NON-LEAGUE CLUB DIRECTORY 2015

(37th Edition)

EDITORS
MIKE WILLIAMS & TONY WILLIAMS

NON-LEAGUE CLUB DIRECTORY 2015
ISBN 978-1-869833-75-6

Editors
Mike Williams
(Tel: 01548 531 339)
tw.publications@btinternet.com)
Tony Williams
(Tel: 01823 490 684)
Email: t.williams320@btinternet.com

Published by Tony Williams Publications Ltd
(Tel: 01548 531 339)
Email: tw.publications@btinternet.com

Printed by Polestar Wheatons (Exeter, Devon)

Sales & Distribution
T.W. Publications (01548 531 339)

Front Cover: Boston United's Carl Piergianni heads the ball despite the attentions of two Solihull Moor's defenders. Boston's 2-1 win ensured the end of Solihull's bid to make the Conference North play-off's.
Photo: Jonathan Holloway.

KENSINGTON PALACE

Association football is enjoyed by all ages across the length and breadth of the country. The great thing about football in this country is that there are levels of the game available for all - whatever their standard.

There are leagues for inter-village rivalries, leagues for work teams and groups of friends - leagues for almost every type of group imaginable, not to mention semi-professional and full-time players. These competitions make up our country's impressive 'Non-League football', involving all clubs below the Premier League and The Football League.

Like you, I am a football fan. I have loved the game from a very young age - as a player, and as a supporter of club and country. As President of The Football Association, I am honoured to be involved with a sport that reaches every community and is part of the fabric of our society.

The team spirit that develops on the pitch and in the dressing room is something that should be encouraged and nurtured – a sporting tradition that forms part of our way of life.

This Non-League Club Directory provides an annual record for the massive world of football enthusiasts who play, administer and support their local clubs across England. Read it with pleasure, then head outside for a game!

CONTENTS

FRONT SECTION

NON-LEAGUE CLUB DIRECTORY

STEP 1

STEP 2

STEP 3

STEP 4

STEP 5/6

STEP 7

OTHER LEAGUES

FA COMPETITIONS

BACK SECTION

It is my great pleasure to welcome you all to the latest edition of the Non-League Club Directory.

In my first year as FA Chairman I have been particularly struck by the dedication and commitment shown by volunteers involved in all aspects of the non-league game. Those tens of thousands of people are the cornerstone of what makes English football so special and they deserve full praise. I was particularly glad some of them were included in our 'grassroots heroes' celebration at Buckingham Palace last season.

Not that I was in any doubt about their importance before arriving at The FA. For more than half a century I have been watching football in this country - and not just with Manchester United and Brentford, where I have been a director and chairman respectively - but as a fan travelling far and wide watching games at every level. It is incredible how you can go to a pitch in any part of England and see competitive football being played to such a good standard – and usually with a loyal band of supporters behind them.

It is also a fitting year to be writing these notes as the 2014/15 season marks 40 years since the start of one of our flagship competitions – The FA Vase.

With more than 500 clubs taking part from Step 5 and below, it is an important part of our sporting calendar. The Vase gives thousands of footballers, many of whom playing for teams at the heart of their local community, the chance to dream of running out in a final at Wembley Stadium – as Sholing did in winning last season.

In supporting The FA Vase and, of course, The FA Trophy, we must also remember how we need to do everything possible to protect and promote the game across the country. While times are tough in terms of government funding, The FA can and will do more to support facilities investment – especially around 3G pitches.

The pressure on our army of volunteers and the negative impact on players is increased when winter weather takes hold or when local authorities make cut-backs. We are aware of this at The FA and this is a major part of the work with my FA Chairman's England Commission.

This facilities debate, along with other issues around the importance of coaching and the matter of helping young players to achieve their full potential, has driven our research over the past year and in the months to come.

All of the measures being put forward are done so with the best interest of English football in its widest sense at heart. I understand the reservations some have about certain proposals but we would always look to preserve the integrity of our pyramid system and the potential for clubs to rise through the ranks. In fact, I would argue our ideas are aimed at protecting this important aspect of our game in the face of increasing financial demands on smaller clubs.

Overall, a successful England team can only come with the right structure in place below the elite level.

If a community club doesn't have players coming through because they can't see a way through to the top, then the ramifications will be felt throughout the pyramid. If fewer players keep going with football after school, then they won't join their local team. That team will have a reduced talent pool and perhaps the lower league club nearby won't have the chance to sign them, nurture them and see them go on to greatness – and make some much-needed money in the process.

We must tackle this problem, or at least have the debate to see if anything can be done without dismissing ideas from the outset. We might well ultimately decide the benefits of a proposal are outweighed by being too detrimental to the game we know and love - I was clear on this in my initial report - but how will we know unless we ask the question?

Rest assured, while we have the debate and listen to the ongoing feedback and opinions sparked by our initial open consultation, we will continue to cherish the non-league game. Without it English football would simply not be the same.

Greg Dyke
FA Chairman

THE EDITORS

TONY WILLIAMS
Editor

Educated at Malvern College, one of the country's best football schools in the late sixties, he represented England Under 18 against Scotland at Celtic Park before serving as an administrative officer in the Royal Air Force for five years.

He was on Reading's books from the age of 16 to 22, but also represented F.A. Amateur XI's and the R.A.F. while playing mainly in the old Isthmian League for Corinthian Casuals, Dulwich Hamlet and Kingstonian and joining Hereford United and Grantham during R.A.F. postings.

After taking an F.A. Coaching badge he coached at Harrow Borough, Epsom & Ewell and Hungerford Town and was asked to edit Jimmy Hill's Football Weekly after initial experience with the Amateur Footballer. Monthly Soccer and Sportsweek followed before he had the idea for a football Wisden and was helped by The Bagnall Harvey Agency to find a suitable generous sponsor in Rothmans.

After launching the Rothmans Football Yearbook in 1970 as its founder and co-compiler with Roy Peskett, he was asked to join Rothmans (although a non-smoker!) in the company's public relations department and was soon able to persuade the Marketing Director that Rothmans should become the first ever sponsor of a football league.

After a season's trial sponsoring the Hellenic and Isthmian Leagues, it was decided to go national with the Northern and Western Leagues and for four years he looked after the football department at Rothmans, with Jimmy Hill and Doug Insole presenting a brilliant sponsorship package which amongst many other innovations included three points for a win and goal difference.

So Non-League football led the way with league sponsorship and two, now well accepted, innovations.

Sportsmanship and goals were also rewarded in a sponsorship that proved a great success for football and for Rothmans. Indeed the sportsmanship incentives could be of great value to-day in the Football Association's bid to improve the game's image by ridding the game of dissent and cheating.

After the cigarette company pulled out of their sports sponsorship Tony produced the first Non-League Annual and later The Football League Club Directory, launching 'Non-League Football' magazine with "The Mail on Sunday" and then "Team Talk."

After his ten years with Hungerford Town, he moved West and served Yeovil Town as a Director for seven years but was thrilled when David Emery's plans for the exciting Non-League Media emerged and came into reality, thus giving the grass roots of the game the publicity and promotion that he and his team had been attempting to set up since the Annual (now Directory) was launched in 1978.

The aim of the company has always been to promote the non-league 'family,' its spirit and its general development. So a plaque from The Football Association inscribed 'To Tony Williams for his continued promotion of all that's good in football' was greatly appreciated as was the trophy to commemorate the thirtieth edition of the Directory and the recent GLS "Lifetime Award' for promoting non-league football.

MIKE WILLIAMS
Editorial Manager

What started out as a holiday job in 1988 helping put together (literally in those days) the Non-League Club Directory and League Club Directory, in the end forged a career which saw him work for Coventry City Football Club, e-comsport in London and finally return to TW Publications in 2003.

During his eight year spell with TW Publications he learned the ropes of all aspects of publishing culminating in the roll of production manager for the Non-League Club Directory, Team Talk Magazine, the League Club Directory and many more publications published by the company.

1995 saw the opportunity to take up the post of Publications Manager at Coventry City Football Club, and the transfer was made in the April of that year. Sky Blue Publications was formed and the League Club Directory became their leading title. Re-branded as the Ultimate Football Guide he was to deal with all aspects of the book, from design to sales and was also put on a steep learning curve into the world of Premiership programme production. The three years spent at the Midland's club gave him a great insight into all departments of a Premiership club, having produced publications for them all.

Leaving Coventry City F.C. in 1998, and after a spell working on a world wide football player database for e-comsport in London, he returned to the West Country in 2001 to set up his own design/publishing company, which incorporated working on the Directory again. 2009 saw the full time switch to TW Publications and the responsibilities of publishing the Directory.

Having gone to a rugby school his football playing career was delayed. However, becoming the youngest player to have played for the First XV and representing Torbay Athletics club at 100 and 200m proved his sporting pedigree. At the age of 20 he begun his football career which, at it's height, saw him playing for Chard Town in the Western League Premier Division.

Now enjoying his time helping run local side Loddiswell Athletic in the South Devon League, with the odd appearance here and there for their Reserve team (when needed), he relishes the challenge of maintaining the club's position in the Premier Division.

ACKNOWLEDGMENTS

It dawned on me as I was sending the first pages off to the printers that I, in some capacity or another, have now worked on 26 of the 37 edition's of the Non-League Club Directory - and oh how things have changed over those years!

Back in the day, if you wanted a photograph on a page, cut and paste literally was, get out a knife, cut the image out, put on some glue and paste it on the page. Nowadays when the book is ready to go to the printers I simply drag a file containing 944 pages from one side of my computer screen to the other, and after ten minutes or so it's at the printers - again, back in the day we would physically take 944 individual pages to the printers!

However, the one thing that has stayed constant throughout those year's is the support and help we get from those that contribute to the book. Some have been involved for longer than I but their enthusiasm for our publication has not falter and goes a long way to making sure we return each new season. Again as always I can't list everyone who has helped but please know that we very much appreciate your continued support.

'OUR TEAM' OF PHOTOGRAPHERS

Peter Barnes, Graham Brown, Keith Clayton, Alan Coomes, Jonathan Holloway, 'Uncle Eric' Marsh, Roger Turner, Bill Wheatcroft and Gordon Whittington.

FA COMPETITIONS DEPARTMENT

Steve Clark, Chris Darnell and Scott Bolton

CONTRIBUTORS

Alan Allcock. Alan Constable. Anthony Golightly. Cyril Windiate. Elaine Waumsley. Louise Edwards. Mark Edmonds. Phil Hiscox. Wendy Juggins. Robin Flight. Ron Holpin.

Arthur Evans (Photographer & reports).
Dr. Andrew Sarnecki (Pecking Order). James Wright.
Richard Rundle (Football Club History Database).
Mike Simmonds (Schools).

And finally, this year I have two family members to thank!

Firstly to Dad, who's passion for non-League football is second to none and support during the production process is invaluable. And secondly to my daughter, Rosie, who, at 4½, becomes the youngest contributor to the book. Her keenness to help was very supportive but it didn't go unnoticed that it delayed her having to go to bed - things young children will do to stay up an extra 10 minutes!!

Thank you one and all

Mike Williams

THERE'S SO MUCH GOOD IN OUR NATIONAL GAME - SO LET'S PROMOTE IT !

For the last thirty seven years we have enjoyed producing an annual in which we have attempted to report on the previous year's competitions and to promote all that we admired within the non-league game. We also enjoyed producing over a hundred 'Team Talks', a Non-League Monthly Football magazine, plus over twenty other football publications.

Originally The Football Association, with leaders such as Ted Croker and Graham Kelly, encouraged us to develop the non-league publications, that covered 95% of the nation's football under the Football Association's jurisdiction.

So, I was extremely proud to have been commemorated for 'an outstanding contribution to football' at 'The Grassroots Heroes Reception' at Buckingham Palace last October. To attend the function with my son Michael and to receive a medal from Prince William was a wonderful experience.

Since the 1977-1978 edition of our non-league annual we have had wonderful support from Steve Clark, Mike Appleby, Adrian Titcombe, Alan Odell and David Barber at The Football Association with Jack Pearce, Mark Harris, Brian Lee, Dennis Strudwick and Barry Bright particularly supportive senior football executives.

All these dedicated football people still really care about 'their game' and originally the vast majority of those working with them at the Football Association were proud to be involved at Lancaster Gate and Soho Square. They considered it an honour, enjoyed and treasured by the executives who promoted and cared for the game to which they were dedicated.

'Blatant cheating, caught by officials or even proved in hindsight by television, should be punished severely'

With twice as many staff now employed at Wembley Stadium and the massive money involved in football, it isn't surprising that the sheer dedication and love of the game has been overtaken by the need to be financially successful. The changing face of sport can also be traced in our national Rugby Union and Cricket headquarters in a similar fashion.

I have always been impressed with the way that everyone involved with Rugby League, their players, club officials, television commentators and the media, all promote their sport with an impressive loyalty and respect.

That 'old fashioned' love of their sport creates an atmosphere similar to the one in which I grew up, where football people loved and promoted all that was good in their game and tried to protect it from criticism. The Football Association was quite rightly the English game's strongest ally, promoting and protecting their game. Is that the case to-day? I hope it is, but I wonder what percentage of the executives working at the FA headquarters regularly go to football matches?

The early paragraphs in this piece were written at the midway stage of the World Cup in Brazil. The football had been positive, exciting and not ruined by too much diving and general cheating, which last season ruined so many of our games at all levels. (The extraordinary biting incident which is a tragic personal problem-not a reflection on the game itself, took place in the evening after this editorial was originally written). Sadly the media will love the scandal and no doubt we will read nearly as much about this lunatic action as the games themselves.
The World Cup referees seemed to have had the simulation problem under control and used their judgement as to the severity of the injury sustained by the writhing, squealing and ground thumping players, which looks so pitiful and ridiculous to anyone who has played the game or ever really suffered a painful injury. In the World Cup, it was encouraging that the few cheats were usually ignored and, of course, they got up and sprinted back into their position.

Surely a strong attitude could be encouraged in our national competitions by The Football Association, The Premier League and the country's senior Referees. Blatant cheating, caught by officials or even proved in hindsight by television, should be punished severely.

In a similar fashion, if it was announced that any player seen to be holding an opponent at a corner or free kick was perhaps warned once and then dismissed, the really annoying offence would be wiped out within weeks - it would no longer be worth risking. If simulation of injury to get free kicks and opponents into trouble, plus the holding at corners were offences punished severely, it would improve our football and also help young officials within the non-league levels.

We all saw Daniel Sturridge bundled off the ball twice in the World Cup with fouls which would surely warrant a free kick. As he was in the penalty area and looked like scoring and as he didn't throw himsclf screaming to the ground, both referees chose to ignore the incidents. Players shouldn't have to cheat to persuade referees to give correct decisions. So it is important that the senior powers in the game give referees the confidence that honest decisions will encourage more honest players and a far better reputation for the game we love.

I saw a disgraceful non-league game in which eight players finished up playing against nine. The young referee had been completely conned by simulated fouls with screaming coaches not helping the players or the officials. The players were copying the cheating seen on television and the poor referee just couldn't cope or decide what was genuine and what was simulated. I left early and I can't imagine anyone ever wanting to watch a similar performance at this local club.

'I left early and I can't imagine anyone ever wanting to watch a similar performance at this local club'

When we remember the horrific World Cup Final ruined by Holland's attitude in 2010 and compare it with the Dutch display this year against Spain. Surely it is obvious which style of play brings success, support and friends!

The World Cup in general was a terrific advert for the game. Positive attacking play, spectacular goals and the great majority of players playing with a smile, which of course is how it really should be for sportsmen playing the game they love, for fabulous money in the greatest competition being watched by the rest of the world.

Let's hope that in England next season, all of us lucky enough to be involved with our great game, enjoy it in the same spirit and prove we are proud to promote its image on and off the field.

Tony Williams

FOOTBALL LEAGUE

STEP 1

Vanarama Conference

STEP 2

Vanarama Conference North

Vanarama Conference South

STEP 3

SOUTHERN PREMIER

The Evo-Stik League
NORTHERN PREMIER

Ryman football league
ISTHMIAN PREMIER

STEP 4

SOUTHERN DIVISION 1 CENTRAL/SOUTH &WEST	NORTHERN DIV 1 NORTH SOUTH	ISTHMIAN DIVISION 1 NORTH SOUTH

STEP 5/6

Combined Counties	Hellenic	West Counties	Southern Counties East	Wessex
East Midlands Counties	Kent Invicta	Northern Counties East	Spartan South Midlands	West Midlands
Eastern Counties	Midland Combination	Northern League South West	Sussex County	
Essex Senior	Midland Football Alliance North	Peninsular	United Counties	Western

STEP 7

Anglian Combination	Essex Olympian league	Liverpool Combination	Oxfordshire Senior league	Teesside League
Bedford & District league	Gloucestershire County League	Manchester League	Peterborough & District League	Thames Valley League
Cambridgeshire County League	Hampshire League	Middlesex County League	Sheffield & Hallmashire League	Wearside League
Central Midlands League	Herts Senior County League	North Berkshire League	Somerset County League	West Cheshire League
Cheshire Association League	Humber Premier League	Northamptonshire Combination	Staffordshire League	West Lancashire League
Dorset Premier League	Kent County League	Northern Alliance	Suffolk & Ipswich league	West Yorkshire League
Essex & Suffolk Border League	Leicestershire League	Nottinghamshire Senior League	Surrey Elite Intermediate	Wiltshire league

FOOTBALL CONFERENCE PREMIER DIVISION 2013-14

		P	W	D	L	F	A	GD	Pts
1	(P) Luton Town	46	30	11	5	102	35	67	101
2	(P) Cambridge United	46	23	13	10	72	35	37	82
3	Gateshead	46	22	13	11	72	50	22	79
4	Grimsby Town	46	22	12	12	65	46	19	78
5	FC Halifax Town	46	22	11	13	85	58	27	77
6	Braintree Town	46	21	11	14	57	39	18	74
7	Kidderminster Harriers	46	20	12	14	66	59	7	72
8	Barnet	46	19	13	14	58	53	5	70
9	Woking	46	20	8	18	66	69	-3	68
10	Forest Green Rovers	46	19	10	17	80	66	14	67
11	Alfreton Town (-3)	46	21	7	18	69	74	-5	67
12	(R) Salisbury City	46	19	10	17	58	63	-5	67
13	Nuneaton Town	46	18	12	16	54	60	-6	66
14	Lincoln City	46	17	14	15	60	59	1	65
15	Macclesfield Town	46	18	7	21	62	63	-1	61
16	Welling United	46	16	12	18	59	61	-2	60
17	Wrexham	46	16	11	19	61	61	0	59
18	Southport	46	14	11	21	53	71	-18	53
19	Aldershot Town (-10)	46	16	13	17	69	62	7	51
20	Hereford United	46	13	12	21	44	63	-19	51
21	Chester	46	12	15	19	49	70	-21	51
22	Dartford	46	12	8	26	49	74	-25	44
23	(R) Tamworth	46	10	9	27	43	81	-38	39
24	(R) Hyde	46	1	7	38	38	119	-81	10

PLAY-OFFS

Semi-Finals 1st Leg / 2nd Leg

FC Halifax Town 1-0 Cambridge United / Cambridge United 2-0 FC Halifax Town

Grimsby Town 1-1 Gateshead / Gateshead 3-1 Grimsby Town

Final (@ Wembley, 18/5/13) - Att: 19,613

Cambridge United 2-1 Gateshead

	1	2	3	4	5	6	7	8	9	10	11	12	13	14	15	16	17	18	19	20	21	22	23	24
1 Aldershot Town		2-3	3-3	2-1	0-1	2-0	3-0	2-2	2-2	1-2	0-3	1-2	1-0	0-0	2-3	3-3	1-0	2-2	3-2	5-1	6-0	3-1	2-1	2-0
2 Alfreton Town	1-4		3-1	3-1	1-1	0-1	2-1	3-0	3-2	1-1	3-3	2-1	3-0	3-1	1-1	0-5	0-1	1-1	3-2	2-1	4-2	2-2	3-1	1-0
3 Barnet	1-3	1-0		1-1	2-2	3-0	1-0	0-4	2-1	0-1	2-1	2-0	3-2	1-0	1-1	1-2	1-2	1-1	3-1	1-0	1-0	0-0	1-3	1-1
4 Braintree Town	1-0	3-1	0-3		1-0	3-0	1-0	1-0	1-1	0-0	0-0	1-1	2-1	0-1	0-2	1-2	0-1	2-1	0-1	1-0	2-0	2-3	2-0	3-0
5 Cambridge United	4-0	0-1	1-1	1-0		0-1	1-1	5-1	2-1	1-0	1-2	1-0	7-2	5-1	1-0	1-1	3-0	3-0	2-0	3-1	3-0	2-1	2-0	0-0
6 Chester	1-1	0-1	2-1	0-2	0-0		0-0	2-1	1-2	1-1	0-0	0-2	3-2	0-0	3-3	1-1	2-1	3-3	2-2	2-2	2-0	1-3	0-2	0-0
7 Dartford	1-1	1-0	0-2	0-2	3-3	0-1		1-2	0-1	0-1	1-0	2-0	4-3	3-0	1-2	1-2	2-1	1-2	1-1	1-0	2-3	1-2	5-1	1-5
8 FC Halifax Town	4-0	2-0	2-1	0-0	1-1	2-1	2-0		1-0	3-3	4-0	1-1	4-0	1-1	5-1	2-0	2-1	2-2	5-1	1-0	2-0	3-0	3-4	3-2
9 Forrest Green Rovers	3-1	3-1	1-2	0-2	3-2	3-0	1-0	2-1		1-0	2-1	1-1	8-0	1-1	4-1	0-0	2-3	1-0	4-0	3-1	1-2	0-0	2-2	1-1
10 Gateshead	0-0	3-0	1-2	1-0	2-0	3-2	2-0	1-1	1-1		1-2	2-1	4-0	3-1	3-1	0-0	2-2	2-1	3-2	2-2	5-0	1-1	0-2	0-3
11 Grimsby Town	1-1	3-1	2-1	1-0	0-1	2-1	5-2	0-1	3-1	2-2		1-1	1-0	3-1	1-1	1-2	2-3	1-2	2-0	0-0	3-1	1-1	2-2	3-1
12 Hereford United	0-2	3-2	0-1	1-1	1-0	2-2	2-2	3-2	1-0	0-1	0-1		0-0	1-1	1-0	0-0	1-2	0-1	1-0	4-1	1-0	2-1	0-2	0-2
13 Hyde FC	2-2	1-2	0-1	0-3	0-1	1-2	0-2	1-5	2-6	0-2	0-1	2-2		1-3	3-4	0-1	0-3	2-2	0-2	1-2	0-3	0-1	0-2	2-5
14 Kidderminster Harriers	0-0	1-3	1-0	2-2	2-0	3-1	1-2	2-0	4-1	3-1	0-1	2-1	2-1		4-1	0-2	2-1	0-0	3-0	1-1	5-3	2-0	2-0	3-1
15 Lincoln City	0-1	4-1	3-3	2-0	1-0	1-1	0-0	3-1	2-1	0-1	0-2	1-1	3-0	2-0		0-0	1-0	1-2	0-1	1-0	0-0	1-2	2-2	2-0
16 Luton Town	1-0	3-0	2-1	2-3	0-0	3-0	3-0	4-3	4-1	4-2	0-0	7-0	4-1	6-0	3-2		1-1	3-0	2-0	3-0	2-0	2-1	0-1	5-0
17 Macclesfield Town	1-1	0-1	2-0	0-1	0-1	3-2	3-1	2-2	1-2	0-2	1-1	1-0	3-0	1-1	3-1	1-2		0-1	1-0	2-2	2-1	2-1	3-2	3-2
18 Nuneaton Town	2-1	3-0	0-1	1-1	0-0	1-0	3-1	0-1	1-1	1-4	0-1	2-1	1-0	2-1	2-2	0-5	1-0		1-2	3-1	1-0	2-0	0-2	2-0
19 Salisbury City	1-0	0-0	2-1	1-1	0-3	3-1	1-0	3-1	1-4	0-0	1-0	4-1	2-0	1-1	1-2	0-0	3-2	2-1		1-1	0-1	3-0	2-0	2-1
20 Southport	1-0	2-1	1-1	0-4	1-0	0-0	3-0	2-1	2-0	2-1	2-1	0-3	1-1	1-2	0-1	1-0	4-1	1-0	3-1		2-0	2-2	1-1	1-2
21 Tamworth	1-0	1-0	0-0	0-0	0-1	3-4	0-2	2-0	1-2	0-1	0-2	1-0	1-1	0-3	0-0	3-4	1-0	1-1	1-2	4-1		1-1	2-4	2-2
22 Welling United	1-0	1-2	1-1	0-2	2-2	2-0	1-1	0-1	5-2	2-0	1-0	0-1	0-2	1-2	1-0	1-2	1-0	1-2	0-0	4-3	2-0		3-0	1-1
23 Woking	1-2	2-1	0-0	1-0	0-3	0-1	3-0	0-0	2-1	1-2	1-2	3-0	3-2	1-0	0-0	0-4	3-2	2-0	1-3	2-0	2-2	2-4		2-1
24 Wrexham	2-1	2-3	0-1	2-3	1-1	0-2	1-2	0-0	2-0	3-2	0-1	2-0	2-2	0-0	0-1	2-0	1-0	3-0	1-1	1-0	2-0	2-1	2-0	

FOOTBALL CONFERENCE NORTH 2013-14

		P	W	D	L	F	A	GD	Pts
1	(P) AFC Telford United	42	25	10	7	82	53	29	85
2	North Ferriby United	42	24	10	8	80	51	29	82
3	(P) Altrincham	42	24	9	9	95	51	44	81
4	Hednesford Town	42	24	6	12	87	65	22	78
5	Guiseley	42	23	9	10	78	56	22	78
6	Boston United	42	20	12	10	85	60	25	72
7	Brackley Town	42	17	16	9	66	45	21	67
8	Solihull Moors	42	17	14	11	63	52	11	65
9	Harrogate Town (-3)	42	19	9	14	75	59	16	63
10	Bradford Park Avenue	42	15	12	15	66	70	-4	57
11	Barrow	42	14	14	14	50	56	-6	56
12	Colwyn Bay	42	14	13	15	63	67	-4	55
13	Leamington	42	13	13	16	54	53	1	52
14	Stockport County	42	12	14	16	58	57	1	50
15	Worcester City	42	13	11	18	40	53	-13	50
16	Gainsborough Trinity	42	13	6	23	67	85	-18	45
17	Gloucester City	42	11	11	20	64	77	-13	44
18	(W) Vauxhall Motors	42	12	8	22	43	74	-31	44
19	Stalybridge Celtic	42	10	9	23	57	88	-31	39
20	Oxford City (-3)	42	9	13	20	50	70	-20	37
21	(R) Histon	42	7	11	24	41	76	-35	32
22	(R) Workington	42	6	10	26	39	85	-46	28

PLAY-OFFS

Semi-Finals 1st Leg / 2nd Leg

Guiseley 2-0 North Ferriby United / North Ferriby United v Guiseley

Hednesford Town 2-2 Altrincham / Altrincham v Hednesford Town

Final (@ Altrincham FC, 10/5/13) - Att: 4,632

Altrincham 2-1 Guiseley (AET)

	1	2	3	4	5	6	7	8	9	10	11	12	13	14	15	16	17	18	19	20	21	22
1 AFC Telford United		3-1	0-1	2-1	2-1	2-1	4-1	3-0	2-1	4-2	0-1	5-3	3-2	1-2	2-0	4-0	1-1	3-1	2-0	1-0	0-0	2-1
2 Altrincham	1-1		2-1	0-0	1-0	4-1	3-1	3-0	2-0	4-1	1-3	1-3	2-2	3-2	1-1	2-2	1-0	5-0	3-0	5-1	1-2	2-0
3 Barrow	0-3	1-1		4-4	0-1	0-1	1-1	0-6	0-0	1-0	1-0	1-0	2-1	0-0	2-0	1-1	0-2	1-1	2-4	1-1	0-1	2-0
4 Boston United	1-1	3-2	1-0		1-2	2-3	2-1	6-0	2-0	3-0	3-3	4-0	0-0	2-0	2-0	2-1	4-1	4-1	0-0	5-2	2-1	5-3
5 Brackley Town	1-1	1-2	1-2	3-2		0-1	2-2	3-1	1-3	1-2	2-2	1-0	3-0	1-1	1-1	2-1	1-0	3-0	0-0	2-1	0-0	1-1
6 Bradford Park Avenue	3-1	2-4	2-2	1-1	0-5		1-2	4-0	3-1	0-3	0-0	1-2	3-0	3-2	0-4	3-3	2-2	1-1	0-2	0-0	6-1	1-0
7 Colwyn Bay	0-1	1-3	1-2	3-3	2-2	2-2		0-2	1-1	2-2	2-1	1-3	1-0	1-1	0-3	1-1	3-1	1-2	0-0	1-0	0-0	3-2
8 Gainsborough Trinity	1-3	5-4	2-1	0-1	2-2	4-2	0-2		3-3	1-2	2-0	1-2	3-0	1-1	1-4	6-0	2-3	0-2	1-5	1-1	2-1	3-0
9 Gloucester City	1-2	2-0	1-3	1-3	2-2	2-3	2-3	0-1		1-1	5-2	5-1	2-0	3-3	1-1	0-2	0-3	1-0	2-0	2-2	2-1	1-1
10 Guiseley	6-1	2-2	2-1	1-0	0-2	0-2	2-1	3-1	3-1		2-0	1-2	1-1	2-1	1-0	2-0	0-3	3-1	2-0	1-0	0-1	1-0
11 Harrogate Town	2-2	3-2	3-1	4-0	0-1	1-1	2-2	1-1	4-2	2-3		3-1	0-1	1-1	5-0	3-2	2-1	2-1	3-1	1-1	2-0	3-0
12 Hednesford Town	3-3	1-1	3-1	4-2	2-2	2-0	2-1	1-3	4-1	3-2	1-3		2-1	3-2	0-1	3-0	1-2	4-1	3-1	2-0	4-0	4-0
13 Histon	0-1	0-5	0-0	1-2	3-3	1-0	3-1	2-0	1-3	1-1	0-1	0-1		1-1	0-3	2-2	0-3	1-4	2-1	1-2	1-2	3-1
14 Leamington	2-2	0-1	1-1	0-0	3-1	2-0	2-1	0-1	0-1	2-3	1-2	2-1	1-0		0-2	4-0	0-1	1-0	2-1	0-1	1-0	2-0
15 North Ferriby United	2-2	2-1	2-2	3-0	1-1	2-1	2-3	2-0	3-1	2-3	3-2	3-0	4-4	4-1		2-1	1-1	2-0	0-0	2-0	2-1	3-1
16 Oxford City	2-0	1-2	0-1	1-1	0-1	1-1	1-2	1-0	1-0	3-3	1-2	1-2	2-1	2-2	2-3		0-2	2-1	4-1	3-0	0-0	1-1
17 Solihull Borough	2-2	0-1	0-2	1-2	1-0	2-2	2-2	3-2	2-1	0-3	3-0	2-3	0-0	0-0	2-0	2-2		3-3	1-0	1-0	1-1	1-1
18 Stalybridge Celtic	0-2	0-5	1-3	3-3	1-1	2-2	2-3	3-2	2-2	2-3	3-2	0-4	2-1	2-1	2-3	1-1	2-3		0-0	3-2	1-2	2-0
19 Stockport County	4-2	0-0	2-2	1-4	0-2	4-1	0-1	3-1	2-2	3-3	3-1	0-1	1-0	1-1	1-2	2-0	2-2	2-0		4-1	4-0	1-1
20 Vauxhall Motors	2-4	1-2	1-1	2-2	0-3	0-2	0-3	2-1	3-2	0-5	1-0	2-2	4-0	2-1	0-1	1-0	0-2	1-3	2-1		1-0	2-1
21 Worcester City	0-1	1-3	1-0	3-0	1-1	1-2	2-1	2-2	0-1	0-0	1-0	2-2	1-1	0-3	0-1	0-2	3-1	2-1	0-0	2-0		4-0
22 Workington	0-1	1-6	2-3	1-0	0-3	0-2	0-3	4-2	4-2	1-1	0-3	2-2	2-3	1-2	3-3	1-0	0-0	1-0	1-1	0-1	1-0	

FOOTBALL CONFERENCE SOUTH 2013-14

		P	W	D	L	F	A	GD	Pts
1	(P) Eastleigh	42	26	8	8	71	40	31	86
2	Sutton United	42	23	12	7	77	39	38	81
3	Bromley	42	25	5	12	82	50	32	80
4	Ebbsfleet United	42	21	11	10	67	40	27	74
5	(P) Dover Athletic	42	20	9	13	63	38	25	69
6	Havant & Waterlooville	42	19	12	11	57	43	14	69
7	Bath City	42	18	12	12	64	52	12	66
8	Staines Town	42	18	9	15	56	57	-1	63
9	Concord Rangers	42	17	10	15	58	59	-1	61
10	Eastbourne Borough	42	16	10	16	55	59	-4	58
11	Weston-super-Mare	42	16	9	17	50	55	-5	57
12	Gosport Borough	42	16	7	19	46	51	-5	55
13	Boreham Wood	42	14	11	17	65	55	10	53
14	Basingstoke Town	42	15	8	19	55	56	-1	53
15	Bishop's Stortford	42	13	13	16	63	68	-5	52
16	Farnborough	42	15	5	22	62	78	-16	50
17	Chelmsford City	42	14	7	21	57	77	-20	49
18	Maidenhead United	42	12	10	20	55	69	-14	46
19	Whitehawk	42	12	10	20	56	71	-15	46
20	Hayes & Yeading United	42	13	6	23	45	52	-7	45
21	(R) Tonbridge Angels	42	9	13	20	43	77	-34	40
22	(R) Dorchester Town	42	8	7	27	33	94	-61	31

PLAY-OFFS

Semi-Finals 1st Leg / 2nd Leg

Dover Athletic 1-1 Sutton United / Sutton United v Dover Athletic

Ebbsfleet United 4-0 Bromley / Bromley v Ebbsfleet United

Final (@ Ebbsfleet United, 10/5/13) - Att: 4,294

Ebbsfleet United 0-1 Dover Athletic

	1	2	3	4	5	6	7	8	9	10	11	12	13	14	15	16	17	18	19	20	21	22
1 Basingstoke Town		0-0	0-0	1-0	0-1	2-3	0-1	2-1	2-0	1-2	2-0	2-2	4-0	2-1	0-1	0-1	2-2	2-1	0-1	0-0	3-2	1-3
2 Bath City	0-1		2-1	2-2	1-2	4-1	3-1	1-0	0-2	2-1	0-1	2-2	4-2	1-1	3-1	3-2	1-0	1-1	2-2	2-2	1-0	3-1
3 Bishop's Stortford	5-3	1-2		1-3	1-0	1-1	0-1	1-1	2-2	1-0	2-2	3-2	1-3	4-0	2-1	0-0	1-1	1-0	1-2	2-1	0-0	1-2
4 Boreham Wood	1-1	0-1	2-2		1-1	4-3	0-2	5-0	2-2	3-1	0-3	2-1	1-1	2-0	0-2	1-3	2-2	0-2	1-3	7-0	1-1	1-3
5 Bromley	3-2	2-2	3-2	2-1		5-0	1-2	4-1	0-4	2-1	1-2	0-0	3-0	2-1	2-0	2-1	6-1	3-0	2-4	5-1	2-1	4-0
6 Chelmsford City	1-0	1-0	2-1	0-6	3-1		2-2	4-1	0-4	3-0	0-0	1-2	3-1	1-0	0-0	0-0	0-3	3-2	0-2	7-1	1-2	0-2
7 Concord Rangers	1-2	0-2	0-2	0-4	2-3	1-3		1-0	1-2	1-1	3-2	1-2	5-0	0-2	3-3	3-1	4-1	2-1	0-0	2-2	2-0	1-1
8 Dorchester Town	0-4	0-2	1-3	1-4	3-2	2-0	2-2		0-4	0-0	1-2	1-3	1-0	1-1	0-2	0-2	0-3	1-1	0-0	2-1	0-3	2-6
9 Dover Athletic	1-1	2-0	2-3	0-0	0-2	2-2	0-1	1-0		0-0	1-2	2-1	0-1	3-0	0-0	0-1	2-0	1-0	0-1	3-1	1-2	1-1
10 Eastbourne Borough	1-3	3-2	4-1	1-0	1-1	4-2	0-0	0-1	0 4		1-1	1-1	5-2	1-3	0-1	3-1	2-0	2-0	1-1	2-1	2-0	0-2
11 Eastleigh	2-1	2-1	4-2	0-1	2-1	1-0	1-1	6-0	1-0	2-0		3-1	1-0	2-1	0-0	1-0	3-2	1-0	1-0	1-2	3-1	3-2
12 Ebbsfleet United	1-0	1-1	2-1	0-0	1-3	0-2	4-0	4-0	0-2	1-0	3-1		3-0	2-1	0-0	1-0	1-1	3-0	2-0	1-0	1-1	3-1
13 Farnborough	0-3	2-4	4-2	2-0	2-1	2-0	0-2	3-2	1-0	3-3	0-1	0-1		1-0	2-2	1-2	3-0	1-2	1-2	3-2	4-0	2-0
14 Gosport Borough	2-0	3-1	2-1	2-1	1-2	2-1	1-2	1-1	0-1	1-2	0-2	0-2	1-0		0-0	3-0	0-2	2-0	2-2	2-0	0-0	0-2
15 Havant & Waterlooville	4-1	1-0	2-0	1-1	1-0	3-0	1-0	5-1	3-4	1-1	1-0	1-0	2-1	3-0		1-2	1-3	0-2	0-5	1-2	2-0	2-0
16 Hayes & Yeading United	0-0	0-2	2-3	1-0	0-2	4-0	1-0	2-0	1-2	0-1	1-1	1-2	1-2	0-1	0-1		1-2	1-2	0-0	3-0	1-2	3-2
17 Maidenhead United	0-1	0-1	2-2	0-1	0-1	1-1	1-3	1-3	1-2	2-3	1-3	1-0	2-2	1-2	1-3	2-1		3-1	3-2	0-0	0-3	1-0
18 Staines Town	4-5	1-0	2-0	3-1	2-1	3-1	0-1	1-0	2-2	2-1	0-0	1-1	3-2	0-3	1-0	2-1	0-0		2-1	0-0	2-1	2-1
19 Sutton United	4-0	2-2	1-2	1-0	1-0	2-0	1-0	0-1	1-0	4-0	1-1	3-1	3-3	2-0	3-1	2-0	3-2	4-1		1-2	3-0	2-0
20 Tonbridge Angels	2-1	1-1	1-1	0-2	1-1	2-1	2-2	1-2	0-2	2-1	2-1	0-2	1-3	0-2	0-0	1-1	2-4	1-1	1-1		1-0	3-1
21 Weston-Super-Mare	1-0	2-0	2-2	3-0	0-1	2-0	5-0	3-0	2-1	0-1	3-2	0-6	2-1	0-1	1-1	0-3	0-0	0-3	1-1	2-1		2-1
22 Whitehawk	1-0	2-2	1-1	0-2	1-2	0-4	0-2	3-0	0-1	1-2	1-4	1-1	3-1	1-1	2-2	1-0	0-3	3-3	3-3	1-0	0-0	

A.F.C. TELFORD UNITED

Chairman: Ian Dosser
Secretary: Mrs Sharon Bowyer **(T)** 07970 040 106 **(E)** sharon.bowyer@telfordutd.co.uk
Commercial Manager: Paul Riley **(T)** 07855 776 586
Programme Editor: James Baylis **(T)** 07977 481 186
Ground Address: New Bucks Head Stadium, Watling Street, Wellington, Telford TF1 2TU
(T) 01952 640 064 **Manager:** Liam Watson

Club Factfile

Founded: 2004 **Nickname:** The Bucks
Previous Names: AFC Telford United was formed when Telford United folded in May 2004
Previous Leagues: As AFC Telford United: Northern Premier 2004-06
As Telford United: Southern 1969-79. Alliance/Conference 1979-2004

Club Colours (change): All white (Cyan/navy/navy)

Ground Capacity: 6,380 **Seats:** 2,200 **Covered:** 4,800 **Clubhouse:** Yes **Shop:** Yes

Directions
(Sat Nav follow TF1 2NW into Haybridge Road) From M54 Junction 6, A5223 towards Wellington, straight over first roundabout (retail park). Straight over second roundabout (B5067). Left at third roundabout (Furrows garage). Continue over railway bridge and follow road round to the right, then turn left into AFC Telford United Car Park.

Previous Grounds: None - Renovation of the old Bucks Head started in 2000 and was completed in 2003.

Record Attendance: 4,215 v Kendal Town - Northern Premier League play-off final
Record Victory: 7-0 v Runcorn (A) - Northern Premier League Division One 2005-06
Record Defeat: 3-6 v Bradford P.A. (H) - Northern Premier League Division One 2005-06
Record Goalscorer: Kyle Perry - 32 (2004-06)
Record Appearances: Stuart Brock - 132 (2004-09)
Additional Records: Paid £5,000 to Tamworth for Lee Moore 08/12/06
Received £33,000 from Burnley for Duane Courtney 31/08/05
Senior Honours:
Northern Premier League Division 1 Play-off 2004-05, Premier Division Play-off 2006-07. Conference League Cup 2008-09.
Shropshire Senior Cup 2012-13. Conference North 2013-14.

10 YEAR RECORD

04-05	05-06	06-07	07-08	08-09	09-10	10-11	11-12	12-13	13-14
NP 1 3	NP P 10	NP P 3	Conf N 2	Conf N 4	Conf N 11	Conf N 2	Conf 20	Conf 24	Conf N 1

Conference Action

Alfreton's Akinde leaves the Cambridge United defence stranded as he creates space to fire in a shot, which goes the wrong side of the post.

Photo: Bill Wheatcroft.

AFC TELFORD UNITED MATCH RESULTS 2013-14

Date	Comp	H/A	Opponents	Att:	Result		Goalscorers	Pos	No.
Aug 17	CNorth	H	Workington	1640	W	2-1	Byrne 7 Gray 52	8	1
20	CNorth	A	Boston United	1145	D	1-1		7	2
24	CNorth	A	Gloucester City	434	W	2-1	Farrell 3 Clancy 75	6	3
26	CNorth	H	Solihull Moors	1491	D	1-1	Clancy 56	5	4
31	CNorth	A	Gainsborough Trinity	428	W	3-1	Clancy 60 Farrell 62 Grand 80	4	5
Sept 7	CNorth	H	Harrogate Town	1431	L	0-1		9	6
14	CNorth	A	Bradford PA	305	L	1-3	Farrell 15	9	7
21	CNorth	H	Colwyn Bay	1677	W	4-1	Booth 9 Grand 20 McGinn 89 Phenix 90	7	8
24	CNorth	H	Worcester City	1330	D	0-0		8	9
28	***FAC2Q***	***H***	***Hednesford Town***	***1345***	***L***	***1-3***	***Booth 52***		10
Oct 5	CNorth	A	Histon	350	W	1-0	Phenix 61	7	11
19	CNorth	H	North Ferriby United	1368	W	2-0	Gray 50 Phenix 82	7	12
Nov 2	CNorth	A	Stockport County	2710	L	2-4	Cooke 19 Moses 79 (og)	7	13
5	CNorth	A	Brackley Town	216	D	1-1	Owens 18	7	14
9	CNorth	H	Stalybridge Celtic	1527	W	3-1	Farrell 3 Clancy 16 Grogan 62	7	15
12	CNorth	H	Vauxhall Motors	1218	W	1-0	Farrell 7	6	16
16	***FAT3Q***	***H***	***Scarborough United***	***869***	***W***	***6-0***	***Clancy 11 (pen) Grogan 44 48 Farrell 55 Grand 81 Gray 89 (pen)***		17
23	CNorth	A	Barrow	646	W	3-0	Grogan 14 87 Gray 90	6	18
30	***FAT1***	***A***	***Worcester Clty***	***764***	***D***	***0-0***			19
Dec 2	***FAT1r***	***H***	***Worcester Clty***	***603***	***L***	***0-3***			20
7	CNorth	H	Leamington	1563	L	1-2	Gray 74	7	21
14	CNorth	A	Workington	348	W	1-0	Benjamin 15	5	22
21	CNorth	H	Brackley Town	1351	W	2-1	Clancy 78 (pen) Farrell 65	3	23
26	CNorth	A	Hednesford Town	1352	D	3-3	Barnett 45 Grogan 50 Phenix 77	3	24
28	CNorth	H	Boston United	1659	W	2-1	Gray 46 Booth 68	2	25
Jan 1	CNorth	H	Hednesford Town	1903	W	5-3	FARRELL 3 (15 53 79) Barnett 50 Phenix 56	1	26
4	CNorth	A	Harrogate Town	525	D	2-2	Grogan 75 Gray 82	2	27
18	CNorth	H	Barrow	1684	L	0-1		3	28
25	CNorth	A	North Ferriby United	558	D	2-2	Grand 3 Farrell 32	3	29
Feb 1	CNorth	H	Guiseley	1266	W	4-2	Grogan 17 Phenix 76 Whalley 79 Grand 90	3	30
4	CNorth	A	Altrincham	690	D	1-1	Grogan 6	4	31
15	CNorth	H	Stockport County	1819	W	2-0	Owens 23 Clancy 72	2	32
18	CNorth	A	Worcester City	534	W	1-0	Preston 12	2	33
22	CNorth	A	Vauxhall Motors	340	W	4-2	Clancy 16 (pen) 38 McGinn 63 Whalley 90	1	34
March 1	CNorth	H	Bradford PA	1800	W	2-1	Owens 55 Farrell 68 (pen)	1	35
8	CNorth	A	Stalybridge Celtic	517	W	2-0	Owens 8 62	1	36
15	CNorth	H	Histon	1607	W	3-2	Grogan 31 75 Phenix 45	2	37
22	CNorth	H	Oxford City	1531	W	4-0	Whalley 12 40 Owens 18 Farrell 4 (pen)	1	38
29	CNorth	A	Leamington	843	D	2-2	Farrell 15 (pen) McGinn 34	2	39
April 1	CNorth	A	Guiseley	469	L	1-6	Phenix 69	2	40
5	CNorth	H	Altrincham	1785	W	3-1	Grogan 18 Byrne 51 Farrell 67	1	41
8	CNorth	A	Oxford City	312	L	0-2		1	42
12	CNorth	A	Colwyn Bay	629	W	1-0	Farrell 28 (pen)	1	43
19	CNorth	H	Gloucester City	2084	W	2-1	Farrell 30 (pen) Clancy 78	2	44
21	CNorth	A	Solihull Moors	834	D	2-2	Pierpoint 21 (og) Grogan 63	1	45
26	CNorth	H	Gainsborough Trinity	**3724**	W	3-0	Grogan 18 Clancy 63 (pen) Whalley 89	1	46

GOALSCORERS	Lge	FAC	FAT	Total	Pens	Hat-tricks	Cons Run
Farrell	16		1	17	5	1	3
Grogan	12		2	14			2
Clancy	11		1	12	4		3
Phenix	8			8			
Gray	6		1	7	1		2
Owens	6			6			
Grand	4		1	5			2
Whalley	5			5			
Booth	2	1		3			
McGinn	3			3			
Barnett	2			2			
Byrne	2			2			
Benjamin	1			1			
Cooke	1			1			
Preston	1			1			
Opponents	2			2			

Cons Run - Consecutive scoring games.

ALDERSHOT TOWN

Chairman: Shahid Azeem
Secretary: Bob Green (T) 01252 320 211 (E) admin@theshots.co.uk
Commercial Manager: Mark Butler (T) 01252 320 211
Programme Editor: Victoria Rogers (T) 07979 964 264
Ground Address: EBB Stadium, High street, Aldershot, GU11 1TW
(T) 01252 320 211 **Manager:** Andy Scott

Club Factfile

Founded: 1992 **Nickname:** Shots
Previous Names: None
Previous Leagues: Isthmian 1992-2003. Conference 2003-2008. Football League 2008-13.

Club Colours (change): red/blue/red (Cyan/blue/blue)

Ground Capacity: 7,500 **Seats:** 1,800 **Covered:** 6,850 **Clubhouse:** Yes **Shop:** Yes

Directions
Exit from the M3 at junction 4 and take the A331 to Aldershot , after 3 miles take the 4th exit off the A331 and take the Town Centre route to Aldershot.
1.25 miles from the A331 junction the ground will be on your right hand side. Located on the High Street in Aldershot.

Previous Grounds: None

Record Attendance: 7,500 v Brighton & Hove Albion, FA Cup 1st Round, 18/11/2000
Record Victory: 8-0 v Bishop's Stortford (A) Isthmian Premier 05/09/1998
Record Defeat: 0-6 v Worthing (A) Isthmian League Cup 02/03/99
Record Goalscorer: Mark Butler - 155 (1992-96)
Record Appearances: Jason Chewings - 400
Additional Records:

Senior Honours:
Isthmian League Premier Division 2002-03. Conference 2007-08.

10 YEAR RECORD

04-05	05-06	06-07	07-08	08-09	09-10	10-11	11-12	12-13	13-14
Conf 4	Conf 13	Conf 9	Conf 1	FL 2 15	FL 2 6	FL 2 14	FL 2 11	FL 2 24	Conf 19

ALDERSHOT TOWN MATCH RESULTS 2013-14

Date	Comp	H/A	Opponents	Att:	Result		Goalscorers	Pos	No.
Aug 10	CPrem	A	Grimsby Town	4037	D	1-1	Oastler 58	24	1
13	CPrem	H	Dartford	2138	**W**	3-0	B.Williams 18 Oyeleke 61 Wickham 87	24	2
17	CPrem	H	Cambridge United	2022	L	0-1		24	3
24	CPrem	A	Salisbury City	1175	L	0-1		24	4
26	CPrem	H	Woking	**3138**	**W**	2-1	Paterson 1 B.Williams 18	24	5
31	CPrem	A	Southport	1012	L	0-1		24	6
Sept 6	CPrem	H	Macclesfield Town	1752	**W**	1-0	Molesley 66	24	7
13	CPrem	A	Hereford United	1851	**W**	2-0	B.Williams 14 66	22	8
17	CPrem	H	Barnet	1740	D	3-3	B.Williams 3 69 Oyeleeke 64	22	9
21	CPrem	H	Wrexham	1915	**W**	2-0	Molesley 61 Roberts 80	22	10
24	CPrem	A	Welling United	837	L	0-1		23	11
28	CPrem	A	Kidderminster Harriers	2049	D	0-0		22	12
Oct 5	CPrem	H	Grimsby Town	2118	L	0-3		23	13
8	CPrem	H	Luton Town	2693	D	3-3	Goodman 13 Roberts 24 Molesley 45	23	14
12	CPrem	A	Lincoln City	2748	**W**	1-0	B.Williams 48	23	15
19	CPrem	H	Alfreton Town	1732	L	2-3	Gibbs 28 B.Williams 47	23	16
26	***FAC4Q***	***A***	***Shortwood United***	***631***	***D***	***1-1***	***B.Williams 15***		17
29	***FAC4Qr***	***H***	***Shortwood United***	***1233***	***L***	***1-2***	***Paterson***		18
Nov 2	CPrem	H	Chester FC	2029	D	1-1	Gibbs 90	23	19
12	CPrem	A	Cambridge United	3110	L	0-4		23	20
16	Cprem	A	FC Halifax Town	1418	L	0-4		23	21
23	CPrem	H	Southport	1592	**W**	5-1	B.WILLIAMS 3 (1 24 77pen) Smith 12 (og) Mekki 19	23	22
26	CPrem	H	Braintree Town	1215	**W**	2-1	B.Williams 21 Paterson 90	21	23
30	***FAT1***	***H***	***Weston-super-Mare***	***1084***	***D***	***1-1***	***O'Brien 90***		24
Dec 2	***FAT1r***	***A***	***Weston-suoer-Mare***	***283***	***W***	***5-2***	***Young 42 54 O'Brien 56 Paterson 83 Stanley 90***		25
14	***FAT2***	***H***	***Worcester City***	***1158***	***W***	***4-1***	***O'Brien 23 Oyeleke 34 B Williams 66 85***		26
21	CPrem	H	Tamworth	1598	**W**	6-0	Oyeleke 11 Molesley 33 B.Williams 63 pen 73 O'Brien 66 Roberts 77	19	27
28	CPrem	H	Welling United	2058	**W**	3-1	B.Williams 68 (pen) O'Brien 78 86	19	28
Jan 4	CPrem	A	Wrexham	2819	L	1-2	B.Williams 20	20	29
11	***FAT3***	***H***	***Guiseley***	***1632***	***W***	***3-0***	***Parker 22 (og) O'Brien 28 Roberts 63***		30
14	CPrem	A	Gateshead	724	D	0-0		20	31
21	CPrem	A	Barnet	1387	**W**	3-1	Roberts 3 Bubb 48 Molesley 55	19	32
25	CPrem	H	FC Halifax Town	1977	D	2-2	Roberts 45 Stanley 66	19	33
28	CPrem	A	Nuneaton Town	718	L	1-2	Plummer 84	19	34
Feb 4	***FAT4***	***A***	***Havant & Waterlooville***	***1125***	***L***	***1-4***	***B.Williams 81 (pen)***		35
18	CPrem	H	Forest Green Rovers	1407	D	2-2	Mekki 58 Bubb 61	19	36
22	CPrem	A	Hyde	520	D	2-2	B.Williams 37 Partington 85	19	37
25	CPrem	A	Dartford	1125	D	1-1	B.Williams 88	20	38
March 1	CPrem	H	Lincoln City	1944	L	2-3	Bubb 10 Scott 53	21	39
8	CPrem	A	Tamworth	915	L	0-1		21	40
11	CPrem	H	Chester FC	1545	**W**	2-0	B.Williams 21 83	21	41
15	CPrem	H	Nuneaton Town	1606	D	2-2	Scott 63 Rowlands 82	21	42
18	CPrem	H	Kidderminster Harriers	1558	D	0-0		21	43
22	CPrem	A	Braintree Town	1090	L	0-1		21	44
25	CPrem	H	Gateshead	1358	L	1-2	Scott 32	21	45
29	CPrem	H	Hyde	1591	**W**	1-0	Mekki 45	21	46
April 5	CPrem	A	Luton Town	8558	L	0-1		21	47
8	CPrem	A	Alfreton Town	620	**W**	4-1	Rowlands 11 Phillips 16 Oyeleke 57 Molesley 56	21	48
12	CPrem	A	Macclesfield Town	2207	D	1-1	B.Williams 90 (pen)	20	49
18	CPrem	H	Salisbury City	2485	**W**	3-2	B.Williams 16 23 (pen) Oastler 48	19	50
21	CPrem	A	Woking	4728	**W**	2-1	B.Williams 65 (pen) Molesley 83	19	51
26	CPrem	H	Hereford United	3593	L	1-2	Oyeleke 76	19	52

GOALSCORERS	Lge	FAC	FAT	Total	Pens	Hat-tricks	Cons Run
B. Williams	24	1	3	28	8	1	4
Molesley	7			7			
O'Brien	3		4	7			5
Roberts	6		1	7			
Oyeleke	5		1	6			2
Paterson	2	1	1	4			
Bubb	3			3			
Mekki	3			3			
Scott	3			3			
Gibbs	2			2			
Oastler	2			2			
Rowlands	2			2			
Stanley	1		1	2			
Young			2	2			
Goodman	1			1			
Partington	1			1			
Phillips	1			1			
Plummer	1			1			
Wickham	1			1			
Opponents	1		1	2			

Cons Run - Consecutive scoring games.

ALFRETON TOWN

Chairman: Wayne Bradley
Secretary: Bryan Rudkin (T) 07710 444 195 (E) bryanrudkin@hotmail.com
Commercial Manager: Charlotte Webster (T) 07780 472 467
Programme Editor: Image2print Ltd (T)
Ground Address: Impact Arena, North Street, Alfreton, Derbyshire DE55 7FZ
(T) 01773 830 277 **Manager:** Nicky Law

Club Factfile

Founded: 1959 **Nickname:** The Reds
Previous Names: Formed when Alfreton Miners Welfare and Alfreton United merged.
Previous Leagues: Central Alliance (pre reformation 1921-25) 59-61. Midland Combination 1925-27, 61-82. Northern Counties East 1982-87. Northern Premier 1987-99.
Club Colours (change): All red (All blue)

Ground Capacity: 3,600 **Seats:** 1,500 **Covered:** 2,600 **Clubhouse:** Yes **Shop:** Yes

Directions
From M1 Junction 28 Take A38 towards Derby for 2 miles.
Then take slip road onto B600 Turn right at Tjunction towards town centre.
At pedestrian crossing turn left into North Street and the ground is on the right hand side.

Previous Grounds: None

Record Attendance: 5,023 v Matlock Town - Central Alliance 1960
Record Victory: 15-0 v Loughbrough Midland League 1969-70
Record Defeat: 1-9 v Solihull - FAT 1997. 0-8 v Bridlington - 1992
Record Goalscorer: J Harrison - 303
Record Appearances: J Harrison - 560+
Additional Records: Paid £2,000 to Worksop Town for Mick Goddard
Received £7,000 from Ilkeston Town for Paul Eshelby
Senior Honours:
Northern Counties East 1984-85, 2001-02. Northern Premier League Division 1 2002-03.
Conference North 2010-11.
Derbyshire Senior Cup x7

10 YEAR RECORD

04-05	05-06	06-07	07-08	08-09	09-10	10-11	11-12	12-13	13-14
Conf N 14	Conf N 17	Conf N 14	Conf N 16	Conf N 3	Conf N 3	Conf N 1	Conf 15	Conf 13	Conf 11

ALFRETON TOWN MATCH RESULTS 2013-14

Date	Comp	H/A	Opponents	Att:	Result	Goalscorers	Pos	No.
Aug 10	CPrem	A	Dartford	1202	L 0-1		17	1
13	CPrem	H	Kidderminster Harriers	722	W 3-1	Bradley 11 70 Shaw 51	11	2
17	CPrem	H	Salisbury City	463	W 3-2	AKINDE 3 (39 63 78)	5	3
24	CPrem	A	Grimsby Town	3245	L 1-3	Fenton 90	12	4
26	CPrem	H	Hereford United	740	W 2-1	Akinde 12 Law 90	8	5
31	CPrem	A	Forest Green Rovers	1027	L 1-3	Bradley 79	13	6
Sept 7	CPrem	H	Woking	628	W 3-1	Shaw 9 43 Meadows 90	7	7
14	CPrem	A	Macclesfield	1271	W 1-0	Meadows 27	5	8
17	CPrem	H	Cambridge United	731	D 1-1	Clayton 15	7	9
21	CPrem	H	Barnet	783	W 3-1	McGrath 13 Clayton 54 61	3	10
24	CPrem	A	Southport	726	L 1-2	Akinde 49	6	11
28	CPrem	A	Braintree Town	927	L 1-3	Wood 89	11	12
Oct 5	CPrem	H	Forest Green Rovers	582	W 3-2	Shaw 12 Wishart 43 ,51	9	13
8	CPrem	H	Chester	743	L 0-1		10	14
12	CPrem	A	Gateshead		L 0-3		14	15
19	CPrem	A	Aldershot	1732	W 3-2	Shaw 23 Law 31 Speight 56	12	16
26	***FAC4Q***	***A***	***North Ferriby United***	***735***	***W 3-1***	***Speight 39 Akinde 65 McGrath 90***		17
Nov 2	CPrem	H	FC Halifax Town	900	W 3-0	Speight 14 31 J.Akinde 49	9	18
9	***FAC1***	***A***	***Wrexham***	***2415***	***L 1-3***	***Speight 61 (pen)***		19
12	CPrem	A	Tamworth	716	L 0-1		10	20
16	CPrem	H	Braintree Town	904	W 3 1	Akinde 15 Shaw 42 Law 66	6	21
23	CPrem	A	Hyde United	448	W 2 1	Bradley 74 Westwood 78	5	22
26	CPrem	A	Nuneaton Borough	715	L 0-3		6	23
30	***FAT1***	***H***	***Nuneaton Town***	***343***	***L 0-1***			24
Dec 7	CPrem	H	Luton Town	1279	L 0-5		8	25
14	CPrem	A	Kidderminster Harriers	1834	W 3-1	Wylde 52 68 Akinde 89 (pen)	6	26
21	CPrem	H	Dartford	575	W 2-1	Clayton 52 60	4	27
26	CPrem	A	Wrexham	3371	W 3-2	Wylde 73 Akinde 85 Westwood 90	4	28
28	CPrem	H	Southport	976	W 2-1	Wylde 22 Meadows 30	3	29
Jan 1	CPrem	H	Wrexham	756	W 1-0	Akinde 45	3	30
4	CPrem	A	Barnet	1400	L 0-1		3	31
7	CPrem	A	Lincoln City	1877	L 1-4	Fenton 55	3	32
15	CPrem	A	Welling United	677	W 2-1	Law 17 Harrod 58 (pen)	3	33
Feb 8	CPrem	A	Salisbury City	623	D 0-0		3	34
11	CPrem	A	Cambridge United	2106	W 1-0	Wood 25	3	35
22	CPrem	H	Gateshead	817	D 1-1	Shaw 71	3	36
March 1	CPrem	A	Luton Town	8412	L 0-3		4	37
8	CPrem	H	Lincoln City	**1331**	D 1-1	Harrod 61	3	38
11	CPrem	H	Hyde	506	W 3-0	Harrod 18 81 Akinde 50	3	39
15	CPrem	A	Chester	2042	W 1-0	Harrod 61 (pen)	3	40
18	CPrem	H	Tamworth	594	W 4-2	Harrod 41 (pen) Shaw 45 Akinde 73 Clayton 83	3	41
24	CPrem	A	FC Halifax Town	1454	L 0-2		4	42
29	CPrem	H	Nuneaton Town	789	D 1-1	Akinde 32	4	43
April 5	CPrem	H	Welling United	599	D 2-2	Fenton 19 Wood 73	6	44
8	CPrem	H	Aldershot Town	620	L 1-4	Akinde 56	6	45
12	CPrem	A	Woking	1485	L 1-2	Akinde 20	7	46
18	CPrem	H	Grimsby Town	1771	D 3-3	Law 24 Akinde 51 (pen) Clayton 79	8	47
21	CPrem	A	Hereford United	2445	L 2-3	Akinde 7 Harrod 87	9	48
26	CPrem	H	Macclesfield Town	696	L 0-1		11	49

GOALSCORERS	Lge	FAC	FAT	Total	Pens	Hat-tricks	Cons Run
Akinde	17	1		18	3		4
Shaw	8			8			
Clayton	7			7			2
Harrod	7			7	3		4
Law	5			5			
Speight	3	2		5	1		3
Bradley	4			4			
Wylde	4			4			2
Fenton	3			3			
Meadows	3			3			2
Wood	3			3			
McGrath	1	1		2			
Westwood	2			2			
Wishart	2			2			

Cons Run - Consecutive scoring games.

ALTRINCHAM

Chairman: Grahame Rowley
Secretary: Derek Wilshaw (T) 07833 636 381 (E) dwilshaw@altrinchamfootballclub.co.uk
Commercial Manager: Paul Daine (T) 0161 929 3955
Programme Editor: Grahame Rowley (T) 0161 928 1045
Ground Address: The J Davidson Stadium, Moss Lane, Altrincham, Cheshire WA15 8AP
(T) 0161 928 1045 **Manager:** Lee Sinnott

Back row: Simon Richman, James Walshaw, Kyle Perry, Stuart Coburn, Adam Reid, Gianluca Havern, Danny Boshell, Rob Gilroy.
Middle row: Luke Pickering (kitman), George Heslop (matchday secretary), Jake Moult, Scott Leather, Damian Reeves, Mike Williams, Carl Rodgers, Barry Pond (associate director), Ian Senior (g/k coach).
Front row: Alan Ainsley (sports therapist), Brian Smikle, Matt Doughty, Neil Tolson (assistant manager), Paul Daine (director), Shaun Densmore (team captain), Grahame Rowley (chairman), Lee Sinnott (manager), Nicky Clee, James Lawrie, John Skelhorn (kitman).

Club Factfile

Founded: 1903 **Nickname:** The Robins
Previous Names: Broadheath FC 1893-1903.
Previous Leagues: Manchester 1903-11. Lancashire C. 1911-19. Cheshire C. 1919-68. Northern Premier 1968-79,97-99. Conference 1979-97, 99-

Club Colours (change): Red & white stripes/black/red. (Yellow/blue/blue)

Ground Capacity: 6,085 **Seats:** 1,154 **Covered:** Yes **Clubhouse:** Yes **Shop:** Yes

Directions
From M6 junctio19, turn right towards Altrincham into town centre (approx 15 minutes). Turn down Lloyd Street, past Sainsburys on the right. Tesco Extra on left. Then follow signs for Altrincham F.C.

Previous Grounds: Pollitts Field 1903-10.

Record Attendance: 10,275 - Altrincham Boys v Sunderland Boys English Schools Shield 1925.
Record Victory: 9-2 v Merthyr Tydfil - Conference 1990-91.
Record Defeat: 1-13 v Stretford (H) - 04.11.1893.
Record Goalscorer: Jack Swindells - 252 (1965-71).
Record Appearances: John Davison - 677 (1971-86).
Additional Records: Transfer fee paid - £15k to Blackpool for Keith Russell. Received - £50k from Leicester for Kevin Ellison.

Senior Honours:
Cheshire Senior Cup Winners 1904-05, 33-34, 66-67, 81-82. F.A. Trophy Winners 1977-78, 85-86.
Football Alliance Champions 1979-80, 80-81. N.P.L. Premier Champions 1998-99.
Conference North & South Play-off Winners 2004-05.

10 YEAR RECORD

04-05	05-06	06-07	07-08	08-09	09-10	10-11	11-12	12-13	13-14
Conf N 5	Conf 22	Conf 21	Conf 21	Conf 15	Conf 14	Conf 22	Conf N 8	Conf N 4	Conf N 3

ALTRINCHAM MATCH RESULTS 2013-14

Date	Comp	H/A	Opponents	Att:	Result		Goalscorers	Pos	No.
Aug 17	CNorth	A	Worcester City	714	**W**	3-1	Reeves 63 Perry 74 Rodgers 88	4	1
20	CNorth	H	Barrow	1145	**W**	2-1	Lawrie 45 Perry 52	4	2
24	CNorth	H	Stockport County	**2875**	**W**	3-0	Walshaw 42 Reeves 49 70	2	3
26	CNorth	A	Vauxhall Motors	446	**W**	2-1	Perry 19 Walshaw 83	2	4
31	CNorth	H	Histon	825	D	2-2	Walshaw 1 Reeves 62	2	5
Sept 7	CNorth	A	Leamington	853	**W**	1-0	Reeves 20	1	6
14	CNorth	H	Oxford City	820	D	2-2	Walshaw 16 Richman 21	2	7
21	CNorth	A	North Ferriby United	420	L	1-2	Walshaw 77	6	8
24	CNorth	H	Gloucester City	826	**W**	2-0	Richman 27 Smickle 47	3	9
28	***FAC2Q***	***A***	***Trafford***	***829***	***L***	***1-2***	***Walshaw 14 (pen)***		10
Oct 5	CNorth	H	Guiseley	838	**W**	4-1	WALSHAW 3 (50 53 65) Reeves 58	3	11
19	CNorth	H	Brackley Town	855	**W**	1-0	Walshaw 45	2	12
26	CNorth	A	Boston United	1081	L	2-3	Densmore 42 Walshaw 82	2	13
Nov 2	CNorth	H	Hednesford Town	913	L	1-3	Walshaw 15	6	14
8	CNorth	A	Bradford PA	383	**W**	4-2	Reeves 15 42 Wilkinson 71 Clee 79	2	15
19	***FAT3Q***	***A***	***Colwyn Bay***	***280***	***W***	***2-0***	***Wilkinson 66 Walshaw 75***		16
23	CNorth	H	Solihull Borough	840	**W**	1-0	Walshaw 17 (pen)	2	17
30	***FAT1***	***H***	***Leek Town***	***636***	***L***	***1-2***	***Wilkinson 90***		18
Dec 7	CNorth	A	Harrogate Town	547	L	2-3	Leather 28 Perry 71	3	19
10	CNorth	A	Goucester City	320	L	0-2		3	20
21	CNorth	A	Guiseley	613	D	2-2	Havern 17 Rodgers 69	6	21
26	CNorth	H	Stalybridge Celtic	1171	**W**	5-0	Moult 10 52 Perry 14 Reeves 39 Richman 70	5	22
28	CNorth	A	Barrow	736	D	1-1	Reeves 78	5	23
Jan 1	CNorth	A	Stalybridge Celtic	684	**W**	5-0	Moult 18 Leather 31 Perry 48 Reeves 54 Clee 7	4	24
4	CNorth	H	Leamington	972	**W**	3-2	Reeves 5 Perry 53 Walshaw 87	3	25
7	CNorth	A	Gainsborough Trinity	300	L	4-5	Perry 16 74 Rodgers 88 Clee 90	3	26
21	CNorth	H	Worcester CIty	527	L	1-2	Lawrie 80	5	27
Feb 1	CNorth	A	Hednesford Town	703	D	1-1	Densmore 90	6	28
4	CNorth	H	AFC Telford United	690	D	1-1	Walshaw 34	6	29
22	CNorth	H	Colwyn Bay	790	**W**	3-1	WALSHAW 3 (5 10 56)	7	30
March 1	CNorth	H	Workington	259	**W**	2-0	Clee 28 Mwasile 73	6	31
8	CNorth	A	Brackley Town	390	**W**	2-1	Reeves 83 Walshaw 85	4	32
11	CNorth	H	Harrogate Town	704	L	1-3	Reeves 43	5	33
15	CNorth	A	Solihull Borough	438	**W**	1-0	Marshall 45	4	34
22	CNorth	H	Gainborough Trinity	709	**W**	3-0	Walshaw 28 (pen) Leather 74 Lawrie 85	4	35
26	CNorth	H	Bradford PA	582	**W**	4-1	Walshaw 10 74 Reeves 26 Perry 89	3	36
29	CNorth	A	Colwyn Bay	497	**W**	3-1	Reeves 5 Walshaw 26 Clee 96	3	37
April 1	CNorth	H	Boston United	650	D	0-0		3	38
5	CNorth	A	AFC Telford United	1785	L	1-3	Walshaw 73	4	39
8	CNorth	A	Workington	270	**W**	6-1	Walshaw 15 (pen) 40 Densmore 4 Perry 42 69 Moult 52	3	40
12	CNorth	H	North Ferriby United	1160	D	1-1	Wilkinson 79	4	41
15	CNorth	A	Oxford City	283	**W**	2-1	Walshaw 18 Moult 83	3	42
18	CNorth	A	Stockport County	3770	D	0-0		3	43
21	CNorth	H	Vauxhall Motors	812	**W**	5-1	Walshaw 22 50 Havern 27 Reeves 45 Lawrie 73	3	44
26	CNorth	A	Histon	433	**W**	5-0	Leather 6 Clee 10 Reeves 15 24 Lawrie 48	3	45
30	***CNPO SF1***	***A***	***Hednesford Town***	***1209***	***D***	***2-2***	***Reeves 13 Walshaw 59***		46
May 3	***CNPO SF2***	***H***	***Hednesford Town***	***1974***	***W***	***2-1***	***Reeves 85 Lawrie 87***		47
10	***CNPO F***	***H***	***Guiseley***	***4632***	***W***	***2-1***	***Lawrie 51, Wilkinson 120 (AET)***		48

GOALSCORERS	Lge	FAC	FAT	Total	Pens	Hat-tricks	Cons Run
Walshaw	28+1	1	1	31	4	2	5
Reeves	18+2			20			3
Perry	12			12			3
Lawrie	5+2			7			2
Clee	6			6			
Moult	5			5			
Wilkinson	2+1		2	5			2
Leather	4			4			
Densmore	3			3			
Rodgers	3			3			
Havern	2			2			
Richman	2			2			
Marshall	1			1			
Mwasile	1			1			
Smickle	1			1			

Cons Run - Consecutive scoring games.
Play-off goals indicated by +

BARNET

Chairman: Anthony Kleanthous

Secretary: Andrew Adie (T) 020 8381 3800 (E) aadie@barnetfc.com

Commercial Manager: John Meir (T) 020 8381 3800 x1030

Programme Editor: David Bloomfield (T) 02085 243 397

Ground Address: The Hive, Camrose Avenue, Edgware, Middlesex, HA8 6AG

(T) 020 8381 3800 **Manager:** Martin Allen

The West Stand - which can seat 2,684.

Club Factfile

Founded: 1885 **Nickname:** The Bees

Previous Names: New Barnet 1885-88. Barnet 1888-1902 (folded). Barnet Alston 1904-19.

Previous Leagues: Post 1945 - Athenian 1945-65. Southern 1965-79. Conference 1979-91, 2001-05. Football League 1991-2001, 05-13.

Club Colours (change): Black & amber stripes/black/black (Purple & white stripes/white/white)

Ground Capacity: 5,176 **Seats:** 3,434 **Covered:** 5,176 **Clubhouse:** Yes **Shop:** Yes

Directions

Leave M1 at junction 4, take the A41 towards Edgware, at the first roundabout turn right on to the A410 towards Stanmore (London Road), pass the Stanmore Tube Station on your left, at the next set of lights, turn left on the A4140 (Marsh Lane into Honeypot Lane) towards Queensbury/Kingsbury after approx 2 miles turn left at the roundabout by the Tesco petrol station in to Taunton Way, then Camrose Avenue, The Hive is on your left hand side.

Previous Grounds: Underhill 1907-2013

Record Attendance: 11,026 v Wycombe Wanderers FA Amateur Cup 01/01/1953

Record Victory: 7-0 v Blackpool Division 3 11/11/2000

Record Defeat: 1-9 v Peterborough Division 3 05/09/1998

Record Goalscorer: Arthur Morris - 400

Record Appearances:

Additional Records:

Senior Honours:

Athenian League 1931-32, 32-33, 46-47, 58-59, 63-64, 64-65. Southern League Division One 1965-66, Division One South 1977-78.
Football Conference 1990-91, 2004-05.
Amateur Cup 1945-46.

10 YEAR RECORD

04-05	05-06	06-07	07-08	08-09	09-10	10-11	11-12	12-13	13-14
Conf 1	FL 2 18	FL 2 14	FL 2 12	FL 2 17	FL 2 11	FL 2 22	FL 2 22	FL 2 23	Conf 8

BARNET MATCH RESULTS 2013-14

Date	Comp	H/A	Opponents	Att:	Result		Goalscorers	Pos	No.
Aug 10	CPrem	H	Chester	2543	**W**	3-0	Gambin 46 Hyde 63 73	3	1
13	CPrem	A	Tamworth	1379	D	0-0		3	2
17	CPrem	A	Gateshead	639	**W**	2-1	Marsh-Brown 37 Hyde 88	2	3
24	CPrem	H	Nuneaton Borough	1507	D	1-1	Hyde 16	4	4
26	CPrem	A	Braintree Town	1480	**W**	3-0	Marsh-Brown 46 Bryne 72 Hyde 90	1	5
31	CPrem	H	Hyde	1669	**W**	3-2	Marsh-Brown 5 Byrne 40 Crawford 84	2	6
Sept 7	CPrem	A	FC Halifax Town	1651	L	1-2	Weston 65	3	7
14	CPrem	H	Lincoln City	1913	D	1-1	Marsh-Brown 46	4	8
17	CPrem	A	Aldershot Town	1740	D	3-3	Weston 57 Mengerink 78 Crawford 88	5	9
21	CPrem	A	Alfreton Town	783	L	1-3	Marsh-Brown 49	8	10
24	CPrem	H	Macclesfield Town	1179	L	1-2	Vilhete 74	12	11
28	CPrem	H	Salisbury City	1409	**W**	3-1	Abdulla 72 Yiadom 74 Marsh-Brown 88	10	12
Oct 5	CPrem	A	Welling United	1017	D	1-1	Marsh-Brown 72 (pen)	11	13
8	CPrem	A	Woking	1413	D	0-0		11	14
12	CPrem	H	Wrexham	2143	D	1-1	Acheampomg 7	9	15
19	CPrem	A	Hereford United	1632	**W**	1-0	Abdulla 36	8	16
26	***FAC4Q***	***H***	***Concord Rangers***	***1373***	***W***	***3-0***	***Marsh-Brown 20 Lopez 27 72***		17
Nov 2	CPrem	H	Kidderminstre Harriers	1557	**W**	1-0	Villa 25	7	18
8	***FAC1***	***A***	***Preston North End***	***5217***	***L***	***0-6***			19
12	CPrem	H	Welling United	1274	D	0-0		6	20
16	CPrem	H	Cambridge United	2853	D	2-2	Villa 38 Weston 45	7	21
23	CPrem	A	Grimsby Town	3441	L	1-2	Stephens 84	11	22
26	CPrem	A	Dartford	803	**W**	2-0	Marsh-Brown 19 Villa 33	7	23
30	***FAT1***	***A***	***Hayes & Yeading***	***302***	***W***	***1-0***	***Sykes 89***		24
Dec 7	CPrem	H	Dartford	1461	**W**	1-0	Nurse 30	6	25
14	***FAT2***	***H***	***Grimsby Town***	***972***	***L***	***1-2***	***Marsh-Brown 70***		26
21	CPrem	A	Hyde	499	**W**	1-0	Nurse 57	5	27
26	CPrem	H	Luton Town	**3608**	L	1-2	Hyde 69	7	28
28	CPrem	A	Salisbury City	1343	L	1-2	Hyde 20	9	29
Jan 1	CPrem	A	Luton Town	7543	L	1-2	Hyde 70	9	30
4	CPrem	H	Alfreton Town	1400	**W**	1-0	Lopez 40	6	31
18	CPrem	A	Chester	2179	L	1-2	Hyde 84	10	32
Edgar Davids resigns as manager.									
21	CPrem	H	Aldershot Town	1387	L	1-3	Vihete 45	10	33
Ulrich Landvreugd and Dick Schreuder appointed as joint managers.									
25	CPrem	H	Southport	1510	**W**	1-0	Vilhete 74	7	34
Feb 15	CPrem	H	Tamworth	1296	**W**	1-0	Villa 84	9	35
18	CPrem	H	Grimsby Town	1375	**W**	2-1	Vilhete 3 Hyde 81	6	36
22	CPrem	A	Wrexham	2925	**W**	1-0	Hyde 79	4	37
25	CPrem	A	Forest Green Rovers	869	**W**	2-1	Byrne 1 Lopez 42	3	38
March 1	CPrem	H	Woking	1708	L	1-3	Weston 26	3	39
8	CPrem	H	Gateshead	1361	L	0-1		4	40
15	CPrem	A	Kidderminster Harriers	1950	L	0-1		7	41
18	CPrem	A	Macclesfield Town	1153	L	0-2		9	42
22	CPrem	H	Hereford United	1497	**W**	2-0	Marsh-Brown 14 23	6	43
29	CPrem	A	Cambridge United	3386	D	1-1	Dymond 69	9	44
April 5	CPrem	H	Forest Green Rovers	1466	**W**	2-1	Gjokoj 19 Byrne 80	8	45
8	CPrem	A	Southport	774	D	1-1	Byrne 45	8	46
12	CPrem	H	FC Halifax Town	1683	L	0-4		8	47
19	CPrem	A	Nuneaton Borough	852	L	0-1		8	48
21	CPrem	H	Braintree Town	1339	D	1-1	Marsh-Brown 40	8	49
26	CPrem	A	Lincoln City	2812	D	3-3	Abdulla 6 (pen) Allen 57 Hyde 90	8	50

GOALSCORERS	Lge	FAC	FAT	Total	Pens	Hat-tricks	Cons Run
Marsh-Brown	11	1	1	13	1		2
Hyde	12			12			3
Byrne	6			6			2
Lopez	2	2		4			
Vilhete	4			4			2
Villa	4			4			
Weston	4			4			
Abdulla	3			3	1		
Crawford	2			2			
Nurse	2			2			

	Lge	FAC	FAT	Total	Pens	Hat-tricks	Cons Run
Acheampong	1			1			
Allen	1			1			
Dymond	1			1			
Gambin	1			1			
Gjokoj	1			1			
Mengerink	1			1			
Stephens	1			1			
Sykes			1	1			
Yiadom	1			1			

Cons Run - Consecutive scoring games.

BRAINTREE TOWN

Chairman: Lee Harding
Secretary: Tom Woodley **(T)** 07950 537 179 **(E)** tawoodley@talktalk.net
Commercial Manager: Jerry Carter **(T)** 07803 052 304
Programme Editor: Lee Harding **(T)** 07771 810 440
Ground Address: Cressing Road Stadium, off Clockhouse Way, Braintree CM7 3RD
(T) 01376 345 617 **Manager:** Alan Devonshire

Club Factfile

Founded: 1898 **Nickname:** The Iron
Previous Names: Crittall Athletic > 1968, Braintree and Crittall Athletic > 1981, Braintree > 1983
Previous Leagues: N.Essex 1898-1925, Essex & Suffolk Border 1925-29, 55-64, Spartan 1928-35, Eastern Co. 1935-37, 38-39, 52-55, 70-91, Essex Co. 1937-38, London 1945-52, Gt London 1964-66, Met 1966-70, Southern 1991-96, Isthmian 1996-2006

Club Colours (change): Orange/blue/orange (All white)

Ground Capacity: 4,222 **Seats:** 553 **Covered:** 1,288 **Clubhouse:** Yes **Shop:** Yes

Directions
Leave M11 at junction 8A (for Stansted Airport) and follow A120 towards Braintree and Colchester for 17 miles. At Gallows Corner roundabout (with WestDrive Kia on your right) take first exit into Cressing Road. Clockhouse Way and the entrance to the ground are three quarters of a mile on the left and are clearly sign-posted.

Previous Grounds: The Fiar Field 1898-1903, Spalding Meadow and Panfield Lane

Record Attendance: 4,000 v Tottenham Hotspur - Testimonial May 1952
Record Victory: 12-0 v Thetford - Eastern Counties League 1935-36
Record Defeat: 0-14 v Chelmsford City (A) - North Essex League 1923
Record Goalscorer: Chris Guy - 211 (1963-90)
Record Appearances: Paul Young - 524 (1966-77)
Additional Records: Gary Bennett scored 57 goals during season 1997-98
Received £10,000 from Brentford for Matt Metcalf and from Colchester United for John Cheesewright
Senior Honours:
Eastern Counties League 1983-84, 84-85, Essex Senior Cup 1995-96. Isthmian League Premier Division 2005-06.
Conference South Champions 2010-11.
East Anglian Cup x3

10 YEAR RECORD

04-05	05-06	06-07	07-08	08-09	09-10	10-11	11-12	12-13	13-14
Isth P 4	Isth P 1	Conf S 3	Conf S 5	Conf S 14	Conf S 7	Conf S 1	Conf 12	Conf 9	Conf 6

BRAINTREE TOWN MATCH RESULTS 2013-14

Date	Comp	H/A	Opponents	Att:	Result		Goalscorers	Pos	No.
Aug 10	CPrem	A	Hereford United	2033	D	1-1	Smith 8 (og)	9	1
13	CPrem	H	Woking	995	W	2-0	Holman 17 Marks 19	4	2
17	CPrem	H	Kidderminster Harriers	874	L	0-1		12	3
24	CPrem	A	Dartford	1015	W	2-0	Massey 69 Enver-Marum 90	7	4
26	CPrem	H	Barnet	1480	L	0-3		13	5
31	CPrem	A	Macclesfield Town	1264	W	1-0	Enver-Marum 47	9	6
Sept 7	CPrem	H	Forest Green Rovers	944	D	1-1	Davis 45 (pen)	12	7
14	CPrem	A	Grimsby Town	3403	L	0-1		13	8
17	CPrem	A	Salisbury City	594	D	1-1	Marks 28	14	9
21	CPrem	H	Southport	924	W	1-0	Marks 37	12	10
24	CPrem	A	Wrexham	2731	W	3-2	Carrington 3 (og) Wells 21 Tomassen 70 (og)	9	11
28	CPrem	H	Alfreton Town	927	W	3-1	Strutton 61 Marks 84 Sparkes 87	5	12
Oct 5	CPrem	A	Hyde United	402	W	3-0	Strutton 37 57 Cox 67	3	13
8	CPrem	H	Welling United	1119	L	2-3	Strutton 27 Cox 89	5	14
12	CPrem	A	Nuneaton Town	1031	D	1-1	Paine 30	6	15
19	CPrem	H	Chester	1132	W	3-0	Strutton 6 7 Wells 28	4	16
26	***FAC4Q***	***H***	***Weymouth***	***775***	***W***	***2-1***	***Paine 5 Marks 11***		17
Nov 2	CPrem	A	Tamworth	716	D	0-0		6	18
9	***FAC1***	***H***	***Newport County***	***1004***	***D***	***1-1***	***Isaac 9***		19
12	CPrem	H	Luton Town	**1518**	L	1-2	Holman 67	7	20
16	CPrem	A	Alfreton Town	904	L	1-3	Daley 47	10	21
19	***FAC1r***	***A***	***Newport County***	***1406***	***L***	***0-1***			22
23	CPrem	H	FC Halifax Town	943	W	1-0	Davis 62 (pen)	8	23
26	CPrem	A	Aldershot	1215	L	1-2	Davis 16 (pen)	9	24
30	***FAT1***	***H***	***Welling United***	***365***	**W**	***3-0***	***Holman 18 Sparkes 69 Cox 88***		25
Dec 7	CPrem	A	Chester	1736	W	2-0	Holman 34 58	7	26
14	***FAT2***	***H***	***Lincoln City***	***410***	***L***	***1-3***	***Marks 21***		27
26	CPrem	A	Cambridge United	4194	L	0-1		11	28
28	CPrem	H	Tamworth	811	W	2-0	Peters 52 Mulley 76	10	29
Jan 12	CPrem	H	Woking	1270	L	0-1		11	30
Feb 22	CPrem	A	Kidderminster Harriers	1653	D	2-2	Paine 53 Holman 67	17	31
25	CPrem	H	Cambridge United	1016	W	1-0	Sparkes 67	16	32
March 1	CPrem	H	Hyde United	754	W	2-1	Mensah 5 Holman 84	16	33
8	CPrem	H	Hereford United	805	D	1-1	Holman 34	17	34
11	CPrem	H	Wrexham	506	W	2-0	Marks 38 Holman 73 Jakubiak 90	13	35
13	CPrem	A	Forest Green Rovers	841	W	2-0	Holman 36 (pen) Mensah 68	11	36
15	CPrem	A	Lincoln City	2002	L	0-2		12	37
18	CPrem	H	Lincoln City	787	L	0-2		13	38
22	CPrem	H	Aldershot Town	1090	W	1-0	Holman	12	39
25	CPrem	A	Welling United	403	W	2-0	Davis 35 51 (pen)	11	40
27	CPrem	H	Nuneaton Town	802	W	2-1	Streete 8 (og) Holman 17	5	41
29	CPrem	A	Gateshead	859	L	0-1		8	42
April 1	CPrem	A	Suthport	714	W	4-0	Marks 6 Holman 52 77 Mulley 62	6	43
3	CPrem	A	FC Halifax Town	1535	D	0-0		4	44
5	CPrem	H	Salisbury City	905	L	0-1		7	45
8	CPrem	H	Macclesfied Town	739	L	0-1		7	46
12	CPrem	A	Luton Town	10,020	W	3-2	Wells 16 Mulley 21 Isaac 56	6	47
15	CPrem	H	Gateshead	901	D	0-0		6	48
18	CPrem	H	Dartford	1200	W	1-0	Davis 24	6	49
21	CPrem	A	Barnet	1339	D	1-1	Davis 58 (pen)	6	50
26	CPrem	H	Grimsby Town	1489	D	0-0		6	51

GOALSCORERS	Lge	FAC	FAT	Total	Pens	Hat-tricks	Cons Run
Holman	13		1	14	1		3
Marks	6	1	1	8			2
Davis	7			7	5		2
Strutton	6			6			2
Cox	2		1	3			2
Mulley	3			3			
Paine	2	1		3			
Sparkes	2		1	3			
Wells	3			3			
Enver-Marum	2			2			
Isaac	1	1		2			
Mensah	2			2			
Daley	1			1			
Jakubiaki	1			1			
Massey	1			1			
Peters	1			1			
Opponents	4			4			

Cons Run - Consecutive scoring games.

BRISTOL ROVERS

Chairman: Nick Higgs
Secretary: Rod Wesson **(T)** 07970 705 441 **(E)** rodwesson@bristolrovers.co.uk
Commercial Manager: Ian Holtby **(T)** 07778 499 864
Programme Editor: Keith Brookman **(T)** 07968 440 806
Ground Address: Memorial Stadium, Filton Avenue, Horfield, Bristol BS7 0BF
(T) 0117 909 66 48 **Manager:** Darrell Clarke

Club Factfile

Founded: 1883 **Nickname:** Pirates
Previous Names: Black Arabs 1883-84. Eastville Rovers 1884-97. Bristol Eastville Rovers 1897-98.
Previous Leagues: Bristol & District 1892-95, Western 1895-97, Birmingham & District 1897-99. Southern 1899-1920. Football League 1920-2014.

Club Colours (change): Blue & white quarters/blue/white (White/black/black)

Ground Capacity: 11,000 **Seats:** Yes **Covered:** Yes **Clubhouse:** Yes **Shop:** Yes

Directions From South West/Midlands/North - Exit M5 at Junction Junction 16 (sign posted Thornbury, Filton A38). At roundabout take the A38, Gloucester Road (Filton). Keep straight on for 4.4 miles, passing through Patchway, and past Filton Aerodrome. Turn left at traffic lights (opposite The Wellington public house) on to the B4469 (Muller Road). Turn right at the first junction, into Filton Avenue, and the stadium is on the left hand side after 0.1 miles. From East - Exit M4 at Junction 19 (s/p Bristol M32) on to the M32. After 3.1 miles, exit at Junction 2 (s/p B4469 Fishponds, Horfield). At roundabout, turn right (s/p A38, Memorial Stadium) and as the road divides, branch right on to Muller Road. Go straight on, passing through five sets of traffic lights. At the sixth set of lights, turn left into Filton Avenue and the stadium is on the left hand side after 0.1 miles.

Previous Grounds: Eastville 1897-1986. Twerton Park 1986-96.

Record Attendance: 12,011 v West Bromwich Albion, FA Cup Rnd 6, 09/03/2008
Record Victory: 15-1 v Weymouth, FA Cup 3rd Qualifying Round, 17/11/1900
Record Defeat: 0-12 v Luton Town, Division 3 South, 13/04/1936
Record Goalscorer: League: Geoff Bradford - 242 (1949-64)
Record Appearances: League: Stuart Taylor - 546 (1966-80)
Additional Records: Received £2m from Fulham for Barry Hayles (Nov. 1998).
And £2m from West Bromwich Albion for Jason Roberts (July 2000)
Senior Honours:
Southern League 1904-05. Football League Division Three South 1952-53, Division Three 1989-90.

10 YEAR RECORD

04-05	05-06	06-07	07-08	08-09	09-10	10-11	11-12	12-13	13-14
FL 3 12	FL 3 12	FL 2 6	FL 1 16	FL 1 11	FL 1 11	FL 1 22	FL 2 13	FL 2 14	FL 2 23

BRISTOL ROVERS MATCH RESULTS 2013-14

Date	Comp	H/A	Opponents	Att:	Result	No.
Aug 3	FL2	A	Exeter City	5196	L 1-2	1
6	**LC1**	**H**	**Watford**	**4875**	**L 1-3**	2
10	FL2	H	Scunthorpe United	6259	D 0-0	3
17	FL2	A	Newport County	5387	L 0-1	4
24	FL2	H	York City	5569	W 3-2	5
31	FL2	H	Northampton Town	5695	W 1-0	6
Sept 4	**JPT1**	**A**	**Bristol City**	**17888**	**L 1-2**	7
7	FL2	A	Plymouth Argyle	8631	L 0-1	8
14	FL2	A	Dagenham & Redbridge	1423	L 0-2	9
21	FL2	H	Hartlepool United	5579	D 2-2	10
27	FL2	A	Southend United	5489	D 1-1	11
Oct 5	FL2	H	Fleetwood Town	5303	L 1-3	12
12	FL2	A	Mansfield Town	3275	D 1-1	13
19	FL2	H	Wycombe Wanderers	5783	L 0-1	14
22	FL2	A	Accrington Stanley	1101	L 1-2	15
26	FL2	H	Chesterfield	5667	D 0-0	16
NOV 2	FL2	A	Oxford United	6374	W 1-0	17
8	**FAC1**	**H**	**York City**	**4654**	**D 3-3**	18
16	FL2	H	Bury	5534	D 1-1	19
19	**FAC1r**	**A**	**York City**	**2051**	**W 3-2**	20
23	FL2	A	Burton Albion	2302	L 0-1	21
26	FL2	A	Cheltenham Town	3556	D 0-0	22
30	FL2	H	AFC Wimbledon	5860	W 3-0	23
Dec 7	**FAC2**	**H**	**Crawley Town**	**4623**	**D 0-0**	24
14	FL2	A	Morecambe	1514	L 1-2	25
21	FL2	H	Portsmouth	7537	W 2-0	26
26	FL2	A	Torquay United	3461	D 1-1	27
29	FL2	A	Rochdale	2576	L 0-2	28
Jan 8	**FAC2r**	**A**	**Crawley Town**	**2435**	**W 2-1**	29
11	FL2	H	Exeter City	6674	W 2-1	30
14	**FAC3**	**A**	**Birmingham City**	**9914**	**L 0-3**	31
18	FL2	A	York City	3514	D 0-0	32
25	FL2	H	Newport County	7288	W 3-1	33
28	FL2	H	Accrington Stanley	6067	L 0-1	34
Feb 1	FL2	A	Chesterfield	6048	L 1-3	35
8	FL2	H	Oxford United	6493	D 1-1	36
11	FL2	H	Cheltenham Town	5808	W 1-0	37
21	FL2	H	Burton Albion	5957	W 2-0	38
25	FL2	A	Scunthorpe United	3318	D 1-1	39
Mar 1	FL2	A	Northampton Town	5058	D 0-0	40
8	FL2	H	Plymouth Argyle	7799	W 2-1	41
11	FL2	H	Dagenham & Redbridge	5761	L 1-2	42
15	FL2	A	Hartlepool United	3480	L 0-4	43
21	FL2	H	Southend United	6028	D 0-0	44
25	FL2	A	Fleetwood Town	2023	L 1-3	45
29	FL2	H	Morecambe	5647	W 1-0	46
April 1	FL2	A	Bury	2314	L 1-2	47
5	FL2	A	AFC Wimbledon	4322	D 0-0	48
12	FL2	H	Torquay United	6612	L 1-2	49
19	FL2	A	Portsmouth	17998	L 2-3	50
21	FL2	H	Rochdale	8158	L 1-2	51
26	FL2	A	Wycombe Wanderers	6752	W 2-1	52
May 3	FL2	H	Mansfield Town	10594	L 0-1	53

CHESTER

Chairman: Tony Durkin
Secretary: Calvin Hughes (T) 07739 351 711 (E) calvin_hughes@o2.co.uk
Commercial Manager: Dave Riche (T) 01244 371 376 (B)
Programme Editor: Rob Ashcroft (T) 07935 218 619
Ground Address: Swansway Chester Stadium, Bumpers Lane, Chester. CH1 4LT
(T) 01244 371 376 **Manager:** Steve Burr

Club Factfile

Founded: 1885 **Nickname:** Blues
Previous Names: Chester > 1983, Chester City 1983-2010
Previous Leagues: Cheshire 1919-31, Football League 1931-2000, 2004-09, Conference 2000-04, 09-10 (Did not finish the season)

Club Colours (change): Blue and white/blue & white/white with blue hoop (All purple)

Ground Capacity: 6,012 **Seats:** 3,284 **Covered:** Yes **Clubhouse:** Yes **Shop:** Yes

Directions
Stay on the M56 until you reach a roundabout at the end of the motorway. Follow the signs to North Wales & Queensferry A5117. After around one and a half miles you will reach a set of traffic lights where you need to bear left on to the A550 (signposted North Wales & Queensferry). Then from the A550, take the A548 towards Chester. Head straight through the first set of traffic lights and after passing a Vauxhall and then a Renault garage on your left, turn right at the next lights into Sovereign Way. Continue to the end of Sovereign Way and then turn right into Bumpers Lane and the entrance to the Club car park is just down on the right.

Previous Grounds: Faulkner Street 1885-98, The Old Showground 98-99, Whipcord Lane 1901-06, Sealand Road 06-90, Macclesfield FC 90-92

Record Attendance: 20,378 v Chelsea - FA Cup 3rd Round replay 16/01/1952
Record Victory: 12-0 v York City - 01/02/1936
Record Defeat: Not known
Record Goalscorer: Stuart Rimmer - 135
Record Appearances: Ray Gill - 406 (1951-62)
Additional Records: Paid £100,000 to Rotherham for Gregg Blundell.
Received £300,000 from Liverpool for Ian Rush
Senior Honours:
Conference 2003-04, Conference North 2012-13.
Cheshire Senior Cup 1894-95, 96-97, 1903-04, 07-08, 08-09, 30-31, 31-32, 2012-13. Herefordshire Senior Cup 1991-92 (shared).
Welsh Cup 1907-08, 32-33, 46-47. NPL Division One North 2010-11, Premier Division 2011-12.

10 YEAR RECORD

04-05	05-06	06-07	07-08	08-09	09-10	10-11	11-12	12-13	13-14
FL 2 20	FL 2 15	FL 2 18	FL 2 22	FL 2 23	Conf dnf	NP1N 1	NP P 1	Conf N 1	Conf 21

CHESTER MATCH RESULTS 2013-14

Date	Comp	H/A	Opponents	Att:	Result		Goalscorers	Pos	No.
Aug 10	CPrem	A	Chester	2543	L	0-3		22	1
13	CPrem	H	Hereford United	2900	L	0-2		22	2
17	CPrem	H	Woking	2016	L	0-2		23	3
24	CPrem	A	Kidderminster Harriers	2283	L	1-3	Harrison 45	23	4
26	CPrem	H	Forest Green Rovers	2080	L	1-2	Mills 80	23	5
31	CPrem	A	Wrexham	6037	W	2-0	Llnwood 5 L.Turner 17	22	6
Sept 7	CPrem	H	Dartford	2587	D	0-0		21	7
14	CPrem	A	Salisbury City	925	L	1-3	Heath 14	21	8
17	CPrem	H	Macclesfield Town	2012	W	2-1	Chippendale 18 Seddon 30	20	9
21	CPrem	H	Grimsby Town	2363	D	0-0		21	10
24	CPrem	A	Gateshead	610	L	2-3	Harrison 27 Higginbotham 74	22	11
28	CPrem	A	FC Halifax Town	1805	L	1-2	Seddon 18	23	12
Oct 5	CPrem	H	Kidderminster Harriers	2223	D	0-0		22	13
8	CPrem	A	Alfreton Town	743	W	1-0	Reed 33	22	14
12	CPrem	H	Cambridge United	2530	D	0-0		22	15
19	CPrem	A	Braintree Town	1132	L	0-3		22	16
26	***FAC4Q***	***H***	***Gatehead***	***1659***	***L***	***0-1***			17
Nov 2	CPrem	H	Aldershot	2029	D	1-1	Wilkinson 68	22	18
9	CPrem	A	Hyde	1232	W	2-1	Lindfield 40 Mahon 47	21	19
12	CPrem	A	Hereford United	1512	D	2-2	Lindfield 18 Seddon 21	20	20
16	CPrem	H	Luton Town	3291	D	1-1	Seddon 23	21	21
23	CPrem	A	Nuneaton	1221	L	0-1		21	22
30	***FAT1***	***H***	***Barrow***	***1409***	***L***	***1-2***	***Seddon 3***		23
Dec 7	CPrem	H	Braintree Town	1736	L	0-2		22	24
21	CPrem	H	Lincoln City	1850	D	3-3	Menagh 8 10 Rooney 50 (pen)	21	25
26	CPrem	A	Southport	1872	D	0-0		21	26
28	CPrem	H	Gateshead	2017	D	1-1	Killock 10	21	27
Jan 8	*Neil Young steps down as Manager.*								
18	*Steve Burr appointed as the new Manager.*								
18	CPrem	H	Barnet	2179	W	2-1	Turner 34 Reed 85	21	28
21	CPrem	A	Woking	1124	W	1-0	Menagh 29	20	29
25	CPrem	A	Forest Green Rovers	1483	L	0-3		20	30
Feb 1	CPrem	H	Welling United	2074	L	1-3	Taylor 55	20	31
4	CPrem	A	Macclesfield Town	1771	L	2-3	Seddon 19 Rooney 87	20	32
13	CPrem	H	FC Halifax Town	2127	W	2-1	Mahon 55 Menagh 90	19	33
22	CPrem	A	Lincoln City	2354	D	1-1	Taylor 52	20	34
25	CPrem	A	Tamworth	1036	W	4-3	TAYLOR 3 (23 33 60) Rooney 30	19	35
March 1	CPrem	H	Nuneaton Town	2214	D	3-3	Rooney 16 Taylor 35 Killock 70	20	36
7	CPrem	A	Dartford	1610	W	1-0	Seddon 18	19	37
11	CPrem	A	Aldershot Town	1545	L	0-2		19	38
14	CPrem	H	Alfreton Town	2042	L	0-1		20	39
18	CPrem	H	Southport	2274	D	2-2	Hobson 34 Mahon 49	20	40
22	CPrem	A	Luton Town	8475	L	0-3		20	41
25	CPrem	H	Tamworth	1731	W	2-0	Richards-Everton 62 (og) Carlton 67	18	42
29	CPrem	A	Welling United	706	L	0-2		19	43
April 5	CPrem	H	Hyde	2228	W	3-2	Seddon 15 Brizell (og) 23 Hobson 50	18	44
12	CPrem	A	Grimsby Town	4174	L	1-2	Carlton 90	19	45
19	CPrem	H	Wrexham	**4326**	D	0-0		19	46
21	CPrem	A	Cambridge United	3521	W	1-0	Carlton	20	47
26	CPrem	H	Salisbury City	3588	D	2-2	Carlton 14 Rooney 58	21	48

GOALSCORERS	Lge	FAC	FAT	Total	Pens	Hat-tricks	Cons Run
Seddon	7		1	8			2
Taylor	6			6		1	3
Rooney	5			5	1		
Carlton	4			4			2
Menagh	4			4			
Mahon	3			3			
Harrison	2			2			
Hobson	2			2			
Kilock	2			2			
Linfield	2			2			2
Reed	2			2			
L.Turner	2			2			
Chippendale	1			1			
Heath	1			1			
Higginbotham	1			1			
Linwood	1			1			
Mills	1			1			
Wilkinson	1			1			
Opponents	2			2			

Cons Run - Consecutive scoring games.

DARTFORD

Chairman: Bill Archer & David Skinner
Secretary: Peter Martin **(T)** 07976 054 202 **(E)** peter@martinpe.freeserve.co.uk
Commercial Manager: Tina Dyson **(T)** 01322 299 991
Programme Editor: Stephen Kennedy **(T)** 07707 088 349
Ground Address: Princes Park Stadium, Grassbanks, Darenth Road, Dartford DA1 1RT
(T) 01322 299 990/1 **Manager:** Tony Burman

Action from the 2014-15 pre-season friendly v Millwall.

Club Factfile

Founded: 1888 **Nickname:** The Darts
Previous Names: None
Previous Leagues: Kent League 1894-96, 97-98, 99-1902, 09-14, 21-26, 93-96, Southern 1996-2006

Club Colours (change): White/black/white (Blue/white/blue)

Ground Capacity: 4,097 **Seats:** 640 **Covered:** Yes **Clubhouse:** Yes **Shop:** Yes

Directions
From M25 clockwise leave at Junction 1 B to roundabout controlled by traffic lights. Take third exit onto Princes Road, (A225) then second exit at next roundabout. Continue down hill to traffic lights (ground on your left), turn left into Darenth Road then second turning on your left into Grassbanks leading to car park. From M25 anti-clockwise leave at Junction 2 onto slip road A225 to roundabout, then first exit, second exit at next roundabout then down hill to traffic lights turn left into Darenth Road, then second turning on your left into Grassbanks leading to car park.

Previous Grounds: The Brent/Westgate House, Potters Meadow, Engleys Meadow, Summers Meadow, Watling Street

Record Attendance: 4,097 v Horsham YMCA - Isthmian Division 1 South 11/11/2006 and v Crystal Palace - Friendly 20/07/2007
Record Victory: Not known
Record Defeat: Not known
Record Goalscorer: Not known
Record Appearances: Steve Robinson - 692
Additional Records: Paid £6,000 to Chelmsford City for John Bartley
Received £25,000 from Redbridge Forest for Andy Hessenthaler
Senior Honours:
Southern League Division 2 1896-97, Eastern Section 1930-31, 31-32, Southern Championship 30-31, 31-32, 73-74, 83-84, Southern Division 1980-81, League Cup 1976-77, 87-88, 88-89, Championship Shield 1983-84, 87-88, 88-89.
Isthmian League Division 1 North 2007-08, Premier Division 2009-10. Kent Senior Cup 1929-30, 34-35, 38-39, 69-70.

10 YEAR RECORD

04-05	05-06	06-07	07-08	08-09	09-10	10-11	11-12	12-13	13-14
SthE 16	SthE 7	Isth1S 7	Isth1N 1	Isth P 8	Isth P 1	Conf S 10	Conf S 2	Conf 8	Conf 22

DARTFORD MATCH RESULTS 2013-14

Date	Comp	H/A	Opponents	Att:	Result		Goalscorers	Pos	No.
Aug 10	CPrem	H	Alfreton Town	1202	W	1-0	Birchall 42	5	1
13	CPrem	A	Aldershot Town	2138	L	0-3		15	2
17	CPrem	A	FC Halifax	1296	L	0-2		18	3
24	CPrem	H	Braintree Town	1015	L	0-2		19	4
26	CPrem	A	Tamworth	864	W	2-0	Harris 3 Clark 26	15	5
31	CPrem	H	Lincoln City	1386	L	1-3	Bradbrook 59	16	6
Sept 7	CPrem	A	Chester	2587	D	0-0		18	7
14	CPrem	H	Nuneaton	1155	L	1-2	Bradbrook 28	19	8
17	CPrem	A	Luton Town	5433	L	0-3		21	9
21	CPrem	H	Kidderminster Harriers	1020	W	3-0	Price 34 Bradbrook 51 Harris 61	18	10
24	CPrem	A	Grimsby Town	2503	L	2-5	Harris 24 Noble 55	19	11
28	CPrem	H	Southport	1025	W	1-0	Birchall 32	17	12
Oct 5	CPrem	A	Gateshead	561	L	0-2		18	13
8	CPrem	H	Salisbury City	920	D	1-1	Godden 29	20	14
12	CPrem	A	Hereford United	1583	D	2-2	Noble 11 Ibemere 85	20	15
19	CPrem	H	Hyde	1083	W	4-3	GODDEN 3 (12 15 87) Monger 83	18	16
26	***FAC 4Q***	***A***	***Ebbsfleet United***	***2895***	***D***	***1-1***	***Noble 44***		17
29	***FAC4Qr***	***H***	***Ebbsfleet United***	***1901***	***W***	***1-0***	***Bradbrook 54 (pen)***		18
Nov 2	CPrem	A	Forest Green Rovers	960	L	0-1		18	19
9	***FAC1***	***A***	***Salisbury City***	***1313***	***L***	***2-4***	***Burns 68 Cornhill 90***		20
12	CPrem	A	Woking	1157	L	0-3		21	21
16	CPrem	A	Macclesfield Town	1543	L	1-3	Godden 13 (pen)	22	22
19	CPrem	H	Wrexham	816	L	1-5	Burns 3	22	23
23	CPrem	H	Gateshead	975	L	0-1		22	24
26	CPrem	H	Barnet	803	L	0-2		23	25
30	***FAT1***	***H***	***Forest Green Rovers***	***511***	***D***	***1-1***	***Harris 41***		26
Dec 2	***FAT1r***	***A***	***Forest Green Rovers***	***459***	***L***	***0-1***			27
7	CPrem	A	Barnet	1461	L	0-1		23	28
14	CPrem	H	FC Halifax Town	952	L	1-3	Essam 83	23	29
21	CPrem	A	Alfreton Town	575	L	1-2	Bradbrook 16 (pen)	23	30
26	CPrem	H	Welling United	1758	L	1-2	Burns 29	23	31
Jan 10	CPrem	A	Welling United	1336	D	1-1	Stevenson 10	23	32
18	CPrem	A	Salisbury City	850	L	0-1		23	33
21	CPrem	A	Kidderminster Harriers	1580	W	2-1	Cornhill 3 Pugh 23	23	34
25	CPrem	H	Cambridge United	2023	D	3-3	Bradbrook 26 (pen) Cornhill 45 Harris 69	23	35
Feb 8	CPrem	A	Wrexham	2645	W	2-1	Pugh 10 Bradbrook 45	23	36
18	CPrem	H	Woking	1002	W	5-1	Wall 5 45 Cornhill 56 74 Noble 90	22	37
22	CPrem	H	Hereford United	1137	W	2-0	Wall 12 Noble 71	21	38
25	CPrem	H	Aldershot Town	1125	D	1-1	Bradbrook 45 (pen)	22	39
March 1	CPrem	A	Southport	1041	L	0-3		22	40
7	CPrem	H	Chester	1610	L	0-1		22	41
15	CPrem	A	Cambridge United	2885	D	1-1	Wall 90	22	42
22	CPrem	A	Hyde	358	W	2-0	Wall 57 80	22	43
29	CPrem	H	Macclesfield Town	1105	W	2-1	Harris 47 Cornhill 81	22	44
April 1	CPrem	H	Luton Town	**2869**	L	1-2	Suarez 34	22	45
5	CPrem	A	Lincoln City	1947	D	0-0		22	46
10	CPrem	H	Grimsby Town	1257	W	1-0	Cornhill 75	22	47
12	CPrem	H	Forest Green Rovers	1061	L	0-1		22	48
17	CPrem	A	Braintree Town	1200	L	0-1		22	49
21	CPrem	H	Tamworth	1465	L	2-3	Bradbrook 30 90	22	50
26	CPrem	A	Nuneaton Town	903	L	1-3	McAuley 17	22	51

GOALSCORERS	Lge	FAC	FAT	Total	Pens	Hat-tricks	Cons Run
Bradbrook	9	1		10	4		2
Cornhill	6	1		7			2
Harris	5		1	6			2
Wall	6			6			2
Godden	5			5	1	1	
Noble	4	1		5			2
Burns	2	1		3			
Birchall	2			2			
Pugh	2			2			
Clark	1			1			
Essam	1			1			
Ibemere	1			1			
McAuley	1			1			
Monger	1			1			
Price	1			1			
Stevenson	1			1			
Suarez	1			1			

Cons Run - Consecutive scoring games.

DOVER ATHLETIC

Chairman: Jim Parmenter
Secretary: Franke Clarke **(T)** 07794 102 664 **(E)** frank.clarke@doverathletic.com
Commercial Manager: n/a **(T)**
Programme Editor: Chris Collings **(T)** 01304 822 704
Ground Address: Crabble Athletic Ground, Lewisham, Dover, Kent CT17 0JB
(T) 01304 822 373 **Manager:** Chris Kinnear

Club Factfile

Founded: 1983 **Nickname:** The Whites
Previous Names: Dover F.C. until club folded in 1983
Previous Leagues: Southern 1983-93, 2002-04, Conference 1993-2002, Isthmian 2004-2009

Club Colours (change): White/black/black (All pink)

Ground Capacity: 6,500 **Seats:** 1,000 **Covered:** 4,900 **Clubhouse:** Yes **Shop:** Yes

Directions
From outside of Kent, find your way to the M25, then take the M2/A2 (following the signs to Canterbury, then from Canterbury follow signs to Dover) as far as the Whitfield roundabout (there is a McDonald's Drive-Thru on the left). Take the fourth exit at this roundabout, down Whitfield Hill. At the bottom of the hill turn left at the roundabout and follow this road until the first set of traffic lights. At the lights turn right (180 degrees down the hill) and follow the road under the railway bridge, the ground is a little further up the road on the left. There is no parking for supporters within the ground, although parking is available in the rugby ground, which is just inside the main entrance - stewards will direct you. If you have to take the M20/A20 leave the A20 in Folkestone (the exit immediately after the tunnel through the hill) and travel through the Alkham Valley (turn left at the roundabout at the end of the slip-road and then left again, following the signs for Alkham) which will eventually take you near Kearsney train station (turn right into Lower Road just before the railway bridge, before you get to the station).

Previous Grounds: None.

Record Attendance: 4,186 v Oxford United - FA Cup 1st Round November 2002
Record Victory: 7-0 v Weymouth - 03/04/1990
Record Defeat: 1-7 v Poole Town
Record Goalscorer: Lennie Lee - 160
Record Appearances: Jason Bartlett - 359
Additional Records: Paid £50,000 to Farnborough Town for David Lewworthy August 1993
Received £50,000 from Brentford for Ricky Reina 1997
Senior Honours:
Southern League Southern Division 1987-88, Premier Division 1989-90, 92-93, Premier Inter League Cup 1990-91.
Kent Senior Cup 1990-91. Isthmian League Division 1 South 2007-08, Premier Division 2008-09.

10 YEAR RECORD

04-05	05-06	06-07	07-08	08-09	09-10	10-11	11-12	12-13	13-14
Isth P 21	Isth1 5	Isth1S 3	Isth1S 1	Isth P 1	Conf S 2	Conf S 7	Conf S 7	Conf S 3	Conf S 5

DOVER ATHLETIC MATCH RESULTS 2013-14

Date	Comp	H/A	Opponents	Att:	Result		Goalscorers	Pos	No.
Aug 17	CSouth	A	Gosport Borough	592	W	1-0	Stone 58	6	1
20	CSouth	H	Ebbsfleet United	1562	W	2-1	Murphy 68 Orfu 7	4	2
24	CSouth	H	Concord Rangers	681	L	0-1		5	3
26	CSouth	A	Whitehawk	338	W	1-0	Murphy 33 (pen)	4	4
31	CSouth	H	Hayes & Yeading	691	L	0-1		6	5
Sept 7	CSouth	A	Farnborough	1139	L	0-1		9	6
14	CSouth	H	Weston-s-Mare	556	L	1-2	Modester 58	12	7
17	CSouth	A	Sutton United	442	L	0-1		15	8
21	CSouth	A	Bath City	551	W	2-1	Elder 24 Murphy 86	12	9
28	*FAC2Q*	*A*	*Guernsey*	*324*	*W*	*3-2*	*Rogers 8 Elder 41 Modester 67*		10
Oct 5	CSouth	H	Dorchester Town	632	W	1-0	Modester 33	12	11
12	*FAC3Q*	*H*	*AFC Rushden & Diamonds*	*735*	*W*	*3-1*	*Raggett 14 Cross 46 (og) Cogan 75*		12
19	CSouth	H	Havant & Waterlooville	593	D	0-0		9	13
22	CSouth	A	Eastbourne Borough	488	W	4-0	Murphy 13 Modeste 17 Cogan 25 68 (pen)	6	14
26	*FAC4Q*	*H*	*Oxford City*	*880*	*W*	*3-0*	*Elder 25 Cogan 37 Raggett 74*	*7*	15
Nov 2	CSouth	A	Basingstoke Town	352	L	0-2		11	16
9	*FAC1*	*A*	*Corby Town*	*1387*	*W*	*2-1*	*Elder 57 Kinnear 66*		17
16	*FAT3Q*	*H*	*Bath City*	*483*	*W*	*1-0*	*Elder 33*		18
23	CSouth	A	Chelmsford City	591	W	4-0	Goulding 45 (og) Murphy 55 76 Bakare 89 (pen)	12	19
30	*FAT1*	*A*	*East Thurrock United*	*273*	*D*	*1-1*	*Murphy 79*		20
Dec 2	*FAT1r*	*H*	*East Thurrock United*	*295*	*W*	*3-1*	*Bellamy 34 72 Elder 27*		21
7	*FAC 2*	*A*	*MK Dons*	*4060*	*L*	*0-1*			22
10	CSouth	H	Bromley	598	L	0-2		14	23
14	*FAT2*	*H*	*Leamington*	*435*	*W*	*2-0*	*Rogers 50 61*		24
17	CSouth	H	Eastleigh	436	L	1-2	Kinnear 77	14	25
21	CSouth	A	Staines Town	284	D	2-2	Elder 53 Cogan 79 (pen)	12	26
26	CSouth	H	Tonbridge Angels	856	W	3-1	Elder 14 70 Bellamy 22	11	27
28	CSouth	A	Ebbsfleet United	1320	W	2-0	Edwards 1 (og) Charles 32	8	28
Jan 4	CSouth	H	Bishop's Stortford	615	L	2-3	Bellamy 28 Murphy 32	9	29
11	*FAT3*	*A*	*Eastleigh*	*238*	*L*	*2-3*	*Kamara 32 Cogan 54*		30
18	CSouth	A	Dorchester Town	407	W	4-0	GOULDING 3 (30 47 51) Cogan 83	7	31
25	CSouth	A	Boreham Wood	251	D	2-2	Goulding 23 80 (pen)	9	32
Feb	CSouth	H	Chelmsford City	811	D	2 2	Cogan 17 Goulding 19	9	33
11	CSouth	H	Maidenhead United	356	W	2-0	Goulding 50 Winter 61	8	34
15	CSouth	H	Bath City	526	W	2-0	Cogan 53 Modeste 64	6	35
18	CSouth	H	Sutton United	525	L	0-1		6	36
22	CSouth	A	Weston-s-Mare	251	L	1-2	Cogan 67 (pen)	7	37
March 1	CSouth	H	Gosport Borough	623	W	3-0	Murphy 18 Cogan 56 (pen) Bellamy 79	6	38
8	CSouth	H	Basingstoke Town	635	D	1-1	Elder 90	7	39
11	CSouth	A	Bromley	466	W	4-0	Ademola 26 Orlu 42 Cogan 74 (pen) Murphy 90	6	40
15	CSouth	A	Maidenhead United	301	W	2-1	Murphy 98 Modeste 89	5	41
20	CSouth	A	Havant & Waterlooville	457	W	4-3	Goulding 49 Murphy 61 64 Bellamy 82	5	42
22	CSouth	H	Eastbourne Borough	735	D	0-0		5	43
25	CSouth	H	Farnborough	501	L	0-1		5	44
29	CSouth	H	Boreham Wood	721	D	0-0		5	45
April 5	CSouth	A	Bishop's Stortford	451	D	2-2	Modeste 25 Ademola 82	7	46
10	CSouth	A	Tonbridge Angels	533	W	2-0	Orlu 64 Elder 89	5	47
12	CSouth	H	Staines Town	625	W	1-0	Cogan 10 (pen)	5	48
15	CSouth	A	Eastleigh	1006	L	0-1		6	49
19	CSouth	A	Concord Rangers	286	W	2-1	Murphy 74 82	5	50
21	CSouth	H	Whitehawk	695	D	1-1	Davies 83	6	51
26	CSouth	A	Hayes & Yeading	450	W	2-1	Elder 3 Cogan 87 (pen)	5	52
30	*CSPO SF 1*	*H*	*Sutton United*	*1273*	*D*	*1-1*	*Ademola 43*		53
May 3	*CSPO SF 2*	*A*	*Sutton United*	*1671*	*W*	*3-0*	*Modeste 57 73 Ademola 79*		54
10	*CSPO F*	*A*	*Ebbsfleet United*	*4294*	*W*	*1-0*	*Elder 55*		55

GOALSCORERS	Lge	FAC	FAT	Total	Pens	Hat-tricks	Cons Run
Murphy	14		1	15	1		2
Cogan	11	2	1	14	7		2
Elder	7	3	2	12			2
Modeste	8	1		9			2
Goulding	7			7	1	1	4
Bellamy	4		2	6			
Ademola	4			4			2
Orlu	4			4			
Rogers		1	2	3			
Kinnear	1	1		2			
Raggett		2		2			
Bakare				1	1		
Charles	1			1			
Davies	1			1			
Kamara			1	1			
Stone	1			1			
Winter	1			1			
Opponents	2	1		3			

Cons Run - Consecutive scoring games.

EASTLEIGH

Chairman: Stewart Donald
Secretary: Ray Murphy **(T)** 07508 431 451 **(E)** raymurphy@ntlworld.com
Commercial Manager: Mark Jewell **(T)** 07837 665 229
Programme Editor: Jamie Graham **(T)** 07912 482 768
Ground Address: Silverlake Stadium 'Ten Acres', Stoneham Lane, Eastleigh SO50 9HT
(T) 02380 613 361 **Manager:** Richard Hill

Club Factfile

Founded: 1946 **Nickname:** The Spitfires
Previous Names: Swaythling Athletic 1946-59, Swaythling 1973-80
Previous Leagues: Southampton Junior & Senior 1946-59, Hampshire 1950-86, Wessex 1986-2003, Southern 2003-04, Isthmian 2004-05

Club Colours (change): Blue/white/blue (White/blue/white)

Ground Capacity: 3,000 **Seats:** 520 **Covered:** 520+ **Clubhouse:** Yes **Shop:** Yes

Directions
From junction 13 of M3, turn right into Leigh Road, turn right at Holiday Inn, at mini roundabout take second exit, at the next mini roundabout take second exit, then next mini roundabout take first exit. Then take the first turning right (signposted) ground 200 metres on the left.

Previous Grounds: Southampton Common. Westfield >1957.

Record Attendance: 3,191 v Southampton - Friendly July 2007 - League Record: 2,283 v AFC Wimbledon, 28/03/2009
Record Victory: 12-1 v Hythe & Dibden (H) - 11/12/1948
Record Defeat: 0-11 v Austin Sports (A) - 01.01.1947
Record Goalscorer: Johnnie Williams - 177
Record Appearances: Ian Knight - 611
Additional Records: Paid £10,000 to Newport (I.O.W.) for Colin Matthews

Senior Honours:
Southampton Senior League (West) 1950. Wessex League Cup 1992,2003, Division One 2002-03. Hampshire Senior Cup 2011-12. Conference South 2013-14.

10 YEAR RECORD

04-05	05-06	06-07	07-08	08-09	09-10	10-11	11-12	12-13	13-14
Isth P 3	Conf S 8	Conf S 15	Conf S 6	Conf S 3	Conf S 11	Conf S 8	Conf S 12	Conf S 4	Conf S 1

Conference Action

Braintree's Dan Bradley gets his shot away before the Alfreton defender can stop him.

Photo: Bill Wheatcroft.

EASTLEIGH MATCH RESULTS 2013-14

Date	Comp	H/A	Opponents	Att:	Result		Goalscorers	Pos	No.
Aug 17	CSouth	H	Sutton United	682	W	1-0	Odubade 26	8	1
20	CSouth	A	Bath City	645	W	1-0	Strevens 68	6	2
24	CSouth	A	Basingstoke Town	329	L	0-2		6	3
26	CSouth	H	Havant & Waterlooville	153	D	0-0		7	4
31	CSouth	A	Boreham Wood	202	W	3-0	McAllister 41 Fleetwood 61 Reason 82 (pen)	4	5
Sept 7	CSouth	H	Bromley	837	W	2-1	McAllister 30 Fleetwood 31	1	6
14	CSouth	A	Maidenhead United	403	W	3-1	Odubade 18 57 McAllister 79	1	7
17	CSouth	H	Eastbourne Borough	554	W	2-0	Reason 54 Southam 72	1	8
21	CSouth	H	Hayes & Yeading	**1202**	W	1-0	McAllister 54	1	9
28	***FAC2Q***	***H***	***Mangotsfield***	***238***	***W***	***4-0***	***Reason 7 Southam 31 Fleetwood 41 Wilson 84***		10
Oct 5	CSouth	H	Concord Rangers	551	D	1-1	Reason 33	1	11
8	CSouth	A	Ebbsfleet United	799	L	1-3	Strevens 45	1	12
12	***FAC3Q***	***H***	***Oxford City***	***434***	***L***	***2-3***	***Collins 17 Fleetwood 49***		13
19	CSouth	H	Staines Town	663	W	1-0	Reason 14	1	14
Nov 2	CSouth	A	Sutton United	691	D	1-1	McAllistair 6	2	15
9	CSouth	H	Farnborough	571	W	1-0	McAllister 90	2	16
12	CSouth	A	Gosport Borough	562	W	2-0	Odubade 45 Southam 54	1	17
16	***FAT3Q***	***A***	***Maidstone United***	***1397***	***W***	***2-1***	***McAllister 41 Reason 56 (pen)***		18
23	CSouth	H	Tonbridge Angels	536	L	1-2	Collins 58	2	19
30	***FAT1***	***A***	***Bury Town***	***321***	***W***	***3-0***	***Strevens 11 37 McAllister 56***		20
Dec 14	***FAT2***	***H***	***Gateshead***	***330***	***W***	***2-0***	***Collins 32 Fleetwood 72***	***2***	21
17	CSouth	A	Dover Athletic	436	W	2-1	Strevens 79 Fleetwood 90	2	22
26	CSouth	H	Dorchester Town	614	W	2-1	Strevens 20 Reason 46	2	23
28	CSouth	H	Bath City	637	W	2-1	Strevens 15 Collins 80	2	24
Jan 11	***FAT3***	***H***	***Dover Athletic***	***368***	***W***	***3-2***	***Odubade 2 Strevens 80 Collins 90***		25
18	CSouth	H	Gosport Borough	668	W	2-1	McAllister 9 Strevens 72	2	26
21	CSouth	A	Weston-s-Mare	198	L	2-3	McAllister 75 Odubade 90	2	27
25	CSouth	H	Ebbsfleet United	702	W	3-1	REASON 3 (19 (pen) 59 (pen) 73)	2	28
Feb 1	***FAT4***	***H***	***Cambridge United***	***757***	***L***	***0-1***			29
17	CSouth	A	Tonbridge Angel	304	L	1-2	Fleetwood 49	2	30
22	CSouth	A	Farnborough	358	W	1-0	Wright 24	2	31
25	CSouth	H	Maidenhead United	482	W	3-2	Connolly 33 Fleetwood 50 Strevens 90	2	32
March 1	CSouth	H	Weston-s-Mare	602	W	3-1	Wright 60 Reason 64 McAllister 76	2	33
4	CSouth	A	Eastbourne Borough	454	D	1-1	Fleetwood 75	2	34
8	CSouth	A	Concord Rangers	251	L	2-3	Wright 48 Strevens 71	2	35
11	CSouth	H	Chelmsford City	552	W	1-0	Connelly 43	2	36
15	CSouth	H	Bishop's Stortford	601	W	4-2	McAllister 11 WRIGHT 3 (31 56 71)	1	37
18	CSouth	A	Whitehawk	135	W	4-1	Wright 8 McAllister 23 36 Connolly 24	1	38
22	CSouth	A	Staines Town	341	D	0-0		2	39
25	CSouth	H	Dorchester Town	544	W	6-0	REASON 3 (15 45 80) Todd 17 Wright 40 Odubade 89	1	40
30	CSouth	A	Hayes & Yeading	204	D	1 1	McAllister	1	41
April 1	CSouth	A	Bishops Stortford	268	D	2-2	Wright 41 Strevens 60	1	42
5	CSouth	H	Whitehawk	592	W	3-2	Wright 15 Todd 34 Fleetwood 56	1	43
8	CSouth	A	Bromley	1011	W	2-1	Wright 17 58 (pen)	1	44
12	CSouth	A	Chelmsford City	623	D	0-0		1	45
15	CSouth	H	Dover Athletic	1006	W	1-0	Peacock 79	1	46
18	CSouth	H	Basingstoke Town	1505	W	2 1	Odubade 66 Wright 79	1	47
21	CSouth	A	Havant & Waterlooville	932	L	0-1		1	48
26	CSouth	H	Boreham Wood	638	L	0-1		1	49

GOALSCORERS	Lge	FAC	FAT	Total	Pens	Hat-tricks	Cons Run
McAllister	13		2	15			3
Reason	12	1	1	14	4	2	2
Wright	13			13	1	1	3
Strevens	9		3	12			5
Fleetwood	7	2	1	10			2
Odubade	7		1	8			
Collins	2	1	2	5			2
Connolly	3			3			
Southam	2	1		3			
Todd	2			2			
Peacock	1			1			
Wilson		1		1			

Cons Run - Consecutive scoring games.

FC HALIFAX TOWN

Chairman: David Bosomworth

Secretary: Tony Allan (T) 01422 341 222 (E) tonyallan@fchalifaxtown.com

Commercial Manager: Debbie Charlton (T) 07715 372 333

Programme Editor: Greg Stainton (T) 07950 215 604

Ground Address: The Shay Stadium, Shay Syke, Halifax HX1 2YS

(T) 01422 341 222 **Manager:** Neil Aspin

Club Factfile

Founded: 1911 **Nickname:** Shaymen

Previous Names: Halifax Town 1911-2008 then reformed as F.C. Halifax Town

Previous Leagues: Yorkshire Combination 1911-12, Midland 1912-21, Football League 1921-93, 98-2002, Conference 1993-98, 2002-08

Club Colours (change): Blue/white & blue/white & blue (Red/red & white/red & white)

Ground Capacity: 6,561 **Seats:** 2,330 **Covered:** 4,231 **Clubhouse:** Yes **Shop:** Yes

Directions

The Shay Stadium, Shay Syke, Halifax. HX1 2YS (PLEASE NOTE FOR SAT NAV use post code HX1 2YT) From the M62, Junction 26 (7.5 miles, 15 minutes by car. Head south east towards A58/Whitehall Road. Continue straight on to A58/Whitehall Road (signs for Halifax/A58). Continue to follow A58, at a roundabout, take first exit on to A629 Orange Street. Turn right at A629 Broad Street. Continue to follow A629. Go through one roundabout. Turn left at Shaw Hill. The Stadium will be on your left after 100 yards. From the M62, Junction 24 (4.5 miles, 9 minutes by car). Exit on to A629/Blackley New Road heading to Halifax. Continue on A629/Huddersfield Road heading towards Elland and Halifax.

Having gone down steep hill, traffic lights in dip, road inclines. Past Hospital on left, road levels, Athletics Track on right. Traffic lights. Filter right, Stadium on left in 100yds

Previous Grounds: Sandhall Lane 1911-15, Exley 1919-20

Record Attendance: 36,885 v Tottenham Hotspur - FA Cup 5th Round 14/02/1953

Record Victory: 12-0 v West Vale Ramblers - FA Cup 1st Qualifying Road 1913-14

Record Defeat: 0-13 v Stockport County - Division 3 North 1933-34

Record Goalscorer: Albert Valentine

Record Appearances: John Pickering

Additional Records:

Senior Honours:

Conference 1997-98, Conference North Play-offs 2012-13. Northern Premier League Division 1 North 2009-10, Premier Division 2010-11. West Riding County Cup 2012-13.

10 YEAR RECORD

04-05	05-06	06-07	07-08	08-09	09-10	10-11	11-12	12-13	13-14
Conf 9	Conf 4	Conf 16	Conf 20	NP1N 8	NP1N 1	NP P 1	Conf N 3	Conf N 5	Conf 5

FC HALIFAX TOWN MATCH RESULTS 2013-14

Date	Comp	H/A	Opponents	Att:	Result		Goalscorers	Pos	No.
Aug 11	CPrem	A	Cambridge United	2780	L	1-5	Gregory 7	22	1
13	CPrem	H	Wrexham	1674	W	3-2	Maynard 34 Wilson 40 (pen) Gregory 45	16	2
17	CPrem	H	Dartford	1296	W	2-0	Gregory 49 Holsgrove 54	8	3
24	CPrem	A	Macclesfield Town	1720	D	2-2	Gregory 16 Holsgrove 21	11	4
26	CPrem	H	Southp[ort	1583	W	1-0	Holsgove 86	6	5
31	CPrem	A	Salisbury City	820	L	1-3	Brett 87 (og)	10	6
Sept 7	CPrem	H	Barnet	1651	W	2-1	McManus 21 Maynard 50	5	7
14	CPrem	A	Forest Green Rovers	1195	L	1-2	Gardner 34 (pen)	10	8
17	CPrem	H	Grimsby Town	1602	W	4-0	Carber 19 Gardner 27 32 A.Smith 47	6	9
21	CPrem	H	Hereford United	1362	D	1-1	Smith 31 (og)	7	10
24	CPrem	A	Kidderminster Harriers	1703	L	0-2			11
28	CPrem	H	Chester	1805	W	2-1	Gregory 4 Roberts 64	9	12
Oct 5	CPrem	A	Luton Town	6519	L	3-4	Marshall 3 Ainge 19 Gardner 23	11	13
8	CPrem	H	Nuneaton	1197	D	2-2	Gardner 40 Toulson 90	12	14
12	CPrem	A	Woking	1552	D	0-0		11	15
19	CPrem	H	Welling United	1345	W	3-0	GREGORY 3 (7 24 36)	11	16
26	***FAC4Q***	***A***	***Nuneaton Town***	***1043***	***W***	***2-0***	***Gregory 17 McManus 62***		17
Nov 2	CPrem	A	Alfreton Town	900	L	0-3		12	18
12	CPrem	H	Hyde	1037	W	4-0	Maynard 5 Gregory 72 83 (pen) Wilson 76	9	19
16	CPrem	H	Aldershot Town	1418	W	4-0	Gregory 18 Smith 27 McManus 41 Roberts 71	5	20
23	CPrem	A	Braintree Town	943	L	0-1		10	21
26	CPrem	A	Hereford United	1158	L	2-3	Wilson 20 (pen) Ironside 62	11	22
30	***FAT1***	***H***	***Guiseley***	***935***	***L***	***0-1***			23
Dec 7	CPrem	H	Woking	1033	L	3-4	Love 2 Wilson 74 Gardner 81	11	24
14	CPrem	A	Dartford	952	W	2-1	Ironside 63 Wilson 74	10	25
21	CPrem	H	Forest Green Rovers	1262	W	1-0	Roberts 28	8	26
26	CPrem	A	Gateshead	857	D	1-1	Pearson 26	8	27
28	CPrem	H	Lincoln City	1979	W	5-1	Gardner 13 (pen) Gregory 27 Smith 70 Worthington 85 Gray 90	6	28
Jan 1	CPrem	H	Gateshead	1624	D	3-3	Gregory 10 13 Ainge 58	5	29
4	CPrem	A	Tamworth	890	L	0-2		5	30
11	CPrem	A	Wrexham	3214	D	0-0		7	31
18	CPrem	H	Cambridge United	1767	D	1-1	Gregory 76	7	32
25	CPrem	A	Aldershot Town	1977	D	2-2	Gregory 34 83	6	33
Feb 1	CPrem	A	Lincoln City	2077	L	1-3	Crowther 51	9	34
4	CPrem	H	Salisbury City	1003	W	5-1	Maynard 16 GREGORY (3 53 75 pen) Wilson 90	7	35
13	CPrem	A	Chester	2127	L	1-2	Bolton 90	9	36
March 1	CPrem	H	Tamworth	1313	W	2-0	Pearson 14 Maynard 67	9	37
8	CPrem	A	Hyde	901	W	5-1	Crowther 9 GREGORY 3 (27 60 82) Marshall 50	7	38
15	CPrem	A	Welling United	645	W	1-0	Gregory 47 (pen)	5	39
24	CPrem	H	Alfreton Town	1454	W	2-0	Gregory 22 50	5	40
29	CPrem	H	Luton Town	**3586**	W	2-0	Roberts 18 Gregory 69	5	41
April 3rd	CPrem	H	Braintree Town	1535	D	0-0		7	42
5	CPrem	A	Nuneaton Town	1041	W	1-0	Smith 85	5	43
12	CPrem	A	Barnet	1683	W	4-0	Spencer 6 32 Gregory 24 Maynard 53	5	44
15	CPrem	A	Grimsby Town	4374	W	1-0	Maynard 52	3	45
19	CPrem	H	Macclesfield Town	2190	W	2-1	Roberts 18 Smith 22	3	46
21	CPrem	A	Southport	2043	L	1-2	Gregory 5	4	47
26	CPrem	H	Kidderminster Harriers	2089	D	1-1	Wilson 1	5	48
30	**CPO SF1**	**H**	**Cambridge United**	**3668**	**W**	**1-0**	**Gregory 83 (pen)**		49
4	**CPO SF2**	**A**	**Cambridge United**	**6262**	**L**	**0-2**			50

GOALSCORERS	Lge	FAC	FAT	Total	Pens	Hat-tricks	Cons Run
Gregory	30+1	1		32	4	3	4
Gardner	7			7	2		2
Maynard	7			7			2
Wilson	7			7	2		2
Roberts	5			5			
A. Smith	5			5			
Holsgrove	3			3			3
McManus	2	1		3			
Ainge	2			2			
Crowther	2			2			
Ironside	2			2			

	Lge	FAC	FAT	Total	Pens	Hat-tricks	Cons Run
Marshall	2			2			
Pearson	2			2			
Spencer	2			2			
Bolton	1			1			
Carber	1			1			
Gray	1			1			
Love	1			1			
Toulson	1			1			
Worthington	1			1			
Opponents	2			2			

Cons Run - Consecutive scoring games. Play-off goals indicated by +

FOREST GREEN ROVERS

Chairman: Dale Vince OBE
Secretary: Michelle McDonald **(T)** 01453 834 860 **(E)** Michelle.McDonald@fgrfc.com
Commercial Manager: Paula Brown **(T)** 01453 834 860
Programme Editor: Terry Brumpton **(T)** 07771 802 048
Ground Address: The New Lawn, Smiths Way, Nailsworth, Gloucestershire GL6 0FG
(T) 01453 834 860 **Manager:** Ady Pennock

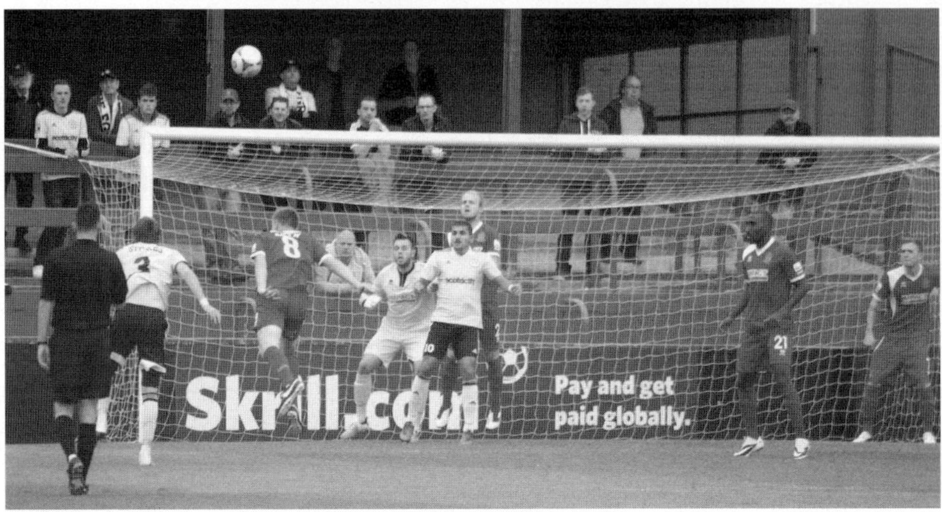

Rovers on the attack against Alfreton Town.
Photo: Bill Wheatcroft.

Club Factfile

Founded: 1890 **Nickname:** Rovers
Previous Names: Stroud FC 1980s-92.
Previous Leagues: Stroud & District 1890-1922, Gloucestershire Northern Senior 1922-67, Gloucestershire Senior 1967-73, Hellenic 1973-82, Southern 1982-89.
Club Colours (change): Green & black hoops/green/green & black hoops (Black & white stripes/black/red)

Ground Capacity: 5,141 **Seats:** 2,000 **Covered:** 1,000 **Clubhouse:** Yes **Shop:** Yes

Directions
Nailsworth is on the A46 between Stroud and Bath. At mini roundabout in town turn up Spring Hill towards Forest Green (signposted) and the stadium is at the top of the hill after the second roundabout.
Satnav users should enter GL6 0ET and not the mail post code. Please note on Matchdays there is a Temporary Traffic Order in place on the highway around the stadium. Car parking is available inside the stadium at £3 per vehicle.

Previous Grounds: Moved to the New Lawn in 2006 - 400 meters away from the old Lawn ground.

Record Attendance: 4,836 v Derby County - FA Cup 3rd Round 03/01/2009
Record Victory: 8-0 v Fareham Town - Southern League Southern Division 1996-97
Record Defeat: 0-7 v Moor Green - Southern League Midland Division 1985-86
Record Goalscorer: Karl Bayliss
Record Appearances: Alex Sykes
Additional Records: Paid £20,000 to Salisbury City for Adrian Randall. Received £35,000 from Nuneaton Borough for Marc McGregor and from Oxford United for Wayne Hatswell.
Senior Honours:
FA Vase 1981-82. Hellenic League 1981-82. Gloucestershire Senior Cup 1984-85, 85-86, 86-87.
Gloucestershire Senior Professional Cup 1984-85, 86-86, 87-87.

10 YEAR RECORD

04-05	05-06	06-07	07-08	08-09	09-10	10-11	11-12	12-13	13-14
Conf 20	Conf 19	Conf 14	Conf 8	Conf 18	Conf 21	Conf 20	Conf 10	Conf 10	Conf 10

FOREST GREEN ROVERS MATCH RESULTS 2013-14

Date	Comp	H/A	Opponents	Att:	Result		Goalscorers	Pos	No.
Aug 10	CPrem	H	Hyde	1158	**W**	8-0	KELLY 3 (25 29 76) Wright 33 Norwood 38 Taylor 60 72 Barnes-Homer 71	1	1
13	CPrem	A	Nuneaton Town	1005	D	1-1	Hodgkiss 78	2	2
17	CPrem	A	Lincoln City	2290	L	1-2	Barry 20	11	3
24	CPrem	H	Luton Town	**1858**	D	0-0		13	4
26	CPrem	A	Chester	2083	**W**	2-1	Wright 6 Barnes-Homer 73	10	5
31	CPrem	H	Alfreton Town	1027	**W**	3-1	Norwood 7 23 Wright 35	6	6
Sept 7	CPrem	A	Braintree Town	944	D	1-1	Norwood 6	6	7
14	CPrem	H	FC Halifax Town	1195	**W**	2-1	Vieira 90 Barry 90	3	8
17	CPrem	A	Welling United	452	L	2-5	Barry 45 Klukowski 62 (pen)	8	9
21	CPrem	A	Cambridge United	2915	L	1-2	Klukowski 57	10	10
24	CPrem	H	Tamworth	1029	L	1-2	Taylor 37	14	11
28	CPrem	H	Gateshead	1149	**W**	1-0	Klukowski 15	12	12
Oct 5	CPrem	A	Alfreton Town	582	L	2-3	Vieira 20 Barnes-Homer 27	14	13
8	CPrem	A	Kidderminster Harriers	2244	L	1-4	Barnes-Homer 6	14	14
12	CPrem	H	Macclesfield Town	1181	L	2-3	Barnes-Homer 10 Klukowki 65 (pen)	14	15
19	CPrem	A	Grimsby Town	3150	L	1-3	Klukowski 24	16	16
21	*Manager David Hockaday leaves the club by mutal consent.*								
26	***FAC4Q***	***H***	***Bishop's Stortford***	***789***	***L***	***0-1***			17
Nov 2	CPrem	H	Dartford	960	**W**	1-0	Norwood 5	15	18
12	*Adrian Pennock appointed Manager.*								
12	CPrem	H	Nuneaton Town	933	**W**	1-0	Kelly 38	14	19
16	CPrem	H	Lincoln City	1128	**W**	4-1	Norwood 21 73 Green 37 Turley 90	13	20
23	CPrem	A	Wrexham	3083	L	0-2		14	21
26	CPrem	A	Salisbury CIty	725	**W**	4-1	Norwood 10 86 Wright 68 Klukowski 82 (pen)	12	22
30	***FAT1***	***A***	***Dartford***	***511***	***D***	***1-1***	***Klukowski 72***		23
Dec 2	***FAT1r***	***H***	***Dartford***	***459***	***W***	***1-0***	***Barnes-Homer 34***		24
14	***FAT2***	***A***	***Chorley***	***790***	***D***	***0-0***			25
17	***FAT2r***	***H***	***Chorley***	***620***	***D***	***0-0***	***Chorley win 3-1 on penalties***		26
21	CPrem	A	FC Halifax Town	1262	L	0-1		13	27
26	CPrem	H	Aldershot	1676	**W**	3-1	Kelly 12 77 Norwood 90	13	28
28	CPrem	A	Hereford United	1848	L	0-1		14	29
Jan 8	CPrem	H	Hereford United	1077	D	1-1	Kelly 53	14	30
18	CPrem	A	Hyde United	496	**W**	6-2	Oshodi 11 67 Norwood 13 86 Kelly 15 Styche 24	14	31
25	CPrem	H	Chester	1483	**W**	3-0	Hughes 23 73 Norwood 65	12	32
Feb 18	CPrem	A	Aldershot Town	1407	D	2-2	Norwood 56 Hughes 64	15	33
22	CPrem	H	Southport	1118	**W**	3-1	Wright 23 30 Klukowski 73	11	34
25	CPrem	H	Barnet	869	L	1-2	Kelly 90	13	35
Match 1	CPrem	A	Gateshead	649	D	1-1	Hughes 75 (pen)	15	36
8	CPrem	H	Cambridge United	1411	**W**	3-2	Norwood 5 Hodgkiss 44 Wright 47	12	37
11	CPrem	H	Salisbury City	918	**W**	4-0	Racine 39 Hodgkiss 42 Hughes 59 Klukowski 90	12	38
13	CPrem	H	Braintree Town	841	L	0-2		12	39
15	CPrem	A	Tamworth	736	**W**	2-1	Klukowski 11 Norwood 47	11	40
18	CPrem	H	Grimsby Town	1219	**W**	2-1	Hughes 3 Oshodi 30	6	41
22	CPrem	H	Welling United	1338	D	0-0		9	42
27	CPrem	A	Southport	1227	L	0-2		11	43
April 1	CPrem	A	Woking	1315	L	1-2	Hughes 63	11	44
5	CPrem	A	Barnet	1466	L	1-2	Norwood 61	13	45
8	CPrem	H	Kidderminster Harriers	1231	D	1-1	Green 13	13	46
12	CPrem	A	Darftord	1061	**W**	1-0	Wright 63	12	47
15	CPrem	A	Macclesfeld Town	1142	**W**	2-1	Klukowski 2 19	8	48
19	CPrem	H	Woking	1245	D	2-2	Norwood 33 Hughes 9		49
21	Cprem	A	Luton Iown	10,044	L	1-4	Klukowski 34 (pen)	10	50
26	CPrem	H	Wrexham	1630	D	1-1	Norwood 14	10	51

GOALSCORERS	Lge	FAC	FAT	Total	Pens	Hat-tricks	Cons Run
Norwood	19			19			3
Klukowski	12		1	13	3		2
Kelly	9			9		1	
Hughes	8			8	1		2
Wright	8			8			
Barnes-Homer	5		1	6			3
Barry	3			3			2
Hodgkiss	3			3			2
Oshodi	3			3			
Taylor	3			3			
Vieira	2			2			
Green	2			2			
Racine	1			1			
Styche	1			1			
Turley	1			1			

Cons Run - Consecutive scoring games.

GATESHEAD

Chairman: Graham Wood
Secretary: Mike Coulson (T) 07912 869 943 (E) mike.coulson@gateshead-fc.com
Commercial Manager: Grahamme McDonnell (T) 07917 886 721
Programme Editor: Jeff Bowron (T) 07801 847 004
Ground Address: International Stadium, Neilson Road, Gateshead NE10 0EF
(T) 0191 478 3883 **Manager:** Gary Mills

Oster looks for a way through the Cambridge United defence during the Conference Play-off final at Wembley. Photo: Peter Barnes.

Club Factfile

Founded: 1930 **Nickname:** Tynesiders, The Heed
Previous Names: Gateshead Town, Gateshead United.
Previous Leagues: Football League 1930-60, Northern Counties east 1960-62, North Regional 1962-68, Northern Premier 1968-70, 73-83, 85-86, 87-90, Wearside 1970-71, Midland 1971-72, Alliance/Conf 1983-85, 86-87, 90-98

Club Colours (change): White/black/black & white (Sky blue with claret/sky blue/sky blue & claret)

Ground Capacity: 11,795 **Seats:** 11,795 **Covered:** 7,271 **Clubhouse:** Yes **Shop:** Yes

Directions
Travelling up on the A1, turn off at the junction with the A194 just north of the Washington Services. Follow the A194 until the roundabout junction with the A184, turn left onto this road. The International Stadium is on the right after approximately 3 miles.

Previous Grounds: Redheugh Park 1930-71

Record Attendance: 11,750 v Newcastle United - Friendly 07/08/95
Record Victory: 8-0 v Netherfield - Northern Premier League
Record Defeat: 0-9 v Sutton United - Conference 22/09/90
Record Goalscorer: Paul Thompson - 130
Record Appearances: James Curtis - 506 (2003-present)
Additional Records: Record transfer fee paid; £9,000 - Paul Cavell, Dagenham & Redbridge 1994
Record transfer fee received; £150,000 Lee Novak, Huddersfield Town 2009
Senior Honours:
Northern Premier League 1982-83, 85-86, Northern Premier League play-off 2007-8, Conference North play-off 2008-9, Durham Challenge Cup 2010-11

10 YEAR RECORD

04-05		05-06		06-07		07-08		08-09		09-10		10-11		11-12		12-13		13-14	
NP P	17	NP P	17	NP P	9	NP P	3	Conf N	2	Conf	20	Conf	15	Conf	8	Conf	17	Conf	3

GATESHEAD MATCH RESULTS 2013-14

Date	Comp	H/A	Opponents	Att:	Result		Goalscorers	Pos	No.
Aug 10	CPrem	A	Kidderminster Harriers	2110	L	1-3	Brodie 43	21	1
13	CPrem	H	Grimsby Town	944	L	1-2	Turnbull 20	19	2
17	CPrem	H	Barnet	639	L	1-2	Larkin 32	21	3
18	*Manager Anthony Smith resigns.*								
24	CPrem	A	Southport	915	L	1-2	Brodie 62	22	4
27	CPrem	H	Macclesfield	631	D	2-2	Magnay 51 Hatch 70	22	5
31	CPrem	A	Woking	1230	W	2-1	Brown 20 Chandler 30	19	6
Sept 3	*Gary Mills appointed as the new Manager.*								
7	CPrem	H	Hereford United	931	W	2-1	Walker 32 42	17	7
14	CPrem	A	Cambridge United	2599	L	0-1		18	8
17	CPrem	H	Wrexham	538	L	0-3		19	9
21	CPrem	A	Tamworth	738	W	1-0	Larkin 24 (pen)	17	10
24	CPrem	H	Chester	610	W	3-2	Magnay 1 Hugill 54 Larkin 56	16	11
28	CPrem	A	Forest Green Rovers	1149	L	0-1		16	12
Oct 5	CPrem	H	Dartford	561	W	2-0	Marwood 43 Ramshaw 58	16	13
8	CPrem	A	Hyde	409	W	2-0	Marwood 10 Hugil 79	13	14
12	CPrem	H	Alfreton Town		W	3-0	Larkin 63 Hugill 78 83	12	15
19	CPrem	A	Nuneaton	946	W	4-1	Marwood 15 Hugill 20 Larkin 57 (pen) Ramshaw 59	10	16
26	***FAC4Q***	***A***	***Chester***	***1659***	***W***	***1-0***	***Curtis 74***		17
Nov 2	CPrem	H	Luton Town	1080	D	0-0		11	18
8	***FAC1***	***A***	***Oxford United***	***3114***	***D***	***2-2***	***Marwood 12 Chandler 51***		19
12	CPrem	A	Wrexham	2469	L	2-3	Marwood 36 Boyes 37	12	20
16	CPrem	H	Salisbury City	839	W	3-2	Walker 1 58 Marwood 46	11	21
23	CPrem	A	Dartford	975	W	1-0	Brown 89	9	22
30	***FAT1***	***H***	***Hednesford Town***	***410***	***W***	***4-1***	***Walker 12 Marwood 45 Tait 87 Maddison 88***		23
Dec 4	***FAC1r***	***H***	***Oxford United***	***2632***	***L***	***0-1****			24
10	CPrem	A	Lincoln City	1411	W	1-0	Walker 56	8	25
14	***FAT 2***	***A***	***Eastleigh***	***330***	***L***	***0-2***			26
21	CPrem	A	Luton Town	6913	L	2-4	Oster 70 Hatch 84	10	27
26	CPrem	H	FC Halifax Town	857	D	1-1	Chandler 57	10	28
28	CPrem	A	Chester	2017	D	1-1	Marwood 68	11	29
Jan 1	CPrem	A	FC Halifax Town	1624	D	3-3	Brown 46 Maddison 76 Marwood 81	12	30
4	CPrem	H	Hyde	502	W	4-0	Maddison 12 Brown 58 Hatch 68 Chandler 73	8	31
11	CPrem	H	Nuneaton	726	W	2-1	Brown 46 Curtis 80	6	32
14	CPrem	H	Aldershot Town	724	D	0-0		4	33
18	CPrem	A	Grimsby Town	3243	D	2-2	Larkin 14 (pen) Maddison 55	4	34
21	CPrem	H	Welling United	621	D	1-1	Maddison 50 (pen)	4	35
Feb 1	CPrem	H	Kidderminster Harriers	625	W	3-1	Oster 52 Marwood 63 Maddison 70	4	36
15	CPrem	H	Woking	1296	L	0-2		5	37
22	CPrem	A	Alfreton Town	817	D	1-1	Maddison 51	7	38
25	CPrem	A	Welling United	455	L	0-2		7	39
March 1	CPrem	H	Forest Green Rovers	649	D	1-1	Hatch 89	8	40
8	CPrem	A	Barnet	1361	W	1-0	Chandler 71	6	41
15	CPrem	A	Salisbury City	685	D	0-0		9	42
22	CPrem	H	Lincoln City	804	W	3-1	Lester 34 Chandler 44 Noble 79	7	43
25	CPrem	A	Aldershot Town	1358	W	2-1	Lester 57 O'Donnell 82	4	44
29	CPrem	H	Braintree Town	859	W	1-0	O'Donnell 90	3	45
April 5	CPrem	H	Tamworth	705	W	5-0	Chandler 36 Ramshaw 72 90 Maddison 89 90	4	46
12	CPrem	A	Hereford United	1783	W	1-0	Marwood 36	4	47
15	CPrem	A	Braintree Town	901	D	0-0		4	48
18	CPrem	H	Southport	2121	D	2-2	Chandler 27 88	5	49
21	CPrem	A	Macclesfield	1628	W	2-0	Larkin 26 Maddison 51	5	50
26	CPrem	H	Cambridge United	2916	W	2-0	Larkin 18 Ramshaw 81	3	51
May 1	**CPO SF1**	**A**	**Grimsby Town**	**5234**	**D**	**1-1**	**Larkin 7**		52
4	**CPO SF1**	**H**	**Grimsby Town**	**8144**	**W**	**3-1**	**Marwood 22 84 O'Donnell 90**		53
18	**CPO F**	**N**	**Cambridge United**	**19613**	**L**	**1-2**	**Lester 80**		54

GOALSCORERS	Lge	FAC	FAT	Total	Pens	Hat-tricks	Cons Run
Marwood	9+2	1	1	13			3
Maddison	9		1	10			
Chandler	8	1		9			
Larkin	8+1			9	2		3
Walker	5		1	6			
Brown	5			5			
Hugill	5			5			3
Ramshaw	5			5			
Hatch	4			4			
Lester	2+1			3			2
O'Donnell	2+1			3			2

	Lge	FAC	FAT	Total	Pens	Hat-tricks	Cons Run
Brodie	2			2			
Curtis	1	1		2			
Magnay	2			2			
Oster	2			2			
Boyes	1			1			
Noble	1			1			
Tait			1	1			
Turnbull	1			1			

Cons Run - Consecutive scoring games.
Play-off goals indicated by +

GRIMSBY TOWN

Chairman: John Fenty
Secretary: Ian Fleming **(T)** 07711 188 542 **(E)** ian@gtfc.co.uk
Commercial Manager: Dave Smith **(T)** 07801 081 874
Programme Editor: Jack Johnson **(T)** 07540 126 369
Ground Address: Blundell Park, Cleethorpes, North East Lincolnshire DN35 7PY
(T) 01472 605 050 **Manager:** Paul Hurst

Club Factfile

Founded: 1878 **Nickname:** The Mariners
Previous Names: Grimsby Pelham 1878-79
Previous Leagues: Football League 1892-2010

Club Colours (change): Black & white stripes/black/red (All blue)

Ground Capacity: 10,033 **Seats:** Yes **Covered:** Yes **Clubhouse:** Yes **Shop:** Yes

Directions From the North/West All routes follow M180 onto the A180 to Grimsby. At first roundabout go straight on then follow signs for Cleethorpes (A180) onto Grimsby Road. Blundell Park is situated behind the Drive Thru' McDonalds. From the South A46 (Lincoln) Follow A46 into Grimsby, go straight on at roundabout after dual carriageway, following signs to Cleethorpes. At the 'Grimsby Institute' get in the right hand lane and keep following signs for Cleethorpes. At Isaac's Hill roundabout turn left onto Grimsby Road, the ground is on the right hand side behind the Drive Thru' at McDonalds.

Previous Grounds: Clee Park, Abbey Park

Record Attendance: 31,657 v Wolverhampton Wanderers - FA Cup 5th Round 20/02/1937
Record Victory: 9-2 v Darwen - Division 2 15/04/1899
Record Defeat: 1-9 v Arsenal - Division 1 28/01/1931
Record Goalscorer: Pat Glover - 180 (1930-39)
Record Appearances: John McDermott - 754 (1987-2007)
Additional Records: Paid £500,000 to Preston North End for Lee Ashcroft 11/08/1998
Received £1.5m from Everton for John Oster July 1997
Senior Honours:
Football League Division 2 1900-01, 33-34, Division 3 North 1925-26, 55-56, Division 3 1979-80, Division 4 1971-72.
Division 2 Play-offs 1997-98.
League Group Cup 1982. Auto Windscreen Shield 1998.

10 YEAR RECORD

04-05		05-06		06-07		07-08		08-09		09-10		10-11		11-12		12-13		13-14	
FL 2	18	FL 2	4	FL 2	15	FL 2	16	FL 2	22	FL 2	23	Conf	11	Conf	11	Conf	4	Conf	4

GRIMSBY TOWN MATCH RESULTS 2013-14

Date	Comp	H/A	Opponents	Att:	Result		Goalscorers	Pos	No.
Aug 10	CPrem	H	Aldershot Town	4037	D	1-1	Hannah 81 (pen)	10	1
13	CPrem	A	Gateshead	944	W	2-1	Hearn 25 Doig 72	6	2
17	CPrem	A	Welling United	807	L	0-1		16	3
24	CPrem	H	Alfreton Town	3245	W	3-1	Hearn 13 Colbeck 39 McLaughlin 57	9	4
26	CPrem	A	Hyde	786	W	1-0	Rodman 72	4	5
31	CPrem	H	Nuneaton	3321	L	1-2	Cook 86	8	6
Sept 7	CPrem	A	Luton Town	6131	D	0-0		11	7
14	CPrem	H	Braintree Town	3403	W	1-0	John-Lewis 13	7	8
17	CPrem	A	FC Halifax Town	1602	L	0-4		10	9
21	CPrem	A	Chester	2363	D	0-0		13	10
24	CPrem	H	Dartford	2503	W	5-2	McLaughlin 32 Pearson 36 Joihn-Lewis 43 Kerr 85 Disley 90	8	11
28	CPrem	H	Tamworth	3105	W	3-1	Pearson 56 Hannah 67 (pen) Hearn 83	4	12
Oct 5	CPrem	A	Aldershot Town	2118	W	3-0	John- Lewis Hannah Hearn 54	2	13
8	CPrem	H	Cambridge United	4386	L	0-1		6	14
12	CPrem	A	Salisbury City		L	0-1		8	15
19	CPrem	H	Forest Green Rovers	3150	W	3-1	Hannah 37 64 (pen) Rodman 84	5	16
26	***FAC4Q***	***H***	***Rushall Olympic***	***1456***	***W***	***3-0***	***Hannah 31 (pen) Pearson 75 Cook 85***		17
Nov 2	CPrem	A	Woking	1432	W	2-1	Hannah 1 Disley 90	4	18
8	***FAC1***	***H***	***Scunthorpe United***	***8306***	***D***	***0-0***			19
16	CPrem	A	Tamworth	1306	W	2-0	Disley 51 Rodman 84	4	20
19	***FAC1r***	***A***	***Scunthorpe***	***5699***	***W***	***2-1***	***John-Lewis 10 McDonald 58***		21
23	CPrem	H	Barnet	3441	W	2-1	Hannah 67 L.Hearn 81	4	22
30	***FAT1***	***A***	***Coalville Town***	***844***	***D***	***1-1***	***Rodman 51***		23
Dec 2	***FAT1r***	***H***	***Coalville Town***	***1102***	***W***	***3-0***	***SOUTHWELL 3 (60 78 86)***		24
7	***FAC2***	***H***	***Northampton Town***	***3828***	***W***	***2-0***	***Pearson 64 McLoughlin 90***		25
10	CPrem	H	Welling United	2487	D	1-1	Southwell 90	5	26
15	***FAT2***	***A***	***Barnet***	***972***	***W***	***2-1***	***Cook 6 Southwell 80***		27
19	CPrem	H	Kidderminster Harriers	3086	W	3-1	Disley 17 Neilson 30 62	3	28
26	CPrem	A	Lincoln City	5421	W	2-0	Hannah10 Disley 39	3	29
28	CPrem	H	Macclesfield Town	4002	L	2-3	Williams 56 (og) Doig 61	4	30
Jan 1	CPrem	H	LIncoln City	**5484**	D	1-1	Disley 38	4	31
4	***FAC3***	***H***	***Huddersfield Town***	***6544***	***L***	***2-3***	***Hannah 25 Disley 62***		32
11	***FAT3***	***H***	***Maidenhead United***	***1623***	***W***	***2-1***	***Colbeck 35 Pearson 40***	***5***	33
18	CPrem	H	Gateshead	3243	D	2-2	McDonald 8 Bignot 82	5	34
28	CPrem	A	Cambridge United	3027	W	2-1	John-Lewis 18 Neilson 55	4	35
Feb 1	***FAT4***	***H***	***Tamworth***	***2795***	***W***	***4-1***	***John-Lewis 17 Tounkara 39 McLoughlin 69 Cook 90***		36
8	CPrem	H	Southport	3306	D	0-0		6	37
15	***FAT S-F 1***	***A***	***Cambridge United***	***3264***	***L***	***1-2***	***John-Lewis 90***		38
18	CPrem	A	Barnet	1375	L	1-2	Disley 58	8	39
22	***FAT S-F 2***	***H***	***Cambridge United***	***3931***	***D***	***1-1***	***Neilson 42***		40
25	CPrem	A	Southport	812	L	1-2	John-Lewis 90	9	41
March 1	CPrem	H	Salisbury City	3269	W	2-0	Disley 3 Rodman 83	7	42
8	CPrem	A	Macclesfield Town	2092	D	1-1	Jennings 36	9	43
11	CPrem	H	Hereford United	3007	D	1-1	Hannah 16	8	44
15	CPrem	H	Wrexham	3506	W	3-1	Neilson 42 Disley 87 Cook 90	6	45
18	CPrem	A	Forest Green Rovers	1219	L	1-2	Neilson 58	8	46
22	CPrem	A	Nuneaton	1585	W	1-0	Rodman 8	5	47
25	CPrem	H	Luton Town	3789	L	1-2	Neilson 19	7	48
29	CPrem	A	Hereford United	2545	W	1-0	Rodman 62	6	49
April 1	CPrem	A	Wrexham	2019	W	1-0	McLaughlin 11	3	50
5	CPrem	A	Kidderminster Harriers	2176	W	1-0	Rodman 20	3	51
8	CPrem	H	Woking	3507	D	2-2	Tounkara 90 John Lewis 90	3	52
12	CPrem	H	Chester	4174	W	2-1	Tounkara 16 Cook 84	3	53
15	CPrem	H	FC Halifax Town	4374	L	0-1		3	54
17	CPrem	A	Alfreton Town	1771	D	3-3	HANNAH 3 (6 32 69 pen)	3	55
21	CPrem	H	Hyde United	4232	W	1-0	Hannah 76	3	56
26	CPrem	A	Braintree Town	1489	D	0-0		4	57
May 1	**CPO SF1**	**H**	**Gateshead**	**5234**	**D**	**1-1**	**Disley 24**		58
4	**CPO SF2**	**A**	**Gateshead**	**8144**	**L**	**1-3**	**Disley 60**		59

GOALSCORERS	Lge	FAC	FAT	Total	Pens	Hat-tricks	Cons Run
Hannah	13	2		15	4	1	2
Disley	9+2	1		12			2
John-Lewis	6	1	2	9			2
Rodman	7		1	8			
Neilson	6		1	7			2
Cook	3	1	2	6			
Hearn	5			5			
Pearson	2	2	1	5			2
Southwell	1		4	5		1	2
McLaughlin	3	1	1	5			
Tounkara	2		1	3			2
Colbeck	1		1	2			
Doig	2			2			
McDonald	1	1		2			
Bignot	1			1			
Jennings	1			1			
Kerr	1			1			
Opponents	1			1			

Cons Run - Consecutive scoring games.
Play-off goals indicated by +

KIDDERMINSTER HARRIERS

Chairman: Ken Rae

Secretary: Robin Lamb (T) 07976 752 493 (E) robin.lamb@harriers.co.uk

Commercial Manager: Mark Searle (T) 07827 930 940

Programme Editor: Matt Wall (T) 07725 536 272

Ground Address: Aggborough Stadium, Hoo Road, Kidderminster DY10 1NB

(T) 01562 823 931 **Manager:** Gary Whild

Photo: Keith Clayton.

Club Factfile

Founded: 1886 **Nickname:** Harriers

Previous Names: Kidderminster > 1891

Previous Leagues: Birmingham 1889-90, 91-1939, 47-48, 60-62. Midland 1890-91. Southern 1939-45, 48-60, 72-83. Birmingham Comb. 1945-47. West Midlands 1962-72. Conference 1983-2000. Football League 2000-05.

Club Colours (change): Red/black/black (Amber/purple/purple)

Ground Capacity: 6,419 **Seats:** 3.175 **Covered:** 3,062 **Clubhouse:** Yes **Shop:** Yes

Directions

From North M5 Junc 3 onto A456 to Kidderminster, From South M5 Junc 6 onto A449 to Kidderminster. Alternatively M40/42 Junc 1 onto A38 to Bromsgrove/A448 to Kidderminster. (All routes follow Brown signs to (SVR) Steam Railway then follow signs to Aggborough). Aggborough is signposted at either end of Hoo Road.

Previous Grounds: None

Record Attendance: 9,155 v Hereford United - 27/11/48

Record Victory: 25-0 v Hereford (H) - Birmingham Senior Cup 12/10/1889

Record Defeat: 0-13 v Darwen (A) - FA Cup 1st Round 24/01/1891

Record Goalscorer: Peter Wassell - 432 (1963-74)

Record Appearances: Brendan Wassell - 686 (1962-74)

Additional Records: Paid £80,000 to Nuneaton Borough for Andy Ducros July 2000
Recieved £380,000 from W.B.A. for Lee Hughes July 1997

Senior Honours:

FA Trophy 1986-87. Conference 1993-94, 1999-2000.

10 YEAR RECORD

04-05	05-06	06-07	07-08	08-09	09-10	10-11	11-12	12-13	13-14
FL 3 23	Conf 15	Conf 10	Conf 13	Conf 6	Conf 13	Conf 6	Conf 6	Conf 2	Conf 7

KIDDERMINSTER HARRIERS MATCH RESULTS 2013-14

Date	Comp	H/A	Opponents	Att:	Result		Goalscorers	Pos	No.
Aug 10	CPrem	H	Gateshead	2110	W	3-1	Gash 13 Gittings 60 Dunkley 81	3	1
13	CPrem	A	Alfreton Town	722	L	1-3	Storer 79	13	2
17	CPrem	A	Braintree Town	874	W	1-0	Storer 89	6	3
24	CPrem	H	Chester	2283	W	3-1	Gowling 32 Johnson 45 Lolley 90	2	4
26	CPrem	A	Nuneaton	1481	L	1-2	Malbon 5	7	5
31	CPrem	H	Luton Town	**2866**	L	0-2		12	6
Sept 7	CPrem	A	Welling United	911	W	2-1	Dance 10 25	8	7
14	CPrem	H	Hyde	1607	W	2-1	Malbon 3 Gash 34	6	8
17	CPrem	A	Tamworth	874	W	3-0	Dance 6 Gash 63 Malbon 90 (pen)	3	9
21	CPrem	A	Dartford	1020	L	0-3		4	10
24	CPrem	H	FC Halifax Town	1703	W	2-0	Gash 21 Lolley 57	3	11
28	CPrem	A	Aldershot Town	2049	D	0-0		3	12
Oct 5	CPrem	A	Chester	2223	D	0-0		4	13
8	CPrem	H	Forest Green Rovers	2244	W	4-1	Storer 12 Byrne 65 Morgan-Smith 72 88 (pen)	2	14
12	CPrem	A	Southport	1018	W	2-1	Lolley 8 Blissett 45	2	15
19	CPrem	H	Lincoln City	2103	W	4-1	Gash 42 Boyce 65 Storer 68 Malbon 90	2	16
27	***FAC4Q***	***H***	***Bradford PA***		***D***	***1-1***	***Byrne 35***		17
29	***FAC4Qr***	***A***	***Bradford PA***	***464***	***W***	***2 1***	***Morgan-Smith 91 Johnson 104***		18
Nov 2	CPrem	A	Barnet	1557	L	0-1		2	19
8	***FAC1***	***H***	***Sutton United***	***2045***	***W***	***4-1***	***Morgan-Smith 13 Gittings 18 Lolley 60 Malbon 90***		20
12	CPrem	A	Macclesfield	1395	D	1-1	Gittings 27	3	21
16	CPrem	H	Wrexham	2532	W	3-1	Lolley 31 64 Dunkley 78	2	22
23	CPrem	H	Tamworth	1951	W	5-3	Malbon 20 Lolley 22 Morgan-Smith 56 77 Storer 83	2	23
30	***FAT1***	***A***	***Bradford PA***	***355***	***L***	***1-2***	***Gash 90***		24
Dec 7	***FAC2***	***H***	***Newport County***	***2636***	***W***	***4-2***	***Gash 19 63 Gittings 28 43***	***3***	25
10	CPrem	A	Woking	1366	L	0-1		3	26
14	CPrem	H	Alfreton Town	1834	L	1-3	Gittings 17	3	27
19	CPrem	A	Grimsby Town	3086	L	1-3	Gash 6	4	28
26	CPrem	H	Hereford United	3420	W	2-1	Gash 10 Jackman 29	5	29
28	CPrem	A	Luton Town	8486	L	0-6		5	30
Jan 4	***FAC3***	***H***	***Peterborough United***	***3858***	***D***	***0-0***			31
7	*Steve Burr leaves his post as Manager, with Andy Thorn replacing him*								
11	CPrem	H	Salisbury City	2034	W	3-0	LOLLEY 3 (18 75 pen 86 pen)	4	32
14	***FAC3r***	***A***	***Peterborough United***	***3483***	***W***	***3-2***	***Gash 49 Byrne 52 Lolley 76***		33
21	CPrem	H	Dartford	1580	L	1-2	Gash 49	6	34
25	***FAC4***	***A***	***Sunderland***	***25,081***	***L***	***0-1***			35
28	CPrem	A	Hereford United	2014	D	1-1	Gowling 65	7	36
Feb 1	CPrem	A	Gateshead	625	L	1-3	Johnson 90	7	37
15	CPrem	A	Lincoln City	2012	L	0-2		10	38
22	CPrem	H	Braintre Town	1653	D	2-2	Morgan-Smith 78 82	10	39
25	CPrem	H	Woking	1448	W	2-0	Morgan-Smith 1 Storer 69	8	40
March 1	CPrem	A	Cambridge United	2528	L	1-5	Malbon 30	10	41
5	*Gary Whilds appointed as Manager*								
8	CPrem	A	Wrexham	3159	D	0-0		10	42
11	CPrem	H	Macklesfield Town	1591	W	2-1	Gittings 1 Morgan-Smith 44	9	43
15	CPrem	H	Barnet	1950	W	1-0	Gash 60	8	44
18	CPrem	A	Aldershot Town	1558	D	0-0		5	45
22	CPrem	H	Southport	1818	D	1-1	Byrne 77	8	46
29	CPrem	A	Salisbury City	2217	D	1-1	Gittings 35	10	47
April 5	CPrem	H	Grimsby Town	2176	L	0-1		10	48
8	CPrem	A	Forest Green Rovers	1231	D	1-1	Wright 49	11	49
12	CPrem	H	Welling United	1882	W	2-0	Gash 77 Blissett 84	9	50
15	CPrem	H	Cambridge United	1938	W	2-0	Bell 67 Gash 76	8	51
18	CPrem	A	Hyde	531	W	3-1	Bell 6 Morgan-Smith Thornton 73 (og)	7	52
21	CPrem	H	Nuneaton Town	2022	D	0-0		7	53
28	CPrem	A	FC Halifax Town	2089	D	1-1	Blissett	7	54

GOALSCORERS	Lge	FAC	FAT	Total	Pens	Hat-tricks	Cons Run
Gash	11	3	1	15			2
Lolley	10	1		11		1	2
Morgan-Smith	9	2		11	1		2
Gittings	6	2		8			
Malbon	7			7	1		2
Storer	6			6			2
Byrne	2	2		4			
Blissett	3			3			
Dance	3			3			
Johnson	2	1		3			
Bell	2			2			2
Dunkley	2			2			
Gowling	2			2			
Boyce	1			1			
Jackman	1			1			
Wright	1			1			
Opponents	1			1			

Cons Run - Consecutive scoring games.

LINCOLN CITY

Chairman: Bob Dorrian
Secretary: John Vickers **(T)** 07881 913 249 **(E)** jv@redimps.com
Commercial Manager: Russell Moore **(T)** 07971 122 234
Programme Editor: John Vickers **(T)** 07881 913 249
Ground Address: Sincil Bank Stadium, Lincoln LN5 8LD
(T) 01522 880 011 **Manager:** Gary Simpson

Club Factfile

Founded: 1884 **Nickname:** Imps
Previous Names: None
Previous Leagues: Midland (Founder Member) 1889-91, 1908-09, 1911-12, 1920-21, Football Alliance 1891-92, Football League (Founder Member) 1892-1908, 1909-11, 1912-20, 1921-86, 1988-2011, Conference 1986-88.

Club Colours (change): Red & white stripes/black/red & white (All sky blue)

Ground Capacity: 9,800 **Seats:** Yes **Covered:** Yes **Clubhouse:** **Shop:** Yes

Directions
From South: Exit A1 at s/p 'Lincoln A46, Sleaford A17' onto the A46. At roundabout after 9.4 mile take 3rd exit (s/p Lincoln South A1434). Keep on A1434, following 'Lincoln and City Centre' signs for 4.3 miles. Then get into inside lane (s/p City Centre, Worksop A7) and go straight on (1st exit) at r'about into the High St. After 0.5 miles get in outside lane, and go straight on at lights (s/p City Ctre, Worksop A57). After 0.1 miles turn right into Scorer Street. **From North:** Exit A1(M) at the r'about after the Fina and Shell garages (s'p Lincoln A57, E. Markham) onto the A57. At junc. after 9.9 miles turn right (s/p Lincoln A57), remaining on A57 which here runs alongside the Foss Dyke. At r'about after 5.9 miles turn right (Lincoln South, Newark A46, Grantham A1) onto the A46. Straight on at r'about after 1.8 miles. At next r'about after 1.6 miles (by BP station) turn left (s/p) Lincoln South B1190, Doddington Ind.Est., into Doddington Rd, Sraight on for 2 miles to T-junction. Here, turn left (no signpost) onto Newark Rd A1434. Keep on A1434 following City Centre signs. Go straight on (1st exit) at r'about into the High St. After (0.5 miles get in outside lane, and go straight on at lights (s/p City Ctre, Worksop A57). After 0.1 miles turn right into Scorer St. Tip: Have some change ready for a small toll bridge (Dunham) en route.

Previous Grounds: John O'Gaunt's 1883-94.

Record Attendance: 23,196 v Derby County, League Cup 4th Round 15/11/1967
Record Victory: 11-1 v Crewe Alexandra, Division Three North 29/09/1951.
Record Defeat: 3-11 v Manchester City, Division Two 23/03/1895.
Record Goalscorer: (League) Andy Graver - 143, 1950-55, 58-61.
Record Appearances: (League) Grant Brown - 407, 1989-2002.
Additional Records: Paid, £75,000 for Tony Battersby from Bury, 08/1998.
Received, £500,000 for Gareth Anisworth from Port Vale, 09/1997.
Senior Honours:
Midland League 1908-09, 20-21. Football League Division Three North 1931-32, 47-48, Division Four 1975-76.
Football Conference 1987-88.

10 YEAR RECORD

04-05	05-06	06-07	07-08	08-09	09-10	10-11	11-12	12-13	13-14
FL 2 6	FL 2 7	FL 2 5	FL 2 15	FL 2 13	FL 2 20	FL 2 23	Conf 17	Conf 16	Conf 14

LINCOLN CITY MATCH RESULTS 2013-14

Date	Comp	H/A	Opponents	Att:	Result	Goalscorers	Pos	No.
Aug 10	CPrem	A	Woking	1845	D 0-0		12	1
13	CPrem	H	Macclesfield Town	2384	W 1-0	Rowe 27	8	2
17	CPrem	H	Forest Green Rovers	2290	W 2-1	Fairhurst 27 86	4	3
24	CPrem	A	Cambridge United	3022	L 0-1		10	4
26	CPrem	H	Wrexham	2610	W 2-0	Tomlinson 38 82	5	5
31	CPrem	A	Dartford	1386	W 2-1	Tomlinson 21 Boyce 43	2	6
Sept 7	CPrem	H	Salisbury City	2646	L 0-1		4	7
14	CPrem	A	Barnet	1913	D 1-1	Nolan 90	8	8
17	CPrem	H	Southport	1879	W 1-0	Miller 26	4	9
21	CPrem	A	Luton Town	6203	L 2-3	Power 20 Tomlinson 51	6	10
24	CPrem	A	Hereford United	1398	L 0-1			11
28	CPrem	H	Hyde	2311	W 3-0	Tomlinson 48 Dixon 79 89	7	12
Oct 5	CPrem	A	Nuneaton Town	1634	D 2-2	Miller 37 Nolan 47	9	13
8	CPrem	H	Tamworth	2603	D 0-0		9	14
12	CPrem	H	Aldershot	2748	L 0-1		9	15
19	CPrem	A	Kidderminster Harriers	2103	L 1-4	Wright 80	13	16
26	***FAC4Q***	***A***	***Worcester City***	***1019***	***D 1-1***	***Boyce 77***		17
29	***FAC4Qr***	***H***	***Worcester City***	***1344***	***W 3-0***	***Tomlinson 31 44 Dixon 65***		18
Nov 2	CPrem	A	Welling United	746	L 0-1		13	19
9	***FAC1***	***H***	***Plymouth Argyle***	***2924***	***D 0-0***			20
12	CPrem	A	Southport	818	W 1-0	Nolan 75	13	21
16	CPrem	A	Forest Green Rovers	1128	L 1-4	Sharp 39	15	22
20	***FAC1r***	***A***	***Plymouth Argyle***	***3324***	***L 0-5***			23
23	CPrem	H	Hereford United	1874	D 1-1	Tomlinson 47	16	24
30	***FAT1***	***H***	***Stalybridge Celtic***	***1023***	***W 5-1***	***Jackson 19 POWER 3 (23 29 56) Folana 90***		25
Dec 10	CPrem	H	Gateshead	1411	L 0-1		16	26
15	***FAT2***	***A***	***Braintree Town***	***410***	***W 3-1***	***Sharp 58 Hamann 90 (og) Foster 90***		27
21	CPrem	A	Chester	1850	D 3-3	Dixon 19 Power 47 (pen) Robinson 90	19	28
26	CPrem	H	Grimsby Town	**5421**	L 0-2		18	29
28	CPrem	A	FC Halifax Town	1979	L 1-5	Tomlinson 25	18	30
Jan 1	CPrem	A	Grimsby Town	5484	D 1-1	Thomas 21 (og)	18	31
4	CPrem	H	Luton Town	2928	D 0-0		18	32
7	CPrem	H	Alfreton Town	1877	W 4-1	Kempson 8 (og) Wright 21 Nolan 80 Sam-Yorke 87	16	33
11	***FAT3***	***H***	***North Ferriby United***	***2037***	***L 0-4***			34
21	CPrem	A	Macclesfield Town	1364	L 1-3	Tomlinson 44	17	35
25	CPrem	H	Woking	2017	D 2-2	Brown 25 Tomlinson 40	17	36
Feb 1	CPrem	H	FC Halifax	2077	W 3-1	TOMLINSON 3 (3 11 53)	17	37
4	CPrem	H	Nuneaton Town	1772	L 1-2	Power 70	18	38
8	CPrem	A	Hyde	646	W 4-3	Sam-Yorke 15 Audel 45 Tomlinson 76 Miller 90	16	39
15	CPrem	H	Kidderminster Harriers	2012	W 2-0	Tomlinson 19 78	14	40
22	CPrem	H	Chester	2354	D 1-1	Sam-Yorke 16	15	41
March 1	CPrem	A	Aldershot	1944	W 3-2	Miller 5 Audel 26 Tomlinson 71	14	42
8	CPrem	A	Alfreton Town	1331	D 1-1	Newton 90	16	43
11	CPrem	H	Welling United	1623	L 1-2	Bright 5	17	44
15	CPrem	H	Braintree Town	2002	W 2-0	Miller 64 Audel 73	14	45
18	CPrem	A	Braintree Town	787	W 2-0	Foster 37 Sheridan 76	12	46
22	CPrem	A	Gateshead	804	L 1-3	Nolan 47	15	47
29	CPrem	A	Tamworth	979	D 0-0		15	48
April 5	CPrem	H	Dartford	1947	D 0-0		15	49
12	CPrem	A	Salisbury City	952	W 2-1	Newton 70 Rowe 90	15	50
18	CPrem	H	Cambridge United	2535	W 1-0	Tomlinson 32 (pen)	14	51
21	CPrem	A	Wrexham	2714	W 1-0	Rowe 31	13	52
26	CPrem	H	Barnet	2812	D 3-3	Brown 7 Bright 46 Tomlinson 54	14	53

GOALSCORERS	Lge	FAC	FAT	Total	Pens	Hat-tricks	Cons Run
Tomlinson	18	2		20	1	1	3
Power	3		3	6	1	1	
Miller	5			5			
Nolan	5			5			
Dixon	3	1		4			
Audel	3			3			
Rowe	3			3			
Sam-Yorke	3			3			
Boyce	1	1		2			
Bright	2			2			
Brown	2			2			
Fairhurst	2			2			
Foster	1		1	2			
Newton	2			2			
Sharp	1		1	2			
Wright	2			2			
Folana			1	1			
Jackson			1	1			
Robinson	1			1			
Sheridan	1			1			
Opponents	2		1	3			

Cons Run - Consecutive scoring games.

MACCLESFIELD TOWN

Chairman: TBC

Secretary: Julie Briggs **(T)** 01625 264 686 **(E)** juliebriggs@mtfc.co.uk

Commercial Manager: TBC **(T)**

Programme Editor: TBC **(T)**

Ground Address: Moss Rose Ground, London Road, Macclesfield SK11 7SP

(T) 01625 264 686 **Manager:** John Askey

Club Factfile

Founded: 1874 **Nickname:** The Silkmen

Previous Names: None

Previous Leagues: Manchester. Cheshire County. Northern Premier. Conference 1987-97. Football League 1997-2012.

Club Colours (change): Blue/white/blue (Petrol green/white/petrol green)

Ground Capacity: 6,335 **Seats:** 2,599 **Covered:** Yes **Clubhouse:** Yes **Shop:** Yes

Directions

From North (M6), Exit Junction 19, Knutsford. Follow the A537 to Macclesfield. Follow signs for the Town Centre. The follow signs A523 Leek, the ground is a mile out of town. The ground is sign-posted from the Town Centre

From South (M6), Exit Junction 17 Sandbach. Follow A534 to Congleton. Then A536 to Macclesfield. After passing the Rising Sun on the left, less than a mile, turn right into Moss Lane. Follow this around and it will bring you to the rear of the ground.

Previous Grounds: Rostron Field 1874-1891.

Record Attendance: 9,008 v Winsford United - Cheshire Senior Cup 04.02.1948.

Record Victory: 15-0 v Chester St Marys - Cheshire Senior Cup Second Round 16.02.1886.

Record Defeat: 1-13 v Tranmere Rovers Reserves - 03.05.1929.

Record Goalscorer: Not known

Record Appearances: Not known

Additional Records:

Senior Honours:

Manchester League 1908-09, 10-11. Cheshire County League 1931-32, 32-33, 53-54, 60-61, 63-64, 67-68.
Northern Premier League 1968-69, 69-70, 86-87. Bob Lord Trophy 1993-94. Conference 1994-95, 96-97, Championship Shield 1996, 1997, 1998.
FA Trophy 1969-70, 95-96. Cheshire Senior cup x20 most recently 1999-2000.

10 YEAR RECORD

04-05	05-06	06-07	07-08	08-09	09-10	10-11	11-12	12-13	13-14
FL 2 5	FL 2 17	FL 2 22	FL 2 19	FL 2 20	FL 2 19	FL 2 15	FL 2 24	Conf 11	Conf 15

MACCLESFIELD TOWN MATCH RESULTS 2013-14

Date	Comp	H/A	Opponents	Att:	Result		Goalscorers	Pos	No.
Aug 10	CPrem	H	Nuneaton Town	1585	L	0-1		19	1
13	CPrem	A	Lincoln City	2386	L	0-1		19	2
17	CPrem	A	Luton Town	6216	D	1-1	Holroyd 63	19	3
24	CPrem	H	FC Halifax	1720	D	2-2	Boden 38 Mackreth 82	20	4
26	CPrem	A	Hyde	631	D	2-2	Boden 19 41	20	5
31	CPrem	H	Braintree Town	1264	L	0-1		21	6
Sept 7	CPrem	A	Aldershot	1752	L	0-1		22	7
14	CPrem	H	Alfreton Town	1271	L	0-1		23	8
17	CPrem	A	Chester	2012	L	1-2	Whitaker 44	23	9
21	CPrem	H	Woking	1195	**W**	3-2	Jennings 12 45 Mackreth 78	23	10
24	CPrem	A	Barnet	1179	**W**	2-1	Jennings 27 35	20	11
28	CPrem	H	Welling United	1321	**W**	2-1	Jennings 64 Holroyd 67	18	12
Oct 5	CPrem	A	Tamworth	864	L	0-1		19	13
8	CPrem	H	Hereford United	1329	**W**	1-0	Jennings 62	18	14
12	CPrem	A	Forest Green Rovers	1181	**W**	3-2	Williams 41 Whittaker 59 Lewis 90	15	15
18	CPrem	H	Southport	1370	D	2-2	Jennings 10 77	15	16
26	***FAC4Q***	***H***	***Vauxhall Motors***	***956***	***W***	***7-0***	***Whittaker 20 Jennings 34 (pen) Boden 47 ROWE 3 (52 59 68) Kay 72***		17
Nov 2	CPrem	H	Wrexham	1978	**W**	3-2	JENNINGS 3 (1pen 40 90)	14	18
9	***FAC1***	***H***	***FACup***	***1835***	***W***	***4-0***	***Jennings 2 74 Boden 70 Winn 89***		19
12	CPrem	H	Kidderminster Harriers	1395	D	1-1	Turnbull 90	15	20
16	CPrem	H	Dartford	1543	**W**	3-1	Boden 66 Jennings 68 69	14	21
23	CPrem	A	Salisbury CIty	843	L	2-3	Jennings 45 (pen) Turnbull 55	15	22
30	***FAT1***	***A***	***Tamworth***	***667***	***L***	***0-2***			23
Dec 7	***FAC2***	***H***	***Brackley***	***2438***	***W***	***3-2***	***Andrew 17 Boden 50 Mackreth 81***		24
10	CPrem	A	Cambridge United	2284	L	0-3		15	25
14	CPrem	H	Salisbury City	1235	**W**	1-0	Rowe 85	14	26
26	CPrem	H	Hyde	1882	**W**	3-0	Turnbull 6 Andrew 29 Holroyd 88	14	27
28	CPrem	A	Grimsby Town	4002	**W**	3-2	Boden 9 Holroyd 22 Andrew 84	12	28
Jan 1	CPrem	A	Hyde	979	**W**	3-0	Boden 64 76 (pen) O'Connnor 60 (og)	11	29
4	***FAC3***	***H***	***Sheffield Wednesday***	***5873***	***D***	***1-1***	***Williams 72***		30
14	***FAC3r***	***A***	***Sheffield Wednesday***	***12,302***	***L***	***1-4***	***Boden 65 (pen)***		31
18	CPrem	A	Nuneaton Town	1002	L	0-1		12	32
21	CPrem	H	LIncoln City	1364	**W**	3-1	Boden 60 Mackreth79 Holroyd 81	11	33
Feb 4	CPrem	H	Chester	1771	**W**	3-2	Boden 22 Williams 33 Holroyd 54	11	34
11	CPrem	H	Luton Town	1705	L	1-2	Andrew 38	11	35
22	CPrem	A	Woking	1144	L	2-3	Boden 6 Pilkington 73	12	36
25	CPrem	A	Hereford United	1013	**W**	2-1	Pilkington 29 Boden 48	11	37
March 1	CPrem	A	Welling United	701	L	0-1		12	38
8	CPrem	H	Grimsby Town	2092	D	1-1	Boden 90 (pen)	13	39
11	CPrem	A	Kidderminster Harriers	1591	L	1-2	Whittaker 45	14	40
15	CPrem	A	Southport	1045	L	1-4	Andrew 16	15	41
18	CPrem	H	Barnet	1153	**W**	2-0	Holroyd 81 Whittaker 87	15	42
22	CPrem	H	Tamworth	1352	**W**	2-1	Andrew 9 Boden 57	13	43
29	CPrem	A	Dartford	1105	L	1-2	Turnbull 42	14	44
April 1	CPrem	H	Cambridge United	1278	L	0-1		15	45
5	CPrem	A	Wrexham	2402	L	0-1		16	46
8	CPrem	A	Braintree Town	739	**W**	1-0	Boden 62	15	47
12	CPrem	H	Aldershot Town	**2207**	D	1-1	Boden 77	14	48
15	CPrem	H	Forest Green Rovers	1142	L	1-2	Boden 38	14	49
19	CPrem	A	FC Halifax Town	2190	L	1-2	Boden 45	14	50
21	CPrem	H	Gateshead	1628	L	0-2		16	51
26	CPrem	A	Alfreton Town	696	**W**	1-0	Boden 89	15	52

GOALSCORERS	Lge	FAC	FAT	Total	Pens	Hat-tricks	Cons Run
Jennings	14	3		17	3		4
Boden	18	4		12	3		4
Holroyd	7			7			2
Andrew	5	1		6			2
Whitaker	4	1		5			
Mackreth	3	1		4			
Rowe	1	3		4		1	
Turnbull	4			4			
Williams	2	1		3			
Pilkington	2			2			2
Kay		1		1			
Lewis	1			1			
Winn		1		1			
Opponents	1			1			

Cons Run - Consecutive scoring games.

NUNEATON TOWN

Chairman: Ian Neale (Chief Exe)
Secretary: Richard Dean **(T)** 02476 385 738 **(E)** richard.dean1955@o2.co.uk
Commercial Manager: Gemma Brown **(T)** 02476 385 738
Programme Editor: Jodie Faries **(T)** 07912 694 811
Ground Address: Liberty Way, Nuneaton CV11 6RR
(T) 02476 385 738 **Manager:** Brian Reid

2013-14 Squad - Back Row (l to r): Paul Egan, John Warren, Theo Streete, Gaz Dean, Dimitar Evtimov, Gavin Cowan, James Belshaw, Adam Walker, Phil Trainer, Richard Hearn, Darryl Strong.
Middle Row: Martin Winstanley, Jason Hood, Mark Bell, James Armson, Greg Pearson, David McNamee, Danny Sleath, Louis Moult, Omar Reiki, Richie Norman, Gemma Brown, Jodie Faries.
Front Row: Delroy Gordon, Andy Brown, Connor Taylor, Kevin Wilkin, Michael Moore, Wes York, Jon Adams, Amari'i Bell

Club Factfile

Founded: 2008 **Nickname:** The Boro
Previous Names: Nuneaton Borough 1937-2008
Previous Leagues: Central Amateur 1937-38, Birmingham Combination 1938-52, West Midlands 1952-58, Southern 1958-79 81-82, 88-90, 2003-04, 08-10, Conference 1979-81, 82-88, 99-03, 04-08
Club Colours (change): Blue & white stripes/white/white (Amber/black/amber)

Ground Capacity: **Seats:** Yes **Covered:** Yes **Clubhouse:** Yes **Shop:** Yes

Directions
From the South, West and North West, exit the M6 at Junction 3 and follow the A444 into Nuneaton. At the Coton Arches roundabout turn right into Avenue Road which is the A4254 signposted for Hinckley. Continue along the A4254 following the road into Garrett Street, then Eastboro Way, then turn left into Townsend Drive. Follow the road round before turning left into Liberty Way for the ground. From the North, exit the M1 at Junction 21 and follow the M69. Exit at Junction 1 and take the 4th exit at roundabout onto A5 (Tamworth, Nuneaton). At Longshoot Junction turn left onto A47, continue to roundabout and take the 1st exit onto A4254, Eastboro Way. Turn right at next roundabout into Townsend Drive, then right again into Liberty Way, CV11 6RR.

Previous Grounds: Manor Park

Record Attendance: 22,114 v Rotherham United - FA Cup 3rd Round 1967 (At Manor Park)
Record Victory: 11-1 - 1945-46 and 1955-56
Record Defeat: 1-8 - 1955-56 and 1968-69
Record Goalscorer: Paul Culpin - 201 (55 during season 1992-93)
Record Appearances: Alan Jones - 545 (1962-74)
Additional Records: Paid £35,000 to Forest green Rovers for Marc McGregor 2000
Received £80,000 from Kidderminster Harriers for Andy Ducros 2000
Senior Honours:
Southern League Midland Division 1981-82, 92-93, Premier Division 1988-99, Premier Division Play-offs 2009-10.
Conference North Play-offs 2011-12.
Birmingham Senior Cup x7.

10 YEAR RECORD

04-05		05-06		06-07		07-08		08-09		09-10		10-11		11-12		12-13		13-14	
Conf N	2	Conf N	3	Conf N	10	Conf N	7	SthE	2	SthP	2	Conf N	6	Conf N	5	Conf	15	Conf	13

NUNEATON TOWN MATCH RESULTS 2013-14

Date	Comp	H/A	Opponents	Att:	Result		Goalscorers	Pos	No.
Aug 10	CPrem	A	Macclesfield Town	1585	**W**	1-0	Moult 23	6	1
13	CPrem	H	Forest Green Rovers	1005	D	1-1	Brown 18	7	2
17	CPrem	H	Southport	919	**W**	3-1	Moult 2 10 Walker 83	7	3
24	CPrem	A	Barnet	1507	D	1-1	Brown 43	6	4
26	CPrem	H	Kidderminster Harriers	1481	**W**	2-1	Moult 83 Pearson 90	3	5
31	CPrem	A	Grimsby Town	3321	**W**	2-1	Cowan 26 Brown 33	3	6
Sept 7	CPrem	H	Wrexham	1561	**W**	2-0	Brown 75 Moult 90	2	7
14	CPrem	A	Dartford	1155	**W**	2-1	Moult 4 8	2	8
17	CPrem	H	Hereford United	1085	**W**	2-1	York 23 Moult 61	1	9
21	CPrem	H	Salisbury City	1355	L	1-2	Moult 73	2	10
24	CPrem	A	Cambridge United	3740	L	0-3		2	11
28	CPrem	A	Woking	1272	L	0-2		2	12
Oct 5	CPrem	H	Lincoln City	1634	D	2-2	York 4 Brown 84	4	13
8	CPrem	A	FC Halifax Town	1197	D	2-2	York 5 90	3	14
12	CPrem	H	Braintree Town	1030	D	1-1	Streete 64	4	15
19	CPrem	H	Gateshead	946	L	1-4	Moult 73	7	16
26	***FAC4Q***	***H***	***FC Halifax Town***	***1043***	***L***	***0-2***			17
Nov 2	CPrem	A	Hyde	447	D	2-2	Ladapo 18 Hibbert 90	10	18
12	CPrem	A	Forest Green Rovers	933	L	0-1		11	19
16	CPrem	A	Welling United	807	**W**	2-1	Arrnson 55 Ladapo 90	9	20
23	CPrem	H	Chester	1221	**W**	1-0	Moult 84	7	21
26	CPrem	H	Alfreton Town	715	**W**	3-0	Walker 27 Hibbert 42 York 88	5	22
30	***FAT1***	***A***	***Alfreton Town***	***343***	***W***	***1-0***	***Moult 53***		23
Dec 7	CPrem	A	Hereford United	1292	**W**	1-0	Moult 40 (pen)	4	24
14	***FAT2***	***A***	***Gosport Borough***	***284***	***D***	***0-0***			25
17	***FAT2r***	***H***	***Gosport Borough***	***423***	***D***	***0-0***	***Gosport won 4-2 on penalties***		26
21	CPrem	H	Woking	895	L	0-2		7	27
26	CPrem	A	Tamworth	1347	D	1 1	Streete 69	7	28
28	CPrem	H	Cambridge United	1478	D	0-0		7	29
Jan 4	CPrem	A	Southport	811	L	0-1		9	30
11	CPrem	A	Gateshead	726	L	1-2	Walker 55	9	31
18	CPrem	H	Macclesfield Town	1002	**W**	1-0	Brown 60	9	32
25	CPrem	A	Luton Town	7310	L	0-3		9	33
28	CPrem	H	Aldershot Town	718	**W**	2-1	Brown 38 Moult 44	6	34
Feb 1	CPrem	A	Salisbury City	740	L	1-2	Sleath 34	6	35
4	CPrem	H	Lincoln City	1772	**W**	2-1	Walker 18 Streete 58	5	36
15	CPrem	H	Hyde	876	**W**	1-0	Armson 2	4	37
22	CPrem	H	Luton Town	**3480**	L	0-5		6	38
1 Mar	CPrem	A	Chester	2214	D	3 3	Moult 30 Brown 43 87	6	39
8	CPrem	H	Welling United	929	**W**	2-0	Brown 62 Hibbert 87	5	40
11	CPrem	H	Tamworth	1097	**W**	1-0	Delfounseo 10	4	41
15	CPrem	A	Aldershot Town	1606	D	2-2	Cowan 27 Armson 42 (pen)	4	42
22	CPrem	H	Grimsby Town	1565	L	0-1		7	43
27	CPrem	A	Braintree Town	802	L	1-2	Hibbert 70	8	44
29	CPrem	A	Alfreton Twn	789	D	1-1	Armson 84	8	45
April 5	CPrem	H	FC Halifax Town	1041	L	0-1		9	46
12	CPrem	A	Wrexham	2706	L	0-3		10	47
18	CPrem	H	Barnet	852	L	0-1		13	48
21	CPrem	A	Kidderminster Harriers	2022	D	0-0		13	49
26	CPrem	H	Dartford	903	**W**	3-1	MOULT 3 (28 37 63)	13	50

GOALSCORERS	Lge	FAC	FAT	Total	Pens	Hat-tricks	Cons Run
Moult	17		1	18	1	1	4
Brown	11			11			2
York	5			5			2
Armson	4			4	1		
Hibbert	4			4			
Walker	4			4			
Streete	3			3			
Cowan	2			2			
Ladapo	2			2			
Delfounseo	1			1			
Pearson	1			1			
Sleath	1			1			

Cons Run - Consecutive scoring games.

SOUTHPORT

Chairman: Charles Clapham
Secretary: Ken Hilton (T) 07802 661 906 (E) secretary@southportfc.net
Commercial Manager: Haydn Preece (T) 07768 000 818
Programme Editor: Rob Urwin (T) programme@southportfc.net
Ground Address: Merseyrail Community Stadium, Haig Avenue, Southport, Merseyside PR8 6JZ
(T) 01704 533 422 **Manager:** Martin Foyle

Club Factfile

Founded: 1881 **Nickname:** The Sandgrounders
Previous Names: Southport Central, Southport Vulcan
Previous Leagues: Preston & District, Lancashire 1889-1903, Lancashire comb. 1903-11, Central 1911-21, Football League 1921-78, Northern Premier 1978-93, 2003-04, Conference 1993-2003
Club Colours (change): Yellow/black/black (All sky blue)

Ground Capacity: 6,008 **Seats:** 1,660 **Covered:** 2,760 **Clubhouse:** Yes **Shop:** Yes

Directions
Leave M6 at junction 26. Join M58 to junction 3. Join A570 signposted Southport, follow A570 through Ormskirk Town Centre following signs for Southport. At the big roundabout (McDonalds is on the left) take the fourth exit. Proceed along this road until you reach the 2nd set of pedstrian lights and take the next left into Haig Avenue.

Previous Grounds: Sussex Road Sports Ground, Scarisbrick New Road, Ash Lane (later named Haig Avenue)

Record Attendance: 20,010 v Newcastle United - FA Cup 1932
Record Victory: 8-1 v Nelson - 01/01/31
Record Defeat: 0-11 v Oldham Athletic - 26/12/62
Record Goalscorer: Alan Spence - 98
Record Appearances: Arthur Peat - 401 (1962-72)
Additional Records: Paid £20,000 to Macclesfield Town for Martin McDonald

Senior Honours:
Lancashire Senior Cup 1904-05. Liverpool Senior Cup 1930-31, 31-32, 43-44, 62-63, 74-75, 90-91, 92-93, 98-99, Shared 57-58, 63-64. Football League Division 4 1972-73. Northern Premier League Challenge Cup 1990-91. Northern Premier League Premier Division 1992-93. Conference North 2004-05, 2009-10.

10 YEAR RECORD

04-05	05-06	06-07	07-08	08-09	09-10	10-11	11-12	12-13	13-14
Conf N 10	Conf 18	Conf 23	Conf N 4	Conf N 5	Conf N 1	Conf 21	Conf 7	Conf 20	Conf 18

SOUTHPORT MATCH RESULTS 2013-14

Date	Comp	H/A	Opponents	Att:	Result		Goalscorers	Pos	No.
Aug 10	CPrem	A	Luton Town	2210	W	1-0	Milligan 22	7	1
13	CPrem	A	Hyde	769	W	2-1	Hattersley 78 Thames 90	1	2
17	CPrem	A	Nuneaton Town	919	L	1-3	Aaron Chalmers 8	7	3
24	CPrem	H	Gateshead	915	W	2-1	Ledsham 34 45	3	4
26	CPrem	A	F C Halifax Town	1583	L	0-1		9	5
31	CPrem	H	Aldershot Town	1012	W	1-0	Osawe 27	5	6
Sept 7	CPrem	A	Tamworth	933	L	1-4	Osawe 20	9	7
14	CPrem	H	Welling United	825	D	2-2	Almond 51 Hattersley 62	11	8
17	CPrem	A	Lincoln City	1879	L	0-1		12	9
21	CPrem	A	Braintree Town	924	L	0-1		14	10
24	CPrem	H	Alfreton Town	726	W	2-1	Fitzpatrick 68 Osawe 83	13	11
28	CPrem	A	Dartford	1025	L	0-1		15	12
Oct 5	CPrem	H	Woking	873	D	2-1	Milligan 19	13	13
8	CPrem	A	Wrexham	2734	L	0-1		15	14
12	CPrem	H	Kidderminster Harriers	1018	L	1-2	Smith 42	17	15
18	CPrem	A	Macclesfield Town	1370	D	2-2	Hattersley 61 Milligan 90 (pen)	17	16
26	***FAC4Q***	***H***	***Marske United***	***943***	***W***	***6-2***	***Hattersley 4 12 Brown 6 Ellington 8 Milligan 32 Ledsham 53***		17
Nov 2	CPrem	H	Cambridge United	1006	W	1-0	M.Brown 2	16	18
9	***FAC1***	***A***	***Leyton Orient***	***3024***	***L***	***2-5***	***George 21 Flynn 87***		19
12	CPrem	H	Lincoln City	818	L	0-1		17	20
16	CPrem	H	Hereford United	876	L	0-3		18	21
23	CPrem	A	Aldershot	1592	L	1-5	Irle-Bi 85	18	22
26	CPrem	A	Luton Town	6057	L	0-3		18	23
30	***FAT1***	***H***	***Boston United***	***496***	***L***	***1-2***	***Ellington 8***		24
Dec 21	CPrem	A	Salisbury City	724	D	1-1	Hattersley 64	20	25
26	CPrem	H	Chester	1872	D	0-0		19	26
28	CPrem	A	Alfreton Town	976	L	1-2	Brodie 76	20	27
Jan 4	CPrem	H	Nuneaton	811	W	1-0	Hattersley 88	19	28
11	CPrem	H	Hyde United	871	D	1-1	Hattersley 78	19	29
18	CPrem	A	Hereford United	1569	L	1-4	Akrigg 60	19	30
21	CPrem	H	Wrexham	911	L	1-2	Brown 4	21	31
25	CPrem	A	Barnet	1510	L	0-1		22	32
Feb 8	CPrem	A	Grimsby Town	3306	D	0-0		21	33
15	CPrem	H	Salisbury City	719	W	3-1	Ledsham 3 Hattersley 29 Brown 88	20	34
22	CPrem	A	Forest Green Rovers	1118	L	1-3	O'Sullivan 48	22	35
25	CPrem	H	Grimsby Town	812	W	2-1	Brown 36 Osawe 68	20	36
March 1	CPrem	H	Dartford	1041	W	3-0	Hattersley 12 Walker 71 Osawe 78	19	37
8	CPrem	A	Woking	1504	L	0-2		20	38
15	CPrem	H	Macclesfield	1045	W	4-1	Nsiala 13 Walker 34 Osawe 63 Hattersley 83	19	39
18	CPrem	A	Chester FC	2274	D	2-2	Ledsham 56 89	19	40
22	CPrem	A	Kidderminster Harriers	1818	D	1-1	Hattersley 27	16	41
27	CPrem	H	Forest Green Rovers	1227	W	2-0	Ledsham 49 O'Sullivan 62	18	42
April 1	CPrem	H	Braintree Town	714	L	0-4		18	43
5	CPrem	A	Cambridge United	2717	L	1-3	Walker 16	19	44
8	CPrem	H	Barnet	774	D	1-1	Brown 3	18	45
12	CPrem	H	Tamworth	1006	W	2-0	Walker 50 72	18	46
18	CPrem	A	Gateshead	2121	D	2-2	George 2 Walker 54	18	47
21	CPrem	H	FC Halifax Town	**2043**	W	2-1	George 70 Fitzpatrick 79	18	48
26	CPrem	A	Welling United	521	L	3-4	George 15 Mukendi 22 O'Sullivan 38	18	49

GOALSCORERS	Lge	FAC	FAT	Total	Pens	Hat-tricks	Cons Run
Hattersley	10	2		12			2
Ledsham	6	1		7			
Brown	5	1		6			2
Osawe	6			6			2
Walker	6			6			2
George	3	1		4			3
Milligan	3	1		4	1		
O'Sullivan	3			3			
Ellington	1	1		2			
Fitzpatrick	2			2			
Akrigg	1			1			
Almond	1			1			
Brodie	1			1			
Chalmers (Aaron)	1			1			
Flynn		1		1			
Irle-Bi	1			1			
Mukendi	1			1			
Nsiala	1			1			
Smith	1			1			
Thames	1			1			

Cons Run - Consecutive scoring games.

TORQUAY UNITED

Chairman: Thea Bristow
Secretary: Tim Herbert (T) 07722 282 999 (E) operations@torquayunited.com
Commercial Manager: Dean Edwards (T) 01803 328 666
Programme Editor: Tim Herbet (T) 07722 282 999
Ground Address: Plainmoor, Torquay, Devon TQ1 3PS
(T) 01803 328 666 **Manager:** Chris Hargreaves

Club Factfile

Founded: 1899 **Nickname:**
Previous Names: Torquay United & Ellacombe merged to form Torquay Town 1910, then merged with Babbacombe to form Torquay Utd in 1921
Previous Leagues: Western 1921-27. Football League 1927-2007, 09-14. Conference 2007-09.

Club Colours (change): Yellow/blue/white (All blue)

Ground Capacity: 6,500 **Seats:** Yes **Covered:** Yes **Clubhouse:** Yes **Shop:** Yes

Directions
BY ROAD FROM THE NORTH/EAST (A30/M5): At the junction of the A30/M5 take A38 signposted Plymouth. After 3 miles take left fork on A380 signposted Torquay. After a further 10 miles at Penn Inn roundabout take 2nd exit to Torquay. At Kerswell Gardens take the A3022 to Torquay. At Lowes Bridge turn left into Hele Rd (B3199) and continue until a double roundabout is reached. Turn left and immediately right into Westhill Road. Take the fifth turning on the right (St Marychurch Rd) then second left into St Paul's Rd. Continue on into St Paul's Crescent and the ground is on the left. Main entrance from Westlands Lane.
BY ROAD FROM THE WEST (A38): At Goodstone Junction on the A38 take exit marked Newton Abbot and join the A383. After 4.5 miles, at the Dyrons roundabout, take second exit on to the A382 signposted Totnes. At traffic lights turn right (A382) on the inner ring road until its junction with the A381. Turn left on the A381 signposted Torquay until the Penn Inn roundabout. Take the third exit signposted A380 to Torquay and follow the same directions as from the North/East.

Previous Grounds: Recreation Ground. Cricketfield Road > 1910.

Record Attendance: 21,908 v Huddersfield Town, FA Cup 4th Rnd, 29/01/1955.
Record Victory: 9-0 v Swindon Town, Division Three South, 08/03/1952
Record Defeat: 2-10 v Fulham, Division Three South, 07/09/1931
Record Goalscorer: Sammy Collins - 219 in 379 games (1948-58) Also scored 40 during the 1955-56 season.
Record Appearances: Dennis Lewis - 443 (1947-59)
Additional Records: Received £650,000 from Crewe for Rodney Jack (July 1998)

Senior Honours:
League: Torquay & District 1909-09. Plymouth & District 1911-12. Southern Western Section 1926-27.
FA/County Cups: Devon Senior Cup 1910-11, 21-22. Devon Bowl/Devon St Luke's Bowl 1933-34, 34-35, 36-37,45-46, 47-48, 48-49, 54-55 (shared), 57-58, 60-61, 69-70, 70-71, 71-72, 95-96 (shared), 97-98, 2006-07.

10 YEAR RECORD

04-05	05-06	06-07	07-08	08-09	09-10	10-11	11-12	12-13	13-14
FL 1 21	FL 2 20	FL 2 24	Conf 3	Conf 4	FL 2 17	FL 2 7	FL 2 5	FL 2 19	FL 2 24

TORQUAY UNITED MATCH RESULTS 2013-14

Date	Comp	H/A	Opponents	Att:	Result	No.
Aug 3	FL2	H	AFC Wimbledon	3441	D 1-1	1
6	**LC1**	**A**	**Swindon Town**	**5662**	**L 0-1**	2
10	FL2	A	Morecambe	1555	D 1-1	3
17	FL2	H	Oxford United	3176	L 1-3	4
24	FL2	A	Northampton Town	4088	**W** 2-1	5
31	FL2	H	Hartlepool United	2646	D 0-0	6
Sept 3	**JPT1**	**H**	**Portsmouth**	**1951**	**D 0-0**	7
7	FL2	A	Fleetwood Town	2426	L 1-4	8
14	FL2	A	Rochdale	2138	L 0-1	9
21	FL2	H	Cheltenham Town	2407	**W** 4-2	10
28	FL2	A	Newport County	3557	L 1-2	11
Oct 5	FL2	H	York City	2559	L 0-3	12
12	FL2	A	Wycombe Wanderers	3466	L 2-3	13
19	FL2	H	Mansfield Town	2473	D 0-0	14
22	FL2	A	Burton Albion	2005	L 0-2	15
26	FL2	H	Portsmouth	3843	D 1-1	16
Nov 2	FL2	A	Bury	2997	**W** 3-1	17
9	**FAC1**	**H**	**Rochdale**	**1976**	**L 0-2**	18
16	FL2	H	Chesterfield	2361	L 0-2	19
23	FL2	A	Accrington Stanley	1279	L 1-2	20
26	FL2	H	Plymouth Argyle	3866	D 1-1	21
30	FL2	A	Scunthorpe United	3358	L 1-3	22
Dec 14	FL2	H	Southend United	2144	**W** 1-0	23
21	FL2	A	Dagenham & Redbridge	1675	**W** 1-0	24
26	FL2	H	Bristol Rovers	3461	D 1-1	25
29	FL2	H	Exeter City	**4231**	L 1-3	26
Jan 1	FL2	A	Plymouth Argyle	10126	L 0-2	27
4	FL2	H	Morecambe	2004	D 1-1	28
11	FL2	A	AFC Wimbledon	4339	**W** 2-0	29
25	FL2	A	Oxford United	4744	L 0-1	30
Feb 1	FL2	A	Portsmouth	15474	**W** 1-0	31
11	FL2	H	Northampton Town	2051	L 1-2	32
15	FL2	A	Chesterfield	5912	L 1-3	33
22	FL2	H	Accrington Stanley	2218	L 0-1	34
25	FL2	H	Burton Albion	1583	D 1-1	35
Mar 1	FL2	A	Hartlepool United	3437	L 0-3	36
8	FL2	H	Fleetwood Town	2245	L 0-1	37
11	FL2	H	Rochdale	1627	**W** 2-1	38
15	FL2	A	Cheltenham Town	3105	L 0-1	39
18	FL2	H	Bury	1738	**W** 2-1	40
22	FL2	H	Newport County	2874	L 0-1	41
25	FL2	A	York City	3416	L 0-1	42
29	FL2	A	Southend United	6556	L 0-1	43
April 5	FL2	H	Scunthorpe United	2234	L 0-1	44
12	FL2	A	Bristol Rovers	6612	**W** 2-1	45
18	FL2	H	Dagenham & Redbridge	2425	L 0-1	46
21	FL2	A	Exeter City	5221	**W** 2-1	47
26	FL2	A	Mansfield Town	3389	**W** 3-1	48
May 3	FL2	H	Wycombe Wanderers	3149	L 0-3	49

WELLING UNITED

Chairman: Paul Websdale
Secretary: Barrie Hobbins **(T)** 0208 301 1196 **(E)** wellingutdfcsecretary@hotmail.co.uk
Commercial Manager: Paul White **(T)** 0777 556 755
Programme Editor: Matthew Panting **(T)** Wellingpress@Hotmail.co.uk
Ground Address: Park View Road Ground, Welling, Kent DA16 1SY
(T) 0208 301 1196 **Manager:** Jamie Day

2013-14 Squad with the Conference South trophy.

Club Factfile

Founded: 1963 **Nickname:** The Wings
Previous Names: None
Previous Leagues: Eltham & District 1963-71, London Spartan 1971-77, Athenian 1978-81, Southern 1981-86, 2000-04, Conference 1986-2000

Club Colours (change): Red/red/white (All blue)

Ground Capacity: 4,000 **Seats:** 1,070 **Covered:** 1,500 **Clubhouse:** Yes **Shop:** Yes

Directions
M25 to Dartford then A2 towards London.
Take Bexleyheath/Blackfen/Sidcup,turn off (six miles along A2) then follow A207 signed welling.
Ground is 1 mile From A2 on main road towards Welling High Street.

Previous Grounds: Butterfly Lane, Eltham 1963-78

Record Attendance: 4,100 v Gillingham - FA Cup
Record Victory: 7-1 v Dorking - 1985-86
Record Defeat: 0-7 v Welwyn Garden City - 1972-73
Record Goalscorer: Not known
Record Appearances: Not known
Additional Records: Paid £30,000 to Enfield for Gary Abbott
Received £95,000 from Birmingham City for Steve Finnan 1995
Senior Honours:
Southern League 1985-86. Conference South 2012-13.
Kent Senior Cup 1985-86, 98-99, 2008-09. London Senior Cup 1989-90. London Challenge Cup 1991-92.

10 YEAR RECORD

04-05	05-06	06-07	07-08	08-09	09-10	10-11	11-12	12-13	13-14
Conf S 16	Conf S 9	Conf S 8	Conf S 16	Conf S 7	Conf S 9	Conf S 6	Conf S 3	Conf S 1	Conf 16

WELLING UNITED MATCH RESULTS 2013-14

Date	Comp	H/A	Opponents	Att:	Result		Goalscorers	Pos	No.
Aug 10	CPrem	A	Wrexham	4011	L	1-2	Healy 43	16	1
14	CPrem	H	Cambridge United	1010	D	2-2	Lafayette 37 Clarke 43	17	2
17	CPrem	H	Grimsby Town	807	W	1-0	Lafayette 85	15	3
24	CPrem	A	Woking	1430	W	4-2	Howe 15 (og) Bergquist 19 Beautyman 29 Pires 67	8	4
26	CPrem	H	Salisbury City	725	D	0-0		11	5
31	CPrem	A	Hereford United	1527	L	1-2	Lafayette 90	14	6
Sept 7	CPrem	H	Kidderminster Harriers	911	L	1-2	Fazackerly 81	15	7
14	CPrem	A	Southport	825	D	2-2	Clarke 48 Lafayette76	15	8
17	CPrem	H	Forest Green Rovers	452	W	5-2	Bergquist 9 Pires 19 Clarke 66 (pen) 69 Dyer 80	13	9
21	CPrem	A	Hyde	427	W	1-0	Healy 37	11	10
24	CPrem	H	Aldershot Town	837	W	1-0	Dyer 15	7	11
28	CPrem	A	Macclesfield Town	1321	L	1-2	Lafatette 83	13	12
Oct 5	CPrem	H	Barnet	1017	D	1-1	Healy 29	12	13
8	CPrem	A	Braintree Town	1119	W	3-2	Day 31 Clarke 72 Dyer 82	8	14
12	CPrem	H	Tamworth	803	W	2-0	Clarke 63 Pires 82	6	15
19	CPrem	A	FC Halifax Town	1345	L	0-3		9	16
26	***FAC 4Q***	***A***	***Brislington***	***700***	***W***	***1-0***	***Clarke 68***		17
Nov 2	CPrem	H	Lincoln City	746	W	1-0	Gallagher 53	8	18
9	***FAC1***	***H***	***Luton Town***	***1555***	***W***	***2-1***	***Clarke 28 Healy 44***		19
12	CPrem	A	Barnet	1274	D	0-0		8	20
16	CPrem	H	Nuneaton Town	807	L	1-2	Lafayette 53 (pen)	12	21
23	CPrem	A	Luton Town	6592	L	1-2	Dyer 47	12	22
30	***FAT1***	***A***	***Braintree Town***	***365***	***L***	***0-3***			23
Dec7	***FAC2***	***A***	***Plymouth Argyle***	***4706***	***L***	***1-3***	***Lafayete 53***		24
10	CPrem	A	Grimsby Town	2487	D	1-1	Healy 11	13	25
21	CPrem	H	Wrexham	633	D	1-1	Guthrie 29	12	26
26	CPrem	A	Dartford	1758	W	2-1	Lafayette 74 Guthrie 80	12	27
28	CPrem	A	Aldershot Town	2058	L	1-3	Lafayette 50	13	28
Jan 10	CPrem	H	Dartford	1336	D	1-1	Lafayette 18 (pen)	14	29
14	CPrem	H	Hyde	436	L	0-2		14	30
18	CPrem	H	Woking	809	W	3-0	Healy 62 75 Clarke 83	13	31
21	CPrem	A	Gateshead	621	D	1-1	Healy 10	13	32
25	CPrem	H	Alfreton Town	677	L	1-2	Guthrie 43	14	33
Feb 1	CPrem	A	Chester	2074	W	3-1	Cornick 16 Lafayette 40 Healy 53	12	34
22	CPrem	A	Tamworth	742	D	1-1	Guthrie 41	14	35
25	CPrem	H	Gateshead	455	W	2-0	Healy 7 Mawson 59	12	36
March 1	CPrem	H	Macclesfield Town	701	W	1-0	Hudson 62	11	37
8	CPrem	A	Nuneston Town	929	L	0-2		11	38
11	CPrem	A	Lincoln City	1623	W	2-1	Wakefield 37 Beautyman 40	11	39
15	CPrem	H	FC Halifax Town	645	L	0-1		13	40
18	CPrem	A	Cambridge United	2012	L	1-2	Sho-Silva 71	14	41
22	CPrem	A	Forest Green Rovers	1338	D	0-0		14	42
25	CPrem	H	Braintree Town	403	L	0-2		14	43
29	CPrem	H	Chester	706	W	2-0	Karaglannis 57 Lafayette 89	13	44
April 5	CPrem	A	Alfreton Town	599	D	2-2	Taylor 2 Lafayette 62 (pen)	14	45
8	CPrem	H	Hereford United	480	L	0-1		14	46
12	CPrem	A	Kidderminster Harriers	1882	L	0-2		17	47
19	CPrem	H	Luton Town	**2650**	L	1 2	Lafayette 80	17	48
21	CPrem	A	Salisbury City	895	L	0-3		17	49
26	CPrem	H	Southport	521	W	4-3	Lafayette 10 73 (pen) Beautyman 49 Gallagher 57	16	50

GOALSCORERS	Lge	FAC	FAT	Total	Pens	Hat-tricks	Cons Run
Lafayette	15	1		16	5		3
Healy	9	1		10			2
Clarke	7	2		9	1		2
Dyer	4			4			
Guthrie	4			4			
Beautyman	3			3			
Pires	3			3			
Bergguist	2			2			
Gallagher	2			2			
Cornick	1			1			
Day	1			1			
Fazackerly	1			1			
Hudson	1			1			
Karaglannis	1			1			
Mawson	1			1			
Sho-Silva	1			1			
Taylor	1			1			
Wakefield	1			1			
Opponents	1			1			

Cons Run - Consecutive scoring games.

WOKING

Chairman: Mike Smith
Secretary: Derek Powell (T) 01483 772 470 (E) derek.powell@wokingfc.co.uk
Commercial Manager: Nicky Banger (T) 01483 772 470
Programme Editor: Anthony Scott (T) 07769 114 476
Ground Address: Kingfield Stadium, Kingfield Road, Woking, Surrey GU22 9AA
(T) 01483 772 470 **Manager:** Garry Hill

2014-15 Squad - Back row (l-r): Jake Cole, Theo Lewis, Aaron Howe, Adam Brice, Reece Beckles.
Middle row: Stuart Baverstock (Kitman), Joe Jones, John Goddard, Giuseppe Sole, Keiran Murtagh, Malcolm Jobling (Kitman)
Front row: Josh Payne, Scott Rendell, Steve Thompson (Coach), Garry Hill (Manager), Joe McNerney, Mark Ricketts (Captain), James Clarke

Club Factfile

Founded: 1889 **Nickname:** The Cards
Previous Names: None
Previous Leagues: Isthmian 1911-92.

Club Colours (change): Red and white halves/black/white (All yellow)

Ground Capacity: 6,000 **Seats:** 2,500 **Covered:** 3,900 **Clubhouse:** Yes **Shop:** Yes

Directions
Exit M25 Junction 10 and follow A3 towards Guildford. Leave at next junction onto B2215 through Ripley and join A247 to Woking. Alternatively exit M25 junction 11 and follow A320 to Woking Town Centre. The ground is on the outskirts of Woking opposite the Leisure Centre.

Previous Grounds: Wheatsheaf, Ive Lane (pre 1923)

Record Attendance: 6,000 v Swansea City - FA Cup 1978-79 and v Coventry City - FA Cup 1996-97
Record Victory: 17-4 v Farnham - 1912-13
Record Defeat: 0-16 v New Crusaders - 1905-06
Record Goalscorer: Charlie Mortimore - 331 (1953-65)
Record Appearances: Brian Finn - 564 (1962-74)
Additional Records: Paid £60,000 to Crystal Palace for Chris Sharpling
Received £150,000 from Bristol Rovers for Steve Foster
Senior Honours:
Surrey Senior Cup 1912-13, 26-27, 55-56, 56-57, 71-72, 90-91, 93-94, 95-96, 99-2000, 2003-04, 2011-12, 2013-14. FA Amateur Cup 1957-58.
Isthmian League Cup 1990-91, Premier Division 1991-92. FA Trophy 1993-94, 94-95, 96-97.
Vauxhall Championship Shield 1994-95. GLS Conference Cup 2004-05. Conference South 2011-12.

10 YEAR RECORD

04-05	05-06	06-07	07-08	08-09	09-10	10-11	11-12	12-13	13-14
Conf 8	Conf 11	Conf 15	Conf 17	Conf 21	Conf S 5	Conf S 5	Conf S 1	Conf 12	Conf 9

WOKING MATCH RESULTS 2013-14

Date	Comp	H/A	Opponents	Att:	Result	Goalscorers	Pos	No.
Aug 10	CPrem	H	Lincoln City	1845	D 0-0		13	1
13	CPrem	A	Braintree Town	995	L 0-2		17	2
17	CPrem	A	Chester	2016	**W** 2-0	Williams 59 McNerney 63	17	3
24	CPrem	H	Welling United	1430	L 2-4	Johnson 38 McNerney 69	17	4
26	CPrem	A	Aldershot Town	3138	L 1-2	Williams 74	18	5
31	CPrem	H	Gateshead	1230	L 1-2	Williams 90 (pen)	20	6
Sept 7	CPrem	A	Alfreton Town	628	L 1-3	Williams 10 (pen)	20	7
13	CPrem	H	Tamworth	1246	D 2-2	Rendell 70 Williams 78 (pen)	20	8
17	CPrem	A	Hyde	387	**W** 2-0	Betsy 74 87	18	9
21	CPrem	A	Macclesfield	1195	L 2-3	Sole 80 Betsy 90	20	10
24	CPrem	H	Luton Town	1955	L 0-4		21	11
28	CPrem	H	NuneatonTown	1272	**W** 2-0	Rendell 13 Payne 49	21	12
Oct 5	CPrem	A	Southport	873	L 1-2	Rendell 3	21	13
8	CPrem	H	Barnet	1413	D 0-0		21	14
12	CPrem	H	FC Halifax Town	1552	D 0-0		21	15
19	CPrem	A	Wrexham	3183	L 0-2		21	16
26	***FAC4Q***	***H***	***Luton Town***	***1452***	***L 0-1***			17
Nov 2	CPrem	H	Grimsby Town	1432	L 1-2	Betsy 28	21	18
12	CPrem	H	Dartford	1157	**W** 3-0	Marriott 63 Rendell 75 McNerney 77	22	19
16	CPrem	H	Hyde	1381	**W** 3-2	Marriott 14 74 Rendell 47	19	20
23	CPrem	A	Cambridge United	3515	L 0-2		19	21
30	***FAT1***	***A***	***Hereford United***	***1040***	***W 3-0***	***Rendell 10 36 Marriott 33***		22
Dec 7	CPrem	A	FC Halifax Town	1033	**W** 4-3	MARRIOTT 3 (9 13 73) Rendell 16	18	23
10	CPrem	H	Kidderminster Harriers	1166	**W** 1-0	Rendell 64	17	24
14	***FAT 2***	***A***	***North Ferriby United***	***201***	***L 0-4***		***17***	25
21	CPrem	A	Nuneaton Town	895	**W** 2-0	Marriott 50 Betsy 60	16	26
26	CPrem	H	Salisbury City	2112	L 1-3	Marriott 14	16	27
Jan 11	CPrem	H	Braintree Town	1270	**W** 1-0	McNerney	17	28
18	CPrem	A	Welling United	809	L 0-3		18	29
21	CPrem	H	Chester	1124	L 0-1		18	30
25	CPrem	A	Lincoln City	2017	D 2-2	Betsy 19 Sole 73	18	31
Feb 3	CPrem	H	Hereford United	1131	**W** 3-0	Marriott 24 Murtagh 26 Payne 88	18	32
11	CPrem	A	Salisbury City	624	L 0-2		18	33
15	CPrem	A	Gateshead	706	**W** 2-0	Nutter 1 Goddard 70	16	34
18	CPrem	A	Dartford	1002	L 1-5	Rendell 4	17	35
22	CPrem	H	Macclesfield Town	1144	**W** 3-2	Marriott 61 Goddard 69 Rendell 78	16	36
25	CPrem	A	Kidderminster Harriers	1448	L 0-2		17	37
March 1	CPrem	A	Barnet	1708	**W** 3-1	Payne 23 Rendell 37 (pen) 88	17	38
8	CPrem	H	Southport	1504	**W** 2-0	Rendell 55 Murtagh 80	14	39
17	CPrem	A	Luton Town	6683	**W** 1-0	Sole 87	14	40
29	CPrem	H	Wrexham	2117	**W** 2-1	Rendell 20 Jones 57	16	41
April 1	CPrem	H	Forest Green Rovers	1315	**W** 2-1	Rendell 68 (pen) Marriott 82	12	42
5	CPrem	A	Hereford United	2140	**W** 2-0	Rendell 20 Newton 35	11	43
8	CPrem	A	Grimsby Town	3507	D 2-2	Betsy 84 Murtagh 90	12	44
12	CPrem	H	Alfreton Town	1485	**W** 2-1	Jones 80 Marriott 85	10	45
19	CPrem	A	Forest Green Rovers	1245	D 2-2	Johnson 68 Goddard 90	10	46
21	CPrem	H	Aldershot Town	**4728**	L 1-2	Johnson 72	12	47
26	CPrem	A	Tamworth	788	**W** 4-2	Sole 8 Rendell 13 55 Betsy 90	9	48

GOALSCORERS	Lge	FAC	FAT	Total	Pens	Hat-tricks	Cons Run
Rendell	17		2	19	2		3
Marriott	12		1	13		1	2
Betsy	8			8			2
Williams	5			5	3		4
McNerney	4			4			2
Sole	4			4			
Goddard	3			3			
Johnson	3			3			2
Murtagh	3			3			
Payne	3			3			
Jones	2			2			
Newton	1			1			
Nutter	1			1			

Cons Run - Consecutive scoring games.

WREXHAM

Chairman: Don Bircham (Chief Exe)
Secretary: Geraint Parry (T) 07801 749 021 (E) geraint.parry@wrexhamfc.tv
Commercial Manager: Steven Cook (T) 07921 371 766
Programme Editor: Terry Brumpton (T) 07771 802 048
Ground Address: Racecourse Ground, Mold road, Wrexham LL11 2AN
(T) 01978 891 864 **Manager:** Kevin Wilkin

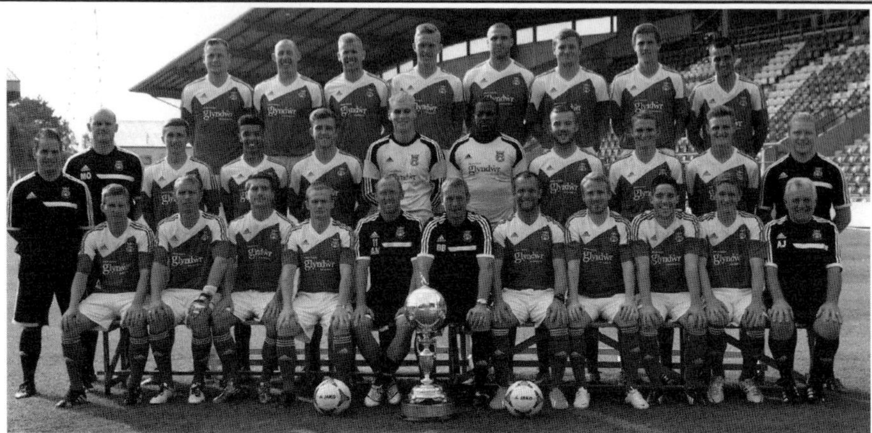

2013/14 Squad - Back Row (l-r): Joe Clarke, Stephen Wright, Andy Bishop, Jonathan Royle, Mark Creighton, Leon Clowes, Rob Ogleby, Kyle Parle.
Middle (l-r): Christos Christofides (physio), Michael Oakes (coach), Jay Colbeck, Theo Bailey-Jones, Anthony Stephens, Andy Coughlin, Joslain Mayebi, Steve Tomassen, Johnny Hunt, Bradley Reid (now Wolves), Phil Davies (asst physio).
Front (l-r): Jay Harris, Brett Ormerod, Adrian Cieslewicz, Dean Keates, Andy Morrell (manager), Billy Barr (asst manager), Neil Ashton, Kevin Thornton, Robbie Evans, Nick Rushton, Alan Jones (kitman).

Club Factfile

Founded: 1872 **Nickname:** The Robins
Previous Names: Wrexham Athletic for the 1882-83 season only
Previous Leagues: The Combination 1890-94, 1896-1906, Welsh League 1894-96, Birmingham & District 1906-21, Football League 1921-2008
Club Colours (change): Red & black hoops/black/red (White with black trim/white/white)

Ground Capacity: 15,500 **Seats:** 10,100 **Covered:** 15,500 **Clubhouse:** Yes **Shop:** Yes

Directions
From Wrexham by-pass (A483) exit at Mold junction (A451).
Follow signs for Town Centre and football ground is half a mile on the left hand side.

Previous Grounds: Rhosddu Recreation Ground during the 1881-82 and 1882-83 seasons.

Record Attendance: 34,445 v Manchester United - FA Cup 4th Round 26/01/57
Record Victory: 10-1 v Hartlepool United - Division Four 03/03/62
Record Defeat: 0-9 v v Brentford - Division Three
Record Goalscorer: Tommy Bamford - 201 (1928-34)
Record Appearances: Arfon Griffiths - 592 (1959-79)
Additional Records: Paid £800,000 to Birmingham City for Bryan Hughes March 1997
Received £210,000 from Liverpool for Joey Jones October 1978
Senior Honours:
Welsh FA Cup 1877-78, 81-82, 92-93, 96-97, 1902-03, 04-05, 08-09, 09-10, 10-11, 13-14, 14-15, 20-21, 23-24, 24-25, 30-31, 56-57, 57-58, 59-60, 71-72, 74-75, 77-78, 85-86, 94-95. Welsh Lge 1894-95, 95-96. Combination 1900-01, 01-02, 02-03, 04-05. Football Lge Div. 3 1977-78. FAW Prem. Cup 1997-98, 99-2000, 00-01, 02-03, 03-04. F. Lge Trophy 2004-05. FA Trophy 2012-13.

10 YEAR RECORD

04-05	05-06	06-07	07-08	08-09	09-10	10-11	11-12	12-13	13-14
FL 1 22	FL 2 13	FL 2 19	FL 2 24	Conf 10	Conf 11	Conf 4	Conf 2	Conf 5	Conf 17

WREXHAM MATCH RESULTS 2013-14

Date	Comp	H/A	Opponents	Att:	Result		Goalscorers	Pos	No.
Aug 10	CPrem	A	Welling United	4011	W	2-1	Clarke 17 Ogleby 83	4	1
13	CPrem	A	FC Halifax Town	1674	L	2-3	Ainge 22 (og) Cieslewicz 80	14	2
17	CPrem	A	Tamworth	1128	D	2-2	Ormerod 37 Reid 79	14	3
24	CPrem	H	Hyde	3304	D	2-2	Thornton 24 Ntame 27	15	4
26	CPrem	A	Lincoln City	2610	L	0-2		16	5
31	CPrem	H	Chester	**6037**	L	0-2		17	6
Sept 7	CPrem	A	Nuneaton	1561	L	0-2		19	7
13	CPrem	H	Luton Town	3122	W	2-0	Bishop 21 Hunt 58		8
17	CPrem	A	Gateshead	538	W	3-0	Ormerod 55 Tomassen 65 Bishop 71	15	9
21	CPrem	A	Aldershot	1915	L	0-2		16	10
24	CPrem	H	Braintree Town	2731	L	2-3	Hunt 29 Harris 34	18	11
28	CPrem	H	Cambridge United	3136	D	1-1	Clowes 6	19	12
Oct 5	CPrem	A	Salisbury City	986	L	1-2	Anyinsah 40	20	13
8	CPrem	H	Southport	2734	W	1-0	Anyinsah 75	19	14
13	CPrem	A	Barnet	2143	D	1-1	Keates 90	19	15
19	CPrem	H	Woking	3183	W	2-0	Keates 21 Clarke 90	14	16
26	***FAC4Q***	***H***	***Hyde***	***1848***	***W***	***2-0***	***Ogleby 22 67***		17
Nov 2	CPrem	A	Macclesfield Town	1978	L	2-3	Anyinsah 13 Ormerod 80	17	18
8	***FAC1***	***H***	***Alfreton Town***	***2415***	***W***	***3-1***	***Bishop 24 49 Harris 72***		19
12	CPrem	H	Gateshead	2469	W	3-2	BISHOP 3 (23 77 (pen 90)	16	20
16	CPrem	A	Kidderminster Harriers	2532	L	1-3	Cieslewicz 71	16	21
19	CPrem	A	Dartford	876	W	5-1	Ormorod 15 34 Clarke 23 Ogleby 31 Hunt 76	15	22
23	CPrem	H	Forest Green Rovers	3083	W	2-0	Morrrell 30 Hunt 36	13	23
30	***FAT1***	***H***	***Gresley Rovers***	***1257***	***W***	***2-1***	***Hunt 17 Morrell 41***		24
Dec 8	***FAC2***	***H***	***Oxford United***	***2906***	***L***	***1-2***	***Clarke 29***		25
14	***FAT2***	***A***	***Luton Town***	***1617***	***L***	***0-2***			26
21	CPrem	A	Welling United	633	D	1-1	Hunt 38	14	27
26	CPrem	H	Alfreton Town	3371	L	2-3	Carrington 64 Clowes 97	15	28
28	CPrem	A	Hyde United	952	W	5-2	OGLEBY 3 (12 39 71) Clarke 63 Artell 89	15	29
Jan 1	CPrem	A	Alfreton Town	756	L	0-1		15	30
4	CPrem	H	Aldershot	2819	W	2-1	Clarke 15 Harris 87	13	31
11	CPrem	H	FC Halifax Town	3214	D	0-0		13	32
21	CPrem	A	Southport	911	W	2-1	Artell 14 Anyinsah 87	12	33
28	CPrem	H	Tamworth	2160	W	2-0	Bishop 12 Hunt 90	11	34
Feb 8	CPrem	H	Dartford	2645	L	1-2	Clarke 21	12	35
18	CPrem	A	Cambridge United	2231	D	0-0		12	36
22	CPrem	H	Barnet	2925	L	0-1		13	37
25	CPrem	A	Luton Town	7526	L	0-5		14	38
March 1	CPrem	A	Hereford United	1884	W	2-0	Hunt 10 Ogleby 42	13	39
8	CPrem	H	Kidderminster Harriers	3159	D	0-0		15	40
11	CPrem	A	Braintree Town	699	L	0-3		16	41
15	CPrem	A	Grimsby Town	3506	L	1-3	Pearson 45 (og)	17	42
18	CPrem	H	Hereford United	2056	W	2-0	Graham 1 (og) Carrington 63	16	43
22	CPrem	H	Salisbury CIty	2850	D	1-1	Ashton 24 (pen)	16	44
29	CPrem	A	Woking	2117	L	1-2	Hunt 22	17	45
April 1	CPrem	H	Grimsby Town	2019	L	0-1		17	46
5	CPrem	H	Macclesfield Town	2402	W	1-0	Hunt 12	17	47
12	CPrem	H	Nuneaton	2706	W	3-0	Hunt 54 Bishop 70 Ashton 90	16	48
19	CPrem	A	Chester	4326	D	0-0		16	49
21	CPrem	H	Lincoln City	2714	L	0-1		15	50
26	CPrem	A	Forest Green Rovers	1630	D	1-1	Hunt 90 (pen)	17	51

GOALSCORERS	Lge	FAC	FAT	Total	Pens	Hat-tricks	Cons Run
Hunt	11		1	12	1		3
Bishop	7	2		9	1	1	2
Ogleby	6	2		8		1	
Clarke	6	1		7			
Ormerod	5			5			
Anyinsah	4			4			2
Harris	2	1		3			
Artell	2			2			
Ashton	2			2	1		
Carrington	2			2			

	Lge	FAC	FAT	Total	Pens	Hat-tricks	Cons Run
Cieslewicz	2			2			
Clowes	2			2			
Keates	2			2			
Morrell	1		1	2			
Ntame	1			1			
Reid	1			1			
Thornton	1			1			
Tomassen	1			1			
Opponents	3			3			

Cons Run - Consecutive scoring games.

LUTON TOWN MATCH RESULTS 2013-14

Date	Comp	H/A	Opponents	Att:	Result	Goalscorers	Pos	No.
Aug 10	CPrem	A	Southport	2210	L 0-1		18	1
13	CPrem	H	Salisbury City	6520	W 2-0	Taiwo 64 (pen) Guttridge 81	12	2
17	CPrem	H	Macclesfield Town	6216	D 1-1	Guttridge 90	13	3
24	CPrem	A	Forest Green Rovers	1858	D 0-0		14	4
26	CPrem	H	Cambridge United	7517	D 0-0		14	5
31	CPrem	A	Kidderminster Harriers	2866	W 2-0	Howells 70 (pen) 81 (pen)	11	6
Sept 7	CPrem	H	Grimsby Town	6131	D 0-0		13	7
13	CPrem	A	Wrexham	3122	L 0-2		13	8
17	CPrem	H	Dartford	5433	W 3-0	Benson 30 Guttridge 33 Lawless 64	11	9
21	CPrem	H	Lincoln City	6203	W 3-2	Cullen 46 80 Guttridge 77	9	10
24	CPrem	A	Woking	1955	W 4-0	Cullen 29 45 Lacey 35 Gray 70	5	11
28	CPrem	A	Hereford United	2386	D 0-0		6	12
Oct 5	CPrem	H	FC Halifax Town	6519	W 4-3	Gutteridge 16 Benson 33 Gray 39 Wall 83	5	13
8	CPrem	A	Aldershot Town	2693	D 3-3	Gray 4 Parry 26 Whalley 80 (pen)	4	14
12	CPrem	H	Hyde	7081	W 4-1	GRAY 3 (16 55 79) Gutteridge 51	3	15
19	CPrem	A	Tamworth	2066	W 4-3	Smith 32 Barry 41 Benson 46 54	3	16
26	***FAC4Q***	***A***	***Woking***	***1452***	***W 1-0***	***Cullen 35***		17
Nov 2	CPrem	A	Gateshead	1080	D 0-0		3	18
9	***FAC1***	***A***	***Welling Uited***	***1555***	***L 1-2***	***Benson 57***		19
12	CPrem	A	Braintree Town	1518	W 2-1	Benson 30 Parry 65	2	20
16	CPrem	A	Chester	3291	D 1-1	Gray 11	3	21
23	CPrem	H	Welling United	6592	W 2-1	Gray 17 19	3	22
26	CPrem	H	Southport	6057	W 3-0	McNulty 30 Smith 66 Gray 75	2	23
30	***FAT1***	***A***	***Staines Town***	***621***	***D 0-0***			24
Dec 2	***FAT1r***	***H***	***Staines Town***	***911***	***W 2-0***	***Parry 49 Whalley 72***		25
7	CPrem	A	Alfreton Town	1279	W 5-0	Gray 10 14 Benson 13 Guttridge 18 Lawless 67	2	26
14	***FAT2***	***H***	***Wrexham***	***1617***	***W 2-0***	***Cullen 15 Ashton 75 (og)***		27
21	CPrem	H	Gateshead	6913	W 4-2	Benson 16 Lawless 27 60 Gray 30	2	28
26	CPrem	A	Barnet	3608	W 2-1	Benson 22 Lawless 34	2	29
28	CPrem	H	Kidderminster Harriers	8488	W 6-0	Guttridge 28 86 Benson 52 Howells 56 (pen) 70 Griffiths 79	1	30
Jan 1	CPrem	H	Barnet	7543	W 2-1	Gray 2 Benson 31	1	31
4	CPrem	A	Lincoln City	2928	D 0-0		1	32
11	***FAT3***	***A***	***Cambridge United***	***3194***	***D 2-2***	***Innis 4 Wall 48***		33
14	***FAT3r***	***H***	***Cambridge United***	***2312***	***L 0-1***			34
25	CPrem	H	Nuneaton Town	7310	W 3-0	GRAY 3 (50 64 77)	1	35
Feb 11	CPrem	A	Macclesfield Town	1705	W 2-1	Gray 9 82	1	36
15	CPrem	H	Hereford United	7111	W 7-0	GRAY 3 (12 68 82) Benson 49 Howells 56 (pen) Ruddock 60 Lawless 90	1	37
22	CPrem	A	Nuneaton Town	3480	W 5-0	Benson 34 81 Gray 64 Guttridge 70 Howells 85	1	38
25	CPrem	H	Wrexham	7526	W 5-0	Guttridge 3 17 Gray 9 Benson 38 Howells 70 (pen)	1	39
March 1	CPrem	H	Alfreton Town	8412	W 3-0	Guttridge 29 Gray 52 Benson 86	1	40
8	CPrem	A	Salisbury CIty	2633	D 0-0		1	41
11	CPrem	A	Cambridge United	6050	D 1-1	Cullen 90	1	42
14	CPrem	H	Woking	6683	L 0-1		1	43
22	CPrem	H	Chester	8475	W 3-0	Robinson 70 Gray 82 Benson 90	1	44
25	CPrem	A	Grimsby Town	3789	W 2-1	Robinson 21 Benson 61	1	45
29	CPrem	A	FC Halifax Town	3586	L 0-2		1	46
April 1	CPrem	A	Dartford	2869	W 2-1	Ruddock 83 Gray 86	1	47
5	CPrem	H	Aldershot Town	8558	W 1-0	McGeehan 85	1	48
8	CPrem	H	Tamworth	8554	W 2-0	McGeehan 49 Cullen 65	1	49
12	CPrem	H	Braintree Town	10,020	L 2-3	Howells 62 (pen) Wall 65	1	50
19	CPrem	A	Welling United	2650	W 2 1	Cullen 28 Gray 73	1	51
21	CPrem	H	Forest Green Rovers	**10,044**	W 4-1	Gray 45 (pen) 60 McGeehan 56 Cullen 90	1	52
26	CPrem	A	Hyde	2729	W 1-0	Wall 70	1	53

GOALSCORERS	Lge	FAC	FAT	Total	Pens	Hat-tricks	Cons Run		Lge	FAC	FAT	Total	Pens	Hat-tricks	Cons Run
Gray	30			30	1	3	6	Ruddock	2			2			
Benson	17	1		18			4	Smith	2			2			
Guttridge	13			13			3	Whalley	1		1	2	1		
Cullen	8	1	1	10			2	Griffiths	1			1			
Howells	8			8	5			Innis			1	1			
Lawless	6			6			2	Lacey	1			1			
Parry	3		1	4				McNulty	1			1			
Wall	3		1	4				Taiwo	1			1	1		
McGeehan	3			3			2	Opponents			1	1			
Robinson	2			2				Cons Run - Consecutive scoring games.							

CAMBRIDGE UNITED MATCH RESULTS 2013-14

Date	Comp	H/A	Opponents	Att:	Result	Goalscorers	Pos	No.
Aug 11	CPrem	H	FC Halifax	2780	W 5-1	Cunnington 13 (pen) 67 Donaldson 36 Sam-Yorke 49 71	2	1
14	CPrem	A	Welling United	1010	D 2-2	Donaldson 33 Arnold 68	3	2
17	CPrem	A	Aldershot Town	2022	W 1-0	Oastlier 12 (og)	1	3
24	CPrem	H	Lincoln City	3012	W 1-0	Berry 41	1	4
26	CPrem	A	Luton Town	7517	D 0-0		2	5
31	CPrem	H	Tamworth	2527	W 3-0	Cunnington 38 (pen) Berry 58 66	1	6
Sept 7	CPrem	A	Hyde	766	W 1-0	Cunnington 42	1	7
14	CPrem	H	Gateshead	2599	W 1-0	Cunnington 16	1	8
17	CPrem	A	Alfreton Town	731	D 1-1	Donaldson 60	2	9
21	CPrem	H	Forest Green Rovers	2915	W 2-1	Berry 1 Champion 53	1	10
24	CPrem	H	Nuneaton Town	3740	W 3-0	Berry 22 Appiah 74 Dunk 89	1	11
28	CPrem	A	Wrexham	3136	D 1-1	Appiah 17	1	12
Oct 5	CPrem	H	Hereford United	3381	W 1-0	Appiah 7	1	13
8	CPrem	A	Grimsby Town	4386	W 1-0	Cunnington 68	1	14
12	CPrem	A	Chester	2530	D 0-0		1	15
19	CPrem	H	Salisbury City	3622	W 2-0	Appiah 49 56	1	16
26	***FAC4Q***	***A***	***Needham Market***	***1784***	***W 1-0***	***Cunnington 74***		17
Nov 2	CPrem	A	Southport	1006	L 0-1		1	18
12	CPrem	H	Aldershot Town	3110	W 4-0	Berry 45 Appiah 51 Cunnington 56 Arnold 71	1	19
16	CPrem	A	Barnet	2853	D 2-2	Appiah 29 32	1	20
19	***FAC1***	***A***	***Bury***	***1712***	***D 0-0***			21
23	CPrem	H	Woking	3515	W 2-0	Dunk 3 15	1	22
30	***FAT1***	***A***	***Salisbury City***	***727***	***W 1-0***	***Arnold 51***		23
Dec 2	***FAC1r***	***H***	***Bury***	***3342***	***W 2-1***	***Berry 56 84***		24
8	***FAC2***	***H***	***Sheffeld United***	***4593***	***L 0-2***			25
10	CPrem	H	Macclesfield	2284	W 3-1	Appiah 18 27 Gillies 81	1	26
14	***FAT2***	***A***	***St Albans City***	***887***	***W 2-1***	***Arnold 32 Pierre 90***		27
21	CPrem	A	Hereford United	1558	L 0-1		1	28
26	CPrem	H	Braintree Town	4194	W 1-0	Berry 20	1	29
28	CPrem	A	Nuneaton Town	1478	D 0-0		2	30
Jan 11	***FAT3***	***H***	***Luton Town***	***3194***	***D 2-2***	***Elliott 73 Chambers 75***		31
14	***FAT3r***	***A***	***Luton Town***	***2312***	***W 1-0***	***Chambers 39***		32
18	CPrem	A	FC Halifax Town	1767	D 1-1	Elliott 65	2	33
21	CPrem	A	Tamworth	833	W 1-0	Hughes 64	2	34
25	CPrem	A	Dartford	2023	D 3-3	Bird 2 16 Berry 79	2	35
28	CPrem	H	Grimsby Town	3027	L 1-2	Berry 54	2	36
Feb 1	***FAT 4***	***A***	***Eastleigh***	***757***	***W 1-0***	***Berry 69 (pen)***		37
11	CPrem	H	Alfreton Town	2106	L 0-1		2	38
15	***FAT S-F 1***	***H***	***Grimsby Town***	***3264***	***W 2-1***	***Bird 21 56***		39
18	CPrem	H	Wrexham	2231	D 0-0		2	40
22	***FAT S-F 2***	***A***	***Grimsby Town***	***3931***	***D 1-1***	***Bird 8***		41
25	CPrem	A	Braintree Town	1016	L 0-1		2	42
March 1	CPrem	H	Kidderminster Harriers	2528	W 5-1	Coulson 42 Bird 53 Sam-Yorke 55 Berry 79 (Pen) Pugh 90	2	43
8	CPrem	A	Forest Green Rovers	1411	L 2-3	Coulson 8 Arnold 10	2	44
11	CPrem	H	Luton Town	**6050**	D 1-1	Elliott 62	2	45
15	CPrem	H	Dartford	2885	D 1-1	Elliott 67	2	46
18	CPrem	H	Welling United	2002	W 2-1	Cunnington 64 (pen) Sam-Yorke 75	2	47
23	***FAT Final***	***N***	***Gosport Borough***	***18,123***	***W 4-0***	***Bird 38 Donaldson 51 60 Berry 78 (pen)***		48
26	CPrem	A	Salisbury City	695	W 3-0	Bird 42 Taylor 61 Donaldson 63	2	49
29	CPrem	H	Barnet	3386	D 1-1	Gillies 23 (pen)	2	50
April 1	CPrem	A	Macclesfield	1278	W 1-0	Berry 87 (pen)		51
5	CPrem	H	Southport	2717	W 3-1	Berry 25 (pen) Chadwick 51 Pugh 68	2	52
10	CPrem	A	Woking	1805	W 3-0	Sam-Yorke 17 Chadwick 25 Hughes 85	2	53
12	CPrem	H	Hyde	2804	W 7-2	Gillies 2 PUGH 4 (18 20 47 50) Chambers 26 Barnes-Homer 90	2	54
15	CPrem	A	Kidderminster Harriers	1938	L 0-2		2	55
18	CPrem	A	Lincoln City	2535	L 0-1		2	56
21	CPrem	H	Chester	3521	L 0-1		2	57
26	CPrem	A	Gateshead	2916	L 0-2		2	58
30	**CPO SF1**	**A**	**FC Halifax Town**	**3668**	**L 0-1**			59
May 4	**CPO SF2**	**H**	**FC Halifax Town**	**6262**	**W 2-0**	**Sam-Yorke 11 38**		60
18	**CPO F**	**N**	**Gateshead**	**19613**	**W 2-1**	**Hughes 51, Donaldson 71**		61

GOALSCORERS	Lge	FAC	FAT	Total	Pens	Hat-tricks	Cons Run
Berry	12	2	2	16	4	1	3
Appiah	10			10			3
Cunnington	8	1		9	3		3
Bird	4		4	8			2
Donaldson	4+1		2	7			2
Sam-Yorke	5+2			7			
Pugh	6			6		1	
Arnold	3		2	5			
Elliott	3		1	4			2
Chambers	1		2	3			2
Dunk	3			3			

	Lge	FAC	FAT	Total	Pens	Hat-tricks	Cons Run
Gilies	3			3	1		
Hughes	2+1			3			
Chadwick	2			2			2
Coulson	2			2			2
Barnes-Homer	1			1			
Champion	1			1			
Pierre			1	1			
Taylor	1			1			
Opponents	1			1			

Cons Run - Consecutive scoring games.
Play-off goals indicated by +

Football Conference Play-off Final 2013-14

At Wembley, 18/5/13 - Att: 19,613

Cambridge United 2-1 Gateshead

Photos by Peter Barnes.

Conference Premier Division Statistics 2013-14

	MCV	MCD	MCwW	MCwD	MCSG	MCwS	TGS	MCCS	TNCS
Aldershot Town	3	2	8	6	10	3	13	2	12
Alfreton Town	5	3	8	5	12	3	12	2	7
Barnet	5	4	5	7	19	3	9	3	17
Braintree Town	4	3	5	6	9	3	15	2	21
Cambridge United	4	4	4	17	12	4	14	6	27
Chester	2	5	8	5	7	3	18	3	12
Dartford	3	7	15	6	6	3	18	2	10
FC Halifax Town	5	4	6	10	10	2	8	7	18
Forest Green Rovers	3	5	5	5	12	3	11	3	12
Gateshead	5	4	5	12	7	2	11	4	18
Grimsby Town	3	2	5	14	17	2	10	3	19
Hereford United	2	5	13	5	7	5	19	2	11
Hyde	1	13	29	2	3	6	24	1	2
Kidderminster Harriers	3	3	6	8	6	2	14	3	14
Lincoln City	3	2	5	6	13	2	15	2	17
Luton Town	7	1	3	14	7	2	12	5	27
Macclesfield Town	4	4	9	8	9	3	13	2	9
Nuneaton Town	5	3	10	9	10	4	16	6	14
Salisbury City	3	4	7	8	10	4	14	2	14
Southport	2	6	9	4	6	2	13	1	9
Tamworth	2	4	8	4	4	5	20	3	14
Welling United	3	4	7	4	10	2	12	2	13
Woking	6	4	6	9	11	4	13	2	16
Wrexham	3	3	6	4	15	3	15	3	15

MCV - Most Consecutive Victories I MCD - Most Consecutive Defeats
MCwW - Most Consecutive without a Win I MCwD - Most Consecutive without a defeat
MCSG - Most Consecutive Scoring Games I MCwS - Most Consecutive without Scoring
TGS - Total Games without Scoring I MCCS - Most Consecutive Clean Sheets
TNCS - Total Number of Clean Sheets

Best Home League Attendances 2013-2014

	Att:	Opponents	Score
Aldershot Town	3,593	Hereford United	L 1-2
Alfreton Town	1,771	Grimsby Town	D 3-3
Barnet	3,608	Luton Town	L 1-2
Braintree Town	1,518	Luton Town	L 1-2
Cambridge Utd	6,050	Luton Town	D 2-2
Chester	4,326	Wrexham	D 0-0
Dartford	2,869	Luton Town	L 1-2
FC Halfax Town	3,586	Luton Town	W 2-0
Forest Green R	1,858	Luton Town	D 0-0
Gateshead	2,916	Cambridge Utd	W 2-0
Grimsby Town	5,484	Lincoln City	D 1-1
Hereford United	2,545	Grimsby Town	L 0-1
Hyde	2,729	Luton Town	L 0-1
Kidderminster H	3,420	Hereford United	W 2-1
Lincoln City	5,421	Grimsby Town	L 0-2
LutonTown	10,044	Forest Green R	W 4-1
Macclesfield T	2,207	Aldershot Town	D 1-1
Nuneaton Town	3,480	Luton Town	L 0-5
Salisbury City	2,633	Luton Town	D 0-0
Southport	2,210	Luton Town	W 1-0
Tamworth	2,066	Luton Town	L 3-4
Welling United	2,650	Luton Town	L 1-2
Woking	4.728	Aldershot Town	L 1-2
Wrexham	7,526	Luton Town	L 0-5

HAT-TRICK HEROS

	Club	Goals	Opponents	Score
Brett Williams	Aldershot Town	3	Southport (H)	W 5-1
Matty Taylor	Chester	3	Tamworth (A)	W 4-3
Matt Godden	Dartford	3	Hyde (H)	W 4-3
Lee Gregory	FC Halifax Town	3	Welling U (H)	W 3-0
Lee Gregory	FC Halifax Town	3	Salisbury C (H)	W 5-1
Lee Gregory	FC Halifax Town	3	Hyde (A)	W 5-1
Dayle Southwell	Grimsby Town	3	Coalville Town (H)	W 3-0
Ross Hannah	Grimsby Town	3	Alfreton Town(A)	D 3-3
Joe Lolley	Kidderminster H	3	Salisbury C (H)	W 3-0
Alan Power	Lincoln City	3	Stalybridge Cletic	W 5-1
Ben Tomlinson	LIncoln City	3	FC Halifax Town	W 3-1
Andre Gray	Luton Town	3	Hyde (H)	W 4-1
Andre Gray	Luton Town	3	Nuneaton T (H)	W 3-0
Andre Gray	Luton Town	3	Hereford U (H)	W 7-0
Connor Jennings	Macclesfield Town	3	Wrexham (H)	W 3-2
Adam Marriott	Woking	3	FC Halifax T	W 4-3
Andy Bishop	Wrexham	3	Gateshead (H)	W 3-2
Rob Ogleby	Wrexham	3	Hyde (A)	W 5-2
Brett Williams	Aldershot Town	3	Southport (H)	W 5-1
Matty Taylor	Chester	3	Tamworth (A)	W 4-3
Matt Godden	Dartford	3	Hyde (H)	W 4-3
Lee Gregory	FC Halifax Town	3	Welling U (H)	W 3-0
Lee Gregory	FC Halifax Town	3	Salisbury C (H)	W 5-1
Louis Moult	Nuneaton Town	3	Dartford (h)	W 3-1

A.F.C. FYLDE

Chairman: David Haythornthwaite
Secretary: Martin Benson (T) 07545 735 154 (E) clubsecretary@afcfylde.co.uk
Commercial Manager: Charlie Hay (T) 07525 323 775
Programme Editor: Chris Park (T) 07714 306 931
Ground Address: Kellamergh Park, Bryning Lane, Warton, Preston PR4 1TN
(T) 01772 682 593 **Manager:** Dave Challinor

The Coasters starting XI observing a minute's silence v Matlock Town in Nov 2013

Club Factfile

Founded: 1988 **Nickname:** The Coasters
Previous Names: Wesham FC and Kirkham Town amalgamated in 1988 to form Kirkham & Wesham > 2008
Previous Leagues: West Lancashire, North West Counties 2007-09. Northern Premier 2009-14.

Club Colours (change): All white (Blue and yellow stripes/black/black)

Ground Capacity: 1,426 **Seats:** 282 **Covered:** 282 **Clubhouse:** Yes **Shop:** Yes

Directions
AFC Fylde is based in an area called 'The Fylde Coast' located between Blackpool and Preston. Kellamergh Park is located in WARTON. EXIT via Junction 3 M55 (signposted A585 Fleetwood/Kirkham). Up approach and turn left towards signs for Kirkham. In around 3/4 mile you will approach a roundabout. Then follow the signs for Wrea Green and Lytham St. Annes (2nd exit) B5259. After another 500 yards you will approach a new roundabout (go straight on) and 1/4 mile you will go over main Preston/Blackpool railway bridge and drop down almost immediately to a small mini roundabout (pub on left called Kingfisher). Carry on straight over this and up to main roundabout (another 200 yards) at junction of main Preston/Blackpool A583. Go straight over roundabout and drive on into Wrea Green Village. At 2nd mini roundabout in the centre of the village (Church on right and Primary School) take left turn into Bryning Lane, signposted on The Green (small white signpost) to Warton (2 miles).The Green will now be on your right as you exit out of the village and in around 1.8 miles you will come to the Birley Arms Pub on your left. Turn left at The Birley Arms Pub Car park and continue to drive through the car park down an access road and park in the Main Club Car Park.

Previous Grounds: Coronation Road > 2006

Record Attendance: 1,418 v FC United of Manchester, NPL P, 13/10/12.
Record Victory: Not known
Record Defeat: Not known
Record Goalscorer: Not known
Record Appearances: Not known
Additional Records:

Senior Honours:
West Lancashire League 1999-2000, 00-01, 01-02, 03-04, 04-05, 05-06, 06-07.
FA Vase 2007-08.
North West Counties League 2008-09. Northern Premier Division 1 North 2011-12. Lancashire FA Challenge Trophy 2011-12.

10 YEAR RECORD

04-05	05-06	06-07	07-08	08-09	09-10	10-11	11-12	12-13	13-14
WYkP 1	WYkP 1	WYkP 1	NWC2 2	NWCP 1	NP1N 13	NP1N 5	NP1N 1	NP P 5	NP P 2

A.F.C. FYLDE MATCH RESULTS 2013-14

Date	Comp	H/A	Opponents	Att:	Result		Goalscorers	Pos	No.
Aug 17	NPL	H	Stafford Rangers	361	W	2-1	Winter 59 Lloyd-Goldrick 82	7	1
20	NPL	A	FC United	1649	D	0-0		8	2
24	NPL	A	Grantham Town	220	W	2-1	Barnes 33 Blinkhorn 47	3	3
26	NPL	H	Chorley	588	L	0-1		9	4
31	NPL	A	Worksop Town	251	W	6-1	Blinkhorn 22 30 Winter 24 Lloyd-Goldrick 33 43 Barnes 57	2	5
Sept 3	NPL	H	Droylsden	227	W	5-0	Blinkhorn 23 Hughes 36 Winter 65 Hankin 69 Booth 78	2	6
7	NPL	H	Matlock Town	363	W	2-0	Blinkhorn 42 Winter 46	1	7
10	NPL	A	Nantwich Town	200	D	1-1	Barnes 61	2	8
14	***FAC1Q***	***A***	***Blyth Spartans***	***386***	***W***	***3-1***	***Lloyd-McGoldrick 34 Blinkhorn 50 Rainford 90***		9
17	NPL	H	Marine	182	D	0-0		1	10
21	NPL	A	Whitby Town	212	W	2-0	Hughes 5 Blinkhorn 10	1	11
24	NPL	A	Witton Albion	292	W	1-0	Lloyd-McGoldrick 34	2	12
28	***FAC2Q***	***H***	***Ashton United***	***302***	***L***	***0-1***			13
Oct 5	NPL	H	Buxton	359	D	2 2	Lloyd-McGoldrick 45 Dorney 75	1	14
12	NPL	A	Barwell	232	W	3-0	Blinkhorn 26 Winter 45 Rainford 90	1	15
16	NPL	A	Trafford	218	L	0-2		2	16
19	***FAT1Q***	***H***	***Kendal Town***	***254***	***D***	***1-1***	***Blinkhorn 63***		17
23	***FAT1Qr***	***A***	***Kendal Town***	***170***	***W***	***2-1***	***Russell 11 Winter 41***		18
26	NPL	H	Whitby Town	281	W	3-1	Sumner 76 (pen) Blinkhorn 78 Lloyd 89	2	19
29	NPL	A	Droylsden	109	W	10-0	B.BARNES 5 M.Barnes Winter, Denson, Russell, Lloyd	2	20
Nov 2	***FAT 2Q***	***A***	***Rushall Olympic***	***121***	***W***	***1-0***	***B.Barnes 87***		21
5	NPL	H	Nantwich Town	204	L	1-2	Lloyd-McGoldrick 10	3	22
9	NPL	A	Matlock Town	343	D	1-1	Russell 50	3	23
16	***FAT 3Q***	***A***	***Curzon Ashton***	***217***	***L***	***1-2***	***B.Barnes 33***		24
23	NPL	H	Frickley Athletic	291	W	2-0	Denson 23 Hughes 53	3	25
30	NPL	A	Stocksbridge PS	176	W	1-0	Eckersley 38	3	26
Dec 7	NPL	A	Stafford Rangers	311	D	2-2	Dorney 81 Denson 90	3	27
14	NPL	H	FC United	**709**	L	0-2		4	28
21	NPL	A	Kings Lynn Town	482	L	0-2		4	29
26	NPL	H	Skelmersdale United	343	L	2-3	B.Barnes 8 Sumner 74	4	30
28	NPL	H	Ilkeston	314	L	1-2	Baker 48 (og)	6	31
Jan 1	NPL	A	Chorley	1020	L	1-3	Cooke 22	10	32
4	NPL	H	Worksop Town	254	W	3-2	Booth 3 Blinkhorn 58 Scott 63 (og)	7	33
11	NPL	H	Ashton United	265	W	1-0	Lloyd 40	5	34
18	NPL	A	Marine	338	W	2-1	Allen 37 Lloyd-McGoldrick 90	4	35
25	NPL	H	Witton Albion	248	W	3-0	Allen 1 35 Cooke 57	4	36
Feb 1	NPL	A	Buxton	167	W	4-0	Lloyd-McGoldrick 41 83 M.Barnes 68 Russell 90	5	37
4	NPL	H	Trafford	189	W	2-1	Mason 26 (og) Lloyd McGoldrick 27	3	38
15	NPL	A	Ashton United	175	D	1-1	Allen 30	3	39
22	NPL	H	Barwell	251	W	1-0	Blinkhorn 48	3	40
March 1	NPL	A	Blyth Spartans	386	D	1-1	Allen 86 (pen)	4	41
8	NPL	H	Rushall Olymppi	274	W	2-1	B.Barnes 32 Sumner 76	3	42
15	NPL	A	Stamford	268	W	3-1	Blinkhorn 5 Cooke 31 Russell 40	2	43
22	NPL	H	Stamford	238	W	2-0	Blinkhorn 39 Lloyd-McGoldrick 88	4	44
29	NPL	A	Frickley Athletic	203	W	2-0	Cooke 47 Allen 90	4	45
April 1	NPL	A	Rushall Olympic	146	D	2-2	Allen 18 Winter 71	3	46
5	NPL	H	Stocksbridge PS	274	W	5-0	Booth 25 Haigh 29 (og) ALLEN 3 (45 49 58)	3	47
8	NPL	A	Ilkeston Town	305	W	1-0	Blinkhorn 79	3	48
16	NPL	H	Blyth Spartans	304	W	5-1	M.Barnes 15 Winter 27 Lloyd-McGoldrick 51 (pen) 85 Mullen 89	3	49
19	NPL	H	Grantham Town	148	L	1-2	Allen 64	3	50
21	NPL	A	Skelmersdale United	273	W	5-0	Allen 8 75 (pen) BLINKHORN 3 (20 22 34)	3	51
26	NPL	H	King's Lynn Town	337	W	1-0	Blinkhorn 73	3	52
29	**NPL PO SF**	**H**	**Worksop Town**	**576**	**W**	**3-1**	**ALLEN 3 (19 65 90 pen)**		53
May 3	**NPL PO F**	**H**	**Ashton United**	**1191**	**D**	**1-1**	**Cooke 70 (AFC Fylde won 4-3 on penalties aet)**		54

GOALSCORERS	Lge	FAC	FAT	Total	Pens	Hat-tricks	Cons Run
Blinkhorn	17	1	1	19		1	3
Allen	13+3			16	3	2	3
Lloyd-Goldrick	13	1		14	1		
B. Barnes	7		2	9			
Winter	8		1	9			3
M. Barnes	6			6			
Cooke	4+1			5			
Russell	4		1	5			
Booth	3			3			
Denson	3			3			
Hughes	3			3			
Lloyd	3			3			
Sumner	3			3	1		
Dorney	2			2			
Rainford	1	1		2			
Eckersley	1			1			
Hankin	1			1			
Mullen	1			1			
Opponents	4			4			

Cons Run - Consecutive scoring games.
Play-off goals indicated by +

BARROW

Chairman: Paul Casson

Secretary: Russell Dodd (T) 07789 757 639 (E) secbafc@aol.com

Commercial Manager: Lyndsay Aspin (T) 07402 375 051

Programme Editor: Bob Herbert (T) 01229 829 133

Ground Address: Furness Building Society Stadium, Wilkie Road, Barrow-in-Furness LA14 5UW

(T) 01299 823 061 **Manager:** Darren Edmondson

Club Factfile

Founded: 1901 **Nickname:** Bluebirds

Previous Names: None

Previous Leagues: Lancashire Combination 1901-21. Football League 1921-72. Northern Premier 1972-79, 83-84, 86-89, 92-98, 99-04. Conference 1979-83, 84-86, 89-92, 98-99.

Club Colours (change): Blue & white/white with blue trim/blue with white trim (All yellow with black trim)

Ground Capacity: 4,500 **Seats:** 1,000 **Covered:** 2,200 **Clubhouse:** Yes **Shop:** Yes

Directions

M6 Junction 36, onto A590 signposted Barrow. Follow A590 all the way to the outskirts of Barrow (approx. 27 miles) entering via Industrial route. In a further 2 miles you pass the Fire Station on the right hand side, take next left into Wilkie Road, the ground is on the right.

Previous Grounds: Strawberry & Little Park, Roose.

Record Attendance: 16,854 v Swansea Town - FA Cup 3rd Round 1954

Record Victory: 12-0 v Cleator - FA Cup 1920

Record Defeat: 1-10 v Hartlepool United - Football League Division 4 1959

Record Goalscorer: Colin Cowperthwaite - 282 (December 1977 - December 1992)

Record Appearances: Colin Cowperthwaite - 704

Additional Records: Paid £9,000 to Ashton United for Andy Whittaker (07/94)
Received £40,000 from Barnet for Kenny Lowe (01/91)

Senior Honours:
Lancashire Senior Cup 1954-55. Lancashire Challenge Trophy 1980-81. Northern Premier League 1983-84, 88-89, 97-98.
FA Trophy 1989-90, 2009-10.

10 YEAR RECORD

04-05	05-06	06-07	07-08	08-09	09-10	10-11	11-12	12-13	13-14
Conf N 16	Conf N 14	Conf N 16	Conf N 5	Conf 20	Conf 15	Conf 18	Conf 13	Conf 22	Conf N 11

BARROW MATCH RESULTS 2013-14

Date	Comp	H/A	Opponents	Att:	Result		Goalscorers	Pos	No.
Aug 17	CNorth	H	Brackley Town	884	L	0-1		15	1
20	CNorth	A	Altrincham	145	L	1-2	Davies 53	21	2
24	CNorth	A	Bradford PA	315	D	2-2	Arnison 8 (pen) Sheridan 75 (pen)	15	3
26	CNorth	H	Harrogate Town	727	W	1-0	Sheridan 54	14	4
31	CNorth	A	Hednesford Town	648	L	1-3	Johnson 24	17	5
Sept 7	CNorth	H	Gloucester City	751	D	0-0		16	6
14	CNorth	A	Gainsborough Trinity	415	L	1-2	Rushton 68	18	7
17	CNorth	H	Colwyn Bay	540	D	1-1	Arnison 69	17	8
21	CNorth	H	Histon	593	W	2-1	Johnson 26 Sheridan 44	14	9
28	***FAC2Q***	***H***	***Ramsbottom United***	***677***	***W***	***3-0***	***Mills 27 Meechan 44 (pen) 77 (pen)***		10
Oct 5	CNorth	A	Boston United	1041	L	0-1		16	11
8	CNorth	H	Stockport County	684	L	2-4	Ruston 59 (pen) Allen 74	16	12
12	***FAC3Q***	***A***	***Atherstone Town***	***823***	***W***	***4-0***	***Arnison 23 38 Meecham 42 Davies 44***		13
19	CNorth	A	Vauxhall Motors	230	D	1-1	Allen 39	16	14
26	***FAC4Q***	***H***	***Brackley Town***	***409***	***D***	***0-0***			15
29	***FAC4Qr***	***A***	***Brackley Town***	***830***	***L***	***0-1***			16
Nov 2	CNorth	A	Guiseley	431	L	1-2	Sheridan 21	18	17
9	CNorth	H	North Ferriby United	287	D	2 2	Rushton 17 Arnison 87	18	18
12	CNorth	H	Stalybridge Celtic	642	D	1-1	Carver 16	18	19
16	***FAT3Q***	***H***	***Stockport County***	***727***	***D***	***2-2***	***Platt 28 (og) Rushton 48 (pen)***		20
19	***FAT3Qr***	***A***	***Stockport County***	***812***	***W***	***3-2***	***O'Donnell 26 Rushton 28 Walker 70***		21
23	CNorth	H	AFC Telford United	646	L	0-3		19	22
30	***FAT1***	***A***	***Chester***	***1409***	***W***	***2-1***	***Carver 58 74***		23
Dec 7	CNorth	H	Gainsborough Trinity	421	L	0-6		22	24
14	***FAT2***	***H***	***Maidenhead United***	***560***	***L***	***0-2***			25
21	CNorth	H	Solihull Borough	454	L	0-2		22	26
26	CNorth	A	Workington	581	W	3-2	Rushton 3 60 Arnison 83 (pen)	21	27
28	CNorth	H	Altrincham	736	D	1-1	Harvey 4	21	28
Jan 1	CNorth	H	Workington	931	W	2-0	Rushton 45 Lacey 80	20	29
7	CNorth	A	Stalybridge Celtic	313	W	3-1	Rushton 17 Davies 55 Parkinson 85	19	30
14	CNorth	A	Brackley Town	218	W	2-1	Cowperthwaite 22 Arnison 88	18	31
18	CNorth	A	AFC Telford United	1684	W	1-0	Sheridan 76	16	32
28	CNorth	H	Guiseley	593	W	1-0	Rushton 12	14	33
Feb 1	CNorth	H	Leamington	734	D	0-0		13	34
4	CNorth	A	Oxford City	197	W	1-0	Marsh 15	12	35
8	CNorth	H	North Ferriby United	963	W	2-0	Rushton 11 (pen) 81	10	36
18	CNorth	A	Gloucester CIty	421	W	3-1	Sheridon 21 Rushton 64 O'Donnell 84	10	37
22	CNorth	H	Oxford City	**1011**	D	1-1	Marsh 40	9	38
March 1	CNorth	A	Colwyn Bay	493	W	2-1	Cowperthwaite 10 Rushton 77	9	39
4	CNorth	A	Stockport County	2457	D	2-2	Harvey 36 Rushton 67	9	40
8	CNorth	H	Worcester City	901	L	0-1		10	41
15	CNorth	A	Leamington	548	D	1-1	Corner 16	11	42
22	CNorth	H	Boston United	808	D	4-4	REYNOLDS 3 (21 45 57) Cowperthwaite 81	11	43
29	CNorth	H	Vauxhall Motors	808	D	1-1	Arnison 24 (pen)	11	44
April 5	CNorth	A	Histon	311	D	0-0		11	45
8	CNorth	A	Worcester City	314	L	0-1		11	46
12	CNorth	A	Solihull Moors	343	W	2-0	Burns 45 Lacey 83	11	47
19	CNorth	H	Bradford PA	733	L	0-1		12	48
21	CNorth	A	Harrogate Town	582	L	1-3	Reynolds 39	12	49
26	CNorth	H	Hednesford Town	799	W	1-0	Sheridon 21	11	50

GOALSCORERS	Lge	FAC	FAT	Total	Pens	Hat-tricks	Cons Run
Rushton	13		2	15	3		2
Arnison	6	2		8	3		
Sheridan	7			7	1		
Reynolds	4			4		1	
Carver	1		2	3			
Cowperthwaite	3			3			
Davies	2	1		3			
Meechan		3		3	2		
Allen	2			2			
Harvey	2			2			
Johnson	2			2			
Lacey	2			2			
Marsh	2			2			
O'Donnell	1		1	2			
Burns	1			1			
Corner	1			1			
Mills		1		1			
Parkinson	1			1			
Walker			1	1			
Opponents			1	1			

Cons Run - Consecutive scoring games.

BOSTON UNITED

Chairman: David Newton
Secretary: John Blackwell (T) 07860 663 299 (E) admin@bufc.co.uk
Commercial Manager: Craig Singleton (T) 07966 952 694
Programme Editor: Craig Singleton (T) craig.singleton@bufc.co.uk
Ground Address: Jakemans Stadium, York Street, Boston PE21 6JN
(T) 01205 364 406 **Manager:** Dennis Greene

2013-14 Squad

Club Factfile

Founded: 1933 **Nickname:** The Pilgrims
Previous Names: Reformed as Boston United when Boston Town folded in 1933
Previous Leagues: Midland 1933-58, 62-64, Southern 1958-62, 98-2000, United Counties 1965-66, West Midlands 1966-68, Northern Premier 1968-79, 93-98, 2008-10, Alliance/Conference 1979-93, 2000-02, 07-08, Football League 2002-07

Club Colours (change): Amber and black halves/black/black (Green/white/green with white hoops)

Ground Capacity: 6,645 **Seats:** 5,711 **Covered:** 6,645 **Clubhouse:** Yes **Shop:** Yes

Directions: A1 to A17 Sleaford to Boston-Over Boston Railway Station crossing, bear right at the Eagle Public House-To light over Haven Bridge-straight along John Adams Way(Dual Carriageway) -Turn right at traffic lights into main ridge, then right again into York Street(This is opposite Eagle Fisheries)-Ground is signposted after Railway crossing.

Previous Grounds: None

Record Attendance: 10,086 v Corby Town - Floodlights inauguration 1955
Record Victory: 12-0 v Spilsby Town - Grace Swan Cup 1992-93
Record Defeat: Not known.
Record Goalscorer: Chris Cook - 181
Record Appearances: Billy Howells - 500+
Additional Records: Paid £30,000 to Scarborough for Paul Ellender, 08/2001
Received £50,000 from Bolton Wanderers for David Norris 2000
Senior Honours:
Central Alliance League 1961-62. United Counties League 1965-66. West Midlands League 1966-67, 67-68.
Northern Premier League 1972-73, 73-74, 76-77, 77-78, League Cup 1973-74, 75-76. Southern League 1999-2000. Conference 2001-02.

10 YEAR RECORD

04-05	05-06	06-07	07-08	08-09	09-10	10-11	11-12	12-13	13-14
FL 2 16	FL 2 11	FL 2 23	Conf N 10	NP P 16	NP P 3	Conf N 3	Conf N 11	Conf N 16	Conf N 6

BOSTON UNITED MATCH RESULTS 2013-14

Date	Comp	H/A	Opponents	Att:	Result	Goalscorers	Pos	No.
Aug 17	CNorth	A	Stockport County	3317	**W** 4-1	Garner 7 Newsham 55 Weir-Daley 57 Miller 65	2	1
20	CNorth	H	AFC Telford United	1145	D 1-1	Bore 42	5	2
24	CNorth	H	Leamington	1086	**W** 2-0	Miller 53 Newsham 78	4	3
26	CNorth	A	North Ferriby United	618	L 0-3		7	4
31	CNorth	H	Worcester City	919	**W** 2-1	Newsham 25 Weir-Daley 52	7	5
Sept 7	CNorth	A	Vauxhall Motors	214	D 2-2	Weir-Daley 44 Newsham 90	7	6
14	CNorth	H	Guiseley	1022	**W** 3-0	Piergianni 60 Newsham 66 90	5	7
17	CNorth	A	Oxford City	234	D 1-1	Ross 90	6	8
21	CNorth	A	Gloucester City	337	**W** 3-1	Ross 34 Piergianni 51 Garner 56	5	9
24	CNorth	H	Bradford PA	1099	L 2-3	Newsham 56 82 (pen)	6	10
28	***FAC2Q***	***A***	***Stafford Rangers***	***519***	***W 4-0***	***Miller 18 80 Weir-Daley 29 (pen) 66***		11
Oct 5	CNorth	H	Barrow	1041	**W** 1-0	Miller 54	5	12
12	***FAC3Q***	***A***	***Brackley Town***	***406***	***L 0-2***			13
19	CNorth	H	Harrogate Town	921	D 3-3	Newsham 11 23 (Pen) Weir-Daley 28	6	14
26	CNorth	H	Altrincham	1081	**W** 3-2	Marshall 8 Weir-Daley 45 Garner 75	3	15
Nov 2	CNorth	A	Brackley Town	364	L 2-3	Austin 52 (og) Newsham 69	6	16
9	CNorth	H	Colwyn Bay	1028	**W** 2-1	Weir-Daley 59 Piergianni 79	4	17
12	CNorth	A	Gainsborough Trinity	746	**W** 1-0	Miller 17	2	18
16	***FAT3Q***	***H***	***Redditch United***	***784***	***W 4-1***	***Piergianni 22 Miller 70 75 Hall 81***		19
23	CNorth	A	Bradford PA	401	D 1-1	Ross 76	4	20
30	***FAT1***	***A***	***Southport***	***496***	***W 2-1***	***Newsham 37 Piergianni 51***		21
Dec 7	CNorth	A	Guiseley	470	L 0-1		6	22
14	***FAT2***	***A***	***Tamworth***	***688***	***L 0-2***			23
21	CNorth	A	Stalybridge Celtic	354	D 3-3	Sansara19 Fairclough 68 Newsham 74	7	24
26	CNorth	H	Histon	1361	D 0-0		7	25
28	CNorth	A	AFC Telford United	1659	L 1-2	Newsham 41	7	26
Jan 4	CNorth	H	Vauxhall Motors	931	**W** 5-2	Newsham 12 52 Garner 45 Miller 74 Ross 77 (pen)	7	27
7	CNorth	H	Workington	797	**W** 5-3	MILLER 3 (6 31 39) Semple 80 Newsham 83 (pen)	5	28
11	CNorth	A	Hednesford Town	650	L 2-4	Miller 31 63	7	29
18	CNorth	H	Solihull Moors	1102	**W** 4-1	Garner 38 MILLER 3 (40 55 90pen)	6	30
28	CNorth	H	Stockport County	917	D 0-0		5	31
Feb 1	CNorth	H	Gainsborough Trinity	1255	**W** 6-0	NEWSHAM 3 (8 20 86) Miller 29 (pen) Semple 34 Garner 75	5	32
4	CNorth	A	Histon	353	**W** 2-1	Newsham 4 Weir-Daley 80	3	33
8	CNorth	H	Brackley Town	1207	L 1-2	McGhee 27	4	34
22	CNorth	A	Harrogate Town	632	L 0-4		4	35
March 1	CNorth	H	Hednesford Town	1102	**W** 4-0	Miller 12 (pen) Garner 16 Agnew 56 Milnes 79	4	36
8	CNorth	A	Workington	397	L 0-1		7	37
15	CNorth	H	Oxford City	1023	**W** 2-1	Miller 68 (pen) Marshall 77	6	38
22	CNorth	A	Barrow	88	D 4-4	MILLER 3 (8 89 90) Milnes 62	6	39
29	CNorth	H	Gloucester City	1208	**W** 2-0	Agnew 28 Miller 90 (pen)	5	40
April 1	CNorth	A	Altrincham	650	D 0-0		6	41
5	CNorth	A	Soihull Moors	459	**W** 2-1	Miller 37 (pen) 77	6	42
8	CNorth	A	Colwyn Bay	257	D 3-3	Smyth 48 (og) Miller 78 Mills 90	6	43
12	CNorth	H	Stalybridge Celtic	1133	**W** 4-1	Kanadu 73 Weir-Daley 77 Milnes 79 90	5	44
19	CNorth	A	Leamington	792	D 0-0		6	45
21	CNorth	H	North Ferriby United	**1567**	**W** 2-0	McGhee 70 Miller 80 (pen)	6	46
26	CNorth	A	Worcester City	854	L 0-3		6	47

GOALSCORERS	Lge	FAC	FAT	Total	Pens	Hat-tricks	Cons Run
Miller	24	2	2	28	7	3	4
Newsham	20		1	21	3	1	3
Weir-Daley	8	2		10	1		3
Garner	7			7			
Piergianni	3		1	5			
Milnes	4			4			
Ross	4			4	1		2
Agnew	2			2			
Marshall	2			2			
McGhee	2			2			
Semple	2			2			
Bore	1			1			
Fairclough	1			1			
Hall			1	1			
Kanadu	1			1			
Mills	1			1			
Sansara	1			1			
Opponents	2			2			

Cons Run - Consecutive scoring games.

BRACKLEY TOWN

Chairman: Francis Oliver

Secretary: Pat Ashby (T) 07969 825 636 (E) pat.ashby55@btinternet.com

Commercial Manager: Jan Butters (T) 07766 226 655

Programme Editor: Steve Goodman (T) 07595 204 940

Ground Address: St James Park, Churchill Way, Brackley NN13 7EJ

(T) 01280 704 077 **Manager:** Jon Brady

Club Factfile

Founded: 1890 **Nickname:** Saints

Previous Names: None

Previous Leagues: Banbury & District, North Buckinghamshire, Hellenic 1977-83, 94-97, 99-2004, United Counties 1983-84, Southern 1997-99

Club Colours (change): Red and white stripes/red/red (All yellow)

Ground Capacity: 3,500 **Seats:** 300 **Covered:** 1,500 **Clubhouse:** Yes **Shop:** Yes

Directions
Take A43 from Northampton or Oxford, or A422 from Banbury to large roundabout south of town. Take exit marked Brackley (South) and follow towards the town (Tesco store on left). Pass the Locomotive public house and take first turning right, signposted Football Club, into Churchill Way - road leads into Club car park.

Previous Grounds: Banbury Road, Manor Road, Buckingham Road > 1974

Record Attendance: 960 v Banbury United - 2005-06

Record Victory: Not known

Record Defeat: Not known

Record Goalscorer: Paul Warrington - 320

Record Appearances: Terry Muckelberg - 350

Additional Records: Received £2,000 from Oxford City for Phil Mason 1998

Senior Honours:

Hellenic League Premier Division 1996-97, 2003-04, Division 1 Cup 1982-83. Southern League Division 1 Midlands 2006-07.
Southern Premier Division 2011-12. Northamptonshire Senior Cup 2011-12.

10 YEAR RECORD

04-05	05-06	06-07	07-08	08-09	09-10	10-11	11-12	12-13	13-14
SthW 7	SthW 3	SthM 1	SthP 8	SthP 11	SthP 5	SthP 9	SthP 1	Conf N 3	Conf N 7

BRACKLEY TOWN MATCH RESULTS 2013-14

Date	Comp	H/A	Opponents	Att:	Result	Goalscorers	Pos	No.
Aug 17	CNorth	A	Barrow	884	W 1-0	Reid 64	11	1
20	CNorth	H	Histon	281	W 3-0	Kaziboni 26 Solkhon 52 Diggin 90	3	2
24	CNorth	H	Worcester City	312	D 0-0		5	3
26	CNorth	A	Oxford City	483	W 1-0	Diggin 76	3	4
31	CNorth	H	North Ferriby United	283	D 1-1	Reid 84	3	5
Sept 7	CNorth	A	Guiseley	607	W 2-0	Reid 13 Nisevic 33	2	6
14	CNorth	H	Stalybridge	303	W 3-0	DIGGIN 3 (5 71 87)	1	7
17	CNorth	A	Gloucester City		D 2-2	Diggin 47 Austin 86	2	8
21	CNorth	A	Harrogate Town	410	W 1-0	Griffin 47	2	9
28	***FAC2Q***	***H***	***Gresley***	***312***	***D 1-1***	***Walker 71***		10
Oct 1	***FAC2Qr***	***A***	***Gresley***	***302***	***W 1-0***	***Solkhon 58***		11
5	CNorth	H	Vauxhall Motors	320	W 2-1	Diggin 13 (pen) Reid 58	2	12
12	***FAC3Q***	***H***	***Brackley Town***	***406***	***W 2-0***	***Walker 43 Diggin 86***		13
19	CNorth	A	Altrincham	855	L 0-1		4	14
26	***FAC4Q***	***H***	***Barrow***	***409***	***D 0-0***			15
29	***FAC4Qr***	***A***	***Barrow***	***830***	***W 1-0****	***Reid 45 (pen)***		16
2 Nov	CNorth	H	Boston United	364	W 3 2	Towers 3 Reid 26 Mills 40	3	17
5	CNorth	H	AFC Telford United	216	D 1 1	Walker 64	3	18
9	***FAC1***	***A***	***Gillingham***	***3004***	***D 1 1***	***Martin 69 (og)***		19
16	***FAT3Q***	***H***	***Leek Town***	***187***	***D 0-0***			20
18	***FAC1r***	***H***	***Gillingham***	***1772***	***W 1-0***	***Walker 21***		21
23	CNorth	H	Hednesford Town	448	W 1-0	Diggin 86	3	22
26	***FAT3Qr***	***A***	***Leek Town***	***236***	***L 1 2***	***Story 80***		23
30	CNorth	A	Colwyn Bay	240	D 2 2	Diggin 3 Story 90	3	24
3 Dec	CNorth	A	Solihull Moors	239	L 0-1			25
7	***FAC2***	***A***	***Macclesfield Town***	***2438***	***L 2 3***	***Diggin 38 Story 71***		26
10	CNorth	A	Gainsborough Trinity	317	D 2 2	Mills 14 Diggin 72		27
14	CNorth	A	Stockport County	1941	W 2-0	Story 63 Diggin 73	2	28
21	CNorth	A	AFCTelford United	1351	L 1 2	Griffin 17		29
26	CNorth	H	Leamington	**529**	D 1 1	Solkhon 81	4	30
28	CNorth	A	Histon	408	D 3 3	Diggin 7 Griffin 36 Nisevic 65	4	31
1 Jan	CNorth	A	Leamington	504	L 1 3	Griffin 28	6	32
11	CNorth	H	Gainsborough Trinity	269	W 3 1	Moore 8 74 Mills 27 (pen)	6	33
14	CNorth	H	Barrow	218	L 1 2	Moore 49	6	34
18	CNorth	A	Vauxhall Motors	146	W 3-0	Claire 19 (og) Moore 36 61	4	35
25	CNorth	H	Workington	315	D 1 1	Diggin 54	4	36
1 Feb	CNorth	H	Solihull Moors	263	W 1-0	Moore 49	4	37
8	CNorth	A	Boston Unied	1207	W 2 1	Moore 6 Piergianni 72 (og)	3	38
22	CNorth	A	Stalybridge Celtic	332	D 1 1	Solkhon 58	4	39
25	CNorth	H	Guiseley	172	L 1 2	Mulligan 90	5	40
1 Mar	CNorth	H	Harrogate Town	293	D 2 2	Moore 8 Solkhon 59	5	41
8	CNorth	H	Altrincham	390	L 1 2	Bridges 17	8	42
15	CNorth	A	Workington	314	W 3-0	Clerima 14 Moore 29 Bridges 75	7	43
18	CNorth	H	Gloucester City	197	L 1 3	Reid 78	8	44
22	CNorth	H	Bradford PA	266	L 0-1		8	45
29	CNorth	A	Bradford PA	352	W 5-0	Walker 8 Clerima 25 Moore 37 (pen) 59 Diggin 82	7	46
1 Apr	CNorth	A	Hednesford Town	468	D 2 2	Odihambo-Anoclet 37 Walker 69	7	47
5	CNorth	H	Colwyn Bay	235	D 2 2	Rowe 77 Diggin 89	7	48
12	CNorth	H	Stockport County	350	D 0-0		7	49
19	CNorth	A	Worcester City	568	D 1 1	Rowe 53	7	50
21	CNorth	H	Oxford City	430	W 2 1	Moore 63 Austin 77	6	51
26	CNorth	A	North Ferriby United	673	D 1 1	Rowe 88	7	52

GOALSCORERS	Lge	FAC	FAT	Total	Pens	Hat-tricks	Cons Run
Diggin	15	2		17	1	1	3
Moore	12			12	1		3
Reid	6	1		7	1		2
Walker	3	3		6			2
Solkhon	4	1		5			
Griffin	4			4			2
Story	2	1	1	4			2
Mills	3			3	1		
Rowe	3			3			
Austin	2			2			
Bridges	2			2			
Clerima	2			2			
Nisevic	2			2			
Kaziboni	1			1			
Mulligan	1			1			
Odihambo-Anoclet	1			1			
Towers	1			1			
Opponents	2	1		3			

Cons Run - Consecutive scoring games.

BRADFORD PARK AVENUE

Chairman: Dr. John Dean
Secretary: Colin Barker (T) 07863 180 787 (E) colin.barker1@tesco.net
Commercial Manager: Kevin Hainsworth (T) 07912 271 498
Programme Editor: Tim Parker (T) 07738 675 776
Ground Address: Horsfall Stadium, Cemetery Road, Bradford, West Yorkshire BD6 2NG
(T) 01274 604 578 **Manager:** John Deacey

2014-15 Squad

Club Factfile

Founded: 1907 **Nickname:** Avenue
Previous Names: Reformed in 1988
Previous Leagues: Southern 1907-08, Football League 1908-70, Northern Premier 1970-74, West Riding Co.Am. 1988-89, Central Midlands 1989-90, North West Counties 1990-95
Club Colours (change): Green & white stripe/green/green (Blue, red & pink/pink/pink)

Ground Capacity: 5,000 **Seats:** 1,247 **Covered:** 2,000 **Clubhouse:** Yes **Shop:** Yes

Directions
M62 to junction 26. Join M606 leave at second junction. At the roundabout take 2nd exit (A6036 signposted Halifax) and pass Odsal Stadium on the left hand side. At next roundabout take the 3rd exit (A6036 Halifax, Horsfall Stadium is signposted). After approximately one mile turn left down Cemetery Road immediately before the Kings Head Public House. Ground is 150 yards on the left.

Previous Grounds: Park Ave. 1907-73, Valley Parade 1973-74, Manningham Mills 1988-89, McLaren Field 1985-93, Batley 1993-96

Record Attendance: 2,100 v Bristol City - FA Cup 1st Round 2003
Record Victory: 11-0 v Derby Dale - FA Cup 1908
Record Defeat: 0-7 v Barnsley - 1911
Record Goalscorer: Len Shackleton - 171 (1940-46)
Record Appearances: Tommy Farr - 542 (1934-50)
Additional Records: Paid £24,500 to Derby County for Leon Leuty 1950
Received £34,000 from Derby County for Kevin Hector 1966
Senior Honours:
Football League Division 3 North 1928. North West Counties League 1994-95.
Northern Premier League Division 1 2000-01, Division 1 North 2007-08. Premier Division Play-offs 2011-12.
West Riding Senior Cup x9. West Riding County Cup x2.

10 YEAR RECORD

04-05	05-06	06-07	07-08	08-09	09-10	10-11	11-12	12-13	13-14
Conf N 22	NP P 21	NP 1 4	NP1N 1	NP P 7	NP P 2	NP P 3	NP P 4	Conf N 7	Conf N 10

BRADFORD PARK AVENUE MATCH RESULTS 2013-14

Date	Comp	H/A	Opponents	Att:	Result		Goalscorers	Pos	No.
Aug 17	CNorth	A	Leamington	657	L	0-2		19	1
19	CNorth	H	North Ferriby United	346	L	0-4		22	2
24	CNorth	H	Barrow	315	D	2-2	Boshell 4 Knowles 12	20	3
26	CNorth	A	Stalybridge Celtic	364	D	2-2	Marshall 8 Chilaka 63	18	4
31	CNorth	H	Oxford City	302	D	3-3	Boshell 51 Clayton 69 Mallory 90	18	5
Sept 7	CNorth	A	Worcester City	636	W	2-1	Walker 17 Mallory 86	15	6
14	CNorth	H	AFC Telford United	305	W	3-1	Knowles 29 Boshell 23 Marshall 77 (pen)	11	7
17	CNorth	A	Guiseley	500	W	2-0	Swain 1 Marshall 44	9	8
21	CNorth	H	Solihull Moors	305	D	2-2	Walker 18 Boshell 61	11	9
24	CNorth	A	Boston United	1099	W	3-2	Walker 10 Davidson 5 Mallory 60	7	10
28	***FAC2Q***	***A***	***Guisley***	***595***	***W***	***2-1***	***Davidson 27 Marshall 45***		11
Oct 5	CNorth	A	Solihull Moors	374	D	2-2	Marshall 37 Howarth 87	8	12
12	***FAC3Q***	***H***	***Penrith AFC***	***427***	***W***	***2-1***	***Marshal 62 (pen) Howarth 90***		13
19	CNorth	A	Colwyn Bay	313	D	2-2	Chilaka 7 Davidson 83	8	14
27	***FAC4Q***	***H***	***Kidderminster Harriers***	***464***	***D***	***1-1***	***Davidson 25***		15
30	***FAC4Qr***	***H***	***Kidderminster Harriers***	***355***	***L***	***1-2***	***Chilaka 39***		16
Nov 2	CNorth	H	Gloucester City	265	L	1-3	Edwards 31 (pen)	8	17
9	CNorth	A	Gainsborough Trinity	436	L	2-4	Walker 30 Davidson 55	8	18
11	CNorth	H	Altrincham	383	L	2 4	Boshell 2 Deacey 31	8	19
16	***FAT3Q***	***A***	***Harrogate Town***	***572***	***D***	***1-1***	***Boshell 61***	***16***	20
18	***FAT3Qr***	***H***	***Harrogate Town***	***189***	***W***	***4-0***	***KNOWLES 3 (24 53 83) Boshell 42 (pen)***		21
23	CNorth	H	Boston United	401	D	1-1	Davidson 50	10	22
Dec 7	CNorth	A	Vauxhal Motors	180	W	2-0	Walker 38 59	9	23
9	CNorth	H	Guiseley	405	L	0-3		9	24
14	***FAT2***	***A***	***Guiseley***	***476***	***L***	***0-3***			25
17	CNorth	A	Hednesford Town	483	L	0-2		10	26
21	CNorth	A	Histon	314	L	0-1		12	27
26	CNorth	A	Stockport County	2108	L	1-4	Beesley 45	12	28
28	CNorth	A	North Ferriby United	319	W	3-0	Knowles 10 Hotte 61 Walker 74	12	29
Jan 4	CNorth	H	Worcester City	288	W	6 1	Boshell 13 80 (pen) Deacey 39 Beesley 41 Clayton 62 Gardner 86	12	30
11	CNorth	A	Gloucester City	294	W	3-2	Deacey 21 Clayton 24 Davidson 63	12	31
18	CNorth	H	Hednesford Town	354	L	1-2	Gardner 90	12	32
20	CNorth	H	Leamington	369	W	3-2	Glover 75 Walker 95 Chilaka 90	11	33
25	CNorth	A	Harrogate Town	597	D	1-1	Walker 77	11	34
Feb 10	CNorth	H	Stockport County	**569**	L	0-2		13	35
Mar 1	CNorth	A	AFC Telford United	1800	L	1-2	Glover 82	14	36
3	CNorth	H	Vauxhall Motors	232	D	0-0		14	37
8	CNorth	H	Colwyn Bay	390	L	1-2	Beesley 34	15	38
12	CNorth	H	Workington	269	W	1-0	Chilaka 25	15	39
15	CNorth	H	Harrogate Town	371	D	0-0		13	40
19	CNorth	H	Gainsborough Trinity	237	W	4-0	Walker 15 Marshall 44 (Pen) Beesley 50 Chilaka 57	12	41
22	CNorth	A	Brackley Town	266	W	1-0	Walker 89	12	42
26	CNorth	A	Altrincham	582	L	1-4	Deacy 42	12	43
29	CNorth	H	Brackley Town	352	L	0-5		12	44
April 5	CNorth	A	Workington	303	W	2-0	Walker 53 Beesley 68	12	45
12	CNorth	H	Histon	312	W	3-0	Chilaka 31 44 Walker 74	11	46
19	CNorth	A	Barrow	733	W	1-0	Beesley 16	10	47
21	CNorth	H	Stalybridge Celtic	369	D	1-1	Chilaka 40	10	48
26	CNorth	A	Oxford City	251	D	1-1	Marshall 79	10	49
									50

GOALSCORERS	Lge	FAC	FAT	Total	Pens	Hat-tricks	Cons Run
Walker	13			13			2
Boshell	7		2	9	2		
Chilaka	8	1		9			
Marshall	6	2		8	3		3
Davidson	5	2		7			2
Knowles	3		3	6		1	
Beesley	5			5			
Deacey	4			4			
Clayton	3			3			
Mallory	3			3			2
Howarth	1	1		2			2
Gardner	2			2			
Glover	2			2			
Edwards	1			1	1		
Hotte	1			1			
Swain	1			1			

Cons Run - Consecutive scoring games.

CHORLEY

Chairman: Ken Wright
Secretary: Graham Watkinson (T) 0773 995 2167 (E) graham.watkinson@chorleyfc.com
Commercial Manager: Jeremy Lee (T) 07774 197 303
Programme Editor: Josh Vosper (T) 07773 688 936
Ground Address: Victory Park Stadium, Duke Street, Chorley, Lancashire PR7 3DU
(T) 01257 230 007 **Manager:** Garry Flitcroft

Club Factfile

Founded: 1883 **Nickname:** Magpies
Previous Names: None
Previous Leagues: Lancashire Alliance 1890-94, Lancashire 1894-1903, Lancashire Combination 1903-68, 69-70, Northern Premier 1968-69, 70-72, 82-88, Cheshire County 1970-82, Conference 1988-90
Club Colours (change): Black and white stripes/black/black (Red/red/red)

Ground Capacity: 4,100 **Seats:** 900 **Covered:** 2,800 **Clubhouse:** Yes **Shop:** Yes

Directions

M61 leave at junction 6, follow A6 to Chorley, going past the Yarrow Bridge Hotel on Bolton Road. Turn left at first set of traffic lights into Pilling Lane, first right into Ashley St. Ground 2nd entrance on left.

M6 junction 27, follow Chorley, turn left at lights, A49 continue for 2 ½ miles, turn right onto B5251. Drive through Coppull and into Chorley for about 2 miles. On entering Chorley turn right into Duke Street 200 yards past Plough Hotel. Turn right into Ashby Street after Duke Street school, and first right into Ground.

Previous Grounds: Dole Lane 1883-1901, Rangletts Park 1901-05, St George's Park 1905-20

Record Attendance: 9,679 v Darwen - FA Cup 1931-32
Record Victory: Not known
Record Defeat: Not known
Record Goalscorer: Peter Watson - 371 (158-66)
Record Appearances: Not known
Additional Records: Received £30,000 from Newcastle United for David Eatock 1996
Senior Honours:
Lancashire Alliance 1892-93. Lancashire League 1896-97, 98-99. Lancashire Combination x11.
Cheshire County League 1975-76, 76-77, 81-82. Northern Premier League 1987-88.
Lancashire FA Trophy x14. Lancashire Combination League cup x3. Northern Premier Premier Division 2013-14.

10 YEAR RECORD

04-05		05-06		06-07		07-08		08-09		09-10		10-11		11-12		12-13		13-14	
NP 1	16	NP 1	18	NP 1	23	NP1N	14	NP1N	14	NP1N	16	NP1N	3	NP P	3	NP P	8	NP P	1

CHORLEY MATCH RESULTS 2013-14

Date	Comp	H/A	Opponents	Att:	Result		Goalscorers	Pos	No.
Aug 17	NPL	A	Barwell	223	W	3-1	Stephenson 44 87 Whitham 89	3	1
20	NPL	H	Ashton United	631	D	3-3	Hine 6 Stephenson 48 51	2	2
24	NPL	H	Whitby Town	590	D	0-0		7	3
26	NPL	A	AFC Fylde	588	W	1-0	Stephenson 24	2	4
31	NPL	A	Frickley Athletic	235	D	0-0		5	5
Sept 2	NPL	H	Trafford	621	W	6-2	STEPHENSON 3 (26 56 71) Hine 45 Teague 61 Baker 88	4	6
7	NPL	H	Stafford Rangers	896	W	3-0	Whitham 44 Jarvis 57 Dean 60	2	7
10	NPL	A	Matlock Town	282	W	2-1	Cottrell 32 Baker 74	1	8
14	***FAC1Q***	***A***	***FC United***	***1318***	***W***	***1-0***	***Whitham 62***		9
17	NPL	A	Skelmersdale Utd	397	L	0-1		2	10
21	NPL	H	Kings Lynn Town	696	W	1-0	Hine 49 (pen)	2	11
24	NPL	H	Blyth Spartans	685	W	3-0	Stephenson 23 Dean 27 88	1	12
28	***FAC2Q***	***A***	***Vauxhall Motors***	***366***	***L***	***0-4***			13
Oct 5	NPL	A	Stamford	281	D	1-1	Ross 35	2	14
15	NPL	A	Nantwich Town	172	W	1-0	Hine 11	2	15
19	***FAT1Q***	***A***	***Whitby Town***	***219***	***W***	***1-0***	***Stephenson 30***		16
26	NPL	A	Worksop Town	282	W	4-1	Whitham 14 Hine 44 78 Roscoe 72	3	17
29	NPL	A	Trafford	369	W	5-0	Dean 20 Walmsley 56 Stephenson 59 Roscoe 74 Wiles 90	2	18
Nov 2	***FAT2Q***	***A***	***Soham Town Rangers***	***196***	***W***	***2-1***	***Hine 13 60 (pen)***		19
5	NPL	H	Matlock Town	595	W	3-1	Cottrell 6 Dean 52 Teague 63	2	20
9	NPL	A	Stafford Rangers	483	W	3-1	Hine 26 (pen) Dean 46 Teague 61	1	21
16	***FAT3Q***	***H***	***Matlock Town***	***772***	***W***	***2-0***	***Hine 84 90***		22
23	NPL	H	Ilkeston	1017	W	2-1	Stephenson 27 Dean 45	2	23
30	***FAT1***	***H***	***Curzon Ashton***	***595***	***W***	***2-1***	***Dean 5 Hine 90***		24
Dec 2	NPL	A	Droylsden	264	W	5-0	Whitham 24 35 Dean 78 90 Jarvis 82	1	25
7	NPL	H	Barwell	697	L	1-2	Mather 52	2	26
14	***FAT2***	***H***	***Forest Green Rovers***	***790***	***D***	***0-0***			27
17	***FAT2r***	***A***	***Forest Green Rovers***	***508***	***D***	***0-0***	***(Won 3-1 on penalties aet)***		28
21	NPL	H	Buxton	748	D	0-0		2	29
26	NPL	A	Marine	534	W	1-0	Jarvis 45	2	30
28	NPL	A	Stocksbridge PS	293	D	2-2	Jarvis 60 O'Brien 67	3	31
Jan 1	NPL	H	AFC Fylde	1020	W	3-1	Hine 11 45 Dean 45	2	32
4	NPL	H	Grantham Town	813	W	3-1	Dean 36 Hine 64 Whitham 76	2	33
11	***FAT3***	***A***	***Tamworth***	***1209***	***D***	***1-1***	***Mather 52***		34
15	***FAT3r***	***H***	***Tamworth***	***1393***	***D***	***2-2***	***Cotrell 25 Teague 90 (Lost 5-6 on penalties aet)***		35
18	NPL	H	Skelmersdale United	1968	W	4-1	Jarvis 25 Dean 39 Dorney 44 Hine 84	2	36
25	NPL	A	Blyth Spartans	437	L	1-3	Utterson 20 (og)	2	37
Feb 1	NPL	H	Stamford	875	W	3-0	Lawlor 37 (og) Dean 64 (pen) 86	1	38
8	NPL	A	Kings Lynn Town	804	W	2-0	Stephenson 74 Whitham 85 (pen)	1	39
11	NPL	H	Frickley Athletic	593	W	2-0	Dean 74 Whitham 90	1	40
22	NPL	A	Grantham Town	260	D	1-1	Mather 87	1	41
25	NPL	H	Rushall Olympic	614	L	0-1		1	42
March 1	NPL	A	Witton Albion	497	D	2-2	Almond 82 Zibaka 90	1	43
4	NPL	H	FC United	**2171**	L	0-1		1	44
8	NPL	H	Worksop Town	1150	W	1-0	O'Brien 18	1	45
15	NPL	A	Rushall Olympic	253	L	0-1		1	46
22	NPL	H	Nantwich Town	829	W	5-1	Cartwright 24 Dean 45 56 Davies 58 (og) Hine 89	1	47
26	NPL	A	Ashton Uited	354	L	1-2	Teague 52	2	48
29	NPL	A	Ilkeston Town	436	W	3-2	Cartwright 5 Dean 25 (pen) Reid 67 (og)	2	49
April 1	NPL	H	Witton Albion	639	W	1-0	Whitham 78	1	50
5	NPL	H	Droylsden	849	W	13-1	Dorney 2 81 Hine 5 Henghan 7 (og) Cartwright 8 69 Murphy 12 (og) Whitham 36 86 DEAN 3 (44 52 pen 84) Stephenson 89	1	51
8	NPL	A	FC United	4152	D	2-2	Dean 12 Hine 59	1	52
12	NPL	H	Stocksbridge PS	1007	W	3-1	Hine 14 69 Stephenson 16	1	53
19	NPL	A	Whitby Town	447	D	1-1	Teague 23	1	54
21	NPL	H	Marine	2128	W	4-0	Dean 17 48 Stephenson 26 Almond 87	1	55
26	NPL	A	Buxton	1483	W	2-0	Hine 42 89	1	56

GOALSCORERS	Lge	FAC	FAT	Total	Pens	Hat-tricks	Cons Run
Dean	24		1	25	3	1	3
Hine	18		5	23	3		
Stephenson	15		1	16			
Whitham	11	1		12	1		
Teague	5		1	6			
Cottrell	2		1	3			
Dorney	3			3			
Jarvis	3			3			2
Mather	2		1	3			
Cartwright	4			4			
Almond	2			2			
Baker	2			2			
O'Brien	2			2			
Roscoe	2			2			2
Ross	1			1			
Walmsey	1			1			
Wiles	1			1			
Zibaka	1			1			
Opponents	6			6			

Cons Run - Consecutive scoring games.

COLWYN BAY

Chairman: David Messom

Secretary: Paul Edwards (T) 07990 730 323 (E) pauledwardscbfc@gmail.com

Commercial Manager: Karen Edwards (T) 07776 167 860

Programme Editor: Roger Skinner (T) 07783 287 406

Ground Address: Red Lion Foods Stadium, Llanelian Road, Old Colwyn, North Wales LL29 8UN

(T) 01492 514 680 **Manager:** Frank Sinclair

Club Factfile

Founded: 1885 **Nickname:** The Bay / Seagulls

Previous Names: None

Previous Leagues: North Wales Coast 1901-21, 33-35, Welsh National 1921-30, North Wales Combination 1930-31, Welsh League (North) 1945-84, North West Counties 1984-91

Club Colours (change): Sky blue and claret/maroon/sky blue & claret (Red & navy/white/red & white hoop)

Ground Capacity: 2,500 **Seats:** 250 **Covered:** 700 **Clubhouse:** Yes **Shop:** Yes

Directions

From Queensferry take the A55 and exit at Junction 22 signposted Old Colwyn at end of slip road turn left, up the hill to the mini roundabout, straight across onto Llanelian Road, ground is approx half mile on the right.

Previous Grounds: Eirias Park

Record Attendance: 5,000 v Borough United at Eirias Park 1964

Record Victory: Not known

Record Defeat: Not known

Record Goalscorer: Peter Donnelly

Record Appearances: Bryn A Jones

Additional Records:

Senior Honours:

Northern League Division 1 1991-92, Division 1 Play-off 2009-10

10 YEAR RECORD

04-05	05-06	06-07	07-08	08-09	09-10	10-11	11-12	12-13	13-14
NP 1 13	NP 1 12	NP 1 5	NP1S 7	NP1N 4	NP1N 4	NP P 2	Conf N 12	Conf N 18	Conf N 12

COLWYN BAY MATCH RESULTS 2013-14

Date	Comp	H/A	Opponents	Att:	Result		Goalscorers	Pos	No.
Aug 17	CNorth	A	Histon	307	L	1 3	Connor 59	16	1
20	CNorth	H	Stalybridge Celtic	309	L	1 3	Ennis 41	20	2
24	CNorth	H	Guiseley	282	D	2 2	Ennis 85 Darkwah 90	17	3
26	CNorth	A	Stockport County	2561	W	1-0	Matthews 77	15	4
31	CNorth	H	Leamington	344	D	1-1	Hopley 12	14	5
Sept 7	CNorth	A	Oxford City	252	W	2-1	Meadowcroft 57 89	11	6
14	CNorth	H	Worcester City	310	D	0-0		10	7
17	CNorth	A	Barrow	540	D	1-1	Moss 45	12	8
21	CNorth	A	AFC Telford	1677	L	1-4	Crowther 6	13	9
28	***FAC2Q***	***H***	***Harrogate Town***	***259***	***W***	***1-0***	***Hopley 87***		10
Oct 5	CNorth	H	North Ferriby United	257	L	0-3		14	11
12	***FAC3Q***	***H***	***Ossett Town***	***344***	***W***	***2-1***	***Ellison 10 Darkwah 41***		12
19	CNorth	H	Bradford PA	313	D	2-2	Hopley 23 Moss 28	14	13
26	***FAC4Q***	***H***	***Corby Town***	***552***	***L***	***1-3***	***Hopley 76***		14
Nov 2	CNorth	H	Solihull Moors	239	W	3-1	Sanna 8 Hopley 24 Evans 80	15	15
5	CNorth	A	Hednesford Town	566	L	1-2	M.Williams 64	15	16
9	CNorth	A	Boston United	1028	L	1-2	Royle 43 (pen)	15	17
12	CNorth	A	Gloucester City	257	W	3-2	Royle 31 Hopley 60 Evans 71		18
19	***FAT1***	***H***	***Altrincham***	***280***	***L***	***0-2***			19
23	CNorth	A	Gainsborough Trinity	279	L	0-2		15	20
30	CNorth	H	Brackley Town	240	D	2-2	Darkwah 36 (pen) M.Williams 88	14	21
Dec 7	CNorth	A	Workington	314	W	3-0	Evans 21 41 Hopley 51	13	22
14	CNorth	H	Histon	244	W	1-0	Hopley 22	12	23
21	CNorth	A	North Ferriby United	318	W	3-2	Ellison 24 40 S.Williams 30	10	24
26	CNorth	H	Vauxhall Motors	289	W	1-0	M.Williams 25	10	25
28	CNorth	A	Stalybridge Celtic	340	W	3-2	S.Williams 2 M.Williams 33 Evans 41	8	26
Jan 1	CNorth	A	Vauxhall Motors	257	W	3-0	M. Williams 31 Evans 59 Darkwah 80	7	27
11	CNorth	H	Oxford City	367	D	1-1	Hopley 72	8	28
18	CNorth	A	Worcester City	571	L	1-2	Ellison 90 (pen)	9	29
25	CNorth	A	Gainsborough Trinity	371	W	2-0	Holpey 22 Ellison 75	9	30
Feb 8	CNorth	A	Solihull Moors	363	D	2-2	Ellison 55 (pen) 63	9	31
22	CNorth	A	Altrincham	790	L	1-3	S.Williams 81	10	32
25	CNorth	H	Gloucester City	209	D	1-1	Ellison 45 (pen)	9	33
Mar 1	CNorth	H	Barrow	493	L	1-2	Hopley 90	10	34
4	CNorth	H	Harrogate Town	213	W	2-1	Royle 53 Ellison 58	10	35
8	CNorth	A	Bradford PA	334	W	2-1	Ellison 27 M Williams 73	9	36
15	CNorth	H	Hednesford Town	322	L	1-3	Darkwah 55	10	37
22	CNorth	A	Harrogate Town	547	D	2-2	S.Williams 16 Hopley 78	10	38
29	CNorth	H	Altrincham	497	L	1-3	Hopley 29	10	39
April 1	CNorth	H	Workington	158	W	3-2	Stevens 33 (pen) 69 (pen) Hopley 87	10	40
5	CNorth	A	Brackley Town	235	D	2-2	Crowther 22 Ellison 90	10	41
8	CNorth	H	Boston United	257	D	3-3	Stevens 2 (pen) M.Williams 20 S Williams 88	10	42
12	CNorth	H	AFC Telford United	629	L	0-1		10	43
19	CNorth	A	Guiseley	520	L	1-2	Ellison 57 (pen)	11	44
21	CNorth	H	Stockport County	**1056**	D	0-0		11	45
26	CNorth	A	Leamington	570	L	1-2	Darkwah 13	12	46

GOALSCORERS	Lge	FAC	FAT	Total	Pens	Hat-tricks	Cons Run
Hopley	12	2		14			
Ellison	11	1		12	4		
M Williams	7			7			
Darkwah	5	1		6	1		
Evans	6			6			
S Williams	5			5			
Royle	3			3	1		
Stevens	3			3	3		
Crowther	2			2			
Ennis	2			2			
Meadowcroft	2			2			
Moss	2			2			
Connor	1			1			
Matthews	1			1			
Sanna	1			1			

Cons Run - Consecutive scoring games.

GAINSBOROUGH TRINITY

Chairman: Nick Tinker
Secretary: David Tinsley **(T)** 0771 733 8109 **(E)** davidtinsley@yahoo.co.uk
Commercial Manager: John Myskiw **(T)** 07977 751 549
Programme Editor: Kristan Smith **(T)** kristan@kristansmith.com
Ground Address: The Northolme, Gainsborough, Lincolnshire DN21 2QW
(T) 01427 613 295 (office) 613 688 (Social C) **Manager:** Steve Housham

Manager, Steve Housham, meets Fergil, the club shark (mascot!)

Club Factfile

Founded: 1873 **Nickname:** The Blues
Previous Names: Trinity Recreationists
Previous Leagues: Midland Counties 1889-96, 1912-60, 61-68, Football League 1896-1912, Central Alliance 1960-61, Northern Premier 1968-2004
Club Colours (change): All blue (Orange/black/orange)

Ground Capacity: 4,340 **Seats:** 504 **Covered:** 2,500 **Clubhouse:** Yes **Shop:** Yes

Directions
The Northolme is situated on the A159, Gainsborough to Scunthorpe road, approximately a third of a mile north of the Town Centre. Public Car Park on the right 150 yards before the Ground. Any person parked illegally in the Streets around the Ground will be issued with a ticket from the Police.

Previous Grounds: None

Record Attendance: 9,760 v Scunthorpe United - Midland League 1948
Record Victory: 7-0 v Fleetwood Town and v Great Harwood Town
Record Defeat: 1-7 v Stalybridge Celtic - Northern Premier 2000-01 and v Brentford - FA Cup 03-04.
Record Goalscorer: Not known
Record Appearances: Not known
Additional Records: Paid £3,000 to Buxton for Stuart Lowe
Received £30,000 from Lincoln City for Tony James
Senior Honours:
Midland Counties League 1890-91, 1927-28, 48-49, 66-67
Lincolnshire Senior Cup x18

10 YEAR RECORD

04-05	05-06	06-07	07-08	08-09	09-10	10-11	11-12	12-13	13-14
Conf N 11	Conf N 16	Conf N 12	Conf N 11	Conf N 13	Conf N 14	Conf N 18	Conf N 4	Conf N 8	Conf N 16

GAINSBOROUGH TRINITY MATCH RESULTS 2013-14

Date	Comp	H/A	Opponents	Att:	Result		Goalscorers	Pos	No.
Aug 17	CNorth	A	Vauxhall Motors	151	L	1-2	Davis 79	12	1
20	CNorth	H	Guiseley	425	L	1-2	Park 90	18	2
24	CNorth	H	Stalybridge Celtic	422	L	0-2		22	3
26	CNorth	A	Histon	331	L	0-2		22	4
31	CNorth	H	AFC Telford United	428	L	1-3	Davis 40	22	5
Sept 7	CNorth	A	Stockport County	2802	L	1-3	Lacey 69	22	6
14	CNorth	H	Barrow	415	**W**	2-1	Clayton 24 Jones 90	22	7
17	CNorth	A	Worcester City	347	D	2-2	Oates 26 52	22	8
21	CNorth	A	Leamington	561	**W**	1-0	Griffin 47	18	9
28	***FAC2Q***	***H***	***Rushall Olympic***	***433***	***W***	***2-0***	***Stamp 50 Davies 74***		10
Oct 5	CNorth	H	Harrogate Town	401	**W**	2-0	Russell 35 (pen) Barraclough 28	13	11
19	CNorth	A	Solihull Moors	383	L	2-3	Stamp 6 Taylor 82	17	12
Nov 2	CNorth	A	Workington	265	L	2-4	Russell 12 (pen) Barraclough 39	19	13
9	CNorth	H	Bradford PA	436	**W**	4-2	Barraclough 17 Yussuf 40 Ward 82 Clayton 89	16	14
12	CNorth	H	Boston United	**746**	L	0-1		17	15
16	***FAT3Q***	***A***	***Leamington***	***375***	***L***	***0-2***			16
23	CNorth	A	Colwyn Bay	279	**W**	2-0	Howe 49 McMahon 74	17	17
Dec 7	CNorth	A	Barrow	529	**W**	6-0	McMAHON 3 (23 43 80) Barraclough 26 61 Russell 50 (pen)	15	18
10	CNorth	H	Brack;ey Town	317	D	2-2	McMahon 65 Wootton 70	14	19
14	CNorth	H	Vauxhall Motors	334	D	1-1	Tames 58	14	20
21	CNorth	A	Gloucester Clty	268	**W**	1-0	Barraclough 58	14	21
Jan 1	CNorth	A	North Ferriby United	374	L	0-2		16	22
4	CNorth	H	Stockport County	579	L	1-5	Stamp 64	17	23
7	CNorth	H	Altrincham	300	**W**	5-4	Davis 3 Wootton 34 Barraclough 31 90 Russell 56	15	24
11	CNorth	A	Brackley Town	269	L	1-3	Stamp 67	15	25
18	CNorth	H	Workington	371	**W**	3-0	Barraclough 5 Russell 21 70 (pen)	13	26
25	CNorth	H	Colwyn Bay	371	L	0-2		14	27
Feb 1	CNorth	A	Boston United	1255	L	0-6		16	28
8	CNorth	H	Leamington	358	D	1-1	Russell 41	17	29
22	CNorth	H	Worcester Clty	298	**W**	2-1	Barraclough 52 Howe 54	15	30
March 4	CNorth	H	Solihull Moors	265	L	2-3	Davis 9 Margetts 62	17	31
8	CNorth	A	Hednesford Town	556	**W**	3-1	Bateson 24 Margetts 69 88	15	32
11	CNorth	H	North Ferriby United	299	L	1-4	Davis 43	16	33
15	CNorth	H	Gloucester City	459	D	3-3	Margetts 12 16 Russell 82	16	34
19	CNorth	A	Bradford PA	237	L	0-4		17	35
22	CNorth	A	Altrincham	709	L	0-3		17	36
29	CNorth	A	Harrogate Town	516	D	1-1	Margetts 45	17	37
April 3	CNorth	A	Oxford City	233	L	0-1		17	38
5	CNorth	H	Hednesford Town	343	L	1-2	Stamp 15	17	39
8	CNorth	A	Guiseley	506	L	1-3	Stamp 55	18	40
12	CNorth	H	Oxford City	321	**W**	6-0	Young 24 MARGETTS 3 (27 54 56) Roberts 53 Toner 81	17	41
19	CNorth	A	Stalybridge Celtic	446	L	2-3	Regan 31 (og) Russell 58	18	42
21	CNorth	H	Histon	363	**W**	3-1	Stamp 9 Margetts 20 Leary 90	16	43
26	CNorth	A	AFC Telford United	3724	L	0-3		16	44

GOALSCORERS	Lge	FAC	FAT	Total	Pens	Hat-tricks	Cons Run
Barraclough	10			10			
Margetts	10			10		1	
Russell	9			9	4		
Stamp	6	1		7			
McMahon	5			5		1	
Davis	5	1		6			
Oates	2			2			
Clayton	2			2			
Howe	2			2			
Wootton	2			2			
Bateson	1			1			
Griffin	1			1			
Jones	1			1			
Lacey	1			1			
Leary	1			1			
Park	1			1			
Roberts	1			1			
Tames	1			1			
Taylor	1			1			
Ward	1			1			
Young	1			1			
Yousuf	1			1			
Opponents	1			1			

Cons Run - Consecutive scoring games.

GLOUCESTER CITY

Chairman: Nigel Hughes
Secretary: Shaun Wetson **(T)** 07813 931 781 **(E)** secretary@gloucestercityafc.com
Commercial Manager: **(T)**
Programme Editor: Mike Dunstan **(T)** 07899 743 951
Ground Address: Cheltenham Tn FC, The Abbey Business Stad., Whaddon Rd GL52 5NA
(T) 01242 573 558 (Cheltenham Town No.) **Manager:** Tim Harris

Club Factfile

Founded: 1889 **Nickname:** The Tigers
Previous Names: Gloucester Y.M.C.A.
Previous Leagues: Bristol & District (now Western) 1893-96, Gloucester & Dist. 1897-1907, North Gloucestershire 1907-10, Gloucestershire North Senior 1920-34, Birmingham Combination 1935-39, Southern 1939-2000
Club Colours (change): Yellow & black stripes/black/black (All white)

Ground Capacity: 7,289 **Seats:** Yes **Covered:** Yes **Clubhouse:** Yes **Shop:** Yes

Directions
From the North (M5) leave at Jnctn 10, follow road A4019) towards Cheltenham, keep going straight through traffic lights until you reach a roundabout, PC World will be on your left and McDonalds on your right. Turn left here, after 500 yards you will then come to a double roundabout, go straight over, keep going for another 300 yards then turn right into Swindon Lane, follow the road over the level crossing and 2 mini roundabouts until you come to a large roundabout, go straight over, signposted Prestbury, continue past Racecourse and turn right into Albert Road, follow this to the end then turn left at roundabout into Prestbury Road, 200yards turn into Whaddon Road.

Previous Grounds: Longlevens 1935-65, Horton Road 1965-86, Meadow Park 1986-2007, Corinium Stadium Cirencester 2007-10

Record Attendance: Longlevens: 10,500 v Tottenham - Friendly 1952. Meadow Park: 4,000 v Dagenham & Red. - FAT 3rd Q Rnd 12/04/97
Record Victory: 10-1 v Sudbury Town (H) - FA Cup 3rd Qualifying Round 17/10/98
Record Defeat: 1-12 v Gillingham - 09/11/46
Record Goalscorer: Reg Weaver - 250 (1930s)
Record Appearances: Stan Myers & Frank Tredgett - (1950s)
Additional Records: Paid £25,000 to Worcester City for Steve Ferguson 1990-91
Received £25,000 from AFC Bournemouth for Ian Hedges 1990
Senior Honours:
Southern League Cup 1955-56, Midland Division 1988-89, Premier Division Play-off 2008-09.
Gloucestershire Senior Cup x19

10 YEAR RECORD

04-05	05-06	06-07	07-08	08-09	09-10	10-11	11-12	12-13	13-14
SthP 15	SthP 13	SthP 10	SthP 6	SthP 3	Conf N 18	Conf N 14	Conf N 14	Conf N 11	Conf N 17

GLOUCESTER CITY MATCH RESULTS 2013-14

Date	Comp	H/A	Opponents	Att:	Result	Goalscorers	Pos	No.
Aug 17	CNorth	A	North Ferriby United	342	L 1-3	Wilson 12	17	1
20	CNorth	H	Worcester City	**566**	**W** 2-1	Wilson 51 Hutchinson 14 (og)	11	2
24	CNorth	H	AFC Telford United	434	L 1-3	Hogg 13	14	3
26	CNorth	A	Leamington	637	**W** 1-0	Wilson 90	13	4
31	CNorth	H	Guiseley	284	D 1-1	Edwards 73 (pen)	12	5
Sept 7	CNorth	A	Barrow	751	D 0-0		12	6
14	CNorth	A	Workington	373	L 2-4	Harris 24 Edwards 45 (pen)	13	7
17	CNorth	H	Brackley Town	234	D 2-2	Edwards 73 Wilson 77	14	8
21	CNorth	H	Boston United	337	L 1-3	Weir 4 (pen)	15	9
24	CNorth	A	Altrincham	826	L 0-2		15	10
29	***FAC2Q***	***H***	***Havant & Waterlooville***	***336***	***D 1-1***	***Wilson 67***		11
Oct 1	***FAC2Qr***	***A***	***Havant & Waterloovile***		***W 3-2***	***Groves 22 Wilson 46 Hogg 67***		12
5	CNorth	A	Hednesford Town	750	L 1-4	Weir 53 (pen)	17	13
12	***FAC3Q***	***A***	***Yate Town***	***609***	***D 2 2***	***Wilson 57 Edwards 90 (pen)***		14
16	***FAC3Qr***	***H***	***Yate Town***	***520***	***W 7 0***	***PARKER 3 (5 22 25) Mullins 17 Wilson 65 Morford 85 Webb 90***		15
19	CNorth	A	Stockport County	2727	D 2 2	Morford 57 Rawlings 64	18	16
26	***FAC4Q***	***H***	***Hampton & Richmond B***	***663***	***W 3-1***	***Mullins 52 Turt 82 Webb 89***		17
29	CNorth	H	Solihull Moors	313	L 0-3		19	18
Nov 2	CNorth	A	Bradford PA	265	L 1-3	Edwards 31 (pen)	20	19
9	***FAC1***	***H***	***Fleetwood Town***	***1183***	***L 0-2***			20
12	CNorth	H	Colwyn Bay	257	L 2-3	Walden 42 47	21	21
16	***FAT3Q***	***A***	***Boreham Wood***	***133***	***W 1-0***	***Walden 57***		22
23	CNorth	A	Vauxhall Motors	147	L 2-3	Edwards 26 Mullins 31	22	23
30	***FAT1***	***A***	***Ebbsfleet United***	***740***	***L 0-3***			24
Dec 7	CNorth	H	Hednesford Town	421	**W** 5-1	Kotwica 11 Mullins 23 Walden 57 Morford 80 90	20	25
10	CNorth	H	Altrincham	320	**W** 2-0	Walden 14 36	19	26
14	CNorth	A	Harrogate Town	1428	L 2-4	Lidiard 76 Wilson 80	19	27
21	CNorth	H	Gainsborough Trinity	268	L 0-1		20	28
26	CNorth	A	Oxford City	273	D 0-1		20	29
28	CNorth	A	Worcester City	796	**W** 1-0	Walden 20	19	30
Jan 11	CNorth	H	Bradford PA	294	L 2-3	Groves 78 Morford 87	21	31
18	CNorth	A	Stalybridge Celtic	327	D 2-2	Webb 60 Mullins 88	21	32
Feb 18	CNorth	H	Barrow	421	L 1-3	Griffin 20	21	33
22	CNorth	H	North Ferriby United	252	D 1-1	Hogg 26	21	34
25	CNorth	A	Colwyn Bay	209	D 1-1	Groves 27	21	35
March 1	CNorth	A	Solihull Moors	433	L 1-2	Harris 15	21	36
4	CNorth	H	Histon	462	**W** 2-1	Griffin 32 Mann 82	20	37
8	CNorth	H	Stockport County	328	**W** 2-0	Mann 31 Hogg 74	19	38
15	CNorth	A	Gainsborough Trinity	459	D 3-3	Griffin 6 Walden 23 Goddard 48	19	39
18	CNorth	A	Brackley Town	197	**W** 3-1	Gosling 57 Griffin 80 Hogg 88	18	40
22	CNorth	H	Stalybridge Celtic	339	**W** 1-0	Griffin 27	18	41
25	CNorth	A	Histon	217	**W** 3-1	Groves 14 Griffin 26 86	17	42
29	CNorth	A	Boston United	1208	L 0-2		18	43
April 1	CNorth	H	Oxford City	303	L 0-2		18	44
6	CNorth	H	Harrogate Town	217	**W** 5-2	PARKER 3 (45 54 74) Gosling 64 Griffin 86	16	45
12	CNorth	H	Vauxhall Motors	297	D 2-2	Harris 45 Jarvis 66	16	46
15	CNorth	H	Workington	324	D 1-1	Harris 81	16	47
19	CNorth	A	AFC Telford United	2084	L 1-2	Gosling 14	17	48
21	CNorth	H	Leamington	527	D 3-3	Mann 3 80 Morford 60	17	49
26	CNorth	A	Guiseley	748	L 1-3	Jones 4	17	50

GOALSCORERS	Lge	FAC	FAT	Total	Pens	Hat-tricks	Cons Run
Wilson	5	4		9			2
Griffin	8			8			4
Walden	7		1	8			2
Edwards	5	1		6	4		2
Morford	5	1		6			2
Parker	3	3		6		2	
Hogg	4	1		5			
Mullins	3	2		5			
Groves	3	1		4			
Harris	4			4			2
Mann	4			4			2
Gosling	3			3			
Webb	1	2		3			
Weir	2			2	2		
Goddard	1			1			
Jarvis	1			1			
Jones	1			1			
Kotwica	1			1			
Lidiard	1			1			
Rawlings	1			1			
Turt		1		1			
Opponents	1			1			

Cons Run - Consecutive scoring games.

GUISELEY

Chairman: Philip Rogerson
Secretary: Adrian Towers (T) 07946 388 739 (E) admin@guiseleyafc.co.uk
Commercial Manager: (T)
Programme Editor: Rachel O'Connor (T) 0113 250 6205
Ground Address: Nethermoor Park, Otley Road, Guiseley, Leeds LS20 8BT
(T) 01943 873 223 (Office) 872 872 (Club) **Manager:** Steve Kittrick

Club Factfile

Founded: 1909 **Nickname:** The Lions
Previous Names: None
Previous Leagues: Wharfedale, Leeds, West Riding Counties, West Yorkshire, Yorkshire 1968-82, Northern Counties East 1982-91, Northern Premier 1991-2010

Club Colours (change): White/navy/navy (All yellow)

Ground Capacity: 3,000 **Seats:** 427 **Covered:** 1,040 **Clubhouse:** Yes **Shop:** Yes

Directions
From the West M62, M606 then follow signs to A65 through Guiseley to Ground on Right. From South and East M1 and M621 towards Leeds City Centre. Continue on M621 to Junction 2, follow Headingly Stadium signs to A65 towards Ilkley then as above. From North West From Skipton, A65 Ilkley, via Burley By-pass A65 towards Leeds, Ground quarter of a mile on left after Harry Ramsden's roundabout From North/NE A1M, leave at A59, towards Harrogate, then A658 signed Leeds Bradford Airport, at Pool turn right onto A659 Otley, continue towards Bradford/Leeds, to Harry Ramsden roundabout then A65 Leeds ground quarter of a mile on left.

Previous Grounds: None

Record Attendance: 2,486 v Bridlington Town - FA Vase Semi-final 1st Leg 1989-90
Record Victory: Not known
Record Defeat: Not known
Record Goalscorer: Not known
Record Appearances: Not known
Additional Records:

Senior Honours:
Northern Counties East 1990-91. FA Vase 1990-91.
Northern Premier League Division 1 1993-94, Premier Division 2009-10, Challenge Cup 2008-09.

10 YEAR RECORD

04-05	05-06	06-07	07-08	08-09	09-10	10-11	11-12	12-13	13-14
NP P 10	NP P 14	NP P 6	NP P 6	NP P 3	NP P 1	Conf N 5	Conf N 2	Conf N 2	Conf N 5

GUISELEY MATCH RESULTS 2013-14

Date	Comp	H/A	Opponents	Att:	Result		Goalscorers	Pos	No.
Aug 17	CNorth	H	Solihull Borough	338	L	0-3		21	1
20	CNorth	A	Gainsborough Trinity	425	W	2-1	Brooksby 44 Rothery 80	13	2
24	CNorth	A	Colwyn Bay	282	D	2-2	Ellis 18 Hobson 61	12	3
26	CNorth	H	Workington	417	W	1-0	Lawlor 90	9	4
31	CNorth	A	Gloucester City	284	D	1-1	Potts 19	10	5
Sept 7	CNorth	H	Brackley Town	607	L	0-2		13	6
14	CNorth	A	Boston United	1022	L	0-3		14	7
17	CNorth	H	Bradford PA	500	L	0-2		15	8
21	CNorth	H	Hednesford Town	469	L	1-2	Burns 90	16	9
28	***FAC2Q***	***H***	***Bradford PA***	***595***	***L***	***1-2***	***Lawlor 51***		10
Oct 5	CNorth	A	Altrincham	838	L	1-4	Potts 3	20	11
19	CNorth	H	Histon	405	D	1-1	Johnson 42	20	13
22	CNorth	A	North Ferriby United	315	W	3-2	Rothery 32 (pen) Brooksby 41 70	17	14
2Nov 2	CNorth	H	Barrow	431	W	2-1	Johnson 45 Swain 90	14	15
9	CNorth	A	Leamington	655	W	3-2	Forrest 18 Hall 28 Rea 36	13	16
16	***FAT3Q***	***H***	***Histon***	***404***	***W***	***3-0***	***Hall 25 Johnson 58 Brooksby 90***		17
23	CNorth	H	Oxford City	409	W	2-0	Johnson 15 25	12	18
26	CNorth	A	Worcester City	337	D	0-0		11	19
30	***FAT1***	***A***	***FC Halifax Town***	***935***	***W***	***1-0***	***Johnson 45***		20
Dec 7	CNorth	H	Boston United	470	W	1-0	Forrest 45	10	21
9	CNorth	A	Bradford PA	405	W	3-0	Forrest 2 54 Rothery 70 (pen)	8	22
14	***FAT2***	***H***	***Bradford PA***	***476***	***W***	***3-0***	***Parker 9 Rothery 90 Johnson 90***		23
21	CNorth	H	Altrincham	613	D	2-2	Johnson 8 Rothery 90	9	24
26	CNorth	A	Harrogate Town	828	W	3-2	ROTHERY 3 (24 pen 40 pen 71)	9	25
Jan 11	***FAT3***	***A***	***Aldershot Town***	***1632***	***L***	***0-3***			26
21	CNorth	A	Solihull Moors	336	W	3-0	Hall 40 Lawlor 47 Brooksby 74	10	27
28	CNorth	A	Barrow	593	L	0-1		10	28
Feb 1	CNorth	A	AFC Telford United	1266	L	2-4	Boyes 45 Rothery 67 (pen)	10	29
8	CNorth	H	Worcester City	399	L	0-1		12	30
25	CNorth	A	Brackley Town	172	W	2-1	Lawlor 19 Johnson 87	12	31
March 1	CNorth	A	Histon	277	D	1-1	Johnson 83	12	32
4	CNorth	H	Leamington	323	W	2-1	Ellis 14 Holsgrove 42	11	33
8	CNorth	H	Vauxhall Motors	439	W	1-0	Holsgrove 90	11	34
11	CNorth	H	Stockport County	502	W	2-0	Lawlor 26 Brooksby 71	10	35
15	CNorth	A	Stockport County	2764	D	3-3	Brooksby 38 Boyes 59 Ellis 67	9	36
18	CNorth	H	Salybridge Celtic	336	W	3-1	Ellis 50 73 Hall 59	9	37
22	CNorth	H	North Ferriby United	554	W	1-0	Rothery 10	9	38
26	CNorth	A	Stalybridge Celtic	253	W	3-2	Boyes 8 Johnson 76 Brooksby 78	6	39
29	CNorth	A	Oxford City	364	D	3-3	Brooksby 27 Johnson 38 Boyes 81	8	40
April 1	CNorth	H	AFC Telford United	469	W	6-1	Ellis 32 Rothery 38 48 (pen) Boyes 53 Johnson 79 89	5	41
5	CNorth	A	Vauxhall Motors	176	W	5-0	Ellis 12 Boyes 15 28 Johnson 25 Rothery 37 (pen)	5	42
8	CNorth	H	Gainsborough Trinity	506	W	3-1	Johnson 33 Boyes 53 Brooksby 66	5	43
12	CNorth	A	Hednesford Town	574	L	2-3	Johnson 12 Boyes 16	6	44
15	CNorth	H	Harrogate Town	815	W	2-0	Lawler 10 Boyes 44	5	45
19	CNorth	H	Colwyn Bay	620	W	2-1	Boyes 68 Rothery 72	5	46
21	CNorth	A	Workington	357	D	1-1	Boyes 59	5	47
26	CNorth	H	Gloucester City	748	W	3-1	Boyes 31 42 Potts 80	5	48
30	***CNPO SF1***	***H***	***North Ferriby United***	***1164***	***W***	***2-0***	***Boyes 37 Johnson 49***		49
May 3	***CNPO SF2***	***A***	***North Ferriby United***	***924***	***W***	***1-0***	***Brooksby 60***		50
10	***CNPO F***	***A***	***Altrincham***	***4632***	***L***	***1-2***	***Forrest 70 (AET)***		51

GOALSCORERS	Lge	FAC	FAT	Total	Pens	Hat-tricks	Cons Run
Johnson	14+1		3	18			6
Boyes	14+1			15			11
Rothery	13		1	14	5	1	4
Brooksby	9+1		1	11			2
Ellis	7			7			2
Lawlor	5	1		6			
Forrest	4+1			5			2
Hall	3		1	4			2
Potts	3			3			
Holsgrove	2			2			2
Burns	1			1			
Hobson	1			1			
Parker			1	1			
Rea	1			1			
Swain	1			1			

Cons Run - Consecutive scoring games.

Play-off goals indicated by +

HARROGATE TOWN

Chairman: Irving Weaver
Secretary: Mike Bligh **(T)** 07775 940 539 **(E)** mikebligh@harrogatetownafc.com
Commercial Manager: Garry Plant **(T)** 07740 822 497
Programme Editor: Peter Arnett **(T)** 07894 401 110
Ground Address: The CNG Stadium, Wetherby Road, Harrogate HG2 7SA
(T) 01423 880 675 **Manager:** Simon Weaver

Club Factfile

Founded: 1935 **Nickname:** Town
Previous Names: Harrogate Hotspurs 1935-48.
Previous Leagues: West Riding 1919-20, Yorkshire 1920-21, 22-31, 57-82, Midland 1921-22, Northern 1931-32, Harrogate & Dist. 1935-37, 40-46, W. Riding Co.Am. 1937-40, W. Yorks. 1946-57, N.C.E. 1982-87, N.P.L. 1987-2004
Club Colours (change): Yellow & black stripe/black/yellow (All blue)

Ground Capacity: 3,291 **Seats:** 502 **Covered:** 1,300 **Clubhouse:** Yes **Shop:** Yes

Directions
A61 to Harrogate, turn right on to A658, and at roundabout take A661, proceed through second set of lights (Woodlands pub) ground approx. 500 mtrs on the right. From A1 Wetherby. Leave A1 at Wetherby on to A661 to Harrogate. Stay on this road and when reaching Harrogate at Woodland pub lights, ground 500mtrs on the right.

Previous Grounds: None

Record Attendance: 4,280 v Railway Athletic - Whitworth Cup Final 1950
Record Victory: 13-0 v Micklefield
Record Defeat: 1-10 v Methley United - 1956
Record Goalscorer: Jimmy Hague - 135 (1956-58 and 1961-76)
Record Appearances: Paul Williamson - 428 (1980-81, 1982-85, and 1986-93)
Additional Records:

Senior Honours:
West Riding County Cup 1962-63, 72-73, 85-86. Northern Premier League Division 1 2001-02.
West Riding Challenge Cup x2.

10 YEAR RECORD

04-05	05-06	06-07	07-08	08-09	09-10	10-11	11-12	12-13	13-14
Conf N 6	Conf N 5	Conf N 6	Conf N 6	Conf N 9	Conf N 21	Conf N 12	Conf N 15	Conf N 6	Conf N 9

HARROGATE TOWN MATCH RESULTS 2013-14

Date	Comp	H/A	Opponents	Att:	Result	Goalscorers	Pos	No.
Aug 17	CNorth	A	Oxford City	186	**W** 2-1	Worsfield 26 30	9	1
20	CNorth	H	Vauxhall Motors	628	D 1-1	Bolder 26	8	2
24	CNorth	H	North Ferriby United	442	**W** 5-0	Franks 13 Hall 42 Rowe 49 77 Wright 88	3	3
26	CNorth	A	Barrow	727	L 0-1		6	4
31	CNorth	H	Stockport County	918	**W** 3-1	Bolder 37 Woods 39 Hall 41	5	5
Sept 7	CNorth	A	AFC Telford United	1431	**W** 1-0	Nelthorpe 54	3	6
14	CNorth	H	Histon	548	L 0-1		7	7
17	CNorth	A	Stalybridge Celtic	270	L 2-3	Novakowski 4 Haedy 10	8	8
21	CNorth	H	Brackley Town	410	L 0-1		10	9
28	***FAC2Q***	***A***	***Colwyn Bay***	***259***	***L 0-1***			10
Oct 5	CNorth	A	Gainsborough Trinity	401	L 0-2		12	11
19	CNorth	A	Boston United	921	D 3-3	Hardy 68 Rowe 71 Southwell 85 (pen)	12	12
22	CNorth	H	Workington	318	**W** 3-0	Hardy 2 56 Nelthorpe 31	11	13
Nov 2	CNorth	H	Oxford City	358	**W** 3-2	Killock 73 Hardy 66 69	12	14
9	CNorth	H	Worcester City	443	**W** 2-0	Worsfold 74 Rowe 89	10	15
16	***FAT 3Q***	***H***	***Bradford PA***	***572***	***D 1-1***	***Hall 25***		16
18	***FAT3Qr***	***A***	***Bradford PA***	***189***	***L 0-4***			17
23	CNorth	A	Workington	295	**W** 3-0	Worsfold 61(pen) 72 Hall 73	9	18
30	CNorth	A	Solihull Moors	287	L 0-3		9	19
Dec 7	CNorth	H	Altrincham	547	**W** 3-2	Worsfield 26 30	8	20
10	CNorth	A	Hednesford Town	458	**W** 3-1	C.Taylor 30 Hardy 47 Hall 84	8	21
14	CNorth	H	Gloucester City	**1428**	**W** 4-2	WOODS 3 (43 46 59) Nelthorpe 69	6	22
21	CNorth	A	Worcester City	403	L 0-1		8	23
26	CNorth	H	Guiseley	828	L 2-3	Killock 34 Mallory 90	8	24
28	CNorth	A	Vauxhall Motors	267	L 0-1		9	25
Jan 4	CNorth	H	AFC Telford United	525	D 2-2	Merris 45 Killock 80	9	26
11	CNorth	H	Stalybridge Celtic	454	**W** 2-1	Hall 28 Nowakowski 58	9	27
18	CNorth	A	Leamington	609	**W** 2-1	Worsfold 36 Sellars 79	8	28
25	CNorth	H	Bradford PA	597	D 1-1	Worsfold 27	8	29
Feb 8	CNorth	H	Hednesford Town	477	**W** 3-1	Hall 10 43 Heath 26	8	30
15	CNorth	A	Histon	291	**W** 1-0	Hall 66	7	31
22	CNorth	H	Boston United	632	**W** 4-0	Hall 21 47 Killock 56 Rowe 80	6	32
March 1	CNorth	A	Brackley Town	293	D 2-2	Nowakowski 2 Rowe 31	8	33
4	CNorth	A	Colwyn Bay	213	L 1-2	Royal 31	8	34
8	CNorth	H	Solihull Moors	508	**W** 2-1	Hall 2 Worsfold 38	6	35
11	CNorth	A	Altrincham	704	**W** 3-1	Worsfold 33 Hall 50 Nelthorpe 71	3	36
15	CNorth	A	Bradford PA	371	D 0-0		5	37
22	CNorth	H	Colwyn Bay	547	D 2-2	Hall 39 Brown 90	5	38
29	CNorth	H	Gainsborough Trinity	516	D 1-1	Worsfold 83	6	39
April 6	CNorth	A	Gloucester City	317	L 2-5	Heath 47 Worsfold 49	8	40
12	CNorth	H	Leamington	545	D 1-1	Worsfold 66	8	41
15	CNorth	A	Guiseley	815	L 0-2		8	42
19	CNorth	A	North Ferriby United	663	L 2 3	Worsfold 26 Brown 37	9	43
21	CNorth	H	Barrow	582	**W** 3 1	Brown 2 Worsfold 50 Clayton 62	9	44
26	CNorth	A	Stockport County	3126	L 1 3	Rowe 34	9	45

GOALSCORERS	Lge	FAC	FAT	Total	Pens	Hat-tricks	Cons Run
Worsfield	16			16	1		3
Hall	13		1	14			3
Hardy	7			7			3
Rowe	7			7			
Nelthorpe	4			4			
Killock	4			4			
Woods	4			4		1	
Brown	3			3			2
Novakowski	3			3			
Bolder	2			2			
Heath	2			2			
Clayton	1			1			
Franks	1			1			
Mallory	1			1			
Merris	1			1			
Royal	1			1			
Sellars	1			1			
Southwell	1			1	1		
C.Taylor	1			1			
Wright	1			1			

Cons Run - Consecutive scoring games.

HEDNESFORD TOWN

Chairman: Stephen Price
Secretary: Terry McMahon **(T)** 07901 822 040 **(E)** mcmahon64@gmail.com
Commercial Manager: **(T)**
Programme Editor: Scott Smith **(T)** 07518 144 801
Ground Address: Keys Park, Park Road, Hednesford, Cannock WS12 2DZ
(T) 01543 422 870 **Manager:** Rob Smith

Club Factfile

Founded: 1880 **Nickname:** The Pitmen
Previous Names: Hednesford 1938-74
Previous Leagues: Walsall & District, Birmingham Combination 1906-15, 45-53, West Midlands 1919-39, 53-72, 74-84, Midland Counties 1972-74, Southern 1984-95, 2001-2005, 2009-11, Conference 1995-2001, 05-06, Northern Premier 2006-09
Club Colours (change): White/black/black & white (Sky blue/white/sky blue & white)

Ground Capacity: 6,039 **Seats:** 1,011 **Covered:** 5,335 **Clubhouse:** Yes **Shop:** Yes

Directions Leave M6 at J11 and follow the signs for Cannock. At the next island take the third exit towards Rugeley (A460). On reaching the A5 at Churchbridge island, rejoin the A460 signposted Rugeley and follow this road over five traffic islands. At the sixth traffic island, by a Texaco petrol station, turn right past a McDonalds restaurant and follow this road to the next island which is 'Cross Keys Island'. Go over this island to the next small island and turn right. Keys Park football ground is on left.

Previous Grounds: The Tins 1880-1903. The Cross Keys 1903-95.

Record Attendance: 3,169 v York City - FA Cup 3rd Round 13/01/1997
Record Victory: 12-1 v Redditch United - Birmingham Combination 1952-53
Record Defeat: 0-15 v Burton - Birmingham Combination 1952-53
Record Goalscorer: Joe O'Connor - 230 in 430 games
Record Appearances: Kevin Foster - 463
Additional Records: Paid £12,000 to Macclesfield Town for Steve Burr
Received £50,000 from Blackpool for Kevin Russell
Senior Honours:
Southern League Premier Division 1994-95. FA Trophy 2004-05.
Staffordshire Senior Cup x3 Most recently 2012-13. Birmingham Senior Cup 1935-36, 2012-13.

10 YEAR RECORD

04-05	05-06	06-07	07-08	08-09	09-10	10-11	11-12	12-13	13-14
SthP 4	Conf N 22	NP P 7	NP P 8	NP P 8	SthP 4	SthP 2	NP P 5	NP P 2	Conf N 4

HEDNESFORD TOWN MATCH RESULTS 2013-14

Date	Comp	H/A	Opponents	Att:	Result		Goalscorers	Pos	No.
Aug 17	CNorth	A	Stalybridge	465	W	4-0	Francais 13 DURRELL 3 (49 pen 64 76)	1	1
20	CNorth	H	Leamington	**708**	W	3-2	Wolfe 73 Durrell 79 Rey 88	2	2
24	CNorth	H	Oxford City	581	W	3-0	Riley 50 Durrell 86 88	1	3
26	CNorth	A	Worcester City	741	D	2-2	Riley 25 Durrell 44 (pen)	2	4
31	CNorth	H	Barrow	646	W	3-1	Durrell 15 (pen) McPherson 18 Harvey 58	1	5
Sept 7	CNorth	A	North Feriby United	523	L	0-3		4	6
14	CNorth	H	Vauxhall Motors	577	W	2-0	Durrell 14 36	3	7
17	CNorth	A	Histon	308	W	1-0	Durrell 16 (pen)	1	8
21	CNorth	A	Guiseley	469	W	2-1	Harvey 60 Durrell 80	1	9
28	***FAC2Q***	***A***	***AFC Telford United***	***1345***	***W***	***3-1***	***Durrell 55 88 Rey 79***		10
Oct 5	CNorth	H	Gloucester City	750	W	4-1	Osborne 39 43 Durrell 80 (pen) Harvey 90	1	11
12	***FAC3Q***	***H***	***West Auckland Town***	***820***	***D***	***2-2***	***Wolfe 70 Harvey 77***		12
15	***FAC3Qr***	***A***	***West Auckland Town***		***D***	***2-2***	***Riley 25 Francis 53 (Hednesford won on penalties - aet)***		13
19	CNorth	A	Workington	442	D	2 2	Osborne 48 Bailey 70	1	14
26	***FAC4Q***	***A***	***Stamford***	***668***	***W***	***2-0***	***Durrell 55 (pen) 79 (pen)***		15
Nov 2	CNorth	A	Altrincham	913	W	3-1	Thompson-Brown 8 Durrell 25 84	1	16
5	CNorth	H	Colwyn Bay	566	W	2 1	Francis 9 Osborne 34	1	17
9	***FAC1***	***H***	***Crawley Town***	***2231***	***L***	***1-2***	***Durrell 78 (pen)***		18
16	***FAT3Q***	***H***	***Workington AFC***	***551***	***W***	***3-0***	***Riley 27 Francis 30 Durrell 61***		19
23	CNorth	A	Brackley Town	484	L	0-1		1	20
30	***FAT1***	***A***	***Gateshead***	***410***	***L***	***1-4***	***Francis 82***		21
Dec 7	CNorth	A	Gloucester City	421	L	1-5	Woolfe 64	4	22
10	CNorth	H	Harrogate Town	458	L	1-3	Pearson 4	5	23
14	CNorth	H	Stalybridge Celtic	454	W	4-1	McCone 5 Durrell 53 Pearson 71 Woolfe 76	3	24
17	CNorth	H	Bradford PA	483	W	2-0	Osborne 8 Bailey 75	1	25
21	CNorth	A	Vauxhall Motors	206	D	2-2	Riley 51 Francis 54	1	26
26	CNorth	H	AFC Telford United	1252	D	3-3	Byrne 17 (og) Robinson 52 McCone 57	1	27
28	CNorth	A	Leamington	803	L	1-2	Blissett 24	3	28
Jan 1	CNorth	A	AFC Telford United	1903	L	3-5	McPherson 8 Francis 24 Blissett 76	5	29
4	CNorth	H	North Ferriby United	645	L	0-1		5	30
11	CNorth	H	Boston United	650	W	4-2	Robinson 13 McCone 27 Harvey 32 Blissett 46	5	31
14	CNorth	H	Stockport County	585	W	3-1	Harvey 15 56 Osborne 51	2	32
18	CNorth	A	Bradford PA	354	W	2-1	Taylor 12 Durrell 90	2	33
25	CNorth	A	Solihull Moors	602	W	3-2	Riley 75 Harvey 83 Francis 87	2	34
Feb 1	CNorth	H	Altrincham	703	D	1-1	Taylor 85	2	35
8	CNorth	A	Harrogate Town	477	L	1-3	Disney 36 (Pen)	3	36
15	CNorth	H	Solihull Moors	602	L	1-2	Anagho-Ntamark 77	3	37
22	CNorth	H	Histon	552	W	2-1	Woolfe 51 Robinson 53	3	38
March 1	CNorth	A	Boston United	1102	L	0-4		3	39
8	CNorth	H	Gainsborough Trinity	556	L	1-3	Harvey 44	3	40
15	CNorth	A	Colwyn Bay	322	W	3-1	McCone 7 Hopley 35 (og) Osborne 47	3	41
22	CNorth	H	Workington	490	W	4-0	Osborne 19 85 Robinson 88 90	3	42
29	CNorth	A	Stockport County	2669	W	1-0	Anagho-Ntamark 12	4	43
April 1	CNorth	H	Brackley Town	468	D	2-2	Sullivan 85 Riley 88	4	44
5	CNorth	A	Gainsborough Trinity	343	W	2-1	Johnson 12 Riley 71	3	45
12	CNorth	H	Guiseley	574	W	3-2	Thorley 19 McCone 30 Glover 34	3	46
19	CNorth	A	Oxford City	335	W	2-1	McPherson 15 Johnson 72	4	47
21	CNorth	H	Worcester City	668	W	4-0	McPherson 60 Reily 76 Disney 90 Sullivan 90	4	48
26	CNorth	A	Barrow	799	L	0-1		4	49
30	***CNPO SF1***	***H***	***Altrincham***	***1209***	***D***	***2-2***	***Melbourne 33 Glover 56***		50
May 3	***CNPO SF2***	***A***	***Altrincham***	***1974***	***L***	***1-2***	***Thorley 80***		51

GOALSCORERS	Lge	FAC	FAT	Total	Pens	Hat-tricks	Cons Run
Durrell	17	5	1	23	7	1	5
Harvey	8	1		9			2
Osborne	9			9			2
Francis	5	1	2	8			
Riley	6	1	1	8			
McCone	5			5			
Robinson	5			5			
Woolfe	4	1		5			
McPherson	4			4			2
Blissett	3			3			2
Anagho-Ntamark	2			2			
Bailey	2			2			
Disney	2			2	1		
Glover	1+1			2			
Johnson	2			2			
Pearson	2			2			
Rey	1	1		2			
Sullivan	2			2			
Taylor	2			2			
Thorley	1+1			2			
Melbourne	0+1			1			
Thompson-Brown	1			1			
Opponents	2			2			

Cons Run - Consecutive scoring games.
PLay-off goals indicated by +

HYDE FC

Chairman: Tahir Khan
Secretary: Andrew McAnulty **(T)** 07866 165 957 **(E)** secretary@hydefc.co.uk
Commercial Manager: Alan Hackney **(T)** 07803 555 124
Programme Editor: Emily Liles **(T)** 07817 645 151
Ground Address: Ewen Fields, Walker Lane, Hyde SK14 5PL
(T) 0161 367 7273 **Manager:** Scott McNiven

Action from the Ray Stanley Memorial Shield which Hyde won 5-4 on penalties against Altrincham, during the 2014-15 pre-season.

Club Factfile

Founded: 1885 **Nickname:** The Tigers
Previous Names: Hyde F.C., Hyde United > 2011.
Previous Leagues: Lancashire & Cheshire 1919-21, Manchester 1921-30, Cheshire County 1930-68, 1970-82, Northern Premier 1968-70, 1983-2004

Club Colours (change): Red/black/red (Sky/navy/sky)

Ground Capacity: 4,073 **Seats:** 550 **Covered:** 4,073 **Clubhouse:** Yes **Shop:** Yes

Directions
M60 (Manchester Orbital Motorway) to Junction 24, take the M67 (towards Sheffield) to junction 3 (Hyde/Dukinfield/Stalybridge). Once on exit slipway, keep to the right-hand lane heading for Hyde town centre. At the traffic lights at end of the slipway turn right, then at the second set of lights turn left (Morrisons on left) onto Mottram Road. Turn right at next lights onto Lumn Road. Left at Give Way sign onto Walker Lane. Ground entrance is on left, just after Hyde Leisure Pool, and is clearly signposted. Please note for Satnav, use SK14 5PL

Previous Grounds: None

Record Attendance: 7,600 v Nelson - FA Cup 1952
Record Victory: 9-1 v South Liverpool 04/1991
Record Defeat: 0-26 v Preston North End - FA Cup 1887
Record Goalscorer: David Nolan - 117 in 404 appearances (1992-2003). Ged Kimmins - 117 in 274 appearances (1993-98)
Record Appearances: Steve Johnson - 623 (1976-1988)
Additional Records: Paid £8,000 to Mossley for Jim McCluskie 1989
Received £50,000 from Crewe Alexandra for Colin Little 1995
Senior Honours:
Northern Premier League Division 1 2003-04, Premier Division 2004-05, League Cup x3. Conference North 2011-12.
Cheshire Senior Cup x6. Manchester Premier cup x6.

10 YEAR RECORD

04-05	05-06	06-07	07-08	08-09	09-10	10-11	11-12	12-13	13-14
NP P 1	Conf N 11	Conf N 8	Conf N 9	Conf N 20	Conf N 15	Conf N 19	Conf N 1	Conf 18	Conf 24

HYDE FC MATCH RESULTS 2013-14

Date	Comp	H/A	Opponents	Att:	Result		Goalscorers	Pos	No.
Aug 10	CPrem	A	Forest Green Rovers	1158	L	0-8		23	1
13	CPrem	H	Southport	769	L	1-2	Collins 28	23	2
17	CPrem	H	Hereford United	509	D	2-2	Collins 21 Tomsett 42	20	3
24	CPrem	A	Wrexham	3304	D	2-2	Collins 13 (pen) Spencer 90 (pen)	21	4
26	CPrem	H	Grimsby Town	786	L	0-1		21	5
31	CPrem	A	Barnet	1669	L	2-3	Tomsett 46 78	23	6
Sept 7	CPrem	H	Cambridge United	766	L	0-1		23	7
14	CPrem	A	Kidderminster Harriers	1607	L	1-2	Collins 15	24	8
17	CPrem	H	Woking	387	L	0-2		24	9
21	CPrem	H	Welling United	427	L	0-1		24	10
24	CPrem	A	Salisbury City	638	L	0-2		24	11
28	CPrem	A	Lincoln City	2311	L	0-3		24	12
Oct 5	CPrem	H	Braintree Town	402	L	0-3		24	13
8	CPrem	H	Gateshead	409	L	0-2		24	14
12	CPrem	A	Luton Town	7081	L	1-4	Nulty (og)	24	15
19	CPrem	A	Dartford	1083	L	3-4	Spencer 34 (pen) 43 Almond 54	24	16
26	***FAC4Q***	***A***	***Wrexham***	***1848***	***L***	***0-2***			17
Nov 2	CPrem	H	Nuneaton Town	447	D	2-2	Almond 27 Spencer 90	24	18
9	CPrem	H	Chester	1232	L	1-2	Almond 3	24	19
12	CPrem	A	FC Halifax	1037	L	0-4		24	20
16	CPrem	A	Woking	1381	L	2-3	Spencer 14 Gray 43	24	21
23	CPrem	H	Alfreton Town	448	L	1-2	Spencer 66	24	22
30	***FAT1***	***H***	***North Ferriby United***	***256***	***L***	***1-2***	***O'Donnell 5***		23
Dec 21	CPrem	H	Barnet	499	L	0-1		24	24
26	CPrem	A	Macclesfield	1882	L	0-3		24	25
28	CPrem	H	Wrexham	952	L	2-5	Hughes 28 Spencer 33	24	26
Jan 1	CPrem	H	Macclesfield Town	979	L	0-3		24	27
4	CPrem	A	Gateshead	502	L	0-4		24	28
11	CPrem	A	Southport	871	D	1-1	Spencer 38	24	29
14	CPrem	A	Welling United	436	W	2-0	Almond 58 Hughes 75	24	30
18	CPrem	H	Forest Green Rovers	496	L	2-6	Blakeman 21 Carlton 50	24	31
25	CPrem	H	Tamworth	369	L	0-3		24	32
Feb 8	CPrem	H	Lincoln City	646	L	3-4	Hughes 41 65 Brizell 68	24	33
11	CPrem	A	Tamworth	616	D	1-1	Brizell 70	24	34
15	CPrem	A	Nuneaton Town	876	L	0-1		24	35
22	CPrem	H	Aldershot Town	520	D	2-2	Blakeman 39 Clark 75	24	36
March 1	CPrem	A	Braintree Town	754	L	1-2	Brown 37	24	37
8	CPrem	H	FC Halifax Town	901	L	1-5	Brown 56	24	38
11	CPrem	A	Alfreton Town	506	L	0-3		24	39
15	CPrem	A	Hereford United	1378	D	0-0		24	40
22	CPrem	H	Dartford	358	L	0-2		24	41
29	CPrem	A	Aldershot Town	1591	L	0-1		24	42
April 5	CPrem	A	Chester	2228	L	2-3	Blakeman 57 64	24	43
8	CPrem	H	Salisbury City	275	L	0-2		24	44
12	CPrem	A	Cambridge United	2804	L	2-7	Poole 13 Thurston 66	24	45
18	CPrem	H	Kidderminster Harriers	531	L	1-3	Blakeman 32	24	46
21	CPrem	A	Grimsby Town	4232	L	0-1		24	47
26	CPrem	H	Luton Town	**2729**	L	0-1		24	48

GOALSCORERS	Lge	FAC	FAT	Total	Pens	Hat-tricks	Cons Run
Spencer	8			8	2		2
Blakeman	5			5			
Almond	4			4			2
Collins	4			4	1		3
Hughes	4			4			
Tomsett	3			3			
Brizell	2			2			2
Brown	2			2			2
Carlton	1			1			
Clark	1			1			
Gray	1			1			
O'Donnell			1	1			
Poole	1			1			
Thurston	1			1			
Opponents	1			1			

Cons Run - Consecutive scoring games.

LEAMINGTON

Chairman: Jim Scott
Secretary: Richard Edy (T) 07762 866 123 (E) matchsecretary@leamingtonfc.co.uk
Commercial Manager: Nic Sproul (T) 07710 112 292
Programme Editor: Sally Ellis (T) programme@leamingtonfc.co.uk
Ground Address: New Windmill Ground, Harbury Lane, Whitmarsh, Leamington CV33 9QB
(T) 01926 430 406 **Manager:** Paul Holleran

Club Factfile

Founded: 1892 **Nickname:** The Brakes
Previous Names: Leamington Town 1892-1937, Lockheed Borg & Beck 1944-46 , Lockheed Leamington 1946-73, AP Leamington 1973-88
Previous Leagues: Birmingham Combination, Birmingham & District, West Midlands Regional, Midland Counties, Southern, Midland Combination, Midland Alliance 2005-07. Southern 2007-13.

Club Colours (change): Gold with black trim/black with gold trim/gold with black trim (White with black trim/white/black with white trim)

Ground Capacity: 5,000 **Seats:** 120 **Covered:** 720 **Clubhouse:** Yes **Shop:** Yes

Directions
From West and North – M40 Southbound – Exit J14 and take A452 towards Leamington. Ahead at 1st island. Next island take 2nd exit A452 (Europa Way). Next island take 4th exit (Harbury Lane) signposted Harbury and Bishops Tachbrook. Next island take 3rd exit (Harbury Lane). At traffic lights continue straight ahead Harbury Lane. Ground is 1.5 miles on left.
From South – M40 northbound – Exit J13. Turn right onto A452 towards Leamington. At 1st island take 3rd exit A452 (Europa Way) and follow as above (Europa Way onwards).

Previous Grounds: Old Windmill Ground

Record Attendance: 1,380 v Retford United - 17/02/2007
Record Victory: Not known
Record Defeat: Not known
Record Goalscorer: Josh Blake - 166
Record Appearances: Josh Blake - 314
Additional Records:

Senior Honours:
Birmingham & District 1961-62. West Midlands Regional 1962-63. Midland Counties 1964-65.
Southern League 1982-83, 2012-13, Division 1 Midlands 2008-09.
Midland Combination Division 2 2000-01, Premier Division 2004-05. Midland Alliance 2006-07, League cup 2005-06.

10 YEAR RECORD

04-05	05-06	06-07	07-08	08-09	09-10	10-11	11-12	12-13	13-14
MCmP 1	MidAl 5	MidAl 1	SthM 2	SthM 1	SthP 10	SthP 5	SthP 7	SthP 1	Conf N 13

LEAMINGTON MATCH RESULTS 2013-14

Date	Comp	H/A	Opponents	Att:	Result		Goalscorers	Pos	No.
Aug 17	CNorth	H	Bradford PA	657	W	2-0	Dodd 16 (pen) Moore 19	7	1
20	CNorth	A	Hednesford Town	708	L	2-3	Chilton 26 Moore 34	10	2
24	CNorth	A	Boston United	1086	L	0-2		13	3
26	CNorth	H	Gloucester City	637	L	0-1		16	4
31	CNorth	A	Colwyn Bay	344	D	1-1	Towers 58	15	5
Sept 7	CNorth	H	Altrincham	**853**	L	0-1		17	6
14	CNorth	A	Stockport County	2925	D	1-1	Johnson 2	17	7
17	CNorth	H	Solihull Moors	548	L	0-1		18	8
21	CNorth	H	Gainsborough T	561	L	0-1		21	9
28	FAC2Q	A	Solihull Moors	479	D	1-1	Johnson 71		10
Oct 1	***FAC2Qr***	***H***	***Solihull Moors***		***L***	***1-2***	***Johnson 65***		11
5	CNorth	A	Workington	359	W	2-1	L.Moore 29 Johnson 90	18	12
19	CNorth	H	Stalybridge Celtic	676	W	1-0	Owen 90	13	13
26	CNorth	A	Stalybridge Celtic	383	L	1-2	S.Moore 77	15	14
Nov 2	CNorth	A	Vauxhall Motors	181	L	1-2	Green 85	16	15
9	CNorth	H	Guiseley	655	L	2-3	Johnson 28 Dodd 52 (pen)	19	16
12	CNorth	A	Worcester City	486	W	3-0	S.Moore 10 Chilton 23 Dodd 55 (pen)	16	17
16	***FAT3Q***	***H***	***Gainsborough T***	***375***	***W***	***2-0***	***Chilton 32 S.Moore 77***		18
23	CNorth	H	Histon	545	W	1-0	Dodd 77 (pen)	14	19
30	***FAT1***	***H***	***Northwich Victoria***	***357***	***D***	***0-0***			20
Dec 2	***FAT1r***	***A***	***Northwich Vctoria***	***131***	***W***	***1-0***	***S.Moore 86***		21
7	CNorth	A	AFC Telford United	1563	W	2-1	S.Moore 55 71	14	22
10	CNorth	A	North Ferriby United	226	L	1-4	S.Moore 44	15	23
14	***FAT2***	***A***	***Dover Athletic***	***435***	***L***	***0-2***			24
21	CNorth	H	Workington	509	W	2-0	Daly 10 Johnson 28	15	25
26	CNorth	A	Brackley Town	520	D	1-1	S.Moore 60	15	26
28	CNorth	H	Hednesford Town	803	W	2-1	Johnson 46 S.Moore 66	13	27
Jan 1	CNorth	H	Brackley Town	504	W	3-1	S.Moore 17 26 Johnson 76	11	28
4	CNorth	A	Altrincham	972	L	2-3	Dodd 57 (pen) Magunda 73	11	29
11	CNorth	A	Solihull Moors	877	D	0-0		11	30
14	CNorth	H	North Ferriby United	409	L	0-2		11	31
18	CNorth	H	Harrogate Town	609	L	1-2	Newton 19	11	32
20	CNorth	A	Bradford PA	369	L	2-3	Newton 55 Dodd 87	12	33
Feb 1	CNorth	A	Barrow	734	D	0-0		12	34
8	CNorth	A	Gainsborough Trinity	358	D	1-1	Chilton 27	15	35
March 1	CNorth	H	Stockport County	1038	W	2-1	Newton 73 83	13	36
4	CNorth	A	Guiseley	323	L	1-2	Newton 4	13	37
8	CNorth	A	Oxford City	349	D	2-2	Newton 25 37	14	38
11	CNorth	H	Vauxhall Motors	308	L	0-1		15	39
15	CNorth	H	Barrow	548	D	1-1	Dodd 45 (pen)	15	40
22	CNorth	A	Histon	301	D	1-1	Clappison 76 (og)	14	41
25	CNorth	H	Oxford CIty	389	W	4-0	Chilton 13 Flanagan 23 Hicks 36 Newton 65	14	42
29	CNorth	H	AFC Telford United	843	D	2-2	Newton 27 Hicks 45 (pen)	14	43
April 5	CNorth	H	Worcester City	657	W	1-0	Chilton 8	13	44
12	CNorth	A	Harrogate Town	545	D	1-1	Mace 27	13	45
19	CNorth	H	Boston United	792	D	0-0		13	46
21	CNorth	A	Gloucester City	527	D	3-3	Johnson 14 Newton 84 Dodd 90	13	47
26	CNorth	H	Colwyn Bay	570	W	2-1	Flanagan 21 Newton 70	13	48

GOALSCORERS	Lge	FAC	FAT	Total	Pens	Hat-tricks	Cons Run
S.Moore	11		2	13			3
Newton	11			11			3
Johnson	8	1		9			2
Dodd	8			8	6		
Chilton	5		1	6			
Flanagan	2			2			
Hicks	2			2	1		2
Daley	1			1			
Green	1			1			
Mace	1			1			
Magunda	1			1			
L.Moore	1			1			
Owen	1			1			
Towers	1			1			
Opponents	1			1			

Cons Run - Consecutive scoring games.

LOWESTOFT TOWN

Chairman: Gary Keyzor
Secretary: Terry Lynes **(T)** 0793 087 2947 **(E)** terrylynes@fsmail.net
Commercial Manager: Rachel Beamish **(T)** 07826 931 358
Programme Editor: Terry Lynes **(T)** 0793 087 2947
Ground Address: Crown Meadow, Love Road, Lowestoft NR32 2PA
(T) 01502 573 818 **Manager:** Micky Chapman and Ady Gallagher

2013-14 promotion winning squad - Back row (l-r): Robert Eagle, Bally Smart, David Tarawali (Now Kirkley & Pakefield), Danny Cunningham (Now Bury Town), Erkan Okay, Jack Ainsley, Sam Gaughran, Bradley Woods-Garness, Chris Henderson, Stuart Ainsley.
Middle Row: Curtley Williams, Saul Otobo (Now Mt Police), Jack Defty, Lee Smith (Now Biggleswade), Will Viner (Now Cheshunt), Ashlee Jones, Jake Jessup, Curtis Haynes-Brown, Dale Cockrill, Michael Frew
Front Row: Emma Boon (Sports Therapist), Adam Smith, Ady Gallagher, Micky Chapman, Craig Fleming, Dan Gleeson, George Neeve (kitman)

Club Factfile

Founded: 1880 **Nickname:** The Trawler Boys or Blues
Previous Names: Original club merged with Kirkley in 1887 to form Lowestoft and became Lowestoft Town in 1890
Previous Leagues: North Suffolk 1897-35, Eastern Counties 1935-2009. Isthmian 2009-2014.

Club Colours (change): All blue (All white)

Ground Capacity: 3,000 **Seats:** 466 **Covered:** 500 **Clubhouse:** Yes **Shop:** Yes

Directions
Head for Lowestoft town centre. After crossing Bascule Bridge and railway station turn right at traffic lights (sp A12 Yarmouth) into Katwyck Way. After 300 yards take 1st exit at roundabout into Raglan Street. At 'T' junction turn left into Love Road and ground is about 100 yards on right.

Previous Grounds: None

Record Attendance: 5,000 v Watford - FA Cup 1st Round 1967
Record Victory: Not Known
Record Defeat: Not Known
Record Goalscorer: Not Known
Record Appearances: Not Known
Additional Records:

Senior Honours:
Eastern Counties League 1935-36 (shared), 37-38, 62-63, 64-65, 65-66, 66-67, 67-68, 69-70, 70-71, 77-78, 2005-06, 08-09.
Isthmian League Division 1 North 2009-10.
Suffolk Senior Cup 1902-03, 22-23, 25-26, 31-32, 35-36, 46-47, 47-48, 48-49, 55-56.

10 YEAR RECORD

04-05	05-06	06-07	07-08	08-09	09-10	10-11	11-12	12-13	13-14
ECP 4	ECP 1	ECP 3	ECP 11	ECP 1	Isth1N 1	Isth P 4	Isth P 3	Isth P 2	Isth P 4

LOWESTOFT TOWN MATCH RESULTS 2013-14

Date	Comp	H/A	Opponents	Att:	Result	Goalscorers	Pos	No.
Aug 10	IsthP	A	Dulwich Hamlet	542	L 0-2	Hill 45	20	1
13	IsthP	H	Thamesmead Town	520	W 5-0	Smith 7 30 Eagle 26 Henderson 33 84	8	2
17	IsthP	H	Bognor Regis Town	532	W 2-0	Ainsley 4 Cunningham 90	7	3
20	IsthP	A	Canvey Island	341	D 0-0		8	4
24	IsthP	A	AFC Hornchurch	210	L 1-2	Henderson 36	11	5
26	IsthP	H	Leiston	653	W 3-0	Frew 62 Woods-Garness 74 Eagle 77	9	6
31	IsthP	A	Wingate & Finchley	122	D 0-0		10	7
Sept 7	IsthP	H	Hendon	585	L 2-3	Woods-Garness 1 (pen) Eagle 64	10	8
10	IsthP	H	Grays Athletic	257	D 2-2	Smith 42 90	11	9
14	***FAC1Q***	***A***	***Harlow Town***	***236***	***L 1-2***	***Frew 21***		10
21	IsthP	A	Enfield Town	363	D 2-2	Smith 39 Frew 54	12	11
24	IsthP	A	East Thurrock United	143	W 1-0	Haynes-Brown 90	11	12
Oct 5	IsthP	A	Maidstone United	2041	L 0-2		11	13
12	IsthP	H	Carshalton Athletic	500	W 5-0	REED 4 (2 14 20 24) Smith 44	11	14
19	***FAT1Q***	***A***	***Enfield Town***	***240***	***L 1-2***	***Gaughran 48***		15
26	IsthP	H	Kingstonian	501	W 2-0	Reed 32 Smith 85	8	16
Nov 2	IsthP	H	AFC Hornchurch	530	W 3-0	Eagle 49 Smith 52 Gaughram 74	7	17
9	IsthP	H	Cray Wanderers	462	L 0-2		8	18
16	IsthP	A	Lewes	706	W 2-0	Osei 51 Eagle 73	7	19
23	IsthP	H	Margate	511	W 3-0	Reed 3 Osei 42 Gaughram 66	7	20
30	IsthP	A	Metropolitan Police	166	D 0-0		7	21
Dec 7	IsthP	H	Hampton & Richmond B	404	L 0-3		8	22
14	IsthP	A	Thamesmead Town	76	D 2-2	Porter 16 (og) Reed 89	8	23
21	IsthP	H	Dulwich Hamlet	389	W 2-0	Gaughran 48 Jarvis 55	6	24
26	IsthP	A	Leiston	545	W 1-0	Reed 14	6	25
28	IsthP	H	Canvey Island	498	W 2-1	Henderson 71 72	6	26
Jan 11	IsthP	A	Harrow Borough	135	D 1-1	Henderson 89	7	27
14	IsthP	A	Bognor Regis Town	392	L 1-4	Henderson 24	7	28
18	IsthP	H	Bury Town	568	L 1-3	Reed 45	8	29
21	IsthP	H	East Thurrock United	288	W 3-0	Reed 40 Osie 50 Frew 90	8	30
Feb 4	IsthP	H	Wealdstone	446	D 1-1	Reed 56	7	31
22	IsthP	A	Carshalton Athletic	147	W 1-0	Reed 47	7	32
25	IsthP	A	Billericay Town	208	W 1-0	Henderson 69	7	33
March 1	IsthP	H	Maidstone United	671	W 2-1	Henderson 72 Reed 90	7	34
8	IsthP	A	Cray Wanderers	137	W 4-0	Reed 8 77 Eagle 24 Henderson 59	7	35
10	IsthP	A	Hendon	183	W 1-0	Ainsley 86 (pen)		36
15	IsthP	H	Lewes	601	D 1-1	Eagle 9	6	37
22	IsthP	A	Margate	365	L 0-3		7	38
25	IsthP	H	Wingate & Finchley	348	W 7-0	Frew 20 AINSLEY 3(27 52 (pen) 63) Smith 50 Reed 62 Doddington 87	7	39
29	IsthP	H	Metropolitan Police	525	D 1-1	Okay 64	7	40
April 5	IsthP	A	Hampton & Richmond B	344	W 2-1	Eagle 6 Henderson 45	7	41
8	IsthP	A	Wealdstone	852	D 0-0		7	42
12	IsthP	A	Kingstonian	552	L 0-1		7	43
15	IsthP	H	Enfield Town	513	W 2-0	Okay 62 Reed 77	7	44
17	IsthP	A	Grays Athletic	175	D 1-1	Henderson 13	7	45
19	IsthP	H	Billericay Town	688	W 1-0	Reed 75	5	46
21	IsthP	A	Bury Town	589	W 2-1	Ainsley 20 64 (pen)	4	47
26	IsthP	H	Harrow Borough	845	W 3-0	Eagle 44 Bamment 68 Frew 90	4	48
30	***IsthP PO SF***	***A***	***Bognor Regis Town***	***941***	***W 2-1***	***Haynes-Brown 42 Reed 85***		49
May 5	***IsthP PO F***	***H***	***AFC Hornchurch***	***2697***	***W 3-0***	***Eagle 29, Reed 49, Haynes-Brown 52***		50

GOALSCORERS	Lge	FAC	FAT	Total	Pens	Hat-tricks	Cons Run
Reed	18+2			20		1	4
Henderson	12			12			3
Eagle	9+1			10			
Smith	9			9			2
Ainsley	7			7	3	1	
Frew	4	1		5			2
Gaughan	3		1	4			
Haynes-Brown	1+2			3			
Woods-Garness	2			2	1		
Bamment	1			1			
Cunningham	1			1			
Doddington	1			1			
Hill	1			1			
Jarvis	1			1			
Opponents	1			1			

Cons Run - Consecutive scoring games.

Play-off goals indicated by +

NORTH FERRIBY UNITED

Chairman: Les Hare
Secretary: Steve Tather (T) 07845 378 512 (E) tather@tather39.karoo.co.uk
Commercial Manager: Les Hare (T) 07813 688 220
Programme Editor: Richard Watts (T) 07814 836 504
Ground Address: Eon Visual Media Stadium, Grange Lane, Church Road, North Ferriby HU14 3AB
(T) 01482 634 601 **Manager:** Billy Heath

Club Factfile

Founded: 1934 **Nickname:** United
Previous Names: None
Previous Leagues: East Riding Church, East Riding Amateur, Yorkshire 1969-82, Northern Counties East 1982-2000. Northern Premier 2000-13.

Club Colours (change): White with green trim/green/green (All yellow with green trim)

Ground Capacity: 3,000 **Seats:** 250 **Covered:** 1,000 **Clubhouse:** Yes **Shop:** Yes

Directions
Main Leeds to Hull road A63 or M62. North Ferriby is approx. 8 miles west of Hull.
Proceed through village past the Duke of Cumberland Hotel.
Turn right down Church Road. Ground mile down on left.

Previous Grounds: Not known

Record Attendance: 1,927 v Hull City - Charity game 2005
Record Victory: 9-0 v Hatfield Main - Northern Counties East 1997-98
Record Defeat: 1-7 v North Shields - Northern Counties East 1991
Record Goalscorer: Mark Tennison - 161
Record Appearances: Paul Sharp - 497 (1996-2006)
Additional Records: Andy Flounders scored 50 during season 1998-99
Received £60,000 from Hull City for Dean Windass
Senior Honours:
Northern Counties East 1999-2000. Northern Premier League Division 1 2004-05, Premier Division 2012-13.
East Riding Senior Cup 1970-71, 76-77, 77-78, 78-79, 90-91, 96-97, 97-98, 98-99, 99-2000, 00-01, 01-02, 02-03, 06-07, 07-08, 08-09, 09-10, 10-11, 12-13.

10 YEAR RECORD

04-05	05-06	06-07	07-08	08-09	09-10	10-11	11-12	12-13	13-14
NP 1 1	NP P 5	NP P 13	NP P 15	NP P 10	NP P 4	NP P 5	NP P 9	NP P 1	Conf N 2

NORTH FERRIBY UNITED MATCH RESULTS 2013-14

Date	Comp	H/A	Opponents	Att:	Result		Goalscorers	Pos	No.
Aug 17	CNorth	H	Gloucester CIty	342	W	3-1	Clark 6 Jarman 26 Hone 45	6	1
19	CNorth	A	Bradford PA	346	W	4-0	M.Wilson 10 King 61 Jarman 66 A.Wilson 84	1	2
24	CNorth	A	Harrogate Town	442	L	0-4		8	3
26	CNorth	H	Boston United	618	W	3-0	Anderson 40 Jarman 46 81	4	4
31	CNorth	A	Brackley Town	283	D	1-1	Jarman 60	6	5
Sept 7	CNorth	H	Hednesford Town	523	W	3-0	Yates 1 A .Wilson 45 86	5	6
14	CNorth	A	Solihull Moors	352	L	0-2		8	7
17	CNorth	H	Workington	256	W	3-1	Jarman 7 Kendall 33 50	5	8
21	CNorth	H	Altrincham	420	W	2-1	Jarman 29 49	3	9
28	***FAC2Q***	***A***	***Buxton***	***284***	***W***	***4-1***	***Jarman 2 Yates 71 A.Wilson 79 King 81***		10
Oct 5	CNorth	A	Colwyn Bay	257	W	3-0	A.WILSON 3 (6 52 90)	4	11
8	CNorth	A	Vauxhall Motors	185	W	1-0	A.Wilson 58	2	12
12	***FAC3Q***	***H***	***Runcorn Linnets***	***520***	***W***	***2-0***	***Jarman 59 66***		13
19	CNorth	A	AFC Telford United	1368	L	0-2		3	14
22	CNorth	H	Guiseley	315	L	2-3	King 10 A Wilson 47	3	15
26	***FAC4Q***	***H***	***Alfreton Town***	***735***	***L***	***1-3***	***Jarman 15***		16
Nov 2	CNorth	A	Worcester City	471	W	1-0	Kendall 58	2	17
9	CNorth	A	Barrow	287	D	2-2	A.Wilson 2 Kendall 78	2	18
16	***FAT3Q***	***A***	***Stourbridge***	***437***	***D***	***2-2***	***Jarman 13 (pen) 84***		19
19	***FAT3Qr***	***H***	***Stourbridge***	***134***	***W***	***4-0***	***King 26 Hone 31 Kendall 45 69***		20
23	CNorth	A	Stockport County	2608	W	2-1	A.Wilson 19 66	3	21
30	***FAT1***	***A***	***Hyde***	***256***	***W***	***2-1***	***Jarman 1 (pen) Clarke 25***		22
Dec 7	CNorth	H	Solihull Moors	335	D	1-1	A.Wilson 62	2	23
10	CNorth	H	Leamington	226	W	4-1	King 24 Jarman 37 54 A.Wilson 40	1	24
14	***FAT2***	***H***	***Woking***	***201***	***W***	***4-0***	***M.Wilson 36 Clark 50 King 81 90***		25
21	CNorth	H	Colwyn Bay	318	L	2-3	Jarman 78 Fry 80	4	26
28	CNorth	H	Bradford PA	319	W	2-1	Hone 61 A.Wilson 74	6	27
Jan 1	CNorth	H	Gainsborough Trinity	374	W	2-0	Hone 41 Howe 60 (og)	2	28
4	CNorth	A	Hednesford Town	645	W	1-0	A. Wilson 43	1	29
11	***FAT 3***	***A***	***LIncoln City***	***2037***	***W***	***4-0***	***King 25 90 Kendall 43 Jarman 70 (pen)***		30
14	CNorth	A	Leamington	409	W	2-0	Hone 45 King 56	1	31
18	CNorth	H	Hston	389	D	4-4	Jarman 18 (pen) Kendall 43 52 Peat 55	1	32
21	CNorth	A	Oxford CIty	135	W	3-2	Kendall 17 A.Wilson 7 65	1	33
25	CNorth	H	AFC Telford United	558	D	2-2	Kendall 17 18	1	34
Feb 1	***FAT4***	***H***	***Gosport Borough***	***398***	***L***	***1-2***	***Lisles 48***		35
8	CNorth	A	Barrow	963	L	0-2		1	36
15	CNorth	H	Oxford City	402	W	2-1	King 55 Jarman 79	1	37
22	CNorth	A	Goucester City	252	D	1-1	Yates 48	2	38
March 1	CNorth	H	Vauxhall Motors	241	W	2-0	Hone 18 Jarman 61	2	39
8	CNorth	A	Histon	304	W	3-0	King 12 Emerton 17 McMahon 81	2	40
11	CNorth	A	Gainsborough Trinity	299	W	4-1	JARMAN 3 (32 pen 35 pen 71pen) King 90	1	41
15	CNorth	H	Worcester City	333	W	2-1	Jarman 38 (pen) Gray 73	1	42
22	CNorth	A	Guiseley	554	L	0-1		2	43
25	CNorth	A	Workington	242	D	3-3	King 13 Clarke 63 Jarman 85	2	44
29	CNorth	H	Stalybridge Celtic	366	W	2-0	Jarman 48 (pen) A.Wilson 90	1	45
April 5	CNorth	H	Stockport County	440	D	0-0		2	46
12	CNorth	A	Altrincham	160	D	1-1	Kendall 15	2	47
16	CNorth	A	Stalybridge Celtic	303	W	3-2	King 1 Wilde 70 Jarman 78 (pen)	1	48
19	CNorth	H	Harrogate Town	663	W	3-2	Jarman 27 (pen) Gray 62 A.Wilson 69	1	49
21	CNorth	A	Boston United	1567	L	0-2		2	50
26	CNorth	H	Brackley Town	673	D	1-1	Clark 18	2	51
30	***CNPO SF1***	***A***	***Guiseley***	***1164***	***L***	***0-2***			52
May 3	***CNPO SF2***	***H***	***Guiseley***	***924***	***L***	***0-1***			53

GOALSCORERS	Lge	FAC	FAT	Total	Pens	Hat-tricks	Cons Run
N.Jarman	22	4	4	30	11	1	3
A.Wilson	20	1		21		1	3
King	9	1	5	15			2
Kendall	10		3	13			3
Hone	5		1	6			2
Clark	3		2	5			
Yates	2	1		3			
Gray	2			2			
M.Wilson	1		1	2			
Anderson	1			1			
Emerton	1			1			
Fry	1			1			
Lisles			1	1			
McMahon	1			1			
Peat	1			1			
Opponents	1			1			

Cons Run - Consecutive scoring games.

OXFORD CITY

Chairman: Brian Cox
Secretary: John Shepperd **(T)** 07748 628 911 **(E)** shepoxf@tiscali.co.uk
Commercial Manager: Colin Taylor **(T)** 07817 885 396
Programme Editor: Colin Taylor **(T)** ctoxford@btinternet.com
Ground Address: Court Place Farm, Marsh Lane, Marston, Oxford OX3 0NQ
(T) 01865 744 493 **Manager:** Justin Merritt

Club Factfile

Founded: 1882 **Nickname:** City
Previous Names: None
Previous Leagues: Isthmian 1907-88, 94-2005, South Midlands 1990-93, Spartan South Midlands 2005-06

Club Colours (change): Blue and white hoops/blue/blue (All yellow)

Ground Capacity: 3,000 **Seats:** 300 **Covered:** 400 **Clubhouse:** Yes **Shop:** Yes

Directions
From the South - Travel north from Newbury on the A34 past Abingdon and take the Oxford Ring Road toward London (East). Stay on Ring Road over 5 roundabouts following signs for London & M40 East. At the last Headington roundabout go straightover North towards Banbury & Northampton on A40. Within a mile a flyover is visible as the exit from the Ring Road. Turn left under the flyover and left again toward Marsh Lane. Turn right at the T Junction and the ground is on your left just before the Pedestrian Crossing. From the East - Leave the M40 at Junction 8 and follow the A40 to the Headington roundabout going straightover towards Banbury & Northampton A40. Within a mile a flyover is visible as the exit from the Ring Road. Turn left under the flyover and left again toward Marsh Lane. Turn right at the T Junction and the ground is on your left just before the Pedestrian Crossing. From the North - Leave the M40 at Junction 9 along the A34 toward Oxford. After 5 miles leave A34 following signs for Londan A40 for the next two roundabouts. Leave the A40 at the Marston slip road just before the flyover. Go over the A40 on the flyover into Marsh Lane and the ground is on your left before the Pedestrian Crossing.

Previous Grounds: The White House 1882-1988, Cuttleslowe Park 1990-91, Pressed Steel 1991-93

Record Attendance: 9,500 v Leytonstone - FA Amateur Cup - 1950
Record Victory: Not known
Record Defeat: Not known
Record Goalscorer: John Woodley
Record Appearances: John Woodley
Additional Records: Paid £3,000 to Woking for S Adams
Received £15,000 from Yeovil Town for Howard Forinton
Senior Honours:
FA Amateur Cup 1905-06. Oxford Senior Cup x3
Spartan South Midlands League Premier Division 2005-06. Southern Premier Play-offs 2011-12.

10 YEAR RECORD

04-05		05-06		06-07		07-08		08-09		09-10		10-11		11-12		12-13		13-14	
SthW	21	SSM P	1	SthW	12	SthW	4	SthP	6	SthP	13	SthP	14	SthP	2	Conf N	10	Conf N	20

OXFORD CITY MATCH RESULTS 2013-14

Date	Comp	H/A	Opponents	Att:	Result		Goalscorers	Pos	No.
Aug 17	CNorth	H	Harrogate Town	186	L	1-2	Pond 42	13	1
20	CNorth	A	Solihull Moors	303	D	2-2	Symons 72 Willmott 89	15	2
24	CNorth	A	Hednesford Town	581	L	0-3		19	3
26	CNorth	H	Brackley Town	483	L	0-1		20	4
31	CNorth	A	Bradford PA	302	D	3-3	Symons 18 Winters 23 Cook 34	20	5
Sept 7	CNorth	H	Colwyn Bay	252	L	1-2	Stonehouse 88	21	6
14	CNorth	A	Altrincham	820	D	2-2	Leather 23 (og) Pond 68 (pen)	21	7
17	CNorth	H	Boston Uited	234	D	1-1	Winters 90	21	8
21	CNorth	A	Vauxhall Motors	131	L	0-1		22	9
28	***FAC2Q***	***H***	***Maidenhead United***	***249***	***W***	***1-0***	***Cook 86***		10
Oct 5	CNorth	H	Stalybridge Celtic	223	W	2-1	Cook 15 Basham 16	21	11
12	***FAC3Q***	***A***	***Eastleigh***	***434***	***W***	***3-2***	***Robinson 2 Cook 10 Willmott 77***		12
19	CNorth	H	Worcester City	291	D	0-0		21	13
26	***FAC4Q***	***A***	***Dover Athletic***	***880***	***L***	***0-3***			14
Nov 2	CNorth	A	Harrogate Town	358	L	2-3	Jackson 71 Winters 89	22	15
9	CNorth	H	Stockport County	542	W	4-1	Winters 18 Symons 50 Pond 68 Jackson 87	18	16
12	CNorth	A	Histon	202	D	2-2	Jackson 18 Winters 83		17
17	***FAT 3Q***	***A***	***Hendon***	***197***	***L***	***1-2***	***Benjamin 44***		18
23	CNorth	A	Guiseley	409	L	0-2		18	19
30	CNorth	H	Vauxhall Motors	212	W	3-0	Ballard 53 Symons 56 Jackson 63	18	20
Dec 8	CNorth	A	Worcester City	442	W	2-0	Regan 17 (og) Robinson 22	17	21
10	CNorth	H	Workington	210	D	1-1	Learoyd 52	16	22
21	CNorth	A	Stockport County	1884	L	0-2		17	23
26	CNorth	H	Gloucester CIty	273	W	1-0	Winters 6	18	24
28	CNorth	H	Solihull Moors	297	L	0-2		18	25
Jan 11	CNorth	A	Colwyn Bay	367	D	1-1	Jackson 90	18	26
21	CNorth	H	North Ferriby Uited	135	L	2-3	Cook 60 (pen) 64	20	27
Feb 4	CNorth	H	Barrow	197	L	0-1		20	28
15	CNorth	A	North Ferriby United	402	L	1-2	Pond 60 (pen)	20	29
22	CNorth	A	Barrow	1011	D	1-1	Basham 45	20	30
Mar 4	CNorth	A	Workington	336	L	0-1		21	31
8	CNorth	H	Leamington	349	D	2-2	McEachran 28 Jackson 62	21	32
15	CNorth	A	Boston United	1023	L	1-2	McEachran 40	21	33
18	CNorth	H	Histon	203	W	2-1	Basham 18 Symons 81	21	34
22	CNorth	A	AFC Telford United	1531	L	0-4		21	35
25	CNorth	A	Leamington	389	L	0-4		21	36
29	CNorth	H	Guiseley	364	D	3-3	Jackson 40 Basham 83 Pond 86	21	37
April 1	CNorth	A	Gloucester City	303	W	2-0	Winters 58 Soloman 90	21	38
3	CNorth	H	Gainsborough Trinity	233	W	1-0	Preece 87	19	39
5	CNorth	A	Stalybridge Celtic	377	D	1-1	Pond 85	19	40
8	CNorth	H	AFC Telford United	312	W	2-0	Learoyd 54 Winters 86	19	41
12	CNorth	A	Gainsborough Trinity	321	L	0-6		19	42
15	CNorth	H	Altrincham	283	L	1-2	Jackson 90	19	43
19	CNorth	H	Hednesford Town	335	L	1-2	Ballard 45	19	44
21	CNorth	A	Brackley Town	430	L	1-2	Mullings 53	19	45
26	CNorth	H	Bradford PA	251	D	1-1	McEachran 18	20	46

GOALSCORERS	Lge	FAC	FAT	Total	Pens	Hat-tricks	Cons Run
Jackson	8			8			
Winters	8			8			3
Cook	4	2		6	1		3
Pond	6			6	2		
Symons	5			5			
Basham	4			4			
McEachran	3			3			2
Ballard	2			2			
Learoyd	2			2			
Robinson	1	1		2			
Willmott	1	1		2			
Benjamin			1	1			
Mullings	1			1			
Preece	1			1			
Soloman	1			1			
Stonehouse	1			1			
Opponents	2			2			

Cons Run - Consecutive scoring games.

SOLIHULL MOORS

Chairman: Trevor Stevens
Secretary: Tim Delaney **(T)** 07827 963 212 **(E)** sec.smfc@gmail.com
Commercial Manager: Ben Seifas **(T)** 0121 705 6770
Programme Editor: Ben Seifas **(T)** ben.seifas@solihullmoorsfc.co.uk
Ground Address: The Autotech Stadium, Damson Park, Damson Parkway, Solihull B91 2PP
(T) 0121 705 6770 **Manager:** Marcus Bignot

Club Factfile

Founded: 2007 **Nickname:** Moors
Previous Names: Today's club was formed after the amalgamation of Solihull Borough and Moor Green in 2007
Previous Leagues: None

Club Colours (change): Blue & yellow hoops/blue/blue & yellow hoops (Red, white & black hoops/black/red & white hoops)

Ground Capacity: 3,050 **Seats:** 280 **Covered:** 1,000 **Clubhouse:** Yes **Shop:** Yes

Directions
Leave the M42 at Junction 6 and take the A45 towards Birmingham, after approximately 2 miles, at the traffic lights, take the left hand filter lane onto Damson Parkway. Follow the road for approximately 1 mile where the Autotech Stadium is situated on the right hand side, continue over the traffic lights (for the Land Rover factory entrance) to the traffic island and come back on yourself to find the entrance to the Football Club on the left just after the traffic lights. Use B92 9EJ as the postcode for SatNav purposes.

Previous Grounds: None

Record Attendance: 1,076 v Rushden & Diamonds - FA Cup 4th Qualifying Round 27/10/2007
Record Victory: 4-1 v Southport - Conference South 05/04/2008
Record Defeat: 1-6 v Kettering Town - Conference South 01/01/2008
Record Goalscorer: Not known
Record Appearances: Carl Motteram - 71 (2007-09)
Additional Records:

Senior Honours:
None

10 YEAR RECORD

04-05	05-06	06-07	07-08	08-09	09-10	10-11	11-12	12-13	13-14
			Conf N 17	Conf N 16	Conf N 17	Conf N 7	Conf N 19	Conf N 9	Conf N 8

SOLIHULL MOORS MATCH RESULTS 2013-14

Date	Comp	H/A	Opponents	Att:	Result		Goalscorers	Pos	No.
Aug 17	CNorth	A	Guiseley	338	W	3-0	Gough 4 Bogle 44 54 (pen)	3	1
20	CNorth	H	Oxford City	303	D	2-2	Bogle 56 Wint 90	6	2
24	CNorth	H	Histon	235	D	0-0		10	3
26	CNorth	A	AFC Telford United	1491	D	1-1	Beswick 20	12	4
30	CNorth	H	Vauxhall Motors	315	W	1-0	Wint 35	8	5
Sept 7	CNorth	A	Stalybridge Celtic	398	W	3-1	Beswick 16 Bogle 34 Peirpoint 81	6	6
14	CNorth	H	North Ferriby United	352	W	2-0	Bogle 69 (pen) Denny 72	4	7
17	CNorth	A	Leamington	548	W	1-0	Birch 56	3	8
21	CNorth	A	Bradford PA	305	D	2-2	Bogle 3 13 (pen)	4	9
28	***FAC2Q***	***H***	***Leamington***	***479***	***D***	***1-1***	***Birch 51***		10
Oct 1	***FAC2Qr***	***A***	***Leamington***		***W***	***2-1***	***English 7 Wint 45***		11
5	CNorth	H	Bradford Park Avenue	374	D	2-2	Till 19 Beswick 55 (pen)	6	12
12	***FAC3Q***	***H***	***Worksop Town***	***465***	***W***	***4-0***	***Beswick 6 78 Bogle 45 Elvins 65***		13
19	CNorth	H	Gainsborough Trinity	383	W	3-2	Pierpoint 45 Beswick 86 89	5	14
26	***FAC4Q***	***A***	***Tamworth***	***1035***	***L***	***1-4***	***Bogle 65***		15
29	CNorth	A	Gloucester City	313	W	3-0	Elvins 37 Langden 45 Bogle 52	5	16
Nov 2	CNorth	A	Colwyn Bay	239	L	1-3	Bogle 66 (pen)	5	17
9	CNorth	H	Workington	330	D	1-1	Denny 17	5	18
16	***FAT 3Q***	***H***	***Coalville Town***	***388***	***L***	***1-2***	***Blackwood 90***		19
23	CNorth	A	Altrincham	840	L	0-1		7	20
30	CNorth	H	Harrogate Town	287	W	3-0	Bogle 24 87 Beswick 69	7	21
Dec 2	CNorth	H	Brackley	239	W	1-0	Bogle 12 (pen)		22
7	CNorth	A	North Ferriby United	335	D	1-1	Bogle 45	1	23
21	CNorth	A	Barrow	454	W	2-0	Wint 33 Beswick 37	2	24
26	CNorth	H	Worcester CIty	575	D	1-1	Beswick 63	2	25
28	CNorth	A	Oxford City	297	W	2-0	Till 18 Bogle 58	1	26
Jan 4	CNorth	H	Stalybridge Celtic	423	D	3-3	Bogle 13 (pen) Birch 86 90	4	27
11	CNorth	H	Leamington	**877**	D	0-0		4	28
18	CNorth	A	Boston United	1102	L	1-4	Bogle 45	7	29
21	CNorth	H	Guiseley	336	L	0-3		7	30
25	CNorth	H	Hednesford Town	602	L	2-3	Birch 32 Beswick 73	7	31
28	CNorth	A	Worcester CIty	361	L	1-3	Beswick 56	7	32
Feb 1	CNorth	H	Brackley Town	263	L	0-1		7	33
8	CNorth	H	Colwyn Bay	363	D	2-2	Knights 29 Beswick 68 (pen)	7	34
15	CNorth	A	Hednesford Town	602	W	2-1	Angus 57 English 81	6	35
22	CNorth	A	Stockport County	2396	D	2-2	Beswick 7 Taylor 85	8	36
March1	CNorth	H	Gloucester City	433	W	2-1	Giglio 2 (og) Beswick 75	7	37
4	CNorth	A	Gainsbrough Trinity	265	W	3-2	English 29 32 Beswick 90	4	38
8	CNorth	A	Harrogate Town	508	L	1-2	Beswick 17 (pen)	5	39
15	CNorth	H	Altrincham	438	L	0-1		8	40
22	CNorth	H	Stockport County	525	W	1-0	Bogle 51	7	41
29	CNorth	A	Workington	384	D	0-0		9	42
April 5	CNorth	H	Boston United	459	L	1-2	Bogle 63	9	43
12	CNorth	H	Barrow	343	L	0-2		9	44
19	CNorth	A	Histon	307	W	3-0	English 9 Taylor 52 Knights 59	8	45
21	CNorth	H	AFC Telford United	834	D	2-2	Fleet 6 English 12	8	46
26	CNorth	A	Vauxhall Motors	215	W	2-0	Taylor 45 Knights 58	8	47

GOALSCORERS	Lge	FAC	FAT	Total	Pens	Hat-tricks	Cons Run
Bogle	18	2		20	6		3
Beswick	15	2		17	3		4
English	5	1		6			2
Birch	4	1		5			
Wint	4			4			
Knight	3			3			
Taylor	3			3			
Denny	2			2			
Elvins	1	1		2			
Peirpoint	2			2			
Till	2			2			
Angus	1			1			
Blackwood			1	1			
Fleet	1			1			
Gough	1			1			
Langdon	1			1			
Opponents	1			1			

Cons Run - Consecutive scoring games.

STALYBRIDGE CELTIC

Chairman: Rob Gorski

Secretary: John Hall **(T)** 07813 864 492 **(E)** celticblueblood@hotmail.com

Commercial Manager: Phil Brennan **(T)** 07538 110 439

Programme Editor: Nick Shaw **(T)** 07973 424 975

Ground Address: Bower Fold, Mottram Road, Stalybridge, Cheshire SK15 2RT

(T) 0161 338 2828 **Manager:** Keith Briggs

Club Factfile

Founded: 1909 **Nickname:** Celtic

Previous Names: None

Previous Leagues: Lancashire Combination 1911-12, Central League 1912-21, Southern 1914-15, Football League 1921-23, Cheshire Co. 1923-82, North West Co. 1982-87, N.P.L. 1987-92, 98-2001, Conference 1992-98, 01-02

Club Colours (change): Royal blue & white/white/blue (Green/black/black)

Ground Capacity: 6,500 **Seats:** 1,500 **Covered:** 2,400 **Clubhouse:** Yes **Shop:** Yes

Directions

Leave the M6 at junction 19 (Northwich). At the roundabout at the end of the slip road turn right (exit 3 of 4) to join the A556 towards Altrincham. Stay on the A556 for 5 miles to a roundabout with the M56. Turn right at the roundabout (exit 3 of 4) onto the M56. Stay on the M56 for 6 1/2 miles to junction 3 (M60 signposted Sheffield, M67) Stay on the M60 for 7 miles to junction 24 (M67, Denton) At the roundabout turn right (exit 4 of 5) to join the M67. Stay on the M67 to the very end, Junction 4. At the roundabout turn left (exit 1 of 4) onto the A57 (Hyde Road). After 1/2 a mile you will reach a set of traffic lights (signposted Stalybridge). Turn left onto B6174 (Stalybridge Road). Almost immediately, there is a mini roundabout. Turn left (exit 1 of 5) onto Roe Cross Road (A6018). Follow this road for 1 3/4 miles passing the Roe Cross Inn on the right and through the cutting (the road is now called Mottram Road). When you pass the Dog and Partridge on the right, you will be almost there. Bower Fold is on the left opposite a sharp right turn next to the Hare and Hounds pub. If the car park is full (it usually is), parking can be found on the streets on the right of Mottram Road.

Previous Grounds: None

Record Attendance: 9,753 v West Bromwich Albion - FA Cup replay 1922-23

Record Victory: 16-2 v Manchester NE - 01/05/1926 and v Nantwich - 22/10/1932

Record Defeat: 1-10 v Wellington Town - 09/03/1946

Record Goalscorer: Harry Dennison - 215

Record Appearances: Kevan Keelan - 395

Additional Records: Cecil Smith scored 77 goals during the 1931-32 season
Paid £15,000 to Kettering Town for Ian Arnold 1995. Received £16,000 from Southport for Lee Trundle.

Senior Honours:

Manchester Senior Cup 1922-23.
Northern Premier League Premier Division 1991-92, 2000-01.
Cheshire Senior Cup x2.

10 YEAR RECORD

04-05	05-06	06-07	07-08	08-09	09-10	10-11	11-12	12-13	13-14
Conf N 19	Conf N 7	Conf N 18	Conf N 2	Conf N 6	Conf N 9	Conf N 10	Conf N 6	Conf N 13	Conf N 19

STALYBRIDGE CELTIC MATCH RESULTS 2013-14

Date	Comp	H/A	Opponents	Att:	Result		Goalscorers	Pos	No.
Aug 17	CNorth	H	Hednesford Town	465	L	0-4		22	1
20	CNorth	A	Colwyn Bay	309	W	2-1	McConville 36 Dumin 81	14	2
24	CNorth	A	Gainsborough T	422	W	2-0	Pepper 49 McConville 62	9	3
26	CNorth	H	Bradford PA	364	D	2-2	McConville 5 84	10	4
31	CNorth	A	Workington	424	L	0-1		13	5
Sept 7	CNorth	H	Solihull Moors	398	L	2-3	Anoruo 56 88	14	6
14	CNorth	A	Brackley Town	303	L	0-3		16	7
17	CNorth	H	Harrogate Town	270	W	3-2	McConville 56 Wilkinson 75 Anorou 82	13	8
21	CNorth	H	Stockport County	**1560**	D	0-0		12	9
28	***FAC2Q***	***H***	***Worksop Town***	***328***	***L***	***3-5***	***Hatch 39 McConville 57 Platt 60 (pen)***		10
Oct 5	CNorth	A	Oxford City	223	L	1-2	Warburton 21	12	11
19	CNorth	A	Leamington	676	L	0-1		15	12
22	CNorth	H	Vauxhall Motors	214	W	3-2	Anoruo 50 Warburton 54 Platt 76	12	13
26	CNorth	H	Leamington	383	W	2-1	Anoruo 36 Platt 39	10	14
Nov 2	CNorth	H	Histon	402	W	2-1	Anoruo 35 McConville 40	9	15
9	CNorth	A	AFC Telford United	1527	L	1-3	Byrne 90 (og)	11	16
12	CNorth	A	Barrow	642	D	1-1	Platt 83 (pen)	10	17
16	***FAT3Q***	***H***	***Vauxhall Motors***	***315***	***W***	***3-0***	***Pepper 46 Platt 49 Buckley 75***		18
23	CNorth	H	Worcester CIty	378	L	1-2	Platt 81 (pen)	11	19
30	***FAT1***	***A***	***Lincoln City***	***1023***	***L***	***1-5***	***Marsh 69***	***12***	20
Dec 7	CNorth	A	Histon	244	W	4-1	McConville 6 Dowie 18 (og) Marsh 21 Pepper 86	11	21
14	CNorth	A	Hednesford Town	454	L	1-4	Marsh 57	13	22
21	CNorth	H	Boston United	354	D	3-3	Marsh 9 66 Platt 15	13	23
26	CNorth	A	Altrincham	1171	L	0-5		13	24
28	CNorth	H	Colwyn Bay	340	L	2-3	Tunnicliffe 15 Pepper 90	14	25
Jan 1	CNorth	H	Altrincham	684	L	0-5		14	26
4	CNorth	A	Solihull Borough	423	D	3-3	Anoruo 35 55 Platt 79	16	27
7	CNorth	H	Barrow	313	L	1-3	Ennis 36	17	28
11	CNorth	A	Harrogate Town	454	L	1-2	McConville 26	17	29
18	CNorth	H	Gloucester City	327	D	2-2	Platt 7 McConville 31	17	30
Feb 8	CNorth	A	Stockport County	3107	L	0-2		19	31
22	CNorth	H	Brackley Town	332	D	1-1	Sharpe 87 (og)	19	32
March 1	CNorth	A	Worcester CIty	531	L	1-2	Ennis 39	19	33
8	CNorth	H	AFC Telford United	517	L	0-2		20	34
15	CNorth	A	Vauxhall Motors	227	W	3-1	Platt 43 55 (pen) Croasdale 67	18	35
18	CNorth	A	Guiseley	336	L	1-3	Bembo-Leta 8	19	36
22	CNorth	A	Gloucester City	339	L	0-1		19	37
26	CNorth	H	Guiseley	253	W	2-3	McConville 45 Dickenson 52	19	38
29	CNorth	A	North Ferriby United	366	L	0-2		20	39
April 5	CNorth	H	Oxford City	377	D	1-1	Ennis 83	21	40
12	CNorth	A	Boston United	1133	L	1-4	Bemba-Leta	21	41
16	CNorth	H	North Ferriby United	303	L	2-3	Ennis 10 Dickinson 68 (pen)	21	42
19	CNorth	H	Gainsborough Trinity	446	W	3-2	Dickenson 9 74 Regan 63	20	43
21	CNorth	A	Bradford PA	369	D	1-1	Green 73	20	44
26	CNorth	H	Workington	472	W	2-0	Ennis 21 McConville 51	19	45

GOALSCORERS	Lge	FAC	FAT	Total	Pens	Hat-tricks	Cons Run
McConville	11	1		12			3
Platt	9	1	1	11	4		3
Anoruo	8			8			3
Ennis	5			5			
Marsh	4		1	5			3
Dickenson	4			4	1		2
Pepper	3		1	4			
Bembo-Leta	2			2			
Warburton	2			2			
Buckley			1	1			
Crossdale	1			1			
Durnin	1			1			
Green	1			1			
Hatch		1		1			
Regan	1			1			
Tunnicliff	1			1			
Wilkinson	1			1			
Opponents	3			3			

Cons Run - Consecutive scoring games.

STOCKPORT COUNTY

Chairman: n/a

Secretary: Mark Lockyear **(T)** 07981 885 470 **(E)** mark.lockyear@stockportcounty.com

Commercial Manager: Chris Jolley **(T)** 07803 616 613

Programme Editor: Chris Jolley **(T)** chris.jolley@stockportcounty.com

Ground Address: Edgeley Park, Hardcastle Road, Stockport SK3 9DD

(T) 0161 286 8888 x 257 **Manager:** Alan Lord

Club Factfile

Founded: 1883 **Nickname:** County or Hatters

Previous Names: Heaton Norris Rovers 1883-88, Heaton Norris 1888-90.

Previous Leagues: Football League 1900-2011.

Club Colours (change): Royal blue/white/ royal white (White/black/black & white)

Ground Capacity: 10,800 **Seats:** Yes **Covered:** Yes **Clubhouse:** **Shop:** Yes

Directions

From The South (M6): Exit the M6 at Junction 19 (sign-posted 'Manchester Airport, Stockport A55, M56 East') and at the r'about turn right onto the A556. At the Bowden r'about after 4.2 miles, turn right (sign-posted 'Manchester M56) onto the M56. Exit the M56 after 6.9 miles (sign-posted 'Stockport M60, Sheffield M67') onto the M60. Exit the M60 at Junction 1 ('sign-posted 'Stockport Town Centre and West'). At the r'about turn right and continue through to the second set of lights and turn left (ignoring the sign directing you to Stockport Co.) and follow the road to the left, which is Chestergate. At the lights turn right up King Street, past the fire station on the right to the top of the hill, turn right at the r'about signed Edgeley. Continue down Hardcastle street turning left after the bus stop signed Caroline Street. **From the North** (M62 from Leeds): Follow the M62 onto the M60 and continue south. Exit the M60 at Junction 1 ('sign-posted Stockport Town centre') At the roundabout turn right and continue through to the second set of lights and turn left (ignoring the sign directing you to Stockport Co.) and follow the road to the left, which is Chestergate. At the traffic lights turn right up King Street, past the fire station on the right to the top of the hill, turn right at the roundabout signed Edgeley. Continue down Hardcastle street turning left after the bus stop signed Caroline Street. At the end of Caroline St turn right where you will see the main car park on the left. (not available on Match Days)

Previous Grounds: Nursery Inn, Green Lane 1889-1902.

Record Attendance: 27,833 v Liverpool, FA Cup 5th Round 11/02/1950.

Record Victory: 13-0 v Halifax Town, Division Three North 06/01/1934.

Record Defeat: 1-8 v Chesterfield, Division Two 19/04/1902.

Record Goalscorer: (League) Jack Connor - 132, 1951-56.

Record Appearances: (League) Andy Thorpe - 489, 1978-86, 88-92.

Additional Records: Paid, £800,000 for Ian Moore from Nottingham Forest, 07/1998.
Received, £1,600,000 for Alun Armstrong from Middlesbrough, 02/1998.

Senior Honours:
League Division Three North 1921-22, 36-37, Division Four 1966-67.

10 YEAR RECORD

04-05		05-06		06-07		07-08		08-09		09-10		10-11		11-12		12-13		13-14	
FL 1	24	FL 2	22	FL 2	8	FL 2	4	FL 1	18	FL 1	24	FL 2	24	Conf	16	Conf	21	Conf N	14

STOCKPORT COUNTY MATCH RESULTS 2013-14

Date	Comp	H/A	Opponents	Att:	Result		Goalscorers	Pos	No.
Aug 17	CNorth	H	Boston United	3317	L	1-4	Dennis 29 (pen)	20	1
20	CNorth	A	Workington	562	D	1-1	Howard 47	17	2
24	CNorth	A	Altrincham	2875	L	0-3		21	3
26	CNorth	H	Colwyn Bay	2561	L	0-1		21	4
31	CNorth	A	Harrogate Town	918	L	1-3	Howard 86	21	5
Sept 7	CNorth	H	Gainsborough Trinity	2802	**W**	3-1	Dennis 41 Jevons 52 90	19	6
14	CNorth	H	Leamington	2925	D	1-1	Jevons 72	19	7
17	CNorth	A	Vauxhall Motors	404	L	1-2	Jevons 8	20	8
21	CNorth	A	Stalybridge Celtic	1560	D	0-0		20	9
28	***FAC2Q***	***H***	***Brighouse Town***	***1704***	***W***	***1-0***	***Jacobs 67***		10
Oct 5	CNorth	H	Worcester CIty	2332	**W**	4-0	Jacobs 9 Turner 25 Jevons 44 60	15	11
8	CNorth	A	Barrow	684	**W**	4-2	Turner 11 40 Jevons 26 51 (pen)	11	12
12	FAC3Q	H	Rushall Olympic	2135	L	0-1			13
19	CNorth	H	Gloucester City	2727	D	2-2	Turner 16 Webb 55 (og)	11	14
26	CNorth	A	Histon	508	L	1-2	Duxberry 47	13	15
Nov 2	CNorth	H	AFC Telford United	2710	**W**	4-2	Turner 9 Charnock 32 Tunnicliffe 61 Dennis 78	13	16
9	CNorth	A	Oxford City	542	L	1-4	Stonehouse 1 (og)	14	17
16	***FAT3Q***	***A***	***Barrow***	***727***	***D***	***2-2***	***Jevons 13 (pen) Fogbola 75***		18
19	***FAT3Qr***	***H***	***Barrow***	***812***	***L***	***2-3***	***Jevons 15 Howard 89***		19
23	CNorth	H	North Ferriby United	2608	L	1-2	Jevons 83	16	20
Dec 14	CNorth	H	Brackley Town	1941	L	0-2		18	21
21	CNorth	H	Oxford City	1884	**W**	2-0	Howard 1 85	18	22
26	CNorth	H	Bradford PA	2108	**W**	4-1	Dickenson 6 Turner 20 Howard 54 Jevons 58 (pen)	17	23
28	CNorth	H	Workington	2282	D	1-1	Jevons 5 (pen)	17	24
Jan 4	CNorth	A	Gainsborough Trinity	579	**W**	5-1	DENNIS 3 (3 14 55) Howard 41 Churchman 70	15	25
14	CNorth	A	Hednesford Town	585	L	1-3	Dennis 66	16	26
25	CNorth	H	Histon	2070	**W**	1-0	Platt 6	15	27
28	CNorth	A	Boston United	917	D	0-0		15	28
Feb 4	CNorth	H	Vauxhall Motors	1428	**W**	4-1	Dennis 23 57 Howard 49 Jevons 75	13	29
8	CNorth	H	Stalybridge Celtic	3107	**W**	2-0	Dennis 8 Duxbury 17	11	30
10	CNorth	A	Bradford PA	569	**W**	2-0	Jevons 71 (pen) Howard 90	10	31
15	CNorth	A	AFC Telford United	1819	L	0-2		10	32
22	CNorth	A	Solihull Moors	2396	D	2-2	Jevons 53 Battersby 57	11	33
March 1	CNorth	A	Leamington	1038	L	1-2	Howard 66	11	34
4	CNorth	H	Barrow	2457	D	2-2	Lofthouse 22 Oates 33	12	35
8	CNorth	A	Gloucester City	328	L	0-2		12	36
11	CNorth	A	Guiseley	502	L	0-2		12	37
15	CNorth	H	Guiseley	2764	D	3-3	JEVONS 3 (41 75 90 pen)	12	38
22	CNorth	A	Solihull Moors	525	L	0-1		13	39
25	CNorth	A	Worcester City	376	D	0-0		13	40
29	CNorth	H	Hednesford Town	2669	L	0-1		13	41
April 5	CNorth	A	North Ferriby United	440	D	0-0		14	42
12	CNorth	A	Brackley Town	390	D	0-0		15	43
18	CNorth	H	Altrincham	**3770**	D	0-0		14	44
22	CNorth	A	Colwyn Bay	1056	D	0-0		14	45
26	CNorth	H	Harrogate Town	3126	**W**	3-1	Jevons 44 88 Duxbury 45	14	46

GOALSCORERS	Lge	FAC	FAT	Total	Pens	Hat-tricks	Cons Run
Jevons	19		2	21	6	1	3
Dennis	10			10	1	1	2
Howard	8		1	9			
Turner	5			5			2
Duxbury	3			3			
Tunnicliffe	3			3			
Jacobs	1	1		2			2
Battersbu	1			1			
Charnock	1			1			
Churchman	1			1			
Dickenson	1			1			
Fogbola			1	1			
Lofthouse	1			1			
Oates	1			1			
Platt	1			1			
Opponents	2			2			

Cons Run - Consecutive scoring games.

TAMWORTH

Chairman: Bob Andrews
Secretary: Rod Hadley **(T)** 01827 657 98 **(E)** clubsec@thelambs.co.uk
Commercial Manager: TBC **(T)**
Programme Editor: Terry Brumpton **(T)** 07771 802 048
Ground Address: The Lamb Ground, Kettlebrook, Tamworth, Staffordshire B77 1AA
(T) 01827 657 98 opt. 3 **Manager:** Dale Belford

Club Factfile

Founded: 1933 **Nickname:** The Lambs
Previous Names: None
Previous Leagues: Birmingham Combination 1933-54, West Midlands (originally Birmingham League) 1954-72, 84-88, Southern 1972-79, 83-84, 89-2003, Northern Premier 1979-83
Club Colours (change): All red (White/black/white)

Ground Capacity: 4,100 **Seats:** 518 **Covered:** 1,191 **Clubhouse:** Yes **Shop:** Yes

Directions
M42 Junction 10. Take A5/A51 to Town centre, then follow the signs for Kettlebrook and Tamworth FC.

Previous Grounds: Jolly Sailor Ground 1933-34

Record Attendance: 5,500 v Torquay United - FA Cup 1st Round 15/11/69
Record Victory: 14-4 v Holbrook Institue (H) - Bass Vase 1934
Record Defeat: 0-11 v Solihull (A) - Birmingham Combination 1940
Record Goalscorer: Graham Jessop - 195
Record Appearances: Dave Seedhouse - 869
Additional Records: Paid £7,500 to Ilkeston Town for David Hemmings December 2000
Received £7,500 from Telford United for Martin Myers 1990
Senior Honours:
Birmingham Senior Cup 1960-61, 65-66, 68-69. West Midlands League 1964-65, 65-66, 71-72, 87-88. FA Vase 1988-89. Southern League Premier Division 2002-03. Conference North 2008-09.

10 YEAR RECORD

04-05	05-06	06-07	07-08	08-09	09-10	10-11	11-12	12-13	13-14
Conf 15	Conf 20	Conf 22	Conf N 15	Conf N 1	Conf 16	Conf 19	Conf 18	Conf 19	Conf 23

TAMWORTH MATCH RESULTS 2013-14

Date	Comp	H/A	Opponents	Att:	Result		Goalscorers	Pos	No.
Aug 10	CPrem	A	Salisbury City	958	W	1-0	Thomas 32	8	1
13	CPrem	H	Barnet	1379	D	0-0		9	2
17	CPrem	H	Wrexham	1128	D	2-2	Jones 19 Byfield 84	10	3
24	CPrem	A	Hereford United	864	L	0-1		16	4
31	CPrem	A	Cambridge United	2527	L	0-3		18	5
26	CPrem	H	Dartford	864	L	0-2		17	6
Sept 7	CPrem	H	Southport	933	W	4-1	Baker 12 (pen) Peniket 66 78 George 61 (og)	16	7
13	CPrem	A	Woking	1246	D	2-2	Baker 24 Peniket 84	15	8
17	CPrem	H	Kidderminster Harriers	874	L	0-3		17	9
21	CPrem	H	Gateshead	736	L	0-1		19	10
24	CPrem	A	Forest Green Rovers	829	W	2 1	Baker 26 (pen) Wright 53	18	11
28	CPrem	A	Grimsby Town	3105	L	1-3	Todd 73	20	12
Oct 5	CPrem	H	Macclesfield Town	864	W	1-0	Elford-Alliyu 18	17	13
8	CPrem	A	Lincoln City	2603	D	0-0		17	14
12	CPrem	A	Welling United	803	L	0-2		18	15
19	CPrem	H	Luton Town	**2066**	L	3-4	Courtney 13 78 Elford-Alliyu 64 (pen)	20	16
26	***FAC4Q***	***H***	***Solihull Moors***	***1035***	***W***	***4-1***	***Peniket 5 Chadwick 30 40 Richards 54***		17
Nov 2	CPrem	H	Braintree Town	716	D	0-0		20	18
8	***FAC1***	***H***	***Cheltenham Town***	***1566***	***W***	***1-0***	***Chadwick 20***		19
12	CPrem	H	Alfreton Town	716	W	1-0	Chadwick 23	18	20
16	CPrem	H	Grimsby Town	1306	L	0-3		20	21
23	CPrem	A	Kidderminster Harriers	1951	L	3-5	Peniket 49 Morgan 60 Chadwick 89	20	22
30	***FAT1***	***H***	***Macclesfield Town***	***667***	***W***	***2-0***	***Todd 82 Richards - Everton 89***		23
Dec 8	***FAC2***	***H***	***Bristol City***	***2860***	***L***	***1-2***	***Todd 89***		24
14	***FAT2***	***H***	***Boston United***	***688***	***W***	***2-0***	***Todd 64 Richards 79***		25
21	CPrem	A	Aldershot	1598	L	0-6		22	26
26	CPrem	H	Nuneaton Town	1347	D	1-1	Chadwick 9	22	27
Jan 4	CPrem	H	FC Halifax Town	890	W	2-0	Kerry 45 Todd 59	21	28
11	***FAT3***	***H***	***Chorley***	***1209***	***D***	***1-1***	***Chadwick 59 (pen)***		29
15	***FAT3r***	***A***	***Chorley***	***1393***	***D***	***2-2****	***Chadwick 10 Thomas 60 Won 6-5 on pens***		30
21	CPrem	H	Cambridge United	833	L	0-1		22	31
25	CPrem	A	Hyde	369	W	3-0	Peniket 10 Richards 60 Chadwick 77	21	32
28	CPrem	A	Wrexham	2160	L	0-2		21	33
Feb 1	***FAT4***	***A***	***Grimsby Town***	***2795***	***L***	***1-4***	***Chadwick 53***		34
11	CPrem	H	Hyde	616	D	1-1	Byfield 44	20	35
15	CPrem	A	Barnet	1296	L	0-1		22	36
18	CPrem	H	Salisbury City	564	L	1-2	Hildreth 32	23	37
22	CPrem	H	Welling United	742	D	1-1	Godden 84	23	38
25	CPrem	H	Chester FC	1036	L	3-4	Godden 43 75 Peniket 82	23	39
March 1	CPrem	A	FC Halifax Town	1313	L	0-2		23	40
8	CPrem	H	Aldershot Town	915	W	1-0	Barnes-Homer 68	23	41
15	CPrem	H	Forest Green Rovers	736	L	1-2	Godden 89 (pen)	23	42
18	CPrem	A	Alfreton Town	594	L	2-4	Peniket 7 Godden 67 (pen)	23	43
22	CPrem	A	Macclesfield Town	1352	L	1-2	Thornton 40	23	44
25	CPrem	A	Chester FC	1731	L	0-2		23	45
29	CPrem	H	Lincoln City	979	D	0-0		23	46
April 5	CPrem	A	Gateshead	705	L	0-5		23	47
8	CPrem	A	Luton Town	8554	L	0-2		23	48
12	CPrem	A	Southport	1006	L	0-2		23	49
18	CPrem	H	Hereford United	1154	W	1-0	Kerry 62	21	50
21	CPrem	A	Dartford	1465	W	3-2	Reindorf 60 Thornton 73 (pen) 90	23	51
26	CPrem	H	Woking	788	L	2-4	Reindorf 51 57	23	52

GOALSCORERS	Lge	FAC	FAT	Total	Pens	Hat-tricks	Cons Run
Chadwick	4	3	3	10	1		2
Peniket	7	1		8			2
Godden	5			5	2		2
Todd	2	1	2	5			3
Baker	3			3	2		2
Reindorf	3			3			2
Richards	1	1	1	3			
Thornton	3			3	1		
Byfield	2			2			
Courtney	2			2			
Elford-Alliyu	2			2	1		

	Lge	FAC	FAT	Total	Pens	Hat-tricks	Cons Run
Kerry	2			2			
Thomas	1		1	2			
Barnes-Homer	1			1			
Hilred	1			1			
Jones	1			1			
Morgan	1			1			
Richards-Everton			1	1			
Wright	1			1			
Opponents	1			1			

Cons Run - Consecutive scoring games.

WORCESTER CITY

Chairman: Anthony Hampson
Secretary: Joe Murphy (T) 07837 086 205 (E) joe.murphy@rpsgroup.com
Commercial Manager: n/a (T)
Programme Editor: Rob Bazley (T) 07814 145 039
Ground Address: c/o Kidderminster H., Aggborough Stadium, Hoo Road, Kidderminster, DY10 1NB
(T) 01562 823 931 **Manager:** Carl Heeley

Club Factfile

Founded: 1902 **Nickname:** City
Previous Names:
Previous Leagues: West Midlands, Birmingham, Southern 1938-79, 85-2004, Alliance 1979-85

Club Colours (change): Blue & white stripes/blue/blue (Green/black/black)

Ground Capacity: 4,004 **Seats:** 1,125 **Covered:** 2,000 **Clubhouse:** Yes **Shop:** Yes

Directions
NORTH - Take the M5 coming off at junction 3, follow signs for Severn Valley Railway, take the A456 to Kidderminster, turn left at traffic lights (opposite the Land Oak pub) onto the A449 to Worcester, at the next set of traffic lights turn right towards the Town Centre, then left onto Hoo Road (just before the roundabout at the bottom of hill), the ground should be 300 yards on the left hand side. SOUTH - Take the M5 to junction 6, follow A440 towards Kidderminster, turn right at the first island near McDonalds Drive Thru, take the first left into Hoo Road (opposite the Viaduct Pub), you should find the ground after half a mile on the right hand side.

Previous Grounds: Severn Terrace, Thorneloe, Flagge Meadow. St George's Lane 1905-2013.

Record Attendance: 17,042 v Sheffield United - FA Cup 4th Round 24/01/1959
Record Victory: 18-1 v Bilston - Birmingham League 21/11/1931
Record Defeat: 0-10 v Wellington - Birmingham League 29/08/1920
Record Goalscorer: John Inglis - 189 (1970-77)
Record Appearances: Bobby McEwan - 596 (1959-75)
Additional Records: Paid £8,500 to Telford United for Jim Williams 1981
Received £27,000 from Everton for John Barton
Senior Honours:
Birmingham League 1913-14, 24-25, 28-29, 29-30.
Southern League Cup 1939-40, 2000-01, Division 1 1967-68, 76-77, Premier 1978-79.
Birmingham Senior Cup 1975-76. Worcestershire Senior Cup x26 (last win 1996-97)

10 YEAR RECORD

04-05	05-06	06-07	07-08	08-09	09-10	10-11	11-12	12-13	13-14
Conf N 7	Conf N 8	Conf N 9	Conf N 12	Conf S 16	Conf S 20	Conf N 16	Conf N 7	Conf N 15	Conf N 15

WORCESTER CITY MATCH RESULTS 2013-14

Date	Comp	H/A	Opponents	Att:	Result		Goalscorers	Pos	No.
Aug 17	CNorth	H	Altrincham	714	L	1-3	Glover 27	18	1
20	CNorth	A	Gloucester City	566	L	1-2	Williams 58	21	2
24	CNorth	A	Brackley Town	312	D	0-0		18	3
26	CNorth	H	Hednesford Town	741	D	2-2	Nti 1 57	17	4
31	CNorth	A	Boston United	919	L	1-2	Nti 41	19	5
Sept 7	CNorth	H	Bradford PA	636	L	1-2	Moore 60	20	6
14	CNorth	A	Colwyn Bay	310	D	0-0		20	7
17	CNorth	H	Gainsborough Trinity	347	D	2-2	Geohaghon 54 Moore 90 (pen)	20	8
21	CNorth	H	Workington	559	W	4-0	Moore 12 17 Geohaghon 56 Glover 59	17	9
24	CNorth	A	AFC Telford United	1330	D	0-0		16	10
28	***FAC2Q***	***H***	***Coventry Sphinx***	***514***	***W***	***4-0***	***Toundry 29 Thompson 80 Nti 86 Lemmon 89***		11
Oct 5	CNorth	A	Stockport County	2332	L	0-4		19	12
12	***FAC3Q***	***H***	***Rugby Town***	***704***	***D***	***0-0***			13
15	***FAC3Qr***	***A***	***Rugby Town***	***327***	***W***	***2-0***	***Glover 56 Thorley 64 (pen)***		14
19	CNorth	A	Oxford City	291	D	0-0		19	15
26	***FAC4Q***	***H***	***Lincoln City***	***1019***	***D***	***1-1***	***A.Williams 55***		16
29	***FAC4Qr***	***A***	***Lincoln City***	***1344***	***L***	***0-3***			17
Nov 2	CNorth	H	North Ferriby United	471	L	0-1		21	18
9	CNorth	A	Harrogate Town	443	L	0-2		22	19
12	CNorth	H	Leamington	486	L	0-3		22	20
17	***FAT3Q***	***H***	***Ramsbottom United***	***341***	***W***	***3-0***	***MOORE 3 (40 67 78)***		21
23	CNorth	A	Stalybridge Celtic	378	W	2-1	Khan 2 Nti 89	20	22
26	CNorth	H	Guiseley	337	D	0-0		18	23
30	***FAT1***	***H***	***AFC Telford United***	***764***	***D***	***0-0***			24
Dec 2	***FAT1r***	***A***	***AFC Telford United***	***603***	***W***	***3-0***	***Nti 18 Williams 21 30***		25
8	CNorth	H	Oxford City	442	L	0-2		19	26
14	***FAT 2***	***A***	***Aldershot***	***1158***	***L***	***1-4***	***Moore 12***		27
21	CNorth	H	Harrogate Town	403	W	1-0	Nelson-Addy 11	19	28
26	CNorth	A	Solihull Moors	575	D	1-1	Moore 84	19	29
28	CNorth	H	Gloucester CIty	796	L	0-1		20	30
Jan 4	CNorth	A	Bradford PA	288	L	1-6	Moore 10	21	31
11	CNorth	A	Histon	294	W	2-1	Nti 3 52	20	32
18	CNorth	H	Colwyn Bay	571	W	2-1	Nti 70 Williams 78	20	33
21	CNorth	A	Altrincham	527	W	2-1	Brown 50 Nti 78	19	34
22	CNorth	A	Vauxhall Motors	172	L	0-1		19	35
28	CNorth	H	Solihull Moors	361	W	3-1	Leslie 2 Moore 55 Nelson-Addy 90	17	36
Feb 8	CNorth	A	Guiseley	399	W	1-0	Brown 51	16	37
15	CNorth	H	AFC Telford United	534	L	0-1		16	38
22	CNorth	A	Gainsborough Trinity	298	L	1-2	Nil 29	17	39
March 1	CNorth	H	Stalybridge Celtic	531	W	2-1	Nti 17 Williams 79	15	40
8	CNorth	A	Barrow	901	W	1-0	Nti 56	13	41
15	CNorth	A	North Ferriby United	333	L	1-2	Nti 43	17	42
23	CNorth	H	Vauxhall Motors	434	W	2-0	Deeney 37 Nti 89	15	43
25	CNorth	H	Stockport County	376	D	0-0		15	44
29	CNorth	H	Histon	432	D	1-1	Moore 90 (pen)	15	45
April 5	CNorth	A	Leamington	657	L	0-1		15	46
8	CNorth	H	Barrow	314	W	1-0	Devaney 71	14	47
12	CNorth	A	Workington	241	L	0-1		14	48
19	CNorth	H	Brackley Town	568	D	1-1	Moore 68 (pen)	14	49
21	CNorth	A	Hednesford Town	668	L	0-4		15	50
26	CNorth	H	Boston United	**854**	W	3-1	Nelson-Addy 53 Weir 60 77	15	51

GOALSCORERS	Lge	FAC	FAT	Total	Pens	Hat-tricks	Cons Run
Nti	13	1	1	15			2
Moore	10		3	13	3	1	2
Glover	2	1		3			
Nelson-Addy	3			3			
Brown	2			2			
Geohaghon	2			2			2
Weir	2			2			
Deeney	1			1			
Devaney	1			1			
Khan	1			1			
Lemmon		1		1			
Leslie	1			1			
Thompson		1		1			
Thorley		1		1	1		
Toundry		1		1			
Williams	4		2	6			

Cons Run - Consecutive scoring games.

BASINGSTOKE TOWN

Chairman: Rafi Razzak
Secretary: Richard Trodd (T) 07887 507 447 (E) richard.trodd@ntlworld.com
Commercial Manager: John Gaston (T) 07782 379 400
Programme Editor: James Holly (T) 07834 285 042
Ground Address: Camrose Ground, Western Way, Basingstoke RG22 6EZ
(T) 01256 327 575 **Manager:** Jason Bristow

Club Factfile

Founded: 1896 **Nickname:** Dragons
Previous Names: None
Previous Leagues: Hampshire 1900-40, 45-71, Southern 1971-87, Isthmian 1987-2004

Club Colours (change): Blue/blue/yellow (All white with blue trim)

Ground Capacity: 6,000 **Seats:** 651 **Covered:** 2,000 **Clubhouse:** Yes **Shop:** Yes

Directions
Leave M3 at junction 6 and turn left onto South Ringway which is the A30.
Straight over first roundabout. At second roundabout turn left into Winchester Road.
Proceed past ground on right to roundabout.
Take fifth exit into Western Way. Ground on right.

Previous Grounds: Castle Field 1896-1947

Record Attendance: 5,085 v Wycombe Wanderers - FA Cup 1st Round replay 1997-98
Record Victory: 10-1 v Chichester City (H) - FA Cup 1st Qualifying Round 1976
Record Defeat: 0-8 v Aylesbury United - Southern League April 1979
Record Goalscorer: Paul Coombs - 159 (1991-99)
Record Appearances: Billy Coomb
Additional Records: Paid £4,750 to Gosport Borough for Steve Ingham

Senior Honours:
Hampshire League 1967-68, 69-70, 70-71. Southern League Southern Division 1984-85.
Hampshire Senior Cup 1970-71, 89-90, 95-96, 2007-08.

10 YEAR RECORD

04-05	05-06	06-07	07-08	08-09	09-10	10-11	11-12	12-13	13-14
Conf S 6	Conf S 19	Conf S 19	Conf S 15	Conf S 18	Conf S 15	Conf S 13	Conf S 5	Conf S 14	Conf S 14

BASINGSTOKE TOWN MATCH RESULTS 2013-14

Date	Comp	H/A	Opponents	Att:	Result	Goalscorers	Pos	No.
Aug 17	CSouth	A	Concord Rangers	306	W 2-1	Ibe 38 George 90	4	1
20	CSouth	H	Gosport Borough	460	W 2-1	Williams 25 (pen) Matthews 7	3	2
24	CSouth	H	Eastleigh	329	W 2-0	Gatson 38 Barrett 82	2	3
26	CSouth	A	Weston-s-Mare	286	L 0-1		3	4
31	CSouth	H	Staines Town	377	W 2-1	Ibe 17 Williams 41	2	5
Sept 7	CSouth	A	Whitehawk	334	L 0-1		4	6
14	CSouth	H	Ebbsfleet United	371	D 2-2	Williams 35 Barrett 48	5	7
21	CSouth	A	Bromley	681	L 2-3	Partridge 9 McAuley 50	8	8
28	***FAC2Q***	***H***	***Weston-s-Mare***	***336***	***L 1-3***	***Partridge 20***		9
Oct 5	CSouth	H	Hays & Yeading U	351	L 0-1		8	10
12	CSouth	A	Havant & Waterlooville	956	L 1-4	Strugnell 41 (og)	13	11
19	CSouth	H	Boreham Wood	281	W 1-0	Reynolds 85 (og)	11	12
26	CSouth	A	Dorchester Town	435	W 4-0	McAuley 4 Williams 39 41 Barrett 79	8	13
Nov 2	CSouth	H	Dover Athletic	352	W 2-0	Jenkinson 21 Partridge 81	5	14
9	CSouth	A	Maidenhead United	314	W 1-0	Barrett 43	4	15
16	***FAT3Q***	***H***	***Hampton & Richmond B***	***403***	***W 3-1***	***Green 30 McAuley 45 Williams 52***		16
23	CSouth	A	Ebbsfleet United	953	L 0-1		4	17
30	***FAT1***	***H***	***Havant & Waterlooville***	***354***	***D 0-0***		***6***	18
Dec 2	***FAT1r***	***A***	***Havant & Waterlooville***	***210***	***L 0-1***			19
7	CSouth	A	Chelmsford City	561	L 0-1		9	20
14	CSouth	H	Bromley	340	L 0-1			21
21	CSouth	A	Bishop's Stortford	357	L 3-5	McAuley 47 Jenkinson 56 Wright 85 (og)	11	22
26	CSouth	H	Farnborough	447	W 4-0	Ibe 6 Williams 14 McAuley 44 Soares 90	9	23
Jan 11	CSouth	H	Bath City	354	D 0-0		11	24
14	CSouth	H	Whitehawk	207	L 1-3	Ibe 33	12	25
18	CSouth	A	Eastbourne Borough	511	W 3-1	Wright 11 McAuley 24 Williams 87 (pen)	8	26
25	CSouth	H	Sutton United	**462**	L 0-1		11	27
Feb 3	CSouth	A	Boreham Wood	112	D 1-1	Partridge 27	11	28
22	CSouth	A	Bath City	519	W 1-0	Smart 83	10	29
March 1	CSouth	H	Maidenhead United	272	D 2-2	Holder-Spooner 11 Jenkinson 48	10	30
6	CSouth	A	Farnborough Town	226	W 3-0	Williams 3 82 (pen) Ray 40	9	31
8	CSouth	A	Dover Athletic	635	D 1-1	Soares 12	10	32
11	CSouth	H	Eastbourne Borough	183	L 1-2	Soares 13	10	33
15	CSouth	A	Sutton United	2172	L 0-4		12	34
18	CSouth	H	Tonbridge Angels	167	D 0-0		12	35
22	CSouth	H	Havant & Waterlooville	344	L 0-1		14	36
29	CSouth	H	Dorchester Town	548	W 2-1	Enver-Marum 30 90	12	37
April 3	CSouth	A	Hayes & Yeading	115	D 0-0		13	38
5	CSouth	A	Tonbridge Angels	354	L 1-2	McAuley 72	14	39
8	CSouth	H	Chelmsford City	182	L 2-3	Williams 10 Enver-Marum 50	14	40
12	CSouth	H	Bishop's Stortford	200	D 0-0		14	41
15	CSouth	A	Gosport Borough	425	L 0-2		15	42
18	CSouth	A	Eastleigh	1505	L 1-2	Enver-Marum 90	15	43
21	CSouth	H	Weston-s-Mare	191	W 3-2	Envor-Marum 15 71 McAuley 43	15	44
23	CSouth	H	Concord Rangers	137	L 0-1		15	45
26	CSouth	A	Staines Town	307	W 5-4	BIGNALL 3 (18 38 63) Daly 21 Soares 66	14	46

GOALSCORERS	Lge	FAC	FAT	Total	Pens	Hat-tricks	Cons Run
Williams	9		1	10	3		
Enver-Marum	7			7			2
McAuley	6		1	7			2
Barrett	4			4			
Ibe	4			4			
Partridge	3	1		4			2
Soares	4			4			2
Bignall	3			3		1	
Jenkinson	3			3			
Daley	1			1			

	Lge	FAC	FAT	Total	Pens	Hat-tricks	Cons Run
Gatson	1			1			
George	1			1			
Green			1	1			
Holder-Spooner	1			1			
Matthews	1			1			
Ray	1			1			
Smart	1			1			
Wright	1			1			
Opponents	3			3			

Cons Run - Consecutive scoring games.

BATH CITY

Chairman: Paul Williams
Secretary: Quentin Edwards **(T)** 07785 795 532 **(E)** qcath@blueyonder.co.uk
Commercial Manager: Bob Chester **(T)** 07786 092 836
Programme Editor: Mark Stillman **(T)** 07929 110 109
Ground Address: Twerton Park, Twerton, Bath, Somerset BA2 1DB
(T) 01225 423 087 **Manager:** Lee Howells

2014-15 Squad - Back row (l-r): Ashley Kington, Andy Watkins, Ross Stearn, Martin Slocombe, Dan Bowman, Chris Allen, Zak Evans, Pat Keary
Middle row: Jim Rollo (player-coach), Adi Britton (director of football), Elliott Gibbons, Sekani Simpson, David Pratt, Frankie Artus, Jason Mellor, Chas Hemmings, Andy Gallinagh, Ben Adelsbury, Dan Ball, Lee Williams (physio), John Freegard (coach)

Club Factfile

Founded: 1889 **Nickname:** The Romans
Previous Names: Bath AFC 1889-92. Bath Railway FC 1902-05. Bath Amateurs 1913-23 (Reserve side)
Previous Leagues: Western 1908-21. Southern 1921-79, 88-90, 97-2007. Alliance/Conference 1979-88, 90-97.

Club Colours (change): Black & white/black/black (Yellow/blue/blue)

Ground Capacity: 8,840 **Seats:** 1,017 **Covered:** 4,800 **Clubhouse:** Yes **Shop:** Yes

Directions
Take Junction 18 off M4. 3rd exit off roundabout and follow A46 (10 miles) to Bath City Centre. Along Pulteney Road then right into Claverton Street and then follow A36 Lower Bristol Road (1.5 miles). Left under Railway bridge (signs Bath City FC) into Twerton High Street and ground is 2nd turning on left.

Previous Grounds: The Belvoir Ground 1889-92 & 1902-15. Lambridge Show Ground 1919-32.

Record Attendance: 18,020 v Brighton & Hove Albion - FA Cup 1960
Record Victory: 8-0 v Boston United - 1998-99
Record Defeat: 0-9 v Yeovil Town - 1946-47
Record Goalscorer: Paul Randall - 106
Record Appearances: David Mogg - 530
Additional Records: Paid £15,000 to Bristol City for Micky Tanner. Received £80,000 from Southampton for Jason Dodd.

Senior Honours:
Southern Lge Western Div.2 1928-29. Southern Lge Western Division 1933-34. Southern League 1959-60, 77-78, 2006-07.
Southern League Cup 1978-79. Somerset Premier Cup 1951-52, 52-53, 57-58, 59-60, 65-66, 67-68, 69-70, 77-78, 80-81, 81-82, 83-84, 84-85, 85-86, 88-89, 89-90, 93-94, 94-95, 2007-08. Conference South Play-offs 2009-10.

10 YEAR RECORD

04-05	05-06	06-07	07-08	08-09	09-10	10-11	11-12	12-13	13-14
SthP 6	SthP 2	SthP 1	Conf S 8	Conf S 8	Conf S 4	Conf 10	Conf 23	Conf S 11	Conf S 7

BATH CITY MATCH RESULTS 2013-14

Date	Comp	H/A	Opponents	Att:	Result		Goalscorers	Pos	No.
Aug 17	CSouth	A	Bishop's Stortford	417	W	2-1	Watkins 43 Pratt 53	5	1
20	CSouth	H	Eastleigh	645	L	0-1		10	2
24	CSouth	H	Gosport Borough	514	D	1-1	Pratt 45	12	3
31	CSouth	H	Concord Rangers	485	W	3-1	Stearn 15 59 Preece 68	10	4
Sept 7	CSouth	A	Ebbsfleet United	856	D	1-1	Salmon 69	12	5
14	CSouth	H	Tonbridge Angels	541	D	2-2	Stearn 23 Pratt 49	10	6
17	CSouth	A	Staines Town	224	L	0-1		12	7
21	CSouth	H	Dover Athletic	551	L	0-2		14	8
28	***FAC2Q***	***H***	***Gosport Borough***	***441***	***W***	***2-0***	***Pratt 14 Stearn 86***		9
Oct 5	CSouth	A	Chelmsford City	619	L	0-1		14	10
12	***FAC3Q***	***A***	***Bridgwater Town***	***722***	***W***	***3-0***	***Pratt 9 Allen 29 32***		11
19	CSouth	A	Whitehawk	261	D	2-2	Low 53 Allen 65 (pen)	18	12
26	***FAC4Q***	***H***	***Salisbury City***	***1068***	***L***	***0-1***			13
29	CSouth	A	Farnborough	352	W	4 2	Stearn 25 Ball 60 Keats 77 Pratt 90	14	14
Nov 2	CSouth	H	Havant & Waterlooville	451	W	3-1	STEARN 3 (17 71 75)	13	15
9	CSouth	A	Dorchester Town	516	W	2-0	Ball 3 12	11	16
12	CSouth	H	Sutton United	476	D	2-2	Pratt 60 Steam 82	10	17
16	***FAT3Q***	***A***	***Dover Athletic***	***483***	***L***	***0-1***			18
23	CSouth	H	Maidenhead United	501	W	1-0	Pratt 23	10	19
30	CSouth	A	Boreham Wood	151	W	1-0	Watkins 7	5	20
Dec 7	CSouth	H	Boreham Wood	541	D	2-2	Watkins 45 Preece 46	8	21
26	CSouth	H	Weston-s-Mare	**852**	W	1-0	Rollo 55	7	22
28	CSouth	A	Eastleigh	637	L	1-2	Low 29	7	23
Jan 4	CSouth	H	Staines Town	538	D	1-1	Pratt 80	7	24
11	CSouth	A	Basingstoke Town	354	D	0-0		7	25
18	CSouth	H	Bromley	755	L	1-2	Keats 35	9	26
21	CSouth	A	Tonbridge Angels	298	D	1-1	Muggeridge 18 (og)	8	27
25	CSouth	A	Eastbourne Borough	514	L	2-3	Connelly 31 Allen 68	10	28
Feb 1	CSouth	H	Bishop's Stortford	547	W	2-1	Keats 9 80	5	29
4	CSouth	A	Hayes & Yeading	97	W	2-0	Platt 45 Watkins 70	5	30
8	CSouth	H	Whitehawk	540	W	3-1	Keats 64 Stearn 71 Low 74	4	31
15	CSouth	A	Dover Athletic	526	L	0-2		5	32
18	CSouth	A	Weston-s~Mare	357	L	0 2		5	33
22	CSouth	H	Basingstoke Town	519	L	0-1		6	34
March 1	CSouth	A	Bromley	857	D	2-2	Ball 14 Watkins 66	7	35
4	CSouth	H	Ebbsfleet United	483	D	2-2	Watkins 21 61	6	36
8	CSouth	A	Maidenhead United	351	W	1-0	Low 85	6	37
15	CSouth	H	Dorchester Town	555	W	1-0	Burnell 47	6	38
22	CSouth	H	Chelmsford City	1374	W	4-1	Adelsbury 27 Stearn 55 Watkins 70 Pratt 90	6	39
24	CSouth	A	Havant & Waterlooville	471	L	0-1		6	40
29	CSouth	A	Sutton United	554	D	2-2	Pratt 45 85	7	41
April 5	CSouth	H	Eastbourne Borough	593	W	2-1	Watkins 34 Keats 57	6	42
12	CSouth	H	Hayes & Yeading	553	W	3-2	Pratt 34 (pen) 84 Watkins 90	7	43
19	CSouth	A	Gosport Borough	517	L	1-3	Pratt 45 (pen)	7	44
21	CSouth	H	Farnborough	571	W	4-2	Pratt 23 77 Burnell 58 Stearn 71	7	45
26 -	CSouth	A	Concord Rangers	302	W	2-0	Connelly 76 Stearn 90	7	46

GOALSCORERS	Lge	FAC	FAT	Total	Pens	Hat-tricks	Cons Run
Pratt	16	2		18	2		3
Stearn	12	1		13		1	2
Watkins	10			10			2
Keats	6			6			
Allen	2	2		4	1		
Ball	4			4			
Low	4			4			
Burnell	2			2			
Connelly	2			2			
Preece	2			2			

	Lge	FAC	FAT	Total	Pens	Hat-tricks	Cons Run
Adelsbury	1			1			
Rollo	1			1			
Salmon	1			1			
Opponents	1			1			

Cons Run - Consecutive scoring games.

BISHOP'S STORTFORD

Chairman: Luigu Del Basso
Secretary: Ian Kettridge **(T)** 07904 169 017 **(E)** ianket@aol.com
Commercial Manager: John Turner **(T)** 077100 79158
Programme Editor: Dave Ryan **(T)** 07828 470 015
Ground Address: ProKit Uk Stadium, Woodside Park, Dunmow Road, Bishop's Stortford CM23 5RG
(T) 01279 306 456 **Manager:** Rod Stringer

Club Factfile

Founded: 1874 **Nickname:** Blues or Bishops
Previous Names: None
Previous Leagues: East Herts 1896-97, 1902-06, 19-21, Stansted & District 1906-19, Herts County 1921-25, 27-29, Herts & Essex Border 1925-27, Spartan 1929-51, Delphian 1951-63, Athenian 1963-73, Isthmian 1974-2004
Club Colours (change): All blue (White/black/black)

Ground Capacity: 4,000 **Seats:** 298 **Covered:** 700 **Clubhouse:** Yes **Shop:** Yes

Directions
Woodside Park is situated 1/4 mile from Junction 8 of M11.
Follow A1250 towards Bishop's Stortford Town Centre, entrance to the ground is signposted through Woodside Park Industrial Estate.

Previous Grounds: Rhodes Avenue 1919-1997.

Record Attendance: 6,000 v Peterborough Town - FA Cup 2nd Round 1972-73 and v Middlesbrough - FA Cup 3rd Round replay 1982-83
Record Victory: 11-0 v Nettleswell & Buntwill - Herts Junior Cup 1911
Record Defeat: 0-13 v Cheshunt (H) - Herts Senior Cup 1926
Record Goalscorer: Post 1929 Jimmy Badcock - 123
Record Appearances: Phil Hopkins - 543
Additional Records:

Senior Honours:
Athenian League 1969-70. FA Amateur Cup 1973-74. Isthmian League Division 1 1980-81. FA Trophy 1980-81.
London Senior Cup 1973-74. Premier Inter League Cup 1989-90. Herts Senior Cup x10 Most recently 2011-12.

10 YEAR RECORD

04-05	05-06	06-07	07-08	08-09	09-10	10-11	11-12	12-13	13-14
Conf S 10	Conf S 15	Conf S 5	Conf S 10	Conf S 9	Conf S 18	Conf S 16	Conf N 10	Conf N 17	Conf S 15

BISHOP'S STORTFORD MATCH RESULTS 2013-14

Date	Comp	H/A	Opponents	Att:	Result		Goalscorers	Pos	No.
Aug 17	CSouth	H	Bath City	417	L	1-2	Asante 85	14	1
19	CSouth	A	Boreham Wood	251	D	2-2	Vassell 23 Francis 74	14	2
24	CSouth	A	Sutton United	405	**W**	2-1	Prestedge 60 Johnson 75	9	3
26	CSouth	H	Bromley	451	**W**	1-0	Miller 65	6	4
31	CSouth	A	Maidenhead United	384	D	2-2	Francis 11 Vassell 39	8	5
Sept 7	CSouth	H	Havant & Waterlooville	428	**W**	2-1	Francis 88 Sykes 90	6	6
14	CSouth	A	Dorchester Town	373	**W**	3-1	Johnson 26 Symons 42 Sykes 88	4	7
21	CSouth	A	Eastbourne	514	L	1-4	Vassell 90	7	8
29	***FAC 2Q***	***A***	***Hendon***	***269***	***W***	***5-0***	***VASSELL 4 (32pen 34 39pen 49) Church 71***		9
Oct 5	CSouth	H	Gosport Borough	**504**	**W**	4-0	Francis 9 Johnson 41 Akurang 53 Vassell 71 (pen)	7	10
12	***FAC3Q***	***A***	***Chipstead***	***204***	***W***	***6-1***	***VASSELL3 (40 pen 54 pen 60) Miller 56 Akurang 70 89***		11
19	CSouth	A	Hayes & Yeading United	136	**W**	3-2	Akurang 51 Church 73 Prestedge 84	4	12
22	CSouth	H	Ebbsfleet United	511	**W**	3-2	Akurang 10 26 Vassell 54	2	13
26	***FAC4Q***	***A***	***Forest Green Rovers***	***789***	***W***	***1-0***	***Prestedge 52***		14
Nov 2	CSouth	H	Tonbridge Angels	573	**W**	2-1	Prestedge 27 Vassell 40	3	15
10	***FAC1***	***H***	***Northampton Town***	***2548***	***L***	***1-2***	***Prestedge 81***		16
16	***FAT3Q***	***A***	***Whitehawk***	***107***	***L***	***1-2***	***Asante 12***		17
23	CSouth	A	Whitehawk	159	D	1-1	Akurang 44	3	18
Dec 7	CSouth	A	Staines Town	230	L	0-2		7	19
10	CSouth	A	Weston-super-Mare	124	D	2-2	Prestedge (2)	6	20
21	CSouth	H	Basingstoke	357	**W**	5-3	Enver-Marum 23 32 Akurang 53 83 Francis 82	5	21
26	CSouth	A	Chelmsford City	728	L	1-2	McNaughton 79	6	22
28	CSouth	H	Boreham Wood	430	L	1-3	Prestedge 52 (pen)	6	23
Jan 4	CSouth	A	Dover Athletic	615	**W**	3-2	Miller 57 Akurang 69 Woodall 84	4	24
18	CSouth	A	Ebbsfleet United	907	L	1-2	Akurang 23	5	25
Feb 1	CSouth	A	Bath City	547	L	1-2	Richens 20	10	26
4	CSouth	H	Staines Town	288	**W**	1-0	Johnson 8	8	27
22	CSouth	H	Concord Rangers	212	**W**	2-0	Francis 21 Goodacre 27 (og)	8	28
March 8	CSouth	A	Tonbridge Angels	406	D	1-1	Akurang 72	9	29
11	CSouth	H	Dorchester Town	257	D	1-1	Richens 87	9	30
13	CSouth	H	Hayes & Yeading United	244	D	0-0		8	31
15	CSouth	A	Eastleigh	601	L	2-4	Church 24 Prestedge 52 (pen)	9	32
18	CSouth	H	Concord Rangers	260	D	0-1		12	33
22	CSouth	H	Farnborough	360	L	1-3	Church 68	11	34
25	CSouth	H	Whitehawk	226	L	1-2	Prestedge 20	12	35
27	CSouth	H	Weston-s-Mare	244	D	0-0		12	36
29	CSouth	A	Gosport Borough	1010	L	1-2	Prestedge 86	13	37
April 1	CSouth	H	Eastleigh	268	D	2-2	Prestedge 16 Young 34	13	38
3	CSouth	H	Eastbourne Borough	231	**W**	1-0	Woodall 37	12	39
5	CSouth	H	Dover Atheltic	451	D	2-2	Woodall 6 Prestedge	12	40
8	CSouth	A	Farnborough	291	L	2-4	Woodall 53 Akurang 75	12	41
10	CSouth	H	Chelmsford City	755	D	1-1	McNaughton 75	12	42
12	CSouth	A	Basingstoke Town	200	D	0-0		12	43
14	CSouth	A	Havant & Waterlooville	462	L	0-2		12	44
19	CSouth	H	Sutton United	478	L	1-2	Prestedge 56 (pen)	13	45
21	CSouth	A	Bromley	549	L	2-3	Richens 44 Herd 48	13	46
26	CSouth	H	Maidenhead United	430	D	1-1	Gilbey 90 (og)	15	47

GOALSCORERS	Lge	FAC	FAT	Total	Pens	Hat-tricks	Cons Run
Prestedge	12	2		14	3		3
Akurang	11	2		13			4
Vassell	6	7		13	5	1	4
Francis	6			6			2
Church	3	1		4			
Johnson	4			4			
Woodall	4			4			3
Miller	2	1		3			
Richens	3			3			
Asante	1		1	2			

	Lge	FAC	FAT	Total	Pens	Hat-tricks	Cons Run
Enver-Marum	2			2			
McNaughton	2			2			
Sykes	2			2			
Herd	1			1			
Symons	1			1			
Young	1			1			
Opponents	2			2			

Cons Run - Consecutive scoring games.

BOREHAM WOOD

Chairman: Danny Hunter
Secretary: Billy Hunter **(T)** 07758 253 537 **(E)** billy@borehamwoodfootballclub.co.uk
Commercial Manager: Mandee Morris **(T)** 020 8953 5097
Programme Editor: John Gill **(T)** 07956 275 111
Ground Address: Meadow Park, Broughinge Road, Boreham Wood WD6 5AL
(T) 0208 953 5097 **Manager:** Ian Allinson

2013-14 Squad.

Club Factfile

Founded: 1948 **Nickname:** The Wood
Previous Names: Boreham Wood Rovers and Royal Retournez amalgamated in 1948 to form today's club
Previous Leagues: Mid Herts 1948-52, Parthenon 1952-57, Spartan 1956-66, Athenian 1966-74, Isthmian 1974-2004, Southern 2004-10

Club Colours (change): White/black/white (All sky blue)

Ground Capacity: 4,502 **Seats:** 600 **Covered:** 1,568 **Clubhouse:** Yes **Shop:** Yes

Directions
Leave A1 at A5135 and follow A5135 towards Borehamwood.
Cross two mini roundabouts then at large roundabout turn right (second exit) into Brook Road then take first right after car park for Broughinge Road.

Previous Grounds: Eldon Avenue 1948-63

Record Attendance: 4,030 v Arsenal - Friendly 13/07/2001
Record Victory: Not known
Record Defeat: Not known
Record Goalscorer: Mickey Jackson
Record Appearances: Dave Hatchett - 714
Additional Records: Received £5,000 from Dagenham & Redbridge for Steve Heffer

Senior Honours:
Athenian League 1973-74. Isthmian League Division 2 1976-77, Division 1 1994-95, 2000-01.
Southern League East 2005-06, Premier Division Play-off 2009-10.
Herts Senior cup 1971-72, 98-99, 2001-02. London Challenge Cup 1997-98.

10 YEAR RECORD

04-05	05-06	06-07	07-08	08-09	09-10	10-11	11-12	12-13	13-14
SthE 7	SthE 1	Isth P 7	Isth P 19	Isth P 18	Isth P 4	Conf S 14	Conf S 8	Conf S 9	Conf S 13

BOREHAM WOOD MATCH RESULTS 2013-14

Date	Comp	H/A	Opponents	Att:	Result		Goalscorers	Pos	No.
Aug 17	CSouth	A	Tonbridge Angels	446	W	2-0	Ball 15 58	2	1
19	CSouth	H	Bishop's Stortford	251	D	2-2	Simmonds 33 Ball 34	7	2
24	CSouth	H	Hayes & Yeading	201	L	1-3	Reid 5 (og)	10	3
26	CSouth	A	Staines Town	219	L	1-3	Simmonds 84	15	4
31	CSouth	H	Eastleigh	202	L	0-2		18	5
Sept 7	CSouth	H	Weston-s-Mare	214	L	0-3		19	6
14	CSouth	H	Gosport Borough	151	W	2-0	Simmonds 27 Poate 41 (og)	18	7
17	CSouth	A	Farnborough	338	L	0-2		20	8
21	CSouth	A	Ebbsfleet United	711	D	0-0		18	9
28	***FAC2Q***	***A***	***Barton Rovers***	***172***	***D***	***0-0***			10
30	***FAC2Qr***	***H***	***Barton Rovers***	***174***	***W***	***3-0***	***Cox 38 Simmonds 58 Note 64***		11
Oct 5	CSouth	H	Bromley	218	D	1-1	Sterling-Parker 90	18	12
12	***FAC3Q***	***A***	***Maidstone United***	***1781***	***W***	***2-0***	***Sullivan 56 (og) Garrard 64 (pen)***		13
19	CSouth	A	Basingstoke Town	281	L	0-1		20	14
26	***FAC4Q***	***H***	***Heybridge Swifts***	***237***	***W***	***1-0***	***Ball 83***		15
Nov 2	CSouth	A	Chelmsford CIty	569	W	6-0	Montgomery 24 72 Moll 28 Lipman 52 Hastings 55 Ball 71	18	16
9	***FAC1***	***H***	***Carlisle United***	***901***	***D***	***0-0***			17
16	***FAT3Q***	***H***	***Gloucester City***	***133***	***L***	***0-1***			18
19	***FAC1r***	***A***	***Carlisle United***	***1484***	***L***	***1-2***	***Garrard 29 (pen)***		19
23	CSouth	A	Eastbourne Borough	527	L	0-1		20	20
26	CSouth	H	Maidenhead United	138	D	2-2	Reynolds 6 Whichelow 10	19	21
30	CSouth	H	Bath City	151	L	0-1		20	22
Dec 7	CSouth	A	Bath City	541	D	2-2	Noto 45 Brown 90	20	23
9	CSouth	H	Sutton United	201	L	1-3	Montgomery 89	20	24
14	CSouth	H	Weston-s-Mare	115	D	1-1	Ball 48	18	25
21	CSouth	A	Whitehawk	57	W	2-0	Jeffrey 37 89	17	26
26	CSouth	H	Concord Rangers	151	L	0-2		18	27
28	CSouth	A	Bishop's Stortford	430	W	3-1	Noto 19 88 (pen) Jeffrey 39	17	28
Jan 11	CSouth	H	Dorchester Town	173	W	5-0	Jeffrey 40 Reynolds 52 83 Whitchelow 53 Lipman 71	15	29
25	CSouth	H	Dover Athletic	251	D	2-2	Forbes 55 (og) Montgomery 57	16	30
Feb 3	CSouth	H	Basingstoke Town	112	D	1-1	Montgomery 1	17	31
22	CSouth	A	Bromley	550	L	1-2	Garrard 70	18	32
March 1	CSouth	H	Tonbridge Angels	203	W	7-0	Reynolds 6 MORAIS 3 (21 41 54) Oyenuga 48 Montgomery 78 Angol 82	16	33
5	CSouth	H	Havant &Waterlooville	128	L	0-2		16	34
8	CSouth	A	Dorchester Town	401	W	4-1	Montgomery 9 87 Oyenuga 11 Whichelow 18	16	35
11	CSouth	A	Maidenhead United	179	W	1-0	Morais 90	14	36
15	CSouth	A	Gosport Borough	550	L	1-2	Morias 90	15	37
17	CSouth	H	Farnborough	131	D	1 1	Noto 55		38
20	CSouth	A	Concord Rangers	148	W	4-0	Morais 16 90 Mawer 39 Reynolds 50	14	39
22	CSouth	H	Ebbsfleet United	274	W	2-1	Thalasittis 17 (og) Angol 47	13	40
29	CSouth	A	Dover Athletic	721	D	0-0		13	41
April 1	CSouth	A	Sutton United	418	L	0-1		13	42
5	CSouth	H	Chelmsford City	**352**	W	4-3	Angol 3 16 Todd 34 Fleetwood 56	13	43
9	CSouth	H	Eastbourne Borough	141	W	3-1	Montgomery 5 Angol 23 (pen) Oyenuga 33	12	44
12	CSouth	H	Whitehawk	131	L	1-3	Morias 90	13	45
16	CSouth	A	Havant & Waterlooville	562	D	1-1	Shakes 37	13	46
19	CSouth	A	Hayes & Yeading	115	L	0-1		14	47
21	CSouth	H	Staines Town	155	L	0-2		14	48
26	CSouth	A	Eastleigh	639	W	1-0	Morgan 12	13	49

GOALSCORERS	Lge	FAC	FAT	Total	Pens	Hat-tricks	Cons Run
Montgomery	9			9			2
Morais	8			8		1	2
Ball	5	1		6			2
Angol	5			5	1		2
Noto	4	1		5	1		
Reynolds	5			5			
Garrard	2	2		4	2		
Jeffery	4			4			
Simmonds	3	1		4			
Oyenuga	3			3			
Whichelow	3			3			
Lipman	2			2			
Brown	1			1			
Cox		1		1			
Fleetwood	1			1			
Hastings	1			1			
Mawer	1			1			
Moll	1			1			
Morgan	1			1			
Shakes	1			1			
Sterling-Parker	1			1			
Todd	1			1			
Opponents	4	1		5			

Cons Run - Consecutive scoring games.

BROMLEY

Chairman: Ashley Reading & Derek Reading
Secretary: Colin Russell (T) 07970 031 511 (E) colin@bromleyfc.co.uk
Commercial Manager: Barry Wickenden (T) 020 8460 5291
Programme Editor: Matt Hall (T) 07982 226 359
Ground Address: The Stadium, Hayes Lane, Bromley, Kent BR2 9EF
(T) 020 8460 5291 **Manager:** Mark Goldberg

Photo: Keith Clayton.

Club Factfile

Founded: 1892 **Nickname:** The Lillywhites
Previous Names: None
Previous Leagues: South London, Southern, London, West Kent, South Surburban, Kent, Spartan 1907-08, Isthmian 1908-11, 52-2007, Athenian 1919-1952
Club Colours (change): White with black trim/white with black trim/white (All red)

Ground Capacity: 5,000 **Seats:** 1,300 **Covered:** 2,500 **Clubhouse:** Yes **Shop:** Yes

Directions
From M25 Motorway: Leaving the M25 at Junction 4, follow the A21 to Bromley and London, for approximately 4 miles and then fork left onto the A232 signposted Croydon/Sutton. At the 2nd set of traffic lights turn right into Baston Road (B265), following it for about 2 miles as it becomes Hayes Street and then Hayes Lane. Bromley FC is on right hand side of road just after a mini roundabout. From the Croydon/Surrey areas use the A232, turn left into Baston Road (B265), following it for about 2 miles as it becomes Hayes Street and then Hayes Lane. From West London use the South Circular Road as far as West Dulwich and then via Crystal Palace, Penge, Beckenham and Bromley South areas. From North and East London use the Blackwall Tunnel and then the A20 road as far as Sidcup. Then use the A232 to Keston Common, turn right into Baston Road (B265), following it for about 2 miles as it becomes Hayes Street and then Hayes Lane.

Previous Grounds: White Hart Field. Widmore Road. Plaistow Cricket Ground.

Record Attendance: 10,798 v Nigeria - 1950
Record Victory: 13-1 v Redhill - Athenian League 1945-46
Record Defeat: 1-11 v Barking - Athenian League 1933-34
Record Goalscorer: George Brown - 570 (1938-61)
Record Appearances: George Brown
Additional Records: Received £50,000 from Millwall for John Goodman

Senior Honours:
Amateur Cup 1910-11, 37-38, 48-49.
Isthmian League 1908-09, 09-10, 53-54, 60-61. Athenian League 1922-23, 48-49, 50-51.
Kent Senior Cup 1949/50, 76-77, 91-92, 96-97, 2005-06, 06-07. Kent Amateur Cup x12. London Senior Cup x4

10 YEAR RECORD

04-05	05-06	06-07	07-08	08-09	09-10	10-11	11-12	12-13	13-14
Isth1 4	Isth P 11	Isth P 2	Conf S 11	Conf S 13	Conf S 12	Conf S 11	Conf S 17	Conf S 15	Conf S 3

BROMLEY MATCH RESULTS 2013-14

Date	Comp	H/A	Opponents	Att:	Result		Goalscorers	Pos	No.
Aug 17	CSouth	A	Hayes & Yeading	173	W	2-0	Kiernan 32 Joseph-Dubois 81	3	1
20	CSouth	H	Whitehawk	605	W	4-0	Swaine 15 May 21 Goldberg 24 Joseph-Dubois 65	1	2
24	CSouth	H	Tonbridge Angels	666	W	5-1	Jason-Dubois 22 Goldberg 30 Kiernan 54 Swaine 77 Clarke 90	1	3
26	CSouth	A	Bishop's Stortford	451	L	0-1		2	4
31	CSouth	H	Gosport Borough	503	W	2-1	Joseph-Dubois 34 Smith 71	1	5
Sept 7	CSouth	A	Eastleigh	837	L	1-2	Goldberg 50	2	6
14	CSouth	H	Staines Town	584	W	3-0	Nicholls 57 Goldberg 66 Joseph-Dubois 90	2	7
17	CSouth	A	Concord Rangers	334	W	3-2	Buchanan 7 Joseph-Dubois 51 Goldberg 75	2	8
21	CSouth	H	Bsingstoke Town	681	W	3-2	Goldberg 19 Mullings 38 Smith 75	2	9
28	***FAC2Q***	***H***	***Burgess Hill Town***	***506***	***W***	***1-0***	***Mullings 20***		10
Oct 5	CSouth	A	Boreham Wood	218	D	1-1	Swallow 48	2	11
12	***FAC3Q***	***H***	***Heybridge Swifts***	***540***	***L***	***1-2***	***Erskine 45***		12
19	CSouth	A	Sutton United	894	L	0-1		2	13
26	CSouth	A	Maidenhead United	288	W	1-0	May J 66	2	14
Nov 2	CSouth	H	Dorchester Town	430	W	4-1	Anderson 18 Swaine 36 Goldberg 58 Buchanan 76	1	15
5	CSouth	H	Chelmsford City	548	W	5-0	GOLDBERG 3 (11 43 72) Anderson 42 May 82	1	16
16	***FAT3Q***	***A***	***Ebbsfleet United***	***556***	***L***	***1-4***	***May J 67***		17
23	CSouth	H	Havant & Waterlooville	425	W	2-0	Joseph-Dubois 52 Nicholls 60	1	18
Dec 7	CSouth	H	Farnborough	580	W	3-0	Kiernan 16 May.J 29 Joseph-Dubois 41.	1	19
10	CSouth	A	Dover Athletic	598	W	2-0	Anderson 39 Goldberg 83	1	20
14	CSouth	A	Basingstoke Town	340	W	1-0	Joseph-Dubois 38	1	21
21	CSouth	A	Weston-s-Mare	610	W	1-0	Goldberg 37	1	22
26	CSouth	H	Ebbsfleet United	**1344**	D	0-0		1	23
28	CSouth	A	Whitehawk	290	W	2-1	Goldberg 57 71	1	24
Jan 1	CSouth	A	Ebbsfleet United	998	W	3-1	Joseph-Dubois 28 Reid 56 Goldberg 81	1	25
14	CSouth	H	Concord Rangers	305	L	1-2	Swaine 38	1	26
18	CSouth	A	Bath City	755	W	2-1	Goldberg 18 Joseph-Dubois 59	1	27
25	CSouth	H	Hayes & Yeading	1066	W	2-1	Swaine 26 McDonnell 29	1	28
Feb 15	CSouth	A	Dorchester Town	417	L	2-3	May 82 Modeste 64	1	29
22	CSouth	H	Boreham Wood	550	W	2-1	Goldberg 13 Joseph-Dubois 16	1	30
March 1	CSouth	H	Bath City	857	D	2-2	Goldberg 20 Waldren 51	1	31
4	CSouth	H	Sutton United	795	L	2-4	Joseph-Dubois 42 55	1	32
8	CSouth	A	Chelmsford CIty	738	L	1-3	Joseph-Dubois 46	1	33
11	CSouth	H	Dover Athletic	466	L	0-4		1	34
15	CSouth	A	Farnborough	309	L	1-2	Dennis 83	2	35
18	CSouth	H	Eastbourne Borough	378	W	2-1	May 28 Swaine 72	2	36
22	CSouth	H	Maidenhead United	610	W	6-1	Goldberg 28 68 (pen) Joseph-Dubois 23 45 May 65 Dennis 90	1	37
25	CSouth	A	Staines Town	212	L	1-2	Waldren 41	2	38
29	CSouth	A	Eastbourne Borough	682	D	1-1	Dennis 77	2	39
April 5	CSouth	A	Havant & Waterlooville	576	L	0-1		3	40
8	CSouth	H	Eastleigh	1011	L	1-2	Swaine 45	3	41
12	CSouth	H	Weston-s-Mare	352	W	2-1	Goldberg 50 (pen) May 90	3	42
19	CSouth	A	Tonbridge Angels	672	D	1-1	Goldberg 9	3	43
21	CSouth	H	Bishop's Stortford	549	W	3-2	May 57 Goldberg 78 Waldren 87	3	44
26	CSouth	A	Gosport Borough	577	W	2-1	Elder 3 Cogan 87 (pen)	3	45
30	***CSPO SF 1***	***A***	***Ebbsfeet United***	***1693***	***L***	***0-4***			46
May 3	***CSPO SF 2***	***H***	***Ebbsfleet United***	***1441***	***W***	***1-0***	***Waldren 25***		47

GOALSCORERS	Lge	FAC	FAT	Total	Pens	Hat-tricks	Cons Run
Goldberg	23			23	2	1	4
Joseph-Dubois	17			17			3
May	9		1	10			
Swaine	7			7			2
Waldren	3+1			4			
Anderson	3			3			2
Dennis	3			3			
Kiernan	3			3			
Mullings	1	1		2			2
Smith	2			2			
Buchanan	2			2			
Nicholls	2			2			
Clarke	1			1			
Cogan				1	1		
Elder	1			1			
Erskine		1		1			
McDonnell	1			1			
Modeste	1			1			
Reid	1			1			
Swallow	1			1			

Cons Run - Consecutive scoring games.

Play-off goals indicated by +

CHELMSFORD CITY

Chairman: Trevor Smith
Secretary: Alan Brown **(T)** 07963 626 381 **(E)** algbrown@blueyonder.co.uk
Commercial Manager: Mick Hooker **(T)** 07957 814 639
Programme Editor: Ken Carr **(T)** 07943 553 436
Ground Address: Melbourne Park Stadium, Salerno Way, Chelmsford CM1 2EH
(T) 01245 290 959 **Manager:** Mark Hawkes

Club Factfile

Founded: 1938 **Nickname:** City or Clarets
Previous Names: None
Previous Leagues: Southern League 1938-2004. Isthmian 2004-08

Club Colours (change): Claret/white/white (White & blue/blue/blue)

Ground Capacity: 3,000 **Seats:** 1,300 **Covered:** 1,300 **Clubhouse:** Yes **Shop:** Yes

Directions
Leave A12 at J15 and head towards Chelmsford. At the roundabout turn left into Westway. Turn left onto the A1060 signposted Sawbridgeworth. At the second set of traffic lights turn right into Chignal Road. Turn right into Melbourne Avenue. Salerno Way is on your left. At the end of the football pitches and immediately before the block of flats, turn left at the mini roundabout in Salerno Way to enter the Stadium car park.

Previous Grounds: New Writtle Street 1938-97, Maldon Town 1997-98, Billericay Town 1998-2005

Record Attendance: 16,807 v Colchester United - Southern League 10/09/1949. Salerno Way: 2,998 v Billericay Town - Isthmian Jan. 2006
Record Victory: 10-1 v Bashley (H) - Southern League 26/04/2000
Record Defeat: 1-10 v Barking (A) - FA Trophy 11/11/1978
Record Goalscorer: Tony Butcher - 287 (1957-71)
Record Appearances: Derek Tiffin - 550 (1950-63)
Additional Records: Paid £10,000 to Dover Athletic for Tony Rogers 1992
Received £50,000 from Peterborough United for David Morrison
Senior Honours:
Southern League 1945-46, 67-68, 71-72, Southern Division 1988-89, League Cup 1945-46, 59-60, 90-91.
Essex Professional Cup 1957-58, 69-70, 70-71, 73-74, 74-75. Non-League Champions Cup 1971-72.
Essex Senior Cup 1985-86, 88-89, 92-93, 2002-03. Isthmian League Premier Division 2007-08.

10 YEAR RECORD

04-05	05-06	06-07	07-08	08-09	09-10	10-11	11-12	12-13	13-14
Isth P 8	Isth P 10	Isth P 3	Isth P 1	Conf S 5	Conf S 3	Conf S 4	Conf S 6	Conf S 5	Conf S 17

CHELMSFORD CITY MATCH RESULTS 2013-14

Date	Comp	H/A	Opponents	Att:	Result		Goalscorers	Pos	No.
Aug 19	CSouth	H	Concord Rangers	320	D	2-2	Goulding 17 (pen) Long 20	10	1
24	CSouth	H	Staines Town	**602**	**W**	3-2	Goulding 33 41 Brayley 75	8	2
26	CSouth	A	Tonbridge Angels	510	L	1-2	Brayley 90 (pen)	13	3
31	CSouth	H	Weston-s-Mare	581	L	1-2	Long 36	17	4
Sept 7	CSouth	A	Hayes & Yeading	218	L	0-4		18	5
14	CSouth	H	Whitehawk	587	L	0-2		20	6
17	CSouth	A	Ebbsfleet United	696	**W**	2-0	Edmans 74 Derry 88	19	7
21	CSouth	A	Dorchester Town	357	L	0-2		20	8
28	***FAC2Q***	***A***	***Biggleswade Town***	***329***	***L***	***0-2***			9
Oct 5	CSouth	H	Bath City	619	**W**	1-0	Edmans 39	20	10
19	ConfS	H	Eastbourne Borough	574	**W**	3-0	Redwood 37 Haines 71 Long 79	14	11
22	ConfS	A	Farnborough	373	L	0-2		14	12
26	ConfS	A	Gosport Borough	501	L	1-2	Derry 87 (pen)	15	13
Nov 2	ConfS	H	Boreham Wood	569	L	0-6		17	14
5	ConfS	A	Bromley	548	L	0-5		17	15
16	***FAT3Q***	***H***	***St Albans City***	***429***	***L***	***1-2***	***Moraes 32***		16
23	ConfS	H	Dover Athletic	591	L	0-4		19	17
25	ConfS	A	Havant & Waterlooville	390	L	0-3		19	18
30	ConfS	H	Farnborough	475	**W**	3-1	Long 16 Ward 43 Brayley 79	16	19
Dec 7	ConfS	H	Basingstoke Town	561	**W**	1-0	Edmans 80	16	20
10	ConfS	A	Maidenhead United	263	D	1-1	Callander 13	16	21
14	ConfS	H	Hayes & Yeading	718	D	0-0		16	22
26	ConfS	H	Bishop's Stortford	728	**W**	2-1	Callander 13 24	15	23
Jan 11	ConfS	H	Sutton United	717	L	0-2		17	24
18	ConfS	A	Whitehawk	148	**W**	4-0	Edmans 33 Callander 35 Cheek 69 89	15	25
21	ConfS	A	Concord Rangers	409	**W**	3-1	Callander 7 Cheek 44 Edmans 86	13	26
Feb 1	ConfS	A	Dover Athletic	811	D	2-2	Davis 73 Forecast 90	13	27
3	ConfS	H	Ebbsfleet United	652	L	1-2	Edmans 25	13	28
22	ConfS	H	Maidenhead United	648	L	0-3		13	29
March 1	ConfS	A	Sutton United	707	L	0-2		15	30
8	ConfS	H	Bromley	738	**W**	3-1	Cheek 32 St Aimie 32 Smith 78	14	31
11	ConfS	A	Eastleigh	552	L	0-1		15	32
15	ConfS	A	Eastbourne Borough	601	L	2-4	Watts 24 (og) Cheek 52	16	33
17	ConfS	H	Dorchester Town	562	**W**	4 1	St Aimie 60 Cheek 65 Ward 77 Edmans 90	16	34
22	ConfS	A	Bath City	1374	L	1-4	Callander 65	18	35
29	ConfS	H	Havant & Waterlooville	613	D	0-0		16	36
April 5	ConfS	A	Boreham Wood	352	L	3-4	Lock 7 Smith 41 (pen) Callander 84	20	37
8	ConfS	A	Basingstoke Town	182	**W**	3-2	Smith 15 (pen) Cheek75 90	17	38
10	ConfS	A	Bishop's Stortford	755	D	1-1	Hughes 90	17	39
12	ConfS	H	Eastleigh	623	D	0-0		17	40
19	ComfS	A	Staines Town	373	L	1-3	Callender 35	19	41
21	ConfS	H	Tonbridge Angels	842	**W**	7-1	CHEEK 4 (28 43 85 90) Callender 17 59 Lovell (og)	17	42
23	ConfS	H	Gosport Borough	776	**W**	1-0	Ward 58	17	43
26	ConfS	A	Weston-s-Mare	464	L	0-2		17	44

GOALSCORERS	Lge	FAC	FAT	Total	Pens	Hat-tricks	Cons Run
Cheek	12			12		1	2
Callender	10			10			2
Edmans	7			7			2
Long	4			4			
Brayley	3			3	1		
Goulding	3			3	1		
Smith	3			3	2		2
Derry	2			2	1		
St Aimie	2			2			
Ward	2			2			
Davis	1			1			
Forecast	1			1			
Haines	1			1			
Hughes	1			1			
Lock	1			1			
Moraes			1	1			
Redwood	1			1			
Opponents	2			2			

Cons Run - Consecutive scoring games.

CONCORD RANGERS

Chairman: Antony Smith
Secretary: Chris Crerie **(T)** 0790 952 8818 **(E)** concordrangers@btinternet.com
Commercial Manager: tbc **(T)**
Programme Editor: Alan Jessop-Peacock **(T)** 0798 387 2000
Ground Address: Aspect Arena, Thames Road, Canvey Island, Essex SS8 0HH
(T) 01268 515 750 **Manager:** Danny Cowley

Club Factfile

Founded: 1967 **Nickname:** Beachboys
Previous Names: None
Previous Leagues: Southend & District, Southend Alliance, Essex Intermediate 1988-91, Essex Senior 1991-2008.

Club Colours (change): All yellow (All blue)

Ground Capacity: 1,500 **Seats:** Yes **Covered:** Yes **Clubhouse:** Yes **Shop:**

Directions
Take the A13 to Sadlers Farm at Benfleet, follow the road onto Canvey Way signposted Canvey Island (A130) next roundabout (Waterside Farm) take 3rd exit onto Canvey Island 1st exit, signposted seafront / Industrial area next roundabout 1st exit, next roundabout 1st exit. Next landmark is a set of traffic lights (King Canute Pub on the left, carry on through to a mini r/bout passing a school on the right turn right into Thorney Bay Road, Thames Road is the 3rd turning on the right, Concord Rangers is approx 1 mile along Thames Road.

Previous Grounds: Waterside

Record Attendance: 1,500 v Lee Chapel North - FA Sunday Cup 1989-90
Record Victory: Not Known
Record Defeat: Not Known
Record Goalscorer: Not Known
Record Appearances: Not Known
Additional Records:

Senior Honours:
Essex Intermediate League Division 2 1990-91. Essex Senior League 1997-98, 2003-04, 07-08.
Essex Senior Cup 2013-14.

10 YEAR RECORD

04-05	05-06	06-07	07-08	08-09	09-10	10-11	11-12	12-13	13-14
ESen 9	ESen 7	ESen 7	ESen 1	Isth1N 5	Isth1N 2	Isth P 8	Isth P 14	Isth P 4	Conf S 9

CONCORD RANGERS MATCH RESULTS 2013-14

Date	Comp	H/A	Opponents	Att:	Result	Goalscorers	Pos	No.
Aug 17	CSouth	H	Basingstoke Town	306	L 1-2	Easterford 83	15	1
19	CSouth	A	Chelmsford City	320	D 2-2	Hallett 11 Easterford 41	14	2
24	CSouth	A	Dover Athletic	681	**W** 1-0	Spendlove 65	11	3
26	CSouth	H	Sutton United	320	D 0-0		11	4
31	CSouth	A	Bath City	485	L 1-3	Collins 57	16	5
Sept 7	CSouth	H	Dorchester Town	284	**W** 1-0	King 86	13	6
14	CSouth	A	Eastbourne Borough	500	D 0-0		11	7
17	CSouth	H	Bromley	334	L 2-3	Higgins 19 Ogilvie 23	14	8
21	CSouth	H	Maidenhead United	295	**W** 4-1	Higgins 23 57 Gordon 65 King 81	10	9
28	***FAC2Q***	***H***	***St Ives Town***	***238***	***W 4-3***	***Ogilvie 11 Cowley 17 50 Higgins 28***		10
Oct 5	CSouth	A	Eastleigh	551	D 1-1	Gordon 13	10	11
12	***FAC3Q***	***H***	***Histon***	***307***	***W 2-1***	***Cowley 75 White 79***		12
19	CSouth	A	Weston-s-Mare	209	L 0-5		15	13
26	***FAC4Q***	***A***	***Barnet***	***1373***	***L 0-3***			14
Nov 2	CSouth	A	Ebbsfleet United	687	L 0-4		16	15
12	CSouth	H	Whitehawk	280	D 1 1	Higgins 90	16	16
16	***FAT3Q***	***A***	***Dulwich Hamlet***	***462***	***D 1-1***	***Higgins 23***		17
19	***FAT3Qr***	***H***	***Dulwich Hamlet***	***156***	***W 4-3****	***White 17 Higgins 46 120 Harris 117***		18
23	CSouth	A	Staines Town	151	**W** 1-0	Ogilvie 50	15	19
26	CSouth	H	Farnborough	142	**W** 5-0	White 13 Powell 50 OGILVIE 3 (8 55 64)	15	20
30	***FAT1***	***A***	***Gosport Borough***	***192***	***L 0-1***			21
Dec 7	CSouth	H	Gosport Borough	203	L 0-2		15	22
10	CSouth	H	Eastbourne Borough	184	D 1-1	Hughes-Mason 47	15	23
14	CSouth	A	Dorchester Town	356	D 2-2	Cawley 65 White 71	15	24
26	CSouth	A	Boreham Wood	151	**W** 2-0	Higgins 7 (pen) Collins 85	14	25
Jan 11	CSouth	H	Hayes & Yeading	327	**W** 3-1	Stokes 40 61 White 90	13	26
14	CSouth	A	Bromley	305	**W** 2-1	Higgins 41 (pen) 56	10	27
21	CSouth	H	Chelmsford City	**409**	L 1-3	Stokes 51	12	28
Feb 22	CSouth	H	Bishop's Stortford	212	L 0-2		12	29
25	CSouth	H	Staines Town	156	**W** 2-1	Collins 13 Stokes 48	12	30
March 1	CSouth	A	Whitehawk	154	**W** 2-0	Cawley 24 Collins 71	11	31
8	CSouth	H	Eastleigh	251	**W** 3-2	Collins 37 Stokes 77 Cawley 90	11	32
13	CSouth	H	Havant & Waterlooville	182	D 3-3	Glazier 35 (pen) Cawley 66 Spendlove 90	12	33
15	CSouth	A	Hayes & Yeading	94	L 0-1		13	34
18	CSouth	A	Bishop's Stortford	260	**W** 1-0	Stokes 90	10	35
20	CSouth	H	Boreham Wood	148	L 0-4		10	36
22	CSouth	H	Weston-s-Mare	169	**W** 2-0	Taaffe 45 Cawley 50	10	37
29	CSouth	A	Farnborough	335	**W** 2-0	Taaffe 12 Ogilvie 79	9	38
April 1	CSouth	A	Tonbridge Angels	274	D 2-2	Collins 17 King 89	10	39
5	CSouth	A	Gosport Borough	375	**W** 2-1	Taaffe 69 Stokes 88	8	40
8	CSouth	H	Tonbridge Angels	180	D 2-2	Cawley 70 Stokes 76	9	41
10	CSouth	A	Maidenhead United	253	**W** 3-1	Glazier 19 (pen) King 38 Njie 50	6	42
12	CSouth	A	Havant & Waterlooville	604	L 0-1		8	43
19	CSouth	H	Dover Athletic	286	L 1-2	Stokes 63	9	44
21	CSouth	A	Sutton United	635	L 0-1		9	45
23	CSouth	A	Basingstoke Town	137	**W** 1 0	Taaffe 45	9	46
24	CSouth	H	Ebbsfleet United	250	L 1-2	Gordon 73	9	47
26	CSouth	H	Bath City	302	L 0-2		9	48

GOALSCORERS	Lge	FAC	FAT	Total	Pens	Hat-tricks	Cons Run
Higgins	7	1	3	11	2		3
Stokes	9			9			2
Cawley	5	3		8			
Ogilive	6	1		7		1	2
Collins	6			6			3
White	3	1	1	5			
Gordon	3			3			
King	4			4			
Taffe	4			4			2
Easterford	2			2			
Glazier	2			2	2		
Spendlove	2			2			
Hallett	1			1			
Harris			1	1			
Hughes-Mason	1			1			
Nije	1			1			
Powell	1			1			

Cons Run - Consecutive scoring games.

EASTBOURNE BOROUGH

Chairman: Len Smith
Secretary: Mrs Jan Field **(T)** 07749 572 693 **(E)** janfield38@sky.com
Commercial Manager: Sharon Hind **(T)** 07850 582 434
Programme Editor: Anthony Scott **(T)** 07769 114 476
Ground Address: Langney Sports Club, Priory Lane, Eastbourne BN23 7QH
(T) 01323 766 265 **Manager:** Tommy Widdrington

Club Factfile

Founded: 1966 **Nickname:** Borough
Previous Names: Langney Sports > 2001
Previous Leagues: Eastbourne & Hastings, Sussex County, Southern

Club Colours (change): Red/black/red (All yellow)

Ground Capacity: 4,151 **Seats:** 542 **Covered:** 2,500 **Clubhouse:** Yes **Shop:** Yes

Directions
From M25 take M23/A23 eastbound to A27 Polegate by pass pick up and follow signs for crematorium 50yds past crematorium turn right at mini roundabout into Priory Road Stadium 100yds on left.

Previous Grounds: None

Record Attendance: 3,770 v Oxford United - FA Cup 1st Round 05/11/05
Record Victory: 10-1 v Haywards Heath Town - Sussex County Division One 1991-92
Record Defeat: 0-8 v Sheppey United (A) - FA Vase 09/10/93 and v Peachaven & Tels (A) - Sussex Co. Div.1 09/11/93
Record Goalscorer: Nigel Hole - 146
Record Appearances: Darren Baker - 689
Additional Records: Paid £1,800 to Yeovil Town for Yemi Odoubade.
Received £15,000 from Oxford United for Yemi Odoubade.
Senior Honours:
Sussex County League 1999-2000, 02-03. Sussex Senior Cup 2001-02.

10 YEAR RECORD

04-05	05-06	06-07	07-08	08-09	09-10	10-11	11-12	12-13	13-14
Conf S 5	Conf S 17	Conf S 7	Conf S 2	Conf 13	Conf 19	Conf 23	Conf S 18	Conf S 12	Conf S 10

Conference Action

Midfield tussle between Cambridge United and AFC Halifax during one of the Conference Play-off semi finals.

Photo: Peter Barnes.

EASTBOURNE BOROUGH MATCH RESULTS 2013-14

Date	Comp	H/A	Opponents	Att:	Result		Goalscorers	Pos	No.
Aug 17	CSouth	A	Weston-s-Mare	207	W	1-0	Raymond 67 (pen)	7	1
20	CSouth	H	Tonbridge Angels	678	W	2-2	Levy 79 Johnson 90	5	2
24	CSouth	H	Ebbsfleet United	641	D	1-1	Shephard 17	3	3
26	CSouth	A	Hayes & Yeading	486	W	1-0	Johnson 51	1	4
Sept 7	CSouth	A	Staines Town	350	L	1-2	Johnson 38	7	5
14	CSouth	H	Concord Rangers	500	D	0-0		8	6
17	CSouth	A	Eastleigh	554	L	0-2		10	7
21	CSouth	H	Bishops Stortford	514	W	4-1	Lok 45 Johnson 61 90 Levy 78	6	8
28	***FAC2Q***	***H***	***Farnborough***	***560***	***D***	***0-0***			9
Oct 1	***FAC2Qr***	***A***	***Farnborough***		***W***	***2-0***	***Lok 50 Shephard 53***		10
8	CSouth	H	Farnborough	503	W	5-2	SHEPHARD 3 (2 46 69) Lok 42 Levy 88	5	11
12	***FAC3Q***	***A***	***Ebbsfleet United***	***901***	***L***	***0-2***			12
19	CSouth	A	Chelmsford City	574	L	0-3		8	13
22	CSouth	H	Dover Athletic	488	L	0-4		9	14
26	CSouth	A	Havant & Waterlooville	745	D	1-1	Johnson 36	10	15
Nov 2	CSouth	H	Maidenhead United	514	W	2-0	Hart 49 Johnson 75	8	16
16	***FAT3Q***	***H***	***Maidenhead United***	***384***	***L***	***0-1***			17
21	CSouth	H	Boreham Wood	527	W	1-0	Lok 83	7	18
30	CSouth	A	Dorchester Town	407	D	0-0		7	19
Dec 7	CSouth	H	Weston-s-Mare	483	W	2-0	Taylor 18 88	4	20
10	CSouth	A	Concord Rangers	184	D	1-1	Taylor 69	5	21
14	CSouth	H	Staines Town	547	W	2-0	Taylor 27 Deaman 34	3	22
26	CSouth	H	Whitehawk	**683**	L	0-2		5	23
28	CSouth	A	Tonbridge Angels	608	L	1-2	Lok 78	5	24
Jan 18	CSouth	H	Basingstoke Town	511	L	1-3	Deaman 77	11	25
25	CSouth	H	Bath City	514	W	3-2	Long 21 Hammond 55 Lok 90	6	26
Feb 4	CSouth	A	Whitehawk	201	W	2-1	Reynolds 11 Akokhia 77	7	27
8	CSouth	H	Dorchester Town	445	L	0-1		7	28
22	CSouth	H	Sutton United	420	D	1-1	Hammond 24	9	29
25	CSouth	A	Gosport Borough	270	W	2-1	Lok 33 46	7	30
March 4	CSouth	H	Eastleigh	454	D	1-1	Simpemba 41	8	31
8	CSouth	H	Havant & Waterlooville	537	L	0-1		8	32
11	CSouth	A	Basingstoke Town	183	W	2-1	Rowe 27 Hammond 30	8	33
15	CSouth	H	Chelmsford City	568	W	4-2	Long 37 Watts 41 Hammond 58 73	7	34
18	CSouth	A	Bromley	378	L	1-2	Hammond 84	7	35
22	CSouth	A	Dover Athletic	735	D	0-0		7	36
25	CSouth	A	Maidenhead United	143	W	3-2	Stinson 17 Simpemba 63 Long 90	7	37
29	CSouth	H	Bromley	682	D	1-1	Derry 70	8	38
April 3	CSouth	A	Bishop's Stortford	231	L	0-1		8	39
5	CSouth	A	Bath City	593	L	1-2	Johnson 10	9	40
9	CSouth	A	Eastbourne Borough	141	L	1-3	Hammond 11	10	41
12	CSouth	H	Gosport Borough	470	L	1-3	Derry 43	10	42
17	CSouth	A	Ebbsfleet United	933	L	0-1		10	43
21	CSouth	H	Hayes & Yeading	602	W	3-2	Stinson 28 Johnson 52 Lok 87	10	44
26	CSouth	A	Farnborough	345	D	3-3	Rowe 12 Raymond 25 Worrall 64	10	45

GOALSCORERS	Lge	FAC	FAT	Total	Pens	Hat-tricks	Cons Run
Lok	8	1		9			
Johnson	8			8			2
Hammond	7			7			
Shephard	5	1		6		1	2
Taylor	4			4			
Levy	3			3			
Deaman	2			2			
Derry	2			2			
Long	2			2			
Raymond	2			2	1		

	Lge	FAC	FAT	Total	Pens	Hat-tricks	Cons Run
Rowe	2			2			
Stinson	2			2			
Akokhia	1			1			
Hart	1			1			
Reynolds	1			1			
Simpemba	1			1			
Watts	1			1			
Worrall	1			1			

Cons Run - Consecutive scoring games.

EBBSFLEET UNITED

Chairman: Dr Abdulla M.S. Al-Humaidi
Secretary: Peter Danzey (T) 07403 285 385 (E) peter.danzey@eufc.co.uk
Commercial Manager: Dave Archer (T) 07713 872 141
Programme Editor: Ed Miller (T) 07986 677 503
Ground Address: Stonebridge Road, Northfleet, Kent DA11 9GN
(T) 01474 533 796 **Manager:** Steve Brown

Club Factfile

Founded: 1946 **Nickname:** The Fleet
Previous Names: Gravesend United and Northfleet United merged in 1946 to form Gravesend and Northfleet > 2007
Previous Leagues: Southern 1946-79, 80-96. Alliance 1979-80, Isthmian 1997-2001

Club Colours (change): Red/white/red (White/black/black)

Ground Capacity: 4,184 **Seats:** 500 **Covered:** 3,000 **Clubhouse:** Yes **Shop:** Yes

Directions
A2 to Ebbsfleet/Eurostar International Junction.
Follow Brown signs to 'The Fleet'.

Previous Grounds: Gravesend United: Central Avenue

Record Attendance: 12,036 v Sunderland - FA Cup 4th Round 12/02/1963
Record Victory: 8-1 v Clacton Town - Southern League 1962-63
Record Defeat: 0-9 v Trowbridge Town - Southern League Premier DIvision 1991-92
Record Goalscorer: Steve Portway - 152 (1992-94, 97-2001)
Record Appearances: Ken Burrett - 537
Additional Records: Paid £8,000 to Wokingham Town for Richard Newbery 1996 and to Tonbridge for Craig Williams 1997
Received £35,000 from West Ham United for Jimmy Bullard 1998
Senior Honours:
Southern League 1956-57, Division 1 South 1974-75, Southern Division 1994-95. Isthmian League Premier 2001-02.
FA Trophy 2007-08. Kent Senior Cup 1948-49, 52-53, 80-81, 99-00, 00-01, 01-02.

10 YEAR RECORD

04-05	05-06	06-07	07-08	08-09	09-10	10-11	11-12	12-13	13-14
Conf 14	Conf 16	Conf 7	Conf 11	Conf 14	Conf 22	Conf S 3	Conf 14	Conf 23	Conf S 4

EBBSFLEET UNITED MATCH RESULTS 2013-14

Date	Comp	H/A	Opponents	Att:	Result	Goalscorers	Pos	No.
Aug 17	CSouth	H	Havant & Waterlooville	973	D 0-0		11	1
20	CSouth	A	Dover Athletic	1562	L 1-2	Cook 39	16	2
24	CSouth	A	Eastbourne Borough	641	D 1-1	Thalassitis 27	18	3
26	CSouth	H	Maidenhead United	835	D 1-1	Thalassitis10 (pen)	16	4
31	CSouth	A	Dorchester Town	422	W 3-1	Bricknell 38 87 Cook 57	11	5
Sept 7	CSouth	H	Bath City	856	D 1-1	Huke 25	14	6
14	CSouth	A	Basingstoke Town	371	D 2-2	Rance 3 Huke 90	15	7
17	CSouth	H	Chelmsford City	796	L 0-2		16	8
21	CSouth	H	Boreham Wood	711	D 0-0		15	9
28	***FAC2Q***	***H***	***Folkstone Invicta***	***737***	***W 1-0***	***McMahon 6***		10
Oct 5	CSouth	A	Weston-s-Mare	356	W 6-0	Slocombe 5 (og) Bricknell 28 Osborn 43 48 Cook 70 73	15	11
8	CSouth	H	Eastleigh	799	W 3-1	Bricknell 19 48 McMahon 89	8	12
12	***FAC3Q***	***H***	***Eastbourne Borough***	***901***	***W 2-0***	***B.May 17 28***		13
19	CSouth	H	Gosport Borough	731	W 2-1	Long 2 B.May 53	6	14
22	CSouth	A	Bishop's Stortford	511	L 2-3	Huke 89 Cook 90	7	15
26	***FAC4Q***	***H***	***Dartford***	***2895***	***D 1-1***	***Cook 65***		16
29	***FAC4Qr***	***A***	***Dartford***	***1901***	***L 0-1***			17
Nov 2	CSouth	H	Concord Rangers	687	W 4-0	B.May 11 Thalassitis 37 Pugh 52 Palmer 82	6	18
16	***FAT3Q***	***H***	***Bromley***	***556***	***W 4-1***	***Thalassittis 15 Palmer 33 B.May 48 Bricknell 90***		19
23	CSouth	H	Basingstoke Town	953	W 1-0	Thalassittis 51	5	20
26	CSouth	A	Hayes & Yeading United	139	W 2-1	Long 81 Mitchell 81 (og)	3	21
30	***FAT1***	***H***	***Gloucester CIty***	***740***	***W 3-0***	***Bricknell 42 Thalassitis 53 McMahon 87***		22
Dec 7	CSouth	H	Whitehawk	752	W 3-1	Osborn 23 Thalassitis 54 58	3	23
14	***FAT2***	***A***	***Whitstable Town***	***742***	***W 2-1***	***Cook 40 Thalassitis 89***	***3***	24
21	CSouth	H	Sutton United	724	W 2 0	Bricknell 12 62	3	25
26	CSouth	A	Bromley	1344	D 0-0			26
28	CSouth	H	Dover Athletic	1320	L 0-2		3	27
Jan 1	CSouth	H	Bromley	998	L 1-3	Bricknell 88	3	28
11	***FAT3***	***A***	***Havant & Waterlooville***	***709***	***L 0-1***			29
14	CSouth	A	Farnborough	219	W 1-0	Bricknell 73	3	30
18	CSouth	H	Bishop's Stortford	907	W 2-1	B.May 75 Palmer 84	3	31
25	CSouth	A	Eastleigh	702	L 1-3	Bricknell 52	3	32
Feb 1	CSouth	H	Weston-s-Mare	865	D 1-1	Bricknell 56	2	33
3	CSouth	A	Chelmsford City	652	W 2-1	Thalassitis 62 McMahon 68	3	34
15	CSouth	H	Staines Town	791	W 3-0	Bricknell 5 McMahon 32 Acheampong 38	3	35
March 1	CSouth	H	Farnborough	850	W 3-0	Cook 6 Rance 47 B.May 80	4	36
4	CSouth	A	Bath City	483	D 2-2	Bricknell 30 Cook 82	4	37
8	CSouth	H	Hayes & Yeading United	821	W 1-0	Acheampong 21	4	38
11	CSouth	A	Tonbridge Angels	467	W 2-0	Osborn 43 Rance 62	3	39
15	CSouth	A	Whitehawk	285	D 1-1	Mambo 5	4	40
22	CSouth	A	Boreham Wood	274	L 1-2	Bricknell 90	4	41
27	CSouth	A	Gosport Borough	349	W 2-0	Bricknell 30 McMahon 55	4	42
29	CSouth	H	Tonbridge Angels	1102	W 1-0	Thalassitis 39	4	43
April 5	CSouth	A	Staines Town	362	D 1-1	B.May 27	4	44
12	CSouth	A	Sutton United	721	L 1-3	McMahon 48	4	45
17	CSouth	A	Havant & Waterlooville	501	L 0-1		4	46
18	CSouth	H	Eastbourne Borough	933	W 1-0	Cook 47	4	47
21	CSouth	A	Maidenhead United	398	L 0-1		4	48
23	CSouth	A	Concord Rangers	250	W 2-1	Cook 15 McMahon 83	4	49
26	CSouth	H	Dorchester Town	**1670**	W 4-0	McMahon 12 40 Thalassitis 69 Osborn 73	4	50
30	***CSPO SF 1***	***H***	***Bromlcy***	***1693***	***W 4-0***	***D.May 1 Bricknell 9 (pen) Howe 60 McMahon 80***		51
May 3	***CSPO SF 2***	***A***	***Bromley***	***1441***	***L 0-1***			52
10	***CSPO F***	***H***	***Dover Athletic***	***4294***	***L 0-1***			53

GOALSCORERS	Lge	FAC	FAT	Total	Pens	Hat-tricks	Cons Run
Bricknell	15+1		2	18	1		2
Thalassitis	9		3	12	1		3
Cook	9	1	1	11			2
McMahon	8+1	1	1	11			2
B. May	5+1	2	1	9			2
Osborn	5			5			
Huke	3			3			
Palmer	2		1	3			2
Rance	3			3			
Acheampong	2			2			
Long	2			2			
Howe	0+1			1			
Mambo	1			1			
Pugh	1			1			
Opponents	2			2			

Cons Run - Consecutive scoring games.

Play-off goals indicated by +

FARNBOROUGH

Chairman: Simon Gardener
Secretary: Jim Hardy **(T)** 07722 504 278 **(E)** info@farnboroughfc.co.uk
Commercial Manager: Jim Hardy **(T)** 07913 207 607
Programme Editor: Kevin Dyer **(T)**
Ground Address: Paddy Power Park, Cherrywood Road, Farnborough, Hants GU14 8DU
(T) 01252 541 469 **Manager:** Spencer Day

Club Factfile

Founded: 1967 **Nickname:** Boro
Previous Names: Farnborough Town 1967-2007
Previous Leagues: Surrey Senior 1968-72, Spartan 1972-76, Athenian 1976-77, Isthmian 1977-89, 99-2001, Alliance/Conference 1989-90, 91-93, 94-99, Southern 1990-91, 93-94, 2007-10

Club Colours (change): Yellow & blue/blue/yellow (All white)

Ground Capacity: 4,190 **Seats:** 627 **Covered:** 1,350 **Clubhouse:** Yes **Shop:** Yes

Directions
Leave the M3 at Junction 4 and take the A331 signed to Farnham, after a few hundred yards exit at the second slip road- signed A325 Farnborough, turn right at the roundabout and cross over the dual carriageway and small roundabout, passing the Farnborough Gate shopping centre on your left hand side, at the next roundabout turn left (first exit) onto the A325. Go over a pelican crossing and at the next set of lights take the right filter into Prospect Avenue. At the end of this road turn rightat the roundabout into Cherrywood Road, the ground is half a mile on the right hand side.

Previous Grounds: None as Farnborough. Queens Road as Farnborough Town

Record Attendance: 2,230 v Corby Town - Southern Premier 21/03/2009
Record Victory: 7-0 v Newport (I.O.W.) (A) - Southern League Division 1 South & West 01/12/2007
Record Defeat: 0-4 v Hednesford Town (A) - Southern League Premier Division 04/03/2010
Record Goalscorer: Dean McDonald - 35 (in 53+3 Appearances 2009-10)
Record Appearances: Nic Ciardini - 147 (2007-10)
Additional Records:

Senior Honours:
Southern League Division 1 South & West 2007-08, Premier Division 2009-10.
Farnborough Town: Southern League Premier Division 1990-91, 93-94. Isthmian League Division 1 1984-85, Premier Division 2000-01.
Hampshire Senior Cup 1974-75, 81-82, 83-84, 85-86, 90-91, 2003-04.

10 YEAR RECORD

04-05	05-06	06-07	07-08	08-09	09-10	10-11	11-12	12-13	13-14
Conf 21	Conf S 3	Conf S 11	SthW 1	SthP 2	SthP 1	Conf S 2	Conf S 16	Conf S 13	Conf S 16

FARNBOROUGH MATCH RESULTS 2013-14

Date	Comp	H/A	Opponents	Att:	Result		Goalscorers	Pos	No.
Sept 7	CSouth	H	Dover Athletic	**1139**	**W**	1-0	Tarpey 77	20	1
11	CSouth	A	Havant & Waterlooville	469	L	1-2	Huggins 90	20	2
14	CSouth	A	Sutton United	465	D	3-3	Bennet 34 Donnelly 39 Huggins 87	19	3
17	CSouth	H	Boreham Wood	338	**W**	2-0	Donnelly 25 90	18	4
21	CSouth	A	Staines Town	410	L	2-3	Connolly 11 Monshas 79	19	5
28	***FAC2Q***	***A***	***Eastbourne Borough***	***560***	***D***	***0-0***			6
Oct 1	***FAC2Qr***	***H***	***Eastbourne Borough***		***L***	***0-2***			7
5	CSouth	H	Whitehawk	483	**W**	2-0	Connolly 26 Page 81	16	8
8	CSouth	A	Eastbourne Borough	503	L	2-5	Doyle 81 Macklin 89	16	9
12	CSouth	H	Hayes & Yeading	714	L	1-2	Huggins 12	16	10
19	ConfS	A	Tonbridge Angels	445	**W**	3-1	Hammond 18 Donnelly 41 75	13	11
22	ConfS	H	Chelmsford City	373	**W**	2-0	Donnelly 31 Webb 72 (og)	9	12
29	ConfS	H	Bath City	352	L	2-4	Hammond 44 Donnelly 49		13
Nov 2	ConfS	H	Weston-super-Mare	400	**W**	4-0	Tarpey 20 50 Huggins 43 Donnelly 58	10	14
5	ConfS	A	Maidenhead United	247	D	2-2	Donnelly 62 (pen) Lee 86	8	15
9	ConfS	A	Eastleigh	571	L	0-1		9	16
16	***FAT 3Q***	***A***	***Staines Town***	***299***	***D***	***2-2***	***Tarpey 74 Donnelly 77 (pen)***		17
19	***FAT 3Qr***	***H***	***Staines Town***	***230***	***L***	***0-2***			18
22	ConfS	H	Gosport Borough	341	**W**	1-0	Tarpey 63	9	19
26	ConfS	A	Concord Rangers	142	L	0-5		11	20
30	ConfS	A	Chelmsford City	475	L	1-3	Lee 37	11	21
Dec7	ConfS	A	Bromley	580	L	0-3		13	22
26	ConfS	A	Badingstoke	447	L	0-4		16	23
28	ConfS	A	Havant & Waterlooville	388	D	2-2	Donnelly 67 Huggins 80	15	24
Jan 11	ConfS	H	Staines Town	313	L	1 2	Page 45	16	25
14	ConfS	H	Ebbsflee United	219	L	0-1		16	26
Feb 1	ConfS	H	Dorchester Town	292	**W**	3-2	Colmer 19 (og) Nurse 63 Page 69	16	27
4	ConfS	H	Tonbridge Angels	225	**W**	3-2	Berry 5 54 Sykes 9	14	28
15	ConfS	H	Whitehawk	162	L	1-3	Page 85	15	29
22	ConfS	A	Eastleigh	358	L	0-1		15	30
25	ConfS	H	Hayes & Yeading Utd	122	**W**	2-1	Page 34 Ball 55	13	31
Mar 1	ConfS	A	Ebbsfleet United	850	L	0-3		14	32
6	ConfS	H	Basingstoke Town	226	L	0-3		14	33
8	ConfS	H	Sutton United	345	L	1-2	French 88	15	34
15	ConfS	H	Bromley	309	**W**	2-1	Ball 53 Hooper 81	14	35
17	ConfS	A	Boreham Wood	131	D	1-1	Hooper 24	15	36
22	ConfS	A	Bishop's Stortford	360	**W**	3-1	Doyle 45 Bennett 79 Fearn 82 (pen)	15	37
25	ConfS	A	Dover Athletic	1139	**W**	1-0	Tarpey 77	20	38
29	ConfS	H	Concord Rangers	335	L	0-2		15	39
April 1	ConfS	A	Gosport Borough	311	L	0-1		16	40
5	ConfS	A	Weston-s-Mare	210	L	1-2	Hooper 45	15	41
8	ConfS	H	Bishop's Stortford	291	**W**	4-2	Huggins 24 76 Page 41 Ball 60	15	42
12	ConfS	A	Dorchester Town	320	L	0-1		15	43
19	ConfS	H	Maidenhead United	320	**W**	3-0	Colmer 68 Huggins 81 Hooper 83		44
21	ConfS	A	Bath City	571	L	2-4	Colmer 3 Hooper 90	16	45
26	ConfS	H	Eastborough Borough	345	D	3-3	Huggins 2 Hooper 31 Ball 90	16	46

GOALSCORERS	Lge	FAC	FAT	Total	Pens	Hat-tricks	Cons Run
Donnelly	10		1	11	2		5
Huggins	9			9			2
Page	7			7			
Hooper	6			6			3
Tarpey	4		1	5			
Ball	4			4			
Connolly	2			2			
Bennet	2			2			
Berry	2			2			
Colmer	2			2			
Doyle	2			2			

	Lge	FAC	FAT	Total	Pens	Hat-tricks	Cons Run
Hammond	2			2			
Lee	2			2			
Fearn	1			1	1		
French	1			1			
Mackin	1			1			
Monshas	1			1			
Nurse	1			1			
Sykes	1			1			
Opppnents	2			2			

Cons Run - Consecutive scoring games.

GOSPORT BOROUGH

Chairman: Mark Hook
Secretary: Brian Cosgrave **(T)** 07984 960 537 **(E)** brian.cosgrave@hotmail.co.uk
Commercial Manager: Jon Gardner **(T)** 07775 533 446
Programme Editor: Keith Fuller **(T)** programme@gosportboroughfc.co.uk
Ground Address: GDL Stadium, Privett Park, Privett Road, Gosport, Hampshire PO12 0SX
(T) 023 9250 1042 (Match days only) **Manager:** Alex Pike

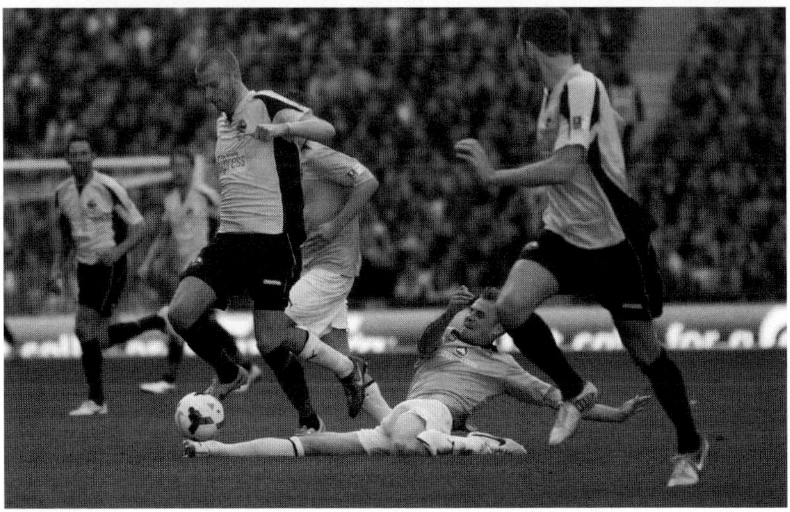

Gosney skips past Cambridge United's Tait during the 2013-14 FA Trophy final at Wembley. Photo: Keith Clayton.

Club Factfile

Founded: 1944 **Nickname:** The 'Boro'
Previous Names: Gosport Borough Athletic
Previous Leagues: Portsmouth 1944-45, Hampshire 1945-78, Southern 1978-92, Wessex 1992-2007

Club Colours (change): Yellow/blue/blue (Blue/yellow/yellow)

Ground Capacity: 4,500 **Seats:** 450 **Covered:** 600 **Clubhouse:** Yes **Shop:** Yes

Directions
Exit M27 at J11. TakeA32 Fareham to Gosport road.
After 3 miles take the 3rd exit at Brockhurst r/a, into Military Road.
At next r/a take 1st exit into Privett Road. Ground is approx. 400 yards on left.

Previous Grounds: None

Record Attendance: 4,770 v Pegasus - FA Amateur Cup 1951
Record Victory: 14-0 v Cunliffe Owen - Hampshire League 1945-46
Record Defeat: 0-9 v Gloucester City - Southern Premier Division 1989-90 and v Lymington & N.M. - Wessex Lge 99-2000
Record Goalscorer: Justin Bennett- 196 (as at May 2014)
Record Appearances: Tony Mahoney - 765
Additional Records:

Senior Honours:
Hampshire League 1945-46, 76-77, 77-78. Hampshire Senior Cup 1987-88. Wessex League Cup 1992-93.
Wessex League 2006-07. Southern Division 1 South & West Play-offs 2011-12, Premier Division Play-offs 2012-13.

10 YEAR RECORD

04-05	05-06	06-07	07-08	08-09	09-10	10-11	11-12	12-13	13-14
Wex1 4	Wex1 5	WexP 1	Sthsw 11	Sthsw 12	Sthsw 8	Sthsw 13	Sthsw 3	SthP 5	Conf S 12

GOSPORT BOROUGH MATCH RESULTS 2013-14

Date	Comp	H/A	Opponents	Att:	Result		Goalscorers	Pos	No.
Aug 17	CSouth	H	Dover Athletic	592	L	0-1		17	1
20	CSouth	A	Basingstoke Town	460	L	1-2	Brown 28	18	2
24	CSouth	A	Bath City	513	D	1-1	Brown 45	19	3
26	CSouth	H	Dorchester Town	486	D	1-1	Wooden 21	20	4
31	CSouth	A	Bromley	503	L	1-2	Bennett 85 (pen)	20	5
Sept 7	CSouth	H	Maidenhead United	485	L	0-2		21	6
14	CSouth	A	Boreham Wood	151	L	0-2		21	7
21	CSouth	H	Tonbridge Angels	418	W	2-0	Brown 53 Williams 80	21	8
28	FAC2Q	A	Bath City	441	L	0-2			9
Oct 5	CSouth	A	Bishop's Stortford	504	L	0-4		21	10
19	CSouth	A	Ebbsfleet United	731	L	1-2	Pearce 31	22	11
26	CSouth	H	Chelmsford City	501	W	2-1	Brown 19 Sills 34	15	12
Nov 2	CSouth	A	Whitehawk	201	D	1-1	Brown 90	21	13
12	CSouth	H	Eastleigh	562	L	0-2		21	14
16	FAT3Q	H	Dorchester Town	206	W	3-0	Dunford 24 90 Bennett 89		15
22	CSouth	A	Farnborough	341	L	0-1		22	16
26	CSouth	H	Staines Town	231	W	2-0	Richardson 56 Gosney 76	21	17
30	FAT1	H	Concord Rangers	192	W	1-0	Gosney 18		18
Dec 7	CSouth	A	Concord Rangers	203	W	2-0	Wooden 43 Williams 86	17	19
14	FAT2	H	Nuneaton Town	284	D	0-0			20
17	FAT2r	A	Nuneaton Town	426	D	0-0	won 4-3 on penalties		21
26	CSouth	A	Havant & Waterlooville	776	L	0-3		21	22
Jan	FAT3	A	Hungerford Town	384	W	1-0	Brown 73		23
18	CSouth	A	Eastleigh	668	L	1-2	Woodward 76	21	24
25	CSouth	A	Weston-s-Mare	202	W	1-0	Brown 46	21	25
Feb 1	FAT4	A	North Ferriby United	398	W	2-1	Igoe 9 Sills 31		26
4	CSouth	H	Sutton United	261	D	2-2	Igoe 36 (pen) Gosney 39	21	27
11	CSouth	H	Whitehawk	219	L	0-2		21	28
17	FAT S-F 1	A	Havant & Waterlooville	1314	D	1-1	Sills 47		29
22	FAT S-F 2	H	Havant & Waterlooville	2901	W	2-0	Sills 45 60		30
25	CSouth	H	Eastbourne Borough	270	L	1-2	Wooden 75	21	31
March 1	CSouth	A	Dover Athletic	623	L	0-3		22	32
8	CSouth	A	Staines Town	231	W	3-0	WILLIAMS 3 (25 34 49)	22	33
11	CSouth	H	Havant & Waterlooville	441	D	0-0		22	34
13	CSouth	A	Maidenhead United	193	W	2-1	Bennett 61 89	20	35
15	CSouth	H	Boreham Wood	550	W	2-1	Bennett 6 53	19	36
18	CSouth	A	Sutton United	433	L	0-2		20	37
23	FAT Final	N	Cambridge United	18,123	L	0-4			38
25	CSouth	A	Tonbridge Angels	273	W	2-0	Forbes 50 Brown 89	19	39
27	CSouth	H	Ebbsfkleet United	349	L	0-2		19	40
29	CSouth	H	Bishop's Stortford	1010	W	2-1	Poate 37 (pen) Prior 48	17	41
April 1	CSouth	H	Farnborough	311	W	1-0	Bennett 65	15	42
3	CSouth	H	Weston-s-Mare	335	D	0-0		16	43
5	CSouth	H	Concord Rangers	375	L	1-2	Carmichael 39	17	44
8	CSouth	H	Hayes & Yeading	316	W	3-0	Wooden 19 Scott 56 Williams 69	16	45
12	CSouth	A	Eastbourne Borough	470	W	3-1	Poate 20 (pen) Smith 47 Bennett 90	16	46
15	CSouth	H	Basingstoke Town	425	W	2-0	Williams 33 Wooden 78	14	47
17	CSouth	A	Hayes & Yeading	122	W	1-0	Woodward 58	13	48
19	CSouth	H	Bath City	517	W	3-1	Smith 30 Wooden 51 Pearce 63	10	49
21	CSouth	A	Dorchester Town	414	D	2-2	Williams 50	11	50
23	CSouth	A	Chelmsford City	776	L	0-1		11	51
26	CSouth	H	Bromley	577	L	1-2	Pearce 46	12	52

GOALSCORERS	Lge	FAC	FAT	Total	Pens	Hat-tricks	Cons Run
Bennett	7		1	8	1		
Brown	7		1	8			2
Williams	8			8		1	
Wooden	6			6			
Sills	1		4	5			
Gosney	2		1	3			
Pearce	3			3			
Dunford			2	2			
Igoe			1	2	1		
Poate				2	2		
Smith	2			2			
Woodward	2			2			
Carmichael	1			1			
Forbes	1			1			
Richardson	1			1			
Prior	1			1			
Scott	1			1			

Cons Run - Consecutive scoring games.

HAVANT AND WATERLOOVILLE

Chairman: Derek Pope
Secretary: Trevor Brock (T) 07768 271 143 (E) trevor.brock52@yahoo.com
Commercial Manager: Adrian Aymes (T) 07814 150 032
Programme Editor: Adrian Aymes (T) aaymes2125@aol.com
Ground Address: Westleigh Park, Martin Road, West Leigh, Havant PO7 5TH
(T) 02392 787 822 **Manager:** Lee Bradbury

Club Factfile

Founded: 1998 **Nickname:** Hawks
Previous Names: Havant Town and Waterlooville merged in 1998
Previous Leagues: Southern 1998-2004

Club Colours (change): White/navy/white (All red)

Ground Capacity: 4,800 **Seats:** 562 **Covered:** 3,500 **Clubhouse:** Yes **Shop:** Yes

Directions
Ground is a mile and a half from Havant Town Centre. Take A27 to Havant then turn onto B2149 (Petersfield Road). Turn right at next junction after HERON pub into Bartons Road then take first right into Martin Road.

Previous Grounds: None

Record Attendance: 4,400 v Swansea City - FA Cup 3rd Round 05/01/2008
Record Victory: 9-0 v Moneyfields - Hampshire Senior Cup 23/10/2001
Record Defeat: 0-5 v Worcester City - Southern Premier 20/03/2004
Record Goalscorer: James Taylor - 138
Record Appearances: James Taylor - 297
Additional Records: Paid £5,000 to Bashley for John Wilson
Received £15,000 from Peterborough United for Gary McDonald
Senior Honours:
Southern League Southern Division 1998-99. Russell Cotes Cup 2003-04

10 YEAR RECORD

04-05	05-06	06-07	07-08	08-09	09-10	10-11	11-12	12-13	13-14
Conf S 13	Conf S 6	Conf 4	Conf S 7	Conf S 15	Conf S 6	Conf S 9	Conf S 19	Conf S 10	Conf S 6

HAVANT & WATERLOOVILLE MATCH RESULTS 2013-14

Date	Comp	H/A	Opponents	Att:	Result	Goalscorers	Pos	No.
Aug 17	ConfS	A	Ebbsfleet United	973	D 0-0		10	1
24	ConfS	H	Weston-s-Mare	447	W 2-0	Kabba 46 Nanetti 76 (pen)	7	2
26	ConfS	A	Eastleigh	153	D 0-0		10	3
31	ConfS	H	Tonbridge Angels	423	L 1-2	Kabba 47	15	4
Sept 7	ConfS	A	Bishops Stortford	428	L 1-2	Nanetti 33	17	5
11	ConfS	H	Farnborough	469	W 2-1	Ciardini 64 Woodford 82	11	6
14	ConfS	H	Hayes & Yeading	490	L 1-2	Ciardini 89 (pen)	16	7
17	ConfS	A	Whitehawk	189	D 2-2	Jones 50 73	13	8
21	ConfS	H	Sutton United	530	L 0-5		16	9
29	***FAC2Q***	***A***	***Gloucester City***	***336***	***D 1-1***	***Oli 57***		10
Oct 2	***FAC2Qr***	***H***	***Gloucester City***		***L 2-3***	***Nanetti 30 (pen) Kabba 90***		11
5	ConfS	A	Maidenhead United	307	W 3-1	Kabba 22 49 Walker 70 (pen)	16	12
12	ConfS	H	Basingstoke Town	**956**	W 4-1	Przespoleski 15 Jones 37 Ciardini 41 (pen) Oli 66	11	13
19	ConfS	H	Dover Athletic	593	D 0-0		10	14
26	ConfS	H	Eastbourne Borough	745	D 1-1	Ryan 40	11	15
Nov 2	ConfS	A	Bath City	451	L 1-3	Kabba 49	13	16
16	***FAT3Q***	***A***	***Sutton United***	***374***	***W 2-1***	***Nanetti 15 (pen) Kabba 80***		17
23	ConfS	A	Bromley	425	L 0-2		14	18
25	ConfS	H	Chelmsford City	390	W 3-0	Jones 10 Ciardini 40 Kabba 59	14	19
30	***FAT1***	***A***	***Basingstoke Town***	***354***	***D 0-0***			20
Dec 2	***FAT1r***	***H***	***Basingstoke Town***	***210***	***W 1-0***	***Kabba 11***		21
7	ConfS	H	Dorchester Town	497	W 5-1	Oli 14 Jones 25 Kabba 42 Waker 77 Strugnell 80	12	22
14	***FAT2***	***A***	***Whitehawk***	***150***	***D 1-1***	***Harris 65***		23
16	***FAT2r***	***H***	***Whitehawk***	***189***	***W 3-1***	***Przespolewski 36 Strugnell 42 Ciardini 60 (pen)***		24
26	ConfS	H	Gosport Borough	776	W 3-0	Kabba 28 Oli 64 Przespolewski 90	10	25
28	ConfS	A	Farnborough	388	D 2-2	Oli 40 Kabba 45	13	26
Jan 11	***FAT3***	***H***	***Ebbsfleet United***	***709***	***W 1-0***	***Atangana 61***		27
Feb 4	***FAT4***	***H***	***Aldershot Town***	***1125***	***W 4-1***	***Oli 47 Atangana 51 Przespolewski 72 Ciardini 75***		28
11	ConfS	A	Dorchester Town	208	W 2-0	Jones 23 46	14	29
17	***FAT S-F 1***	***H***	***Gosport Borough***	***1314***	***D 1-1***	***Ciardini 59***		30
22	***FAT S-F 2***	***A***	***Gosport Borough***	***2901***	***L 0-2***			31
March 1	ConfS	A	Hayes & Yeading	170	W 1-0	Woodford 82	13	32
5	ConfS	A	Boreham Wood	128	W 2-0	Ryan 44 Blanchett 90	12	33
8	ConfS	A	Eastbourne Borough	537	W 1-0	Atangana 31	12	34
11	ConfS	A	Gosport Borough	441	D 0-0		11	35
13	CobfS	A	Concord Rangers	182	D 3-3	Donnelly 41 Atangana 73 Nanetti 90	11	36
15	ConfS	H	Staines Town	541	L 0-2		11	37
17	ConfS	H	Ebbsfleet United	501	W 1 0	Przespolewski 76	9	38
20	ConfS	H	Dover Athletic	457	L 3-4	Donnelly 21 Strugnell 76 Ciardini 81	9	39
22	ConfS	A	Basingstoke Town	344	W 1-0	Kabba 19	9	40
24	ConfS	H	Bath City	471	W 1-0	Ciardini 56	7	41
27	ConfS	H	Whitehawk	478	W 2-0	Nanetti 52 Donnelly 73	6	42
29	ConfS	A	Chelmsford City	613	D 0-0		6	43
April 1	ConfS	A	Staines Town	204	L 0-1		6	44
3	ConfS	A	Sutton United	451	L 1-3	Ryan 41	6	45
5	ConfS	H	Bromley	576	W 1-0	Bassele 45	5	46
12	ConfS	H	Concord Rangers	604	W 1-0	Ciardini 79 (pen)	6	47
14	ConfS	H	Bishop'a Stortford	462	W 2-0	Donnelly 8 (pen) Nanetti 10	5	48
16	ConfS	H	Boreham Wood	562	D 1-1	Blanchett 21	6	49
18	ConfS	A	Weston -s -Mere	230	D 1-1	Atangana 16	5	50
21	ConfS	H	Eastleigh	932	W 1-0	Ciardini 10	5	51
23	ConfS	H	Maidenhead United	532	L 1-3	Hutchinson 90	5	52
26	ConfS	A	Tonbridge Angels	515	D 0-0		6	53

GOALSCORERS	Lge	FAC	FAT	Total	Pens	Hat-tricks	Cons Run
Kabba	11	1	2	14			2
Ciardini	7		3	10	4		2
Jones	7			7			
Nanetti	5	1	1	7	3		
Oli	4	1	1	6			2
Atangana	3		2	5			2
Przespoleski	3		2	5			2
Donnelly	4			4	1		
Ryan	4			4			
Strugnell	3		1	4			

	Lge	FAC	FAT	Total	Pens	Hat-tricks	Cons Run
Blanchett	2			2			
Walker	2			2	1		
Woodford	2			2			
Basselke	1			1			
Harris			1	1			
Hutchinson	1			1			
Opponents	1			1			

Cons Run - Consecutive scoring games.

HAYES & YEADING UNITED

Chairman: Tony O'Driscoll
Secretary: Bill Gritt (T) 07710 102 004 (E) secretary@hyufc.com
Commercial Manager: Derrick Matthews (T) 0208 573 2075 (B)
Programme Editor: Andy Corbett (T) 07540 940 169
Ground Address: The Stadium, Beaconsfield Road, Hayes UB4 0SL
(T) 0208 573 2075 **Manager:** Phil Babb

Construction of the new stand continues however, the club are enjoying the benefits of the ground development, in particular the new 3G pitch.
Photo courtesy: www.hyufc.com

Club Factfile

Founded: 2007 **Nickname:**
Previous Names: Hayes - Botwell Mission 1909-29. Hayes and Yeading merged to form today's club in 2007
Previous Leagues: Isthmian

Club Colours (change): Red/black/black & white (Blue/blue/black & white)

Ground Capacity: 6,000 **Seats:** 2,500 **Covered:** 3,900 **Clubhouse:** Yes **Shop:** Yes

Directions From the M40/A40(M) Head eastbound towards London, take the Target Roundabout exit signposted Northolt, Harrow & Hayes. At the top of the slip road take the fourth exit (the first after the exit towards London) onto the A312 towards Hayes. The next roundabout (The White Hart) is about is about 1 mile and a half on. Here ignore signs to Yeading (third exit) instead take the second exit towards Hayes & Heathrow to stay on the A312 (Hayes-By - Pass). At the next roundabout again ignore signs to Yeading and carry straight over. Take the next exit signposted Southall and Uxbridge (A4020 Uxbridge Road). At the top of the slip road take the first exit towards Southall and follow the directions below Head eastbound along the (A4020) Uxbridge Road. Head eastbound along the (A4020) Uxbridge Road signposted towards Southall. Get into the far right hand lane as soon as you can and turn right into Springfield Road at the next set of Traffic Lights (There is a petrol station and a retail development with a Wickes on the corner of Springfield Road). Follow the road to the School, the Road bears left into Beaconsfield Road, and about 100 yards on your right is the entrance to the ground. **NB: First team home fixtures will initially be played at Woking's Kingfield Stadium. (see Woking FC).**

Previous Grounds: Kingfield Stadium (Woking FC) 2012-13.

Record Attendance: 1,881 v Luton Town - Conference Premier 06/03/2010
Record Victory: 8-2 v Hillingdon Borough (A) - Middlesex Senior Cup 11/11/08
Record Defeat: 0-8 v Luton Town (A) - Conference Premier 27/03/10
Record Goalscorer: Josh Scott - 40 (2007-09)
Record Appearances: James Mulley - 137 (2007-10)
Additional Records:

Senior Honours:
Conference South Play-offs 2008-09

10 YEAR RECORD

04-05	05-06	06-07	07-08	08-09	09-10	10-11	11-12	12-13	13-14
			Conf S 13	Conf S 4	Conf 17	Conf 16	Conf 21	Conf S 17	Conf S 20

HAYES & YEADING MATCH RESULTS 2013-14

Date	Comp	H/A	Opponents	Att:	Result		Goalscorers	Pos	No.
Aug 17	ConfS	H	Bromley	173	L	0-1		20	1
20	ConfS	A	Maidenhead United	460	**W**	2-1	Reid 19 (pen)	19	2
24	ConfS	A	Boreham Wood	201	**W**	3-1	Williams 8 English 19 Inman 70	15	3
26	ConfS	H	Eastbourne Borough	174	L	0-1		17	4
31	ConfS	A	Dover Athletic	691	**W**	1-0	Schoburgh 71	12	5
Sept 7	ConfS	H	Chelsford City	218	**W**	4-0	Inman 37 89 Merrifield 45 Reid 55 (pen)	8	6
14	ConfS	A	Havant & Waterloovile	490	**W**	2-1	Mills 9 (pen) Bossman 14	6	7
21	ConfS	A	Eastleigh	1202	L	0-1		9	8
29	***FAC2Q***	***A***	***Tonbridge Angels***	***198***	***D***	***0-0***			9
Oct 1	***FAC2Qr***	***H***	***Tonbridge Angels***	***297***	***L***	***1-2***	***Merrified 79***		10
5	ConfS	A	Basingstoke Town	351	**W**	1-0	Mitchell 72	9	11
12	ConfS	A	Farnborough	714	**W**	2-1	Soares 79 Mills 90 (pen)	4	12
19	ConfS	H	Bishop's Stortford	136	L	2-3	Mitchell 19 Soares 44	7	13
26	ConfS	A	Weston-s-Mare	210	**W**	3-0	Reid 50 84 Williams 66	5	14
Nov 2	ConfS	A	Staines Town	298	L	1-2	Bossman 27	7	15
9	ConfS	H	Whitehawk	97	**W**	3-2	Soares 28 Reid 56 English 63	5	16
17	***FAT 3Q***	***H***	***Bognor Regis Town***	***250***	***W***	***2 1***	***Reid 28 Everitt 81***		17
23	ConfS	H	Weston-s-Mare	120	L	1-2	Mitchell 62	6	18
26	ConfS	H	Ebbsfleet United	139	L	1-2	Reid 24	7	19
30	***FAT1***	***H***	***Barnet***	***302***	***L***	***0-1***			20
Dec 7	ConfS	H	Tonbridge Amgels	114	**W**	3-0	Reid 17 (pen) Mills 42 Mitchell 90	6	21
14	ConfS	A	Chelmsford City	718	D	0-0		6	22
26	ConfS	A	Sutton United	537	L	0-2		11	23
28	ConfS	H	Maidenhead United	159	L	1-2	English 86	11	24
Jan 11	ConfS	A	Concord Rangers	327	L	1-3	Hippolyte 63	12	25
25	ConfS	A	Bromley	1066	L	1-2	Inman 78	14	26
Feb 4	ConfS	H	Bath City	97	L	0-2		15	27
25	ConfS	H	Farnborough	122	L	1-2	Hughes-Mason 90	16	28
March 1	ConfS	H	Havant & Waterlooville	170	L	0-1		17	29
8	ConfS	A	Ebbsfleet United	821	L	0-1		18	30
11	ConfS	H	Staines Town	112	L	1-2	Williams 40	18	31
13	ConfS	A	Bishop's Stortford	244	D	0-0		17	32
15	ConfS	H	Concord Rangers	94	**W**	1-0	Ladapo 22	17	33
20	ConfS	A	Tonbridge Angels	273	D	1-1	Williams 23	17	34
25	ConfS	H	Sutton United	145	D	0-0		18	35
30	ConfS	H	Eastleigh	204	D	1 1	Cox 71	18	36
April 1	ConfS	A	Whitehawk	112	L	0-1		19	37
3	ConfS	H	Basingstoke Town	115	D	0-0		19	38
5	ConfS	H	Dorchester Town	107	**W**	2-0	Cox 66 Inman 78	16	39
8	ConfS	A	Gosport Borough	316	L	0-3		18	40
12	ConfS	A	Bath City	553	L	2-3	Cox 4 72	19	41
15	ConfS	A	Dorchester Town	316	**W**	2-0	Ladapo 13 Williams 83	18	42
17	ConfS	H	Gosport Brough	122	L	0-1		16	43
19	ConfS	H	Boreham Wood	115	**W**	1-0	Ladapo 82	17	44
21	ConfS	A	Eastbourne Borough	602	L	2-3	Cox 54	18	45
26	ConfS	H	Dover Athletic	**450**	L	1-2	Mitchell 23	20	46

GOALSCORERS	Lge	FAC	FAT	Total	Pens	Hat-tricks	Cons Run
Reid	7		1	8	3		
Williams	5			5			
Cox	5			5			
Inman	5			5			
Mitchell	4			4			
English	3			3			
Ladapo	3			3			
Merrifield	2	1		3			
Mills	3			3	2		
Bossman	1			1			
Everitt			1	1			
Hippolyte	1			1			
Hughes-Mason	1			1			
Schoburgh	1			1			
Soares	1			1			
Williams	1			1			

Cons Run - Consecutive scoring games.

HEMEL HEMPSTEAD TOWN

Chairman: David Boggins
Secretary: Dean Chance (T) 07858 990 550 (E) dean.chance@ntlworld.com
Commercial Manager: Duncan Cockling (T) 07919 305 213
Programme Editor: Marc Willmore (T) 07595 371 908
Ground Address: Vauxhall Road, Adeyfield Road, Hemel Hempstead HP2 4HW
(T) 01442 251 251 **Manager:** Dean Brennan

Club Factfile

Founded: 1885 **Nickname:** The Tudors
Previous Names: Hemel Hempstead FC
Previous Leagues: Spartan 1922-52, Delphian 1952-63, Athenian 1963-77, Isthmian 1977-2004

Club Colours (change): All red (Green/white/white)

Ground Capacity: 3,152 **Seats:** 300 **Covered:** 900 **Clubhouse:** Yes **Shop:** Yes

Directions
Leave M1 at Junction 8 - follow dual carriageway over two roundabouts.
Get into outside lane and after 100 yards turn right.
Follow road to mini-roundabout turn left, next large roundabout take third exit into ground car park.

Previous Grounds: Crabtree Lane

Record Attendance: 3,500 v Tooting & Mitcham - Amateur Cup 1962 (Crabtree Lane)
Record Victory: Not known
Record Defeat: Not known
Record Goalscorer: Dai Price
Record Appearances: John Wallace - 1012
Additional Records:

Senior Honours:
Isthmian League Division 3 1998-99. Herts Senior Cup x8 Most recently 2012-13. Herts Charity Cup x6.
Southern Premier Division 2013-14.

10 YEAR RECORD

04-05	05-06	06-07	07-08	08-09	09-10	10-11	11-12	12-13	13-14
SthP 19	SthW 4	SthP 5	SthP 7	SthP 5	SthP 20	SthP 15	SthP 19	SthP 4	SthP 1

Conference Action

Ricky Miller (left) who scored both goals for visitors Boston United, is chased by this Solihull Moors defender in their end of season Conference North encounter.

Photo: Jonathan Holloway.

HEMEL HEMPSTEAD TOWN MATCH RESULTS 2013-14

Date	Comp	H/A	Opponents	Att:	Result		Goalscorers	Pos	No.
Aug 17	SPL	A	Hitchin Town	330	L	0-2		21	1
20	SPL	H	Corby Town	326	W	6-0	Toomey 2 12 Parkes 34 75 King 61 Mpi 90	8	2
24	SPL	H	Hungerford Town	291	W	2-1	Thorne 2 Mackey 80	4	3
26	SPL	A	Banbury United	265	W	3-0	Pearce 8 Mpi 81 Parkes 90	4	4
31	SPL	A	Burnham	210	W	3-0	Mackey 27 Pearce 36 Talbot 55	2	5
Sept 3	SPL	H	Bedford Town	421	W	6-1	Mackey 10 88 HUTTON 3 (36 57 90) King 61	2	6
7	SPL	H	St Neots Town	689	W	2-0	Toomey 51 78	1	7
14	***FAC1Q***	***A***	***St Margaretsbury***	***97***	***W***	***7-0***	***Thorne 18 Mackey 45 61 Hutton 45 Toomey 57 60 Parkes 90***		8
17	SPL	A	Bashley	102	W	4-1	Hutton 18 Stevenson 68 (og) Mpi 76 80	1	9
21	SPL	A	Weymouth	676	W	3-0	Toomey 8 54 Thorne 47	1	10
28	***FAC2Q***	***H***	***Witham Town***	***425***	***D***	***1-1***	***Pearce 9***		11
Oct 1	***FAC2Qr***	***A***	***Witham Town***	***156***	***W***	***4-3***	***Parkes 5 Toomey 84 Mackey 89 Pearce 90***		12
5	SPL	H	Redditch United	483	W	5-0	Toomey 2 Talbot 25 Pearce 35 Hutton 87 Mpl 90	1	13
8	SPL	H	Arlesey Town	450	W	3-0	Mackey 32 66 Mpi 75	1	14
12	***FAC3Q***	***H***	***Dulwich Hamlet***	***949***	***W***	***3-1***	***Mathew 26 Toomey 48 Mpi 72***		15
19	***FAT1Q***	***H***	***AFC Hornchurch***	***511***	***W***	***3-2***	***Hutton 11 Toomey 17 Mackey 41***		16
21	SPL	A	St Albans City	677	D	2-2	Toomey 44 Diarra 90	1	17
26	***FAC4Q***	***H***	***Sutton United***	***1455***	***D***	***3-3***	***Toomey 3 Mackey 45 48 (pen)***		18
29	***FAC4Qr***	***A***	***Sutton United***	***662***	***L***	***0 2***			19
Nov 2	***FAT2Q***	***H***	***North Greenford United***	***350***	***W***	***9-1***	***MACKAY 3 (25 30 59) CARVALHO 3(64 75 87) Pearce 74 McDonald 75 (og) Parkes 80***		20
5	SPL	H	Bashley	318	W	10-0	Hawkins 11 PEARCE 3 (14 34 77) MACKAY 5 (22 26 31 57 79) Maeden 55 (og)	1	21
9	SPL	A	St Neots Town	436	L	1-4	Mpi 49	1	22
16	***FAT3Q***	***A***	***Hungerford Town***	***137***	***L***	***0-5***			23
23	SPL	A	Frome Town	173	D	1-1	Diarra 90	2	24
26	SPL	H	AFC Totton	238	W	8-1	Pearce 13 Mackey 24 (pen) 29 Toomey 32 Talbot 39 Parkes 40 Mpi 70 79	2	25
30	SPL	A	Cambridge City	247	D	1-1	Toomey 15	2	26
Dec 7	SPL	H	Truro City	495	W	3-0	Murphy 33 Pearce 71 Mpi 82	1	27
10	SPL	A	Bedford Town	191	W	3-0	MACKEY 3 (25 74 83)	1	28
14	SPL	A	Chippenham Town	337	W	3-0	Mackey 45 Parkes 53 Toomey 79	1	29
17	SPL	H	Burnham	361	W	3-0	Mackey 40 (pen) Allen 64 Hutton 74	1	30
26	SPL	H	Banbury United	386	W	5-3	Blackett 25 Toomey 39 Mackey 62 Mpi 67 Parkes 90	1	31
28	SPL	A	Corby Town	409	W	2-0	Hutton 12 Pearce 63	1	32
Jan 1	SPL	A	Chesham United	1104	W	3-1	Parkes 26 Toomey 30 Mackey 64 (pen)	1	33
7	SPL	H	Bideford	344	W	4-1	Mackey 42 (pen) Toomey 49 Blackett 55 Mpi 82	1	34
11	SPL	A	Bideford	275	L	0-1		1	35
18	SPL	H	Frome Town	540	L	0-1		1	36
25	SPL	A	AFC Totton	320	W	4-1	MACKEY 3 (38 51 57) Pearce 65	1	37
Feb 4	SPL	H	Biggleswade Town	351	W	3-0	Mackey 3 Toomey 11 Parkes 75	1	38
8	SPL	A	Truro City	253	W	6-1	PARKES 3 (2 15 19) TOOMEY 3 (44 67 81)	1	39
22	SPL	A	Stourbridge	547	W	4-1	Toomey 1 PARKES 3 (32 pen 33 90)	1	40
March 1	SPL	A	Redditch United	235	L	0-1		1	41
5	SPL	H	Poole Town	369	W	1-0	Allen 25	1	42
8	SPL	H	Weymouth	641	W	4-1	MACKEY 3 (4 14 45) Allen 26	1	43
11	SPL	H	Cambridge City	520	D	1-1	Toomey 56	1	44
15	SPL	A	Arlesey Town	278	W	3-2	Parkes 8 Hutton 44 Allen 90	1	45
22	SPL	A	Poole Town	501	W	2-0	Mackey 13 72	1	46
25	SPL	H	Stourbridge	432	W	4-3	Mackey 3 Thorne 43 Toomey 67 77	1	47
April 1	SPL	H	Chippenham Town	498	W	2-0	Mackey 47 77 (pen)	1	48
5	SPL	H	St Albans City	999	D	0-0		1	49
12	SPL	H	Hitchin Town	775	D	0-0		1	50
19	SPL	A	Hungerford Town	273	W	4-0	Thorne 11 Toomey 44 Parkes 58 Hawkins 74	1	51
21	SPL	H	Chesham United	**1943**	W	2-1	Hutton 9 Talbot 67	1	52
26	SPL	A	Biggleswade Town	345	L	2-5	Hawkins 14 29	1	53

GOALSCORERS	Lge	FAC	FAT	Total	Pens	Hat-tricks	Cons Run
Mackey	33	5	4	42	6	5	4
Toomey	23	4	1	28		1	4
Parkes	15	2	1	18	1	2	3
Mpi	13			13			2
Pearce	9	2	1	12		1	2
Hutton	8	1	1	10		1	
Thorne	4	1		5			
Allen	4			4			2
Hawkins	4			4			
Talbot	4			4			
Carvalho			3	3		1	
Blackett	2			2			
Diarra	2			2			
King	1			1			
Matthews	1			1			
Murphy	1			1			
Stephenson	1			1			
Opponents	2		1	3			

Cons Run - Consecutive scoring games.

MAIDENHEAD UNITED

Chairman: Peter Griffin
Secretary: Ken Chandler (T) 07863 183 872 (E) kenneth.chandler@btinternet.com
Commercial Manager: n/a (T)
Programme Editor: Roy Bannister (T) 07930 115 748
Ground Address: York Road, Maidenhead, Berkshire SL6 1SF
(T) 01628 636 314 **Manager:** Johnson Hippolyte

Club Factfile

Founded: 1870 **Nickname:** Magpies
Previous Names: Maidenhead F.C and Maidenhead Norfolkians merged to form today's club
Previous Leagues: Southern 1894-1902, 2006-07, West Berkshire 1902-04, Gr. West Suburban 1904-22, Spartan 1922-39, Gr. West Comb. 1939-45, Corinthian 1945-63, Athenian 1963-73, Isthmian 1973-2004, Conf. 2004-06

Club Colours (change): Black & white stripes/black/white (Yellow/blue/yellow)

Ground Capacity: 4,500 **Seats:** 400 **Covered:** 2,000 **Clubhouse:** Yes **Shop:** Yes

Directions
The Ground is in the town centre.
200 yards from the station and two minutes walk from the High Street.
Access from M4 Junctions 7 or 8/9.

Previous Grounds: Kidwells Park (Norfolkians)

Record Attendance: 7,920 v Southall - FA Amateur Cup Quarter final 07/03/1936
Record Victory: 14-1 v Buckingham Town - FA Amateur Cup 06/09/1952
Record Defeat: 0-14 v Chesham United (A) - Spartan League 31/03/1923
Record Goalscorer: George Copas - 270 (1924-35)
Record Appearances: Bert Randall - 532 (1950-64)
Additional Records: Received £5,000 from Norwich City for Alan Cordice 1979

Senior Honours:
Corinthian League 1957-58, 60-61, 61-62. Berks & Bucks Senior Cup1894-95, 1895-96, 1911-12, 1927-28, 1929-30, 1930-31, 1931-32, 1938-39, 1945-46, 1955-56, 1956-57, 1960-61, 1962-63, 1965-66, 1969-70, 1997-98, 1998-99, 2001-02, 2002-03, 2009-10.
Southern League Premier Division Play-offs 2006-07.

10 YEAR RECORD

04-05	05-06	06-07	07-08	08-09	09-10	10-11	11-12	12-13	13-14
Conf S 20	Conf S 22	SthP 4	Conf S 17	Conf S 6	Conf S 16	Conf S 19	Conf S 20	Conf S 19	Conf S 18

MAIDENHEAD UNITED MATCH RESULTS 2013-14

Date	Comp	H/A	Opponents	Att:	Result		Goalscorers	Pos	No.
Aug 17	ConfS	A	Whitehawk	151	W	3-0	Pacquette 21 75 Pritchard 85	1	1
20	ConfS	H	Hayes & Yeading United	460	W	2-1	Ruby 69 Pacquette 71	2	2
26	ConfS	A	Ebbsfleet United	835	D	1-1	Tilson-Lascaris 41	5	3
31	ConfS	H	Bishops Stortford	384	D	2-2	Green 24 Mendy 74	7	4
Sept 7	ConfS	A	Gosport Borough	485	W	2-0	Tilson-Lascaris 25 Pacquette 58	5	5
14	ConfS	H	Eastleigh	403	L	1-3	Pacquette16	7	6
17	ConfS	A	Weston-s-Mare	170	D	0-0		8	7
21	ConfS	H	Concord Rangers	295	L	1-4	Tilson-Lascaris 29	11	8
28	***FAC 2Q***	***A***	***Oxford City***	***249***	***L***	***0-1***			9
Oct 5	ConfS	H	Havant & Waterlooville	307	L	1-3	Malcolm 27	11	10
19	ConfS	H	Dorchester Town	301	L	1-3	Hippolyte 86	18	11
26	ConfS	H	Bromley	288	L	0-1		16	12
Nov 2	ConfS	A	Eastbourne Borough	514	L	0-2		19	13
5	ConfS	H	Farnborough	247	D	2-2	Clifton 45 (pen) Pacquette 56	15	14
9	ConfS	H	Basingstoke Town	314	L	0-1		15	15
16	***FAT3Q***	***A***	***Eastbourne Borough***	***384***	***W***	***1-0***	***Grant 68***		16
23	ConfS	A	Bath City	501	L	0-1		18	17
26	ConfS	A	Boreham Wood	138	D	2-2	Pacquette 34 Solomon 50	18	18
30	***FAT1***	***A***	***Daventry Town***	***203***	***W***	***1-0***	***Malcolm 67***		19
Dec 7	ConfS	A	Sutton United	472	L	2-3	Clifton 28 Pacquette 45	21	20
10	ConfS	H	Chelmsford City	253	D	1-1	Pritchard 56	18	21
14	***FAT2***	***A***	***Barrow***	***560***	***W***	***2-0***	***Pacquette 53 Green 86***		22
26	ConfS	H	Staines Town	355	W	3-1	Green 20 Grant 75 Boungow 37 (og)	17	23
28	ConfS	A	Hayes & Yeading United	159	W	2-1	Pacquette 4 Green 24	18	24
Jan 11	***FAT3***	***A***	***Grimsby Town***	***1623***	***L***	***1-2***	***Tilson-Lascaris 46***		25
21	ConfS	A	Staines Town	409	D	0-0		18	26
Feb 4	ConfS	H	Weston-s-Mare	170	L	0-3		18	27
11	ConfS	A	Dover Athletic	356	L	0-2		19	28
22	ConfS	A	Chelmsford City	648	W	3-0	Soloman 13 Grant 16 Constant 90	19	29
25	ConfS	A	Eastleigh	482	L	2-3	Tilson-Lascaris 12 Ruby 45	19	30
March 1	ConfS	A	Basingstoke Town	272	D	2-2	Pritchard 53 Erskine 78	19	31
4	ConfS	A	Tonbridge Angels	332	W	4-2	GREEN 4 (15 34 82 89)	17	32
8	ConfS	H	Bath City	351	L	0-1		17	33
11	ConfS	H	Boreham Wood	179	L	0-1		14	34
13	ConfS	H	Gosport Borough	193	L	1-2	Clifton 3	18	35
15	ConfS	H	Dover Athletic	301	L	1-2	Clifton 12	18	36
22	ConfS	A	Bromley	610	L	1-6	Grant 52	21	37
25	ConfS	H	Eastbourne Borough	143	L	2-3	Pacquette 44 Constant 83	21	38
29	ConfS	H	Whitehawk	245	W	1-0	Grant 15	20	39
April 1	ConfS	A	Dorchester Town	270	W	3-0	Green 57 (pen) 65 Pritchard 67	20	40
5	ConfS	H	Sutton United	356	W	3-2	Grant 45 Green 72 78	18	41
10	ConfS	H	Concord Rangers	253	L	1-3	Soloman 89	19	42
12	ConfS	H	Tonbridge Angels	**472**	D	0-0		20	43
19	ConfS	A	Farnborough	320	L	0-3		20	44
21	ConfS	H	Ebbsfleet United	398	W	1-0	Green 43	20	45
23	ConfS	A	Havant & Waterlooville	532	W	3-1	Clifton 25 36 Green 49	19	46
26	ConfS	A	Bishop's Stortford	430	D	1-1	Erskine 28	18	47

GOALSCORERS	Lge	FAC	FAT	Total	Pens	Hat-tricks	Cons Run
Green	13		1	14	1	1	3
Pacquette	10		1	11			2
Grant	7		1	8			
Clifton	6			6	1		2
Tilson-Lascaris	4		1	5			
Pritchard	4			4			
Soloman	3			3			
Constant	2			2			
Erskine	2			2			
Malcolm	1		1	2			

	Lge	FAC	FAT	Total	Pens	Hat-tricks	Cons Run
Ruby	2			2			
Hippolyte	1			1			
Mendy	1			1			
Opponents	1			1			

Cons Run - Consecutive scoring games.

ST ALBANS CITY

Chairman: Nick Archer
Secretary: Steve Eames (T) 01727 848914 (E) steveeames@sacfc.co.uk
Commercial Manager: Tom Noman (T) 07876 801 484
Programme Editor: Lee Wood (T) woodL1@btconnect.com
Ground Address: Clarence Park, York Road, St. Albans, Herts AL1 4PL
(T) 01727 848 914 **Manager:** James Gray & Graham Golds

Club Factfile

Founded: 1908 **Nickname:** The Saints
Previous Names: None
Previous Leagues: Herts County 1908-10, Spartan 1908-20, Athenian 1920-23, Isthmian 1923-2004, Conference 2004-11. Southern 2011-14.

Club Colours (change): Yellow/blue/white (Sky blue/navy/sky blue)

Ground Capacity: 5,007 **Seats:** 667 **Covered:** 1,900 **Clubhouse:** Yes **Shop:** Yes

Directions
From the M25 (Clockwise) Exit M25 at junction 21A(A405). Follow signs to St. Albans from slip road. At Noke Hotel roundabout (Shell garage will be straight ahead), bear right on A405 and stay on A405 until London Colney roundabout (traffic light controlled). Turn left onto A1081. Follow road for approx 1 mile until mini roundabout (Great Northern pub on left). Turn right into Alma Road. At traffic lights turn right into Victoria Street and continue to junction with Crown pub. Go straight across into Clarence Road, ground is first on left about 50 yards past junction or take the next turning on the left into York Road, ground entrance is at the end of the road on the left. From the M25 (Counter-clockwise) Exit M25 at junction 22 (A1081). Follow signs to St. Albans from slip road. At London Colney roundabout (traffic light controlled) exit onto A1081. Follow road for approx 1 mile until mini roundabout (Great Northern pub on left). Turn right into Alma Road. At traffic lights turn right into Victoria Street and continue to junction with Crown pub. Go straight across into Clarence Road, ground is first on left about 50 yards past junction or take the next turning on the left into York Road, ground entrance is at the end of the road on the left.

Previous Grounds: None

Record Attendance: 9,757 v Ferryhill Athletic - FA Amateur Cup 1926
Record Victory: 14-0 v Aylesbury United (H) - Spartan League 19/10/1912
Record Defeat: 0-11 v Wimbledon (H) - Isthmian League 1946
Record Goalscorer: Billy Minter - 356 (Top scorer for 12 consecutive season from 1920-32)
Record Appearances: Phil Wood - 900 (1962-85)
Additional Records: Paid £6,000 to Yeovil Town for Paul Turner August 1957
Received £92,759 from Southend United for Dean Austin 1990
Senior Honours:
Athenian League 1920-21, 21-22. Isthmian League 1923-24, 26-27, 27-28.
London Senior Cup 1970-71.

10 YEAR RECORD

04-05	05-06	06-07	07-08	08-09	09-10	10-11	11-12	12-13	13-14
Conf S 14	Conf S 2	Conf 24	Conf S 19	Conf S 12	Conf S 13	Conf S 22	SthP 8	SthP 11	SthP 4

ST ALBANS CITY MATCH RESULTS 2013-14

Date	Comp	H/A	Opponents	Att:	Result		Goalscorers	Pos	No.
Aug 17	SPL	A	Poole Town	100	L	1-2	Ngoyi 20	18	1
19	SPL	H	Hungerford Town	383	W	2-0	O'Leary 32 Goss 63	7	2
24	SPL	H	Banbury United	348	W	3-2	Henry 73 90 Keenleyside 89	7	3
26	SPL	A	Chesham United	503	L	0-1		12	4
31	SPL	H	Corby Town	374	W	1-0	Henry 88		5
Sept 2	SPL	A	Hitchin Town	512	D	1-1	Frendo 16	8	6
7	SPL	A	AFC Totton	386	W	5-2	FRENDO 4(29 41 45 52) Nwokeji 82	5	7
14	FAC 1Q	H	Enfield Town	423	W	6-1	NWOKEJI 3 (31 52 83) Frendo 39 Goss 49 Paul 90		8
16	SPL	H	Cambridge City	327	L	0-1		6	9
21	SPL	H	Stourbridge	338	L	1-2	Frendo 90	11	10
28	FAC2Q	H	Billericay Town	372	W	2-0	Nwokeji 17 Frendo 56		11
Oct 5	SPL	A	Truro City	100	W	7-3	Watters 9 Kaloczi 11 Locke 22 Chappell 72 Bailey 76 Henry 90 Frendo 90		12
8	SPL	A	Bedford Town	226	D	2-2	Martin 20 Bailey 33	10	13
12	FAC3Q	H	Tonbridge Angels	605	W	2-1	Frendo 8 Nwokeji 73		14
19	FAT1Q	A	Witham Town	85	W	3-0	Nwokeji 24 Frendo 58 71 (pen)		15
21	SPL	H	Hemel Hempstead T	677	D	2-2	Nwokeji 10 Frendo 28	10	16
26	FAC 4Q	A	Chatham Town	849	W	2-0	Frendo 45 Keenleyside 48		17
28	SPL	H	HItchin Town	355	W	2-1	Wharton 10 Frendo 33 (pen)	7	18
Nov 2	FAT2Q	H	Billericay Town	313	D	3-3	Nwokeji 16 61 Frendo 74		19
5	FAT2Qr	A	Billericay Town	201	D	2-2	Comley 47 Bailey 78 (won 4-2 on pens aet)		20
9	FAC1	H	Mansfield Town	3251	L	1-8	Locke 8		21
16	FAT3Q	A	Chelmsford City	429	W	2-1	Frendo 19 (pen) Ngoyi 89		22
20	SPL	A	Cambridge City	216	W	3-0	Keenleyside 20 41 Wharton 76 (og)	8	23
23	SPL	A	St Neots Town	364	W	3-2	Kaloczi 36 60 Lowe 80	7	24
30	FAT 1	A	Tonbridge Angels	484	D	0-0			25
Dec 2	FAT1r	H	Tonbridge Angels	303	W	4-0	Comley 25 Nwokeji 57 Hall 66 Henry 73		26
7	SPL	A	Weymouth	444	W	3-0	Comley 10 Martin 55 Frendo 80	8	27
14	FAT2	H	Cambridge United	887	L	1 2	Frendo 61 (pen)		28
16	SPL	H	Bashley	280	W	2-0	Frendo 2 (pen) 46	6	29
21	SPL	A	Redditch United	227	W	3-1	Frendo 42 90 Kaloczi 86	6	30
26	SPL	H	Chesham United	730	D	2-2	Lowe 3 Kaloczi 56	7	31
28	SPL	A	Hungerford Town	206	L	1-3	Boardman 80 (og)	7	32
Jan 4	SPL	H	Frome Town	363	W	4-0	Lowe 29 Keenleyside 50 Comley 53 Frendo 68	6	33
11	SPL	A	Chippenham Town	405	D	1-1	Frendo 77	7	34
13	SPL	H	AFC Totton	266	W	4-2	Lowe 48 Gilbert 56 Frendo 62 Chappell 68	6	35
18	SPL	H	St Neots Town	812	D	1-1	Nwokeji 39	5	36
25	SPL	H	Arlesey Town	640	W	5-0	Frendo 19 (pen) 90 Comley 41 Graham 89 Lowe 90	5	37
28	SPL	A	Burnham	150	W	3-2	Comley 45 Frendo 50 Kaloczi 67	4	38
Feb 4	SPL	A	Arlesey Town	242	W	3-2	Locke 7 Taylor 51 Frendo 56	4	39
8	SPL	H	Weymouth	762	W	3-0	Frendo 11 42 Dean 25	3	40
10	SPL	H	Bideford	363	D	1-1	Frendo 19 (pen)	3	41
15	SPL	A	Bideford Town	219	L	0-1		3	42
17	SPL	H	Chippenham Town	352	W	1-0	Frendo 20	3	43
22	SPL	H	Redditch United	515	W	2-1	Frendo 13 Bailey 75	3	44
March 1	SPL	H	Truro City	784	L	1-3	Bailey 54	3	45
5	SPL	A	Corby Town	234	L	0-2		3	46
8	SPL	A	Stourbridge	477	W	1-0	Concanon 20	3	47
10	SPL	A	Biggleswade Town	281	D	0-0		3	48
15	SPL	H	Bedford Town	713	W	2-1	Henry 18 Kaloczi 62	3	49
22	SPL	A	Bashley	192	W	2-1	Gilbert 38 Frendo 59	3	50
29	SPL	H	Burnham	640	W	5-2	Martin 19 Wales 58 90 Sykes 65 Watters 90 (pen)	3	51
April 5	SPL	A	Hemel Hempstead T	999	D	0-0		3	52
12	SPL	H	Poole Town	581	L	0-1		4	53
19	SPL	A	Banbury United	308	W	5-1	Wales 1 Frendo 37 41 Chappell 50 Comley 65	4	54
21	SPL	H	Biggleswade Town	724	W	1-0	Sykes 20	4	55
26	SPL	A	Frome Town	352	D	0-0		4	56
30	SPL PO SF	A	Cambridge City	768	W	4-2	Frendo 5 Wales 23 Martin 48 Comley 82		57
May 5	SPL PO F	A	Chesham United	2960	W	3-1	Frendo 36 59 Wales 45		58

GOALSCORERS	Lge	FAC	FAT	Total	Pens	Hat-tricks	Cons Run
Frendo	29+3	4	5	41	7	1	6
Nwokeji	3	5	4	12		1	3
Comley	5+1		2	8			2
Kaloczi	7			7			2
Henry	5		1	6			
Bailey	4		1	5			
Keenleyside	4	1		5			
Lowe	5			5			
Wales	3+2			5			
Martin	3+1			4			
Chappell	3			3			
Locke	2	1		3			
Gilbert	2			2			
Goss	1	1		2			
Ngoyi	1		1	2			
Sykes	2			2			
Watters	2			2	1		
Concannon	1			1			
Dean	1			1			
Graham	1			1			
Hall	1		1	1			
O'Leary	1			1			
Paine	1			1			
Paul		1		1			
Taylor	1			1			
Wharton	1			1			
Opponents	2			2			

Cons Run - Consecutive scoring games. Play-off goals indicaed by +

STAINES TOWN

Chairman: Matthew Boon
Secretary: Steven Parsons (T) 07850 794 315 (E) steve@stainestownfootballclub.co.uk
Commercial Manager: Roy Lewis (T) 07977 012 699
Programme Editor: Steve Parsons (T) 07850 794 315
Ground Address: Wheatsheaf Park, Wheatsheaf Lane, Staines TW18 2PD
(T) 01784 469 240 **Manager:** Marcus Gayle

2014-15 Squad

Club Factfile

Founded: 1892 **Nickname:** The Swans
Previous Names: Staines Albany & St Peters Institute merged in 1895. Staines 1905-18, Staines Lagonda 1918-25, Staines Vale (WWII)
Previous Leagues: Great Western Suburban, Hounslow & District 1919-20, Spartan 1924-35, 58-71, Middlesex Senior 1943-52, Parthenon 1952-53, Hellenic 1953-58, Athenian 1971-73, Isthmian 1973-2009

Club Colours (change): Old gold/blue/white (All white)

Ground Capacity: 3,000 **Seats:** 300 **Covered:** 850 **Clubhouse:** Yes **Shop:** Yes

Directions
Leave M25 at Junction 13. If coming from the North (anticlockwise), bear left onto A30 Staines By-Pass; if coming from the South (clockwise), go round the roundabout and back under M25 to join By-Pass. Follow A30 to Billet Bridge roundabout, which you treat like a roundabout, taking last exit, A308, London Road towards Town Centre. At 3rd traffic lights, under iron bridge, turn left into South Street, passing central bus station, as far as Thames Lodge (formerly Packhorse). Turn left here, into Laleham Road, B376, under rail bridge. After 1km, Wheatsheaf Lane is on the right, by the traffic island. Ground is less than 100 yds on left. Please park on the left.

Previous Grounds: Groundshared with Walton & Hersham and Egham Town whilst new Wheatsheaf stadium was built 2001-03.

Record Attendance: 2,750 v Banco di Roma - Barassi Cup 1975 (70,000 watched the second leg)
Record Victory: 14-0 v Croydon (A) - Isthmian Division 1 19/03/1994
Record Defeat: 1-18 - Wycombe Wanderers (A) - Great Western Suburban League 27/12/1909
Record Goalscorer: Alan Gregory - 122
Record Appearances: Dickie Watmore - 840
Additional Records:

Senior Honours:
Spartan League 1959-60. Athenian League Division 2 1971-72, Division 1 1974-75, 88-89.
Middlesex Senior cup 1975-76, 76-77, 77-78, 88-89, 90-91, 94-95, 97-98, 2009-10, 12-13. Barassi Cup 1975-76.
Isthmian Full Members Cup 1994-95, Premier Division Play-off 2008-09.

10 YEAR RECORD

04-05	05-06	06-07	07-08	08-09	09-10	10-11	11-12	12-13	13-14
Isth P 9	Isth P 6	Isth P 12	Isth P 2	Isth P 2	Conf S 8	Conf S 15	Conf S 15	Conf S 18	Conf S 8

STAINES TOWN MATCH RESULTS 2013-14

Date	Comp	H/A	Opponents	Att:	Result		Goalscorers	Pos	No.
Aug 17	ConfS	H	Dorchester Town	176	W	1-0	Theophanous 66 (pen)	9	1
20	ConfS	A	Sutton United	484	L	1-4	Taylor 65	11	2
24	ConfS	A	Chelmsford City	602	L	2-3	Johnson 16 Ferguson 45	17	3
26	ConfS	H	Boreham Wood	219	W	3-1	Beadle 51 Russell 9 (og) Russell 39 (og)	9	4
31	ConfS	A	Basingstoke Town	377	L	1-2	Theophanous 13	13	5
Sept 7	ConfS	H	Eastbourne Borough	350	W	2-1	Theophanous 66 (pen) Worsfold 39	10	6
14	ConfS	A	Bromley	584	L	0-3		14	7
17	ConfS	H	Bath City	224	W	1-0	Theophanous 89	9	8
21	ConfS	H	Farnborough	**410**	W	3-2	THEOPHANOUS 3 (23 34 64 pen)	5	9
28	***FAC2Q***	***A***	***Aylesbury United***	***203***	***W***	***3-0***	***Theophanous 55 88 Beadle 90***		10
Oct 5	ConfS	A	Tonbridge Angels	468	D	1-1	Theophanous 10	5	11
12	***FAC3Q***	***H***	***Sittingburne***	***357***	***W***	***4-1***	***Theophanous 23 Ngamvoulo 45 Johnson 79 Akinsanya 90***		12
19	ConfS	A	Eastleigh	663	L	0-1		12	13
26	***FAC4Q***	***H***	***Poole Town***	***357***	***D***	***0-0***			14
29	***FAC4Qr***	***A***	***Poole town***	***935***	***W***	***1-0***	***Theophanous 70***		15
Nov 2	ConfS	H	Hayes & Yeading	396	W	2-1	Pashaj 22 Ferguson 62	12	16
9	***FAC1***	***A***	***Brentford***	***5263***	***L***	***0-5***			17
12	ConfS	H	Weston-s-Mare	203	W	2-1	Neville 26 Beadle 71	7	18
16	***FAT3Q***	***H***	***Farnborough***	***299***	***D***	***2-2***	***M'Boungou 28 Theophanous 48***		19
19	***FAT3Qr***	***A***	***Farnborough***	***230***	***W***	***2-0***	***Ngamvoulou 34 Beadle 90***		20
23	ConfS	H	Concord Rangers	151	L	0-1		13	21
26	ConfS	A	Gosport Borough	231	L	0-2		13	22
30	***FAT1***	***H***	***Luton Town***	***621***	***D***	***0-0***			23
Dec 2	***FAT1r***	***A***	***Luton Town***	***911***	***L***	***0-2***			24
7	ConfS	H	Bishop's Stortford	230	W	2-0	Theophanous 37 Beadle 77	10	25
14	ConfS	A	Eastbourne Borough	547	L	0-2		11	26
21	ConfS	H	Dover Athletic	284	D	2-2	Theophanous 7 30	9	27
26	ConfS	A	Maidenhead United	355	L	1-3	Beadle 45	12	28
28	ConfS	H	Sutton United	377	W	2-1	Brown 3 Ferrell 27	10	29
Jan 4	ConfS	A	Bath City	538	D	1-1	Ferrell 90	8	30
7	ConfS	A	Whitehawk	126	D	3-3	NGAMVOULOU 3 (21 80 82)	8	31
11	ConfS	A	Farnborough	313	W	2 1	Willcock 43 M'Boungou 75	7	32
21	ConfS	H	Maidenhead United	235	D	0-0		6	33
Feb 4	ConfS	A	Bishop's Stortford	288	L	0-1		9	34
15	ConfS	A	Ebbsfleet United	791	L	0-3		10	35
25	ConfS	A	Concord Rangers	156	L	1-2	Brown 75	11	36
March 1	ConfS	A	Dorchester Town	426	D	1-1	Theophanous 45	12	37
8	ConfS	H	Gosport Borough	231	L	0-3		13	38
11	ConfS	A	Hayes & Yeading	112	W	2-1	Worsfold 57 Brown 90	13	39
15	ConfS	A	Havant & Waterlooville	541	W	2-0	Theophanous 42 Lodge 60	10	40
22	ConfS	H	Eastleigh	341	D	0-0		12	41
25	ConfS	H	Bromley	212	W	2-1	Santos 14 Theophanous 89	11	42
29	ConfS	A	Weston-s-Mare	250	W	3-0	M'Boungou 5 30 Theophanous 8	10	43
April 1	ConfS	H	Havant & Waterlooville	204	W	1-0	Pashaj 73	9	44
5	ConfS	H	Ebbsfleet United	362	D	1-1	Corcoran 90 (og)	10	45
8	ConfS	H	Whitehawk	237	W	2-1	M'Boungou 23 Theophanous 43	8	46
12	ConfS	A	Dover Athletic	625	L	0-1		9	47
15	ConfS	H	Tonbridge Angels	257	D	0-0		9	48
19	ConfS	H	Chelmsford City	373	W	3-1	Beadle 17 Theophanous 33 Ming 72 (pen)	8	49
21	ConfS	A	Boreham Wood	155	W	2-0	Brown 15 Pashaj 74	8	50
26	ConfS	H	Basingstoke Town	307	L	4-5	Roe-Beadle 43 Theophanous 72 Brown 87 Felix 90	8	51

GOALSCORERS	Lge	FAC	FAT	Total	Pens	Hat-tricks	Cons Run
Theophanous	18	4	1	23	3		5
Beadle	5	1	1	7			
M'Boungou	4		1	5			
Ngamvoulo	3	1	1	5		1	
Brown	4			4			2
Pashaj	3			3			
Ferrell	2			2			2
Johnson	1	1		2			
Ferguson	2			2			
Worsfold	2			2			
Akinsanya		1		1			
Felix	1			1			
Lodge	1			1			
Ming	1			1	1		
Neville	1			1			
Roe-Beadle	1			1			
Santos	1			1			
Taylor	1			1			
Willcock	1			1			
Opponents	3			3			

Cons Run - Consecutive scoring games.

SUTTON UNITED

Chairman: Bruce Elliott
Secretary: Ray Ward (T) 07908 611 354 (E) honsec@suttonunited.net
Commercial Manager: Graham Baker (T) 07816 088 281
Programme Editor: Lyall Reynolds (T) 07809 416 866
Ground Address: Borough Sports Ground, Gander Green Lane, Sutton, Surrey SM1 2EY
(T) 0208 644 4440 **Manager:** Paul Doswell

Club Factfile

Founded: 1898 **Nickname:** The U's
Previous Names: None
Previous Leagues: Sutton Junior, Southern Suburban, Athenian 1921-63, Isthmian 1963-86, 91-99, 2000-04, 2008-11, Conference 1999-2000, 04-08
Club Colours (change): All amber (All white)

Ground Capacity: 7,032 **Seats:** 765 **Covered:** 1,250 **Clubhouse:** Yes **Shop:** Yes

Directions
Travel along the M25 to junction 8. Then north on the A217 for about 15-20 minutes. Ignoring signs for Sutton itself, stay on the A217 to the traffic lights by the Gander Inn (on the left), turn right into Gander Green Lane. The Borough Sports Ground is about 200 yards up this road on the left hand side, if you reach West Sutton station you have gone too far.

Previous Grounds: Western Road, Manor Lane, London Road, The Find

Record Attendance: 14,000 v Leeds United - FA Cup 4th Round 24/01/1970
Record Victory: 11-1 v Clapton - 1966 and v Leatherhead - 1982-83 both Isthmian League
Record Defeat: 0-13 v Barking - Athenian League 1925-26
Record Goalscorer: Paul McKinnon - 279
Record Appearances: Larry Pritchard - 781 (1965-84)
Additional Records: Received £100,000 from AFC Bournemouth for Efan Ekoku 1990

Senior Honours:
Athenian League 1927-28, 45-46, 57-58. Isthmian League 1966-67, 84-85, 98-99, 2010-11.
London Senior Cup 1957-58, 82-83. Surrey Senior Cup 1945-46, 64-65, 67-68, 69-70, 79-80, 82-83, 83-84, 84-85, 85-86, 86-87, 87-88, 92-93, 94-95, 98-99, 2002-03. Anglo Italian Cup 1978-79. Bob Lord Trophy 1990-91.

10 YEAR RECORD

04-05	05-06	06-07	07-08	08-09	09-10	10-11	11-12	12-13	13-14
Conf S 15	Conf S 13	Conf S 13	Conf S 22	Isth P 5	Isth P 2	Isth P 1	Conf S 4	Conf S 6	Conf S 2

SUTTON UNITED MATCH RESULTS 2013-14

Date	Comp	H/A	Opponents	Att:	Result	Goalscorers	Pos	No.
Aug 17	ConfS	A	Eastleigh	682	L 0-1		18	1
20	ConfS	H	Staines Town	484	**W** 4-1	Taylor 17 54 Dundas 57 Ifil 74 (og)	8	2
24	ConfS	H	Bishops Stortford	405	L 1-2	Allen 19 (og)	13	3
26	ConfS	A	Concord Rangers	320	D 0-0		12	4
31	ConfS	H	Whitehawk	441	**W** 2-0	Stuart 50 Dundas 79	9	5
Sept 7	ConfS	A	Tonbridge Angels	549	D 1-1	Miles 82 (og)	11	6
14	ConfS	H	Farnborough	465	D 3-3	Sinclair 32 Dundas 72 Folkes 84	9	7
17	ConfS	H	Dover Athletic	442	**W** 1-1	McDonald 18	6	8
21	ConfS	A	Havant & Waterlooville	530	**W** 5-0	Haysman 34 Riviere 45 Dundas 70 Slabber 76 79	4	9
28	***FAC2Q***	***A***	***Whitehawk***	***267***	***W 1-0***	***Haysman 3***		10
Oct 5	ConfS	H	Eastbourne Borough	1021	**W** 4-0	Taylor 6 19 Haysman 66 McDonald 86	4	11
12	***FAC3Q***	***A***	***Lewes***	***1173***	***W 1-0***	***Slabber 12***		12
19	ConfS	H	Bromley	894	**W** 1-0	Slabber 49	3	13
26	***FAC4Q***	***A***	***Hemel Hempstead Town***	***1455***	***D 3-3***	***Nelson 23 Dundas 35 Fuseini 40***		14
29	***FAC4Qr***	***H***	***Hemel Hempstead Town***	***662***	***W 2-0***	***Fuseini 12 Dundas 86***		15
Nov 2	ConfS	H	Eastleigh	691	D 1-1	Dundas 48 (pen)	4	16
9	***FAC1***	***A***	***Kidderminster Harriers***	***2045***	***L 1-4***	***Clough 10***		17
12	Conf S	A	Bath City	476	D 2-2	Nelson 41 Slabber 57	6	18
16	***FAT3Q***	***H***	***Havant & Waterlooville***	***374***	***L 1-2***	***Dundas 83***		19
23	ConfS	H	Dorchester Town	646	L 0-1		8	20
26	ConfS	A	Weston-s-Mare	128	D 1 1	Slabber 35	7	21
Dec 7	ConfS	H	Maidenhead United	472	**W** 3-2	Slabber 20 42 Dundas 51	5	22
9	ConfS	A	Boreham Wood	201	**W** 3-1	Scannell 43 Dundas 48 (pen) Slabber 73	4	23
14	ConfS	H	Tonbridge Angels	486	L 1-2	Clough 14	4	24
21	ConfS	A	Ebbsflet United	724	L 0 2		4	25
26	ConfS	H	Hayes & Yeading United	537	**W** 2-0	Scannell 64 Williams 88	4	26
28	ConfS	A	Staines Town	377	L 1-2	Slabber 64	4	27
Jan 11	ConfS	A	Chelmsford City	717	**W** 2-0	Slabber 63 Binns 87	3	28
25	ConfS	A	Basingstoke Town	462	**W** 1-0	Taylor 16	4	29
Feb 4	ConfS	A	Gosport Borough	261	D 2-2	Downer 45 Slabber 68	4	30
15	ConfS	H	Weston-s-Mare	439	**W** 3-0	TAYLOR 3 (19 39 78)	4	31
18	ConfS	A	Dover Athletic	525	**W** 1-0	Dundas 3	4	32
22	ConfS	A	Eastbourne Borough	420	D 1-1	Slabber 48	3	33
March 1	ConfS	H	Chelmsford City	707	**W** 2-0	McCallum 1 Dundas 89	3	34
4	ConfS	A	Bromley	795	**W** 4-2	Slabber 20 Sinclair 82 90 Dundas 90	3	35
8	ConfS	A	Farnborough	345	**W** 2-1	Scannell 34 Taylor 40	3	36
15	ConfS	H	Basingstoke Town	**2172**	**W** 4-0	Scannell 5 McCallum 25 39 Sinclair 76	3	37
18	ConfS	H	Gosport Borough	433	**W** 2-0	McCallum 41 Taylor 48	3	38
22	ConfS	A	Dorchester Town	456	D 0 0		3	39
25	ConfS	A	Hayes & Yeading United	145	D 0-0		3	40
29	ConfS	H	Bath City	554	D 2-2	Clough 82 Dundas 88	3	41
April 1	ConfS	H	Boreham Wood	418	**W** 1-0	Spillaine 87	3	42
3	ConfS	H	Havant & Waterlooville	451	**W** 3-1	Haysman 2 Taylor 50 Dundas 83	2	43
5	ConfS	A	Maidenhead United	356	L 2-3	Taylor 8 68	2	44
12	ConfS	H	Ebbsfleet United	721	**W** 3-1	Taylor 67 86 Downer 71	2	45
19	ConfS	A	Bishop's Stortford	478	**W** 2-1	McCallum 61 Dundas 89	2	46
21	ConfS	H	Concord Rangers	635	**W** 1-0	Dundas 78	2	47
26	ConfS	A	Whitehawk	307	D 3-3	Binns 27 45 Dundas 43	2	48
30	***CSPO SF 1***	***A***	***Dover Athletic***	***1273***	***D 1-1***	***Dundas 1***		49
May 3	***CSPO SF 2***	***H***	***Dover Athletic***	***1671***	***L 0-3***			50

GOALSCORERS	Lge	FAC	FAT	Total	Pens	Hat-tricks	Cons Run
Dundas	15+1	2	1	19	2		4
Taylor	15			15		1	3
Slabber	13	1		14			3
McCallum	5			5			
Haysman	3	1		4			3
Scannell	4			4			2
Sinclair	4			4			
Clough	2	1		3			
Binns	2			2			
Downer	2			2			
Fuseini		2		2			2
McDonald	2			2			
Nelson	1	1		2			
Folkes	1			1			
Ifil	1			1			
Riviere	1			1			
Spillaine	1			1			
Stuart	1			1			
Williams	1			1			
Opponents	3			3			2

Cons Run - Consecutive scoring games.

Play-off goals indicated by +

WEALDSTONE

Chairman: Howard Krais
Secretary: Paul Fruin **(T)** 0779 003 8095 **(E)** paul@pfruin.orangehome.co.uk
Commercial Manager: Paul Rumens **(T)** 07710 929 692
Programme Editor: Mark Hyde **(T)** 07721 893 861
Ground Address: St. Georges Stadium, Grosvenor Vale, Ruislip, Middlesex HA4 6JQ
(T) 07790 038 095 - 01895 637 487 (SC) **Manager:** Gordon Bartlett

Isthmian Premier Division Champions 2013-14!
Photo: Steve Foster/Wealdstone FC

Club Factfile

Founded: 1899 **Nickname:** The Stones
Previous Names: None
Previous Leagues: Willesden & District 1899-1906, 08-13, London 1911-22, Middlesex 1913-22, Spartan 1922-28, Athenian 1928-64, Isthmian 1964-71, 95-2006, 2007-14. Southern 1971-79, 81-82, 88-95, Conference 1979-81, 82-88

Club Colours (change): Royal blue/white/royal blue (All yellow)

Ground Capacity: 2,300 **Seats:** 300 **Covered:** 450 **Clubhouse:** Yes **Shop:**

Directions

From the M1: Follow Signs for Heathrow Airport on the M25. Come off at Junction 16 onto the A40, come off at The Polish War Memorial junction A4180 sign posted to Ruislip, continue on West End Road, right into Grosvenor Vale after approx 1.5 miles, the ground is at the end of the road.
From the M25: Follow Take Junction 16 Off M25 onto A40. Then come off at The Polish War Memorial junction A4180 sign posted to Ruislip, continue on West End Road, right into Grosvenor Vale after approx 1.5 miles, the ground is at the end of the road.
From the M4: Junction 4B, take the M25 towards Watford, come off Junction 16 and join A40, come off at The Polish War Memorial junction A4180 sign posted to Ruislip, continue on West End Road, right into Grosvenor Vale after approx 1.5 miles, the ground is at the end of the road.

Previous Grounds: Lower Mead Stadium, Watford FC, Yeading FC, Northwood FC

Record Attendance: 13,504 v Leytonstone - FA Amateur Cup 4th Round replay 05/03/1949 (at Lower Mead Stadium)
Record Victory: 22-0 v The 12th London Regiment (The Rangers) - FA Amateur Cup 13/10/1923
Record Defeat: 0-14 v Edgware Town (A) - London Senior Cup 09/12/1944
Record Goalscorer: George Duck - 251
Record Appearances: Charlie Townsend - 514
Additional Records: Paid £15,000 to Barnet for David Gipp
Received £70,000 from Leeds United for Jermaine Beckford
Senior Honours:
Athenian League 1951-52. Southern League Division 1 South 1973-74, Southern Division 1981-82. Conference 1984-85.
Isthmian League Division 3 1996-97, Premier 2013-14. FA Amateur Cup 1965-66. London Senior Cup 1961-62. FA Trophy 1984-85.
Middlesex Senior Cup x11

10 YEAR RECORD

04-05		05-06		06-07		07-08		08-09		09-10		10-11		11-12		12-13		13-14	
Isth P	18	Isth P	18	SthP	19	Isth P	13	Isth P	7	Isth P	6	Isth P	12	Isth P	4	Isth P	3	Isth P	1

WEALDSTONE MATCH RESULTS 2013-14

Date	Comp	H/A	Opponents	Att:	Result		Goalscorers	Pos	No.
Aug 10	IsthP	A	Maidstone United	2138	D	1-1	Moore 57	15	1
12	IsthP	H	Bognor Regis Town	544	D	2-2	Parker 22 Godfrey 35	17	2
17	IsthP	H	Wingate & Finchley	425	D	2-2	Moore 10 Pett 43	16	3
20	IsthP	A	Hampton & Richmond B	429	W	3-0	Cronin 42 (pen) Brewer 70 (og) Dean 88	10	4
24	IsthP	A	Harrow Borough	452	W	2-0	Moore 61 Grant 83	8	5
26	IsthP	H	Enfield Town	602	W	4-1	Moore 42 McGleish 56 Pett 86	5	6
31	IsthP	H	Cray Wanderers	460	W	7-1	Cronin 13 (pen) Moore 32 McGleish 37 Godfrey 45 Grant 74 Bailey 89 Hutchinson 90	3	7
Sept 7	IsthP	A	Bury Town	737	W	1-0	Pett 10	2	8
11	IsthP	A	AFC Hornchurch	251	D	1-1	Moore 10	2	9
14	***FAC1Q***	***H***	***Kings Langley***	***332***	***W***	***6-1***	***Cronin 19 Parker 21 49 McGleish 58 Grant 78 Hutchinson 85***		10
21	IsthP	H	Thamesmead Town	686	W	2-0	Moore 33 62	1	11
23	IsthP	H	Lewes	651	D	2-2	Moore 26 Pett 36	1	12
28	***FAC2Q***	***H***	***Haringey Borough***	***314***	***W***	***4-1***	***McGleish 38 48 Pett 81 Dean 90***		13
Oct 5	IsthP	H	Margate	591	L	0-1		5	14
12	***FAC3Q***	***A***	***AFC Hornchurch***	***506***	***L***	***1-6***	***Okimo 89***		15
19	***FAT1Q***	***A***	***Leiston***	***184***	***W***	***3-0***	***McGleish 45 Little 56 Pett 68***		16
26	IsthP	H	Grays Atheltic	554	W	3-1	McGleish 50 (pen) Hamblin 75 Pett 83	6	17
Nov 2	***FAT2Q***	***H***	***Maidstone United***	***524***	***D***	***2-2***	***Hamblin 34 McGleish 36***		18
5	***FAT2Qr***	***A***	***Maidstone United***	***824***	***L***	***0-1***			19
9	IsthP	H	Carshalton Athletic	448	W	3-1	Pett 32 Godfrey 55 McGleish 74	5	20
16	IsthP	A	Cray Wanderers	226	W	3-0	McGleish 66 88 Cronin 78 (pen)	4	21
23	IsthP	H	Leiston	492	W	3-1	McGleish 27 45 Pett 48	3	22
30	IsthP	A	Dulwich Hamlet	843	W	4-1	Pigden 36 Little 37 45 McGleish 39	2	23
Dec 7	IsthP	H	Metropolitan Police	516	D	1-1	Wright 77	3	24
9	IsthP	A	Kingstonian	492	W	1-0	McGleish 20	2	25
14	IsthP	A	Bognor Regis Town	506	W	3-1	Little 18 Pett 29 Wright 61	2	26
21	IsthP	H	Maidstone United	743	W	2-1	Cronin 47 (pen) 81	1	27
26	IsthP	A	Enfield Town	591	W	4-2	McGleish 6 34 Pett 60 90	1	28
28	IsthP	H	Hampton & Richmond B	833	L	1-3	Cronin 25 (pen)	1	29
Jan 11	IsthP	A	Canvey Island	397	L	2-3	Pett 36 Wright 66	1	30
25	IsthP	H	Bury Town	707	W	3-0	McGleish 6 90 Malcolm 58	3	31
Feb 4	IsthP	A	Lowestoft Town	446	D	1-1	McGleish 48	3	32
15	IsthP	A	Thamesmead Town	195	W	2-0	Malcolm 2 Cronin 57 (Pen)	3	33
17	IsthP	H	AFC Hornchurch	685	W	2-0	McGleish 38 Pett 86	3	34
22	IsthP	H	Hendon	693	D	1-1	Wright 83	3	35
24	IsthP	H	Harrow Borough	801	W	3-0	Malcolm 15 Godfrey 47 Pigden 67	3	36
March 8	IsthP	A	Carshalton Athletic	441	W	4-2	Malcolm 2 43 Bailey 47 75	2	37
11	IsthP	A	Wingate & Finchley	265	W	2-0	Bentley 45 McCluskey 47	1	38
15	IsthP	H	East Thurrock United	686	W	5-0	McGLEISH 3 (26 35 56) Bailey 44 Pett 90	1	39
17	IsthP	A	Hendon	575	D	0-0		1	40
22	IsthP	A	Leiston	374	W	2-0	Penny 5 McGleish 61	1	41
25	IsthP	A	Lewes	356	W	3-0	Pett 17 Pigden 68 McGleish 75	1	42
29	IsthP	H	Dulwich Hamlet	**1151**	D	2-2	McGleish 33 Pett 42	1	43
31	IsthP	H	Billericay Town	726	W	2-0	Cronin 70 (pen) 80 Wright	1	44
April 3	IsthP	A	East Thurrock United	299	W	3-0	Penny 32 McCluskie 34 58	1	45
5	IsthP	A	Metropolitan Police	354	L	1-2	Cronin 11 (pen)	1	46
8	IsthP	H	Lowestoft Town	852	D	0-0		1	47
12	IsthP	A	Grays Athletic	473	D	1-1	McGleish 88	1	48
15	IsthP	A	Margate	429	W	1-0	Penny 83	1	49
19	IsthP	H	Kingstonian	895	L	0-4		1	50
21	IsthP	A	Bllericay Town	424	L	2-4	Malcolm 5 Wright 71	1	51
26	IsthP	H	Canvey Island	906	W	2-0	Penny 81 Dean 90	1	52

GOALSCORERS	Lge	FAC	FAT	Total	Pens	Hat-tricks	Cons Run
McGleish	22	3	2	27		1	4
Pett	15	1	1	17			2
Cronin	10	1		11	9		
Moore	9			9			3
Malcolm	6			6			
Wright	6			6			
Bailey	5			5			
Godfrey	4			4			
Little	3		1	4			
Penny	4			4			
Dean	2	1		3			
Grant	2	1		3			
McCluskey	3			3			
Parker	1	2		3			
Pigden	3			3			
Hamblin	1		1	2			
Hutchinson	1	1		2			
Bentley	1			1			
Okimp		1		1			
Opponents	1			1			

Cons Run - Consecutive scoring games.

WESTON-SUPER-MARE

Chairman: Paul Bliss
Secretary: Richard Sloane (T) 07711 078 589 (E) wsmsecretary@gmail.com
Commercial Manager: Neil Keeling (T) 07919 037 343
Programme Editor: Dave Pinnock (T) 01934 621 818 (B)
Ground Address: Woodspring Stadium, Winterstoke Road, Weston-super-Mare BS24 9AA
(T) 01934 621 618 **Manager:** Micky Bell

Club Factfile

Founded: 1899 **Nickname:** Seagulls
Previous Names: Borough or Weston-super-Mare
Previous Leagues: Somerset Senior, Western League

Club Colours (change): White & black stripe/white/white (Orange & black stripe/black/orange)

Ground Capacity: 3,000 **Seats:** 278 **Covered:** 2,000 **Clubhouse:** Yes **Shop:** Yes

Directions
Leave the M5 at Junction 21, take the dual carriageway A370 and continue straight until the 4th roundabout with ASDA on the right.
Turn left into Winterstoke Road, bypassing a mini roundabout and continue for 1/2 mile.
Woodspring Stadium is on the right.

Previous Grounds: Langford Road, Winterstoke Road

Record Attendance: 2,623 v Woking - FA Cup 1st Round replay 23/11/1993 (At Winterstoke Road)
Record Victory: 11-0 v Paulton Rovers
Record Defeat: 1-12 v Yeovil Town Reserves
Record Goalscorer: Matt Lazenby - 180
Record Appearances: Harry Thomas - 740
Additional Records: Received £20,000 from Sheffield Wednesday for Stuart Jones

Senior Honours:
Somerset Senior Cup 1923-24, 26-67.
Western League 1991-92.

10 YEAR RECORD

04-05	05-06	06-07	07-08	08-09	09-10	10-11	11-12	12-13	13-14
Conf S 11	Conf S 14	Conf S 21	Conf S 20	Conf S 17	Conf S 21	Conf S 12	Conf S 13	Conf S 7	Conf S 11

Conference Action

Boston United's No.8, Junior Konadu is confronted by Solihull midfielder,Richard Taundry at the Autotech Stadium. Solihull's 1-2 defeat extinguished their play-off hopes.

Photo: Jonathan Holloway.

WESTON-SUPER-MARE MATCH RESULTS 2013-14

Date	Comp	H/A	Opponents	Att:	Result	Goalscorers	Pos	No.
Aug 17	ConfS	H	Eastbourne Borough	207	L 0-1		19	1
20	ConfS	A	Dorchester Town	400	W 3-0	Plummer 22 (pen) Grubb 63 McClaggon 86	9	2
24	ConfS	A	Havant & Waterlooville	447	L 0-2		14	3
26	ConfS	H	Basingstoke Town	286	W 1-0	Diallo 75	8	4
31	ConfS	A	Chelmsford City	581	W 2-1	Diallo 55 Plummer 80 (pen)	5	5
Sept 7	ConfS	H	Boreham Wood	214	W 3-0	Laird 49 Plummer 62 Ingram 88	3	6
14	ConfS	A	Dover Athletic	556	W 2-1	Plummer 66 Diallo 90	3	7
17	ConfS	H	Maidenhead United	170	D 0-0		3	8
21	ConfS	A	Whitehawk	156	D 0-0		3	9
28	***FAC2Q***	***A***	***Basingstoke Town***	***336***	***W 3-1***	***Diallo 18 Hemmings 47 Kirk 77***		10
Oct 5	ConfS	H	Ebbsfleet United	356	L 0-6		3	11
12	***FAC3Q***	***H***	***Brislington***	***315***	***W 3-2***	***Kirk 48 Ingram 86 (pen)***		12
19	ConfS	H	Concord Rangers	209	W 5-0	Diallo 43 Grubb 53 Fiddes 80 Slocombe 89 Ingram 90	5	13
26	ConfS	H	Hayes & Yeading	210	L 0-3		6	14
Nov 2	ConfS	A	Farnborough	400	L 0-4		9	15
12	ConfS	A	Staines Town	516	L 1-2	Kington 83	11	16
16	***FAT3Q***	***H***	***TivertonTown***	***285***	***D 1-1***	***Pigton 80***		17
19	***FATQ3r***	***A***	***Tiverton Town***	***245***	***W 2-1***	***Harris 16 Kington 19***		18
23	ConfS	A	Hayes & Yeading	120	W 2-1	Hemmings 24 84	11	19
26	ConfS	H	Sutton United	128	D 1-1	Fiddes 62	8	20
30	***FAT1***	***A***	***Aldershot Town***	***1084***	***D 1-1***	***Plummer 76***		21
Dec 2	***FAT1r***	***H***	***Aldershot Town***	***283***	***L 2-5***	***Kirk 62 Plummer 75***		22
7	ConfS	A	Eastbourne Borough	483	L 0-2		11	23
10	ConfS	H	Bishop's Stortford	124	D 2-2	Kington Hemmings	11	24
14	ConfS	A	Boreham Wood	115	D 1-1	Kington 75	9	25
21	ConfS	H	Bromley	**610**	L 0-1		10	26
26	ConfS	A	Bath City	852	L 0-1		13	27
28	ConfS	H	Dorchester Town	232	W 3-0	Ash 20 Kington 70 Camper 80	9	28
Jan 11	ConfS	H	Tonbridge Angels	258	W 2-1	Plummer 37 Kington 90 (pen)	9	29
21	ConfS	H	Eastleigh	198	W 3-2	Hemmings 35 Grubb 78 Fiddes 88	5	30
25	ConfS	H	Gosport Borough	202	L 0-1		5	31
Feb 1	ConfS	A	Ebbsfleet United	865	D 1-1	Kington 82	6	32
4	ConfS	A	Maidenhead United	170	W 3-0	Grubb 17 78 Fiddes 86	6	33
15	ConfS	A	Sutton United	439	L 0-3		7	34
18	ConfS	H	Bath City	357	W 2-0	Kington 76 (pen) Grubb 90	6	35
22	ConfS	H	Dover Athletic	251	W 2-1	Kington 48 (pen) Grubb 85	5	36
Mar 1	ConfS	A	Eastleigh	602	L 1-3	Hemmings 71	5	37
8	ConfS	H	Whitehawk	245	W 2-1	Ingram 5 Kington 90 (pen)	5	38
15	ConfS	A	Tonbridge Angels	360	L 0-1		8	39
22	ConfS	A	Concord Rangers	169	L 0-2		8	40
27	ConfS	A	Bishop's Stortford	244	D 0-0		9	41
29	ConfS	H	Staines Town	250	L 0-3		11	42
April 3	ConfS	A	Gosport Borough	335	D 0-0		11	43
5	ConfS	H	Farnborough	210	W 2-1	Camper 45 Kington 70	11	44
12	ConfS	A	Bromley	352	L 1-2	Grubb 78	11	45
18	ConfS	H	Havant & Waterloville	230	D 1-1	Laird 85	11	46
21	ConfS	A	Basingstoke Town	191	L 2-3	Fiddes 45 Laird 76	12	47
26	ConfS	H	Chelmsford City	464	W 2-0	Grubb 42 Ash 60	11	48

GOALSCORERS	Lge	FAC	FAT	Total	Pens	Hat-tricks	Cons Run
Kington	10		1	11	4		2
Grubb	9			9			2
Plummer	5		2	7	2		3
Hemmings	5	1		6			
Diallo	4	1		5			2
Fiddes	5			5			
Ingram	3	1		4	1		2
Kirk		2	1	3			
Laird	3			3			
Ash	2			2			

	Lge	FAC	FAT	Total	Pens	Hat-tricks	Cons Run
Camper	2			2			
Harris			1	1			
McClaggon	1			1			
Pigton			1	1			
Slocombe	1			1			

Cons Run - Consecutive scoring games.

WHITEHAWK

Chairman: John Summers
Secretary: John Rosenblatt **(T)** 07724 519 370 **(E)** johnrosenblatt@whitehawkfc.com
Commercial Manager: TBC **(T)**
Programme Editor: Peter Smith **(T)** 07801 412 278
Ground Address: The Enclosed Ground, East Brighton Park, Wilson Avenue, Brighton BN2 5TS
(T) 01273 601 244 **Manager:** Steve King

Club Factfile

Founded: 1945 **Nickname:** Hawks
Previous Names: Whitehawk & Manor Farm Old Boys untill 1958.
Previous Leagues: Brighton & Hove District, Sussex County > 2010. Isthmian 2010-13.

Club Colours (change): All red (All blue)

Ground Capacity: 3,000 **Seats:** Yes **Covered:** 500 **Clubhouse:** Yes **Shop:** No

Directions
From N (London) on M23/A23 – after passing Brighton boundary sign & twin pillars join A27 (sp Lewes); immediately after passing Sussex University (on L) leave A27 via slip rd at sp B2123, Falmer, Rottingdean; at roundabout at top of slip rd turn R onto B2123 (sp Falmer, Rottingdean); in 2m at traffic lights in Woodingdean turn R by Downs Hotel into Warren Road; in about 1m at traffic lights turn L into Wilson Ave, crossing racecourse; in 1¼m turn L at foot of hill (last turning before traffic lights) into East Brighton Park; follow lane for the ground.

Previous Grounds: None

Record Attendance: 2,100 v Bognor Regis Town - FA Cup 1988-89
Record Victory: Not known
Record Defeat: Not known
Record Goalscorer: Billy Ford
Record Appearances: Ken Powell - 1,103
Additional Records:

Senior Honours:
Sussex County League Division 1 1961-62, 63-64, 83-84, 2009-10. Division 2 1967-68, 80-81.
Isthmian League Division 1 South 2011-12, Premier Division 2012-13.
Sussex Senior Cup 1950-51, 61-62, 2011-12. Sussex RUR Charity Cup x3.

10 YEAR RECORD

04-05	05-06	06-07	07-08	08-09	09-10	10-11	11-12	12-13	13-14
SxC1 3	SxC1 3	SxC1 2	SxC1 2	SxC1 13	SxC1 1	Isth1S 3	Isth1S 1	Isth P 1	Conf S 19

WHITEHAWK MATCH RESULTS 2013-14

Date	Comp	H/A	Opponents	Att:	Result	Goalscorers	Pos	No.
Aug 17	ConfS	H	Maidenhead United	151	L 0-3		22	1
20	ConfS	A	Bromley	605	L 0-4		22	2
24	ConfS	A	Dorchester Town	403	**W** 6-2	MILLS 5 (7 22 31 35 88) Fraser 15	18	3
26	ConfS	H	Dover Athletic	338	L 0-1		18	4
31	ConfS	A	Sutton United	441	L 0-2		19	5
Sept 7	ConfS	H	Basingstoke Town	334	**W** 1-0	El Abd 20	16	6
14	ConfS	A	Chelmsford City	587	**W** 2-0	Codmore 35 Erskine 78	13	7
17	ConfS	H	Havant & Waterloville	189	D 2-2	Robinson 17 Gargan 43	11	8
21	ConfS	H	Weston-s-Mare	156	D 0-0		13	9
28	***FAC2Q***	***H***	***Sutton United***	***267***	***L 0-1***			10
Oct 5	ConfS	A	Farnborough	483	L 0-2		13	11
19	ConfS	H	Bath City	281	D 2-2	Robinson 3 Gargan 35	17	12
26	ConfS	A	Tonbridge Angels	376	L 1-3	Taylor 82	18	13
Nov 2	ConfS	H	Gosport Borough	201	D 1-1	Mills 33	15	14
9	ConfS	A	Hayes & Yeading	97	L 2-3	Fraser 40 Mills 87	16	15
12	ConfS	A	Concord Rangers	280	D 1-1	Gargan 89	16	16
16	***FAT3Q***	***H***	***Bishop's Stortford***	***107***	***W 2-1***	***Francis 5 (og) El Abd 84***		17
23	ConfS	H	Bishop's Stortford	159	D 1-1	Mills 68	17	18
30	***FAT1***	***A***	***Arlesey Town***	***181***	***W 5-1***	***Parsons 14 49 Mills 17 Robinson 58 68***		19
Dec 7	ConfS	A	Ebbsfleet United	752	L 1-3	Cadmore 12	18	20
14	***FAT2***	***H***	***Havant & Waterlooville***	***150***	***D 1-1***	***El-Abd 90***		21
16	***FAT2r***	***A***	***Havant & Waterlooville***	***189***	***L 1-3***	***Mills 76***		22
21	ConfS	H	Boreham Wood	57	L 0-2		21	23
26	ConfS	A	Eastbourne Borough	683	**W** 2-0	Mills 34 80		24
28	ConfS	H	Bromley	290	L 1-2	Da Silva 32	20	25
Jan 7	ConfS	H	Staines Town	126	D 3-3	Fraser 7 Da Silva 22 Gargan 90	20	26
14	ConfS	A	Basingstoke Town	207	**W** 3-1	Mills 22 Fraser 64 Addai 90	18	27
18	ConfS	H	Chelmsford City	148	L 0-4		18	28
4	ConfS	H	Eastbourne Borough	201	L 1-2	Addai 2	20	29
8	ConfS	A	Bath City	540	L 1-3	Mills 17	20	30
11	ConfS	A	Gosport Borough	219	**W** 2-0	Carew 34 Robinson 67	18	31
15	ConfS	H	Farnborough	162	**W** 3-1	El-Abd 61 Robinson 62 Carew 70	17	32
March 1	ConfS	H	Concord Rangers	154	L 0-2		18	33
8	ConfS	A	Weston-s-Mare	245	L 1-2	Fairhurst 56	19	34
15	ConfS	H	Ebbsfleet United	285	D 1-1	Mills 52	20	35
18	ConfS	H	Eastleigh	135	L 1-4	Robinson 83	21	36
22	ConfS	H	Tonbridge Angels	194	**W** 1-0	Fairhurst 57	18	37
25	ConfS	A	Bishop's Stortford	226	**W** 2-1	Robinson 37 Mills 65	17	38
27	ConfS	A	Havant & Waterlooville	478	L 0-2		17	39
29	ConfS	A	Maidenhead United	245	L 0-1		18	40
April	ConfS	H	Hayes & Yeading	112	**W** 1-0	El Abd 52	17	41
5	ConfS	A	Eastleigh	592	L 2-3	Mills 7 Robinson 31 (pen)	19	42
8	ConfS	A	Staines Town	237	L 1-2	Green 80	20	43
12	ConfS	A	Boreham Wood	131	**W** 3-1	Robinson 35 (pen) Cadmore 40 Green 83 (pen)	18	44
18	ConfS	H	Dorchester Town	199	**W** 3-0	Fairhurst 32 Mills 73 82	18	45
21	ConfS	A	Dover Athletic	695	D 1-1	Parsons 3	19	46
26	ConfS	H	Sutton United	**356**	D 3-3	Robinson 32 (pen) Mills 37 Fairhurst 76	19	47

GOALSCORERS	Lge	FAC	FAT	Total	Pens	Hat-tricks	Cons Run
Mills	18		2	20			
Robinson	9		2	11	3		
El Abd	3		2	5			
Fairhurst	4			4			
Fraser	4			4			
Gargan	4			4			
Cadmore	3			3			
Parsons	1		2	3			
Addai	2			2			
Carew	2			2			
De Silva	2			2			
Green	2			2	1		
Erskine	1			1			
Taylor	1			1			
Opponents			1	1			

Cons Run - Consecutive scoring games.

Conference North Division Statistics 2013-14

	MCV	MCD	MCwW	MCwD	MCSG	MCwS	TGS	MCCS	TNCS
AFC Telford United	7	2	3	11	13	2	5	4	13
Altrincham	4	3	4	7	19	1	3	2	13
Barrow	5	3	7	14	7	3	14	5	13
Boston United	3	2	5	9	8	2	10	2	13
Brackley Town	3	2	4	13	19	2	7	4	20
Bradford Park Avenue	3	5	7	13	21	4	10	4	12
Colwyn Bay	6	2	6	8	22	2	6	2	9
Gainsborough Trinity	2	6	8	5	10	2	11	3	8
Gloucester City	3	4	7	8	11	3	11	2	8
Guiseley	5	6	8	13	18	3	8	7	14
Harrogate Town	3	5	7	8	11	3	10	1	7
Hednesford Town	5	4	5	11	13	1	5	2	10
Histon	2	5	20	5	6	3	17	2	7
Leamington	3	3	10	9	9	2	12	5	13
North Ferriby United	6	3	3	9	21	1	7	4	17
Oxford City	3	4	9	5	5	2	13	2	7
Solihull Moors	4	5	8	14	16	1	8	2	16
Stalybridge Celtic	3	3	13	3	11	1	11	1	4
Stockport County	3	3	14	5	7	7	16	4	13
Vauxhall Motors	3	3	5	3	4	3	16	2	8
Worcester City	3	4	8	3	5	4	20	3	18
Workington	2	4	15	2	5	3	18	2	5

MCV - Most Consecutive Victories I MCD - Most Consecutive Defeats
MCwW - Most Consecutive without a Win I MCwD - Most Consecutive without a defeat
MCSG - Most Consecutive Scoring Games I MCwS - Most Consecutive without Scoring
TGS - Total Games without Scoring I MCCS - Most Consecutive Clean Sheets
TNCS - Total Number of Clean Sheets

Best Home League Attendances 2013-2014

	Att:	Opponents	Score
AFC Telford United	3724	Gainsborough Trinity	W 3-0
Altrincham	2875	Stockport County	W 3-0
Barrow	1011	Barrow	D 1-1
Boston United	1567	North Ferriby United	W 2-0
Brackley Town	529	Leamington	D 1-1
Bradford PA	569	Stockport County	L 0-2
Colwyn Bay	497	Altrincham	L 1-3
Gainsborough Trinity	746	Boston United	L 0-1
Goucester City	566	Worcester City	W 2-1
Guseley	815	Harrogate Town	W 2-0
Harrogate Town	1428	Gloucester City	W 4-2
Hednesford Town	1252	AFC Telford United	D 3-3
Histon	508	Stockport County	W 2-1
Leamington	1038	Stockport County	W 2-1
North Ferriby United	673	Brackley Town	D 1-1
Oxford City	542	Stockport County	W 4-1
Solihull Moors	834	AFC Telford UNited	D 2-2
Stalybridge Celtic	1500	Stockport County	D 0-0
Stockport County	3770	Altrincham	D 0-0
Vauxhall Motors	446	Altrincham	L 1-2
Worcester City	854	Boston United	W 3-1
Workington	931	Barrow	L 0-2

HAT-TRICK HEROS

	Club	Goals	Opponents	Score
Adam Farrell	AFC Telford United	3	Hednesford Town (h)	W 5-3
James Walshaw	Altrincham	3	Guiseley (h)	W 4-1
James Walshaw	Altrincham	3	Colwyn Bay (h)	W 3-1
Ricky Miller	Boston United	3	Workington (h)	W 5-3
Ricky Miller	Boston United	3	Solihull Moors (h)	W 4-1
Marc Newsham	Boston United	3	Gainsborough Trinity (h)	W 6-0
Ricky Miller	Boston United	3	Barrow (a)	D 4-4
Lewis McMahon	Gainsborough Trinity	3	Barrow (a)	W 6-0
Jonno Margetts	Gainsborough Trinity	3	Oxford City (h)	W 6-0
Joe Parker	Gloucester City	3	Yate Town (h) (FACup)	W 7-0
Joe Parker	Gloucester City	3	Harrogate Town (h)	W 5-2
Gavin Rothery	Guiseley	3	Harrogate Town (a)	W 3-2
Michael Woods	Harrogate Town	3	Gloucester City (h)	W 4-2
Elliott Durrell	Stalybridge Celtic	3	Hednesford Town (a)	W 4-0
Nathan Jarman	North Ferriby United	3 pens	Gainsboorough Trinity (a)	W 4-1
Anthony Wilson	North Ferriby United	3	Colwyn Bay (a)	W 3-0
Kristian Dennis	Stockport County	3	Gaimsborough Trinity (a)	W 5-1
Ethan Moore	Worcester City	3	Ramsbothom U (FATrophy)	W 3-0

Conference South Division Statistics 2013-14

	MCV	MCD	MCwW	MCwD	MCSG	MCwS	TGS	MCCS	TNCS
Basingstoke Town	5	4	6	4	6	5	17	4	13
Bath City	3	3	6	5	6	3	11	2	11
Bishops Stortford	7	3	10	7	18	2	6	2	10
Boreham Wood	2	4	9	5	6	3	16	4	16
Bromley	5	2	4	9	10	1	6	6	12
Chelmsford City	2	7	7	5	4	2	17	2	9
Concord Rangers	3	3	4	6	6	3	13	2	12
Dorchester Town	2	5	9	3	5	3	21	2	6
Dover Athletic	4	4	4	7	12	3	13	3	19
Eastbourne Borough	2	5	6	5	4	3	15	3	11
Eastleigh	7	2	3	12	24	2	9	3	20
Ebbsfleet United	8	3	4	9	16	2	7	3	18
Farnborough	5	4	7	4	8	2	14	1	9
Gosport Borough	5	3	7	6	7	3	18	5	18
Havant & Waterlooville	3	2	5	12	10	2	12	4	24
Hayes & Yeading United	3	7	9	3	7	2	16	2	13
Maidenhead United	3	6	10	5	8	3	13	2	12
Staines Town	3	3	6	8	6	4	16	2	15
Sutton United	6	2	6	16	15	2	6	5	20
Tonbridge Angels	2	3	7	4	9	3	16	2	8
Weston-Super-Mare	4	2	8	7	7	5	17	2	11
Whitehawk	2	3	9	4	11	3	12	2	8

MCV - Most Consecutive Victories I MCD - Most Consecutive Defeats
MCwW - Most Consecutive without a Win I MCwD - Most Consecutive without a defeat
MCSG - Most Consecutive Scoring Games I MCwS - Most Consecutive without Scoring
TGS - Total Games without Scoring I MCCS - Most Consecutive Clean Sheets
TNCS - Total Number of Clean Sheets

Best Home League Attendances 2013-2014

	Att:	Opponents	Score
Basingstoke Town	548	Dorchester Town	W 2-1
Bath City	852	Weston-s-Mare	W 1-0
Bishop's Stortford	755	Chelmsford City	D 1-1
Boreham Wood	352	Chelmsford City	W 4-3
Bromley	134	Ebbsfleet United	D 0-0
Chelmsford City	842	Tonbridge Angels	W 7-1
Concord Rangers	409	Chelmsford City	L 1-3
DorchesterTown	614	Eastleigh	L 1-2
Dover Athletic	856	Tonbridge Angels	W 3-1
Eastbourne Borough	683	Whitehawk	L 0-2
Eastleigh	1505	Basingstoke Town	W 2-1
Ebbsfleet United	1670	Dorchester Town	W 4-0
Farnborough	714	Hayes & Yeading	L 1-2
Gosport Borough	592	Dover Athletic	L 0-1
Havant & Waterlooville	956	Basingstoke Town	W 4-1
Hayes & Yeading	450	Dover Atletic	L 1-2
Maidenhead United	472	Tonbridge Angels	D 0-0
Staines Town	410	Farnborough	W 3-2
Sutton United	2172	Basingstoke Town	W 4-0
Tonbridge Angels	672	Bromley	D 1-1
Weston-a-Mare	610	Bromley	L 0-1
Whyteleaf	356	Sutton united	D 3-3

HAT-TRICK HEROS

	Club	Goals	Opponents	Score
Nicholas Bignall	Basingstoke Town (a)	3	Staines Town (a)	W 5-4
Ross Stearn	Bath City (h)	3	Havant & Waterlooville (h)	W 3-1
Kyle Vassell	Bishop's Stortford	4	Hendon (a) FA Cup	W 5-0
Kyle Vassell	Bishop's Stortford	3	Chipstaed (a) FA Cup	W 6-1
Junior Morais	Boreham Wood	3	Tonbridge Angels (h)	W 7-0
Bradley Goldberg	Bromley	3	Chelmsford City (h)	W 5-0
Michael Cheek	Chelmsford City	4	Tonbridge Angels (h)	W 7-1
Gary Ogilvie	Concord Rangers	3	Farnborough (h)	W 5-0
Jeff Goulding	Dover Athletic	3	Dorchester Town (a)	W 4-0
Chris Shephard	Eastbourne Borough	3	Farnborough (h)	W 5-2
Jai Reason	Eastleigh	3	Ebbsfleet United (h)	W 3-1
Ben Wright	Eastleigh	3	Bishop's Stortford (h)	W 4-0
Jai Reason	Eastleigh	3	Dorchester Town (h)	W 6-2
Rory Williams	Gosport Borough	3	Staines Town (a)	W 3-0
Danny Green	Maidenhead United	4	Tonbridge Angels (a)	W 4-2
Louie Theophanous	Staines Town	3	Farnborough (h)	W 3-2
Stephane Ngamvoulou	Staines Town	3	Whitehawk (a)	D 3-3
Jamie Taylor	Sutton United	3	Weston-s-Mare	W 3-0
Danny Mills	Whyteleaf	5	Dorchester Town (h)	W 6-2

PREMIER DIVISION 2013-14

		P	W	D	L	F	A	GD	Pts
1	(P) Chorley	46	29	10	7	107	39	68	97
2	FC United of Manchester	46	29	9	8	108	52	56	96
3	(P) AFC Fylde	46	28	9	9	97	41	56	93
4	(W) Worksop Town	46	27	7	12	120	87	33	88
5	Ashton United	46	24	8	14	92	62	30	80
6	Skelmersdale United	46	24	5	17	92	79	13	77
7	Rushall Olympic	46	21	12	13	79	65	14	75
8	Blyth Spartans	46	20	12	14	79	78	1	72
9	Whitby Town	46	18	16	12	82	64	18	70
10	Trafford	46	20	8	18	77	73	4	68
11	Kings Lynn Town	46	20	8	18	76	77	-1	68
12	Matlock Town	46	18	13	15	61	53	8	67
13	Buxton	46	16	14	16	63	60	3	62
14	Barwell	46	17	11	18	62	67	-5	62
15	Grantham Town	46	17	10	19	77	78	-1	61
16	Witton Albion	46	17	9	20	77	80	-3	60
17	Ilkeston	46	17	8	21	81	77	4	59
18	Stamford	46	17	7	22	75	85	-10	58
19	Nantwich Town	46	14	14	18	77	71	6	56
20	Marine	46	13	14	19	68	76	-8	53
21	Frickley Athletic	46	12	13	21	62	80	-18	49
22	(R) Stafford Rangers	46	9	8	29	56	112	-56	35
23	(R) Stocksbridge Park Steels	46	5	8	33	60	130	-70	23
24	(R) Droylsden	46	2	3	41	40	182	-142	9

PLAY-OFFS

Semi-Finals: FC United of Manchester 1-2 (Aet) Ashton United I AFC Fylde 3-1 Worksop Town

Final: AFC Fylde 1-1 Ashton United (AFC Fylde won 4-3 after penalties)

	1	2	3	4	5	6	7	8	9	10	11	12	13	14	15	16	17	18	19	20	21	22	23	24
1 AFC Fylde		1-0	1-0	5-1	2-2	0-1	5-0	0-2	2-0	1-2	1-2	1-0	0-0	2-0	1-2	2-1	2-3	2-1	2-0	5-0	2-1	3-1	3-0	3-2
2 Ashton United	1-1		0-1	3-3	2-0	2-1	4-1	2-1	2-2	2-1	1-3	5-1	4-1	0-0	1-0	2-0	4-1	4-0	2-1	3-2	2-0	3-4	1-4	2-3
3 Barwell	0-3	1-0		1-2	1-0	1-3	2-2	0-3	1-1	2-2	1-1	1-3	2-0	0-0	2-2	3-1	5-0	2-0	1-0	2-1	0-0	1-1	0-2	1-3
4 Blyth Spartans	1-1	2-1	2-1		0-1	3-1	3-0	0-1	2-0	2-1	3-2	1-3	2-2	1-2	2-2	3-2	2-1	6-2	2-1	3-0	2-1	0-7	4-2	3-3
5 Buxton	0-4	1-2	3-0	2-1		0-2	4-2	0-2	1-1	3-1	1-2	6-1	2-2	1-1	2-0	1-2	2-0	2-2	2-2	0-1	1-2	1-1	3-1	2-4
6 Chorley	3-1	3-3	1-2	3-0	0-0		13-1	0-1	2-0	3-1	2-1	1-0	4-0	3-1	5-1	0-1	4-1	3-0	3-0	3-1	6-2	0-0	1-0	1-0
7 Droylsden	0-10	0-9	1-2	0-0	1-1	0-5		1-4	2-3	0-3	1-5	1-2	0-4	1-4	1-6	1-5	0-3	2-3	0-3	2-3	0-6	0-2	4-3	3-4
8 FC Unitd of Manc.	0-0	3-2	2-0	3-0	1-2	2-2	4-1		3-0	3-0	4-1	2-0	1-0	2-1	2-1	0-2	1-3	4-0	6-0	6-2	1-1	1-3	3-1	4-4
9 Frickley Athletic	0-2	0-2	2-1	0-1	0-1	0-0	2-0	1-2		3-2	0-1	2-2	1-1	1-3	2-0	4-2	4-3	2-0	1-1	2-2	2-1	1-1	0-0	2-2
10 Grantham Town	1-2	0-1	0-1	4-2	0-1	1-1	6-0	1-5	2-1		2-0	2-0	3-1	1-1	0-5	3-0	1-2	3-2	1-1	3-2	2-1	3-1	0-0	3-1
11 Ilkeston	0-1	1-2	4-2	0-1	0-2	2-3	5-1	3-3	1-0	0-2		3-4	1-2	1-3	3-1	0-1	2-1	0-0	3-0	6-1	1-1	0-2	1-1	0-0
12 Kings Lynn Town	2-0	2-1	3-2	0-1	3-1	0-2	2-1	0-0	3-0	1-1	3-1		2-3	0-4	0-0	6-0	3-3	5-1	2-1	3-3	2-2	3-0	3-0	1-3
13 Marine	1-2	0-1	1-1	1-1	0-2	0-1	5-1	0-2	2-1	3-3	2-3	2-3		3-0	1-0	1-2	2-2	5-2	1-3	3-0	1-2	1-1	2-1	0-1
14 Matlock Town	1-1	0-0	2-1	1-1	1-1	1-2	2-0	1-1	0-0	4-1	1-0	2-0	0-0		2-1	1-1	2-1	0-2	2-0	3-0	3-2	2-0	0-1	1-0
15 Nantwich Town	1-1	2-2	2-0	1-1	1-1	0-1	4-0	1-1	2-1	1-1	2-2	2-0	1-2	1-1		3-2	2-2	4-1	3-1	2-1	0-1	4-3	0-2	2-3
16 Rushall Olympic	2-2	2-1	0-0	0-0	2-2	1-0	0-1	1-1	4-1	3-1	3-2	3-1	1-1	6-1	1-1		1-0	2-0	0-2	1-1	1-2	0-0	2-0	2-2
17 Skelmersdale Utd	0-5	1-1	1-0	4-3	2-0	1-0	7-3	1-3	3-2	1-2	2-0	3-0	4-1	1-0	2-1	1-0		3-2	0-1	6-0	3-1	4-2	1-3	2-1
18 Stafford Rangers	2-2	1-2	2-3	2-2	1-1	1-3	3-1	2-1	0-2	2-2	2-4	0-1	2-2	1-3	1-0	2-5	0-2		2-1	3-1	1-4	0-2	2-2	0-2
19 Stamford	1-3	2-1	0-2	3-4	1-0	1-1	4-0	2-3	6-4	1-2	0-2	3-0	2-4	1-0	2-2	3-4	2-0	2-0		4-3	2-2	1-2	3-1	2-2
20 Stocksbridge PS	0-1	0-2	1-2	1-1	2-3	2-2	3-1	1-4	3-4	4-3	2-3	0-0	1-1	3-1	1-5	1-2	0-4	0-3	1-3		1-3	0-3	2-2	4-5
21 Trafford	2-0	4-1	2-4	2-1	0-0	0-5	1-0	2-3	4-1	2-1	2-5	1-2	1-0	2-1	0-1	3-1	2-0	1-2	0-2	1-0		0-3	3-3	0-2
22 Whitby Town	1-2	1-2	2-2	2-1	1-0	1-1	5-2	3-2	2-2	1-1	1-1	4-0	0-0	1-0	4-2	0-0	2-2	2-1	1-2	4-0	1-1		1-1	2-5
23 Witton Albion	0-1	1-2	1-2	0-1	0-1	2-2	5-1	2-5	2-1	2-1	2-1	1-0	2-3	1-0	3-2	2-4	2-3	5-0	2-1	4-1	0-4	3-1		2-2
24 Worksop Town	1-6	3-2	4-3	3-2	3-1	1-4	3-0	2-0	1-3	3-1	5-2	1-4	5-1	4-2	3-1	1-3	3-2	5-0	6-1	3-2	1-2	3-0	2-3	

DIVISION ONE NORTH 2013-14

		P	W	D	L	F	A	GD	Pts
1	(P) Curzon Ashton	42	31	6	5	92	36	56	99
2	Darlington 1883	42	28	6	8	101	37	64	90
3	Warrington Town	42	27	6	9	86	47	39	87
4	Bamber Bridge	42	26	5	11	81	45	36	83
5	(P) Ramsbottom United (-3)	42	25	8	9	112	57	55	80
6	Lancaster City	42	24	8	10	75	52	23	80
7	Farsley	42	21	12	9	76	51	25	75
8	Ossett Town	42	19	8	15	66	63	3	65
9	Northwich Victoria	42	16	15	11	73	52	21	63
10	Kendal Town	42	17	5	20	83	84	-1	56
11	(W) Cammell Laird	42	15	9	18	65	64	1	54
12	Salford City	42	15	7	20	68	80	-12	52
13	Harrogate Railway Athletic	42	14	6	22	52	66	-14	48
14	Burscough	42	13	9	20	58	82	-24	48
15	Mossley	42	13	8	21	73	90	-17	47
16	New Mills	42	12	9	21	68	95	-27	45
17	Clitheroe	42	12	7	23	55	81	-26	43
18	Radcliffe Borough	42	12	7	23	57	93	-36	43
19	Padiham	42	12	6	24	61	92	-31	42
20	Prescot Cables	42	10	10	22	63	86	-23	40
21	Ossett Albion	42	7	8	27	40	80	-40	29
22	(W) Wakefield	42	7	7	28	55	127	-72	28

PLAY-OFFS

Semi-Finals: Darlington 1883 0-2 Ramsbottom United I Warrington Town 0-1 Bamber Bridge

Final: Bamber Bridge 2-3 Ramsbottom United

	1	2	3	4	5	6	7	8	9	10	11	12	13	14	15	16	17	18	19	20	21	22
1 Bamber Bridge		2–0	1–0	2–0	0–1	0–3	0–1	3–0	2–1	0–1	5–1	2–1	1–1	4–0	4–0	5–1	2–2	4–0	2–1	3–1	2–1	0–3
2 Burscough	1–4		2–3	2–3	0–1	0–7	0–0	2–1	4–0	0–1	0–3	3–2	1–2	0–0	1–2	3–4	2–2	1–3	1–1	2–0	1–0	0–0
3 Cammell Laird	0–1	2–1		1–0	0–1	0–2	2–3	2–4	2–3	2–3	1–1	5–0	0–0	0–1	1–2	2–0	2–1	2–1	2–1	2–2	4–2	0–0
4 Clitheroe	0–2	4–2	2–2		0–3	2–3	1–0	0–2	3–0	2–2	3–1	3–2	2–0	0–2	3–2	2–3	3–1	4–0	2–4	2–2	1–2	1–0
5 Curzon Ashton	3–2	1–1	2–0	1–0		1–0	1–2	1–0	3–1	1–0	2–1	2–2	0–0	2–0	0–2	2–2	6–0	3–1	2–2	4–0	5–0	2–3
6 Darlington 1883	1–0	1–2	3–1	6–0	0–4		3–0	0–0	3–1	0–2	4–0	2–0	0–1	7–0	4–1	3–0	2–2	3–0	0–1	2–2	5–1	2–0
7 Farsley	0–0	1–2	2–2	4–1	0–1	4–2		0–0	1–2	2–1	3–0	2–1	2–2	4–1	1–1	4–1	3–1	2–0	3–2	2–3	2–2	0–3
8 Harrogate Railway Athletic	1–2	1–0	4–1	3–2	0–1	0–2	1–1		3–1	1–3	0–2	5–0	2–1	2–3	0–1	4–0	2–1	2–2	0–4	0–1	2–0	0–2
9 Kendal Town	2–3	3–1	2–2	2–0	0–3	1–5	3–0	3–1		0–1	6–5	4–5	2–2	3–2	0–2	2–1	3–0	5–1	2–3	2–0	5–0	1–1
10 Lancaster City	0–2	1–1	1–0	1–1	1–0	0–0	2–2	2–1	2–2		2–1	0–1	1–0	1–0	2–1	1–1	2–0	4–1	1–3	2–1	5–2	3–1
11 Mossley	2–3	0–2	2–0	1–1	2–3	1–2	1–0	2–0	1–3	2–1		3–3	2–4	3–2	1–2	0–1	4–2	3–1	4–3	3–1	2–2	2–2
12 New Mills	0–2	4–2	3–0	2–1	1–3	0–3	0–4	4–1	0–4	2–1	2–1		2–2	2–2	2–0	2–3	0–0	0–3	2–3	0–2	8–2	2–3
13 Northwich Victoria	4–0	2–3	3–0	3–0	1–1	1–1	3–3	1–0	2–1	3–1	2–0	2–1		1–1	4–0	2–0	1–1	4–0	3–4	1–2	2–3	0–2
14 Ossett Albion	2–3	1–2	0–2	1–2	2–3	2–3	0–1	0–2	1–3	0–2	1–0	0–0	0–0		1–4	0–3	1–1	1–2	1–2	1–2	2–0	1–2
15 Ossett Town	1–0	3–3	1–1	2–0	2–1	1–2	0–1	1–1	1–0	0–3	3–3	3–3	1–0	0–1		3–1	2–1	0–1	2–0	0–3	2–3	0–1
16 Padiham	6–1	1–2	1–3	2–0	1–4	0–2	1–2	1–1	2–1	0–0	2–3	1–2	3–2	0–0	2–5		2–2	0–1	1–4	0–1	4–3	2–4
17 Prescot Cables	0–5	3–0	0–3	2–2	2–3	0–0	0–3	0–1	1–2	1–2	0–1	7–1	2–1	3–2	3–2	3–0		4–3	0–3	3–1	4–0	0–2
18 Radcliffe Borough	0–2	1–1	0–6	1–0	1–2	1–2	2–3	3–1	1–0	1–4	3–3	4–0	3–4	3–0	1–1	1–0	2–2		1–1	0–2	0–1	1–2
19 Ramsbottom United	0–0	7–1	0–2	4–1	1–3	3–0	1–1	5–0	3–0	6–0	3–1	1–1	2–2	2–0	2–2	1–2	5–3	8–0		5–2	3–1	3–2
20 Salford City	2–1	3–4	2–2	1–1	0–2	0–2	2–4	2–0	6–3	2–1	6–2	1–3	0–0	0–3	1–2	2–1	2–0	3–3	1–2		2–3	1–2
21 Wakefield	0–3	1–2	1–3	2–0	2–3	1–5	0–3	2–3	3–3	4–9	1–1	1–1	1–1	2–2	1–5	0–3	0–1	1–4	2–3	2–0		0–7
22 Warrington Town	1–1	1–0	3–0	3–0	1–5	1–4	0–0	2–0	2–1	2–3	3–2	2–1	1–3	2–0	0–1	7–2	3–2	2–0	1–0	3–1	4–0	

DIVISION ONE SOUTH 2013-14

		P	W	D	L	F	A	GD	Pts
1	(P) Halesowen Town	40	29	4	7	80	38	42	91
2	Coalville Town	40	27	8	5	101	35	66	89
3	Leek Town	40	28	4	8	86	35	51	88
4	(P) Belper Town	40	24	9	7	98	50	48	81
5	Mickleover Sports	40	22	7	11	82	62	20	73
6	Sutton Coldfield Town	40	19	7	14	74	53	21	64
7	Scarborough Athletic	40	18	7	15	73	57	16	61
8	Newcastle Town	40	18	5	17	66	65	1	59
9	Gresley	40	17	5	18	66	67	-1	56
10	Carlton Town	40	15	10	15	58	55	3	55
11	Romulus	40	16	7	17	66	64	2	55
12	Chasetown	40	14	10	16	52	59	-7	52
13	Goole AFC	40	15	6	19	61	76	-15	51
14	Loughborough Dynamo	40	13	8	19	62	77	-15	47
15	Rainworth Miners Welfare	40	12	10	18	52	72	-20	46
16	Sheffield	40	12	8	20	69	80	-11	44
17	Lincoln United	40	10	6	24	55	88	-33	36
18	Brigg Town	40	9	8	23	49	94	-45	35
19	Market Drayton Town	40	8	11	21	56	105	-49	35
20	Bedworth United	40	9	7	24	48	83	-35	34
21	Kidsgrove Athletic	40	7	9	24	41	80	-39	30

Feb 2014 - Eastwood Town resigned - record expunged.

PLAY-OFFS

Semi-Finals: Colaville Town 2-3 Mickleover Sports I Leek Town 0-2 Belper Town

Final: Belper Town 1-0 Mickleover Sports

	1	2	3	4	5	6	7	8	9	10	11	12	13	14	15	16	17	18	19	20	21
1 Bedworth United		1–3	3–3	2–0	1–1	0–3	1–4	1–2	0–1	1–1	0–2	1–1	2–1	1–3	0–2	2–3	0–1	1–2	0–3	1–3	1–0
2 Belper Town	6–2		3–0	0–1	1–4	0–1	5–1	4–1	0–2	4–0	1–0	5–0	3–0	0–1	4–0	2–0	2–2	4–1	2–0	2–0	2–2
3 Brigg Town	0–2	2–6		0–2	1–1	0–2	3–1	2–1	2–2	2–1	0–4	0–3	2–1	2–2	1–2	1–2	1–3	1–0	0–3	2–1	2–3
4 Carlton Town	2–0	1–1	1–2		2–2	1–2	4–2	2–1	1–3	0–1	2–3	0–0	3–1	4–0	0–2	2–1	1–1	5–0	0–3	1–0	1–0
5 Chasetown	2–1	0–1	1–0	2–1		0–3	0–1	2–1	1–3	1–0	1–3	4–1	0–0	1–0	0–2	2–1	0–0	2–1	4–0	4–3	1–1
6 Coalville Town	6–1	4–2	5–1	5–0	3–1		1–0	0–2	0–1	2–0	0–0	2–1	4–0	4–1	1–3	4–0	4–1	1–2	2–0	1–1	1–1
7 Goole	3–1	2–6	2–1	1–3	3–1	0–3		1–3	0–0	3–2	0–3	2–1	1–1	4–1	1–2	1–0	3–2	1–1	1–3	0–3	0–1
8 Gresley	0–2	0–0	2–1	1–1	5–2	3–3	2–1		0–2	5–3	4–1	0–0	0–1	2–2	1–3	3–0	1–0	2–1	0–2	2–0	2–1
9 Halesowen Town	5–0	3–4	3–0	0–2	0–0	0–3	3–2	5–0		2–0	1–0	2–1	1–0	3–1	2–1	3–2	1–0	1–0	3–0	3–0	0–1
10 Kidsgrove Athletic	2–0	0–1	2–2	1–1	2–1	2–2	1–1	2–1	2–2		2–0	1–2	0–3	0–0	2–2	0–3	4–1	2–1	1–1	2–3	0–3
11 Leek Town	1–0	1–1	4–1	1–0	3–0	0–1	2–1	2–0	4–1	1–0		1–0	2–1	5–0	4–0	2–1	0–1	1–0	2–2	2–1	3–2
12 Lincoln United	1–3	4–1	4–2	0–3	1–2	1–4	1–0	2–1	1–3	2–1	1–5		5–6	2–2	0–2	2–3	1–2	2–1	3–3	0–1	1–4
13 Loughborough Dynamo	1–1	1–2	0–0	2–4	1–2	2–1	0–2	4–3	1–2	4–0	0–8	3–1		1–4	2–4	1–1	2–3	1–1	2–1	3–2	1–2
14 Market Drayton Town	2–2	2–2	2–4	2–2	2–1	1–7	2–2	1–2	0–3	2–1	1–2	3–1	2–3		1–4	0–4	1–4	3–2	2–4	3–2	1–1
15 Mickleover Sports	5–3	1–1	3–0	2–2	2–1	1–1	2–2	3–2	2–4	1–0	2–3	1–2	0–3	4–1		2–0	2–1	2–1	2–1	3–4	2–1
16 Newcastle Town	1–3	2–2	3–3	2–0	0–0	0–3	2–3	1–0	2–1	4–0	2–0	1–2	2–1	4–1	1–0		2–1	2–4	2–0	3–5	2–0
17 Rainworth Miners Welfare	1–0	1–4	1–3	1–1	3–1	0–1	0–3	3–2	0–2	2–1	0–5	2–2	0–0	3–3	1–1	1–2		0–0	1–2	3–1	0–0
18 Romulus	0–1	0–1	3–0	1–0	2–2	2–5	2–0	3–2	0–2	4–0	1–2	3–2	3–2	0–0	4–3	2–2	4–2		4–2	3–0	1–2
19 Scarborough Athletic	1–0	3–3	4–0	3–0	1–0	1–3	1–2	0–1	3–1	5–0	1–1	2–0	1–3	3–0	2–2	2–1	4–0	1–3		1–3	2–0
20 Sheffield	4–4	1–3	1–1	0–0	2–1	2–2	2–3	1–3	2–3	2–0	1–2	4–0	2–2	3–1	1–5	1–2	3–1	1–1	1–1		2–4
21 Sutton Coldfield Town	1–3	3–4	5–1	4–2	1–1	1–1	4–0	2–3	0–1	3–2	2–1	2–1	0–1	6–0	1–0	3–0	2–3	1–2	2–1	2–0	

LEAGUE CHALLENGE CUP 2013-14

PRELIMINARY ROUND

Lincoln United	2–0	Wakefield
Loughborough Dynamo	2–0	Rainworth Miners Welfare
Mossley	4–3	Padiham
Newcastle Town	1–0	Market Drayton Town

ROUND 1

Barwell	5–0	Coalville Town
Belper Town	3–0	Ilkeston
Burscough	3–0	Warrington Town
Carlton Town	1–1	Buxton (6–5p)
Chasetown	2–0	Newcastle Town
Darlington 1883	5–1	Blyth Spartans
Droylsden	2–3	Frickley Athletic
Gresley	1–1	Eastwood Town (4–2p)
Goole	0–4	Farsley
Grantham Town	5–0	Bedworth United
Harrogate Railway Ath.	3–0	Stocksbridge P.S.
Kendal Town	1–3	Chorley
Kidsgrove Athletic	1–1	Halesowen Town (5–4p)
Lancaster City	1–3	Bamber Bridge
Marine	0–0	Ashton United (3–4p)
Mickleover Sports	4–0	Matlock Town
Mossley	0–2	A.F.C. Fylde
Nantwich Town	5–0	Leek Town
New Mills	2–4	Rushall Olympic
Northwich Victoria	0–2	Trafford
Ossett Albion	1–3	Scarborough Athletic
Prescot Cables	0–6	Skelmersdale United
Radcliffe Borough	3–0	Clitheroe
Ramsbottom United	1–2	F.C. United
Romulus	2–2	Stafford Rangers (3–4p)
Salford City	0–1	Cammell Laird
Sheffield	2–3	Ossett Town
Stamford	6–0	Lincoln United
Sutton Coldfield Town	2–4	Loughborough Dynamo
Whitby Town	0–0	Brigg Town (5–6p)
Witton Albion	1–0	Curzon Ashton
Worksop Town	3–3	King's Lynn Town (7-6p)

ROUND 2

A.F.C. Fylde	3–1	Burscough
Barwell	2–0	Rushall Olympic
Brigg Town	2–0	Scarborough Athletic
Cammell Laird	2–3	Bamber Bridge
Carlton Town	3–2	Mickleover Sports
Chorley	1–4	Witton Albion
Darlington 1883	1–3	Ossett Town
F.C. United	2–0	Ashton United
Frickley Athletic	1–0	Belper Town
Grantham Town	0–2	Gresley
Harrogate Railway Ath.	0–0	Farsley (2–4p)
Kidsgrove Athletic	2–3	Chasetown
Loughborough Dynamo	4–2	Stafford Rangers
Trafford	0–4	Nantwich Town
Radcliffe Borough	0–2	Skelmersdale United
Stamford	3–1	Worksop Town

ROUND 3

A.F.C. Fylde	4–0	Nantwich Town
Brigg Town	2–5	Frickley Athletic
Chasetown	3–1	Barwell
Witton Albion	0–4	Skelmersdale United
Farsley	1–0	Bamber Bridge
Loughborough Dynamo	3–2	Gresley
Ossett Town	1–2	F.C. United
Stamford	1–3	Carlton Town

QUARTER FINALS

A.F.C. Fylde	4–1	Chasetown
Frickley Athletic	2–0	Loughborough Dynamo
Carlton Town	2–1	F.C. United
Skelmersdale United	4–0	Farsley

SEMI-FINALS

Carlton Town	2–4	Skelmersdale United
Frickley Athletic	0–0	A.F.C. Fylde (3–4p)

FINAL

A.F.C. Fylde	1-0	Skelmersdale United
	Att: 358	

Premier Division Statistics 2013-14

	MCV	MCD	MCwW	MCwD	MCSG	MCwS	TGS	MCCS	TNCS
AFC Fylde	6	5	6	17	23	2	7	3	21
Ashton United	8	4	5	9	11	1	6	3	13
Barwell	4	5	9	9	8	2	13	3	12
Blyth Spartans	3	3	7	7	11	1	8	1	10
Buxton	3	7	9	6	13	2	12	2	12
Chorley	11	1	4	12	13	3	10	4	23
Droylsden	1	26	40	1	5	4	20	1	2
FC United of Manchester	13	3	4	14	35	2	5	2	16
Frickley Athletic	3	5	8	6	7	2	14	1	7
Grantham Town	3	4	11	5	18	1	7	1	8
Ilkeston FC	3	4	6	4	11	2	11	1	6
Kings Lynn Town	4	4	4	4	5	2	14	1	7
Marine	2	4	6	4	6	1	9	1	8
Matlock Town	3	2	8	5	9	3	15	4	15
Nantwich Town	3	3	9	6	9	2	10	2	7
Rushall Olympic	6	3	4	7	14	3	12	3	14
Skelmersdale United	6	4	7	9	19	3	9	2	12
Stafford Rangers	2	7	9	5	4	2	17	2	6
Stamford	3	3	4	5	9	2	10	2	11
Stocksbridge Park Steels	2	14	23	3	8	1	13	1	2
Trafford	3	5	5	5	17	3	9	2	10
Whitby Town	5	4	6	11	10	1	8	2	14
Witton Albion	3	4	7	8	12	2	10	2	8
Worksop Town	5	3	3	12	16	1	4	2	9

MCV - Most Consecutive Victories I MCD - Most Consecutive Defeats
MCwW - Most Consecutive without a Win I MCwD - Most Consecutive without a defeat
MCSG - Most Consecutive Scoring Games I MCwS - Most Consecutive without Scoring
TGS - Total Games without Scoring I MCCS - Most Consecutive Clean Sheets
TNCS - Total Number of Clean Sheets

Best Home League Attendances 2013-2014

	Att:	Opponents	Score
AFC Fylde	709	FC United	L 0-2
Ashton United	1008	FC United	L 1-2
Barwell	1809	FC United	L 0-3
Blyth Spartans	932	DC United	L 0-2
Buxton	1112	FC United	L 0-2
Chorley	2171	FC United	L 0-1
Droylsden	754	FC United	L 1-4
FC United	4152	Chorley	D 2-2
Frickley Athletic	420	FC United	L 0-2
Grantham Town	739	FC United	L 1-5
Ilkeston Town	974	FC United	D 3-3
Kings Lynn Town	1440	FC United	D 0-0
Marine	940	FC United	L 0-2
Matlock Town	978	FC United	D 1-1
Nantwich Town	672	FC United	D 1-1
Rushall Olympic	539	FC United	D 1-1
Spennymoor Utd	1000	FC United	L 1-3
Stafford Rangers	1032	FC United	W 2-1
Stamford	1204	FC United	L 2-3
Stocksbridge PS	891	FC United	L 1-4
Trafford	1374	FC United	L 2-3
Whitby Town	818	FC United	W 3-2
Witton Albion	693	FC United	D 2-2
Worksop Town	837	FC United	W 2-0

HAT-TRICK HEROS

	Club	Goals	Opponents	Score
Richie Allen	AFC Fylde	3	Stocksbridge PS (h)	W 5-0
Richie Allen	AFC Fylde	3	Worksop (h) Play-Off	W 3 0
Bradley Barnes	AFC Fylde	5	Droylsden (a)	W 10-0
Matt Blinkhorn	AFC Fylde	3	Skelmersdale Utd (a)	W 5-0
Matty Chadwick	Ashton United	3	Droylsden (a)	W 9-0
Martin Pilkington	Ashton United	3	Droylsden (a)	W 9-0
Connor Gudger	Barwell	3	Worksop Town (a)	L 3-4
Danny Newton	Barwell	3	Stafford Rangers (a)	W 5-0
Craig Hubbard	Blyth Spartans	3	Skelmersdale U (a)	L 3-4
Craig Hubbard	Blyth Spartans	3	Skelmersdale U9h) FAT	W 6-0
Dan Maguire	Blyth Spartans	3	Stafford Rangers (h)	W 6-2
Darren Stephenson	Chorley	3	Trafford (h)	W 6-2
Tom Greaves	FC United	3	Stamford (h)	W 6-2
Gavin Allott	Frickley Athletic	3	Rushall Olympic (h)	W 4-2
Gavin Allott	Frickley Athletic	3	Grantham Town (h)	W 3 2
Jake Picton	Frickley Athletic	3	Sheffield (h) FAC	W 4-1
Jack McGovern	Grantham Town	3	Droylsden (h)	W 6-0
Greg Smith	Grantham Town	3	Marine (h)	W 3-1
Andy Hall	King's Lynn Town	3	Skelmersdale U (h)	D 3-3
Dan Jacob	King's Lynn Town	3	Rushall Olympic (h)	W 6-0
Joe Fowler	Marine	3	Stafford Rangers (h)	W 5-2
Leon Spink	Rushall Olympic	3	Barwell (a) FA Trophy	W 4-0
Dean Astbury	Spennymoor Utd	3	Stocksbridge PS (h)	W 6-0
Dean Astbury	Spennymoor Utd	3	Kings Lynn T (a)	D 3-3
Ryan Robbins	Stamford	3	AFC Wulfranians (h) FAC	W 4-1
Ryan Robbins	Stamford	3	Marine (a)	W 3-1
Jordan Smith	Stamford	3	Frickley Athletic (h)	W 6-4
Michael Oates	Trafford	3	Wakefield (h) FAT	W 6-1
Stefan Payne	Trafford	5	Droylsden (a)	W 5-1
Stefan Payne	Trafford	3	Stocksbridge PS (a)	W 3-1
Kyle Wilson	Witton Albion	3	Droylsden	W 5-1
Leon Mettam	Worksop Town	3	Whitby Town (a)	W 5-2
Leon Mettam	Worksop Town	3	Barwell (h)	W 4-3
Leon Mettam	Worksop Town	3	Stamford (h)	W 5-1
Leon Mettam	Worksop Town	3	Ilkeston Town (h)	W 5-2
Leon Mettam	Worksop Town	3	Blyth Spartans (h)	W 3-2

ASHTON UNITED

Chairman: Terry Hollis
Secretary: Andy Finnigan (T) 07866 360200 (E) secretary@ashtonutd.com
Commercial Manager: (T)
Programme Editor: Russ Gratton (T) 07850 554 296
Ground Address: Hurst Cross, Surrey Street, Ashton-u-Lyne OL6 8DY
(T) 0161 339 4158 **Manager:** Paul Phillips & Steve Halford

2014-15 Squad.

Club Factfile

Founded: 1878 **Nickname:** Robins
Previous Names: Hurst 1878-1947
Previous Leagues: Manchester, Lancashire Combination 1912-33, 48-64, 66-68, Midland 1964-66, Cheshire County 1923-48, 68-82, North West Counties 1982-92

Club Colours (change): Red and white halves/red/red (Blue & black halves/blue/blue)

Ground Capacity: 4,500 **Seats:** 250 **Covered:** 750 **Clubhouse:** Yes **Shop:** Yes

Directions
From the M62 (approx 7.5 miles) Exit at Junction 20, take A627M to Oldham exit (2.5 miles) Take A627 towards Oldham town centre At King Street Roundabout take Park Road Continue straight onto B6194 Abbey Hills Road Follow B6194 onto Lees Road Turn right at the stone cross memorial and 1st right into the ground. From the M60 (approx 2.5 miles); Exit at Junction 23, take A635 for Ashton town centre Follow by-pass to B6194 Mossley Road. At traffic lights turn left into Queens Road Continue onto B6194 Lees Road Turn left at the stone cross memorial and 1st right into the ground.

Previous Grounds: Rose HIll 1878-1912

Record Attendance: 11,000 v Halifax Town - FA Cup 1st Round 1952
Record Victory: 11-3 v Stalybridge Celtic - Manchester Intermediate Cup 1955
Record Defeat: 1-11 v Wellington Town - Cheshire League 1946-47
Record Goalscorer: Not known
Record Appearances: Micky Boyle - 462
Additional Records: Paid £9,000 to Netherfield for Andy Whittaker 1994
Received £15,000 from Rotherham United for Karl Marginson 1993
Senior Honours:
Manchester League 1911-12. Lancs Comb. 1916-17. NWCL Div. Two 1987-88, Div. One 1991-92, League cup 1991-92, Challenge Cup 1991-92. Manchester Challenge Shield 1992-93. Northern Premier League Division 1 Cup 1994-95, 96-97, 98-99, League Challenge Cup 2010-11. Manchester Senior Cup 1894-95, 1913-14, 75-76, 77-78. Manchester Premier Cup 1979-80, 82-83, 91092, 2000-01, 01-02, 02-03.

10 YEAR RECORD

04-05	05-06	06-07	07-08	08-09	09-10	10-11	11-12	12-13	13-14
Conf N 21	NP P 15	NP P 18	NP P 10	NP P 9	NP P 12	NP P 14	NP P 12	NP P 10	NP P 5

ASHTON UNITED MATCH RESULTS 2013-14

Date	Comp	H/A	Opponents	Att:	Result		Goalscorers	Pos	No.
Aug 17	NPL	H	Grantham Town	133	W	2-1	Gee 28 (pen) O'Neill 84	8	1
20	NPL	A	Chorley	631	D	3-3	Pilkington 72 78 Rick 88	5	2
24	NPL	A	Skelmersdale United	186	D	1-1	Pilkington 58	9	3
26	NPL	H	Droylsden	282	W	4-1	Denham 7 O'Neill 15 Rick 18 Gee 59	1	4
31	NPL	A	Nantwich Town	255	D	2-2	Rick 63 Coppin 75	4	5
Sept 4	NPL	H	Matlock Town	177	D	0-0		8	6
7	NPL	H	Trafford	153	W	2-0	Rick 59 Pilkington 65	7	7
11	NPL	A	Buxton	238	W	2-1	Young 34 O'Neill 86	2	8
14	***FAC1Q***	***H***	***Witton Albion***	***152***	***W***	***2-1***	***Pilkington 20 Gee 69***		9
17	NPL	A	Blyth Spartans	241	L	1-2	Gee 26	5	10
21	NPL	H	Stamford	110	W	2-1	Young 55 Jarvis 64 (og)	4	11
28	***FAC2Q***	***A***	***AFC Fylde***	***302***	***W***	***1-0***	***Pilkington 2***		12
Oct 2	NPL	H	Frickley Athletic	101	D	2-2	Pilkington 25 65	4	13
5	NPL	A	Rushhall Olympic	181	L	1-2	Pilkington 17	8	14
12	***FAC3Q***	***A***	***Stamford AFC***	***301***	***L***	***2-4***	***Coppin 6 Logan 75***		15
16	NPL	H	Whittby Town	104	L	3-4	Lynch 10 Coppin 60 82	10	16
19	***FAT1Q***	***H***	***Sheffield***	***104***	***L***	***0-3***			16
26	NPL	H	Marine	111	W	4-1	O'Neill 11 Pilkington 44 59 Chadwick 90	11	17
29	NPL	A	Matlock Town	273	D	0-0		11	18
Nov 2	NPL	A	Kings Lynn Town	504	L	1-2	Coppin 17	12	19
9	NPL	A	Trafford	196	L	1-4	Coppin 9	16	20
16	NPL	H	Worksop Town	160	L	2-3	Pilkington 5 Chadwick 78	16	21
30	NPL	A	Ilkerston Town	523	W	2-1	Chadwick 45 Gorton 85	16	22
Dec 7	NPL	A	Grantham Town	181	W	1-0	Gee 57	16	23
11	NPL	H	Nantwich Town	148	W	1-0	Johnson 30	13	24
21	NPL	A	Witton Albion	302	W	2-1	Gorton 30 O'Neill 90	11	25
26	NPL	H	FC United	**1008**	W	2-1	Gee 80 (pen) Johnson 85	7	26
28	NPL	H	Stafford Rangers	167	W	4-0	Chadwick 9 Rick 36 Johnson 53 Coppin 77	7	27
Jan 1	NPL	A	Droylsden	157	W	9-0	PILKINGTON 3 (11 51 76) CHADWICK 3 (22 44 45) Gee 31 Coppin 36 O'Neill 83	5	28
8	NPL	H	Buxton	166	W	2-0	Chadwick 4 Gorton 38	4	29
11	NPL	A	AFC Fylde	265	L	0-1		6	30
18	NPL	H	Blyth Spartans	147	D	3-3	Chadwick 3 90 Pilkington 56	6	31
25	NPL	A	Frickley Athletic	197	W	2-0	Baguley 6 64	6	32
Feb 1	NPL	H	Rushall Olympic	132	W	2-0	Chalmers 18 Pilkington 45	4	33
8	NPL	A	Stamford	259	L	1-2	Rick 84	5	34
15	NPL	H	AFC Fylde	175	D	1-1	Russell 16 (og)	5	35
22	NPL	A	Worksop Town	313	L	2-3	Johnson 14 Gorton 77	6	36
25	NPL	H	Barlone	133	L	0-1		6	37
March 1	NPL	H	Kings Lynn Town	177	W	5-1	Higgins 14 Johnson 29 79 Pilkington 45 Kosylo 50	6	38
6	NPL	A	Marine	336	W	1-0	Baguley 78	6	39
12	NPL	H	Stocksbridge PS	104	W	3-2	Gee 47 Gorton 72 Kosylo 90	6	40
15	NPL	H	Barwell	137	L	0-1		6	41
22	NPL	A	Whitby Town	263	W	2-1	Chalmers 48 Pilkington 70	6	42
26	NPL	H	Chorley	354	W	2-1	Gorton 9 Johnson 79	5	43
29	NPL	A	Stocksbridge PS	85	W	2-0	Pilkington 53 Chadwick 57	5	44
April 5	NPL	H	Ilkeston Town	188	L	1-3	Baguley 57	5	45
12	NPL	A	Stafford Rangers	288	W	2-1	Baguley 80 Johnson 86	5	46
19	NPL	H	Skelmersdale United	246	W	4-1	Pilkington 9 41 Lynch 72 Johnson 89	5	47
21	NPL	A	FC United	3056	L	2-3	Lynch 1 Chadwick 24	5	48
26	NPL	H	Witton Albion	158	L	1-4	Chadwick 90	5	49
29	**NPL PO SF**	**A**	**FC United**	**2956**	**W**	**2-1**	**Johnson 90 Higgins 120 (aet)**		50
May 3	**NPL PO F**	**A**	**AFC Fylde**	**1191**	**D**	**1-1**	**Pilkington 7 (AFC Fylde won 4-3 on penalties aet)**		51

GOALSCORERS	Lge	FAC	FAT	Total	Pens	Hat-tricks	Cons Run
Pilkington	20+1	2		23		1	3
Chadwick	13			13		1	2
Johnson	9+1			10			2
Coppin	7	1		8			2
Gee	7	1		8	2		2
Gorton	6			6			
O'Neill	6			6			
Rick	6			6			2
Baguley	5			5			2
Lynch	3			3			2
Chalmers	2			2			
Higgins	1+1			2			
Kosylo	2			2			
Young	2			2			
Denham	1			1			
Logan		1		1			
Opponents	2			2			

Cons Run - Consecutive scoring games.

BARWELL

Chairman: David Laing

Secretary: Mrs Shirley Brown **(T)** 07961 905 141 **(E)** shirley.brown16@ntlworld.com

Commercial Manager: Contact secretary **(T)**

Programme Editor: Dave Richardson **(T)** 0116 246 0137

Ground Address: Kirkby Road Sports Ground, Kirkby Road, Barwell LE9 8FQ

(T) 07961 905 141 **Manager:** Jimmy Ginnelly

Club Factfile

Founded: 1992 **Nickname:** Canaries

Previous Names: Barwell Athletic FC and Hinckley FC amalgamated in 1992.

Previous Leagues: Midland Alliance 1992-2010, Northern Premier League 2010-11. Southern 2011-13.

Club Colours (change): Yellow/green/yellow (All blue)

Ground Capacity: 2,500 **Seats:** 256 **Covered:** 750 **Clubhouse:** Yes **Shop:** Yes

Directions

FROM M6 NORTH/M42/A5 NORTH: From M6 North join M42 heading towards Tamworth/Lichfield, leave M42 at Junction 10(Tamworth Services) and turn right onto A5 signposted Nuneaton. Remain on A5 for approx 11 miles, straight on at traffic lights at Longshoot Motel then at next roundabout take first exit signposted A47 Earl Shilton. In about 3 miles at traffic lights go straight on and in 1 mile at roundabout take first exit signposted Barwell. In about 1.5 miles, centre of village, go straight over mini roundabout and then in 20 metres turn right into Kirkby Road. Entrance to complex is 400 metres on right opposite park.

FROM M1 SOUTH: From M1 South Take M69)Signposted Coventry) Take Junction 2 Off M69 (Signposted Hinckley) Follow signs to Hinckley . Go straight on at traffic lights with Holywell Pub on the right. The road bears to the right at next traffic lights turn right signposted Earl Shilton/Leicester. Keep on this road past golf club on right at Hinckley United Ground on left and at large roundabout take second exit signposted Barwell. In about 1.5 miles, centre of village, go straight over mini roundabout and then in 20 metres turn right into Kirkby Road. Entrance to complex is 400 metres on right opposite park.

Previous Grounds: None

Record Attendance: 1,279 v Whitley Bay, FA Vase Semi-Final 2009-10.

Record Victory: Not known

Record Defeat: Not known

Record Goalscorer: Andy Lucas

Record Appearances: Adrian Baker

Additional Records:

Senior Honours:

Midland Alliance League Cup 2005-06, Champions 2009-10.
Northern Premier Division One South 2010-11.

10 YEAR RECORD

04-05	05-06	06-07	07-08	08-09	09-10	10-11	11-12	12-13	13-14
MidAl 13	MidAl 9	MidAl 6	MidAl 10	MidAl 2	MidAl 1	NP1S 1	SthP 9	SthP 7	NP P 14

Northern Premier League Action

Max Harrop (plain shirt) sees his intended chip saved by Stafford Rangers keeper, Andy Jones. His team, Nantwich Town, lost their league match at Marston Road.

Photo: Jonathan Holloway.

BARWELL MATCH RESULTS 2013-14

Date	Comp	H/A	Opponents	Att:	Result		Goalscorers	Pos	No.
Aug 17	NPL	H	Chorley	223	L	1-3	Albrighton 64	20	1
20	NPL	A	Stafford Rangers	441	**W**	3-2	NEWTON 3 (43 45pen 56)	17	2
24	NPL	A	Witton Albion	319	**W**	2-1	Blakeley 70 Newton 90	5	3
26	NPL	H	King's Lynn Town	294	L	1-3	Barlone 44 (pen)	7	4
31	NPL	H	Marine	228	**W**	2-0	Newton 17 Lavery 84	6	5
Sept 2	NPL	A	Ilkeston	496	L	2-4	Lavery 7 Newton 9	7	6
7	NPL	A	Whitby Town	262	D	2-2	Gudger 69 78	15	7
10	NPL	H	Stamford	217	**W**	1-0	Newton 29	10	8
14	***FAC1Q***	***A***	***Corby Town***	***269***	***L***	***0-3***			9
21	NPL	H	Stocksbridge PS	134	**W**	2-1	Newton 5 34	10	10
24	NPL	H	Rushall Olympic	180	**W**	3-1	Towers 17 Tolley 52 (og) Newton 73	6	11
28	NPL	H	Blyth Spartans	213	L	1-2	Newton 37	6	12
Oct 5	NPL	A	Skelmersdale	242	L	0-1		12	13
12	NPL	H	AFC Fylde	232	L	0-3		14	14
16	NPL	A	Matock Town	247	L	1-2	Barlone 18 (pen)	16	15
19	***FAT1Q***	***H***	***Rushall Olympic***	***153***	***L***	***0-4***			16
22	NPL	H	Frickley Athletic	107	D	1-1	Spencer 51	16	17
26	NPL	A	Nantwich Town	205	L	0-2		16	18
29	NPL	H	Ilkeston Town	168	D	1-1	Barlone 35	16	19
Nov 2	NPL	A	Worksop	258	L	3-4	GUDGER 3 (19 46 48)	16	20
5	NPL	A	Stamford	158	**W**	2-0	Griffith 10 Barlone 37	14	21
9	NPL	H	Whitby Town	203	D	1-1	Barlone 80 (pen)	14	22
16	NPL	A	Marine	382	D	1-1	Quinn 10	15	23
23	NPL	H	Trafford	151	D	0-0		15	24
30	NPL	A	Buxton	233	L	0-3		17	25
Dec 7	NPL	A	Chorley	697	**W**	2-1	Kirk 18 Barlone 22	15	26
14	NPL	H	Stafford Rangers	182	**W**	2-0	Kirk 18 Barlone 52	14	27
21	NPL	A	FC United	1661	L	0-2		16	28
26	NPL	H	Grantham Town	182	D	2-2	Charley 41 Barlone 81	16	29
28	NPL	A	Blyth Spartans	355	L	1-2	Weale 72	16	30
Jan 1	NPL	A	Kings Lynn Town	492	L	2-3	Barlone 54 Spencer73	16	31
18	NPL	H	Worksop Town	244	L	1-3	Charley 2	18	32
Feb 15	NPL	H	Droylsden	86	D	2-2	Griffiths-Junior 83 Lower 90	19	33
22	NPL	A	AFC Fylde	251	L	0-1		20	34
25	NPL	H	Ashton United	133	**W**	1-0	Barlone 25	20	35
March 1	NPL	A	Frickley Athletic	208	L	1-2	Barlone 42	20	36
4	NPL	A	Stocksbridge PS	104	**W**	2-1	Gudger 31 Julien 90	19	37
8	NPL	H	Nantwich Town	157	D	2-2	Griffiths 37 Barlone 45	20	38
11	NPL	A	Rushall Olympic	124	D	0-0		20	39
15	NPL	A	Ashton United	137	**W**	1-0	Barlone 40	18	40
22	NPL	H	Matlock Town	157	D	0-0		18	41
29	NPL	A	Trafford	218	**W**	4-2	Preston 20 Love 21 Charley 40 Griffiths 55 (pen)	16	42
April 1	NPL	H	Skelmersdale United	137	**W**	5-0	Julien 5 Hardwick (og) Gudger 45 55 Love 62	15	43
5	NPL	H	Buxton	172	**W**	1-0	Barlone 14	13	44
8	NPL	A	Droylsden	83	**W**	2-1	Barlone 20 26	11	45
19	NPL	H	Witton Albion	158	L	0-2		15	46
21	NPL	A	Grantham Town	218	**W**	1-0	Love 42	15	47
26	NPL	H	FC United	**1809**	L	0-3		14	48

GOALSCORERS	Lge	FAC	FAT	Total	Pens	Hat-tricks	Cons Run
Barlone	16			16	3		2
Newton	11			11	1		3
Gudger	8			8		1	
Charley	3			3			
Griffiths	3			3	1		
Love	3			3			
Julien	2			2			
Kirk	2			2			
Lavery	2			2			2
Spencer	2			2			

	Lge	FAC	FAT	Total	Pens	Hat-tricks	Cons Run
Albrighton	1			1			
Blakeley	1			1			
Griffiths-Junior	1			1			
Lower	1			1			
Preston	1			1			
Quinn	1			1			
Towers	1			1			
Weale	1			1			
Opponents	2			2			

Cons Run - Consecutive scoring games.

BELPER TOWN

Chairman: Alan Benfield
Secretary: Ian Wright (T) 07768 948 506 (E) info@belpertownfc.co.uk
Commercial Manager: (T)
Programme Editor: David Laughlin (T) 07768 010 604
Ground Address: Christchurch Meadow, Bridge Street, Belper DE56 1BA
(T) 01773 825 549 **Manager:** Peter Duffield

Club Factfile

Founded: 1883 **Nickname:** Nailers
Previous Names: None
Previous Leagues: Central Alliance 1957-61, Midland Counties 1961-82, Northern Counties East 1982-97

Club Colours (change): Yellow/black/black (All white)

Ground Capacity: 2,650 **Seats:** 500 **Covered:** 850 **Clubhouse:** Yes **Shop:** Yes

Directions
From North: Exit M1: Exit junction 28 onto A38 towards Derby. Turn off at A610 (signposted 'Ripley/Nottingham') 4th exit at roundabout towards Ambergate. At junction with A6 (Hurt Arms Hotel) turn left to Belper. Ground on right just past first set of traffic lights. Access to the ground is by the lane next to the church.
From South: Follow A6 north from Derby towards Matlock. Follow A6 through Belper until junction with A517. Ground on left just before traffic lights at this junction. Access to the ground is by the lane next to the church.
NB. Please do not attempt to bring coaches into the ground – these can be parked outside

Previous Grounds: Acorn Ground > 1951

Record Attendance: 3,200 v Ilkeston Town - 1955
Record Victory: 15-2 v Nottingham Forest 'A' - 1956
Record Defeat: 0-12 v Goole Town - 1965
Record Goalscorer: Mick Lakin - 231
Record Appearances: Craig Smithurst - 678
Additional Records: Paid £2,000 to Ilkeston Town for Jamie Eaton 2001
Received £2,000 from Hinckley United for Craig Smith
Senior Honours:
Central Alliance League 1958-59, Derbyshire Senior Cup 1958-59, 60-61, 62-63, 79-80.
Midland Counties 1979-80. Northern Counties East 1984-85.

10 YEAR RECORD

04-05	05-06	06-07	07-08	08-09	09-10	10-11	11-12	12-13	13-14
NP 1 17	NP 1 9	NP 1 19	NP 1 8	NP1S 2	NP1S 6	NP1S 14	NP1S 6	NP1S 3	NP1S 4

Northern Premier League Action

Josh Hancock (Witton) puts away the penalty against Skelmersdale

Photo: Keith Clayton.

BLYTH SPARTANS

Chairman: Tony Platten
Secretary: Ian Evans (T) 07905 984 308 (E) generalmanager@blythspartans.com
Commercial Manager: Contact secretary (T)
Programme Editor: Matt Riggs (T) 07933 916 245
Ground Address: Croft Park, Blyth, Northumberland NE24 3JE
(T) 01670 352 373 **Manager:** Tom Wade

Club Factfile

Founded: 1899 **Nickname:** Spartans
Previous Names: None
Previous Leagues: Northumberland 1901-07, Northern All. 1907-13, 46-47, North Eastern 1913-39, Northern Com. 1945-46, Midland 1958-60, Northern Counties 1960-62, Northern 1962-94, Northern Premier 1994-2006. Conference 2006-13.

Club Colours (change): Green & white stripes/black/green (Yellow with green flash/green/green)

Ground Capacity: 4,435 **Seats:** 563 **Covered:** 1,000 **Clubhouse:** Yes **Shop:** Yes

Directions From the Tyne Tunnel, take the A19 signposted MORPETH. At second roundabout take the A189 signposted ASHINGTON. From A189 take A1061 signposted BLYTH. At 1st roundabout follow signs A1061 to BLYTH. Go straight across next two roundabouts following TOWN CENTRE/SOUTH BEECH. At next roundabout turn left onto A193 go straight across next roundabout, and at the next turn right into Plessey Rd and the ground is situated on your left. Team coach should the turn left into William St (3rd left) and reverse up Bishopton St to the designated parking spot.

Previous Grounds: None

Record Attendance: 10,186 v Hartlepool United - FA Cup 08/12/1956
Record Victory: 18-0 v Gateshead Town - Northern Alliance 28/12/1907
Record Defeat: 0-10 v Darlington - North Eastern League 12/12/1914
Record Goalscorer: Not known.
Record Appearances: Eddie Alder - 605 (1965-68)
Additional Records: Received £30,000 from Hull City for Les Mutrie

Senior Honours:
North Eastern League 1935-36. Northern League 1972-73, 74-75, 75-76, 79-80, 80-81, 81-82, 82-83, 83-84, 86-87, 87-88.
Northern League Division 1 1994-95. Northern Premier League Premier Division 2005-06.

10 YEAR RECORD

04-05	05-06	06-07	07-08	08-09	09-10	10-11	11-12	12-13	13-14
NP P 12	NP P 1	Conf N 7	Conf N 18	Conf N 15	Conf N 13	Conf N 9	Conf N 21	NP P 16	NP P 8

BLYTH SPARTANS MATCH RESULTS 2013-14

Date	Comp	H/A	Opponents	Att:	Result		Goalscorers	Pos	No.
Aug 17	NPL	A	Marine	305	D	1-1	Kendrick 26 (pen)	11	1
20	NPL	H	Trafford	311	W	2-1	Kendrick 20 (pen) Maguire 37	7	2
24	NPL	H	Worksop Town	302	D	3-3	Dale 37 Kendrick 53 (pen) Wearmouth 62	10	3
26	NPL	A	Stocksbridge PS	191	D	1-1	Nolan 90	13	4
31	NPL	H	Matlock Town	315	L	1-2	Kendrick 63	16	5
Sept 2	NPL	A	Frickley Athletic	227	W	1-0	Dale 85	11	6
7	NPL	H	Grantham Town	429	W	2-1	Maguire 66 Dale 87 (pen)	9	7
10	NPL	A	Droylsden	121	D	0-0		9	8
14	***FAC1Q***	***H***	***AFC Hyde***	***386***	***L***	***1-3***	***Wade 5***		9
17	NPL	H	Ashton United	241	W	2-1	Parker 82 Wade 88	6	10
20	NPL	A	Witton Albion	441	W	1-0	Dale 82 (pen)	5	11
24	NPL	A	Chorley	685	L	0-3		5	12
28	NPL	A	Barwell	213	W	2-1	Maguire 48 Buddle 87	3	13
Oct 5	NPL	H	Nantwich Town	381	D	2-2	Purewal 54 Maguire 55	4	14
12	NPL	A	Skelmersdale U	286	L	3-4	HUBBARD 3 (7 29 45)	7	15
15	NPL	H	Ilkeston	311	W	3-2	Hubbard 7 (pen) Maguire 48 56	4	16
19	***FAT1Q***	***H***	***Skelmersdale U***	***340***	***W***	***6-0***	***HUBBARD 3 (58 61 67) Davis 81Kendrick 88 Maguire 90***		17
26	NPL	H	Kings Lynn Town	403	L	1-3	Mullen 40	6	18
29	NPL	H	Frickley Athletic	329	W	2-0	Andrews 14 Mullen 60	5	19
Nov 2	***FAT2Q***	***H***	***Ramsbottom United***	***298***	***L***	***0-1***			20
5	NPL	H	Droylsden	242	W	3-0	Wade 30 Andrews 37 Cummings 90	4	21
9	NPL	A	Grantham Town	214	L	2-4	Andrews 4 74	5	22
16	NPL	A	Buxton	204	L	1-2	Hubbard 85	6	23
23	NPL	H	Rushall Olympic	240	W	3-2	Buddle 19 Maguire 47 Robinson 85	5	24
30	NPL	A	FC United	1690	L	0-3		6	25
Dec 7	NPL	H	Marine	272	D	2-2	Shaw 48 (og) Maguire 55	7	26
14	NPL	A	Trafford	165	L	1-2	Maguire 71	8	27
21	NPL	H	Stamford	242	W	2-1	Maguire 29 64	6	28
26	NPL	A	Whitby Town	370	L	1-2	Dale 22	6	29
28	NPL	H	Barwell	355	W	2-1	Maguire 48 85	8	30
Jan 1	NPL	H	Stocksbridge PS	279	W	3-0	Robinson 49 Maguire 73 Hooks 82	8	31
11	NPL	H	Stafford Rangers	315	W	6-2	MAGUIRE 3 (6 9 16) Watson 22 Dale 61 Wade 89	8	32
18	NPL	A	Ashton United	147	D	3 3	Wade 32 Homer 61 Wearmouth 82	8	33
25	NPL	H	Chorley	437	W	3-1	Maguire 44 Hooks 45 Parker 82	8	34
Feb 8	NPL	H	Witton Albion	337	W	4-2	Dale 6 60 (pen) Maguire 80 89	6	35
15	NPL	A	Stafford Rangers	319	D	2-2	Dale 23 Parker 34	6	36
22	NPL	H	Buxton	391	L	0-1		7	37
March 1	NPL	H	AFC Fylde	386	D	1-1	Maguire 35	7	38
8	NPL	A	Kings Lynn Town	576	W	1-0	Dale 69	9	39
15	NPL	H	Skelmersdale United	329	W	2-1	Dale 32 Maguire 48	7	40
22	NPL	A	Ikeston Town	305	W	1-0	Maguire 11	7	41
29	NPL	A	Rushall Olympic	168	D	0-0		7	42
April 1	NPL	A	Matlock Town	208	D	1-1	Davis 84	7	43
5	NPL	H	FC United	**932**	L	0-1		8	44
12	NPL	A	Nantwich Town	189	D	1-1	Purewal 66	7	45
16	NPL	A	AFC Fylde	304	L	1-5	Purewal 79	7	46
19	NPL	A	Worksop Town	340	L	2-3	Dale 43 60	8	47
21	NPL	A	Whitby Town	501	L	0-7		8	48
26	NPL	A	Stamford	449	W	4-3	Wade 11 Maguire 33 Wearmouth 42 Robinson 64	8	49

GOALSCORERS	Lge	FAC	FAT	Total	Pens	Hat-tricks	Cons Run
Maguire	24		1	25		1	3
Dale	12			12	3		2
Hubbard	5		3	8	1	2	3
Wade	5	1		6			2
Kendrick	4		1	5	3		3
Andrews	4			4			2
Parker	3			3			
Purewal	3			3			2
Robinson	3			3			
Wearmouth	3			3			

	Lge	FAC	FAT	Total	Pens	Hat-tricks	Cons Run
Buddle	2			2			
Davis	1		1	2			
Hooks	2			2			
Mullen	2			2			
Cummings	1			1			
Homer	1			1			
Nolan	1			1			
Watson	1			1			
Opponents	1			1			

Cons Run - Consecutive scoring games.

BUXTON

Chairman: David Hopkins
Secretary: Don Roberts **(T)** 07967 822 448 **(E)** admin@buxtonfc.co.uk
Commercial Manager: Contact secretary **(T)**
Programme Editor: Danny Hopkins **(T)** 07891 973 656
Ground Address: The Silverlands, Buxton, Derbyshire SK17 6QH
(T) 01298 23197 **Manager:** Martin McIntosh

Club Factfile

Founded: 1877 **Nickname:** The Bucks
Previous Names: None
Previous Leagues: Combination 1891-99, Manchester 1899-1932, Cheshire County 1932-40, 46-73, Northern Premier 1973-98, Northern Counties East 1998-2006

Club Colours (change): All royal blue (All red)

Ground Capacity: 4,000 **Seats:** 490 **Covered:** 2,500 **Clubhouse:** Yes **Shop:** Yes

Directions
FROM STOCKPORT (A6): Turn left at first roundabout after dropping down the hill into the town, turn right at next roundabout, right at traffic lights (London Road pub) to Buxton Market Place. After two sets of pedestrian lights turn right at Royles shop then turn immediate left and follow road approx 500 metres to ground (opposite police station.)
FROM BAKEWELL (A6): Turn left at roundabout on to Dale Road and follow road to traffic lights then as above.
FROM MACCLESFIELD/CONGLETON/LEEK: Follow road to Burbage traffic lights and take right fork in the road at the Duke of York pub (Macclesfield Road.) Then at next traffic lights turn left (London Road pub) and follow as above.
FROM ASHBOURNE (A515): Go straight on at first traffic lights (London Road pub) and follow directions as above.

Previous Grounds: The Park (Cricket Club) 1877-78. Fields at Cote Heath and Green Lane 1878-84.

Record Attendance: 6,000 v Barrow - FA Cup 1st Round 1961-62
Record Victory: Not known
Record Defeat: Not known
Record Goalscorer: Mark Reed - 236 (in 355 + 46 sub appearances 2002-07, 2009-)
Record Appearances: David Bainbridge - 642
Additional Records: Paid £5,000 to Hyde United for Gary Walker 1989
Received £16,500 from Rotherham for Ally Pickering 1989
Senior Honours:
Manchester League 1931-32, Lge cup 1925-26, 26-27. Cheshire Co. League 1972-73, Lge Cup 1956-57, 57-58, 68-69.
N.C.E. League 2005-06, Presidents Cup 2004-05, 05-06. N.P.L. Division 1 2006-07, President's Cup 1981-82, 2006-07.
Derbyshire Senior Cup 1938-39, 45-46, 56-57, 59-60, 71-72, 80-81, 85-86, 86-87, 2008-09.

10 YEAR RECORD

04-05	05-06	06-07	07-08	08-09	09-10	10-11	11-12	12-13	13-14
NCEP 9	NCEP 1	NP 1 1	NP P 5	NP P 14	NP P 8	NP P 6	NP P 13	NP P 7	NP P 13

BUXTON MATCH RESULTS 2013-14

Date	Comp	H/A	Opponents	Att:	Result		Goalscorers	Pos	No.
Aug 17	NPL	H	Grantham Town	133	W	3-1	Morris 44 64 Osborne 82	2	1
20	NPL	A	Frickley Athletic	270	W	1-0	Reed 77	1	2
24	NPL	A	Droylsden	158	D	1-1	Morris 10	1	3
26	NPL	H	Ilkeston	414	L	1-2	Morris 11	8	4
31	NPL	H	Whitby Town	284	D	1-1	Reed 76	9	5
Sept 2	NPL	A	Stocksbridge PS	208	W	3-2	King 10 Harris 24 Niven 32	6	6
7	NPL	A	Marine	454	W	2-0	Thornhill 17 Morris 45	5	7
11	NPL	H	Ashton United	238	L	1-1	Lynch 77 (og)	9	8
14	***FAC1Q***	***A***	***Prescot Cables***	***220***	***W***	***1-0***	***Osborne 76***		9
21	NPL	H	Skelmersdale U	316	W	2-0	Osborne 58 King 64	7	10
25	NPL	H	Worksop Town	271	L	2-4	Osborne 7 45	9	11
28	***FAC2Q***	***H***	***North Ferriby United***	***284***	***L***	***1-4***	***Morris 61 (pen)***		12
Oct 5	NPL	A	AFC Fylde	359	D	2-2	Osborne 13 Morris 57	13	13
8	NPL	A	Stamford	200	L	0-1		13	14
12	NPL	H	Nantwich Town	309	W	2-0	Morris 2 11	10	15
15	NPL	A	Grantham Town	136	W	1-0	Istead 88	6	16
19	***FAT1Q***	***H***	***Darlington 1883***	***443***	***D***	***1-1***	***Thornhill 68***		17
22	***FAT1Qr***	***A***	***Darlington 1883***	***766***	***D***	***3-3***	***Morris 65 Thornhill 70 King 88 (Won 4-3 on pens aet)***		18
26	NPL	A	Trafford	253	D	0-0		8	19
30	NPL	H	Stocksbridge Park Steels	170	L	0-1		8	20
Nov 9	NPL	H	Marine	236	D	2-2	King 32 Harris 81	11	21
12	***FAT2Q***	***A***	***Sheffield FC***	***252***	***L***	***0-1***			22
16	NPL	H	Blyth Spartans	204	W	2-1	Stevens 54 Morris 68	10	23
23	NPL	A	Stafford Rangers	363	D	1-1	Reed 82	10	24
30	NPL	H	Barwell	233	W	3-0	King 24 Morris 27 (pen) Thornhill 50	8	25
Dec 7	NPL	A	Witton Albion	300	W	1-0	Morris 55	6	26
14	NPL	H	Frickley Athletic	219	D	1-1	Morris 15	6	27
21	NPL	A	Chorley	748	D	0-0		8	28
28	NPL	H	FC United	1112	L	0-2		11	29
Jan 4	NPL	H	Rushall Olympic	214	L	1-2	Morris 6	15	30
8	NPL	A	Ashton United	166	L	0-2		15	31
11	NPL	A	King's Lynn Town	653	L	1-3	Thornhill 67	15	32
Feb 1	NPL	H	AFC Fylde	167	L	0-4		16	33
8	NPL	A	Skelmersdale United	211	L	0-2		16	34
19	NPL	A	Worksop Town	282	L	1-3	Morris 57	16	35
22	NPL	A	Blyth Spartans	391	W	1-0	Taylor 59	16	36
27	NPL	H	Stamford	151	D	2-2	Morris 36 76 (pen)	16	37
March 1	NPL	A	Rushall Olympic	213	D	2-2	Hardy 22 Davies 42	16	38
8	NPL	H	Trafford	241	L	1-2	King 42	19	39
13	NPL	H	King's Lynn Town	151	W	6-1	Morris 30 (pen) 52 Thornhill 32 Hardy 35 51 Palmer 45	15	40
15	NPL	A	Ilkeston	454	W	2-0	Hardy 39 73	14	41
22	NPL	H	Grantham Town	230	W	3-1	Reed 56 Hardy 70 Davies 85	14	42
25	NPL	A	Nantwich Town	151	D	1-1	Hardy 17	14	43
29	NPL	H	Stafford Rangers	257	D	2-2	Reed 48 60	13	44
April 5	NPL	A	Barwell	172	L	0-1		14	45
9	NPL	H	Matlock Town	531	D	1-1	Reed 84	14	46
12	NPL	A	FC United	3330	W	2-1	Brooks 10 Thornhill 60	14	47
16	NPL	A	Whitby Town	226	L	0-1		14	48
19	NPL	H	Droylsden	210	W	4-2	Morris 40 Reed 46 Brooks 67 King 75	13	49
21	NPL	A	Matlock Town	434	D	1-1	Morris 60	13	50
26	NPL	H	Chorley	**1483**	L	0-2		13	51

GOALSCORERS	Lge	FAC	FAT	Total	Pens	Hat-tricks	Cons Run
Morris	20	1	1	22	4		3
Reed	8			8			
Hardy	7			7			4
King	6		1	7			
Thornhill	5		2	7			
Osborne	5	1		6			3
Brooks	2			2			
Davis	2			2			
Harris	2			2			
Istead	1			1			
Niven	1			1			
Palmer	1			1			
Stevens	1			1			
Taylor	1			1			
Opponents	1			1			

Cons Run - Consecutive scoring games.

NON
LEAGUE DAY
06.09.14
Support your
LOCAL
FOOTBALL CLUB
nonleagueday.co.uk

CURZON ASHTON

Chairman: Harry Galloway
Secretary: Robert Hurst **(T)** 07713 252 310 **(E)** office@curzon-ashton.co.uk
Commercial Manager: **(T)**
Programme Editor: Ian Seymour **(T)** 07908 721 003
Ground Address: Tameside Stadium, Richmond Street, Ashton-u-Lyme OL7 9HG
(T) 0161 330 6033 **Manager:** John Flanagan

Club Factfile

Founded: 1963 **Nickname:** Curzon
Previous Names: Club formed when Curzon Road and Ashton Amateurs merged.
Previous Leagues: Manchester Amateur, Manchester > 1978, Cheshire County 1978-82, North West Counties 1982-87, 98-2007, Northern Premier 1987-97, Northern Counties East 1997-98,
Club Colours (change): All royal blue (All red)

Ground Capacity: 4,000 **Seats:** 527 **Covered:** 1,100 **Clubhouse:** Yes **Shop:** Yes

Directions From Stockport (south) direction Leave the M60 at junc 23 (Ashton-U-Lyne). Turn left at the top of the slip road, go straight through the next set of lights, and bear right (onto Lord Sheldon Way) at the next set. Continue on this road until you come to a set of traffic lights with the Cineworld Cinema on your right. Turn left here onto Richmond St. Over the bridge, across the mini-roundabout and then first left down to the ground. From Oldham (north) direction Leave the M60 at junc 23 (Ashton-U-Lyne) and turn right at the top of the slip road signposted A635 Manchester. Turn right at the second set of traffic lights, sign posted Ashton Moss, and then follow directions as from the south.

Previous Grounds: Katherine Street > 204, Stalybridge Celtic FC 2004-06

Record Attendance: 1,826 v Stamford - FA Vase Semi-final
Record Victory: 7-0 v Ashton United
Record Defeat: 0-8 v Bamber Bridge
Record Goalscorer: Alan Sykes
Record Appearances: Alan Sykes
Additional Records:

Senior Honours:
Northern Premier Division One North 2013-14.
Manchester Premier Cup x5

10 YEAR RECORD

04-05		05-06		06-07		07-08		08-09		09-10		10-11		11-12		12-13		13-14	
NWC1	4	NWC1	7	NWC1	2	NP1N	4	NP1N	4	NP1N	3	NP1N	4	NP1N	2	NP1N	7	NP1N	1

Northern Premier League Action

Stafford Rangers winger, Matt Berkeley (striped shirt) finds himself being held back by his Nantwich Town opponent. Although already relegated, Stafford pulled off a hard fought 1-0 win.

Photo: Jonathan Holloway.

F.C. UNITED OF MANCHESTER

Chairman: Andy Walsh (General Manager)
Secretary: Lindsey Howard **(T)** 0161 273 8950 **(E)** office@fc-utd.co.uk
Commercial Manager: **(T)**
Programme Editor: Tony Howard **(T)** 0161 273 8950
Ground Address: Stalybridge Celtic FC, Bower Fold, Mottram Road, Stalybridge SK15 2RT
(T) 0161 338 2828 (Grd) 0161 273 8950 (Office) **Manager:** Karl Marginson

Club Factfile

Founded: 2005 **Nickname:** F.C.
Previous Names: None
Previous Leagues: North West Counties 2005-07

Club Colours (change): Red/white/black (White/black/white)

Ground Capacity: 6,108 **Seats:** 1,200 **Covered:** 2,400 **Clubhouse:** Yes **Shop:** Yes

Directions Leave the M6 at junction 19 (Northwich). At the roundabout at the end of the slip road turn right (exit 3 of 4) to join the A556 towards Altrincham. Stay on the A556 for 5 miles to a roundabout with the M56. Turn right at the roundabout (exit 3 of 4) onto the M56. Stay on the M56 for 6 1/2 miles to junction 3 (M60 signposted Sheffield, M67) Stay on the M60 for 7 miles to junction 24 (M67, Denton) At the roundabout turn right (exit 4 of 5) to join the M67. Stay on the M67 to the very end, Junction 4. At the roundabout turn left (exit 1 of 4) onto the A57 (Hyde Road). After 1/2 a mile you will reach a set of traffic lights (signposted Stalybridge). Turn left onto B6174 (Stalybridge Road). Almost immediately, there is a mini roundabout. Turn left (exit 1 of 5) onto Roe Cross Road (A6018). Follow this road for 1 3/4 miles passing the Roe Cross Inn on the right and through the cutting (the road is now called Mottram Road). When you pass the Dog and Partridge on the right, you will be almost there. Bower Fold is on the left opposite a sharp right turn next to the Hare and Hounds pub. If the car park is full (it usually is), parking can be found on the streets on the right of Mottram Road.

Previous Grounds: Gigg Lane (Bury FC) 2005-14.

Record Attendance: 6,731 v Brighton & Hove Albion, FA Cup 2nd Round 08/12/2010
Record Victory: 10-2 v Castleton Gabriels 10/12/2005. 8-0 v Squires Gate 14/10/06, Glossop N.E. 28/10/06 & Nelson 05/09/10
Record Defeat: 1-5 v Bradford Park Avenue 24/03/2010. 1-5 v Matlock Town 05/09/2010
Record Goalscorer: Rory Patterson - 99 (2005-08)
Record Appearances: Jerome Wright - 249
Additional Records: Simon Carden scored 5 goals against Castleton Gabriels 10/12/2005.
Longest unbeaten run (League): 22 games 03/12/2006 - 18/08/2007.

Senior Honours:
North West Counties League Division 2 2005-06, Division 1 2006-07.
Northern Premier League Division 1 North Play-off 2007-08.

10 YEAR RECORD

04-05	05-06	06-07	07-08	08-09	09-10	10-11	11-12	12-13	13-14
	NWC2 1	NWC1 1	NP1N 2	NP P 6	NP P 13	NP P 4	NP P 6	NP P 3	NP P 2

F.C. UNITED OF MANCHESTER MATCH RESULTS 2013-14

Date	Comp	H/A	Opponents	Att:	Result		Goalscorers	Pos	No.
Aug 17	NPL	A	Whitby Town	327	L	0-2		23	1
20	NPL	H	AFC Fylde	1649	D	0-0		20	2
24	NPL	H	Stamford	1629	W	6-0	GREAVES 3 (9 30 54) Wolfenden 29 Walwyn 80 90	12	3
26	NPL	A	Trafford	1374	W	3-2	Mulholland 33 Walwyn 77 Greaves 90	5	4
31	NPL	A	Grantham Town	739	W	5-1	Neville 28 Greaves 40 Walwyn 68 84 Wright 90	1	5
Sept 2	NPL	H	Witton Albion	1614	W	3-1	Banks 13 (Pen) Greaves 32 Stott 60	1	6
7	NPL	H	Rushall Olympic	1860	L	0-2		8	7
10	NPL	A	Frickley Athletic	420	W	2-3	Greaves 57 70	6	8
14	***FAC1Q***	***H***	***Chorley***	***1318***	***L***	***0-1***			9
21	NPL	A	Stafford Rangers	1032	L	1-2	Stott 65 (pen)	9	10
28	NPL	H	Whitby Town	1524	L	1-3	Wright 79	15	11
Oct 5	NPL	H	Marine	1528	W	1-0	Daniels 58	11	12
8	NPL	A	Nantwich Town	672	D	1-1	Pearson 45	11	13
12	NPL	A	Kings Lynn	1440	D	0-0		8	14
15	NPL	H	Skelmersdale Utd	1429	L	1-3	Walwyn 80	10	15
19	***FAT1Q***	***A***	***Witton Albion***	***693***	***D***	***2-2***	***Walwyn 60 Wolfenden 81***		16
26	NPL	H	Stocksbridge Park Steels	1542	W	6-2	Norton 4 65 Walwyn 34 Mulholland 74 Daniels 82 89	9	17
Nov 5	***FAT1Qr***	***H***	***Witton Albion***	***369***	***L***	***1-2***	***Greaves 70***		18
9	NPL	A	Rushall Olympic	539	D	1-1	Norton 60	13	19
16	NPL	H	Frickley Athletic	1706	W	3-0	Gardner 55 (og) Davies 61 Greaves 90	11	20
23	NPL	A	Matlock Town	978	D	1-1	Greaves 53	11	21
26	NPL	A	Droylsden	754	W	4-1	GREAVES 3 (16 57 76) Stott 44 (pen)	6	22
30	NPL	H	Blyth Spartans	1690	W	3-0	Davies 34 Daniels 63 Greaves 85	5	23
Dec	NPL	H	Worksop Town	1600	D	4-4	Daniels 50 Greaves 51 60 Wolfenden 60	5	24
14	NPL	A	AFC Fylde	709	W	2-0	Daniels 35 Byrne 66	5	25
21	NPL	H	Barwell	1661	W	2-0	Wolfenden 75 Davies 86	5	26
26	NPL	A	Ashton United	1008	L	1-2	Norton 39	5	27
28	NPL	A	Buxton	1112	W	2-0	Wolfenden 51 Norton 53	4	28
Jan	NPL	A	Ilkeston	974	D	3-3	Daniels 39 Greaves 72 90	6	29
18	NPL	A	Whitby Town	818	L	2-3	Jones 30 Greaves 59	10	30
21	NPL	H	Trafford	1598	W	1-1	Byrne 5	10	31
Feb1	NPL	A	Marine	940	W	2-0	Davies 35 Wright 84 (pen)	9	32
18	NPL	H	Nantwich Town	1416	W	2-1	Greaves 29 Norton 54	7	33
22	NPL	H	Ilkeston	1793	W	4-1	Greaves 38 51 Wright 48 79 (pen)	5	34
Mar 1	NPL	H	Droylsden	1974	W	4-1	Jones 33 Wolfenden 34 Wright 44 Brownhill 57		35
4	NPL	A	Chorley	2171	W	1-0	Greaves 90	5	36
8	NPL	A	Stocksbridge Park Steels	841	W	4-1	Raglan 2 34 Wolfenden 52 Mulholland 52	5	37
15	NPL	H	Kings Lynn Town	2083	W	2-0	Norton 25 90	5	38
18	NPL	H	Stafford Rangers	1589	W	4-0	Greaves 7 59 Raglan 45 Daniels 74	3	39
22	NPL	A	Skelmersdale United	1000	W	3-1	Wright 24 Greaves 77 Brownhill 84	3	40
25	NPL	A	Witton Albion	612	W	5-2	Raglan 15 Greaves 28 31 North 45 Wolfenden 66	1	41
29	NPL	H	Matlock Town	2044	W	2-1	Greaves 48 64	1	42
Apr 5	NPL	A	Blyth Spartans	932	W	1-0	Wolfenden 65	1	43
8	NPL	H	Chorley	**4152**	D	2-2	Raglan 83 Greaves 86	2	44
12	NPL	H	Buxton	3330	L	1-2	Greaves 3	2	45
15	NPL	H	Grantham Town	1732	W	3-0	Wolfenden 65 88 Greaves 69	2	46
19	NPL	A	Stamford	1204	W	3-2	Norton 34 84 og 47	2	47
21	NPL	H	Ashton United	3056	W	3-2	Greaves 62 Norton 72 Daniels 90	2	48
26	NPL	A	Barwell	1809	W	3-0	Davies 22 Norton 30 Byrne 88	2	49
29	***NPL PO SF***	***H***	***Ashton United***	***2956***	***L***	***1-2***	***Wright 59 (pen)***		50

GOALSCORERS	Lge	FAC	FAT	Total	Pens	Hat-tricks	Cons Run
Greaves	33		1	34		2	5
Norton	12			12			2
Wolfenden	10		1	11			
Daniels	9			9			3
Walwyn	7		1	8			3
Wright	7+1			8	3		2
Davies	5			5			
Raglan	5			5			
Byrne	3			3			
Mulholland	3			3			

	Lge	FAC	FAT	Total	Pens	Hat-tricks	Cons Run
Stott	3			3	2		
Brownhill	2			2			
Jones	2			2			
Banks	1			1	1		
Neville	1			1			
North	1			1			
Pearson	1			1			
Opponents	2			2			

Cons Run - Consecutive scoring games.

Play-off goal indicated by +

FRICKLEY ATHLETIC

Chairman: Gareth Dando
Secretary: Steve Pennock (T) 07985 291 074 (E) stevepennock99@gmail.com
Commercial Manager: (T)
Programme Editor: Gareth Dando (T) 07709 098 469
Ground Address: Tech5 Stadium, Westfield Lane, South Elmsall, Pontefract WF9 2EQ
(T) 01977 642 460 **Manager:** Karl Rose

Club Factfile

Founded: 1910 **Nickname:** The Blues
Previous Names: Frickley Colliery
Previous Leagues: Sheffield, Yorkshire 1922-24, Midland Counties 1924-33, 34-60, 70-76, Cheshire County 1960-70, Northern Premier 1976-80, Conference 1980-87

Club Colours (change): All royal blue (All yellow)

Ground Capacity: 2,087 **Seats:** 490 **Covered:** 700 **Clubhouse:** Yes **Shop:** Yes

Directions

From North : Leave A1 to join A639, go over flyover to junction. Turn left and immediately right, signed South Elmsall. Continue to roundabout and take 2nd exit to traffic lights and turn left onto Mill Lane (B6474). Turn right at the T-junction and continue down hill to next T-junction. Turn right and immediately left up Westfield Lane. The ground is signposted to the left after about half a mile.

From South : Exit M18 at J2 onto A1 (North). Leave A1 for A638 towards Wakefield. Continue on A638, going straight on at the first roundabout and turn left at next roundabout to traffic lights. Continue as above from traffic lights.

Previous Grounds: None

Record Attendance: 6,500 v Rotherham United - FA Cup 1st Round 1971
Record Victory: Not known
Record Defeat: Not known
Record Goalscorer: K Whiteley
Record Appearances: Not known
Additional Records: Received £12,500 from Boston United for Paul Shirtliff and from Northampton Town for Russ Wilcox

Senior Honours:
Sheffield & Hallamshire Senior Cup x11 Most recently 2012-13.

10 YEAR RECORD

04-05	05-06	06-07	07-08	08-09	09-10	10-11	11-12	12-13	13-14
NP P 18	NP P 2	NP P 16	NP P 14	NP P 11	NP P 15	NP P 18	NP P 19	NP P 18	NP P 21

FRICKLEY ATHLETIC MATCH RESULTS 2013-14

Date	Comp	H/A	Opponents	Att:	Result		Goalscorers	Pos	No.
Aug 17	NPL	A	Stamford	227	L	4-6	Allott 12 Gray 43 Fox 72 Hinsley 90	19	1
20	NPL	H	Buxton	270	L	0-1		22	2
24	NPL	H	Rushall Olympic	158	**W**	4-2	Hinsley 5 ALLOTT 3 (32 50 66)	19	3
26	NPL	A	Whitby Town	301	D	2-2	Picton 74 Gray 85	19	4
31	NPL	H	Chorley	235	D	0-0		21	5
Sept 7	NPL	A	Skelmersdale U	258	L	2-3	Allott 28 30	22	6
10	NPL	H	FC United	**420**	L	1-2	Allott 17	22	7
14	***FAC1Q***	***H***	***Sheffield***	***222***	***W***	***4-1***	***PICTON 3 (12 57 78) Hinsley 18***		8
17	NPL	H	Trafford	180	**W**	2-1	McFadzean 42 Bloor 68	18	9
21	NPL	A	Matlock Town	322	D	0-0		18	10
28	***FAC2 Q***	***H***	***Marske United***	***302***	***L***	***1-3***	***Kenny 90***		11
Oct 2	NPL	A	Ashton United	101	D	2-2	Bloor 46 Picton 75 (pen)	18	12
5	NPL	H	Stafford Rangers	221	**W**	2-0	Hinsley 5 Dyer-Stewart 87	18	13
12	NPL	A	Ilkeston	517	L	0-1		18	14
15	NPL	H	Kings Lynn	196	D	2-2	Allott 29 (pen) 54	19	15
19	***FAT1Q***	***H***	***Brigg Town***	***136***	***L***	***1-2***	***Hinsley 49***		16
22	NPL	A	Barwell	107	D	1-1	Fearon 90	20	17
26	NPL	H	Droylsden	168	**W**	2-0	Villeman 2 Denton 54	18	18
29	NPL	A	Blyth Spartans	329	L	0-2		18	19
Nov 2	NPL	H	Ilkeston	233	L	0-1		18	20
9	NPL	H	Skelmersdale United	190	**W**	4-3	Denton 6 Allott 28 78 Picton 45	19	21
16	NPL	A	FC United	1706	L	0-3		19	22
23	NPL	A	AFC Fylde	291	L	0-2		20	23
30	NPL	H	Grantham Town	208	**W**	3-2	ALLOTT 3 (25 pen 45 pen 90)	19	24
Dec 7	NPL	H	Stamford	197	D	1-1	Allott 69 (Pen)	19	25
14	NPL	A	Buxton	219	D	1-1	Maguire 71	18	26
21	NPL	H	Worksop Town	257	D	2-2	Allott 5 16 (pen)	19	27
26	NPL	A	Stocksbridge PS	279	**W**	4-3	Collishaw 21 Allott 39 (pen) 90 Hinsley 54	19	28
Jan 1	NPL	H	Whitby Town	218	D	1-1	Hinsley 5	19	29
4	NPL	A	Marine	269	L	1-2	Allott 82	19	30
11	NPL	H	Witton Albion	228	D	0-0		19	31
18	NPL	A	Trafford	265	L	1-4	Picton 90	20	32
25	NPL	H	Ashton United	197	L	0-2		20	33
Feb 1	NPL	A	Stafford Rangers	310	**W**	2-0	Allott 37 Moke 55	18	34
8	NPL	H	Matlock Town	234	L	1-3	Ghaichem 84	19	35
11	NPL	A	Chorley	593	L	0-3		19	36
22	NPL	H	Nantwich Town	207	**W**	2-0	Picton 61 74	19	37
March 1	NPL	H	Barwell	208	**W**	2-1	Denton 75 Hindsley 86	19	38
8	NPL	A	Droylsden	123	**W**	3 2	Moke 19 Rouse 40 (og) Allott 76	18	39
15	NPL	A	Nantwich Town	236	L	1-2	Ghaichem 56	20	40
22	NPL	A	King's Lynn Town	480	L	0-3		21	41
29	NPL	H	AFC Fylde	203	L	0-2		21	42
April 5	NPL	A	Grantham Town	255	L	1-2	Hinsley 82	21	43
8	NPL	A	Witton Albion	304	L	1-2	Moke 42	21	44
12	NPL	H	Marine	245	D	1-1	Osborne 6	21	45
19	NPL	A	Rushall Olympic	138	L	1-4	Allott 85	21	46
21	NPL	H	Stocksbridge PS	210	D	2-2	Allott 26 32	21	47
26	NPL	A	Worksop Town	334	**W**	3-1	Ghaichem 61 Allott 64 Sharry 81	21	48

GOALSCORERS	Lge	FAC	FAT	Total	Pens	Hat-tricks	Cons Run
Allott	25			25	6	2	3
Hinsley	7	1	1	9			2
Picton	6	3		9	1	1	
Denton	3			3			
Ghaichem	3			3			
Moke	3			3			
Bloor	2			2			
Gray	2			2			
Colishaw	1			1			
Dyer-Stewart	1			1			
Fearon	1			1			
Fox	1			1			
Kenny		1		1			
Maguire	1			1			
McFadzean	1			1			
Osbourne	1			1			
Sharry	1			1			
Vileman	1			1			
Opponents	1			1			

Cons Run - Consecutive scoring games.

GRANTHAM TOWN

Chairman: Peter Railton
Secretary: Patrick Nixon **(T)** 07747 136 033 **(E)** psnixon@hotmail.com
Commercial Manager: **(T)**
Programme Editor: Mike Koranski **(T)** 01476 562 104
Ground Address: South Kesteven Sports Stadium, Trent Road, Gratham NG31 7XQ
(T) 01476 591 818 (office) **Manager:** J Albans & W Hallcro

Club Factfile

Founded: 1874 **Nickname:** Gingerbreads
Previous Names: Not known
Previous Leagues: Midland Amateur Alliance, Central Alliance 1911-25, 59-61, Midland Counties 1925-59, 61-72, Southern 1972-79, 85-2006, Northern Premier 1979-85
Club Colours (change): Black & white stripes/black/black (Orange/orange or black/orange or black)

Ground Capacity: 7,500 **Seats:** 750 **Covered:** 1,950 **Clubhouse:** Yes **Shop:** Yes

Directions

FROM A1 NORTH Leave A1 At A607 Melton Mowbray exit. Turn left at island on slip road into Swingbridge Lane. At T junction turn left into Trent Road ground is 100yds on right.
FROM A52 NOTTINGHAM. Pass over A1 and at first island turn right into housing estate & Barrowby Gate. Through housing estate to T junction. Turn right and then immediately left into Trent road ground is 100 yards on the left.
FROM A607 MELTON MOWBRAY. Pass under A1 and take next left A1 South slip road. At island turn right into Swingbridge Road then as for A1 North above. From all directions follow brown signs for Sports Complex, which is immediately behind the stadium.

Previous Grounds: London Road

Record Attendance: 3,695 v Southport - FA Trophy 1997-98
Record Victory: 13-0 v Rufford Colliery (H) - FA Cup 15/09/1934
Record Defeat: 0-16 v Notts County Rovers (A) - Midland Amateur Alliance 22/10/1892
Record Goalscorer: Jack McCartney - 416
Record Appearances: Chris Gardner - 664
Additional Records: Received £20,000 from Nottingham Forest for Gary Crosby

Senior Honours:
Southern League Midland Division 1997-98. Lincolnshire Senior Cup x21 Most recently 2011-12.
Northern Premier Division 1 South 2011-12.

10 YEAR RECORD

04-05	05-06	06-07	07-08	08-09	09-10	10-11	11-12	12-13	13-14
SthP 13	SthP 11	NP P 22	NP 1 6	NP1S 13	NP1S 11	NP1S 5	NP1S 1	NP P 19	NP P 15

GRANTHAM TOWN MATCH RESULTS 2013-14

Date	Comp	H/A	Opponents	Att:	Result	Goalscorers	Pos	No.
Aug 17	NPL	A	Ashton United	133	L 1-2	King 64	15	1
20	NPL	H	Worksop Town	268	W 3-1	Meikle 28 72 Graham 64	11	2
24	NPL	H	AFC Hyde	220	L 1-2	G.Smith 29	17	3
26	NPL	A	Stamford	432	W 2-1	Hawes 38 Pilero 47	14	4
31	NPL	H	FC United	**739**	L 1-5	G. Smith 47	19	5
Sept 2	NPL	A	Kings Lynn Town	670	D 1-1	Lee 51 (og)	16	6
7	NPL	A	Blyth Spartans	249	L 1-2	Buddle 29 (og)	18	7
10	NPL	H	Stocksbridge PS	94	W 3-2	G. Smith 31 80 Watson 54	11	8
14	***FAC1Q***	***A***	***Stamford***	***318***	***D 0-0***			9
17	***FAC1Qr***	***H***	***Stamford***	***215***	***L 2-3***	***McDonald 35 (pen) Towey 47***		10
21	NPL	A	Marine	271	D 3-3	Hawes 7 G. Smith 63 66	16	11
24	NPL	A	Stafford Rangers	340	D 2-2	Hawes 79 G. Smith 90	15	12
28	NPL	H	Ilkeston	302	W 2-0	McGhee 11 G. Smith 49		13
Oct 5	NPL	H	Trafford	216	W 2-1	G. Smith 11 Lewis 47	14	14
12	NPL	A	Droylsden	162	W 3-0	Graham 7 Lewis 14 Towey 19	11	15
15	NPL	H	Buxton	136	L 0-1		11	16
19	***FAT1Q***	***H***	***Soham Town Rangers***	***217***	***D 2-2***	***K.Smith 12 G.Smith 76***		17
22	***FAT1Qr***	***A***	***Soham Town Rangers***	***125***	***L 1-4***	***Hawes 90 (aet)***		18
26	NPL	H	Skelmersdale United	206	L 1-2	Fairclough 59	14	19
29	NPL	H	Kings Lynn Town	253	W 2-0	G.Smith 55 74	11	20
Nov 2	NPL	A	Stocksbridge PS	134	L 3-4	G.Smith 29 35 Towey 54	13	21
9	NPL	H	Blyth Spartans	214	W 4-2	Burbeary 1 45 (pen) McGhee 20 G.Smith 28	10	22
16	NPL	A	Whitby Town	278	D 1-1	Burbeary 42	12	23
23	NPL	H	Witton Albion	189	D 0-0		12	24
30	NPL	A	Frickley Athletic	208	L 2-3	Sanders 1 Burbeary 30 (pen)	13	25
Dec 7	NPL	H	Ashton United	181	L 0 1		16	26
14	NPL	A	Worksop Town	418	L 1-3	Lavell-Moore 74 (og)	17	27
21	NPL	H	Nantwich Town	175	L 0-5		17	28
26	NPL	A	Barwell	182	D 2-2	Towey 16 Dixon 55	18	29
28	NPL	A	Rushall Olympic	179	L 1-3	Meikle 31	20	30
Jan 1	NPL	H	Stamford	243	D 1-1	Burbeary 16	20	31
4	NPL	A	Chorley	813	L 1-3	Burbeary 20	20	32
11	NPL	H	Matlock Town	249	D 1-1	King 78 (pen)	20	33
18	NPL	A	Ilkeston Town	457	W 2-0	Grimes 57 Lister 85	17	34
Feb 1	NPL	A	Trafford	195	L 1-2	Lister 62	17	35
8	NPL	H	Marine	182	W 3-1	G.SMITH 3 (16 66 81)	17	36
22	NPL	H	Chorley	260	D 1-1	G.Smith 63	17	37
March 1	NPL	H	Whitby Town	230	W 3-1	Grimes 8 Meikle 37 Ridley 51	18	38
4	NPL	A	Matlock Town	292	L 1-4	Grimes 70 (pen)	18	39
8	NPL	A	Skelmersdale United	237	W 2 1	G.Smith 27 Grimes 41 (pen)	17	40
15	NPL	H	Droylsden	221	W 6-0	McGOVERN 3 (38 89 90 pen) Grimes 39 (pen) G.Smith 61 Meikle 64	16	41
22	NPL	A	Buxton	230	L 1-3	Hempenstall 68	17	42
25	NPL	H	Stafford Rangers	138	W 3-2	Hempenstall 26 Jacklin 57 Lister 84	15	43
29	NPL	A	Witton Albion	319	L 1-2	Towey 45	15	44
April 5	NPL	H	Frickley Athletic	255	W 2-1	Lister 86 Towey 89	15	45
12	NPL	H	Rushall Olympic	202	W 3-0	Grimes 49 78 Hemperstall 52	16	46
15	NPL	A	FC United	1732	L 0-3		16	47
19	NPL	A	AFC Fylde	348	W 2-1	Hempenstall 46 50	14	48
21	NPL	H	Barwell	218	L 0-1		14	49
26	NPL	A	Nantwich Town	281	D 1-1	Potts 37	15	50

GOALSCORERS	Lge	FAC	FAT	Total	Pens	Hat-tricks	Cons Run
G. Smith	20		1	21		1	4
Grimes	7			7	3		4
Burbeary	6			6	2		2
Towey	5	1		6			
Hempenstall	5			5			2
Meikle	5			5			
Hawes	3		1	4			2
Lister	4			4			2
McGovern	3			3	1	1	
Graham	2			2			
Lewis	2			2			
King	2			2	1		
McGhee	2			2			
Dixon	1			1			
Fairclough	1			1			
Jacklin	1			1			
McDonald		1		1	1		
Pilero	1			1			
Potts	1			1			
Ridley	1			1			
Sanders	1			1			
K. Smith			1	1			
Watson	1			1			
Opponents	3			3			

Cons Run - Consecutive scoring games.

HALESOWEN TOWN

Chairman: Colin Brookes
Secretary: Andrew While (T) 07976 769 972 (E) info@ht-fc.com
Commercial Manager: Mike Burke (T) 07505 102 767
Programme Editor: Rob Edmonds (T) 0121 602 0068
Ground Address: The Grove, Old Hawne Lane, Halesowen B63 3TB
(T) 0121 550 9433 **Manager:** John Hill

Club Factfile

Founded: 1873 **Nickname:** Yeltz
Previous Names: None
Previous Leagues: West Midlands 1892-1905, 06-11, 46-86, Birmingham Combination 1911-39

Club Colours (change): Blue/blue/white (Yellow/black/yellow)

Ground Capacity: 3,150 **Seats:** 525 **Covered:** 930 **Clubhouse:** Yes **Shop:** Yes

Directions
Leave M5 at Junction 3, follow A456 Kidderminster to first island and turn right (signposted A459 Dudley).
Turn left at next island (signposted A458 Stourbridge).
At next island take third exit into Old Hawne Lane.
Ground about 400 yards on left.

Previous Grounds: None

Record Attendance: 5,000 v Hendon - FA Cup 1st Round Proper 1954
Record Victory: 13-1 v Coventry Amateurs - Birmingham Senior cup 1956
Record Defeat: 0-8 v Bilston - West Midlands League 07/04/1962
Record Goalscorer: Paul Joinson - 369
Record Appearances: Paul Joinson - 608
Additional Records: Paid £7,250 to Gresley Rovers for Stuart Evans
Received £40,000 from Rushden & Diamonds for Jim Rodwell
Senior Honours:
FA Vase 1984-85, 85-86 (R-up 1982-83). Southern League Midland Division 1989-90, Western Division 2001-02.
Birmingham Senior Cup 1983-84, 97-98. Staffordshire Senior Cup 1988-89.
Worcestershire Senior Cup 1951-52, 61-62, 2002-03, 04-05. Northern Premier Division One South 2013-14.

10 YEAR RECORD

04-05		05-06		06-07		07-08		08-09		09-10		10-11		11-12		12-13		13-14	
SthP	9	SthP	8	SthP	6	SthP	3	SthP	10	SthP	8	SthP	21	Sthsw	12	NP1S	7	NP1S	1

ILKESTON

Chairman: Dave Mantle
Secretary: Andrew Raisin **(T)** 07813 357 393 **(E)** a.raisin@ilkestonfc.co.uk
Commercial Manager: **(T)**
Programme Editor: Declan Harrop **(T)** 97446 976 265
Ground Address: New Manor Ground, Awsworth Road, Ilkeston, Derbyshire DE7 8JF
(T) 0115 944 428 **Manager:** Kevin Wilson

Club Factfile

Founded: 2010 **Nickname:** The Robins
Previous Names: None
Previous Leagues: None

Club Colours (change): All red (Blue & white stripes/white/blue)

Ground Capacity: 3,029 **Seats:** 550 **Covered:** 2,000 **Clubhouse:** Yes **Shop:** Yes

Directions
M1 Junction 26, take the A610 signed Ripley, leave at the first exit on to the A6096 signed Awsworth / Ilkeston, at the next island take the A6096 signed Ilkeston, keep on this road for about half a mile, then turn right into Awsworth Road, Signed Cotmanhay (Coaches can get down this road) the ground is about half a mile on the left hand side down this road. Car Parking available at the ground £1 per car.

Previous Grounds: None.

Record Attendance: 2,680 v Chelsea - pre-season friendly July 2013. Competitive: 1,670 v Leek Town - NPL Divi.1S P-Off Final 28.4.2012.
Record Victory: 7-0 v Sheffield FC - Evo-Stik League D1S P-Off SF 23.4.2012 & v Heanor Town (H) Derbys Sen Cup 2012-13.
Record Defeat: 1-5 v Northwich Victoria (H) - FA Trophy Third Qualifying Round 28.11.2011.
Record Goalscorer: Gary Ricketts - 32
Record Appearances: Ryan Wilson - 88
Additional Records:

Senior Honours:
Northern Premier League Division One South Play-Off 2011-12.
Derbyshire Senior Challenge Cup 2012-13, 13-14.

10 YEAR RECORD

04-05	05-06	06-07	07-08	08-09	09-10	10-11	11-12	12-13	13-14
							NP1S 3	NP P 12	NP P 17

Northern Premier League Action

Stafford Rangers No.5, Darren Bullock heading clear despite a challenge from Earl Davies of Nantwich at Marston Road.

Photo: Jonathan Holloway.

ILKESTON MATCH RESULTS 2013-14

Date	Comp	H/A	Opponents	Att:	Result	Goalscorers	Pos	No.
Aug 17	NPL	A	Whitby Town	327	D 1-1	Fisher 57	12	1
19	NPL	H	Stamford	537	W 3-0	Palmer 51 Jones 52 (og) Wilson 69	1	2
24	NPL	H	Marine	523	L 1-2	Reid 74	13	3
26	NPL	A	Buxton	414	W 2-1	Ricketts 89 90	6	4
31	NPL	A	Stafford Rangers	431	W 4-2	Webster 14 33 Ricketts 89 Richards 90	3	5
Sept 2	NPL	H	Barwell	496	W 4-2	Webster 27 (pen) 44 (pen) Hooton 54 Ricketts 90	1	6
7	NPL	H	Witton Albion	**576**	D 1-1	Richards 34	3	7
10	NPL	A	Rushall Olympic	186	L 2-3	Wilson 21 (pen) Hooton 70	6	8
14	***FAC 1Q***	***H***	***Belper Town***	***515***	***L 1-2***	***Webster 71***		9
21	NPL	H	Droysden	400	W 5-1	Maguire 34 Reid 44 73 Grant 64 (og) Stokes 90	6	10
23	NPL	H	KIngs Lynn Town	425	L 3-4	Ricketts 29 74 Webster 48 (pen)		11
28	NPL	A	Grantham Town	302	L 0-2		7	12
Oct 5	NPL	A	Stocksbridge PS	260	W 3-2	Richards 11 Maguire 26 Gordon 46	5	13
12	NPL	H	Frickley Athletic	517	W 1-0	Webster 79 (pen)	5	14
15	NPL	A	Blyth Spartans	311	L 2-3	Wilson 15 Webster 75 (pen)	8	15
19	***FAT 1Q***	***A***	***Gresley***	***372***	***L 1-2***	***Ricketts 79***		16
21	NPL	H	Nantwich Town	287	W 3 1	Stokes 6 (pen) 46 Ricketts 90	5	17
26	NPL	A	Matlock Town	498	L 0-1		5	18
29	NPL	A	Barwell	168	D 1-1	Ricketts 85	5	19
Nov 2	NPL	A	Frickley Athletic	233	W 1-0	Baker 71	5	20
4	NPL	H	Rushall Olympic	385	L 0-1		5	21
9	NPL	A	Witton Albion	390	L 1-2	Ricketts 62	8	22
16	NPL	H	Stafford Rangers	553	D 0-0		9	23
23	NPL	A	Chorley	1017	L 1-2	Hooton 81	9	24
30	NPL	H	Ashton United	523	L 1-2	Wilson 75 (pen)	11	25
Dec 7	NPL	H	Whitby Town	370	L 0-2		11	26
14	NPL	A	Stamford	307	W 2-0	Wilson 28 Waite 80 (pen)	11	27
21	NPL	H	Trafford	359	D 1-1	Reid 71	13	28
26	NPL	A	Worksop Town	501	L 2-5	Ricketts 6 Salt 85 (og)	15	29
28	NPL	A	AFC Fylde	314	W 2-1	Hooton 80 88	12	30
Jan 4	NPL	H	FC United	974	D 3-3	Reid 48 75 Maguire 89	14	31
11	NPL	A	Skelmersdale United	353	L 0-2		14	32
18	NPL	H	Grantham Town	457	L 0-2		14	33
25	NPL	A	Kings Lynn Town	745	L 1-3	Waite 62	15	34
Feb 8	NPL	A	Droylsden	135	W 5-1	Waite 6 61 Barrington 15 Wilson 28 (pen) Reid 90	14	35
15	NPL	H	Skelmersdale United	399	W 2-1	Reid 28 Waite	12	36
22	NPL	A	FC United	1793	L 1-4	Waite 34	12	37
24	NPL	H	Stocksbridge PS	315	W 6-1	Wilson 15 (pen) 30 (pen) Storey 46 Richards 65 89 Wiliams 85	12	38
March 1	NPL	A	Nantwich Town	260	D 2-2	Richards 10 Maguire 51	12	39
8	NPL	H	Matlock Town	501	L 1 3	Richards 32	13	40
15	NPL	H	Buxton	454	L 0-2		15	41
22	NPL	H	Blyth Spartans	305	L 0-1		16	42
29	NPL	H	Chorley	436	L 2-3	Maguire 32 Williams 90	17	43
5 Apr 2014	NPL	A	Ashton United	188	W 3 1	Maguire 6 Duffy 9 Grantham 79	17	44
8	NPL	H	AFC Fylde	305	L 0-1		17	45
19	NPL	A	Marine	378	W 3-2	Williams 34 Duffy 44 Wilson 81(pen)	16	46
21	NPL	H	Worksop Town	530	D 0-0		16	47
26	NPL	A	Trafford	300	W 5-2	Maguire 68 Mason 72 (og) Reid 81 (pen) Shaw 88 Williams 90	17	48

GOALSCORERS	Lge	FAC	FAT	Total	Pens	Hat-tricks	Cons Run
Ricketts	10		1	11			
Wilson	9			9	6		
Reid	9			9	1		
Webster	7	1		8	4		
Maguire	8			7			2
Richards	8			7			3
Waite	6			6	1		4
Hooton	5			5			
Williams	4			4			
Stokes	3			3	1		
Duffy	2			2			
Baker	1			1			
Barrington	1			1			
Fisher	1			1			
Gordon	1			1			
Grantham	1			1			
Palmer	1			1			
Shaw	1			1			
Story	1			1			
Opponents	4			4			

Cons Run - Consecutive scoring games.

KING'S LYNN TOWN

Chairman: Keith Chapman
Secretary: Norman Cesar **(T)** 07887 373 956 **(E)** secretary@kltown.co.uk
Commercial Manager: **(T)**
Programme Editor: Barry Fish **(T)** 01533 673 180
Ground Address: The Walks Stadium, Tennyson Road, King's Lynn PE30 5PB
(T) 01553 760 060 **Manager:** Gary Setchell

Club Factfile

Founded: 1879 **Nickname:** Linnets
Previous Names: King's Lynn > 2010
Previous Leagues: N'folk & Suffolk, Eastern Co. 1935-39, 48-54, UCL 1946-48, Midland Co. 1954-58, NPL 1980-81, Southern, Conf

Club Colours (change): Yellow with blue pin stripe/blue with yellow trim/yellow (Turquoise with black pin stripe/black/turquoise)

Ground Capacity: 8,200 **Seats:** 1,200 **Covered:** 5,000 **Clubhouse:** Yes **Shop:** Yes

Directions
At the roundabout, at the junction of A47 and the A17, follow the A47, signposted King's Lynn and Norwich. Travel along the dual carriageway for approx. one and a half miles branching off left, following the signs for Town Centre, onto the Hardwick roundabout. Take the first exit, following the signs for Town Centre, travel through two sets of traffic lights until reaching a further set of traffic lights at the Southgates roundabout. Take the fourth exit onto Vancouver Avenue, and travel for approx. 300 metres, going straight across a mini roundabout, The Walks is a further 200 metres along on the left hand side, with car parking outside the ground. The changing rooms and hospitality suite are located at the rear of the main stand.

Previous Grounds: None

Record Attendance: **Att:** 12,937 v Exeter City FAC 1st Rnd 1950-51.
Record Victory: Not known
Record Defeat: Not known
Record Goalscorer: Malcolm Lindsey 321.
Record Appearances: Mick Wright 1,152 (British Record)
Additional Records:

Senior Honours:
Southern League Division 1 East 2003-04, Premier Division 2007-08, League Cup 2004-05.
Northern Premier Division One South 2012-13.

10 YEAR RECORD

04-05		05-06		06-07		07-08		08-09		09-10		10-11		11-12		12-13		13-14	
SthP	11	SthP	3	SthP	3	SthP	1	Conf N	17	NP P	dnf	UCL P	2	UCL P	2	NP1S	1	NP P	11

KING'S LYNN MATCH RESULTS 2013-14

Date	Comp	H/A	Opponents	Att:	Result		Goalscorers	Pos	No.
Aug 17	NPL	A	Nantwich Town	298	L	0-2		24	1
20	NPL	H	Rushall Olympic	665	W	6-0	JACOB 3 (21 25 53) Thomson 30 Hall 68 Clarke 87	9	2
24	NPL	H	Siocksbridge PS	617	D	3-3	Jacob 67 73 Mulready 90	11	3
26	NPL	A	Barwell	294	W	3-1	Jacob 61 90 Thomson 84 (pen)	4	4
31	NPL	A	Witton Albion	349	L	0-1		11	5
Sept 3	NPL	H	Grantham Town	670	D	1-1	Thomson 15	10	6
7	NPL	H	Droylsden	677	W	2-1	Gulliver 55 Duffy 70	10	7
11	NPL	A	Worksop Town	270	W	4-1	Tolley 49 Fryatt 54 Duffy 80 (pen) 88	4	8
14	*FAC 1Q*	*H*	*Cambridge City*	*705*	*L*	*1-4*	*Duffy 49 (pen)*		9
17	NPL	H	Matlock Town	381	L	0-4		8	10
21	NPL	A	Chorley	696	L	0-1		11	11
23	NPL	H	Ilkeston Town	425	W	4-3	Duffy 35 Thomson 39 Jacob 75 Clarke 86	7	12
28	NPL	H	Marine	554	L	2-3	Gulliver 41 Duffy 51	10	13
Oct 5	NPL	H	Whitby Town	532	W	3-2	Jacob 34 Hall 42 Quigley 57	7	14
12	NPL	H	FC United	**1440**	D	0-0		9	15
15	NPL	A	Frickley Athletic	196	D	2-2	Jones 43 Hall 80 (pen)	9	16
19	*FAT1Q*	*H*	*Cambridge City*	*695*	*L*	*1-2*	*Thomson 21*		17
26	NPL	A	Blyth Spartans	403	W	3-1	Jones 11 Hall 56 Mills 83	7	18
29	NPL	A	Grantham Town	253	L	0-2		8	19
Nov 2	NPL	H	Ashton United	504	W	2-1	Fryatt 46 Thomson 73	8	20
16	NPL	H	Witton Albion	571	W	3-0	Fryatt 8 Duffy 33 Goodfellow 55	7	21
23	NPL	A	Skelmersdale United	226	L	0-3		8	22
30	NPL	H	Stafford Rangers	511	W	5-1	Duffy 22 Fryatt 50 Thomson 72 Clarke 90 Hall 90	7	23
Dec 7	NPL	H	Marine	272	D	2-2	Shaw 48 (og) Maguire 55	7	24
10	NPL	H	Worksop Town	389	L	1-3	Duffy 71	7	25
14	NPL	A	Rushall Olympic	153	L	1-3	McDonald 52	9	26
21	NPL	H	AFC Fylde	482	W	2-0	Goodfellow 54 Mulready 90	7	27
26	NPL	A	Stamford	460	L	0-3		10	28
28	NPL	A	Marine	354	W	3-2	Duffy 38 Hall 45 Quigley 54	9	29
Jan 1	NPL	H	Barwell	492	W	3-2	Duffy 30 (pen) Mulready 76 89	7	30
4	NPL	A	Trafford	213	W	2-1	Duffy 23 (pen) Clarke 33	4	31
11	NPL	H	Buxton	653	W	3-1	Clarke 36 Thomson 51Jones 54	4	32
18	NPL	A	Matlock Town	366	L	0-2		5	33
25	NPL	H	Ilkeston Town	745	W	3-1	Sanders 86 Fryatt 88 Duffy 90	5	34
Feb 8	NPL	H	Chorley	804	L	0-2		7	35
22	NPL	H	Trafford	602	D	2-2	Payne 49 Oates 90	8	36
25	NPL	A	Droylsden	118	W	2-1	Fryatt 64 Jones 70	6	37
March 1	NPL	A	Ashton United	177	L	1-5	Bell 45	8	38
8	NPL	H	Blyth Spartans	576	L	0-1		9	39
12	NPL	A	Buxton	183	L	1-6	Mulready 83	9	40
15	NPL	A	FC United	2083	L	0-2		10	41
22	NPL	H	Frickley Athletic	480	W	3-0	Thomson 20 Quigley 57 Jones 73	9	42
29	NPL	H	Skelmersdale United	528	D	3-3	HALL 3 (15 20 31)	9	43
April 5	NPL	A	Stafford Rangers	315	W	1-0	Thomson 81	9	44
9	NPL	A	Whitby Town	206	L	0-4		9	45
19	NPL	A	Stocksbridge PS	136	D	0-0		11	46
21	NPL	H	Stamford	569	W	2-1	Hall 32 Mulready 79	10	47
26	NPL	A	AFC Fylde	337	L	0-1		11	48

GOALSCORERS	Lge	FAC	FAT	Total	Pens	Hat-tricks	Cons Run
Duffy	12	1		13	3		3
Jacob	9			9			
Hall	9			9	1	1	
Thomson	8		1	9	2		
Fryatt	6			6			2
Mulready	6			6			
Clarke	5			5			2
Jones	5			5			
Quigley	3			3			
Goodfellow	2			2			
Gulliver	2			2			
Bell	1			1			
Maguire	1			1			
Mills	1			1			
McDonald	1			1			
Oates	1			1			
Payne	1			1			
Sanders	1			1			
Tolley	1			1			
Opponents	1			1			

Cons Run - Consecutive scoring games.

MARINE

Chairman: Paul Leary
Secretary: Richard Cross **(T)** 07762 711 714 **(E)** richard@marinefc.com
Commercial Manager: contact secretary **(T)**
Programme Editor: Dave McMillan **(T)** 07949 483 003
Ground Address: Arriva Stadium, College Road, Crosby, Liverpool L23 3AS
(T) 0151 924 1743 **Manager:** Carl Macauley

Club Factfile

Founded: 1894 **Nickname:** Mariners
Previous Names: None
Previous Leagues: Liverpool Zingari, Liverpool County Combination, Lancashire Combination 1935-39, 46-69, Cheshire County 1969-79
Club Colours (change): White/black/black (Yellow/green/green)

Ground Capacity: 3,185 **Seats:** 400 **Covered:** 1,400 **Clubhouse:** Yes **Shop:** Yes

Directions
From the East & South: Leave the M62 at junction 6 and take the M57 to Switch Island at the end. At the end of the M57 take the A5036 (signposted Bootle & Docks). At the roundabout, at the end of the road (by Docks), turn right onto the A565 following signs for 'Crosby' and 'Marine AFC' and follow this road for 1 mile. After passing the Tesco Express on your right, turn left at the traffic lights (by Merchant Taylors' School) into College Road. The ground is half a mile on your left
From the North: Leave the M6 at junction 26 and join the M58. Travel along the M58 to Switch Island at the end. Take the A5036 (signposted Bootle & Docks) and follow directions above.

Previous Grounds: Waterloo Park 1894-1903

Record Attendance: 4,000 v Nigeria - Friendly 1949
Record Victory: 14-0 v Sandhurst - FA Cup 1st Qualifying Round 01/10/1938
Record Defeat: 2-11 v Shrewsbury Town - FA Cup 1st Round 1995
Record Goalscorer: Paul Meachin - 200
Record Appearances: Peter Smith 952
Additional Records: Paid £6,000 to Southport for Jon Penman October 1985
Received £20,000 from Crewe Alexandra for Richard Norris 1996
Senior Honours:
Northern Premier League Premier Division 1993-94, 84-95.
Lancashire Junior Cup 1978-79, Lancashire Trophy x3. Lancashire Amateur Cup x5. Lancashire Senior Cup x6.
Liverpool Non-League Cup x3. Liverpool Challenge Cup x3.

10 YEAR RECORD

04-05	05-06	06-07	07-08	08-09	09-10	10-11	11-12	12-13	13-14
NP P 15	NP P 3	NP P 4	NP P 7	NP P 13	NP P 9	NP P 9	NP P 7	NP P 11	NP P 20

Northern Premier League Action

Stafford Rangers full-back attempts to get past his marker during his sides 1-0 home win against Nantwich Town on Easter Monday. It was Stafford's last home game of the season.

Photo: Jonathan Holloway.

MARINE MATCH RESULTS 2013-14

Date	Comp	H/A	Opponents	Att:	Result	Goalscorers	Pos	No.
Aug 17	NPL	H	Blyth Spartans	305	D 1-1	Fowler 90 (pen)	13	1
20	NPL	A	Witton Albion	363	**W** 3-2	Fowler 33 Astbury 75 83	6	2
24	NPL	A	Ilkeston	523	**W** 2-1	Astbury 40 Devine 85	2	3
26	NPL	H	Skelmersdale U	458	D 2-2	Fowler 44 (Pen) Astbury 45	3	4
31	NPL	A	Barwell	228	L 0-2		10	5
Sept 2	NPL	H	Nantwich Town	313	**W** 1-0	Fowler 85	7	6
7	NPL	H	Buxton	454	L 0-2		12	7
10	NPL	A	Stafford Rangers	282	D 2-2	Goulding 21 (pen) Parle 90	11	8
14	***FAC 1Q***	***H***	***Curzon Ashton***	***233***	***L 2-4***	***Barnes 28 Jones 57***		9
17	NPL	A	AFC Fylde	182	D 0-0		12	10
21	NPL	H	Grantham Town	271	D 3-3	Fowler 35 75 Jones 52	13	11
28	NPL	A	Kings Lynn Town	554	**W** 3-2	Gulliver 41 Fowler 65 Jones 73	13	12
Oct 1	NPL	H	Droysden	260	**W** 5-1	Jones 26 34 Fowler 38 Shaw 73 Monaghan 80	4	13
5	NPL	A	FC United	1528	L 0-1		9	14
12	NPL	H	Stocksbridge PS	323	**W** 3-0	Rendell 5 Summer 23 Jones 78	8	15
15	NPL	A	Rushall Olympic	108	D 1-1	Fowler 45 (pen)	6	16
19	***FAT1Q***	***H***	***Burscough***	***238***	***D 1-1***	***Sumner 12***		17
22	***FAT1Qr***	***A***	***Burscough***	***205***	***W 1-0***	***Beesley 22 (og)***		18
26	NPL	A	Ashton United	111	L 1-4	Sumner 72	10	19
29	NPL	A	Nantwich Town	159	**W** 2-1	Rainford 49 Sumner 64	6	20
Nov 2	***FAT 2Q***	***A***	***Coalville Town***	***178***	***L 0-5***			21
5	NPL	H	Stafford Rangers	258	**W** 5-2	FOWLER 3 (11pen 15 31) Monaghan 13 Corrigan 73	6	22
9	NPL	A	Buxton	236	D 2-2	Fowler 18 90	7	23
16	NPL	H	Barwell	382	D 1-1	Fowler 14	5	24
23	NPL	H	Stamford	277	L 1-3	Devine 90	7	25
30	NPL	A	Whitby Town	226	D 0-0		9	26
Dec 7	NPL	A	Blyth Spartans	272	D 2-2	Fowler 29 Monaghan 33	10	27
10	NPL	H	Trafford	269	L 1-2	Noon 50	10	28
14	NPL	H	Witton Albion	347	**W** 2-1	Rainford 75 Devine 89	7	29
21	NPL	A	Matlock Town	268	D 0-0		9	30
26	NPL	H	Chorley	534	L 0-1		11	31
28	NPL	H	King's Lynn Town	354	L 2-3	Rainford 25 90 (pen)	13	32
Jan 1	NPL	A	Skelmersdale United	303	L 1-4	Noon 84	14	33
4	NPL	H	Frickley Athletic	269	**W** 2-1	Monaghan 29 56	11	34
11	NPL	A	Srocksbridge PS	105	D 1-1	Monaghan 29	11	35
18	NPL	H	AFC Fylde	338	L 1-2	Fowler 21 (pen)	11	36
Feb 1	NPL	H	FC United	**940**	L 0-2		13	37
8	NPL	A	Grantham Town	182	L 1-3	Roberts-Nurse 22	15	38
22	NPL	A	Droysden	141	**W** 4-0	Wright 3 Fowler 6 (pen) Jones 9 14	13	39
March 1	NPL	A	Trafford	227	L 0-1		15	40
8	NPL	H	Ashton United	336	L 0-1		16	41
15	NPL	A	Worksop Town	330	L 1-5	Salt 80 (og)	19	42
22	NPL	H	Rushall Olympic	295	L 1-2	Rey 85	20	43
29	NPL	A	Stamford	320	**W** 4-2	Fowler 3 Monaghan 12 Harvey 68 Rey 90	20	44
April 5	NPL	H	Whitby Town	244	D 1-1	Shaw 75	20	45
12	NPL	A	Frickley Athletic	245	D 1-1	Fowler 75 (pen)	20	46
16	NPL	H	Worksop Town	302	L 0-1		20	47
19	NPL	H	ILkeston Town	378	L 2-3	Fowler 7 87	20	48
21	NPL	A	Chorley	2128	L 0-4		20	49
26	NPL	H	Matlock Town	369	**W** 3-0	Jones 55 Devine 73 Parle 90	20	50

GOALSCORERS	Lge	FAC	FAT	Total	Pens	Hat-tricks	Cons Run
Fowler	22			22	7	1	3
Jones	8	1		9			
Monaghan	7			7			2
Astbury	4			4			
Devine	4			4			
Rainford	4			4	1		
Sumner	3		1	4			2
Parle	3			3			
Rey	3			3			2
Shaw	3			3			
Noon	2			2			
Barnes		1		1			
Corrigan	1			1			
Goulding	1			1	1		
Gulliver	1			1			
Harvey	1			1			
Roberts-Nurse	1			1			
Rendell	1			1			
Wright	1			1			
Opponents	1		1	2			

Cons Run - Consecutive scoring games.

MATLOCK TOWN

Chairman: Tom Wright

Secretary: Keith Brown **(T)** 07831 311 427 **(E)** clubshop@matlocktownfc.com

Commercial Manager: Tom Wright **(T)** 07850 065 968

Programme Editor: Tom Wright **(T)** 07850 065 968

Ground Address: Autoworld Arena, Causeway Lane, Matlock, Derbyshire DE4 3AR

(T) 01629 583 866 **Manager:** Mark Atkins

Club Factfile

Founded: 1885 **Nickname:** The Gladiators

Previous Names: None

Previous Leagues: Midland Combination 1894-96, Matlock and District, Derbyshire Senior, Central Alliance 1924-25, 47-61, Central Combination 1934-35, Chesterfield & District 1946-47, Midland Counties 1961-69

Club Colours (change): All royal blue (All yellow)

Ground Capacity: 5,500 **Seats:** 560 **Covered:** 1,200 **Clubhouse:** Yes **Shop:** Yes

Directions
On A615, ground is 500 yards from Town Centre and Matlock BR.

Previous Grounds: None

Record Attendance: 5,123 v Burton Albion - FA Trophy 1975

Record Victory: 10-0 v Lancaster City (A) - 1974

Record Defeat: 0-8 v Chorley (A) - 1971

Record Goalscorer: Peter Scott

Record Appearances: Mick Fenoughty

Additional Records: Paid £2,000 for Kenny Clark 1996
Received £10,000 from York City for Ian Helliwell

Senior Honours:
FA Trophy 1974-75. Anglo Italian Non-League Cup 1979.
Derbyshire Senior Cup x7.

10 YEAR RECORD

04-05	05-06	06-07	07-08	08-09	09-10	10-11	11-12	12-13	13-14
NP P 11	NP P 9	NP P 5	NP P 16	NP P 15	NP P 7	NP P 11	NP P 14	NP P 17	NP P 12

MATLOCK TOWN MATCH RESULTS 2013-14

Date	Comp	H/A	Opponents	Att:	Result		Goalscorers	Pos	No.
Aug 17	NPL	A	Trafford	229	L	1-2	Thomas 29	16	1
20	NPL	H	Stocksbridge PS	328	**W**	3-0	White 7 Thomas 22 47	10	2
24	NPL	H	Nantwich Town	179	**W**	2-1	Harcourt 17 Gregory 63	5	3
26	NPL	A	Worksop Town	356	L	2-4	Gregory 26 Thomas 44 (pen)	12	4
31	NPL	A	Blyth Spartans	315	**W**	2-1	Holland 14 Gregory 52	6	5
Sept 4	NPL	A	Ashton United	177	D	0-0		9	6
7	NPL	A	AFC Fylde	363	L	0-2		13	7
10	NPL	H	Chorley	282	L	1-2	Thomas 55	15	8
14	***FAC1Q***	***A***	***Basford United***	***169***	***W***	***2-0***	***Holland 56 White 84***		9
17	NPL	A	Kings Lynn Town	381	**W**	4-0	McMahon 13 80 Thomas 25 Holland 41	12	10
21	NPL	H	Frickley Athletic	322	D	0-0		18	11
24	NPL	H	Stamford	271	W	2-0	Holland 56 58	8	12
28	***FAC2Q***	***A***	***Carlton Town***	***161***	***L***	***0-1***			13
Oct 5	NPL	A	Droysden	108	**W**	4-1	Thomas 20 (pen) 49 (pen) Gregory 76 Holland 90	6	14
12	NPL	A	Stafford Rangers	412	**W**	3-1	Thomas 23 (pen) White 56 58	4	15
16	NPL	H	Barwell	247	**W**	2-1	Harcourt 15 Thomas 53	4	16
19	***FAT1Q***	***H***	***Hinckley United - Matlock Town receive a bye as Hinckley United disbanded***						17
22	NPL	A	Skelmersdale United	191	L	0-1		4	18
26	NPL	H	Ilkeston Town	496	**W**	1-0	Holland 84	4	19
29	NPL	H	Ashton United	273	D	0-0		4	20
Nov 2	***FAT 2Q***	***H***	***St Neots Town***	***244***	***W***	***2-0***	***Harcourt 15 Holland 88***		21
5	NPL	A	Chorley	595	L	1-3	Grayson 87	5	22
9	NPL	H	AFC Fylde	343	D	1-1	Holland 38	6	23
16	***FAT3Q***	***A***	***Chorley***	***772***	***L***	***0-2***			24
23	NPL	H	FC United	**978**	D	1-1	Holland 17	6	25
30	NPL	A	Witton Albion	328	L	0-1		10	26
Dec 7	NPL	H	Trafford	254	**W**	3-2	Tuton 16 Harcourt 40 Ashmore 75	9	27
14	NPL	A	Stocksbridge PS	178	L	1-3	White 32	10	28
21	NPL	H	Marine	268	D	0-0		12	29
28	NPL	A	Whitby Town	315	L	0-1		15	30
Jan 1	NPL	H	Worksop Town	351	**W**	1-0	Nyoni 22	11	31
11	NPL	A	Grantham Town	249	D	1-1	Ashmore 45	13	32
18	NPL	H	King's Lynn Town	366	**W**	2-0	McMahon 38 71	13	33
Feb 1	NPL	H	Droylsden	256	**W**	2-0	Thomas 20 Holland 54 (pen)	11	34
8	NPL	A	Frickley Athletic	234	**W**	3-1	Ashmore 17 Tuton 30 47	10	35
22	NPL	A	Rushall Olympic	176	L	1-6	Tuton 36	11	36
March 1	NPL	H	Skelmersdale United	367	L	2-1	Tuton 20 Holland 74	11	37
4	NPL	H	Grantham Town	292	**W**	4-1	Holland 31(pen) 39 Tuton 64 73	9	38
8	NPL	A	Ilkeston	501	**W**	3-1	Holland 25 Hoggery 30 Tuton 42	8	39
15	NPL	H	Stafford Rangers	346	L	0-2		9	40
18	NPL	A	Stamford	184	L	0-1		9	41
22	NPL	A	Barwell	157	D	0-0		10	42
25	NPL	H	Rushall Olympic	166	D	1-1	Holland 76	9	43
29	NPL	A	FC United	2044	L	1-2	Holland 44	10	44
April 1	NPL	H	Blyth Spartans	208	D	1-1	Ashmore 64	9	45
6	NPL	H	Witton Albion	270	L	0-1		10	46
9	NPL	A	Buxton	531	D	1-1	Foster 90 (pen)	10	47
12	NPL	H	Whitby Town	281	**W**	2-0	Nyoni 12 McDonald 65	9	48
19	NPL	A	Nantwich Town	229	D	1-1	Holland 11	9	49
21	NPL	H	Buxton	434	D	1-1	Radford 89	9	50
26	NPL	A	Marine	369	L	0-3		12	51

GOALSCORERS	Lge	FAC	FAT	Total	Pens	Hat-tricks	Cons Run
Holland	16	1	1	18	2		3
Thomas	11			11	3		2
Tuton	8			8			5
White	4	1		5			
Ashmore	4			4			
Gregory	4			4			
Harcourt	3		1	4			
McMahon	4			4			
Nyoni	2			2			
Foster				1	1		
Grayson	1			1			
Hoggery	1			1			
McDonald	1			1			
Radford	1			1			

Cons Run - Consecutive scoring games.

NANTWICH TOWN

Chairman: Jon Gold

Secretary: Janet Stubbs **(T)** 07725 892 922 **(E)** nantwichtownfc@hotmail.co.uk

Commercial Manager: **(T)**

Programme Editor: Michael Chatwin **(T)** 01270 621 771

Ground Address: Weaver Stadium, Waterlode, Kingsley Fields, Nantwich, CW5 5BS

(T) 01270 621 771 **Manager:** Danny Johnson

The Nantwich supporters cheer on their team against Stafford Rangers.
Photo: Jonathan Holloway.

Club Factfile

Founded: 1884 **Nickname:** Dabbers

Previous Names: Nantwich

Previous Leagues: Shropshire & Dist. 1891-92, Combination 1892-94, 1901-10, Cheshire Junior 1894-95, Crewe & Dist. 1895-97, North Staffs & Dist. 1897-1900, Cheshire 1900-01, Manchester 1910-12, 65-68, Lancs. Com. 1912-14, Cheshire Co. 1919-38, 68-82, Crewe & Dist. 1938-39, 47-48, Crewe Am. Comb. 1946-47, Mid-Cheshire 1948-65, North West Co. 1982-2007

Club Colours (change): Green/white/green (Red/black/red & black hoops)

Ground Capacity: 3,500 **Seats:** 350 **Covered:** 495 **Clubhouse:** Yes **Shop:** Yes

Directions

M6 Jun 16 A500 towards Nantwich. Over 4 roundabouts onto A51 towards Nantwich Town Centre, through traffic lights and over railway crossing. Over next r/bout then left at next r/bout past Morrisons supermarket on right. Continue over r/bout through traffic lights. Ground on right at next set of traffic lights.
SATNAV Postcode: CW5 5UP

Previous Grounds: London Road/Jackson Avenue (1884-2007)

Record Attendance: 5,121 v Winsford United - Cheshire Senior Cup 2nd Round 1920-21

Record Victory: 20-0 v Whitchurch Alexandra (home) 1900/01 Cheshire League Division 1, 5 April 1901

Record Defeat: 2-16 v Stalybridge Celtic (away) 1932/33 Cheshire County League, 22 Oct 1932

Record Goalscorer: John Scarlett 161 goals (1992/3 to 2005/6). **Goals in a season:** Bobby Jones 60 goals (1946/7)

Record Appearances: Not known

Additional Records: Gerry Duffy scored 42 during season 1961-62
Record Fee Received undisclosed fee from Crewe Alexandra for Kelvin Mellor - Feb 2008

Senior Honours:

FA Vase Winners 2005/06. Cheshire Senior Cup Winners 1932/33, 1975/76, 2007/08 & 2011/12. Cheshire County League Champions 1980/81.
Mid-Cheshire League Champions 1963/64. North West Counties League Challenge Cup Winners 1994/95.
Cheshire Amateur Cup Winners 1895/96 & 1963/64.

10 YEAR RECORD

04-05	05-06	06-07	07-08	08-09	09-10	10-11	11-12	12-13	13-14
NWC1 16	NWC1 4	NWC1 3	NP1S 3	NP P 3	NP P 10	NP P 17	NP P 10	NP P 14	NP P 19

NANTWICH TOWN MATCH RESULTS 2013-14

Date	Comp	H/A	Opponents	Att:	Result		Goalscorers	Pos	No.
Aug 17	NPL	H	Kings Lynn Town	133	W	2-0	Corden 7 Burns 83	5	1
20	NPL	A	Skelmersdale U	221	L	1-2	Burns 88	12	2
24	NPL	A	Matlock Town	179	L	1-2	Clayton 41	18	3
26	NPL	H	Witton Albion	418	L	0-2		21	4
31	NPL	H	Ashton United	255	D	2-2	Burns 50 White 68	22	5
Sept 2	NPL	A	Marine	313	L	0-1		22	6
7	NPL	A	Stocksbridge PS	178	W	5-1	Burns 44 70 Harrop 56 Degan 89 Devanney 90	16	7
10	NPL	H	AFC Fylde	121	D	1-1	Burns 67	17	8
14	***FAC1Q***	***H***	***Rugby Town***	***232***	***L***	***1-2***	***Burns 40***		9
17	NPL	A	Rushall Olympic	167	D	1-1	Burns 49	17	10
21	NPL	H	Worksop Town	263	L	2-3	Devenney 33 Bailey 74	17	11
28	NPL	A	Droylsden	111	W	6-1	Burns 33 Harrop 34 Courtney 37 Frost 65 Bailey 83 Moore 90	17	12
Oct 5	NPL	A	Blyth Spartans	381	D	2-2	Devanney 7 Burns 19 (pen)	17	13
8	NPL	H	FC United	**672**	D	1-1	Burns 64	17	14
12	NPL	A	Buxton	309	L	0-2		17	15
15	NPL	H	Chorley	172	L	0-1		17	16
19	***FAT1Q***	***A***	***Droylsden***	***114***	***W***	***3-0***	***Burns 62 Deegan 77 89***		17
21	NPL	A	Ilkeston	287	L	1 3	Burns 49	19	18
26	NPL	H	Barwell	205	W	2-0	Burns 82 Deegan 83	19	19
29	NPL	H	Marine	159	L	1-2	Burns 89	19	20
Nov 2	***FAT 2Q***	***A***	***St Ives Town***	***282***	***W***	***4-1***	***Bailey 56 Frost 81 Courtney 86 Jones 90***		21
5	NPL	A	AFC Fylde	204	W	2-1	Burns 70 (pen) Deegan 76	17	22
9	NPL	H	Stocksbridge PS	243	W	2-1	Foster 71 Deegan 85	17	23
16	***FAT3Q***	***A***	***Northwich Victoria***	***146***	***L***	***0-2***			24
23	NPL	H	Whitby Town	159	W	4-3	Foster 54 Harrop 59 Clayton 81 Deegan 90	16	25
30	NPL	A	Trafford	222	D	1-0	Jones 90	12	26
Dec 7	NPL	A	Kings Lynn Town	508	D	0-0		13	27
11	NPL	A	Ashton United	148	L	0-1		14	28
14	NPL	H	Skelmersdale United	303	D	2-2	Deegan 17 Jones 32	16	29
21	NPL	A	Grantham Town	179	W	5-0	Foster 8 39 Deegan 24 Abadaki 51 Clayton 69 (pen)	15	30
26	NPL	H	Stafford Rangers	507	W	4-1	Agadaki 13 Deegan 48 Foster 67 Burns 77 (pen)	13	31
Jan 4	NPL	H	Droylsden	284	W	4-0	Deegan 2 Harrop 45 Burns 51 Foster 66	12	32
11	NPL	A	Stamford	330	D	2-2	Burns 36 (pen) Foster 65	12	33
Feb 4	NPL	H	Rushall Olympic	164	W	3-2	Jones 43 Burns 69 Harrop 78	12	34
18	NPL	A	FC United	1416	L	1-2	Burns 39	13	35
22	NPL	A	Frickley Athletic	207	L	0-2		14	36
25	NPL	A	Witton Albion	301	L	2-3	Burns 62 72	14	37
March 1	NPL	H	Ilkeston Town	280	D	2-2	Burns 15 (pen) Foster 36	14	38
4	NPL	H	Stamford	163	W	3-1	Foster 1 Eastwood 39 Burns 90	13	39
8	NPL	A	Barwell	157	D	2-2	Oates 63 Hackney76	13	40
15	NPL	H	Frickley Athletic	236	W	2-1	Devanney 57 Deegan 72	12	41
22	NPL	A	Chorley	829	L	1-5	Davies 31	13	42
25	NPL	H	Buxton	151	D	1-1	Pearson 32	12	43
29	NPL	A	Whitby Town	247	L	2-4	Burns 8 Deegan 88	14	44
April 2	NPL	A	Worksop Town	421	L	1-3	Burns 88	14	45
5	NPL	H	Trafford	253	L	0-1		16	46
12	NPL	H	Blyth Spartans	189	D	1-1	Meaney 26	17	47
19	NPL	H	Matlock Town	227	D	1-1	Frost 49	18	48
21	NPL	A	Stafford Rangers	394	L	0-1		18	49
26	NPL	H	Grantham Town	281	D	1-1	Deegan 25	19	50

GOALSCORERS	Lge	FAC	FAT	Total	Pens	Hat-tricks	Cons Run
Burns	25	1	1	27	5		5
Deegan	12		2	14			4
Foster	9			9			4
Devanney	4			4			
Harrop	4			4			
Jones	3		1	4			
Bailey	2		1	3			2
Courtney	2		1	3			
Frost	2		1	3			
Clayton	2			2	1		
Agadaki	2			2			

	Lge	FAC	FAT	Total	Pens	Hat-tricks	Cons Run
Carson	1			1			
Corden	1			1			
Eastwood	1			1			
Davies	1			1			
Hackney	1			1			
Meany	1			1			
Moore	1			1			
Oats	1			1			
Pearson	1			1			
White	1			1			

Cons Run - Consecutive scoring games.

Click Back in Time!

Over 37 years of publishing the Non-League Club Directory has filled a room full of information and photographs covering the game we know and love.

What we intend, over time, is to create a website that shares with you everything we have accumulated, which we hope will bring back some fond memories of season's gone by.

A unique look back at how the game has evolved since the 1940s will also make for interesting reading, including league tables from season's gone by.

Log on to **www.non-leagueclubdirectory.co.uk** today and see how many faces from teams gone by you recognise

RAMSBOTTOM UNITED

Chairman: Harry Williams
Secretary: Tony Cunningham **(T)** 07973 416 580 **(E)** anthony.cunningham@hotmail.co.uk
Commercial Manager: **(T)**
Programme Editor: Rob Moss **(T)** 07944 038 512
Ground Address: The Harry Williams Stadium, Acrebottom (off Bridge Street) BL0 0BS.
(T) 07973 416 580 **Manager:** Anthony Johnson

Club Factfile

Founded: 1966 **Nickname:** The Rams
Previous Names: None
Previous Leagues: Bury Amateur, Bolton Combination & Manchester League

Club Colours (change): Blue/blue/white (Red/black/red).

Ground Capacity: **Seats:** Yes **Covered:** Yes **Clubhouse:** Yes **Shop:** No

Directions

From South,M66(north) to junction1,take the A56 towards Ramsbottom, after 1 mile turn left at traffic lights down Bury New Road follow the road towards the centre then turn left just before the railway crossing, ground runs parallel with the railway line.

From the North leave the A56 (Edenfield by pass) at the start of the M66, follow the signs for Ramsbottom into the centre turn left down Bridge street then after 100 yards turn immediately right after the railway level crossing ground parallel with railway line.

Previous Grounds:

Record Attendance: **Att:** 1,653 v FC United of Manchester 07.04.2007.
Record Victory: 9-0 v Stantondale (Home, NWCFL Division Two, 9th November 1996)
Record Defeat: 0-7 v Salford City (Away, NWCFL Division One, 16th November 2002)
Record Goalscorer: Russell Brierley - 176 (1996-2003). **Record in a season:** Russell Brierley - 38 (1999-2000)
Record Appearances: Not known
Additional Records:

Senior Honours:
North West Counties Division Two 1996-97, Premier Division 2011-12.

10 YEAR RECORD

04-05	05-06	06-07	07-08	08-09	09-10	10-11	11-12	12-13	13-14
NWC1 5	NWC1 18	NWC1 8	NWC1 16	NWCP 14	NWCP 4	NWCP 2	NWCP 1	NP1N 6	NP1N 5

RUSHALL OLYMPIC

Chairman: John C Allen
Secretary: Peter Athersmith (T) 07771 361 002 (E) rushallolympic@yahoo.co.uk
Commercial Manager: Darren Stockall (T) 07870 236 013
Programme Editor: Darren Stockall (T) 07870 236 013
Ground Address: Dales Lane off Daw End Lane, Rushall, Nr Walsall WS4 1LJ
(T) 01922 641 021 **Manager:** Neil Kitching

Club Factfile

Founded: 1951 **Nickname:** The Pics
Previous Names: None
Previous Leagues: Walsall Amateur 1952-55, Staffordshire County (South) 1956-78, West Midlands 1978-94, Midland Alliance 1994-2005, Southern 2005-08
Club Colours (change): Gold and black/black/black (Red & white/red/red)

Ground Capacity: 2,500 **Seats:** 200 **Covered:** 200 **Clubhouse:** Yes **Shop:** Yes

Directions
M6 J10 follow signs for Walsall stay on this dual carriage way for about four miles until you come to the Walsall Arboretum and turn left following signs for Lichfield A461. Go under the bridge and you will come to McDonald's on your right, turn right into Daw End Lane. Go over the canal bridge and turn right opposite the Royal Oak Public House and the ground is on the right.
Alternative: From the A38 to it's junction with the A5 (Muckley Corner Hotel) take the A461 to Walsall after about five miles you will reach some traffic lights in Rushall by Mcdonald's, turn left into Daw End Lane go over the canal bridge and turn right opposite The Royal Oak Public House the ground is on the right.

Previous Grounds: Rowley Place 1951-75, Aston University 1976-79

Record Attendance: 2,000 v Leeds United Ex players
Record Victory: Not known
Record Defeat: Not known
Record Goalscorer: Graham Wiggin
Record Appearances: Alan Dawson - 400+
Additional Records:

Senior Honours:
West Midlands League 1979-80. Midland Alliance 2004-05.

10 YEAR RECORD

04-05	05-06	06-07	07-08	08-09	09-10	10-11	11-12	12-13	13-14
MidAl 1	SthW 10	SthM 15	SthM 5	NP1S 5	NP1S 12	NP1S 3	NP P 8	NP P 6	NP P 7

Northern Premier League Action

Nantwich Town's top goal scorer, Aaron Burns looks to turn past Stafford's Joe Ballinger.

Photo: Jonathan Holloway.

RUSHALL OLYMPIC MATCH RESULTS 2013-14

Date	Comp	H/A	Opponents	Att:	Result		Goalscorers	Pos	No.
Aug 17	NPL	H	Skelmersdale United	178	W	2-0	Caines 43 (pen)	10	1
20	NPL	A	Kings Lynn Town	665	L	0-6		19	2
24	NPL	A	Frickley Athletic	158	L	2-4	Bottomer 20 (pen) Obeng 62	21	3
26	NPL	H	Stafford Rangers	297	W	2-0	Adebola 5 Obeng 76	16	4
31	NPL	H	Stocksbridge PS	149	D	1-1	Bottomer 22 (pen)	14	5
Sept 2	NPL	A	Stamford	218	W	4-3	Eckersley 15 Adebola 29 Craddock 69 Wood 90	8	6
7	NPL	A	FC United	1860	W	2-0	Adebola 51 Obeng 80 (pen)	8	7
10	NPL	H	Ilkeston	186	W	3-2	Obeng 51 Adebola 56 Craddock 90	5	8
14	***FAC1Q***	***A***	***Hinckley United***	***260***	***W***	***3-0***	***Adebola 25 Haynes 80 Palmer 90***		9
17	NPL	H	Nantwich Town	167	D	1-1	Craddock 61	4	10
21	NPL	A	Trafford	204	L	1-3	Craddock 5	8	11
24	NPL	A	Barwell	180	L	1-3	Walker 83	9	12
28	***FAC2Q***	***A***	***Gainsborough Trinity***	***433***	***L***	***0-2***	**Result awarded to Rushall, Gainsborough removed.**		13
Oct 5	NPL	H	Ashton United	181	W	2-1	Ramsey-Dickson 41 54	10	14
12	***FAC3Q***	***A***	***Stockport County***	***2135***	***W***	***1-0***	***Turner 63***		15
15	NPL	H	Marine	108	D	1-1	Obeng 15 (pen	9	16
19	***FAT1Q***	***A***	***Barwell***	***153***	***W***	***4-0***	***Obeng 55 SPINK 3 (75 82 86)***		17
26	***FAC4Q***	***A***	***Grimsby Town***	***1456***	***L***	***0-3***			18
29	NPL	H	Stamford	148	L	0-2		16	19
Nov 2	***FAT2Q***	***H***	***AFC Fylde***	***121***	***L***	***0-1***			20
4	NPL	A	Ilkeston	385	W	1-0	Allinson 33 (og)	15	21
9	NPL	H	FC United	**539**	D	1-1	Ramsey-Dickson 49	15	22
16	NPL	A	Stocksbridge PS	183	W	2-1	Craddock 1 Duggan 75	13	23
23	NPL	A	Blyth Spartans	240	L	2-3	Martin 79 (pen) Mugisha 68	13	24
30	NPL	H	Worksop Town	190	D	2-2	Martin 16 Duggan 82	14	25
Dec 7	NPL	A	Skelmersdale United	201	L	0-1		17	26
14	NPL	H	Kings Lynn Town	153	W	3-1	Mugisha 17 Adebola 45 Dacres 50	15	27
21	NPL	A	Droylsden	131	W	5-1	Palmer 16 Obeng 21 Duggon 24 Mugisha 53 Caines 90 (pen)	14	28
26	NPL	H	Witton Albion	192	W	2-0	Obeng 26 Craddock 90	12	29
28	NPL	H	Grantham Town	179	W	3-1	Obeng 29 Palmer 42 84	10	30
Jan 1	NPL	A	Stratford Town	323	W	5-2	Craddock 7 Palmer 27 Adebola 38 Caines 66 (pen) Dacres 71	9	31
4	NPL	A	Buxton	214	W	2-1	Palmer 57 Adebola 67	5	32
11	NPL	H	Whitby Town	227	D	0-0		7	33
Feb 1	NPL	A	Ashton United	132	L	0-2		10	34
4	NPL	A	Nantwich Town	164	L	2-3	Adebola 9 Mugisha 90	10	35
22	NPL	H	Matlock Town	176	W	6-1	Dance 48 81 (pen) Ashton 67 Radford 72 (og) Mugisha 76 87	10	36
25	NPL	A	Chorley	614	W	1-0	Wood 86	8	37
March 1	NPL	H	Buxton	213	D	2-2	Mugisha 44 Dance 90 (pen)	9	38
8	NPL	A	AFC Fylde	274	L	1-2	Ashton 90	10	39
11	NPL	H	Barwell	124	D	0-0		10	40
15	NPL	H	Chorley	253	W	1-0	Obeng 13	8	41
18	NPL	A	Whitby Town	164	D	0-0		8	42
22	NPL	A	Marine	295	W	2-1	Craddock 37 Dance 54 (pen)	8	43
25	NPL	A	Matlock Town	166	D	1-1	Obeng 47	8	44
29	NPL	H	Blyth Spartans	168	D	0-0		8	45
April 1	NPL	H	AFC Fylde	146	D	2-2	Obeng 36 85	8	46
5	NPL	A	Worksop Town	387	W	3-1	Mugisha 11 71 Dance 47	7	47
12	NPL	A	Grantham Town	202	L	0-3		8	48
15	NPL	H	Trafford	156	L	1-2	Obeng 2	8	49
19	NPL	H	Frickley Athletic	138	W	4-1	Dacres 36 51 Spencer 56 Mugisha 81	7	50
21	NPL	A	Witton Albion	324	W	4-2	Spencer 7 74 Mugisha 40 82	6	51
26	NPL	H	Droylsden	173	L	0-1		6	52

GOALSCORERS	Lge	FAC	FAT	Total	Pens	Hat-tricks	Cons Run
Obeng	13		1	14	2		3
Mugisha	12			12			2
Adebola	8	1		9			4
Craddock	8			8			2
Palmer	5	1		6			3
Dance	5			5	3		
Dacres	4			4			
Caines	3			3	2		
Duggen	3			3			
Ramsey-Dickson	3			3	1		
Spencer	3			3			

	Lge	FAC	FAT	Total	Pens	Hat-tricks	Cons Run
Spink			3	3		1	
Ashton	2			2			
Bottomer	2			2	2		
Martin	2			2	1		2
Wood	2			2			
Eckersley	1			1			
Haynes		1		1			
Turner		1		1			
Walker	1			1			
Opponents	2			2			

Cons Run - Consecutive scoring games.

SKELMERSDALE UNITED

Chairman: Christopher Lloyd
Secretary: Bryn Jones **(T)** 07904 911 234 **(E)** skemsaint@sky.com
Commercial Manager: **(T)**
Programme Editor: Neil Leatherbarrow **(T)** 07855 701 512
Ground Address: Stormy Corner, Selby Place, Statham Road WN8 8EF
(T) 01695 722 123 **Manager:** Tommy Lawson

Club Factfile

Founded: 1882 **Nickname:** Skem
Previous Names: None
Previous Leagues: Liverpool County Combination, Lancashire Combination 1891-93, 1903-07, 21-24, 55-56, 76-78, Cheshire County 1968-71, 78-82, Northern Premier 1971-76, North West Counties 1983-2006
Club Colours (change): All royal blue (All bright red)

Ground Capacity: 2,300 **Seats:** 240 **Covered:** 500 **Clubhouse:** Yes **Shop:** Yes

Directions
Exit M58 J4 (signposted Skelmersdale), carry straight on at next roundabout (Hope Island) into Glenburn Road, left at next roundabout (Half Mile Island) into Neverstitch Road (signposted Stanley Industrial Estate). Immediately right at next roundabout into Staveley Road and then left into Statham Road. Ground is 500 yards on left in Selby Place.

Previous Grounds: None

Record Attendance: 7,000 v Slough Town - FA Amateur Cup Semi-final 1967
Record Victory: Not known
Record Defeat: Not known
Record Goalscorer: Stuart Rudd - 230
Record Appearances: Robbie Holcroft - 422 including 398 consecutively
Additional Records: Paid £2,000 for Stuart Rudd
Received £4,000 for Stuart Rudd
Senior Honours:
FA Amateur Cup 1970-71. Barassi Anglo-Italian Cup 1970-71.
Northern Premier Division One North 2013-14.
Lancashire Junior Cup x2. Lancashire Non-League Cup x2.

10 YEAR RECORD

04-05		05-06		06-07		07-08		08-09		09-10		10-11		11-12		12-13		13-14	
NWC1	6	NWC1	2	NP 1	15	NP1N	3	NP1N	2	NP1N	5	NP1N	2	NP1N	7	NP1N	1	NP P	6

SKELMERSDALE UNITED MATCH RESULTS 2013-14

Date	Comp	H/A	Opponents	Att:	Result	Goalscorers	Pos	No.
Aug 17	NPL	A	Rushall Olympic	178	L 0-1		18	1
20	NPL	H	Nantwich Town	221	**W** 2-1	Strickland 43 Burnett 82	15	2
24	NPL	H	Ashton United	186	D 1-1	Hughes 32	15	3
26	NPL	A	Marine	458	D 2-2	Wright 58 Hibbert 90	17	4
31	NPL	A	Droylsden	183	**W** 3-0	Morning 34 Rogan 38 Burton 40	8	5
Sept 2	NPL	H	Stafford Rangers	235	**W** 3-2	Morning 30 Rogan 34 Leadbetter 88 (pen)	5	6
7	NPL	H	Frickley Athletic	258	**W** 3-2	Leadbetter 50 (pen) 88 Morning 84	4	7
10	NPL	A	Witton Albion	293	**W** 3-3	Rogan 7 Holt 17 Morning 71	3	8
14	***FAC 1Q***	***A***	***Northwich Victoria***	***187***	***W 3-0***	***Leadbetter 17 (pen) Rogan 27 Tuck 71***		9
17	NPL	H	Chorley	397	**W** 1-0	Burton 88	1	10
21	NPL	A	Buxton	316	L 0-2		3	11
28	***FAC 2Q***	***A***	***West Auckland T***	***362***	***L 0-5***			12
Oct 1	NPL	A	Trafford	185	L 0-2		5	13
5	NPL	H	Barwell	242	**W** 1-0	Astbury 67	3	14
12	NPL	H	Blyth Spartans	286	**W** 4-3	Morning 5 Tuck 35 42 (pen) Strickland 79	2	15
15	NPL	A	FC United	1429	**W** 3-1	Burton 10 Hughes 27 Astbury 48	1	16
18	***FAT1Q***	***A***	***Blyth Spartans***	***340***	***L 0-6***			17
22	NPL	H	Matlock Town	191	**W** 1-0	Dunn 83	1	18
26	NPl	A	Grantham Town	206	**W** 2-1	Strickland 64 (pen) Hughes 74	1	19
Nov 2	NPL	A	Stafford Rangers	366	**W** 2-0	Tuck 4 8	1	20
9	NPL	A	Frickey Athletic	190	L 3-4	Tuck 51 Wylie 56 Holt 85	2	21
16	NPL	H	Droylsden	300	**W** 7-3	O'Reilly 12 Tuck 27 47 Astbury 53 90 Hughes 69 Morning 83	1	22
23	NPL	H	Kings Lynn Town	226	**W** 3-0	Hughes 64 Dunn 9 Morning 82	1	23
30	NPL	A	Stamford	240	L 0-2		1	24
Dec 7	NPL	H	Rushall Olympic	201	**W** 1-0	Ince 87	1	25
14	NPL	A	Nantwich Town	303	D 2-2	Astbury 13 Laird 90	1	26
21	NPL	H	Stocksbridge PS	219	**W** 6-0	Laird 22 ASTBURY 3 (31 56 73) Hughes 46 Dunn 53	1	27
26	NPL	A	AFC Fylde	343	**W** 3-2	Laird 28 (pen) Dunn 46 Hughes 76	1	28
28	NPL	A	Worksop Town	542	L 2-3	Prince 54 Strickland 55	1	29
Jan 1	NPL	H	Marine	303	**W** 4-1	Hughes 37 Astbury 38 53 Goulding 40 (og)	1	30
4	NPL	A	Whitby Town	268	D 2-2	Ince 53 Astbury 55	1	31
11	NPL	H	Ilkeston	353	**W** 2-0	Hughes 5 Astbury 28	1	32
18	NPL	A	Chorley	1968	L 1-4	Hardwick 54	1	33
Feb 8	NPL	H	Buxton	211	**W** 2-0	Prince 12 Dunn 43	2	34
15	NPL	A	Ilkeston	399	L 1-2	Astbury 45	2	35
22	NPL	H	Whitby Town	220	**W** 4-2	Morning 22 Ince 86 Astbury 88 90	2	36
March 1	NPL	A	Matlock Town	367	L 1-2	Astbury 32	2	37
4	NPL	H	Trafford	215	**W** 3-1	Astbury 5 75 Simm 87	2	38
8	NPL	H	Grantham Town	237	L 1-2	McCarthy 69	2	39
15	NPL	A	Blyth Spartans	329	L 1-2	Jackson 42	3	40
18	NPL	H	Witton Albion	201	L 1-3	Miller 81	5	41
22	NPL	H	FC United	**1000**	L 1-3	Dunn 81	5	42
29	NPL	A	Kings Lynn Town	528	D 3-3	ASTBURY 3 (1 36 77)	6	43
April 1	NPL	A	Barwell	137	L 0-5		6	44
5	NPL	H	Stamford	182	L 0-1		6	45
8	NPL	H	Worksop Town	194	**W** 2-1	Dunn 59 Strickland 90	6	46
19	NPL	A	Ashton United	246	L 1-4	Miller 46	6	47
21	NPL	H	AFC Fylde	273	L 0-5		7	48
26	NPL	A	Stocksbridge PS	108	**W** 4-0	McCarthy 11 Greene 34 Holden 38 67	7	49

GOALSCORERS	Lge	FAC	FAT	Total	Pens	Hat-tricks	Cons Run
Astbury	21			21		2	4
Hughes	8			8			2
Morning	8			8			4
Tuck	7	1		8	1		3
Dunn	7			7			
Strickland	5			5	1		
Leadbetter	3	1		4	3		2
Rogan	3	1		4			2
Burton	3			3			
Ince	3			3			
Laird	3			3	1		3
Holdon	2			2			
Holt	2			2			
Jackson	2			2			
McCarthy	2			2			
Miller	2			2			
Prince	2			2			
Burnett	1			1			
Greene	1			1			
Hardwick	1			1			
Hibbert	1			1			
O'Reilly	1			1			
Simm	1			1			
Wright	1			1			
Wylie	1			1			
Opponents	1			1			

Cons Run - Consecutive scoring.

STAMFORD

Chairman: Robert Feetham
Secretary: Phil Bee (T) 07772 646 776 (E) phil.bee1947@hotmail.co.uk
Commercial Manager: (T)
Programme Editor: Andrianna Curtis (T) 07867 960 900
Ground Address: Kettering Road, Stamford, Lincs PE9 2JS
(T) 01780 763 079 **Manager:** David Staff

Club Factfile

Founded: 1894 **Nickname:** The Daniels
Previous Names: Stamford Town and Rutland Ironworks amalgamated in 1894 to form Rutland Ironworks > 1896
Previous Leagues: Peterborough, Northants (UCL) 1908-55, Central Alliance 1955-61, Midland counties 1961-72, United Counties 1972-98, Southern 1998-2007
Club Colours (change): All red (Yellow/blue/yellow)

Ground Capacity: 2,000 **Seats:** 250 **Covered:** 1,250 **Clubhouse:** Yes **Shop:** Yes

Directions
Travel on A1 Southbound. Leave A1 by A43 slip road.
At junction turn left. Ground is one mile on the left.

Previous Grounds: None

Record Attendance: 4,200 v Kettering Town - FA Cup 3rd Qualifying Round 1953
Record Victory: 13-0 v Peterborough Reserves - Northants League 1929-30
Record Defeat: 0-17 v Rothwell - FA Cup 1927-28
Record Goalscorer: Bert Knighton - 248
Record Appearances: Dick Kwiatkowski - 462
Additional Records:
Senior Honours:
FA Vase 1979-80. United Counties League x7. Lincolnshire Senior Cup, Senior Shield. Lincolnshire Senior 'A' Cup x3.

10 YEAR RECORD

04-05	05-06	06-07	07-08	08-09	09-10	10-11	11-12	12-13	13-14
SthE 21	SthE 4	SthP 8	NP P 20	NP1S 7	NP1S 10	NP1S 19	NP1S 7	NP1S 4	NP P 18

STAMFORD MATCH RESULTS 2013-14

Date	Comp	H/A	Opponents	Att:	Result		Goalscorers	Pos	No.
Aug 17	NPL	H	Frickley Athletic	227	W	6-4	Robbins 3 SMITH 3 (28pen 36 90) Woodhead 53 (og) Lawlor 82	1	1
19	NPL	A	Ilkeston	537	L	0-3		11	2
24	NPL	A	FC United	1629	L	0-6		20	3
26	NPL	H	Grantham Town	432	L	1-2	Jones 6	22	4
31	NPL	A	Trafford	182	W	2-0	Robbins 45 72	20	5
Sept 3	NPL	H	Rushall Olympic	218	L	3-4	Robbins 20 57 Blakely 53	20	6
7	NPL	H	Worksop Town	320	D	2-2	Smith 4 Blakely 34	19	7
10	NPL	A	Barwell	217	L	0-1		19	8
14	***FAC1Q***	***H***	***Grantham Town***	***318***	***D***	***0-0***			9
17	***FAC1Qr***	***A***	***Grantham Town***	***215***	***W***	***3-2***	***Smith 75 Wesley 89 90***		10
21	NPL	A	Ashton United	110	L	1-2	Robbins 7	21	11
24	NPL	A	Matlock Town	271	L	0-2		21	12
28	***FAC2Q***	***H***	***AFC Wulfranians***	***225***	***W***	***4-1***	***ROBBINS 3 (5 4179) Richards 86***		13
Oct 5	NPL	H	Chorley	281	D	1-1	Burgess 17	21	14
8	NPL	H	Buxton	200	W	1-0	Richards 90	21	15
12	***FAC 3Q***	***H***	***Ashton United***	***301***	***W***	***4-2***	***Smith 38 Challinor 45 Moyo 51 Westley 84***		16
16	NPL	H	Stocksbridge PS	201	W	4-3	Jarvis 20 Richards 53 Moyo 55 81	21	17
19	***FAT1Q***	***H***	***Kidsgove Athletic***	***151***	***L***	***1-2***	***Wesley 81***		18
22	NPL	A	Stafford Rangers	246	L	1-2	Smith 41	21	19
26	***FAC4Q***	***H***	***Hednesford Town***	***668***	***L***	***0-2***			20
29	NPL	A	Rushall Olympic	148	W	2-0	Haines 33 Wesley 59	20	21
Nov 2	NPL	H	Whitby Town	203	L	1-2	Robbins 58 (pen)	20	22
5	NPL	H	Barwell	158	L	0-2		20	23
9	NPL	A	Worksop Town	318	L	1-6	Richards 68	21	24
16	NPL	H	Trafford	271	D	2-2	Robbins 29 90	21	25
23	NPL	A	Marine	277	W	3-1	ROBBINS 3(35 50 83)	21	26
30	NPL	H	Skelmersdale United	240	W	2-0	Robbins 23 Shariff 54	20	27
Dec 7	NPL	A	Frickley Athletic	197	D	1-1	Shariff 66	20	28
14	NPL	H	Ilkeston Town	307	L	0-2		21	29
21	NPL	A	Blyth Spartans	242	L	1-2	Challinor 90	21	30
26	NPL	H	Kings Lynn Town	460	W	3-0	Challinor 5 45 Lawlor 61	20	31
28	NPL	H	Droylsden	327	W	4-0	Richards 57 79 (pen) Jones 59 Shariff 74	18	32
Jan 1	NPL	A	Grantham Town	218	D	1-1	Smith 71	18	33
11	NPL	H	Nantwich Town	330	D	2-2	Robbins 2 (pen) Shariff 83	18	34
Feb 1	NPL	A	Chorley	875	L	0-3		20	35
8	NPL	H	Ashton United	259	W	2-1	Robbins 4 (pen) Shariff 90	18	36
22	NPL	H	Witton Albion	286	W	3-1	Carr 2 Binns 33 85	18	37
27	NPL	A	Buxton	151	D	2-2	Jarvis 20 Robbins 24	18	38
March 1	NPL	H	Stafford Rangers	348	W	2-0	Richards 45 Jarvis 62	17	39
4	NPL	A	Nantwich Town	163	L	1-4	Smith 75	17	40
8	NPL	A	Whitby Town	259	W	2-1	Carr 62 Smith 72	15	41
11	NPL	A	Witton Albion	244	L	1-2	Smith 68	15	42
15	NPL	H	AFC Fylde	268	L	1 3	Robinson 25	16	43
18	NPL	H	Matlock Town	184	W	1-0	Robbins 21	16	44
22	NPL	A	AFC Fylde	238	L	0-2		16	45
29	NPL	H	Marine	320	L	2-4	Carr 63 Robbins 73 (pen)	18	46
April 5	NPL	A	Skelmersdale United	182	W	1-0	Jones 14	18	47
8	NPL	A	Stocksbridge PS	91	W	3-1	Robbins 66 Shariff 77 90	14	48
12	NPL	A	Droysden	133	W	3-0	Smith 21 Shariff 33 Richards 71	15	49
19	NPL	H	FC United	**1204**	L	2-3	Robbins 3 Sharriff 44	16	50
21	NPL	A	Kings Lynn Town	569	L	1-2	Robbins 45	16	51
26	NPL	H	Blyth Spartans	449	L	3-4	Smith 21 Robinson 30 Challinor 31	18	52

GOALSCORERS	Lge	FAC	FAT	Total	Pens	Hat-tricks	Cons Run
Robbins	21	3		24	4	2	3
Smith	11	2		13	1	1	3
Shariff	9			9			3
Richards	7	1		8	1		
Challinor	4	1		5			2
Wesley		3	1	4			
Carr	3			3			
Jarvis	3			3			
Jones	3			3			
Moyo	2	1		3			
Binns	2			2			
Blakely	2			2			
Lawler	2			2			
Robinson	2			2			
Burgess	1			1			
Opponents	1			1			

Cons Run - Consecutive scoring games.

STOURBRIDGE

Chairman: Andy Pountney
Secretary: Clive Eades (T) 07958 275 986 (E) clive.eades2@capita.co.uk
Commercial Manager: (T)
Programme Editor: Nigel Gregg (T) 07531 963 288
Ground Address: War Memorial Athletic Ground, High Street, Amblecote DY8 4HN
(T) 01384 394 040 **Manager:** Gary Hackett

Club Factfile

Founded: 1876 **Nickname:** The Glassboys
Previous Names: Stourbridge Standard 1876-87
Previous Leagues: West Midlands (Birmingham League) 1892-1939, 54-71, Birmingham Combination 1945-53, Southern 1971-2000. Midland Alliance 2000-06. Southern 2006-14.

Club Colours (change): Red and white stripes/red/red (Yellow with green trim/green/yellow with green trim)

Ground Capacity: 2,000 **Seats:** 250 **Covered:** 750 **Clubhouse:** Yes **Shop:** Yes

Directions
From Stourbridge Ring-Road follow signs A491 to Wolverhampton.
The ground is on the left within 300 yards immediately beyond the third traffic lights and opposite the Royal Oak public house.

Previous Grounds: None

Record Attendance: 5,726 v Cardiff City - Welsh Cup Final 1st Leg 1974
Record Victory: Not known
Record Defeat: Not known
Record Goalscorer: Ron Page - 269
Record Appearances: Ron Page - 427
Additional Records: Received £20,000 from Lincoln City for Tony Cunningham 1979

Senior Honours:
Southern League Division 1 North 1973-74, Midland Division 90-91, League Cup 92-93. Midland Alliance 2001-02, 02-03.
Worcestershire Junior Cup 1927-28. Hereford Senior Cup 1954-55. Birmingham Senior Cup x3.
Worcestershire Senior Cup x11 Most recently 2012-13.

10 YEAR RECORD

04-05	05-06	06-07	07-08	08-09	09-10	10-11	11-12	12-13	13-14
MidAl 8	MidAl 2	SthM 7	SthM 3	SthP 16	SthP 9	SthP 8	SthP 6	SthP 2	SthP 5

STOURBRIDGE MATCH RESULTS 2013-14

Date	Comp	H/A	Opponents	Att:	Result		Goalscorers	Pos	No.
Aug 17	SPL	A	AFC Totton	202	W	4-1	GEDDES 3 (13 pen 30 pen 41 pen) Broadhust 48	1	1
20	SPL	H	St Neots Town	447	W	2-1	Billingham 28 Richards 90	1	2
24	SPL	H	Chesham United	172	L	2-3	Geddes 45 (pen) 60 (pen)	5	3
26	SPL	A	Redditch United	316	W	6-1	Benbow 24 ROWE 4 (39 54 72 88) Geddes 84 (Pen)	3	4
31	SPL	A	Bedford Town	267	L	0-2		8	5
Sept 3	SPL	H	Chippenham Town	445	L	0-1		9	6
7	SPL	H	Burnham	551	W	1-0	Richards 74	7	7
14	***FAC1Q***	***A***	***Evesham United***	***265***	***W***	***3-0***	***N.Bennett 10 Geddes 59 (pen) Benbow 88***		8
17	SPL	A	Hungerford Town	100	L	0-1		9	9
21	SPL	A	St Albans City	338	W	2-1	Billingham 19 Geddes 61 (pen)	7	10
28	***FAC2Q***	***H***	***Sutton Coldfield***	***373***	***W***	***3-2***	***Billingham 67 71 Geddes 90***		11
Oct 5	SPL	H	Poole Town	466	W	5-2	Canavan 42 Geddes 49 (pen) 84 (pen) Fitzpatrick 73 90	8	12
8	SPL	H	Corby Town	317	W	3-1	Fitzpatrick 57 Richards 68 Casgoine 77 (og)	6	13
19	***FAT1Q***	***H***	***Banbury United***	***321***	***W***	***3-2***	***Rowe 10 Agbor 59 Brown 90***		14
26	***FAC4Q***	***A***	***Workington***	***519***	***W***	***3-1***	***Oliver 10 Richards 61 Benbow 77***		15
29	SPL	A	Chippenham Town	317	W	9-0	ROWE 5 (7 21 70 82 87) Geddes 23 67 Benbow 78 85	5	16
Nov 2	***FAT2Q***	***A***	***Mickleover Sports***	***186***	***W***	***2-1***	***Benbow 64 Geddes 90 (pen)***		17
9	***FAC1***	***H***	***Biggleswade Town***	***1605***	***W***	***4-1***	***Rowe 12 17 Richards 60 Benbow 87***		18
13	SPL	A	Cambridge City	241	L	1-2	Geddes 60	5	19
16	***FAT3Q***	***H***	***North Ferriby United***	***437***	***D***	***2 2***	***Benbow 68 Richards 90***		20
19	***FAT3Qr***	***A***	***North Ferriby United***	***134***	***L***	***0 4***			21
23	SPL	A	Bideford	231	W	1-0	Gerring 62 (og)	6	22
26	SPL	A	Biggleswade Town	126	D	2-2	Billingham 25 Rowe 90	7	23
30	SPL	H	Weymouth	470	W	7-0	Rowe 11 BENBOW 3 (20 36 58) Billingham 34 Knight 86 Washbourne 90	6	24
Dec 2	SPL	A	Burnham	123	L	0-2		6	25
7	***FAC 2***	***A***	***Stevenage***	***2160***	***L***	***0-4***			26
14	SPL	H	Arlesey Town	328	L	0-2		7	27
17	SPL	H	Frome Town	249	W	7-0	GEDDES 3 (11 31 pen 38) Benbow 22 Brown 52 Richards 86 Oliver 90	6	28
23	SPL	H	Redditch United	637	W	5-1	Benbow 16 Bennett 41 Canavan 79 Fitzpatrick 80 Rowe 89	6	29
28	SPL	A	St Neots Town	356	D	1-1	Geddes 28 (pen)	6	30
Jan 4	SPL	H	Hitchin Town	400	D	1-1	Benbow 12	7	31
7	SPL	H	Bedford Town	261	W	2-1	Benbow 76 Brown 77	4	32
11	SPL	A	Truro City	401	D	1-1	Rowe 64	5	33
18	SPL	H	Bideford	573	L	0-4		6	34
21	SPL	A	Bashley	108	W	4-1	Benbow 8 Canavan 16 Broadhurst 61 Knight 74	5	35
28	SPL	H	Truro City	260	D	2-2	Brown 53 89	6	36
Feb 1	SPL	A	Weymouth	492	W	5-0	Canavan 5 Geddes 16 55 Billingham 70 Fitzpatrick 86	6	37
8	SPL	H	Bashley	379	W	4-1	Geddes 23 Brown 54 Billingham 60 Broadhurst 90	5	38
15	SPL	A	Arlesey Town	151	W	5-1	BILLINGHAM 3 (15 31 34) Geddes 21 (pen) Brown 24	4	39
22	SPL	H	Hemel Hempstead T	547	L	1-4	Geddes 79	6	40
27	SPL	A	Banbury United	162	W	4-0	Billingham 33 78 Benbow 38 58	5	41
March 8	SPL	H	St Albans City	477	D	0-1		5	42
11	SPL	H	Hungerford Town	253	L	1-2	Richards 40	5	43
15	SPL	A	Corby Town	361	W	4-2	Geddes 4 80 (pen) Knight 64 Brown 67	5	44
18	SPL	H	Biggleswade Town	319	W	2-1	Gentle 59 (og) Brown 68	5	45
22	SPL	H	Cambridge City	504	W	3-2	BENBOW 3 (31 55 72)	4	46
25	SPL	A	Hemel Hempstead T	432	L	3-4	Benbow 38 Billingham 55 71	4	47
29	SPL	A	Frome Town	224	W	2-0	Broadhurst 5 Haines 22	4	48
April 3	SPL	A	Poole Town	341	W	2-1	Benbow 61 Geddes 73 (pen)	4	49
12	SPL	H	AFC Totton	583	W	3-0	Harris 33 Billingham 56 Sansara 79	5	50
19	SPL	A	Chesham United	461	W	1-0	Geddes 68	5	51
21	SPL	H	Banbury United	670	W	5-0	Broadhurst 10 Brown 39 48 Smikle 58 Billingham 65	5	52
26	SPL	A	Hitchin Town	476	D	1-1	Smikle 15	5	53
29	***SPL PO SF***	***A***	***Chesham United***	***728***	***L***	***1-2***	***Brown 21***		54

GOALSCORERS	Lge	FAC	FAT	Total	Pens	Hat-tricks	Cons Run
Geddes	25	2	1	28	16	1	4
Benbow	17	3	2	22	1	2	4
Billingham	15	2		17		1	3
Rowe	14	1	1	16		2	
Brown	11+1		1	13			
Richards	5	2	1	8			
Broadhurst	5			5			
Fitzpatrick	5			5			2
Canavan	4			4			
Knight	3			3			
Bennett	1	1		2			
Oliver	1	1		2			
Smikle	2			2			2
Agbor			1	1			
Haines	1			1			
Harris	1			1			
Sansara	1			1			
Washbourne	1			1			
Opponents	3			3			

Cons Run - Consecutive scoring games. Play-off goals indicated by +

TRAFFORD

Chairman: John Eadie
Secretary: Graham Foxall (T) 07796 864 151 (E) davem@traffordfc.co.uk
Commercial Manager: (T)
Programme Editor: Dave Murray (T) 07551 982 299
Ground Address: Shawe View, Pennybridge Lane, Flixton Urmston M41 5DL
(T) 0161 747 1727 **Manager:** Garry Vaughan

Club Factfile

Founded: 1990 **Nickname:** The North
Previous Names: North Trafford 1990-94
Previous Leagues: Mid Cheshire 1990-92, North West Counties 1992-97, 2003-08, Northern Premier 1997-2003

Club Colours (change): All white (All yellow)

Ground Capacity: 2,500 **Seats:** 292 **Covered:** 740 **Clubhouse:** Yes **Shop:** Yes

Directions
Anti-Clockwise exit at J10 (Trafford Centre) and turn right towards Urmston B5214. Straight across two roundabouts. First lights turn right into Moorside Road, at next roundabout take second exit in to Bowfell Road. At next lights turn sharp left then immediately right in to Pennybridge Lane next to Bird In Hand Pub, parking on left 100 yards.
Or Leave M60 at J8, taking A6144 towards Lymm, Partington, Carrington. At second set of traffic lights turn right on B5158 towards Flixton. Remain on B5158 crossing railway bridge at Flixton Station and turn right at next set of traffic lights. Passing Bird in Hand Pub take immediate right in to Pennybridge Lane. Parking on left 100 yards.

Previous Grounds: Not known

Record Attendance: 803 v Flixton - Northern Premier League Division 1 1997-98
Record Victory: Not known
Record Defeat: Not known
Record Goalscorer: Garry Vaughan - 88
Record Appearances: Garry Vaughan - 293
Additional Records:

Senior Honours:
North West Counties Division 1 1996-97, 2007-08.
Manchester Challenge Trophy 2004-05. Northern Premier President's Cup 2008-09.

10 YEAR RECORD

04-05	05-06	06-07	07-08	08-09	09-10	10-11	11-12	12-13	13-14
NWC1 12	NWC1 15	NWC1 5	NWC1 1	NP1N 15	NP1N 12	NP1N 14	NP1N 12	NP1N 4	NP P 10

TRAFFORD MATCH RESULTS 2013-14

Date	Comp	H/A	Opponents	Att:	Result		Goalscorers	Pos	No.
Aug 17	NPL	H	Matlock Town	229	W	2-1	Oates 32 Brown 79	9	1
20	NPL	A	Blyth Spartans	311	L	1-2	Payne 17 (pen)	13	2
24	NPL	A	Stafford Rangers	390	W	4-1	Smart 22 67 Nsangou 80 Payne 90	4	3
26	NPL	H	FC United	**1374**	L	2-3	Payne 48 Oates 58	8	4
31	NPL	H	Stamford	182	L	0-2		15	5
Sept 3	NPL	A	Chorley	621	L	2-6	Brown 8 Oates 90	19	6
7	NPL	A	Ashton United	153	L	0-2		20	7
10	NPL	H	Whitby Town	106	L	0-3		21	8
14	***FAC1Q***	***A***	***Droylsden***	***186***	***W***	***5-1***	***PAYNE 5 (22 36 60 75 77)***		9
17	NPL	A	Frickley Athletic	180	L	1-2	Lacy 36	21	10
21	NPL	H	Rushall Olympic	204	W	3-1	Oates 43 Ashton 49 61	19	11
28	***FAC2Q***	***H***	***Altrincham***	***829***	***W***	***2-1***	***Fallon 11 Oates 64***		12
Oct 1	NPL	H	Skelmersdale United	185	W	2-0	McKenzie 37 Payne 88	18	13
5	NPL	A	Grantham Town	216	L	1-2	Payne 34	19	14
12	***FAC3Q***	***A***	***Corby Town***	***531***	***L***	***2-4***	***Payne 33 (pen) Lacy 43***		15
16	NPL	H	AFC Fylde	218	W	2-0	Smart 56 Payne 59 (pen)	17	16
19	***FAT1Q***	***H***	***Wakefield***	***159***	***W***	***6-1***	***OATES 3 (14 26 80) Welsh 22 Palmer 62 Payne 89 (pen)***		17
26	NPL	H	Buxton	253	D	0-0		20	18
29	NPL	H	Chorley	367	L	0-5		20	19
Nov 2	***FAT 2Q***	***A***	***Gresley***	***304***	***L***	***0-2***			20
6	NPL	A	Whitby Town	178	D	1-1	Fallon 86	21	21
9	NPL	H	Ashton United	196	W	4-1	Payne 33 84 Oates 41 Mbalanda 88		22
12	NPL	A	Stamford	271	D	2-2	Payne 3 33	20	23
23	NPL	A	Barwell	151	D	0-0		19	24
30	NPL	H	Nantwich Town	222	D	0-1		21	25
Dec 7	NPL	A	Matlock Town	254	L	2-3	Hackney 15 Ashton 69	21	26
10	NPL	A	Marine	269	W	2-1	Schofield 3 Mbalanda 10	20	27
14	NPL	H	Blyth Spartans	165	W	2-1	Mbalanda 16 54	18	28
21	NPL	A	Ilkeston	359	D	1-1	Oates 82	18	29
26	NPL	H	Droylsden	217	W	1-0	Jones 48	17	30
28	NPL	H	Witton Albion	234	D	3-3	Ashton 48 Mason 87 Bayuno 90	17	31
Jan 4	NPL	H	King's Lynn Town	213	L	1-2	Bayuno 45	17	32
11	NPL	A	Worksop Town	352	W	2-1	Schofield 60 Payne 84	16	33
18	NPL	H	Frickley Athletic	265	W	4-1	Oates 25 67 Andrews 73 Payne 83	15	34
21	NPL	A	FC United	1598	D	1-1	Mason 22	14	35
Feb 1	NPL	H	Grantham Town	195	W	2-1	Hackney 71 Payne 88	12	36
4	NPL	A	AFC Fylde	189	L	1-2	Payne 10	13	37
22	NPL	A	Kings Lynn Town	602	D	2-2	Payne 49 Oates 90	15	38
March 1	NPL	H	Marine	227	W	1-0	Wright 72 (og)	13	39
4	NPL	A	Skelmersdale United	215	L	1-3	Payne 64 (pen)	13	40
8	NPL	A	Buxton	241	W	2-1	Oates 63 Hackney 76	12	41
15	NPL	H	Stocksbridge PS	157	W	1-0	Ashton 26	11	42
18	NPL	H	Worksop Town	161	L	0-2		12	43
22	NPL	A	Stocksbridge PS	93	W	3-1	PAYNE 3 (40 65 68)	11	44
29	NPL	H	Barwell	218	L	2-4	Payne 16 Hackney 78	12	45
April 5	NPL	A	Nantwich Town	253	W	1-0	Andrews 81	11	46
12	NPL	A	Witton Albion	356	W	4-0	Payne 33 39 Heron 69 Derbyshire 86	11	47
15	NPL	A	Rushall Olympic	156	W	2-1	Heron 41 Payne 44	10	48
18	NPL	H	Stafford Rangers	324	L	1-2	Andrews 78	10	49
21	NPL	A	Droylsden	203	W	6-0	Payne 39 65 Hackney 41 49 Ashton 47 Andrews 57	10	50
26	NPL	H	Ilkeston Town	300	L	2-5	Nsangou 35 Riley 73	10	51

GOALSCORERS	Lge	FAC	FAT	Total	Pens	Hat-tricks	Cons Run
Payne	25	6	1	32	4	2	3
Oates	10	1	3	14		1	
Ashton	6			6			
Hackney	6			6			
Andrews	4			4			
Mbalanda	4			4			2
Smart	3			3			
Bayuno	2			2			2
Brown	2			2			
Fallon	1	1		2			
Heron	2			2			2
Lacy	1	1		2			
Mason	2			2			
Nsangou	2			2			
Schofield	2			2			
Derbyshire	1			1			
Jones	1			1			
McKenzie	1			1			
Palmer			1	1			
Riley	1			1			
Welsh			1	1			
Opponents	1			1			

Cons Run - Consecutive scoring games.

WHITBY TOWN

Chairman: Anthony Graham Manser
Secretary: Peter Tyreman **(T)** 01947 605 153 **(E)**
Commercial Manager: **(T)**
Programme Editor: Paul Connolly **(T)** 07798 746 865
Ground Address: Turnbull Ground, Upgang Lane, Whitby, North Yorks YO21 3HZ
(T) 01947 604 847 **Manager:** Darren Williams

Club Factfile

Founded: 1926 **Nickname:** Seasiders
Previous Names: Whitby United (pre 1950)
Previous Leagues: Northern League 1926-97

Club Colours (change): All royal blue (All white)

Ground Capacity: 2,680 **Seats:** 622 **Covered:** 1,372 **Clubhouse:** Yes **Shop:** Yes

Directions
On entering Whitby from both the A169 and A171 roads, take the first fork and follow signs for the "West Cliff".
Then turn left at the Spa Shop and Garage, along Love Lane to junction of the A174.
Turn right and the ground is 600 yards on the left.

Previous Grounds: None

Record Attendance: 4,000 v Scarborough - North Riding Cup 18/04/1965
Record Victory: 11-2 v Cargo Fleet Works - 1950
Record Defeat: 3-13 v Willington - 24/03/1928
Record Goalscorer: Paul Pitman - 382
Record Appearances: Paul Pitman - 468
Additional Records: Paid £2,500 to Newcastle Blue Star for John Grady 1990
Received £5,000 from Gateshead for Graham Robinson 1997
Senior Honours:
Rothmans National Cup 1975-76, 77-78. Northern League 1992-93, 96-97. FA Vase 1996-97.
Northern Premier League Division 1 1997-98.
North Riding Senior Cup x5.

10 YEAR RECORD

04-05	05-06	06-07	07-08	08-09	09-10	10-11	11-12	12-13	13-14
NP P 4	NP P 6	NP P 11	NP P 12	NP P 19	NP P 14	NP P 16	NP P 17	NP P 13	NP P 9

WHITBY TOWN MATCH RESULTS 2013-14

Date	Comp	H/A	Opponents	Att:	Result		Goalscorers	Pos	No.
Aug 17	NPL	H	Ilkeston Town	327	D	1-1	Farrell 9	14	1
20	NPL	A	Droylsden	180	W	2-0	Armstrong 73 Farrell 90	4	2
24	NPL	A	Chorley	590	D	0-0		8	3
26	NPL	H	Frickley Athletic	301	D	2-2	Armstrong 65 Portas 66	11	4
31	NPL	A	Buxton	284	D	1-1	McTiernan 67	12	5
Sept 4	NPL	H	Worksop Town	274	L	2-5	Armstrong 42 49	15	6
7	NPL	H	Barwell	262	D	2-2	Armstrong 21 56	14	7
10	NPL	A	Trafford	106	W	3-0	Armstrong 27 Rundle 43 Henry 60	13	8
14	***FAC1Q***	***H***	***West Auckland Town***	***284***	***D***	***1-1***	***Henry 3***		9
17	***FAC1Qr***	***A***	***West Auckland Town***	***265***	***L***	***1-4***	***Armstrong 55***		10
21	NPL	H	Fylde	212	L	1-2	Rundle 65	15	11
25	NPL	H	Stocksbridge PS	168	W	4-0	Rundle 5 Bullock 22 Mason 33 Farrell 50	13	12
28	NPL	A	FC United	1524	W	3-1	Armstrong 6 Henry 42 Farrell 90	8	13
Oct 5	NPL	A	Kings Lynn Town	532	L	0-3		15	14
12	NPL	H	Witton Albion	273	D	1-1	Armstrong 34	15	15
16	NPL	A	Ashton United	104	W	4-3	Farrell 17 77 Mason 58 Armstrong 62	11	16
19	***FAT1***	***H***	***Chorley***	***219***	***L***	***0-1***			17
26	NPL	A	AFC Fylde	281	L	1-3	Farrell 31 (pen)	13	18
30	NPL	A	Worksop Town	249	L	0-3		13	19
Nov 2	NPL	A	Stamford	203	W	2-1	Snaith 12 43	14	20
6	NPL	H	Trafford	178	D	1-1	McTiernan 88	12	21
9	NPL	A	Barwell	203	D	1-1	Snaith 59	12	22
16	NPL	H	Grantham Town	278	D	1-1	Armstrong 88	14	23
23	NPL	A	Nantwich Town	159	L	3-4	Mason 17 Armstrong 27 65	14	24
30	NPL	H	Marine	226	D	0-0		15	25
Dec 7	NPL	A	Ilkeston	370	W	2-0	Armstrong 6 Bullock 60	12	26
14	NPL	H	Droylsden	198	W	5-2	Snaith 34 Armstrong 47 82 Pell 53 Rundle 60	12	27
21	NPL	A	Stafford Rangers	313	W	2-0	Pell 17 Henry 47	10	28
26	NPL	H	Blyth Spartans	370	W	2-1	Henry 39 Armstrong 87	8	29
28	NPL	H	Matlock Town	315	W	1-0	Armstrong 34	5	30
Jan 1	NPL	A	Frickley Athletic	218	D	1-1	Robinson 56	6	31
4	NPL	H	Skelmersdale United	268	D	2-2	Snaith 8 Armstrong 51	9	32
11	NPL	A	Rushall Olympic	227	D	0-0		10	33
18	NPL	H	FC United	**818**	W	3-2	Armstrong 8 84 Snaith 47	7	34
25	NPL	A	Stocksbridge PS	148	W	3-0	Armstrong 10 Farrell 17 39	7	35
Feb	NPL	A	Skelmersdale United	220	L	2-4	Armstrong 19 Farrell 61	9	36
March 1	NPL	A	Grantham Town	230	L	1-3	Farrell 22	10	37
8	NPL	H	Stamford	259	L	1-2	Armstrong 83	11	38
15	NPL	A	Witton Albion	428	L	1-3	Farrell 35	13	39
18	NPL	H	Rushall Olympic	164	D	0-0		11	40
22	NPL	H	Ashton United	173	L	1-2	McTiernon 73	12	41
29	NPL	H	Nantwich Town	247	W	4-2	Henry 30 81 Robinson 67 (pen) Mason 72	11	42
April 5	NPL	A	Marine	244	D	1-1	Mason 47	12	43
9	NPL	H	Kings Lynn Town	206	W	4-0	Henry 19 Mason 58 Snaith 73 Boagey 87	11	44
12	NPL	A	Matlock Town	281	L	0-2		12	45
16	NPL	A	Buxton	226	W	1-0	Mason 6	12	46
19	NPL	H	Chorley	447	D	1-1	Atmstrong 48	12	47
21	NPL	A	Blyth Spartans	501	W	7-0	Portas 7 Farrell 38 (pen) 88 Armstrong 45 90 Rundle 53 Mason 70	10	48
26	NPL	H	Stafford Rangers	362	W	2-1	Henry 28 Armstrong 67	9	49

GOALSCORERS	Lge	FAC	FAT	Total	Pens	Hat-tricks	Cons Run
Armstrong	28	1		29			3
Farrell	14			14	2		3
Henry	8	1		9			2
Mason	8			8			3
Snaith	7			7			
Rundle	5			5			2
McTierrnan	3			3			
Bullock	2			2			
Pell	2			2			2
Portas	2			2			
Robinson	2			2	1		
Boagey	1			1			

Cons Run - Consecutive scoring games.

WITTON ALBION

Chairman: Mark Harris
Secretary: Andrea Harris **(T)** 07970 663 412 **(E)** wafc43008@o2.co.uk
Commercial Manager: **(T)**
Programme Editor: David Kettle **(T)** 07734 603 811
Ground Address: Help for Heros Stadium, Wincham Park, Chapel Street, Wincham, CW9 6DA
(T) 01606 430 08 **Manager:** Brian Pritchard

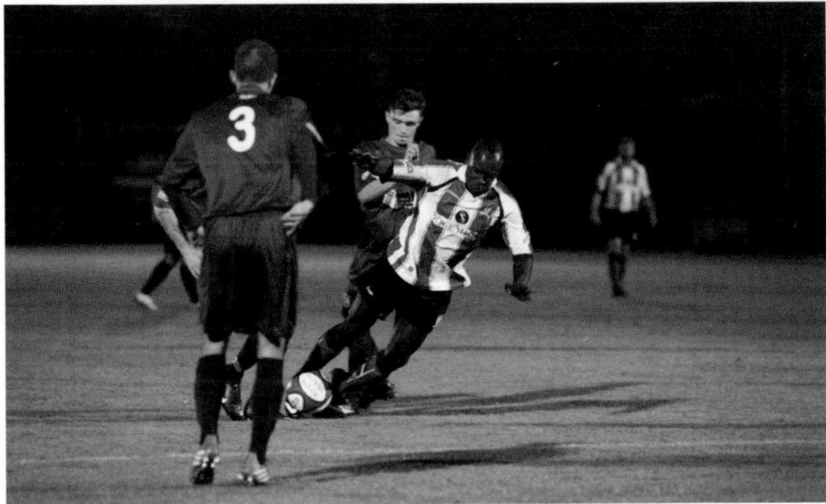

Cliff Moyo is tackled by a Skelmsdale defender.
Photo: Keith Clayton.

Club Factfile

Founded: 1887 **Nickname:** The Albion
Previous Names: None
Previous Leagues: Lancashire Combination, Cheshire County > 1979, Northern Premier 1979-91, Conference 1991-94

Club Colours (change): Red & white stripes/blue/red (Navy blue & yellow/yellow/yellow)

Ground Capacity: 4,500 **Seats:** 650 **Covered:** 2,300 **Clubhouse:** Yes **Shop:** Yes

Directions
M6 Junction 19: Follow A556 for Northwich for three miles, through two sets of traffic lights. Turn right at the beginning of the dual carriageway onto A559. After ¾ mile turn right at traffic lights by Slow & Easy Public House, still following A559. After a further ¾ mile turn left a Black Greyhound Public House (signposted). Follow the road through the industrial estate for about ½ mile. Turn left immediately after crossing the canal bridge (signposted) **From M56 Junction 10:** Follow the A558 (Northwich Road) towards Northwich for approximately 6 miles. Turn right at the crossroads by the Black Greyhound Public House (signposted). Follow the road through the industrial estate for about ½ mile. Turn left immediately after crossing the canal bridge (signposted)

Previous Grounds: Central Ground (1910-1989)

Record Attendance: 3,940 v Kidderminster Harries - FA Trophy Semi-final 13/04/1991
Record Victory: 13-0 v Middlewich (H)
Record Defeat: 0-9 v Macclesfield Town (A) - 18/09/1965
Record Goalscorer: Frank Fidler - 175 (1947-50)
Record Appearances: Brian Pritchard - 729
Additional Records: Paid £12,500 to Hyde United for Jim McCluskie 1991
Received £11,500 from Chester City for Peter Henderson
Senior Honours:
Northern Premier League Premier Division 1990-91, Division 1 North Play-offs 2011-12. Cheshire Senior Cup x7.

10 YEAR RECORD

04-05	05-06	06-07	07-08	08-09	09-10	10-11	11-12	12-13	13-14
NP 1 8	NP 1 8	NP P 2	NP P 2	NP P 20	NP1S 7	NP1N 10	NP1N 3	NP1N 4	NP P 16

WITTON ALBION MATCH RESULTS 2013-14

Date	Comp	H/A	Opponents	Att:	Result		Goalscorers	Pos	No.
Aug 17	NPL	A	Buxton	133	L	1-3	Wilson 59	22	1
20	NPL	H	Marine	363	L	2-3	Hancock 8 29	23	2
24	NPL	H	Barwell	319	L	1-2	Andrews 33	23	3
26	NPL	A	Nantwich Town	418	W	2-0	Wilson 23 Hancock 63 (pen)	20	4
31	NPL	H	KIngs Lynn	349	W	1-0	Tuck 87	18	5
Sept 3	NPL	A	FC United	1614	L	1-3	Sheehan 80	18	6
7	NPL	A	Ilkeston	576	D	1-1	Wilson 90	17	7
10	NPL	H	Skelmersdale United	293	L	2-3	Andrews 14 Hancock 81 (pen)	18	8
14	***FAC 1Q***	***A***	***Ashton United***	***152***	***L***	***1-2***	***Powell 54***		9
21	NPL	H	Blyth Spartans	441	L	0-1		20	10
24	NPL	H	AFC Fylde	292	L	0-1		20	11
28	NPL	A	Stocksbridge PS	146	D	2-2	Dawson 52 Wilson 74	20	12
Oct 5	NPL	A	Worksop Town	244	W	2-3	Walker 22 69 Hancock 75	20	13
12	NPL	A	Whitby Town	273	D	1-1	Andrews 27	19	14
15	NPL	H	Droylsden	217	W	5-1	Hancock 3 Walker 6 WILSON 3 (9 51 71)	17	15
19	***FAT1Q***	***H***	***FC United***	***693***	***D***	***2-2***	***Wilson 46 Hancock 89 (pen)***		16
26	NPL	H	Stafford Rangers	379	W	5-0	Andrews 4 Walker 10 19 Thompson 15 67	17	17
Nov 5	***FAT1Qr***	***A***	***FC United***	***369***	***W***	***2-1***	***Thompson 17 Andrews 87***		18
9	NPL	H	Ilkeston	390	W	2-1	Powell 60 Hancock 79	18	19
12	***FAT2Q***	***H***	***Leek Town***	***290***	***L***	***1-2***	***Hancock 26***		20
16	NPL	A	Kings Lynn	571	L	0-3		18	21
23	NPL	A	Grantham Town	189	D	0-0		18	22
30	NPL	H	Matlock Town	328	W	1-0	Gardner 20	18	23
Dec 7	NPL	H	Buxton	300	L	0-1		18	24
14	NPL	A	Marine	347	L	1-2	Dawson 51	20	25
21	NPL	H	Ashton United	302	L	1-2	Harrison 81	20	26
26	NPL	A	Rushall Olympic	192	L	0-2		21	27
28	NPL	A	Trafford	234	D	3-3	Jackson 5 Powell 83 90	21	28
Jan 11	NPL	A	Frickley Athetic	228	D	0-0		21	29
18	NPL	H	Stocksbridge PS	322	W	4-1	Simm 22 Powell 57 Andrews 85 90	21	30
25	NPL	A	AFC Fylde	246	L	0-3		21	31
Feb 1	NPL	H	Worksop Town	294	D	2-2	Powell 52 Hancock 74	21	32
8	NPL	A	Blyth Spartans	337	L	2-4	Andrews 7 Powell 37	21	33
22	NPL	A	Stamford	286	L	1-3	Breeze 74	21	34
25	NPL	H	Nantwich Town	301	W	3-2	Titchiner 14 32 Hancock 61	21	35
March 1	NPL	H	Chorley	497	D	2-2	Hancock 23 Titchenor 28	21	36
8	NPL	A	Stafford Rangers	393	D	2-2	Powell 19 Andrews 85	21	37
11	NPL	H	Stamford	244	W	2-1	Bakkor 45 Hancock 47	21	38
15	NPL	H	Whitby Town	428	W	3-1	Andrews 55 Titchiner 67 Dawson 84	21	39
18	NPL	A	Skelmersdale United	201	W	3-1	Powell 2 Titchiner 35 Bakkor 77	19	40
22	NPL	A	Droylsden	135	L	3-4	Andrews 48 69 Bakkor 49	19	41
25	NPL	H	FC United	**612**	L	2-5	Titchiner 36 Andrews 62	19	42
29	NPL	H	Grantham Town	319	W	2-1	Hancock 24 Titchiner 37	19	43
April 1	NPL	A	Chorley	639	L	0-1		19	44
5	NPL	A	Matlock Town	270	W	1-0	Bodle 40	19	45
8	NPL	H	Frickley Athletic	304	W	2-1	Picton 13 (og) Titchiner 83	17	46
12	NPL	H	Trafford	358	L	0-4		18	47
19	NPL	A	Barwell	158	W	2-0	Bakkor 7 Andrews 76	17	48
21	NPL	H	Rushall Olympic	324	L	2-4	Hancock 7 Andrews 36	17	49
26	NPL	A	Ashton United	158	W	4-1	Sheehan 30 Andrews 71 Dawson 82 Hancock 88	16	50

GOALSCORERS	Lge	FAC	FAT	Total	Pens	Hat-tricks	Cons Run
Hancock	14		2	16	3		2
Andrews	15		1	16			3
Powell	9			9			2
Tichener	8			8			2
Wilson	7		1	8			2
Walker	5			5			
Bakkor	4			4			2
Dawson	4			4			
Thompson	2		1	3			2
Sheehan	2			2			
Bodle	1			1			
Breeze	1			1			
Gardner	1			1			
Harrison	1			1			
Jackson	1			1			
Simm	1			1			
Tuck	1			1			
Opponents	1			1			

Cons Run - Consecutive scoring games.

WORKINGTON

Chairman: Glenn Heathcote
Secretary: Alec Graham **(T)** 07788 537 811 **(E)** alec.graham@workingtonafc.com
Commercial Manager: **(T)**
Programme Editor: Paul Armstrong **(T)** 07951 243 717
Ground Address: Borough Park, Workington, Cumbria CA14 2DT
(T) 01900 602 871 **Manager:** Gavin Skelton

Club Factfile

Founded: 1884 **Nickname:** Reds
Previous Names: None
Previous Leagues: Cumberland Assoc. 1890-94, Cumberland Senior 1894-1901, 03-04. Lancashire 1901-03, Lancashire Comb. 1904-10, North Eastern 1910-11, 21-51, Football League 1951-77, N.P.L. 1977-2005. Conference 2005-14.

Club Colours (change): Red/white/red (White/black/black & white hoops)

Ground Capacity: 2,500 **Seats:** 500 **Covered:** 1,000 **Clubhouse:** Yes **Shop:** Yes

Directions
A66 into Workington. At traffic lights at bottom of hill (HSBC opposite), turn left towards town centre. Approach traffic lights in centre lane (Washington Central Hotel on your right) and turn right. Continue on this road, passing over a mini roundabout, a pedestrian crossing and a further set of traffic lights. You will come to the Railway Station (facing you), carry on through the junction and bear right, passing the Derwent Park Stadium (Rugby League/speedway), then left and Borough Park becomes visible ahead of you.

Previous Grounds: Various 1884-1921, Lonsdale Park 1921-37

Record Attendance: 21,000 v Manchester United - FA Cup 3rd round 04/01/1958
Record Victory: 17-1 v Cockermouth Crusaders - Cumberland Senior League 19/01/1901
Record Defeat: 0-9 v Chorley (A) - Northern Premier League 10/11/1987
Record Goalscorer: Billy Charlton - 193
Record Appearances: Bobby Brown - 419
Additional Records: Paid £6,000 to Sunderland for Ken Chisolm 1956
Received £33,000 from Liverpool for Ian McDonald 1974
Senior Honours:
North West Counties League 1998-99
Cumberland County Cup x23

10 YEAR RECORD

04-05	05-06	06-07	07-08	08-09	09-10	10-11	11-12	12-13	13-14
NP P 2	Conf N 13	Conf N 3	Conf N 14	Conf N 12	Conf N 4	Conf N 11	Conf N 13	Conf N 14	Conf N 22

WORKINGTON MATCH RESULTS 2013-14

Date	Comp	H/A	Opponents	Att:	Result		Goalscorers	Pos	No.
Aug 17	CNorth	A	AFC Telford	1630	L	1-2	Tinnion 54	14	1
20	CNorth	H	Stockport County	**562**	D	1-1	May	16	2
24	CNorth	H	Vauxhall Motors	353	L	0-1		18	3
26	CNorth	A	Guiseley	417	L	0-1		18	4
31	CNorth	H	Stalybridge Celtic	424	**W**	1-0	Allison 23	16	5
Sept 7	CNorth	A	Histon	405	L	1-3	Jackson 86	18	6
14	CNorth	H	Gloucester City	373	**W**	4-2	Allison 22 Wilson 40 Built 73 Edwards 90 (pen)	15	7
17	CNorth	A	North Ferriby United	256	L	1-3	Jackson 62	16	8
21	CNorth	A	Worcester City	559	L	0-4		19	9
28	***FAC2Q***	***H***	***Burscough***	***381***	***W***	***2-1***	***Dodd 29 (og) Wilson 40***		10
Oct 5	CNorth	H	Leamington	359	L	1-2	Jackson 7	22	11
12	***FAC3Q***	***A***	***Guisborough Town***	***524***	***W***	***4-1***	***Wordsworth 39 Wright 55 Forrest 67 Tinnion 87***		12
19	CNorth	H	Hednesford Town	442	D	2-2	Forrest 13 35	22	13
22	CNorth	A	Harrogate Town	318	L	0-3		22	14
26	***FAC4Q***	***H***	***Stourbridge***	***519***	***L***	***1-3***	***McLuckie 86***		15
Nov 2	CNorth	H	Gainsborough Trinity	265	**W**	4-2	Jackson 37 May 44 McLuckie 52 Allison 76	17	16
9	CNorth	A	Solihull Moors	330	D	1-1	Hindmarsh 65	17	17
16	***FAT3Q***	***A***	***Hednesford Town***	***551***	***L***	***0-3***			18
23	CNorth	H	Harrogate Town	295	L	0-3		21	19
Dec 7	CNorth	H	Colwyn Bay	314	L	0-3		21	20
10	CNorth	A	Oxford City	210	D	1-1	McKenna 65	21	21
14	CNorth	H	AFC Telford United	346	L	0-1		21	22
21	CNorth	A	Leamington	509	L	0-2		21	23
26	CNorth	H	Barrow	581	L	2-3	Tinnion 20 Jackson 37	22	24
28	CNorth	A	Stockport County	2282	D	1-1	Jackson 2	22	25
Jan 1	CNorth	H	Barrow	931	L	0-2		22	26
4	CNorth	H	Histon	347	L	2-3	Hindmarsh 32 Haley 62	22	27
7	CNorth	A	Boston Unlted	797	L	3-5	Wordswoth 21 Jackson 27 48 (pen)	22	28
18	CNorth	A	Gainborough Trinity	371	L	0-3		22	29
25	CNorth	A	Brackley Town	315	D	1-1	Jackson 61 (pen)	22	30
March 1	CNorth	A	Altrincham	859	L	0-2		22	31
4	CNorth	H	Oxford City	336	**W**	1-0	McKenna 24	22	32
8	CNorth	H	Boston United	397	**W**	1-0	McKenna 84	22	33
12	CNorth	A	Bradford PA	269	L	0-1		22	34
15	CNorth	H	Brackley Town	314	L	0-3		22	35
22	CNorth	A	Hednesford Town	490	L	0-4		22	36
25	CNorth	H	North Ferriby United	242	D	3-3	Allison 28 70 Abadaki 82	22	37
29	CNorth	H	Solihull Moors	384	D	0-0		22	38
April 1	CNorth	A	Canvey Island	158	L	2-3	Jackson 55 Wright 59	22	39
5	CNorth	H	Bradford PA	303	L	0-2		22	40
8	CNorth	H	Altrincham	270	L	1-6	Abadaki 77	22	41
12	CNorth	H	Worcester City	241	**W**	1-0	Jackson 90	22	42
15	CNorth	A	Gloucester Clty	324	D	1-1	Jackson 40 (pen)	22	43
19	CNorth	A	Vauxhall Motors	168	L	1-2	May	22	44
21	CNorth	H	Guiseley	357	D	1-1	Abadaki 52	22	45
26	CNorth	A	Stalybridge Celtic	472	L	0-2		22	46

GOALSCORERS	Lge	FAC	FAT	Total	Pens	Hat-tricks	Cons Run
Jackson	12			12	3		2
Allison	5			5			
Abadaki	3			3			
Forrest	2	1		3			
May	3			3			
McKenna	3			3			2
Tinnion	2	1		3			
McLuckie	1	1		2			2
Hindmarsh	2			2			
Wilson	1	1		2			
Wordsworth	1	1		2			
Wright	1	1		2			
Built	1			1			
Edwards	1			1	1		
Haley	1			1			
Opponents		1		1			

Cons Run - Consecutive scoring games.

BAMBER BRIDGE

Chairman: Francis Doyle
Secretary: George Halliwell (T) 07970 042 954 (E)
Commercial Manager: (T)
Programme Editor: Peter Nowell (T) 07766 196 246
Ground Address: Sir Tom Finney Stadium, Brownedge Road, Bamber Bridge PR5 6UX
(T) 01772 909 690 **Manager:** Neil Crowe

Club Factfile

Founded: 1952 **Nickname:** Brig
Previous Names: None
Previous Leagues: Preston & District 1952-90, North West Counties 1990-93

Club Colours (change): White/black/black (All red)

Ground Capacity: 3,000 **Seats:** 554 **Covered:** 800 **Clubhouse:** Yes **Shop:** Yes

Directions
Junction 29, A6 (Bamber Bridge by-pass)onto London Way. First roundabout take 3rd exit Brownedge Road (East) then take first right. Ground on left at the bottom of the road.

Previous Grounds: King George V, Higher Wallton 1952-86

Record Attendance: 2,300 v Czech Republic - Pre Euro '96 friendly
Record Victory: 8-0 v Curzon Ashton - North West Counties 1994-95
Record Defeat: Not known
Record Goalscorer: Not known
Record Appearances: Not known
Additional Records: Paid £10,000 to Horwich RMI for Mark Edwards
Received £15,000 from Wigan Athletic for Tony Black 1995
Senior Honours:
ATDC Lancashire Trophy 1994-95.
Northern Premier League Premier Division 1995-96, Challenge Cup 1995-96.

10 YEAR RECORD

04-05		05-06		06-07		07-08		08-09		09-10		10-11		11-12		12-13		13-14	
NP P	21	NP 1	13	NP 1	13	NP1N	5	NP1N	11	NP1N	14	NP1N	7	NP1N	10	NP1N	9	NP1N	4

BRIGHOUSE TOWN

Chairman: Ray McLaughlin
Secretary: Malcolm Taylor (T) 07884 182 970 (E) malctay@blueyonder.co.uk
Commercial Manager: (T)
Programme Editor: Ray McLaughlin (T) 07929 053 819
Ground Address: Dual Seal Stadium, St Giles Rd, Hove Edge, Brighouse, HD6 2PL
(T) 01484 380 088 **Manager:** Paul Quinn

Club Factfile

Founded: 1963 **Nickname:** Town
Previous Names: Blakeborough
Previous Leagues: Huddersfield Works. 1963-75. West Riding County Amateur 1975-08.

Club Colours (change): Orange/black/orange. (Yellow/green/yellow).

Ground Capacity: 1,000 **Seats:** 100 **Covered:** 200 **Clubhouse:** Yes **Shop:**

Directions
Leave M62 at jct 26 go onto A58 Halifax. Carry on to third set of traffic lights at Hipperholme. Turn left at lights onto A644 Brighouse past Brighouse Juniors pitch on right. Take next left in 100 metres then next left into Spout House Lane. Follow road past Old Pond PH road bears right, carry on and as road begins to bear left turn right into lane, gate 20 metres on left into car park.

Previous Grounds: Green Lane.

Record Attendance:
Record Victory:
Record Defeat:
Record Goalscorer:
Record Appearances:
Additional Records:

Senior Honours:
West Riding County Amateur League: Prem Div - 1990/91 1994/95 1995/96 2000/01 2001/02, Prem Cup - 1993/94, 95/96 98/99, 00/01; Div 1 - 1988/89. Northern Counties East Premier 2013-14.

10 YEAR RECORD

04-05		05-06		06-07		07-08		08-09		09-10		10-11		11-12		12-13		13-14	
WRCP	4	WRCP	3	WRCP	3	WRCP	8	NCE1	15	NCE1	2	NCEP	16	NCEP	4	NCEP	2	NCEP	1

Northern Premier League Action

Nantwich Town's top goal scorer, Aaron Burns looks to turn past Stafford's Joe Ballinger.

Photo: Jonathan Holloway.

BURSCOUGH

Chairman: Mike Swift
Secretary: Stan Petheridge **(T)** 07815 954 304 **(E)** stanpeth@fsmail.net
Commercial Manager: **(T)**
Programme Editor: Stan Petheridge **(T)** 07815 954 304
Ground Address: Victoria Park, Bobby Langton Way, Mart Lane, Burscough L40 0SD
(T) 01704 896 776 **Manager:** Derek Goulding

Club Factfile

Founded: 1946 **Nickname:** Linnets
Previous Names: None
Previous Leagues: Liverpool County Combination 1946-53, Lancashire Combination 1953-70, Cheshire County 1970-82, North West Counties 1982-98, Northern Premier League 1998-2007, Conference 2007-09
Club Colours (change): All green (Sky blue/navy/sky)

Ground Capacity: 2,500 **Seats:** 270 **Covered:** 1,000 **Clubhouse:** Yes **Shop:** Yes

Directions
M6 to J27. Follow signs for 'Parbold' (A5209), carry on through Newburgh into Burscough passing Briars Hall Hotel on left. Turn right at second mini-roundabout into Junction Lane (signposted 'Burscough & Martin Mere') into village, over canal. Take second left into Mart Lane to ground at end.

Previous Grounds: None

Record Attendance: 4,798 v Wigan Athletic - FA Cup 3rd Qualifying Round 1950-51
Record Victory: 10-0 v Cromptons Rec - 1947 and v Nelson - 1948-49 both Lancashire Combination
Record Defeat: 0-9 v Earltown - Liverpool County Combination 1948-49
Record Goalscorer: Wes Bridge - 188
Record Appearances: Not known
Additional Records: Johnny Vincent scored 60 goals during the 1953-64 season
Louis Bimpson scored 7 goals in one game.
Senior Honours:
North West Counties League Division 1 1982-83. FA Trophy 2002-03. Northern Premier League Premier Division 2006-07.
Liverpool Challenge Cup x3. Liverpool Non-League Senior Cup x2.

10 YEAR RECORD

04-05	05-06	06-07	07-08	08-09	09-10	10-11	11-12	12-13	13-14
NP P 6	NP P 7	NP P 1	Conf N 8	Conf N 21	NP P 16	NP P 19	NP P 22	NP1N 11	NP1N 14

CLITHEROE

Chairman: Anne Barker
Secretary: Chris Musson (T) 07503 240 629 (E)
Commercial Manager: (T)
Programme Editor: Chris Musson (T) 07503 240 629
Ground Address: Shawbridge, off Pendle Road, Clitheroe, Lancashire BB7 1DZ
(T) 01200 444 487 **Manager:** Simon Garner

Club Factfile

Founded: 1877 **Nickname:** The Blues
Previous Names: Clitheroe Central 1877-1903.
Previous Leagues: Blackburn & District, Lancashire Combination 1903-04, 05-10, 25-82, North West Counties 1982-85

Club Colours (change): All blue (Red/black/red)

Ground Capacity: 2,400 **Seats:** 250 **Covered:** 1,400 **Clubhouse:** Yes **Shop:**

Directions
M6 junction 31, A59 to Clitheroe (17 miles) at 5th roundabout turn left after half a mile at Pendle Road. Ground is one mile behind Bridge Inn on the right.

Previous Grounds: None

Record Attendance: 2,050 v Mangotsfield - FA Vase Semi-final 1995-96
Record Victory: Not known
Record Defeat: Not known
Record Goalscorer: Don Francis
Record Appearances: Lindsey Wallace - 670
Additional Records: Received £45,000 from Crystal Palace for Carlo Nash

Senior Honours:
North West Counties League 1984-85, 2003-04.
Lancashire Challenge Trophy 1984-85. East Lancashire Floodlit Trophy 1994-95.

10 YEAR RECORD

04-05	05-06	06-07	07-08	08-09	09-10	10-11	11-12	12-13	13-14
NP 1 19	NP 1 16	NP 1 16	NP1N 13	NP1N 12	NP1N 8	NP1N 6	NP1N 19	NP1N 8	NP1N 17

DARLINGTON 1883

Chairman: Martin Jesper
Secretary: Harry Dunn (T) 07807 831 299 (E) secretary@dfc1883.co.uk
Commercial Manager: (T)
Programme Editor: Ray Simpson (T) 07976 434 111
Ground Address: Bishop Auckland FC, Heritage Park, Bishop Auckland, Co. Durham DL14 9AE
(T) 01388 604 605 **Manager:** Martin Gray

Club Factfile

Founded: 1883 **Nickname:** The Quakers
Previous Names: Darlington FC 1883-2012
Previous Leagues: Northern League 1883-1908, 2012-13, North Eastern 1908-21, Football League 1921-89, 91-2010, Conference 1989-90, 10-12.
Club Colours (change): White & black hoops/black/black (All green)

Ground Capacity: 2,004 **Seats:** 250 **Covered:** 722 **Clubhouse:** Yes **Shop:** Yes

Directions
Leave the A1(m) at junction 57 for Darlington. Follow road to roundabout. From here take the first exit off and follow road to second roundabout (Reg Vardy on right). Head straight over and follow signs for Teesside until you reach next roundabout. Turn left here and stadium is on right hand side.

Previous Grounds: Feethams > 2003, Reynolds Arena, Hurworth Moor.

Record Attendance: **Record Att:** 21,023 v Bolton Wanderers - League Cup 3rd Round 14/11/1960
Record Victory: 9-2 v Lincoln City - Division 3 North 07/01/1928
Record Defeat: 0-10 v Doncaster Rovers - Division 4 25/01/1964
Record Goalscorer: Alan Walsh - 100, Jerry Best - 80
Record Appearances: Ron Greener - 490, John Peverell - 465, Brian Henderson - 463
Additional Records: Paid £95,000 to Motherwell for Nick Cusack January 1992.
Received £400,000 from Dundee United for Jason Devos October 1998
Senior Honours:
Northern League 1895-96, 99-1900, 2012-13. North Eastern League 1912-13, 20-21. Football League Division 3 1924-25, Division 4 1990-91, Division 3 North Cup 1933-34. Durham Senior Cup 1919-20. FA Trophy 2010-11.

10 YEAR RECORD

04-05	05-06	06-07	07-08	08-09	09-10	10-11	11-12	12-13	13-14
FL 2 8	FL 2 8	FL 2 11	FL 2 6	FL 2 12	FL 2 24	Conf 7	Conf 22	NL 1 1	NP1N 2

DROYLSDEN

Chairman: David Pace

Secretary: S Quinn **(T)** 07887 933 095 **(E)** alphagroup@jlservices.co.uk

Commercial Manager: **(T)**

Programme Editor: Bryan Pace **(T)** 07763 318 860

Ground Address: The Butchers Arms Ground, Market Street, Droylsden, M43 7AY

(T) 0161 370 1426 **Manager:** David Pace

Club Factfile

Founded: 1892 **Nickname:** The Bloods

Previous Names: None

Previous Leagues: Manchester, Lancashire Combination 1936-39, 50-68, Cheshire County 1939-50, 68-82, North West Counties 1982-87, Northern Premier 1986-2004

Club Colours (change): All red (Yellow/blue/blue)

Ground Capacity: 3,000 **Seats:** 500 **Covered:** 2,000 **Clubhouse:** Yes **Shop:** Yes

Directions

From junction 23 M60 follow signs A635 Manchester, then A662 signed Droylsden, at town centre traffic lights turn right into Market Street, through next set of lights and the main entrance to the ground is 75 yards on your left.

Previous Grounds: None

Record Attendance: 4,250 v Grimsby, FA Cup 1st Round 1976.

Record Victory: 13-2 v Lucas Sports Club

Record Defeat: Not known

Record Goalscorer: E. Gillibrand - 275 (1931-35)

Record Appearances: Paul Phillips - 326

Additional Records: Received £11,000 from Crewe Alexandra for Tony Naylor 1990

Senior Honours:

Northern Premier League Division 1 1998-99. Conference North 2006-07.
Manchester Premier Cup x3. Manchester Senior Cup x3.

10 YEAR RECORD

04-05	05-06	06-07	07-08	08-09	09-10	10-11	11-12	12-13	13-14
Conf N 3	Conf N 4	Conf N 1	Conf 24	Conf N 7	Conf N 5	Conf N 8	Conf N 9	Conf N 21	NP P 24

FARSLEY A.F.C.

Chairman: John Palmer
Secretary: Joshua Greaves (T) 07725 999 758 (E) office@farsleyafc.com
Commercial Manager: (T)
Programme Editor: Robert Winterbottom (T) 07736 037 604
Ground Address: Throstle Nest, Newlands, Pudsey, Leeds, LS28 5BE
(T) 0113 255 7292 **Manager:** Neil Parsley

Club Factfile

Founded: 2010 **Nickname:** The Villagers
Previous Names: Farsley Celtic > 2010
Previous Leagues: Northern Counties East 2010-11.

Club Colours (change): Royal blue macron with white chest trim/blue/blue (Yellow macron with band of blue & white/yellow/yellow)np

Ground Capacity: 4,000 **Seats:** 300 **Covered:** 1,500 **Clubhouse:** Yes **Shop:** Yes

Directions
Farsley is sandwiched between Leeds and Bradford approximately 1 mile from the junction of the Leeds Outer Ring Road (A6110) and the A647 towards Bradford. At the junction, take the B6157 towards Leeds, passing the police station on the left hand side. At New Street (the junction cornered by Go Outdoors) turn left. Newlands is approximately 300 yards on the right. Throstle Nest is situated at the end of Newlands with parking available outside the ground.

Previous Grounds: None

Record Attendance:
Record Victory: 8-0 v Arnold Town (H) Northern Counties East Premier 2010-11.
Record Defeat: 5-1 v Tadcaster Albion, President's Cup Final 27/04/11.
Record Goalscorer: Not known
Record Appearances: Not known
Additional Records: None

Senior Honours:
Northern Counties East Premier Division 2010-11.

10 YEAR RECORD

04-05	05-06	06-07	07-08	08-09	09-10	10-11	11-12	12-13	13-14
						NCEP 1	NP1N 4	NP1N 14	NP1N 7

HARROGATE RAILWAY ATHLETIC

Chairman: Nigel Corner
Secretary: Dave Shepherd (T) 07816 986 799 (E) mail4rail@ntlworld.com
Commercial Manager: (T)
Programme Editor: Dave Shepherd (T) 07816 986 799
Ground Address: Station View, Starbeck, Harrogate, North Yorkshire HG2 7JA
(T) 01423 883 104 **Manager:** Billy Miller

Club Factfile

Founded: 1935 **Nickname:** The Rail
Previous Names: None
Previous Leagues: West Yorkshire, Harrogate & District, Yorkshire 1955-73, 80-82, Northern Counties East 1982-2006

Club Colours (change): Red/green/red (All blue)

Ground Capacity: 3,500 **Seats:** 800 **Covered:** 600 **Clubhouse:** Yes **Shop:** No

Directions
From All Areas I would suggest using the M1 A1 Link Road heading North. Once on the A1 North stay on it until Junction 47. Exit at Junction 47 and take the 1st Exit at the Roundabout A59 heading towards Knaresborough and Harrogate. At the next Roundabout take the 3rd exit A59 Knaresborough. Stay on the A59 through Knaresborough and on towards Harrogate, after approx 1 mile from Knaresborough you will enter Starbeck. Proceed through Starbeck over the Railway Crossing. Station View is the 1st Right after the Railway Crossing. The Ground is at the far end of Station View. If you are coming from Harrogate towards Knaresborough on the A59 turn left immediately prior to pelican crossing just before the Railway Crossing. The Ground is at the far end of Station View.

Previous Grounds: None

Record Attendance: 3,500 v Bristol City - FA Cup 2nd Round 2002-03
Record Victory: Not known
Record Defeat: Not known
Record Goalscorer: Not known
Record Appearances: Not known
Additional Records: Received £1,000 from Guiseley for Colin Hunter

Senior Honours:
Northern Counties East Division 2 North & League cup 1983-84, Division 1 1989-99.

10 YEAR RECORD

04-05	05-06	06-07	07-08	08-09	09-10	10-11	11-12	12-13	13-14
NCEP 3	NCEP 3	NP 1 12	NP1N 12	NP1N 18	NP1N 17	NP1N 20	NP1N 21	NP1N 18	NP1N 13

KENDAL TOWN

Chairman: Haydon Munslow
Secretary: Craig Campbell **(T)** 07980 660 428 **(E)** info@kendaltownfootballclub.co.uk
Commercial Manager: Graham O'Callaghan **(T)**
Programme Editor: Merrill Tummey **(T)** 07733 135 796
Ground Address: The Northgate Stadium, Parkside Road, Kendal, Cumbria LA9 7BL
(T) 01539 727 472 **Manager:** David Foster

Club Factfile

Founded: 1919 **Nickname:** Town
Previous Names: Netherfield AFC 1919-2000
Previous Leagues: Westmorland, North Lancashire Combination 1945-68, Northern Premier 1968-83, North West Counties 1983-87

Club Colours (change): Black and white stripes/black/red (Pale blue/navy/navy)

Ground Capacity: 2,490 **Seats:** 450 **Covered:** 1000 **Clubhouse:** Yes **Shop:** Yes

Directions
M6 junction 36, via A590/591/A6 to Kendal (South). At first traffic lights turn right, left at roundabout, right into Parkside Road. Ground on right over brow of hill.

Previous Grounds: None

Record Attendance: 5,184 v Grimsby Town - FA Cup 1st Round 1955
Record Victory: 11-0 v Great Harwood - 22/03/1947
Record Defeat: 0-10 v Stalybridge Celtic - 01/09/1984
Record Goalscorer: Tom Brownlee
Record Appearances: Not known
Additional Records: Received £10,250 from Manchester City for Andy Milner 1995

Senior Honours:
Westmorlands Senior Cup x12. Lancashire Senior Cup 2002-03.

10 YEAR RECORD

04-05	05-06	06-07	07-08	08-09	09-10	10-11	11-12	12-13	13-14
NP 1 5	NP 1 3	NP P 19	NP P 11	NP P 5	NP P 5	NP P 8	NP P 11	NP P 21	NP1N 10

LANCASTER CITY

Chairman: Stuart Houghton
Secretary: Barry Newsham **(T)** 07759 530 901 **(E)** lancastercityfc@btinternet.com
Commercial Manager: Jim Johnstone **(T)** 07551 642 343
Programme Editor: Andrew Satterthwaite **(T)** 07947 145 915
Ground Address: Giant Axe, West Road, Lancaster LA1 5PE
(T) 01524 382 238 **Manager:** Darren Peacock

Club Factfile

Founded: 1905 **Nickname:** Dolly Blues
Previous Names: None
Previous Leagues: Lancashire Combination 1905-70, Northern Premier League 1970-82, 87-2004, North West Counties 1982-87, Conference 2004-07
Club Colours (change): Blue/white/blue (Yellow/blue/yellow)

Ground Capacity: 3,064 **Seats:** 513 **Covered:** 900 **Clubhouse:** Yes **Shop:** Yes

Directions From the South: Exit M6 at Junction 33. At roundabout take the second exit onto the A6, pass through Galgate and then Lancaster University on the right until the next roundabout. Take the second main exit into Lancaster and follow signs for the railway station. At the traffic lights by Waterstones Bookshop turn immediately left. Take the second right onto Station Road and follow downhill on West Road and take the first right into the ground. From the North: Exit M6 at Junction 34 and turn left onto the A683. Follow signs for railway station into City around the one way system. Move over to the right hand side lane at the police station and through traffic lights. Manoeuvre into the left-hand lane until traffic lights at Waterstones Bookshop. Follow directions as from the south.

Previous Grounds: None

Record Attendance: 7,500 v Carlisle United - FA Cup 1936
Record Victory: 8-0 v Leyland Motors (A) - 1983-84
Record Defeat: 0-10 v Matlock Town - Northern Premier League Division 1 1973-74
Record Goalscorer: David Barnes - 130
Record Appearances: Edgar J Parkinson - 591
Additional Records: Paid £6,000 to Droylsden for Jamie Tandy
Received £25,000 from Birmingham City for Chris Ward
Senior Honours:
Lancashire Junior Cup (ATS Challenge Trophy) 1927-28, 28-29, 30-31, 33-34, 51-52, 74-75.
Northern Premier League Division 1 1995-96.

10 YEAR RECORD

04-05	05-06	06-07	07-08	08-09	09-10	10-11	11-12	12-13	13-14
Conf N 13	Conf N 15	Conf N 24	NP1N 11	NP1N 7	NP1N 2	NP1N 8	NP1N 6	NP1N 13	NP1N 6

MOSSLEY

Chairman: Harry Hulmes
Secretary: Harry Hulmes **(T)** 07944 856 343 **(E)** harry.hulmes@mossleyafc.com
Commercial Manager: **(T)**
Programme Editor: John Cawthorne **(T)** 01457 511 053
Ground Address: Seel Park, Market Street, Mossley, Lancashire OL5 0ES
(T) 01457 832 369 **Manager:** Peter Band & Lloyd Morrison

Club Factfile

Founded: 1903 **Nickname:** Lilywhites
Previous Names: Park Villa 1903-04, Mossley Juniors
Previous Leagues: Ashton, South East Lancashire, Lancashire Combination 1918-19, Cheshire County 1919-72, Northern Premier 1972-95, North West Counties 1995-2004
Club Colours (change): White/black/white (Orange/white/orange)

Ground Capacity: 4,500 **Seats:** 200 **Covered:** 1,500 **Clubhouse:** Yes **Shop:** Yes

Directions
Exit M60 Junction 23 following A635 Ashton-under-Lyne. Take 3rd exit off roundabout then 3rd exit off next roundabout (Asda) and then 3rd exit off next roundabout signed Mossley A670. At junction turn right on to Mossley Rd through traffic lights. After approx 2.5 miles drop down hill entering Mossley town centre. Passing supermarket on left turn right before next traffic lights. Continue up the hill and left into Market Street. Ground is approx 200 yards on the left.

Previous Grounds: None

Record Attendance: 7,000 v Stalybridge Celtic 1950
Record Victory: Not known
Record Defeat: Not known
Record Goalscorer: David Moore - 235 (1974-84)
Record Appearances: Jimmy O'Connor - 613 (1972-87)
Additional Records: Paid £2,300 to Altrincham for Phil Wilson
Received £25,000 from Everton for Eamonn O'Keefe
Senior Honours:
Northern Premier League 1978-79, 79-80, Challenge Cup 78-79, Division 1 2005-06.
Manchester Challenge Trophy 2011-12. Manchester Premier Cup 2012-13.

10 YEAR RECORD

04-05	05-06	06-07	07-08	08-09	09-10	10-11	11-12	12-13	13-14
NP 1 7	NP 1 1	NP P 20	NP1N 15	NP1N 10	NP1N 7	NP1N 15	NP1N 14	NP1N 5	NP1N 15

NEW MILLS

Chairman: Raymond Coverley
Secretary: Emma Adrio **(T)** 07878 551 324 **(E)** newmillsfs@yahoo.co.uk
Commercial Manager: **(T)**
Programme Editor: Glynn Jones **(T)** 07445 380 064
Ground Address: Church Lane, New Mills, SK22 4NP
(T) 01663 747 435 **Manager:** Roy Soule

Club Factfile

Founded: pre1890 **Nickname:** The Millers
Previous Names: New Mills St Georges until 1919
Previous Leagues: Manchester, North West Counties, Cheshire

Club Colours (change): Amber & black/amber/black (White/white/black).

Ground Capacity: 1,650 **Seats:** 120 **Covered:** 400 **Clubhouse:** Yes **Shop:**

Directions

Via Buxton: Follow the A6 By-Pass, go straight through the roundabout, under railway bridge and about 1 mile further on turn right onto Marsh Lane (Past Furness Vale primary school), this road takes you straight to the ground. Coach drivers should proceed on the A6 a couple of miles turning right opposite the Swan.

From Chesterfield, take the A619 then the A623 and after the hair pin bend at Sparrow pit, proceed down the A623 turning right onto the A6 By-Pass, Follow directions as above.

Previous Grounds: Not known

Record Attendance: Att: 4,500 v Hyde United, Manchester Junior Cup 09/09/1922
Record Victory: 20-3 v Winton United, Manchester Junior Cup 10/11/1962
Record Defeat: Not known
Record Goalscorer: In a season - Neville Holdgate - 62 1937-38
Record Appearances: Not known
Additional Records:

Senior Honours:
Manchester League Premier Division 1924, 26, 56, 63, 65, 66, 67, 68, 70, 71.
North West Counties Division Two 2007-08, Challenge Cup 2008-09, Premier Division 2010-11.

10 YEAR RECORD

04-05	05-06	06-07	07-08	08-09	09-10	10-11	11-12	12-13	13-14
NWC2 9	NWC2 12	NWC2	NWC2 1	NWCP 2	NWCP 2	NWCP 1	NP1S 9	NP1N 3	NP1N 16

NORTHWICH VICTORIA

Chairman: Derek Nuttall
Secretary: Dave Thomas **(T)** 07798 564 596 **(E)** admin@northwichvics.co.uk
Commercial Manager: **(T)**
Programme Editor: Jason Dudley **(T)** 07765 764 856
Ground Address: Flixton FC, Valley Road, Flixton, Manchester M41 8RQ
(T) 0161 458 2903 **Manager:** James Gannon

Club Factfile

Founded: 1874 **Nickname:** Vics, Greens or Trickies
Previous Names: None
Previous Leagues: The Combination 1890-92, 1894-98, Football League 1892-94, Cheshire 1898-1900, Manchester 1900-12 Lancashire 1912-19, Cheshire County 1919-68, Northern Premier 1968-79, Conference 1979-2010
Club Colours (change): Green and white hoops/white/white (Yellow/blue/blue)

Ground Capacity: 6,000 **Seats:** 4,264 **Covered:** 3,500 **Clubhouse:** Yes **Shop:** Yes

Directions
Leave M60 at junction 10, take B5214 signposted Urmston. At second roundabout take 3rd exit, take right only lane on the exit on Daveyhulme Road. Follow this road to Valley Road. Just after left hand bend, 1.5miles. Ground is at far end of the road.

Previous Grounds: The Drill Field. Victoria Stadium. Stafford Rangers FC.

Record Attendance: 11,290 v Witton Albion - Cheshire League Good Friday 1949
Record Victory: 17-0 v Marple Association 1883
Record Defeat: 3-10 v Port Vale - 1931
Record Goalscorer: Peter Burns - 160 (1955-65)
Record Appearances: Ken Jones - 970 (1969-85)
Additional Records: Paid £12,000 to Hyde United for Malcolm O'Connor August 1988. Received £50,000 from Leyton Orient for Gary Fletcher June 1921 and from Chester City for Neil Morton October 1990.
Senior Honours:
FA Trophy 1983-84.
Conference North 2005-06.
Cheshire Senior Cup x16 Most recent 2013-14. Staffordshire Senior Cup x3.

10 YEAR RECORD

04-05	05-06	06-07	07-08	08-09	09-10	10-11	11-12	12-13	13-14
Conf 19	Conf N 1	Conf 13	Conf 19	Conf 22	Conf N 12	NP P 12	NP P 2	NP1S 8	NP1N 9

OSSETT ALBION

Chairman: Dominic Riordan
Secretary: Stephen Hanks (T) 07792 221 088 (E) ossettalbion@sky.com
Commercial Manager: (T)
Programme Editor: Stephen Hanks (T) 07792 221 088
Ground Address: Queens Terrace, Dimple Wells, Ossett, Yorkshire WF5 8JU
(T) 01924 273 746 **Manager:** Richard Tracey

Club Factfile

Founded: 1944 **Nickname:** Albion
Previous Names: Not known
Previous Leagues: Heavy Woollen Area 1944-49, West Riding County Amateur 1949-50, West Yorkshire 1950-57, Yorkshire 1957-82, Northern Counties East 1982-2004
Club Colours (change): Gold/black/black (All white)

Ground Capacity: 3,000 **Seats:** Yes **Covered:** 750 **Clubhouse:** Yes **Shop:** Yes

Directions
From M1 Junction 40: Follow Wakefield signs for 200 yards. Turn right at traffic lights (Holiday Inn on the corner). At the end of Queens Drive turn right and then 2nd left onto Southdale Road. At the end of Southdale Road turn right then immediately left onto Dimple Wells Road, the ground is facing. NOTE: There is a weight limit on Southdale Road. Coaches will need to continue on Station Road to the end, turn left, then at the end left again. Take 1st right onto Priory Road following for 200 yards turning left twice.

Previous Grounds: Fearn House

Record Attendance: 1,200 v Leeds United - Opening of floodlights 1986
Record Victory: 12-0 v British Ropes (H) - Yorkshire League Division 2 06/05/1959
Record Defeat: 2-11 v Swillington (A) - West Yorkshire League Division 1 25/04/1956
Record Goalscorer: John Balmer
Record Appearances: Peter Eaton - 800+ (22 years)
Additional Records:

Senior Honours:
Northern Counties East League Division 1 1986-87, Premier Division 1998-99, 2003-04, League Cup 1983-84, 2002-03.
West Riding County Cup x4.

10 YEAR RECORD

04-05	05-06	06-07	07-08	08-09	09-10	10-11	11-12	12-13	13-14
NP 1 12	NP 1 14	NP 1 11	NP1N 6	NP1N 6	NP1N 21	NP1N 22	NP1N 18	NP1N 20	NP1N 21

OSSETT TOWN

Chairman: James Rogers
Secretary: Neil Spofforth **(T)** 07818 400 808 **(E)** spofforth10@gmail.com
Commercial Manager: **(T)**
Programme Editor: Neil Spofforth **(T)** 07818 400 808
Ground Address: Ingfield, Prospect Road, Ossett, Wakefield WF5 9HA
(T) 01924 280 028 **Manager:** John Reed

Club Factfile

Founded: 1936 **Nickname:** Town
Previous Names: None
Previous Leagues: Leeds 1936-39, Yorkshire 1945-82, Northern Counties East 1983-99

Club Colours (change): All red (Blue & yellow stripes/blue/blue)

Ground Capacity: 4,000 **Seats:** 360 **Covered:** 1,000 **Clubhouse:** Yes **Shop:** Yes

Directions
From M1 Junction 40: Take A638 signposted Ossett Town Centre. Take first left off A638 onto Wakefield Road, sixth left turn into Dale Street (B6120) to traffic lights. Turn left at lights. The Ground is in front of you opposite the bus station. The entrance to the Ground is just before the Esso petrol station.

Previous Grounds: Wakefield Road 1936-39. Back Lane.

Record Attendance: 2,600 v Manchester United - Friendly 1989
Record Victory: 10-1 v Harrogate RA (H) - Northern Counties East 27/04/1993
Record Defeat: 0-7 v Easington Colliery - FA Vase 08/10/1983
Record Goalscorer: Dave Leadbitter
Record Appearances: Steve Worsfold
Additional Records: Received £1,350 from Swansea Town for Dereck Blackburn

Senior Honours:
West Riding County Cup 1958-59, 81-82

10 YEAR RECORD

04-05	05-06	06-07	07-08	08-09	09-10	10-11	11-12	12-13	13-14
NP P 16	NP P 11	NP P 10	NP P 18	NP P 12	NP P 19	NP P 21	NP1N 17	NP1N 12	NP1N 8

PADIHAM

Chairman: Frank Heys

Secretary: Alan Smith **(T)** 07775 717 698 **(E)** alansmithpadihamfc@yahoo.co.uk

Commercial Manager: **(T)**

Programme Editor: Alan Smith **(T)** 07775 717 698

Ground Address: Arbories Memorial Sports Ground, Well Street, Padiham BB12 8LE

(T) 0777 571 7698 **Manager:** Steve Wilkes

Club Factfile

Founded: 1878 **Nickname:** Caldersiders

Previous Names: None

Previous Leagues: Lancashire Combination. East Lancashire Amateur. North East Lancashire. West Lancashire. North West Counties > 2013.

Club Colours (change): All royal blue. (Red/blue/red).

Ground Capacity: 1,688 **Seats:** 159 **Covered:** Yes **Clubhouse:** Yes **Shop:**

Directions

M65 to Junction 8, then follow A6068 signposted Clitheroe and Padiham. At traffic lights at bottom of hill turn right into Dean Range/Blackburn Road towards Padiham. At next junction turn into Holland Street opposite church, then into Well St at the side of Hare & Hounds Pub to ground.

Previous Grounds: Wyre Street 1878-1916.

Record Attendance: **Att:** 9,000 v Burnley, Dec.1884 (at Calderside Ground).

Record Victory:

Record Defeat:

Record Goalscorer:

Record Appearances:

Additional Records:

Senior Honours:

West Lancashire League 1999-00. North West Counties League 2012-13.

10 YEAR RECORD

04-05	05-06	06-07	07-08	08-09	09-10	10-11	11-12	12-13	13-14
NWC2 4	NWC2 5	NWC2 3	NWC2 12	NWC1 2	NWCP 10	NWCP 4	NWCP 15	NWCP 1	NP1N 19

PRESCOT CABLES

Chairman: Tony Zeverona
Secretary: Doug Lace (T) 07753 143 273 (E) prescotcables@hotmail.com
Commercial Manager: (T)
Programme Editor: Paul Watkinson (T) 0151 426 4593
Ground Address: Valerie Park, Eaton Street, Prescot L34 6HD
(T) 0151 430 0507 **Manager:** Neil Prince

Club Factfile

Founded: 1884 **Nickname:** Tigers
Previous Names: Prescot > 1995
Previous Leagues: Liverpool County Combination, Lancashire Combination 1897-98, 1918-20, 27-33, 36-76, Mid Cheshire 1976-78, Cheshire County 1978-82, North West Counties 1982-2003

Club Colours (change): Amber/black/black (All red)

Ground Capacity: 3,000 **Seats:** 500 **Covered:** 600 **Clubhouse:** Yes **Shop:** Yes

Directions
From North: M6 to Junction 26, onto M58 to Junction 3. Follow A570 to junction with A580 (East Lancs Road). (Approach junction in right hand lane of the two lanes going straight on). Cross A580 and take first road on right (Bleak Hill Road). Follow this road through to Prescot (2 miles). At traffic lights turn right, straight on at large roundabout (do not follow route onto Prescot by-pass) and right at next lights. 100 yards turn right at Hope and Anchor pub into Hope Street. Club will be in sight at bottom of road. **From South:** M6 to Junction 21a (M62 junction 10). Follow M62 towards Liverpool, to junction 7. Follow A57 to Rainhill and Prescot. Through traffic lights at Fusilier pub, 100 yards turn right at Hope and Anchor pub (as above). **From East:** Follow M62 as described in 'From South' or A580 East Lancs Road to Junction with A570 (Rainford by-pass), turn left and take first right. Follow route as 'From North'.

Previous Grounds: None

Record Attendance: 8,122 v Ashton National - 1932
Record Victory: 18-3 v Great Harwood - 1954-55
Record Defeat: 1-12 v Morecambe - 1936-37
Record Goalscorer: Freddie Crampton
Record Appearances: Harry Grisedale
Additional Records:

Senior Honours:
Lancashire Combination 1956-57. North West Counties League 2002-03.
Liverpool Non-League Cup x4. Liverpool Challenge Cup x6.

10 YEAR RECORD

04-05	05-06	06-07	07-08	08-09	09-10	10-11	11-12	12-13	13-14
NP P 5	NP P 13	NP P 14	NP P 13	NP P 22	NP1N 15	NP1N 21	NP1N 16	NP1N 17	NP1N 20

RADCLIFFE BOROUGH

Chairman: David Chalmers (Chief Executive)
Secretary: Ric Fielding **(T)** 07877 696 097 **(E)** rbfc@hotmail.co.uk
Commercial Manager: **(T)**
Programme Editor: Peter Lofthouse **(T)** 0161 724 8346
Ground Address: Stainton Park, Pilkington Road, Radcliffe, Lancashire M26 3PE
(T) 0161 724 8346 **Manager:** Paul McGuire

Club Factfile

Founded: 1949 **Nickname:** Boro
Previous Names: None
Previous Leagues: South East Lancashire, Manchester 1953-63, Lancashire Combination 1963-71, Cheshire County 1971-82, North West Counties 1982-97

Club Colours (change): Blue/blue/white (All red)

Ground Capacity: 3,100 **Seats:** 350 **Covered:** 1,000 **Clubhouse:** Yes **Shop:** Yes

Directions
M62 junction 17 – follow signs for 'Whitefield' and 'Bury'.
Take A665 to Radcliffe via by-pass to Bolton Road. Signposted to turn right into Unsworth Street opposite Turf Hotel.
The Stadium is on the left approximately half a mile turning Colshaw Close East.

Previous Grounds: Ashworth Street. Bright Street > 1970.

Record Attendance: 2,495 v York City - FA Cup 1st Round 2000-01
Record Victory: Not known
Record Defeat: Not known
Record Goalscorer: Ian Lunt - 147
Record Appearances: David Bean - 401
Additional Records: Paid £5,000 to Buxton for Gary Walker 1991
Received £20,000 from Shrewsbury Town for Jody Banim 2003
Senior Honours:
North West Counties 19984-85. Northern Premier League Division 1 1996-97.

10 YEAR RECORD

04-05	05-06	06-07	07-08	08-09	09-10	10-11	11-12	12-13	13-14
NP P 9	NP P 18	NP P 21	NP1N 16	NP1N 16	NP1N 10	NP1N 18	NP1N 15	NP1N 15	NP1N 18

Follow us on Twitter
or Facebook
twitter
f
For news about the Directory.
Updates from around the Non-League world.
Latest news from all FA Competitions.
Plus have your say on anything Football related.
LOG ON TO: www.non-leagueclubdirectory.co.uk
and join in today!

SALFORD CITY

Chairman: Karen Baird
Secretary: Andrew Giblin (T) 07867 823 713 (E) andrewgiblin@aol.com
Commercial Manager: (T)
Programme Editor: Gareth Lyons (T)
Ground Address: Moor Lane, Kersal, Salford, Manchester M7 3PZ
(T) 0161 792 6287 **Manager:** Phil Power

2014-15 Squad - Back row (l-r): Stuart Rudd (assistant manager), Simon Wiles, Jacob Hazel, Phil Edgehill, Mike Smith, Ashley Dunn, Andy Robertson, Paul Linwood, Aaron Walters, Andy Smart, Trialist, Dave Chadwick (coach). Front row: Chris Williams, Ephraim Miti, Jamie Rother, James Moss, Sam Madeley, Danny Warrender, Chris Lynch, Nicky Platt, James Kirby, Josh Messer.

Club Factfile

Founded: 1940 **Nickname:** Ammies
Previous Names: Salford Central 1940-63, Salford Amateurs 1963 until merger with Anson Villa, Salford F.C. > 1990
Previous Leagues: Manchester 1963-80, Cheshire County 1980-82, North West Counties 1982-2008

Club Colours (change): Red/white/white (White/black/black)

Ground Capacity: 8,000 **Seats:** 260 **Covered:** 600 **Clubhouse:** Yes **Shop:** No

Directions
M62 to Junction 17 (Prestwich, Whitefield). Take A56 Bury New Road towards Manchester.
Continue through four sets of traffic lights.
Turn right into Moor Lane. Ground 500 yards on left.
Take first left after ground (Oaklands Road), first left again into Nevile Road and follow along to main entrance.

Previous Grounds:

Record Attendance: 3,000 v Whickham - FA Vase 1980
Record Victory: Not known
Record Defeat: Not known
Record Goalscorer: Not known
Record Appearances: Not known
Additional Records:

Senior Honours:
Manchester League Premier Division 1975, 76, 77, 79. North West Counties League Cup 2006.

10 YEAR RECORD

04-05	05-06	06-07	07-08	08-09	09-10	10-11	11-12	12-13	13-14
NWC1 18	NWC1 5	NWC1 4	NWC1 2	NP1N 20	NP1N 11	NP1N 12	NP1N 13	NP1N 16	NP1N 12

SCARBOROUGH ATHLETIC

Chairman: David Holland
Secretary: Sally Elwick (T) 07851 113 757 (E) info@scarboroughathletic.com
Commercial Manager: (T)
Programme Editor: Nick Finch (T) 07800 635 273
Ground Address: Bridlington FC, Queensgate, Bridlington, East Yorks YO16 7LN
(T) 01723 379 113 (office) **Manager:** Rudy Funk

Club Factfile

Founded: 2007 **Nickname:** The Seadogs
Previous Names: Formed after Scarborough F.C. folded in 2007.
Previous Leagues: Northern Counties East 2007-13.

Club Colours (change): All red & white (Light blue & navy/light blue/light blue).

Ground Capacity: 3000 **Seats:** 500 **Covered:** 1,200 **Clubhouse:** Yes **Shop:** No

Directions
From South (Hull, Beeford, Barmston): Approach Bridlington on the A165, passing golf course on right and Broadacres Pub, Kingsmead Estate on left. Straight through traffic lights to roundabout by B&Q. Turn right. At traffic lights turn left and over the railway bridge. At roundabout bear left and carry on heading north up Quay Road. After traffic lights turn right into Queensgate. Ground is 800 yards up the road on the right.
From South and West (Driffield, Hull, York): Approach Bridlington on A614. (This was formally the A166). Straight on at traffic lights (Hospital on right) and follow the road round the bend. At roundabout straight across to mini roundabout and bear right (second exit). Follow road around to right and to traffic lights. Straight on. At next traffic lights (just after Kwikfit) turn left into Queensgate. Ground is 800 yards up the road on the right.
From North (Scarborough): Approach Bridlington (Esso garage on right) at roundabout turn left then at mini roundabout second exit. Follow road around to right and to traffic lights. Straight on. At next traffic lights (just after Kwikfit) turn left into Queensgate. Ground is 800 yards up the road on the right.

Previous Grounds: None

Record Attendance: **Att:** 791 v Leeds Carnegie N.C.E. Div.1 - 25.04.09.
Record Victory: 13-0 v Brodsworth, Northern Counties East, 2009-10.
Record Defeat:
Record Goalscorer:
Record Appearances:
Additional Records:

Senior Honours:
Northern Counties East Division One 2008-09, Premier 2012-13.

10 YEAR RECORD

04-05	05-06	06-07	07-08	08-09	09-10	10-11	11-12	12-13	13-14
			NCE1 5	NCE1 1	NCEP 5	NCEP 10	NCEP 3	NCEP 1	NP1S 7

SPENNYMOOR TOWN

Chairman: Bradley Groves (Chief Executive)
Secretary: Steven Lawson (T) 07871 206 474 (E) stevenlawson_16@hotmail.co.uk
Commercial Manager: B Beasley & C Ponfret (T)
Programme Editor: Mike Rowcroft (T) 07770 500 593
Ground Address: Brewery Field, Durham Road, Spennymoor DL16 6JN
(T) 01388 827 248 **Manager:** Jason Ainsley

Club Factfile

Founded: 1904 **Nickname:** Moors
Previous Names: Amalgamation of Evenwood Town & Spennymoor United in 2005-06.
Previous Leagues: Northern League 2005-14.

Club Colours (change): Black & white stripes/black/white (All maroon)

Ground Capacity: 3,000 **Seats:** 224 **Covered:** 800 **Clubhouse:** Yes **Shop:** Yes

Directions Leave the A1(M) at junction 59, then at roundabout take the 1st exit onto the A167. At roundabout take the 2nd exit onto the A167 At Rushyford roundabout take the 3rd exit onto the A167. At roundabout take the 3rd exit onto the A167. At Thinford Roundabout take the 1st exit onto the A688. At roundabout take the 1st exit onto the A688. At roundabout take the 3rd exit onto Saint Andrew's Lane. At roundabout take the 1st exit onto Saint Andrew's Lane. At mini roundabout take 2nd exit onto King Street. At mini roundabout take 2nd exit onto King Street/Durham Road. Bear right onto Durham Road. Take 3rd exit on left onto Wood Vue.

Previous Grounds:

Record Attendance: 2,670 v Darlington, Northern League 2012-13.
Record Victory: 10-0 v Billingham Town (H), Northern League Division One, 18/03/2014
Record Defeat: 2-8 v Clitheroe (A), FA Cup 2nd Qualifying Round, 29/09/2007
Record Goalscorer: Gavin Cpgdon - 103
Record Appearances: Lewis Dodds - 227
Additional Records: Northern League record points tally of 109 during 2012-13.

Senior Honours:
League: Northern League Division Two 2006-07, Division One 2009-10, 2010-11, 2011-12, 2013-14.
FA/County Cups: Durham Challange Cup 2011-12, FA Vase 2012-13.

10 YEAR RECORD

04-05	05-06	06-07	07-08	08-09	09-10	10-11	11-12	12-13	13-14
	NL 2 8	NL 2 1	NL 1 12	NL 1 4	NL 1 1	NL 1 1	NL 1 1	NL 1 2	NL 1 1

WARRINGTON TOWN

Chairman: Toby Macormac
Secretary: Chris Henshall **(T)** 07969 123 786 **(E)** info@warringtontown.co.uk
Commercial Manager: **(T)**
Programme Editor: Paul Roach **(T)** 07982 781 772
Ground Address: Cantilever Park, Common Lane, Latchford, Warrington WA4 2RS
(T) 01925 653 044 **Manager:** Shaun Reid

Club Factfile

Founded: 1948 **Nickname:** The Town
Previous Names: Stockton Heath Albion 1949-61
Previous Leagues: Warrington & District 1949-52, Mid Cheshire 1952-78, Cheshire County 1978-82, North West Counties 1982-90 Northern Premier 1990-97
Club Colours (change): Yellow and blue/blue/yellow (Blue & white/white/blue)

Ground Capacity: 2,000 **Seats:** 350 **Covered:** 650 **Clubhouse:** Yes **Shop:** Yes

Directions
From M62 Junction 9 Warrington Town Centre: Travel 1 mile south on A49, turn left at traffic lights into Loushers Lane, ground ½ mile on right hand side. From M6 North or South Junction 20: Follow A50 (Warrington signs) for 2 miles, cross Latchford Swingbridge, turn immediate left into Station Road, ground on left.

Previous Grounds: London Road 1948-65

Record Attendance: 2,600 v Halesowen Town - FA Vase Semi-final 1st leg 1985-86
Record Victory: Not known
Record Defeat: Not known
Record Goalscorer: Steve Hughes - 167
Record Appearances: Neil Whalley
Additional Records: Paid £50,000 to Preston North End for Liam Watson Received £60,000 from P.N.E. for Liam Watson
Players to progress - Roger Hunt, Liverpool legend and 1966 World Cup winner.
Senior Honours:
North West Counties 1989-90, Division 2 2000-01, League Cup 1985-86, 87-88, 88-89

10 YEAR RECORD

04-05	05-06	06-07	07-08	08-09	09-10	10-11	11-12	12-13	13-14
NP 1 20	NP 1 19	NP 1 22	NP1S 13	NP1N 19	NP1N 9	NP1N 9	NP1N 11	NP1N 10	NP1N 3

BRIGG TOWN

Chairman: Simon Harris
Secretary: Martin North (T) 07891 122 242 (E) briggtownfc@chessmail.co.uk
Commercial Manager: (T)
Programme Editor: Michael Harker (T) 01302 852 404
Ground Address: The Hawthorns, Hawthorn Avenue, Brigg DN20 8PG*
(T) 01652 651 605 **Manager:** Scott Hellewell

2013-2014 Squad

Club Factfile

Founded: 1864 **Nickname:** Zebras
Previous Names: Not known
Previous Leagues: Lincolnshire 1948-76, Midland Counties 1976-82, Northern Counties East 1982-2004

Club Colours (change): Black and white stripes/black/red (Pink/white/pink)

Ground Capacity: 2,500 **Seats:** 370 **Covered:** Yes **Clubhouse:** Yes **Shop:** Yes

Directions
From M180 (Exit 4 - Scunthorpe East) A18 to Brigg. Leave Town via Wrawby Road, following signs for Airport and Grimsby. 100 metres after Sir John Nelthorpe Lower School, and immediately after bus stop/shelter, turn left into Recreation ground (signposted "Football Ground") and follow road into club car park.

*SAT NAV postcode DN20 8DT

Previous Grounds: Old Manor House Convent, Station Road > 1939, Brocklesby 1939-59

Record Attendance: 2,000 v Boston United - 1953
Record Victory: Not known
Record Defeat: Not known
Record Goalscorer: Not known
Record Appearances: Not known
Additional Records:

Senior Honours:
Midland Counties League 1977-78. FA Vase 1995-96, 2002-03. Northern Counties East Premier Division 2000-01.
Lincolnshire League x8, League Cup x5. Lincolnshire 'A' Senior Cup x4. Lincolnshire 'B' Senior Cup x5.

10 YEAR RECORD

04-05	05-06	06-07	07-08	08-09	09-10	10-11	11-12	12-13	13-14
NP 1 8	NP 1 8	NP 1 17	NP 1 16	NP1S 20	NP1S 15	NP1S 4	NP1S 17	NP1S 13	NP1S 18

CARLTON TOWN

Chairman: Michael Garton

Secretary: Paul Shelton (T) 07854 586 875 (E) info@carltontownfc.co.uk

Commercial Manager: (T)

Programme Editor: Des Oldham (T) 07772 550 763

Ground Address: Bill Stokeld Stadium, Stoek Lane, Gedling, Nottingham NG4 2QP*

(T) 0115 940 3192 **Manager:** Les McJannet

Photo: Keith Clayton.

Club Factfile

Founded: 1904 **Nickname:** Town

Previous Names: Sneinton

Previous Leagues: Notts Alliance, Central Midlands, Northern Counties East

Club Colours (change): All navy blue & yellow (Maroon & orange/maroon & orange/orange)

Ground Capacity: 1,500 **Seats:** 164 **Covered:** 100 **Clubhouse:** Yes **Shop:** No

Directions

From M1 J26 take A610 to Nottingham Ring Road. Follow signs for Mansfield (A60) for approx 4 miles via 2 roundabouts until reaching junction with A60 at Arnold. Take right turn at Vale Hotel on to Thackerays Lane. Proceed to roundabout and take 3rd exit on to Arno Vale Road. Proceed through traffic lights to top of hill and continue straight on at next lights on to Arnold Lane. Continue past golf course, the old Gedling Colliery and church to mini roundabout. Continue straight on to the old junction with A612. (Southwell) must turn right here and at next set of lights turn left and follow the loop road to the next junction. Take left turn on to the new A612 Gedling By Pass and follow to the next set of traffic lights at Severn Trent Works. Turn left on to Stoke Lane. Entrance to Carlton Town is immediate right. **[Ground must be accessed via the new A612 between Netherfield and Burton Joyce. Football club is signposted in both directions on the approach to the ground).**

*Sat Nav postcode NG4 2QW

Previous Grounds:

Record Attendance: 1,000 - Radio Trent Charity Match

Record Victory: Not known

Record Defeat: Not known

Record Goalscorer: Not known

Record Appearances: Not known

Additional Records:

Senior Honours:

Notts Alliance League Division 2 1984-85, Division 1 1992-93. Central Midlands Supreme Division 2002-03.
Northern Counties East Division 1 2005-06.
Notts Senior Cup 2012-13.

10 YEAR RECORD

04-05		05-06		06-07		07-08		08-09		09-10		10-11		11-12		12-13		13-14	
NCE1	3	NCE1	1	NCEP	3	NP 1	10	NP1S	4	NP1S	9	NP1S	8	NP1S	2	NP1S	12	NP1S	10

CHASETOWN

Chairman: Mike Joiner
Secretary: John Richards **(T)** 07866 902 093 **(E)** chastownfc@gmail.com
Commercial Manager: **(T)**
Programme Editor: Pamela Mullins **(T)** 07981 192 345
Ground Address: The Scholars, Church Street, Chasetown, Walsall WS7 3QL
(T) 01543 682 222 **Manager:** Craig Harris

2013-2014 Squad - Back Row (L-R): Alex Morris, Todd Evans, Jud Ellis, Gary Hay, Grant Beckett, Alex Forde, Ryan Price, John Birt (gk coach), Danny Watson, Richard Teesdale, Nick Wellecomme, Chris Slater, Ted Highfield (Physio), Avun Jephcott. Front Row: Danny Bragoli, Theo Robinson, Louis Keenan, Andy Westwood, Simon Brown, Jack Farmer, Richard Upton (coach), Craig Harris (Manager), Kevin Sweeney (Coach), Tesfa Robinson, Paul Sullivan, Danny Smith, Lee Butler, Marco Adaggio.

Club Factfile

Founded: 1954 **Nickname:** The Scholars
Previous Names: Chase Terrace Old Scholars 1954-72
Previous Leagues: Cannock Youth 1954-58, Lichfield & District 1958-61, Staffordshire County 1961-72, West Midlands 1972-94, Midland Alliance 1994-2006, Southern 2006-09

Club Colours (change): Royal blue/royal blue/white (All bright red)

Ground Capacity: 2,000 **Seats:** 151 **Covered:** 220 **Clubhouse:** Yes **Shop:** Yes

Directions
From the M42 junction10 towards Tamworth or from the M6 Junction 11 or 12 towards Cannock or the A38 southbound from Derby - follow signs for A5 towards Brownhills, At the traffic lights at the Terrace Restaurant turn towards Burntwood onto the A5195. Straight over first island towards Chasetown and Hammerwich, over toll road and at second island turn left into Haney Hay Road which leads into Highfields Road signposted Chasetown, up the hill to mini island, then straight on into Church Street past the church on left and school on right. Ground is on the left at end of road. If using M6 Toll exit at junction T6 Burntwood - turn left out of Toll booths and left at second island and follow over toll road as above.

Previous Grounds: Burntwood Recreation

Record Attendance: 2,420 v Cardiff City - FA Cup 3rd Round January 2008
Record Victory: 14-1 v Hanford - Walsall Senior Cup 1991-92
Record Defeat: 1-8 v Telford United Reserves - West Midlands League
Record Goalscorer: Tony Dixon - 197
Record Appearances: Not known
Additional Records:

Senior Honours:
West Midlands League 1978, League Cup x2.
Midland Alliance 2005-06.
Walsall Senior Cup x2.

10 YEAR RECORD

04-05		05-06		06-07		07-08		08-09		09-10		10-11		11-12		12-13		13-14	
MidAl	2	MidAl	1	SthM		SthM	7	SthM	4	NP1S	2	NP P	10	NP P	20	NP1S	5	NP1S	12

COALVILLE TOWN

Chairman: Glyn Rennocks
Secretary: Peter Walford **(T)** 07534 675 127 **(E)** info@coalvilletownfc.co.uk
Commercial Manager: **(T)**
Programme Editor: Wayne McDermott **(T)** 07876 140 248
Ground Address: Owen Street Sports Ground, Owen St, Coalville LE67 3DA
(T) 01530 833 365 **Manager:** Adam Stevens

Club Factfile

Founded: 1994 **Nickname:** The Ravens
Previous Names: Ravenstoke Miners Ath. 1926-58. Ravenstoke FC 1958-95. Coalville 1995-98.
Previous Leagues: Coalville & Dist. Amateur. North Leicester. Leicestershire Senior. Midland Alliance > 2011.

Club Colours (change): Black & white/black/black (Red & yellow stripes/red/red)

Ground Capacity: 2,000 **Seats:** 240 **Covered:** 240 **Clubhouse:** Yes **Shop:** Yes

Directions
From the M42/A42 take the exit signposted Ashby and follow A511 to Coalville and Leicester. After approx. 3 miles and at the first roundabout take the second exit (A511). At the next roundabout take the 3rd exit into Coalville Town Centre. At the traffic lights go straight over to mini-roundabout then straight on for 50 meters before turning right into Owen Street. Ground is at the top of Owen Street on the left.

Previous Grounds: None

Record Attendance: 1,500.
Record Victory: Not known
Record Defeat: Not known
Record Goalscorer: Not known
Record Appearances: Nigel Simms.
Additional Records: 153 goals scored during 2010-11 season.
Senior Honours:
Leicestershire Senior Cup 1999-00. Leicestershire Senior 2001-02, 02-03. Midland Football Alliance 2010-11.
Leicestershire Challenge Cup 2012-13.

10 YEAR RECORD

04-05	05-06	06-07	07-08	08-09	09-10	10-11	11-12	12-13	13-14
MidAl 3	MidAl 8	MidAl 18	MidAl 8	MidAl 3	MidAl 2	MidAl 1	NP1S 14	NP1S 2	NP1S 2

GOOLE AFC

Chairman: Baron Bloom
Secretary: Andrew Morris **(T)** 07751 457 254 **(E)**
Commercial Manager: **(T)**
Programme Editor: Graeme Wilson **(T)** 07908 969 637
Ground Address: Victoria Pleasure Gardens, Marcus Road, Goole DN14 6SL
(T) 01405 762 794 (Match days) **Manager:** Curtis Woodhouse

Club Factfile

Founded: 1997 **Nickname:** The Badgers
Previous Names: Goole Town > 1996.
Previous Leagues: Central Midlands 1997-98.
Northern Counties East 2000-04.
Club Colours (change): All red with yellow trim (Yellow/black with yellow trim/yellow with black trim)

Ground Capacity: 3,000 **Seats:** 200 **Covered:** 800 **Clubhouse:** Yes **Shop:** Yes

Directions
Leave the M62 at Junction 36 and follow signs to Goole Town Centre.
Turn right at the 2nd set of traffic lights into Boothferry Road. Turn right again after 300 yards into Carter Street.
The Victoria Pleasure Grounds is at the end of the road. 366 Metres from Goole Railway Station.

Previous Grounds: None

Record Attendance: 976 v Leeds United - 1999
Record Victory: Not known
Record Defeat: Not known
Record Goalscorer: Kevin Severn (1997-2001)
Record Appearances: Phil Dobson - 187 (1999-2001)
Additional Records:

Senior Honours:
Central Midlands 1997-98.
Northern Counties East Division 1 1999-2000, Premier Division 2003-04.

10 YEAR RECORD

04-05	05-06	06-07	07-08	08-09	09-10	10-11	11-12	12-13	13-14
NCEP 1	NP 1 21	NP 1 7	NP 1 9	NP1S 18	NP1S 18	NP1S 13	NP1S 10	NP1N 21	NP1S 13

Northern Premier League Action

Brigg Town in FA Cup action away to Arnold Town in the Preliminary Round..

Photo: Bill Wheatcroft.

GRESLEY

Chairman: Barry North
Secretary: Ian Collins (T) 07733 055 212 (E) office@gresleyfc.com
Commercial Manager: (T)
Programme Editor: Robin Mansfield (T) 07855 847 337
Ground Address: The Moat Ground, Moat Street, Church Gresley, Derbyshire DE11 9RE
(T) 01283 215 316 **Manager:** Martin Rowe

Club Factfile

Founded: 2009 **Nickname:**
Previous Names: Gresley Rovers
Previous Leagues: East Midlands 2009-11. Midland Football Alliance 2011-12.

Club Colours (change): All red (Blue/navy blue/blue)

Ground Capacity: **Seats:** Yes **Covered:** Yes **Clubhouse:** Yes **Shop:** Yes

Directions
From the South: Follow the M42 northbound to Junction 11, turn off onto the A444 toward Burton Upon Trent. Turn right onto the A514 (Castle Road) toward Gresley and follow the road up the hill to the traffic island at the top. Continue on the A514 over the island and take the second road on the left (School Street), the next left into Moat Street where the Moat Ground is located. **From the North-East:** Follow the M1 south to junction 23a, turn off on to the A42 southbound. Continue on the A42 to Ashby-de-la-Zouch then turn off onto the A511 toward Swadlincote. At Woodville turn off the A511 onto the A514 toward Church Gresley, follow the road signs to Gresley, the School Street turn off is second on the right after the Gresley island. Take the first turn on the left in School Street to take you to the ground. **From the North-West:** From Stoke-on-Trent follow the A50 toward Burton-Upon-Trent, turn on to the A511 and continue through Burton. Turn off the A511 onto the A444 toward Nuneaton. Follow the A444 until you reach the turn off for the A514. Turn left onto the A514 (Castle Road) toward Gresley and follow the road up the hill to the traffic island at the top. Continue on the A514 over the island and take the second road on the left (School Street), the next left into Moat Street where the Moat Ground is located.

Previous Grounds: None

Record Attendance: 861 v Whitehawk (FA Vase Quarter Final 27th Feb 2010)
Record Victory: 9-0 v Anstey Nomads 30th August 2010 (EMCL)
Record Defeat: 1-5 v Westfields (MFA)
Record Goalscorer: Royce Turville - 61
Record Appearances: Jamie Barrett - 142
Additional Records:

Senior Honours:
East Midlands Counties League 2010-11. Midland Alliance 2011-12.

10 YEAR RECORD

04-05	05-06	06-07	07-08	08-09	09-10	10-11	11-12	12-13	13-14
					EMC 2	EMC 1	MidAl 1	NP1S 11	NP1S 9

KIDSGROVE ATHLETIC

Chairman: John Rowley
Secretary: Les Morris (T) 07879 466 523 (E)
Commercial Manager: (T)
Programme Editor: Neil Clowes (T) 07950 209 204
Ground Address: The Seddon Stadium, Hollinwood Road, Kidsgrove, Staffs ST7 1DQ
(T) 01782 782 412 **Manager:** Neil Gill

Club Factfile

Founded: 1952 **Nickname:** The Grove
Previous Names: None
Previous Leagues: Buslem and Tunstall 1953-63, Staffordshire County 1963-66, Mid Cheshire 1966-90, North West Counties 1990-2002
Club Colours (change): All blue (All red)

Ground Capacity: 4,500 **Seats:** 1,000 **Covered:** 800 **Clubhouse:** Yes **Shop:** Yes

Directions
Leave the M6 at Junction 16, join the A500 towards Stoke-on-Trent. Take the 2nd exit signposted Newcastle & Kidsgrove. Top of the slip road, turn left onto A34 Kidsgrove/Congleton. Straight over at roundabout. At 1st set of traffic lights (by Caudwell Arms pub) turn right onto A34. Continue to next set of lights, turn right into Cedar Avenue. Continue then take 2nd right into Lower Ash Road. Take 3rd left into Hollinwood Road, Ground on left at top.

Previous Grounds: Vickers and Goodwin 1953-60

Record Attendance: 1,903 v Tiverton Town - FA Vase Semi-final 1998
Record Victory: 23-0 v Cross Heath W.M.C. - Staffordshire Cup 1965
Record Defeat: 0-15 v Stafford Rangers - Staffordshire Senior Cup 20/11/2001
Record Goalscorer: Scott Dundas - 53 (1997-98)
Record Appearances: Not known
Additional Records: Paid £10,000 to Stevenage Borough for Steve Walters
Received £3,000 for Ryan Baker 2003-04
Senior Honours:
Mid Cheshire League x4, League Cup x3.
North West Counties Division 1 1997-98, 2001-02, Challenge Cup 1997-98.
Staffordshire Senior Cup 2010-11.

10 YEAR RECORD

04-05	05-06	06-07	07-08	08-09	09-10	10-11	11-12	12-13	13-14
NP 1 10	NP 1 17	NP 1 8	NP 1 17	NP1S 15	NP1S 4	NP1S 7	NP1S 13	NP1S 18	NP1S 21

Northern Premier League Action

Mickleover's number 10 looks set to shoot at goal, however, the Harborough Town defender has other ideas during this Preliminary round FA Cup tie.

Photo: Bill Wheatcroft.

LEEK TOWN

Chairman: Andrew Wain

Secretary: Brain Wain (T) 07967 204 470 (E)

Commercial Manager: (T)

Programme Editor: Tracy Reynolds (T) 07540 161 017

Ground Address: Harrison Park, Macclesfield Road, Leek, Cheshire ST13 8LD

(T) 01538 399 278 **Manager:** Lee Casswell

Club Factfile

Founded: 1946 **Nickname:** The Blues

Previous Names: None

Previous Leagues: Staffordshire Co., Manchester 1951-54, 57-73, West Midlands (B'ham) 1954-56,Cheshire Co. 1973-82, North West Counties 1982-87, N.P.L. 1987-94, 95-97, Southern 1994-95, Conference 1997-99

Club Colours (change): All blue (Amber & black/black/black)

Ground Capacity: 3,000 **Seats:** 650 **Covered:** 3,000 **Clubhouse:** Yes **Shop:** Yes

Directions

From the South: Leave M6 at J15, over roundabout on to the A500, go over the flyover, up the slip road, onto the A50 and follow the signs to Leek. Go straight over the roundabout (Britannia Building on the left) to large set of lights. Go straight across St. Georges Street to top of road to junction, turn left, go down the hill for about a half a mile. The Ground is on the left. **From the North:** Leave M6 at J19. Take Macclesfield signs. Follow into Macclesfield then take A523 Leek/Buxton signs. Follow these to Leek. Ground is situated on the right as you come into Leek. From West Midlands: M6 J15. A500 towards Stoke, over flyover, take A50 past Brittania Stadium. After approx 3 miles join A53 signposted Leek. On entering the town, straight ahead up St Edwards St. (Remainder as above)

Previous Grounds: None

Record Attendance: 5,312 v Macclesfield Town - FA Cup 1973-74

Record Victory: Not known

Record Defeat: Not known

Record Goalscorer: Dave Sutton - 144

Record Appearances: Gary Pearce - 447

Additional Records: Paid £2,000 to Sutton Town for Simon Snow
Received £30,000 from Barnsley for Tony Bullock

Senior Honours:
Northern Premier League 1996-97. Staffordshire Senior Cup 1995-96.

10 YEAR RECORD

04-05	05-06	06-07	07-08	08-09	09-10	10-11	11-12	12-13	13-14
NP P 7	NP P 12	NP P 17	NP P 19	NP1S 9	NP1S 8	NP1S 16	NP1S 5	NP1S 10	NP1S 3

LINCOLN UNITED

Chairman: Malcolm Cowling
Secretary: Pete Doyle (T) 07971 034 693 (E) peterdoyle150@gmail.com
Commercial Manager: Allen Crombie (T)
Programme Editor: Mark Shillito (T) 07447 501 544
Ground Address: NTR Stadium, Ashby Avenue, Hartsholme, Lincoln LN6 0DY
(T) 01522 696 400 **Manager:** David Frecklington

Action from Lincoln United's visit to Chastown last season.
Photo: Jonathan Holloway.

Club Factfile

Founded: 1938 **Nickname:** United
Previous Names: Lincoln Amateurs > 1954
Previous Leagues: Lincolnshire 1945-46, 60-67, Lincoln 1946-60, Yorkshire 1967-82, Northern Counties East 1982-86, 92-95, Central Midlands 1982-92

Club Colours (change): All white (Red & blue/blue/red)

Ground Capacity: 2,714 **Seats:** 400 **Covered:** 1,084 **Clubhouse:** Yes **Shop:** Yes

Directions
Along Lincoln Relief Road (A46) until reaching roundabout with exit for Birchwood. Take this exit which is Skellingthorpe Road for approximately 1 mile, at 30 mph sign turn right into Ashby Avenue. Entrance to ground is 200 yards on right.

Previous Grounds: Skew Bridge 1940s, Co-op Sports Ground > 1960s, Hartsholme Cricket Club > 1982

Record Attendance: 2,000 v Crook Town - FA Amateur Cup 1st Round 1968
Record Victory: 12-0 v Pontefract Colliery - 1995
Record Defeat: 0-7 v Huddersfield Town - FA Cup 1st Round 16/11/1991
Record Goalscorer: Tony Simmons - 215
Record Appearances: Steve Carter - 447
Additional Records: Paid £1,000 to Hucknall Town for Paul Tomlinson December 2000
Received £3,000 from Charlton Athletic for Dean Dye July 1991
Senior Honours:
Northern Counties East Division 1 1985-86, 92-93, Premier Division 1994-95.

10 YEAR RECORD

04-05	05-06	06-07	07-08	08-09	09-10	10-11	11-12	12-13	13-14
NP P 14	NP P 19	NP P 15	NP P 20	NP1S 10	NP1S 19	NP1S 12	NP1S 18	NP1S 20	NP1S 17

LOUGHBOROUGH DYNAMO

Chairman: Vaughan Williams
Secretary: Brian Pugh **(T)** 07716 846 626 **(E)** contact@loughboroughdynamofc.co.uk
Commercial Manager: **(T)**
Programme Editor: **(T)**
Ground Address: Nanpantan Sports Ground, Nanpantan Road, Loughborough LE11 3YE
(T) 01509 237 148 **Manager:** Tommy Brookbanks

Club Factfile

Founded: 1955 **Nickname:** Dynamo
Previous Names: None
Previous Leagues: Loughborough Alliance 1957-66, Leicestershire & District 1966-71, East Midlands 1971-72, Central Alliance 1972-89, Leicestershire Senior 1989-2004, Midland Alliance 2004-08
Club Colours (change): Gold/black/gold (Blue with red shoulder flash/blue/red)

Ground Capacity: 1,500 **Seats:** 250 **Covered:** Yes **Clubhouse:** Yes **Shop:** No

Directions
From M1: At Junction 23 turn towards Loughborough (A512). At 1st set of traffic lights turn right on to Snells Nook Lane.. At 1st crossroads ("Priory" pub on left) turn left on to Nanpantan Rd. Turn (1st) right after 0.75 miles on to Watermead Lane. The ground is at the end of the lane. **From Leicester (A6):** Turn left at 3rd roundabout on Epinal Way (Ring Road) on to Forest Road. After 2 miles turn (5th) left on to Watermead Lane. **From Nottingham (A60):** Turn right at 1st set of traffic lights in Loughborough. Go through next 4 sets of traffic lights. Turn left at the first roundabout on to Epinal Way straight on at next roundabout and then take the third exit at following roundabout on to Forest Road. After 2 miles turn (5th) left on to Watermead Lane.

Previous Grounds: None

Record Attendance: Not known
Record Victory: Not known
Record Defeat: Not known
Record Goalscorer: Not known
Record Appearances: Not known
Additional Records:

Senior Honours:
Leicestershire Senior League Division 1 2001-02, Premier Division 2003-04.
Leicestershire Senior Cup 2002-03, 03-04.

10 YEAR RECORD

04-05	05-06	06-07	07-08	08-09	09-10	10-11	11-12	12-13	13-14
MidAl 14	MidAl 13	MidAl 9	MidAl 2	NP1S 14	NP1S 14	NP1S 17	NP1S 8	NP1S 16	NP1S 14

MARKET DRAYTON TOWN

Chairman: Nicky Millington
Secretary: Rod Poe (T) 07572 283 090 (E) opoe2nt@btinternet.com
Commercial Manager: (T)
Programme Editor: Rod Pope (T) 07572 283 090
Ground Address: Greenfields Sports Ground, Greenfields Lane, Market Drayton TF9 3SL
(T) 01630 661 780 **Manager:** Darren Garner

Club Factfile

Founded: 1969 **Nickname:**
Previous Names: Little Drayton Rangers > 2003
Previous Leagues: West Midlands (Regional) 1969-2006, Midland Alliance 2006-09

Club Colours (change): Red/red/white (White/white/navy blue)

Ground Capacity: **Seats:** **Covered:** **Clubhouse:** Yes **Shop:** Nk

Directions

Take the A41 to Ternhill Island, turn right on A53 for Newcastle-under-Lyne. Straight on at first island (by Muller factory). At next island turn right to town centre (by Gingerbread Inn). Approx 200yds take 2nd right into Greenfields Lane. Ground 150 yards on right, car park opposite.

From Stoke-on-Trent take A53 for Shrewsbury, at Gingerbread Inn turn left for town centre then as above.

Previous Grounds: Not known

Record Attendance: 440 vs. AFC Telford, Friendly 11/07/09. 229 vs. Witton Albion, Unibond South 25/08/09
Record Victory: (League) 9-0 Home vs. Racing Club Warwick 10/03/09
Record Defeat: Not known
Record Goalscorer: Not known
Record Appearances: Not known
Additional Records:

Senior Honours:
West Midlands (Regional) League 2005-06. Midland Alliance 2008-09.

10 YEAR RECORD

04-05		05-06		06-07		07-08		08-09		09-10		10-11		11-12		12-13		13-14	
WMP	2	WMP	1	MidAl	13	MidAl	3	MidAl	1	NP1S	13	NP1S	18	NP1S	16	NP1S	15	NP1S	19

Northern Premier League Action

Chasetown's, Luke Bottomer is on the attack in their 4-1 win over visitors Lincoln United at the Scholars Ground.

Photo: Jonathan Holloway.

MICKLEOVER SPORTS

Chairman: Stuart Clarke
Secretary: Tony Shaw **(T)** 07966 197 246 **(E)**
Commercial Manager: **(T)**
Programme Editor: James Edge **(T)** 07964 217 945
Ground Address: Mickleover Sports Club, Station Road, Mickleover Derby DE3 9JG
(T) 01332 512 826 **Manager:** Glen Kirkwood

The Mickleover players look set to take advantage of this freekick during their FAC Preliminary tie with Harborough Town. Photo: Bill Wheatcroft.

Club Factfile

Founded: 1948 **Nickname:** Sports
Previous Names: Mickleover Old Boys 1948-93
Previous Leagues: Central Midlands 1993-99, Northern Counties East 1999-2009

Club Colours (change): Red and black stripes/black/red (All blue)

Ground Capacity: 1,500 **Seats:** 280 **Covered:** 500 **Clubhouse:** Yes **Shop:** Yes

Directions

M1 NORTH - J28. A38 to Derby. At Markeaton Island right A52 Ashbourne, 2nd left Radbourne Lane, 3rd Left Station Road 50 yds.

M1 SOUTH – J25. A52 to Derby. Follow signs for Ashbourne, pick up A52 at Markeaton Island (MacDonalds) then as above.

FROM STOKE A50 – Derby. A516 to A38 then as above.

Previous Grounds: None

Record Attendance: Not known
Record Victory: Not known
Record Defeat: Not known
Record Goalscorer: Not known
Record Appearances: Not known
Additional Records: Won 16 consecutive League matches in 2009-10 - a Northern Premier League record

Senior Honours:
Central Midlands Supreme Division 1998-99. Northern Counties East Division 1 2002-03, Premier Division 2008-09.
Northern Premier League Division 1 South 2009-10.

10 YEAR RECORD

04-05		05-06		06-07		07-08		08-09		09-10		10-11		11-12		12-13		13-14	
NCEP	7	NCEP	13	NCEP	7	NCEP	14	NCEP	1	NP1S	1	NP P	15	NP P	21	NP1S	21	NP1S	5

NEWCASTLE TOWN

Chairman: Alistair Miller
Secretary: Ray Tatton (T) 07792 292 849 (E) rftatton@tiscali.co.uk
Commercial Manager: (T)
Programme Editor: Ray Tatton (T) 07792 292 849
Ground Address: The Aspire Stadium, Buckmaster Avenue, Clayton, ST5 3BX
(T) 01782 662 350 **Manager:** Ivan Lodge

Club Factfile

Founded: 1964 **Nickname:** Castle
Previous Names: Parkway Hanley, Clayton Park & Parkway Clayton. Merged as NTFC in 1986.
Previous Leagues: Newcatle & District, Staffs Co & Mid Cheshire, North West Counties

Club Colours (change): Blue/blue/white (White/black/red)

Ground Capacity: 4,000 **Seats:** 300 **Covered:** 1,000 **Clubhouse:** Yes **Shop:** Yes

Directions
FROM M6: Leave the M6 at Junction 15 and immediately turn left up the bank (signposted A519 Newcastle.) Go to the second roundabout and turn right into Stafford Avenue. Take the first left into Tittensor Road (signposted Newcastle Town FC.) Go to the end and the ground is below in the parkway. (Entrance through the gateway signposted Newcastle Town FC.) **FROM A50 DERBY:** Follow the A50 to the end and join the A500 (signposted M6 South) just past Stoke City Football Ground. Follow the A500 to the Motorway and at the roundabout turn right up the bank (A519 Newcastle.) Go to the second roundabout and turn right into Stafford Avenue. Take the first left into Tittensor Road (signposted Newcastle Town FC.) Go to the end and the ground is below in the parkway. (Entrance through the gateway signposted Newcastle Town FC.)

Previous Grounds: None

Record Attendance: 3,948 v Notts County - FA Cup 1996
Record Victory: Not known
Record Defeat: Not known
Record Goalscorer: Andy Bott - 149
Record Appearances: Dean Gillick - 632
Additional Records:

Senior Honours:
Mid Cheshire League 1985-86. Walsall Senior Cup 1993-94, 94-95.

10 YEAR RECORD

04-05	05-06	06-07	07-08	08-09	09-10	10-11	11-12	12-13	13-14
NWC1 2	NWC1 6	NWC1 12	NWC1 3	NWCP 3	NWCP 1	NP1S 2	NP1S 15	NP1S 17	NP1S 8

Northern Premier League Action

The Mickleover player tries to block the Harborough Town defender's clearance during this FA Cup Preliminary round tie.

Photo: Bill Wheatcroft.

NORTON UNITED

Chairman: Stephen Beaumont
Secretary: Dennis Vickers (T) 07401 737 377 (E) nortonian1@aol.com
Commercial Manager: (T)
Programme Editor: Kevin Harris (T) 07792 550 638
Ground Address: Norton CC & MWI Community Drive, Smallthorne, Stoke-on-Trent ST6 1QF
(T) 01782 838 290 **Manager:** Scott Dundas

2013-14 Squad with the North West Counties Premier Division Trophy.

Club Factfile

Founded: 1989 **Nickname:**
Previous Names: None
Previous Leagues: Stafford County Senior 1990-94. Midland 1994-2001. North West Counties > 2014.

Club Colours (change): Red & black/black/black (Black & white stripes/white/white)

Ground Capacity: **Seats:** No **Covered:** Yes **Clubhouse:** Yes **Shop:**

Directions

From the South A50 (or Junction 15 M6) to A500. Head North to A53. Turn right and head for Leek over a flyover and through a big crossroadsunder a road bridge. Turn left into Norton Drive just before a petrol station. At the end of Norton Drive turn left then turn right into Community Drive and ground is 100 yards on the right.

From the North M6 Junction 16. Take the A500 towards Stoke and after about 6 miles turn left for Tunstall/Burslem. After 600 yards turn right at small roundabout and in to Burslem. Through the main traffic lights and up Moorland Road to Smallthorne. At the roundabouts take the third exit down Ford Green Road. 400 yards turn right at the post office into Community Drive, ground is about 300 yards on the left.

Previous Grounds:

Record Attendance: **Att:** 1,382 v FC United of Manchester 09/04/2006.
Record Victory:
Record Defeat:
Record Goalscorer:
Record Appearances:
Additional Records:

Senior Honours:
League: Midland League 1996-97, 98-99, 2000-01. North West Counties League Premier Division 2013-14.
FA/County Cups: Staffordshire Senior Vase 1998-99, 2003-04.

10 YEAR RECORD

04-05		05-06		06-07		07-08		08-09		09-10		10-11		11-12		12-13		13-14	
NWC2	5	NWC2	8	NWC2	17	NWC2	8	NWC1	12	NWC1	3	NWC1	7	NWC1	2	NWCP	14	NWCP	1

RAINWORTH MINERS WELFARE

Chairman: Mark Hawkins
Secretary: Les Lee (T) 07889 561 787 (E)
Commercial Manager: (T)
Programme Editor: Paul Fryer (T) 07534 530 254
Ground Address: Welfare Ground, Kirklington Road, Rainworth, Mansfield NG21 0JY
(T) 01623 792 495 **Manager:** Scott Rickards

Club Factfile

Founded: 1922 **Nickname:** The Wrens
Previous Names: Rufford Colliery
Previous Leagues: Notts Alliance 1922-03, Central Midlands League 2003-07, Northern Counties East 2007-10

Club Colours (change): All White (All royal blue).

Ground Capacity: 2,201 **Seats:** 221 **Covered:** 350 **Clubhouse:** Yes **Shop:** No

Directions
From M1 (Junction 29) – take A617. At Pleasley turn right onto the new Mansfield Bypass road which is still the A617 and follow to Rainworth. At roundabout with B6020 Rainworth is off to the right, but it is better to go straight over onto the new Rainworth Bypass and then right at the next roundabout (the ground can be seen on the way along the Bypass) At mini roundabout, turn right onto Kirklington Road and go down the hill for ¼ mile – ground and car park on the right
Alternatively you can reach the new A617 Bypass from the A38 via Junction 28 on the M1. From A614 at roundabout, take the A617 to Rainworth for 1 mile. Left at 1st roundabout into village. At mini roundabout right into Kirklington road – ¼ mile down hill as above.

Previous Grounds: None

Record Attendance: 5,071 v Barton Rovers FA Vase SF 2nd Leg, 1982. (A record for a Vase match outside of the final)
Record Victory: Not known
Record Defeat: Not known
Record Goalscorer: Not known
Record Appearances: Not known
Additional Records:
Senior Honours:
Notts Senior Cup Winners 1981-82

10 YEAR RECORD

04-05	05-06	06-07	07-08	08-09	09-10	10-11	11-12	12-13	13-14
CM Su 20	CM Su 9	CM Su 3	NCE1 4	NCE1 2	NCEP 2	NP1S 20	NP1S 19	NP1N 14	NP1S 15

Northern Premier League Action

Jonathan Gould, the Chasetown No.11 keeps his balance despite the close attentions of these Lincoln Utd defenders. Chasetown won 4-1 to keep Lincoln battling against possible relegation..

Photo: Jonathan Holloway.

ROMULUS

Chairman: Richard Evans

Secretary: Peter Lowe (T) 07738 604 391 (E) peterwloweuk@yahoo.co.uk

Commercial Manager: Andy Mitchell (T)

Programme Editor: Paul Dockerill (T) 07711 856 551

Ground Address: Sutton Coldfield FC, Central Ground, Coles Lane B72 1NL

(T) 0121 354 2997 **Manager:** Dave Barnett

Club Factfile

Founded: 1979 **Nickname:** The Roms

Previous Names: None

Previous Leagues: Midland Combination 1999-2004, Midland Alliance 2004-07, Southern 2007-2010

Club Colours (change): Red and white/red/red (Yellow/yellow/black)

Ground Capacity: 4,500 **Seats:** 200 **Covered:** 500 **Clubhouse:** Yes **Shop:** Yes

Directions

From M42 Junc 9, take A4097 (Minworth sign). At island, follow signs to Walmley Village. At traffic lights turn right (B4148). After shops turn left at traffic lights into Wylde Green Road. Over railway bridge turn right into East View Road, which becomes Coles Lane.

Previous Grounds: Penns Lane.

Record Attendance: Not known

Record Victory: Not known

Record Defeat: Not known

Record Goalscorer: Not known

Record Appearances: Not known

Additional Records: Players who have progress: Dean Sturridge, Stuart Bowen, Luke Rogers, Darius Vassell and Zat Knight.

Senior Honours:

Midland Combination Division One 1999-00, Premier Division 2003-04, Challenge Cup 03-04.

10 YEAR RECORD

04-05		05-06		06-07		07-08		08-09		09-10		10-11		11-12		12-13		13-14	
MidAl	12	MidAl	4	MidAl	2	SthM	10	SthM	11	SthM	8	NP1S	10	NP1S	20	NP1S	19	NP1S	11

SHEFFIELD

Chairman: Mick Wadsworth
Secretary: Bill Towning **(T)** 07557 107 158 **(E)**
Commercial Manager: **(T)**
Programme Editor: Stuart James **(T)** 07709 225 110
Ground Address: The BT Local Business Stadium, Sheffield Road, Dronfield S18 2GD
(T) 01246 292 622 **Manager:** Mick Wadsworth

Club Factfile

Founded: 1857 **Nickname:** Not known
Previous Names: None
Previous Leagues: Yorkshire 1949-82

Club Colours (change): Red/black/red (All blue)

Ground Capacity: 1,456 **Seats:** 250 **Covered:** 500 **Clubhouse:** Yes **Shop:** Yes

Directions
From the South – M1 to Junc 29, A617 into Chesterfield. At Roundabout follow A61 Sheffield. This is a dual carriageway passing over 2 roundabouts. At the 3rd roundabout take the 3rd exit signposted Dronfield. The Coach and Horses Public House is at the bottom of the hill on the right and the BT Local Business Stadium directly behind it. Entrance to the ground is by turning right at the traffic lights and immediate right into the Club Car Park. **From the East** - M18 to M1 north to Junc 33 (Sheffield). Turn towards Sheffield and take the 3rd exit from dual carriageway signposted' Ring Road / Chesterfield'. Go straight on at traffic island so that you are travelling alongside dual carriageway for a short period. At the junction turn left onto A61 Chesterfield. This is a dual carriageway passing through numerous traffic lights and two traffic islands. Follow Chesterfield sign at all times. After passing Graves Tennis centre on your left, turn left at next traffic island (still signposted Chesterfield). At next traffic island take 2nd exit signposted Dronfield The Coach and Horses Public House is at the bottom of the hill on the right and the BT Local Business Stadium directly behind it. Entrance to the ground is by turning right at the traffic lights and immediate right into the Club Car Park.

Previous Grounds: Abbeydale Park, Dore 1956-89, Sheffield Amateur Sports Stadium, Hillsborough Park 1989-91, Don Valley Stadium 1991-97

Record Attendance: 2,000 v Barton Rovers - FA Vase Semi-final 1976-77
Record Victory: Not known
Record Defeat: Not known
Record Goalscorer: Not known
Record Appearances: Not known
Additional Records: Paid £1,000 to Arnold Town for David Wilkins. Received £1,000 from Alfreton for Mick Godber 2002.
World's first ever Football Club.
Senior Honours:
FA Amateur Cup 1902-03. Northern Counties East Division 1 1988-89, 90-91, League Cup 2000-01, 04-05.
Sheffield and Hallamshire Senior Cup 1993-94, 2004-05, 05-06.

10 YEAR RECORD

04-05	05-06	06-07	07-08	08-09	09-10	10-11	11-12	12-13	13-14
NCEP 4	NCEP 4	NCEP 2	NP 1 4	NP1S 11	NP1S 5	NP1S 11	NP1S 4	NP1S 9	NP1S 16

Northern Premier League Action

Nick Wellecomme of Chasetown, looks to get in a cross in to the Lincoln Utd penalty area in a match that went ahead despite a rain soaked pitch. It paid off with a win for the home team.

Photo: Jonathan Holloway.

SPALDING UNITED

Chairman: Chris Toynton

Secretary: Audrey Fletcher (T) 07778 411 916 (E) tulips@uk2.net

Commercial Manager: (T)

Programme Editor: Ray Tucker (T) ray.tucker@talktalk.net

Ground Address: Sir Halley Stewart Playing Fields, Winfrey Avenue, Spalding PE11 1DA

(T) 01775 712 047 **Manager:** Pat Rayment

Photo: Jake Whitely

Club Factfile

Founded: 1921 **Nickname:** Tulips

Previous Names: Not known

Previous Leagues: Peterborough, United Counties 1931-55,68-78,86-88,91-99,03-04, 11-14 Eastern Counties 1955-60, Central Alliance 1960-61, Midland Co. 1961-68, Northern Counties East 1982-86, Southern 1988-91, 99-03. NPL 2003-11.

Club Colours (change): All royal blue (Orange/black/black)

Ground Capacity: 2,700 **Seats:** 300 **Covered:** 500 **Clubhouse:** Yes **Shop:** Yes

Directions

From the North follow the A52 and pick up the A16 south, as you near Spalding follow A16 By-pass past the New Power Station (on right). Carry on the by-pass to Springfields Roundabout, (McDonalds is on the left) turn right. Follow signs to Spalding Town Centre over Fulney Bridge on the Holbeach Road and travel approx ¾ mile from by-pass. Turn right over second bridge forming the roundabout then straight over into West Elloe Avenue. Continue down to traffic lights (Approx 400 yards). Turn left into Pinchbeck Road. After approx 300 yards turn right at the traffic lights. Turn left at the next set of traffic lights into Winfrey Avenue. The Ground is on the left.

Previous Grounds: Not known

Record Attendance: 6,972 v Peterborough - FA Cup 1982

Record Victory: Not known

Record Defeat: Not known

Record Goalscorer: Not known

Record Appearances: Not known

Additional Records:

Senior Honours:

United Counties League 1954-55, 75-75, 87-88, 98-99, 2003-04, 13-14. Northern Counties East 1983-84.
Lincolnshire Senior Cup 1952-53.

10 YEAR RECORD

04-05	05-06	06-07	07-08	08-09	09-10	10-11	11-12	12-13	13-14
NP 1 18	NP 1 20	SthM 19	NP 1 18	NP1S 17	NP1S 21	NP1S 22	UCL P 13	UCL P 3	UCL P 1

STAFFORD RANGERS

Chairman: Mike Hughes
Secretary: Mike Hughes **(T)** 07850 996 386 **(E)** info@staffordrangersfc.co.uk
Commercial Manager: **(T)**
Programme Editor: Chris Elsey **(T)** 07715 934 258
Ground Address: Marston Road, Stafford ST16 3BX*
(T) 01785 602 430 **Manager:** Neil Kitching

Photo: Jonathan Holloway.

Club Factfile

Founded: 1876 **Nickname:** Rangers
Previous Names: None
Previous Leagues: Shropshire 1891-93, Birmingham 1893-96, N. Staffs. 1896-1900, Cheshire 1900-01, Birmingham Comb. 1900-12, 46-52, Cheshire County 1952-69, N.P.L. 1969-79, 83-85, Alliance 1979-83, Conf. 1985-95, 2005-11. Southern >2005.

Club Colours (change): Black & white stripes/black/black (All red)

Ground Capacity: 6,000 **Seats:** 4,264 **Covered:** 3,500 **Clubhouse:** Yes **Shop:** Yes

Directions
M6 Junction 14. Follow signs for Uttoxeter and Stone. Straight over at 1st and 2nd (A34) islands, 3rd right sign posted Common Road and Astonfields Road Ind. Estate. The ground is straight ahead after three quarters of a mile. The route from the Motorway is highlighted by the standard football road signs.
*Sat Nav ST16 3UF

Previous Grounds: None

Record Attendance: 8,536 v Rotherham United - FA Cup 3rd Round 1975
Record Victory: 14-0 v Kidsgrove Athletic - Staffordshire Senior Cup 2003
Record Defeat: 0-12 v Burton Town - Birmingham League 1930
Record Goalscorer: M. Cullerton - 176
Record Appearances: Jim Sargent
Additional Records: Paid £13,000 to VS rugby for S. Butterworth
Received £100,000 from Crystal Palace for Stan Collymore

Senior Honours:
Northern Premier League 1971-72, 84-85. FA trophy 1971-72.
Staffordshire Senior Cup x7

10 YEAR RECORD

04-05	05-06	06-07	07-08	08-09	09-10	10-11	11-12	12-13	13-14
Conf N 8	Conf N 2	Conf 20	Conf 23	Conf N 18	Conf N 16	Conf N 20	NP P 16	NP P 15	NP P 22

STOCKSBRIDGE PARK STEELS

Chairman: Allen Bethel

Secretary: Michael Grimmer (T) 07801 626 725 (E) mickgrimmer@gmail.com

Commercial Manager: (T)

Programme Editor: Philip Burkenshaw (T) 07713 096 918

Ground Address: Look Local Stadium, Bracken Moor Lane, Stocksbridge, Sheffield S36 2AN

(T) 0114 288 8305 (Match days) **Manager:** Christopher Hilton

Club Factfile

Founded: 1986 **Nickname:** Steels

Previous Names: Stocksbridge Works and Oxley Park merged in 1986

Previous Leagues: Northern Counties East 1986-96

Club Colours (change): Yellow/blue/blue (Red/white/red)

Ground Capacity: 3,500 **Seats:** 400 **Covered:** 1,500 **Clubhouse:** Yes **Shop:** Yes

Directions

From West onto A616. Immediately you reach the Stocksbridge bypass turn Right signed (Stocksbridge West), then continue until you reach the shopping centre approx 1.5 miles. 300 yards past the centre you will see Gordons Autos on your left. Turn right directly opposite signed (Nanny Hill) and continue up the hill for Approx 500 yds, Ground is on the Left.

From M1- From North Junction 36 on to A61 Sheffield to McDonalds Roundabout. From South Junction 35a on to A616 Manchester to McDonalds Roundabout. From McDonalds roundabout on A616 Manchester for approx 6 miles then take Stocksbridge West exit, then continue until you reach the shopping centre approx 1.5 miles. 300yds past the centre you will see Gordons Autos on your Left. Turn right directly opposite signed (Nanny Hill) and continue up the hill for Approx 500yds, ground on Left.

Previous Grounds: Stonemoor 1949-51, 52-53

Record Attendance: 2,050 v Sheffield Wednesday - opening of floodlights October 1991

Record Victory: 17-1 v Oldham Town - FA Cup 2002-03

Record Defeat: 0-6 v Shildon

Record Goalscorer: Trevor Jones - 145

Record Appearances: Not known

Additional Records: Paul Jackson scored 10 v Oldham Town in the 2002-03 FA Cup - a FA Cup record
Received £15,000 from Wolverhampton Wanderers for Lee Mills

Senior Honours:

Northern Counties East Division 1 1991-92, Premier Division 1993-94, League Cup 1994-95.
Sheffield Senior Cup 1951-52, 92-93, 95-96, 98-99

10 YEAR RECORD

04-05	05-06	06-07	07-08	08-09	09-10	10-11	11-12	12-13	13-14
NP 1 14	NP 1 6	NP 1 6	NP1S 5	NP1S 3	NP P 11	NP P 13	NP P 18	NP P 20	NP P 23

SUTTON COLDFIELD TOWN

Chairman: Nick Thurston

Secretary: Bill Worship (T) 07837 375 369 (E) billandpatworship@tiscali.co.uk

Commercial Manager: (T)

Programme Editor: Lyn Coley (T) 0121 240 5421

Ground Address: Central Ground, Coles Lane, Sutton Coldfield B72 1NL

(T) 0121 354 2997 **Manager:** Neil Tooth

Club Factfile

Founded: 1897 **Nickname:** Royals

Previous Names: Sutton Coldfield F.C. 1879-1921

Previous Leagues: Central Birmingham, Walsall Senior, Staffordshire County, Birmingham Combination 1950-54, West Midlands (Regional) 1954-65, 79-82, Midlands Combination 1965-79

Club Colours (change): All blue (All yellow)

Ground Capacity: 4,500 **Seats:** 200 **Covered:** 500 **Clubhouse:** Yes **Shop:** Yes

Directions

From M42 Junc 9, take A4097 [Minworth sign]. At island, follow signs to Walmley Village. At traffic lights turn right [B4148]. After shops turn left at traffic lights into Wylde Green Road. Over railway bridge turn right into East View Road, which becomes Coles Lane.

Previous Grounds: Meadow Plat 1879-89, Coles Lane 1890-1919

Record Attendance: 2,029 v Doncaster Rovers - FA Cup 1980-81

Record Victory: Not known

Record Defeat: Not known

Record Goalscorer: Eddie Hewitt - 288

Record Appearances: Andy Ling - 550

Additional Records: Paid £1,500 to Gloucester for Lance Morrison, to Burton Albion for Micky Clarke and to Atherstone United for Steve Farmer 1991. Received £25,000 from West Bromwich Albion for Barry Cowdrill 1979

Senior Honours:

West Midlands League 1979-80. Midland Combination x2.

10 YEAR RECORD

04-05		05-06		06-07		07-08		08-09		09-10		10-11		11-12		12-13		13-14	
SthW	18	SthW	7	SthM	12	SthM	4	SthM	6	SthM	6	NP1S	6	NP1S	12	NP1S	6	NP1S	6

TIVIDALE

Chairman: Chris Dudley
Secretary: Leon Murray (T) 07939 234 813 (E) leon@tividalefc.co.uk
Commercial Manager: (T)
Programme Editor: Kris Tarplee (T) 07963 400 173
Ground Address: The Beeches, Packwood Road, Tividale, West Mids B69 1UL
(T) 01384 211 743 **Manager:** Ian Long

Club Factfile

Founded: 1953 **Nickname:**
Previous Names: Tividale Hall Youth Club 1953-56
Previous Leagues: Warwickshire & West Midlands Alliance 1956-66. West Midlands (Regional) 1966- 2011. Midland Alliance 2011-14.

Club Colours (change): All yellow (All navy blue)

Ground Capacity: 3,000 **Seats:** Yes **Covered:** Yes **Clubhouse:** Yes **Shop:**

Directions M5 Junction 2. Take A4123 towards Dudley. After approx 1.5 miles and after footbridge, take left up Trafalgar Road. Take 2nd right into Elm Terrace and then 1st left into Birch Crescent. Take 1st right into Packwood Road and ground is at end of road.

Previous Grounds: Moved to The Beeches in 1974.

Record Attendance: Not known
Record Victory: Not known
Record Defeat: Not known
Record Goalscorer: Not known
Record Appearances: Not known
Additional Records:

Senior Honours:
Warwickshire & West Midlands Alliance Premier 1964-65. West Midlands (Regional) League Division One 1972-73, Premier Division 2010-11.
Midland Alliance 2013-14.
Walsall Senior Cup 1984-85, 2000-01.

10 YEAR RECORD

04-05	05-06	06-07	07-08	08-09	09-10	10-11	11-12	12-13	13-14
WMP 16	WMP 8	WMP 2	WMP 11	WMP 13	WMP 7	WMP 1	MidAl 4	MidAl 8	MidAl 1

Northern Premier League Action

Midfield action between Lincoln Utd and Chasetown (dark shirts) in their Northern Premier League (Div 1 South) clash.

Photo: Jonathan Holloway.

Click Back in Time!

Over 37 years of publishing the Non-League Club Directory has filled a room full of information and photographs covering the game we know and love.

What we intend, over time, is to create a website that shares with you everything we have accumulated, which we hope will bring back some fond memories of season's gone by.

A unique look back at how the game has evolved since the 1940s will also make for interesting reading, including league tables from season's gone by.

Log on to **www.non-leagueclubdirectory.co.uk** today and see how many faces from teams gone by you recognise

PREMIER DIVISION 2013-14

		P	W	D	L	F	A	GD	Pts
1	(P) Hemel Hempstead Town	44	32	6	6	128	38	90	102
2	Chesham United	44	29	5	10	102	47	55	92
3	Cambridge City	44	27	7	10	95	49	46	88
4	(P) St Albans City	44	25	10	9	89	49	40	85
5	Stourbridge	44	26	6	12	114	54	60	84
6	Hungerford Town	44	26	6	12	83	45	38	84
7	Poole Town (-3)	44	25	10	9	82	48	34	82
8	Bideford	44	18	13	13	75	64	11	67
9	Biggleswade Town	44	16	16	12	85	61	24	64
10	Redditch United	44	20	3	21	68	85	-17	63
11	Corby Town	44	18	6	20	65	68	-3	60
12	Weymouth	44	18	6	20	69	80	-11	60
13	Hitchin Town	44	16	11	17	63	52	11	59
14	Frome Town	44	16	9	19	63	74	-11	57
15	Arlesey Town	44	15	10	19	68	79	-11	55
16	St Neots Town	44	15	9	20	74	76	-2	54
17	Truro City	44	15	9	20	68	84	-16	54
18	Chippenham Town	44	14	6	24	59	87	-28	48
19	Banbury United	44	14	5	25	64	116	-52	47
20	Burnham	44	12	8	24	60	91	-31	44
21	(R) AFC Totton	44	10	7	27	58	119	-61	37
22	(R) Bedford Town	44	6	6	32	46	114	-68	24
23	(R) Bashley	44	4	4	36	33	131	-98	16

Oct 2013 - Hinckley United folded - record expunged.

PLAY-OFFS

Semi-Finals: Chesham United 2-1 Stourbridge I Cambridge City 2-4 St Albans City

Final: Chesham United 1-3 St Albans City

	1	2	3	4	5	6	7	8	9	10	11	12	13	14	15	16	17	18	19	20	21	22	23
1 A.F.C. Totton		2–2	1–3	3–1	1–1	2–2	1–5	2–1	3–2	0–2	3–1	2–1	0–5	1–4	0–5	1–3	3–1	0–3	2–5	2–2	1–4	2–3	0–1
2 Arlesey Town	2–2		2–1	0–1	3–0	1–1	3–2	2–2	0–2	3–2	1–0	1–1	1–2	2–3	0–0	5–2	2–2	0–3	2–3	1–1	1–5	1–1	2–3
3 Banbury United	3–4	3–2		3–3	3–0	1–0	6–4	2–2	1–5	0–4	2–0	3–1	1–2	0–3	2–1	0–7	0–0	2–0	1–5	0–1	0–4	1–2	0–0
4 Bashley	0–2	1–4	2–3		0–2	0–1	0–7	1–2	0–6	0–1	3–1	1–3	0–4	1–4	0–2	0–2	0–3	2–3	1–2	1–3	1–4	2–2	0–3
5 Bedford Town	3–2	0–2	2–0	0–1		2–4	1–5	3–3	0–4	0–3	0–3	2–4	0–2	0–3	0–1	1–4	1–5	1–2	2–2	1–2	2–0	0–1	0–3
6 Bideford	4–0	0–1	2–2	4–2	4–0		1–1	4–0	1–4	1–4	4–1	1–1	2–2	1–0	3–1	0–0	0–0	4–3	1–0	3–2	0–1	0–0	2–1
7 Biggleswade Town	1–1	2–1	1–2	0–0	4–1	3–0		1–1	1–2	3–2	3–3	0–1	2–0	5–2	3–2	0–1	2–2	0–0	0–0	2–2	2–2	2–1	2–1
8 Burnham	2–3	1–2	1–2	1–1	3–1	1–3	0–3		0–3	1–3	4–1	2–1	1–1	0–3	1–0	1–0	2–0	2–4	2–3	1–0	2–0	1–2	1–3
9 Cambridge City	3–0	2–1	3–1	7–1	1–0	1–1	1–1	7–2		1–2	2–1	1–0	2–0	1–1	3–2	0–0	1–2	4–1	0–3	3–2	2–1	4–1	4–2
10 Chesham United	4–1	3–3	8–0	4–1	3–0	2–2	2–1	1–2	3–0		2–0	2–1	2–1	1–3	1–2	1–0	0–2	3–1	1–0	3–0	0–1	4–2	0–0
11 Chippenham Town	1–2	0–1	2–0	2–0	1–4	2–4	1–3	2–1	1–0	0–3		0–0	3–3	0–3	2–0	2–3	1–2	3–0	1–1	2–1	0–9	3–1	2–1
12 Corby Town	3–1	1–3	4–2	3–1	2–0	3–0	1–1	0–3	0–2	2–1	2–2		0–1	0–2	1–2	0–2	0–3	2–3	2–0	1–0	3–4	3–2	3–1
13 Frome Town	1–0	0–1	3–2	1–2	4–4	2–0	0–0	4–1	0–0	1–4	0–5	1–3		1–1	2–0	0–2	1–3	4–0	0–0	5–4	0–2	1–2	1–2
14 Hemel Hempstead Town	8–1	3–0	5–3	10–0	6–1	4–1	3–0	3–0	1–1	2–1	2–0	6–0	0–1		0–0	2–1	1–0	5–0	0–0	2–0	4–3	3–0	4–1
15 Hitchin Town	1–1	1–0	5–0	1–0	6–1	0–1	1–0	1–1	1–0	1–2	3–1	0–2	1–2	2–0		0–2	2–2	0–2	1–1	4–0	1–1	2–3	3–2
16 Hungerford Town	4–0	3–0	3–1	3–1	2–0	2–1	1–1	2–3	3–2	0–1	1–1	1–2	0–0	0–4	2–3		2–0	0–2	3–1	1–0	1–0	6–0	2–1
17 Poole Town	2–0	5–3	4–1	5–0	1–3	3–3	2–1	0–0	0–1	1–0	3–1	3–1	4–2	0–2	1–0	0–0		2–1	2–1	2–0	1–2	1–0	2–2
18 Redditch United	2–1	1–3	2–3	4–0	2–0	3–1	2–2	2–1	4–1	1–2	3–0	1–3	1–0	1–0	1–0	0–5	0–2		1–3	0–0	1–6	3–1	0–4
19 St Albans City	4–2	5–0	3–2	2–0	2–1	1–1	1–0	5–2	0–1	2–2	1–0	1–0	4–0	2–2	2–1	2–0	0–1	2–1		1–1	1–2	1–3	3–0
20 St Neots Town	6–0	3–1	3–1	3–1	2–2	2–0	3–4	4–2	1–2	0–5	1–2	0–3	3–1	4–1	1–1	3–0	1–1	2–3	2–3		1–1	2–0	0–2
21 Stourbridge	3–0	0–2	5–0	4–1	2–1	0–3	2–1	1–0	3–2	2–3	0–1	3–1	7–0	1–4	1–1	1–2	5–2	5–1	0–1	2–1		2–2	7–0
22 Truro City	3–2	2–0	5–0	5–0	2–2	0–2	0–2	3–0	0–1	1–1	1–3	0–0	0–2	1–6	1–1	1–2	0–2	1–0	3–7	2–3	1–1		2–1
23 Weymouth	2–1	2–1	0–1	2–0	4–1	3–2	2–2	2–1	1–1	2–4	4–1	1–0	2–0	0–3	1–1	1–3	0–3	3–0	0–3	1–2	0–5	2–5	

DIVISION ONE CENTRAL 2013-14

		P	W	D	L	F	A	GD	Pts
1	(P) Dunstable Town	42	28	6	8	94	44	50	90
2	Rugby Town	42	27	8	7	100	45	55	89
3	Kettering Town	42	27	7	8	86	41	45	88
4	Daventry Town	42	27	5	10	82	40	42	86
5	(P) Slough Town	42	26	5	11	101	51	50	83
6	Barton Rovers	42	24	8	10	79	48	31	80
7	Royston Town	42	21	10	11	80	58	22	73
8	Beaconsfield SYCOB	42	22	7	13	79	60	19	73
9	Northwood	42	21	6	15	72	62	10	69
10	Uxbridge	42	18	7	17	84	70	14	61
11	Egham Town	42	17	9	16	80	58	22	60
12	Aylesbury United	42	16	9	17	64	72	-8	57
13	St Ives Town	42	16	8	18	68	77	-9	56
14	Chalfont St Peter	42	14	8	20	49	60	-11	50
15	Potters Bar Town	42	13	10	19	61	86	-25	49
16	Aylesbury	42	14	6	22	56	73	-17	48
17	Marlow	42	12	11	19	73	84	-11	47
18	AFC Hayes	42	12	8	22	51	74	-23	44
19	Leighton Town	42	6	13	23	45	85	-40	31
20	North Greenford United	42	7	5	30	52	114	-62	26
21	(R) Chertsey Town	42	6	4	32	38	117	-79	22
22	(R) Ashford Town (Mx)	42	5	6	31	32	107	-75	21

PLAY-OFFS

Semi-Finals: Rugby Town 0-3 Slough Town I Kettering Town 1-0 Daventry Town

Final: Kettering Town 2-3 Slough Town

	1	2	3	4	5	6	7	8	9	10	11	12	13	14	15	16	17	18	19	20	21	22
1 AFC Hayes		1-2	3-1	2-5	0-2	0-1	0-1	0-2	1-2	0-2	0-4	2-1	2-2	0-0	3-1	1-0	1-1	2-1	0-6	1-1	0-1	0-4
2 Ashford Town (Middlesex)	2-1		0-0	1-2	0-1	1-4	0-1	0-2	2-1	0-1	2-2	0-2	3-1	0-4	1-2	0-3	0-2	0-2	1-1	0-1	0-5	0-4
3 Aylesbury	1-1	5-0		3-1	2-0	3-3	1-3	1-2	1-2	0-4	0-3	2-3	3-0	2-0	3-1	0-2	1-0	0-3	0-0	5-1	3-1	0-3
4 Aylesbury United	3-2	1-0	1-3		1-1	2-0	1-0	1-0	0-2	1-3	0-0	0-3	1-1	0-1	3-1	0-0	0-0	0-1	0-2	3-3	3-3	1-2
5 Barton Rovers	1-0	2-0	3-2	4-0		1-1	2-1	7-2	1-2	2-0	3-1	3-1	2-0	4-1	5-1	0-3	1-3	4-0	1-4	2-2	1-2	1-1
6 Beaconsfield SYCOB	4-1	2-0	3-1	4-1	0-4		1-1	0-1	1-0	2-3	3-2	0-2	1-1	1-1	3-2	0-2	6-1	2-2	1-4	0-2	3-1	3-1
7 Chalfont St Peter	2-2	3-1	0-1	1-3	1-2	2-1		2-1	1-1	0-1	1-2	1-3	2-3	2-3	2-1	0-1	1-0	0-1	0-2	0-1	0-1	1-1
8 Chertsey Town	1-4	3-4	4-3	1-3	0-1	1-2	0-1		0-2	0-5	1-4	0-3	0-0	1-1	1-3	0-2	1-2	0-2	2-6	0-4	0-4	0-5
9 Daventry Town	3-0	5-2	4-0	2-0	3-1	1-0	0-1	2-0		0-3	2-0	0-3	5-0	1-1	4-1	2-0	5-0	0-0	5-0	5-1	2-2	2-1
10 Dunstable Town	1-0	8-2	3-1	3-0	0-1	2-3	2-1	2-1	3-1		0-1	4-1	2-2	2-0	4-1	3-2	1-1	2-2	3-0	2-1	3-2	1-0
11 Egham Town	1-1	4-0	0-1	1-2	1-1	0-3	2-0	4-1	4-1	1-2		0-3	0-2	4-1	1-0	2-4	6-0	1-2	1-1	1-2	2-2	1-4
12 Kettering Town	3-1	4-0	3-0	4-3	0-3	1-1	1-1	2-0	2-0	2-0	1-0		5-1	1-1	1-0	3-0	4-0	5-0	0-2	4-1	1-5	2-1
13 Leighton Town	2-3	4-0	0-2	0-1	0-1	2-3	1-1	0-0	1-2	1-6	0-0	0-0		4-2	1-1	1-3	1-2	1-2	0-1	1-1	1-0	2-2
14 Marlow	0-3	2-1	4-1	3-2	1-1	2-0	1-4	1-2	1-2	2-1	2-4	1-3	0-0		4-2	2-0	6-0	2-4	2-6	3-3	2-2	1-1
15 North Greenford United	0-3	3-0	0-0	3-4	1-3	0-4	0-2	3-2	0-1	3-1	0-5	2-3	2-3	3-1		0-1	2-3	0-5	1-5	0-3	1-7	3-6
16 Northwood	2-1	1-1	0-1	1-1	2-1	0-1	2-0	8-3	0-3	1-3	0-1	0-0	4-2	2-7	3-0		1-2	3-1	2-1	3-0	0-2	2-1
17 Potters Bar Town	2-1	1-1	2-1	0-3	1-2	2-0	1-1	7-0	0-1	1-1	1-1	2-0	4-1	3-3	1-1	1-1		1-4	0-1	1-2	0-3	3-2
18 Royston Town	1-3	2-2	2-0	1-2	2-2	3-1	3-0	4-0	0-1	0-0	2-2	0-0	2-1	4-0	3-3	2-2	4-2		1-0	1-4	0-1	1-0
19 Rugby Town	2-0	1-0	3-2	1-1	2-0	0-1	0-0	8-1	2-1	0-0	3-1	1-1	4-0	3-2	2-2	4-2	6-1	6-1		1-0	0-4	3-1
20 St Ives Town	1-1	4-0	2-0	2-4	0-0	1-4	3-4	2-1	1-1	1-4	3-2	0-1	3-0	1-0	0-1	4-5	2-1	0-5	0-3		0-3	0-1
21 Slough Town	1-2	4-2	2-0	5-3	4-0	1-3	5-1	1-0	3-1	4-0	1-3	0-2	4-1	2-1	3-0	0-1	4-3	2-1	1-2	1-0		1-2
22 Uxbridge	1-2	5-1	1-1	2-1	0-2	1-3	2-3	1-1	0-2	0-3	0-5	4-2	3-1	2-1	4-1	5-1	3-2	1-3	3-1	2-5	1-1	

DIVISION ONE SOUTH & WEST 2013-14

		P	W	D	L	F	A	GD	Pts
1	(P) Cirencester Town	42	29	5	8	95	45	50	92
2	Merthyr Town	42	28	5	9	111	58	53	89
3	Tiverton Town	42	26	8	8	80	51	29	86
4	(P) Paulton Rovers	42	24	9	9	102	54	48	81
5	Swindon Supermarine	42	24	7	11	91	52	39	79
6	Shortwood United	42	23	9	10	91	44	47	78
7	North Leigh	42	22	6	14	84	46	38	72
8	Taunton Town (-1)	42	21	7	14	71	58	13	69
9	Yate Town	42	20	8	14	81	69	12	68
10	Stratford Town	42	19	5	18	103	86	17	62
11	Mangotsfield United	42	18	7	17	65	62	3	61
12	Didcot Town	42	17	6	19	70	85	-15	57
13	Wimborne Town	42	16	7	19	78	70	8	55
14	Bridgwater Town	42	14	11	17	62	64	-2	53
15	Cinderford Town	42	13	10	19	69	79	-10	49
16	Evesham United	42	12	11	19	66	80	-14	47
17	Clevedon Town	42	12	5	25	48	96	-48	41
18	(S) Godalming Town	42	10	9	23	47	79	-32	39
19	(W) Thatcham Town	42	11	6	25	41	99	-58	39
20	Bishops Cleeve	42	11	1	30	52	94	-42	34
21	Fleet Town	42	7	8	27	43	90	-47	29
22	(R) Guildford City	42	7	6	29	45	134	-89	27

PLAY-OFFS

Semi-Finals: Merthyr Town 5-2 Swindon Supermarine I Tiverton Town 1-3 Paulton Rovers

Final: Merthyr Town 0-2 Paulton Rovers

	1	2	3	4	5	6	7	8	9	10	11	12	13	14	15	16	17	18	19	20	21	22
1 Bishops Cleeve		2-0	0-3	0-4	0-5	1-3	1-2	0-2	5-0	0-2	3-0	1-0	0-5	0-2	2-1	2-4	0-3	1-3	3-4	3-0	1-3	0-2
2 Bridgwater Town	5-1		1-1	1-3	1-0	0-0	1-1	0-0	2-2	4-2	0-3	0-2	1-1	2-0	1-3	4-3	1-1	3-1	6-3	1-2	1-1	1-1
3 Cinderford Town	4-1	2-0		1-3	0-1	2-3	1-3	5-0	1-0	4-2	1-3	0-3	0-4	2-3	1-1	1-3	1-3	1-3	1-1	0-2	1-1	1-2
4 Cirencester Town	2-0	1-4	2-0		7-0	3-1	2-1	2-2	2-2	6-1	2-1	4-1	0-0	2-2	2-1	2-0	0-1	3-1	7-0	0-0	4-3	0-1
5 Clevedon Town	2-3	1-2	1-2	3-0		0-2	1-1	3-2	1-0	2-1	2-3	0-2	0-2	1-7	0-5	1-5	1-2	1-1	1-1	0-4	3-1	3-1
6 Didcot Town	0-4	2-2	1-1	3-2	6-2		1-3	1-0	2-0	3-2	2-2	3-4	2-1	1-3	2-3	1-4	2-3	0-3	4-0	0-1	1-0	2-0
7 Evesham United	2-3	3-2	0-3	2-3	3-1	1-2		2-1	1-1	1-1	0-3	1-4	4-0	2-3	2-1	1-1	2-2	4-4	5-0	1-1	2-6	3-0
8 Fleet Town	0-2	0-2	1-3	0-1	2-0	1-2	0-0		2-1	2-3	1-1	1-2	2-1	2-2	1-2	2-7	3-0	0-1	2-3	0-3	2-1	0-6
9 Godalming Town	1-0	1-3	2-2	1-2	0-2	3-0	2-3	1-0		1-0	0-3	2-2	2-2	0-5	4-3	1-2	1-1	0-1	1-2	0-2	0-1	3-1
10 Guildford City	1-0	0-3	1-3	0-5	3-2	1-2	2-2	3-2	0-0		1-2	2-3	0-7	1-3	0-0	0-1	1-1	2-1	0-3	1-4	0-3	3-3
11 Mangotsfield United	4-2	0-0	1-0	2-3	1-1	0-2	3-2	2-0	1-1	5-3		4-0	1-2	1-1	1-0	2-0	1-0	1-2	1-2	0-1	1-0	1-2
12 Merthyr Town	1-0	3-0	4-4	3-1	6-0	5-1	1-0	3-1	5-0	12-0	3-0		3-2	3-2	2-1	5-1	3-1	1-0	4-0	3-3	3-2	3-3
13 North Leigh	2-1	2-1	4-1	0-1	0-1	2-1	2-0	3-1	5-0	8-0	4-2	2-1		1-1	2-2	0-4	1-0	0-1	1-0	3-2	0-1	3-0
14 Paulton Rovers	4-1	1-0	3-1	0-1	0-0	3-3	3-1	1-2	2-1	4-0	2-0	5-2	1-0		0-3	3-4	1-1	2-3	4-0	4-0	7-0	1-2
15 Shortwood United	1-0	2-0	6-1	1-2	0-1	4-1	2-0	1-1	2-0	4-0	4-0	0-0	2-1	3-6		2-1	1-1	3-1	3-0	3-3	3-0	0-0
16 Stratford Town	5-2	1-2	1-3	0-2	3-1	1-1	0-1	2-2	1-3	4-0	3-2	0-1	2-1	1-2	0-4		4-3	5-3	7-1	2-4	4-2	3-3
17 Swindon Supermarine	5-3	2-0	2-2	3-2	2-0	2-4	3-0	4-1	4-1	5-0	4-1	1-0	2-0	3-0	2-3	3-1		4-1	5-0	1-2	2-0	1-2
18 Taunton Town	3-1	1-0	0-0	1-0	2-0	4-0	2-1	3-0	1-2	2-3	2-1	2-1	1-3	1-1	1-1	2-1	1-3		3-0	1-2	0-0	2-2
19 Thatcham Town	0-0	3-1	1-3	0-1	1-2	2-0	1-1	0-0	0-2	3-1	1-1	0-2	0-1	0-3	0-6	1-5	0-2	0-3		3-1	1-0	3-1
20 Tiverton Town	1-0	3-1	2-1	1-2	2-0	4-1	2-1	2-1	2-1	2-0	2-3	4-1	0-0	0-0	0-2	4-3	3-0	2-1	1-0		4-4	1-0
21 Wimborne Town	1-2	1-2	2-2	0-1	4-1	5-2	6-0	2-1	2-1	8-1	0-1	2-1	2-1	1-2	0-2	3-3	1-0	1-2	2-0	2-0		3-3
22 Yate Town	2-1	2-1	2-3	1-3	6-1	1-0	2-1	7-0	1-3	4-1	1-0	2-3	0-5	2-3	2-0	3-1	1-3	2-0	2-1	1-1	2-1	

LEAGUE CUP

PRELIMINARY ROUND

AFC Totton	1-3	Wimborne Town

ROUND 1

Hemel Hempstead Town	2 – 4	Aylesbury United
Hinckley United	v	Corby Town (w/o)
Hungerford Town	3 – 1	Didcot Town
Stratford Town	4 – 6	Redditch United
Arlesey Town	4 – 3	Biggleswade Town
Ashford Town	1 – 3	Northwood
Barton Rovers	0 – 1	Royston Town
Bideford	3 – 2	Taunton Town
Chertsey Town	0 – 3	Slough Town
Dunstable Town	1 – 0	Aylesbury
Egham Town	6 – 1	Guildford City
Evesham United	1 – 3	Bishop's Cleeve
Marlow	4 – 0	Fleet Town
Merthyr Town	4 – 1	Shortwood United
North Greenford United	2 – 4	Uxbridge
St Neots Town	5 – 0	Hitchin Town
Thatcham Town	0 – 3	Beaconsfield SYCOB
A.F.C. Hayes	0 – 4	Burnham
Bedford Town	2 – 3	St Ives Town
Chalfont St Peter	1 – 1	Godalming Town (3-4p)
Chesham United	5 – 0	Potters Bar Town
Cinderford Town	0 – 1	Cirencester Town
Frome Town	1 – 2	Chippenham Town
Leighton Town	2 – 2	St Albans City (1-4p)
Poole Town	1 – 1	Wimborne Town (5-4p)
Swindon Supermarine	3 – 0	North Leigh
Kettering Town	5 – 0	Daventry Town
Bashley	0 – 5	Weymouth
Bridgwater Town	3 – 3	Truro City (6-5p)
Paulton Rovers	1 – 2	Yate Town
Rugby Town	5 – 2	Banbury United
Tiverton Town	4 – 1	Clevedon Town

ROUND 2

Redditch United	3 – 2	Rugby Town
St Albans City	2 – 4	Beaconsfield SYCOB
Godalming Town	3 – 0	Egham Town
Hungerford Town	4 – 0	Bishop's Cleeve
Merthyr Town	2 – 2	Chippenham Town (6-5p)
Slough Town	5 – 1	Uxbridge
St Ives Town	2 – 3	Royston Town
Tiverton Town	4 – 2	Bridgwater Town
Swindon Supermarine	0 – 3	Cirencester Town
Arlesey Town	0 – 3	Kettering Town
Bideford	0 – 1	Yate Town
Burnham	6 – 2	Northwood
St Neots Town	3 – 0	Corby Town
Weymouth	4 – 0	Poole Town
Aylesbury United	2 – 2	Chesham United (4-3p)
Dunstable Town	4 – 3	Marlow

ROUND 3

Beaconsfield SYCOB	2 – 0	Godalming Town
Burnham	3 – 3	Slough Town (4-2p)
Dunstable Town	0 – 3	St Neots Town
Merthyr Town	1 – 1	Yate Town (4-2p)
Weymouth	1 – 2	Tiverton Town
Cirencester Town	1 – 4	Hungerford Town
Kettering Town	4 – 5	Redditch United
Royston Town	6 - 0	Aylesbury United

QUARTER FINALS

Redditch United	3 – 1	Beaconsfield SYCOB
Hungerford Town	7 – 3	Burnham
Merthyr Town	0 – 2	Tiverton Town
St Neots Town	3 – 2	Royston Town

SEMI-FINALS

Redditch United	1 – 3	St Neots Town
Tiverton Town	3 – 1	Hungerford Town

FINAL (2 Legs)

Tiverton Town	0 – 0	St Neots Town
St Neots Town	1 – 0	Tiverton Town

Premier Division Statistics 2013-14

	MCV	MCD	MCwW	MCwD	MCSG	MCwS	TGS	MCCS	TNCS
AFC Totton	3	8	16	4	6	3	13	1	1
Arlesey Town	4	4	4	7	11	2	9	2	12
Banbury United	3	9	12	5	12	3	13	3	7
Bashley	1	10	15	2	7	4	21	1	4
Bedford Town	3	19	31	3	6	3	19	2	3
Bideford	5	2	4	10	14	2	11	3	13
Biggleswade Town	4	2	8	7	12	2	11	2	12
Burnham	3	7	7	5	14	2	9	1	7
Cambridge City	6	2	6	8	11	1	7	4	15
Chesham United	12	3	4	12	22	2	5	4	18
Chippenham Town	2	4	8	3	11	1	11	2	10
Corby Town	3	4	4	5	19	2	12	2	10
Frome Town	3	5	11	4	9	2	15	4	14
Hemel Hempstead Town	9	2	3	17	17	2	8	4	21
Hitchin Town	6	3	7	6	11	2	13	2	12
Hungerford Town	10	4	4	12	11	2	13	7	23
Poole Town	5	3	3	13	9	2	11	3	19
Redditch United	3	3	7	5	8	2	11	3	14
St Albans City	4	2	3	10	16	2	9	3	19
St Neots Town	3	4	4	9	12	2	12	2	6
Stourbridge	9	3	3	9	12	3	9	3	12
Truro City	3	5	5	5	10	2	11	2	9
Weymouth	4	3	5	5	12	2	9	3	14

MCV - Most Consecutive Victories I MCD - Most Consecutive Defeats
MCwW - Most Consecutive without a Win I MCwD - Most Consecutive without a defeat
MCSG - Most Consecutive Scoring Games I MCwS - Most Consecutive without Scoring
TGS - Total Games without Scoring I MCCS - Most Consecutive Clean Sheets
TNCS - Total Number of Clean Sheets

Best Home League Attendances 2013-2014

	Att:	Opponents	Score
AFCTotton	505	Banbury United	L 1-3
Arlesey Town	526	Hitchin Town	D 0-0
Banbury United	350	Truro City	L 1-2
Bashley	288	Poole Town	L 0-3
Bedford Town	512	St Neots Town	L 1-2
Bideford	549	Truro City	D 0-0
Biggleswade Town	435	Cambridge City	L 1-2
Burnham	210	Hemel Hempstead T	L 0-3
Bideford	549	Truro City	D 0-0
Cambridge City	438	Poole Town	W 1-0
Chesham United	1104	Hemel Hempstead T	L 1-3
Chippenham Town	495	St Albans City	D 1-1
Corby Town	550	Bedford Town	W 2-0
Frome Town	392	Weymouth	L 1-2
Hemel Hempstead Town	1943	Chesham United	W 2-1
Hitchin Town	570	Cambridge City	W 1-0
Hungerford Town	273	Hemel Hempstead T	L 0-4
Poole Town	1053	Weymouth	D 2-2
Redditch United	316	Stourbridge	L 1-6
St Albans City	812	St Neots Town	D 1-1
St Neots Town	464	Hitchin Town	D 1-1
Stourbridge	870	Banbury United	W 5-0
Truro City	527	Bideford	L 0-2
Weymouth	1065	Poole Town	L 0-3

HAT-TRICK HEROS

	Club	Goals	Opponents	Score
Claudio Dias	Banbury United	3	Hemel Hempstead T (a)	L 3-5
Andy Phillips	Bedford Town	3	Greenhouse London (a) FAC	W 6-2
Andy Phillips	Bedford Town	3	Chippenham Town (a)	W 4-1
Ashley Yeoman	Bideford Town	3	St Neots Town (h)	W 3-2
Sam Reed	Bigglewade Town	3	Bashley (a)	W 7-0
Adam Marriott	Cambridge City	3	Bedford Town (a)	W 4-0
Adam Marriott	Cambridge City	5	Bashley (h)	W 7-1
Adam Marriott	Cambridge City	3	Burnham (h)	W 7-2
Adam Marriott	Cambridge City	4	Bashley (a)	W 6-0
Drew Roberts	Chesham United	3	Chippenham Town (a)	W 3-0
Drew Roberts	Chesham United	3	Banbury United (h)	W 8-0
Chris Dillon	Chesham United	4	Weymouth (a)	W 4-2
Alan Griffin	Chippenham Town	3	Redditch United	W 3-0
Tom Knighton	Chippenham Town	3	Frome Town	W 5-0
Tommy Berwick	Corby Town	3	Bashley (h)	W 3-1
Claudio Hoban	Corby Town	4	Bedford Town (a)	W 4-2
Ben Wood	Frome Town	3	AFC Totton (a)	W 5-0
Wilson Carvalho	Hemel Hempstead T	3	North Greenford United (h) FAC	W 9-1
Dave Hutton	Hemel Hempstead T	3	Bedford Town (h)	W 6-1
Ben Mackey	Hemel Hempstead T	3	Morth Greenford United (h) FAC	W 9-1
Ben Mackey	Hemel Hempstead T	3	AFC Totton (a)	W 4-1
Ben Mackey	Hemel Hempstead T	5	Bashley (h)	W 10-0
Ben Mackey	Hemel Hempstead T	3	Bedford Town (a)	W 3-0
Ben Mackey	Hemel Hempstead T	3	Weymouth (h)	W 4-1
Jordan Parkes	Hemel Hempstead T	3	Stourbridge (a)	W 4-1
Jordan Parkes	Hemel Hempstead T	3	Truro City (a)	W 6-1
Jordan Parkes	Hemel Hempstead T	3	Bashley (h)	W 10-0
Chris Toomey	Hemel Hempstead T	3	Truro City (a)	W 6-1
Mark Draycott	Hungerford Town	3	AFC Totton (h)	W 4-0
Mark Draycott	Hungerford Town	3	Banbury United (a)	W 7-0
Josh Parsons	Hungerford Town	3	Redditch United (a)	W 4-0
Justin Bennett	Poole Town	3	Bedford Town (a)	W 5-1
Steve Devlin	Poole Town	3	Bashley (h)	W 5-0
Richard Gillespie	Poole Town	4	Banbury United (h)	W 4-1
Jermaine Hylton	Redditch United	3	Cambridge City (h)	W 4-1
John Frendo	St Albans City	4	AFC Totton (a)	W 5-2
Mark Nwokeji	St Albans City	3	Enfield Town (h) FAC	W 6-1
Lewis Hilliard	St Neots Town	3	Biggleswade Town (h)	L 3-4
Shane Tolley	St Neots Town	3	Frome Town (a)	L 4-5
Luke Benbow	Stourbridge	3	Weymouth (h)	W 7-0
Luke Benbow	Stourbridge	3	Cambridge City (h)	W 3-2
Ben Billingham	Stourbridge	3	Arlesey Town (a)	W 5-1
Sean Geddes	Stourbridge	3 pens	Frome Town (h)	W 7-0
Ryan Rowe	Stourbridge	5	Chippenham Town (a)	W 9-0

ARLESEY TOWN

Chairman: Manny Cohen
Secretary: Chris Sterry (T) 07540 201 473 (E) chris.sterry@ntlworld.com
Commercial Manager: (T)
Programme Editor: Jason Marshall (T) jasonmarshall1@live.co.uk
Ground Address: Armadillo Stadium, Hitchin Road, Arlesey SG15 6RS
(T) 01462 734 504 **Manager:** Zema Abbey

Club Factfile

Founded: 1891 **Nickname:** The Blues
Previous Names: None
Previous Leagues: Biggleswade & Dist., Bedfordshire Co. (South Midlands) 1922-26, 27-28, Parthenon, London 1958-60, United Co. 1933-36, 82-92, Spartan South Mid. 1992-2000, Isthmian 2000-04, 06-08, Southern 2004-07

Club Colours (change): Light blue/dark blue/dark blue (Yellow/black/black)

Ground Capacity: 2,920 **Seats:** 150 **Covered:** 600 **Clubhouse:** Yes **Shop:** Yes

Directions

From the A1 exit at Baldock(J10) and follow the signs for Stotfold then Arlesey. You will enter Arlesey from the area known as Church End, this is the opposite end of Arlesey, but as there is only one main street just follow keep driving until you pass the Biggs Wall building and the ground is on your left.

Coming of the M1 at Luton and follow the signs for Hitchin, pass Hitchin Town FC on the Shefford Road and turn right into Turnpike Lane, this is Ickleford. Follow the road out of Ickleford and bear left away from the Letchworth turning, the ground is a little further on, on the right.

Previous Grounds: The Bury. Lamb Meadow.

Record Attendance: 2,000 v Luton Town Reserves - Bedfordshire Senior Cup 1906
Record Victory: Not known
Record Defeat: Not known
Record Goalscorer: Not known
Record Appearances: Gary Marshall
Additional Records:

Senior Honours:
South Midlands Premier Division x5. United Counties Premier Division 1984-85. FA Vase 1994-95.
Isthmian League Division 3 2000-01. Southern League Division 1 Central 2010-11.
Bedfordshire Senior Cup 1965-66, 78-79, 96-97, 2010-11.

10 YEAR RECORD

04-05	05-06	06-07	07-08	08-09	09-10	10-11	11-12	12-13	13-14
SthE 14	SthE 10	Isth1N 18	Isth1N 15	SthC 18	SthC 9	SthC 1	SthP 18	SthP 6	SthP 15

Southern League Action

Sam Reed (Biggleswade) attempts an overhead kick between Ben Gerring and Jack Furzer (Bideford).

Photo: Keith Clayton.

ARLSEY TOWN MATCH RESULTS 2013-14

Date	Comp	H/A	Opponents	Att:	Result		Goalscorers	Pos	No.
Aug 17	SPL	A	Redditch United	183	W	3-1	Hayles 34 (pen) McNamara 65 Prosper 74	3	1
20	SPL	H	Chesham United	188	W	3-2	Farrell 37 Forsythe 75 78	4	2
24	SPL	H	Corby Town	181	D	1-1	Hatch 86	3	3
26	SPL	A	Hitchin Town	502	L	0-1		8	4
31	SPL	H	Hinckley United	141	W	3-1	Hayles 35 Prosper 61 Farrell 63	6	5
Sept 4	SPL	A	Cambridge City	224	L	1-2	Forsythe 61	7	6
7	SPL	A	Frome Town	170	W	1-0	Frater 39	6	7
14	FAC1Q	A	Hitchin Town	431	D	1-1	Osei-Siribour 14		8
17	FAC1Qr	H	Hitchin Town	257	W	2-0	Hatch 36 71		9
21	SPL	H	Bideford	122	D	1-1	Hatch 76	9	10
28	FAC2Q	A	Thurrock	167	W	1-0	Prosper 4		11
Oct 1	SPL	H	Biggleswade Town	201	W	3-2	Osei-Siribour 16 Powell 79 Hatch 90	6	12
5	SPL	A	Bashley	133	W	4 1	Hatch 17 Osei-Siribour 24 Powell 41 Frater 90	5	13
8	SPL	A	Hemel Hempstead T	450	L	0-3		7	14
12	FAC3Q	A	Hampton & Richmond B	406	L	1-5	Hatch 6		15
19	FAT1Q	H	Waltham Abbey	94	W	3-0	Pemberton 23 Hayles 37 70		16
22	SPL	H	Burnham	63	D	2-2	Osie-Siribour 3 Farrell 89	7	17
26	SPL	A	AFC Totton	221	D	2 2	Powell 19 Farrell 69	7	18
29	SPL	H	Cambridge City	190	L	0-2		8	19
Nov 5	FAT2	H	Poole Town	114	W	3-2	McNamara 21 Frater 56 Farrell 83		20
9	SPL	H	Frome Town	142	L	1-2	Frater 64	10	21
16	FAT3Q	H	Marlow	149	W	2-0	Farrell 28 Hayles 30		22
23	SPL	A	Weymouth	401	L	1-2	McNamara 53	14	23
30	FAT1	H	Whitehawk	181	L	1-5	Hayles 41		24
Dec 2	SPL	A	Biggleswade Town	188	L	1-2	Farrell 51		25
7	SPL	H	Bedford Town	202	W	3-0	Hayles 19 Mbala 63 65	16	26
10	SPL	H	Banbury United	83	W	2-1	N'Guessen 58 McNamara 78	12	27
14	SPL	A	Stourbridge	328	W	2-0	N'Guessen 31 Hatch 86	10	28
17	SPL	H	Hungerford Town	102	W	5-2	Taverner 11 N'Guessen 23 29 Hayles 46 McNamara 79	10	29
21	SPL	H	Truro City	137	D	1-1	Taverner 39	9	30
26	SPL	H	Hitchin Town	526	D	0-0		10	31
28	SPL	A	Chesham United	342	D	3-3	N'Guessen 44 88 McNamara 90	10	32
Jan 11	SPL	A	Banbury United	255	L	2-3	N'Guessen 33 Taverner 61	11	33
14	SPL	A	Chippenham Town	212	W	1-0	Medina 6	8	34
18	SPL	H	Weymouth	172	L	2-3	McNamara 48 Nsue 63	8	35
21	SPL	H	Poole Town	106	D	2-2	Taverner 37 McNamara 61	8	36
25	SPL	A	St Albans City	640	L	0-5		9	37
Feb 4	SPL	H	St Albans City	242	L	2-3	Hayles 8 68	10	38
8	SPL	A	Bedford Town	217	W	2-0	McNamara 42 Mouko Nsue 67	8	39
15	SPL	H	Stourbridge	151	L	1-5	Nsue 23	9	40
18	SPL	A	St Neots Town	252	L	1-3	Hayles 27	10	41
22	SPL	A	Truro City	312	L	0-2		11	42
March 1	SPL	H	Bashley	113	L	0-1		12	43
4	SPL	H	Chippenham Town	102	W	1-0	Farrell 28	11	44
8	SPL	A	Bideford	224	W	1-0	Basmel 70	10	45
15	SPL	H	Hemel Hempstead	278	L	2-3	Basmel 14 Taylor 42	12	46
22	SPL	A	Hungerford Town	88	L	0-3		13	47
29	SPL	H	AFC Totton	137	D	2-2	Hayles 12 Farrell 20	15	48
April 5	SPL	A	Burnham	93	W	2-1	Gallagher 61 McNamara 89	13	49
12	SPL	H	Redditch United	150	L	0-3		15	50
19	SPL	A	Corby Town	196	W	3-1	Hayles 1 McNamara 11 Basmel 12	15	51
21	SPL	H	St Neots Town	227	D	1-1	Hayles 33	15	52
26	SPL	A	Poole Town	250	L	3-5	Hatch 26 Hayles 6 Shaw 77	15	53

GOALSCORERS	Lge	FAC	FAT	Total	Pens	Hat-tricks	Cons Run
Hayles	10		4	14	1		3
McNamara	10		1	11			2
Hatch	6	3		9			2
Farrell	6		2	8			2
N'Guessen	7			7			3
Frater	3		1	4			2
MOsie-Siribour	3	1		4			2
Taverner	4			4			2
Basmel	3			3			2
Forsyth	3			3			
Nsue	3			3			
Powell	3			3			
Prosper	2	1		3			
Bala	2			2			
Gallagher	1			1			
Medina	1			1			
Pemberton			1	1			
Shaw	1			1			
Taylor	1			1			

Cons Run - Consecutive scoring games.

BANBURY UNITED

Chairman: Kim Dumbleton
Secretary: Barry Worlsey (T) 07941 267 567 (E) bworsley@btinternet.com
Commercial Manager: (T)
Programme Editor: David Shadbolt (T) djshadbolt@tiscali.o.uk
Ground Address: Spencer Stadium, off Station Road, Banbury OX16 5TA
(T) 01295 263 354 **Manager:** Edwin Stein

Club Factfile

Founded: 1931 **Nickname:** Puritans
Previous Names: Spencer Villa 1931-34. Banbury Spencer. Club reformed in 1965 as Banbury United
Previous Leagues: Banbury Junior 1933-34, Oxon Senior 1934-35, Birmingham Combination 1935-54, West Midlands 1954-66, Southern 1966-90, Hellenic 1991-2000
Club Colours (change): Red/gold/red (White/blue/blue)

Ground Capacity: 6,500 **Seats:** 250 **Covered:** 250 **Clubhouse:** Yes **Shop:** Yes

Directions
From M40, Junction 11, head towards Banbury, over first roundabout, left at next roundabout into Concorde Avenue. Straight on at next roundabout, taking left hand lane, and turn left at traffic lights, turn first right into Station Approach. At station forecourt and car park, take narrow single track road on extreme right and follow to Stadium.(Direct SatNav to OX16 5AB).

Previous Grounds: Middleton Road 1931-34.

Record Attendance: 7,160 v Oxford City - FA Cup 3rd Qualifying Round 30/10/1948
Record Victory: 12-0 v RNAS Culham - Oxon Senior Cup 1945-46
Record Defeat: 2-11 v West Bromwich Albion 'A' - Birmingham Combination 1938-39
Record Goalscorer: Dick Pike and Tony Jacques - 222 (1935-48 and 1965-76 respectively)
Record Appearances: Jody McKay - 576
Additional Records: Paid £2,000 to Oxford United for Phil Emsden
Received £20,000 from Derby County for Kevin Wilson 1979
Senior Honours:
Hellenic Premier 1999-2000. Oxford Senior Cup 1978-79, 87-88, 2003-04.

10 YEAR RECORD

04-05	05-06	06-07	07-08	08-09	09-10	10-11	11-12	12-13	13-14
SthP 17	SthP 7	SthP 13	SthP 9	SthP 19	SthP 12	SthP 16	SthP 16	SthP 16	SthP 19

BANBURY UNITED MATCH RESULTS 2013-14

Date	Comp	H/A	Opponents	Att:	Result		Goalscorers	Pos	No.
Aug 17	SPL	H	Chippenham Town	210	W	2-0	Morgan 32 Simpson 45	20	1
20	SPL	A	Burnham	177	W	2-1	Evangelinos 31 Isaac 88	5	2
24	SPL	A	St Albans City	348	L	2-3	Isaac 78 Gomez de Menezes 80	6	3
26	SPL	H	Hemel Hempstead T	265	L	0-3		13	4
31	SPL	H	Frome Town	182	L	1-2	Isaac 80	16	5
Sept 3	SPL	A	Hinckley United	211	D	1-1	Pinto 26	15	6
7	SPL	A	Redditch United	221	W	3-2	Isaac 37 Bridges 62 (pen) 72	10	7
14	***FAC1Q***	***H***	***Cirencester Town***	***171***	***L***	***1-2***	***Talabi 5***		8
17	SPL	H	Corby Town	157	W	3-1	Simpson 15 Isaac 66 Pinto 82	8	9
21	SPL	H	Hitchin Town	290	W	2-1	Simpson 32 52	6	10
Oct 5	SPL	A	AFC Totton	505	W	3-1	Simpson 32 Lawless 44 54	6	11
8	SPL	A	Hungerford Town	100	L	1-3	Lawless 34	9	12
12	SPL	H	Truro City	**350**	L	1-2	Isaac 57	9	13
19	***FAT1Q***	***A***	***Stourbridge***	***321***	***L***	***2-3***	***Talabi 48 Lawless 27***		14
26	SPL	A	Bashley	168	W	3-2	Pinto 22 Bridges 62 90	7	15
Nov	SPL	H	Redditch United	250	W	2-0	Talabi 45 Lawless 53	6	16
19	SPL	H	Bedford Town	123	W	3-0	Isaac 20 Skendl 29 Lawless 39	5	17
23	SPL	H	Poole	317	D	0-0		5	18
26	SPL	A	Bideford	158	D	2-2	Lawless 30 (pen) Isaac 40	6	19
30	SPL	H	St Neots Town	271	L	0-1		7	20
Dec 7	SPL	A	Biggleswade Town	180	W	2-1	Talabi 57 Simpson 88	6	21
10	SPL	A	Arlesey Town	83	L	1-2	Talabi 64	6	22
14	SPL	H	Weymouth	325	D	0-0		6	23
18	SPL	A	Corby Town	167	L	2-4	Morgan 16 Bridges 30 (pen)	6	24
26	SPL	A	Hemel Hempstead Town	386	L	3-5	DIAS 3 (51 58 79)	10	25
28	SPL	H	Burnham	269	D	2-2	Bridges 81 (pen) Green 90	10	26
Jan 11	SPL	H	Arlesey Town	255	W	3-2	Talabi 31 Evangelinos 53 Lawless 72	8	27
15	SPL	A	Frome Town	133	L	2-3	Bridges 40 (pen) Abrahams 45	9	28
25	SPL	H	Bideford	229	W	1-0	Martin 19	8	29
Feb 1	SPL	A	St Neots Town	374	L	1-3	Martin 36	8	30
4	SPL	A	Chesham United	212	L	0-8		8	31
19	SPL	A	Cambridge City	205	L	1-2	Pinto 30	11	32
22	SPL	H	Chesham United	276	L	0-4		14	33
27	SPL	H	Stourbridge	162	L	0-4		14	34
March 1	SPL	H	AFC Totton	178	L	3-4	Talabi 21 Isaac 29 Blossom 89	14	35
8	SPL	A	Hitchin Town	322	L	0-5		18	36
15	SPL	H	Hungerford Town	228	L	0-7		18	37
22	SPL	A	Truro City	369	L	0-3		19	38
29	SPL	H	Bashley	217	D	3-3	Skendl 53 Martin 57 Talabi 69	19	39
April 1	SPL	A	Poole Town	216	L	1-4	Dias 85	19	40
5	SPL	A	Bedford Town	216	L	0-2		20	41
8	SPL	H	Biggleswade Town	147	W	6-4	York 4 (og) Pinto 25 Dias 50 Isaac 57 79 Skendl 65	18	42
12	SPL	A	Chippenham Town	325	L	0-2		20	43
15	SPL	A	Weymouth	310	W	1-0	Evangelinos 65	18	44
19	SPL	H	St Albans City	308	L	1-5	Fathers 28	18	45
21	SPL	A	Stourbridge	670	L	0-5		18	46
26	SPL	H	Cambridge City	324	L	1-5	Talabi 72	19	47

GOALSCORERS	Lge	FAC	FAT	Total	Pens	Hat-tricks	Cons Run
Isaac	11			11			2
Talabi	7	1	1	9			2
Lawless	7		1	8	1		2
Bridges	7			7	3		
Simpson	6			6			3
Dias	5			5		1	
Pinto	4			4			
Evangelinos	3			3			
Martin	3			3			2
Skendl	3			3			
Morgan	2			2			
Abrahams	1			1			
Blossom	1			1			
Fathers	1			1			
Gomez de Menazes	1			1			
Green	1			1			
Opponents	1			1			

Cons Run - Consecutive scoring games.

BIDEFORD

Chairman: Roy Portch
Secretary: Kevin Tyrrell (T) 07929 078 613 (E) info@bidefordafc.co.uk
Commercial Manager: (T)
Programme Editor: Ian Knight (T) ianknight@bidefordafc.co.uk
Ground Address: The Sports Ground, Kingsley Road, Bideford EX39 2LH
(T) 01237 474 974 **Manager:** Sean Joyce

Photo: Keith Clayton.

Club Factfile

Founded: 1949 **Nickname:** The Robins
Previous Names: Bideford Town
Previous Leagues: Devon & Exeter 1947-49, Western 1949-72, 75-2010, Southern 1972-75

Club Colours (change): All red (All blue)

Ground Capacity: 6,000 **Seats:** 375 **Covered:** 1,000 **Clubhouse:** Yes **Shop:**

Directions
Exit M5 at J.27. A361 to Barnstaple. Turn left onto A39 to Bideford.
9 miles turn left into town.
Ground on right hand side as entering town centre.

Previous Grounds: None

Record Attendance: 6,000 v Gloucester City - FA Cup 4th Qualifying Round
Record Victory: Not known
Record Defeat: Not known
Record Goalscorer: Tommy Robinson - 259
Record Appearances: Derek May - 527
Additional Records:

Senior Honours:
Western League 1963-64, 70-71, 71-72, 81-82, 82-83, 2001-02, 03-04, 04-05, 05-06, 09-10, Division 1 1951-52, Division 3 1949-50.
Southern Division 1 South & West 2011-12.
Devon Senior Cup 1979-80

10 YEAR RECORD

04-05	05-06	06-07	07-08	08-09	09-10	10-11	11-12	12-13	13-14
WestP 1	WestP 1	WestP 4	WestP 6	WestP 6	WestP 1	Sthsw 10	Sthsw 1	SthP 20	SthP 8

BIDEFORD MATCH RESULTS 2013-14

Date	Comp	H/A	Opponents	Att:	Result		Goalscorers	Pos	No.
Aug 17	SPL	A	Chesham United	282	D	2-2	Clifford 6 Howe 58	9	1
20	SPL	H	AFC Totton	230	W	4-0	Howe 35 65 Downing 55 80	7	2
24	SPL	H	Biggleswade Town	220	D	1-1	Duff 82	9	3
26	SPL	A	Truro City	527	W	2-0	Duff 39 Groves 87	6	4
31	SPL	A	Bashley	150	W	1-0	Halpin 29	3	5
Sept 3	SPL	H	Weymouth	341	W	2-1	Howe 20 Squire 52	3	6
7	SPL	H	Bedford Town	249	W	4-0	Duff 35 60 Hockley 42 (pen) Gerring 88	2	7
14	***FAC1Q***	***H***	***Larkhall***	***221***	***W***	***3-0***	***Bye 42 Howe 44 Clifford 77***		8
17	SPL	A	Poole Town	239	D	3-3	Downing 1 Duff 20 Groves 36	3	9
21	SPL	A	Arlesey Town	122	D	1-1	Groves 45	2	10
28	***FAC 2Q***	***A***	***Yate Town***	***268***	***L***	***1-2***	***Howe 28***		11
Oct 5	SPL	H	Corby Town	216	D	1-1	Halpin 15	4	12
8	SPL	H	Chippenham Town	191	W	4-1	Downing 10 Hockley 65 (pen) 79 Yeoman 77	3	13
26	SPL	H	St Neots Town	215	W	3-2	YEOMAN 3 (24 75 pen 82)	3	14
Nov 3	***FAT1***	***A***	***Hendon***	***220***	***L***	***0-1***			15
9	SPL	A	Bedford Town	187	W	4-1	Howe 1 Downing 24 30 Yeoman 78	3	16
16	SPL	H	Bashley	237	W	4-2	Downing 14 Halpin 42 55 Farkins 78	3	17
23	SPL	H	Stourbridge	231	L	0-1		3	18
26	SPL	H	Banbury United	158	D	2-2	Phillips 83 87	3	19
30	SPL	A	Burnham	155	W	3-1	Downing 21 70 Howell 87	3	20
Dec 7	SPL	H	Cambridge CIty	220	L	1-4	Hockley 75	4	21
14	SPL	A	Redditch United	129	L	1-3	Hockley 55 (pen)	5	22
21	SPL	H	Hitchin Town	234	W	3-1	Merceica 25 Duff 72 Howe 80	4	23
26	SPL	H	Truro CIty	**549**	D	0-0		5	24
28	SPL	A	AFC Totton	285	D	2-2	Merceica 31 Gerring 36	4	25
Jan 4	SPL	H	Hungerford Town	245	D	0-0		4	26
7	SPL	A	Hemel Hempstead T	344	L	1-4	Phillips 81 (pen)	5	27
11	SPL	H	Hemel Hempstead T	275	W	1-0	Hockley 44	4	28
14	SPL	H	Poole Town	183	D	0-0		4	29
18	SPL	A	Stourbrdge	573	W	3-0	Hockley 52 (pen) Duff 72 Squire 79	4	30
25	SPL	A	Banbury United	229	L	0-1		4	31
28	SPL	A	Frome Town	167	L	0-2		5	32
Feb 1	SPL	H	Burnham	193	W	4-0	Duff 12 Hockley 35 Downing 55 Farkins 80	4	33
4	SPL	A	Weymouth	261	L	2-3	Downing 21 Gerring 86	5	34
10	SPL	A	St Albans City	363	D	1-1	Downing 2	6	35
15	SPL	H	St Albans City	219	W	1-0	Sullivan 20	5	36
22	SPL	A	Hitchin Town	321	W	1-0	Duff 81	5	37
March 1	SPL	A	Corby Town	282	L	0-3		6	38
8	SPL	H	Arlesey Town	224	L	0-1		6	39
15	SPL	A	Chippenham Town	307	W	4-2	Howe 6 35 Hockley 48 74	6	40
19	SPL	A	Cambridge City	174	D	1-1	Howe 60		41
29	SPL	A	St Neots Town	353	L	0-2		8	42
April 5	SPL	H	Redditch United	214	W	4-3	Squire 38 Duff 48 85 Phillips 47	8	43
12	SPL	H	Chesham United	231	L	1-4	Groves 85	8	44
19	SPL	A	Biggleswade Town	140	L	0-3		8	45
21	SPL	H	Frome Town	207	D	2-2	Squire 8 Duff 42	8	46
26	SPL	A	Hungerford Town	211	L	1-2	Howe 43 (pen)	8	47

GOALSCORERS	Lge	FAC	FAT	Total	Pens	Hat-tricks	Cons Run
Duff	12			12			2
Downng	12			12			
Hockley	10			10	4		2
Howe	9	2		9	1		2
Yeoman	9			9	1	1	2
Halpin	4			4			
Phillips	4			4	1		
Squire	4			4			
Groves	3			3			
Clifford	1	1		2			

	Lge	FAC	FAT	Total	Pens	Hat-tricks	Cons Run
Farkins	2			2			
Gerring	2			2			
Mercieca	2			2			
Bye		1		1			
Howell	1			1			
Sullivan	1			1			

Cons Run - Consecutive scoring games.

BIGGLESWADE TOWN

Chairman: Maurice Dorrington
Secretary: Mike Draxter (T) (E) michaeldraxler@hotmail.com
Commercial Manager: (T)
Programme Editor: David Simpson (T) simpson_david@hotmail.co.uk
Ground Address: The Carlsberg Stadium, Langford Road, Biggleswade SG18 9JJ
(T) 01767 318 202 (Matchdays) **Manager:** Chris Nunn

Club Factfile

Founded: 1874 **Nickname:** The Waders
Previous Names: Biggleswade FC
Previous Leagues: Biggleswade & District, Bedford & District, Spartan South Midlands 1951-55, 80-2009, Eastern Counties 1955-63, United Counties 1963-80

Club Colours (change): White with green trim/green/green (Blue & black stripes/black/blue & black)

Ground Capacity: 3,000 **Seats:** 300 **Covered:** 400 **Clubhouse:** Yes **Shop:**

Directions
From the south – up the A1, past the first roundabout (Homebase) signposted Biggleswade. At next roundabout (Sainsburys) turn right onto A6001. As you approach the Town Centre, go straight over the mini roundabout following signs for Langford (Teal Road). At traffic lights, turn right (still heading towards Langford). Continue along Hitchin Street over two mini roundabouts and as you pass under the A1, the ground entrance is 200 yards on the right. From the north – exit A1 at the Sainsburys roundabout and follow instructions as above.

Previous Grounds: Fairfield

Record Attendance: 2,000
Record Victory: Not known
Record Defeat: Not known
Record Goalscorer: Not known
Record Appearances: Not known
Additional Records:

Senior Honours:
Spartan South Midlands Premier Division 2008-09. Bedfordshire Premier Cup 2009. Bedfordshire Senior Challenge Cup 2012-13.

10 YEAR RECORD

04-05	05-06	06-07	07-08	08-09	09-10	10-11	11-12	12-13	13-14
SSM P 10	SSM P 15	SSM P 18	SSM P 3	SSM P 1	SthM 12	SthC 4	SthC 8	SthC 4	SthP 9

BIGGLESWADE TOWN MATCH RESULTS 2013-14

Date	Comp	H/A	Opponents	Att:	Result		Goalscorers	Pos	No.
Aug 17	SPL	H	Bashley	140	D	0-0		15	1
21	SPL	A	Cambridge City	293	D	1-1	Allinson	14	2
24	SPL	A	Bideford	220	D	1-1	Lewis 8	14	3
26	SPL	H	Bedford Town	330	W	4-1	Lewis 22 York 52 S Reed 66 Knight 79	11	4
31	SPL	A	Poole Town	262	L	1-2	S.Reed 83	13	5
Sept 3	SPL	H	Burnham	135	D	1-1	S.Reed 57	14	6
7	SPL	H	Hungerford Town	145	L	0-1		17	7
15	FAC1Q	A	Wingate & Finchley	108	D	0-0			8
17	***FAC1Qr***	***H***	***Wingate & Finchley***	***79***	***W***	***4-3***	***S.Reed 13 L.Reed 42 74 Gentle 54***		9
21	SPL	A	Redditch United	197	D	2-2	Donnelly 11 York 63	19	10
28	***FAC2Q***	***H***	***Chelmsford City***	***329***	***W***	***2-0***	***Daniel 32 York 44***		11
Oct 1	SPL	A	Arlesey Town	201	L	2-3	L.Reed 45 Key 61	19	12
5	SPL	H	Weymouth	178	W	2-1	Peacock 13 L.Reed 45	16	13
12	***FAC3Q***	***H***	***Leatherhead***	***366***	***W***	***5-1***	***Witham 45 L.Reed 52 Key 67 90 Donnelly 87***		14
19	***FAT1Q***	***H***	***Chesham United***	***168***	***L***	***0-1***			15
26	***FAC 4Q***	***H***	***Canvey Island***	***678***	***W***	***1-0***	***Donnelly 80***		16
29	SPL	A	Burnham	125	W	3-0	Peacock 9 Donnelly 85 Allinson 89	10	17
Nov 9	***FAC1***	***A***	***Stourbridge***	***1605***	***L***	***1-4***	***Key 14***		18
12	SPL	A	St Neots Town	306	W	4-3	Donnelly 5 89 Daniel 19 Witham 80	11	19
16	SPL	H	Chippenham Town	154	D	3-3	Donnelly 3 Gentle 20 S.Reed 45	13	20
19	SPL	A	Hungerford Town	62	D	1-1	S.Reed 19	10	21
23	SPL	A	Truro City	384	W	2-0	S.Reed 19 Daniel 87	10	22
26	SPL	H	Stourbridge	126	D	2-2	S.Reed 77 L.Reed 90	10	23
30	SPL	A	AFC Totton	290	W	5-1	S Reed 14 47 Donnelly 51 Allinson 56 Peacock 70		24
Dec 2	SPL	H	Arlesey Town	188	W	2-1	Peacock 54 Smith 73	7	25
7	SPL	H	Banbury United	180	L	1-2	York 70	9	26
11	SPL	A	Corby Town	175	D	1-1	Donnelly 17	9	27
14	SPL	A	Hitchin Town	371	L	0-1		10	28
17	SPL	H	Chesham United	135	W	3-2	Donnelly 22 Gentle 54 Key 67	8	29
26	SPL	A	Bedford Town	339	W	5-1	S.Reed 1 43 York 6 27 Mason 87	8	30
28	SPL	H	Cambridge CIty	435	L	1-2	L.Reed 45	8	31
Jan 11	SPL	A	Chesham United	315	L	1-2	Gentle 48	9	32
21	SPL	H	Frome Town	110	W	2-0	Witham 3 Donnelly 67	8	33
Feb 4	SPL	A	Hemel Hempstead	351	L	0-3		9	34
22	SPL	A	Frome Town	163	D	0-0		12	35
March 1	SPL	A	Weymouth	441	D	2-2	Poole 13 (og) Daniel 57	11	36
8	SPL	H	Redditch United	181	D	0-0		13	37
10	SPL	H	St Albans City	281	D	0-0		14	38
18	SPL	A	Stourbridge	319	L	1-2	Donnelly 37	15	39
22	SPL	H	St Neots Town	315	D	2-2	S.Reed 43 50	15	40
25	SPL	H	Poole Town	140	D	2-2	Donnelly 15 S Reed 88	14	41
29	SPL	A	Chippenham Town	284	W	3-1	Mason 27 30 Peacock 45	13	42
April 1	SPL	H	AFC Totton	106	D	1-1	Donnelly 37	14	43
5	SPL	H	Corby Town	170	L	0-1		15	44
8	SPL	A	Banbury United	147	L	4-6	York 13 Donnelly 24 Woolf 36 Allinson 45	15	45
10	SPL	H	Hitchin Town	280	W	3-2	Allinson 13 48 (pen) S.Reed 83	13	46
12	SPL	A	Bashley	125	W	7-0	S.REED 3 (29 pen 52 59 pen) Woolf 37 83 Daniel 79 Peacock 85	12	47
15	SPL	H	Truro City	131	W	2-1	Daniel 9 Allinson 24	10	48
19	SPL	H	Bideford	140	W	3-0	Short 33 Daniel 70 L.Reed 76	9	49
21	SPL	A	St Albans City	724	L	0-1		9	50
26	SPL	H	Hemel Hempstead	**345**	W	5-2	L.Reed 41 Key 45 Donnelly 71 Daniel 87 Mason 90	9	51

GOALSCORERS	Lge	FAC	FAT	Total	Pens	Hat-tricks	Cons Run
S. Reed	18	1		19	2	1	4
Donnelly	14	1	1	16			2
L. Reed	6	3		9			3
Daniel	7	1		8			3
Key	4	2	1	7			
York	6	1		7			2
Allinson	7			7	1		2
Peacock	6			6			
Gentle	3	1		4			
Mason	4			4			

	Lge	FAC	FAT	Total	Pens	Hat-tricks	Cons Run
Witham	2	1		3			
Woolf	3			3			
Lewis	2			2			
Knight	1			1			
Short	1			1			
Smith	1			1			
Opponents	1			1			

Cons Run - Consecutive scoring games.

BURNHAM

Chairman: Gary Reeves
Secretary: Gary Reeves (T) 07919 415 141 (E) burnhamfcsec@aol.com
Commercial Manager: Alan Hickman (T) 07946 349 452
Programme Editor: (T)
Ground Address: The Gore, Wymers Wood Road, Burnham, Slough SL1 8JG
(T) 01628 668 654 **Manager:** Gary Meakin

Club Factfile

Founded: 1878 **Nickname:** The Blues
Previous Names: Burnham & Hillingdon 1985-87
Previous Leagues: Hellenic 1971-77, 95-99, Athenian 1977-84, London Spartan 1984-85, Southern 1985-95

Club Colours (change): Blue and white halves/blue/blue (Red and black hoops/red/red)

Ground Capacity: 2,500 **Seats:** Yes **Covered:** Yes **Clubhouse:** Yes **Shop:** Yes

Directions
Approx. 2 miles from M4 junction 7 and 5 miles from M40 junction 2. From M40 take A355 to A4 signposted Maidenhead. From M4 take A4 towards Maidenhead until you reach roundabout with Sainsbury Superstore on left. Turn right into Lent Rise Road and travel approx 11/2 miles over 2 double roundabouts. 100 yards after second double roundabout fork right into Wymers Wood Road. Ground entrance on right.

Previous Grounds: Baldwin Meadow until 1920s

Record Attendance: 2,380 v Halesowen Town - FA Vase 02/04/1983
Record Victory: 18-0 v High Duty Alloys - 1970-71
Record Defeat: 1-10 v Ernest Turner Sports - 1963-64
Record Goalscorer: Fraser Hughes - 65 (1969-70)
Record Appearances: Not known
Additional Records:

Senior Honours:
Hellenic League 1975-76, 98-99, League Cup 1975-76, 98-99, Division 1 Cup 1971-72.
Southern League Division One Central 2012-13.

10 YEAR RECORD

04-05		05-06		06-07		07-08		08-09		09-10		10-11		11-12		12-13		13-14	
SthW	9	SthW	4	Sthsw	3	Sthsw	10	Sthsw	17	SthM	3	SthC	14	SthC	15	SthC	1	SthP	20

BURNHAM MATCH RESULTS 2013-14

Date	Comp	H/A	Opponents	Att:	Result		Goalscorers	Pos	No.
Aug 17	SPL	A	Corby Town	251	W	3-0	Blake 19 John 28 Gray 88	2	1
20	SPL	H	Banbury United	177	L	1-2	Upward 42	9	2
24	SPL	H	Frome Town	114	D	1-1	Blake 52	11	3
26	SPL	A	Hungerford Town	140	W	3-2	Driver 3 Burnell 28 65	7	4
31	SPL	H	Hemel Hempstead	**210**	L	0-3		10	5
Sept 3	SPL	A	Biggleswade Town	135	D	1-1	Driver 86	13	6
7	SPL	A	Stourbridge	551	L	0-1		15	7
14	***FAC1Q***	***A***	***Beaconsfield SYCOB***	***129***	***W***	***4-2***	***Burnell 26 Gray 58 Driver 60 Dobson 84***		8
21	SPL	A	Poole Town	249	D	0-0		17	9
28	***FAC 2Q***	***A***	***Didcot Town***	***103***	***L***	***1-2***	***Burnell 90***		10
Oct 5	SPL	H	Chippenham Town	138	W	4-1	Charles-Smith 8 Gray 30 Dobson 32 (pen) 45	13	11
8	SPL	H	Redditch United	121	L	2-4	Dobson 7 (Pen) 48 (pen)	13	12
19	***FAT1Q***	***H***	***Paulton Rovers***	***92***	***W***	***2-1***	***Charles-Smith 13 Togwell 75***		13
22	SPL	A	Arlesey Town	63	D	2-2	Charle-Smith 22 Dobson 72	12	14
26	SPL	A	Hitchin Town	238	D	1-1	Dobson 45	12	15
29	SPL	H	Biggleswade Town	125	L	0-3		13	16
Nov 2	***FAT2Q***	***A***	***Marlow***	***201***	***L***	***0-2***			17
9	SPL	A	Bashley	113	W	2-1	Blake 48 53	13	18
16	SPL	A	Bedford Town	185	D	3-3	Blake 2 Togwell 53 Bollard 81	14	19
22	SPL	H	Cambridge City	120	L	0-3		19	20
30	SPL	H	Bideford Town	155	L	1-3	Charles-Smith 17	19	21
Dec 2	SPL	H	Stourport	123	W	2-0	Blake 9 90	16	22
7	SPL	A	Chesham United	313	W	2-1	Driver 65 Blake 90	14	23
14	SPL	H	St Neots Town	124	W	1-0	Kabamba 80	13	24
17	SPL	A	Hemel Hempstead	361	L	0-3		14	25
26	SPL	H	Hungerford Town	133	W	1-0	Baddeley 48	12	26
28	SPL	A	Banbury United	269	D	2-2	Upward 2 48	13	27
Jan 11	SPL	H	Bedford Town	143	W	3-1	Blake 62 Smith 87 (pen) Couch 88	12	28
14	SPL	H	Hitchin Town	125	W	1-0	Blake 11	10	29
18	SPL	A	Cambridge City	249	L	2-7	Driver 63 Sears 70	10	30
25	SPL	H	Bashley	125	D	1-1	Webb 3	11	31
28	SPL	H	St Albans City	150	L	2-3	Webb 2 Hippolyte 4	12	32
Feb 1	SPL	A	Bideford	193	L	0-4		12	33
15	SPL	A	St Neots Town	262	L	2-4	Togwell 45 Kebamba 90	15	34
25	SPL	H	Truro City	109	L	1-2	Kebamba 19	15	35
March 1	SPL	A	Chippenham Town	308	L	1-2	Driver 72	19	36
8	SPL	H	Poole Town	160	W	2-0	Kebamba 14 50	16	37
11	SPL	H	Chesham United	175	L	1-2	Couch 85	16	38
15	SPL	A	Redditch United	201	L	1-2	Blake 48	17	39
18	SPL	A	AFC Totton	247	L	1-2	Hippolyte 47 (pen)	17	40
22	SPL	H	Weymouth	120	L	1-3	Hippolyte 15	18	41
25	SPL	A	Weymouth	321	L	1-2	Kabamba 9	18	42
29	SPL	A	St Albans City	640	L	2-5	Driver 8 Hippolyte 90	18	43
April 5	SPL	H	Arlesey Town	93	L	1-2	Couch 62	18	44
12	SPL	H	Corby Town	102	W	2-1	Munday 24 Kebamba 64	18	45
19	SPL	A	Frome Town	242	L	1-4	Couch 3	20	46
21	SPL	H	AFC Totton	107	L	2-3	Blake 16 Kebamba 36	20	47
26	SPL	A	Truro City	333	L	0-3		20	48
									49

GOALSCORERS	Lge	FAC	FAT	Total	Pens	Hat-tricks	Cons Run
Blake	12			12			2
Kebamba	8			8			2
Dobson	6	1		7	3		2
Driver	6	1		7			
Burnell	2	2		4			
Charles-Smith	3		1	4			2
Couch	4			4			
Hippolyte	4			4	1		2
Gray	2	1		3			
Togwell	2		1	3			
Upward	3			3			
Gray	2			2			
Webb	2			2			2
Baddeley	1			1			
Bollard	1			1			
John	1			1			
Munday	1			1			
Sears	1			1			
Smith	1			1	1		

Cons Run - Consecutive scoring games.

CAMBRIDGE CITY

Chairman: Kevin Satchell
Secretary: Andy Dewey (T) 07720 678 585 (E) andy@cambridgecityfc.com
Commercial Manager: (T) 07887 748 002
Programme Editor: Chris Farrington (T) ccfc.editor@googlemail.com
Ground Address: City Ground, Milton Road, Cambridge CB4 1UY
(T) 01223 233 226 **Manager:** Gary Roberts

Club Factfile

Founded: 1908 **Nickname:** Lilywhites
Previous Names: Cambridge Town 1908-51
Previous Leagues: Bury & District 1908-13, 19-20, Anglian 1908-10, Southern Olympian 1911-14, Southern Amateur 1913-35, Spartan 1935-50, Athenian 1950-58, Southern 1958-2004

Club Colours (change): White/black/white (All light blue)

Ground Capacity: 2,722 **Seats:** 526 **Covered:** 220 **Clubhouse:** Yes **Shop:** Yes

Directions
Take Junction 13 on M11 and head for City Centre. At mini roundabout turn left then straight on at traffic lights. The road then runs parallel with the river. On reaching traffic lights controlling entry to one way system, get into middle lane up beside Staples Office Furniture and follow lane behind Staples where it becomes nearside lane. Stay in this lane until road straightens then take first left. Ground is behind Westbrook Centre.

Previous Grounds: None

Record Attendance: 12,058 v Leytonstone - FA Amateur Cup 1st Round 1949-50
Record Victory: Not known
Record Defeat: Not known
Record Goalscorer: Gary Grogan
Record Appearances: Mal Keenan
Additional Records: Paid £8,000 to Rushden & Diamonds for Paul Coe
Received £100,000 from Millwall for Neil Harris 1998
Senior Honours:
Southern League 1962-63, Southern Division 1985-86.
Suffolk Senior Cup 1909-10. East Anglian x9. Cambridgeshire Professional Cup 2012-13.

10 YEAR RECORD

04-05	05-06	06-07	07-08	08-09	09-10	10-11	11-12	12-13	13-14
Conf S 2	Conf S 7	Conf S 13	Conf S 14	SthP 4	SthP 6	SthP 4	SthP 5	SthP 8	SthP 3

CAMBRIDGE CITY MATCH RESULTS 2013-14

Date	Comp	H/A	Opponents	Att:	Result		Goalscorers	Pos	No.
Aug 17	SPL	A	Frome Town	206	D	0-0		16	1
21	SPL	H	Biggleswade Town	293	D	1-1	Abbs 35	15	2
24	SPL	H	Poole Town	230	L	1-2	Beech 33	18	3
26	SPL	A	St Neots Town	451	W	2-1	Dawkin 31 Abbs 88	14	4
31	SPL	A	Weymouth	655	D	1-1	Beech 3	14	5
Sept 4	SPL	H	Arlesey Town	224	W	2-1	Dawkin 65 Marriott 85	11	6
8	SPL	H	Chippenham Town	322	W	2-1	Marriott 9 Beasant 84	10	7
14	***FAC1Q***	***A***	***Kings Lynn Town***	***705***	***W***	***5-1***	***Bacon 7 Lewis 12 Marriott 35 Ramm 40 Beasant 77***		8
16	SPL	A	St Albans City	327	W	1-0	Marriott 15	5	9
21	SPL	H	AFC Totton	219	W	3-0	Marriott 53 88 Prada 75	5	10
28	***FAC2Q***	***A***	***AFC Rushden & Diamonds***	***815***	***L***	***2-3***	***Clarke 28 (og) Dawkin 31 (pen)***		11
Oct 5	SPL	A	Bedford Town	344	W	4-0	MARRIOTT 3 (17 36 48) Bacon 25	3	12
8	SPL	A	Chesham United	312	L	0-3		5	13
19	FAT1	A	Kings Lynn Town	605	W	2-1	Marriott 44 51	4	14
26	SPL	A	Truro City	350	W	1-0	Dawkin 12		15
29	SPL	A	Arlesey Town	190	W	2-0	Marriott 37 (pen) 73 (pen)	3	16
Nov 2	***FAT2Q***	***A***	***Scarborough Athletic***	***442***	***D***	***0-0***			17
6	***FAT2Qr***	***H***	***Scarborough Athletic***	***227***	***L***	***1-2***	***Marriott 58 (pen)***		18
9	SPL	A	Chippenham Town	347	L	0-1		4	19
13	SPL	H	Stourbridge	241	W	2-1	Chaffey 53 Dawkin 81	3	20
20	SPL	H	St Albans City	216	L	0-3		4	21
22	SPL	A	Burnham	120	W	3-0	Beech 9 20 Marriott 68	3	22
30	SPL	H	Hemel Hempstead Town	247	D	1-1	Pepper 82	4	23
Dec 7	SPL	A	Bideford	220	W	4-1	Beasant 11 Martin 26 Burns 55 Brighton 60	3	24
11	SPL	H	Redditch United	174	W	4-1	Marriott 22 Dawkin 40 47 Brighton 66	3	25
14	SPL	H	Bashley	251	W	7-1	MARRIOTT 5 (9 14 63 pen 70 76) Dawkin 47 78	3	26
18	SPL	H	Hitchin Town	288	W	3-2	Beech 26 Bossman 29 Marriott 90 (pen)	3	27
26	SPL	H	St Neots Town	371	W	3-2	Dawkins 17 Marriott 62 Bossman 65	2	28
28	SPL	A	Biggleswade Town	435	W	2-1	Brighton 26 Beech 77	2	29
Jan 11	SPL	A	Redditch United	220	L	1-4	Marriott 43 (pen)	3	30
18	SPL	H	Burnham	249	W	7-2	Burns 5 Chaffey Bossman 27 41 MARRIOTT 3 (16 35 49)	3	31
Feb 19	SPL	H	Banbury United	205	W	3-1	Ryan 20 (og) Beech 57 Dawkin 68	4	32
22	SPL	H	Hungerford Town	325	D	0-0		4	33
26	SPL	H	Weymouth	231	W	4-2	Marriott 26 53 Bossman 40 74	4	34
Mar 2	SPL	H	Bedford Town	301	W	1-0	Marriott 53	3	35
4	SPL	A	Hungerford Town	117	L	2-3	Bossman 48 Marriott 66	3	36
8	SPL	A	AFC Totton	325	L	2-3	Marriott 6 12	4	37
11	SPL	A	Hemel Hempstead Town	520	D	1-1	Marriott 45 (pen)	4	38
14	SPL	H	Chesham United	370	L	1-2	Marriott 24	4	39
19	SPL	H	Bideford	174	D	1 1	Beech 57	5	40
22	SPL	A	Stourbridge	504	L	2-3	Marriott 88 90 (pen)	5	41
29	SPL	H	Truro City	265	W	4-1	Marriott 13 Beech 45 Dawkin 63 Lawton 67	5	42
April 2	SPL	A	Corby Town	215	W	2-0	Beech 34 Marriott 76	3	43
5	SPL	A	Hitchin Town	570	L	0-1		3	44
8	SPL	A	Bashley	91	W	6-0	MARRIOTT 4 (27 59 pen 81 84) Beech 71 Dawkin 78	3	45
12	SPL	H	Frome Town	310	W	2-0	Kelly 13 Marriott 90	3	46
19	SPL	H	Poole Town	**438**	W	1-0	Beech 50	3	47
21	SPL	H	Corby Town	412	W	1-0	Burns 4	3	48
26	SPL	A	Banbury United	324	W	5 1	Chaffey 8 Dawkin 29 Burns 45 Beech 60 (pen) Brighton 83	3	49
30	***SPL PO SF***	***H***	***St Albans City***	***768***	***L***	***2-4***	***Kelly 45 Marriott 62***		50

GOALSCORERS	Lge	FAC	FAT	Total	Pens	Hat-tricks	Cons Run
Marriott	42+1	1	1	45	10	4	6
Dawkin	12	1		13	1		
Beech	12			12	1		2
Bossman	7			7			
Brighton	5			5			2
Burns	4			4			2
Chaffey	4			4			
Beasant	2	1		3			
Abbs	2			2			
Bacon	1	1		2			
Kelly	1+1			2			
Lawton	1			1			
Lewis		1		1			
Martin	1			1			
Pepper	1			1			
Prada	1			1			
Ramm		1		1			
Opponents	1	1		2			

Cons Run - Consecutive scoring games.

Play-off goals indicated by +

CHESHAM UNITED

Chairman: Brian McCarthy

Secretary: Alan Lagden (T) (E) secretary@cheshamunited.co.uk

Commercial Manager: (T)

Programme Editor: Steve Doman (T) cufcprogramme@talktalk.net

Ground Address: The Meadow, Amy Lane, Amersham Road, Chesham HP5 1NE

(T) 01494 783 964 **Manager:** Andy Leese

Action from the 2014-15 pre-season friendly with Wycombe Wanderers.
Photo: Trevor Hyde

Club Factfile

Founded: 1917 **Nickname:** The Generals

Previous Names: Chesham Town and Chesham Generals merged in 1917 to form Chesham United.

Previous Leagues: Spartan 1917-47, Corinthian 1947-63, Athenian 1963-73, Isthmian 1973-2004

Club Colours (change): All claret (Yellow/black/yellow)

Ground Capacity: 5,000 **Seats:** 284 **Covered:** 2,500 **Clubhouse:** Yes **Shop:** Yes

Directions

From M25 Junction 20 take A41 (Aylesbury), leave A41 at turn-off for Chesham (A416), pass through Ashley Green into Chesham. Follow signs to Amersham, still on A416 pass two petrol stations opposite each other and at next roundabout take third exit into ground.

From M1 Junction 8 follow signs for Hemel Hempstead then joining the A41 for Aylesbury, then as above.

Previous Grounds: None

Record Attendance: 5,000 v Cambridge United - FA Cup 3rd Round 05/12/1979

Record Victory: Not known

Record Defeat: Not known

Record Goalscorer: John Willis

Record Appearances: Martin Baguley - 600+

Additional Records: Received £22,000 from Oldham Athletic for Fitz Hall

Senior Honours:

Isthmian League 1992-93, Division 1 1986-87, 97-97. Berks & Bucks Senior Cup x12.

10 YEAR RECORD

04-05		05-06		06-07		07-08		08-09		09-10		10-11		11-12		12-13		13-14	
SthP	12	SthP	22	Sthsw	15	SthM	6	SthM	5	SthM	4	SthP	6	SthP	4	SthP	3	SthP	2

CHESHAM UNITED MATCH RESULTS 2013-14

Date	Comp	H/A	Opponents	Att:	Result		Goalscorers	Pos	No.
Aug 17	SPL	H	Bideford Town	282	D	2-2	Roberts 30 Potton 46	10	1
20	SPL	A	Arlesey Town	188	L	2-3	Dillon 51 Watters 62	16	2
24	SPL	A	Stourbridge	172	W	3-2	Lambert 5 (pen) Effiong 34 Potton	12	3
26	SPL	H	St Albans City	503	W	1-0	Effiong 4	9	4
31	SPL	A	Hungerford Town	140	W	1-0	Wales 44	7	5
Sept 3	SPL	H	Bashley	251	W	4-1	Roberts12 70 Dillon 61 Potton 86	4	6
7	SPL	H	Truro City	477	W	4-2	Dillon 39 52 Roberts 43 (pen) 79	4	7
14	***FAC1Q***	***H***	***Royston Town***	***255***	***L***	***1-2***	***Roberts 15***		8
17	SPL	A	Bedford town	159	W	3-0	Thomas 45 Dillon &0 Effiong 90	2	9
21	SPL	A	Corby Town	221	L	1-2	Braithwaite 86	3	10
Oct 5	SPL	H	Hinckley United	331	W	3-0	Roberts 20 (pen) Potton 53 73	2	11
8	SPL	H	Cambridge City	312	W	3-0	Wales 31 Roberts 38 Potton 74	2	12
12	SPL	A	Chippenham Town	349	W	3-0	ROBERTS 3 (12 29 56)	2	13
19	***FAT1Q***	***A***	***Biggleswade Town***	***109***	***L***	***1-0***	***Braithwaite 53***		14
22	SPL	A	St Neots Town	224	W	5-0	Wales 16 Dillon 25 Potton 37 87 Roberts 49	2	15
26	SPL	H	Redditch United	339	W	3-1	Roberts 18 Dillon 29 Potton 56	2	16
29	SPL	A	Bashley	134	W	1-0	Dillon 14	1	17
Nov 2	***FAT2Q***	***H***	***Weymouth***	***276***	***W***	***2-1***	***Dillon 2 Wales 14***		18
5	SPL	H	Bedford Town	264	W	3-0	Roberts 47 55 Kyriacou 65	1	19
9	SPL	A	Truro City	461	D	1-1	Dillon 71	1	20
16	***FAT3Q***	***A***	***Margate***	***317***	***W***	***3-0***	***Roberts 5 90 Wales 90***		21
23	SPL	H	AFC Totton	360	W	4-0	Gordon 28 Roberts 54 77 Potton 70	1	22
26	SPL	H	Poole Town	321	L	0-2		1	23
30	***FAT1Q***	***A***	***Hungerford Town***	***211***	***L***	***0-2***			24
Dec 7	SPL	H	Burnham	313	L	1-2	Fotheringham 7	2	25
10	SPL	H	Hungerford Town	251	W	1-0	Potton 32	2	26
14	SPL	A	Frome Town	182	W	4-1	Potton 15 18 Wales 20 Roberts 79	2	27
17	SPL	A	Biggleswade Town	135	L	2-3	Potton 33 50	2	28
26	SPL	A	St Albans City	730	D	2-2	Little 25 Kyriacou 44	3	29
28	SPL	H	Arlesey Town	342	D	3-3	Dillon 25 M'Bala 36 (og) Wales 90	3	30
Jan 1	SPL	H	Hemel Hempstead	**1104**	L	1-3	Roberts 49	3	31
11	SPL	H	Biggleswade Town	315	W	2-1	Roberts 6 20	2	32
18	SPL	A	AFC Totton	276	W	2-0	Potton 28 Roberts 90	2	33
Feb 1	SPL	H	Hitchin Town	451	L	1-2	Wilson 30	2	34
4	SPL	H	Banbury United	212	W	8-0	Ryan 8 (og) Dillon 27 55 ROBERTS 3 (34 50 79pen) Potton 45 47	2	35
15	SPL	H	Frome Town	317	W	2-1	Roberts 44 (pen) 64	2	36
22	SPL	A	Banbury United	276	W	4-0	Dillon 13 29 Roberts 34 88	2	37
24	SPL	A	Hitchin Town	243	W	2-1	Roberts 21 Dillon 90	2	38
March 4	SPL	A	Weymouth	413	W	4-2	DILLON 4 (11 23 29 73)	2	39
8	SPL	H	Corby Town	366	W	2-1	Dillon 7 Roberts 27	2	40
11	SPL	A	Burnham	175	W	3-1	Roberts 9 Dillon 48 Stewart 80	2	41
15	SPL	A	Cambridge City	370	W	2-1	Potton 17 Dillon 37	2	42
22	SPL	H	Chippenham Town	345	W	2-0	Stewart 42 Potton 57	2	43
29	SPL	A	Redditch United	220	W	2-1	Roberts 45 (pen) 48	2	44
April 5	SPL	H	St Neots Town	339	W	3-0	Dillon 29 58 Little 44	2	45
12	SPL	A	Bideford Town	231	W	4-1	Brown 15 Roberts 40 Potton 47 55	2	46
17	SPL	A	Poole Town	315	L	0-1		2	47
19	SPL	H	Stourbridge	461	L	0-1		2	48
21	SPL	A	Hemel Hempstead T	1943	L	1-2	Little 56	2	49
26	SPL	H	Weymouth	391	D	0-0		2	50
29	***SPL PO SF***	***H***	***Stourbridge***	***728***	***W***	***2-1***	***Roberts 31 Dillon 64***		51
May 5	***SPL PO F***	***H***	***St Albans City***	***2960***	***L***	***1-3***	***Potton 6***		52

GOALSCORERS	Lge	FAC	FAT	Total	Pens	Hat-tricks	Cons Run
Roberts	31+1	1	2	35	5	1	4
Dillon	24+1		1	26		1	6
Potton	19+1			20			3
Wales	5		2	7			
Effiong	3			3			2
Little	3			3			
Braithwaite	1		1	2			
Kyriacou	2			2			
Stewart	2			2			
Brown	1			1			
Gordon	1			1			
Fotherby	1			1			
Lambert	1			1	1		
Thomas	1			1			
Watters	1			1			
Wilson	1			1			
Opponents	2			2			

Cons Run - Consecutive scoring games.

CHIPPENHAM TOWN

Chairman: Neil Blackmore

Secretary: Angela Townsley **(T)** 07909 634 875 **(E)** angelatownsley.chiptownfc@gmail.com

Commercial Manager: **(T)**

Programme Editor: Angela Townsley **(T)** angelatownsley.chiptownfc@gmail.com

Ground Address: Hardenhuish Park, Bristol Road, Chippenham SN14 6LR

(T) 01249 650 400 **Manager:** Mark Collier

Club Factfile

Founded: 1873 **Nickname:** The Bluebirds

Previous Names: None

Previous Leagues: Hellenic, Wiltshire Senior, Wiltshire Premier, Western

Club Colours (change): All royal blue (Green/black/black)

Ground Capacity: 3,000 **Seats:** 300 **Covered:** 1,000 **Clubhouse:** Yes **Shop:** Yes

Directions

Exit 17 from M4. Follow A350 towards Chippenham for three miles to first roundabout, take second exit (A350); follow road to third roundabout (junction with A420). Turn left and follow signs to town centre. Ground is 1km on left hand side adjacent to pedestrian controlled traffic lights. Car/Coach park next to traffic lights.

Previous Grounds: Played at four different locations before moving in to Hardenhuish on 24/09/1919.

Record Attendance: 4,800 v Chippenham United - Western League 1951

Record Victory: 9-0 v Dawlish Town (H) - Western League

Record Defeat: 0-10 v Tiverton Town (A) - Western League

Record Goalscorer: Dave Ferris

Record Appearances: Ian Monnery

Additional Records:

Senior Honours:

Western League 1951-52. Les Phillips Cup 1999-2000. Wiltshire Senior Cup. Wiltshire Senior Shield x4.

10 YEAR RECORD

04-05		05-06		06-07		07-08		08-09		09-10		10-11		11-12		12-13		13-14	
SthP	2	SthP	4	SthP	7	SthP	4	SthP	8	SthP	3	SthP	7	SthP	11	SthP	15	SthP	18

CHIPPENHAM TOWN MATCH RESULTS 2013-14

Date	Comp	H/A	Opponents	Att:	Result		Goalscorers	Pos	No.
Aug 17	SPL	A	Banbury United	210	L	0-2		20	1
20	SPL	H	Poole Town	350	L	1-2	McLennan 18	21	2
Nathan Rudge resigned as Manager - Steve Winter in temporary charge before being made full-time Manager.									3
24	SPL	H	Hitchin Town	265	W	2-0	Griffin 29 McLennon 72	16	4
26	SPL	A	Frome Town	307	W	5-0	Phillips 20 Guthrie 27 KNIGHTON 3 (73 75 90)	10	5
31	SPL	H	AFC Totton	289	L	1 2	Griffin 23 (pen)	12	6
Sept 3	SPL	A	Stourbridge	455	W	1-0	Purnell 83	10	7
8	SPL	A	Cambridge City	322	L	1-2	Guthrie 39	13	8
14	***FAC1Q***	***A***	***Yate Town***	***248***	***L***	***2-3***	***McLennon 42 Horsell 85 (og)***		9
21	SPL	H	Bedford Town	299	L	1-4	Knighton 29	15	10
28	SPL	H	Redditch United	266	W	3-0	GRIFFIN 3 (26 65 pen 81)	13	11
Oct 5	SPL	A	Burnham	138	L	1-4	Murden 47	15	12
8	SPL	A	Bideford	191	L	1-4	Griffin 25	15	13
12	SPL	H	Chesham United	349	L	0-3		16	14
19	***FAT1Q***	***H***	***Chertsey Town***	***224***	***W***	***3-0***	***Blake 34 (og) Knighton 61 Phillips 90***		15
29	SPL	H	Stourbridge	317	L	0-9		18	16
Steve Winter sacked as Manager.									17
Nov 2	***FAT 2Q***	***A***	***Bognor Regis Town***	***367***	***L***	***1-4***	***Knighton 51***		18
4	SPL	A	Redditch United	168	L	0-4		20	19
Mark Collier appointed as new Manager.									20
9	SPL	H	Cambridge City	347	W	1-0	Phillips 43	16	21
16	SPL	A	Biggleswade Town	154	D	3-3	Knighton 34 Griffin 73 McLennon 75	19	22
19	SPL	H	Truro City	266	W	3-1	Dean 51 Griffin 55 59	13	23
26	SPL	A	Weymouth	339	L	1-4	Griffin 14	17	24
30	SPL	A	Poole Town	331	L	1-3	Dean 69	18	25
Dec 7	SPL	A	Corby Town	312	D	2-2	Guthrie 63 Phillips 66	18	26
10	SPL	A	AFC Totton	237	L	1-3	Ferguson 35	18	27
14	SPL	H	Hemel Hempstead T	337	L	0-3		18	28
26	SPL	H	Frome Town	400	D	3-3	Griffin 28 59 Dean 44	16	29
Jan 11	SPL	H	St Albans City	495	D	1-1	King 89	18	30
14	SPL	H	Arlesey Town	212	L	0-1		20	31
25	SPL	H	Weymouth	452	W	2-1	Dean 24 King 48	20	32
28	SPL	H	St Neots Town	209	W	2-1	Griffin 15 Dean 74	19	33
Feb 8	SPL	H	Corby Town	337	D	0-0		19	34
11	SPL	A	Bashley	93	L	1-3	Griffin 40	19	35
17	SPL	A	St Albans City	219	L	0-1		19	36
22	SPL	H	Bashley	319	W	2-0	Guthrie 49 Griffin 60	20	37
March 1	SPL	H	Burnham	308	W	2-1	Dean 46 Griffin 76	20	38
4	SPL	A	Arlesey Town	102	L	0-1		20	39
8	SPL	A	Bedford Town	169	W	3-0	Guthrie 8 Phillips 47 52	20	40
15	SPL	H	Bideford	307	L	2-4	Dean 86 Griffin 87	20	41
22	SPL	A	Chesham United	345	L	0-2		20	42
29	SPL	H	Biggleswade Town	284	L	1-3	King 86	20	43
April 1	SPL	A	Hemel Hempstead T	498	L	0-2		20	44
5	SPL	A	Truro City	341	W	3-1	Phillips 27 King 49 Griffin 58	19	45
12	SPL	H	Banbury United	325	W	2-0	Griffin 37 Guthrie 54	19	46
17	SPL	H	Hungerford Town	164	D	1-1	Griffin 40	19	47
19	SPL	A	Hitchin Town	293	L	1-3	McLennon 24	19	48
21	SPL	H	Hungerford Town	369	L	2-3	Harris 37 45	19	49
26	SPL	A	St Neots Town	453	W	2-1	McLennon 24 (pen) Griffin 72	18	50

GOALSCORERS	Lge	FAC	FAT	Total	Pens	Hat-tricks	Cons Run
Griffin	21			21	2	1	3
Dean	7			7			2
Knighton	5		2	7			1
Phillips	6		1	7			
Guthrie	6			6			
McLennon	4	1		5	1		
King	4			4			
Harris	2			2			
Ferguson	1			1			
Murden	1			1			
Pennell	1			1			
Opponents		1	1	2			

Cons Run - Consecutive scoring games.

Soccer Books Limited

72 ST. PETERS AVENUE (Dept. NLD)
CLEETHORPES
N.E. LINCOLNSHIRE
DN35 8HU
ENGLAND

Tel. 01472 696226 Fax 01472 698546

Web site www.soccer-books.co.uk
e-mail info@soccer-books.co.uk

Established in 1982, Soccer Books Limited has one of the largest ranges of English-Language soccer books available. We continue to expand our stocks even further to include many more titles including German, French, Spanish and Italian-language books.

With well over 200,000 satisfied customers over the past 30 years, we supply books to virtually every country in the world but have maintained the friendliness and accessibility associated with a small family-run business. The range of titles we sell includes:

Yearbooks – All major yearbooks including editions of the Sky Sports Football Yearbook (previously Rothmans), Supporters' Guides, South American Yearbooks, North & Central American Yearbooks, Asian Football Yearbooks, Yearbooks of African Football, Non-League Club Directories, Almanack of World Football.

Club Histories – Complete Statistical Records, Official Histories, Definitive Histories plus many more including photographic books.

World Football – World Cup books, European Championships History, Statistical histories for the World Cup, European Championships, South American and European Club Cup competitions and foreign-language Season Preview Magazines for dozens of countries.

Biographies & Who's Whos – of Managers and Players plus Who's Whos etc.

Encyclopedias & General Titles – Books on Stadia, Hooligan and Sociological studies, Histories and hundreds of others, including the weird and wonderful!

DVDs – Season reviews for British clubs, histories, European Cup competition finals, World Cup matches and series reviews, player profiles and a selection of almost 60 F.A. Cup Finals with many more titles becoming available all the time.

For a printed listing showing a selection of our titles, contact us using the information at the top of this page. Alternatively, our web site offers a secure ordering system for credit and debit card holders and Paypal users and lists our full range of 2,000 new books and 400 DVDs.

CIRENCESTER TOWN

CIRENCESTER TOWN FOOTBALL CLUB

Chairman: Stephen Abbley
Secretary: Scott Griffin (T) 01285 654 543 (E) scott.griffin@cirentownfc.plus.com
Commercial Manager: (T)
Programme Editor: Scott Griffin (T) scott.griffin@cirentownfc.plus.com
Ground Address: The Corinium Stadium, Kingshill Lane, Cirencester GL7 1HS
(T) 01285 654 543 **Manager:** Brian Hughes

The squad celebrate winning the Southern League Division One South & West title 2013-14.

Club Factfile

Founded: 1889 **Nickname:** Centurions
Previous Names: None
Previous Leagues: Hellenic

Club Colours (change): Red & black stripes/black/red (Orange/white/orange)

Ground Capacity: 4,500 **Seats:** 550 **Covered:** 1,250 **Clubhouse:** Yes **Shop:** Yes

Directions
Go along the dual carriageway, the Cirencester North-South outer bypass which links the M4 at Junction 15, Swindon, with the M5 at Junction 11a, Gloucester. That road is identified on the road signs and road maps as A419(T) from Swindon or A417(T) from the M5. It is about 20 or so minutes road time from both the M4 and the M5 junctions, traffic permitting. Come off the bypass at the Burford Road Junction (named on the road signs). There is a big services located there - fuel, food and a Travelodge. At that junction, go up the slip road to a roundabout. At the roundabout, turn away from Cirencester Town Centre, (If you are coming from the south, go over the bypass and straight over another roundabout) and up to the traffic lights. Turn right at the traffic lights and follow the road to a T-junction. Turn right, the road takes you back over the bypass, and then turn first left into Kingshill Lane. The Ground is half a mile on the right, past Kingshill School and the Council Playing Fields - See more at: http://www.southern-football-league.co.uk/clubs/cirencester-town#sthash.6fp1KGuA.dpuf

Previous Grounds: Smithfield Stadium

Record Attendance: 2,600 v Fareham Town - 1960
Record Victory: Not known
Record Defeat: Not known
Record Goalscorer: Not known
Record Appearances: Not known
Additional Records: Paid £4,000 to Gloucester City for Lee Smith

Senior Honours:
Hellenic League Premier Division 1995-96. Southern Division One South & West 2013-14.
Gloucestershire Senior Amateur Cup 1989-90. Gloucestershire County Cup 1995-96.

10 YEAR RECORD

04-05	05-06	06-07	07-08	08-09	09-10	10-11	11-12	12-13	13-14
SthP 7	SthP 18	SthP 21	SthP 21	Sthsw 14	Sthsw 5	SthP 13	SthP 22	Sthsw 11	Sthsw 1

CORBY TOWN

Chairman: Stevie Noble
Secretary: Gerry Lucas (T) 07932 6333 43 (E) info@corbytownfc.co.uk
Commercial Manager: (T) commercial@corbytownfc.co.uk
Programme Editor: (T) media@corbytownfc.co.uk
Ground Address: Steel Park, Jimmy Kane Way, Rockingham Road, Corby NN17 2FB
(T) 01536 406 640 **Manager:** Tommy Wright

Club Factfile

Founded: 1947 **Nickname:** The Steelmen
Previous Names: Stewart & Lloyds (Corby) > 1947
Previous Leagues: United Counties 1935-52. Midland 1952-58. Southern 1958-2009

Club Colours (change): White/black/black (Pink/black & white/pink)

Ground Capacity: 3,893 **Seats:** 577 **Covered:** 1,575 **Clubhouse:** Yes **Shop:** Yes

Directions
From A14, Exit at Jnc 7, Keep left, at first roundabout take A6003 Oakham/Uppingham stay on this road for approx. 7 miles (ignore signs for Corby to your right en route) straight over two roundabouts at second B.P. petrol station on right. At next roundabout approx 1 mile ahead turn right onto A6116 for 300 yards entrance to Ground between Rugby Club and Rockingham Forest Hotel (Great Western).

Previous Grounds: Occupation Road 1948-85.

Record Attendance: 2,240 v Watford - Friendly 1986-87
Record Victory: Not known
Record Defeat: Not known
Record Goalscorer: David Holbauer - 159 (1984-95)
Record Appearances: Derek Walker - 601
Additional Records: Paid £2,700 to Barnet for Elwun Edwards 1981
Received £20,000 from Oxford United for Matt Murphy 1993
Senior Honours:
United Counties League 1950-51, 51-52. Southern League Premier Division 2008-09.
Northants Senior Cup x7 Most recently 2012-13.

10 YEAR RECORD

04-05	05-06	06-07	07-08	08-09	09-10	10-11	11-12	12-13	13-14
SthW 12	SthE 2	SthP 20	SthP 16	SthP 1	Conf N 6	Conf N 13	Conf N 17	Conf N 20	SthP 11

CORBY TOWN MATCH RESULTS 2013-14

Date	Comp	H/A	Opponents	Att:	Result		Goalscorers	Pos	No.
Aug 17	SPL	H	Burnham	251	L	0-3		24	1
20	SPL	A	Hemel Hempstead Town	326	L	0-6		24	2
24	SPL	A	Arlesey Town	181	D	1-1	Berwick 82	23	3
26	SPL	H	Hinckley United	302	W	3-1	Moyo 14 Shariff 49 Hurst 90	17	4
31	SPL	A	St Albans City	374	L	0-1		20	5
Sept 4	SPL	H	St Neots Town	317	W	1-0	Moreman 63	17	6
7	SPL	H	Bashley	261	W	3-1	BERWICK 3 (56 60 (pen) 62)	12	7
14	***FAC1Q***	***H***	***Barwell***	***269***	***W***	***3-0***	***Malone 24 Berwick 42 Moreman 50***		8
17	SPL	A	Banbury United	157	L	1-3	Wright 61	13	9
21	SPL	H	Chesham United	221	W	2-1	Malone 54 Braithwaite 88 (og)	12	10
28	***FAC2Q***	***A***	***Mickleover Sports***	***270***	***D***	***3-3***	***Berwick 3 Shariff 7 Wright 19***		11
Oct 2	***FAC2Qr***	***H***	***Mickleover Sports***	***228***	***W***	***5-2***	***James 38 Berwick 55 (pen) Gascoigne 60 Shariff 76 82***		12
5	SPL	A	Bideford	216	D	1-1	Shariff 75	12	13
8	SPL	A	Stourbridge	317	L	1-3	S.Hendrie 39	12	14
12	***FAC3Q***	***H***	***Trafford***	***531***	***W***	***4-2***	***Malone 5 49 McGowan 13 Smart 57 (og)***		15
19	***FAT1Q***	***A***	***Daventry Town***	***159***	***L***	***1-2***	***Berwick 17***		16
26	***FAC4Q***	***A***	***Colwyn Bay***	***552***	***W***	***3-1***	***Hendrie 22 Rooney 82 Ives 90***		17
29	SPL	A	St Neots Town	261	W	3-0	Rooney 15 72 Wright 27	11	18
Nov 9	***FAC1***	***H***	***Dover Athletic***	***1387***	***L***	***1 2***	***Carruthers 90***		19
16	SPL	H	Weymouth	390	W	3-1	Rooney 40 S.Hendry 54 80	17	20
23	SPL	A	Redditch United	216	W	3-1	Berwick 75 89	12	21
27	SPL	H	Hitchin Town	251	L	1-2	Carruthers 20	12	22
30	SPL	A	Frome Town	170	W	3-1	Wright 5 36 Ives 90	11	23
Dec 7	SPL	H	Chippenham Town	312	D	2-2	Ives 45 Verma 76	13	24
11	SPL	H	Biggleswade Town	175	D	1-1	Hendrie 15	13	25
14	SPL	A	Truro City	386	D	0-0		14	26
18	SPL	H	Banbury United	167	W	4-2	Rooney 26 Mills 27 50 Wright 61	11	27
28	SPL	H	Hemel Hempstead Town	409	L	0-2		16	28
Jan 11	SPL	A	Weymouth	551	L	0-1		16	29
14	SPL	A	Bashley	100	W	3-1	Malone 21 40 Rooney 24 (Pen)	16	30
25	SPL	A	Hitchin Town	395	W	2-0	Verma 59 Carruthers 68	14	31
28	SPL	A	Hungerford Town	75	W	2-1	Hendry 38 Verma 88	10	32
Feb 1	SPL	H	Frome Town	312	L	0-1		11	33
8	SPL	A	Chippenham Town	337	D	0-0		11	34
15	SPL	H	Truro City	247	W	3-2	Mills 34 (pen) Verma 36 67	8	35
18	SPL	A	Bedford Town	164	W	4-2	HOBAN 4 (8 25 37 pen 49)	8	36
22	SPL	A	Poole Town	280	L	1-3	Hoban 72	8	37
March 1	SPL	H	Bideford	282	W	3-0	Carruthers 69 84 Mills 88	8	38
5	SPL	H	St Albans City	234	W	2-0	Wright 50 Mills 77 (pen)	7	39
8	SPL	H	Chesham United	368	L	1-2	Hoban 22	7	40
15	SPL	H	Stourbridge	361	L	3-4	Verma 18 Taylor 43 Mills 58 (pen)	9	41
19	SPL	H	Poole Town	208	L	0-3		10	42
22	SPL	A	AFC Totton	398	L	1-2	Mills 33	10	43
26	SPL	H	AFC Totton	131	W	3-1	Hoban 3 Mills 68 (pen) Ives 70	10	44
29	SPL	H	Hungerford Town	253	L	0-2		10	45
April 2	SPL	H	Cambridge CIty	215	L	0-2		10	46
5	SPL	A	Biggleswade Town	170	W	1-0	John 28	9	47
12	SPL	A	Burnham	102	L	1-2	Mills 49	9	48
16	SPL	H	Redditch United	236	L	2-3	Thomas 57 Mills 87 (pen)	9	49
19	SPL	H	Arlesey Town	196	L	1-3	Ives 8	12	50
21	SPL	A	Cambridge City	412	L	0-1		13	51
26	SPL	H	Bedford Town	**550**	W	2-0	Mills 59 (pen) Ives 76	11	52

GOALSCORERS	Lge	FAC	FAT	Total	Pens	Hat-tricks	Cons Run
Mills	11			11	6		
Berwick	6	3	1	10	2	1	2
Hoban	7			7	1		
Hendrie	5	1		6			
Ives	5	1		6			
Malone	3	3		6			
Wright	5	1		6			
Verma	6			6			
Rooney	4	1		5	1		
Shariff	2	3		5			2
Carruthers	3	1		4			
Moreman	1	1		2			
Gascoigne		1		1			
Hurst	1			1			
James		1		1			
John	1			1			
McGowan		1		1			
Moyo	1			1			
Taylor	1			1			
Thomas	1			1			
Opponents	1	1		2			

Cons Run - Consecutive scoring games.

DORCHESTER TOWN

Chairman: Neil Butterworth
Secretary: David Martin **(T)** 07971 172 795 **(E)** dorchdave@gmail.com
Commercial Manager: Richard Coole **(T)** commercial@dorchestertownfc.com
Programme Editor: **(T)** media@dorchestertownfc.com
Ground Address: The Avenue Stadium, Weymouth Avenue, Dorchester DT1 2RY
(T) 01305 262 451 **Manager:** Phil Simkin

Club Factfile

Founded: 1880 **Nickname:** The Magpies
Previous Names: None
Previous Leagues: Dorset, Western 1947-72

Club Colours (change): Black & white/black/black (Yellow/blue/yellow)

Ground Capacity: 5,009 **Seats:** 710 **Covered:** 2,846 **Clubhouse:** Yes **Shop:** Yes

Directions
The stadium is located at the junction of A35 Dorchester Bypass and the A354 to Weymouth, adjacent to Tesco. There is a coach bay for the team coach at the front of the stadium. Any supporters coach should park on the railway embankment side of the stadium.

Previous Grounds: Council Recreation Ground, Weymouth Avenue 1908-1929, 1929-90, The Avenue Ground 1929

Record Attendance: 4,159 v Weymouth - Southern Premier 1999
Record Victory: 7-0 v Canterbury (A) - Southern League Southern Division 1986-87
Record Defeat: 0-13 v Welton Rovers (A) - Western League 1966
Record Goalscorer: Not known
Record Appearances: Derek 'Dinkie' Curtis - 458 (1950-66)
Additional Records: Denis Cheney scored 61 goals in one season. Paid £12,000 to Gloucester City for Chris Townsend 1990. Received £35,000 from Portsmouth for Trevor Sinclair.
Senior Honours:
Western League 19954-55. Southern League 1985-86, Division 1 East 2002-03. Dorset Senior Cup x8 Most recently 2011-12.

10 YEAR RECORD

04-05	05-06	06-07	07-08	08-09	09-10	10-11	11-12	12-13	13-14
Conf S 8	Conf S 11	Conf S 17	Conf S 21	Conf S 19	Conf S 17	Conf S 17	Conf S 11	Conf S 8	Conf S 22

DORCHESTER TOWN MATCH RESULTS 2013-14

Date	Comp	H/A	Opponents	Att:	Result		Goalscorers	Pos	No.
Aug 17	CSouth	A	Staines Town	176	L	0-1		16	1
20	CSouth	H	Weston-s-Mare	400	L	0-3		21	2
24	CSouth	H	Whitehawk	403	L	2-6	Crittendon 12 Watson 89	22	3
26	CSouth	A	Gosport Borough	486	D	1-1	Walker 73	21	4
31	CSouth	H	Ebbsfleet United	422	L	1-2	Watson 66	21	5
Sept 7	CSouth	A	Concord Rangers	284	L	0-1		22	6
14	CSouth	H	Bishop's Stortford	373	L	1-3		22	7
21	CSouth	H	Chelmsford City	357	**W**	2-0	Way 14 Crittenden 89	22	8
28	***FAC2Q***	***H***	***Shortwood United***	***279***	***L***	***0-1***			9
Oct 5	CSouth	A	Dover Athletic	632	L	0-1		22	10
19	CSouth	A	Maidenhead United	301	**W**	3-1	Jermyn 37 Goodship 39 88	21	11
26	CSouth	H	Badingstoke Town	435	L	0-4		22	12
Nov 2	CSouth	A	Bromley	430	L	1-4	Crittenden 68 (pen)	22	13
9	CSouth	H	Bath City	516	L	0-2		22	14
16	***FAT3Q***	***A***	***Gosport Borough***	***206***	***L***	***0-3***			15
23	CSouth	A	Sutton United	646	**W**	1-0	Goodship 63	21	16
30	CSouth	H	Eastbourne Borough	407	D	0-0		22	17
Dec 7	CSouth	A	Havant & Waterlooville	497	L	1-5	Way 26	22	18
10	CSouth	H	Tonbridge Angels	281	**W**	2-1	Goodship 45 Munday 89	22	19
14	CSouth	H	Concord Rangers	356	D	2-2	Crittenden 58 Wakefield 69	22	20
26	CSouth	H	Eastleigh	**614**	L	1-2	Wakefield 61	22	21
28	CSouth	A	Weston-s-Mare	232	L	0-3		22	22
Jan 11	CSouth	A	Boreham Wood	173	L	0-5		22	23
18	CSouth	H	Dover Athletic	407	L	0-4		22	24
Feb 1	CSouth	A	Farnborough	292	L	2-3	Lanahan 32 Munday 79	22	25
8	CSouth	A	Eastbourne Borough	445	**W**	1-0	Lanahan 53	22	26
11	CSouth	H	Havnt & Waterlooville	208	L	0-2		22	27
15	CSouth	H	Bromley	417	**W**	3-2	Craig 43 Yeoman 51 Gleeson 90	21	28
22	CSouth	A	Tonbridge Angels	405	**W**	2-1	Crittenden 36 Jermyn 89	21	29
March 1	CSouth	H	Staines Town	426	D	1-1	Crittenden 76 (pen)	21	30
8	CSouth	H	Boreham Wood	401	L	1-4	Crittenden 76 (pen)	21	31
11	CSouth	A	Bisho's Stortford	257	D	1-1	Walker 48	21	32
15	CSouth	A	Bath City	555	L	0-1		22	33
17	CSouth	A	Chelmsford City	561	L	1 4	Losasso 86	22	34
22	CSouth	H	Sutton United	456	D	0-0		22	35
25	CSouth	A	Eastleigh	544	L	0-6		22	36
29	CSouth	A	Basingstoke Town	548	L	1-2	Losasso 78	22	37
April 1st	CSouth	H	Maidenhead United	270	L	0-3		22	38
5	CSouth	A	Hayes & Yeading	107	L	0-2		22	39
12	CSouth	H	Farnborough	320	**W**	1-0	Jermyn 37	22	40
15	CSouth	H	Hayes & Yeading	316	L	0-2		22	41
19	CSouth	A	Whtehawk	199	L	0-3		22	42
21	CSouth	H	Gosport Borough	414	D	1-1	Chamberlain 7	22	43
26	CSouth	A	Ebbsfleet United	1670	L	0-4		22	44

GOALSCORERS	Lge	FAC	FAT	Total	Pens	Hat-tricks	Cons Run
Crittendon	7			7	3		
Goodship	4			4			
Jermyn	3			3			
Lanahan	2			2			
Losasso	2			2			
Munday	2			2			
Wakefield	2			2			
Walker	2			2			
Way	2			2			
Watson	2			2			
Chamerlain	1			1			
Craig	1			1			
Gleeson	1			1			
Martin	1			1			
Yeoman	1			1			

Cons Run - Consecutive scoring games.

NON
LEAGUE DAY
06.09.14
Support your
LOCAL
FOOTBALL CLUB
nonleagueday.co.uk

DUNSTABLE TOWN

Chairman: Roger Dance
Secretary: Malcolm Aubrey (T) (E) malcolm.aubrey@openreach.co.uk
Commercial Manager: (T)
Programme Editor: Paul Harris (T) hpauljharris@aol.com
Ground Address: Creasey Park Stadium, Brewers Hill Rd, Dunstable LU6 1BB
(T) 07798 716 263 **Manager:** Darren Croft & Paul Reeves

Celebrations after clinching the Spartan South Midlands title.
Photo: Gordon Whittington.

Club Factfile

Founded: 1883 **Nickname:** The Blues
Previous Names: Dunstable Town 1883-1976. Dunstable FC 1976-98.
Previous Leagues: Metropolitan & District 1950-61, 64-65. United Counties 1961-63. Southern 1965-76, 2004-09. Spartan South Midlands 1998-2003, 09-13. Isthmian 2003-04.

Club Colours (change): Blue & white (Red & white)

Ground Capacity: 3,500 **Seats:** 350 **Covered:** 1000 **Clubhouse:** Yes **Shop:** Yes

Directions From the south: When travelling on the A5, go straight across the lights in the centre of Dunstable. Turn left at the next main set of lights into Brewers Hill Road. You will immediately pass the Fire Station on your left. Carry on until you hit the first roundabout, Go over the roundabout and take the immediate right into Creasey Park Drive. From the north: When travelling south on the A5, go through the chalk cutting and over the first set of traffic lights. At the next set of lights, turn right into Brewers Hill Road. Then proceed as above. From the East: Turn right at the traffic lights in the centre of Dunstable. Turn left at the next main set of traffic lights into Brewers Hill Road. Then proceed as above. From the east: When coming into Dunstable, go straight across the first roundabout you come to. Then turn left at the double mini-roundabout into Drovers Way. Follow this road for about 1/2 mile as it bears to the right and becomes Brewers Hill Road. Go over two mini-roundabouts and just before you hit the larger roundabout, turn left into Creasey Park Drive.

Previous Grounds: Kingsway 1950-58.

Record Attendance: 10,000 (approx) v Manchester United, friendly, July 1974
Record Victory: 12-0 v Welwyn Garden City, Spartan South Midlands League 2009-10.
Record Defeat: 0-13 v Arsenal, Metropolitan League
Record Goalscorer: Not known
Record Appearances: Not known
Additional Records: Received £25,000 from Reading for Kerry Dixon 1980.

Senior Honours:
Spartan South Midlands Division One 1999-00, Premier 2002-03, 12-13. Southern Division One Central 2013-14.
Bedfordshire Senior Cup 1895–96, 1956–57, 59–60, 79–80, 82–83, 85–86, 86–87, 87–88, 88–89, 2002–03, 06–07, 08–09.
Bedforshire Premier Cup 1980–81, 82–83, 90–91, 2006–07, 11-12.

10 YEAR RECORD

04-05	05-06	06-07	07-08	08-09	09-10	10-11	11-12	12-13	13-14
SthP 20	SthW 21	SthM 11	SthM 13	SthM 21	SSM P 7	SSM P 7	SSM P 2	SSM P 1	SthC 1

FROME TOWN

Chairman: Jeremy Alderman
Secretary: Ian Pearce (T) 07811 511 222 (E) ian@frometownfc.co.uk
Commercial Manager: Brian Stevens (T) info@frometownfc.co.uk
Programme Editor: AM Print & Copy (T)
Ground Address: Blindmans Brewery Stadium, Badgers Hill, Berkley Road, Frome BA11 2EH
(T) 01373 464 087 **Manager:** Adrian Foster

Club Factfile

Founded: 1904 **Nickname:** The Robins
Previous Names: None
Previous Leagues: Wiltshire Premier 1904, Somerset Senior 1906-19, Western 1919, 63-2009

Club Colours (change): All red (Yellow/blue/yellow)

Ground Capacity: 2,200 **Seats:** 575 **Covered:** 575 **Clubhouse:** Yes **Shop:** Yes

Directions
From Bath, take A36 and then A361. At third roundabout, follow A361 and at fourth roundabout take A3098. Take first right and ground is one mile on left hand side. From south follow A36 (Warminster) and take A3098 to Frome. At T Junction turn right and take second exit at roundabout. Ground is first right and follow road for one mile on left hand side.

Previous Grounds: None

Record Attendance: 8,000 v Leyton Orient - FA Cup 1st Round 1958
Record Victory: Not Known
Record Defeat: Not Known
Record Goalscorer: Not Known
Record Appearances: Not Known
Additional Records:

Senior Honours:
Somerset County League 1906-07, 08-09, 10-11.
Western League Division 1 1919-20, 2001-02, Premier Division 1962-63, 78-79.
Somerset Senior Cup 1932-33, 33-34, 50-51 Somerset Premier Cup 1966-67, 68-69 (shared), 82-83, 2008-09.

10 YEAR RECORD

04-05	05-06	06-07	07-08	08-09	09-10	10-11	11-12	12-13	13-14
WestP 3	WestP 7	WestP 3	WestP 4	WestP 2	Sthsw 6	Sthsw 4	SthP 12	SthP 18	SthP 14

FROME TOWN MATCH RESULTS 2013-14

Date	Comp	H/A	Opponents	Att:	Result		Goalscorers	Pos	No.
Aug 17	SPL	H	Cambridge City	206	D	0-0		17	1
20	SPL	A	Weymouth	785	L	0-2		20	2
24	SPL	A	Burnham	114	D	1-1	Baggridge 28	20	3
26	SPL	H	Chippenham Town	307	L	0-5		22	4
31	SPL	A	Banbury United	182	**W**	2-1	Ferguson 45 Walden 90	19	5
Sept 4	SPL	H	Poole Town	263	L	1-3	Baggridge 12	20	6
7	SPL	H	Arlesey Town	170	L	0-1		21	7
14	***FAC1Q***	***H***	***Bognor Regis Town***	***218***	***D***	***1-1***	***Morzetti 90 (og)***		8
18	***FAC1Qr***	***A***	***Bognor Regis Town***	***310***	***L***	***0-4***			9
21	SPL	H	Hungerford Town	151	L	0-2		23	10
24	SPL	A	Truro City	244	**W**	2-0	Lavelle 42 (pen) Cooper 79	20	11
Manager Derek Graham leaves the club.									
Oct 5	SPL	A	Hitchin Town	300	**W**	2-1	Lavelle 65 Baggridge 88	17	12
12	SPL	H	Bedford Town	190	D	4-4	Ledgister 16 82 (pen) Wood 51 87	16	13
Brian O'Donnell appointed as the new Manager.									
19	***FAT1***	***H***	***Poole Town***	***224***	***D***	***1-1***	***Agbo 45***		14
Nov 2	***FAT1r***	***A***	***Poole Town***	***245***	***L***	***1-3***	***Ledgister 5***		15
9	SPL	A	Arlesey Town	142	**W**	2-1	Wood 23 Smith 51	15	16
12	SPL	A	AFC Totton	327	**W**	5-0	Baggridge 9 WOOD 3 (31 58 90) Mundy 56	12	17
16	SPL	H	Truro City	223	L	1-2	Smith 65	15	18
23	SPL	H	Hemel Hempsted Town	173	D	1-1	Baggridge 61	15	19
25	SPL	A	Redditch United	112	L	0-1		15	20
30	SPL	H	Corby Town	170	L	1 3	Stephenson 54	19	21
Dec 7	SPL	A	St Neots Town	252	L	1-3	Baggridge 59	19	22
14	SPL	H	Chesham United	182	L	1-4	Wood 43	19	23
17	SPL	A	Stourbridge	240	L	0-7		17	24
26	SPL	A	Chippenham Town	400	D	3-3	Groves 11 Vance 75 Wood 90	20	25
28	SPL	H	Weymouth	**392**	L	1-2	Groves 58	20	26
Jan 4	SPL	A	St Albans City	363	L	0-4		20	27
11	SPL	H	Bashley	241	L	1-2	Hulbert 90	19	28
15	SPL	H	Banbury United	133	**W**	3-2	Sallis 4 Francis 43 Wood 47	18	29
18	SPL	A	Hemel Hempstead Town	540	**W**	1-0	Franks 49	18	30
21	SPL	A	Biggleswade Town	110	L	0-2		18	31
25	SPL	H	Redditch United	221	**W**	4-0	Thomson 6 Hulbert 64 Smith 57 Mateus 79	17	32
28	SPL	H	Bideford	167	**W**	2-0	Miller 61 (pen) Baggridge 72	16	33
Feb 1	SPL	A	Corby Town	312	**W**	1-0	Smith 79	16	34
15	SPL	A	Chesham United	317	L	1-2	Groves 55	17	35
22	SPL	H	Biggleswade Town	163	D	0-0		16	36
March 1	SPL	H	Hitchin Town	223	**W**	2-0	Stephenson 9 Wood 12	17	37
8	SPL	A	Hungerford Town	127	D	0-0		16	38
15	SPL	H	AFC Totton	221	**W**	1-0	Wood 36	16	39
17	SPL	A	Poole Town	284	L	2-4	Wallace 45 Miller 60 (pen)	14	40
22	SPL	A	Bedford Town	174	**W**	2-0	Baggridge 6 Mundy 71	12	41
26	SPL	H	St Neots Town	126	**W**	5-4	Wood 38 Groves 44 Baggridge 53 Vallis 57 Miller 75 (pen)	12	42
29	SPL	H	Stourbridge	224	L	0-2		11	43
April 5	SPL	A	Bashley	128	**W**	4-0	Baggridge 20 Thomson 28 Cooper 79 Miller 83 (pen)	14	44
12	SPL	A	Cambridge City	310	L	0-2		14	45
19	SPL	H	Burnham	242	**W**	4-1	Vallis 12 Miller 61 (pen) Thomson 79 Smith 83	14	46
21	SPL	A	Bideford	207	D	2-2	Vance 65 Vallence 70	14	47
26	SPL	H	St Albans City	352	D	0-0		14	48

GOALSCORERS	Lge	FAC	FAT	Total	Pens	Hat-tricks	Cons Run
Wood	12			12		1	
Baggridge	10			10			
Miller	5			5	5		
Smith	5			5			
Groves	4			4			2
Ledgister	2		1	3	1		
Mundy	3			3			
Vallis	3			3			
Cooper	2			2			
Hulbert	2			2			
Lavelle	2			2	1		2

	Lge	FAC	FAT	Total	Pens	Hat-tricks	Cons Run
Stephenson	2			2			
Thomson	2			2			
Vance	2			2			
Agbo			1	1			
Francis	1			1			
Franks	1			1			
Ferguson	1			1			
Mateus	1			1			
Vallance	1			1			
Walden	1			1			
Wallace	1			1			
Opponents		1		1			

Cons Run - Consecutive scoring games.

HEREFORD UNITED

Chairman: David Keyte

Secretary: Lee Symonds **(T)** 0844 2761 939 **(E)** club@herefordunited.co.uk

Commercial Manager: **(T)**

Programme Editor: **(T)**

Ground Address: Edgar Street Athletic Ground, Blackfriars Street, Hereford HR4 9JU

(T) 0844 2761 939 **Manager:**

Club Factfile

Founded: 1924 **Nickname:** The Bulls

Previous Names: St Martins and RAOC amalgamated in 1924 to form Hereford United.

Previous Leagues: Birminham. Birmingham Combination. Southern 1939-72. Football League 1972-97, 2006-12. Conference 1997-2006, 12-14.

Club Colours (change): White/black/white (All orange)

Ground Capacity: 8,843 **Seats:** 2,761 **Covered:** 6,082 **Clubhouse:** Yes **Shop:** Yes

Directions

Edgar Street is in the heart of the City of Hereford.

The main road, Edgar Street, which lends it's name to the ground is the main A49 which runs directly through Hereford City Centre in a North-South direction.

Previous Grounds: None

Record Attendance: 18,114 v Sheffield Wednesday - FA Cup 3rd Round 04.01.1958

Record Victory: (League) 6-0 v Burnley (A) - Division Four 24.01.1987

Record Defeat: (League) 1-7 v Mansfield Town - Division Three

Record Goalscorer: (League) Stewart Phillips - 93, 1980-91. Goals in a Season - Dixie McNeil - 35, 1975-76.

Record Appearances: (League) Mel Pejic - 412, 1980-92.

Additional Records: Received £440,000 from Queen's Park Rangers for Darren Peacock 1990.
Paid £80,000 to Walsall for Dean Smith 1994.

Senior Honours:
Football League Division Three 1974-76. Southern League Division One 1958-59. Welsh Cup 1989-90.

10 YEAR RECORD

04-05		05-06		06-07		07-08		08-09		09-10		10-11		11-12		12-13		13-14	
Conf	2	Conf	2	FL 2	16	FL 2	3	FL 1	21	FL 2	16	FL 2	21	FL 2	23	Conf	6	Conf	20

HEREFORD UNITED MATCH RESULTS 2013-14

Date	Comp	H/A	Opponents	Att:	Result		Goalscorers	Pos	No.
Aug 10	CPrem	H	Braintree Town	2033	D	1-1	Walker 79	11	1
13	CPrem	A	Chester	2900	**W**	2-0	Graham 45 Smith 50	5	2
17	CPrem	A	Hyde	509	D	2-2	Bush 15 Rankine 70	9	3
24	CPrem	H	Tamworth	1864	**W**	1-0	Smith 51	5	4
26	CPrem	A	Alfreton Town	740	L	1-2	Sharp 45	8	5
31	CPrem	H	Welling United	1527	**W**	2-1	Sharp 49 Rankine 84	7	6
Sept 7	CPrem	A	Gateshead	931	L	1-2	West 74	10	7
13	CPrem	H	Aldershot Town	1851	L	0-2		12	8
17	CPrem	A	NuneatonTown	1085	L	1-2	McDonald 53	16	9
21	CPrem	A	FC Halifax Town	1362	D	1-1	Brodie 8	15	10
24	CPrem	H	Lincoln City	1398	**W**	1-0	Bush 85	15	11
28	CPrem	H	Luton Town	2386	D	0-0		14	12
Oct 5	CPrem	A	Cambridge United	3381	L	0-1		15	13
8	CPrem	A	Macclesfield Town	1329	L	0-1		16	14
12	CPrem	H	Dartford	1583	D	2-2	Krans 49 Dyer 60	15	15
19	CPrem	H	Barnet	1632	L	0-1		19	16
26	***FAC4Q***	***A***	***AFC Hornchurch***	***713***	***W***	***1-0***	***O'Keefe 90***		17
31	CPrem	A	Salisbury City	1112	L	1-4	Smith 59	19	18
Nov 10	***FAC1***	***A***	***Burton Albion***	***2069***	***L***	***0-2***			19
12	CPrem	H	Chester	1512	D	2-2	Jarrett 17 (og) Dyer 38	19	20
16	CPrem	A	Southport	876	**W**	3-0	Collins 23 Rankine 69 Dyer 89	17	21
23	CPrem	A	Lincoln City	1874	D	1-1	Artus 89	17	22
26	CPrem	H	FC Halifax Town	1158	**W**	3 2	O'Keefe 37 Collins 73 Odhiambo76	17	23
30	***FAT1***	***H***	***Woking***	***1040***	***L***	***0-3***			24
Dec 7	CPrem	H	NuneatonTown	1292	L	0-1		17	25
21	CPrem	H	Cambridge United	1558	**W**	1-0	Rankine 24	17	26
26	CPrem	A	Kidderminster Harriers	3420	L	1-2	O'Keefe 90	17	27
28	CPrem	H	Forest Green Rovers	1848	**W**	1-0	Brown 26	16	28
Jan 9	CPrem	A	Forest Green Rovers	1077	D	1-1	Bush 76		29
18	CPrem	H	Southport	1569	**W**	4-1	Brown 31 Rankine 53 89 Walker 55	16	30
25	CPrem	H	Salisbury City	2016	**W**	1-0	Collins 52	16	31
28	CPrem	H	Kidderminster Harriers	2014	D	1-1	O'Keefe 61	15	32
Feb 3	CPrem	A	Woking	1131	L	0-3		15	33
15	CPrem	A	Luton Town	7111	L	0-7		17	34
22	CPrem	A	Dartford	1137	L	0-2		18	35
25	CPrem	H	Macclesfield Town	1013	L	1-2	Collins 78	18	36
March 1	CPrem	H	Wrexham	1884	L	0-2		18	37
9	CPrem	A	Braintree Town	805	D	1-1	Walker 36	18	38
11	CPrem	A	Grimsby Town	3007	D	1-1	McDonald 22	18	39
15	CPrem	H	Hyde	1378	D	0-0		18	40
18	CPrem	A	Wrexham	2056	L	0-2		18	41
22	CPrem	A	Barnet	1497	L	0-2		19	42
29	CPrem	H	Grimsby Town	**2545**	L	0-1		20	43
April 5	CPrem	H	Woking	2140	L	0-2		20	44
8	CPrem	A	Welling United	480	**W**	1-0	James 61	20	45
12	CPrem	H	Gateshead	1783	L	0-1		21	46
18	CPrem	A	Dartford	1154	L	0-1		21	47
21	CPrem	H	Alfreton Town	2445	**W**	3-2	James 29 Collins 61 Bowman 71	21	48
26	CPrem	A	Aldershot Town	3593	**W**	2-1	Smith 28 Rankine 88	20	49

GOALSCORERS	Lge	FAC	FAT	Total	Pens	Hat-tricks	Cons Run
Rankine	7			7			
Collins	5			5			
O'Keefe	3	1		4			
Smith	4			4			
Bush	3			3			
Dyer	3			3			2
Walker	3			3			
Brown	2			2			
James	2			2			
McDonald	2			2			
Sharp	2			2			2
Artus	1			1			
Bowman	1			1			
Brodie	1			1			
Graham	1			1			
Krans	1			1			
Odhiambo	1			1			
West	1			1			
Opponents	1			1			

Cons Run - Consecutive scoring games.

HISTON

Chairman: Russell Hands
Secretary: Howard Wilkins (T) 01223 237 373 (E) secretary@histonfc.co.uk
Commercial Manager: (T)
Programme Editor: Howard Wilkins (T) 01223 237 373
Ground Address: The Glass World Stadium, Bridge Road, Impington, Cambridge CB24 9PH
(T) 01223 237 373 **Manager:** Brian Page

The squad on the last day of the 2013-14 season.
Back row (l-r): Eugene Libertucci, Michael Built, Ben Clappison, Will De Havilland, Calum Kitscha, Salim Relizani, Danny Rumens, Caspar Irso-Coombes, Nick Freeman, Ryan Baxter.
Front row: Charlie Naylor, Matty Waters, Luis McCoy, Ashley White, Peter Clark, Charlie Day, Curtis Fulcher, George Root.

Club Factfile

Founded: 1904 **Nickname:** The Stutes
Previous Names: Histon Institute
Previous Leagues: Cambridgeshire 1904-48, Spartan 1948-60, Delphian 1960-63, Eastern Counties 1966-2000, Southern 2000-05. Conference 2005-14.
Club Colours (change): Red and black stripes/black/black (Blue & white stripes/blue/blue)

Ground Capacity: 3,250 **Seats:** 450 **Covered:** 1,800 **Clubhouse:** Yes **Shop:** Yes

Directions
From the M11 (Northbound) Junc 14, take the A14 eastbound signed towards Newmarket. Take the first exit off the A14 and at the roundabout, take the first exit onto the B1049. Go straight over the traffic lights, past the Holiday Inn Hotel (on your right) and the entrance to the club is half a mile on your right.

Previous Grounds: None

Record Attendance: 6,400 v King's Lynn - FA Cup 1956
Record Victory: 11-0 v March Town - Cambridgeshire Invitation Cup 15/02/01
Record Defeat: 1-8 v Ely City - Eastern Counties Division One 1994
Record Goalscorer: Neil Kennedy - 292
Record Appearances: Neil Andrews and Neil Kennedy
Additional Records: Paid £6,000 to Chelmsford City for Ian Cambridge 2000. Received £30,000 from Manchester United for Guiliano Maiorana.
Senior Honours:
Eastern Counties League Cup 1990-91, Eastern Counties League 1999-2000, Southern League Premier 2004-05, Conference South 2006-07. Cambridgeshire Professional Cup 2012-13.

10 YEAR RECORD

04-05	05-06	06-07	07-08	08-09	09-10	10-11	11-12	12-13	13-14
SthP 1	Conf S 5	Conf S 1	Conf 7	Conf 3	Conf 18	Conf 24	Conf N 16	Conf N 19	Conf N 21

HISTON MATCH RESULTS 2013-14

Date	Comp	H/A	Opponents	Att:	Result		Goalscorers	Pos	No.
Aug 17	CNorth	H	Colwyn Bay	307	**W**	3-1	Beckles 62 Taaffe 66 Sheppard 88 (pen)	5	1
20	CNorth	A	Brackley	281	L	0-3		12	2
24	CNorth	A	Solihull Moors	235	D	0-0		11	3
26	CNorth	H	Gainsborough Trinity	331	**W**	2-0	Hicks 13 Clerima 33	9	4
31	CNorth	A	Altrincham	825	D	2-2	Sheppard 13 Hicks 41	9	5
Sept 7	CNorth	H	Workington	405	**W**	3-1	Day 23 Hicks 45 Built 73	8	6
14	CNorth	A	Harrogate Town	548	**W**	1-0	Hicks 61	8	7
17	CNorth	H	Hednesford Town	308	L	0-1		7	8
21	CNorth	A	Barrow	593	L	1-2	Reynolds 90 (og)	8	9
28	***FAC2Q***	***A***	***Royston Town***	***525***	***W***	***4-0***	***Taaffe 45 75 Built 63 Sheppard 88***		10
Oct 5	CNorth	H	AFC Telford United	350	L	0-1		9	11
12	***FAC3Q***	***A***	***Concord Rangers***	***307***	***L***	***1-2***	***Shepherd 40 (pen)***		12
19	CNorth	A	Guiseley	405	D	1-1	McDonald 73	9	13
26	CNorth	H	Stockport County	**508**	**W**	2-1	McDonald 52 Taaffe 80	8	14
Nov 2	CNorth	A	Stalybridge Celtic	402	L	1-2	Sheppard 86 (pen)	10	15
9	CNorth	H	Vauxhall Motors	325	L	1-2	Taaffe 15	12	16
12	CNorth	H	Oxford City	202	D	2-2	Taaffe 10 Sheppard 27	12	17
16	***FAT3Q***	***A***	***Guiseley***	***404***	***L***	***0-3***			18
23	CNorth	A	Leamington	545	L	0-1		13	19
Dec 7	CNorth	H	Stalybridge Celtic	244	L	1-4	Grant 52	16	20
14	CNorth	A	Colwyn Bay	244	L	0-1		12	21
21	CNorth	H	Bradford PA	314	**W**	1-0	Taaffe 67	16	22
26	CNorth	A	Boston United	1361	D	0-0		16	23
28	CNorth	H	Brackley Town	408	D	3-3	Phillips 50 Sheppard 80 (pen) Waters 90	16	24
Jan 4	CNorth	A	Workington	347	**W**	3-2	Mills 4 30 Taaffe 50	14	25
11	CNorth	H	Worcester City	294	L	1-2	Mills 54	14	26
18	CNorth	A	North Ferriby United	389	D	4-4	Taaffe 3 82 Hicks 11 Freeman 50	15	27
25	CNorth	A	Stockport County	2070	L	0-1		16	28
Feb 4	CNorth	H	Boston United	353	L	1-2	Taaffe 81 (pen)	18	29
8	CNorth	A	Vauxhall Motors	131	L	0-4		18	30
15	CNorth	H	Harrogate Town	291	L	0-1		18	31
22	CNorth	A	Hednesford Town	552	L	1-2	Hicks 54	18	32
March 1	CNorth	H	Guisley	277	D	1-1	Built 79	18	33
4	CNorth	A	Gloucester City	462	L	0-2		18	34
8	CNorth	H	North Ferriby United	304	L	0-3		18	35
15	CNorth	A	AFC Telford United	1607	L	2-3	O'Malley 73 de Havilland 81	20	36
18	CNorth	A	Oxford City	203	L	1-2	Hicks 1	20	37
22	CNorth	H	Leamington	301	D	1-1	Liburcucci 86	20	38
25	CNorth	H	Gloucester City	217	L	1-3	Yussuf 17	20	39
29	CNorth	A	Worcester City	432	D	1-1	O'Malley 72	19	40
April 5	CNorth	H	Barrow	311	D	0-0		20	41
12	CNorth	A	Bradford PA	312	L	0-3		20	42
19	CNorth	H	Solihull Moors	307	L	0-3		21	43
21	CNorth	A	Gainsborough Trinity	363	L	1-3	Clappison	21	44
26	CNorth	H	Altrincham	433	L	0-5		21	45

GOALSCORERS	Lge	FAC	FAT	Total	Pens	Hat-tricks	Cons Run
Taaffe	9	2		11	1		2
Hicks	7			7			4
Sheppard	5	2		7	4		
Built	2	1		3			
Mills	3			3			2
McDonald	2			2			2
O'Malley	2			2			
Beckles	1			1			
Clappison	1			1			
Clerima	1			1			

	Lge	FAC	FAT	Total	Pens	Hat-tricks	Cons Run
Day	1			1			
de Havilland	1			1			
Freeman	1			1			
Grant	1			1			
Liburcucci	1			1			
Phillips	1			1			
Waters	1			1			
Yussuf	1			1			
Opponents	1			1			

Cons Run - Consecutive scoring games.

HITCHIN TOWN

Chairman: Terry Barratt
Secretary: Roy Izzard **(T)** 07803 202 498 **(E)** roy.izzard@hitchintownfc.co.uk
Commercial Manager: Fred Andrews **(T)** 01462 452 980
Programme Editor: **(T)**
Ground Address: Top Field, Fishponds Road, Hitchin SG5 1NU
(T) 01462 459 028 (match days only) **Manager:** Mark Burke

Club Factfile

Founded: 1865 **Nickname:** Canaries
Previous Names: Hitchin FC 1865-1911. Re-formed in 1928
Previous Leagues: Spartan 1928-39, Herts & Middlesex 1939-45, Athenian 1945-63, Isthmian 1964-2004

Club Colours (change): Yellow/green/green (All green)

Ground Capacity: 5,000 **Seats:** 500 **Covered:** 1,250 **Clubhouse:** Yes **Shop:** Yes

Directions
From East A1 to J8 onto A602 to Hitchin.
At Three Moorhens Pub roundabout, take third exit (A600) towards Bedford, over next roundabout and lights, turn right at next roundabout, turnstiles on left, parking 50 yards on.

Previous Grounds: None

Record Attendance: 7,878 v Wycombe Wanderers - FA Amateur Cup 3rd Round 08/02/1956
Record Victory: 13-0 v Cowley and v RAF Uxbridge - both Spartan League 1929-30
Record Defeat: 0-10 v Kingstonian (A) and v Slough Town (A) - 1965-66 and 1979-80 respectively
Record Goalscorer: Paul Giggle - 214 (1968-86)
Record Appearances: Paul Giggle - 769 (1968-86)
Additional Records: Paid £2,000 to Potton United for Ray Seeking
Received £30,000 from Cambridge United for Zema Abbey, January 2000
Senior Honours:
AFA Senior Cup 1931-32. London Senior Cup 1969-70. Isthmian League Division 1 1992-93.
Herts Senior Cup x19 (a record)

10 YEAR RECORD

04-05		05-06		06-07		07-08		08-09		09-10		10-11		11-12		12-13		13-14	
SthP	18	SthP	14	SthP	11	SthP	18	SthP	20	SthC	2	SthC	2	SthP	14	SthP	13	SthP	13

HITCHIN TOWN MATCH RESULTS 2013-14

Date	Comp	H/A	Opponents	Att:	Result		Goalscorers	Pos	No.
Aug 17	SPL	H	Hemel Hempstead T	330	W	2-0	Burns 24 Martin 79	5	1
20	SPL	A	Hinckley United	246	W	2-0	Donnelly 1 Lowe 25	2	2
24	SPL	A	Chippenham Town	265	L	0-2		8	3
26	SPL	H	Arlesey Town	502	W	1-0	Donnelly 37	5	4
31	SPL	A	Truro City	412	D	1-1	McGeorge 27	6	5
Sept 2	SPL	H	St Albans City	512	D	1-1	Noone 29	5	6
7	SPL	H	Poole Town	451	D	2-2	King 21 79	9	7
14	***FAC1Q***	***H***	***Arlesey Town***	***431***	***D***	***1-1***	***King 22***		8
17	***FAC1Qr***	***A***	***Arlesey Town***	***257***	***L***	***0-2***			9
21	SPL	A	Banbury United	290	L	1-2	Burns 38	13	10
Oct 5	SPL	H	Frome Town	300	L	1-2	Burns 76	14	11
7	SPL	H	St Neots Town	309	W	4-0	Burns 11 28 King 83 90	11	12
12	SPL	A	Redditch United	175	L	0-1		16	13
19	***FAT1Q***	***A***	***Wingate & Finchley***	***81***	***D***	***2-2***	***Burns 20 31***		14
21	***FAT1Qr***	***H***	***Wingate & Finchley***	***114***	***L***	***0-1***			15
26	SPL	H	Burnham	238	D	1-1	McGeorge 38 (pen)	13	16
28	SPL	A	St Albans City	355	L	1-2	Webb 74	13	17
Nov 2	SPL	H	Truro City	320	L	2-3	Webb 15 Martin 50	17	18
16	SPL	A	AFC Totton	320	W	5-0	Martin 15 Forsythe 17 Pearson 22 Webb 58 Donnelly 90	18	19
23	SPL	H	Bashley	277	W	1-0	Donnelly 81	13	20
27	SPL	A	Corby Town	251	W	2-1	Pearson 5 Martin 35 (pen)	12	21
Dec 7	SPL	A	Hungerford Town	117	W	3-2	Leech 9 Martin 30 48	11	22
9	SPL	H	Weymouth	250	W	3-2	Donnelly 12 Webb 59 Forsyth 78	11	23
16	SPL	H	Biggleswade Town	371	W	1-0	Donnelly 30	8	24
18	SPL	A	Cambridge CIty	288	L	2-3	Martin 29 Dixon 69	8	25
21	SPL	A	Bideford Town	234	L	1-3	Dixon 89	11	26
26	SPL	A	Arlesey Town	526	D	0-0		11	27
Jan 4	SPL	A	Stourbridge	400	D	1-1	Jones 90	11	28
11	SPL	H	AFC Totton	314	D	1-1	Leech 71	10	29
14	SPL	A	Burnham	125	L	0-1		12	30
25	SPL	H	Corby Town	395	L	0-2		15	31
Feb 1	SPL	A	Chesham United	451	W	2-1	Lambert 18 (og) Donnelly 59	13	32
10	SPL	H	Bedford Town	221	W	6-1	Martin19 Donnelly 20 72 Forsythe 33 Barker 39 King 90	9	33
22	SPL	H	Bideford	321	L	0-1		13	34
24	SPL	H	Chesham United	243	L	1-2	Donnelly 41	13	35
March 1	SPL	A	Frome Towen	223	L	0-2		13	36
8	SPL	H	Banbury Town	322	W	5-0	Donnelly 2 Bryant 11 Lench 19 Martin 52 King 90	11	37
11	SPL	A	Bashley	106	W	2-0	Lench 18 Martin 43 (pen)	11	38
15	SPL	A	St Neots Town	464	D	1-1	Bryant 22	11	39
22	SPL	H	Redditch United	277	L	0-2		12	40
29	SPL	A	Weymouth	527	D	1-1	Lench 64	14	41
April 5	SPL	H	Cambridge City	**570**	W	1-0	Smith 3	12	42
7	SPL	H	Hungerford Town	235	L	0-2		12	43
10	SPL	A	Biggleswade Town	280	L	2-3	Rolfe 67 King 89	12	44
12	SPL	A	Hemel Hempstead T	775	D	0-0		13	45
15	SPL	A	Poole Town	301	L	0-1		13	46
19	SPL	H	Chippenham Town	293	W	3-1	Wharton 37 70 Jones 45 (pen)	13	47
21	SPL	A	Bedford Town	305	W	1-0	Walton 84	12	48
26	SPL	H	Stourbridge	476	D	1-1	King 66	13	49

GOALSCORERS	Lge	FAC	FAT	Total	Pens	Hat-tricks	Cons Run
Donnelly	10			10			2
Martin	10			10	2		2
King	8	1		9			2
Burns	5		2	7			3
Lench	5			5			
Webb	4			4			3
Forsythe	3			3			
Bryant	2			2			
Dixon	2			2			2
Jones	2			2	1		
McGeorge	2			2	1		
Pearson	2			2			
Wharton	2			2			
Barker	1			1			
Lowe	1			1			
Noone	1			1			
Rolph	1			1			
Smith	1			1			
Walton	1			1			
Opponents	1			1			

Cons Run - Consecutive scoring games.

HUNGERFORD TOWN

Chairman: Steve Skipworth
Secretary: John Smyth **(T)** **(E)** john.smyth@saxon-brands.com
Commercial Manager: Ron Tarry, Ray Brown, **(T)**
Programme Editor: John Smyth **(T)** john.smyth@saxon-brands.com
Ground Address: Bulpitt Lane, Hungerford RG17 0AY
(T) 01488 682 939 **Manager:** Bobby Wilkinson

Club Factfile

Founded: 1886 **Nickname:** The Crusaders
Previous Names: None
Previous Leagues: Newbury & District, Swindon & District, Hellenic 1958-78, 2003-09, Isthmian 1978-2003

Club Colours (change): White/royal blue/royal blue (All red)

Ground Capacity: 2,500 **Seats:** 170 **Covered:** 400 **Clubhouse:** Yes **Shop:** Yes

Directions
From M4 Junction, take A338 to Hungerford. First Roundabout turn right on to A4, next roundabout first left, 100 yards roundabout 1st left up High Street, go over three roundabouts, at fourth roundabout turn first left signposted 'Football Club'. Take second left into Bulpitt Lane, go over crossroads, ground on left.

Previous Grounds: None

Record Attendance: 1,684 v Sudbury Town - FA Vase Semi-final 1988-89
Record Victory: Not known
Record Defeat: Not known
Record Goalscorer: Ian Farr - 268
Record Appearances: Dean Bailey and Tim North - 400+
Additional Records: Paid £4,000 to Yeovil Town for Joe Scott
Received £3,800 from Barnstaple Town for Joe Scott
Senior Honours:
Hellenic Division 1 1970-71, Premier Division 2008-09, League Cup 2006-07, 07-08.
Berks & Bucks Senior Cup 1981-82. Basingstoke Senior Cup 2012-13.
Isthmian representatives in Anglo Italian Cup 1981.

10 YEAR RECORD

04-05	05-06	06-07	07-08	08-09	09-10	10-11	11-12	12-13	13-14
Hel P 17	Hel P 16	Hel P 3	Hel P 3	Hel P 1	Sthsw 17	Sthsw 7	Sthsw 5	Sthsw 2	SthP 6

HUNGERFORD TOWN MATCH RESULTS 2013-14

Date	Comp	H/A	Opponents	Att:	Result		Goalscorers	Pos	No.
Aug 17	SPL	H	Hinckley United	145	D	2-2	Moran 3 (og) Brown 73	12	1
19	SPL	A	St Albans City	383	L	0-2		18	2
24	SPL	A	Hemel Hempstead T	291	L	1-2	Draycott 65 (pen)	21	3
26	SPL	H	Burnham	140	L	2-3	Draycott 50 (pen) Goodger 80	23	4
31	SPL	H	Chesham United	140	L	0-1		23	5
Sept 2	SPL	A	Redditch United	137	W	5-0	Draycott 7 74 PARSONS 3 (14 36 40)	20	6
7	SPL	A	Biggleswade Town	145	W	1-0	Parsone 64	16	7
14	FAC 1Q	H	Cove	100	W	4-0	Parsons 4 55 O'Brien 57 Wood 78		8
17	SPL	H	Stourbridge	100	W	1-0	Draycott 2	12	9
21	SPL	A	Frome Town	151	W	2-0	Parsons 6 Rees 34	10	10
28	FAC2Q	A	Bashley	177	W	3-0	Boardman 9 Brown 38 Gray 47		11
Oct 5	SPL	H	St Neots Town	105	W	1-0	Draycott 15	10	12
8	SPL	H	Banbury United	100	W	3-1	Gray 42 43 Brown 83	8	13
12	FAC3Q	A	Poole Town	551	L	0-2			14
19	FAT1Q	H	Bashley	112	W	4-2	Brown 16 Draycott 22 73 Clark 24		15
29	SPL	H	Redditch United	98	L	0-2		11	16
Nov 2	FAT2Q	A	Folkestone Invicta	242	D	1-1	Day 88		17
5	FAT2Qr	H	Folkestone Invicta	100	D	1-1	Draycott 22 (won 5-4 on pens aet)		18
9	SPL	A	Weymouth	501	W	3-1	Brown 32 69 Draycott 39	9	19
16	FAT3Q	H	Hemel Hempstead T	137	W	5-0	Stow 7 Draycott 43 51 (pen) Brown 79 Gray 90		20
19	SPL	H	Biggleswade Town	62	D	1-1	Stow	8	21
23	SPL	H	Bedford Town	98	W	2-0	Brewer 10 Herring 33	9	22
26	SPL	H	Truro City	90	W	6-0	Stow 46 Boardman 53 Legg 60 Brown 66 79 Hopkins 82	8	23
30	FAT1	H	Chesham United	211	W	2-0	Draycott 31 Stow 90		24
Dec 7	SPL	H	Hitchin Town	117	L	2-3	Draycott 17 (pen) Stow 38	10	25
10	SPL	A	Chesham United	251	L	0-1		10	26
14	FAT2	A	Leek Town	496	W	1-0	Draycott 84		27
17	SPL	A	Arlesey Town	102	L	2-5	Draycott 58 (pen) Goodger 77	12	28
26	SPL	A	Burnham	133	L	0-1		14	29
28	SPL	H	St Albans City	206	W	3-1	Stanley 6 Goodger 42 Draycott 90	12	30
Jan 4	SPL	A	Bideford	245	D	0-0		12	31
11	FAT3	H	Gosport Borough	384	L	0-1			32
18	SPL	A	Bedford Town	234	W	4-1	Draycott 6 (pen) Stanley 41 Reeves 83 Burnell 89	13	33
28	SPL	A	St Neots Town	75	L	1-2	O'Brien 71	14	34
Feb 11	SPL	A	Poole Town	183	D	0-0		15	35
15	SPL	H	AFC Totton	106	W	4-0	DRAYCOTT 3 (30 82 83) Clark 90	12	36
18	SPL	A	AFC Totton	225	W	3-1	Gray 44 Brown 58 Burnell 79	9	37
22	SPL	A	Cambridge City	325	D	0-0		9	38
March 1	SPL	A	St Neots Town	324	L	0-3		9	39
4	SPL	H	Cambridge CIty	117	W	3-2	Clark 28 Draycott 61 O'Brien 82	9	40
8	SPL	H	Frome Town	127	D	0-0		9	41
11	SPL	A	Stourbridge	253	W	2-1	Draycott 61 (pen) Hopper 70	9	42
15	SPL	A	Banbury United	228	W	7-0	DRAYCOTT 3 (1 12 65) Hopper 49 72 Brown 84 Goodger 87	8	43
22	SPL	H	Arlesey Town	88	W	3-0	Brown 53 83 Stanley 65	8	44
25	SPL	A	Bashley	82	W	2-0	Brown 27 Draycott 3	8	45
29	SPL	A	Corby Town	253	W	2-0	Brown 15 Clark 66	8	46
April 1	SPL	A	Truro City	212	W	2-1	Fisher 41 (og) Brown 78	7	47
5	SPL	H	Weymouth	176	W	2-1	Brown 71 Goodger 80	6	48
7	SPL	A	Hitchn Town	235	W	2-0	Day 30 Brown 65	6	49
10	SPL	H	Poole Town	214	W	2-0	Brown 7 49	6	50
15	SPL	H	Bashley	109	W	3-1	Goodger 74 Brown 78 Clark 90	6	51
17	SPL	H	Chippenham Town	164	D	1-1	Draycott 1	4	52
19	SPL	H	Hemel Hempstead T	273	L	0-4		6	53
21	SPL	A	Chippenham Town	369	W	3-2	Brown 55 78 Clark 77	6	54
26	SPL	H	Bideford	211	W	2-1	Goodger 88 Draycott 90	6	55

GOALSCORERS	Lge	FAC	FAT	Total	Pens	Hat-tricks	Cons Run
Draycott	22		7	29	7	2	2
Brown	19	1	2	22			8
Goodger	7			7			
Parsons	5	2		7		1	3
Clark	5		1	6			
Gray	3	1	1	5			
Stow	3		2	5			
Hooper	3			3			2
O'Brien	2	1		3			
Stanley	3			3			
Boardman	1	1		2			
Burnell	2			2			
Day	1		1	2			
Brewer	1			1			
Herring	1			1			
Hopkins	1			1			
Legg	1			1			
Rees	1			1			
Reeves	1			1			
Wood		1		1			
Opponents	2			2			

Cons Run - Consecutive scoring games.

PAULTON ROVERS

Chairman: David Bissex
Secretary: Andy Harris **(T)** 07760 377 302 **(E)** footballsecretary.prfc@gmail.com
Commercial Manager: Chris Fenwick **(T)** 07706 106 387
Programme Editor: Andy Harris **(T)** 07760 377 302
Ground Address: Athletic Ground, Winterfield Road, Paulton, Bristol BS39 7RF
(T) 01761 412 907 **Manager:** Nick Bunyard

The squad celebrate after their play-off victory over Merthyr Town which won them promotion to the Premier Division.

Club Factfile

Founded: 1881 **Nickname:** The Robins or Rovers
Previous Names: Not known
Previous Leagues: Wiltshire Premier, Somserset Senior, Western

Club Colours (change): All maroon (All blue with yellow trim/blue/blue)

Ground Capacity: 5,000 **Seats:** 253 **Covered:** 2,500 **Clubhouse:** Yes **Shop:** Yes

Directions
From A39 at Farrington Gurney, follow A362 marked Radstock for two miles.
Turn left at roundabout, take B3355 to Paulton and ground is on the right.

Previous Grounds: Chapel Field, Cricket Ground, Recreation Ground

Record Attendance: 2,000 v Crewe Alexandra - FA Cup 1906-07
Record Victory: Not known
Record Defeat: Not known
Record Goalscorer: Graham Colbourne
Record Appearances: Steve Tovey
Additional Records:

Senior Honours:
Somerset Senior Cup x12.
Somerset Premier Cup 2012-13.

10 YEAR RECORD

04-05	05-06	06-07	07-08	08-09	09-10	10-11	11-12	12-13	13-14
SthW 8	SthW 17	Sthsw 2	Sthsw 7	Sthsw 10	Sthsw 7	Sthsw 11	Sthsw 7	Sthsw 5	Sthsw 4

POOLE TOWN

Chairman: Clive Robbins
Secretary: Bill Reid (T) 01794 517 991 (E) secretary@pooletownfc.co.uk
Commercial Manager: Mark Bumford (T)
Programme Editor: Jack Amey (T)
Ground Address: Tatnam Ground, Oakdale School, School Lane, Poole BH15 3JR
(T) 07771 604 289 (Match days) **Manager:** Tommy Killick

Poole Town in action last season.
Photo: Andrew Orman.

Club Factfile

Founded: 1880 **Nickname:** The Dolphins
Previous Names: Poole Rovers 1884, Poole Hornets 1886 - amalgamated on 20.09.1890 to form Town. Know as Poole & St. Mary's 1919-20.
Previous Leagues: Dorset 1896-1903, 04-05, 10-11. Hampshire 1903-04, 05-10, 11-23, 34-35, 96-2004. Western 1923-26, 30-34, 35-57. Southern 1926-30, 57-96. Wessex 2004-11.
Club Colours (change): Red & white halves/red/red & white (All sky blue)

Ground Capacity: 2,000 **Seats:** 154 **Covered:** 200 **Clubhouse:** Yes **Shop:** Yes

Directions
Follow the A35 into Poole and at the roundabout by the fire station take the second exit into Holes Bay Road (A350). At next roundabout take 1st exit onto Broadstone Way (A349) and turn right at Wessex Gate East traffic lights into Willis Way. Turn right into Fleets Way and continue until you see Poole Motor Cycles. Turn left into Palmer Road opposite Poole Motor Cycles and take first right into School Lane which will take you into the Club/School car park. The ground is on the right hand side. Nearest Railway Station: Poole (3/4 mile)

Previous Grounds: Ye Old Farm Ground. Wimborne Road Rec > 1933. Poole Stadium 1933-94. Hamworthy Utd FC 1994-96. Holt Utd 1996.

Record Attendance: **Att:** 10,224 v Queens Park Rangers, FA Cup 1st Rnd Replay, 1946 (at Poole Stadium).
Record Victory: 11-0 v Horndean (A) Hampshire League 11/02/1998
Record Defeat: 1-8 v East Cowes VA (A) Hampshire League 01/05/2001.
Record Goalscorer: Not known
Record Appearances: Not known
Additional Records: Got to 3rd Round of FA Cup in 1926 v Everton. Transfer fee paid £5,000 for Nicky Dent 1990. Transfer fee received £70,000 for Charlie Austin from Swindon Town 2009.
Senior Honours:
Western League 1956-57. Dorset Senior Cup x13 Most recently 2012-13.
Wessex League Champions 2008-09, 09-10, 10-11. Southern Division One South & West 2012-13.

10 YEAR RECORD

04-05	05-06	06-07	07-08	08-09	09-10	10-11	11-12	12-13	13-14
Wex2 2	Wex1 8	WexP 4	WexP 4	WexP 1	WexP 1	WexP 1	Sthsw 2	Sthsw 1	SthP 7

POOLE TOWN MATCH RESULTS 2013-14

Date	Comp	H/A	Opponents	Att:	Result		Goalscorers	Pos	No.
Au 17	SPL	H	St Albans City	100	W	2-1	Petts 30 Devlin 60	7	1
20	SPL	A	Chippenham Town	350	W	2-1	Devlin 64 (pen) 90	6	2
24	SPL	A	Cambridge City	230	W	2-1	Spetch 5 Gillespie 10	2	3
26	SPL	H	Weymouth	**1053**	D	2-2	Gillespie 60 64	2	4
31	SPL	H	Biggleswade Town	262	W	2-1	Preston 25 Gillespie 90	1	5
Sept 4	SPL	A	Frome Town	263	W	3-1	Cann 7 Devlin 33 (pen) Spetch 70	1	6
7	SPL	A	Hitchin Town	451	D	2-2	Gillespie 88 Spetch 90	3	7
14	***FAC1Q***	***H***	***Brockenhurst***	***280***	***W***	***2-0***	***Brookes 5 Gillespie 90***		8
17	SPL	H	Bideford	239	D	3-3	Gillespie 9 17 Spetch 87	4	9
21	SPL	H	Burnham	249	D	0-0		4	10
28	***FAC2Q***	***A***	***Hamworthy United***	***353***	***W***	***4-2***	***Devlin 7 Brookes 21 Cann 47 Preston 63***		11
Oct 5	SPL	A	Stourbridge	466	L	2-5	Gillespie 81 90	7	12
8	SPL	A	Truro City	306	W	2-0	Brookes 32 Gillespie 60	4	13
13	***FAC23Q***	***H***	***Hungerford Town***	***551***	***W***	***2-0***	***Davies 6 Brooks 71***		14
19	***FAT1Q***	***A***	***Frome Town***	***224***	***D***	***1-1***	***Devlin 79 (pen)***		15
26	***FAC4Q***	***A***	***Staines Town***	***357***	***D***	***0-0***			16
29	***FAC4Qr***	***H***	***Staines Town***	***935***	***L***	***0-1***			17
Nov 2	***FAT1Qr***	***A***	***Frome Town***	***245***	***W***	***3-1***	***Spetch 84 Devlin 109 (pen) Charles 111 (aet)***		18
5	***FAT2***	***A***	***Arlesey Town***	***114***	***L***	***2-3***	***Preston 62 69***		19
16	SPL	H	St Neots Town	402	W	2-0	Cann 13 Brooks 52	11	20
23	SPL	A	Banbury United	317	D	0-0		8	21
26	SPL	A	Chesham United	321	W	2-0	Emmerson 8 Brooks 78	5	22
30	SPL	H	Chippenham Town	331	W	3-1	Devlin 43 45 (pen) Charles 90 (pen)	5	23
Dec 7	SPL	A	Bashley	288	W	3-0	Whisken 44 Cann 60 Charles 79	5	24
14	SPL	H	Redditch United	224	W	2-1	Charles 23 Preston 90	4	25
26	SPL	A	Weymouth	1065	W	3-0	Cann 36 Elliott 47 Brooks 77	4	26
Jan 11	SPL	A	St Neots Town	375	D	1-1	Spetch 90	6	27
14	SPL	A	Bideford	183	D	0-0		7	28
21	SPL	A	Arlesey Town	106	D	2-2	Willetts 19 (og) Cann 70	7	29
Feb 4	SPL	A	Bedford Town	142	W	5-1	BENNETT 3 (14 19 75) Brooks 73 Chiedozie 83	7	30
11	SPL	H	Hungerford Town	183	D	0-0		7	31
22	SPL	H	Corby Town	280	W	3-1	Devlin 16 Chiedozie 33 46	7	32
March 5	SPL	A	Hemel Hempstead T	369	L	0-1		7	33
8	SPL	A	Burnham	160	L	0-2		8	34
11	SPL	H	AFC Totton	283	W	2-0	Bennett 4 62	7	35
15	SPL	H	Truro City	382	W	1-0	Preston 16	7	36
17	SPL	H	Frome Town	284	W	4-2	Whisken 20 Elliott 22 Devlin 63 69 (pen)	7	37
19	SPL	A	Corby Town	208	W	3 0	Charles 9 Brooks 33 Devlin 45 (Pen)	7	38
22	SPL	H	Hemel Hempstead T	501	L	0-2		7	39
25	SPL	A	Biggleswade Town	140	D	2-2	Devlin 45 (pen) Charles 56	7	40
27	SPL	A	Redditch United	182	W	2-0	Dibba 44 Gillespie 69	6	41
29	SPL	H	Bedford Town	280	L	1-3	Grant 55 (og)	6	42
April 1	SPL	H	Banbury United	216	W	4-1	GILLESPIE 4 (12 35 51pen 61)	6	43
3	SPL	H	Stourbridge	341	L	1-2	Devlin 62	6	44
5	SPL	A	AFC Totton	380	L	1-3	Burbidge 63	7	45
10	SPL	A	Hungerford Town	214	L	0-2		7	46
12	SPL	A	St Albans City	581	W	1-0	Elliott 57	7	47
15	SPL	H	Hitchin Town	301	W	1-0	Elliott 53	7	48
17	SPL	H	Chesham United	315	W	1-0	Elliott 84	7	49
19	SPL	H	Cambridge City	438	L	0-1		7	50
21	SPL	H	Bashley	314	W	5-0	DEVLIN 3 (45 63 80 pen) Burbidge 48 50	7	51
26	SPL	H	Arlesey Town	250	W	5-3	Chiedozie 30 Davies 60 Burbidge 62 Devlin 70 Cann 89	7	52

GOALSCORERS	Lge	FAC	FAT	Total	Pens	Hat-tricks	Cons Run
Gillespie	15	1		16	1	1	3
Devlin	15	1	2	18	9	1	2
Brooks	6	3		9			
Cann	6	1		7			
Charles	5		1	6	1		3
Preston	3	1	2	6			
Spetch	5		1	6			
Bennett	5			5		1	
Elliott	5			5			3
Burbidge	4			4			

	Lge	FAC	FAT	Total	Pens	Hat-tricks	Cons Run
Chiedozie	4			4			
Davies	2			2			
Whiken	2			2			
Dibba	1			1			
Emmerson	1			1			
Petts	1			1			
Opponents	2			2			

Cons Run - Consecutive scoring games.

REDDITCH UNITED

Chairman: Chris Swan
Secretary: Dave Jones (T) (E) secretaryrufc@ymail.com
Commercial Manager: (T)
Programme Editor: Sallie Swan & Craig Swan (T) programmeeditor.reds@yahoo.com
Ground Address: Valley Stadium, Bromsgrove Road, Redditch B97 4RN
(T) 01527 67450 **Manager:** Liam McDonald

Club Factfile

Founded: 1891 **Nickname:** The Reds
Previous Names: Redditch Town
Previous Leagues: Birmingham combination 1905-21, 29-39, 46-53, West Midlands 1921-29, 53-72, Southern 1972-79, 81-2004, Alliance 1979-80. Conference 2004-11.

Club Colours (change): Red/black/black (All blue)

Ground Capacity: 5,000 **Seats:** 400 **Covered:** 2,000 **Clubhouse:** Yes **Shop:** Yes

Directions M42 J2, at island first exit onto the A441 for 2 miles, next island first exit onto Birmingham Road A441 for 1.2 miles then at island third exit onto Middlehouse Lane B4184 for 0.3 miles. At traffic lights (next to the fire station) turn left onto Birmingham Road for 0.2 miles then turn right into Clive Road for 0.3 miles. At island take first exit onto Hewell Road for 0.2 miles then at 'T' junction right onto Windsor Street for 0.1 miles. At traffic lights (next to bus station) continue straight ahead onto Bromsgrove Road for 0.3 miles and at the brow of the hill, turn right into the ground's entrance.

Previous Grounds: HDA Sports Ground, Millsborough Road

Record Attendance: 5,500 v Bromsgrove Rovers - Wets Midlands League 1954-55
Record Victory: Not known
Record Defeat: Not known
Record Goalscorer: Not known
Record Appearances: Not known
Additional Records: Paid £3,000 to Halesowen Town for Paul Joinson. Received £40,000 from Aston Villa for David Farrell. Played nine games in nine days at the end of the 1997-98 season.
Senior Honours:
Worcestershire Senior Cup 1893-94, 29-30, 74-75, 76-76, 2007-08, 13-14.
Birmingham Senior Cup 1924-25, 31-32, 38-39, 76-77, 2004-05.
Southern League Division 1 North 1975-76, Western Division 2003-04. Staffordshire Senior Cup 1990-91.

10 YEAR RECORD

04-05	05-06	06-07	07-08	08-09	09-10	10-11	11-12	12-13	13-14
Conf N 9	Conf N 20	Conf N 19	Conf N 13	Conf N 14	Conf N 19	Conf N 21	SthP 15	SthP 19	SthP 10

REDDITCH UNITED MATCH RESULTS 2013-14

Date	Comp	H/A	Opponents	Att:	Result		Goalscorers	Pos	No.
Aug 17	SPL	H	Arlesey Town	183	L	1-3	Headley 45	19	1
20	SPL	A	Bedford Town	230	W	2-1	Headley 31 Patterson 90	11	2
24	SPL	A	Weymouth	773	L	0-3		17	3
26	SPL	H	Stourbridge	**316**	L	1-6	Ahenkorah 68	20	4
31	SPL	A	St Neots Town	231	W	3-2	Patterson 4 Ahenkorah 40 Austin 85	18	5
Sept 2	SPL	H	Hungerford Town	137	L	0-5		18	6
7	SPL	H	Banbury United	221	L	2-3	Headley 41 (pen) 71	20	7
14	***FAC1Q***	***A***	***Atherstone Town***	***307***	***D***	***3-3***	***Molyneux 19 24 Caines 90***		8
16	***FAC1Qr***	***H***	***Atherstone Town***	***183***	***L***	***1-2***	***Molyneux 15***		9
21	SPL	H	Biggleswade Town	197	D	2-2	Ahenkorah 26 Balllinger 54	20	10
28	SPL	A	Chippenham Town	266	L	0-3		21	11
Oct 5	SPL	A	Hemel Hempstead U	483	L	0-5		21	12
8	SPL	A	Burnham	121	W	4-2	Ahenkorah 37 Sterling-James 44 Clarke 52 Sammons 90	19	13
12	SPL	H	Hitchin Town	175	W	1-0	Molyneux 65	18	14
23	***FAT1Q***	***H***	***Chasetown***	***172***	***W***	***2-0***	***Headley 47 Sammons 77***		15
26	SPL	A	Chesham United	339	L	1-3	Headley 78 (pen)	14	16
29	SPL	A	Hungerford Town	97	W	2-0	Bridgewater 72 Ahenkorah 90	9	17
Nov 2	***FAT2Q***	***H***	***Brigg Town***	***193***	***W***	***5-0***	***Hylton 49 65 Sammons 44 Patterson 78 Bridgewater 79***		18
4	SPL	H	Chippenham Town	168	W	3-0	Sammons 50 Hylton 60 Headley 82 (pen)	10	19
9	SPL	A	Banbury United	250	L	0-2		11	20
16	***FAT3Q***	***A***	***Boston United***	***784***	***L***	***1-4***	***Slade 63***		21
23	SPL	H	Corby Town	216	L	1-3	Headley 28	18	22
25	SPL	H	Frome Town	112	W	1-0	Ballinger 23	11	23
30	SPL	A	Truro City	368	L	0-1		15	24
Dec 7	SPL	H	AFC Totton	141	W	2-1	Headley 15 Ballinger 89	12	25
11	SPL	A	Cambridge City	174	L	1-4	Sammons 78	14	26
14	SPL	A	Poole Town	224	L	1-2	Youngs 25 (pen)	15	27
16	SPL	H	Bideford	129	W	3-1	Eminoglu 52 86 (pen) Hylton 90	13	28
21	SPL	H	St Albans City	227	L	1-3	Headley 47	14	29
26	SPL	A	Stourbridge	637	L	1-5	Sterling-James 36	15	30
28	SPL	H	Bedford Town	252	W	2-0	Youngs 48 Mutton 55	14	31
Jan 11	SPL	H	Cambridge City	220	W	4-1	HYLTON 3 (22 84 90) Birch 24	13	32
25	SPL	A	Frome Town	221	L	0-4		18	33
Feb 18	SPL	A	Bashley	132	W	3-2	Molyneux 10 Youngs 32 Hylton 76	16	34
22	SPL	A	St Albans City	515	L	1-2	Stirling-James 34	16	35
March 1	SPL	H	Hemel Hempstead T	235	W	1-0	Sammons 85	15	36
3	SPL	H	St Neots Town	105	D	0-0		13	37
8	SPL	A	Biggleswade Town	181	D	0-0		15	38
12	SPL	H	Truro City	163	W	3 1	Sammons 62 Youngs 71 Young 90	12	39
15	SPL	H	Burnham	201	W	2-1	Headley 53 Lavender 59 (og)	10	40
22	SPL	A	Hitchin Town	277	W	2-0	Ahenkorah 29 31	11	41
27	SPL	H	Poole Town	182	L	0-2		11	42
29	SPL	H	Chesham United	220	L	1-2	Sammons 39	11	43
April 5	SPL	A	Bideford	214	L	3-4	Hylton 30 90 Sammons 83	14	44
8	SPL	A	AFC Totton	272	W	3-0	Sammons 21 90 Molyneux 74	11	45
12	SPL	A	Arlesey Town	150	W	3-0	Youngs 40 42 (pen) Sammons 63	10	46
16	SPL	A	Corby Town	236	W	3-2	Oshungbure 27 Sterling-James 42 Hylton 79	9	47
19	SPL	H	Weymouth	293	L	0-4		10	48
26	SPL	H	Bashley	193	W	4-0	Sterling-Jame 15 Molyneux 42 60 Hylton 87	10	49

GOALSCORERS	Lge	FAC	FAT	Total	Pens	Hat-tricks	Cons Run
Hylton	10		2	12		1	
Sammons	10		2	12			3
Headley	10		1	11	3		2
Molyneux	5	3		8			2
Youngs	6			6	2		
Ahenkorah	5			5			2
Sterling-James	5			5			
Ballinger	3			3			
Patterson	2		1	3			
Bridgewater	1		1	2			2
Eminoglu	2			2	1		
Austin	1			1			
Bird	1			1			
Caines		1		1			
Clarke	1			1			
Oshungbure	1			1			
Mutton	1			1			
Slade			1	1			
Young	1			1			
Opponents	1			1			

Cons Run - Consecutive scoring games.

Click Back in Time!

Over 37 years of publishing the Non-League Club Directory has filled a room full of information and photographs covering the game we know and love.

What we intend, over time, is to create a website that shares with you everything we have accumulated, which we hope will bring back some fond memories of season's gone by.

A unique look back at how the game has evolved since the 1940s will also make for interesting reading, including league tables from season's gone by.

Log on to **www.non-leagueclubdirectory.co.uk** today and see how many faces from teams gone by you recognise

SLOUGH TOWN

Chairman: Steve Easterbrook
Secretary: Kath Lathey (T) 07792 126 124 (E) gensec@sloughtownfc.net
Commercial Manager: (T)
Programme Editor: Glen Riley (T) programme@sloughtownfc.net
Ground Address: Sharing with Beaconsfield SYCOB, Holloways Park, Slough Road HP9 2SE
(T) 01494 676 868 **Manager:** Neil Baker & Jon Underwood

Club Factfile

Founded: 1890 **Nickname:** The Rebels
Previous Names: None
Previous Leagues: Southern Alliance 1892-93, Berks & Bucks 1901-05, Gt Western Suburban 1909-19, Spartan 1920-39, Herts & Middx 1940-45, Corinthian 1946-63, Athenian 1963-73, Isthmian 1973-90, 94-95, Conf. 1990-94

Club Colours (change): Amber/navy blue/amber (All purple)

Ground Capacity: 3,500 **Seats:** 200 **Covered:** Yes **Clubhouse:** Yes **Shop:** Yes

Directions
Leave M40 at Junction 2, take A355 towards Slough, only 50 yards off the roundabout on the A355 is slip road on right with sign giving Club name. Turn right through gate and clubhouse is 200 metres on the right. The ground is 'signposted' from both sides of the carriageway (A355).

Previous Grounds:

Record Attendance: 8,000 v Liverpool - Schoolboys 1976
Record Victory: 17-0 v Railway Clearing House - 1921-22
Record Defeat: 1-11 v Chesham Town - 1909-10
Record Goalscorer: Tony Norris - 84 (1925-26)
Record Appearances: Terry Reardon - 458 (1964-81)
Additional Records: Paid £18,000 to Farnborough Town for Colin Fielder
Received £22,000 from Wycombe Wanderers for Steve Thompson
Senior Honours:
Isthmian League 1980-81, 89-90. Athenian League x3. Berks & Bucks Senior Cup x10.

10 YEAR RECORD

04-05	05-06	06-07	07-08	08-09	09-10	10-11	11-12	12-13	13-14
Isth P 13	Isth P 17	Isth P 22	Sthsw 21	Sthsw 16	SthM 5	SthC 5	SthC 2	SthC 6	SthC 5

Southern League Action

Vincente (Chalfont) and De La Salle (Royston) in Division One Central action.

Photo: Keith Clayton.

ST. NEOTS TOWN

Chairman: Mike Kearns
Secretary: Gary Wilson (T) 01480 470 012 (E) enquiries@stneotstownfc.co.uk
Commercial Manager: Mark Davies (T)
Programme Editor: (T)
Ground Address: Rowley Park, Kester Way, Cambridge Road, St Neots, PE19 6SN
(T) 01480 470 012 **Manager:** Gary King & Zema Abbey

Celebrations after winning the Southern League Cup.
Photo: Gordon Whittington.

Club Factfile

Founded: 1879 **Nickname:** Saints
Previous Names: St Neots 1879-1924. St. Neots & District 1924-1951.
Previous Leagues: S Midlands, Cent. Alliance, UCL, Eastern Co., Hunts, United Counties > 2011.

Club Colours (change): All dark blue (All red)

Ground Capacity: 3,000 **Seats:** 250 **Covered:** 850 **Clubhouse:** Yes **Shop:** No

Directions
From St Neots town centre, take the B1428 Cambridge Road, after going under the railway bridge, turn left at the first roundabout into Dramsell Rise. Follow the road up the hill to Kester Way and the ground. If approaching from Cambridge on the A428, turn right at the first roundabout as you approach St Neots onto the Cambridge Road. At the second roundabout, turn right into Dramsell Rise and follow as above. If travelling via the A1, follow signs for the A428 Cambridge. Go straight over roundabout with Tescos on left hand side, then turn left at next roundabout. Follow final instructions above as if approaching from Cambridge.

Previous Grounds: Rowley Park >2008.

Record Attendance: Att: 2,000 v Wisbech 1966
Record Victory: Not known
Record Defeat: Not known
Record Goalscorer: Not known
Record Appearances: Not known
Additional Records: 105 points obtained in the 2010-11 season - a United Counties record.

Senior Honours:
United Counties League 1967-68, 2010-11. Division One 1994-95.Southern League Division 1 Central 2011-12.
Huntingdonshire Senior Cup x37 Most recently 2013-14. Huntingdonshire Premier Cup 2001-02.

10 YEAR RECORD

04-05	05-06	06-07	07-08	08-09	09-10	10-11	11-12	12-13	13-14
UCL P 14	UCL P 4	UCL P 17	UCL P 8	UCL P 17	UCL P 2	UCL P 1	SthC 1	SthP 12	SthP 16

ST. NEOTS TOWN MATCH RESULTS 2013-14

Date	Comp	H/A	Opponents	Att:	Result		Goalscorers	Pos	No.
Aug 17	SPL	H	Weymouth	354	L	0-2		22	1
20	SPL	A	Stourbridge	447	L	1-2	Sear 52	22	2
24	SPL	A	Bashley	209	W	3-1	Benjamin 49 53 Hillard 58 (pen)	15	3
27	SPL	H	Cambridge Clty	451	L	1-2	Sear 12	18	4
31	SPL	H	Redditch United	231	L	2-3	Sear 69 Safee 90	21	5
Sept 4	SPL	A	Corby Town	317	L	0-1		22	6
7	SPL	A	Hemel Hempstead	669	L	0-2		22	7
14	***FAC 1Q***	***H***	***Wroxham***	***232***	***W***	***3-1***	***Hilliard 3 Sear 17 Hurst 49***		8
21	SPL	H	Truro City	307	W	2-0	Hurst 39 Safee 74	16	9
28	***FAC2Q***	***A***	***Canvey Island***	***256***	***D***	***2-2***	***Hillard 4 Adjie 74***		10
Oct 1	***FAC2Qr***	***H***	***Canvey Island***	***289***	***L***	***1-2***	***Sear 71***		11
5	SPL	A	Hungerford Town	105	L	0-1		19	12
7	SPL	A	Hitchin Town	307	L	0-4		20	13
19	***FAT1Q***	***A***	***Halesowen Town***	***273***	***W***	***3-1***	***Deeney 24 Woolley 39 Adjei 79***		14
22	SPL	H	Chesham United	224	L	0-5		21	15
26	SPL	A	Bideford	215	L	2-3	Sear 65 Davies 88 (pen)	22	16
29	SPL	H	Corby Town	261	L	0-3		22	17
Nov 2	***FAT2Q***	***A***	***Matlock Town***	***244***	***L***	***0-2***			18
9	SPL	H	Hemel Hempstead T	436	W	4 1	Adjei 23 Hilliard 50 Woolley 56 Davies 88	21	19
12	SPL	H	Biggleswade Town	306	L	3-4	HILLIARD 3 (28 79 pen 83)	21	20
16	SPL	A	Poole Town	402	L	0-2		21	21
23	SPL	H	St Albans City	364	L	2-3	Davies 37 Nolan 52	22	22
26	SPL	H	Bedford Town	281	D	2-2	Davies 76 Frater 90	21	23
30	SPL	A	Banbury United	271	W	1-0	Davies 2	21	24
Dec 7	SPL	H	Frome Town	252	W	3-1	Nolan 13 37 Thomas 83	20	25
14	SPL	A	Burnham	124	L	0-1		20	26
21	SPL	H	AFC Totton	293	W	6-0	Woolley 11 Nolan 12 57 Davies 13 Hilliard 47 (Pen) Tolley 77	19	27
26	SPL	A	Cambridge City	371	L	2-3	Tolley 86 90 (pen)	18	28
28	SPL	H	Stourbridge	356	D	1-1	Davies 82	19	29
Jan 11	SPL	H	Poole Town	375	D	1-1	Hilliard 27	19	30
18	SPL	A	St Albans City	812	D	1-1	Thomas 32	19	31
25	SPL	A	Bedford Town	512	W	2-1	Tolley 37 43	19	32
28	SPL	A	Chippenham Town	209	L	1-2	Tolley 68	20	33
Feb 1	SPL	H	Banbury United	374	W	3-1	Ferrari 45 Hilliard 81 Woolley 90	19	34
15	SPL	H	Burnham	262	W	4-2	Hoyte 18 Tolley 34 50 Thomas 68	18	35
18	SPL	H	Arlesey Town	252	W	3-1	Tolley 49 Woolley 71 Hilliard 74	18	36
22	SPL	A	AFC Totton	286	D	2-2	Woolley 7 Tolley 23	18	37
March 1	SPL	H	Hungerford Town	324	W	3-0	Tolley 50 Deeley 68 Hilliard 73 (pen)	18	38
3	SPL	A	Redditch United	105	D	0-0		18	39
8	SPL	A	Truro City	417	W	3-2	Hilliard 18 Woolley 55 Nolan 81	14	40
15	SPL	H	Hitchin Town	**464**	D	1-1	Davies 4	15	41
22	SPL	A	Biggleswade Town	315	D	2-2	Davies 48 (pen) Tolley 88	16	42
26	SPL	A	Frome Town	126	L	4-5	TOLLEY 3 (20 45 55) Hilliard 41 (pen)	16	43
29	SPL	H	Bideford Town	353	W	2-0	Tolley 39 72	16	44
April 5	SPL	A	Chesham United	339	L	0-3		16	45
12	SPL	A	Weymouth	546	W	2 1	Farrell 15 Tolley 64	16	46
19	SPL	H	Bashley	318	W	3-1	Tolley 40 Ford 88 Hilliard 90 (pen)	16	47
21	SPL	A	Arlesey Town	227	D	1-1	Farroll 20	16	48
26	SPL	H	Chippenham Town	453	L	1-2	Ferrari 33	16	49

GOALSCORERS	Lge	FAC	FAT	Total	Pens	Hat-tricks	Cons Run
Tolley	19			19	1	1	4
Hillard	13	2		15	6	1	2
Davies	9			9	1		3
Woolley	6		1	7			
Sear	4	2		6			2
Adjie	1	1	1	3			
Thomas	3			3			
Benjamin	2			2			
Farrell	2			2			
Ferrari	2			2			
Hurst	1	1		2			
Safee	2			2			
Deeney	1		1	2			
Ford	1			1			
Frater	1			1			
Hoyle	1			1			

Cons Run - Consecutive scoring games.

TRURO CITY

Chairman: Peter Masters
Secretary: Tracey Finemore (T) (E) traceyfinemore@truocityfc.net
Commercial Manager: (T)
Programme Editor: Dave Deacon (T) davedeacs@hotmail.com
Ground Address: Treyew Road, Truro, Cornwall TR1 2TH
(T) 01872 225 400 / 278 853 (Social Club) **Manager:** Steve Tully

Photo: Keith Clayton.

Club Factfile

Founded: 1889 **Nickname:** City, White Tigers, The Tinmen
Previous Names: None
Previous Leagues: Cornwall County, Plymouth & District, South Western, Western 2006-08, Southern 2008-11.

Club Colours (change): All white (Red & black stripes/red/red)

Ground Capacity: 3,500 **Seats:** 1,675 **Covered:** Yes **Clubhouse:** Yes **Shop:**

Directions
On arriving at Exeter, leave the M5 at junction 31 and join the A30. Travel via Okehampton, Launceston, and Bodmin.. At the end of the dual carriageway (windmills on right hand side) take left hand turning signposted Truro. After approximately 7 miles turn right at traffic lights, travel downhill crossing over three roundabouts, following signs for Redruth. Approximately 500 metres after third roundabout signed 'Arch Hill', ground is situated on left hand side.

Previous Grounds: None

Record Attendance: 1,400 v Aldershot - FA Vase
Record Victory: Not known
Record Defeat: Not known
Record Goalscorer: Not known
Record Appearances: Not known
Additional Records: 115 points & 185 goals, Western League Division One (42 games) 2006-07.
Became first British club to achieve five promotions in six seasons.
Senior Honours:
South Western League 1960-61, 69-70, 92-93, 95-96, 97-98. Western League Division 1 2006-07, Premier Division 07-08.
FA Vase 2006-07. Southern League Division 1 South & West 2008-09, Premier Division 2010-11.
Cornwall Senior Cup x15

10 YEAR RECORD

04-05	05-06	06-07	07-08	08-09	09-10	10-11	11-12	12-13	13-14
SWest 6	SWest 2	West1 1	WestP 1	Sthsw 1	SthP 11	SthP 1	Conf S 14	Conf S 22	SthP 17

TRURO CITY MATCH RESULTS 2013-14

Date	Comp	H/A	Opponents	Att:	Result	Goalscorers	Pos	No.
Aug 17	SPL	H	Bedford Town	421	D 2-2	Afful 32 Copp 90	13	1
20	SPL	A	Bashley	212	D 2-2	Middleton 8 (og) Morris 40 (og)	12	2
26	SPL	H	Bideford	**527**	L 0-2		15	3
31	SPL	H	Hitchin Town	412	D 1-1	Ash 90	16	4
Sept 3	SPL	A	AFC Totton	355	W 3-2	Sims 29 Afful 32 Andrew 89	12	5
7	SPL	A	Chesham United	477	L 2-4	Andrew 45 Broomfield 66	14	6
10	***FAC 1Q***	***H***	***Street***	***365***	***W 1-0***	***Eddy 89***		7
21	SPL	A	St Neots Town	307	L 0-2		18	8
24	SPL	H	Frome Town	244	L 0-2		18	9
28	***FAC 2Q***	***A***	***Brislington***	***172***	***L 2-3***	***Cooke 10 Slateford 22***		10
Oct 5	SPL	H	St Albans City	100	L 3-7	Watson 48 68 Cooke 81	20	11
8	SPL	H	Poole Town	306	L 0-2		21	12
12	SPL	A	Banbury United	350	W 2-1	Slateford 78 Eddy 87	17	13
19	***FAT1Q***	***A***	***Tiverton Town***	***312***	***L 2-3***	***Pugh 51 Slateford 80***		14
26	SPL	H	Cambridge City	350	L 0-1		20	15
29	SPL	H	AFC Totton	295	W 3-2	Eddy 2 73 Kendall 75	16	16
Nov 2	SPL	A	Hitchin Town	320	W 3-2	Tully 23 Eddy 45 Slateford 48	12	17
9	SPL	H	Chesham United	461	D 1 1	Kendall 76	14	18
16	SPL	A	Frome Town	223	W 2-1	Brokenshire 23 Pugh 40	11	19
19	SPL	A	Chippenham Town	266	L 1-3	Cooke 87	12	20
23	SPL	H	Biggleswade Town	384	L 0-2		16	21
26	SPL	A	Hungerford Town	90	L 0-6		18	22
30	SPL	H	Redditch United	368	W 1-0	Eddy 71	14	23
Dec 7	SPL	A	Hemel Hempstead T	495	L 0-3		17	24
14	SPL	H	Corby Town	386	D 0-0		17	25
21	SPL	A	Arlesey Town	137	D 1-1	Afful 9	17	26
26	SPL	A	Bideford Town	549	D 0-0		15	27
28	SPL	H	Bashley	401	W 5-0	Watson 42 64 Brokenshire 45 Cooke 75 Tully 90 (pen)	17	28
Jan 11	SPL	H	Stourbridge	401	D 1-1	Watson 35	17	29
18	SPL	A	Stourbridge	260	L 2-2	Brokenshire 28 Watson 81	17	30
Feb 8	SPL	H	Hemel Hempstead T	253	L 1-6	Eddy 83	18	31
15	SPL	A	Corby Town	247	L 2-3	Watson 59 White 83	19	32
22	SPL	H	Arlesey Town	312	W 2-0	Eddy 6 Watson 10	19	33
25	SPL	A	Burnham	109	W 2-1	Tully 42 (pen) Cooke 80	18	34
March 1	SPL	A	St Albans City	784	W 3-1	Cooke 15 Green 56 90	17	35
8	SPL	H	St Neots Town	417	L 2-3	Watson 64 74	19	36
12	SPL	A	Redditch United	163	L 1 3	Lowry 20	19	37
15	SPL	A	PooleTown	382	L 0-1		19	38
22	SPL	H	Banbury United	369	W 5-0	Cooke 8 Berrow 18 Kendall 43 Copp 53 Eddy 66	17	39
29	SPL	A	Cambridge City	265	L 1-4	Green 77	17	40
April 1	SPL	H	Hungerford Town	212	L 1-2	White 6	17	41
5	SPL	H	Chippenham Town	341	L 1-3	Kendall 25	17	42
8	SPL	H	Weymouth	346	W 2-1	Afful 24 Slateford 41	18	43
12	SPL	A	Bedford Town	224	W 1-0	Green 60	17	44
15	SPL	A	Biggleswade Town	131	L 1-2	Cooke 10	17	45
21	SPL	A	Weymouth	672	W 5-2	Kendlall 5 Watson 9 57 Slateford 49 Eddy 86	17	46
26	SPL	H	Burnham	333	W 3-0	Watson 15 (pen) Cooke 37 62	17	47

GOALSCORERS	Lge	FAC	FAT	Total	Pens	Hat-tricks	Cons Run
Watson	13			13	1		3
Cooke	9	1		10			2
Eddy	9	1		10			2
Slateford	4	1	1	6			2
Kendle	5			5			
Afful	4			4			
Green	4			4			
Brokenshire	3			3			
Tulley	3			3	2		
Andrew	2			2			
Copp	2			2			
Lowry-Sims	2			2			
Pugh	1		1	2			
White	2			2			
Ash	1			1			
Berrow	1			1			
Broomfield	1			1			
Sims	1			1			
Opponents	2			2			

Cons Run - Consecutive scoring games.

WEYMOUTH

Chairman: Nigel Biddlecombe
Secretary: Nigel Biddlecombe **(T)** 07880 508 240 **(E)** biddie@weymoff.com
Commercial Manager: **(T)**
Programme Editor: Ian White **(T)** whiteij7544@btinterneti.com
Ground Address: Bob Lucas Stadium, Radipole Lane, Weymouth DT4 9XJ
(T) 01305 785 558 **Manager:** Jason Matthews

Club Factfile

Founded: 1890 **Nickname:** The Terras
Previous Names: None
Previous Leagues: Dorset, Western 1907-23, 28-49, Southern 1923-28, 49-79, 89-2005, Alliance/Conference 1979-89, 2005-10
Club Colours (change): Claret & blue/dark blue/dark blue (Yellow & blue/blue/blue)

Ground Capacity: 6,600 **Seats:** 800 **Covered:** Yes **Clubhouse:** Yes **Shop:** Yes

Directions
Approach Weymouth from Dorchester on the A354.
Turn right at first roundabout onto Weymouth Way, continue to the next roundabout then turn right (signposted Football Ground).
At the next roundabout take third exit into the ground.

Previous Grounds: Recreation Ground > 1987.

Record Attendance: 4,995 v Manchester United - Ground opening 21/10/97
Record Victory: Not known
Record Defeat: Not known
Record Goalscorer: W 'Farmer' Haynes - 275
Record Appearances: Tony Hobsons - 1,076
Additional Records: Paid £15,000 to Northwich Victoria for Shaun Teale
Received £100,000 from Tottenham Hotspur for Peter Guthrie 1988
Senior Honours:
Southern League 1964-65, 65-66. Conference South 2005-06.
Dorset Senior Cup x27

10 YEAR RECORD

04-05	05-06	06-07	07-08	08-09	09-10	10-11	11-12	12-13	13-14
Conf S 7	Conf S 1	Conf 11	Conf 18	Conf 23	Conf S 22	SthP 18	SthP 17	SthP 9	SthP 12

Southern League Action

Power-Simpson (Chalfont) saves at the feet of Hammond (Royston).

Photo: Keith Clayton.

WEYMOUTH MATCH RESULTS 2013-14

Date	Comp	H/A	Opponents	Att:	Result		Goalscorers	Pos	No.
Aug 17	SPL	A	St Neots Town	183	W	2-0	Ford 6 Walker 12 (pen)	6	1
20	SPL	H	Frome Town	785	W	2-0	Poole 38 Yetton 51	6	2
24	SPL	H	Redditch United	773	W	3-0	Poole 25 Baines 51 (og) Burbidge 67	1	3
26	SPL	A	Poole Town	1053	D	2-2	Yetton 45 Burbidge 78	1	4
31	SPL	H	Cambridge City	655	D	1-1	Ford 73	4	5
Sept 3	SPL	A	Bideford	341	L	1-2	Yetton 42	5	6
14	***FAC 1Q***	***A***	***Fareham Town***	***323***	***W***	***1-0***	***Yetton 49***		7
17	SPL	H	AFC Totton	459	W	2-1	Poole 23 Yetton 25	5	8
28	***FAC2Q***	***H***	***Bognor Regis Town***	***598***	***D***	***2-2***	***Yetton 85 Joyce 87***		9
Oct 1	***FAC2Qr***	***A***	***Bognor Regis Town***	***414***	***W***	***4-1***	***S. Walker 65 (Pen) Ford 66 Yetton 67 84***		10
5	SPL	A	Biggleswade	178	L	1-2	Walker 76 (pen)	11	11
12	***FAC3Q***	***A***	***Cirencester Town***	***366***	***W***	***2-1***	***Yetton 21 60***		12
19	***FAT1Q***	***H***	***Bridgwater Town***	***428***	***W***	***1-0***	***Yetton 63***		13
26	***FAC4Q***	***H***	***Braintree Town***	***775***	***L***	***1-2***	***Poole 90***		14
Nov 2	***FAT2Q***	***A***	***Chesham United***	***276***	***L***	***1-2***	***Joyce 56***		15
5	SPL	A	AFC Totton	332	W	1-0	Joyce 29	11	16
9	SPL	H	Hungerford Town	501	L	1-3	S.Walker 9	12	17
16	SPL	A	Corby Town	390	L	1-3	Wright 14 (og)	16	18
23	SPL	H	Arlesey Town	401	W	2-1	Joyce 43 Allen 62	11	19
26	SPL	H	Chippenham Town	339	W	4-1	Yetton 32 82 Ford 62 Allen 78	11	20
30	SPL	A	Stourbridge	470	L	0-7		12	21
Dec 7	SPL	H	St Albans City	444	L	0-4		15	22
9	SPL	A	Hitchin Town	250	L	2-3	S.Walker 18 M.Walker 54	15	23
14	SPL	A	Banbury United	325	D	0-0		16	24
21	SPL	H	Bedford Town	436	W	4-1	Yetton 20 88 Burbidge 24 85	15	25
26	SPL	H	Poole Town	**1065**	L	0-3		14	26
28	SPL	A	Frome Town	392	W	2-1	Yetton 76 87	15	27
Jan 11	SPL	H	Corby Town	551	W	1-0	Burbidge 51	14	28
18	SPL	A	Arlesey Town	172	W	3-2	M.Walker 36 Yetton 43 S. Walker 80 (pen)	12	29
25	SPL	A	Chippenham Town	452	L	1-2	Yetton 63	12	30
Feb 1	SPL	H	Stourbridge	492	L	0-5		14	31
4	SPL	H	Bideford	261	W	3-2	Rigg 20 53 Yetton 61	10	32
8	SPL	A	St Albans CIty	762	L	0-3		12	33
22	SPL	A	Bedford Town	220	W	3-0	Poole 6 Hutchins 28 Kelly 39	10	34
26	SPL	A	Cambridge City	231	L	2 4	Kelly 20 Walker 67	10	35
March 1	SPL	H	Biggleswade Town	441	D	2-2	Joyce 46 Yetton 70 (pen)	10	36
4	SPL	H	Chesham United	413	L	2-4	Rigg 48 Yetton 57	11	37
8	SPL	A	Hemel Hempstead Town	641	L	1-4	Yetton 54	12	38
15	SPL	H	Bashley	447	W	2-0	Richards 50 Yetton 77	13	39
18	SPL	A	Bashley	184	W	3-0	Yetton 37 (pen) 53 Vassell 72	10	40
22	SPL	A	Burnham	120	W	3-0	Kelly 6 Yetton 70 Vassell 86	9	41
25	SPL	H	Burnham	321	W	2-1	Yetton 57 Vassell 80	9	42
29	SPL	H	Hitchin Town	527	D	1-1	Vassell 72	9	43
April 5	SPL	A	Hungerford Town	176	L	1-2	Yetton 25	10	44
8	SPL	A	Truro City	346	L	1-2	Yetton 8	10	45
12	SPL	H	St Neots Town	546	L	1-2	Yetton 55	11	46
15	SPL	H	Banbury United	310	L	0-1		11	47
19	SPL	A	Redditch United	293	W	4-0	Colwell 12 Green 54 Vassell 83 Rigg 88	11	48
21	SPL	H	Truro City	672	L	2-5	Yetton 2 23	11	49
26	SPL	A	Chasham United	391	D	0-0		12	50

GOALSCORERS	Lge	FAC	FAT	Total	Pens	Hat-tricks	Cons Run
Yetton	26	6	1	33	2		7
S. Walker	5	1		6	1		
Burbidge	5			5			
Joyce	3	1	1	5			2
Poole	4	1		5			
Vassel	5			5			4
Ford	3	1		4			
Rigg	4			4			
Kelly	3			3			2
M. Walker	3			3			
Allen	2			2			2
Colwell	1			1			
Green	1			1			
Hutchings	1			1			
Richards	1			1			
Opponents	2			2			

Cons Run - Consecutive scoring games.

A.F.C. HAYES

Chairman: Barry Stone
Secretary: Barry Crump (T) (E) afchayesfootballsec@hotmail.co.uk
Commercial Manager: (T)
Programme Editor: Graham White (T) grassrootspublications@btconnect.com
Ground Address: Farm Park, Kingshill Avenue, Hayes UB4 8DD
(T) 020 8845 0110 **Manager:** Ian Crane

Photo: Keith Clayton.

Club Factfile

Founded: 1974 **Nickname:** The Brook
Previous Names: Brook House > 2007.
Previous Leagues: Spartan South Midlands, Isthmian

Club Colours (change): Blue and white stripes/blue/blue (Yellow & black stripes/black/yellow)

Ground Capacity: 2,000 **Seats:** 150 **Covered:** 200 **Clubhouse:** Yes **Shop:** No

Directions
From the A40 McDonalds Target roundabout take A312 south towards Hayes.
At White Hart roundabout take third exit into Yeading Lane.
Turn right at first traffic lights into Kingshill Avenue.
Ground approx one miles on the right-hand side.

Previous Grounds: None

Record Attendance: Not known
Record Victory: Not known
Record Defeat: Not known
Record Goalscorer: Not known
Record Appearances: Not known
Additional Records:

Senior Honours:
Spartan South Midlands Premier South 1997-98, Premier Cup 1999-2000, Challenge Trophy 2003-04.
Isthmian Associate Members Trophy 2005-06.
Middlesex Senior Cup 2008-09.

10 YEAR RECORD

04-05	05-06	06-07	07-08	08-09	09-10	10-11	11-12	12-13	13-14
Conf S 12	Conf S 20	Conf S 20	Sthsw 14	Sthsw 9	Sthsw 21	SthC 19	SthC 10	SthC 15	SthC 18

AYLESBURY

Chairman: Danny Martone

Secretary: Ian Brown (T) 07947 338 462 (E) brownzola@aol.com

Commercial Manager: (T)

Programme Editor: Christine Martone (T) martone040@hotmail.com

Ground Address: Haywood Way, Aylesbury, Bucks. HP19 9WZ

(T) 01296 421 101 **Manager:** Steve Bateman

Photo: Keith Clayton.

Club Factfile

Founded: 1930 **Nickname:** The Moles

Previous Names: Negretti & Zambra FC 1930-54, Stocklake 1954-2000, Haywood United > 2000, Haywood FC 2000-06, Aylesbury Vale 2006-09.

Previous Leagues: Aylesbury District. Wycombe & District. Chiltern, Spartan South Midlands

Club Colours (change): Red with black trim/black/red (Silver & white/red/red)

Ground Capacity: **Seats:** Yes **Covered:** Yes **Clubhouse:** Yes **Shop:** No

Directions

When entering Aylesbury from all major routes, join the ring road and follow signposts for A41 Bicester and Waddesdon. leave the ring road at the roundabout by the Texaco Garage and Perry dealership. From the Texaco Garage cross straight over four roundabouts. At the fifth roundabout with the Cotton Wheel Pub on the right hand side, turn right into Jackson Road. Take the second left into Haywood Way, club is at the bottom of the road. If entering Aylesbury from Bicester (A41), turn left into Jackson Road by the Cotton Wheel Pub, and then second left into Haywood Way.

Previous Grounds: Negretti & Zambra King's Cross 1930-49. Stocklake Industrial Estate 1949-87.

Record Attendance: Not known

Record Victory: Not known

Record Defeat: Not known

Record Goalscorer: Not known

Record Appearances: Not known

Additional Records: Not known

Senior Honours:

Spartan South Midlands League Division 1 2003-04, Premier Division 2009-10.

Wycombe Senior Cup 1994-95.

10 YEAR RECORD

04-05	05-06	06-07	07-08	08-09	09-10	10-11	11-12	12-13	13-14
SSM P 3	SSM P 5	SSM P 5	SSM P 9	SSM P 15	SSM P 1	SthC 8	SthC 20	SthC 12	SthC 16

AYLESBURY UNITED

Chairman: Graham Read
Secretary: Steve Baker (T) 07768 353 265 (E) stevepb42@hotmail.com
Commercial Manager: (T)
Programme Editor: Steve Baker (T) stevepb42@hotmail.com
Ground Address: Leighton Town FC, Lake Street, Leighton Buzzard, Beds LU7 1RX
(T) 01296 487 367 (Office) 07710 551 971 **Manager:** Tony Joyce

Club Factfile

Founded: 1897 **Nickname:** The Ducks
Previous Names: None
Previous Leagues: Post War: Spartan >1951, Delphian 51-63, Athenian 63-76, Southern 76-88, 2004-10, Conf. 88-89, Isthmian 89-2004. Spartan South Midlands 2010-13.
Club Colours (change): Green & white (Orange & black)

Ground Capacity: 2,800 **Seats:** 155 **Covered:** 300 **Clubhouse:** Yes **Shop:** No

Directions
From Aylesbury: Take the A418 towards Leighton Buzzard and at the bypass turn right onto the A505. Go straight over the first two roundabouts; then turn left at the third onto the A4146. Stay on the A4146 at the next two roundabouts (second exit, first exit), then carry straight on at the next mini-roundabout. The entrance to the ground is about 50 yards after this mini-roundabout on the left. Car parking is on your left as you turn. Travel from the Midlands using the M1: Leave the M1 at junction 15 and take the A508 towards Milton Keynes. After 9 miles you will reach the A5 roundabout. Take the first exit and travel about 8 miles to the roundabout at the end of the dual carriageway. Take the second exit and follow the A5 towards Dunstable. After about 3 miles you will arrive at another roundabout (Flying Fox pub is on your left) take the third exit towards Heath & Reach and Leighton Buzzard. Follow this road for about 4 miles until you arrive at a large roundabout in Leighton Buzzard then take the first exit. At the next roundabout take the second exit, you will then go through 2 sets of lights. The ground and car park is on the right, immediately after the lights and opposite a petrol station.
Previous Grounds: Turnfurlong Lane. Buckingham Road >2006

Record Attendance: Turnfurlong Lane - 7,440 v Watford FAC 1st Rnd 1951-52. Buckingham Road - 6,031 v England 04/06/1988.
Record Victory: 10-0 v Hornchurch & Upminster (H), Delphain League 17/04/1954
Record Defeat: 0-9 v Bishop's Stortford (A), Delphain League 08/10/1955
Record Goalscorer: Cliff Hercules - 301 (1984-2002)
Record Appearances: Cliff Hercules - 651+18 (1984-2002)
Additional Records:
Senior Honours:
Southern League 1987-88. Berks & Bucks Senior Cup x5 2012-13. Isthmian Cup 1994-95.

10 YEAR RECORD

04-05	05-06	06-07	07-08	08-09	09-10	10-11	11-12	12-13	13-14
SthP 10	SthP 21	SthM 6	SthM 8	SthM 10	SthM 22	SSM P 6	SSM P 4	SSM P 2	SthC 12

Southern League Action

Brian haule (Beaconsfield) opens the scoring against Ashford.

Photo: Keith Clayton.

BARTON ROVERS

Chairman: Darren Whiley
Secretary: Iain Rennie (T) 01582 707 772 (E)
Commercial Manager: (T)
Programme Editor: Kev King (T) programme@bartonrovers.com
Ground Address: Sharpenhoe Road, Barton-le-Clay, Bedford MK45 4SD
(T) 01582 707 772 **Manager:** Dan Kennoy

Club Factfile

Founded: 1898 **Nickname:** Rovers
Previous Names: None
Previous Leagues: Luton & district 1947-54, South Midlands 1954-79, Isthmian 1979-2004

Club Colours (change): Royal blue with white trim/royal blue/royal blue (Yellow with black trim/black/yellow)

Ground Capacity: 4,000 **Seats:** 160 **Covered:** 1,120 **Clubhouse:** Yes **Shop:** Yes

Directions
Leave M1 at J12 head towards Harlington.
Follow signs through Sharpenhoe Village to Barton.
At T-junction in village turn right, continue 500 yards and turn right into ground on concrete roadway adjacent to playing fields.

Previous Grounds: None

Record Attendance: 1,900 v Nuneaton Borough - FA Cup 4th Qualifying Round 1976
Record Victory: Not known
Record Defeat: Not known
Record Goalscorer: Richard Camp - 152 (1989-98)
Record Appearances: Tony McNally - 598 (1988-2005)
Additional Records: Paid £1,000 to Hitchin Town for B. Baldry 1980
Received £1,000 from Bishop's Stortford for B. Baldry 1981
Senior Honours:
South Midlands League 1970-71, 71-72, 72-73, 74-75, 75-76, 76-77.
Bedfordshire Senior Cup 1971-72, 72-73, 80-81, 81-82, 89-90, 97-98, 98-99. Bedfordshire Premier Cup 1995-96.

10 YEAR RECORD

04-05		05-06		06-07		07-08		08-09		09-10		10-11		11-12		12-13		13-14	
SthE	8	SthE	19	SthM	20	SthM	11	SthM	17	SthM	21	SthC	12	SthC	11	SthC	14	SthC	6

BEACONSFIELD SYCOB

Chairman: Fred Deanus
Secretary: Robin Woolman **(T)** **(E)** robin.woolman@btinternet.com
Commercial Manager: **(T)**
Programme Editor: Karl McKenzie **(T)** karlmckenzie1@hotmail.co.uk
Ground Address: Holloways Park, Windsor Road, Beaconsfield, Bucks HP9 2SE
(T) 01494 676 868 **Manager:** Andy Hurley

Club Factfile

Founded: 1994 **Nickname:** The Rams
Previous Names: Slough YCOB and Beaconsfield United merged in 1994
Previous Leagues: Spartan South Midlands 1004-2004, 07-08, Southern 2004-07

Club Colours (change): Red and white quarters/white with red trim/red and white (Yellow with blue trim/blue/yellow & blue)

Ground Capacity: **Seats:** **Covered:** **Clubhouse:** Yes **Shop:**

Directions
Leave Junction 2 of M40, take A355 towards Slough, 50 yards off roundabout turn left and at next roundabout turn complete right, coming back towards A355 to continue across A355, then turn right and 150 yards on left is sign to club. Go through gate and clubhouse is 200 yards on right.

Previous Grounds: None

Record Attendance: Not known
Record Victory: Not known
Record Defeat: Not known
Record Goalscorer: Allan Arthur
Record Appearances: Allan Arthur
Additional Records:

Senior Honours:
Spartan South Midlands 2000-01, 03-04, 07-08. Berks and Bucks Senior Trophy 2003-04

10 YEAR RECORD

04-05	05-06	06-07	07-08	08-09	09-10	10-11	11-12	12-13	13-14
SthE 14	SthW 13	Sthsw 22	SSM P 1	Sthsw 4	SthM 19	SthC 22	SthC 5	SthC 5	SthC 8

BEDFORD TOWN

Bedford Town F.C.

Chairman: David Howell
Secretary: James Smiles **(T)** 07986 714 418 **(E)** james.smiles@bedfordeagles.net
Commercial Manager: **(T)**
Programme Editor: Dave Swallow **(T)** david.swallow@bedfordeagles.net
Ground Address: The Eyrie, Meadow Lane, Cardington, Bedford MK44 3SB
(T) 01234 831 558 **Manager:** Craig Adams

2014-15 Squad.

Club Factfile

Founded: 1989 **Nickname:** The Eagles
Previous Names: Original Bedford Town founded in 1908 folded in 1982
Previous Leagues: South Midlands 1989-94, Isthmian 1994-2004, Southern 2004-06, Conference 2006-07

Club Colours (change): All blue (Gold with black trim/black/black)

Ground Capacity: 3,000 **Seats:** 300 **Covered:** 1,000 **Clubhouse:** Yes **Shop:** Yes

Directions
From A1: Take A603 from Sandy to Bedford, go through Willington and ground is a mile and a half on right, signposted Meadow Lane. From M1: Off at Junction 13, take A421, carry on A421 onto Bedford Bypass and take A603 Sandy turn off. Ground is on left.

Previous Grounds: Allen Park, Queens Park, Bedford Park Pitch 1991-93

Record Attendance: 3,000 v Peterborough United Ground opening 06/08/1993
Record Victory: 9-0 v Ickleford and v Cardington
Record Defeat: 0-5 v Hendon
Record Goalscorer: Jason Reed
Record Appearances: Eddie Lawley
Additional Records:

Senior Honours:
Isthmian League Division 2 1998-99. Bedfordshire Senior Cup 1994-95. Southern League Play-offs 2005-06.

10 YEAR RECORD

04-05	05-06	06-07	07-08	08-09	09-10	10-11	11-12	12-13	13-14
SthP 5	SthP 5	Conf S 22	SthP 19	SthP 15	SthP 18	SthP 17	SthP 10	SthP 10	SthP 22

BEDWORTH UNITED

Chairman: Neill Rayson-Randle
Secretary: Andy Stickley **(T)** 07740 869 757 **(E)** andrew.stickley@live.co.uk
Commercial Manager: **(T)**
Programme Editor: Barry Walker **(T)** bedworthunitededitor@gmail.com
Ground Address: The Oval, Coventry Road, Bedworth CV12 8NN
(T) 02476 314 752 **Manager:** Stuart Storer

2013-14 Squad.

Club Factfile

Founded: 1896 **Nickname:** Greenbacks
Previous Names: Bedworth Town 1947-68
Previous Leagues: Birmingham Combination 1947-54, Birmingham/West Midlands 1954-72. Southern 1972-2013. Northern Premier 2013-14.

Club Colours (change): All green (Gold/black/gold)

Ground Capacity: 7,000 **Seats:** 300 **Covered:** 300 **Clubhouse:** Yes **Shop:** Yes

Directions
11/2 miles from M6 J3, take B4113 Coventry–Bedworth Road and after third set of traffic lights (Bedworth Leisure Centre). Ground 200 yards on right opposite cemetery.
Coaches to park in Leisure Centre.

Previous Grounds: British Queen Ground 1911-39

Record Attendance: 5,127 v Nuneaton Borough - Southern League Midland Division 23/02/1982
Record Victory: Not known
Record Defeat: Not known
Record Goalscorer: Peter Spacey - 1949-69
Record Appearances: Peter Spacey - 1949-69
Additional Records: Paid £1,750 to Hinckley Town for Colin Taylor 1991-92
Received £30,000 from Plymouth Argyle for Richard Landon
Senior Honours:
Birmingham Combination x2. Birmingham Senior Cup x3. Midland Floodlit Cup 1981-82, 92-93. Southern Division 1 Central Play-offs 2011-12.

10 YEAR RECORD

04-05	05-06	06-07	07-08	08-09	09-10	10-11	11-12	12-13	13-14
SthW 15	SthW 16	SthM 16	SthM 15	SthM 14	SthM 16	SthC 15	SthC 3	SthP 21	NP1S 20

CHALFONT ST PETER

Chairman: Denis Mair
Secretary: John Carroll (T) 07950 981 008 (E) jc.chalfontfc@fsmail.net
Commercial Manager: (T)
Programme Editor: Ian Doorbar (T) 07985 943 395
Ground Address: Mill Meadow, Gravel Hill, Amersham Road, Chalfont St Peter SL9 9QX
(T) 01753 885 797 **Manager:** Danny Edwards

Chalfont's Vincente shields the ball from Royston's De La Salle.
Photo: Keith Clayton.

Club Factfile

Founded: 1926 **Nickname:** Saints
Previous Names: None
Previous Leagues: G W Comb. Parthernon. London. Spartan. L Spartan. Athenian. Isthmian, Spartan South Midlands 2006-11.

Club Colours (change): Red/green/red. (All yellow).

Ground Capacity: 4,500 **Seats:** 220 **Covered:** 120 **Clubhouse:** Yes **Shop:** Yes

Directions
Follow A413 (Amersham Road).
The ground is adjacent to the Chalfont Community Centre off Gravel Hill which is part of the A413.
Players and officials can park inside the ground.
The A413 is the Denham to Aylesbury road.

Previous Grounds: None

Record Attendance: **Att:** 2,550 v Watford benefit match 1985 **App:** Colin Davies
Record Victory: Not known
Record Defeat: Not known
Record Goalscorer: Not known
Record Appearances: Not known
Additional Records:

Senior Honours:
Isthmian Lge Div 2 87-88, Berks & Bucks Intermediate Cup 52-53.
Spartan South Midlands Premier Division 2010-11.

10 YEAR RECORD

04-05	05-06	06-07	07-08	08-09	09-10	10-11	11-12	12-13	13-14
Isth2 11	Isth2 8	SSM P 6	SSM P 2	SSM P 3	SSM P 2	SSM P 1	SthC 12	SthC 16	SthC 14

DAVENTRY TOWN

Chairman: Iain Humphrey
Secretary: Nigel Foster **(T)** 07454 521 773 **(E)** dtfcsecretary@sky.com
Commercial Manager: Jim Davis **(T)**
Programme Editor: Nigel Foster **(T)** 07454 521 773
Ground Address: Communications Park, Browns Road, Daventry, Northants NN11 4NS
(T) 01327 311 239 **Manager:** Darran Foster

The team line up before their FA Cup tie with Chesterfield.
Photo: Keith Clayton.

Club Factfile

Founded: 1886 **Nickname:** The Town
Previous Names: Not known
Previous Leagues: Northampton Town (pre-1987), Central Northways Comb 1987-89, United Counties 1989-2010.

Club Colours (change): Purple/white/purple (White/purple/white)

Ground Capacity: 2,000 **Seats:** 250 **Covered:** 250 **Clubhouse:** Yes **Shop:**

Directions
From Northampton or J.16 of the M1, follow A45 westbound into Daventry, crossing the A5 on the way.
At first roundabout bear left along A45 Daventry Bypass.
At next roundabout go straight over onto Browns Road.
The Club is at the top of this road on the left.

Previous Grounds: Not known

Record Attendance: 850 v Utrecht (Holland) - 1989
Record Victory: Not known
Record Defeat: Not known
Record Goalscorer: Not known
Record Appearances: Not known
Additional Records:

Senior Honours:
United Counties League Division 1 1989-90, 90-91, 2000-01, 2007-08, Premier Division 2009-10.

10 YEAR RECORD

04-05	05-06	06-07	07-08	08-09	09-10	10-11	11-12	12-13	13-14
UCL P	UCL P	UCL P	UCL 1 1	UCL P 7	UCL P 1	SthC 2	SthC 16	SthC 8	SthC 4

EGHAM TOWN

Chairman: Patrick Bennett
Secretary: Daniel Bennett (T) 07932 612 424 (E) sales@beautiful-bathrooms.co.uk
Commercial Manager: (T)
Programme Editor: Stephen Bennett (T) patonofwalton@btconnect.com
Ground Address: Runnymead Stadium, Tempest Road, Egham TW20 8XD
(T) 01784 437 055 **Manager:** Lee Passmore

Photo: Keith Clayton.

Club Factfile

Founded: 1877 **Nickname:** Sarnies
Previous Names: Runnymead Rovers 1877-1905. Egham F.C. 05-63.
Previous Leagues: Spartan. Athenian. Isthmian. Southern. Combined Counties 2006-13.

Club Colours (change): Red & white (Green & black)

Ground Capacity: 5500 **Seats:** 262 **Covered:** 3300 **Clubhouse:** Yes **Shop:** No

Directions
From M25 - J13 - Take the A30, heading south. The road runs parallel with the M25 briefly, and sweeps round a sharp left hand bend, under the M25. Stay right, down to the r'about in front of you just the other side of the M25. Go round the r'about and back under the M25.This road is called The Causeway. Carry on down this road, over the small r'about at Sainsbury's and at the bigger r'about turn right (signposted B3376 - Thorpe, Chertsey, Woking). Proceed down Thorpe Rd, over a level crossing, to a mini r'about, go over, and on the left, after the green turn into Pond Road. Left into Wards Place then first right and you will see the entrance to the football ground.

Previous Grounds: Moved to Recreation Ground - now Runnymead Stadium - in 1963.

Record Attendance: 1400 v Wycombe Wanderers, FAC 2nd Qual. 1972-73.
Record Victory: Not known
Record Defeat: Not known
Record Goalscorer: Mark Butler (153).
Record Appearances: Dave Jones (850+).
Additional Records:

Senior Honours:
Spartan League Champions 1971-72. Athenian League Division 2 Champions.
Combined Counties League 2012-13.

10 YEAR RECORD

04-05	05-06	06-07	07-08	08-09	09-10	10-11	11-12	12-13	13-14
SthW 22	Isth2 5	CCP 10	CCP 12	CCP 13	CCP 4	CCP 13	CCP 4	CCP 1	SthC 11

GODALMING TOWN

Chairman: Kevin Young
Secretary: Glenn Moulton **(T)** **(E)** secretary@godalmingtownfc.co.uk
Commercial Manager: Kevin Marshall **(T)** commercial@godalmingtownfc.co.uk
Programme Editor: Nick Mitchell **(T)** info@godalmingtownfc.co.uk
Ground Address: Weycourt, Meadrow, Guildford, Surrey GU7 3JE
(T) 01483 417 520 **Manager:** Andy Hunt

Godalming No.9 tries to escape the attentions of Cinderford's full back, Archer.
Photo: Jonathan Holloway.

Club Factfile

Founded: 1950 **Nickname:** The G's
Previous Names: Godalming United 1950-71. Godalming & Farncombe 1971-79. Godalming Town 1979-92. Godalming & Guildford 1992-2005.
Previous Leagues: Combined Counties, Southern 2006-08

Club Colours (change): Yellow & green (White & black)

Ground Capacity: 3,000 **Seats:** 200 **Covered:** 400 **Clubhouse:** Yes **Shop:** Yes

Directions
A3100 from Guildford, pass the Manor Inn on the left and then the petrol station on the right. Wey Court is 50 yards further along the road on the right hand side.
A3100 from Godalming, pass the Three Lions pub on the left and then turn left into Wey Court immediately after the Leathern Bottle pub.
Parking: Please note that the club car park is for players and officials only. Spectators are asked to use the public car park next door to the ground.

Previous Grounds: Recreation Ground 1950-71. Brief spell at Broadwater Park whilst work was done on Weycourt.

Record Attendance: 1,305 v AFC Wimbledon - 2002
Record Victory: Not Known
Record Defeat: Not Known
Record Goalscorer: Not Known
Record Appearances: Shaun Elliott - 360+
Additional Records:

Senior Honours:
Combined Counties League Premier Division 1983-84, 2005-06.
Surrey Senior Cup 2012-13.

10 YEAR RECORD

04-05	05-06	06-07	07-08	08-09	09-10	10-11	11-12	12-13	13-14
CCP 4	CCP 1	Isth1S 22	Sthsw 12	Isth1S 9	Isth1S 4	Isth1S 17	Isth1S 5	SthC 3	Sthsw 18

HANWELL TOWN

Chairman: Bob Fisher
Secretary: Clive Cooke (T) 07791 314 689 (E) clivecooke2@sky.com
Commercial Manager: (T)
Programme Editor: Bob Fisher (T)
Ground Address: Reynolds Field, Preivale Lane, Perivale, Greenford, UB6 8TL
(T) 020 8998 1701 **Manager:** Ray Duffy

Club Factfile

Founded: 1920 **Nickname:** Magpies
Previous Names: None
Previous Leagues: Dauntless. Wembley & Dist. Middlesex. London Spartan. Southern.

Club Colours (change): Black & white stripes/black/black (Red/white/red)

Ground Capacity: 1,250 **Seats:** 175 **Covered:** 600 **Clubhouse:** Yes **Shop:** No

Directions
From West - Exit M25 at junction 16 and follow A40(M) towards London. Continue over Greenford Flyover and get into nearside lane, signposted Ealing & Perivale. Exit and turn right across the A40 and the ground is immediatley on the left.
From East - At Hanger Lane Giratory take the A40 exit towards Oxford. The first exit is signposted Perivale/Ealing. Take the slip road and then left at traffic lights . Take the first left again into Perivale Lane.

Previous Grounds: Moved to Reynolds Field in 1981.

Record Attendance: **Att:** 600 v Spurs, floodlight switch on, 1989.
Record Victory: Not known
Record Defeat: Not known
Record Goalscorer: Keith Rowlands
Record Appearances: Phil Player 617 (20 seasons)
Additional Records:

Senior Honours:
London Spartan Senior Div. 83-84. London Senior Cup 1991-92, 92-93.
Spartan South Midlands Premier 2013-14.

10 YEAR RECORD

04-05	05-06	06-07	07-08	08-09	09-10	10-11	11-12	12-13	13-14
SSM P 2	SSM P 3	SthS 21	SSM P 9	SSM P 7	SSM P 13	SSM P 15	SSM P 21	SSM P 6	SSM P 1

Southern League Action

Shennan (AFC Hayes) and Wallace (Uxbridge) contest for the ball.

Photo: Keith Clayton.

KETTERING TOWN

Chairman: Ritchie Jeune
Secretary: Neil Griffin (T) 01536 217 006 (E)
Commercial Manager: Martin Bellamy (T)
Programme Editor: Paul Cooke (T) companioncooke@btinternet.com
Ground Address: Latimer Park, Burton Latimer, Kettering NN15 5PS
(T) 01536 217 006 **Manager:** Scott Machin & Thomas Bailie

Club Factfile

Founded: 1872 **Nickname:** The Poppies
Previous Names: Kettering > 1924
Previous Leagues: Midland 1892-1900, also had a team in United Counties 1896-99, Southern 1900-30, 1950-79, 2001-02, Birmingham 1930-50, Alliance/Conference 1979-2001, 02-03, Isthmian 2003-04

Club Colours (change): Red & black (Blue & white)

Ground Capacity: **Seats:** Yes **Covered:** Yes **Clubhouse:** Yes **Shop:**

Directions
From Junction 10 of the A14 turn due South at the roundabout onto Kettering Road (signposted Burton Latimer). After 200 yards turn right at the roundabout onto Attendiez Way. Go over the next roundabout and follow the road around Morrison's warehouse. The road becomes Polwell Lane and the entrance to Latimer Park is on the left just after Morrison's warehouse.
If approaching from the South, take the A6 to its junction with the A14 and follow the directions above or, if travelling up the A509 turn right at the roundabout just after Isham (signposted Burton Latimer) onto Station Road and continue for half a mile past the Weetabix and Alumasc factories before turning left onto Polwell Lane. The entrance to Latimer Park is on the right after 50 yards.

Previous Grounds: North Park, Green Lane, Rockingham Road > 2011. Nene Park 2011-13.

Record Attendance: 11,536 v Peterborough - FA Cup 1st Round replay 1958-59
Record Victory: 16-0 v Higham YMCI - FA Cup 1909
Record Defeat: 0-13 v Mardy - Southern League Division Two 1911-12
Record Goalscorer: Roy Clayton - 171 (1972-81)
Record Appearances: Roger Ashby
Additional Records: Paid £25,000 to Macclesfield for Carl Alford 1994. Recieved £150,000 from Newcastle United for Andy Hunt
Senior Honours:
Southern League 1927-28, 56-57, 72-73, 2001-02. Conference North 2007-08.

10 YEAR RECORD

04-05	05-06	06-07	07-08	08-09	09-10	10-11	11-12	12-13	13-14
Conf N 4	Conf N 6	Conf N 2	Conf N 1	Conf 8	Conf 6	Conf 14	Conf 24	SthP 22	SthC 3

Southern League Action

Hammond (Royston) makes it 3-0 against Chalfont.

Photo: Keith Clayton.

LEIGHTON TOWN

Chairman: Terry McCafferty

Secretary: Malcolm McCormick **(T)** **(E)** malcolmmccormick@btinternet.com

Commercial Manager: **(T)**

Programme Editor: Andrew Parker **(T)** andrewparker-leightontownfc@virginmedia.com

Ground Address: Lake Street, Leighton Buzzard, Beds LU7 1RX

(T) 01525 373 311 **Manager:** Craig Bicknell

Club Factfile

Founded: 1885 **Nickname:** Reds

Previous Names: Leighton United 1922-63

Previous Leagues: Leighton & District, South Midlands 1922-24, 26-29, 46-54, 55-56, 76-92, Spartan 1922-53, 67-74, United Counties 1974-76, Isthmian

Club Colours (change): Red & white (All blue)

Ground Capacity: 2,800 **Seats:** 155 **Covered:** 300 **Clubhouse:** Yes **Shop:** No

Directions

Ground is situated just south of Town Centre on the A4146 Leighton Buzzard to Hemel Hemstead Road.
Entrance to car park and ground is opposite Morrisons Supermarket Petrol Station.
1/2 mile south of town centre.

Previous Grounds: Wayside

Record Attendance: 1,522 v Aldershot Town - Isthmian League Division 3 30/01/1993

Record Victory: v Met Railway (H) - Spartan League 1925-26

Record Defeat: 0-12 v Headington United (A) - Spartan League 18/10/1947

Record Goalscorer: Not known

Record Appearances: Not known

Additional Records:

Senior Honours:

South Midlands League 1966-67, 91-92. Isthmian League Division 2 2003-04.
Bedfordshire Senior Cup 1926-27, 67-68, 69-70, 92-93.

10 YEAR RECORD

04-05	05-06	06-07	07-08	08-09	09-10	10-11	11-12	12-13	13-14
SthE 10	SthW 8	SthM 18	SthM 9	SthM 8	SthM 10	SthC 7	SthC 13	SthC 21	SthC 19

MARLOW

Chairman: Terry Staines
Secretary: David White (T) 01628 483 970 (E) terry.staines@ntlworld.com
Commercial Manager: (T)
Programme Editor: Terry Staines (T) terry.staines@ntlworld.com
Ground Address: Alfred Davies Memorial Ground, Oak tree Road, Marlow SL7 3ED
(T) 01628 483 970 **Manager:** Mark Bartley

2013-14 Squad.

Club Factfile

Founded: 1870 **Nickname:** The Blues
Previous Names: Great Marlow
Previous Leagues: Reading & District, Spartan 1908-10, 28-65, Gt Western Suburban, Athenian 1965-84, Isthmian 1984-2004. Southern 2004-12. Hellenic 2012-13.
Club Colours (change): All royal blue (All red)

Ground Capacity: 3,000 **Seats:** 250 **Covered:** 600 **Clubhouse:** Yes **Shop:**

Directions
From M40 (Junction 4 High Wycombe) or M4 (Junction 8/9 Maidenhead) take A404, leave at the A4155 junction signposted Marlow.
Follow A4155 towards Marlow then turn right at Esso service station into Maple Rise.
At crossroads follow straight ahead into Oak Tree Road.
Ground 100 yards on left.

Previous Grounds: Crown ground 1870-1919, Star Meadow 1919-24

Record Attendance: 3,000 v Oxford United - FA Cup 1st Round 1994
Record Victory: Not known
Record Defeat: Not known
Record Goalscorer: Kevin Stone
Record Appearances: Mick McKeown - 500+
Additional Records: Paid £5,000 to Sutton United for Richard Evans
Received £8,000 from Slough Town for David Lay
Senior Honours:
Isthmian League Division 1 1987-88, League Cup 92-93. Hellenic League Premier Division 2012-13.
Berks & Bucks Senior Cup x11

10 YEAR RECORD

04-05		05-06		06-07		07-08		08-09		09-10		10-11		11-12		12-13		13-14	
SthW	13	SthW	6	Sthsw	7	Sthsw	9	SthM	9	SthM	15	SthC	11	SthC	22	Hel P	1	SthC	17

NORTH GREENFORD UNITED

Chairman: John Bivens
Secretary: Mrs Barbara Bivens **(T)** 07915 661 580 **(E)** barbarabivens@talktalk.net
Commercial Manager: **(T)**
Programme Editor: Graham Wither **(T)** grassrootspublications@btconnect.com
Ground Address: Berkeley Fields, Berkley Avenue, Greenford UB6 0NX
(T) 0208 422 8923 **Manager:** Paul Palmer

Club Factfile

Founded: 1944 **Nickname:** Blues
Previous Names: None
Previous Leagues: London Spartan, Combined Counties 2002-10

Club Colours (change): Royal blue & white (Red & white)

Ground Capacity: 2,000 **Seats:** 150 **Covered:** 100 **Clubhouse:** Yes **Shop:** No

Directions
A40 going towards London. At the Greenford Flyover come down the slip road, keep in the left hand lane, turn left onto the Greenford Road (A4127). At the third set of traffic lights, turn right into Berkeley Av. Go to the bottom of the road. There is a large car park. We are on the right hand side.

Previous Grounds:

Record Attendance: 985 v AFC Wimbledon
Record Victory: Not known
Record Defeat: Not known
Record Goalscorer: John Hill - 98
Record Appearances: Not known
Additional Records:

Senior Honours:
Combined Counties League Premier Division 2009-10

10 YEAR RECORD

04-05	05-06	06-07	07-08	08-09	09-10	10-11	11-12	12-13	13-14
CCP 2	CCP 13	CCP 5	CCP 6	CCP 2	CCP 1	SthC 20	SthC 18	SthC 19	SthC 20

Southern League Action

Alderton (Chertsey) outjumps Stanislaus (Egham).

Photo: Keith Clayton.

NORTHWOOD

Chairman: Ian Barry
Secretary: Alan Evans (T) 07960 744 349 (E) alan.evansnfc@btopenworld.com
Commercial Manager: (T) enquiries@northwoodfc.com
Programme Editor: Ken Green (T) ken.green01@ntlworld.com
Ground Address: Northwood Park, Chestnut Avenue, Northwood, Middlesex HA6 1HR
(T) 01923 827 148 **Manager:** Mark Burgess

Club Factfile

Founded: 1926 **Nickname:** Woods
Previous Names: Northwood United 1926-1945.
Previous Leagues: Harrow & Wembley 1932-69, Middlesex 1969-78, Hellenic 1979-84, London Spartan 1984-93, Isthmian 1993-2005, 2007-10, Southern 2005-07
Club Colours (change): All red (Yellow & blue)

Ground Capacity: 3,075 **Seats:** 308 **Covered:** 932 **Clubhouse:** Yes **Shop:** No

Directions
M25 Junction 18, take A404 through Rickmansworth to Northwood. After passing under grey railway bridge, take first right into Chestnut Avenue. Ground is in grounds of Northwood Park, entrance is 400 metres on left.
(Ground is 20 minutes from J.18).

Previous Grounds: Northwood Recreation Ground 1926-1928. Northwood Playing Fields 1928-1971.

Record Attendance: 1,642 v Chlesea - Friendly July 1997
Record Victory: 15-0 v Dateline (H) - Middlesex Intermediate Cup 1973
Record Defeat: 0-8 v Bedfont - Middlesex League 1975
Record Goalscorer: Not known
Record Appearances: Chris Gell - 493+
Additional Records: Lawrence Yaku scored 61 goals during season 1999-2000

Senior Honours:
Isthmian League Division 1 North 2002-03, Charity Shield 2002.
Middlesex Premier Cup 1994-95.

10 YEAR RECORD

04-05	05-06	06-07	07-08	08-09	09-10	10-11	11-12	12-13	13-14
Isth P 17	SthP 19	SthP 22	Isth1N 10	Isth1N 6	Isth1N 10	SthC 20	SthC 7	SthC 13	SthC 9

Southern League Action

John Flood (Chertsey) gets the block on Joshua Andrew (Egham).

Photo: Keith Clayton.

POTTERS BAR TOWN

Chairman: Mark Martyn
Secretary: Alan Evans **(T)** 0783 363 2965 **(E)** potters_bar_sec@hotmail.co.uk
Commercial Manager: Jeff Barnes **(T)** 07785 765 793
Programme Editor: Jeff Barnes **(T)** jeff@jeffbarnes.co.uk
Ground Address: Pakex Stadium, Parkfield, Watkins Rise, Potters Bar EN6 1QB
(T) 01707 654 833 **Manager:** Jack Friend

Photo: Alan Coomes.

Club Factfile

Founded: 1960 **Nickname:** Grace or Scholars
Previous Names: None
Previous Leagues: Barnet & District 1960-65, North London Combination 1965-68, Herts Senior County 1968-91, Spartan South Midlands 1991-2005, Southern 2005-06. Isthmian 2006-13.
Club Colours (change): Maroon/white/white (All yellow)

Ground Capacity: 2,000 **Seats:** 150 **Covered:** 250 **Clubhouse:** Yes **Shop:** Yes

Directions
M25 junction 24 enter Potters Bar along Southgate Road (A111) turn right into High Street at first lights (A1000) then left into The Walk after half a mile. Ground is 200 yards on the right - opposite Potters Bar Cricket Club.

Previous Grounds: None

Record Attendance: 268 v Wealdstone - FA Cup 1998 (4,000 watched a charity match in 1997)
Record Victory: Not known
Record Defeat: Not known
Record Goalscorer: Not known
Record Appearances: Not known
Additional Records:

Senior Honours:
Spartan South Midlands League Premier 1996-97, 2004-05.

10 YEAR RECORD

04-05	05-06	06-07	07-08	08-09	09-10	10-11	11-12	12-13	13-14
SSM P 1	SthE 15	Isth1N 14	Isth1N 17	Isth1N 19	Isth1N 14	Isth1N 13	Isth1N 12	Isth1N 10	SthC 15

ROYSTON TOWN

Chairman: Steve Jackson
Secretary: Terry McKinnell (T) 07772 086 709 (E) terry.mckinnell@talktalk.net
Commercial Manager: (T)
Programme Editor: Kelly Taylor (T) info@abaconsultants.com
Ground Address: Garden Walk, Royston, Herts, SG8 7HP
(T) 01763 241 204 **Manager:** Steve Castle

2013-14 Squad.

Club Factfile

Founded: 1872 **Nickname:** Crows
Previous Names: None
Previous Leagues: Cambridgeshire & Herts Co. Isthmian

Club Colours (change): White & black (Red & white)

Ground Capacity: **Seats:** Yes **Covered:** Yes **Clubhouse:** Yes **Shop:**

Directions
From A505 (Town Bypass) take A10 towards town centre (signposted London).
Go straight on at next roundabout.
Garden Walk is on the left after the 3rd set of pedestrian lights (opposite Catholic Church).
Entrance to ground is approx 75 metres on left.

Previous Grounds: Royston Heath, Mackerell Hall and Newmarket Road before acquiring Garden Walk in 1931.

Record Attendance: Att: 876 v Aldershot Town, 1993-94.
Record Victory: Not known
Record Defeat: Not known
Record Goalscorer: Not known
Record Appearances: Not known
Additional Records:

Senior Honours:
Herts County Champions 1976-77. South Midlands Div.1 1978-79, 2008-09, Premier Division 2011-12.

10 YEAR RECORD

04-05	05-06	06-07	07-08	08-09	09-10	10-11	11-12	12-13	13-14
SSM P 16	SSM P 18	SSM P 20	SSM1 5	SSM1 1	SSM P 4	SSM P 3	SSM P 1	SthC 7	SthC 7

RUGBY TOWN

Chairman: Brian Melvin

Secretary: Doug Wilkins **(T)** 07976 284 614 **(E)** dougwilkins44@hotmail.com

Commercial Manager: **(T)**

Programme Editor: Neil Melvin **(T)** neil@melbros.com

Ground Address: Butlin Road, Rugby, Warwicks CV21 3SD

(T) 01788 844 806 **Manager:** Dave Stringer

Club Factfile

Founded: 1956 **Nickname:** The Valley

Previous Names: Valley Sports 1956-71, Valley Sport Rugby 1971-73, VS Rugby 1973-2000, Rugby United 2000-05

Previous Leagues: Rugby & District 1956-62, Coventry & Partnership, North Warwickshire 1963-69, United Counties 1969-75
West Midlands 1975-83

Club Colours (change): Sky blue & white (All maroon)

Ground Capacity: 6,000 **Seats:** 750 **Covered:** 1,000 **Clubhouse:** Yes **Shop:** Yes

Directions

From M6 J.1 North and South, take A426 signed Rugby at third island turn left into Boughton Road.
Continue along Boughton Road after passing under viaduct turn right at traffic lights, B5414 up the hill take second left at mini island into Butlin Road.

Previous Grounds: None

Record Attendance: 3,961 v Northampton Town - FA Cup 1984

Record Victory: 10-0 v Ilkeston Town - FA Trophy 04/09/1985

Record Defeat: 1-11 v Ilkeston Town (A) - 18/04/1998

Record Goalscorer: Danny Conway - 124

Record Appearances: Danny Conway - 374

Additional Records: Paid £3,500 for R Smith, I Crawley and G Bradder
Received £15,000 from Northampton Town for Terry Angus

Senior Honours:

FA Vase 1982-83. Southern League Midland Division 1986-87. Midland Combination Division 1 2001-02.
Birmingham Senior Cup 1988-89, 91-92

10 YEAR RECORD

04-05	05-06	06-07	07-08	08-09	09-10	10-11	11-12	12-13	13-14
	SthP 15	SthP 17	SthP 15	SthP 17	SthP 22	SthC 6	SthC 6	SthC 2	SthC 2

ST. IVES TOWN

Chairman: Gary Clarke
Secretary: Marina Howlett **(T)** 01480 463 207 **(E)**
Commercial Manager: Mark Taylor **(T)**
Programme Editor: Martin Bailey **(T)**
Ground Address: Westwood Road, St. Ives PE27 6WU
(T) 01480 463 207 **Manager:** Ricky Marheineke

Club Factfile

Founded: 1887 **Nickname:** Saints
Previous Names: None
Previous Leagues: Cambridgeshire, Central Amateur, Hunts, Peterborough & District. United Counties > 2013.

Club Colours (change): White & black (All red)

Ground Capacity: **Seats:** Yes **Covered:** Yes **Clubhouse:** Yes **Shop:** No

Directions
From A1123 Houghton Road rurn right at traffic lights into Ramsey Road. After Fire Station turn right into Westwood Road. Ground at end of road on right hand side immediately before St Ivo Recreation Centre Car Park.

Previous Grounds: Meadow Lane.

Record Attendance: 767 v Needham Market, FA Vase 5th Rnd 2007-08. 801 v Cambridge United, pre-season friendly, 2009-10.
Record Victory:
Record Defeat:
Record Goalscorer:
Record Appearances:
Additional Records:
Senior Honours:
Hunts Senior Cup 1900/01, 1911/12, 1922/23, 1925/26, 1929/30, 1981/82, 1986/87, 1987/88, 2006/07, 2008/09, 2011-12. Hunts Premier Cup 2006-07, 2008/09. United Counties League Cup 2009-10.

10 YEAR RECORD

04-05	05-06	06-07	07-08	08-09	09-10	10-11	11-12	12-13	13-14
UCL 1 3	UCL P 9	UCL P 10	UCL P 5	UCL P 6	UCL P 10	UCL P 11	UCL P 3	UCL P 2	SthC 13

Southern League Action

Woods (Uxbridge) and Dyett (AFC Hayes) shape up to cross and block.

Photo: Keith Clayton.

UXBRIDGE

Chairman: Alan Holloway

Secretary: Roger Stevens (T) 01895 236 879 (E) sec@uxbridgefc.co.uk

Commercial Manager: (T)

Programme Editor: Sharon Madigan (T) program.editor@uxbridgefc.co.uk

Ground Address: Honeycroft Road, West Drayton, Middlesex UB7 8HX

(T) 01895 443 557 **Manager:** Tony Choules

Uxbridge's Tomkins, beats AFC Hayes' Khaira from the penalty spot.
Photo: Keith Clayton.

Club Factfile

Founded: 1871 **Nickname:** The Reds

Previous Names: Uxbridge Town 1923-45

Previous Leagues: Southern 1894-99, Gt Western Suburban 1906-19, 20-23, Athenian 1919-20, 24-37, 63-82, Spartan 1937-38, London 1938-46, Gt Western Comb. 1939-45, Corinthian 1946-63, Isthmian

Club Colours (change): Red/white/red (Sky blue/navy/navy)

Ground Capacity: 3,770 **Seats:** 339 **Covered:** 760 **Clubhouse:** Yes **Shop:**

Directions
M4 to Junction 4 (Heathrow),
take A408 towards Uxbridge for 1 mile,
turn left into Horton Road.
Ground 1/2 mile on right.

Previous Grounds: RAF Stadium 1923-48, Cleveland Road 1948-78

Record Attendance: 1,000 v Arsenal - Opening of the floodlights 1981

Record Victory: Not known

Record Defeat: Not known

Record Goalscorer: Phil Duff - 153

Record Appearances: Roger Nicholls - 1,054

Additional Records:

Senior Honours:
Middlesex Senior Cup 1893-94, 95-96, 1950-51, 2000-01. London Challenge Cup 1993-94, 96-97, 98-99.

10 YEAR RECORD

04-05	05-06	06-07	07-08	08-09	09-10	10-11	11-12	12-13	13-14
SthE 4	SthE 14	Sthsw 8	Sthsw 5	Sthsw 13	Sthsw 15	SthC 13	SthC 4	SthC 11	SthC 10

A.F.C. TOTTON

Chairman: Andy Straker
Secretary: Alec Hayter (T) (E) alechayter@onetel.com
Commercial Manager: (T)
Programme Editor: Stephen Cain (T) stephen.cain@trescal.com
Ground Address: Testwood Stadium, Salisbury Road, Calmore, Totton SO40 2RW
(T) 02380 868 981 **Manager:** Stephen Riley

Club Factfile

Founded: 1886 **Nickname:** Stags
Previous Names: Totton FC until merger with Totton Athletic in 1975
Previous Leagues: Hampshire 1982-86, Wessex 1986-2008

Club Colours (change): All blue (All yellow)

Ground Capacity: 3,000 **Seats:** 500 **Covered:** 500 **Clubhouse:** Yes **Shop:** Yes

Directions
From the M27 Junction 2. From the east take the first exit at the roundabout or from the west take the third exit at the roundabout. Take the first left within 100 yards, signposted Totton Central.
At the T junction turn left and you will find the entrance to the ground approximately 1 mile on the left hand side, just before the Calmore Roundabout.

Previous Grounds: South testwood Park 1886-1933.

Record Attendance: 600 v Windsor & Eton - FA Cup 4th Qualifying Round 1982-83
Record Victory: Not known
Record Defeat: Not known
Record Goalscorer: Not known
Record Appearances: James Sherlington
Additional Records:

Senior Honours:
Hampshire League 1981-82, 84-85. Wessex League Premier Division 2007-08.
Southern League Division South & West 2010-11.
Hampshire Senior Cup 2010-11.

10 YEAR RECORD

04-05	05-06	06-07	07-08	08-09	09-10	10-11	11-12	12-13	13-14
Wex1 8	Wex1 4	WexP 2	WexP 1	Sthsw 3	Sthsw 2	Sthsw 1	SthP 3	SthP 14	SthP 21

BASHLEY

Chairman: Mike Cranidge
Secretary: Tim Allan (T) 07809 224 893 (E) tim@upthebash.co.uk
Commercial Manager: (T)
Programme Editor: (T)
Ground Address: Bashley Road Ground, Bashley Road, New Milton, Hampshire BH25 5RY
(T) 01425 620 280 **Manager:** Paul Gazzard & John Pyatt

Club Factfile

Founded: 1947 **Nickname:** The Bash
Previous Names: None
Previous Leagues: Bournemouth 1953-83, Hampshire 1983-86, Wessex 1986-89, Southern 1989-2004, Isthmian 2004-06

Club Colours (change): Gold/black/black (White/blue/blue)

Ground Capacity: 4,250 **Seats:** 250 **Covered:** 1,200 **Clubhouse:** Yes **Shop:** Yes

Directions
Take the A35 from Lyndhurst towards Christchurch, turn left onto B3058 towards New Milton.
The ground is on the left hand side in Bashley village.

Previous Grounds: None

Record Attendance: 3,500 v Emley - FA Vase Semi-final 1st Leg 1987-88
Record Victory: 21-1 v Co-Operative (A) - Bournemouth League 1964
Record Defeat: 2-20 v Air Speed (A) - Bournemouth League 1957
Record Goalscorer: Richard Gillespie - 134
Record Appearances: John Bone - 829
Additional Records: Paid £7,500 to Newport (IOW) for Danny Gibbons and from Dorchester Tn for David Elm. Received £15,000 from Salisbury for Craig Davis, from Eastleigh for Paul Sales and from AFC Bournemouth for Wade Elliott.
Senior Honours:
Wessex League 1986-87, 87-88, 88-89. Southern League Southern Division 1989-90, Division 1 South & West 2006-07.

10 YEAR RECORD

04-05	05-06	06-07	07-08	08-09	09-10	10-11	11-12	12-13	13-14
Isth1 14	Isth1 9	Sthsw 1	SthP 5	SthP 14	SthP 7	SthP 11	SthP 13	SthP 17	SthP 23

BISHOP'S CLEEVE

Chairman: David Walker
Secretary: Nigel Green (T) 07919 518 880 (E) negreen@tiscali.co.uk
Commercial Manager: (T)
Programme Editor: Nigel Green (T) negreen@tiscali.co.uk
Ground Address: Kayte Lane, Bishop's Cleeve, Cheltenham GL52 3PD
(T) 01242 676 166 **Manager:** Steve Cleal

Club Factfile

Founded: 1892 **Nickname:** Villagers
Previous Names:
Previous Leagues: Cheltenham, North Gloucestershire, Hellenic 1983-2006

Club Colours (change): Green, black & white (Blue & white)

Ground Capacity: 1,500 **Seats:** 50 **Covered:** 50 **Clubhouse:** Yes **Shop:** Yes

Directions
From Cheltenham take A435 towards Evesham.
Pass racecourse, take right at traffic lights then first left into Kayte Lane.
Ground 1⁄2 mile on left.

Previous Grounds: Stoke Road and ground shared with Moreton Town, Wollen Sports, Highworth Town and Forest Green Rovers

Record Attendance: 1,300 v Cheltenham Town - July 2006
Record Victory: Not known
Record Defeat: Not known
Record Goalscorer: Kevin Slack
Record Appearances: John Skeen
Additional Records:

Senior Honours:
Hellenic League Division 1 1986-87, Premier League Cup 1988.
Gloucestershire Junior Cup North. Gloucestershire Senior Amateur Cup North x3.

10 YEAR RECORD

04-05	05-06	06-07	07-08	08-09	09-10	10-11	11-12	12-13	13-14
Hel P 3	Hel P 2	SthM 13	SthM 12	Sthsw 18	Sthsw 11	Sthsw 15	Sthsw 11	Sthsw 21	Sthsw 20

Southern League Action

Reis Stanislaus (Egham) and Daniel Alderton (Chertsey) tussle for the ball.

Photo: Keith Clayton.

BRIDGWATER TOWN 1984

Chairman: Alan Hurford
Secretary: Roger Palmer (T) 07587 775 227 (E) palmer449@btinternet.com
Commercial Manager: (T)
Programme Editor: Roger Palmer (T) palmer449@btinternet.com
Ground Address: Fairfax Park, College Way, Bath Road, Bridgwater, Somerset TA6 4TZ
(T) 01278 446 899 **Manager:** Richard Fey

Club Factfile

Founded: 1984 **Nickname:** The Robins
Previous Names: Bridgwater Town
Previous Leagues: Somerset Senior, Western

Club Colours (change): Red & white (Yellow & blue)

Ground Capacity: 2,500 **Seats:** 128 **Covered:** 500 **Clubhouse:** Yes **Shop:** Yes

Directions
Southbound from Bristol M5 J.23- enter town on A39 from Glastonbury. Ground is between Bridgwater College and Rugby Ground by railway bridge.
Northbound from Taunton – M5 J.24- enter town on A38, follow signs for Glastonbury (A39). Ground is between Bridgwater College and Rugby Ground as you pass over railway bridge.

Previous Grounds: None

Record Attendance: 1,112 v Taunton Town - 26/02/1997
Record Victory: Not Known
Record Defeat: Not Known
Record Goalscorer: Not Known
Record Appearances: Not Known
Additional Records:

Senior Honours:
Somerset Senior League x3. Somerset Senior Cup 1993-94, 95-96. Western League Division 1 1995-96.

10 YEAR RECORD

04-05	05-06	06-07	07-08	08-09	09-10	10-11	11-12	12-13	13-14
WestP 6	WestP 11	WestP 2	Sthsw 6	Sthsw 7	Sthsw 3	Sthsw 18	Sthsw 15	Sthsw 19	Sthsw 14

CINDERFORD TOWN

Chairman: Ashley Saunders
Secretary: Robert Maskell (T) 07835 511 774 (E) maskellbilly@yahoo.co.uk
Commercial Manager: (T)
Programme Editor: Liam Maskell (T) liam.maskell@gmail.com
Ground Address: The Causeway, Hildene, Cinderford, Gloucestershire GL14 2QH
(T) 01594 827 147 / 822 039 **Manager:** John Brough

Photo: Peter Holloway

Club Factfile

Founded: 1922 **Nickname:** The Foresters
Previous Names: None
Previous Leagues: Gloucestershire Northern Senior 1922-39, 60-62, Western 1946-59, Warwickshire Combination 1963-64, West Midlands 1965-69, Gloucestershire Co. 1970-73, 85-89, Midland Comb. 1974-84, Hellenic 1990-95

Club Colours (change): White & black (All yellow)

Ground Capacity: 3,500 **Seats:** 250 **Covered:** 1,000 **Clubhouse:** Yes **Shop:** Yes

Directions
Take A40 west out of Gloucester, then A48 for 8 miles. Turn right at Elton Garage onto A4151 (Forest of Dean). Continue through Littledean, climb steep hill, turn right at crossroads (football ground), then second left into Latimer Road. Or if coming from Severn Bridge take A48 Chepstow through Lydney, Newnham then left at Elton Garage – then as above.

Previous Grounds: Mousel Lane, Royal Oak

Record Attendance: 4,850 v Minehead - Western League 1955-56
Record Victory: 13-0 v Cam Mills - 1938-39
Record Defeat: 0-10 v Sutton Coldfield - 1978-79
Record Goalscorer: Not known
Record Appearances: Russel Bowles - 528
Additional Records:

Senior Honours:
Western League Division 2 1956-57. Midland Combination 1981-82. Hellenic Premier Division 1994-95, League Cup 94-95.
Gloucestershire Senior Amateur Cup North x6. Gloucestershire Junior Cup North 1980-81.
Gloucestershire Senior Cup 2000-01.

10 YEAR RECORD

04-05	05-06	06-07	07-08	08-09	09-10	10-11	11-12	12-13	13-14
SthW 16	SthW 15	SthM 9	SthM 16	SthM 11	Sthsw 16	Sthsw 12	Sthsw 10	Sthsw 10	Sthsw 15

CLEVEDON TOWN

Chairman: Steve Spicer
Secretary: Brian Rose (T) 07768 100 632 (E) brian.rose@blueyonder.co.uk
Commercial Manager: (T)
Programme Editor: Dave Wright (T) smallwavedave@hotmail.com
Ground Address: Hand Stadium, Davis Lane, Clevedon BS21 6TG
(T) 01275 871 600 **Manager:** Paul McLoughlin

Club Factfile

Founded: 1880 **Nickname:** Seasiders
Previous Names: Clevedon FC and Ashtonians merged in 1974
Previous Leagues: Weston & District, Somerset Senior, Bristol Charity, Bristol & District, Bristol Suburban, Western 1974-93

Club Colours (change): Burgandy & blue (Blue & white)

Ground Capacity: 3,500 **Seats:** 300 **Covered:** 1,600 **Clubhouse:** Yes **Shop:** Yes

Directions
Exit J20 from M5, at bottom of slip road, turn left at roundabout into Central Way.
At next roundabout turn left to Kenn Road.
Stay on Kenn Road out of town, cross river, take 1st left into Davis Lane, over motorway.
Ground 200m on right.

Previous Grounds: Dial Hill until early 1890s, Teignmouth Road > 1991

Record Attendance: 2,300 v Billingham Synthonia - FA Amateur Cup 1952-53
Record Victory: 18-0 v Dawlish Town (H) - Western League Premier Division 24/04/1993
Record Defeat: 3-13 v Yate YMCA (A) - Bristol Combination 1967-68
Record Goalscorer: Not known
Record Appearances: Not known
Additional Records:

Senior Honours:
Somerset Senior Cup 1901-02, 04-05, 28-29, 2000-01, 01-02. Somerset Premier Cup x4.
Southern League Western Division 1992-93, 2005-06, Midland Division 1998-99.

10 YEAR RECORD

04-05	05-06	06-07	07-08	08-09	09-10	10-11	11-12	12-13	13-14
SthW 4	SthW 1	SthP 18	SthP 11	SthP 18	SthP 21	Sthsw 20	Sthsw 20	Sthsw 15	Sthsw 17

DIDCOT TOWN

Chairman: John Bailey
Secretary: Pat Horsman **(T)** 07882 154 612 **(E)** pjh@didcottownfc.co.uk
Commercial Manager: **(T)**
Programme Editor: Steve Clare **(T)** stclare@tiscali.co.uk
Ground Address: Draycott Engineering Loop Meadow Stadium, Bowmont Water, Didcot OX11 7GA
(T) 01235 813 138 **Manager:** Ian Concannon

2013-14 Squad

Club Factfile

Founded: 1907 **Nickname:** Railwaymen
Previous Names: Didcot Village and Northbourne Wanderers amalgamated to form Didcot Town in 1907.
Previous Leagues: Metropolitan 1957-63, Hellenic 1963-2006

Club Colours (change): Red & white (Blue & gold)

Ground Capacity: 5,000 **Seats:** 250 **Covered:** 200 **Clubhouse:** Yes **Shop:** Yes

Directions
From A34 take A4130 towards Didcot.
At first roundabout take first exit, at next roundabout take third exit, then straight across next two roundabouts.
At fifth roundabout turn right into Avon Way.
Follow Avon Way for 1/2 mile till you get to a mini roundabout.
Straight across it, ground is on the left after 100 yards, in Bowmont Water.

Previous Grounds: Fleet Meadow. Edmonds Park. Cow Lane. Haydon Road. Station Road 1923-99.

Record Attendance: 1,512 v Jarrow roofing - FA Vase Semi-final 2005
Record Victory: Not known
Record Defeat: Not known
Record Goalscorer: Ian Concanon
Record Appearances: Not known
Additional Records:

Senior Honours:
Hellenic League Premier Division 1953-54, 2005-06, Division 1 1976-77, 87-88, League Cup x6.
FA Vase 2004-05. Berks & Bucks Senior Trophy 2001-02, 02-03, 05-06.

10 YEAR RECORD

04-05	05-06	06-07	07-08	08-09	09-10	10-11	11-12	12-13	13-14
Hel P 2	Hel P 1	Sthsw 10	Sthsw 3	Sthsw 5	SthP 15	SthP 19	Sthsw 16	Sthsw 17	Sthsw 12

EVESHAM UNITED

Chairman: Jim Cockerton

Secretary: Mike Peplow (T) 07889 011 539 (E) footballsecretary@eveshamunitedfcl.com

Commercial Manager: Bern Jordan (T)

Programme Editor: Mike Peplow (T) 07889 011 539

Ground Address: Jubilee Stadium, Cheltenham Rd, Evesham WR11 2LZ

(T) 01386 442 303 **Manager:** Paul Collicut

Club Factfile

Founded: 1945 **Nickname:** The Robins

Previous Names: Not known

Previous Leagues: Worcester, Birmingham Combination, Midland Combination 1951-55, 65-92,
West Midlands (Regional) 1955-62

Club Colours (change): Red and white stripes/white/red (Blue and white stripes/blue/blue)

Ground Capacity: **Seats:** Yes **Covered:** Yes **Clubhouse:** Yes **Shop:** Yes

Directions

FROM M5 NORTH: Leave M5 motorway at Junction 7 and follow B4084 through Pershore onto Evesham. At traffic lights in Evesham with River Avon and Bridge on left, take right hand lane and turn right into Cheltenham Road signposted A46, M5 Southbound, Oxford and Cheltenham. Continue through two sets of traffic lights passing Tesco Garage and Ambulance Station on left before reaching roundabout. Ground situated on right at roundabout. **FROM M5 SOUTH:** Leave M5 motorway at Junction 9 signposted Tewkesbury and Evesham. Take 3rd exit signposted Ashchurch and Evesham. Follow A46 (Evesham) through Beckford before reaching roundabout on outskirts of Evesham. Ground situated on left at roundabout. **FROM M42:** Leave M42 motorway at Junction 3 (A435) signposted Redditch and Evesham. Continue on A435 (Evesham) through Studley then A46 until reaching roundabout on outskirts of Evesham. Take left hand exit onto Evesham by-pass (A46), signposted M5 South, Cheltenham and Oxford. Proceed on by-pass going over three r'abouts before reaching ground, which is situated on 4th r'about at end of by-pass.

Previous Grounds: The Crown Meadow > 1968, Common Reed 1968-2006. Ground shared with Worcester City 2006-12.

Record Attendance: 2,338 v West Bromwich Albion - Friendly 18/07/1992

Record Victory: 11-3 v West Heath United

Record Defeat: 1-8 v Ilkeston Town

Record Goalscorer: Sid Brain

Record Appearances: Rob Candy

Additional Records: Paid £1,500 to Hayes for Colin Day 1992
Received £5,000 from Cheltenham Town for Simon Brain

Senior Honours:

Midland Combination Premier Division 1991-92, Division 1 1965-66, 67-68, 68-69.
Southern League Division 1 Midlands 2007-08.
Worcestershire Senior Urn x2

10 YEAR RECORD

04-05	05-06	06-07	07-08	08-09	09-10	10-11	11-12	12 13	13-14
SthW 3	SthP 20	SthM 5	SthM 1	SthP 9	SthP 16	SthP 12	SthP 20	Sthsw 14	Sthsw 16

FLEET TOWN

Chairman: Steve Cantle
Secretary: John Goodyear (T) (E) fleettownfc@hotmail.com
Commercial Manager: (T)
Programme Editor: Martin Griffiths (T) mgriffiths@ntlworld.com
Ground Address: Calthorpe Park, Crookham Road, Fleet, Hants GU51 5FA
(T) 01252 623 804 **Manager:** Craig Davis

Club Factfile

Founded: 1890 **Nickname:** The Blues
Previous Names: Fleet FC 1890-1963
Previous Leagues: Hampshire 1961-77, Athenian, Combined Counties, Chiltonian, Wessex 1989-95, 2000-02, Southern 1995-2000, 02-04, 07-08, Isthmian 2004-07, 2008-11.
Club Colours (change): All blue (Yellow & black/black/yellow & black)

Ground Capacity: 2,000 **Seats:** 250 **Covered:** 250 **Clubhouse:** Yes **Shop:** Yes

Directions
Leave the M3 at Junction 4a, and follow the signs for Fleet. Head along the A3013, Fleet Road. Carry on along the street passing the main shopping street, through several pedestrian crossings for about 1 mile. When you get to the Oatsheaf Pub crossroads head straight across. Ground is 300yds down the hill on the right.

Previous Grounds: Watsons Meadow > 1923.

Record Attendance: 1,336 v AFC Wimbledon, Isthmian League 08/01/2005
Record Victory: 15-0 v Petersfield , Wessex League 26/12/1994
Record Defeat: 0-7 v Bashley, Southern League 12/04/2004
Record Goalscorer: Mark Frampton - 428
Record Appearances: Mark Frampton - 250
Additional Records: Paid £3,000 to Aldershot for Mark Russell

Senior Honours:
Wessex League 1994-95.
Aldershot Senior Cup 1993, 95, 96, 2000, 08, 09, 10. Basingstoke Senior Cup 2006, 08, 10. Hampshire Senior Cup 2009.

10 YEAR RECORD

04-05	05-06	06-07	07-08	08-09	09-10	10-11	11-12	12-13	13-14
Isth1 19	Isth1 14	Isth1S 5	Sthsw 2	Isth1S 3	Isth1S 6	Isth1S 13	SthC 21	SthC 18	Sthsw 21

LARKHALL ATHLETIC

Chairman: Paul Rankin
Secretary: Tracey Hill **(T)** 07825 774 683 **(E)** larkhallathletic@gmail.com
Commercial Manager: Tracey Hill **(T)** 07825 774 683
Programme Editor: **(T)**
Ground Address: Plain Ham, Charlcombe Lane, Larkhall, Bath BA1 8DJ
(T) 01225 334 952 **Manager:** Wayne Thorne

2014-15 Back row: Jas Maddison (therapist); Ross Lye; Jake Gardner; Luke Bryan; Chris Snoddy; Alex Shaftoe; Ollie Price; Tyler Sibbick; Brad Norris; Luke Scott.
Front row: Steve Bridges; Joe Tumelty; Rob Hobbs; Scott Lye (captain); Lee Collier (assistant manager); Wayne Thorne (manager); Matty Brown (coach); Matt Ralph; Simon Gilbert; Jamie Lyons; Charlie Maddison.

Club Factfile

Founded: 1914 **Nickname:** Larks
Previous Names: None
Previous Leagues: Somerset Senior. Western 1976-2014.

Club Colours (change): All royal blue (All yellow)

Ground Capacity: 1,000 **Seats:** Yes **Covered:** 50 **Clubhouse:** Yes **Shop:**

Directions
Take the A4 east from Bath City Centre towards Chippenham/M4. After approximately 1 mile after Cleveland Bridge junction (keep straight ahead) fork left into St Saviours Road (turning is signposted 'Larkhall Local Shops'). In Larkhall Square take first left exit (Salisbury Road) and turn right at t-junction. Follow the road round to the left and up the hill. You are now on Charlcombe Lane. The ground is on the right, on a parallel lane, as Charlcombe Lane narrows. Continue for approximately 100 yards, turn around in Woolley Lane on the right and go back down the hill, this time keeping to the top lane on the left hand side. Plain Ham is on the left just past the junction with Charlcombe Lane. - See more at: http://www.southern-football-league.co.uk/clubs/larkhall-athletic#sthash.wz786mka.dpuf

Previous Grounds: None

Record Attendance: 280 v Tunbridge Wells, FA Vase, Feb 2013
Record Victory: 8-0 v Oldland Abbotonians, 2007
Record Defeat: 1-6 v Exmouth Town, 2001
Record Goalscorer: Ben Highmore scored 52 goals during the 2008-09 season.
Record Appearances: Luke Scott - 600+ (as at July 2014)
Additional Records:

Senior Honours:
Somerset Senior Cup 1975-76, 2003-04. Somerset Senior Champions. Western Division One 1988-89, 93-94, 94-95, 08-09.
Western Premier Division 2010-11, 13-14. Les Phillips Cup 2013-14.

10 YEAR RECORD

04-05	05-06	06-07	07-08	08-09	09-10	10-11	11-12	12-13	13-14
West1 5	West1 7	West1 5	West1 3	West1 1	WestP 14	WestP 1	WestP 3	WestP 5	WestP 1

MANGOTSFIELD UNITED

Chairman: Mike Richardson
Secretary: David Jones (T) 07903 655 723 (E) davidj693@hotmail.co.uk
Commercial Manager: (T)
Programme Editor: Bob Smale (T) bob_smale@yahoo.co.uk
Ground Address: Cossham Street, Mangotsfield, Bristol BS16 9EN
(T) 0117 956 0119 **Manager:** Richard Thompson

2013-14 Squad - Back Row l-tr, John House (Kit), Jamie Reid, Charlie Hitchings, Shaun Lamb, Kevin Sawyer, Ryan Bath, Rhys Baird, Lee Marshall, Ryan Bennett, Ben Hunt, Kyle Thomas, Doug Pringle (physio)
Front Row l-r, Alex Kite, Ashley Williams, Marcus Duharty, Josh Egan, Richard Thompson (Manager), Neil Arndale (capt), Lee Barlass (Coach), Kyle Tooze, Tom Parrinello, Lewis Powell, Liam Monelle.

Club Factfile

Founded: 1950 **Nickname:** The Field
Previous Names: None
Previous Leagues: Bristol & District 1950-67. Avon Premier Combination 1967-72. Western 1972-2000.

Club Colours (change): Maroon, sky blue & white (yellow & black)

Ground Capacity: 2,500 **Seats:** 300 **Covered:** 800 **Clubhouse:** Yes **Shop:** Yes

Directions
Exit the M32 at Junction 1 and follow the A4174 towards Downend following signs to Mangotsfield.
Turn left into Cossham Street, the ground is approx 300 yards on the right.

Previous Grounds: None

Record Attendance: 1,253 v Bath City - F.A. Cup 1974
Record Victory: 17-0 v Hanham Sports (H) - 1953 Bristol & District League
Record Defeat: 3-13 v Bristol City United - Bristol & District League Division 1
Record Goalscorer: John Hill
Record Appearances: John Hill - 600+
Additional Records: In the last 10 matches of the 2003/04 season, the club went 738 minutes (just over 8 games) without scoring and then finished the campaign with 13 goals in the last two, which included a 9-0 away win.
Senior Honours:
Gloucestershire Senior Cup 1968-69, 75-76, 2002-03, 12-13. Somerset Premier Cup 1987-88. Western League 1990-91.
Southern League Division One West 2004-05. Gloucestershire F.A. Trophy x6.

10 YEAR RECORD

04-05	05-06	06-07	07-08	08-09	09-10	10-11	11-12	12-13	13-14
SthW 1	SthP 10	SthP 9	SthP 14	SthP 22	Sthsw 9	Sthsw 3	Sthsw 14	Sthsw 13	Sthsw 11

MERTHYR TOWN

Chairman: Meurig Price
Secretary: Jamie Mack **(T)** 07823 776 422 **(E)** merthysec@gmail.com
Commercial Manager: Brent Carter **(T)** 07983 615 504
Programme Editor: Malcolm Johnson **(T)** malc.johnson@talk21.com
Ground Address: Penydarren Park, Park Terrace, Merthyr Tydfil CF47 8RF
(T) 07980 363 675 **Manager:** Steve Jenkins

Club Factfile

Founded: 2010 **Nickname:** Martyrs
Previous Names: None
Previous Leagues: Western League 2010-12.

Club Colours (change): White & black (All yellow)

Ground Capacity: **Seats:** Yes **Covered:** Yes **Clubhouse:** Yes **Shop:**

Directions
Leave the M4 at Junction 32 and join the A470 to Merthyr Tydfil. After approx 22 miles at the fourth roundabout take 3rd exit. At next roundabout go straight on and go straight on through two sets of traffic lights. At third set turn left (ground signposted Merthyr Tydfil FC from here). After 50 yards take first right, then first right just after Catholic Church into Park Terrace. The ground is at the end of the road approx. 200 yards on.

Previous Grounds: None

Record Attendance:
Record Victory:
Record Defeat:
Record Goalscorer:
Record Appearances:
Additional Records:

Senior Honours:
Western League Division One 2010-11, Premier Division 2011-12.

10 YEAR RECORD

04-05	05-06	06-07	07-08	08-09	09-10	10-11	11-12	12-13	13-14
						West1 1	WestP 1	Sthsw 3	Sthsw 2

NORTH LEIGH

Chairman: Peter King
Secretary: Keith Huxley (T) 01993 851 497 (E) keith.huxley08@tiscali.co.uk
Commercial Manager: (T)
Programme Editor: Mike Burnell (T) 01993 845 507
Ground Address: Eynsham Hall Park, North Leigh, Witney, Oxon OX29 6SL
(T) 07583 399 577 **Manager:** Mark Gee

Club Factfile

Founded: 1908 **Nickname:** The Millers
Previous Names: None
Previous Leagues: Witney & District, Hellenic 1990-2008

Club Colours (change): Yellow/black/yellow (Dark blue with red trim)

Ground Capacity: 2,000 **Seats:** 100 **Covered:** 200 **Clubhouse:** Yes **Shop:** No

Directions
Ground is situated off A4095 Witney to Woodstock road, three miles east of Witney.
Entrance 300 yards east of main park entrance.

Previous Grounds: None

Record Attendance: 426 v Newport County - FA Cup 3rd Qualifying Round 16/10/2004
Record Victory: Not known
Record Defeat: Not known
Record Goalscorer: P Coles
Record Appearances: P King
Additional Records:

Senior Honours:
Hellenic Premier Division 2001-02, 02-03, 07-08. Oxon Charity Cup x2.
Oxfordshire Senior Cup 2011-12.

10 YEAR RECORD

04-05	05-06	06-07	07-08	08-09	09-10	10-11	11-12	12-13	13-14
Hel P 7	Hel P 4	Hel P 2	Hel P 1	Sthsw 8	Sthsw 10	Sthsw 6	Sthsw 6	Sthsw 9	Sthsw 7

Southern League Action

Cinderford's Clayton Green, takes the ball past this Godalming player in their hard fought 1-0 win.

Photo: Jonathan Holloway.

SHOLING

Chairman: David Daiper

Secretary: Greg Dickson **(T)** 07948 832 944 **(E)** secretary.sholingfc@gmail.com

Commercial Manager: Gary Cassell **(T)**

Programme Editor: Chris Lewis **(T)** chrislewis@tiscali.co.uk

Ground Address: VT Group Sportsground, Portsmouth Road, Sholing, SO19 9PW

(T) 02380 403 829 **Manager:** Dave Fear & Mick Marsh

2013-14 Squad - Back Row L - R Mick Marsh (Coach), Marc Diaper, Pete Castle, Byron Mason, Lewis Fennemore, Matt Renouf, Dan Miller, James Thomson, Matt Brown, Lee Webber, James Taylor, Lee Bright, Adam Camfield, Lee Wort, Mick Brown (Asst Manager), Kevin Harnett (Director of Football).
Front Row L - R Danny Cox, Tyronne Bowers, Mike Carter, Barry Mason, Alex Sawyer, Kevin Brewster, Marvin McLean, Ashley Jarvis.

Club Factfile

Founded: 1916 **Nickname:** The Boatmen

Previous Names: Woolston Works, Thornycrofts (Woolston) 1918-52, Vospers 1960-2003, Vosper Thorneycroft FC/VTFC 2003-10

Previous Leagues: Hampshire 1991-2004, Wessex 2004-09. Southern 2009-13.

Club Colours (change): Red & white/black/red & white (Yellow & blue/yellow/yellow)

Ground Capacity: **Seats:** Yes **Covered:** Yes **Clubhouse:** Yes **Shop:**

Directions
Leave the M27 at J8 and follow the signs towards Hamble. As you drive up dual carriageway (remain in the L/H lane), you come to Windover roundabout. Take the second exit towards Hamble. Take the R/H lane and carry on straight across the small roundabout. After 200 yards bear right across a second small roundabout (2nd exit). After about 100 yards turn right into Portsmouth Road. Follow straight on for about half mile. VT ground is on right opposite a lorry entrance.

Previous Grounds:

Record Attendance: **Att:** 150
Record Victory: Not known
Record Defeat: Not known
Record Goalscorer: George Diaper - 100+
Record Appearances: Not known
Additional Records:

Senior Honours:
Hampshire Premier Division 2000-01, 03-04. FA Vase 2013-14.
Wessex Premier 2013-14.

10 YEAR RECORD

04-05	05-06	06-07	07-08	08-09	09-10	10-11	11-12	12-13	13-14
Wex1 12	Wex1 13	WexP 3	WexP 2	WexP 2	Sthsw 4	Sthsw 2	Sthsw 4	Sthsw 7	WexP 1

SHORTWOOD UNITED

Chairman: Peter Webb

Secretary: Mark Webb (T) 07792 323784 (E) squish.shortwoodfc@live.co.uk

Commercial Manager: Jim Cunneen (T) 07714 661 797

Programme Editor: Paul Benneyworth (T) prbrab@btinternet.com

Ground Address: Meadowbank, Shortwood, Nailsworth GL6 0SJ

(T) 01453 833 936 **Manager:** John Evans

2013-14 Squad

Club Factfile

Founded: 1900 **Nickname:** The Wood

Previous Names: None.

Previous Leagues: Gloucestershire County. Hellenic >2012.

Club Colours (change): Red & white/black/black (All royal blue)

Ground Capacity: 2,000 **Seats:** 50 **Covered:** 150 **Clubhouse:** Yes **Shop:** No

Directions

When entering Nailsworth from Stroud turn right at mini roundabout, when coming from Cirencester go straight over roundabout, and when from Bath turn left at mini roundabout.

Proceed up Spring Hill 30 yards turn left at Raffles Wine Warehouse, straight through town turn left at Brittannia Pub carry on for 1 mile until you come to Shortwood village you will see sign post on fork in the road keep to the left follow on for quarter of a mile ground opposite church.

Previous Grounds: Played at Nailsworth Playing Field, Table Land and Wallow Green before moving to Meadowbank in 1972.

Record Attendance: Att: 1,000 v Forest Green Rovers, FA Vase 5th Rnd 1982.

Record Victory:

Record Defeat:

Record Goalscorer: Peter Grant.

Record Appearances: Peter Grant.

Additional Records: Gloucestershire Lge Champions 1981-82.

Senior Honours:

Hellenic League Champions 1984-85, 91-92.

Gloucestershire Senior Cup (x 2).

10 YEAR RECORD

04-05	05-06	06-07	07-08	08-09	09-10	10-11	11-12	12-13	13-14
Hel P 15	Hel P 15	Hel P 8	Hel P 5	Hel P 2	Hel P 2	Hel P 6	Hel P 2	Sthsw 8	Sthsw 6

STRATFORD TOWN

Chairman: Craig Hughes
Secretary: Brian Rose (T) 07833 776 834 (E) brian_rose@nfumutual.co.uk
Commercial Manager: Melanie Tweedle (T) 07968 600 300
Programme Editor: Mark Bickley (T) info@stratfordtownfc.org
Ground Address: The DCS Stadium, Knights Lane, Tiddington, Stratford Upon Avon CV37 7BZ
(T) 01789 269 336 **Manager:** Carl Adams

Club Factfile

Founded: 1943 **Nickname:** The Town
Previous Names: Straford Rangers 1943-49. Stratford Town Amateurs 1964-70.
Previous Leagues: Worcestershire/Midland Comb. Birmingham & Dist. W.Mid (Reg). Hellenic. Midland Alliance > 2013.

Club Colours (change): All royal blue. (Tangerine/black/tangerine)

Ground Capacity: **Seats:** Yes **Covered:** Yes **Clubhouse:** Yes **Shop:** Yes

Directions
From Town Centre follow signs for Banbury (A422) and Oxford (A3400). Cross Clopton Bridge and turn immediately left onto B4086 towards Wellesbourne. After approx 1 mile you enter the village of Tiddington. Turn 1st right into Knights Lane. Ground is approx 800 yards on right (100 yards after school).

Previous Grounds: A number of pitches before Alcester Road by the late 1940s.

Record Attendance: **Att:** 1,078 v Aston Villa, Birmingham Senior Cup, Oct. 1996.
Record Victory: Not known
Record Defeat: Not known
Record Goalscorer: Not known
Record Appearances: Not known
Additional Records:

Senior Honours:
Worcestershire/Midland Combination 1956-57, 86-87.
Birmingham Senior Cup 1962-63. Midland Alliance 2012-13, League Cup 2002-03, 03-04, 10-11.

10 YEAR RECORD

04-05	05-06	06-07	07-08	08-09	09-10	10-11	11-12	12-13	13-14
MidAl 11	MidAl 15	MidAl 4	MidAl 7	MidAl 6	MidAl 3	MidAl 5	MidAl 8	MidAl 1	Sthsw 10

SWINDON SUPERMARINE

Chairman: Jez Webb
Secretary: Judi Moore **(T)** 07785 970 954 **(E)** judimoore6@aol.com
Commercial Manager: **(T)**
Programme Editor: Keith Yeomans **(T)** supermarinefc@aol.com
Ground Address: The Webbs Stadium, South Marston, Swindon SN3 4BZ
(T) 01793 828 778 **Manager:** Dave Webb

Club Factfile

Founded: 1992 **Nickname:** Marine
Previous Names: Club formed after the amalgamation of Swindon Athletic and Supermarine
Previous Leagues: Wiltshire, Hellenic1992-2001.

Club Colours (change): All blue (All red)

Ground Capacity: 3,000 **Seats:** 300 **Covered:** 300 **Clubhouse:** Yes **Shop:** Yes

Directions

From M5 Junction 11a, take the A417 to Cirencester, then A419 Swindon. At the A361 junction by Honda Factory take road to Highworth. After one mile Club is on 4th roundabout.

From M4 Junction 15, take A419 towards Swindon Cirencester, take A361, then as above .

From A420 Swindon take A419 to Cirencester, near Honda factory take A361, then as above.

Previous Grounds: Supermarine: Vickers Airfield > Mid 1960s

Record Attendance: 1,550 v Aston Villa
Record Victory: Not known
Record Defeat: Not known
Record Goalscorer: Damon York - 136 (1990-98)
Record Appearances: Damon York - 314 (1990-98)
Additional Records: Paid £1,000 to Hungerford Town for Lee Hartson

Senior Honours:
Hellenic League Premier Division 1997-98, 2000-01, Challenge Cup 97-97, 99-2000.

10 YEAR RECORD

04-05	05-06	06-07	07-08	08-09	09-10	10-11	11-12	12-13	13-14
SthW 19	SthW 5	Sthsw 4	SthP 12	SthP 13	SthP 14	SthP 10	SthP 21	Sthsw 4	Sthsw 5

TAUNTON TOWN

Chairman: Kevin Sturmey
Secretary: Andy Power (T) 07769 695 192 (E) admin@tauntontown.com
Commercial Manager: Kevin Sturmey (T) 07778 434 055
Programme Editor: Andy Power (T) 07769 695 192
Ground Address: Wordsworth Drive, Taunton, Somerset TA1 2HG
(T) 01823 254 909 / 278 191 **Manager:** Leigh Robinson

Club Factfile

Founded: 1947 **Nickname:** The Peacocks
Previous Names: None
Previous Leagues: Western 1954-77, 83-2002, Southern 1977-83

Club Colours (change): Claret & sky blue (yellow & blue)

Ground Capacity: 2,500 **Seats:** 300 **Covered:** 1,000 **Clubhouse:** Yes **Shop:** Yes

Directions
From M5 Junction 25 follow signs to Town Centre.
Proceed along Toneway then bear left at roundabout into Chritchard Way.
At traffic lights proceed into Wordsworth Drive and the ground is on the left.

Previous Grounds: None

Record Attendance: 3,284 v Tiverton Town - FA Vase Semi-final 1999
Record Victory: 12-0 v Dawlish Town (A) - FA Cup Preliminary Round 28/08/1993
Record Defeat: 0-8 v Cheltenham Town (A) - FA Cup 2nd Qualifying Round 28/09/1991
Record Goalscorer: Tony Payne
Record Appearances: Tony Payne
Additional Records: Reg Oram scored 67 in one season

Senior Honours:
Western League 1968-69, 89-90, 95-96, 98-99, 99-2000, 2000-01. FA Vase 2000-01.
Somerset Premier Cup 2002-03, 05-06.

10 YEAR RECORD

04-05	05-06	06-07	07-08	08-09	09-10	10-11	11-12	12-13	13-14
SthW 17	SthW 18	Sthsw 5	Sthsw 18	Sthsw 20	Sthsw 19	Sthsw 9	Sthsw 17	Sthsw 18	Sthsw 8

TIVERTON TOWN

Chairman: Dave Wright
Secretary: Ramsey Findlay (T) 07761 261 990 (E) ramsayfindlay@hotmail.co.uk
Commercial Manager: John Fournier (T) 07980 543 634
Programme Editor: John Fournier (T) tivertontown@btinternet.com
Ground Address: Ladysmead, Bolham Road, Tiverton, Devon EX16 6SG
(T) 01884 252 397 **Manager:** Martyn Rogers

Owen Howe (right) in action for Tivvy
during their 2014-15 pre-season friendly against Port Vale.

Club Factfile

Founded: 1913 **Nickname:** Tivvy
Previous Names: None
Previous Leagues: Devon and Exeter, Western

Club Colours (change): Black & gold (All white)

Ground Capacity: 3,500 **Seats:** 520 **Covered:** 2,300 **Clubhouse:** Yes **Shop:** Yes

Directions
M5 Junction 27, follow A361 to Tiverton's second exit at roundabout, turning left.
Continue for about 400 yards, crossing roundabout until reaching mini-roundabout.
Carry on straight across. Ground is 200 yards on right.

Previous Grounds: None

Record Attendance: 3,000 v Leyton Orient - FA Cup 1st Round Proper 1994-95
Record Victory: 10-0 v Exmouth Town, Devon St Lukes Cup 16/02/1994
Record Defeat: 2-6 v Stafford Rangers (A) - Southern League 2001-02 & Heavitree United, Les Philips Cup 29/11/1997
Record Goalscorer: Phil Everett
Record Appearances: Not known
Additional Records:

Senior Honours:
FA Vase 1997-98, 98-99. Western League x5. Southern League Cup 2006-07.
Devon Senior Cup 1955-56, 65-66. East Devon Senior Cup x7.

10 YEAR RECORD

04-05	05-06	06-07	07-08	08-09	09-10	10-11	11-12	12-13	13-14
SthP 8	SthP 12	SthP 15	SthP 17	SthP 12	SthP 19	SthP 20	Sthsw 9	Sthsw 16	Sthsw 3

WANTAGE TOWN

Chairman: Tony Woodward

Secretary: John Culley **(T)** 07921 243 263 **(E)** john_clly@yahoo.co.uk

Commercial Manager: **(T)**

Programme Editor: Ros Shepperd **(T)** ross.sheppard@hotmail.co.uk

Ground Address: Alfredian Park, Manor Road, Wantage OX12 8DW

(T) 01235 764 781 **Manager:** Gary Ackling

Celebrating their Hellenic League Premier Division title.

Club Factfile

Founded: 1892 **Nickname:** Alfredians

Previous Names: None.

Previous Leagues: Swindon & District. North Berkshire. Reading & District. Hellenic > 2014.

Club Colours (change): Green & white

Ground Capacity: 1,500 **Seats:** 50 **Covered:** 300 **Clubhouse:** Yes **Shop:** No

Directions Proceed to Market Square. Take road at southeast corner (Newbury Street signposted to Hungerford). Continue for approximately a quarter of a mile take right turning into the ground. Clearly marked 'Wantage Town FC'.

Previous Grounds:

Record Attendance: Att. 550 v Oxford United, July 2003.

Record Victory:

Record Defeat:

Record Goalscorer:

Record Appearances:

Additional Records:

Senior Honours:

Hellenic Division 1 East 1980-81, 03-04, Premier Division 2010-11, 13-14.

Oxon Senior Cup 1982-83.

10 YEAR RECORD

04-05	05-06	06-07	07-08	08-09	09-10	10-11	11-12	12-13	13-14
Hel P 10	Hel P 9	Hel P 11	Hel P 12	Hel P 11	Hel P 5	Hel P 1	Hel P 12	Hel P 2	Hel P 1

WIMBORNE TOWN

Chairman: Paul Miller
Secretary: Peter Barham (T) 07956 833 316 (E) wimbornefc@aol.com
Commercial Manager: (T)
Programme Editor: Graham Dunn (T) magpies.graham@gmail.com
Ground Address: The Cuthbury, Cowgrove Road, Wimborne, Dorset, BH21 4EL
(T) 01202 884 821 **Manager:** Steve Cuss

Club Factfile

Founded: 1878 **Nickname:** Magpies
Previous Names: None
Previous Leagues: Dorset, Dorset Combination, Western 1981-86, Wessex 1986-2010

Club Colours (change): Black and white stripes/black/black (Sky blue & navy blue)

Ground Capacity: 3,250 **Seats:** 275 **Covered:** 425 **Clubhouse:** Yes **Shop:** Yes

Directions
On the Wimborne To Blandford Road (B3082), turn left into Cowgrove Road just past Victoria Hospital.
Postcode for Sat nav is BH21 4EL.

Previous Grounds: None

Record Attendance: 3,250 v Bamber Bridge
Record Victory: Not known
Record Defeat: Not known
Record Goalscorer: Jason Lovell
Record Appearances: James Sturgess
Additional Records:

Senior Honours:
FA Vase 1991-92. Wessex League 1991-92, 93-94, 99-2000.
Dorset Senior Amateur Cup 1936-37, 63-64.

10 YEAR RECORD

04-05	05-06	06-07	07-08	08-09	09-10	10-11	11-12	12-13	13-14
Wex1 7	Wex1 12	WexP 6	WexP 3	WexP 4	WexP 2	Sthsw 19	Sthsw 19	Sthsw 12	Sthsw 13

Southern League Action

Kieron Thomas is brought down in the penalty area by this Godalming defender but the referee only awarded a free-kick in Cinderford's favour at their Causeway Ground..

Photo: Jonathan Holloway.

YATE TOWN

Chairman: Colin Pick

Secretary: Terry Tansley **(T)** 07875 272 126 **(E)** admin@yatetownfc.com

Commercial Manager: **(T)**

Programme Editor: Terry Tansley **(T)** admin@yatetownfc.com

Ground Address: Lodge Road, Yate, Bristol BS37 7LE

(T) 01454 228 103 **Manager:** Robert Cousins

2014-15 Squad - Back Row. Karl Trotter. Daniel Lane. Jacob Staines. Jacob Cox. Thomas Seery. Martin Horsell. Joe Chandler. Jordan Rogers. Josh Dempsey. Mitch Harrison. Martin Lenihan. Ricky Hulbert. Lewis Haldane. Steve Carter. Front Row. Lewis Shipp. Bradley Abraham. Nuno Felix. Michael Meaker. Michael Bryant. Rob Cousins. Ross Staley. Jake Jackson. Shaun Wimble.

Club Factfile

Founded: 1906 **Nickname:** The Bluebells

Previous Names: Yate Rovers 1906-1930s. Yate YMCA 1933-58.

Previous Leagues: Bristol Premier Combination > 1968, Gloucestershire County 1968-83, Hellenic 1983-89, 2000-03, Southern 1989-2000

Club Colours (change): White/blue navy/white (All yellow)

Ground Capacity: 2,000 **Seats:** 236 **Covered:** 400 **Clubhouse:** Yes **Shop:** Yes

Directions

From East: leave M4 J18, enter Yate on A432 via Chipping Sodbury bypass. Turn right at first small roundabout (Link Road), straight over next roundabout into Goose Green Way, over more roundabouts and 2 major sets of traffic lights. Turn right at third set of lights (by The Fox), then immediately left into Lodge Road. Ground 200m on right. From North: M5 (South) exit J14, B4509/B4060 into Chipping Sodbury. Turn right into Chipping Sodbury High Street, down Bowling Hill and right at first roundabout into Goose Green Way – then as above. From South: Leave M5 at J15, then join M5. Leave M4 at J19, take second exit onto M32. Leave M32 at J1, at roundabout take first exit onto A4174. Continue on A4174 over traffic lights, then at roundabout take first exit onto A432. Enter Yate on A432, at traffic lights turn left into Stover Road (B4059), then at roundabout take second exit – still on B4059. Left at traffic lights (Fox PH) and immediately left into Lodge Road.

Previous Grounds: Yate Aerodrome 1954-60. Sunnyside Lane 1960-84.

Record Attendance: 2,000 v Bristol Rovers v Bristol Rovers Past XI - Vaughan Jones testimonial 1990

Record Victory: 13-3 v Clevedon - Bristol Premier Combination 1967-68

Record Defeat: Not known

Record Goalscorer: Kevin Thaws

Record Appearances: Gary Hewlett

Additional Records: Paid £2,000 to Chippenham Town for Matt Rawlings 2003
Received £15,000 from Bristol Rovers for Mike Davis

Senior Honours:

Hellenic League 1987-88, 88-89. Gloucestershire Senior Cup 2004-05, 05-06.

10 YEAR RECORD

04-05	05-06	06-07	07-08	08-09	09-10	10-11	11-12	12-13	13-14
SthW 2	SthP 6	SthP 14	SthP 10	SthP 21	Sthsw 13	Sthsw 14	Sthsw 13	Sthsw 6	Sthsw 9

Ryman
football league

PREMIER DIVISION 2013-14

		P	W	D	L	F	A	GD	Pts
1	(P) Wealdstone	46	28	12	6	99	43	56	96
2	Kingstonian	46	25	10	11	80	44	36	85
3	Bognor Regis Town	46	26	7	13	95	65	30	85
4	(P) Lowestoft Town	46	24	12	10	76	40	36	84
5	AFC Hornchurch	46	24	11	11	83	53	30	83
6	Dulwich Hamlet	46	25	7	14	96	65	31	82
7	Maidstone United	46	23	12	11	92	57	35	81
8	Hendon	46	21	7	18	84	69	15	70
9	Leiston	46	19	10	17	73	71	2	67
10	Billericay Town	46	19	9	18	66	64	2	66
11	Margate	46	18	10	18	70	67	3	64
12	Hampton & Richmond Borough	46	18	10	18	72	70	2	64
13	Canvey Island	46	17	11	18	65	65	0	62
14	Grays Athletic	46	17	10	19	74	82	-8	61
15	Bury Town	46	17	9	20	60	65	-5	60
16	Lewes	46	14	17	15	67	67	0	59
17	Metropolitan Police	46	15	13	18	58	59	-1	58
18	Harrow Borough	46	15	13	18	66	72	-6	58
19	Enfield Town	46	13	12	21	64	90	-26	51
20	East Thurrock United	46	13	10	23	66	84	-18	49
21	Wingate & Finchley	46	14	7	25	57	84	-27	49
22	(R) Thamesmead Town	46	12	10	24	61	90	-29	46
23	(R) Carshalton Athletic	46	8	6	32	40	101	-61	30
24	(R) Cray Wanderers	46	7	5	34	40	137	-97	26

PLAY-OFFS

Semi-Finals: Kingstonian 0-1 AFC Hornchurch I Bognor Regis Town 1-2 Lowestoft Town

Final: Lowestoft Town 3-0 AFC Hornchurch

		1	2	3	4	5	6	7	8	9	10	11	12	13	14	15	16	17	18	19	20	21	22	23	24
1	AFC Hornchurch	1-2	1-0	0-0	1-1	2-1	1-2	1-1	3-0	3-0	1-2	2-3	2-4	1-2	0-0	4-2	0-1	2-1	1-0	3-2	1-0	2-0	1-1	3-0	
2	Billericay Town	2-2		1-2	0-0	1-4	3-1	1-2	2-0	0-1	0-2	4-0	1-2	2-1	0-1	3-2	4-1	0-1	0-1	3-3	0-2	1-2	3-2	4-2	1-0
3	Bognor Regis	1-1	1-0		5-2	5-0	2-4	4-0	4-2	3-1	5-1	0-3	4-0	3-2	3-0	0-0	0-0	3-1	4-1	1-2	5-3	2-0	2-1	1-3	1-0
4	Bury Town	3-2	0-1	2-0		0-1	0-1	1-0	0-4	0-0	3-3	2-1	0-0	3-2	0-4	0-3	0-2	2-1	1-2	1-2	1-1	2-1	0-0	0-1	2-0
5	Canvey Island	1-1	1-2	1-3	0-2		3-2	4-0	2-1	2-1	2-1	1-0	2-1	1-3	0-0	0-1	2-3	3-3	0-0	0-1	2-0	1-1	2-2	3-2	2-0
6	Carshalton Athletic	0-1	1-0	1-3	1-3	1-1		0-2	0-4	1-2	1-4	1-1	2-0	1-2	0-2	1-3	0-1	1-0	0-1	1-2	0-6	1-1	0-4	2-4	0-4
7	Cray Wanderers	1-6	0-1	1-2	1-3	2-1	0-0		0-6	1-3	1-2	3-2	1-1	0-1	0-6	0-4	2-2	1-5	0-4	0-5	1-4	4-1	3-4	0-3	2-2
8	Dulwich Hamlet	2-3	2-1	0-2	1-0	1-0	3-1	4-0		3-0	2-2	3-2	2-2	3-2	2-0	1-1	2-3	4-2	2-0	2-0	2-0	1-2	2-0	1-4	4-2
9	East Thurrock Utd	1-2	2-2	4-2	2-2	2-0	2-3	3-0	1-4		1-1	3-0	0-1	1-3	6-1	2-0	1-2	0-2	0-1	3-1	1-4	1-1	3-1	0-3	0-1
10	Enfield Town	0-2	1-2	2-1	1-0	3-3	2-2	1-0	3-4	3-5		1-1	3-0	1-0	3-2	0-1	1-3	2-1	2-2	1-1	1-1	2-1	3-1	2-4	0-3
11	Grays Athletic	1-5	2-2	3-4	4-3	1-4	1-4	3-0	0-0	2-0	2-0		1-3	2-0	1-3	0-0	3-2	4-2	1-1	0-1	3-0	0-0	1-4	1-1	2-0
12	Hampton & Richmond	1-1	0-1	4-3	3-0	0-2	4-0	4-0	0-1	1-0	2-0	0-2		1-1	5-2	4-1	0-2	1-1	1-2	1-3	1-2	1-3	0-1	0-3	2-0
13	Harrow Borough	1-2	1-1	0-0	0-2	2-0	2-1	4-2	3-1	2-2	1-1	2-2	3-2		1-3	0-0	1-1	2-0	1-1	4-1	0-0	1-2	1-2	0-2	0-2
14	Hendon	0-1	1-2	1-0	1-0	4-2	1-0	2-0	1-2	2-2	0-3	2-3	3-4	1-2		1-2	3-1	1-1	0-1	3-5	2-3	4-1	5-2	0-0	1-1
15	Kingstonian	1-1	0-2	1-2	2-1	3-1	5-1	4-0	2-1	3-0	3-0	4-1	1-0	2-2	1-4		2-0	4-1	1-0	0-3	2-0	1-2	4-1	0-1	1-0
16	Leiston	2-3	2-2	5-2	0-4	0-2	0-1	4-1	2-1	3-1	6-1	4-1	0-0	0-1	1-0	0-0		2-2	0-1	1-0	1-0	1-1	3-0	0-2	0-2
17	Lewes	1-5	1-1	1-1	1-4	1-0	2-0	4-1	2-0	2-2	3-1	0-1	1-1	1-1	0-2	1-1	5-1		0-2	1-0	3-0	2-2	1-1	0-3	3-0
18	Lowestoft Town	3-0	1-0	2-0	1-3	2-1	5-0	0-2	2-0	3-0	2-0	2-2	0-3	3-0	2-3	2-0	3-0	1-1		2-1	3-0	1-1	5-0	1-1	7-0
19	Maidstone United	1-1	2-1	1-2	1-1	1-1	1-0	3-0	4-3	1-1	3-0	2-1	7-2	4-4	1-1	2-0	2-2	0-0	2-0		4-0	1-1	4-0	1-1	5-0
20	Margate	1-2	1-2	1-1	1-2	1-1	1-0	5-0	2-4	1-1	1-0	2-5	2-2	3-1	2-3	1-2	1-1	1-1	3-0	1-0		1-0	2-1	0-1	3-2
21	Metropolitan Police	2-1	0-2	0-2	0-3	0-1	3-0	7-1	0-0	1-2	3-1	1-2	1-3	2-0	0-1	0-2	2-1	0-0	0-0	1-2	0-2		3-1	2-1	3-1
22	Thamesmead Town	1-2	3-3	1-2	4-2	2-0	1-1	2-1	1-3	1-0	1-1	1-0	1-1	0-1	0-4	2-2	2-4	2-0	2-2	4-1	0-2	0-0		0-2	1-2
23	Wealdstone	2-0	2-0	2-2	3-0	2-0	3-1	7-1	2-2	5-0	4-1	3-1	1-3	3-0	1-1	0-4	3-1	2-2	0-0	2-1	0-1	1-1	2-0		2-2
24	Winggate & Finchley	0-3	5-0	3-0	1-0	0-4	4-0	1-1	2-3	4-3	1-1	1-3	1-2	3-1	1-0	0-4	0-1	1-3	0-0	2-4	0-0	0-3	3-1	0-2	

DIVISION ONE NORTH 2013-14

		P	W	D	L	F	A	GD	Pts
1	(P) VCD Athletic	46	32	3	11	116	54	62	99
2	(P) Witham Town	46	30	8	8	109	54	55	98
3	Heybridge Swifts	46	28	9	9	108	59	49	93
4	Harlow Town	46	27	10	9	105	59	46	91
5	Needham Market	46	25	12	9	85	44	41	87
6	Thurrock	46	26	9	11	99	60	39	87
7	Dereham Town	46	22	11	13	98	65	33	77
8	Soham Town Rangers	46	24	4	18	92	75	17	76
9	Maldon & Tiptree	46	21	13	12	82	68	14	76
10	AFC Sudbury	46	21	13	12	76	63	13	76
11	Romford	46	21	5	20	76	69	7	68
12	Chatham Town	46	20	8	18	74	76	-2	68
13	Aveley	46	20	5	21	81	81	0	65
14	Redbridge	46	16	11	19	78	84	-6	59
15	Cheshunt	46	12	17	17	74	75	-1	53
16	Tilbury	46	14	11	21	56	74	-18	53
17	Burnham Ramblers	46	14	10	22	69	100	-31	52
18	Waltham Abbey	46	14	8	24	71	90	-19	50
19	Brentwood Town	46	11	13	22	71	92	-21	46
20	Barkingside	46	12	10	24	76	120	-44	46
21	Ware	46	12	9	25	73	93	-20	45
22	Wroxham	46	10	6	30	77	123	-46	36
23	(R) Waltham Forest	46	6	7	33	43	118	-75	25
24	(R) Erith & Belvedere	46	6	4	36	44	137	-93	22

PLAY-OFFS

Semi-Finals: Witham Town 1-0 Needham Market I Heybridge Swifts 0-3 Harlow Town

Final: Witham Town 3-0 Harlow Town

	1	2	3	4	5	6	7	8	9	10	11	12	13	14	15	16	17	18	19	20	21	22	23	24
1 AFC Sudbury		2-0	4-2	1-0	3-0	0-2	2-2	2-0	1-1	0-0	1-5	1-1	0-0	3-1	1-3	1-2	1-1	1-0	1-1	2-1	3-0	2-1	1-2	1-0
2 Aveley	2-1		5-0	2-1	3-0	3-1	3-3	1-3	3-1	0-1	1-2	2-3	1-1	1-3	1-0	2-1	2-1	2-0	0-2	4-2	1-2	1-1	0-3	6-1
3 Barkingside	1-4	2-0		3-3	1-3	2-2	2-1	1-1	3-0	3-4	3-2	2-4	1-1	3-5	0-2	0-2	0-3	3-0	0-5	4-5	4-3	1-1	0-6	1-1
4 Brentwood Town	1-2	1-3	2-1		0-1	1-3	3-1	2-4	2-0	0-2	0-5	2-0	1-3	2-2	2-1	3-2	2-2	1-2	0-1	2-3	4-0	2-1	1-2	0-0
5 Burnham Ramblers	1-4	1-4	5-0	3-3		1-2	1-4	1-1	0-1	2-5	1-1	1-1	1-2	2-2	0-2	2-2	3-2	3-1	1-6	0-2	1-0	2-1	1-2	2-1
6 Chatham Town	0-0	1-2	2-3	2-2	2-0		2-2	3-2	1-1	0-2	1-4	1-0	0-0	4-1	0-2	2-0	1-2	3-1	1-2	1-0	2-1	3-0	2-4	1-1
7 Cheshunt	2-2	1-1	2-0	0-0	2-3	3-1		4-1	3-2	1-1	2-2	1-4	0-3	3-2	4-0	0-1	1-2	0-0	0-2	0-1	1-1	2-2	1-1	1-3
8 Dereham Town	2-0	5-1	4-2	2-2	0-0	3-0	0-0		4-1	2-1	1-3	6-1	0-1	0-2	4-2	3-1	0-2	2-2	1-2	1-0	10-1	4-1	1-4	4-0
9 Erith & Belvedere	0-4	1-2	0-6	2-4	1-3	1-4	0-2	0-3		0-2	3-2	2-4	0-3	3-1	1-1	0-3	1-0	0-2	0-1	3-2	1-2	2-6	1-4	0-0
10 Harllow Town	1-1	2-0	8-3	5-1	3-1	2-0	2-2	2-2	3-2		3-4	2-2	2-1	2-2	1-0	1-2	1-1	3-0	3-2	3-4	4-0	1-0	2-0	3-0
11 Heybridge Swifts	2-0	3-1	1-0	3-1	2-0	0-2	1-1	2-2	7-0	2-1		0-0	1-1	6-1	3-1	1-3	0-5	3-2	3-0	5-2	0-2	3-1	2-1	7-2
12 Maldon & Tiptree	3-2	4-1	2-2	3-1	4-4	2-3	2-0	2-0	4-1	2-0	2-1		4-2	2-1	0-1	1-3	1-1	3-1	1-2	1-0	2-1	2-1	1-1	4-1
13 Needham Market	2-0	3-1	2-2	0-0	1-2	7-1	1-2	3-2	2-1	1-1	2-1	1-1		1-0	3-0	1-0	2-3	3-2	0-0	4-0	1-0	1-0	1-0	2-2
14 Redbridge	2-3	1-2	4-1	1-1	2-2	0-1	1-1	0-1	1-0	2-4	1-1	0-0	2-1		5-2	3-0	1-1	1-1	0-1	3-2	2-1	3-2	1-1	4-0
15 Romford	1-2	2-0	4-1	2-3	2-0	2-2	2-6	1-2	4-1	0-1	1-3	0-0	3-2	5-0		1-0	3-1	1-1	2-0	0-2	4-0	2-1	2-3	3-0
16 Sohaam Town R.	2-2	4-3	2-2	2-0	3-2	5-1	4-2	3-1	2-0	1-1	1-2	4-2	2-1	4-1	0-2		2-3	3-0	1-3	4-1	4-1	0-2	5-2	2-6
17 Thurrock	1-3	2-1	3-0	4-1	6-0	1-0	1-0	1-3	10-1	5-1	3-2	1-1	1-0	2-1	1-2	2-0		1-2	2-6	2-0	3-2	2-2	3-0	2-1
18 Tilbury	1-1	2-1	1-2	3-1	4-2	0-2	2-1	0-0	2-0	0-2	0-2	0-1	0-2	2-0	2-1	2-0	1-1		2-1	2-3	1-1	2-1	0-3	4-1
19 VCD Athletic	1-2	3-1	4-1	3-1	2-0	3-2	2-2	1-3	6-2	1-2	1-2	3-2	1-2	3-1	6-0	0-2	2-0	3-2		2-0	4-1	3-2	3-1	8-0
20 Waltham Abbey	0-2	2-2	0-2	0-0	0-3	2-1	3-1	1-1	5-0	1-3	0-1	0-0	0-3	1-4	0-1	2-0	2-1	2-2	1-3		2-2	1-2	4-1	4-0
21 Waltham Forest	3-3	1-2	0-1	3-3	2-3	1-3	0-4	0-4	0-2	1-0	0-2	0-2	0-4	0-1	0-4	1-3	1-2	0-0	0-5	2-2		1-2	1-5	3-2
22 Ware	3-0	0-2	1-3	5-5	3-3	0-1	2-0	4-0	3-2	0-5	1-1	2-1	1-3	3-4	1-0	3-5	0-1	0-0	0-2	3-3	1-0		0-3	2-1
23 Witham	5-1	2-1	4-0	1-0	4-0	2-1	3-1	1-1	3-2	2-5	1-1	3-0	0-0	2-0	0-0	1-0	2-2	3-0	4-1	3-0	4-1	4-2		4-1
24 Wroxham	2-3	3-4	2-2	1-4	1-2	3-4	1-2	1-2	7-1	3-2	1-2	4-0	2-5	1-3	3-2	3-0	2-3	4-2	0-3	4-3	0-1	4-3	1-2	

DIVISION ONE SOUTH 2013-14

		P	W	D	L	F	A	GD	Pts
1	(P) Peacehaven & Telscombe	46	33	8	5	128	55	73	107
2	Folkestone Invicta	46	27	8	11	102	59	43	89
3	(P) Leatherhead (-6)	46	28	8	10	93	46	47	86
4	Guernsey	46	23	12	11	93	65	28	81
5	Hastings United (-1)	46	24	7	15	73	62	11	78
6	Burgess Hill Town	46	22	11	13	88	67	21	77
7	Merstham	46	23	7	16	82	64	18	76
8	Hythe Town	46	22	7	17	87	71	16	73
9	Walton Casuals	46	22	4	20	90	94	-4	70
10	Faversham Town	46	18	14	14	78	69	9	68
11	Tooting & Mitcham United	46	17	12	17	79	75	4	63
12	Ramsgate	46	18	8	20	84	79	5	62
13	Chipstead	46	18	8	20	79	83	-4	62
14	Sittingbourne	46	16	13	17	69	75	-6	61
15	Worthing	46	17	8	21	80	98	-18	59
16	Horsham	46	15	11	20	66	78	-12	56
17	Corinthian-Casuals	46	15	10	21	69	73	-4	55
18	Herne Bay	46	15	9	22	69	72	-3	54
19	Three Bridges	46	15	8	23	71	88	-17	53
20	Whitstable Town	46	14	11	21	61	78	-17	53
21	Walton & Hersham	46	14	9	23	75	92	-17	51
22	Redhill	46	13	6	27	72	96	-24	45
23	(R) Crawley Down Gatwick	46	9	6	31	51	139	-88	33
24	(R) Eastbourne Town	46	6	11	29	60	121	-61	29

PLAY-OFFS

Semi-Finals: Folkestone Invicta 3-2 Hastings United I Leatherhead 3-2 Guernsey

Final: Folkstone Invicta 1-1 Leatherhead (Leatherhead won 3-1 after penalties)

	1	2	3	4	5	6	7	8	9	10	11	12	13	14	15	16	17	18	19	20	21	22	23	24
1 Burgess Hill Town		4-0	3-0	1-1	2-0	2-0	0-0	0-3	1-1	3-2	1-0	4-5	0-0	3-2	1-2	1-0	2-1	7-1	2-1	0-0	3-2	6-1	2-1	4-1
2 Chipstead	0-0		1-0	4-0	2-2	0-1	4-3	1-3	0-1	3-4	3-1	2-3	0-3	1-2	1-1	1-3	1-1	2-1	3-4	4-1	1-1	3-2	1-0	0-3
3 Corinthian-Casuals	0-2	3-4		1-2	4-0	1-1	2-3	1-2	2-2	1-4	1-1	0-4	0-0	1-3	2-0	3-1	7-0	1-1	1-0	0-0	0-1	1-2	0-0	1-0
4 Crawley Down G.	1-4	4-3	2-4		6-1	1-2	3-2	1-1	2-6	3-3	0-2	0-6	0-5	1-3	0-1	0-0	2-1	0-3	2-3	0-0	1-2	0-5	0-2	1-2
5 Eastbourne Town	1-1	1-2	0-0	6-0		3-6	2-3	3-3	3-2	1-1	0-2	2-0	2-2	1-0	0-2	0-4	0-2	2-4	0-3	0-2	1-3	0-4	0-3	2-2
6 Faversham Town	2-1	5-3	2-3	2-1	3-1		2-2	1-2	2-0	1-0	2-1	2-3	1-1	1-2	3-0	5-2	0-2	2-1	1-1	3-1	2-2	0-1	0-0	0-0
7 Folkstone Invicta	4-1	1-3	2-1	8-0	1-1	2-1		1-1	2-1	2-1	4-0	1-1	2-0	3-2	2-3	3-1	3-1	5-0	4-2	3-0	4-2	0-1	1-0	3-1
8 Guernsey	3-1	1-0	2-1	11-0	4-2	2-1	2-2		2-0	4-2	0-1	5-1	2-0	0-1	2-2	0-4	0-1	1-1	1-1	2-1	1-2	2-1	2-1	4-1
9 Hastings United	3-2	0-2	2-1	1-0	3-0	0-0	3-0	0-4		1-0	2-1	3-2	2-2	2-2	1-2	3-1	2-1	1-1	1-0	3-1	2-1	1-0	3-1	4-0
10 Herne Bay	3-1	1-2	1-2	1-0	3-2	1-1	2-1	0-1	0-2		2-2	0-1	2-0	4-0	1-2	1-0	0-3	1-1	4-1	3-1	1-2	0-2	1-0	0-1
11 Horsham	0-2	2-2	1-3	1-0	2-1	1-1	1-5	6-2	2-0	1-0		0-2	2-2	0-1	1-4	2-2	0-2	3-1	1-0	1-2	1-1	3-1	3-1	1-1
12 Hythe Town	3-0	2-0	4-3	1-1	2-3	1-2	2-3	1-1	1-2	1-1	1-1		1-0	3-2	1-2	2-3	1-0	3-0	3-1	1-1	0-2	6-0	1-1	4-2
13 Leatherhead	2-3	3-0	3-0	2-1	5-0	1-3	1-0	2-0	3-0	1-0	2-1	0-1		1-0	0-0	4-0	3-1	3-0	2-1	5-1	3-3	1-0	1-2	2-0
14 Merstham	1-1	1-4	0-1	1-3	5-0	4-1	0-2	3-3	2-0	3-1	1-0	0-2	3-2		0-3	0-2	3-2	2-0	5-1	3-1	3-0	3-2	5-0	1-2
15 Peacehaven & Tel.	3-2	2-1	3-1	10-0	4-1	0-0	3-0	2-0	2-1	4-2	5-5	4-0	3-0	3-1		5-1	3-1	2-0	2-3	2-2	2-2	5-0	4-1	6-0
16 Ramsgate	1-2	0-2	1-1	4-2	2-0	2-3	2-1	2-1	5-0	5-1	4-2	1-0	0-1	1-1	3-1		1-3	2-4	5-0	2-1	1-1	2-3	1-2	3-0
17 Redhill	3-4	0-1	0-3	6-0	4-4	2-1	0-1	0-1	0-4	1-2	2-1	3-1	1-2	1-1	1-4	1-0		2-3	0-0	0-3	0-3	2-3	3-3	3-1
18 Sittingbourne	2-2	1-1	0-0	5-2	3-0	0-0	0-3	1-1	2-1	4-2	2-0	0-1	0-1	1-0	3-3	3-1	3-3		0-1	2-0	1-2	0-4	1-0	3-0
19 Three Bridges	2-2	1-3	3-2	1-2	1-1	1-3	2-3	1-4	1-2	2-1	0-1	3-0	1-4	1-2	0-1	0-0	5-2	2-0		1-4	5-2	1-1	1-0	4-2
20 Tooting & Mitcham	0-2	2-2	5-1	2-0	3-4	4-2	0-0	2-2	1-0	0-0	2-1	4-1	1-2	0-1	3-5	3-4	2-1	0-0	2-0		2-1	4-3	6-0	2-1
21 Walton & Hersham	5-1	1-3	1-4	1-2	3-1	2-2	0-3	4-0	2-0	1-2	0-1	0-4	0-5	1-4	1-2	1-1	2-3	0-4	2-2	0-1		0-2	3-4	2-1
22 Walton Casuals	2-1	3-1	1-3	2-0	2-2	5-3	1-2	2-2	0-1	0-6	2-3	3-1	2-4	1-1	4-2	3-1	3-2	2-3	1-2	3-2	1-5		3-1	3-1
23 Whitstable Town	1-0	3-2	3-1	0-1	3-2	0-0	1-1	1-3	1-1	0-0	1-1	0-1	2-3	1-2	1-3	4-1	3-2	1-1	2-4	2-2	3-2	0-1		2-1
24 Worthing	1-1	2-0	0-1	7-3	3-2	4-2	2-1	3-0	2-3	2-2	5-3	3-2	2-4	0-0	0-4	2-2	4-2	3-2	2-1	2-2	2-1	5-2	1-3	

NON
LEAGUE DAY
06.09.14
Support your
LOCAL
FOOTBALL CLUB
nonleagueday.co.uk

Isthmian League Premier Division Statistics 2013-14

	MCV	MCD	MCwW	MCwD	MCSG	MCwS	TGS	MCCS	TNCS
AFC Hornchurch	6	3	4	15	18	2	5	2	14
Billericay Town	3	3	6	4	9	1	13	3	12
Bognor Regis Town	6	2	4	10	14	2	9	4	12
Bury Town	6	4	9	9	7	4	21	4	13
Canvey Island	3	3	4	9	15	4	14	2	10
Carshalton Athletic	2	6	7	2	5	3	19	1	6
Cray Wanderers	2	8	11	3	5	6	22	1	3
Dulwich Hamlet	7	4	7	7	21	1	6	3	17
East Thurrock United	2	4	13	6	11	3	15	1	8
Enfield Town	3	6	10	7	12	3	11	2	6
Grays Athletic	5	7	8	5	14	2	11	3	14
Hampton & Richmond Borough	3	3	5	8	12	3	13	2	12
Harrow Borough	3	3	7	4	10	3	11	2	8
Hendon	4	4	6	5	10	1	10	3	13
Kingstonian	3	3	3	13	7	2	12	6	21
Leiston	4	4	11	6	12	3	14	4	11
Lewes	3	3	11	13	10	3	9	3	11
Lowestoft Town	5	2	5	8	15	2	10	3	24
Maidstone United	4	3	4	9	14	2	7	2	16
Margate	3	3	4	8	10	2	11	3	13
Metropolitan Police	4	4	7	7	7	4	17	2	9
Thamesmead Town	3	5	10	7	17	2	12	2	9
Wealdstone	5	2	3	15	20	1	5	5	21
Wingate & Finchley	4	5	8	5	12	3	19	4	13

MCV - Most Consecutive Victories I MCD - Most Consecutive Defeats
MCwW - Most Consecutive without a Win I MCwD - Most Consecutive without a defeat
MCSG - Most Consecutive Scoring Games I MCwS - Most Consecutive without Scoring
TGS - Total Games without Scoring I MCCS - Most Consecutive Clean Sheets
TNCS - Total Number of Clean Sheets

Best Premier League Attendances 2013-2014

	Att:	Opponents	Score
AFC Hornchurch	485	Maidstone United	1-0
Billercay Town	434	Kingstonian	3-2
Bognor Regis Town	603	Lewes	3-1
Bury Town	737	Wealdstone	0-1
Canvey Island	461	Enfield	2-1
Carshalton Athletic	441	Wealdstone	2-4
Cray Wanderers	521	Maidstone United	0-5
Dulwich Hamlet	1388	Kingstonian	1-1
East Thurrock United	314	Bognor Regis Town	4-2
Enfield Town	662	East Thurrock Utd	3-5
Grays Athletic	303	Maidstone United	0-1
Hampton & Richmond B	769	Maidstone United	1-3
Harrow Borough	452	Wealdstone	0-2
Hendon	575	Wealdstone	0-0
Kingstonian	678	Maidstone United	0-3
Leiston	545	Lowestoft Town	0-1
Lewes	788	Metropolitan Police	2-2
Lowestoft Town	845	Harrow Borough	3-0
Maidstone United	2296	Dulwich Hamlet	4-3
Margate	887	Maidstone United	1-0
Metropolitan Police	425	Bury	0-3
Thamesmead Town	305	Maidstone United	4-1
Wealdstone	1151	Dulwich Hamlet	2-2
Wingate & Finchley	345	Enfield Town	1-1

HAT-TRICK HEROS

	Club	Goals	Opponents	Score
Stefan Payne	AFC Hornchurch	3	Leiston (a)	W 3-2
Carl Rook	AFC Hornchurch	3	Spalding (a) FACup	W 4-1
Terry Dodd	Bognor Regis Town	3	Chippenham T (h) FATrophy	W 4-1
Terry Dodd	Bognor Regis Town	3	Bury Town (h)	W 5-2
Terry Dodd	Bognor Regis Town	3	Lowetoft Town (h)	W 4-1
Jay Curran	Canvey Island	3 pens	Aveley (a) FA Cup	W 5-2
John Sands	Canvey Island	3	Lewes (h)	D 3-3
Ero Ozturner	Dulwich Hamlet	3	Enfield Town (a)	W 4 3
Eron Ozturner	Dulwich Hamlet	3	Cray Wanderers (a)	W 6-0
Eron Ozturner	Dulwich Hamlet	3	East Thurrock Utd (a)	W 4-1
Sam Higgins	East Thurrock United	3	Hendon (h)	W 6-1
Joel Ledgister	Hampton & Richmond B.	3	Ashford Town(h) FAC	W 4-2
Charlie Moone	Hampton & Richmond B.	3	Arlesey Town (h) FAC	W 5-1
Charlie Moone	Hampton & Richmond B.	3	Kingstonian (h)	W 4-1
Belal Aite-Ouakrim	Hampton & Richmond B.	3	Bury Town (h)	W 3-0
Charlie Moone	Hampton & Richmond B.	3	Bognor Regis Town (h)	W 4-3
Ben Harris	Hampton & Richmond B.	3	AFC Hornchurch (a)	W 3-2
Steve Butterworth	Harrow Borough	3	Cray Wanderers (h)	W 4-2
Andre McCollin	Kingstonian	4	Grays Athletiv (h)	W 4-0
Andre McCollin	Kingstonian	3	Lewis (h)	W 4-1
Andre McCollin	Kingstonian	3	Carshalton Athletic (a)	W 3-1
Joe Francis	Leiston	3	Thamesmead Town(h)	W 3-0
Luke Blewden	Lewes	3	Leiston (a)	W 5-1
Jake Reed	Lowestoft Town	4	Carshalton Athletic (h)	W 5-0
Stuart Ainsley	Lowestoft Town	3	Wingate & Finchley(h)	W 7-0
Frannie Collin	Maidstone United	3	Cray Wanderers (a)	W 5-0
Fabio Saraiva	Maidstone United	3	Wingate & Finchley (a)	W 4-2
Jefferson Louis	Margate	3	Carshalton Athletiv (a)	W 6-0
Tyrus Gordon-Young	Thamesmead	3	Grays Athletic (a)	W 4-1
Scott McGleish	Wealdstone	3	East Thurrock United (h)	W 5-0
Ahmet Rifat	Wingate & Finchley	3	Billericay Town (h)	W 5-0

A.F.C. HORNCHURCH

Chairman: Colin McBride

Secretary: Peter Butcher **(T)** 07918 645 109 **(E)** peter.butcher5@btinternet.com

Commercial Manager: Peter Butcher **(T)** 07918 645 109

Programme Editor: Peter Butcher **(T)** 07918 645 109

Ground Address: The Stadium, Bridge Avenue, Upminster, Essex RM14 2LX

(T) 01708 220 080 **Manager:** Jim McFarlane

Club Factfile

Founded: 2005 **Nickname:** The Urchins

Previous Names: Formed in 2005 after Hornchurch F.C. folded

Previous Leagues: Essex Senior 2005-06. Isthmian 2006-12. Conference 2012-13.

Club Colours (change): Red and white stripes/black/black

Ground Capacity: 3,500 **Seats:** 800 **Covered:** 1,400 **Clubhouse:** Yes **Shop:** Yes

Directions

Bridge Avenue is off A124 between Hornchurch and Upminster.

Previous Grounds: None

Record Attendance: 3,500 v Tranmere Rovers - FA Cup 2nd Round 2003-04

Record Victory: Not known

Record Defeat: Not known

Record Goalscorer: Not known

Record Appearances: Not known

Additional Records: Won the Essex League with a record 64 points in 2005-06

Senior Honours:

Since reformation in 2005: Essex Senior League, League Cup and Memorial Trophy 2005-06.
Isthmian League Division 1 North 2006-07, Premier Division Play-offs 2011-12.
Essex Senior Cup 2012-13.

10 YEAR RECORD

04-05	05-06	06-07	07-08	08-09	09-10	10-11	11-12	12-13	13-14
Conf S 17	ESen 1	Isth1N 1	Isth P 4	Isth P 6	Isth P 9	Isth P 10	Isth P 2	Conf S 20	Isth P 5

AFC HORNCHURCH MATCH RESULTS 2013-14

Date	Comp	H/A	Opponents	Att:	Result		Goalscorers	Pos	No.
Aug 10	IsthP	H	Lewes	259	L	0-1		18	1
12	IsthP	A	Margate	329	W	2-1	Rook 25 (pen) Yuseff 90	14	2
17	IsthP	A	Cray Wanderers	147	W	6-1	Rook 11 Hayles 21 Styles 24 Purcell 32 62 Bourne 53	6	3
20	IsthP	H	Bury Town	218	D	0-0		7	4
24	IsthP	H	Lowestoft Town	210	W	2-1	Bourne 49 Purcell 90	6	5
26	IsthP	A	Billericay Town	386	D	2-2	Purcell 60 65	6	6
31	IsthP	A	Dulwich Hamlet	607	W	3-2	Purcell 22 Payne 67 80	5	7
Sept 7	IsthP	H	East Thurrock United	328	W	3-0	Bourne 41 Purcell 55 57	3	8
11	IsthP	H	Wealdstone	251	D	1-1	Yuseff 90	4	9
14	***FAC1Q***	***H***	***East Thurrock United***	***273***	***D***	***1-1***	***Rook 78***		10
17	***FAC 1Qr***	***A***	***East Thurrock United***	***156***	***W***	***2-1***	***Spencer 28 Bourne 55***		11
21	IsthP	A	Leiston	223	W	3-2	PAYNE 3 (31 85 88)	4	12
24	IsthP	A	Enfield Town	312	W	2-0	Curley 14 Payne 78		13
28	***FAC 2Q***	***A***	***Spalding United***	***366***	***W***	***4-1***	***ROOK 3 (3 59 64 pen) Yuseff 85***		14
Oct 1	IsthP	H	Carshalton Athletic	192	W	2-1	Rook 12 Payne 58	1	15
5	IsthP	A	Grays Athletic	303	W	5-1	Bremner 15 Payne 16 63 Rook 49 Baker 90 (og)	1	16
19	***FAT1Q***	***A***	***Hemel Hempstead T***	***501***	***L***	***2-3***	***Curley 14 Hayles 80***		17
26	***FAC4Q***	***H***	***Hereford United***	***713***	***L***	***0-1***			18
Nov 2	IsthP	A	Lowestoft Town	530	L	0-3		4	19
9	IsthP	A	Thamesmead	96	W	2-1	Purcell 20 Payne 90	3	20
12	IsthP	H	Harrow Borough	180	L	2-4	Purcell 50 70	3	21
16	IsthP	H	Kingstonian	360	D	0-0		3	22
19	IsthP	H	Bognor Regis Town	145	W	1-0	Purcell 71	1	23
23	IsthP	A	Maidstone United	1879	D	1-1	Bremner 12	2	24
30	IsthP	H	Wingate & Finchley	187	W	3-0	Rook 7 Purcell 26 Payne 72	1	25
Dec 7	IsthP	A	Hendon	141	W	1-0	Rainford 61	1	26
14	IsthP	H	Margate	238	W	3-2	Spencer 35 64 Payne 61	1	27
26	IsthP	H	Billericay Town	444	L	1-2	Purcell 45		28
28	IsthP	A	Bury Town	367	L	2-3	Payne 48 90	4	29
Jan 11	IsthP	A	Metropolitan Police	151	L	1-2	Purcell 60	5	30
21	IsthP	H	Enfield Town	200	W	3-0	Payne 32 Purcell 50 89	6	31
25	IsthP	A	East Thurrock United	306	W	2-1	Payne 12 44	5	32
Feb 15	IsthP	H	Leiston	255	W	4-2	Payne 7 38 Purcell 36 Bremner 68	4	33
17	IsthP	A	Wealdstone	685	L	0-2		5	34
22	IsthP	A	Bognor Regis Town	433	D	1-1	Purcell 3	5	35
25	IsthP	H	Canvey Island	232	D	1-1	Purcell 84	5	36
March 1	IsthP	H	Grays Athletic	341	L	1-2	Coyne 53	4	37
8	IsthP	H	Thamesmead Town	219	W	2-0	Payne 7 Purcell 90	5	38
12	IsthP	A	Lewes	311	W	5-1	Eyong 3 Payne 27 69 Purcell 16 (pen) 77	5	39
15	IsthP	A	Kingstonian	281	D	1-1	Purcell 14 (pen)	5	40
18	IsthP	H	Cray Wanderers	157	L	1-2	Purcell 29	5	41
22	IsthP	H	Maidstone United	**485**	W	1-0	Payne 25	5	42
25	IsthP	H	Dulwich Hamlet	254	D	1-1	Payne 16	5	43
29	IsthP	A	Wingate & Finchley	203	W	3-0	Purcell 19 54 Eyong 77	3	44
Aprll 1	IsthP	A	Carshalton Athletic	120	W	1-0	Payne 35	3	45
5	IsthP	H	Hendon	300	L	1-2	Purcell 26 (pen)	3	46
10	IsthP	A	Hampton & Richmond	235	D	1-1	Purcell 86	3	47
12	IsthP	A	Harrow Borough	164	W	2-1	Bourne 24 Payne 49	2	48
19	IsthP	H	Hampton & Richmond B	308	L	2-3	Purcell 14 Hayles 64	4	49
21	IsthP	A	Canvey Island	373	D	1-1	Bourne 90	7	50
26	IsthP	H	Metropolitan Police	374	W	1-0	Bourne 48	5	51
30	***IsthP PO SF***	***A***	***Kingstonian***	***641***	***W***	***1-0***	***Hayles***		52
May 5	***IsthP PO F***	***A***	***Lowestoft Town***	***2697***	***L***	***0-3***			53

GOALSCORERS	Lge	FAC	FAT	Total	Pens	Hat-tricks	Cons Run
Payne	23	3		26		2	3
Purcell	29	1		30	3	1	4
Rook	4	4		8	2		2
Bourne	5	2		7			2
Hayles	2+1		1	4			
Bremner	3			3			
Spencer	2	1		3			
Yuseff	2	1		3			
Curley	1		1	2			
Eyong	2			2			
Coyle	1			1			
Rainford	1			1			
Styles	1			1			
Opponents	1			1			

Cons Run - Consecutive scoring games.

Play-off goals indicated by +

BILLERICAY TOWN

Chairman: Steve Kent
Secretary: Ian Ansell (T) 07958 978 154 (E) secretary@billericaytownfc.co.uk
Commercial Manager: (T)
Programme Editor: Gary Clark (T) 07957 004 930
Ground Address: New Lodge, Blunts Wall Road, Billericay CM12 9SA
(T) 01277 652 188 **Manager:** Craig Edwards

Club Factfile

Founded: 1880 **Nickname:** Town or Blues
Previous Names: None
Previous Leagues: Romford & District 1890-1914, Mid Essex 1918-47, South Essex Combination 1947-66, Essex Olympian 1966-71, Essex Senior 1971-77, Athenian 1977-79. Isthmian 1979-2012. Conference 2012-13.
Club Colours (change): Blue & white

Ground Capacity: 3,500 **Seats:** 424 **Covered:** 2,000 **Clubhouse:** Yes **Shop:** Yes

Directions
From the M25 (J29) take the A127 to the Basildon/Billericay (A176) turn-off, (junction after the Old Fortune of War r'about). Take second exit at r'about (Billericay is signposted). Then straight over (2nd exit) at the next roundabout. Continue along that road until you enter Billericay. At the first r'about take the first available exit. At the next r'about (with Billericay School on your left) go straight over (1st exit). At yet another r'about!, turn left into the one-way system. Keep in the left-hand lane and go straight over r'about. At first set of lights, turn left. Blunts Wall Road is the second turning on your right.

Previous Grounds: None

Record Attendance: 3,841 v West Ham United - Opening of Floodlights 1977
Record Victory: 11-0 v Stansted (A) - Essex Senior League 05/05/1976
Record Defeat: 3-10 v Chelmsford City (A) - Essex Senior Cup 04/01/1993
Record Goalscorer: Freddie Claydon - 273
Record Appearances: J Pullen - 418
Additional Records: Leon Gutzmore scored 51 goals during the 1997-98 season.
Received £22,500+ from West Ham United for Steve Jones November 1992
Senior Honours:
FA Vase 1975-76, 76-77, 78-79. Essex Senior Cup 1975-76. Athenian League 1978-79. Isthmian Premier Division 2011-12.
Essex Senior Trophy x2.

10 YEAR RECORD

04-05	05-06	06-07	07-08	08-09	09-10	10-11	11-12	12-13	13-14
Isth P 2	Isth P 7	Isth P 4	Isth P 10	Isth P 11	Isth P 13	Isth P 11	Isth P 1	Conf S 21	Isth P 10

BILLERICAY TOWN MATCH RESULTS 2013-14

Date	Comp	H/A	Opponents	Att:	Result		Goalscorers	Pos	No.
Aug 10	IsthP	A	Harrow Borough	211	D	1-1	Kouassi 29	12	1
13	IsthP	H	East Thurrock United	342	L	0-1		20	2
17	IsthP	H	Thamesmead Town	261	W	3-2	Collis 59 Poole 75 Campbell 81	13	3
20	IsthP	A	Maidstone United	1746	L	1-2	Lee 21	14	4
26	IsthP	H	AFC Hornchurch	386	D	2-2	Sappleton 34 Campbell 52	15	5
Sept 1	IsthP	A	Grays Athletic	313	D	2-2	Sappleton 20 Robinson 75	18	6
7	IsthP	H	Bognor Regis Town	409	L	1-2	Benjamin 34	20	7
10	IsthP	H	Leiston	163	W	4-1	Dunne 17 59 Luke 33 Halle 49 (pen)	18	8
14	***FAC1Q***	***H***	***Leiston***	***210***	***W***	***2-0***	***Sappleton 70 Robinson 90***		9
17	IsthP	A	Canvey Island	312	W	2-0	Sappleton 55 79	12	10
21	IsthP	A	Carshalton Athletic	281	L	0-1		13	11
23	IsthP	A	Hendon	132	W	2-1	Sappleton 8 12	12	12
28	***FAC2Q***	***A***	***St Albans City***	***372***	***L***	***0-2***			13
Oct 5	IsthP	H	Kingstonian	434	W	3-2	Dunne 4 Benjamin 8 Layne 61	10	14
12	IsthP	A	Enfield Town	554	W	2-1	Poole 68 (pen) Luke 87	8	15
19	***FAT1Q***	***A***	***Guernsey***	***1090***	***W***	***2-1***	***Poole 19 (pen) Benjamin 41***		16
26	IsthP	A	Dulwich Hamlet	706	L	1-2	Poole 82 (pen)	10	17
29	IsthP	H	Metropolitan Police	248	L	1-2	Sappleton	10	18
Nov 2	***FAT2Q***	***A***	***St Albans City***	***313***	***D***	***3-3***	***Poole 9 (pen) 90 Luke 51***		19
5	***FAT2Qr***	***H***	***St Albans City***	***201***	***D***	***2-2***	***Webber 9 Scott 58 (lost 2-4 on pens aet)***		20
16	IsthP	A	Leiston	224	D	2-2	Sappleton 46 Bonnet-Johnson 77	11	21
23	IsthP	H	Hampton & Richmond B	301	L	1-2	Benjamin 34	13	22
30	IsthP	A	Cray Wanderers	158	W	1-0	Benjamin 59	10	23
Dec 7	IsthP	H	Lewes	293	L	0-1		13	24
10	IsthP	A	Margate	182	W	2-0	Webb 49 Ekim 79	9	25
14	IsthP	A	East Thurrock United	205	D	2-2	Bryant 22 66	11	26
26	IsthP	A	AFC Hornchurch	444	W	2-1	Sappleton 12 (pen) 16	11	27
Jan 4	IsthP	A	Thamesmead Town	146	D	3-3	Hotte 42 Sappleton 78 90	11	28
21	IsthP	H	Hendon	238	L	0-1		11	29
Feb 4	IsthP	H	Harrow Borough	184	W	2-1	Poole 42 Sappleton 57	13	30
10	IsthP	A	Metropolitan Police	85	W	2-0	Layne 8 39	12	31
25	IsthP	H	Lowestoft Town	208	L	0-1		14	32
March 1	IsthP	A	Kingstonian	255	W	2-0	Ekim 32 Scott 47	14	33
4	IsthP	A	Bognor Regis Town	399	L	0-1		14	34
8	IsthP	A	Bury Town	348	W	1-0	Layne 7	14	35
11	IsthP	H	Canvey Island	321	L	1-4	Scott 83	15	36
15	IsthP	H	Margate	333	L	0-2		15	37
18	IsthP	H	Wingate & Finchley	183	W	1-0	Halle 60 (pen)	13	38
20	IsthP	H	Carshalton Athletic	168	W	3-1	Kouassi 43 Halle 58 Webber 90	13	39
22	IsthP	A	Hampton & Richmond B	325	W	1-0	Halle 59	10	40
25	IsthP	H	Maidstone United	254	D	3-3	Layne 12 61 Mitchell 84	10	41
27	IsthP	H	Enfield Town	273	L	0-2		10	42
29	IsthP	H	Cray Wanderers	289	L	1-2	Halle 26	11	43
31	IsthP	A	Wealdstone	726	L	0 2		11	44
April 5	IsthP	A	Lewes	388	D	1-1	Benjamin 71	11	45
8	IsthP	H	Bury Town	202	D	0-0		11	46
12	IsthP	H	Dulwich Hamlet	371	W	2-0	Ngakam 4 Ekim 33	11	47
15	IsthP	H	Grays Athletiic	232	W	4-0	Ekim 47 73 Layne 54 Poole 74	10	48
19	IsthP	A	Lowestoft Town	688	L	0-1		11	49
21	IsthP	H	Wealdstone	424	W	4-2	Halle 28 Scott 45 Dunne 55 Layne 86	10	50
25	IsthP	A	Wingate & Finchey	228	L	0-5		10	51

GOALSCORERS	Lge	FAC	FAT	Total	Pens	Hat-tricks	Cons Run
Sappleton	13	1		14	1		2
Layne	8			8			
Poole	5		3	8	4		3
Benjamin	5		1	6			2
Halle	6			6	2		3
Ekim	5			5			
Scott	3		1	4			
Dunne	3			3			
Bryant	2			2			
Campbell	2			2			
Dunne	2			2			
Kouassi	2			2			
Luke	2		1	2			
Robinson	1	1		2			
Webber	1		1	2			
Bonnet-Johnson	1			1			
Collis	1			1			
Hotte	1			1			
Lee	1			1			
Mitchell	1			1			
Ngakam	1			1			
Webb	1			1			

Cons Run - Consecutive scoring games.

BOGNOR REGIS TOWN

Chairman: Dominic Reynolds
Secretary: Simon Cook (T) 07527 455 167 (E) sajcook2@aol.com
Commercial Manager: (T)
Programme Editor: Rob Garforth (T) 07791 591 375
Ground Address: Nyewood Lane, Bognor Regis PO21 2TY
(T) 01243 822 325 **Manager:** Jamie Howell

Club Factfile

Founded: 1883 **Nickname:** The Rocks

Previous Names: None

Previous Leagues: West Sussex 1896-1926, Brighton & Hove District 1926-27, Sussex County 1927-72, Southern League 1972-81, Isthmian 1982-2004, Conference 2004-09

Club Colours (change): White with green trim/green/white (Gold/black/gold)

Ground Capacity: 4,100 **Seats:** 350 **Covered:** 2,600 **Clubhouse:** Yes **Shop:** Yes

Directions
West along sea front from pier past Aldwick shopping centre then turn right into Nyewood Lane.

Previous Grounds: None

Record Attendance: 3,642 v Swnsea City - FA Cup 1st Round replay 1984
Record Victory: 24-0 v Littlehampton - West Sussex League 1913-14
Record Defeat: 0-19 v Shoreham - West Sussex League 1906-07
Record Goalscorer: Kevin Clements - 206
Record Appearances: Mick Pullen - 967 (20 seasons)
Additional Records: Paid £2,000 for Guy Rutherford 1995-96. Received £10,500 from Brighton & Hove for John Crumplin and Geoff Cooper, and from Crystal Palace for Simon Rodger.

Senior Honours:
Sussex Professional Cup 1973-74. Sussex Senior Cup x9.
Isthmian League Division 1 South Play-offs 2011-12.

10 YEAR RECORD

04-05	05-06	06-07	07-08	08-09	09-10	10-11	11-12	12-13	13-14
Conf S 9	Conf S 12	Conf S 12	Conf S 18	Conf S 21	Isth P 22	Isth1S 2	Isth1S 2	Isth P 14	Isth P 3

BOGNOR REGIS TOWN MATCH RESULTS 2013-14

Date	Comp	H/A	Opponents	Att:	Result		Goalscorers	Pos	No.
Aug 10	IsthP	H	Grays Athletic	478	L	0-3		22	1
12	IsthP	A	Wealdstone	544	D	2-2	Whyte 42 44	21	2
15	IsthP	A	Lowestoft Town	532	L	0-2		21	3
20	IsthP	H	Carshalton Athletic	380	L	2-4	Robson 18 26	23	4
24	IsthP	H	Metropolitan Police	372	**W**	2 0	Godfrey 64 Wills 81	17	5
26	IsthP	A	Lewes	777	D	1 1	Wills 70	17	6
31	IsthP	H	Canvey Island	433	**W**	5-0	Robson 9 Godfrey 16 Wills 54 Dodd 84 Johnson 90	14	7
Sept 7	IsthP	A	Billericay Town	409	**W**	2-1	Godfrey 23 Dodd 90	11	8
9	IsthP	A	Kingstonian	345	**W**	2-1	Godfrey 23 Johnson 86 (pen)	8	9
14	***FAC1Q***	***A***	***Frome Town***	***218***	***D***	***1-1***	***Godfrey 64***		10
18	***FAC1Qr***	***H***	***Frome Town***	***310***	***W***	***4-0***	***Whyte 37 Pearce 42 Godfrey 56 Dodd 79***		11
21	IsthP	H	Hampton & Richmond	411	**W**	4-0	Pearce 18 59 Godfrey 65 Dodd 69	9	12
24	IsthP	H	Cray Wanderers	415	**W**	4-0	Johnson 10 Pearce 48 Whyte 52 Sackman 54	6	13
28	***FAC2Q***	***A***	***Weymouth***	***598***	***D***	***2-2***	***Johnson 62 (pen) Hopkinsn 66***		14
Oct 7	IsthP	H	Enfield	407	**W**	5-1	Hopkinson 1 Pearce 21 27 Dodd 65 75	6	15
19	***FAT1Q***	***H***	***Thurrock***	***341***	***W***	***2-1***	***Dodd 1 45***		16
26	IsthP	A	Wingate & Finchley	142	L	0-3		7	17
Nov 2	***FAT2Q***	***H***	***Chippenham Town***	***367***	***W***	***4-1***	***Pearce 13 DODD 3 (20 21 77)***		18
5	IsthP	A	Thamesmead Town	94	**W**	2 1	Johnson 22 90 (pen)		19
9	IsthP	H	Dulwich Hamlet	502	**W**	4-2	Hopkinson 66 Johnson 87 (pen) Robson 90 Dodd 90	6	20
17	***FAT3Q***	***A***	***Hayes & Yeading United***	***250***	***L***	***1-2***	***Godfrey 11***		21
19	IsthP	A	AFC Hornchurch	145	L	0-1		6	22
23	IsthP	H	Bury Town	423	**W**	5-2	DODD 3 (18 51 73) Johnson 64 (Pen) Wills 90	6	23
30	IsthP	A	Harrow Borough	174	D	0-0		6	24
Dec 2	IsthP	H	Maidstone United	471	L	1-2	Wills 71	6	25
7	IsthP	H	Margate	402	**W**	5-3	Murombedzi 48 Dodd 55 Pearce 57 Crane 79 83	6	26
10	IsthP	A	Leiston	168	L	2-5	Pearce 27 Robson 40	6	27
14	IsthP	H	Wealdstone	506	L	1-3	Dodd 84	7	28
26	IsthP	H	Lewes	**603**	**W**	3-1	Godfrey 52 Chamberlain 63 Pearce 79	7	29
28	IsthP	A	Carshalton Athletic	230	**W**	3-1	Godfrey 21 Chamberlain 51 Odamesley 57 (og)	7	30
Jan 11	IsthP	H	East Thurrock United	418	**W**	3-1	Dodd 11 33 Wills 24	6	31
14	IsthP	H	Lowestoft Town	392	**W**	4-1	DODD 3 (44 47 48) Hopkinson 51	5	32
21	IsthP	A	Cray Wanderers	126	**W**	2-1	Dodd 6 Wills 39	2	33
Feb 8	IsthP	H	Thamesmead Town	347	**W**	2-1	Crane 32 Dodd 41	5	34
22	IsthP	H	AFC Hornchurch	433	D	1-1	Pearce 64	6	35
24	IsthP	A	Hendon	141	L	0-1		6	36
March 4	IsthP	H	Billericay Town	399	**W**	1-0	Dodd 73 (pen)	6	37
8	IsthP	A	Dulwich Hamlet	792	**W**	2-0	Pearce 16 Thompson 85	4	38
11	IsthP	A	Metropolitan Police	151	**W**	2 0	Crane 25 Dodd 59 (pen)	4	39
15	IsthP	H	Leiston	407	D	0-0		4	40
18	IsthP	A	Canvey Island	237	**W**	3-1	Hopkinson 17 Crane 19 Pearce 89	4	41
22	IsthP	A	Bury Town	410	L	0-2		4	42
25	IsthP	H	Kingstonian	361	D	0-0		4	43
29	IsthP	H	Harrow Borough	387	**W**	3-2	Thompson 26 Robson 49 Crane 81	4	44
April 3	IsthP	A	Enfield Town	375	L	1-2	Robson	4	45
5	IsthP	A	Margate	306	D	1-1	Pearce 16	6	46
10	IsthP	A	Grays Athletic	182	**W**	4-3	Jackman Wills Pearce Hopkinson	3	47
12	IsthP	H	Wingate & Finchley	323	**W**	1-0	Igoe 85 (pen)	3	48
15	IsthP	A	Hampton & Richmond B	339	L	3-4	Chamberlain 52 74 Igoe 90	3	49
19	IsthP	A	Maidstone United	2148	**W**	2-1	Chamberlain 40 Thompson 64	2	50
21	IsthP	H	Hendon	498	**W**	3-2	Pearce 24 Dodd 32 Johnson 76 (pen)	2	51
26	IsthP	A	East Thurrock United	314	L	2-4	Johnson 7 Pearce 14	3	52
30	***IsthP PO SF***	***H***	***Lowestoft Town***	***941***	***L***	***1-2***	***Dodd 10***		53

GOALSCORERS	Lge	FAC	FAT	Total	Pens	Hat-tricks	Cons Run
Dodd	21+1	1	5	28	2	3	4
Pearce	15	1	1	17			3
Johnson	10	1		11	6		2
Godfrey	7	2	1	10			5
Wills	8			8			
Robson	6			6			2
Crane	6			6			
Hopkinson	5	1		6			
Chamberlain	5			5			2
Whyte	3	1		4			
Thompson	3			3			
Igoe	2			2	1		
Jackman	1			1			
Murombedzi	1			1			
Sackman	1			1			
Opponents	1			1			

Cons Run - Consecutive scoring games.
Play-off goals indicated by +

BURY TOWN

Chairman: Russell Ward
Secretary: Mrs Wendy Turner **(T)** 07795 661 959 **(E)** wturner@burytownfc.freeserve.co.uk
Commercial Manager: **(T)**
Programme Editor: Christopher Ward **(T)** 07778 571 812
Ground Address: Ram Meadow, Cotton Lane, Bury St Edmunds IP33 1XP
(T) 01284 754 721 **Manager:** Richard Wilkins

Club Factfile

Founded: 1872 **Nickname:** The Blues
Previous Names: Bury St Edmunds 1872-1885, 1895-1908. Bury Town 1885-95. Bury United 1908-23.
Previous Leagues: Norfolk & Suffolk Border, Essex & Suffolk Border, Eastern Counties 1935-64, 76-87, 97-2006, Metropolitan 1964-71, Southern 1971-76, 87-97
Club Colours (change): All blue with white (orange/black/orange)

Ground Capacity: 3,500 **Seats:** 300 **Covered:** 1,500 **Clubhouse:** Yes **Shop:** Yes

Directions
Follow signs to Town Centre from A14. At second roundabout take first left into Northgate Street then left into Mustow Street at T junction at lights and left again into Cotton Lane. Ground is 350 yards on the right.

Previous Grounds: Kings Road 1888-1978

Record Attendance: 2,500 v Enfield - FA Cup 1986
Record Victory: Not known
Record Defeat: Not known
Record Goalscorer: Doug Tooley
Record Appearances: Doug Tooley
Additional Records: Paid £1,500 to Chelmsford City for Mel Springett
Received £5,500 from Ipswich Town for Simon Milton
Senior Honours:
Eastern Counties League 1963-64.
Suffolk Premier Cup x10 Most recently 2012-13.
Southern League Division One Central 2009-10

10 YEAR RECORD

04-05	05-06	06-07	07-08	08-09	09-10	10-11	11-12	12-13	13-14
ECP 2	ECP 2	Isth1N 17	Isth1N 7	SthC 7	SthC 1	Isth P 3	Isth P 5	Isth P 7	Isth P 15

BURY TOWN MATCH RESULTS 2013-14

Date	Comp	H/A	Opponents	Att:	Result		Goalscorers	Pos	No.
Aug 10	IsthP	A	East Thurrock	173	D	2-2	Clark 55 Bailey-Dennis 71	10	1
13	IsthP	H	Harrow Borough	374	W	3-2	Bailey-Dennis 9 Sands 40 53	3	2
17	IsthP	H	Hampton & Richmond B	356	D	0-0		10	3
20	IsthP	A	AFC Hornchurch	218	D	0-0		11	4
24	IsthP	A	Leiston	254	W	4-0	Sands 17 Bridges 34 45 Semple 64	9	5
26	IsthP	H	Canvey Town	461	L	0-1		11	6
31	IsthP	A	Carshalton Athletic	175	W	3-1	Clark 2 43 Patrick 40	9	7
Sept 7	IsthP	H	Wealdstone	737	L	0-1		9	8
10	IsthP	H	Enfield	251	D	3-3	Bridges 6 Bullard 27 Sands 90	10	9
14	***FAC1Q***	***H***	***Thurrock***	***234***	***L***	***0-1***			10
21	IsthP	A	Metropolitan Police	425	W	3-0	Sands 25 64 Tolley 43	10	11
25	IsthP	A	Grays Athletic	179	L	3 4	Sands 56 Logan 82 Wright 90		12
Oct 1	IsthP	H	Dulwich Hamlet	273	L	0-4		11	13
5	IsthP	H	Hendon	301	L	0-4		14	14
19	***FAT1Q***	***H***	***Dereham***	***217***	***W***	***2-0***	***Tolley 36 52***		15
26	IsthP	A	Cray Wandferers	104	W	3-1	Semple 27 Roulston 30 Bullard 69	9	16
Nov 2	**FATQ2**	**H**	**Chatham Town**	**238**	**W**	**2-1**	**Clark 51 Wales 66**		17
12	IsthP	H	Lewes	293	W	2-1	Short 28 Semple 90	9	18
16	***FAT3Q***	***H***	***Grays Athletic***	***305***	***W***	***5-1***	***Clark 3 (pen) 52 Bailey-Denis 38 Semple 60 Tolley 86***		19
23	IsthP	A	Bognor Regis Town	423	L	2-5	Clark 69 Tolley 86	9	20
30	***FAT1Q***	***H***	***Eastleigh***	***321***	***L***	***0-3***			21
Dec 7	IsthP	A	Maidstone United	1615	D	1-1	Patrick 79	12	22
10	IsthP	H	Wingate & Finchley	202	W	2-0	Williams 42 (og) Tolley 72	9	23
14	IsthP	A	Harrow Borough	101	W	2-0	Bailey-Dennis 15 Clark 89 (pen)	9	24
21	IsthP	H	East Thurrock U	225	D	0-0		9	25
26	IsthP	A	Canvey Island	296	W	2-0	Patrick 3 Roulston 39	8	26
28	IsthP	H	AFC Hornchurch	367	W	3-2	Clark 8 Wright 12 Bentley 52 (og)	8	27
Jan 11	IsthP	H	Thamesmead Town	327	D	0-0		8	28
18	IsthP	A	Lowestoft Town	568	W	3-2	Short 47 Bullard 52 Kennedy 71	8	29
21	IsthP	H	Grays Athletic	275	W	2-1	Clark 8 82	7	30
25	IsthP	A	Wealdstone	707	L	0-3		8	31
Feb 4	IsthP	H	Leiston	353	L	0-2		8	32
11	IsthP	A	Enfield Town	265	L	0-1		8	33
18	IsthP	H	Carshalton Athletic	239	L	0-1		8	34
22	IsthP	H	Margate	305	D	1-1	Brame 36	8	35
March 8	IsthP	H	Billericay Town	346	L	0-1		12	36
11	IsthP	A	Hampton & Richmond B	139	L	0-3		12	37
15	IsthP	A	Wingate & Finchley	118	L	0-1		12	38
18	IsthP	H	Kingstonian	238	L	0-3		13	39
22	IsthP	H	Bognor Regis Town	410	W	2-0	Nwachukwu 29 (pen) Jordan 58	15	40
27	IsthP	A	Hendon	116	L	0-1		16	41
29	IsthP	A	Kingstonian	251	L	1-2	Finch 90	16	42
April 1	IsthP	A	Dulwich Hamlet	477	L	0-1		16	43
5	IsthP	H	Maidstone United	540	L	1-2	Nwachukwu 14	17	44
8	IsthP	A	Billericay Town	202	D	0-0		17	45
12	IsthP	H	Cray Wanderers	305	W	1-0	Nwachukwu 82	16	46
15	IsthP	H	Metropolitan Police	248	W	2-1	Brame 87 Wright 90 (pen)	14	47
19	IsthP	A	Lewes	510	W	4-1	Wales 40 Allen 55 Roulston 73 Bailey 78	14	48
21	IsthP	H	Lowestoft Town	**589**	L	1-2	Bailey 32	15	49
26	IsthP	A	Thamesmead Town	91	L	2-4	Roulston 50 62	15	50

GOALSCORERS	Lge	FAC	FAT	Total	Pens	Hat-tricks	Cons Run
Clark	8		3	11	2		2
Sands	7			7			2
Tolley	4		3	7			
Roulston	5			5			
Bailey-Dennis	3		1	4			
Semple	3		1	4			2
Bridges	3			3			
Bullard	3			3			
Nwachukwu	3			3	1		
Patrick	3			3			
Wright	3			3	1		

	Lge	FAC	FAT	Total	Pens	Hat-tricks	Cons Run
Bailey	2			2			
Brame	2			2			
Jordan	2			2			
Short	2			2			
Wales	1		1	2			
Allen	1			1			
Finch	1			1			
Kennedy	1			1			
Logan	1			1			
Opponents	2			2			

Cons Run - Consecutive scoring games.

CANVEY ISLAND

Chairman: TBA
Secretary: Gary Sutton (T) 07790 025 828 (E) gary.sutton@sky.com
Commercial Manager: (T)
Programme Editor: Glen Eckett (T) 07740 921 532
Ground Address: The Prospects Stadium, Park Lane, Canvey Island, Essex SS8 7PX
(T) 01268 682 991 **Manager:** Danny Heale

Club Factfile

Founded: 1926 **Nickname:** The Gulls
Previous Names: None
Previous Leagues: Southend & District, Thurrock & Thames Combination, Parthenon, Metropolitan, Greater London 1964-71, Essex Senior 1971-95, Isthmian 1995-2004, Conference 2004-06
Club Colours (change): Yellow and sky blue/sky blue/yellow (White with sky blue trim/white with sky blue trim/sky blue)

Ground Capacity: 4,100 **Seats:** 500 **Covered:** 827 **Clubhouse:** Yes **Shop:** Yes

Directions
A130 from A13 or A127 at Sadlers Farm roundabout.
One mile through Town Centre, first right past old bus garage.

Previous Grounds: None

Record Attendance: 3,553 v Aldershot Town - Isthmian League 2002-03
Record Victory: Not Known
Record Defeat: Not Known
Record Goalscorer: Andy Jones
Record Appearances: Steve Ward
Additional Records: Paid £5,000 to Northwich Victoria for Chris Duffy
Received £4,500 from Farnborough Town for Brian Horne
Senior Honours:
Isthmian Division 1 1993-94, Premier Division 2003-04.
FA Trophy 2000-01. Essex Senior Cup 1998-99, 2000-01, 2001-02.

10 YEAR RECORD

04-05	05-06	06-07	07-08	08-09	09-10	10-11	11-12	12-13	13-14
Conf N 18	Conf N 4	Isth1N 6	Isth1N 5	Isth P 12	Isth P 16	Isth P 6	Isth P 8	Isth P 8	Isth P 13

CANVEY ISLAND MATCH RESULTS 2013-14

Date	Comp	H/A	Opponents	Att:	Result		Goalscorers	Pos	No.
Aug 10	IsthP	H	Kingstonian	388	L	0-1		19	1
13	IsthP	A	Cray Wanderers	172	L	1-2	Nash 40	22	2
17	IsthP	A	Lewes	532	L	0-1		22	3
20	IsthP	H	Lowestoft Town	341	D	0-0		22	4
26	IsthP	A	Bury Town	461	W	1-0	Bellotti 18	19	5
31	IsthP	A	Bognor Regis Town	433	L	0-5		21	6
Sept 7	IsthP	H	Enfield	461	W	2-1	Smith 54 (pen) Imber 74 (og)	19	7
11	IsthP	H	Wingate & Finchley	185	W	2-0	Hawes 32 Thomas 82	15	8
14	***FAC1Q***	***A***	***Aveley***	***131***	***W***	***5-2***	***CURRAN 3 (all pens)Thomas 2***		9
17	IsthP	H	Billericay Town	312	L	1-2	Curran 38	15	10
21	IsthP	A	Dulwich Hamlet	171	L	0-1		16	11
24	IsthP	A	Leiston	190	W	2-0	Chatting 26 Bartley 69	14	12
28	***FAC2Q***	***H***	***St Neots Town***	***256***	***D***	***2-2***	***Dumas 19 Bellotti 82***		13
Oct 5	IsthP	A	Carshalton Athletic	223	D	1-1	Thomas 50 (pen)	15	14
8	IsthP	H	Maidstone United	373	L	0-1		15	15
12	***FAC3Q***	***H***	***North Green ford***	***332***	***W***	***2-1***	***Bellotti 40 Curran 90 (pen)***		16
19	***FAT1Q***	***A***	***Heybridge Swifts***	***174***	***W***	***2-1***	***Chatting 26 Edwards 65***		17
26	***FAC4Q***	***A***	***Biggleswade Town***	***678***	***L***	***0-1***			18
Nov 2	***FAT 2Q***	***H***	***East Thurrock United***	***266***	***L***	***0-2***			19
9	IsthP	H	Hampton & Richmond B	273	W	2-1	Sands 40 56	15	20
12	IsthP	H	Grays Athletic	292	W	1-0	Sellers 64	14	21
16	IsthP	A	Metropolitan Police	154	W	1-0	Bartley 90	10	22
21	IsthP	H	Harrow Borough	232	L	1-3	Ademola 24	12	23
25	IsthP	A	Hendon	129	L	2 4	Curran 12 63 (pen)	14	24
30	IsthP	A	Margate	383	D	1-1	Ademola 39	15	25
Dec 2	IsthP	H	Thamsmead Town	204	D	2-2	Stokes 2 (pen) Sellers 34	13	26
7	IsthP	H	East Thurrock United	291	W	2-1	Curran 65 Bartley 90	10	27
14	IsthP	H	Cray Wanderers	391	W	4-0	Talbot 14 (og) Stokes 64 (pen) 72 Alaile 90	10	28
21	IsthP	A	Kingstonian	335	L	1-3	Chatting 13	10	29
26	IsthP	H	Bury Town	296	L	0-2		12	30
28	IsthP	A	Lowestoft Town	498	L	1-2	Belloti 42	14	31
Jan 11	IsthP	H	Wealdstone	397	W	3-2	Hallett 21 Stickland 85 Humphrey 90	12	32
14	IsthP	H	Lewes	239	D	3-3	SANDS 3 (59 62 76)	11	33
21	IsthP	H	Leiston	217	L	2-3	Sands 62 70	13	34
25	IsthP	A	Enfield	435	D	3-3	Hallett 61 84 Curran 75	14	35
Feb 8	IsthP	A	Maidstone United	1794	D	1-1	Curran 50	13	36
11	IsthP	A	Wingate & Finchley	119	W	4-0	Hallett 42 Sands 61 Curran 72 76	11	37
15	IsthP	H	Dulwich Hamlet	341	W	2-1	Curran 33 Chatting 43	10	38
22	IsthP	A	Grays Atheltic	253	W	4-1	Humphrey 23 Chatting 30 Sands 43 Jones 56	9	39
25	IsthP	A	AFC Hornchurch	232	D	1-1	Sands 47	9	40
March 1	IsthP	H	Carshalton Athletic	333	W	3-2	Curran 4 (pen) 88 (pen) Sands 56	8	41
8	IsthP	A	Hampton & Richmond B	333	W	2-0	Jones 38 Chatting 56	9	42
11	IsthP	A	Billericay Town	321	W	4-1	Bryan-Edwards 50 Sands 68 Curran 84 Chatting 90	8	43
15	IsthP	H	Metropolitan Police	341	D	1-1	Curran 54	8	44
18	IsthP	H	Bognor Regis Town	237	L	1-3	Sands 45	8	45
22	IsthP	A	Harrow Borough	161	L	0-2		9	46
29	IsthP	H	Margate	406	W	2-0	Bryan-Edwards 81 Curran 87 (pen)	9	47
April 5	IsthP	A	East Thurrock United	275	L	0-2		10	48
12	IsthP	H	Hendon	330	D	0-0		10	49
19	IsthP	A	Thamesmead Town	101	L	0-2		12	50
21	IsthP	H	AFC Hornchurch	373	D	1 1	Bartley 32	12	51
26	IsthP	A	Wealdstone	906	L	0-2		13	52

GOALSCORERS	Lge	FAC	FAT	Total	Pens	Hat-tricks	Cons Run
Curran	14	4		18	8		4
Sands	13			13		1	3
Chatting	6		1	7			2
Bellotti	4	2		6			
Bartley	4			4			
Hallett	4			4			
Thomas	2	2		4	1		
Ademola	2			2			
Bryan-Edwards	2			2			
Humphrey	2			2			
Jones	2			2			

	Lge	FAC	FAT	Total	Pens	Hat-tricks	Cons Run
Sellers	2			2			
Stokes	2			2	2		
Alaila	1			1			
Dumas		1		1			
Edwards			1	1			
Hawes	1			1			
Nash	1			1			
Smith	1			1	1		
Stickland	1			1			
Opponents	2			2			

Cons Run - Consecutive scoring games.

DULWICH HAMLET

Chairman: Jack Payne
Secretary: Martin Eede (T) 07957 395 948 (E) eede.martin@gmail.com
Commercial Manager: (T)
Programme Editor: John Lawrence (T) 07799 500 415
Ground Address: Champion Hill Stadium, Dog Kennell Hill, Edgar Kail Way SE22 8BD
(T) 0207 274 8707 **Manager:** Gavin Rose

2014-15 pre-season action against Crystal Palace.
Photo: Joel Virgo

Club Factfile

Founded: 1893 **Nickname:** Hamlet
Previous Names: None
Previous Leagues: Camberwell 1894-97, Southern Suburban 1897-1900, 01-07, Dulwich 1900-01, Spartan 1907-08

Club Colours (change): Navy blue and pink/navy blue/navy blue (Red, white & black hoops/red/red)

Ground Capacity: 3,000 **Seats:** 500 **Covered:** 1,000 **Clubhouse:** Yes **Shop:** Yes

Directions
East Dulwich station, 200 yards.
Denmark Hill station, 10 minutes walk.
Herne Hill station then bus 37 stops near ground.
Buses 40 & 176 from Elephant & Castle, 185 from Victoria.

Previous Grounds: Woodwarde Rd 1893-95,College Farm 95-96,Sunray Ave 1896-02,Freeman's Gd,Champ Hill 02-12,Champ Hill (old grd)12-92

Record Attendance: 1,835 v Southport - FA Cup 1998-99
Record Victory: 13-0 v Walton-on-Thames, Surrey Senior Cup, 1936-37
Record Defeat: 1-10 v Hendon, Isthmian league, 1963-64
Record Goalscorer: Edgar Kail - 427 (1919-33)
Record Appearances: Reg Merritt - 576 (1950-66)
Additional Records: Received £35,000 from Charlton Athletic for Chris Dickson 2007

Senior Honours:
FA Amateur Cup 1919-20, 31-32, 33-34, 36-37.
Isthmian League Premier Division x4, Division One 1977-78, Division One South 2012-13. London Senior Cup x5. Surrey Senior Cup x16.
London Challenge Cup 1998-99.

10 YEAR RECORD

04-05	05-06	06-07	07-08	08-09	09-10	10-11	11-12	12-13	13-14
Isth1 15	Isth1 13	Isth1S 8	Isth1S 6	Isth1S 12	Isth1S 12	Isth1S 5	Isth1S 3	Isth1S 1	Isth P 6

DULWICH HAMLET MATCH RESULTS 2013-14

Date	Comp	H/A	Opponents	Att:	Result		Goalscorers	Pos	No.
Aug 10	IsthP	H	Lowestoft	542	W	2-0	Green 26 Ozturner 73 (pen)	5	1
12	IsthP	A	Hendon	251	W	2-1	Ottaway 20 34	2	2
17	IsthP	A	Metropolitan Police	262	D	0-0		4	3
20	IsthP	H	Cray Wanderers	479	W	4-0	Green 12 Ozturner 45 80 Ottaway 70	3	4
24	IsthP	H	Carshalton Athletic	492	W	3-1	Lodge 15 Boyer 49 Ozturner 88	2	5
26	IsthP	A	Grays Athletic	344	D	0-0		2	6
31	IsthP	H	AFC Hornchurch	607	L	2-3	Clunis 35 Ozturner 90 (pen)	4	7
Sept 7	IsthP	A	Harrow Borough	313	L	1-3	Clunis 11	6	8
11	IsthP	A	Thamesmead	202	W	3-1	Boyer 12 Henry-Davies 13 55	6	9
14	***FAC1Q***	***H***	***Shoreham***	***341***	***W***	***6-0***	***Clunis 14 Vidal 23 Oztumer 36 (pen) 42 Boyer 57 Daly 76***		10
21	IsthP	H	Canvey Island	571	W	1-0	James 47	5	11
24	IsthP	H	Margate	466	W	2-0	James 44 Daly 89	6	12
28	***FAC2Q***	***A***	***Margate***	***508***	***W***	***2-1***	***Green 51 Pinnock 62***		13
Oct 1	IsthP	A	Bury Town	273	W	4-0	Oztumer 35 75 (pen) Walker 45 57	2	14
6	IsthP	H	Lewes	712	W	4-2	Brinkhurst 13 (og) Walker 48 James 57 Okoye 69	2	15
12	***FAC3Q***	***A***	***Hemel Hempstead T***	***949***	***L***	***1-2***	***Ozturner 23***		16
19	***FAT1Q***	***H***	***Harrow Borough***	***81***	***W***	***2-1***	***Daly 24 Samuels 90***		17
26	IsthP	H	Billericay Town	706	W	2-1	Ozturner 29 (pen) Clunis 74	2	18
Nov 2	***FAT 2Q***	***H***	***Leatherhead***	***296***	***W***	***3-0***	***Daly 36 80 Ozturner 52 (pen)***		19
9	IsthP	A	Bognor Regis Town	502	L	2-4	Lodge 70 76	4	20
16	***FAT3Q***	***H***	***Concord Rangers***	***462***	***D***	***1-1***	***Oztumer 59 (pen)***		21
19	***FAT3Qr***	***A***	***Concord Rangers***	***156***	***L***	***3-4***	***Lodge 22 Daly 90 Ozturner 120***		22
23	IsthP	A	Enfield Town	270	W	4-3	OZTURNER 3 (25 33 80 pen) Vidal 895	5	23
30	IsthP	H	Wealdstone	843	L	1-4	Ozturner 47	5	24
Dec 7	IsthP	A	Wingate & Finchley	225	W	3-2	Daly 1 Ozturner 55 Green 90	5	25
10	IsthP	H	Hendon	551	W	2-0	Daly 59 Flegg 77 (og)	5	26
17	IsthP	H	Maidstone United	817	W	2-0	Clunis 34 Walker 58	3	27
21	IsthP	A	Lowestoft Town	389	L	0-2		4	28
26	IsthP	H	Grays Athletic	558	W	3-2	Clunis 25 Ozturner 33 Pinney 56		29
28	IsthP	A	Cray Wanderers	334	W	6-0	Clunis 11 OZTURNER 3 (19 50 71) Okaye 64 Samuels 74	2	30
Jan 7	IsthP	A	Leiston	154	L	1-2	Clunis 5	2	31
11	IsthP	A	Kingstonian	590	L	1 2	Page (og) 19	3	32
18	IsthP	H	Hampton & Richmond B	756	D	2-2	Ozturner 10 (pen) Clunis 39	4	33
21	IsthP	A	Margate	242	W	4-2	James 58 Lodge 83 Vidal 90 Ozturner 89	2	34
25	IsthP	H	Harrow Borough	810	W	3-2	Clarke 11 James 63 Ozturner 71	1	35
Feb 4	IsthP	A	East Thurrock United	146	W	4-1	OZTURNER 3 (30 pen 51 90 pen) Clunis 16	1	36
11	IsthP	H	Thamesmead Town	488	W	2-0	Clunis 47 Ozturner 90	1	37
15	IsthP	A	Canvey Island	341	L	1-2	Vidal 20	2	38
22	IsthP	H	East Thurrock United	642	W	3-0	Ozturner 43 82 (pen) Clarke 79	2	39
25	IsthP	A	Carshalton Athletic	277	W	4-0	Clunis 20 Lodge 30 Daly 38 50	1	40
March 1	IsthP	A	Lewes	757	L	0-2		1	41
4	IsthP	H	Metropolitan Police	537	L	1-2	Ozturner 56 (pen)	1	42
8	IsthP	H	Bognor Regis Town	792	L	0-2		1	43
15	IsthP	A	Maidstone United	2296	L	3-4	Clunis 26 Whitnell 50 Ozturner 67	3	44
22	IsthP	H	Enfield Town	732	D	2-2	Lodge 30 Adeniyi 45	2	45
25	IsthP	A	AFC Hornchurch	254	D	1-1	James 78	2	46
29	IsthP	A	Wealdstone	1151	D	2-2	Kavanagh 62 Deen 82	2	47
April 1	IsthP	H	Bury Town	477	W	1-0	Vidal 47	2	48
5	IsthP	H	Wingate & Finchley	668	W	2-2	Daly 37 Lodge 43 68 Vidal 80	2	49
12	IsthP	A	Billericay Town	371	L	0-2		4	50
19	IsthP	H	Leiston	710	L	2-3	Clunis 29 36	6	51
21	IsthP	A	Hampton & Richmond B	505	W	1-0	Ozturner 45	5	52
26	IsthP	H	Kingstonian	**1388**	D	1-1	James 10	6	53

GOALSCORERS	Lge	FAC	FAT	Total	Pens	Hat-tricks	Cons Run
Ozturner	29	3	3	35	12	3	5
Clunis	14	1		15			3
Daly	7	1	4	12			2
Lodge	8		1	9			
James	7			7			
Vidal	6			6			
Walker	4			4			
Boyer	2	1		3			
Green	2	1		3			2
Ottaway	3			3			
Clarke	2			2			
Okoye	2			2			
Adeniyi	1			1			
Dean	1			1			
Henry-Davies	1			1			
Kavanagh	1			1			
Pinney	1			1			
Pinnock	1			1			
Whitnell	1			1			
Sammuels	1		1	2			
Opponents	3			3			

Cons Run - Consecutive scoring games.

EAST THURROCK UNITED

Chairman: Brian Mansbridge
Secretary: Neil Speight **(T)** 07885 313 435 **(E)** speight.n@sky.com
Commercial Manager: **(T)**
Programme Editor: Neil Speight **(T)** 07885 313 435
Ground Address: Rookery Hill, Corringham, Essex SS17 9LB
(T) 01375 644 166 **Manager:** John Coventry

Club Factfile

Founded: 1969 **Nickname:** Rocks
Previous Names: Corringham Social > 1969 (Sunday side)
Previous Leagues: South Essex Combination, Greater London, Metropolitan 1972-75, London Spartan 1975-79, Essex Senior 1979-92, Isthmian 1992-2004, Southern 2004-05
Club Colours (change): Amber with black trim/black (Black & white stripes/white)

Ground Capacity: 3,500 **Seats:** 160 **Covered:** 1,000 **Clubhouse:** Yes **Shop:** Yes

Directions
From A13 London-Southend road,
take A1014 at Stanford-le-Hope for two and half miles,
Ground is on the left.

Previous Grounds: Billet, Stanford-le-Hope 1970-73, 74-76, Grays Athletic 1973-74, Tilbury FC 1977-82, New Thames Club 1982-84

Record Attendance: 1,215 v Woking FA Cup 2003
Record Victory: 7-0 v Coggeshall (H) - Essex Senior League 1984
Record Defeat: 0-9 v Eton Manor (A) - Essex Senior League 1982
Record Goalscorer: Graham Stewart - 102
Record Appearances: Glen Case - 600+
Additional Records: £22,000 from Leyton Orient for Greg Berry 1990
Senior Honours:
Isthmian League Division Three 1999-2000, Division One North 2010-11. East Anglian Cup 2002-03.

10 YEAR RECORD

04-05		05-06		06-07		07-08		08-09		09-10		10-11		11-12		12-13		13-14	
SthE	2	Isth P	12	Isth P	16	Isth P	20	Isth1N	2	Isth1N	5	Isth1N	1	Isth P	10	Isth P	5	Isth P	20

EAST THURROCK UNITED MATCH RESULTS 2013-14

Date	Comp	H/A	Opponents	Att:	Result		Goalscorers	Pos	No.
Aug 10	IsthP	H	Bury Town	173	D	2-2	Bryant 30 39	11	1
13	IsthP	A	Billericay Town	342	W	1-0	Korantang 11	4	2
17	IsthP	A	Kingstonian	261	L	0-3		14	3
20	IsthP	H	Lewes	160	L	0-2		15	4
24	IsthP	H	Grays Athletic	267	W	3-0	Thurgood 45 Bryant 65 90	12	5
26	IsthP	A	Carshalton Athletic	191	W	2-1	Wanadio 57 81	10	6
31	IsthP	H	Hampton & Richmond B	148	L	0-1		11	7
Sept 7	IsthP	A	AFC Hornchurch	328	L	0-3		13	8
10	IsthP	A	Margate	153	D	1-1	McKenzie 85	14	9
14	***FAC1Q***	***A***	***AFC Hornchurch***	***273***	***D***	***1-1***	***Stephen 59 (pen)***		10
17	***FAC1Qr***	***H***	***AFC Hornchurch***	***156***	***L***	***1-2***	***McKenzie 39***		11
21	IsthP	H	Cray Wanderers	124	W	3-0	McKenzie 8 Bryant 60 Eagle 90	11	12
24	IsthP	H	Lowestoft Town	143	L	0-1		13	13
28	IsthP	A	Harrow Borough	128	D	2-2	McKenzie 58 Sheeham 88	13	14
Oct 5	IsthP	A	Thamesmead	56	L	0-1		13	15
19	***FAT1Q***	***A***	***Eastbourne Town***	***110***	***D***	***0-0***			16
22	***FAT1Qr***	***H***	***Eastbourne Town***	***140***	***W***	***6 2***	***McKenzie 14 44 Bryant 30 Hallett 40 Sheehan 54 Stephan 60 (pen)***		17
26	IsthP	H	Leiston	185	L	1-2	McKenzie 64	15	18
Nov 1	***FAT2Q***	***A***	***Canvey Island***	***266***	***W***	***2-0***	***Gilbey 2 Hallett 74***		19
9	IsthP	A	Wingate & Finchley	128	L	3-4	Stephan 57 McKenzie 62 Smith 88	19	20
16	***FAT3Q***	***H***	***Merthyr Town***	***163***	***W***	***4-2***	***Stephan 62 72 Hallett 77 82***		21
23	IsthP	A	Hendon	105	D	2-2	Hallett 50 Bryant 75	19	22
26	IsthP	A	Metropolitan Police	68	W	2-1	Stephan 4 (pen) Hallett 45	18	23
30	***FAT1***	***H***	***Dover Athletic***	***273***	***D***	***1-1***	***Bryant 67***		24
Dec 2	***FAT1r***	***A***	***Dover Athletic***	***295***	***L***	***1-3***	***Thurgood 61***		25
7	IsthP	A	Canvey Island	291	L	1-2	Hopkin 37	19	26
14	IsthP	H	Billericay Town	205	D	2-2	Bryant 22 66	20	27
21	IsthP	A	Bury Town	225	D	0-0		20	28
26	IsthP	H	Carshalton Athletic	115	L	2-3	Stephan 20 (pen) Thurgood 75		29
28	IsthP	A	Lewes	651	D	2-2	Bryant 11 Easterford 24	20	30
Jan 11	IsthP	A	Bognor Regis Town	418	L	1-3	Stephan 13 (pen)	20	31
18	IsthP	H	Enfield Town	293	D	1-1	Stephan 59 (pen)	20	32
21	IsthP	A	Lowestoft Town	288	L	0-3		21	33
25	IsthP	H	AFC Hornchuch	306	L	1-2	Hopkins 39	21	34
Feb 4	IsthP	H	Dulwich Hamlet	146	L	1-4	McKenzie 26	21	35
22	IsthP	A	Dulwich Hamlet	642	L	0-3		22	36
25	IsthP	H	Kingstonian	103	W	2-0	Higgins 13 Drage 51 (og)	20	37
March 1	IsthP	H	Thamesmead Town	101	W	3-1	Higgins 72 Symonds 78 Richmond 79	20	38
8	IsthP	H	Wingate & Finchley	155	L	0-1		20	39
12	IsthP	A	Grays Athletic	240	L	0-2		20	40
15	IsthP	A	Wealdstone	686	L	0-5		21	41
18	IsthP	H	Maidstone United	234	W	3-1	Smith 6 68 Richmond 44	21	42
22	IsthP	H	Hendon	147	W	6-1	HIGGINS 3 (2 39 69) Richmond 44 Gilbey 72 80	20	43
25	IsthP	A	Hampton & Richmond B	136	L	0-1		20	44
29	IsthP	A	Maidstone United	1731	D	1-1	Higgins 3	21	45
April 1	IsthP	H	Harrow Borough	136	L	1-3	Higgins 27 (pen)	21	46
3	IsthP	H	Wealdstone	299	L	0-3		21	47
5	IsthP	H	Canvey Island	275	W	2-0	Higgins 13 (pen) 19	21	48
8	IsthP	H	Margate	141	L	1-4	Stephan 61 (pen)	21	49
12	IsthP	A	Leiston	198	L	1-3	Higgins 30	21	50
15	IsthP	A	Cray Wanderers	132	W	3-1	Higgins 3 85 Bryant 19	21	51
19	IsthP	H	Metropolitan Police	145	D	1 1	Smith 48	20	52
23	IsthP	A	Enfield Town	662	W	5 3	Gilbey 8 Sheehan 12 Chalk 14 (og) Richmond 24 Smith 74	20	53
26	IsthP	H	Bognor Regis Town	**314**	W	4 2	Bryant 33 Gilbey 55 70 Higgins 80	20	54

GOALSCORERS	Lge	FAC	FAT	Total	Pens	Hat-tricks	Cons Run
Bryant	11		2	13			
Higgins	13			13	2	1	2
McKenzie	6	1	2	9			2
Stephan	5	1	3	9	7		2
Gilbey	5		1	6			
Hallett	2		4	6			
Smith	5			5			
Richmond	4			4			2
Sheehan	2		1	3			
Thurgood	2		1	3			
Hopkins	2			2			
Wanadio	2			2			
Eagle	1			1			
Easterford	1			1			
Korantang	1			1			
Simmnds	1			1			
Opponents	2			2			

Cons Run - Consecutive scoring games.

ENFIELD TOWN

Chairman: Paul Millington
Secretary: Nigel Howard (T) 07969 831 140 (E) nigel.howard71@gmail.com
Commercial Manager: (T)
Programme Editor: Ken Brazier (T) 07855 647 008
Ground Address: Queen Elizabeth Stadium, Donkey Lane, Enfield EN1 3PL
(T) 0208 350 4064 **Manager:** George Borg

Photo taken at pre-season friendly against YB SK Beveren 26th July 2014 (played at KSK Svelta Melsele)
Back Row: (left to right): Pat Folan (coach), Bradley Quinton (player coach), Jamie Pyper, Nathan McDonald (goalkeeper), Ryan Doyle, Taylor Hastings, Liam Hope, Phil Kane, George Borg (manager), Neil Butterfield (kit man).
Front row: Vincent Romanelli, Neil Cousins, Joe Stevens, Jordan Lockie, Corey Whitely, Nathan Livings

Club Factfile

Founded: 2001 **Nickname:** ET's or Towners
Previous Names: Broke away from Enfield F.C. in 2001
Previous Leagues: Essex Senior League

Club Colours (change): White/blue/blue (Red & yellow hoops/red/red & yellow hoops)

Ground Capacity: **Seats:** Yes **Covered:** Yes **Clubhouse:** **Shop:**

Directions

From the M25: Head towards London on the A10 from junction 25. Turn right into Carterhatch Lane at the Halfway House pub. Donkey Lane is first left after the pub.

From London/North Circular Road: Head north up the A10 and turn left to Carterhatch Lane at the Halfway House pub. Donkey Lane is first left after the pub.

Previous Grounds: Brimsdown Rovers FC 2001-2010

Record Attendance: 562 v Enfield - Middlesex Charity Cup 2002-03
Record Victory: 7-0 v Ilford (A) - 29/04/2003
Record Defeat: Not known
Record Goalscorer: Dan Clarke - 68
Record Appearances: Stuart Snowden - 147
Additional Records:

Senior Honours:
Essex Senior League 2002-03, 04-05. Isthmian League Division 1 North Play-offs 2011-12.

10 YEAR RECORD

04-05	05-06	06-07	07-08	08-09	09-10	10-11	11-12	12-13	13-14
ESen 1	SthE 3	Isth1N 3	Isth1N 12	Isth1N 12	Isth1N 4	Isth1N 6	Isth1N 2	Isth P 16	Isth P 19

ENFIELD TOWN MATCH RESULTS 2013-14

Date	Comp	H/A	Opponents	Att:	Result		Goalscorers	Pos	No.
Aug 10	IsthP	H	Metropolitan Police	341	**W**	2-1	Hope 21 64	6	1
12	IsthP	A	Kingstonian	342	L	0-3		16	2
17	IsthP	A	Grays Athletic	254	L	0-2		17	3
20	IsthP	H	Margate	354	D	1-1	Hope	16	4
24	IsthP	H	Hendon	289	**W**	3-2	Wallace 2 Hope 48 90 (pen)	13	5
26	IsthP	A	Wealdstone	602	L	1-4	Bailey 45 (og)	14	6
31	IsthP	H	Thamesmead Town	339	**W**	3-1	Wallace 35 Campbell 57 Hope 82	13	7
Sept 7	IsthP	A	Canvey Island	461	L	1-2	Osei 77	14	8
10	IsthP	A	Bury Town	251	D	3-3	Hope 19 Kendall 25 Sands 87	14	9
14	***FAC1Q***	***A***	***St Albans City***	***423***	***L***	***1-6***	***Kendall 80***		10
21	IsthP	H	Lowestoft Town	363	D	2-2	Wild 59 Whiteley 84	14	11
24	IsthP	H	AFC Hornchurch	312	L	0-2		16	12
Oct 5	IsthP	A	Bognor Regis Town	407	L	1-5	Whiteley 50	16	13
12	IsthP	H	Billericay Town	554	L	1-2	Kirby 20	20	14
19	***FAT1Q***	***H***	***Lowestoft Town***	***240***	***W***	***2-1***	***Campbell 62 Hope 84***		15
22	IsthP	A	Lewes	287	L	1-3		20	16
26	IsthP	A	Maidstone United	1933	L	0-3		21	17
Nov 2	***FAT2Q***	***H***	***Grays Athletic***	***260***	***L***	***0-1***			18
12	IsthP	H	Wingate & Finchley	295	L	0-3		21	19
23	IsthP	H	Dulwich Hamet	270	L	3-4	Hope 54 Olando 59 Campbell 89	21	20
30	IsthP	A	Leiston	221	L	1-6	Osie 58	22	21
Dec 7	IsthP	H	Carshalton Athletic	321	D	2-2	Hope 5 O'Brien 18	22	22
14	IsthP	H	Kingstonian	338	L	0-1		22	23
26	IsthP	H	Wealdstone	591	L	2-4			24
28	IsthP	A	Margate	391	L	0-1		23	25
Jan 11	IsthP	H	Cray Wanderers	334	**W**	1-0	Brayley 46	22	26
18	IsthP	A	East Thurrock United	293	D	1-1	Hope 42 (pen)	22	27
21	IsthP	A	AFC Hornchurch	200	L	0-3		22	28
25	IsthP	H	Canvey Island	435	D	3-3	Hope 4 (pen) 90 Stevens 90	22	29
Feb 3	IsthP	A	Hendon	180	**W**	3-0	Hope 38 Campbell 57 Richards 86	22	30
11	IsthP	H	Bury Town	265	**W**	1-0	Stevens 55	22	31
25	IsthP	A	Metropolitan Police	142	L	1-3	Og 43	21	32
March 4	IsthP	A	Thamesmead Town	106	D	1-1	Hope 72 (pen)	22	33
8	IsthP	A	Harrow Borough	244	D	1-1	Hope 55 (pen)	22	34
11	IsthP	H	Harrow Borough	287	**W**	1-0	Whiteley 30	21	35
15	IsthP	H	Hampton & Richmond B	371	**W**	3-0	Hope 29 Whiteley 39 Richards 59	20	36
18	IsthP	H	Grays Athletic	357	D	1-1	Quinton 85	20	37
22	IsthP	A	Dulwich Hamlet	732	D	2-2	Richards 44 Quinton 81	21	38
27	IsthP	A	Billericay Town	275	**W**	2-0	Hope 8 (pen) Whitely 70	20	39
29	IsthP	H	Leiston	379	L	1-3	Head 16 (og)	20	40
Apr 1	IsthP	A	Hampton & Richmond B	242	L	0-2		20	41
3	IsthP	H	Bognor Regis Town	375	**W**	2-1	Robson 25 Kirby 85	20	42
5	IsthP	A	Carshalton Athletic	392	**W**	4-1	Whiteley 20 45 Quinton 52 Stevens 84	19	43
8	IsthP	H	Lewes	337	**W**	2-1	Hope 55 Campbell 75	19	44
12	IsthP	H	Maidstone United	594	D	1-1	Hope 40 (pen)	19	45
15	IsthP	A	Lowestoft Town	513	L	0-2		19	46
19	IsthP	A	Wingate & Finchley	345	D	1-1	Hahn 53	19	47
21	IsthP	H	East Thurrock United	**662**	L	3-5	Doyle 1 Hahn 12 Hope 90	19	48
26	IsthP	A	Cray Wanderers	318	**W**	2-1	Lockie 39 Doyle 74	19	49

GOALSCORERS	Lge	FAC	FAT	Total	Pens	Hat-tricks	Cons Run
Hope	20	1		21	7		2
Whiteley	7			7			2
Campbell	4		1	5			
Quinton	3			3			2
Richards	3			3			
Stevens	3			3			
Doyle	2			2			
Hahn	2			2			2
Kendall	1	1		2			2
Kirby	2			2			
Osei	2			2			
Wallace	2			2			
Brayley	1			1			
Lockie	1			1			
O'Brien	1			1			
Orlando	1			1			
Robson	1			1			
Sands	1			1			
Wild	1			1			
Opponents	2			2			

Cons Run - Consecutive scoring games.

GRAYS ATHLETIC

Chairman: Keith Burns
Secretary: Janet Packer **(T)** 07738 355 619 **(E)** graysathleticfc@hotmail.co.uk
Commercial Manager: **(T)**
Programme Editor: Glyn Balmer **(T)** 07870 592 382
Ground Address: Aveley FC, Mill Field, Mill Field Road, Aveley RM15 4SJ
(T) 07752 161 633 **Manager:** Jody Brown

Club Factfile

Founded: 1890 **Nickname:** The Blues
Previous Names: None
Previous Leagues: Athenian 1912-14, 58-83, London 1914-24, 26-39, Kent 1924-26, Corinthian 1945-58, Isthmian 1958-2004, Conference 2004-10

Club Colours (change): All royal blue (All white)

Ground Capacity: 4,000 **Seats:** 400 **Covered:** 400 **Clubhouse:** Yes **Shop:** No

Directions
London - Southend A1306, turn into Sandy Lane at Aveley.

Previous Grounds: Recreation Ground Bridge Road. Rookery Hill (East Thurrock Utd). Rush Green Road.

Record Attendance: 9,500 v Chelmsford City - FA Cup 4th Qualifying Round 1959
Record Victory: 12-0 v Tooting & Mitcham United - London League 24/02/1923
Record Defeat: 0-12 v Enfield (A) - Athenian League 20/04/1963
Record Goalscorer: Harry Brand - 269 (1944-52)
Record Appearances: Phil Sammons - 673 (1982-97)
Additional Records:

Senior Honours:
Conference South 2004-05. FA Trophy 2004-05, 05-06. Isthmian Division One North 2012-13.
Essex Senior Cup x8

10 YEAR RECORD

04-05	05-06	06-07	07-08	08-09	09-10	10-11	11-12	12-13	13-14
Conf S 1	Conf 3	Conf 19	Conf 10	Conf 19	Conf 23	Isth1N 10	Isth1N 5	Isth1N 1	Isth P 14

GRAYS ATHLETIC MATCH RESULTS 2013-14

Date	Comp	H/A	Opponents	Att:	Result		Goalscorers	Pos	No.
Aug 10	IsthP	A	Bognor Regis Town	478	W	3-0	Carlos 21 West 64 Gonzales 78	4	1
13	IsthP	H	Leiston	214	W	3-2	Hammond 11 Lalite 41 Carlos 86	2	2
17	IsthP	H	Enfield Town	254	W	2-0	Small 57 West 60	2	3
20	IsthP	A	Wingate & Finchley	179	W	3-1	Carlos 33 90 Baker 82	1	4
24	IsthP	A	East Thurrock United	267	L	0-3		3	5
26	IsthP	H	Dulwich Hamlet	344	D	0-0		3	6
Sept 1	IsthP	H	Billericay Town	313	D	2 2	Duru 55 Carlos 59	5	7
Sept 7	IsthP	A	Kingstonian	394	L	1-4	Duru 13	8	8
10	IsthP	A	Lowestoft	257	D	2-2	Gaughran 48 (og) Hammond 90	8	9
15	***FAC1Q***	***H***	***Romford***	***217***	***W***	***2-1***	***Carlos 7 Beaney 61***		10
21	IsthP	H	Margate	234	W	3-0	Hammond 79 West 88 90	7	11
25	IsthP	H	Bury Town	179	W	4 3	Small 33 Carlos 64 (pen) 66 Baker 76		12
29	***FAC2Q***	***H***	***Tilbury***	***368***	***W***	***3-0***	***Carlos 35 (pen) West 43 60***		13
Oct 5	IsthP	H	AFC Hornchurch	303	L	1-5	West 87	9	14
19	***FAT1Q***	***H***	***Herne Bay***	***154***	***D***	***1-1***	***Carlos 80 (pen)***		15
22	***FAT1Qr***	***A***	***Herne Bay***	***170***	***W***	***2-1***	***Moses 90 Nightingale 120 (aet)***		16
26	IsthP	A	Wealdstone	554	L	1-3	Hammond 5	11	17
Nov 2	***FAT2Q***	***A***	***Enfield Town***	***260***	***W***	***1-0***	***Kendall 42 (og)***		18
12	IsthP	A	Canvey Island	292	L	0-1		13	19
16	***FAT3Q***	***A***	***Bury Town***	***305***	***L***	***1-5***	***Carlos 25***		20
23	IsthP	H	Metropolitan Police	174	D	0-0		15	21
30	IsthP	A	Hampton & Richmond	303	W	2-0	West 37 Carlos 85	11	22
Dec 7	IsthP	H	Harrow Borough	178	W	2-0	Carlos 79 Pope 90	9	23
11	IsthP	H	Hendon	127	L	1-3	Hammond 70		24
14	IsthP	A	Leiston	221	L	1-4	Carlos 86	13	25
26	IsthP	A	Dulwich Hamlet	558	L	2-3	Hammond 31 Nouble 67		26
Jan 11	IsthP	H	Maidstone United	**393**	L	0-1		17	27
18	IsthP	A	Thamesmead Town	117	L	0-1		17	28
21	IsthP	A	Bury Town	275	L	1-2	Beaney 38	18	29
Feb 22	IsthP	H	Canvey Island	253	L	1-4	Yala 3	19	30
25	IsthP	H	Lewes	156	W	4-2	Bunce 21 Nouble 33 56 Yala 50	18	31
March 1	IsthP	A	AFC Hornchurch	341	W	2-1	Nouble 11 (pen) Carlos 35	18	32
5	IsthP	H	Wingate & Finchley	165	W	2-0	Yala 14 Bunce 19	17	33
8	IsthP	A	Lewes	425	W	1-0	Carlos 25	16	34
12	IsthP	H	East Thurrock United	240	W	2-0	Carlos 15 Dixon 70	15	35
15	IsthP	H	Carshalton Athletic	227	L	1-4	Griffiths 67	16	36
18	IsthP	A	Enfield Town	357	D	1-1	Bunce 86	16	37
20	IsthP	H	Cray Wanderers	146	W	3-0	Small 21 Benjamin 75 Carlos 83	15	38
22	IsthP	A	Met Police	123	W	2-1	Benjamin 22 26	13	39
25	IsthP	A	Cray Wanderers	125	L	2-3	Bunce 16 Benjamin 88	13	40
27	IsthP	A	Margate	248	W	5-2	Bunce 27 Carlos 42 90 Benjamin 61 89	12	41
29	IsthP	H	Hampton & Richmond B	193	L	1-3	Orome 39	12	42
April 2	IsthP	H	Kingstonian	189	D	0-0		12	43
5	IsthP	A	Harrow Borough	153	D	2-2	Griffiths 20 Nouble 33	12	44
8	IsthP	A	Carshalton Athletic	130	D	1-1	Carlos 76	12	45
10	IsthP	H	Bognor Regis Town	182	L	3-4	Griffiths 11 Carlos 32 44	12	46
12	IsthP	H	Wealdstone	173	D	1-1	Wilson 72	14	47
15	Isth P	A	Billericay Town	232	L	0-4		15	48
17	IsthP	H	Lowestoft Town	175	D	1-1	Nouble 48 (pen)	14	49
19	IsthP	A	Hendon	144	W	3-2	Benjamin 6 90 Nouble 83	13	50
21	IsthP	H	Thamesmead Town	167	L	1-4	Carlos 40	14	51
26	IsthP	A	Maidstone United	1984	L	1-2	Benjamin 87	14	52

GOALSCORERS	Lge	FAC	FAT	Total	Pens	Hat-tricks	Cons Run
Carlos	21	2	1	24	2		2
Benjamin	9			9			4
West	6	2		8			2
Nouble	7			7	1		2
Hammond	6			6			
Bunce	5			5			2
Griffiths	3			3			
Small	3			3			
Yala	3			3			
Baker	2			2			
Beaney	1	1		2			
Duru	2			2			2
Dixon	1			1			
Gonzales	1			1			
Goodfellow	1		1	1			
Lalite	1			1			
Moses			1	1			
Nightingale			1	1			
Orome	1			1			
Pope	1			1			
Wilson	1			1			
Opponents	1		1	2			

Cons Run - Consecutive scoring games.

HAMPTON & RICHMOND BOROUGH

Chairman: Steve McPherson
Secretary: Nick Hornsey (T) 07768 861 446 (E) secretary@hamptonfc.net
Commercial Manager: (T)
Programme Editor: Rob Overfield (T) 07967 537 845
Ground Address: Accord Beveree Stadium, Beaver Close, Station Road, Hampton TW12 2BX
(T) 0208 8979 2456 **Manager:** Darren Powell & Paul Barry

2013-14 Squad.

Club Factfile

Founded: 1921 **Nickname:** Beavers or Borough
Previous Names: Hampton > 1999
Previous Leagues: Kingston & District, South West Middlesex, Surrey Senior 1959-64, Spartan 1964-71, Athenian 1971-73, Isthmian 1973-2007

Club Colours (change): Red with blue flash/blue/red (Sky blue/white/sky blue)

Ground Capacity: 3,000 **Seats:** 300 **Covered:** 800 **Clubhouse:** Yes **Shop:** Yes

Directions
From M25; Exit M25 at Junction 10 (M3 Richmond). Exit M3 at Junction 1 and take 4th exit (Kempton Park, Kingston). After approximately 3 miles turn left in to High Street, Hampton. Immediately turn left on to Station Road. The entrance to the ground is 200 yards on the right hand side.

Previous Grounds: None

Record Attendance: 2,520 v AFC Wimbledon - 11/10/2005
Record Victory: 11-1 v Eastbourne United - Isthmian League Division 2 South 1991-92
Record Defeat: 0-13 v Hounslow Town - Middlesex Senior Cup 1962-63
Record Goalscorer: Peter Allen - 176 (1964-73)
Record Appearances: Tim Hollands - 750 (1977-95)
Additional Records: Paid £3,000 to Chesham United for Matt Flitter June 2000
Received £40,000 from Queens Park Rangers for Leroy Phillips
Senior Honours:
Isthmian League Premier Division 2006-07.
Spartan League x4. London Senior Cup x2. Middlesex Senior Challenge Cup 2011-12.

10 YEAR RECORD

04-05	05-06	06-07	07-08	08-09	09-10	10-11	11-12	12-13	13-14
Isth P 6	Isth P 5	Isth P 1	Conf S 3	Conf S 2	Conf S 14	Conf S 18	Conf S 21	Isth P 13	Isth P 12

HAMPTON & RICHMOND BOROUGH MATCH RESULTS 2013-14

Date	Comp	H/A	Opponents	Att:	Result		Goalscorers	Pos	No.
Aug 10	IsthP	H	Margate	345	L	1-2	Moone 25 (pen)	16	1
13	IsthP	A	Lewes	516	D	1-1	Moone 18	19	2
17	IsthP	A	Bury	356	D	0-0		19	3
20	IsthP	H	Wealdstone	429	L	0-3		21	4
26	IsthP	A	Kingstonian	504	L	0-3		24	5
31	IsthP	A	East Thurrock U	148	**W**	1-0	Bray 81	19	6
Sept 7	IsthP	H	Maidstone United	**769**	L	1-3	Rocastle 89	21	7
14	***FAC1 Q***	***H***	***Ashford Town (Middlesex)***	***235***	***W***	***4-2***	***LEDGISTER 3 Simmonds***		8
17	IsthP	H	Cray Wanderers	149	**W**	4-0	Wells 74 Turner 81 Moone 86 Simmonds 89	20	9
21	IsthP	A	Bognor Regis Town	411	L	0-4		21	10
24	IsthP	A	Wingate & Finchley	116	**W**	2-1	Moone 21 23	17	11
28	***FAC2Q***	***H***	***Bedford Town***	***312***	***W***	***1-0***	***Moone 13***		12
Oct 5	IsthP	A	Leiston	194	D	0-0		17	13
12	***FAC3Q***	***H***	***Arlesey Town***	***406***	***W***	***5-1***	***MOONE 3 (921 55) Thompson 54 Simmonds 86***		14
19	***FAT1Q***	***H***	***Bedford Town***	***209***	***D***	***1-1***	***Lake 47***		15
22	***FAT1Qr***	***A***	***Bedford Town***	***162***	***W***	***2-0***	***Turner 22 Moone 66***		16
26	***FAC4Q***	***A***	***Gloucester City***	***683***	***L***	***1-3***	***Moone 28***		17
29	IsthP	H	Hendon	201	**W**	5-2	Moone (4) Brewer	15	18
Nov 2	***FAT2Q***	***H***	***Metropolitan Police***	***227***	***W***	***2-1***	***Aite-Ouakrim 62 75***		19
5	IsthP	H	Harrow Borough	169	D	1 1	Moone 24		20
9	IsthP	A	Canvey Island	273	L	1-2	Moone 7	17	21
16	***FAT3Q***	***A***	***Basingstoke Town***	***403***	***L***	***1-3***	***Thompson 35***		22
24	IsthP	A	Billericay Town	301	**W**	2-1	Moone 15 89	17	23
26	IsthP	A	Thamesmead Town	57	D	1-1		17	24
30	IsthP	H	Grays Athletic	303	L	0-2		17	25
Dec 7	IsthP	A	Lowestoft Town	404	**W**	3-0	Moone 20 51 Thompson 58	16	26
14	IsthP	H	Lewes	329	D	1-1	Moone 53	16	27
21	IsthP	A	Margate	266	D	2-2	Moone 17 (pen) Wanadio 66	16	28
26	IsthP	H	Kingstonian	505	**W**	4-1	Lake 45 MOONE 3 (74 77 88)		29
28	IsthP	A	Wealdstone	833	**W**	3 1	Hickey 35 Moone 45 Turner 84	13	30
Jan 11	IsthP	H	Carshalton Athletic	379	**W**	4-0	Moone 10 Tarpey 11 62 Harris 60	11	31
18	IsthP	A	Dulwich Hamlet	756	D	2-2	Moone 49 90	11	32
21	IsthP	H	Wingate & Finchley	269	**W**	2-0	Moone 15 Lake 33	11	33
25	IsthP	A	Maidstone United	1983	L	2-7	Tarpey 2 Turner 31	11	34
Feb 4	IsthP	A	Metropolitan Police	162	**W**	3-1	Moone 18 90 Tarpey 73	9	35
22	IsthP	A	Harrow Borough	161	L	2-3	Tarpey 14 90 (pen)	12	36
25	IsthP	H	Cray Wanderers	108	D	1-1	Tarpey 61	12	37
Match 1	IsthP	H	Leiston	395	L	0-2		15	38
8	IsthP	H	Canvey Island	333	L	0-2		15	39
11	IsthP	H	Bury Town	139	**W**	3-0	AITE-OUAKRIM 3 (8 41 49)	14	40
15	IsthP	A	Enfield Town	371	L	0-3		14	41
18	IsthP	H	Metropolitan Police	120	L	1-3	Carder 68	15	42
22	IsthP	H	Billericay Town	325	L	0-1		17	43
25	IsthP	H	East Thurrock United	136	**W**	1-0	Turner 55	16	44
29	IsthP	A	Grays Athletic	193	**W**	3-1	Tarpey 9 76 Moone 35	13	45
April 1	IsthP	H	Enfield Town	242	**W**	2-0	Tarpey 10 Moone 12	12	46
5	IsthP	H	Lowestoft Town	344	L	1-2	Brewer 64	13	47
7	IsthP	A	Hendon	163	**W**	4-3	Brewer 17 Osman 45 Moone 78 90	11	48
10	IsthP	H	AFC Hornchurch	235	D	1-1	Roberts	11	49
12	IsthP	A	Thamesmead Town	232	L	0-1		12	50
15	IsthP	H	Bognor Regis Town	339	**W**	4-3	Tarpey 2 MOONE 3 (32 65 pen 73)	11	51
19	IsthP	A	AFC Hornchurch	308	**W**	3-2	HARRIS 3 (9 pen 12 81)	10	52
21	IsthP	H	Dulwich Hamlet	505	L	0-1		11	53
26	IsthP	A	Carshalton Athletic	268	L	0-2		12	54

GOALSCORERS	Lge	FAC	FAT	Total	Pens	Hat-tricks	Cons Run
Moone	36	5	1	40	3	4	8
Tarpey	11			11	1		4
Aite-Ouakrim	3		2	5		1	
Turner	4		1	5			
Harris	4			4	1	1	
Thompson	2	1	1	4			
Brewer	3			3			2
Lake	2		1	3			
Ledgister		3		3		1	
Simmonds	1	2		3			2

	Lge	FAC	FAT	Total	Pens	Hat-tricks	Cons Run
Bray	1			1			
Carder	1			1			
Hickey	1			1			
Osman	1			1			
Roberts	1			1			
Rocastle	1			1			
Wanadio	1			1			
Wells	1			1			

Cons Run - Consecutive scoring games.

HARROW BOROUGH

Chairman: Peter Rogers
Secretary: Peter Rogers **(T)** 07956 185 685 **(E)** peter@harrowboro.co.uk
Commercial Manager: **(T)**
Programme Editor: Peter Rogers **(T)** 07956 185 685
Ground Address: Earlsmead, Carlyon Avenue, South Harrow HA2 8SS
(T) 0844 561 1347 **Manager:** Dave Anderson

2013-14 Squad - Back Row: Bill Tumbridge, Danny Leech,Ronnel Dennis,Garry Jones, Michael Barima, James Regis, Michael Peacock, Saheed Sankoh.
Middle Row: Chris Croft,Rhys Murrell-Williamson, Simeon Akinola,Kevant Serbonij, Max Oberschmidt, Shaun Lucian, Zsolt Mezei, Christopher Benjamin,Attila Fekete, Peter Rogers.
Front Row: Daniel Llacer, Terrell Lewis, James Burgess ,Samantha Backhouse, Dave Anderson ,Darron Wilkinson, Leroy Griffiths, Adam Louth,Ruddock Yala

Club Factfile

Founded: 1933 **Nickname:** Boro
Previous Names: Roxonian 1933-38, Harrow Town 1938-66
Previous Leagues: Harrow & District 1933-34, Spartan 1934-40, 45-58, West Middlesex Combination 1940-41, Middlesex Senior 1941-45, Delphian 1956-63, Athenian 1963-75

Club Colours (change): All red (All blue)

Ground Capacity: 3,070 **Seats:** 350 **Covered:** 1,000 **Clubhouse:** Yes **Shop:** Yes

Directions
From the M25 junction 16, take the M40 East towards Uxbridge and London. Continue onto A40, passing Northolt Aerodrome on the left hand side. At the Target Roundabout junction (A312) turn left towards Northolt.
Just after passing Northolt Underground Station on the left hand side, turn left at the next set of traffic lights, onto Eastcote Lane, becoming Field End Road.
At next roundabout, turn right onto Eastcote Lane. At a small parade of shops, take the turning on the right into Carlyon Avenue. Earlsmead is the second turning on the right.

Previous Grounds: Northcult Road 1933-34.

Record Attendance: 3,000 v Wealdstone - FA Cup 1st Qualifying Road 1946
Record Victory: 13-0 v Handley Page (A) - 18/10/1941
Record Defeat: 0-8 on five occasions
Record Goalscorer: Dave Pearce - 153
Record Appearances: Les Currell - 582, Colin Payne - 557, Steve Emmanuel - 522
Additional Records:

Senior Honours:
Isthmian League 1983-84.
Middlesex Senior Cup 1982-83, 92-93. Middlesex Premier Cup 1981-82.
Middlesex Senior Charity Cup 1979-80, 92-93, 2005-06, 06-07

10 YEAR RECORD

04-05	05-06	06-07	07-08	08-09	09-10	10-11	11-12	12-13	13-14
Isth P 16	Isth P 16	Isth P 19	Isth P 16	Isth P 14	Isth P 14	Isth P 5	Isth P 17	Isth P 15	Isth P 18

HARROW BOROUGH MATCH RESULTS 2013-14

Date	Comp	H/A	Opponents	Att:	Result		Goalscorers	Pos	No.
Aug 10	IsthP	H	Billericay Town	211	D	1-1	Lucian 77	13	1
13	IsthP	A	Bury Town	374	L	2-3	Lucien 20 (pen) 65	18	2
17	IsthP	A	Margate	303	L	1-3	Walsh 17 (og)	20	3
20	IsthP	H	Kingstonian	170	D	0-0		20	4
24	IsthP	H	Wealdstone	**452**	L	0-2		22	5
26	IsthP	A	Metropolitan Police	120	L	0-2		23	6
31	IsthP	A	Leiston	200	**W**	1-0	Akinola 90	20	7
Sept 7	IsthP	H	Dulwich Hamlet	313	**W**	3-1	Lucian 27 Berry 63 Barrington 90	18	8
9	IsthP	H	Hendon	259	L	1-3	Akinola 55	18	9
14	***FAC1Q***	***H***	***North Greenford United***	***135***	***D***	***2-2***	***Akinola 54 Murrell-Willamson 87***		10
17	***FAC1Qr***	***A***	***North Greenford United***	***135***	***L***	***1-2***	***Murrell-Williamson 25***		11
21	IsthP	A	Maidstone United	1935	D	4-4	Akinola 25 45 Peacock 73 Homer 79	19	12
24	IsthP	A	Carshalton Athletic	144	**W**	2-1	Berry 76 (pen) Dennis 89	15	13
28	IsthP	H	East Thurrock United	128	D	2-2	Gilbert 43 Lucian 88	15	14
Oct 5	IsthP	H	Wingate & Finchley	139	L	0-2		16	15
19	***FAT1Q***	***A***	***Dulwich Hamlet***	***404***	***L***	***1-2***	***Jones 75***		16
Nov 2	IsthP	H	Cray Wanderers	114	**W**	4-2	Osubu 22 BUTTERWORTH 3 (34 69 85 pen)	14	17
5	IsthP	A	Hampton & Richmond B	169	D	1 1	Butterworth 18		18
12	IsthP	A	AFC Hornchurch	180	**W**	4-2	Butterworth 8 (pen) Osobu 15 Leech 78 Akinola 80	13	19
16	IsthP	H	Thamesmead Town	126	L	1-2	Lucian 73	16	20
23	IsthP	A	Canvey Island	232	**W**	3-1	Osobu 44 56 Butterworth 88 (pen)	11	21
30	IsthP	H	Bognor & Regis Town	174	D	0-0		14	22
Dec 7	IsthP	A	Grays Athletic	178	L	0-2		16	23
14	IsthP	H	Bury Town	101	L	0-2		17	24
26	IsthP	H	Metropolitan Police	147	L	1-2	Butterworth 65		25
28	IsthP	A	Kingstonian	287	D	2-2	Lucian 79 90	18	26
Jan 11	IsthP	H	Lowestoft Town	135	D	1-1	Akinola 35	18	27
18	IsthP	A	Lewes	564	D	1-1	Lucian 82	18	28
21	IsthP	H	Carshalton Athletic	101	**W**	2-1	Osobu 17 Bonsa 70 (og)	17	29
25	IsthP	A	Dulwich Hamlet	810	L	2 3	Hawkins 29 90	17	30
Feb 4	IsthP	A	Billericay Town	184	L	1-2	Bellotti 36	17	31
15	IsthP	H	Maidstone United	264	**W**	4-1	Akinola 11 45 Odameley 37 Osobu 90	17	32
22	IsthP	H	Hampton & Richmond B	161	**W**	3-2	Lucien 13 Akinola 72 Maissiat 73	17	33
24	IsthP	A	Wealdstone	801	L	0-3		17	34
March 1	IsthP	A	Wingate & Finchley	118	L	1-3	Osubu 22 (pen)	17	35
4	IsthP	H	Margate	165	D	0-0		17	36
8	IsthP	H	Enfield	244	D	1-1	Akinola 41	18	37
11	IsthP	A	Enfield	287	L	0-1		19	38
15	IsthP	A	Thamesmead Town	101	**W**	1-0	Bellotti 21	18	39
22	IsthP	H	Canvey Island	161	**W**	2-0	Charles-Smith 44 67	18	40
25	IsthP	H	Leiston	77	D	1-1	Butterworth 45	18	41
29	IsthP	A	Bognor Regis Town	387	L	2-3	Louth 64 Leech 77	18	42
April 1	IsthP	A	East Thurrock United	136	**W**	3-1	Osubo 9 Charles-Smith 29 Gilbert 44	18	43
5	IsthP	H	Grays Atheltic	153	D	2-2	Charles-Smith 52 (pen) 73	18	44
12	IsthP	H	AFC Hornchurch	164	L	1-2	Charles-Smith 72 (pen)	18	45
14	IstthP	A	Hendon	207	**W**	2-1	Osubu 74 Butterworth 90	18	46
19	IsthP	A	Cray Wanderers	120	**W**	1-0	Page 11	18	47
21	IsthP	H	Lewes	152	**W**	2-0	Wolleaston 12 Butterworth 84	17	48
26	IsthP	A	Lowestoft Town	845	L	0-3		18	49

GOALSCORERS	Lge	FAC	FAT	Total	Pens	Hat-tricks	Cons Run
Akinola	10	1		11			2
Lucien	10			10	1		2
Butterworth	10			10	3	1	
Osubu	9			9	1		
Charles-Smith	6			6	2		3
Bellotti	2			2			
Berry	2			2	1		
Gilbert	2			2			
Hawkins	2			2			
Leach	2			2			
Murrell-Williamson		2		2			2
Barrington	1			1			
Dennis	1			1			
Homer	1			1			
Jones			1	1			
Louth	1			1			
Maissant	1			1			
Odameley	1			1			
Page	1			1			
Peacock	1			1			
Wolleaston	1			1			
Opponents	2			2			

Cons Run - Consecutive scoring games.

HENDON

Chairman: Simon Lawrence

Secretary: Graham Etchell **(T)** 07973 698 552 **(E)** hendonfc@freenetname.co.uk

Commercial Manager: **(T)**

Programme Editor: Graham Etchell **(T)** 07973 698 552

Ground Address: Harrow Borough FC, Earlsmead, Carlyon Avenue, South Harrow HA2 8SS

(T) **Manager:** Gary McCann

BACK ROW (L_R): GARY McCANN (Manager), CHRIS SEEBY, SAM FLEGG, JOE McDONNELL, DAVE DIEDHIOU, MICHAEL MURRAY, ELLIOTT BRATHWAITE, FREDDIE HYATT (Asst.Manager)
FRONT ROW: LEE O'LEARY, MAX McCANN, JOSE FIGURA, OLIVER SPRAGUE, ANTHONY THOMAS.
(Photographer Andrew Aleksiejczuk).
Photo taken on 19/04/14

Club Factfile

Founded: 1908 **Nickname:** Dons or Greens

Previous Names: Christ Church Hampstead > 1908, Hampstead Town > 1933, Golders Green > 1946

Previous Leagues: Finchley & District 1908-11, Middlesex 1910-11, London 1911-14, Athenian 1914-63

Club Colours (change): All green & white (All tangerine)

Ground Capacity: 2,450 **Seats:** 350 **Covered:** 950 **Clubhouse:** Yes **Shop:**

Directions

From the M25 junction 16, take the M40 East towards Uxbridge and London. Continue onto A40, passing Northolt Aerodrome on the left hand side. At the Target Roundabout junction (A312) turn left towards Northolt.
Just after passing Northolt Underground Station on the left hand side, turn left at the next set of traffic lights, onto Eastcote Lane, becoming Field End Road.
At next roundabout, turn right onto Eastcote Lane. At a small parade of shops, take the turning on the right into Carlyon Avenue. Earlsmead is the second turning on the right.

Previous Grounds: Claremont Road. Vale Farm (Wembley FC).

Record Attendance: 9,000 v Northampton Town - FA Cup 1st Round 1952

Record Victory: 13-1 v Wingate - Middlesex County Cup 02/02/1957

Record Defeat: 2-11 v Walthamstowe Avenue, Athenian League 09/11/1935

Record Goalscorer: Freddie Evans - 176 (1929-35)

Record Appearances: Bill Fisher - 787 - (1940-64)

Additional Records: Received £30,000 from Luton Town for Iain Dowie

Senior Honours:
FA Amateur Cup 1959-60, 64-65, 71-72. Isthmian League 1964-65, 72-73. European Amateur Champions 1972-73.
Athenian League x3. London Senior Cup 1963-64, 68-69. Middlesex Senior Cup x14

10 YEAR RECORD

04-05	05-06	06-07	07-08	08-09	09-10	10-11	11-12	12-13	13-14
Isth P 11	Isth P 19	Isth P 14	Isth P 7	Isth P 16	Isth P 10	Isth P 15	Isth P 7	Isth P 10	Isth P 8

HENDON MATCH RESULTS 2013-14

Date	Comp	H/A	Opponents	Att:	Result		Goalscorers	Pos	No.
Aug 10	IsthP	A	Thamesmead	81	**W**	4-0	MacLaren 29 Louis 78 Thomas 85 Horner 90	1	1
12	IsthP	H	Dulwich Hamlet	251	L	1-2	Louis 90 (pen)	3	2
17	IsthP	H	Maidstone United	217	L	3-5	Angol 16 Diedhiou 26 Louis 65	15	3
20	IsthP	A	Leiston	212	L	0-1		17	4
24	IsthP	A	Enfield Town	289	L	2-3	Diedhou 31 54	18	5
26	IsthP	H	Wingate & Finchley	184	D	1-1	Angol 94	18	6
31	IsthP	H	Lewes	154	D	1-1	Louis 65	17	7
Sept 7	IsthP	A	Lowestoft Town	585	**W**	3-2	Bennett 49 Morias 56 Fisher 87	17	8
9	IsthP	A	Harrow Borough	259	**W**	3-1	Louis 4 5 Taggart 89	10	9
15	***FAC1Q***	***H***	***Biggleswade United***	***138***	***W***	***7-1***	***Taggart 19 33 Bennett 42 Seeby 73 THOMAS 3 (84 87 90)***		10
21	IsthP	H	Kingstonian	192	L	1-2	Murray 38	15	11
23	IsthP	H	Billericay Town	132	L	1-2	Diedhiou 10	17	12
29	***FAC2Q***	***H***	***Bishop's Stortford***	***269***	***L***	***0-5***			13
Oct 5	IsthP	A	Bury	301	**W**	4-0	MacLaren 12 McCluskey 21 Louis 47 Thomas 78 (pen)	14	14
19	***FAT1Q***	***A***	***Cray Wanderers***	***81***	***W***	***4-1***	***Taggart 27 Seeby 40 Louis 47 87***		15
26	IsthP	H	Thamesmead Town	103	**W**	5-2	Taggart 4 Louis 43 48 Diedhiou 61 Thomas 88	13	16
29	IsthP	A	Hampton & Richmond B	201	L	2-5	Louis (2)	13	17
Nov 3	***FAT2Q***	***H***	***Bideford***	***220***	***W***	***1-0***	***Diedhiou 87***		18
9	IsthP	H	Metropolitan Police	130	W	4-1	Louis 52 71 McCluskey 62 Bennett 66	13	19
17	***FAT3Q***	***H***	***Oxford City***	***197***	***W***	***2-1***	***McCluskey 66 Thomas 72***		20
23	IsthP	H	East Thurrock United	105	D	2-2	O'Leary 45 Louis 82	16	21
25	IsthP	H	Canvey Island	129	**W**	4-2	Taggart 36 McCluskey 37 Louis 39 47	10	22
Dec 1	***FAT1Q***	***H***	***Whitstable Town***	***211***	***L***	***1-2***	***Louis 69***		23
7	IsthP	H	AFC Hornchurch	141	L	0-1		14	24
11	IsthP	A	Grays Athletic	127	**W**	3-1	Thomas 7 Louis 44 68 (pen)	12	25
14	IsthP	A	Dulwich Hamlet	551	L	0-2		15	26
17	IsthP	A	Cray Wanderers	131	**W**	6-0	Seeby 2 Fisher 21 Louis 24 55 Thomas 44 Flegg 65	11	27
26	IsthP	A	Wingate & Finchley	155	L	0-1			28
28	IsthP	H	Leiston	143	**W**	3-1	Bryon 33 McCluskey 69 Louis 73	10	29
Jan 4	IsthP	A	Maidstone United	1583	D	1-1	McCluskey 49	10	30
11	IsthP	A	Margate	353	**W**	3-2	Louis 19 McLaren 55 Thomas 61	9	31
21	IsthP	A	Billericay Town	238	**W**	1-0	Wallace	9	32
Feb 4	IsthP	H	Enfield Town	180	L	0-3		9	33
15	IsthP	A	Kingstonian	278	**W**	4-1	Bennett 7 Smith 43 Thomas 49 81(pen)	9	34
22	IsthP	A	Wealdstone	693	D	1-1	Taggart 64	10	35
24	IsthP	H	Bognor Regis Town	141	**W**	1-0	Smith 87	8	36
March 4	IsthP	A	Carshalton Athletic	104	**W**	2-0	O'Leary 21 Smith 52	8	37
8	IsthP	A	Metropolitan Police	101	**W**	1-0	Wallace 80	8	38
10	IsthP	H	Lowestoft Town	183	L	0-1		9	39
15	IsthP	H	Cray Wanderers	103	**W**	2-0	Smith 12 McLaren 9	9	40
17	IsthP	H	Wealdstone	**575**	D	0-0		8	41
22	IsthP	A	East Thurrock United	147	L	1-6	Smith 65	8	42
27	IsthP	H	Bury Town	116	**W**	1-0	Smith 26	8	43
29	IsthP	H	Carshalton Athletic	114	**W**	1-0	Smith 44	8	44
April 1	IsthP	A	Lewes	251	**W**	2-0	Smith 21 (pen) 66	8	45
5	IsthP	A	AFC Hornchurch	300	**W**	2-1	Taggart 47 Smith 59 (pen)	8	46
7	IsthP	H	Hampton & Richmond B	163	L	3-4	Thomas 59 64 Murray 60	8	47
12	IsthP	A	Canvey Island	330	D	0-0		8	48
14	IsthP	H	Harrow Borough	207	L	1-2	Smith 59	8	49
19	IsthP	H	Grays Athletic	144	L	2-3	Diedhiou 51 Murray 90 (Pen)	8	50
21	IsthP	A	Bognor Regis Town	498	L	0-3		8	51
26	IsthP	H	Margate	230	L	2-3	Smith 9 Diedhiou 56	8	52

GOALSCORERS	Lge	FAC	FAT	Total	Pens	Hat-tricks	Cons Run
Louis	21		3	24	2		4
Thomas	10	3	1	14	1	1	
Smith	12			12	2		5
Diedhiou	7		1	8			
Taggart	5	2	1	8			2
McCluskey	5		1	6			2
Bennett	3	1		4			
MacLaren	4			4			
Murray	3			3	1		
Seeby	1	1	1	3			
Angol	2			2			
Fisher	2			2			
O'Leary	2			2			
Wallace	2			2			
Bryon	1			1			
Flegg	1			1			
Homer	1			1			
Morias	1			1			

Cons Run - Consecutive scoring games.

KINGSTONIAN

Chairman: John Fenwick
Secretary: Karen Muir **(T)** 07752 926 809 **(E)** karen@muir54.fsnet.co.uk
Commercial Manager: **(T)**
Programme Editor: Robert Wooldridge **(T)** 07884 074 668
Ground Address: Kingsmeadow Stadium, Kingston Road, Kingston KT1 3PB
(T) 0208 330 6869 **Manager:** Tommy Williams

Club Factfile

Founded: 1885 **Nickname:** The K's
Previous Names: Kingston & Suburban YMCA 1885-87, Saxons 1887-90, Kingston Wanderers 1893-1904, Old Kingstonians 1908-19
Previous Leagues: Kingston & District, West Surrey, Southern Suburban, Athenian 1919-29, Isthmian 1929-98, Conference 1998-2001

Club Colours (change): Red and white hoops/black/red & white (Yellow with blue piping/blue/blue)

Ground Capacity: 4,262 **Seats:** 1,080 **Covered:** 2,538 **Clubhouse:** Yes **Shop:** Yes

Directions
Take Cambridge Road from Town Centre (A2043) to Malden Road.
From A3 turn off at New Malden and turn left onto A2043.
Ground is 1 mile on the left which is half a mile from Norbiton BR.

Previous Grounds: Several > 1921, Richmond Road 1921-89

Record Attendance: 4,582 v Chelsea - Freindly
Record Victory: 15-1 v Delft - 1951
Record Defeat: 0-11 v Ilford - Isthmian League 13/02/1937
Record Goalscorer: Johnnie Wing - 295 (1948-62)
Record Appearances: Micky Preston - 555 (1967-85)
Additional Records: Paid £18,000 to Rushden & Diamonds for David Leworthy 1997
Received £150,000 from West Ham United for Gavin Holligan 1999
Senior Honours:
FA Amateur Cup 1932-33. Isthmian League 1933-34, 36-37, 97-98, Division 1 South 2008-09.
FAT Trophy 1998-99, 99-2000. Athenian League x2. London Senior Cup x3. Surrey Senior Cup x3.

10 YEAR RECORD

04-05	05-06	06-07	07-08	08-09	09-10	10-11	11-12	12-13	13-14
Isth P 22	Isth1 7	Isth1S 13	Isth1S 7	Isth1S 1	Isth P 5	Isth P 7	Isth P 11	Isth P 11	Isth P 2

KINGSTONIAN MATCH RESULTS 2013-14

Date	Comp	H/A	Opponents	Att:	Result		Goalscorers	Pos	No.
Aug 10	IsthP	A	Canvey Island	368	W	1-0	McCollin 12 (pen)	8	1
12	IsthP	H	Enfield Town	342	W	3-0	Whiteley 31 (og) Moss 74 Sweeney 90	1	2
17	IsthP	H	East Thurrock United	261	W	3-0	Moss 19 74 McCollin 77	1	3
20	IsthP	A	Harrow Borough	170	D	0-0		3	4
24	IsthP	A	Wingate & Finchley	159	W	4-0	MOSS 3 (10 25 76) McCollin 23 (pen)	1	5
26	IsthP	H	Hampton & Richmond	504	W	1-0	Moss 53	1	6
31	IsthP	A	Maidstone United	1775	L	0-2		1	7
Sept 7	IsthP	H	Grays Athletic	394	W	4-0	McCOLLIN 4 (45 53 58 66)	1	8
9	IsthP	H	Bognor Regis Town	345	L	1-2	McCollin 65	1	9
14	***FAC 1Q***	***A***	***Margate***	***328***	***L***	***1-2***	***McCollin 22***		10
21	IsthP	A	Hendon	292	W	2-1	Drage 1 Moss 33	2	11
24	IsthP	A	Metropolitan Police	244	W	3-0	Knight 5 McCollin 40	1	12
Oct 5	IsthP	A	Billericay Town	434	L	2-3	Kavanagh 25 90	4	13
19	***FAT1Q***	***A***	***Folkestone Invicta***	***230***	***L***	***0-2***			14
26	IsthP	A	Lowestoft Town	501	L	0-2		4	15
Nov 2	IsthP	H	Leiston	226	W	2-0	Kavanagh 45 Moss 67	3	16
9	IsthP	H	Margate	284	W	2-0	Moss 45 Goode 86	2	17
16	IsthP	A	AFC Hornchurch	360	D	0-0		1	18
23	IsthP	H	Lewes	289	W	4-1	McCOLLIN 3 (26 pen 54 90) Moss 88	1	19
Dec 7	IsthP	H	Cray Wanderers	237	W	4-0	McCollin 6 Casey 32 Goode 66 Sweeney 90	2	20
9	IsthP	H	Wealdstone	492	L	0-1		3	21
14	IsthP	A	Enfield Town	338	W	1-0	Moss 54	3	22
21	IsthP	H	Canvey Island	335	W	3-1	McCollin 59 Moss 64 Okojie 84	2	23
26	IsthP	A	Hampton & Richmond B	508	L	1-4	McCollin 28		24
28	IsthP	H	Harrow Borough	287	D	2-2	McCollin 30 (pen) Moss 49	3	25
Jan 12	IsthP	H	Dulwich Hamlet	590	W	2 1	McCollin 35 (pen) Sweeney 86	1	26
18	IsthP	A	Carshalton Athletic	390	W	3-1	McCOLLIN 3 (22 34 pen 84 pen)	1	27
20	IsthP	H	Metropolitan Police	275	L	1 2	Moss 72	4	28
Feb 1	IsthP	H	Maidstone United	**687**	L	0-3		4	29
15	IsthP	H	Hendon	278	L	1-4	Kavanagh 61	6	30
17	IsthP	H	Wingate & Finchley	201	W	1-0	Moss 3	4	31
22	IsthP	A	Thamesmead Town	104	D	2-2	Casey 22 Moss 48	4	32
25	IsthP	A	East Thurrock United	103	L	0-2		5	33
March 1	IsthP	H	Billericay Town	255	L	0-2		5	34
8	IsthP	A	Margate	371	W	2-1	Sweeney 42 McCollin 75	5	35
15	IsthP	H	AFC Hornchurch	281	D	1-1	Moss 58 (pen)	7	36
18	IsthP	A	Bury Town	238	W	3-0	Casey 51 Moss 62 81	6	37
22	IsthP	A	Lewes	478	D	1-1	Moss 36	6	38
25	IsthP	A	Bognor Regis Town	361	D	0-0		6	39
29	IsthP	H	Bury Town	251	W	2-1	Knight 54 Drage 90	6	40
April 2	IsthP	A	Grays Athletic	189	D	0-0		6	41
5	IsthP	A	Cray Wanderers	146	W	4-0	McCollin 23 82 (pen) Page 66 Laidler 88	5	42
8	IsthP	A	Leiston	310	D	0-0		5	43
12	IsthP	H	Lowestoft Town	552	W	1-0	Okojie 75	5	44
19	IsthP	A	Wealdstone	895	W	4-0	McCollin 20 67 (pen) Drage 22 Akinde 81	3	45
21	IsthP	H	Carshalton Athletic	412	W	5-1	Moss 19 68 McCollin 60 90 Akinde 83	3	46
26	IsthP	A	Dulwich Hamlet	1388	D	1-1	Sweeney 45	2	47
30	***IsthP PO SFH***		***AFC Hornchurch***	***641***	***L***	***0-1***			48

GOALSCORERS	Lge	FAC	FAT	Total	Pens	Hat-tricks	Cons Run
McCollin	27	1		28	9	3	5
Moss	22			22		1	3
Kavanagh	5			5			
Sweeney	5			5			
Casey	3			3			
Drage	3			3			
Knight	3			3			
Akinde	2			2			2
Goode	2			?			
Okije	2			2			
Laider	1			1			
Moody	1			1			
Page	1			1			
Opponents	1			1			

Cons Run - Consecutive scoring games.

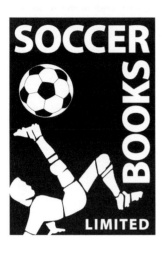

LEATHERHEAD

Chairman: Peter Ashdown
Secretary: Jean Grant (T) 07966 710 089 (E) jeangrant65@hotmail.com
Commercial Manager: (T)
Programme Editor: Neil Grant (T) 07816 772 857
Ground Address: Fetcham Grove, Guildford Road, Leatherhead, Surrey KT22 9AS
(T) 01372 360 151 **Manager:** Richard Brady

Club Factfile

Founded: 1946 **Nickname:** The Tanners
Previous Names: None
Previous Leagues: Surrey Senior 1946-50, Metropolitan 1950-51, Delphian 1951-58, Corinthian 1958-63, Athenian 1963-72

Club Colours (change): Green/white/green (All red)

Ground Capacity: 3,400 **Seats:** 200 **Covered:** 45 **Clubhouse:** Yes **Shop:** Yes

Directions
M25 junction 9 to Leatherhead,
follow signs to Leisure Centre,
ground adjacent.
Half a mile from Leatherhead BR.

Previous Grounds: None

Record Attendance: 5,500 v Wimbledon - 1976
Record Victory: 13-1 v Leyland Motors - Surrey Senior League 1946-47
Record Defeat: 1-11 v Sutton United
Record Goalscorer: Steve Lunn scored 46 goals during 1996-97
Record Appearances: P Caswell - 200
Additional Records: Paid £1,500 to Croydon for B Salkeld
Received £1,500 from Croydon for B Salkeld
Senior Honours:
Athenian League 1963-64.
Surrey Senior Cup 1968-69. Isthmian League cup 1977-78.

10 YEAR RECORD

04-05	05-06	06-07	07-08	08-09	09-10	10-11	11-12	12-13	13-14
Isth1 7	Isth1 10	Isth1S 11	Isth1S 17	Isth1S 15	Isth1S 5	Isth1S 4	Isth P 19	Isth1S 6	Isth1S 3

LEISTON

Chairman: Andrew Crisp
Secretary: David Rees (T) 07977 782 559 (E) gagrees@aol.com
Commercial Manager: (T)
Programme Editor: Mark Barber (T) 07792 292 134
Ground Address: LTAA, Victory Road, Leiston IP16 4DQ
(T) 01728 830 308 **Manager:** Steve BallLeiston_crest

Club Factfile

Founded: 1880 **Nickname:** The Blues
Previous Names: None
Previous Leagues: Suffolk & Ipswich, Eastern Counties > 2011.

Club Colours (change): Blue/white/red (All red)

Ground Capacity: 2,500 **Seats:** 124 **Covered:** 500 **Clubhouse:** **Shop:**

Directions
Take junction 28 off the M25, take the A12/A1023 exit to Chelmsford/Romford/Brentwood, keep left at the fork, follow signs for Chelmsford/A12 (E) and merge onto A12, at the roundabout, take the 3rd exit onto the A14 ramp, merge onto A14, at junction 58, exit toward A12, keep left at the fork, follow signs for Lowestoft/Woodbridge/A12 (N) and merge onto A12, go through 7 roundabouts, turn right onto A1094, turn left onto Snape Rd/B1069, continue to follow B1069, turn left onto Victory Rd, ground will be on the left.

Previous Grounds: Leiston Recreation Ground 1880-1918.

Record Attendance: **Att:** 271 v AFC Sudbury, 13.11.04.
Record Victory: Not known
Record Defeat: Not known
Record Goalscorer: Lee McGlone - 60 (League).
Record Appearances: Tim Sparkes - 154 (League).
Additional Records:

Senior Honours:
Eastern Counties League Premier Division 2010-11. Isthmian League Division 1 North 2011-12.

10 YEAR RECORD

04-05		05-06		06-07		07-08		08-09		09-10		10-11		11-12		12-13		13-14	
ECP	10	ECP	9	ECP	5	ECP	9	ECP	7	ECP	3	ECP	1	Isth1N	1	Isth P	12	Isth P	9

LEISTON MATCH RESULTS 2013-14

Date	Comp	H/A	Opponents	Att:	Result		Goalscorers	Pos	No.
Aug 10	IsthP	H	Cray Wanderers	224	**W**	4-1	Francis 9 Parker 55 Head 72 Heath 85	3	1
14	IsthP	A	Grays Athletic	214	L	2-3	Jefford 17 54	9	2
17	IsthP	A	Carshalton Athletic	158	**W**	1-0	Crisp 75	8	3
20	IsthP	H	Hendon	212	**W**	1-0	Broadley 60	6	4
24	IsthP	H	Bury Town	254	L	0-4		10	5
26	IsthP	A	Lowestoft Town	653	L	0-3		12	6
31	IsthP	H	Harrow Borough	200	L	0-1		13	7
Sept 7	IsthP	A	Margate	491	D	1 1	Parker 21	12	8
10	IsthP	A	Billericay Town	163	L	1-4	Crisp 2	16	9
14	***FAC1Q***	***A***	***Billericay Town***	***210***	***L***	***0-2***			10
21	IsthP	H	AFC Hornchurch	223	L	2-3	Head 77 Redgrave 87	17	11
24	IsthP	H	Canvey Island	190	L	0-2		19	12
Oct 5	IsthP	H	Hampton & Richmond B	194	D	0-0		20	13
12	IsthP	A	Metropolitan Police	108	L	1-2	Ottley-Gooch 38	21	14
19	***FAT1Q***	***H***	***Wealdstone***	***184***	***L***	***0-3***			15
26	IsthP	A	East Thurrock United	185	W	2-1	Stephen 12 (og) Parker 42	17	16
Nov 2	IsthP	A	Kingstonian	226	L	0-2		20	17
9	IsthP	A	Maidstone United	1577	D	2-2	Head 28 Heath 32	20	18
16	IsthP	H	BillericayTown	224	D	2-2	Heath 1 Francis 83	19	19
23	IsthP	A	Wealdstone	492	L	1-3	Parker 68	20	20
30	IsthP	H	Enfield Town	221	**W**	6-1	Ottley-Gooch 10 46 Heath 21 72 Francis 76 Parker 87	19	21
Dec 7	IsthP	A	Thamesmead Town	58	**W**	4-2	Ottley-Gooch 4 29 Henry 43 Heath 61	18	22
10	IsthP	H	Bognor Regis Town	168	**W**	5-2	Francis 17 35 Simmons 25 Jefford 52 Heath 69 (pen)	14	23
14	IsthP	H	Grays Athletic	221	**W**	4-1	Francis 1 90 Nwachuku 13 Anderson 75 (og)	12	24
26	IsthP	H	Lowestoft Town	**545**	L	0-1			25
28	IsthP	A	Hendon	143	L	1-3	Heath 49	16	26
Jan 7	IsthP	H	Dulwich Hamlet	154	**W**	2-1	Parker 23 Francis 52	14	27
11	IsthP	H	Lewes	214	D	2-2	Head 24 Parker 63	14	28
18	IsthP	A	Wingate & Finchley	172	**W**	1-0	Francis 18	12	29
21	IsthP	A	Canvey Island	217	**W**	3-2	Heath 12 34 Boadley 19	12	30
Feb 4	IsthP	A	Bury Town	353	**W**	2-0	Hubble 25 Parker 36	9	31
15	IsthP	A	AFC Hornchurch	255	L	2-4	Ottley-Gooch 58 Henry 68	12	32
18	IsthP	A	Cray Wanderers	107	D	2-2	Tann 69 Boardley 90	11	33
22	IsthP	H	Metropolitan Police	204	D	1-1	Francis 24	11	34
25	IsthP	H	Margate	177	**W**	1-0	Heath 60	10	35
March 1	IsthP	A	Hampton & Richmond B	395	**W**	2-0	Francis 49 Ottley-Gooch 90	9	36
8	IsthP	H	Maidstone United	335	**W**	1-0	Heath 54 (pen)	10	37
15	IsthP	A	Bognor Regis Town	407	D	0-0		10	38
22	IsthP	H	Wealdstone	374	L	0-2			39
25	IsthP	A	Harrow Borough	77	D	1-1	Parker 18	10	40
29	IsthP	A	Enfield Town	379	**W**	3-1	Heath 37 76 Hubble 66	10	41
April 5	IsthP	H	Thamesmead Town	201	**W**	3-0	FRANCIS 3 (49 78 88)	9	42
8	IsthP	H	Kingstonian	310	D	0-0			43
12	IsthP	H	East Thurrock United	198	**W**	3-1	Francis 57 79 Parker 76	9	44
15	IsthP	H	Carshalton Athletic	187	L	0-1		9	45
19	IsthP	A	Dulwich Hamlet	710	**W**	3-2	Parker 9 90 Head 51	9	46
21	IsthP	H	Wingate & Finchley	243	L	0-2		10	47
26	IsthP	A	Lewes	556	L	1-5	Osei 82	9	48
28	IsthP	A	Harrow Borough	77	D	1-1	Parker 18	10	49

GOALSCORERS	Lge	FAC	FAT	Total	Pens	Hat-tricks	Cons Run
Francis	16			16		1	2
Heath	14			14	2		3
Parker	13			13			2
Ottley-Gooch	7			7			2
Head	5			5			
Broadley	3			3			
Jefford	3			3			
Crisp	2			2			
Henry	2			2			
Hubble	2			2			
Osie	1			1			
Nwachuku	1			1			
Redgrave	1			1			
Simms	1			1			
Tann	1			1			
Opponents	2			2			

Cons Run - Consecutive scoring games.

LEWES

Chairman: Terry Parris
Secretary: Kevin Brook **(T)** 07785 074 081 **(E)** clubsecretary@lewesfc.com
Commercial Manager: **(T)**
Programme Editor: Stuart Fuller **(T)** 07947 078 530
Ground Address: The Dripping Pan, Mountfield Road, Lewes, East Sussex BN7 2XD
(T) 01273 470 820 **Manager:** Garry Wilson

Club Factfile

Founded: 1885 **Nickname:** Rooks
Previous Names: None
Previous Leagues: Mid Sussex 1886-1920, Sussex County 1920-65, Athenian 1965-77, Isthmian 1977-2004, Conference 2004-11.

Club Colours (change): Red and black stripes/black/black

Ground Capacity: 3,000 **Seats:** 400 **Covered:** 1,400 **Clubhouse:** Yes **Shop:** Yes

Directions
After leaving the M23, follow the A23 to Brighton. On the outskirts of Brighton join the A27 eastbound. Stay on the A27 for about 5 miles. At the roundabout take first exit into Lewes. Follow this road until you reach traffic lights outside Lewes Prison. Turn right at the lights and follow the road down the hill until you reach a mini roundabout outside the Swan public house. Turn left at roundabout into Southover High Street and continue over next mini roundabout outside the Kings Head public house. At the next roundabout go straight over into Mountfield Road. The Dripping Pan is on your right.

Previous Grounds: Played at Convent Field for two seasons before WWI

Record Attendance: 2,500 v Newhaven - Sussex County League 26/12/1947
Record Victory: Not known
Record Defeat: Not known
Record Goalscorer: 'Pip' Parris - 350
Record Appearances: Terry Parris - 662
Additional Records: Paid £2,000 for Matt Allen
Received £2,500 from Brighton & Hove Albion for Grant Horscroft
Senior Honours:
Mid Sussex League 1910-11, 13-14. Sussex County League 1964-65.
Sussex Senior Cup 1964-65, 70-71, 84-85, 2000-01, 05-06. Athenian League Division 2 1967-68, Division 1 1969-70.
Isthmian League Division 2 2001-02, Division 1 South 2003-04. Conference South 2007-08

10 YEAR RECORD

04-05	05-06	06-07	07-08	08-09	09-10	10-11	11-12	12-13	13-14
Conf S 4	Conf S 4	Conf 9	Conf S 1	Conf 24	Conf S 19	Conf S 21	Isth P 6	Isth P 19	Isth P 16

LEWES MATCH RESULTS 2013-14

Date	Comp	H/A	Opponents	Att:	Result		Goalscorers	Pos	No.
Aug 10	IsthP	A	AFC Hornchurch	259	W	1-0	Olorunda 18	9	1
13	IsthP	H	Hampton & Richmond B	516	D	1-1	Logan 50	5	2
17	IsthP	H	Canvey Island	532	W	1-0	Dixon 5	5	3
20	IsthP	A	East Thurrock United	160	W	2-0	Dixon 27 Olorunda 86	5	4
24	IsthP	A	Maidstone United	1659	D	0-0		5	5
26	IsthP	H	Bognor Regis Town	777	D	1-1	Dixon 7	6	6
31	IsthP	A	Hendon	154	D	1-1	Dixon 86	8	7
Sept 7	IsthP	H	Metropolitan Police	**788**	D	2-2	S Crabb 55 N Crabb 59	7	8
10	IsthP	H	Carshalton Athletic	326	W	2-0	Dixon 6 N.Crabb 47	7	9
14	***FAC1Q***	***A***	***Peacehaven & Telscombe***	***612***	***W***	***3-2***	***Dixon (2) Walder***		10
21	IsthP	A	Wingate & Finchley	107	W	3-1	Olorunda 51 71 N.Crabb 69	6	11
23	IsthP	A	Wealdstone	651	D	2-2	Logan 82 Lovett 90	5	12
28	***FAC 2Q***	***A***	***Chalfont St Peter***	***153***	***W***	***1-0***	***Smith 3***		13
Oct 5	IsthP	A	Dulwich Hamlet	712	L	2-4	Lovett 35 Dixon 59	7	14
12	***FAC3Q***	***H***	***Sutton United***	***1173***	***L***	***0-1***			15
19	***FAT 1Q***	***H***	***Lewes***	***417***	***L***	***1-2***	***Wheeler 6***		16
22	IsthP	H	Enfield Town	287	W	3-1	Austin 14 40 N.Crabb 44	5	17
26	IsthP	H	Margate	570	W	3-0	Wheeler 4 Dixon 46 Smith 79	5	18
Nov 12	IsthP	A	Bury Town	293	L	1-2	Dixon 68	7	19
16	IsthP	H	Lowestoft Town	706	L	0-2		8	20
20	IsthP	H	Cray Wanderers	355	W	4-1	Brinkhurst 31 Lovett 42 54 Smith 89	8	21
23	IsthP	A	Kingstonian	289	L	1-4	N.Crabb 3	8	22
30	IsthP	H	Thamesmead Town	567	D	1-1	N.Crabb 90	8	23
Dec 7	IsthP	A	Billericay Town	293	W	1-0	N.Crabb 45	7	24
14	IsthP	A	Hampton & Richmond B	329	D	1-1	N.Crabb 90	7	25
26	IsthP	A	Bognor Regis Town	603	L	1-3	Penny 86		26
28	IsthP	H	East Thurrock United	651	D	2-2	Penny 48 Dixon 61	9	27
Jan 11	IsthP	A	Leiston	214	D	2-2	N.Crabb 2 Logan 81	10	28
14	IsthP	A	Canvey Island	239	D	3-3	N.Crabb 8 11 Blewden 28	9	29
21	IsthP	H	Harrow Borough	564	D	1-1	Penny 57	9	30
25	IsthP	A	Metropolitan Police	265	D	0-0		10	31
28	IsthP	A	Grays Athletic	156	L	2-4	Dixon 61 Blewden 54	12	32
Feb 23	IsthP	A	Cray Wanderers	317	W	5 1	Austin 17 Blewden 64 Dixon 73 75 (pen) N.Crabb 84	12	33
March 1	IsthP	H	Dulwich Hamlet	757	W	2-0	Ramos 46 (og) Brinkhurst 81	11	34
4	IsthP	H	Maidstone United	570	W	1-0	Logan 27	11	35
8	IsthP	H	Grays Athletic	425	L	0-1		11	36
12	IsthP	H	AFC Hornchurch	311	L	1-5	Blewden 53	11	37
15	IsthP	A	Lowestoft Town	601	D	1-1	Blewden 45	11	38
18	IsthP	A	Carshalton Athletic	69	L	0-1		12	39
22	IsthP	H	Kingstonian	478	D	1 1	Dixon 15 (pen)	12	40
25	IsthP	H	Wealdstone	356	L	0-3		14	41
29	IsthP	A	Thamesmead Twn	66	L	0-2		14	42
April 1	IsthP	H	Hendon	251	L	0-2		15	43
5	IsthP	H	Billericay Town	388	D	1-1	Dixon 68 (pen)	15	44
8	IsthP	A	Enfield Town	337	L	1-2	Blewden 24	17	45
12	IsthP	A	Margate	356	D	1-1	Wheeler 65	17	46
16	IsthP	H	Wingate & Finchley	320	W	3-0	Dixon 56 Blewden 76 87	17	47
18	IsthP	H	Bury Town	510	L	1-4	Ledgister 16	17	48
21	IsthP	A	Harrow Borough	152	L	0-2		17	49
26	IsthP	H	Leiston	556	W	5-1	BLEWDEN 3 (6 12 41) Dixon 22 Wheeler 46	16	50

GOALSCORERS	Lge	FAC	FAT	Total	Pens	Hat-tricks	Cons Run
Dixon	16	2		18	3		2
N.Crabb	12			12			4
Blewden	11			11		1	2
Logan	4			4			
Lovett	4			4			
Olorundo	4			4			
Wheeler	3		1	4			
Austin	3			3			
Penny	3			3			2
Smith	2	1		3			

	Lge	FAC	FAT	Total	Pens	Hat-tricks	Cons Run
Brinkhurst	2			2			
S.Crabb	1			1			
Ledgister	1			1			
Walder		1		1			
Opponents	1			1			

Cons Run - Consecutive scoring games.

MAIDSTONE UNITED

Chairman: (Chief Exec.) Bill Williams
Secretary: Ian Tucker (T) 07968 505 888 (E) itucker@maidstoneunited.co.uk
Commercial Manager: (T)
Programme Editor: Ian Tucker (T) 07968 505 888
Ground Address: The Gallagher Stadium, James Whatman Way, Maidstone, Kent ME14 1LQ
(T) 01622 753 817 **Manager:** Jay Saunders

Club Factfile

Founded: 1992 **Nickname:** The Stones
Previous Names: None
Previous Leagues: Kent County, Kent

Club Colours (change): Amber/black/black (All white with black trim)

Ground Capacity: **Seats:** Yes **Covered:** Yes **Clubhouse:** Yes **Shop:** Yes

Directions
M20 (junction 6) and M2 (junction 3).
Follow signs to Maidstone on the A229.
At the White Rabbit roundabout, take the third exit on to James Whatman Way.

Previous Grounds: London Road 1992-2001, Central Park (Sittingbourne) 2001-02 11-12, The Homelands 2002-11.

Record Attendance: 1,589 v Gillingham - Friendly
Record Victory: 12-1 v Aylesford - Kent League 1993-94
Record Defeat: 2-8 v Scott Sports - 1995-96
Record Goalscorer: Richard Sinden - 98
Record Appearances: Aaron Lacy - 187
Additional Records: Paid £2,000 for Steve Jones - 2000

Senior Honours:
Kent League 2001-02, 05-06, League cup 2005-06. Isthmian Division 1 South 2006-07.
Kent Senior Trophy 2002-03.

10 YEAR RECORD

04-05	05-06	06-07	07-08	08-09	09-10	10-11	11-12	12-13	13-14
Kent P 4	Kent P 1	Isth1S 1	Isth P 17	Isth P 15	Isth P 18	Isth P 20	Isth1S 6	Isth1S 2	Isth P 7

MAIDSTONE UNITED MATCH RESULTS 2013-14

Date	Comp	H/A	Opponents	Att:	Result		Goalscorers	Pos	No.
Aug 10	IsthP	H	Wealdstone	2138	D	1-1	Hill 45	14	1
13	IsthP	A	Carshalton Athletic	374	W	2-1	Collin 37 Brown 87	5	2
17	IsthP	A	Hendon	217	W	5-3	Collin 22 35 Booth 39 Brown 58 66	3	3
20	IsthP	H	Billericay Town	1746	W	2-1	Smth 1 Collin 56	4	4
24	IsthP	H	Lewes	1659	D	0-0		4	5
26	IsthP	A	Margate	887	L	0-1		8	6
31	IsthP	H	Kingstonian	1775	W	2-0	Collin 1 Brown 19	6	7
Sept 7	IsthP	A	Hampton & Richmond B	769	W	3-1	Watt 17 Smith 19 Attwood 38	4	8
11	IsthP	A	Cray Wanderers	521	W	5-0	COLLIN 3 (12 35 62) Attwood 54 Flisher 88	1	9
14	***FAC1Q***	***A***	***Three Bridges***	***263***	***W***	***1-0***	***Collin 60***		10
21	IsthP	H	Harrow Borough	1935	D	4-4	Brown 28 49 Smith 31 Attwood 46	3	11
24	IsthP	H	Thamesmead Town	1517	W	4-0	Sobers 2 Attwood 35 Collin 66 Saraiva 88	3	12
28	***FAC2Q***	***A***	***Merstham***	***306***	***W***	***4-0***	***Collin 4 90 Attwood 36 Fisher 75***		13
Oct 5	IsthP	H	Lowestoft Town	2041	W	2-0	Collin 60 Fisher 63	3	14
8	IsthP	A	Canvey Island	373	W	1-0	Attwood 40	1	15
12	***FAC3Q***	***H***	***Boreham Wood***	***1781***	***L***	***0-2***			16
19	***FAT1Q***	***A***	***Maldon & Tiptree***		***W***	***3-1***	***Brown 47 Saraiva 82 89***		17
26	IsthP	H	Enfield Town	1933	W	3-0	Hill 59 90 Saralva 77	1	18
Nov 2	***FAT2Q***	***A***	***Wealdstone***	***524***	***D***	***2-2***	***Brown 45 Fisher 88***		19
5	***FAT2Qr***	***H***	***Wealdstone***	***824***	***W***	***1-0***	***Attwood 90***		20
9	IsthP	H	Leiston	1577	D	2-2	Phipp 78 Robinson 90	1	21
16	***FAT3Q***	***H***	***Eastleigh***	***1397***	***L***	***1-2***	***Collin 49***		22
23	IsthP	H	AFC Hornchurch	1879	D	1-1	Phipp 10	4	23
Dec 2	IsthP	A	Bognor Regis Town	471	W	2-1	Hill 31 Phipp 50	3	24
7	IsthP	H	Bury Town	1615	D	1-1	Collin 58	4	25
14	IsthP	H	Carshalton Athletic	1559	W	1-0	Collin 10	4	26
17	IsthP	A	Dulwich Hamlet	817	L	0-2		5	27
21	IsthP	A	Wealdstone	743	L	1-2	Attwood 29	5	28
26	IsthP	H	Margate	2002	W	4-0	Attwood 30 Brown 39 Collin 45 Miller 84	5	29
Jan 4	IsthP	H	Hendon	1583	D	1-1	Attwood 54	5	30
11	IsthP	A	Grays Atheltic	393	W	1-0	Saraiva 90	3	31
14	IsthP	A	Wingate & Finchley	197	W	4-2	Collin 6 SARAIVA 3 (18 65 84 pen)	1	32
18	IsthP	H	Metropolitan Police	2019	D	1-1	Collin 54 (pen)	2	33
21	IsthP	A	Thamesmead Town	305	L	1-4	Sobers 53	3	34
25	IsthP	H	Hampton & Richmond B	1953	W	7-2	Attwood 13 Brown 18 Fisher 39 Collin 47 Parkinson 57 Phillips 84 Robertson 86	2	35
Feb 1	IsthP	A	Kingstonian	687	W	3-0	Woolery 63 Attwood 84 90 (pen)	1	36
8	IsthP	H	Canvey Island	1794	D	1-1	Collin 82 (pen)	1	37
11	IsthP	H	Cray Wanderers	1292	W	3-0	Fisher 51 Parkinson 77 Attwood 90 (pen)	1	38
15	IsthP	A	Harrow Borough	264	L	1-4	Collin 30	1	39
22	IsthP	H	Wingate & Finchley	1723	W	5-0	Mills 21 Collin 22 Parkinson 47 Fisher 87 Attwood 90 (pen)	1	40
March 1	IsthP	A	Lowestoft Town	671	L	1-2	Rooney 73	2	41
4	IsthP	A	Lewes	570	L	0-1		2	42
8	IsthP	A	Leiston	335	L	0-1		3	43
15	IsthP	H	Dulwich Hamlet	**2296**	W	4-3	Fisher 37 Harris 59 65 Parkinson 90	2	44
18	IsthP	A	East Thurrock United	234	L	1-3	Attwood 57 (pen)	2	45
22	IsthP	A	AFC Hornchurch	485	L	0-1		3	46
25	IsthP	A	Billericay Town	254	D	3-3	Parkinson 45 72 Attwood 75	3	47
29	IsthP	H	East Thurrock United	1731	D	1-1	Attwood 85	5	48
April 5	IsthP	A	Bury Town	540	W	2-1	Parkinson 6 Attwood 90	4	49
12	IsthP	A	Enfield Town	594	D	1-1	Collin 82 (pen)	6	50
19	IsthP	H	Bognor Regis Town	2148	L	1-2	Watt 71	7	51
21	IsthP	A	Metropolitan Police	243	W	2-1	Collin 60 (pen) Fisher 72	6	52
26	IsthP	H	Grays Athletic	1984	W	2-0	Anderson 15 (og) Collin 64	7	53

GOALSCORERS	Lge	FAC	FAT	Total	Pens	Hat-tricks	Cons Run
Collin	22	3	1	26	4	1	3
Attwood	17	1	1	19	4		3
Brown	8		2	10			3
Fisher	7	1	1	9			
Saraiva	6		2	8	1	1	2
Parkinson	7			7			
Hill	4			4			
Phipp	3			3			2
Smith	3			3			
Harris	2			2			

	Lge	FAC	FAT	Total	Pens	Hat-tricks	Cons Run
Sobers	2			2			
Watt	2			2			
Booth	1			1			
Miller	1			1			
Mills	1			1			
Robertson	1			1			
Robinson	1			1			
Rooney	1			1			
Woolery	1			1			
Opponents	1			1			

Cons Run - Consecutive scoring games.

MARGATE

Chairman: Robert Laslett
Secretary: Ken Tomlinson **(T)** 07710 033 566 **(E)** ken.tomlinson@margate-fc.com
Commercial Manager: n/a **(T)**
Programme Editor: Neil Wyatt **(T)** 07806 865 2092
Ground Address: Hartsdown Park, Hartsdown Road, Margate, Kent CT9 5QZ
(T) 01843 221 769 **Manager:** Terry Brown

Club Factfile

Founded: 1896 **Nickname:** The Gate
Previous Names: None
Previous Leagues: Kent 1911-23, 24-28, 29-33, 37-38, 46-59. Southern 1933-37, 59-2001, Conference 2001-04

Club Colours (change): Royal blue & white hoops/royal blue/white (All amber with black trim)

Ground Capacity: 3,000 **Seats:** 350 **Covered:** 1,750 **Clubhouse:** Yes **Shop:** Yes

Directions
From M25 continue onto M26 merge onto M20, at junction 7, exit onto Sittingbourne Rd/A249 toward Sheerness/Canterbury/Ramsgate, continue to follow A249, take the ramp onto M2, continue onto A299 (signs for Margate/Ramsgate) keep right at the fork, at the roundabout, take the 2nd exit onto Canterbury Rd (Birchington)/A28 continue to follow A28, turn right onto The Square/A28 continue to follow A28, turn right onto George V Ave/B2052, turn right onto Hartsdown Rd/B2052, ground will be on the left.

Previous Grounds: At least six before moving to Hartsdown in 1939.

Record Attendance: 14,500 v Tottenham Hotspur - FA Cup 3rd Round 1973
Record Victory: 8-0 v Tunbridge Wells (H) - 1966-67, v Chatham Town (H) - 1987-88 and v Stalybridge Celtic (H) - 2001-02
Record Defeat: 0-11 v AFC Bournemouth (A) - FA Cup 20/11/1971
Record Goalscorer: Jack Palethorpe scored 66 during 1929-30
Record Appearances: Bob Harrop
Additional Records: Paid £5,000 to Dover Athletic for Steve Cuggy

Senior Honours:
Southern League Premier Division 1935-36, 2000-01, Division 1 1962-63, Division 1 South 1977-78.

10 YEAR RECORD

04-05	05-06	06-07	07-08	08-09	09-10	10-11	11-12	12-13	13-14
Conf S 21	Isth P 14	Isth P 6	Isth P 9	Isth P 19	Isth P 19	Isth P 16	Isth P 15	Isth P 9	Isth P 11

MARGATE MATCH RESULTS 2013-14

Date	Comp	H/A	Opponents	Att:	Result		Goalscorers	Pos	No.
Aug 10	IsthP	A	Hampton & Richmond	345	W	2-1	Walsh 69 Bodkin 90	7	1
13	IsthP	H	AFC Hornchurch	329	L	1-2	Beales 60	13	2
17	IsthP	H	Harrow Borough	303	W	3-1	Ademeno 1 Walsh 52 Attwood 76	9	3
20	IsthP	A	Enfield Town	354	D	1-1	Attwood	9	4
24	IsthP	A	Thamesmead Town	94	W	2-0	Walsh 10 Azeez 90	7	5
26	IsthP	H	Maidstone United	**887**	W	1-0	Kinch 42	4	6
31	IsthP	A	Metropolitan Police	130	W	2-0	Attwood 78 (pen) Azeez 83	2	7
Sept 7	IsthP	H	Leiston	491	D	1-1	Walsh 39	5	8
10	IsthP	H	East Thurrock United	153	D	1-1	Kinch 88	5	9
14	**FAC1Q**	**H**	**Kingstonian**	**328**	**W**	**2-1**	**Walsh 36 Ademeno 60**		10
21	IsthP	A	Grays Athletic	234	L	0-3		8	11
24	IsthP	A	Dulwich Hamlet	466	L	0-2		9	12
28	**FAC2Q**	**H**	**Dulwich Hamlet**	**508**	**L**	**1-2**	**Ademeno 45 (pen)**		13
Oct 5	IsthP	A	Wealdstone	591	W	1-0	Ademeno 2	8	14
12	IsthP	H	Bury Town	401	L	1-2	Sammoutis 10	10	15
19	**FAT1Q**	**A**	**Wroxham**	**124**	**W**	**9-4**	**Sammoutis 10 32 Walsh 23 Ademeno 37 87 Bodkin 41 Kinch 52 Fakinos 71 Dolby 89**		16
26	IsthP	A	Lewes	570	L	0-3		12	17
Nov 2	**FATQ2**	**H**	**Clevedon Town**	**227**	**W**	**4-1**	**Ademeno 8 20 Walsh 37 68**		18
9	IsthP	A	Kingstonian	284	L	0-2		12	19
16	**FAT 3Q**	**H**	**Chesham United**	**317**	**L**	**0-3**			20
19	IsthP	H	Carshalton Athletic	142	W	1-0	Borrowdale 71	10	21
23	IsthP	A	Lowestoft Town	511	L	0-3		10	22
26	IsthP	H	Wingate & Finchley	154	W	3-2	Bodkin 2 (pen) Borrowdale 34 Avery 84	9	23
30	IsthP	H	Canvey Island	393	D	1-1	Borrowdale 81	9	24
Dec 7	IsthP	A	Bognor Regis Town	402	L	3-5	Whiteley 8 Walsh 78 90	11	25
10	IsthP	H	Billericay Town	182	L	1-2	Walsh 45	12	26
14	IsthP	A	AFC Hornchurch	238	L	2-3	Whiteley 30 Walsh 59	14	27
21	IsthP	H	Hampton & Richmond B	266	D	2-2	Bodkin 23 Ademeno 90	13	28
26	IsthP	A	Maidstone United	2002	L	0-4			29
29	IsthP	H	Enfield Town	391	W	1-0	Vines 59	12	30
Jan 11	IsthP	H	Hendon	353	L	2-3	Bodkin 8 Stuart 45	15	31
21	IsthP	H	Dulwich Hamlet	242	L	2-4	Riviere 10 Beales 42	16	32
Feb 4	IsthP	A	Cray Wanderers	153	W	4-1	Phipp 10 Nelson 70 Rents 78 Whiteley 84	16	33
18	IsthP	H	Thamesmead Town	211	W	2-1	Ademeno 40 Wassmer 66	15	34
22	IsthP	A	Bury Town	305	D	1-1	Wassmer 41	15	35
25	IsthP	A	Leiston	177	L	0-1		15	36
March 4	IsthP	A	Harrow Borough	165	D	0-0		15	37
8	IsthP	H	Kingstonian	371	L	1-2	Rents 20	17	38
15	IsthP	A	Billericay Town	333	W	2-0	Louis 9 66 (pen)	17	39
22	IsthP	H	Lowestoft Town	365	W	3-0	Stuart 6 Louis 44 75	16	40
25	IsthP	H	Metropolitan Police	188	W	1-0	Wassmer 38	16	41
27	IsthP	H	Grays Athletic	248	L	2-5	Artemi 31 Wassmer 80	16	42
29	IsthP	A	Canvey Island	406	L	0-2		17	43
April 1	IsthP	A	Wingate & Finchley	128	D	0-0		17	44
5	IsthP	A	Bognor Regis Town	308	D	1-1	Allen 26	16	45
8	IsthP	A	East Thurrock United	141	W	4-1	Allen 27 59 Nelson 46 Riviere 48	15	46
12	IsthP	H	Lewes	356	D	1-1	Louis 26	15	47
15	IsthP	H	Wealdstone	429	L	0-1		16	48
19	IsthP	A	Carshalton Athletic	125	W	6-0	Allen 17 22 LOUIS 3 (28 pen 44 59) Medley 66	16	49
21	IsthP	H	Cray Wanderers	320	W	5-0	Rents 21 Bodkin 47 Ademeno 70 Allen 85 Louis 90	14	50
26	IsthP	A	Hendon	230	W	3-2	Allen 45 Bodkin 48 Medley 86	11	51

GOALSCORERS	Lge	FAC	FAT	Total	Pens	Hat-tricks	Cons Run
Walsh	8	1	3	12			3
Ademeno	5	2	4	11	1		2
Louis	9			9	2	1	2
Allen	7			7			3
Bodkin	6		1	7	1		2
Wassmer	4			4			2
Attwood	3			3	1		
Borrowdale	3			3			2
Kinch	2		1	3			
Rents	3			3			
Sammoutis	1		2	3			
Whiteley	3			3			
Azeez	2			2			
Beales	2			2			
Medley	2			2			
Nelson	2			2			
Riviere	2			2			
Stuart	2			2			
Artemi	1			1			
Dolby			1	1			
Fakinos			1	1			
Phipps	1			1			
Vines	1			1			

Cons Run - Consecutive scoring games.

METROPOLITAN POLICE

Chairman: Des Flanders
Secretary: Tony Brooking **(T)** 07961 334 523 **(E)** tony.brooking@met.police.uk
Commercial Manager: **(T)**
Programme Editor: Rich Nelson **(T)** 07872 110 308
Ground Address: Imber Court, Ember Lane, East Molesey, Surrey KT8 0BT
(T) 0208 398 7358 **Manager:** Jim Cooper

Club Factfile

Founded: 1919 **Nickname:** The Blues
Previous Names: None
Previous Leagues: Spartan 1928-60, Metropolitan 1960-71, Southern 1971-78

Club Colours (change): All blue (All red)

Ground Capacity: 3,000 **Seats:** 297 **Covered:** 1,800 **Clubhouse:** Yes **Shop:** No

Directions
From London A3 take A309 towards Scilly Isles roundabout then right into Hampton Court Way.
Left at first roundabout into Imber Court Road. Ground is in 300 yards.

Previous Grounds: None

Record Attendance: 4,500 v Kingstonian - FA Cup 1934
Record Victory: 10-1 v Tilbury - 1995
Record Defeat: 1-11 v Wimbledon - 1956
Record Goalscorer: Mario Russo
Record Appearances: Pat Robert
Additional Records:

Senior Honours:
Spartan League x7.
Middlesex Senior Cup 1927-28, Surrey Senior Cup 1932-33. London Senior Cup 2009-10.
Isthmian League Division One South 2010-11.

10 YEAR RECORD

04-05	05-06	06-07	07-08	08-09	09-10	10-11	11-12	12-13	13-14
Isth1 5	Isth1 4	Isth1S 6	Isth1S 4	Isth1S 4	Isth1S 10	Isth1S 1	Isth P 12	Isth P 6	Isth P 17

METROPOLITAN POLICE MATCH RESULTS 2013-14

Date	Comp	H/A	Opponents	Att:	Result	Goalscorers	Pos	No.
Aug 10	IsthP	A	Enfield Town	341	L 1-2	Knight 79	17	1
12	IsthP	H	Wingate & Finchley	134	**W** 3-1	Alabi 19 (pen) 45 Knight 90	12	2
17	IsthP	H	Dulwich Hamlet	262	D 0-0		12	3
20	IsthP	A	Thamesmead Town	60	D 0-0		12	4
24	IsthP	A	Bognor Regis Town	372	L 0-2		14	5
26	IsthP	H	Harrow Borough	120	**W** 2-0	Alabi 26 Osie 76	13	6
31	IsthP	H	Margate	130	L 0-2		15	7
Sept 7	IsthP	A	Lewes	788	D 2-2	Sutherland 89 Osie 90	15	8
14	***FAC1Q***	***A***	***Chalfont St Peter***	***60***	***D 0-0***			9
17	***FAC1Qr***	***H***	***Chalfont St Peter***	***67***	***L 0-1***			10
21	IsthP	H	Bury Town	**425**	L 0-3		18	11
24	IsthP	H	Kingstonian	244	L 0-2		20	12
Oct 5	IsthP	A	Cray Wanderers	145	L 1-4	Newton 35	21	13
12	IsthP	H	Leiston	106	**W** 2-1	James 4 Tait 85	19	14
19	FAT1Q	A	Thamesmead Town	102	**W** 2-1	James 37 40		15
26	IsthP	A	Carshalton Athletic	215	D 1-1	Collins 19	19	16
29	IsthP	A	Billericay Town	248	**W** 2-1	Tait 33 Sutherland 40	14	17
Nov 2	***FAT2Q***	***A***	***Hampton & Richmond B***	***227***	***L 1-2***	***Smith 87***		18
9	IsthP	A	Hendon	130	L 1-4	Newton 74	18	19
16	IsthP	H	Canvey Island	154	L 0-1		18	20
23	IsthP	A	Grays Athletic	174	D 0-0		18	21
26	IsthP	H	East Thurrock United	68	L 1-2	Newton 45		22
30	IsthP	H	Lowestoft Town	166	D 0-0		20	23
Dec 7	IsthP	A	Wealdstone	516	D 1-1	Collins 34	20	24
14	IsthP	A	Wingate & Finchley	95	**W** 3-0	Taylor 4 Sutherland 21 Hudson-Odoi 62	19	25
26	IsthP	A	Harrow Borough	147	**W** 2-1	Pattison 10 Collins 48		26
28	IsthP	H	Thamesmead Town	81	**W** 3-1	Hudson-Odoi 6 86 James 41	17	27
Jan 11	IsthP	H	AFC Hornchurch	151	**W** 2-1	Joseph 10 Pattison 90	16	28
18	IsthP	A	Maidstone United	2019	D 1-1	Collins 63	15	29
20	IsthP	A	Kingstonian	275	**W** 2 1	Collins 40 Hudson-Odoi 47	13	30
25	IsthP	H	Lewes	285	D 0-0		13	31
Feb 4	IsthP	H	Hampton & Richmond	162	L 1-3	Collins 34	14	32
11	IsthP	H	Billericay Town	85	L 0-2	Layne 8 39	13	33
22	IsthP	A	Leiston	204	D 1-1	Bird 33	16	34
25	IsthP	H	Enfield Town	142	**W** 3-1	Bird 33 Smith 53 Pink 76	14	35
March 1	IsthP	H	Cray Wanderers	151	**W** 7-1	Newton 8 45 Pink 18 James 40 Bird 43 Collins 55 Neita 84	13	36
4	IsthP	A	Dulwich Hamlet	537	**W** 2-1	Pink 20 35	13	37
8	IsthP	H	Hendon	101	L 0-1		13	38
11	IsthP	H	Bognor Regis Town	151	L 0-2		13	39
15	IsthP	A	Canvey Island	341	D 1-1	Neila 81	13	40
18	IsthP	A	Hampton & Richmond B	120	**W** 3-1	Bird 19 Taylor 47 Hudson-Odoi 84	12	41
22	IsthP	H	Grays Athletic	123	L 1-2	Hudson-Odoi 84	14	42
25	IsthP	A	Margate	188	L 0-1		14	43
29	IsthP	A	Lowestoft Town	525	D 1-1	Hudson-Odoi 48	15	44
April 5	IsthP	H	Wealdstone	354	**W** 2-1	Sutherland 53 Smith 78	14	45
12	IsthP	H	Carshalton Athletic	101	**W** 3-0	Neita 15 James 62 Pink 73	13	46
15	IsthP	A	Bury Town	248	L 1-2	Hudson-Odoi 77 (pen)	13	47
19	IsthP	A	East Thurrock United	145	D 1-1	Collins 15	15	48
21	IsthP	H	Maidstone United	243	L 1-2	Collins 31	16	49
26	IsthP	A	AFC Hornchurch	374	L 0-1		17	50

GOALSCORERS	Lge	FAC	FAT	Total	Pens	Hat-tricks	Cons Run
Collins	9			9			2
Hudson-Odoi	8			8	1		2
James	4		2	6			2
Newton	5			5			
Bird	4			4			3
Pink	4			4			3
Sutherland	4			4			
Alabi	3			3	1		
Neita	3			3			
Smith	2		1	3			
Knight	2			2			
Layne	2			2			
Osie	2			2			
Patterson	2			2			
Tait	2			2			
Taylor	2			2			
Joseph	1			1			

Cons Run - Consecutive scoring games.

PEACEHAVEN & TELSCOMBE

Chairman: Andrew Melbourne
Secretary: Derek Earley (T) 07717 178 483 (E) derek@peacehavenfc.com
Commercial Manager: (T)
Programme Editor: Andrew Melbourne (T) 07818 062 071
Ground Address: The Sports Park, Piddinghoe Ave, Peacehaven, BN10 8RJ
(T) 01273 582 471 **Manager:** Shaun Saunders

Club Factfile

Founded: 1923 **Nickname:**
Previous Names: Formed when Peacehaven Rangers and Telscombe Tye merged.
Previous Leagues: Sussex County > 2013.

Club Colours (change): All black & white (All white)

Ground Capacity: **Seats:** Yes **Covered:** Yes **Clubhouse:** Yes **Shop:**

Directions
From Brighton on A259, over roundabout & Piddinghoe Ave. is next left after 2nd set of lights-ground at end. From Newhaven, Piddinghoe Ave. is 1st right after 1st set of lights. 3 miles from Newhaven(BR). Peacehaven is served by Brighton to Newhaven & Eastbourne buses.

Previous Grounds: The Tye.

Record Attendance:
Record Victory:
Record Defeat:
Record Goalscorer:
Record Appearances:
Additional Records:
Senior Honours:
Sussex County Division One 1978-79, 81-82, 82-83, 91-92, 92-93, 94-95, 95-96, 2012-13, Division Three 2005-06, Division Two 2008-09.
Isthmian Division One South 2013-14.

10 YEAR RECORD

04-05	05-06	06-07	07-08	08-09	09-10	10-11	11-12	12-13	13-14
SxC2 17	SxC3 1	SxC2 5	SxC2 4	SxC2 1	SxC1 2	SxC1 3	SxC1 5	SxC1 1	Isth1S 1

TONBRIDGE ANGELS

Chairman: Steve Churcher
Secretary: Charlie Cole **(T)** 07825 702 412 **(E)** chcole1063@aol.com
Commercial Manager: **(T)**
Programme Editor: Geoff Curtis **(T)** 07930 868 568
Ground Address: Longmead Stadium, Darenth Avenue, Tonbridge, Kent TN10 3LW
(T) 01732 352 417 **Manager:** Steve McKimm

Club Factfile

Founded: 1948 **Nickname:** Angels
Previous Names: Tonbridge Angels, Tonbridge F.C., Tonbridge A.F.C.
Previous Leagues: Southern 1948-80, 93-2004, Kent 1989-93, Isthmian 2004-11.

Club Colours (change): All blue with white trim (All red with white trim)

Ground Capacity: 2,500 **Seats:** 707 **Covered:** 1,500 **Clubhouse:** Yes **Shop:** Yes

Directions
From M25. Take A21 turning at Junction 5 to junction with A225/b245 (signposted Hildenborough). After passing Langley Hotel on left thake slightly hidden left turn into Dry Hill Park Road. Left again at mini roundabout into Shipbourne Road (A227) and then left again at next roundabout into Darenth Avenue' Longmead stadium can be found at the bottom of the hill at the far end of the car park.

Previous Grounds: The Angel 1948-80

Record Attendance: 8,236 v Aldershot - FA Cup 1951
Record Victory: 11-1 v Worthing - FA Cup 1951
Record Defeat: 2-11 v Folkstone - Kent Senior Cup 1949
Record Goalscorer: Jon Main scored 44 goals in one season including seven hat-tricks
Record Appearances: Mark Giham
Additional Records:

Senior Honours:
Kent Senior Cup 1964-65, 74-75

10 YEAR RECORD

04-05	05-06	06-07	07-08	08-09	09-10	10-11	11-12	12-13	13-14
Isth P 20	Isth1 3	Isth P 11	Isth P 8	Isth P 3	Isth P 8	Isth P 2	Conf S 9	Conf S 16	Conf S 21

TONBRIDGE ANGELS MATCH RESULTS 2013-14

Date	Comp	H/A	Opponents	Att:	Result	Goalscorers	Pos	No.
Aug 17	ConfS	H	Boreham Wood	446	L 0-2		21	1
20	ConS	A	Eastbourne Borough	678	L 1-2	Miles 5	20	2
24	ConS	A	Bromley	666	L 1-5	Green 85	21	3
26	ConfS	H	Chelmsford City	510	W 2-1	Muggeridge 37 Browning 82	19	4
31	ConfS	A	Havant & Waterlooville	423	W 2-1	Blewden 9 Harris 89 (og)	14	5
Sept 7	ConfS	H	Sutton United	549	D 1-1	Ijaha 36	15	6
14	ConfS	A	Bath City	541	D 2-2	Pinney 2 Lovell 90	17	7
21	ConfS	A	Gosport Borough	418	L 0-2		17	8
29	***FAC2Q***	***A***	***Hayes & Yeading***	***198***	***D 0-0***			9
Oct 1	***FAC2Qr***	***H***	***Hayes & Yeading***	***297***	***W 2-1***	***Elphick 30 Suarez 43***		10
5	ConfS	H	Staines Town	468	D 1-1	Green 49	17	11
12	***FAC3Q***	***A***	***St Albans City***	***605***	***L 1-2***	***Lovell 41***		12
19	ConfS	H	Farnborough	445	L 1-3	Pinney 44	19	13
26	ConfS	H	Whitehawk	376	W 3-1	Pinney 32 Goodwin 34 Green 76 (pen)	17	14
Nov 2	ConfS	A	Bishop's Stortford	573	L 1-2	Goodwin 14	20	15
16	***FAT 3Q***	***H***	***AFC Sudbury***	***408***	***D 1-1***	***Goodwin 11***		16
19	***FAT 3Qr***	***A***	***AFC Sudbury***	***191***	***W 1-0***	***Watts 58***		17
23	ConfS	A	Eastleigh	536	W 2-1	Goodwin 23 Miles 88	16	18
30	***FAT1***	***H***	***St Albans City***	***484***	***D 0-0***			19
Dec 2	***FAT1r***	***A***	***St Albans City***	***303***	***L 0-4***			20
7	ConfS	A	Hayes & Yeading	114	L 0-3		19	21
10	ConfS	A	Dorchester Town	281	L 1 2	Miles 36	19	22
14	ConfS	A	Sutton United	488	W 2-1	Piper 22 Goodwin 70	17	23
26	ConfS	A	Dover Athletic	856	L 1-3	Green 76	20	24
28	ConfS	H	Eastbourne Borough	608	W 2-1	Lovell 33 82 (pen)	19	25
Jan 11	ConfS	A	Weston-s-Mare	258	L 1-2	McCallum 35	19	26
21	ConfS	H	Bath City	298	D 1-1	Browning 10	19	27
Feb 4	ConfS	A	Farnborough	225	L 2-3	Pinney 79 Bakare 87	19	28
17	ConfS	H	Eastleigh	304	W 2-1	Bakare 9 Lovell 34	19	29
22	ConfS	H	Dorchester Town	405	L 1-2	Bakare 14	20	30
March 1	ConfS	A	Boreham Wood	203	L 0-7		20	31
4	ConfS	H	Maidenhead United	332	L 2-4	Pinney 3 Lovell 55	20	32
8	ConfS	H	Bishop's Stortford	406	D 1-1	Piper 10	20	33
11	ConfS	H	Ebbsfleet United	467	L 0-2		20	34
15	ConfS	H	Weston -s-Mare	380	W 1-0	Teniola 89	21	35
18	ConfS	A	Basingstoke Town	167	D 0-0		18	36
20	ConfS	H	Hayes & Yeading	273	D 1-1	Lovell 73 (pen)	18	37
22	ConfS	A	Whitehawk	194	L 0-1		19	38
25	ConfS	H	Gosport Borough	273	L 0-2		20	39
29	ConfS	A	Ebbsfleet United	1102	L 0-1		21	40
April 1	ConfS	H	Concord Rangers	274	D 2-2	James 46 Lovell 77	21	41
5	ConfS	H	Basingstoke Town	354	W 2-1	Lovell 45 (pen) Bakare 74	21	42
8	ConfS	A	Concord Rangers	180	D 2-2	Bakare 43 Teniola 45	21	43
10	ConfS	H	Dover Athletic	533	L 0-2		21	44
12	ConfS	A	Maidenhead United	472	D 0-0		21	45
15	ConfS	A	Staines Town	257	D 0-0		21	46
19	ConfS	H	Bromley	**672**	D 1-1	Teniola 21	21	47
21	ConfS	A	Chelmsford City	842	L 1-7	Piper 67	21	48
28	ConfS	H	Havant & Waterlooville	515	D 0-0		21	49

GOALSCORERS	Lge	FAC	FAT	Total	Pens	Hat-tricks	Cons Run
Lovell	8	1		9	3		
Bakare	5			5			
Goodwin	4		1	5			
Pinney	5			5			
Green	4			4	1		
Miles	3			3			
Piper	3			3			
Teniola	3			3			
Browning	2			2			
Blewden	1			1			
Elphick		1		1			
Ijaha	1			1			
James	1			1			
McCallum	1			1			
Muggeridge	1			1			
Suarez		1		1			
Watts			1	1			
Opponents	1			1			

Cons Run - Consecutive scoring games.

VICKERS CRAYFORD DARTFORD ATHLETIC

Chairman: Gary Rump
Secretary: Chris Dudley **(T)** 07803 700 261 **(E)** chris.dudley@ntlworld.com
Commercial Manager: **(T)**
Programme Editor: Craig Winn **(T)** 07428 842 771
Ground Address: VCD Athletic Club, Oakwood, Old Road, Crayford DA1 4DN
(T) 01322 524 262 **Manager:** Tony Russell

Club Factfile

Founded: 1916 **Nickname:** The Vickers
Previous Names: Vickers (Erith). Vickers (Crayford)
Previous Leagues: Dartford & District. Kent County. Isthmian

Club Colours (change): Green & white/white (Blue/black/black)

Ground Capacity: **Seats:** Yes **Covered:** Yes **Clubhouse:** Yes **Shop:** No

Directions
Follow A2 until you reach the exit for A220/A223 towards Bexleyheath and Crayford. At the roundabout, take the second exit on to Bourne Road/A223. After just over half a mile, turn right onto the A207 London Road. Keep left at the fork, then turn left onto Crayford High Street/A2000. Where the A2000 bends right, go straight on to pick up Old Road, and the ground is on your right.

Previous Grounds: Groundshared with Thamesmead (5 seasons), Lordswood (2) and Greenwich Boro' (1) whilst waiting for planning at Oakwood.

Record Attendance: 13,500 Away v Maidstone, 1919.
Record Victory:
Record Defeat:
Record Goalscorer:
Record Appearances:
Additional Records:

Senior Honours:
Kent County League 1996-97. Kent League 2008-09. Isthmian Division One North 2013-14.
Kent Senior Trophy 2005-06, 08-09.

10 YEAR RECORD

04-05	05-06	06-07	07-08	08-09	09-10	10-11	11-12	12-13	13-14
Kent P 5	Kent P 6	Kent P 2	Kent P 2	Kent P 1	Isth1N 8	Kent P 3	Kent P 3	Kent P 2	Isth P 1

WINGATE & FINCHLEY

Chairman: Aron Sharpe
Secretary: David Thrilling (T) 07977 007 746 (E) secretary@wingatefinchley.com
Commercial Manager: (T)
Programme Editor: Paul Lerman (T) 07736 282 218
Ground Address: Harry Abraham Stadium, Summers Lane, Finchley N12 0PD
(T) 0208 446 2217 **Manager:** Daniel Nielson

Club Factfile

Founded: 1991 **Nickname:** Blues
Previous Names: Wingate (founded 1946) and Finchley (founded late 1800s) merged in 1991
Previous Leagues: South Midlands 1991-95, Isthmian 1995-2004, Southern 2004-2006

Club Colours (change): Light blue with navy flash/navy (Yellow & black)

Ground Capacity: 8,500 **Seats:** 500 **Covered:** 500 **Clubhouse:** Yes **Shop:** No

Directions
The simplest way to get to The Harry Abrahams Stadium is to get on to the A406 North Circular Road.
If coming from the West (eg via M1), go past Henlys Corner (taking the left fork after the traffic lights) and then drive for about 1 mile. The exit to take is the one immediately after a BP garage. Take the slip road and then turn right at the lights onto the A1000.
If coming from the East (eg via A10, M11) take the A1000 turn off. At the end of the slip road turn left at the lights. Go straight over the next set of lights. Then after 100m pass through another set of lights, then at the next set of lights turn right into Summers Lane. The Abrahams Stadium is a few hundred metres down on the right hand side.

Previous Grounds: None

Record Attendance: 528 v Brentwood Town (Division One North Play-Off) 2010/11
Record Victory: 9-1 v Winslow (South Midlands League) 23/11/1991
Record Defeat: 0-9 v Edgware - Isthmian Division 2 15/01/2000
Record Goalscorer: Marc Morris 650 (including with Wingate FC) FA Record for one Club
Record Appearances: Marc Morris 720 (including with Wingate FC)FA Record for one Club
Additional Records:

Senior Honours:
Isthmian League Cup 2010-11.
London Senior Cup 2010-11.

10 YEAR RECORD

04-05		05-06		06-07		07-08		08-09		09-10		10-11		11-12		12-13		13-14	
SthE	12	SthE	12	Isth1N	9	Isth1N	18	Isth1N	7	Isth1N	3	Isth1N	3	Isth P	13	Isth P	18	Isth P	21

WINGATE & FINCHLEY MATCH RESULTS 2013-14

Date	Comp	H/A	Opponents	Att:	Result	Goalscorers	Pos	No.
Aug 10	IsthP	H	Carshalton Athletic	165	W 4-0	Smith 14 (pen) Weatherstone 53 Mackie 71 Rifat 86	2	1
13	IsthP	A	Metropolitan Police	134	L 1-3	Weatherstone 38	11	2
17	IsthP	A	Wealdstone	425	D 2-2	Shulton 8 Smith 29	11	3
20	IsthP	H	Grays Athletic	179	L 1-3	Rifat 65	13	4
24	IsthP	H	Kingstonian	159	L 0-4		16	5
26	IsthP	A	Hendon	184	D 1 1	Smith 86	16	6
31	IsthP	H	Lowestoft Town	122	D 0-0		16	7
Sept 7	IsthP	A	Thamesmead Town	64	W 2-1	Smith 16 Shulton 83	16	8
11	IsthP	A	Canvey Island	185	L 0-2		19	9
15	FAC1Q	H	Biggleswade Town	108	D 0-0			10
17	FAC1Qr	A	Biggleswade Town	78	L 3-4	Smith 31 (pen) Rifat 35 Weatherstone 54		11
21	IsthP	H	Lewes	107	L 1-3	McCall 45	20	12
24	IsthP	H	Hampton & Richmond	116	L 1-2	Hallam 58	21	13
Oct 5	IsthP	A	Harrow Borough	139	W 2-0	Rifat 47 Smith 87	18	14
19	FAT1Q	H	Hitchin Town	81	D 2-2	Williams 52 McCall 90 (Pen)		15
21	FAT1Qr	A	Hitchin Town	114	W 1-0	Rifat 39		16
26	IsthP	H	Bognor Regis Town	142	W 3-0	Mason 31 Zawadski 63 (og) Axten 64 (og)	14	17
Nov 2	FAT2Q	H	Daventry Town	91	D 1-1	Owen 27		18
5	FAT2Q	A	Daventry Town	124	L 1-3	Stellars 25		19
9	IsthP	H	East Thurrock United	128	W 4-3	Rifat 15 62 Smith 87 90	14	20
12	IsthP	A	Enfield Town	295	W 3-0	McCall 27 (pen) Henry 47 Rifat 50	12	21
23	IsthP	H	Cray Wanderers	110	D 1-1	Laird 90 (pen)	14	22
26	IsthP	A	Margate	154	L 2-3	Morante 1 McCall 40 (pen)	14	23
30	IsthP	A	AFC Hornchurch	187	L 0-3		16	24
Dec 7	IsthP	H	Dulwich Hamlet	225	L 2-3	Smith 64 Mason 69	17	25
10	IsthP	A	Bury Town	202	L 0-2		17	
14	IsthP	H	Metropolitan Police	95	L 0-3		18	
26	IsthP	H	Hendon	155	W 1-0	Bolle 25	18	28
Jan 14	IsthP	H	Maidstone United	197	L 2-4	Sogbanae 32 47	19	29
18	IsthP	H	Leiston	172	L 0-1		19	30
21	IsthP	A	Hampton & Richmnd B	269	L 0-2		20	31
25	IsthP	H	Thamesmead Town	115	W 3-1	Tejan-Sie 5 Bolle 54 Rifat 58	19	32
Feb 4	IsthP	A	Carshalton Athletic	89	W 4-0	Sogbanae 41 Rifat 55 Tajan-Sie 77 Jones 90	17	33
11	IsthP	H	Canvey Island	119	L 0-4		17	34
17	IsthP	A	Kingstonian	201	L 0-1		17	35
22	IsthP	A	Maidstone Uited	1723	L 0-5		18	36
March 1	IsthP	H	Harrow Borough	118	W 3-1	Tejan-Sie 9 Fredericks 52 Read 90	19	37
5	IsthP	A	Grays Athletic	165	L 0-2		19	38
8	IsthP	A	East Thurrock United	115	W 1-0	Kennett 68	19	39
11	IsthP	H	Wealdstone	265	L 0-2		19	40
15	IsthP	H	Bury Town	118	W 1-0	Kennett 14	19	41
18	IsthP	A	Billericay Town	183	L 0-1		19	42
23	IsthP	A	Cray Wanderers	166	D 2 2	Weatherstone 18 Davies 81	19	43
25	IsthP	A	Lowestoft Town	348	D 0-7		19	44
29	IsthP	H	AFC Hornchurch	203	L 0-3		19	45
April 1	IsthP	H	Margate	128	D 0-0		19	46
5	IsthP	A	Dulwich Hamlet	668	L 2-4	Bolle 32 Kennedy 70	20	47
12	IsthP	A	Bognor Regis Town	323	L 0-1		20	48
16	IsthP	A	Lewes	320	L 0-3		20	49
19	IsthP	H	Enfield Town	345	D 1-1	Kennett 55	21	50
21	IsthP	A	Leiston	243	W 2-0	Rifat 12 Fichor 90	21	51
26	IsthP	H	Billericay Town	228	W 5-0	RIFAT 3 (14 48 82) Fisher 17 Shulton 66	21	52

GOALSCORERS	Lge	FAC	FAT	Total	Pens	Hat-tricks	Cons Run
Rifat	13	1		14		1	2
Smith	8	1		9	2		
McCall	3		1	4	3		
Sogbanae	4			4			
Weatherstone	3	1		4			2
Kennett	3			3			
Shulton	3			3			
Tejan-Sie	3			3			2
Fisher	2			2			2
Mason	2			2			
Davies	1			1			
Fredericks	1			1			
Hallam	1			1			
Henry	1			1			
Jones	1			1			
Kennedy	1			1			
Laird	1			1	1		
Mackie	1			1			
Morante	1			1			
Owen			1	1			
Reed	1			1			
Stellars			1	1			
Williams			1	1			
Opponents	2			2			

Cons Run - Consecutive scoring games.

WITHAM TOWN

Chairman: Tony Last

Secretary: Kevin Carroll **(T)** 07743 827 505 **(E)** withamtownfcsecretary@gmail.com

Commercial Manager: **(T)**

Programme Editor: Steve Parker **(T)** 07984 177 888

Ground Address: Village Glass Stadium, Spa Road, Witham CM8 1UN

(T) 01376 511 198 **Manager:** Garry Kimble

2012-13 Squad.

Club Factfile

Founded: 1947 **Nickname:** Town

Previous Names: None.

Previous Leagues: Mid. Essex. Essex & Suff. B. Essex Senior 1971-87. Isthmian 1987-2009

Club Colours (change): White/blue/green (All yellow).

Ground Capacity: 2,500 **Seats:** 157 **Covered:** 780 **Clubhouse:** Yes **Shop:** No

Directions

From M25: At junction 28, take the A12/A1023 exit to Chelmsford/Romford/Brentwood.
At the roundabout, take the 1st exit onto the A12 ramp to Chelmsford/Harwich/A120.
Merge onto A12. At junction 21, exit onto Hatfield Rd/B1389 toward Witham.
Go through 2 roundabouts. Turn left onto Spinks Lane. Turn right onto Highfields Road.
Turn left ground will be on the right.

Previous Grounds: None

Record Attendance: **Att:** 800 v Billericay Town, Essex Senior Lge, May 1976.

Record Victory: Not known

Record Defeat: Not known

Record Goalscorer: Colin Mitchell.

Record Appearances: Keith Dent.

Additional Records:

Senior Honours:

Essex Senior League 1970-71, 85-86, 2011-12.

10 YEAR RECORD

04-05		05-06		06-07		07-08		08-09		09-10		10-11		11-12		12-13		13-14	
Isth2	5	Isth2	2	Isth1N	20	Isth1N	20	Isth1N	21	ESen	2	ESen	3	ESen	1	Isth1N	4	Isth1N	2

A.F.C. SUDBURY

Chairman: Vacant

Secretary: Davis Webb **(T)** 07885 327 510 **(E)** dave-afc@supanet.com

Commercial Manager: **(T)**

Programme Editor: Darren Theobald **(T)** theobaldd@hotmail.co.uk

Ground Address: Kingsmarsh Stadium, Brundon Lane, Sudbury CO10 7HN

(T) 01787 376 213 **Manager:** David Batch

Club Factfile

Founded: 1999 **Nickname:** Yellows

Previous Names: Sudbury Town (1874) and Sudbury Wanderers (1958) merged in 1999

Previous Leagues: Eastern Counties 1999-2006, Isthmian 2006-08, Southern 2008-10

Club Colours (change): Yellow/blue/yellow (All red)

Ground Capacity: 2,500 **Seats:** 200 **Covered:** 1,500 **Clubhouse:** Yes **Shop:** Yes

Directions

From Braintree: Take A131 through Halstead to Sudbury. On descending hill into Sudbury turn left at first set of traffic lights (Kings Head), and then take the first right into Brundon Lane. The road narrows before reaching ground on the right hand side.

From Colchester, Bury St Edmunds and Ipswich: Enter Sudbury and follow signs for Halstead/Chelmsford. Go aross the river bridge and go under the old rail bridge, then turn right at the traffic lights (Kings Head) into Bulmer Road and the first right again into Brundon Lane. The road narrows before reaching ground on the right hand side.

Previous Grounds: The Priory Stadium

Record Attendance: 1,800

Record Victory: Not known

Record Defeat: Not known

Record Goalscorer: Gary Bennett - 172

Record Appearances: Paul Betson - 376

Additional Records:

Senior Honours:

Eastern Counties League 2000-01, 01-02, 02-03, 03-04, 04-05.

Suffolk Premier Cup 2002, 2003, 2004.

10 YEAR RECORD

04-05		05-06		06-07		07-08		08-09		09-10		10-11		11-12		12-13		13-14	
ECP	1	ECP	3	Isth1N	5	Isth1N	2	SthM		SthM	14	Isth1N	7	Isth1N	8	Isth1N	17	Isth1N	10

AVELEY

Chairman: Graham Gennings
Secretary: Craig Johnston **(T)** 07946 438 540 **(E)** craigjohnston@aveleyfc.freeserve.co.uk
Commercial Manager: **(T)**
Programme Editor: Craig Johnston **(T)** 07946 438 540
Ground Address: Mill Field, Mill Road, Aveley, Essex RM15 4SJ
(T) 01708 865 940 **Manager:** Justin Gardner

Club Factfile

Founded: 1927 **Nickname:** The Millers
Previous Names: None
Previous Leagues: Thurrock Combination 1946-49, London 1949-57, Delphian 1957-63, Athenian 1963-73, Isthmian 1973-2004, Southern 2004-06
Club Colours (change): All blue (All red)

Ground Capacity: 4,000 **Seats:** 400 **Covered:** 400 **Clubhouse:** Yes **Shop:** No

Directions
London - Southend A1306, turn into Sandy Lane at Aveley.

Previous Grounds: None

Record Attendance: 3,741 v Slough Town - FA Amateur Cup 27/02/1971
Record Victory: 11-1 v Histon - 24/08/1963
Record Defeat: 0-8 v Orient, Essex Thameside Trophy
Record Goalscorer: Jotty Wilks - 214
Record Appearances: Ken Riley - 422
Additional Records:

Senior Honours:
Athenian League 1970-71. Isthmian League Division 1 North 2008-09.
Thameside Trophy 1980, 2005, 2007.

10 YEAR RECORD

04-05	05-06	06-07	07-08	08-09	09-10	10-11	11-12	12-13	13-14
SthE 17	SthE 20	Isth1N 15	Isth1N 11	Isth1N 1	Isth P 3	Isth P 19	Isth P 20	Isth P 5	Isth1N 13

BARKINGSIDE

Chairman: Jimmy Flanagan

Secretary: Jimmy Flanagan **(T)** 07956 894 194 **(E)** confclothing@aol.com

Commercial Manager: **(T)**

Programme Editor: Jimmy Flanagan **(T)**

Ground Address: Cricketfield Stadium, 3 Cricklefield Place, Ilford IG1 1FY

(T) 020 8552 3995 **Manager:** Matt Frew

Club Factfile

Founded: 1898 **Nickname:** The Side / Sky Blues

Previous Names: None

Previous Leagues: London. Greater London. Met London. Spartan, South Midlands. Essex Senior > 2013.

Club Colours (change): Sky blue & navy/navy blue/navy blue. (All orange)

Ground Capacity: 3,500 **Seats:** 216 **Covered:** Yes **Clubhouse:** Yes **Shop:** No

Directions

Taking the A127, from the east travel towards London before coming to the traffic light controlled junction at Barley Lane, Goodmayes (B177) . Turn Left by taking the slip road and follow Barley Lane to its junction with the traffic light controlled High Road, Goodmayes (A118) (it is the first set of traffic control lights for traffic rather than pedestrians on that road). Turn Right and follow the road past Seven Kings station (which should be on your right) and on towards Ilford. The entrance to the ground is some 400 yards past the station with the Ilford Swimming Baths on the left being the point at which both coaches and those in cars or on foot should turn left into the car parks. Both on Saturday and after 6pm. during the week, the public car park is free of charge.

Previous Grounds: Barkingside High Road. Barkingside Recreation Ground. Oakside > 2014.

Record Attendance: **Att:** 957 v Arsenal Reserves, London League, 1957.

Record Victory:

Record Defeat:

Record Goalscorer:

Record Appearances:

Additional Records: Greater London League 1964-65. Spartan League 1996-97.

Senior Honours:

London Senior Cup 1996-97. Spartan South Midlands League Premier Division 1998-99. Essex Senior Cup 2008-09.

10 YEAR RECORD

04-05	05-06	06-07	07-08	08-09	09-10	10-11	11-12	12-13	13-14
ESen 4	ESen 4	ESen 3	ESen 3	ESen 5	ESen 9	ESen 15	ESen 8	ESen 2	Isth1N 20

BRENTWOOD TOWN

Chairman: Brian Hallett
Secretary: Ray Stevens **(T)** 07768 006 370 **(E)** r.w.stevens@btinternet.com
Commercial Manager: **(T)**
Programme Editor: Ken Hobbs **(T)** 07958 232 829
Ground Address: The Arena, Brentwood Centre, Doddinghurst Road, Brentwood CM15 9NN
(T) 07768 006 370 **Manager:** Danny Dafter & Adam Flanagan

Club Factfile

Founded: 1954 **Nickname:** Blues
Previous Names: Manor Athletic, Brentwood Athletic, Brentwood F.C.
Previous Leagues: Romford & District, South Essex Combination, London & Essex Border, Olympian, Essex Senior

Club Colours (change): Sky blue/white/white (All claret)

Ground Capacity: 1,000 **Seats:** 150 **Covered:** 250 **Clubhouse:** Yes **Shop:** No

Directions
From High Street (Wilson's Corner) turn north into Ongar Road.
Then at third mini roundabout turn right into Doddinghurst Road.

Previous Grounds: King George's Playing Fields (Hartswood), Larkins Playing Fields 1957-93

Record Attendance: 472 v West Ham United - 27/07/2004
Record Victory: Not known
Record Defeat: Not known
Record Goalscorer: Not known
Record Appearances: Not known
Additional Records:

Senior Honours:
Essex Senior League 2000-01, 2006-07, League Cup 1975-76, 78-79, 90-91, 2006-07.
Essex Olympian League Cup 1967-68.

10 YEAR RECORD

04-05		05-06		06-07		07-08		08-09		09-10		10-11		11-12		12-13		13-14	
ESen	14	ESen	8	ESen	1	Isth1N	6	Isth1N	3	Isth1N	12	Isth1N	5	Isth1N	9	Isth1N	9	Isth1N	19

BRIGHTLINGSEA REGENT

Chairman: Terry Doherty

Secretary: Tom Rothery (T) 07794 545 586 (E) t.rothery@sky.com

Commercial Manager: (T)

Programme Editor: Tom Rothery (T) 07794 545 586

Ground Address: North Road, Brightlingsea, Essex CO7 0PL

(T) 01206 304 199 **Manager:** James Webster

The squad celebrate their promotion from the Eastern Counties Premier Division at the end of the 2013-14 season.

Club Factfile

Founded: 1928 **Nickname:** The Rs

Previous Names: Brightlingsea Athletic & Brightlingsea Town merged to form Brightlingsea United 1928-2005. Merged with Regent Park Rangers.

Previous Leagues: Essex Senior 1972-91. Eastern Counties 1990-02, 2011-14. Essex & Suffolk Border 2002-2011.

Club Colours (change): Red & black stripes/red/red (Pink & black/black with white trim/black with white trim)

Ground Capacity: **Seats:** **Covered:** **Clubhouse:** Yes **Shop:**

Directions

Take exit 28 off M25, take slip road left for A12 toward Brentwood / Chelmsford / Romford, turn left onto slip road, merge onto A12, take slip road left for A120, take slip road left for A133, at roundabout, take 2nd exit, turn left onto B1029 / Great Bentley Road, turn right onto B1027 / Tenpenny Hill, and then immediately turn left onto B1029 / Brightlingsea Road, turn left to stay on B1029 / Ladysmith Avenue, bear left onto Spring Road, turn left onto North Road.

Previous Grounds: Bell Green (Bellfield Close). Recreation Ground (Regent Road) > 1920.

Record Attendance: 1,200 v Colchester United, friendly, 1988.

Record Victory:

Record Defeat:

Record Goalscorer:

Record Appearances:

Additional Records:

Senior Honours:

League: Essex Senior 1988-89, 89-90. Essex & Suffolk Border League 2010-11.

10 YEAR RECORD

04-05	05-06	06-07	07-08	08-09	09-10	10-11	11-12	12-13	13-14
						EsSuP 1	EC1 5	EC1 3	ECP 2

BURNHAM RAMBLERS

Chairman: William Hannan
Secretary: Shaun Pugh **(T)** 07525 099 914 **(E)** secretarybrfc@sapugh.gotadsl.co.
Commercial Manager: **(T)**
Programme Editor: Martin Leno **(T)** 07702 592 418
Ground Address: Leslie Fields Stadium, Springfield Road CM0 8TE
(T) 01621 784 383 **Manager:** Keith Wilson

Club Factfile

Founded: 1900 **Nickname:** Ramblers
Previous Names: None
Previous Leagues: North Essex. Mid-Essex. Olympian. South East Essex. Essex Senior > 2013.

Club Colours (change): Navy & sky blue stripes/navy/sky blue (All red).

Ground Capacity: 2,000 **Seats:** 156 **Covered:** 300 **Clubhouse:** Yes **Shop:** No

Directions
A12 Proceed along the A12 until you reach the turn off for Maldon. Carry on through Danbury and then follow the signs for Burnham on Crouch (B1010). *Just before you get to Burnham on Crouch there is a garage on the left-hand side. Springfield Road is about quarter of a mile past the garage on the right. Turn right into Springfield Road, then take the second turning on the right and then first right and drive through the gates of the ground. **A127** Proceed along the A127, and take the A130 turn off sign-posted to Chelmsford. At Rettendon Turnpike (a large roundabout), take the A132 to South Woodham Ferrers. Burnham on Crouch is sign-posted from there (B1012 and then B1010). Continue from * above. **A13** Proceed along A13 and take the A130 turn off sign-posted to Chelmsford. At Rettendon Turnpike (a large roundabout) take the A132 to South Woodham Ferrers. Burnham on Crouch is sign-posted from there (B1012 and then B1010). Continue from * above.

Previous Grounds: None

Record Attendance: **Att:** 1,500 v Arsenal, opening of stand.
Record Victory:
Record Defeat:
Record Goalscorer:
Record Appearances:
Additional Records:

Senior Honours:
Essex Senior League 2012-13.

10 YEAR RECORD

04-05		05-06		06-07		07-08		08-09		09-10		10-11		11-12		12-13		13-14	
ESen	2	ESen	5	ESen	5	ESen	8	ESen	7	ESen	3	ESen	7	ESen	4	ESen	1	Isth1N	17

CHATHAM TOWN

Chairman: Jeff Talbot
Secretary: Henry Longhurst **(T)** 07967 465 554 **(E)** h.longhurst@sky.com
Commercial Manager: **(T)**
Programme Editor: Rachel Willett **(T)** 07951 915 791
Ground Address: Maidstone Road Sports Ground, Maidstone Road, Chatham ME4 6LR
(T) 01634 812 194 **Manager:** Kevin Watson

Club Factfile

Founded: 1882 **Nickname:** Chats
Previous Names: Chatham FC 1882-1974, Medway FC 1974-79
Previous Leagues: Southern 1894-1900, 1920-21, 27-29, 83-88, 2001-, Kent 1894-96, 1901-1905, 29-59, 68-83, 88-2001, Aetolian 1959-64, Metropolitan 1964-68
Club Colours (change): Red & black stripes/black/black (Blue & black stripes/blue/blue)

Ground Capacity: 2,000 **Seats:** 600 **Covered:** 600 **Clubhouse:** Yes **Shop:** Yes

Directions
Exit the M2 at junction 3, and follow directions for Chatham & Town Centre. You will then pass a Homebase & Toys 'R' Us on the left hand side. Continue straight over the roundabout and then there is a split in the road, where you bear right for chatham this is Maidstone Road. Follow this, continuing straight over the cross roads and you will see a petrol station on the left. Bournville Road is opposite the petrol station on the left. Ground entrance is first left.

Previous Grounds: Great Lines, Chatham 1882-90

Record Attendance: 5,000 v Gillingham - 1980
Record Victory: Not known
Record Defeat: Not known
Record Goalscorer: Not known
Record Appearances: Not known
Additional Records: Received Transfer fee of £500. FA Cup Quarter finalists 1888/89.

Senior Honours:
Kent League 1894-95, 1903-04, 04-05, 71-72, 73-74, 75-76, 76-77, 79-80, 2000-01. Aetolian League 1963-64.
Kent Senior Cup 1885-86, 86-87, 87-88, 88-89, 94-95,1904-05, 10-11, 18-19. Kent Senior Shield 1919-20.

10 YEAR RECORD

04-05	05-06	06-07	07-08	08-09	09-10	10-11	11-12	12-13	13-14
SthE 11	SthE 17	Isth1S 16	Isth1S 18	Isth1N 10	Isth1S 17	Isth1S 21	Isth1N 15	Isth1N 13	Isth1N 12

CHESHUNT

Chairman: Dean Williamson
Secretary: Alex Kalinic (T) 07754 831 800 (E) clubsecretary@cheshuntfc.com
Commercial Manager: (T)
Programme Editor: Alex Kalinic (T) 07754 831 800
Ground Address: Cheshunt Stadium, Theobalds Lane, Cheshunt, Herts EN8 8RU
(T) 01992 625 793 **Manager:** Omer Riza

The squad on the last day of the 2013-14 season - Back Row - Steve Rands, Tunde Adewumni, Ross Dedman, Robbie Nash, Will Viner, Milton Elenge, Lewis Payne, Mete Sem, Steve Holmes.
Front Row - Omer Riza, Dan Ferrigno, Ted Llewellyn, John Megicks, Joe Clemo, Josh Cooper, Allen Bossman, Warren Goodhind.

Club Factfile

Founded: 1946 **Nickname:** Ambers
Previous Names:
Previous Leagues: London 1947-51, 56-59, Delphian 1952-55, Aetolian 1960-62, Spartan 1963-64, 88-93, Athenian 1965-76, Isthmian 1977-87, 94-2005, Southern 2006-08

Club Colours (change): Amber/black/black (Sky blue/white/sky blue)

Ground Capacity: 3,500 **Seats:** 424 **Covered:** 600 **Clubhouse:** Yes **Shop:** No

Directions
M25, junction 25 take A10 north towards Hertford.
Third exit at roundabout towards Waltham Cross A121.
First exit at roundabout towards Cheshunt B176.
Under railway bridge then left onto Theobalds Lane.
Ground is 800 yard on the right.

Previous Grounds: Gothic Sports Ground 1946-47. College Road 1947-50. Brookfield Lane 1950-52, 53-58.

Record Attendance: 5,000
Record Victory: v Bromley - FA Amateur Cup 2nd Round 28/01/1950
Record Defeat: 0-10 v Etonn Manor - London League 17/04/1956
Record Goalscorer: Eddie Sedgwick - 148 (1967-72, 1980)
Record Appearances: John Poole - 526 (1970-76, 79-83)
Additional Records: Received £10,000 from Peterborough United for Lloyd Opara

Senior Honours:
London League Premier Division 1950, Division 1 1948, 49. Athenian League Premier Division 1976, Division 1 1968.
Spartan League 1963. Isthmian League Division 2 2003.
London Charity Cup 1974. East Anglian Cup 1975. Herts Charity Cup 2006, 2008.

10 YEAR RECORD

04-05	05-06	06-07	07-08	08-09	09-10	10-11	11-12	12-13	13-14
Isth P 19	SthP 16	SthP 16	SthP 22	Isth1N 14	Isth1N 15	Isth1N 18	Isth1N 18	Isth1N 11	Isth1N 15

CRAY WANDERERS

Chairman: Gary Hillman

Secretary: Kerry Phillips (T) 07718 353 583 (E) kerryphillips@hotmail.com

Commercial Manager: (T)

Programme Editor: Phil Babbs (T) 07977 828 252

Ground Address: Bromley FC, Hayes Lane, Bromley, Kent BR2 9EF

(T) 020 8460 5291 **Manager:** Keith Bird

2014-15 Squad.

Club Factfile

Founded: 1860 **Nickname:** Wanderers or Wands

Previous Names: Cray Old Boys (immediately after WW1); Sidcup & Footscray (start of WW2).

Previous Leagues: Kent 1894-1903, 1906-07, 1909-1914, 1934-38, 1978-2004; West Kent & South Suburban Leagues (before WW1); London 1920-1934, 1951-1959; Kent Amateur 1938-1939, 1946-1951; South London Alliance 1943-1946; Aetolian 1959-1964; Greater London 1964-1966; Metropolitan 1966-1971; Met. London 1971-1975; London Spartan 1975-1978.

Club Colours (change): Amber/black/amber (Pale blue & white stripes/white/pale blue)

Ground Capacity: 5,000 **Seats:** 1,300 **Covered:** 2,500 **Clubhouse:** Yes **Shop:** Yes

Directions

From M25: Leaving the motorway at junction 4, follow the A21 to Bromley and London, for approximately 4 miles and then fork left onto the A232 signposted Croydon/Sutton. At the second set of traffic lights, turn right into Baston Road (B265), following it for about two miles as it becomes Hayes Street and then Hayes Lane. Cray Wanderers FC is on the right hand side of the road just after the mini roundabout. There is ample room for coaches to drive down the driveway, turn round and park.

Previous Grounds: Star Lane (1860s), Derry Downs (until 1898), Fordcroft (1898-1936), Twysdens (1936-1939), St Mary Cray Rec (1940s),

Previous Grounds: Cont. Northfield Farm (1950-51), Tothills (aka Fordcroft, 1951-1955), Grassmeade (1955-1973), Oxford Road (1973-1998).

Record Attendance: (Grassmeade) 2,160vLeytonstone FA Am.C 3rd Rd, 1968-69; (Oxford R) 1,520vStamford - FAV QF 79-80, (Hayes L) 1,082vAFC Wim. - 04-05

Record Victory: 15-0 v Sevenoaks - 1894-95.

Record Defeat: 2-15 (H) and 0-14 (A) v Callenders Athletic - Kent Amateur League, 1947-48.

Record Goalscorer: Ken Collishaw 274 (1954-1965)

Record Appearances: John Dorey - 500 (1961-72).

Additional Records: Unbeaten for 28 Ryman League games in 2007-2008.

Senior Honours:

Kent League 1901-02, 80-81, 2002-03, 03-04 (League Cup 83-84, 2002-03); London League 1956-57, 57-58 (League Cup 54-55); Aetolian League 1962-63 (League Cup 63-64); Greater London League 1965-66 (League Cup 64-65, 65-66); Met. Lge Cup 1970-71; Met. London League & League Cup 1974-75; London Spartan League 1976-77, 77-78. Kent Amateur Cup 1930-31, 62-63, 63-64, 64-65. Kent Senior Trophy 1992-93, 2003-04.

10 YEAR RECORD

04-05		05-06		06-07		07-08		08-09		09-10		10-11		11-12		12-13		13-14	
Isth1	6	Isth1	11	Isth1S	12	Isth1S	3	Isth1S	2	Isth P	15	Isth P	9	Isth P	9	Isth P	17	Isth P	24

DEREHAM TOWN

Chairman: Simon Barnes
Secretary: Nigel Link **(T)** 07885 144 039 **(E)** patnige1954@fsmail.net
Commercial Manager: **(T)**
Programme Editor: Simon Barnes **(T)** 07766 318 550
Ground Address: Aldiss Park, Norwich Road, Dereham, Norfolk NR20 3PX
(T) 01362 690 460 **Manager:** Matt Henman

Club Factfile

Founded: 1884 **Nickname:** Magpies
Previous Names: Dereham and Dereham Hobbies.
Previous Leagues: Norwich District. Dereham & District. Norfolk & Suffolk. Anglian Comb. Eastern Counties > 2013.

Club Colours (change): White & black stripes/black/black. (Green/white/white)

Ground Capacity: 3,000 **Seats:** 50 **Covered:** 500 **Clubhouse:** Yes **Shop:** Yes

Directions
Take the A47 towards Swaffham & Dereham. Do not take first slip road into Dereham. Carry on along the by-pass and take the second slip road, onto the B1110, sign posted B1147 to Bawdeswell, Swanton Morley and the Dereham Windmill. Follow the slip road round and Aldiss Park is 500 yards on your right.

Previous Grounds: None

Record Attendance: **Att:** 3000 v Norwich City, Friendly, 07/2001.
Record Victory:
Record Defeat:
Record Goalscorer:
Record Appearances:
Additional Records:
Senior Honours:
Anglian Combination Division 1 Champions 1989-90, Premier Division 97-98. Norfolk Senior Cup 2005-06, 06-07.
Eastern Counties Premier Division 2012-13.

10 YEAR RECORD

04-05		05-06		06-07		07-08		08-09		09-10		10-11		11-12		12-13		13-14	
ECP	15	ECP	12	ECP	6	ECP	4	ECP	4	ECP	10	ECP	2	ECP	10	ECP	1	Isth1N	7

GREAT WAKERING ROVERS

Chairman: Tony Butcher
Secretary: Daniel Ellis (T) 07828 048 671 (E) secretary@gwrovers.com
Commercial Manager: (T)
Programme Editor: Robert Lilley (T) 07915 082 279
Ground Address: Burroughs Park, Little Wakering Hall Lane, Gt Wakering SS3 0HH
(T) 01702 217 812 **Manager:** Dan Trenkel

Club Factfile

Founded: 1919 **Nickname:** Rovers
Previous Names: Not known
Previous Leagues: Southend & Dist. 1919-81, Southend All. 1981-89, Essex Inter 1989-92, Essex Sen 1992-99, Isth. 1999-2004, Sthn 2004-05

Club Colours (change): Green and white stripes/green/green & white (Yellow/black/yellow & black)

Ground Capacity: 2,500 **Seats:** 150 **Covered:** 300 **Clubhouse:** Yes **Shop:** No

Directions
A127 towards Southend and follow signs for Shoeburyness for about four miles.
Turn left to Great Wakering on B1017 at Bournes Green.
Go down High Street for half a mile and ground is on the left.

Previous Grounds: Great Wakering Rec

Record Attendance: 1,150 v Southend United - Friendly 19/07/2006
Record Victory: 9-0 v Eton Manor - 27/12/1931
Record Defeat: 1-7 v Bowers United - Essex Senior League 01/04/1998
Record Goalscorer: Not known
Record Appearances: Not known
Additional Records:

Senior Honours:
Essex Senior League 1994-95, 2013-14. Isthmian League Division 3.

10 YEAR RECORD

04-05	05-06	06-07	07-08	08-09	09-10	10-11	11-12	12-13	13-14
SthE 20	SthE 13	Isth1N 12	Isth1N 13	Isth1N 13	Isth1N 9	Isth1N 15	Isth1N 22	ESen 4	ESen 1

HARLOW TOWN

Chairman: John Barnett
Secretary: Ray Dyer **(T)** 07841 667 098 **(E)** harlowtownfc@aol.com
Commercial Manager: **(T)**
Programme Editor: Mark Kettley **(T)** sundayonly1@aol.com
Ground Address: The Harlow Arena, off Elizabeth Way, The Pinnacles, Harlow CM19 5BE
(T) 01279 443 196 **Manager:** Danny Chapman

Club Factfile

Founded: 1879 **Nickname:** Hawks
Previous Names: None
Previous Leagues: East Hertfordshire > 1932, Spartan 1932-39, 46-54, London 1954-61, Delphian 1961-63, Athenian 1963-73, Isthmian 1973-92, Inactive 1992-93, Southern 2004-06

Club Colours (change): All red with yellow trim (All yellow)

Ground Capacity: 3,500 **Seats:** 500 **Covered:** 500 **Clubhouse:** Yes **Shop:** Yes

Directions
Barrows Farm is situated on the western side of town just off of the Roydon Road (A1169) on the Pinnacles Industrial Estate.
If coming into Harlow from the M11 (North or South) exit at Junction 7 and follow the A414 until the first roundabout where you turn left onto the A1169. Follow the A1169 signed for Roydon until you see the ground ahead of you at the Roydon Road roundabout. Go straight over the roundabout and the entrance to the ground is on the left.
If coming into town from the west on the A414 turn right at the first roundabout (the old ground was straight ahead) signed Roydon A1169. Follow the A1169 for approx 1 mile and the entrance to the ground is on the right.

Previous Grounds: Marigolds 1919-22, Green Man Field 1922-60

Record Attendance: 9,723 v Leicester City - FA Cup 3rd Round replay 08/01/1980
Record Victory: 14-0 v Bishop's Stortford - 11/04/1925
Record Defeat: 0-11 v Ware (A) - Spartan Division 1 East 06/03/1948
Record Goalscorer: Dick Marshall scored 64 during 1928-29
Record Appearances: Norman Gladwin - 639 (1949-70)
Additional Records:

Senior Honours:
Athenian League Division 1 1971-72. Isthmian League Division 1 1978-79, Division 2 North 1988-89.
Essex Senior cup 1978-79

10 YEAR RECORD

04-05	05-06	06-07	07-08	08-09	09-10	10-11	11-12	12-13	13-14
SthE 15	SthE 9	Isth1N 2	Isth P 15	Isth P 20	Isth1N 22	Isth1N 4	Isth1N 7	Isth1N 21	Isth1N 4

HEYBRIDGE SWIFTS

Chairman: Nick Bowyer
Secretary: Jill Hedgecock (T) 07522 158 487 (E) blackwater1@sky.com
Commercial Manager: (T)
Programme Editor: Pete Calvert (T) 07742 601 629
Ground Address: Scraley Road, Heybridge, Maldon, Essex CM9 8JA
(T) 01621 852 978 **Manager:** Jody Brown

Club Factfile

Founded: 1880 **Nickname:** Swifts
Previous Names: Heybridge FC.
Previous Leagues: Essex & Suffolk Border, North Essex, South Essex, Essex Senior 1971-84

Club Colours (change): Black and white stripes/black/black (Yellow/white/white)

Ground Capacity: 3,000 **Seats:** 550 **Covered:** 1,200 **Clubhouse:** Yes **Shop:** Yes

Directions
Leave Maldon on the main road to Colchester,
pass through Heybridge then turn right at sign to Tolleshunt Major (Scraley Road).
The ground is on the right.

Previous Grounds: One before Scraley Road.

Record Attendance: 2,477 v Woking FA Trophy 1997
Record Victory: Not known
Record Defeat: Not known
Record Goalscorer: Julian Lamb - 115 (post War)
Record Appearances: Hec Askew - 500+. John Pollard - 496
Additional Records: Paid £1,000 for Dave Rainford and for Lee Kersey
Received £35,000 from Southend United for Simon Royce
Senior Honours:
Isthmian League Division 2 North 1989-90, Essex Senior League x3.
Essex Junior Cup 1931-32. East Anglian Cup 1993-94, 94-95.

10 YEAR RECORD

04-05	05-06	06-07	07-08	08-09	09-10	10-11	11-12	12-13	13-14
Isth P 7	Isth P 2	Isth P 12	Isth P 12	Isth P 21	Isth1N 6	Isth1N 9	Isth1N 16	Isth1N 6	Isth1N 3

MALDON & TIPTREE

Chairman: Ed Garty
Secretary: Phil Robinson **(T)** 0775 906 6636 **(E)** robbophil@hotmail.com
Commercial Manager: **(T)**
Programme Editor: Richard Buckby **(T)** buckby1996@hotmail.co.uk
Ground Address: Wallace Binder Ground, Park Drive, Maldon CM9 5JQ
(T) 01621 853 762 **Manager:** Terry Spillane

Club Factfile

Founded: 2010 **Nickname:** The Hoops
Previous Names: Maldon Town (1975) and Tiptree United (1933) merged in 2010 to form today's club
Previous Leagues: None

Club Colours (change): Blue and red stripes/blue/blue (All orange)

Ground Capacity: 2,800 **Seats:** 155 **Covered:** 300 **Clubhouse:** Yes **Shop:**

Directions
From M25 junction 28 travel north on A12 until A414 to Maldon.
Turn right at Safeways roundabout, then over next two roundabouts.
Ground is on the right.

Previous Grounds: None

Record Attendance: Not known
Record Victory: Not known
Record Defeat: Not known
Record Goalscorer: Not known
Record Appearances: Not known
Additional Records:

Senior Honours:
None

10 YEAR RECORD

04-05	05-06	06-07	07-08	08-09	09-10	10-11	11-12	12-13	13-14
						Isth1N 8	Isth1N 11	Isth1N 2	Isth1N 9

NEEDHAM MARKET

Chairman: Keith Nunn
Secretary: Mark Easlea (T) 07795 456 502 (E) m.easlea@sky.com
Commercial Manager: (T)
Programme Editor: Alan Jopling (T) 07824 878 707
Ground Address: Bloomfields, Quinton Road, Needham Market IP6 8DA
(T) 01449 721 000 **Manager:** Mark Morsley

Club Factfile

Founded: 1919 **Nickname:** The Marketmen
Previous Names: None
Previous Leagues: Suffolk & Ipswich Senior, Eastern Counties

Club Colours (change): All red with white trim (Blue & black stripes/black/black)

Ground Capacity: 1,000 **Seats:** 250 **Covered:** 250 **Clubhouse:** Yes **Shop:** Yes

Directions
Quinton Road is off Barretts Lane which in turn is off Needham Market High Street.

Previous Grounds: Young's Meadow 1919. Crowley Park >1996.

Record Attendance: 750 v Ipswich Town - Suffolk Premier Cup 2007
Record Victory: 10-1 v I[swich Wanderers (A) , FA Cup Preliminary Round, 01/09/2007
Record Defeat: 2-6 v Lowestoft Town (A), FA Trophy First round Qualifier, 19/10/2010
Record Goalscorer: Craig Parker - 111 (2007-2011) Most goals in a season - Craig Parker 40 (2011-11).
Record Appearances: Rhys Barber - 334 (2006-2012)
Additional Records: Most goals scored in a season - 196 in 70 games (2007-08)

Senior Honours:
Suffolk Senior Cup 1989-90, 2004-05. Suffolk & Ipswich Senior League 1995-96. East Anglian Cup 2006-07.
Eastern Counties Premier Division 2009-10.

10 YEAR RECORD

04-05	05-06	06-07	07-08	08-09	09-10	10-11	11-12	12-13	13-14
EC1 2	ECP 6	ECP 4	ECP 2	ECP 3	ECP 1	Isth1N 2	Isth1N 4	Isth1N 16	Isth1N 5

REDBRIDGE

Chairman: Jim Chapman
Secretary: Bob Holloway **(T)** 07890 699 907 **(E)** r.holloway338@btinternet.com
Commercial Manager: **(T)**
Programme Editor: Adam Silver **(T)** 07796 880 824
Ground Address: Oakside Stadium, Station Road, Barkingside, Ilford IG6 1NB
(T) 0208 550 3611 **Manager:** Dave Ross & Ricky Eaton

A Redbridge player shields the ball from a Kingstonian player during a match from last season.

Club Factfile

Founded: 1958 **Nickname:** Motormen
Previous Names: Ford United 1958-2004
Previous Leagues: Aetolian 1959-64, Greater London 1964-71, Metropolitan 1971-74, Essex Senior 1974-97, Isthmian 1997-2004, Conference 2004-05
Club Colours (change): Red with black trim/black/black (White and red/red/red)

Ground Capacity: 3,000 **Seats:** 350 **Covered:** 1,000 **Clubhouse:** Yes **Shop:** Yes

Directions
A12 from London, turn left off Eastern Avenue into Horns Road, Barkingside (Greengate). Right into Craven Gardens, right again into Carlton Drive and left into Station Road. Go over bridge and ground is on the right.
Adjacent to Barkingside Underground Station (Central Line).

Previous Grounds: Ford Sports & Social Club > 2000

Record Attendance: 58,000 v Bishop Auckland
Record Victory: Not known
Record Defeat: Not known
Record Goalscorer: Jeff Wood - 196
Record Appearances: Roger Bird
Additional Records:

Senior Honours:
Aetolian League 1959-60, 61-62. Greater London League 1970-71. Essex Senior League 1991-92, 96-97.
Isthmian League Division 3 1998-99, Division 1 2001-02,

10 YEAR RECORD

04-05	05-06	06-07	07-08	08-09	09-10	10-11	11-12	12-13	13-14
Conf S 22	Isth P 22	Isth1N 16	Isth1N 3	Isth1N 8	Isth1N 18	Isth1N 16	Isth1N 6	Isth1N 20	Isth1N 14

ROMFORD

Chairman: Steve Gardener
Secretary: Colin Ewenson **(T)** 07973 717 074 **(E)** ewenson@aol.com
Commercial Manager: **(T)**
Programme Editor: Keith Preston **(T)** 07876 237 918
Ground Address: Thurrock FC, South Way, Ship Lane, Aveley RM19 1YN
(T) 01708 865 492 **Manager:** Paul Martin

Club Factfile

Founded: 1876 **Nickname:** Boro
Previous Names: Original club founded in 1876 folded during WW1, Reformed in 1929 folded again in 1978 and reformed in 1992
Previous Leagues: Athenian 1931-39, Isthmian 1945-59, 97-2002, Southern 1959-78, Essex Senior 1992-96, 2002-09

Club Colours (change): Yellow & blue/white/blue

Ground Capacity: 4,500 **Seats:** 300 **Covered:** 1,000 **Clubhouse:** Yes **Shop:**

Directions
Approaching the ground from the North - along the M25 in a clockwise direction. Leave the motorway at junction 30. At the roundabout take the second exit and stay in the left hand lane. This leads to a large roundabout controlled by traffic lights. The fifth exit is Ship Lane and the ground is approximately 50 yards on the right hand side. Approaching the ground from the South - anti-clockwise on the M25. When going through the Dartford Tunnel take the left hand bore. On coming out of the tunnel take the first exit - junction 31. This leads to a large roundabout controlled by traffic lights. Take the third exit which is Ship Lane. The ground is situated approximately 50 yards on the right hand side.

Previous Grounds: The Mill Field (Aveley FC).

Record Attendance: 820 v Leatherhead - Isthmian Division 2
Record Victory: Not known
Record Defeat: Not known
Record Goalscorer: Danny Benstock
Record Appearances: S Horne - 234
Additional Records:
Senior Honours:
Essex Senior League 1995-96, 2008-09. Isthmian League Division 2 1996-97.

10 YEAR RECORD

04-05	05-06	06-07	07-08	08-09	09-10	10-11	11-12	12-13	13-14
ESen 5	ESen 12	ESen 2	ESen 5	ESen 1	Isth1N 13	Isth1N 12	Isth1N 13	Isth1N 8	Isth1N 11

SOHAM TOWN RANGERS

Chairman: Colin Murfit
Secretary: Simon Cullum (T) 07899 971 680 (E) strfc@live.co.uk
Commercial Manager: (T)
Programme Editor: TBC (T)
Ground Address: Julius Martin Lane, Soham, Ely, Cambridgeshire CB7 5EQ
(T) 01353 720 732 **Manager:** Steve Fallon

Club Factfile

Founded: 1947 **Nickname:** Town or Rangers
Previous Names: Soham Town and Soham Rangers merged in 1947
Previous Leagues: Peterborough & District, Eastern Counties 1963-2008, Southern 2008-11.

Club Colours (change): Green & white stripes/green/green & white (All blue with white trim)

Ground Capacity: 2,000 **Seats:** 250 **Covered:** 1,000 **Clubhouse:** Yes **Shop:** Yes

Directions
Take the turning off the A14 for Soham/Ely. Join the A142 following signs for Ely/Soham. On approaching Soham at the Q8 Petrol Station, continue down the Soham by-pass for approx. 1.5 miles. Turn left after the Bypass Motel, continue bearing left across the Common into Bushel Lane, at end of road, turn right into Hall Street. Julius Martin Lane is 2nd left.

Previous Grounds:

Record Attendance: 3,000 v Pegasus - FA Amateur Cup 1963
Record Victory: Not known
Record Defeat: Not known
Record Goalscorer: Not known
Record Appearances: Not known
Additional Records:

Senior Honours:
Eastern Counties League Premier Division 2007-08

10 YEAR RECORD

04-05	05-06	06-07	07-08	08-09	09-10	10-11	11-12	12-13	13-14
ECP 7	ECP 10	ECP	ECP 1	SthC 15	SthC 11	SthC 17	Isth1N 19	Isth1N 7	Isth1N 8

THAMESMEAD TOWN

Chairman: Terry Hill
Secretary: David Joy (T) 07990 612 495 (E) davejoyo@yahoo.co.uk
Commercial Manager: (T)
Programme Editor: Daniel Parker (T) daniel@duplexity.co.uk
Ground Address: Bayliss Avenue, Thamesmead, London SE28 8NJ
(T) 0208 320 4488 **Manager:** Keith McMahon

Club Factfile

Founded: 1970 **Nickname:** The Mead
Previous Names: None
Previous Leagues: Spartan 1987-91, Kent 1991-2008

Club Colours (change): All green (All light blue)

Ground Capacity: 400 **Seats:** 161 **Covered:** 125 **Clubhouse:** Yes **Shop:**

Directions
From the A2 take the A2018 exit toward Dartford/Wilmington, at the roundabout, take the 1st exit onto Shepherd's Ln/A2018.
At the roundabout, take the 1st exit onto Rochester Way. Slight right at Swan Ln, continue onto Station Rd.
At the roundabout, take the 1st exit onto Crayford Rd/A207, continue to follow A207, slight right to stay on A207, turn left at London Rd/A2000 continue to follow A2000, turn right at Perry St/A2000.
At the roundabout, take the 2nd exit onto Northend Rd/A206, continue to follow A206. Go through 1 roundabout.
At the roundabout, take the 2nd exit onto Bronze Age Way/A2016, continue to follow A2016. Go through 1 roundabout.
At the roundabout, take the 2nd exit onto Eastern Way/A2016. Take the ramp. At the roundabout, take the 3rd exit onto Carlyle Rd/A2041.
At the roundabout, take the 3rd exit onto Crossway. Turn right at Bayliss Ave, take the 1st left onto Chadwick Way. Ground will be on the left.

Previous Grounds: Crossways. Meridian Sports Ground > 1985.

Record Attendance: 400 v Wimbledon - Ground opening 1988
Record Victory: 9-0 v Kent Police - Kent League 19/04/1994
Record Defeat: Not known
Record Goalscorer: Delroy D'Oyley
Record Appearances: Not known
Additional Records:

Senior Honours:
Kent Senior Trophy 2004-05. Kent Premier 2007-08

10 YEAR RECORD

04-05	05-06	06-07	07-08	08-09	09-10	10-11	11-12	12-13	13-14
Kent P 8	Kent P 3	Kent P 4	Kent P 1	Isth1N 18	Isth1N 7	Isth1N 17	Isth1N 10	Isth1N 3	Isth P 22

THURROCK

Chairman: Tommy South
Secretary: Mark Southgate (T) 07979 525 117 (E) mark10tfc@gmail.com
Commercial Manager: (T)
Programme Editor: Tony Flood (T) 07525 493 785
Ground Address: South Way, Ship Lane, Grays, Essex RM19 1YN
(T) 01708 865 492 **Manager:** Mark Stimson

Club Factfile

Founded: 1985 **Nickname:** Fleet
Previous Names: Purfleet > 2003
Previous Leagues: Essex Senior 1985-89, Isthmian 1989-2004

Club Colours (change): Yellow/green/green (All purple)

Ground Capacity: 4,500 **Seats:** 300 **Covered:** 1,000 **Clubhouse:** Yes **Shop:** Yes

Directions
Approaching the ground from the North - along the M25 in a clockwise direction. Leave the motorway at junction 30. At the roundabout take the second exit and stay in the left hand lane. This leads to a large roundabout controlled by traffic lights. The fifth exit is Ship Lane and the ground is approximately 50 yards on the right hand side. Approaching the ground from the South - anti-clockwise on the M25. When going through the Dartford Tunnel take the left hand bore. On coming out of the tunnel take the first exit - junction 31. This leads to a large roundabout controlled by traffic lights. Take the third exit which is Ship Lane. The ground is situated approximately 50 yards on the right hand side.

Previous Grounds: None

Record Attendance: 2,572 v West Ham United - Friendly 1998
Record Victory: 10-0 v Stansted (H) - Essex Senior Lge 1986-87 and v East Ham United (A) - Essex Senior Lge 1987-88
Record Defeat: 0-6 v St Leonards Stamco (A) - FA Trophy 1996-97 and v Sutton United (H) - Isthmian League 1997-98
Record Goalscorer: George Georgiou - 106
Record Appearances: Jimmy McFarlane - 632
Additional Records:

Senior Honours:
Isthmian League Division 2 1991-92.
Essex Senior Cup 2003-04, 05-06.

10 YEAR RECORD

04-05	05-06	06-07	07-08	08-09	09-10	10-11	11-12	12-13	13-14
Conf S 3	Conf S 10	Conf S 18	Conf S 12	Conf S 20	Conf S 10	Conf S 20	Conf S 22	Isth P 21	Isth1N 6

TILBURY

Chairman: Daniel Nash

Secretary: Anthony Mercer (T) 07718 881 593 (E) amercer67@googlemail.com

Commercial Manager: (T)

Programme Editor: Mark Kettlety (T) 07940 322 612

Ground Address: Chadfields, St Chads Road, Tilbury, Essex RM18 8NL

(T) 01375 843 093 **Manager:** Paul Vaughan

Club Factfile

Founded: 1895 **Nickname:** The Dockers

Previous Names:

Previous Leagues: Grays & District/South Essex, Kent 1927-31, London, South Essex Combination (Wartime), Corinthian 1950-57, Delphian 1962-63, Athenian 1963-73, Isthmian 1973-2004, Essex Senior 2004-05

Club Colours (change): Black & white stripes/black/red (Red & yellow stripes/red/yellow)

Ground Capacity: 4,000 **Seats:** 350 **Covered:** 1,000 **Clubhouse:** Yes **Shop:** No

Directions

A13 Southend bound go left at Chadwell St Mary's turning, then right after 400 metres and right again at roundabout (signed Tilbury). Right into St Chads Road after five miles, first right into Chadfields for ground.

Previous Grounds: A couple before moving in to Chafields in 1946-47.

Record Attendance: 5,500 v Gorleston - FA Cup 1949

Record Victory: Not known

Record Defeat: Not known

Record Goalscorer: Ross Livermore - 282 in 305 games

Record Appearances: Nicky Smith - 424 (1975-85)

Additional Records: Received £2,000 from Grays Athletic for Tony Macklin 1990 and from Dartford for Steve Connor 1985

Senior Honours:

Athenian League 1968-69. Isthmian League Division Two 1975-76.
Essex Senior Cup x4.

10 YEAR RECORD

04-05	05-06	06-07	07-08	08-09	09-10	10-11	11-12	12-13	13-14
SthE 22	ESen 3	Isth1N 19	Isth1N 20	Isth1N 11	Isth1N 11	Isth1N 19	Isth1N 3	Isth1N 16	Isth1N 16

WALTHAM ABBEY

Chairman: John Martin
Secretary: David Hodges (T) 07742 364 447 (E) walthamabbeyfc@btconnect.com
Commercial Manager: (T)
Programme Editor: Colin Reed (T) 07712 460 078
Ground Address: Capershotts, Sewardstone Road, Waltham Abbey, Essex EN9 1LU
(T) 01992 711 287 **Manager:** Paul Wickenden

The 2013-14 Squad.

Club Factfile

Founded: 1944 **Nickname:** Abbotts
Previous Names: Abbey Sports amalgamated with Beechfield Sports in 1974 to form Beechfields. Club then renamed to Waltham Abbey in 1976
Previous Leagues: Spartan, Essex & Herts Border, Essex Senior

Club Colours (change): Green and white hoops/white/green (All blue)

Ground Capacity: 2,000 **Seats:** 300 **Covered:** 500 **Clubhouse:** Yes **Shop:** No

Directions
Exit M25 at junction 26 and take 2nd left at roundabout into Honey Lane (A121).
At the Sewardstone roundabout, take third right into Sewarstone Road which takes you over the M25.
Ground is first right before cemetery.

Previous Grounds: None

Record Attendance: Not known
Record Victory: Not known
Record Defeat: Not known
Record Goalscorer: Not known
Record Appearances: Not known
Additional Records:

Senior Honours:
London Spartan League Division 1 1977-78, Senior Division 1978-79.
London Senior Cup 1999. Essex Senior Cup 2004-05.

10 YEAR RECORD

04-05	05-06	06-07	07-08	08-09	09-10	10-11	11-12	12-13	13-14
ESen 3	ESen 2	Isth1N 10	Isth1N 14	Isth1N 4	Isth1N 21	Isth1N 11	Isth1N 14	Isth1N 12	Isth1N 18

WARE

Chairman: Inanc Elitok
Secretary: William Spink (T) 07538 101 463 (E) spink405@btinternet.com
Commercial Manager: (T)
Programme Editor: Mark Kettlety (T) 07940 322 612
Ground Address: Wodson Park, Wadesmill Road, Ware, Herts SG12 0UQ
(T) 01920 462 064 **Manager:** Kem Kemal

Club Factfile

Founded: 1892 **Nickname:** Blues
Previous Names: None
Previous Leagues: East Herts, North Middlesex 1907-08, Herts County 1908-25, Spartan 1925-55, Delphian 1955-63, Athenian 1963-75

Club Colours (change): Blue with white piping/blue/blue (Amber/black/amber)

Ground Capacity: 3,300 **Seats:** 500 **Covered:** 312 **Clubhouse:** Yes **Shop:** Yes

Directions
A10 off junction A602 and B1001 turn right at roundabout after 300 yards and follow Ware sign, past Rank factory. Turn left at main road onto A1170 (Wadesmill Road) Stadium is on the right after 3/4 mile.

Previous Grounds: Highfields, Canons Park, London Road, Presdales Lower Park 1921-26

Record Attendance: 3,800 v Hendon - FA Amateur Cup 1956-57
Record Victory: 10-1 v Wood Green Town
Record Defeat: 0-11 v Barnet
Record Goalscorer: George Dearman scored 98 goals during 1926-27
Record Appearances: Gary Riddle - 654
Additional Records:

Senior Honours:
Isthmian League Division 2 2005-06.
East Anglian Cup 1973-74. Herts Senior Cup x5.

10 YEAR RECORD

04-05		05-06		06-07		07-08		08-09		09-10		10-11		11-12		12-13		13-14	
Isth2	10	Isth2	1	Isth1N	7	Isth1N	4	Isth1N	9	Isth1N	19	Isth1N	14	Isth1N	21	Isth1N	19	Isth1N	21

WROXHAM

Chairman: Tom Jarrett
Secretary: Chris Green (T) 07508 219 072 (E) secretary@wroxhamfc.com
Commercial Manager: (T)
Programme Editor: Mark Kettlety (T) 07940 322 612
Ground Address: Trafford Park, Skinners Lane, Wroxham NR12 8SJ
(T) 01603 783 536 **Manager:** Pawel Guziejko

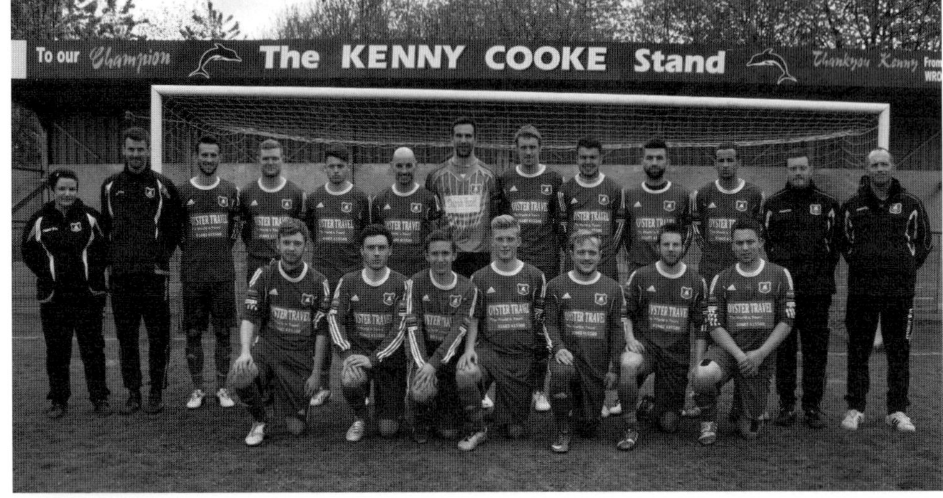

2013-14 Squad.

Club Factfile

Founded: 1892 **Nickname:** Yachtsmen
Previous Names: None
Previous Leagues: East Norfolk. Norwich City. East Anglian. Norwich & Dist. Anglian Comb.

Club Colours (change): Blue & white/blue/blue (White with blue trim/white/blue)

Ground Capacity: 2,500 **Seats:** 50 **Covered:** 250 **Clubhouse:** Yes **Shop:** No

Directions
From Norwich, turn left at former Castle Pub and keep left to ground.
Under two miles from Wroxham & Hoveton BR. Buses 722,724 and 717.

Previous Grounds: Norwich Road, The Avenue and Keys Hill. Moved in to Trafford Park around the time of WWII.

Record Attendance: **Att:** 1,011 v Wisbech Town, Eastern Co. Lge, 16.03.93.
Record Victory: Not known
Record Defeat: Not known
Record Goalscorer: Matthew Metcalf.
Record Appearances: Stu Larter.
Additional Records:

Senior Honours:
Anglian County League 1981-82, 82-83, 83-84, 84-85, 86-87.
Eastern Counties League Division One 1988-89, Prem 91-92, 92-93, 93-94, 96-97, 97-98, 98-99, 2006-07, 11-12.
Norfolk Senior Cup 1992-93, 95-96, 97-98, 99-00, 03-04.

10 YEAR RECORD

04-05		05-06		06-07		07-08		08-09		09-10		10-11		11-12		12-13		13-14	
ECP	5	ECP	8	ECP	1	ECP	3	ECP	5	ECP	8	ECP	3	ECP	1	Isth1N	14	Isth1N	22

BURGESS HILL TOWN

Chairman: Kevin Newell

Secretary: Tim Spencer (T) 07812 644 738 (E) timspencer57@hotmail.com

Commercial Manager: (T)

Programme Editor: Colin Bowman (T) 07816 496 487

Ground Address: Leylands Park, Maple Drive, Burgess Hill, West Sussex RH15 8DL

(T) 01444 254 832 **Manager:** Ian Chapman

Club Factfile

Founded: 1882 **Nickname:** Hillians

Previous Names: None

Previous Leagues: Mid Sussex, Sussex County > 2003, Southern 2003-04

Club Colours (change): Green & black stripes (Yellow with blue trim)

Ground Capacity: 2,250 **Seats:** 307 **Covered:** Yes **Clubhouse:** Yes **Shop:** Yes

Directions

Turn east from A273 London Road into Leylands Road,
take 4th left sign posted Leyland Park.
Nearest station is Wivelsfield.

Previous Grounds: None

Record Attendance: 2,005 v AFC Wimbledon - Isthmian League Division 1 2004-05

Record Victory: Not known

Record Defeat: Not known

Record Goalscorer: Ashley Carr - 208

Record Appearances: Paul Williams - 499

Additional Records:

Senior Honours:

Sussex County League x6 (Most recently 2001-02, 02-03).
Sussex Senior Cup 1883-84, 84-85, 85-86.

10 YEAR RECORD

04-05	05-06	06-07	07-08	08-09	09-10	10-11	11-12	12-13	13-14
Isth1 10	Isth1 19	Isth1S 14	Isth1S 12	Isth1S 19	Isth1S 7	Isth1S 7	Isth1S 20	Isth1S 8	Isth1S 6

CARSHALTON ATHLETIC

Chairman: Paul Dipre
Secretary: Chris Blanchard **(T)** 07583 817 519 **(E)** chrisblanchard@carshaltonathletic.co.uk
Commercial Manager: n/a **(T)**
Programme Editor: Chris Blanchard **(T)** 07583 817 519
Ground Address: War Memorial Sports Ground, Colston Avenue, Carshalton SM5 2PN
(T) 0208 642 8658 **Manager:** Stuart Massey

Club Factfile

Founded: 1905 **Nickname:** Robins
Previous Names: None
Previous Leagues: Southern Suburban > 1911, Surrey Senior 1922-23, London 1923-46, Corinthian 1946-56, Athenian 1956-73, Isthmian 1973-2004, Conference 2004-06
Club Colours (change): All red

Ground Capacity: 8,000 **Seats:** 240 **Covered:** 4,500 **Clubhouse:** Yes **Shop:** Yes

Directions
Turn right out of Carshalton Station exit,
turn right again,
and then left into Colston Avenue.

Previous Grounds: None

Record Attendance: 7,800 v Wimbledon - London Senior Cup
Record Victory: 13-0 v Worthing - Isthmian League Cup 28/01/1991
Record Defeat: 0-11 v Southall - Athenian League March 1963
Record Goalscorer: Jimmy Bolton - 242
Record Appearances: Jon Warden - 504
Additional Records: Paid £15,000 to Enfield for Curtis Warmington
Received £30,000 from Crystal Palace for Ian Cox
Senior Honours:
Isthmian League Division 1 South 2002-03.
Surrey Senior Shield 1975-76. London Challenge Cup 1991-92. Surrey Senior Cup x3.

10 YEAR RECORD

04-05	05-06	06-07	07-08	08-09	09-10	10-11	11-12	12-13	13-14
Conf S 19	Conf S 21	Isth P 13	Isth P 18	Isth P 4	Isth P 17	Isth P 13	Isth P 16	Isth P 20	Isth P 23

CHIPSTEAD

Chairman: Mike Ford

Secretary: Heather Armstrong **(T)** 07525 443 802 **(E)** heather.chipsteadfc@virginmedia.com

Commercial Manager: **(T)**

Programme Editor: Mark Garrett-Budd **(T)** 01737 553 250

Ground Address: High Road, Chipstead, Surrey CR5 3SF

(T) 01737 553 250 **Manager:** Steve Baker

The squad at the end of the 2013-14 season - Back Row: Spike, Steve Baker(Manager), Jack Buckle, Will Turl, Jordan Knight, Roy Butler, Steff Joseph, Julian Osusu, Milan, Adam Willis, Stoney (coach).
Middle Row: Devon Williams, Ben Dyett, Malcolm Cooper(physio)
Front Row: Jordan Berry, Dan Llacer, Dan Moody, Josh, Jess Smith, Sam Charles, Steve Betancourt, Shaun Preddie.

Club Factfile

Founded: 1906 **Nickname:** Chips

Previous Names: None

Previous Leagues: Surrey Intermediate 1962-82, Surrey Premier 1982-86, Combined Counties 1986-2007

Club Colours (change): Green and white hoops/green/black (All red)

Ground Capacity: 2,000 **Seats:** 150 **Covered:** 200 **Clubhouse:** Yes **Shop:** Yes

Directions
From the Brighton Road north bound,
go left into Church Lane and left into Hogcross Lane.
High Road is on the right.

Previous Grounds: None

Record Attendance: 1,170

Record Victory: Not known

Record Defeat: Not known

Record Goalscorer: Mick Nolan - 124

Record Appearances: Not known

Additional Records:

Senior Honours:
Combined Counties Premier 1989-90, 2006-07.

10 YEAR RECORD

04-05	05-06	06-07	07-08	08-09	09-10	10-11	11-12	12-13	13-14
CCP 8	CCP 14	CCP 1	Isth1S 15	Isth1S 21	Isth1S 19	Isth1S 10	Isth1S 12	Isth1S 20	Isth1S 13

CORINTHIAN CASUALS

Chairman: Brian Vandervilt
Secretary: Gary Weir (T) 07508 707 740 (E) secretary@corinthian-casuals.com
Commercial Manager: (T)
Programme Editor: Stuart Tree (T) 07801 858 973
Ground Address: King George's Field, Queen Mary Close, Hook Rise South, KT6 7NA
(T) 0208 397 3368 **Manager:** Matt Howard

Club Factfile

Founded: 1939 **Nickname:** Casuals
Previous Names: Casuals and Corinthians merged in 1939
Previous Leagues: Isthmian 1939-84, Spartan 1984-96, Combined Counties 1996-97

Club Colours (change): Chocolate and pink halves/chocolate/chocolate (All blue)

Ground Capacity: 2,000 **Seats:** 161 **Covered:** 700 **Clubhouse:** Yes **Shop:** Yes

Directions
The ground is situated just off the A3 not far from the Tolworth roundabout. If you are travelling from the M25 you can join the A3 at junction 10 towards London. Stay on the A3 until you reach the 50mph speed limit, continue under the Hook roundabout and move into the lefthand lane for ca. 174 yds. Bear LEFT onto Hook Rise North for 0.2 mile (Tolworth Junction). At roundabout, take the FOURTH exit (as if you were going to rejoin the A3 going towards Portsmouth) then almost immediately take slip road on left onto Hook Rise South for 0.5 mile. If you are travelling from London on the A3 take the Tolworth Junction exit. At roundabout, take the SECOND exit (as if you were going to rejoin the A3 going towards Portsmouth) then almost immediately take slip road on left onto Hook Rise South for 0.5 mile. Turn LEFT into Queen Mary Close. Ground and car park under railway bridge on right hand side. Youth Section pitches and changing rooms are in the park on the left.

Previous Grounds: Kennington Oval, shared with Kingstonian and Dulwich Hamlet

Record Attendance: Not known
Record Victory: Not known
Record Defeat: Not known
Record Goalscorer: Cliff West - 219
Record Appearances: Simon Shergold - 526
Additional Records:

Senior Honours:
London Spartan League Senior Division 1985-86.
Surrey Senior Cup 2010-11.

10 YEAR RECORD

04-05	05-06	06-07	07-08	08-09	09-10	10-11	11-12	12-13	13-14
Isth1 13	Isth1 23	Isth1S 22	Isth1S 20	Isth1S 20	Isth1S 13	Isth1S 20	Isth1S 13	Isth1S 14	Isth1S 17

EAST GRINSTEAD TOWN

Chairman: Richard Tramontin
Secretary: Brian McCorquodale **(T)** 07802 528 513 **(E)** brian.mcc@egtfc.co.uk
Commercial Manager: **(T)**
Programme Editor: Bruce Talbot **(T)** 07966 485 720
Ground Address: The GAC Stadium, East Court, College Lane, East Grinstead RH19 3LS
(T) 01342 325 885 **Manager:** Simon Funnell

Club Factfile

Founded: 1890 **Nickname:** The Wasps
Previous Names: East Grinstead > 1997.
Previous Leagues: Mid Sussex, Sussex County, Souhern Amateur. Sussex County >2014.

Club Colours (change): Yellow & black/black/yellow & black (Blue & yellow/blue & yellow/blue)

Ground Capacity: 3,000 **Seats:** none **Covered:** 400 **Clubhouse:** Yes **Shop:** No

Directions
A264 Tunbridge Wells road (Moat Road) until mini roundabout at bottom of Blackwell Hollow, turn immediately right by club sign then 1st left, ground 200 yards down lane past rifle club on right.

Previous Grounds: None

Record Attendance: Att: 2,006 v Lancing F A Am Cup, November 1947
Record Victory:
Record Defeat:
Record Goalscorer:
Record Appearances: Guy Hill
Additional Records:
Senior Honours:
Sussex County League Division Two 2007-08.

10 YEAR RECORD

04-05		05-06		06-07		07-08		08-09		09-10		10-11		11-12		12-13		13-14	
SxC1	18	SxC2	7	SxC2	11	SxC2	1	SxC1	17	SxC1	15	SxC1	7	SxC1	9	SxC1	8	SxC1	2

FAVERSHAM TOWN

Chairman: Ray Leader
Secretary: Mrs Wendy Walker **(T)** 07789 638 367 **(E)** wendy-walker@hotmail.co.uk
Commercial Manager: **(T)**
Programme Editor: Mark Downs **(T)** 07840 079 992
Ground Address: Salters Lane, Faversham Kent ME13 8ND
(T) 01795 591 900 **Manager:** Ray Turner

Club Factfile

Founded: 1884 **Nickname:** Lillywhites
Previous Names: Faversham Invicta, Faversham Services, Faversham Railway and Faversham Rangers pre War.
Previous Leagues: Metropolitan, Athenian, Kent

Club Colours (change): White/black/black (All yellow)

Ground Capacity: 2,000 **Seats:** 200 **Covered:** 1,800 **Clubhouse:** Yes **Shop:**

Directions From the M25 continue onto M26 9.9 miles. Continue onto M20 8.1 miles. Exit onto Slip Road (M20 J7) 0.2 miles. Bear left 0.1 miles. Continue onto Sittingbourne Road A249 0.9 miles. Bear right onto Detling Hill A249 4.6 miles. Bear left 0.1 miles. Continue onto Slip Road (M2 J5) 0.4 miles. Continue onto M2 10.5 miles. Exit onto Slip Road (M2 J6) 0.1 miles. Turn left onto Ashford Road A251 0.5 miles. Turn right onto Canterbury Road A2 0.2 miles. Turn right onto Westwood Place 0.1 miles.

Previous Grounds: Moved in to Salters Lane in 1948.

Record Attendance: Not Known
Record Victory: Not Known
Record Defeat: Not Known
Record Goalscorer: Not Known
Record Appearances: Not Known
Additional Records:

Senior Honours:
Kent League 1969-70, 70-71, 89-90, 2009-10.

10 YEAR RECORD

04-05	05-06	06-07	07-08	08-09	09-10	10-11	11-12	12-13	13-14
		Kent P 12	Kent P 13	Kent P 4	Kent P 1	Isth1S 8	Isth1S 17	Isth1S 3	Isth1S 10

FOLKESTONE INVICTA

Chairman: Mark Jenner
Secretary: Richard Murrill **(T)** 07810 864 228 **(E)** richardmurrill@gmail.com
Commercial Manager: **(T)**
Programme Editor: Richard Murrill **(T)** 07810 864 228
Ground Address: The Fullicks Stadium, Cheriton Road CT19 5JU
(T) 01303 257 461 **Manager:** Neil Cugley

Club Factfile

Founded: 1936 **Nickname:** The Seasiders
Previous Names: None
Previous Leagues: Kent 1990-98, Southern 1998-2004

Club Colours (change): Black & amber stripes/black/black (White & sky stripes/sky/sky)

Ground Capacity: 4,000 **Seats:** 900 **Covered:** Yes **Clubhouse:** Yes **Shop:** Yes

Directions
Leave the M20 motorway at junction 13, and head south onto the A20 (Cherry Garden Avenue). At the traffic lights, turn left onto the A2034 (Cheriton Road), pass the Harvey Grammar School and Stripes club - the ground is next left before Morrisons' supermarket; opposite the cemetery. Some car parking is available at Stripes.

Previous Grounds: South Road Hythe > 1991, County League matches on council pitches

Record Attendance: 7,881 v Margate - Kent Senior Cup 1958
Record Victory: 13-0 v Faversham Town - Kent League Division 1
Record Defeat: 1-7 v Crockenhill - Kent League Division 1
Record Goalscorer: Not Known
Record Appearances: Not Known
Additional Records:

Senior Honours:
None

10 YEAR RECORD

04-05	05-06	06-07	07-08	08-09	09-10	10-11	11-12	12-13	13-14
Isth P 13	Isth P 13	Isth P 18	Isth P 21	Isth1S 11	Isth1S 2	Isth P 22	Isth1S 4	Isth1S 5	Isth1S 2

GUERNSEY

Chairman: Steve Dewsnip
Secretary: Mark Le Tissier **(T)** 07781 119 169 **(E)** mark.letissier@guernseyfc.com
Commercial Manager: **(T)**
Programme Editor: Andy Richards **(T)** 07447 907 595
Ground Address: Footes Lane Stadium, St Peter Port, Guernsey GY1 2UL
(T) 01481 747 279 **Manager:** Tony Vance

2013-14
Photo: Alan Coomes

Club Factfile

Founded: 2011 **Nickname:** Green Lions
Previous Names: None
Previous Leagues: Combined Counties 2011-13.

Club Colours (change): Green & white/white/green (Sky blue/sky blue/white)

Ground Capacity: 5,000 **Seats:** Yes **Covered:** Yes **Clubhouse:** Yes **Shop:**

Directions
The ground is located centrally in the island, is easily accessible with parking for several hundred cars in the immediate vicinity and on a regular bus route stopping immediately outside the stadium. It is approximately three miles north easterly from Guernsey Airport and one mile west from St Peter Port, the island's capital.

Previous Grounds: None

Record Attendance: 4,290 v. Spennymoor Town, FA Vase semi-final first leg, 23/03/2013
Record Victory: 11-0 v Crawley Down Gatwick, Isthmian Division One South, 01/01/2014
Record Defeat: 2-6 v Horsham, Isthmian Division One South, 14/12/2013
Record Goalscorer: Ross Allen - 163 (Scored 57 in all comps during 2011-12)
Record Appearances: Dom Heaume - 136
Additional Records:

Senior Honours:
Combined Counties League Division One 2011-12, Premier Challenge Cup 2011-12.

10 YEAR RECORD

04-05	05-06	06-07	07-08	08-09	09-10	10-11	11-12	12-13	13-14
							CC1 1	CCP 2	Isth1S 4

HASTINGS UNITED

Chairman: David Walters

Secretary: Darryl Tribbeck **(T)** 07812 822 986 **(E)** darryl@informedfa.co.uk

Commercial Manager: **(T)**

Programme Editor: Dan Willett **(T)** 07590 568 432

Ground Address: The Pilot Field, Elphinstone Road, Hastings TN34 2AX

(T) 01424 444 635 **Manager:** Terry White

Club Factfile

Founded: 1894 **Nickname:** The Us

Previous Names: Hastings and St Leonards Amateurs, Hastings Town > 2002

Previous Leagues: South Eastern 1904-05, Southern 1905-10, Sussex County 1921-27, 52-85, Southern Amateur 1927-46, Corinthian 1946-48

Club Colours (change): Claret/white/white (Light blue/claret/claret)

Ground Capacity: 4,050 **Seats:** 800 **Covered:** 1,750 **Clubhouse:** Yes **Shop:** Yes

Directions

From A1 turn left at third roundabout into St Helens Road.
Then left after one mile into St Helens Park Road leading into Downs Road.
Turn left at T-junction at the end of the road. Ground is 200 yards on the right.

Previous Grounds: Bulverhythe Recreation > 1976

Record Attendance: 4,888 v Nottingham Forest - Friendly 23/06/1996

Record Victory: Not Known

Record Defeat: Not Known

Record Goalscorer: Terry White scored 33 during 1999-2000

Record Appearances: Not Known

Additional Records: Paid £8,000 to Ashford Town for Nicky Dent
Received £30,000 from Nottingham Forest for Paul Smith

Senior Honours:

Southern League Division 1 1991-92, 2001-01, League Cup 1994-95.

10 YEAR RECORD

04-05	05-06	06-07	07-08	08-09	09-10	10-11	11-12	12-13	13-14
Isth1 11	Isth1 12	Isth1S 4	Isth P 14	Isth P 17	Isth P 7	Isth P 18	Isth P 18	Isth P 22	Isth1S 5

HERNE BAY

Chairman: Bill Dordoy
Secretary: John Bathurst **(T)** 07788 718 745 **(E)** johnbhbfc@aol.com
Commercial Manager: **(T)**
Programme Editor: Steve Barton **(T)** 07507 614 868
Ground Address: Safety Net Stadium, Winch's Field, Stanley Gardens, Herne Bay CT6 5SG
(T) 01227 374 156 **Manager:** Sam Denly

Club Factfile

Founded: 1886 **Nickname:** The Bay
Previous Names: None.
Previous Leagues: East Kent. Faversham & Dist. Cantebury & Dist. Kent Am. Athenian.

Club Colours (change): Blue & white/blue/blue (Yellow & black/yellow/yellow)

Ground Capacity: 3,000 **Seats:** 200 **Covered:** 1,500 **Clubhouse:** Yes **Shop:** Yes

Directions
From M25 exit onto Sittingbourne Rd/A249 toward Sheerness.
Continue to follow A249. At the roundabout, take the 1st exit onto the M2 ramp to Canterbury/Dover/Ramsgate.
Merge onto M2. Continue onto Thanet Way/A299.
Continue to follow A299. Take the A291 exit toward Canterbury/Herne Bay.
At the roundabout, take the 2nd exit onto A291. At the roundabout, take the 1st exit onto Canterbury Rd/B2205.
Turn left onto Spenser Rd. Take the 1st left onto Stanley Gardens.
Take the 1st left to stay on Stanley Gardens.

Previous Grounds: Mitchell's Athletic Ground. Herne Bay Memorial Park.

Record Attendance: 2,303 v Margate, FA Cup 4th Qual. 1970-71.
Record Victory: 19-3 v Hythe Wanderers - Feb 1900.
Record Defeat: 0-11 v 7th Dragon Guards - Oct 1907.
Record Goalscorer:
Record Appearances:
Additional Records: Most League Victories in a Season: 34 - 1996-97.

Senior Honours:
Kent League 1991-92, 93-94, 96-97, 97-98, 2011-12, Premier Cup 1996-97, 2009-10, 2010-11.
Kent Senior Trophy 1978-79, 1996-97.

10 YEAR RECORD

04-05	05-06	06-07	07-08	08-09	09-10	10-11	11-12	12-13	13-14
Kent P 2	Kent P 7	Kent P 9	Kent P 6	Kent P 6	Kent P 2	Kent P 2	Kent P 1	Isth1S 19	Isth1S 18

HORSHAM

Chairman: Kevin Borrett

Secretary: John Lines (T) 07721 418 889 (E) johnlines77@googlemail.com

Commercial Manager: (T)

Programme Editor: Jeff Barrett (T) 07712 888 980

Ground Address: Horsham YMCA, Gorings Mead, Horsham RH13 5BP

(T) 01403 266 888 **Manager:** Gary Charman

Horsham (white shirts) in pre-season friendly action away to Horley Town.

Club Factfile

Founded: 1881 **Nickname:** Hornets

Previous Names:

Previous Leagues: West Susses Senior, Sussex County 1926-51, Metropolitan 1951-57, Corinthian 1957-63, Athenian 1963-73

Club Colours (change): Yellow with green flash/green/yellow (White with a black flash/white/white)

Ground Capacity: 1,575 **Seats:** 150 **Covered:** 200 **Clubhouse:** Yes **Shop:**

Directions

Travel north on the A23, turning off onto the A272 at Bolney. Continue on the A272 to Cowfold then follow the A281 to Horsham. On entering the outskirts of the town, follow the A281 (Brighton Road) a short distance and Gorings Mead is a turning on the left. The entrance to the ground is at the bottom of Gorings Mead.

Previous Grounds: Horsham Park, Hurst Park, Springfield Park

Record Attendance: 8,000 v Swindon - FA Cup 1st Round Novmber 1966

Record Victory: 16-1 v Southwick - Sussex County League 1945-46

Record Defeat: 1-11 v Worthing - Sussex Senior Cup 1913-14

Record Goalscorer: Mick Browning

Record Appearances: Mark Stepney

Additional Records:

Senior Honours:

Athenian League Division 1 1972-73. Sussex Senior Cup x7

10 YEAR RECORD

04-05	05-06	06-07	07-08	08-09	09-10	10-11	11 12	12 13	13-14
Isth1 3	Isth1 2	Isth1S 9	Isth P 11	Isth P 13	Isth P 11	Isth P 17	Isth P 22	Isth1S 15	Isth1S 16

HYTHE TOWN

Chairman: Trevor Kennett
Secretary: Martin Giles **(T)** 07908 763 101 **(E)** martinandsuegiles@gmail.com
Commercial Manager: **(T)**
Programme Editor: Richard Giles **(T)** 07923 440 016
Ground Address: Reachfields Stadium, Fort Road, Hythe CT21 6JS
(T) 01303 264 932 / 238 256 **Manager:** Tim Dixon

Club Factfile

Founded: 1910 **Nickname:** The Cannons
Previous Names: Hythe Town 1910-1992, Hythe United 1992-2001
Previous Leagues: Kent Amateur League, Kent League, Southern League, Kent County League, Kent League.

Club Colours (change): All red (All blue)

Ground Capacity: 3,000 **Seats:** 350 **Covered:** 2,400 **Clubhouse:** Yes **Shop:** No

Directions
The Reachfields Stadium is easily accessible from the M20 motorway. Leave the M20 at junction 11, then at the roundabout take the 3rd exit onto the B2068, signposted Hastings, Hythe. At the next roundabout take the 2nd exit onto Ashford Road, A20. Continue forward onto Ashford Road, A20. Entering Newingreen, at the T-junction turn left onto Hythe Road, A261, signposted Hythe. Continue forward down London Road, A261. Entering Hythe, continue forward at the traffic lights onto Scanlons Bridge Road, A2008.
Turn right at the next set of lights onto Dymchurch Road, A259. Either take the 1st left down Fort Road and turn right at the end of Fort Road for the car-park, or after a few hundred yards turn left onto the Reachfields estate. Follow the road round and the stadium will be on your right.

Previous Grounds: South Road.

Record Attendance: 2,147 v Yeading, FA Vase Semi-Final, 1990.
Record Victory: 10-1 v Sporting Bengal, 2008-09
Record Defeat: 1-10 v Swanley Furness, 1997-98
Record Goalscorer: Dave Cook - 113
Record Appearances: Jason Brazier - 350
Additional Records:

Senior Honours:
Kent League 1988-89, 2010-11.
Kent Senior Cup 2011-12.
Kent Senior Trophy 1990-91.

10 YEAR RECORD

04-05	05-06	06-07	07-08	08-09	09-10	10-11	11-12	12-13	13-14
Kent P 6	Kent P 12	Kent P 6	Kent P 4	Kent P 2	Kent P 3	Kent P 1	Isth1S 8	Isth1S 4	Isth1S 8

MERSTHAM

Chairman: Chris Chapman
Secretary: Richard Baxter (T) 07720 290 027 (E) richardbaxter01@hotmail.com
Commercial Manager: (T)
Programme Editor: Kevin Austen (T) 07911 853 353
Ground Address: Moatside Stadium, Weldon Way, Merstham, Surrey RH1 3QB
(T) 01737 644 046 **Manager:** Hayden Bird

Club Factfile

Founded: 1905 **Nickname:** Moatsiders
Previous Names: None
Previous Leagues: Redhill & District, Surrey Senior 1964-78, London Spartan 1978-84, Combined Counties 1984-2008

Club Colours (change): Amber & black/black/amber (All blue)

Ground Capacity: 2,500 **Seats:** 174 **Covered:** 100 **Clubhouse:** Yes **Shop:** No

Directions
Leave Merstham village (A23) by School Hill,
take 5th right (Weldon Way).
Clubhouse and car park on the right.
Ten minutes walk from Merstham BR.

Previous Grounds: None

Record Attendance: 1,587 v AFC Wimbledon - Combined Counties League 09/11/2002
Record Victory: Not Known
Record Defeat: Not Known
Record Goalscorer: Not Known
Record Appearances: Not Known
Additional Records:

Senior Honours:
Combined Counties League Premier Division 2007-08.

10 YEAR RECORD

04-05		05-06		06-07		07-08		08-09		09-10		10-11		11-12		12-13		13-14	
CCP	16	CCP	2	CCP	2	CCP	1	Isth1S	8	Isth1S	16	Isth1S	19	Isth1S	9	Isth1S	12	Isth1S	7

RAMSGATE

Chairman: Phil Fennell

Secretary: Edward Lucas **(T)** 07710 859 034 **(E)** secretary@ramsgate-fc.co.uk

Commercial Manager: **(T)**

Programme Editor: Martin Able **(T)** 07958 993 959

Ground Address: Southwood Stadium, Prices Avenue, Ramsgate, Kent CT11 0AN

(T) 01843 591 662 **Manager:** Dean Hill

2014-15 Squad - Back Row (L to R) Steve King (Coach/U21 Manager), James Olver, Warren Schulz, Tom Ripley, Nick Shaw, Jim Sherman (c), Daren Hawkes, Curtis Robinson, Luke Wheatley, Scott Punton, Nick Blackman.
Front Row: Ira Jackson Jr, Chris Lewis, Toby Smith, Macca Murray, Joe Radford (Goalkeeper Coac), Dean Hill (Player/Manager), Richard Langley (Asst Manager), Chris Walsh, Tom Chapman, Greg Skinner, Dan Barrett.
(Not Pictured): Aaron Beech, Ben Laslett, Carl Munday, Paul Murray (Head Coach), Joe Meadowcroft (Physio).

Club Factfile

Founded: 1945 **Nickname:** Rams

Previous Names: Ramsgate Athletic > 1972

Previous Leagues: Kent 1949-59, 1976-2005, Southern 1959-76

Club Colours (change): All red (Yellow/black/black)

Ground Capacity: 5,000 **Seats:** 400 **Covered:** 600 **Clubhouse:** Yes **Shop:** Yes

Directions

Approach Ramsgate via A299 (Canterbury/London) or A256 (Dover/Folkestone) to Lord of Manor roundabout.
Follow the signpost to Ramsgate along Canterbury Road East, counting via 2nd exit of the 1st roundabout.
At the 2nd roundabout, continue towards Ramsgate on London Road (2nd exit).
Take the 3rd turning on the left, into St Mildred's Avenue, then 1st left into Queen Bertha Road.
After the right hand bend, take left into Southwood Road, and 1st left into Prices Ave. The stadium is at the end of Prices Avenue.

Previous Grounds: None

Record Attendance: 5,200 v Margate - 1956-57

Record Victory: 11-0 & 12-1 v Canterbury City - Kent League 2000-01

Record Defeat: Not Known

Record Goalscorer: Mick Willimson

Record Appearances: Not Known

Additional Records:

Senior Honours:

Kent League Division 1 1949-50, 55-56, 56-57, Premier League 1998-99, 2004-05, Kent League Cup x6.
Isthmian League Division 1 2005-06, League Cup 2007-08.
Kent Senior Cup 1963-64, Kent Senior Trophy x3.

10 YEAR RECORD

04-05		05-06		06-07		07-08		08-09		09-10		10-11		11-12		12-13		13-14	
Kent P	1	Isth1	1	Isth P	8	Isth P	5	Isth P	22	Isth1S	14	Isth1S	9	Isth1S	10	Isth1S	7	Isth1S	12

REDHILL

Chairman: John Park

Secretary: Phil Whatling **(T)** 07929 742 081 **(E)** phil.whatling@btinternet.com

Commercial Manager: **(T)**

Programme Editor: Terry Austin **(T)** 07702 044 487

Ground Address: Kiln Brow, Three Arch Road, Redhill, Surrey RH1 5AE

(T) 01737 762 129 **Manager:** Mike Maher

Club Factfile

Founded: 1894 **Nickname:** Reds/Lobsters

Previous Names: None

Previous Leagues: E & W Surrey. Spartan. Southern Sub. London. Athenian. Sussex County > 2013.

Club Colours (change): Red & white/red/red. (Yellow/blue/blue).

Ground Capacity: 2,000 **Seats:** 150 **Covered:** 150 **Clubhouse:** Yes **Shop:** Yes

Directions

On left hand side of A23 two and a half miles south of Redhill.

Previous Grounds: Wiggie 1894-1896. Memorial Park 1896-1984.

Record Attendance: 0,000 v Hastings U FA Cup 1950

Record Victory:

Record Defeat:

Record Goalscorer: Steve Turner 119

Record Appearances: Brian Medlicott 766

Additional Records:

Senior Honours:

London League 1922-23. Athenian League 1924-25, 83-84.
Surrey Senior Cup 1928-29, 65-66.

10 YEAR RECORD

04-05	05-06	06-07	07-08	08-09	09-10	10-11	11-12	12-13	13-14
SxC1 13	SxC1 18	SxC1 15	SxC1 8	SxC1 7	SxC1 5	SxC1 8	SxC1 10	SxC1 2	Isth1S 22

SITTINGBOURNE

Chairman: Maurice Dunk

Secretary: John PItts (T) 07909 995 210 (E) johncp49@hotmail.com

Commercial Manager: (T)

Programme Editor: Peter Pitts (T) 07785 906 627

Ground Address: The TClarke Stadium, Woodstock Park, Broadoak Road, Sittingbourne ME9 8AG

(T) 01795 410 777 **Manager:** Nick Davis & Matt Wyatt

Club Factfile

Founded: 1886 **Nickname:** Brickies

Previous Names: Sittingbourne United 1881-86

Previous Leagues: Kent 1894-1905, 1909-27, 30-39, 45-59, 68-91, South Eastern 1905-09, Southern 1927-30, 59-67

Club Colours (change): Red & black stripes/black/black & white

Ground Capacity: 3,000 **Seats:** 300 **Covered:** 600 **Clubhouse:** Yes **Shop:** Yes

Directions

From the M2 exit at Junction 5, take A249 towards Sheerness, leave A249 at 1st junction, raised section to Key Street roundabout, take A2 to Sittingbourne.

One way system to town centre, first right into Park Road, Follow signs to Kent Science Park, Park Road becomes Gore Court Road, Gore Court Road becomes Woodstock Road, Woodstock Road becomes Ruins Barn Road.

When houses disappear approximately half a mile, take left as signposted Kent Science Park/Sittingbourne Research Centre into Broadoak Road, down hill passed Research Centre on right, carry on up hill, take left into car park Woodstock Park.

SatNav postcode: ME9 8AG

Previous Grounds: Sittingbourne Rec. 1881-90, Gore Court 1890-92, The Bull Ground 1892-1990. Central Park 1990-2001

Record Attendance: 5,951 v Tottenham Hotspur - Friendly 26/01/1993

Record Victory: 15-0 v Orpington, Kent League 1922-23)

Record Defeat: 0-10 v Wimbledon, SL Cup 1965-66)

Record Goalscorer: Not Known

Record Appearances: Not Known

Additional Records: Paid £20,000 to Ashford Town for Lee McRobert 1993

Received £210,000 from Millwall for Neil Emblem and Michael Harle 1993

Senior Honours:

Southern League Southern Division 1992-93, 95-96. Kent League x7, League cup x4.

Kent Senior Cup 1901-02, 28-29, 29-30, 57-58.

10 YEAR RECORD

04-05		05-06		06-07		07-08		08-09		09-10		10-11		11-12		12-13		13-14	
SthE	19	SthE	18	Isth1S	10	Isth1S	9	Isth1S	6	Isth1S	9	Isth1S	11	Isth1S	19	Isth1S	9	Isth1S	14

SOUTH PARK

South Park F.C
Founded 1897

Chairman: Colin Puplett
Secretary: Nick Thatcher **(T)** 07817 613 674 **(E)** spfcsecretary@hotmail.co.uk
Commercial Manager: **(T)**
Programme Editor: Nick Thatcher **(T)** 07817 613 674
Ground Address: King George's Field, Whitehall Lane, South Park RH2 8LG
(T) 01737 245 963 **Manager:** Joe McElligott

Club Factfile

Founded: 1897 **Nickname:** The Sparks
Previous Names: South Park & Reigate Town 2001-03.
Previous Leagues: Crawley & District > 2006. Combined Counties 2006-14.

Club Colours (change): All red

Ground Capacity: 700 **Seats:** 100 **Covered:** Yes **Clubhouse:** Yes **Shop:** Yes

Directions
From junction 8 of the M25, take A217 and follow signs to Gatwick. Follow through the one way system via Reigate town centre and continue on until traffic lights and crossroads by The Angel public house, turn right at these lights, into Prices Lane, and continue on road. After a sharp right bend into Sandcross Lane past Reigate Garden Centre. Take next left after school into Whitehall Lane.

Previous Grounds: None

Record Attendance: **Att:** 643 v Metropolitan Police, 20/10/2012
Record Victory: Not known
Record Defeat: Not known
Record Goalscorer: Not known
Record Appearances: Not known
Additional Records:

Senior Honours:
League: Combined Counties Premier Division 2013-14.
FA/County Cups: Surrey Premier Cup 2010-11.

10 YEAR RECORD

04-05	05-06	06-07	07-08	08-09	09-10	10-11	11-12	12-13	13-14
		CC1 7	CC1 12	CC1 14	CC1 6	CC1 3	CCP 8	CCP 4	CCP 1

THREE BRIDGES

Chairman: TBA
Secretary: Lorraine Bonner (T) 07701 011 513 (E) lorraine.bonner@lw.com
Commercial Manager: (T)
Programme Editor: Alf Blackler (T) 07758 745 372
Ground Address: Jubilee Field, Three Bridges Rd, Crawley, RH10 1LQ
(T) 01293 442 000 **Manager:** Paul Falli

Club Factfile

Founded: 1901 **Nickname:** Bridges
Previous Names: Three Bridges Worth 1936-52, Three Bridges Utd 53-64
Previous Leagues: Mid Sussex, E Grinstead, Redhill & Dist 36-52

Club Colours (change): Amber & black stripes/black/black. (Blue & white stripes /blue/blue)

Ground Capacity: 3,500 **Seats:** 120 **Covered:** 600 **Clubhouse:** Yes **Shop:**

Directions
Leave the M23 at Junction 10 heading towards Crawley on the A2011 (Crawley Avenue). At the roundabout take the first left heading towards Three Bridges Train Station (Hazelwick Avenue). Pass Tesco on your left and head straight over the roundabout (second exit). As you approach the traffic lights remain in the right hand side lane. After turning right in to Haslett Avenue at these lights move immediately in to the right turn lane at the next set of lights. Turn right at these lights in to Three Bridges Road. Follow the road round to the left then turn left after one hundred yards in to Jubilee Walk (directly opposite the Plough Pub). Follow the road to the end and turn right (still Jubilee Walk) and head straight on where Three Bridges Jubilee Field Stadium is at the far end.

Previous Grounds: None

Record Attendance: 2,000 v Horsham 1948
Record Victory: Not known
Record Defeat: Not known
Record Goalscorer: Not known
Record Appearances: John Malthouse
Additional Records:

Senior Honours:
Sussex RUR Cup 1982-83. Sussex County League Division One 2011-12.

10 YEAR RECORD

04-05	05-06	06-07	07-08	08-09	09-10	10-11	11-12	12-13	13-14
SxC1 7	SxC1 15	SxC1 12	SxC1 6	SxC1 5	SxC1 7	SxC1 5	SxC1 1	Isth1S 21	Isth1S 19

TOOTING & MITCHAM UNITED

Chairman: Steve Adkins
Secretary: Jackie Watkins (T) 07890 102 737 (E) jackie@tmunited.org
Commercial Manager: (T)
Programme Editor: David Penn (T) tmuprogramme@gmail.com
Ground Address: Imperial Fields, Bishopsford Road, Morden, Surrey SM4 6BF
(T) 0208 685 6193 **Manager:** Craig Tanner

Tooting & Mitcham in action during the 2013-14 season.

Club Factfile

Founded: 1932 **Nickname:** The Terrors
Previous Names: Tooting Town (Founded in 1887) and Mitcham Wanderers (1912) merged in 1932 to form Tooting & Mitcham FC.
Previous Leagues: London 1932-37, Athenian 1937-56

Club Colours (change): Black and white stripes/black/black (blue/white/blue)

Ground Capacity: 3,500 **Seats:** 600 **Covered:** 1,200 **Clubhouse:** Yes **Shop:** Yes

Directions
M25 junction 8, take the A217 northbound, this goes through Tadworth and Cheam. It's dual carriageway most of the way, although long stretches have a 40mph speed limit. This leads to a major roundabout with lights (Rose Hill). Take the third exit (Mitcham A217), this is Bishopsford Road and the ground is a mile further on. Go through two sets of lights, the road dips, and the entrance is on the right opposite a petrol station.
From the South: M25 junction 7, M23 then A23 northbound. Turn left onto the A237 after passing under a railway bridge at Coulsdon South station. Through Hackbridge and Beddington, then turn left onto the A239. Turn left again at lights by Mitcham Cricket Green into the A217, the ground is 800 yards on the left.

Previous Grounds: Sandy Lane, Mitcham

Record Attendance: 17,500 v Queens Park Rangers - FA Cup 2nd Round 1956-57 (At Sandy Lane)
Record Victory: 11-0 v Welton Rovers - FA Amateur Cup 1962-63
Record Defeat: 1-8 v Kingstonian - Surrey Senior Cup 1966-67
Record Goalscorer: Alan Ives - 92
Record Appearances: Danny Godwin - 470
Additional Records: Paid £9,000 to Enfield for David Flint
Received £10,000 from Luton Town for Herbie Smith
Senior Honours:
Athenian League 1949-50, 54-55. Isthmian League 1975-76, 59-60, Division 2 2000-01. Full Members Cup 1992-93. London Senior Cup 1942-43, 48-49, 58-59, 59-60, 2006-07, 07-08. Surrey Senior cup 1937-38, 43-44, 44-45, 52-53, 59-60, 75-76, 76-77, 77-78, 2007-07. Surrey Senior Shield 1951-52, 60-61, 61-62, 65-66. South Thames Cup 1969-70.

10 YEAR RECORD

04-05	05-06	06-07	07-08	08-09	09-10	10-11	11-12	12-13	13-14
Isth1 8	Isth1 6	Isth1S 2	Isth1S 2	Isth P 9	Isth P 12	Isth P 14	Isth P 21	Isth1S 16	Isth1S 11

WALTON & HERSHAM

Chairman: Alan Smith
Secretary: Michael Groom (T) 07710 230 694 (E) mhgroom@aol.com
Commercial Manager: (T)
Programme Editor: TBA (T)
Ground Address: Sports Ground, Stompond Lane, Walton-on-Thames KT12 1HF
(T) 01932 245 263 **Manager:** Tony Reid

Club Factfile

Founded: 1945 **Nickname:** Swans
Previous Names: Walton FC (Founded in 1895) amalgamated with Hersham FC in 1945.
Previous Leagues: Surrey Senior, Corinthian 1945-50, Athenian 1950-71

Club Colours (change): All red (Yellow/blue/yellow)

Ground Capacity: 5,000 **Seats:** 400 **Covered:** 2,500 **Clubhouse:** Yes **Shop:** Yes

Directions
From Walton Bridge go over and along New Zealand Avenue, down one way street and up A244 Hersham Road. Ground is second on the right.

Previous Grounds: None

Record Attendance: 10,000 v Crook Town - FA Amateur Cup 6th Round 1951-52
Record Victory: 10-0 v Clevedon - FA Amateur Cup 1960
Record Defeat: 3-11 v Kingstonian - Surrey Shield 1958
Record Goalscorer: Reg Sentance - 220 (During 11 seasons)
Record Appearances: Terry Keen - 449 (During 11 seasons)
Additional Records: Paid £6,000. Received £150,000 from Bristol Rovers for Nathan Ellington 1999.

Senior Honours:
Athenian League 1968-69.
FA Amateur Cup 1972-73. Barassi Cup 1973-74.
Surrey Senior Cup x6. London Senior Cup.

10 YEAR RECORD

04-05	05-06	06-07	07-08	08-09	09-10	10-11	11-12	12-13	13-14
Isth1 2	Isth P 9	Isth P 19	Isth1S 10	Isth1S 14	Isth1S 8	Isth1S 6	Isth1S 11	Isth1S 18	Isth1S 21

WALTON CASUALS

Chairman: Tony Gale
Secretary: Gus Schofield (T) 07415 604 017 (E) g.schofield1@ntlworld.com
Commercial Manager: n/a (T)
Programme Editor: David Symonds (T) 07720 557 530
Ground Address: The Waterside Stadium, Waterside Drive, Walton KT12 2JP
(T) 01932 787 749 **Manager:** Mark Hamms

Club Factfile

Founded: 1948 **Nickname:** The Stags
Previous Names:
Previous Leagues: Surrey Intermediate, Surrey Senior, Suburban, Surrey Premier, Combined Counties

Club Colours (change): Tangerine/black/tangerine (All light blue)

Ground Capacity: 2,000 **Seats:** 153 **Covered:** 403 **Clubhouse:** Yes **Shop:** Yes

Directions
Left off Terrace Road at first major roundabout out of Walton centre.
Ground is next to The Xcel Leisure Centre.

Previous Grounds: Elm Grove Rec. 1948-69. Franklyn Road 1969-71. Stompond Lane 1971-72. Liberty Lane 1972-80.

Record Attendance: 1,748 v AFC Wimbledon - Combined Counties League 12/04/2004
Record Victory: Not Known
Record Defeat: Not Known
Record Goalscorer: Greg Ball - 77
Record Appearances: Craig Carley - 234
Additional Records:

Senior Honours:
Combined Counties League Premier Division 2004-05, League Cup 1999-2000.

10 YEAR RECORD

04-05	05-06	06-07	07-08	08-09	09-10	10-11	11-12	12-13	13-14
CCP 1	Isth1 15	Isth1S 17	Isth1S 16	Isth1S 17	Isth1S 21	Isth1S 12	Isth1S 15	Isth1S 22	Isth1S 9

WHITSTABLE TOWN

Chairman: Gary Johnson
Secretary: Phil Gurr **(T)** 07840 827 796 **(E)** secretary@whitstabletownfc.co.uk
Commercial Manager: n/a **(T)**
Programme Editor: Andy Short **(T)** 07920 068 449
Ground Address: The Belmont Ground, Belmont Road, Belmont, Whitstable CT5 1QP
(T) 01227 266 012 **Manager:** Danny Ward & Jim Ward

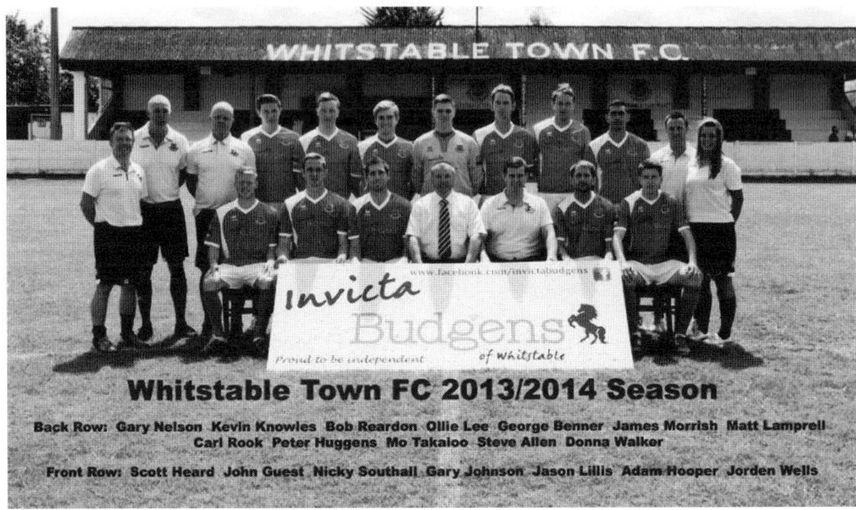

WHITSTABLE TOWN F.C.
www.facebook.com/invictabudgens
Invicta
Budgens
Proud to be independent
of Whitstable
Whitstable Town FC 2013/2014 Season
Back Row: Gary Nelson Kevin Knowles Bob Reardon Ollie Lee George Benner James Morrish Matt Lamprell
Carl Rook Peter Huggens Mo Takaloo Steve Allen Donna Walker
Front Row: Scott Heard John Guest Nicky Southall Gary Johnson Jason Lillis Adam Hooper Jorden Wells

Picture courtesy of Les Biggs.

Club Factfile

Founded: 1886 **Nickname:** Oystermen or Natives
Previous Names:
Previous Leagues: East Kent 1897-1909, Kent 1909-59, Aetolian 1959-60, Kent Amateur 1960-62, 63-64, South East Anglian 1962-63, Greater London 1964-67, Kent 1967-2007

Club Colours (change): Red & white/white/red (Yellow/blue/yellow)

Ground Capacity: 2,000 **Seats:** 500 **Covered:** 1,000 **Clubhouse:** Yes **Shop:** Yes

Directions
From Thanet Way (A299) turn left at Tesco roundabout and Millstrood Road.
Ground at bottom of road,
400 yards from Whitstable BR station.

Previous Grounds:

Record Attendance: 2,500 v Gravesend & Northfleet - FA Cup 19/10/1987
Record Victory: Not known
Record Defeat: Not known
Record Goalscorer: Barry Godfrey
Record Appearances: Frank Cox - 429 (1950-60)
Additional Records:

Senior Honours:
Kent Amateur Cup 1928-29.
Kent League 2006-07, League Trophy 2006-07.

10 YEAR RECORD

04-05	05-06	06-07	07-08	08-09	09-10	10-11	11-12	12-13	13-14
Kent P 3	Kent P 5	Kent P 10	Isth1S 14	Isth1S 16	Isth1S 18	Isth1S 15	Isth1S 18	Isth1S 17	Isth1S 20

WHYTELEAFE

Chairman: Mark Coote
Secretary: Chris Layton (T) 07718 457 875 (E) chris@theleafe.co.uk
Commercial Manager: (T)
Programme Editor: Chris Layton (T) 07718 457 875
Ground Address: 15 Church Road, Whyteleafe, Surrey CR3 0AR
(T) 0208 660 5491 **Manager:** John Fowler

Celebration time after winning the Southern Counties East title.
Photo: Alan Coomes.

Club Factfile

Founded: 1946 **Nickname:** Leafe
Previous Names: Not known
Previous Leagues: Caterham & Ed, Croydon, Thornton Heath & Dist, Surrey Interm. (East) 1954-58, Surrey Sen 58-75, Spartan 75-81, Athenian 81-84, Isthmian 84-2012

Club Colours (change): White with green slash (Red with black slash)

Ground Capacity: 5,000 **Seats:** 400 **Covered:** 600 **Clubhouse:** Yes **Shop:** Yes

Directions
FROM THE M25 AND THE SOUTH: From Junction 6 of the M26 head north along the A22 (signposted to London, Croydon and Caterham). At Wapses Lodge Roundabout, the Ann Summers building is clearly visible opposite, take the third exit. Take the first left adjacent to Whyteleafe South railway station and cross the level crossing. Fork right after 200 yards into Church Road. The ground is a quarter of a mile down the road on the right. FROM THE NORTH: From Purley Cross (where the A23 crosses the A22), head south signposted to Eastbourne and the M25. Pass 'My Old China' (Chinese restaurant) on your right and continue under a railway bridge. Follow the A22 through Kenley and into Whyteleafe. At the first roundabout (with Whyteleafe Tavern opposite), turn right and cross a level crossing adjacent to Whyteleafe Station. Take first left into Church Road keeping St Luke Church to your right. The ground is a quarter of a mile up the road on the left.

Previous Grounds: Not known

Record Attendance: 2,210 v Chester City - FA Cup 1999-2000
Record Victory: Not known
Record Defeat: Not known
Record Goalscorer: Not known
Record Appearances: Not known
Additional Records: Paid £1,000 to Carshalton Athletic for Gary Bowyer
Received £25,000 for Steve Milton
Senior Honours:
Surrey Senior Cup 1968-69.
Southern Counties East (formerly Kent League) 2013-14.

10 YEAR RECORD

04-05	05-06	06-07	07-08	08-09	09-10	10-11	11-12	12-13	13-14
Isth1 9	Isth1 18	Isth1S 20	Isth1S 11	Isth1S 18	Isth1S 15	Isth1S 16	Isth1S 21	Kent P 6	SCE 1

WORTHING

Chairman: Mrs Deborah McKail

Secretary: Gareth Nicholas **(T)** 01903 236 449 **(E)** garethbnicholas@hotmail.co.uk

Commercial Manager: n/a **(T)**

Programme Editor: Alistar McKail **(T)** 07760 110 308

Ground Address: Woodside Road, Worthing, West Sussex BN14 7HQ

(T) 01903 239 575 **Manager:** Lee Brace

Club Factfile

Founded: 1886 **Nickname:** Rebels

Previous Names: None

Previous Leagues: West Sussex 1896-1904, 1905-14, 19-20, Brighton Hove & District 1919-20, Sussex County 1920-40, Corinthian 1948-63, Athenian 1963-77

Club Colours (change): All red (All yellow)

Ground Capacity: 3,650 **Seats:** 500 **Covered:** 1,500 **Clubhouse:** Yes **Shop:**

Directions

A24 or A27 to Grove Lodge roundabout.
A24 (Town Centre exit) and right into South Farm Road.
Over five roundabouts take last on right (Pavilion Road) before level crossing.
Woodside Road on right, ground on left. 1/2 mile from BR.

Previous Grounds: None

Record Attendance: 3,600 v Wimbledon - FA Cup 14/11/1936

Record Victory: 25-0 v Littlehampton (H) - Sussex League 1911-12

Record Defeat: 0-14 v Southwick (A) - Sussex County League 1946-47

Record Goalscorer: Mick Edmonds - 276

Record Appearances: Mark Knee - 414

Additional Records: Received £7,500 from Woking for Tim Read 1990

Senior Honours:

Sussex League 1920-21, 21-22, 26-27, 28-29, 30-31, 33-34, 38-39. Sussex League West 1945-46.
Isthmian League Division 2 1981-82, 92-93, Division 1 1982-83.
Sussex Senior Cup x21.

10 YEAR RECORD

04-05	05-06	06-07	07-08	08-09	09-10	10-11	11-12	12-13	13-14
Isth P 10	Isth P 8	Isth P 20	Isth1S 5	Isth1S 5	Isth1S 3	Isth1S 14	Isth1S 7	Isth1S 10	Isth1S 15

COMBINED COUNTIES LEAGUE

Sponsored by: Cherry Red Records
Founded: 1978
Recent Champions:
2009: Bedfont Green
2010: North Greenford United
2011: Guildford City
2012: Guildford City
2013: Egham Town
combinedcountiesleague.co.uk

PREMIER DIVISION	P	W	D	L	F	A	GD	Pts
1 (P) South Park	42	34	2	6	121	41	80	104
2 Camberley Town	42	27	9	6	88	42	46	90
3 Epsom & Ewell	42	24	6	12	87	61	26	78
4 Westfield	42	24	5	13	72	51	21	77
5 Cove	42	24	4	14	95	67	28	76
6 Windsor	42	21	7	14	98	68	30	70
7 Hartley Wintney	42	20	5	17	94	77	17	65
8 Hanworth Villa	42	18	10	14	82	64	18	64
9 (S) Wembley	42	18	9	15	64	60	4	63
10 Raynes Park Vale	42	18	8	16	79	81	-2	62
11 Molesey	42	15	12	15	70	53	17	57
12 Frimley Green	42	17	6	19	63	82	-19	57
13 (S) Croydon	41	16	5	20	58	81	-23	53
14 Badshot Lea	42	14	10	18	58	84	-26	52
15 Farnham Town (+3)	41	14	9	18	60	70	-10	51
16 Colliers Wood United	42	14	7	21	69	80	-11	49
17 Bedfont Sports	42	11	12	19	52	79	-27	45
18 Mole Valley SCR	42	11	9	22	69	101	-32	42
19 Horley Town	42	12	6	24	60	93	-33	42
20 (R) Ash United	42	12	5	25	62	78	-16	41
21 (R) Alton Town	42	9	7	26	57	93	-36	34
22 (R) Chessington & Hook Utd	42	9	5	28	58	110	-52	32

EL RECORDS PREMIER CHALLENGE CUP

ROUND 1

CB Hounslow United	v	Frimley Green	0-8
Banstead Athletic	v	Colliers Wood United	3-2 aet
Horley Town	v	Epsom & Ewell	2-3
Dorking	v	Cobham	2-1
Worcester Park	v	Molesey	2-1
Epsom Athletic	v	Staines Lammas	2-0

ROUND 2

Bedfont Sports	v	Sheerwater	1-2
Camberley Town	v	Farnham Town	2-1
South Kilburn	v	Spelthorne Sports	0-1
Frimley Green	v	Banstead Athletic	2-2 4-1p
South Park	v	Bedfont & Feltham	1-0
AFC Croydon Athletic	v	Epsom & Ewell	2-7
Eversley & California	v	Hanworth Villa	0-6
Croydon	v	Dorking	5-0
Windsor	v	Alton Town	3-0
Sandhurst Town	v	Ash United	3-1
Chessington & Hook Utd	v	Hartley Wintney	2-1
Wembley	v	Westfield	3-2
Farleigh Rovers	v	Mole Valley SCR	2-4
Worcester Park	v	Cove	3-4
Epsom Athletic	v	Raynes Park Vale	3-0
Badshot Lea	v	Knaphill	3-1

ROUND 3

Sheerwater	v	Camberley Town	0-2
Spelthorne Sports	v	Frimley Green	3-1
South Park	v	Epsom & Ewell	1-2
Hanworth Villa	v	Croydon	2-1
Windsor	v	Sandhurst Town	6-1
Chessington & Hook Utd	v	Wembley	0-3
Mole Valley SCR	v	Cove	1-4
Epsom Athletic	v	Badshot Lea	2-1

QUARTER FINALS

Hanworth Villa	v	Epsom Athletic	4-1
Windsor	v	Cove	3-0
Wembley	v	Epsom & Ewell	2-0
Spelthorne Sports	v	Sheerwater	4-0

SEMI FINALS

Hanworth Villa	v	Windsor	5-4
Wembley	v	Spelthorne Sports	2-6

FINAL

Hanworth Villa	v	Spelthorne Sports	1-0

PREMIER DIVISION	1	2	3	4	5	6	7	8	9	10	11	12	13	14	15	16	17	18	19	20	21	22
1 Alton Town		4-1	0-1	1-2	2-3	4-0	2-1	0-3	2-3	0-1	1-1	1-2	3-1	1-5	2-1	3-1	1-2	1-2	0-4	0-0	2-3	3-1
2 Ash United	1-1		4-0	3-0	1-2	2-0	1-2	2-1	3-1	2-3	0-1	0-1	0-2	3-1	4-0	1-1	2-0	2-3	2-6	1-2	1-2	0-1
3 Badshot Lea	1-1	0-0		4-2	2-2	1-0	2-2	1-2	0-1	1-0	1-1	3-1	0-1	3-1	2-4	2-0	0-6	2-2	0-5	3-1	0-1	2-1
4 Bedfont Sports	1-1	0-2	5-1		0-4	1-4	1-1	0-6	1-1	2-2	0-1	4-0	0-1	1-2	1-1	2-1	1-0	1-1	2-1	3-3	1-2	1-4
5 Camberley Town	4-0	3-1	3-1	3-0		2-0	5-0	3-2	3-0	0-2	3-1	1-0	3-2	1-0	2-0	1-1	0-0	0-1	1-2	3-1	1-1	0-0
6 Chessington & Hook United	4-1	1-2	0-3	2-2	1-3		2-1	0-1	1-0	2-2	3-1	2-4	2-0	2-4	3-3	2-5	2-1	1-5	0-3	2-3	0-2	2-3
7 Colliers Wood United	2-2	0-1	5-0	2-2	5-2	5-1		1-3	0-1	0-2	0-1	3-4	1-1	2-1	3-1	2-5	2-0	4-1	2-3	1-2	2-0	2-2
8 Cove	1-0	1-0	3-2	3-0	1-1	3-2	2-0		0-4	0-3	1-2	1-4	5-2	2-3	1-1	4-2	0-3	3-2	1-2	4-1	1-2	2-4
9 Croydon	0-2	4-3	1-4	1-1	0-1	2-4	1-1	2-6		3-0	2-1	0-1	2-4	0-4	3-2	2-5	2-1	0-1	0-3	1-0	1-0	1-3
10 Epsom & Ewell	0-3	3-0	3-4	1-0	0-2	0-1	4-0	0-1	2-0		3-2	3-0	1-4	4-2	5-3	4-0	2-2	2-2	0-2	0-2	2-1	2-1
11 Farnham Town	1-1	3-6	1-0	0-2	3-3	7-0	1-2	1-2	HW	3-0		0-1	1-1	2-1	2-1	0-2	1-1	3-0	1-0	0-2	1-0	0-2
12 Frimley Green	3-2	1-0	0-2	2-1	2-2	2-1	2-0	2-1	1-4	1-5	3-3		1-0	3-2	5-1	0-0	1-2	0-1	0-1	1-1	1-1	2-5
13 Hanworth Villa	2-1	5-0	2-2	3-0	1-3	2-1	5-2	5-2	1-2	3-3	4-0	3-3		1-2	2-1	1-2	2-2	3-0	0-0	1-1	3-1	3-2
14 Hartley Wintney	6-0	3-1	1-1	5-2	1-2	4-2	0-2	2-4	3-2	4-4	3-2	3-2	0-1		2-0	5-0	0-2	0-4	1-3	2-2	0-1	3-1
15 Horley Town	2-0	2-2	2-1	0-2	1-4	4-0	2-1	0-2	1-2	1-3	2-1	3-2	3-1	1-1		3-2	1-0	0-6	2-3	0-1	1-2	3-2
16 Mole Valley SCR	3-2	2-2	2-2	0-1	0-2	2-2	2-4	2-5	2-2	0-3	2-1	2-0	2-1	1-4	4-4		0-0	2-6	0-3	1-0	1-3	3-2
17 Molesey	5-0	3-2	2-0	0-1	1-2	1-1	1-2	0-3	5-0	1-2	5-0	3-1	1-1	1-1	3-2	5-2		3-3	0-0	1-0	1-3	0-0
18 Raynes Park Vale	4-3	3-2	2-2	0-2	1-4	4-3	1-0	2-1	0-2	1-3	1-2	3-0	2-2	0-2	0-1	4-3	0-0		0-5	4-1	1-3	0-3
19 South Park	8-1	1-0	6-1	5-3	1-0	6-1	3-1	1-6	4-0	0-2	5-2	4-0	3-1	4-0	2-0	4-1	4-1	4-0		2-0	0-4	1-0
20 Wembley	4-2	2-0	2-0	0-0	0-1	4-1	4-1	1-1	3-3	1-3	1-3	2-0	0-2	2-1	2-0	1-0	0-3	2-1	2-4		3-1	1-2
21 Westfield	1-0	4-0	0-1	4-0	1-1	1-0	1-2	1-1	2-1	3-0	1-1	1-4	2-1	2-4	2-0	1-0	3-2	1-2	0-2	0-3		5-2
22 Windsor	2-1	3-2	6-0	1-1	3-2	4-0	3-0	1-3	0-1	1-3	2-2	5-0	2-1	3-5	5-0	5-3	3-0	3-3	3-1	1-1	1-3	

COMBINED COUNTIES - STEP 5/6

DIVISION ONE	P	W	D	L	F	A	GD	Pts
1 (P) Spelthorne Sports (+3)	29	21	8	0	92	23	69	74
2 Eversley & California	30	19	4	7	78	40	38	61
3 (P) Knaphill	30	19	4	7	89	52	37	61
4 Staines Lammas	30	17	6	7	76	44	32	57
5 Bedfont & Feltham	30	17	4	9	68	48	20	55
6 Epsom Athletic	30	17	3	10	85	68	17	54
7 AFC Croydon Athletic	30	16	5	9	64	43	21	53
8 Farleigh Rovers	29	13	6	10	52	46	6	45
9 Worcester Park	30	12	7	11	64	52	12	43
10 South Kilburn (+6)	27	7	4	16	36	57	-21	31
11 Sheerwater	30	8	7	15	35	60	-25	31
12 Banstead Athletic (-3)	30	9	6	15	54	74	-20	30
13 Sandhurst Town	30	7	3	20	46	91	-45	24
14 CB Hounslow United (+3)	29	5	5	19	33	66	-33	23
15 Cobham	29	5	3	21	32	89	-57	18
16 Dorking	27	4	3	20	28	79	-51	15

LEMON RECORDS DIV. ONE CHALLENGE CUP

ROUND 1

AFC Croydon Athletic	v	Knaphill	4-3
Banstead Athletic	v	South Kilburn	2-1
Dorking	v	Cobham	0-1
Epsom Athletic	v	Staines Lammas	1-7
Farleigh Rovers	v	Eversley & California	1-0
Sandhurst Town	v	CB Hounslow United	5-5, 5-4p
Sheerwater	v	Worcester Park	4-1
Spelthorne Sports	v	Bedfont & Feltham	6-1

QUARTER FINALS

Farleigh Rovers	v	Sandhurst Town	2-1
Cobham	v	Spelthorne Sports	0-2
Sheerwater	v	Banstead Athletic	0-1
Staines Lammas	v	AFC Croydon Athletic	2-1 aet

SEMI FINALS

Farleigh Rovers	v	Spelthorne Sports	1-2
Banstead Athletic	v	Staines Lammas	1-4

FINAL

Spelthorne Sports	v	Staines Lammas	1-0

DIVISION ONE	1	2	3	4	5	6	7	8	9	10	11	12	13	14	15	16
1 AFC Croydon Athletic		3-0	0-2	0-1	3-0	4-2	4-3	1-1	0-3	4-5	5-0	2-0	1-0	0-0	1-0	2-0
2 Banstead Athletic	0-2		1-4	2-1	2-3	0-2	5-3	1-0	0-4	1-8	5-0	1-1	2-2	2-2	2-1	0-5
3 Bedfont & Feltham	3-3	5-1		1-0	4-3	2-1	3-5	1-0	0-2	2-1	4-4	6-1	3-2	1-5	2-2	2-3
4 CB Hounslow United	1-3	1-2	0-2		4-0	HW	1-3	2-3	0-3	3-4	0-4	3-0	2-2	0-3	0-5	1-1
5 Cobham	2-3	3-3	1-3	1-1		0-3	0-4	0-3	2-2	0-5	2-1	0-1	2-3	AW	0-2	0-4
6 Dorking	0-4	1-6	1-5	1-2	1-3		0-3	1-3	0-5	0-9	2-1	1-2	AW	1-2	1-3	2-2
7 Epsom Athletic	0-4	4-3	3-2	1-0	4-1	4-1		4-1	6-2	6-0	2-4	4-2	1-3	1-2	10-1	2-1
8 Eversley & California	2-2	3-0	1-0	3-0	3-1	1-1	6-1		2-0	2-0	4-2	5-1	3-2	1-3	1-2	1-0
9 Farleigh Rovers	2-0	2-2	0-6	1-1	3-1	0-0	0-3	0-3		1-4	4-0	1-1	2-0	0-1	1-5	1-0
10 Knaphill	0-5	2-1	3-0	2-1	3-0	3-2	5-1	5-2	0-4		2-0	4-1	5-0	1-3	0-3	2-2
11 Sandhurst Town	4-2	1-4	0-1	1-3	0-2	2-0	1-1	2-11	2-5	1-4		2-1	1-2	2-3	1-1	3-7
12 Sheerwater	1-0	3-4	1-1	2-2	5-1	1-2	0-0	0-1	2-1	0-3	2-1		1-0	2-5	0-2	0-0
13 South Kilburn	1-2	1-0	0-1	1-0	1-2	HW	1-2	2-5	HW	1-1	2-3	4-1		2-2	0-5	3-1
14 Spelthorne Sports	4-1	3-1	2-0	7-1	8-0	4-0	6-1	2-2	3-0	1-1	4-0	0-0	4-0		7-0	2-2
15 Staines Lammas	2-2	0-0	0-1	2-1	5-1	5-1	7-1	3-1	1-1	2-2	6-1	2-3	3-0	0-3		4-0
16 Worcester Park	4-1	4-3	2-1	6-1	5-1	3-1	2-2	1-4	1-2	3-5	0-2	2-0	2-1	1-1	0-2	

CLUB MOVEMENTS

Premier Division - In: Ashford Town (Middx) (R - Southern Div.1 Central). Chertsey Town (R - Southern Div.1 Central). Guildford City (R - Southern Div.1 South & West). Knaphill (P). Spelthorne Sports (P).
Out: Alton Town (R). Ash United (R). Chessington & Hook Utd (R). Croydon (S - Southern Counties East). South Park (P - Isthmian Div.1 South). Wembley (S - Spartan South Midlands Premier).
Division One - In: Alton Town (R). Ash United (R). Chessington & Hook Utd (R).
Out: Knaphill (P). South Kilburn (now Middlesex County). Spelthorne Sports (P).

2013-14 - Hartley Wintney
Photo: Alan Coomes

2013-14 - Raynes Park Vale
Photo: Alan Coomes

ASHFORD TOWN (MIDDLESEX)

Founded: 1958 Nickname: Ash Trees

Secretary: Geoff Knock **(T)** 07928 792 792 **(E)** geoff.knock@btinternet.com

Chairman: Dave Baker **Manager:** Ben Murray **Prog Ed:** Mark Tobin

Ground: Robert Parker Stadium, Stanwell, Staines TW19 7BH **(T)** 01784 245 908

Capacity: 2,550 **Seats:** 250 **Covered:** 250 **Midweek Matchday:** Tuesday **Clubhouse:** Yes **Shop:** No

Colours(change): Tangerine and white stripes/black/tangerine

Previous Names: Ashford Albion 1958-64.

Previous Leagues: Hounslow & Dist 1964-68, Surrey Int. 68-82, Surrey Prem 82-90, Com. Co 90-2000, Isth 00-04, 06-10, Southern 04-06, 10-14

Records: 992 v AFC Wimbledon - Isthmian League Premier Division 26/09/2006

Senior Honours: Surrey Premier League 1982-90. Combined Counties League 1994-95, 95-96, 96-97, 97-98.
Middlesex Charity Cup 2000-01. Middlesex Premier Cup 2006-07. Isthmian League Cup 2006-07.

10 YEAR RECORD

04-05	05-06	06-07	07-08	08-09	09-10	10-11	11-12	12-13	13-14
SthW 6	SthW 2	Isth P 17	Isth P 6	Isth P 10	Isth P 20	SthC 16	SthC 9	SthC 10	SthC 22

BADSHOT LEA

Founded: 1907 Nickname: Baggies

Secretary: Mrs Nicky Staszkiewicz **(T)** 07921 466 858 **(E)** nstaszkiewicz@ashgatepublishing.com

Chairman: Mark Broad **Manager:** Trevor Norris **Prog Ed:** Peter Collison

Ground: Ash United, Shawfields Stadium, Youngs Drive off Shawfield Rd, Ash, GU12 6RE. **(T)** 01252 320 385

Capacity: 2,500 **Seats:** 152 **Covered:** 160 **Midweek Matchday:** Tuesday **Clubhouse:** Yes **Shop:** No

Colours(change): Claret & blue/claret/sky blue

Previous Names:

Previous Leagues: Surrey Intermediate. Hellenic > 2008.

Records: **Att:** 276 v Bisley, 16.04.07.

Senior Honours:

10 YEAR RECORD

04-05	05-06	06-07	07-08	08-09	09-10	10-11	11-12	12-13	13-14
Hel1E 7	Hel1E 12	Hel1E 3	Hel P 11	CCP 7	CCP 10	CCP 6	CCP 17	CCP 7	CCP 14

BEDFONT SPORTS

Founded: 2000 Nickname: The Eagles

Secretary: David Sturt **(T)** 07712 824 112 **(E)** dave.sturt2@blueyonder.co.uk

Chairman: David Reader **Manager:** Mick Snowden **Prog Ed:** Terry Reader

Ground: Bedfont Sports Club, Hatton Road, Bedfont TW14 8JA **(T)** 0208 831 9067

Capacity: 3,000 **Seats:** Yes **Covered:** 200 **Midweek Matchday:** Tuesday **Clubhouse:**

Colours(change): Red & black hoops/black/red & black hoops

Previous Names: Bedfont Sunday became Bedfont Sports in 2000 - Bedfont Eagles (1978) merged with the club shortly afterwards.

Previous Leagues: Middlesex County > 2009

Records:

Senior Honours: Middlesex County Premier Cup 2009-10.

10 YEAR RECORD

04-05	05-06	06-07	07-08	08-09	09-10	10-11	11-12	12-13	13-14
					CC1 9	CC1 4	CC1 2	CCP 13	CCP 17

CAMBERLEY TOWN

Founded: 1895 Nickname: Reds or Town

Secretary: Ben Clifford **(T)** 07876 552 210 **(E)** benjaminclifford@sky.com

Chairman: Christopher Goff **Manager:** Daniel Turkington **Prog Ed:** Andy Vaughan

Ground: Krooner Park, Wilton Road, Camberley, Surrey GU15 2QW **(T)** 01276 65392

Capacity: 1,976 **Seats:** 196 **Covered:** 300 **Midweek Matchday:** Tuesday **Clubhouse:** Yes **Shop:** Yes

Colours(change): Red and white stripes/red & blue/red

Previous Names: None

Previous Leagues: Surrey Senior Lge. Spartan Lge. Athenian Lge. Isthmian Lge.

Records: **Att:** 2066 v Aldershot Town, Isthmian Div.2 25/08/90. **Apps:** Brian Ives.

Senior Honours:

10 YEAR RECORD

04-05	05-06	06-07	07-08	08-09	09-10	10-11	11-12	12-13	13-14
Isth2 12	Isth2 14	CCP 7	CCP 3	CCP 5	CCP 3	CCP 4	CCP 6	CCP 16	CCP 2

CHERTSEY TOWN

Founded: 1890 Nickname: Curfews

Secretary: Chris Gay **(T)** 07713 473 313 **(E)** chrisegay@googlemail.com
Chairman: Steve Powers **Manager:** Kim Harris **Prog Ed:** Chris Gay
Ground: Alwyns Lane, Chertsey, Surrey KT16 9DW **(T)** 01932 561 774
Capacity: 3,000 **Seats:** 240 **Covered:** 760 **Midweek Matchday:** Tuesday **Clubhouse:** Yes **Shop:** Yes

Colours(change): Royal blue & white stripes/royal blue/royal blue
Previous Names: None
Previous Leagues: Metropolitan. Spartan. Athenian. Isthmian, Combined Counties 2006-11. Southern 2011-14.
Records: **Att:** 2150 v Aldershot Town, Isthmian Div.2 04/12/93. **Goals:** Alan Brown (54) 1962-63.
Senior Honours: Surrey Senior Champions 1959, 61, 62. Isthmian League Cup 1994.

10 YEAR RECORD

04-05	05-06	06-07	07-08	08-09	09-10	10-11	11-12	12-13	13-14
Isth2 6	Isth2 6	CCP 8	CCP 8	CCP 3	CCP 2	CCP 2	SthC 17	SthC 20	SthC 21

COLLIERS WOOD UNITED

Founded: 1874 Nickname: The Woods

Secretary: Chris Clapham **(T)** 07812 181 601 **(E)** chrisclapham@blueyonder.co.uk
Chairman: Tony Eldridge **Manager:** Tony Hurrell **Prog Ed:** Chris Clapham
Ground: Wibandune Sports Gd, Lincoln Green, Wimbledon SW20 0AA **(T)** 0208 942 8062
Capacity: 2000 **Seats:** 102 **Covered:** 100 **Midweek Matchday:** Wednesday **Clubhouse:** Yes **Shop:** Yes

Colours(change): Blue/black/black
Previous Names: Vandyke Colliers United
Previous Leagues: Surrey County Senior
Records: **Att:** 151 v Guildford City 06/08/2010. **Win:** 9-1 v Bedfont 05/03/2008.
Senior Honours:

10 YEAR RECORD

04-05	05-06	06-07	07-08	08-09	09-10	10-11	11-12	12-13	13-14
CCP 14	CCP 4	CCP 13	CCP 7	CCP 14	CCP 19	CCP 11	CCP 19	CCP 18	CCP 16

COVE

Founded: 1897 Nickname:

Secretary: Graham Brown **(T)** 07713 250 093 **(E)** secretarycfc@aol.com
Chairman: Matthew Hutton **Manager:** Anthony Millerick **Prog Ed:** Graham Brown
Ground: Oak Farm Fields, 7 Squirrels Lane, Farnborough GU14 8PB **(T)** 01252 543 615
Capacity: 2500 **Seats:** 110 **Covered:** 100 **Midweek Matchday:** Tuesday **Clubhouse:** Yes

Colours(change): Yellow/black/yellow
Previous Names: None
Previous Leagues: Isthmian League. Hampshire.
Records: **Att:** 1798 v Aldershot Town, Isthmian Div.3 01/05/93.
Senior Honours: Aldershot Senior Cup x6 Most recently 2012-13.

10 YEAR RECORD

04-05	05-06	06-07	07-08	08-09	09-10	10-11	11-12	12-13	13-14
CCP 20	CCP 16	CCP 18	CCP 4	CCP 6	CCP 12	CCP 9	CCP 11	CCP 3	CCP 5

EPSOM & EWELL

Founded: 1918 Nickname: E's

Secretary: Peter Beddoe **(T)** 07767 078 132 **(E)** p.beddoe1@ntlworld.com
Chairman: Tony Jeffcoate **Manager:** Lyndon Buckwell **Prog Ed:** Stephen Dyke
Ground: Chipstead FC, High Road, Chipstead, Surrey CR5 3SF **(T)** 01737 553 250
Capacity: 2,000 **Seats:** 150 **Covered:** 200 **Midweek Matchday:** Tuesday **Clubhouse:** Yes

Colours(change): Royal blue & white hoops/royal blue/royal blue
Previous Names: Epsom T (previously Epsom FC) merged with Ewell & Stoneleigh in 1960
Previous Leagues: Corinthian. Athenian. Surrey Senior. Isthmian >2006.
Records: **Att:** 5000 v Kingstonian, FAC 2Q 15/10/49. **Goals:** Tommy Tuite - 391. **Apps:** Graham Morris - 658.
Senior Honours:

10 YEAR RECORD

04-05	05-06	06-07	07-08	08-09	09-10	10-11	11-12	12-13	13-14
Isth2 14	Isth2 15	CCP 17	CCP 10	CCP 4	CCP 5	CCP 10	CCP 14	CCP 5	CCP 3

FARNHAM TOWN
Founded: 1906 Nickname: The Town

Secretary: Sandra Charlton **(T)** 07909 284 167 **(E)** sanboleyn@gmail.com
Chairman: Ray Bridger **Manager:** Paul Tanner **Prog Ed:** Ben Williams
Ground: Memorial Ground, West Street, Farnham GU9 7DY **(T)** 01252 715 305
Capacity: 1,500 **Seats:** 50 **Covered:** **Midweek Matchday:** Tuesday **Clubhouse:**

Colours(change): Claret & sky blue/white, claret & sky blue/sky blue
Previous Names:
Previous Leagues: Spartan 1973-75, London Spartan 1975-80, Combined Co. 1980-92, 93-2006, Isthmian 1992-93 (resigned pre-season).
Records:
Senior Honours: Combined Counties League 1990-91, 91-92, Division 1 2006-07.

10 YEAR RECORD

04-05	05-06	06-07	07-08	08-09	09-10	10-11	11-12	12-13	13-14
CCP 21	CCP 21	CC1 1	CC1 5	CC1 8	CC1 11	CC1 2	CCP 12	CCP 8	CCP 15

FRIMLEY GREEN
Founded: 1919 Nickname: The Green

Secretary: Mark O'Grady **(T)** 07812 026 390 **(E)** mogradyuk@yahoo.co.uk
Chairman: Mark O'Grady **Manager:** Darren Martin **Prog Ed:** Mark O'Grady
Ground: Frimley Green Rec. Ground, Frimley Green, Camberley GU16 6JY **(T)** 01252 835 089
Capacity: 2000 **Seats:** No **Covered:** Yes **Midweek Matchday:** Tuesday **Clubhouse:**

Colours(change): All blue
Previous Names:
Previous Leagues: Surrey Senior. London Spartan. Combined Counties 1981-94. Surrey County Premier 1999-2002.
Records: **Record Att:** 1,152 v AFC Wimbledon 2002-03. **Win:** 6-1 v Farnham Town 21/12/02. **Defeat:** 1-7 v Walton Casuals 2002/03.
Senior Honours: Combined Counties League Division One 2012-13.

10 YEAR RECORD

04-05	05-06	06-07	07-08	08-09	09-10	10-11	11-12	12-13	13-14
CCP 15	CCP 18	CC1 13	CC1 6	CC1 16	CC1 13	CC1 15	CC1 10	CC1 1	CCP 12

GUILDFORD CITY
Founded: 1996 Nickname: The City

Secretary: Barry Underwood **(T)** 07757 730 304 **(E)** barry.underwood@guildfordcityfc.co.uk
Chairman: Mark Redhead **Manager:** Kevin Rayner **Prog Ed:** Lisa Harding
Ground: Spectrum Leisure Centre, Parkway, Guildford GU1 1UP **(T)** 01483 443 322
Capacity: 1100 **Seats:** 269 **Covered:** Yes **Midweek Matchday:** Wednesday **Clubhouse:** Yes **Shop:** Yes

Colours(change): Red & white stripes/black/black
Previous Names: AFC Guildford 1996-2005. Guildford United 2005-06.
Previous Leagues: Surrey Senior. Combined Counties > 2012. Southern 2012-14.
Records: **Att:** 211 v Godalming & Guildford, 2004
Senior Honours: Southern League 1937-38, 55-56, League cup 1962-63, 66-67.
Combined Counties Division One 2003-04, Premier Division 2010-11, 11-12

10 YEAR RECORD

04-05	05-06	06-07	07-08	08-09	09-10	10-11	11-12	12-13	13-14
CCP 12	CCP 17	CCP 21	CCP 2	CCP 20	CCP 7	CCP 1	CCP 1	SthC 9	Sthsw 22

HANWORTH VILLA
Founded: 1976 Nickname: The Vilans

Secretary: Dave Brown **(T)** 07971 650 297 **(E)** david.h.brown@btconnect.com
Chairman: Gary Brunning **Manager:** Gary Jenkins **Prog Ed:** Gary Brunning
Ground: Rectory Meadows, Park Road, Hanworth TW13 6PN **(T)** 020 8831 9391
Capacity: 600 **Seats:** 100 **Covered:** Yes **Midweek Matchday:** Tuesday **Clubhouse:** Yes

Colours(change): Red & white/black/black
Previous Names:
Previous Leagues: Hounslow & District Lge. West Middlesex Lge. Middlesex County League.
Records:
Senior Honours: West Middlesex Div. 1 & Div. 2 Champions. Middlesex County Champions 2002-03, 04-05.

10 YEAR RECORD

04-05	05-06	06-07	07-08	08-09	09-10	10-11	11-12	12-13	13-14
MidCo 1	CC1 7	CC1 6	CC1 2	CC1 2	CCP 17	CCP 5	CCP 3	CCP 9	CCP 8

HARTLEY WINTNEY

Founded: 1897 Nickname: The Row

Secretary: Michael Bradley **(T)** 07754 782 189 **(E)** anfieldarry@btinternet.com

Chairman: Luke Mullen **Manager:** Ben Dillon **Prog Ed:** Luke Mullen

Ground: Memorial Playing Fields,Green Lane, Hartley Wintney RG27 8DL **(T)** 01252 843 586

Capacity: 2,000 **Seats:** 113 **Covered:** Yes **Midweek Matchday:** Tuesday **Clubhouse:** Yes **Shop:** Yes

Colours(change): Orange & black/orange/orange
Previous Names: None
Previous Leagues: Founder members of the Home Counties League (renamed Combined Counties League)
Records: 1,392 v AFC Wimbledon , 25/01/02.
Senior Honours: Combined Counties League 1982-83.

10 YEAR RECORD

04-05	05-06	06-07	07-08	08-09	09-10	10-11	11-12	12-13	13-14
CCP 23	CC1 5	CC1 16	CC1 3	CCP 21	CC1 5	CC1 7	CC1 3	CCP 19	CCP 7

HORLEY TOWN

Founded: 1896 Nickname: The Clarets

Secretary: Mrs Nicky Maybury **(T)** 07753 216 403 **(E)** maybury@hotmail.com

Chairman: Mark Sale **Manager:** Anthony Jupp **Prog Ed:** Feargal Hogan

Ground: The New Defence, Court Lodge Road, Horley RH6 8SP **(T)** 01293 822 000

Capacity: 1800 **Seats:** 101 **Covered:** Yes **Midweek Matchday:** Tuesday **Clubhouse:** Yes **Shop:** Yes

Colours(change): Claret & blue/claret/claret
Previous Names: Horley >1975
Previous Leagues: Surrey Senior, London Spartan, Athenian, Surrey County Senior, Crawley & District
Records: **Att:** 1,500 v AFC Wimbledon, 2003-04. **Goalscorer:** Alan Gates. **Win:** 12-1 v Egham. **Defeat:** 2-8 v Redhill 1956/57.
Senior Honours:

10 YEAR RECORD

04-05	05-06	06-07	07-08	08-09	09-10	10-11	11-12	12-13	13-14
CCP 7	CCP 5	CC1 2	CCP 5	CCP 12	CCP 14	CCP 16	CCP 7	CCP 12	CCP 19

KNAPHILL

Founded: 1924 Nickname: The Knappers

Secretary: Bryan Freeman **(T)** 07876 162 904 **(E)** knaphillfc.honsecretary@gmail.com

Chairman: David Freeman **Manager:** Phil Ruggles **Prog Ed:** Matt Flude

Ground: Brookwood Country Park, Redding Way, Knaphill GU21 2AY **(T)** 01483 475 150

Capacity: 750 **Seats:** **Covered:** **Midweek Matchday:** Tuesday **Clubhouse:**

Colours(change): Red/black/red
Previous Names:
Previous Leagues: Surrey Intermediate > 2007
Records: **Att:** 323 v Guernsey. **Goalscorer:** Matt Baker - 24.
Senior Honours: **Honours:** Woking & District League 1978-79. Surrey Intermediate League Division One 2005-06, Premier 06-07.

10 YEAR RECORD

04-05	05-06	06-07	07-08	08-09	09-10	10-11	11-12	12-13	13-14
			CC1 7	CC1 5	CC1 3	CC1 9	CC1 12	CC1 12	CC1 3

MOLE VALLEY SCR

Founded: 1978 Nickname: Commoners

Secretary: Chris LeBoeuf **(T)** 07966 190 463 **(E)** scrfcsecretary@outlook.com

Chairman: Alan Salmon **Manager:** Darren Salmon **Prog Ed:** Gary Brigden

Ground: Cobham FC, Leg of Mutton Field, Anvil Lane, Downside Bridge Road KT11 1AA **(T)** 01932 866 386

Capacity: 500 **Seats:** No **Covered:** Yes **Midweek Matchday:** Wednesday **Clubhouse:** Yes **Shop:** Yes

Colours(change): Yellow/black/black
Previous Names: Inrad FC. Centre 21 FC . SCR Plough, SCR Grapes, SRC Litten Tree, SCR Kingfisher
Previous Leagues: South Eastern Combination.
Records:
Senior Honours: **Previous Names:** Inrad FC. Centre 21 FC . SCR Plough, SCR Grapes, SRC Litten Tree, SCR Kingfisher.
Previous Leagues: South Eastern Combination.

10 YEAR RECORD

04-05	05-06	06-07	07-08	08-09	09-10	10-11	11-12	12-13	13-14
				CC1 4	CC1 1	CCP 8	CCP 21	CC1 2	CCP 18

MOLESEY

Founded: 1953 Nickname: The Moles

Secretary: Tracy Teague **(T)** 07939 387 277 **(E)** teaguetracy90@gmail.com
Chairman: Tracy Teague **Manager:** Steve Webb **Prog Ed:** John O'Brien
Ground: 412 Walton Road, West Molesey KT8 2JG. **(T)** 020 8979 4283 (Clubhouse)
Capacity: 4,000 **Seats:** 160 **Covered:** Yes **Midweek Matchday:** Tuesday **Clubhouse:** Yes **Shop:** Yes

Colours(change): White/black/black.
Previous Names: None.
Previous Leagues: Surrey Senior. Spartan. Athethian. Isthmian.
Records:
Senior Honours: **Record Att:** 1,255 v Sutton United, Surrey Senior Cup sem-final 1966. **Goalscorer:** Michael Rose (139). **Apps:** Frank Hanley (453).

10 YEAR RECORD

04-05	05-06	06-07	07-08	08-09	09-10	10-11	11-12	12-13	13-14
Isth1 16	Isth1 17	Isth1S 15	Isth1S 22	CCP 11	CCP 8	CCP 3	CCP 5	CCP 10	CCP 11

RAYNES PARK VALE

Founded: 1995 Nickname: The Vale

Secretary: Jon Morris **(T)** 07734 203 699 **(E)** jon.morris042@gmail.com
Chairman: Lee Dobinson **Manager:** Gavin Bolger & Terry Tuvey **Prog Ed:** Mike Hill
Ground: Prince George's Playing Field, Raynes Park SW20 9NB **(T)** 0208 540 8843
Capacity: 1500 **Seats:** 120 **Covered:** 100 **Midweek Matchday:** Tuesday **Clubhouse:** Yes

Colours(change): All blue
Previous Names: Raynes Park > 1995 until merger with Malden Vale.
Previous Leagues: Surrey County Premier Lge. Isthmian.
Records: **Att:** 1871 v AFC Wimbledon (At Carshalton Athletic).
Senior Honours:

10 YEAR RECORD

04-05	05-06	06-07	07-08	08-09	09-10	10-11	11-12	12-13	13-14
CCP 9	CCP 9	CCP 15	CCP 19	CCP 8	CCP 18	CCP 15	CCP 9	CCP 11	CCP 10

SPELTHORNE SPORTS

Founded: 1922 Nickname: Spelly

Secretary: Chris Devlin **(T)** 07956 321 558 **(E)** secretary@spelthornesportsfc.co.uk
Chairman: Ian Croxford **Manager:** Paul Johnson **Prog Ed:** Chris Devlin
Ground: Spelthorne Sports Club, 296 Staines Rd West, Ashford Common, TW15 1RY **(T)** 01932 961 055
Capacity: **Seats:** Yes **Covered:** Yes **Midweek Matchday:** Tuesday **Clubhouse:**

Colours(change): Light & dark blue/dark blue/light blue
Previous Names:
Previous Leagues: Surrey Intermediate (West) > 2009. Surrey Elite Intermediate 2009-11.
Records:
Senior Honours: Surrey Elite Intermediate League 2010-11. Combined Counties Division One 2013-14.

10 YEAR RECORD

04-05	05-06	06-07	07-08	08-09	09-10	10-11	11-12	12-13	13-14
					SuEI 5	SuEI 1	CC1 7	CC1 6	CC1 1

WESTFIELD

Founded: 1953 Nickname: The Field

Secretary: Michael Lawrence **(T)** 07780 684 416 **(E)** michaelgeorgelawrence@hotmail.com
Chairman: Stephen Perkins **Manager:** Martin Beard **Prog Ed:** Pat Kelly
Ground: Woking Park, off Elmbridge Lane, Kingfield, Woking GU22 9BA **(T)** 01483 771 106
Capacity: 1000 **Seats:** Yes **Covered:** Yes **Midweek Matchday:** Tuesday **Clubhouse:** Yes

Colours(change): Yellow/black/black
Previous Names: None
Previous Leagues: Surrey Senior
Records:
Senior Honours: Surrey Senior League 1972-73, 73-74.

10 YEAR RECORD

04-05	05-06	06-07	07-08	08-09	09-10	10-11	11-12	12-13	13-14
CCP 10	CCP 11	CC1 10	CC1 4	CC1 13	CC1 16	CC1 13	CC1 8	CC1 3	CCP 4

WINDSOR

Founded: 1892 Nickname: The Royalists

Secretary: Steve Rowland **(T)** 07887 770 630 **(E)** secretary@windsorfc.net
Chairman: Kevin Stott **Manager:** Mick Woodham **Prog Ed:** Matthew Stevens
Ground: Stag Meadow, St Leonards Road, Windsor, Berks SL4 3DR **(T)** 01753 860 656
Capacity: 3,085 **Seats:** 302 **Covered:** 650 **Midweek Matchday:** Tuesday **Clubhouse:** Yes **Shop:** Yes

Colours(change): All red, white & green
Previous Names: Windsor & Eton 1892-2011.
Previous Leagues: W.Berks, Gt Western, Suburban, Athenian 22-29,63-81, Spartan 29-32, Gt W.Comb. Corinthian 45-50, Met 50-60, Delphian 60-63, Isth 63-06, Sth06-11
Records: 8,500 - Charity Match
Senior Honours: Athenian League 1979-80, 80-81. Isthmian League Division 1 1983-84. Southern League Division 1 South & West 2009-10. Berks & Bucks Senior Cup x11.

10 YEAR RECORD

04-05	05-06	06-07	07-08	08-09	09-10	10-11	11-12	12-13	13-14
Isth P 15	Isth P 21	Sthsw 14	Sthsw 8	Sthsw 2	Sthsw 1	SthP Exp	CCP 2	CCP 6	CCP 6

PREMIER DIVISION GROUND DIRECTIONS

ASHFORD TOWN (MIDDX) - Robert Parker Stadium, Stanwell, Staines TW19 7BH - 01784 245 908
M25 junction 13, A30 towards London, third left at footbridge after Ashford Hospital crossroads, ground sign posted after 1/4 mile on the right down Short Lane, two miles from Ashford (BR) and Hatton Cross tube station.

BADSHOT LEA - See Ash United FC.

BEDFONT SPORTS - Bedfont Sports Club TW14 9QT
From Junction 13, M25 – Staines. At Crooked Billet roundabout turn right onto the A30 Signposted C. London, Hounslow. At Clockhouse Roundabout take the 2nd exit onto the A315 Signposted Bedfont. Turn left onto Hatton Road. Arrive on Hatton Road, Bedfont Sports Club.

CAMBERLEY TOWN - Krooner Park GU15 2QW - 01276 65392
Exit M3 Motorway at Junction 4. At the end of the slip road take the right hand land signposted A331, immediately take the left hand lane signposted Frimley and Hospital (Red H Symbol) and this will lead you up onto the A325. Continue to the roundabout and turn left onto the B3411 (Frimley Road) Continue past Focus DIY store on Left and stay on B3411 for approx 1.5 miles. At the next Mini roundabout turn left into Wilton Road, proceed through industrial estate (past the Peugeot garage) and the entrance to the ground is right at the end.

CHERTSEY TOWN - Alwyns Lane, Chertsey, Surrey KT16 9DW - 01932 561 774
Leave M25 at junction 11, East on St. Peters Way (A317). Left at roundabout in Chertsey Road (A317). Left into Eastworth Road (A317). Straight on into Chilsey Green Road (A320), 3rd exit on roundabout (towards Staines) (A320). 1st right after car showrooms into St. Ann's Road (B375). Right at Coach & Horses in Grove Road (residential). Alwyns Lane is very narrow and not suitable for large motor coaches.

COLLIERS WOOD UTD - Wibbandune Sports Ground SW20 0AA - 0208 942 8062
On A3 Southbound 1 mile from Robin Hood Gate.

COVE - Squirrel Lane GU14 8PB - 01252 543 615
From M3 junction 4, follow signs for A325, then follow signs for Cove FC.

EPSOM & EWELL - Chipstead FC, High Road, Chipstead, Surrey CR5 3SF - 01737 553250
From the Brighton Road north bound, go left into Church Lane and left into Hogcross Lane. High Road is on the right.

FARNHAM TOWN - Memorial Ground, West St. GU9 7DY - 01252 715 305
Follow A31 to Coxbridge roundabout (passing traffic lights at Hickleys corner. Farnham station to left.) At next roundabout take 3rd exit to Farnham town centre. At the mini roundabout take 2nd exit. The ground is to the left.

FRIMLEY GREEN - Frimley Green Recreation Groand GU16 6SY - 01252 835 089
Exit M3 at junction 4 and follow the signs to Frimley High Street. At the mini roundabout in front of the White Hart public house turn into Church Road. At the top of the hill by the Church the road bends right and becomes Frimley Green Road. Follow the road for approx of a mile, go over the mini roundabout which is the entrance to Johnson's Wax factory, and the Recreation Ground is the second turning on the left, just past Henley Drive, which is on your right.

GUILDFORD CITY - Spectrum Leisure Centre, Parkway, Guildford GU1 1UP - 01483 443 322
From Guildford main line station, take no.100 shuttle bus to Spectrum. From London Road Station walk via Stoke Park. From A3, exit at Guildford – follow signs to leisure centre.

HANWORTH VILLA - Rectory Meadows, Park Road TW13 6PN - 0208 831 9391
From M25 and M3 once on the M3 towards London. This becomes the A316, take the A314 (Hounslow Rd) exit signposted Feltham & Hounslow. Turn left onto Hounslow Rd, at the second mini round about (Esso garage on the corner) turn left into Park Rd. Continue down Park Road past the Hanworth Naval Club on the right and Procter's Builders Merchants on the left. Follow the road around the 90 degree bend and continue to the end of the road past the Hanworth Village Hall. Once past the two houses next to the village hall turn left into Rectory Meadows.

HARTLEY WINTNEY - Memorial Playing Fields RG27 8DL - 01252 843 586
On entering Hartley Wintney via the A30 take the turn at the mini roundabout signposted A323 Fleet. Take the 1st right turn, Green Lane, which has St John's Church on the corner. Continue down Green Lane for about 800 metres and turn right into car park, which has a shared access with Greenfields School. Turn left at St John's Church if coming down the A323 from Fleet.

HORLEY TOWN - The New Defence RH6 8RS - 07545 697 234
From centre of town go North up Victoria where it meets the A23, straight across to Vicarage Lane, 2nd left into Court Lodge Road follow it through estate and we are behind adult education centre.

KNAPHILL - Brookwood Country Park GU21 2AY - 01483 475 150
From A3: A322 from Guildford through towards Worplesdon. At Fox Corner rounabaout, take 2bd exit onto Bagshot Road, A322 signposted Bagshot. Pat West Hill Golf Club, at traffice lights turn right onto Brookwood Lye Road, A324 signposted Woking. Turn left into Hermitage Road on A324, up to roundabout, take 1st exit onto Redding Way, then 1st left entering driveway towards car park and ground.

MOLE VALLEY SCR - Cobham FC, Leg of Mutton Field - 07787 383 407
From Cobham High Street, turn right into Downside Bridge Road and turn right into Leg of Mutton Field.

MOLESEY - 412 Walton Road West KT8 0JG - 0208 979 4283
Take A3 towards Cobham/London & exit at Esher-Sandown turn. 1st exit at roundabout to A244 through Esher to Marquis of Granby Pub. 1st exit A309 at next roundabout. 1st exit at end of road turn right, follow until mini roundabout left into Walton Road after 1 mile ground on left.

RAYNES PARK VALE - Prince Georges Fields SW20 9NB (pictured below) - 0208 540 8843
Exit Raynes Park station into Grand Drive cross Bushey Road at the traffic lights continue up Grand Drive for 400 yards entrance on the left follow drive to clubhouse. From the A3. Onto Bushey Road towards South Wimbledon. Grand Drive on the right, ground in Grand Drive on the left hand side.

SPELTHORNE SPORTS - 296 Staines Rd West, Ashford Common, TW15 1RY - 01932 783 625
From M25 (J13) take the A30 exit to London (W)/Hounslow/Staines. At the roundabout, take the 1st exit onto Staines Bypass/A30 heading to London(W)/Hounslow/Staines/Kingston/A308. Turn left onto Staines Bypass/A308 Continue to follow A308. Go through 1 roundabout. Make a U-turn at Chertsey Rd. Ground will be on the left.

WESTFIELD - Woking Park, off Elmbridge Lane GU22 7AA - 01483 771 106
Follow signs to Woking Leisure Centre on the A247.

WINDSOR - Stag Meadow, St Leonards Road, Windsor, Berks SL4 3DR - 01753 860 656
Exit M4 at Junction 6, follow dual carriageway (signposted Windsor) to large roundabout at end, take third exit into Imperial Road, turn left at T-junction into St Leonards Road. Ground approx ½ mile on right opposite Stag & Hounds public house.

A.F.C. CROYDON ATHLETIC
Founded: 2012 Nickname: The Rams

Secretary: Peter Smith **(T)** 07907 588 496 **(E)** secretary@afccroydonathletic.co.uk
Chairman: Paul Smith **Manager:** Anthony Williams **Prog Ed:** Peter Smith
Ground: Mayfield Stadium, off Mayfield Road, Thornton Heath CR7 6DN **(T)**
Colours(change): All maroon

ADDITIONAL INFORMATION: Record Att: 1,372 v AFC Wimbledon 2004-05
Previous Names: Norwood FC and Wandsworth FC amalgamated in 1986 to form Wandsworth & Norwood > 1990. Croydon Athletic 1990-2012.
League honours: London Spartan League 1994-95. Isthmian League Division 3 2001-02, Division 1 South 2009-10.

ALTON TOWN
Founded: 1947 Nickname: The Brewers

Secretary: Jim McKell **(T)** 07740 099 374 **(E)** jim@altontownfc.com
Chairman: Jim McKell **Manager:** Colin Fielder **Prog Ed:** Carl Saunders
Ground: Alton (Bass) Sports Ground, Anstey Road, Alton, Hants GU34 2RL **(T)** **Capacity:** 2,000
Colours(change): White/black/black

ADDITIONAL INFORMATION:
Hants Senior Cup 1958, 1969, 1972 & 1978. Hampshire Champions 2001-02.

ASH UNITED
Founded: 1911 Nickname: Green Army

Secretary: Paul Blair **(T)** 07795 612 664 **(E)** sec@ashunited.co.uk
Chairman: Kevin Josey **Manager:** Alan Reed **Prog Ed:** Paul Burch
Ground: Shawfields Stadium, Youngs Drive off Shawfield Road, Ash, GU12 6RE. **(T)** 01252 320 385 / 345 757 **Capacity:** 2500
Colours(change): All green & red.

ADDITIONAL INFORMATION: Att: 914 v AFC Wimbledon Combined Co 2002-03. **Goals:** Shaun Mitchell (216). **Apps:** Paul Bonner (582).
Aldershot Senior Cup 1998-99, 01-02.

BANSTEAD ATHLETIC
Founded: 1944 Nickname: A's

Secretary: Terry Molloy **(T)** 07958 436 483 **(E)** terrymolloy@leyfield.eclipse.co.uk
Chairman: Terry Molloy **Manager:** Jack Johnson **Prog Ed:** Bob Lockyar
Ground: Merland Rise, Tadworth, Surrey KT20 5JG **(T)** 01737 350 982 **Capacity:** 3500
Colours(change): Amber & black/black/black

ADDITIONAL INFORMATION:
Previous Leagues: London Spartan League. Athenian League. Isthmian > 2006.
Honours: London Spartan LC 1965-67. Athenian LC 190-82.
Record Att: 1400 v Leytonstone, FA Amateur Cup 1953. **Goals:** Harry Clark. **Apps:** Dennis Wall.

BEDFONT & FELTHAM
Founded: 2012 Nickname: The Yellows

Secretary: Derrick Smith **(T)** 07840 128 204 **(E)** derricksmith125@btinternet.com
Chairman: Brian Barry **Manager:** Dean Thomas **Prog Ed:** Rob Healey
Ground: The Orchard, Hatton Road, Bedfont TW14 9QT **(T)** 020 8890 7264 **Capacity:** 1200
Colours(change): Yellow & blue/blue/blue

ADDITIONAL INFORMATION:
Previous Names: Bedfont FC and Feltham (1946) amalgamated in May 2012 but had to wait until 2013-14 before changing the name.

CB HOUNSLOW UNITED
Founded: 1989 Nickname:

Secretary: Stephen Hosmer **(T)** 07900 604 936 **(E)** stephen.hosmer@btinternet.com
Chairman: Frank James **Manager:** Frank James **Prog Ed:** Stephen Hosmer
Ground: Bedfont & Feltham FC, The Orchard, Hatton Road, Bedfont TW14 9QT **(T)** 0208 890 7264 **Capacity:** 1200
Colours(change): All dark blue

ADDITIONAL INFORMATION:
Previous League: Middlesex County.

CHESSINGTON & HOOK UNITED
Founded: 1921 Nickname: Chessey

Secretary: Chris Blackie **(T)** 07748 877 704 **(E)** kandcblackie@googlemail.com
Chairman: Graham Ellis **Manager:** Darren Woods **Prog Ed:** Eric Wicks
Ground: Chalky Lane, Chessington, Surrey KT9 2NF **(T)** 01372 602 263 **Capacity:** 3000
Colours(change): All blue

ADDITIONAL INFORMATION:

COBHAM

Founded: 1892 Nickname: Hammers

Secretary: Tony Skilton **(T)** 07813 347 983 **(E)** hammers063@gmail.com
Chairman: Ken Reed **Manager:** Kevin Petters **Prog Ed:** Sam Merison
Ground: The Reg Madgwick Stadium, Leg O'Mutton Field, Anvil Lane, Cobham KT11 1AA **(T)** 01932 866 386 **Capacity:** 2000
Colours(change): All red

ADDITIONAL INFORMATION: Att: 2000 - Charity game 1975.
Honours: Combined Counties League Cup 2001-02.

DORKING

Founded: 1880 Nickname: The Chicks

Secretary: Simon Coffey **(T)** 07768 104 505 **(E)** coffey_sj@msn.com
Chairman: Grant Ashley **Manager:** Glynn Stephens **Prog Ed:** Bryan Bletso
Ground: Horley Town FC, The New Defence, Anderson Way, Court Lodge, Horley RH6 8SP **(T)** 01293 822 000 **Capacity:** 1,800
Colours(change): Green & red stripes/white/red

ADDITIONAL INFORMATION:
Previous Names: Guildford & Dorking (when club merged 1974). Dorking Town 1977-82.
Previous Leagues: Corinthian, Athenian, Isthmian > 2006.
Record Att: 4500 v Folkstone Town FAC 1955 & v Plymouth Argyle FAC 1993. **Goals:** Andy Bushell. **Apps:** Steve Lunn.

EPSOM ATHLETIC

Founded: 1997 Nickname: The Blue Stallions

Secretary: Peter Beddoe **(T)** 07767 078 132 **(E)** p.beddoe1@ntlworld.com
Chairman: Tony Jeffcoate **Manager:** Lyndon Buckwell **Prog Ed:** Stephen Dyke
Ground: Chessington & Hook United FC, Chalky Lane, Chessington, Surrey KT9 2NF **(T)** 01372 745 777 **Capacity:** 2,000
Colours(change): Royal blue & white hoops/royal blue/royal blue

ADDITIONAL INFORMATION:
Previous League: Surrey Elite > 2012.
Honours: Surrey Elite 2011-12.

EVERSLEY & CALIFORNIA

Founded: 2012 Nickname: Wild Boars

Secretary: Sarah Pyne **(T)** 07969 885 966 **(E)** sarahelizabethpyne@gmail.com
Chairman: Paul Hawke **Manager:** Mark Thomas
Ground: ESA Sports Complex, Fox Lane, Eversley RG27 0NS **(T)** 0118 973 2400 **Capacity:** 300+
Colours(change): Yellow & royal blue stripes/royal blue/royal blue

ADDITIONAL INFORMATION:
Previous League: Surrey Elite Intermediate.
Honours: Surrey Elite Intermediate 2008-09.

FARLEIGH ROVERS

Founded: 1922 Nickname: The Foxes

Secretary: Peter Collard **(T)** 07545 444 820 **(E)** peter.collard@aquatots.com
Chairman: Mark Whittaker **Manager:** Tim Moffatt **Prog Ed:** Peter Collard
Ground: Parsonage Field, Harrow Road, Warlingham CR6 9EX **(T)** 01883 626 483 **Capacity:** 500
Colours(change): Black & red stripes/black/black

ADDITIONAL INFORMATION:
Previous League: Surrey County Premier.
Honours: Surrey County Premier 1982-83.

SANDHURST TOWN

Founded: 1910 Nickname: Fizzers

Secretary: Anne Brummer **(T)** 07955 080 901 **(E)** secretarystfc@hotmail.co.uk
Chairman: Tony Dean **Manager:** Chris Powel
Ground: Bottom Meadow, Memorial Ground, Yorktown Rd, GU47 9BJ **(T)** 01252 878 768 **Capacity:** 1000
Colours(change): Red/black/black.

ADDITIONAL INFORMATION:
Previous Leagues: Reading & District. East Berkshire. Aldershot Senior. Chiltonian.
Record Att: 2,449 v AFC Wimbledon, Combined Counties 17.08.2002.
Honours: Aldershot FA Senior Invitation Challenge Cup 2000-01, 05-06. Combined Counties Premier Challenge Cup 2010-11.

SHEERWATER

Founded: 1958 Nickname: Sheers

Secretary: Trevor Wenden **(T)** 07791 612 008 **(E)** trevor.wenden2@ntlworld.com
Chairman: Peter Cachia **Manager:** John Cook **Prog Ed:** Trevor Wenden
Ground: Sheerwater Recreation Ground, Blackmore Crescent, Woking GU21 5QJ **(T)** 07791 612 008 **Capacity:** 1,000
Colours(change): All royal blue

ADDITIONAL INFORMATION:
Previous League: Surrey County Premier.

STAINES LAMMAS

Founded: 1926 Nickname:

Secretary: Bob Parry **(T)** 07771 947 757 **(E)** bobandtracey1@btopenworld.com
Chairman: Phil Ellery **Manager:** Gavin Bamford **Prog Ed:** Clive Robertson
Ground: Ashford Tn (Mx) FC, The Robert Parker Stadium, Short Lane, Stanwell TW19 7BH **(T)** 01784 245 908 **Capacity:** 2550
Colours(change): All blue

ADDITIONAL INFORMATION:
Record Att: 107 v Hanworth Villa, January 2006. **Goalscorer:** Jay Coombs - 270+ **Win:** 19-1 v Cranleigh (Surrey Senior Lge) 19/03/03.
Honours: Combined Counties Division 1 2007-08, 08-09.

WORCESTER PARK

Founded: 1921 Nickname: The Skinners

Secretary: Kristina Maitre **(T)** 07768 179 938 **(E)** kristinajayne@hotmail.co.uk
Chairman: Sam Glass **Manager:** John Di Palma **Prog Ed:** Darren Talbot
Ground: Skinners Field, Green Lane, Worcester Park, Surrey KT4 8AJ **(T)** 0208 337 4995
Colours(change): All blue

ADDITIONAL INFORMATION:
Previous League: Surrey County Premier.
Honours: Surrey County Premier/Senior League 1999-2000, 2000-01. Combined Counties Division One 2010-11.

DIVISION ONE GROUND DIRECTIONS

AFC CROYDON ATHLETIC - Mayfield Stadium, off Mayfield Road, Thornton Heath CR7 6DN
Directions

ALTON TOWN - Alton (Bass) Sports Ground, Anstey Road, Alton, Hants GU34 2RL
Leave the A31 at the B3004 signposted to Alton. Follow the road round to the left passing Anstey Park on the right, the ground is then immediately on the left – opposite the turning into Anstey Lane. Postcode for Satellite Navigation systems GU34 2RL

ASH UNITED - Shawfields Stadium, Youngs Drive GU12 6RE - 01252 320 385
FROM M3: Get off the M3 at J4, onto the A331: Take 3rd Exit off to Woking. Up to the roundabout turn left into Shawfields Road, follow road for about 500 yards, Football Ground is on the left, take next turning on your left into Youngs Drive where club is 50yards on. FROM M25: Get onto the A3 heading to Guildford/Portsmouth. Keep on this until you reach the A31(Hog's Back). Then go onto the A31 until you reach the exit for the A331 to Aldershot. Follow the signs for Aldershot, which will be the 1st exit off the A331.When you reach the roundabout take the exit for Woking, which will be the 3rd exit off. Up to the roundabout turn left into Shawfields Road, then as above.

BANSTEAD ATHLETIC - Merland Rise KT20 5JG - 01737 350 982
From M25 junction 8 follow signs to Banstead Sports Centre.

BEDFONT & FELTHAM - The Orchard, Hatten Road TW14 9QT - 0208 890 7264
Hatton Road runs alongside the A30 at Heathrow. Ground is opposite the Duke of Wellington Public House.

CB HOUNSLOW UNITED - See Bedfont & Feltham

CHESSINGTON & HOOK UNITED - Chalky Lane KT9 2NF - 01372 745 777
Chalky Lane is off A243 (Opposite Chessington World of Adventures) which leads to Junction 9 on M25 or Hook Junction on the A3.

COBHAM - Leg of Mutton Field - 07787 383 407
From Cobham High Street, turn right into Downside Bridge Road and turn right into Leg of Mutton Field.

2013-14 - AFC Croydon
Photo: Alan Coomes

2013-14 - Dorking
Photo: Alan Coomes

DORKING - See Horley Town FC - 01293 822 000

EPSOM ATHLETIC - See Chessington & Hook United.

EVERSLEY & CALIFORNIA - ESA Sports Complex, Fox Lane, Eversley RG27 0NS - 0118 973 2400

Leave the M3 at junction 4a signposted Fleet/Farnborough. At the roundabout take the 2nd exit towards Yateley.

At the roundabout take the 2nd exit towards Yateley. At the roundabout take the 2nd exit towards Yateley.

At the roundabout take the 1st exit and proceed through Yateley on the Reading Road. At the roundabout take the 2nd exit and follow the road for about 1 mile. Turn right down the first turning for Fox Lane and then follow the road round to the right where the ground will be signposted.

FARLEIGH ROVERS - Parsonage Field, Harrow Road CR6 9EX - 01883 626 483

From M25 junction 6 left at lights up Godstone Hill (Caterham bypass) to roundabout. Take fourth turning off of roundabout. Up Succombs Hill then right into Westhall Rd. Right at the green then second left into Farleigh Rd. Left at mini round about continue still on Farleigh Road. Right at the Harrow Pub. This is Harrow Road. Right at the end of the houses and the ground is behind the houses.

SANDHURST TOWN - Bottom Meadow GU47 9BJ - 01252 878 768

Situated on A321 approx 5 miles from Junction 4 on M3, or approx 8 miles from junction 10 on the M4 Park in Council Offices car park and walk down tarmac footpath beside the stream to ground.

SHEERWATER - Sheerwater Recreation Ground GU21 5QJ - 07791 612 008

From M25(J11) take the A320 towards Woking, At Six Cross roundabout take the exit to Monument Road. At the lights turn left into Eve Road for Sheerwater Estate. First left is Blackmore Crescent, Entrance is Quarter of a mile on left.

STAINES LAMMAS - Ashford T (Mx), The Robert Parker Std, Short Lane, Stanwell TW19 7BH - 01784 245908

M25 junction 13, A30 towards London, third left at footbridge after Ashford Hospital crossroads, ground sign posted after 1/4 mile on the right down Short Lane, two miles from Ashford (BR) and Hatton Cross tube station.

WORCESTER PARK- Skinners Field, Green Lane KT4 8AJ - 0208 337 4995

From M25, come off at A3 turn off and head towards London, then come off at Worcester Park turn off, stay on this road until you pass station on your left and go under bridge, then take first left which is Green Lane, ground is 500 yards on the left.

EAST MIDLAND COUNTIES LEAGUE

Sponsored by: No sponsor
Founded: 2008
Recent Champions:
2009: Kirby Muxloe SC
2010: Dunkirk 2011: Gresley
2012: Heanor Town 2013: Basford United

emc-fl.com

		P	W	D	L	F	A	GD	Pts
1	(P) Thurnby Nirvana	36	25	8	3	107	50	57	83
2	Stapenhill	36	22	8	6	101	53	48	74
3	Ellistown & Ibstock United	36	22	6	8	86	54	32	72
4	Blaby & Whetstone Athletic	36	22	3	11	75	34	41	69
5	Borrowash Victoria	36	22	5	9	87	48	39	68
6	Arnold Town	36	21	4	11	87	55	32	67
7	St Andrews	36	21	6	9	93	56	37	66
8	Sutton Town AFC	36	18	7	11	92	61	31	61
9	Holwell Sports	36	18	7	11	86	68	18	61
10	Graham Street Prims	36	18	4	14	84	62	22	58
11	Bardon Hill	36	14	10	12	69	67	2	52
12	Gedling Miners Welfare	36	11	9	16	60	74	-14	42
13	Holbrook Sports	36	10	3	23	48	79	-31	33
14	Radcliffe Olympic	36	8	8	20	84	102	-18	32
15	Radford	36	9	5	22	54	89	-35	32
16	Greenwood Meadows	36	7	9	20	46	88	-42	30
17	Anstey Nomads	36	8	3	25	50	124	-74	27
18	Aylestone Park	36	5	6	25	38	101	-63	21
19	Barrow Town	36	3	5	28	40	122	-82	14

LEAGUE CUP

ROUND 1

Blaby & Whetstone Ath.	v	Arnold Town	3-2
Ellistown & Ibstock United	v	Holbrook Sports	1-4
St Andrews	v	Aylestone Park	6-1

ROUND 2

Gedling Miners Welfare	v	Graham Street Pims	0-4
St Andrews	v	Anstey Nomads	1-0
Stapenhill	v	Blaby & Whtstone Athletic	3-2
Sutton Town AFC	v	Holbrook Sports	2-1
Greenwood Meadows	v	Borrowash Victoria	2-3
Holwell Sports	v	Thurnby Nirvana	2-1
Radford	v	Barrow Town	1-4
Radcliffe Olympic	v	Bardon Hill	4-2

QUARTER FINALS

Graham Street Prims	v	Borrowash Victoria	3-0
St Andrews	v	Sutton Town AFC	1-4
Barrow Town	v	Holwell Sports	2-5
Radcliffe Olympic	v	Stapenhill	7-4

SEMI FINALS

Holwell Sports	v	Graham Street Prims	0-3
Radcliffe Olympic	v	Sutton Town AFC	3-5

FINAL

Sutton Town AFC	v	Graham Street Prims	2-4

	1	2	3	4	5	6	7	8	9	10	11	12	13	14	15	16	17	18	19
1 Anstey Nomads		1–2	3–1	1–0	2–1	0–1	0–8	0–5	2–2	0–2	0–1	0–3	2–1	2–6	1–3	2–5	1–10	1–7	3–4
2 Arnold Town	3–1		5–1	2–2	8–2	0–1	1–2	1–3	3–0	3–0	2–0	3–0	2–3	4–1	4–0	1–2	0–0	1–0	2–6
3 Aylestone Park	4–1	2–5		5–0	0–0	0–5	0–2	0–1	0–2	1–0	5–1	0–1	1–5	3–3	1–1	1–3	2–2	0–5	0–3
4 Bardon Hill	4–2	2–0	4–2		5–1	2–1	4–4	4–1	2–2	1–3	2–2	3–1	2–2	3–0	2–3	1–1	1–2	0–5	1–2
5 Barrow Town	10–3	2–4	2–0	1–1		0–2	0–2	3–4	0–8	1–4	2–1	0–4	1–2	1–4	1–1	2–2	1–2	0–2	1–5
6 Blaby & Whetstone Athletic	2–0	1–3	5–2	1–0	6–0		0–3	0–1	0–1	0–1	5–1	1–0	0–3	3–2	9–0	1–2	1–2	2–0	1–1
7 Borrowash Victoria	1–2	2–2	4–0	3–0	4–0	1–0		0–1	1–0	3–0	2–0	2–1	2–2	1–1	2–1	1–1	2–3	6–2	2–1
8 Ellistown	5–2	2–1	5–1	1–1	3–0	0–1	0–5		2–2	1–1	7–2	2–1	3–1	5–3	4–0	3–1	1–2	0–2	1–1
9 Gedling Miners Welfare	1–1	1–2	3–0	3–4	1–0	0–5	2–4	2–2		2–1	2–1	2–0	1–2	0–2	4–0	0–4	0–6	0–2	1–1
10 Graham Street Prims	4–1	1–3	10–0	0–1	2–0	0–1	2–0	1–5	5–1		1–2	2–0	5–2	3–3	3–3	4–2	2–3	5–1	0–1
11 Greenwood Meadows	0–2	3–2	2–1	2–4	2–1	0–1	2–1	1–4	2–2	1–2		1–2	1–3	5–2	0–5	0–5	2–2	0–0	2–2
12 Holbrook Sports	2–2	1–4	4–0	0–2	3–1	1–4	3–2	0–2	3–0	1–4	2–2		0–2	4–2	0–3	2–3	1–0	1–2	0–2
13 Holwell Sports	3–4	0–2	3–0	1–1	8–0	2–4	3–2	1–3	4–4	4–5	3–0	2–1		3–2	2–1	3–4	1–1	1–4	3–3
14 Radcliffe Olympic	5–1	2–3	2–2	2–3	4–1	2–2	1–2	4–1	0–2	2–2	0–0	3–3	0–2		4–1	1–2	4–6	1–3	3–5
15 Radford	1–2	1–1	1–0	1–3	3–0	0–3	0–4	2–3	0–4	2–0	1–1	5–1	1–3	2–3		1–2	1–4	0–2	1–3
16 St Andrews	4–2	4–1	2–2	2–2	9–0	0–1	0–2	1–2	4–0	0–2	4–1	3–0	1–2	4–2	2–1		5–4	2–1	0–1
17 Stapenhill	6–1	1–2	3–0	3–0	2–2	3–0	2–3	1–1	1–0	4–1	3–1	3–0	1–2	6–4	3–2	3–2		3–3	0–2
18 Sutton Town AFC	3–2	1–2	0–1	3–2	6–1	0–4	7–1	4–1	2–2	3–4	3–1	4–0	2–2	5–3	1–2	3–3	2–2		1–1
19 Thurnby Nirvana	4–0	4–3	3–0	2–0	3–2	1–1	4–1	2–1	6–3	4–2	3–3	6–2	2–0	7–1	7–4	1–2	0–2	4–1	

CLUB MOVEMENTS

In: Ashby Ivanhoe (P - Leicestershire Senior). Kimberley Miners Welfare (P - Nottinghamshire Senior). South Normanton Athletic (P - Central Midlands Division South).

Out: Thurnby Nirvana (P - United Counties Premier). Sutton Town AFC (W 06/14).

ANSTEY NOMADS

Founded: 1947 Nickname: Nomads

Secretary: Chris Hillebrandt **(T)** 0794 685 6430 **(E)** chille1055@hotmail.com
Chairman: Tony Ford **Manager:** Rob Harris **Prog Ed:** Helen Preston-Hayes
Ground: Cropston Road, Anstey, Leicester LE7 7BP **(T)** 0116279 3783/07946856430
Colours(change): Red & white/black/red (All blue)

ADDITIONAL INFORMATION: Previous Leagues: Leicestershire Senior. Central Alliance. East Midlands Regional.
Record Att: 4,500 v Hayes, 2nd Round FA Amateur Cup.
Senior Honours: Leicestershire Senior League 1951-52, 53-54, 81-82, 82-83, 2008-09. Leicestershire Senior Cup 1994-95.

ARNOLD TOWN

Founded: 1989 Nickname: Eagles

Secretary: Graham Peck **(T)** 07815 458 196 **(E)** graham@peckgraham.orangehome.co.uk
Chairman: Graham Peck **Manager:** Graham Walker **Prog Ed:** Mick Gretton
Ground: Eagle Valley, Oxton Road, Arnold, Nottingham NG5 8PS **(T)** 0115 965 6000
Colours(change): All maroon. (Yellow/blue/yellow)

ADDITIONAL INFORMATION:
Previous Leagues: Central Midland 1989-93. Northern Counites East 1993-2013.
Record Att: 3,390 v Bristol Rovers FAC 1-Dec 1967 **Goalscorer:** Peter Fletcher - 100. **App:** Pete Davey - 346. **Win:** 10-1 **Defeat:** 0-7
Honours: Northern Counties East 1985-86. Central Midlands 92-93. Northern Counties Div.1 93-94.

ASHBY IVANHOE

Founded: 1948 Nickname:

Secretary: Mark Curtis **(T)** 07984 488 993 **(E)** Mark.Curtis@sanctuary-housing.co.uk
Chairman: Stuart Bonser
Ground: NFU Sports Ground, Lower Packington Road, Ashby de la Zouch LE65 1TS **(T)** 07534 336 296
Colours(change): Blue/white/red

ADDITIONAL INFORMATION: Previous Leagues: North Leicestershire League. Leicestershire Senior > 2014.
Senior Honours: Leicestershire Senior League Premier Division 2010-11.

AYLESTONE PARK

Founded: 1968 Nickname:

Secretary: Stuart MacLeod **(T)** 0795 077 9712 **(E)** stumel@btinternet.com
Chairman: Bob Stretton **Manager:** Owen Wright **Prog Ed:** Mick Allard
Ground: Mary Linwood Recreation Ground, Saffron Lane, Leicester LE6 6TG **(T)** 0116 278 5485
Colours(change): All red (All blue)

ADDITIONAL INFORMATION:
Previous Name: Aylestone Park Old Boys > 2007.
Previous Leagues: Leicestershire Senior 1992-2012.
Honours: Leicestershire Senior Cup 2012-13.

BARDON HILL

Founded: 1890 Nickname:

Secretary: Adrian Bishop **(T)** 07999 879 841 **(E)** ade_bish@hotmail.co.uk
Chairman: **Manager:** Steve Titterton and Don Gethfield **Prog Ed:** Adrian Bishop
Ground: Bardon Close, Coalville, Leicester LE67 4BS **(T)** 01530 815 569
Colours(change): Royal blue/royal blue/white (All red)

ADDITIONAL INFORMATION:
Previous Name: Bardon Hill Sports
Previous League: Leics Senior.

BARROW TOWN

Founded: Late 1800s Nickname:

Secretary: Mrs Ann Collington **(T)** 07779 564 819 **(E)** ann.collington@talktalk.net
Chairman: Michael Bland **Manager:** Liam East **Prog Ed:** Steve Chamberlain
Ground: Riverside Park, Bridge Street, Quorn, Leicestershire LE12 8EN **(T)** 0845 872 5860
Colours(change): Red & black/black/red (Yellow/blue/blue)

ADDITIONAL INFORMATION:
Previous League: Leicestershire Senior.
Honours: Leicester Senior League Division One 1992-93.

BLABY & WHETSTONE ATHLETIC

Founded: Nickname:

Secretary: Javeed Virk **(T)** 0782 506 7853 **(E)** javvirk@hotmail.com
Chairman: Mark Jenkins **Manager:** Steve Orme **Prog Ed:** Roger Morris
Ground: Warwick Road, Whetstome, Leicester LE8 6LW **(T)** 0116 286 4852
Colours(change): All navy blue & white (All white)

ADDITIONAL INFORMATION:
Previous Lge: Leicestershire Senior > 2011.

BORROWASH VICTORIA
Founded: Nickname:

Secretary: John Robinson **(T)** 07843 197 950 **(E)** jarobinson@rocketmail.com
Chairman: Fraser Watson **Manager:** Thom Kellogg and Dick Pratley **Prog Ed:** Adrian Randle
Ground: Watkinsons Construction Bowl, Borrowash Rd, Spondon, Derby DE21 7PH **(T)** 01332 683 957
Colours(change): Red & white stripes/black/black (All blue)

ADDITIONAL INFORMATION:
Previous League: Central Midlands

ELLISTOWN & IBSTOCK UNITED
Founded: 2013 Nickname:

Secretary: Sue Matthews **(T)** 07791 963 618 **(E)** suematthews7@hotmail.com
Chairman: Andy Roach **Manager:** Richard Hill & Paul Brown **Prog Ed:** David Craggs
Ground: Terrace Road, Terrace Road, Ellistown, Leicestershire LE67 1GD **(T)** 01530 230 159
Colours(change): All red & white (All yellow & blue)

ADDITIONAL INFORMATION:
Formed when Ellistown and Ibstock United merged in the summer of 2013.

GEDLING MINERS WELFARE
Founded: 1919 Nickname:

Secretary: Norman Hay **(T)** 07748 138 732 **(E)** norman.hay@virginmedia.com
Chairman: Vic Hulme **Manager:** Jonathan Simpson **Prog Ed:** Ian Williams
Ground: Plains Social Club, Plains Road, Mapperley, Nottingham NG3 5RH **(T)** 0115 926 6300
Colours(change): Yellow/royal blue/yellow (All red)

ADDITIONAL INFORMATION:
Previous League: Central Midlands

GRAHAM STREET PRIMS
Founded: 1904 Nickname: Prims

Secretary: Peter Davis **(T)** 07902 403 074 **(E)** j.davis16@sky.com
Chairman: Wayne Harvey-Toon **Prog Ed:** Peter Davis
Ground: Asterdale Sports Centre, Borrowash Road, Spondon, Derbyshire DE21 7PH **(T)** 07902 403 074
Colours(change): Red & white/black/black (All royal blue)

ADDITIONAL INFORMATION:
Previous League: Central Midlands

GREENWOOD MEADOWS
Founded: 1987 Nickname:

Secretary: Christine Burton **(T)** 0771 253 0706 **(E)** christineburton@live.co.uk
Chairman: Mark Burton **Prog Ed:** Martin Asher
Ground: Lenton Lane Ground, Lenton Lane, Nr Clifton Bridge, Nottingham NG7 2SA **(T)** 07712 530 706
Colours(change): Green/black/green (Orange/white/orange)

ADDITIONAL INFORMATION:
Previous League: Central Midlands

HOLBROOK SPORTS
Founded: 1931 Nickname:

Secretary: Paul Romney **(T)** 07833 228 230 **(E)** paul.romney@btinternet.com
Chairman: Howard Williams **Manager:** Paul Romney **Prog Ed:** Paul Romney
Ground: JJN Ground, Shaw Lane, Holbrook, Derbyshire DE56 0TG **(T)** 01332 880 259
Colours(change): All blue (Black & yellow/black/black)

ADDITIONAL INFORMATION:
Previous Names: Holbrook, Holbrook Miners Welfare
Previous League: Central Midlands

HOLWELL SPORTS
Founded: 1902 Nickname:

Secretary: Martin Rooney **(T)** 07957 618 046 **(E)** holwellsportsguy@btinternet.com
Chairman: Graham Lewin **Manager:** Simon Daws **Prog Ed:** Martin Rooney
Ground: Welby Road, Asfordby Hill, Melton Mowbray, Leicestershire LE14 3RD **(T)** 07873 618 046 **Capacity:** 1000
Colours(change): Yellow & green/green/green (All sky blue)

ADDITIONAL INFORMATION: Previous Name: Holwell Works 1902-1988.
Previous League: Leicestershire Senior > 2008
Senior Honours: Leicestershire Senior League Premier 1911-12, 87-88, 91-92, 92-93.

KIMBERLEY MINERS WELFARE
Founded: 1926 Nickname:

Secretary: Danny Staley **(T)** **(E)**
Chairman: Neil Johnson
Ground: Kimberley MWFC, The Stag Ground, Kimberley, Nottingham NG16 2NB **(T)** 07572 863 155
Colours(change):

ADDITIONAL INFORMATION:
Previous Leagues: Spartan League. Notts Combination. Notts Amateur. Notts Alliance. Notts Intermediate. Nottinghamshire Senior > 2014.
Honours: Spartan League 1947-48, 64-65, 65-66. Notts Amateur League 1985-86. Notts Alliance Div.2 1994-95, Div.1 95-96.

RADCLIFFE OLYMPIC
Founded: 1876 Nickname: Olympic

Secretary: Michael Bradley **(T)** 07825 285 024 **(E)** knacks@hotmail.com
Chairman: Rick Bright **Manager:** Kevin Waddley **Prog Ed:** Brendan Richardson
Ground: The Rec. Grd, Wharfe Lane, Radcliffe on Trent, Nottingham NG12 2AN **(T)** 07825 285 024
Colours(change): Blue & red/blue & red/blue (Red & black/red & black/black)

ADDITIONAL INFORMATION:
League Honours: Notts Alliance 1900-01, Div.2 31-32. Notts Realm Div.1 46-47. Midland Amateur Alliance Div.6 65-66, Div.4 66-67, Div.3 67-68. Central Alliance Premier 69-70. East Midlands Regional Div.1 70-71. Central Alliance Premier 80-81.
Notts Alliance Div.1 90-91, Div.3 2001-02, Senior 02-03, Central Midlands Premier 03-04, Supreme 08-09.

RADFORD
Founded: 1964 Nickname:

Secretary: John Holt **(T)** 07508 384 276 **(E)** vote4holt@hotmail.co.uk
Chairman: Bob Thomas **Manager:** Tony Cox **Prog Ed:** John Holt
Ground: Selhurst Street, Off Radford Road, Nottingham NG7 5EH **(T)** 0115 942 3250
Colours(change): Sky blue/claret/claret (Claret/sky/sky)

ADDITIONAL INFORMATION:
Previous Names: Manlove & Allots 1964-71. Radford Olympic 1971-87.
Previous Leagues: Nottinghamshire Sunday 1964-78. East Midlands Regional 1978-83. Central Midlands 1983-2008.
Honours: East Midlands Regional League 1982-83. Central Midlands League Senior Cup 1983-84.

SOUTH NORMANTON ATHLETIC
Founded: 1926 Nickname: The Shiners

Secretary: Stephen Harris **(T)** 07505 366 136 **(E)** manor2@ntlworld.com
Chairman: Phil Bailey **Manager:** Mark Wilson **Prog Ed:** Richard Eyley
Ground: M J Robinson Structures Arena, Lees Lane South Normanton, Derby DE55 2AD **(T)** 07834 206 253
Colours(change): Blue & black/white/black

ADDITIONAL INFORMATION: **Previous Name:** South Normanton Miners Welfare > 1990.
Previous League: Alfreton & District Sunday Lge 1980-87, Mansfield Sunday Lge 1987-90, Central Midlands League 1990-03. Northern Counties East 2003-08.
Club folded in 2008 and reformed in 2014.

ST. ANDREWS
Founded: 1973 Nickname:

Secretary: Les Botting **(T)** 07793 500 937 **(E)** standrewsfc@btconnect.com
Chairman: Andy Ward **Prog Ed:** Les Botting
Ground: Canal Street, Aylestone, Leicester LE2 8LX **(T)** 0116 283 9298
Colours(change): Black & white/black/black (Red & black/white/white)

ADDITIONAL INFORMATION:
Previous League: Leicestershire City League 1973-85. Leicestershire Senior 1985-2008.
League Honours: Leicestershire City Premier x4. Leicestershire Senior x3.

STAPENHILL
Founded: 1947 Nickname:

Secretary: John Holmes **(T)** 07805 411 307 **(E)**
Chairman: Martin Furness **Prog Ed:** John Holmes
Ground: Edge Hill, Maple Grove, Stapenhill DE15 9NN. **(T)** 07805 411 307
Colours(change): All red (All blue)

ADDITIONAL INFORMATION:
Previous Leagues: Leicestershire Senior > 2007, 2008-13. Midland Combination. Midland Alliance 2007-08.
League Honours: Leicestershire Senior 1958–59, 59–60, 86–87, 88–89, 2006–07.

EASTERN COUNTIES LEAGUE

Sponsored by: Thurlow Nunn
Founded: 1935
Recent Champions:
2009: Lowestoft Town
2010: Needham Market
2011: Leiston
2012: Wroxham
2013: Dereham Town
ridgeonsleague.co.uk

PREMIER DIVISION	P	W	D	L	F	A	GD	Pts
1 Hadleigh United	38	26	5	7	105	48	57	83
2 (P) Brightlingsea Regent	38	25	8	5	87	41	46	83
3 Felixstowe & Walton United	38	24	9	5	85	45	40	81
4 Gorleston	38	23	9	6	90	63	27	78
5 Godmanchester Rovers	38	24	5	9	82	43	39	77
6 Norwich United	38	22	7	9	63	42	21	73
7 Haverhill Rovers	38	20	3	15	66	55	11	63
8 Walsham-le-Willows	38	17	10	11	79	54	25	61
9 Newmarket Town	38	15	13	10	76	66	10	58
10 Mildenhall Town	38	16	9	13	74	54	20	57
11 Brantham Athletic	38	15	8	15	71	75	-4	53
12 Kirkley & Pakefield	38	14	8	16	67	72	-5	50
13 Stanway Rovers	38	12	8	18	66	65	1	44
14 CRC	38	12	3	23	66	70	-4	39
15 FC Clacton	38	7	12	19	55	84	-29	33
16 Thetford Town	38	7	9	22	48	83	-35	30
17 Ely City	38	8	6	24	49	85	-36	30
18 Diss Town	38	8	5	25	47	102	-55	29
19 Wivenhoe Town	38	6	7	25	33	79	-46	25
20 (R) Woodbridge Town	38	5	4	29	40	123	-83	19

LEAGUE CUP

PRELIMINARY ROUND

AFC Sudbury Reserves	v	Cornard United	5-2
Brantham Athletic	v	Whitton United	4-1
Debenham LC	v	Norwich United	0-2
Ely City	v	Haverhill Borough	5-1
Haverhill Rovers	v	Godmanchester Rovers	3-2
Stowmarket Town	v	Needham Market Res.	2-2 3-4p
Swaffham Town	v	Gorleston	3-1

ROUND 1

Brightlingsea Regent	v	Stanway Rovers	1-1 4-5p
Diss Town	v	Fakenham Town	2-5
Downham Town	v	Mildenhall Town	1-3
Felixstowe & Walton Utd	v	FC Clacton	1-0
Great Yarmouth Town	v	Dereham Town Reserves	4-3
Halstead Town	v	Team Bury	1-0
Haverhill Rovers	v	CRC	2-0
Ipswich Wanderers	v	Woodbridge Town	5-1
Long Melford	v	AFC Sudbury Reserves	2-2 2-4p
Newmarket Town	v	March Town United	3-0
Needham Market Res.	v	Hadleigh United	1-4
Saffron Walden Town	v	Ely City	2-4
Swaffham Town	v	Norwich United	1-5
Thetford Town	v	Kirkley & Pakefield	1-2
Walsham-le-Willows	v	Braintree Town Reserves	6-2
Wivenhoe Town	v	Brantham Athletic	0-5

ROUND 2

Felixstowe & Walton Utd	v	Walsham-le-Willows	1-0
Great Yarmouth Town	v	Norwich United	1-8
Halstead Town	v	Brantham Athletic	1-2
Ipswich Wanderers	v	Hadleigh United	3-5
Kirkley & Pakefield	v	Fakenham Town	5-0
Mildenhall Town	v	Ely City	2-3
Newmarket Town	v	Haverhll Rovers	3-1
Stanway Rovers	v	AFC Sudbury Reserves	1-2

QUARTER FINALS

AFC Sudbury Reserves	v	Brantham Athletic	0-4
Hadleigh United	v	Newmarket Town	0-2
Kirkley & Pakefield	v	Felixstowe & Walton United	1-3
Norwich United	v	Ely City	0-1

SEMI FINALS

Ely City	v	Newmarket Town	1-1, 2-3p
Felixstowe & Walton Utd	v	Brantham Athletic	3-1

FINAL

Felixstowe & Walton Utd	v	Newmarket Town	1-2

PREMIER DIVISION	1	2	3	4	5	6	7	8	9	10	11	12	13	14	15	16	17	18	19	20
1 Brantham Athletic		1–2	3–2	4–1	3–0	1–1	0–6	0–2	0–0	0–4	1–2	1–3	3–1	1–0	2–0	2–1	2–2	0–2	4–1	5–0
2 Brightlingsea Regent	3–1		2–1	3–1	2–0	3–0	2–0	2–1	5–0	2–4	4–1	6–2	1–1	2–2	2–1	2–1	2–0	2–2	5–0	4–0
3 Cambridge Regional College	2–4	2–0		4–0	0–1	3–1	1–2	1–2	1–2	1–2	1–2	1–1	2–0	2–2	1–2	0–3	0–2	2–0	0–0	5–1
4 Diss Town	3–3	0–0	3–1		1–3	3–3	1–2	1–2	1–3	1–5	1–1	0–3	1–1	3–1	1–3	4–3	2–3	0–11	2–1	3–1
5 Ely City	1–4	1–3	2–3	1–2		0–1	2–3	1–5	1–3	0–5	2–4	0–2	1–3	1–3	0–2	2–1	3–3	0–4	0–1	1–1
6 Clacton	1–1	2–2	1–2	3–0	3–4		1–3	2–3	1–2	0–4	2–2	2–1	2–2	1–4	1–1	2–1	2–1	1–2	2–0	2–3
7 Felixstowe & Walton United	1–1	1–3	3–1	4–1	1–1	3–3		2–1	4–4	4–1	1–0	2–1	2–1	6–2	2–2	3–3	4–0	1–1	1–0	1–0
8 Godmanchester Rovers	2–0	2–2	1–0	3–2	2–3	6–2	0–2		0–0	1–0	0–1	1–1	2–0	0–0	4–2	0–1	1–0	0–2	5–0	2–1
9 Gorleston	3–1	2–2	3–2	4–0	3–1	1–1	1–2	2–4		3–1	1–0	5–2	4–3	2–2	5–4	3–0	3–0	0–0	2–1	4–0
10 Hadleigh United	5–1	1–0	3–1	3–0	3–2	3–0	1–0	2–4	2–2		1–0	7–0	2–1	1–1	0–1	5–2	4–1	2–3	3–1	4–0
11 Haverhill Rovers	4–2	0–1	1–2	0–3	3–2	4–0	3–2	3–4	4–1	1–1		2–1	2–0	2–1	2–4	0–1	3–0	1–2	3–0	2–0
12 Kirkley & Pakefield	1–2	1–3	4–2	3–1	0–2	1–1	0–1	0–2	0–1	3–1	2–1		0–0	4–1	0–0	2–1	5–3	3–3	2–1	2–3
13 Mildenhall Town	4–1	2–0	4–2	4–0	1–1	4–1	0–1	1–3	1–1	1–4	3–0	3–3		0–1	1–2	2–1	3–3	2–1	2–0	7–0
14 Newmarket Town	1–2	0–0	2–1	3–0	1–1	2–1	1–3	1–0	5–7	3–4	4–1	2–2	4–4		5–2	2–1	2–2	1–0	2–2	2–0
15 Norwich United	1–0	1–3	2–1	1–0	1–0	2–0	1–0	1–0	1–2	2–2	0–2	1–0	1–0	3–1		0–1	3–0	1–1	1–1	4–1
16 Stanway Rovers	3–3	1–2	3–2	3–1	1–0	1–1	2–2	0–4	4–2	2–3	0–1	3–1	0–2	4–4	0–0		0–2	1–1	0–1	9–1
17 Thetford Town	3–3	0–2	1–5	1–0	2–3	4–4	0–1	1–1	1–5	1–2	0–1	1–2	0–1	0–3	0–2	2–1		1–2	2–2	2–1
18 Walsham-le-Willows	4–2	1–3	3–1	3–1	2–1	3–2	1–1	2–4	5–1	1–3	2–0	1–3	1–3	1–1	0–2	0–3	0–2		4–0	2–2
19 Wivenhoe Town	1–3	1–3	1–3	4–1	0–2	0–1	1–3	2–3	1–2	1–1	0–2	2–1	0–3	0–3	1–3	1–1	2–1	1–1		1–0
20 Woodbridge Town	2–4	4–2	1–5	1–2	3–3	2–1	1–5	0–5	0–1	1–6	3–5	3–5	1–3	0–1	0–3	0–3	1–1	0–5	2–1	

DIVISION ONE	P	W	D	L	F	A	GD	Pts
1 (P) Whitton United	36	25	8	3	79	36	43	83
2 (P) Fakenham Town	36	23	8	5	94	33	61	77
3 (P) Ipswich Wanderers	36	23	6	7	97	37	60	75
4 Haverhill Borough	36	23	5	8	65	37	28	74
5 Saffron Walden Town	36	20	10	6	91	45	46	70
6 Halstead Town	36	21	7	8	80	39	41	70
7 Swaffham Town	36	21	5	10	94	47	47	68
8 Great Yarmouth Town	36	19	8	9	82	50	32	65
9 Braintree Town Res	36	17	7	12	65	54	11	58
10 Team Bury	36	16	6	14	58	53	5	54
11 Long Melford	36	14	2	20	51	68	-17	44
12 Debenham LC	36	11	7	18	58	63	-5	40
13 Dereham Town Res	36	9	8	19	57	67	-10	35
14 Stowmarket Town	36	11	1	24	53	94	-41	34
15 Needham Market Res	36	10	2	24	52	98	-46	32
16 AFC Sudbury Res	36	10	2	24	49	114	-65	32
17 Downham Town	36	6	5	25	47	120	-73	23
18 Cornard United	36	6	3	27	41	96	-55	21
19 March Town United	36	4	6	26	31	93	-62	18

DIVISION ONE LEAGUE CUP

PRELIMINARY ROUND

AFC Sudbury Reserves	v	Needham Market Reserves	0-4
Cornard United	v	Dereham Town Reserves	2-3
Stowmarket Town	v	Haverhill Borough	6-3

ROUND 1

Debenham LC	v	March Town United	4-0
Downham Town	v	Great Yarmouth Town	0-7
Fakenham Town	v	Dereham Town Reserves	0-1
Halstead Town	v	Braintree Town Reserves	0-1
Long Melford	v	Stowmarket Town	1-3
Saffron Walden Town	v	Team Bury	1-0
Needham Market Res.	v	Whitton United	1-2
Swaffham Town	v	Ipswich Wanderers	6-3

QUARTER FINALS

Dereham Town Reserves	v	Debenham LC	0-1
Saffron Walden Town	v	Braintree Town Reserves	5-2
Stowmarket Town	v	Great Yarmouth Town	1-3
Swaffham Town	v	Whitton United	1-2

SEMI FINALS

Debenham LC	v	Great Yarmouth Town	3-1
Saffron Walden Town	v	Whitton United	1-2

FINAL

Debenham LC	v	Whitton United	2-0

DIVISION ONE	1	2	3	4	5	6	7	8	9	10	11	12	13	14	15	16	17	18	19
1 A.F.C. Sudbury Reserves		1–1	6–1	3–1	1–3	0–7	0–10	5–0	1–2	0–2	0–9	1–3	2–1	0–7	4–1	5–1	1–6	1–4	0–1
2 Braintree Town Reserves	6–2		2–1	1–0	2–1	2–3	0–3	2–2	2–2	0–2	2–3	1–3	1–1	3–0	0–1	2–0	3–2	1–0	2–2
3 Cornard United	0–1	0–1		2–1	2–3	2–2	1–4	0–1	0–2	1–2	0–3	1–4	0–5	4–0	2–3	2–3	1–5	0–1	0–2
4 Debenham LC	0–2	0–3	1–3		5–2	4–1	1–3	0–2	0–3	2–2	0–1	4–2	2–0	3–4	0–0	4–0	4–2	0–1	2–2
5 Dereham Town Reserves	1–2	1–4	8–1	2–2		5–1	2–2	1–2	2–3	1–1	0–2	2–0	1–0	2–1	1–3	3–2	1–1	2–2	0–3
6 Downham Town	1–2	1–0	1–2	1–3	1–1		0–5	4–4	0–4	0–3	1–6	3–0	1–1	5–1	1–4	2–3	1–5	1–5	1–4
7 Fakenham Town	1–0	4–4	8–0	2–1	4–1	6–0		3–2	2–0	0–0	0–0	4–0	3–1	2–1	3–3	3–0	1–1	1–0	1–3
8 Great Yarmouth Town	8–0	2–0	2–1	4–2	3–1	3–0	1–2		0–0	1–0	0–1	2–0	6–0	7–1	0–5	3–2	0–1	1–1	1–1
9 Halstead Town	2–0	0–1	4–0	2–1	3–1	3–0	1–0	4–2		1–2	4–2	0–1	2–1	5–0	2–4	4–1	5–1	0–2	1–2
10 Haverhill Borough	2–0	2–0	3–0	1–1	1–0	4–1	2–3	3–3	3–1		2–1	2–1	5–1	0–1	0–4	4–1	3–2	2–0	0–2
11 Ipswich Wanderers	5–1	1–0	2–2	3–0	1–0	12–1	0–0	1–4	0–0	3–2		4–1	5–0	3–0	0–3	2–1	2–3	1–2	3–0
12 Long Melford	4–0	1–3	2–1	1–3	1–3	3–1	0–2	1–1	2–4	1–2	1–2		2–1	3–2	4–1	2–0	0–3	1–1	0–3
13 March Town United	2–1	1–3	0–2	1–1	0–0	2–0	0–3	0–4	2–2	0–2	1–2	1–2		3–1	1–2	0–7	0–2	0–1	1–5
14 Needham Market Reserves	7–0	2–2	1–2	2–1	2–2	2–1	1–0	0–1	1–4	0–2	0–6	1–2	4–1		1–0	0–1	2–1	1–2	0–5
15 Saffron Walden Town	1–1	6–2	3–1	2–2	1–0	8–0	4–3	2–2	0–0	0–1	1–1	2–1	5–1	6–3		6–0	3–0	1–1	2–2
16 Stowmarket Town	2–1	2–5	2–0	1–2	3–2	0–1	0–3	1–0	0–6	1–2	0–6	1–2	1–1	6–2	3–1		2–4	1–2	2–1
17 Swaffham Town	4–3	0–1	2–1	0–1	2–1	7–0	1–1	1–4	0–1	3–0	2–0	2–0	2–0	6–0	1–1	7–1		4–1	1–0
18 Team Bury	3–1	0–2	4–3	1–4	1–0	2–2	0–1	2–3	1–1	0–1	0–1	2–0	7–1	5–0	0–2	2–1	0–8		1–2
19 Whitton United	5–1	2–1	2–2	1–0	2–1	2–1	2–1	2–1	2–2	1–0	3–3	2–0	4–0	2–1	1–0	2–1	2–2	2–1	

CLUB MOVEMENTS

Premier Division - In: Fakenham Town (P). Ipswich Wanderers (P). Whitton United (P).

Out: Brightlingsea Regant (P - Isthmian Div.1 North). Cambridge Regional College (W). Woodbridge Town (R).

Division One - In: King's Lynn Town Reserves (P - Peterborough & District Premier). Leiston Reserves.

Out: Fakenham Town (P). Ipswich Wanderers (P). Whitton United (P).

BRANTHAM ATHLETIC

Founded: 1887 Nickname:

Secretary: Dan Allen **(T)** 07896 266 074 **(E)** branthamathfc@hotmail.co.uk
Chairman: Peter Crowhurst **Manager:** Paul Abrahams
Ground: Brantham Leisure Centre, New Village, Brantham CO11 1RZ. **(T)** 01206 392 506
Capacity: 1,200 **Seats:** 200 **Covered:** 200 **Midweek Matchday:** Tuesday **Clubhouse:** Yes

Colours(change): All blue. (White/navy/navy)
Previous Names: Brantham & Stutton United 1996-98.
Previous Leagues: Eastern Counties. Suffolk & Ipswich.
Records: **Att:** 1,700 v VS Rugby, FA Vase 5R 1982-83.
Senior Honours: Suffolk & Ipswich Senior League Champions 2007-08.

10 YEAR RECORD

04-05	05-06	06-07	07-08	08-09	09-10	10-11	11-12	12-13	13-14
S&I 1 2	S&I S 14	S&I S 4	S&I S 1	EC1 8	EC1 3	ECP 13	ECP 3	ECP 4	ECP 11

DISS TOWN

Founded: 1888 Nickname: Tangerines

Secretary: Steve Flatman **(T)** 07855 531 341 **(E)** pam@dissfc.wanadoo.co.uk
Chairman: Richard Upson **Manager:** Mike Derbyshire **Prog Ed:** Gary Enderby
Ground: Brewers Green Lane, Diss, Norfolk IP22 4QP **(T)** 01379 651 223
Capacity: **Seats:** **Covered:** **Midweek Matchday:** Tuesday **Clubhouse:** Yes

Colours(change): Tangerine/navy/tangerine (Sky blue/navy/sky blue)
Previous Names:
Previous Leagues: Anglian Combination
Records: 1,731 v Atherton LR, FA Vase Semi Final, 19.03.94.
Senior Honours: Eastern Counties Division One 1991-92. FA Vase winners 1993-94.

10 YEAR RECORD

04-05	05-06	06-07	07-08	08-09	09-10	10-11	11-12	12-13	13-14
ECP 12	ECP 11	ECP 20	EC1 4	EC1 9	EC1 5	EC1 3	ECP 16	ECP 17	ECP 18

ELY CITY

Founded: 1885 Nickname: Robins

Secretary: Derek Oakey **(T)** 07720 542 882 **(E)** derek.oakey@tesco.net
Chairman: Robert Button **Manager:** Brady Stone **Prog Ed:** Barnes Print
Ground: Unwin Sports Ground, Downham Road, Ely CB6 2SH **(T)** 01353 662 035
Capacity: 1,500 **Seats:** 150 **Covered:** 350 **Midweek Matchday:** Tuesday **Clubhouse:** Yes **Shop:** Yes

Colours(change): All red. (All blue).
Previous Names: None.
Previous Leagues: Peterborough. Central Alliance.
Records: **Att:** 260 v Soham, Eastern Counties Div.1, 12.04.93.
Senior Honours: Cambridgeshire Senior Cup 1947-48. Eastern Counties Division 1 1996-97.
Cambridgeshire Invitation Cup 2011-12, 12-13.

10 YEAR RECORD

04-05	05-06	06-07	07-08	08-09	09-10	10-11	11-12	12-13	13-14
EC1 9	EC1 7	EC1 4	EC1 2	ECP 14	ECP 9	ECP 15	ECP 2	ECP 11	ECP 17

FAKENHAM TOWN

Founded: 1884 Nickname: Ghosts

Secretary: Paul Chivers **(T)** 07544 651 815 **(E)** chilvers.paul@yahoo.com
Chairman: Geoffrey Saunders **Manager:** Wayne Anderson **Prog Ed:** Barnes Print
Ground: Clipbush Park, Clipbush Lane, Fakenham, Norfolk NR21 8SW **(T)**
Capacity: **Seats:** **Covered:** **Midweek Matchday:** Wednesday **Clubhouse:**

Colours(change): Yellow & black stripes/black/yellow (Blue & white stripes/blue/blue)
Previous Names:
Previous Leagues:
Records: **Att:** 1,100 v Watford, official opening of new ground.
Senior Honours: Norfolk Senior Cup 1970-71, 72-73, 73-74, 91-92, 93-94, 94-95.

10 YEAR RECORD

04-05	05-06	06-07	07-08	08-09	09-10	10-11	11-12	12-13	13-14
EC1 10	EC1 11	EC1 10	EC1 17	EC1 20	EC1 19	EC1 14	EC1 11	EC1 5	EC1 2

FC CLACTON

Founded: 1892 Nickname: The Seasiders

Secretary: Ian Gunfield **(T)** 07841 031 037 **(E)** ian.gunfield@talk21.com
Chairman: David Ballard **Manager:** Glenn Eldridge **Prog Ed:** Martin Oswick
Ground: Rush Green Bowl, Rush Green Rd, Clacton-on-Sea CO16 7BQ **(T)** 07545 998 242
Capacity: 3,000 **Seats:** 200 **Covered:** Yes **Midweek Matchday:** Tuesday **Clubhouse:** Yes **Shop:** Yes

Colours(change): White/royal blue/royal blue. (All red).
Previous Names: Clacton Town > 2007
Previous Leagues: Eastern Counties. Essex County. Southern League.
Records: **Att:** 3,505 v Romford, FA Cup 1952 at Old Road.
Senior Honours: Eastern Counties Division 1 1994-95, 98-99.

10 YEAR RECORD

04-05	05-06	06-07	07-08	08-09	09-10	10-11	11-12	12-13	13-14
ECP 8	ECP 22	ECP 21	EC1 10	EC1 7	EC1 2	ECP 16	ECP 15	ECP 20	ECP 15

FELIXSTOWE & WALTON UNITED

Founded: 2000 Nickname: Seasiders

Secretary: Tony Barnes **(T)** 07584 010 933 **(E)** tgbarnes@live.co.uk
Chairman: Andy Wilding **Manager:** Kevin O'Donnell **Prog Ed:** Adam Whalley
Ground: Goldstar Ground, Dellwood Avenue, Felixstowe IP11 9HT **(T)** 01394 282 917
Capacity: 2,000 **Seats:** 200 **Covered:** 200 **Midweek Matchday:** Tuesday **Clubhouse:** Yes **Shop:** Yes

Colours(change): Red & white stripes/white/red. (Blue/black/blue).
Previous Names: Felixstowe Port & Town and Walton United merged in July 2000.
Previous Leagues: None
Records:
Senior Honours:

10 YEAR RECORD

04-05	05-06	06-07	07-08	08-09	09-10	10-11	11-12	12-13	13-14
EC1 17	EC1 2	ECP 13	ECP 8	ECP 12	ECP 7	ECP 18	ECP 18	ECP 14	ECP 3

GODMANCHESTER ROVERS

Founded: 1911 Nickname: Goody/Rovers

Secretary: Roger Carpenter **(T)** 07552 771 338 **(E)** rogergrfc@gmail.com
Chairman: Keith Gabb **Manager:** Matt Haniver & Neville Nania **Prog Ed:** Steve Bengree
Ground: Bearscroft Lane, Godmanchester, Huntingdon, Cambs PE29 2LQ **(T)**
Capacity: **Seats:** **Covered:** Yes **Midweek Matchday:** Wednesday **Clubhouse:** Yes

Colours(change): Blue & white stripes/blue/white (Red & white stripes/red/red)
Previous Names: None
Previous Leagues:
Records: **Att:** 138 v Cambridge City Reserves, Dec. 2003.
Senior Honours: Eastern Counties League Division One 2011-12.

10 YEAR RECORD

04-05	05-06	06-07	07-08	08-09	09-10	10-11	11-12	12-13	13-14
EC1 20	EC1 14	EC1 17	EC1 16	EC1 10	EC1 12	EC1 9	EC1 1	ECP 5	ECP 5

GORLESTON

Founded: 1887 Nickname: The Cards

Secretary: Colin Bray **(T)** 07918 186 645 **(E)** colin-bray@sky.com
Chairman: Alan Gordon **Manager:** Richard Daniels
Ground: Emerald Park, Woodfarm Lane, Gorleston, Norfolk NR31 9AQ **(T)** 01493 602 802
Capacity: **Seats:** Yes **Covered:** Yes **Midweek Matchday:** Tuesday **Clubhouse:** Yes

Colours(change): All green (All sky blue)
Previous Names: None
Previous Leagues: Anglian Combination
Records: **Record Att:** 4,473 v Orient, FA Cup 1st Round, 29.11.51.
Senior Honours: Norfolk & Suff. Lge (x 7). Norfolk Senior Cup x16 Most recently 2011-12.
Anglian Comb 1968-69. Eastern Counties 1952-53, 72-73, 79-80, 80-81. Division One 1995-96, 2010-11.

10 YEAR RECORD

04-05	05-06	06-07	07-08	08-09	09-10	10-11	11-12	12-13	13-14
ECP 21	EC1 18	EC1 14	EC1 8	EC1 6	EC1 4	EC1 1	ECP 12	ECP 3	ECP 4

HADLEIGH UNITED

Founded: 1892 Nickname: Brettsiders

Secretary: Louise Hay **(T)** 07962 274 986 **(E)** louise.hay1@yahoo.co.uk
Chairman: Rolf Beggerow **Manager:** Stuart Crawford **Prog Ed:** Nick Barwick
Ground: Millfield, Tinkers Lane, Duke St, Hadleigh IP7 5NF **(T)** 01473 822 165
Capacity: 3,000 **Seats:** 250 **Covered:** 500 **Midweek Matchday:** Tuesday **Clubhouse:** Yes

Colours(change): All navy blue (White/royal blue/royal blue)
Previous Names: None
Previous Leagues: Suffolk & Ipswich.
Records: **Att:** 518 v Halstead Town, FA Vase replay, 17.01.95.
Senior Honours: Suffolk & Ipswich League Champions 1953-54, 56-57, 73-74, 76-77, 78-79.
Suffolk Senior Cup 1968-69, 71-72, 82-83, 2003-04. Eastern Counties League Champions 1993-94, 2013-14.

10 YEAR RECORD

04-05	05-06	06-07	07-08	08-09	09-10	10-11	11-12	12-13	13-14
EC1 16	EC1 21	EC1 9	EC1 5	EC1 2	ECP 18	ECP 9	ECP 11	ECP 8	ECP 1

HAVERHILL ROVERS

Founded: 1886 Nickname: Rovers

Secretary: Julie Ankers **(T)** 07782 120 354 **(E)** julesankers@gmail.com
Chairman: Alastair Shulver **Manager:** Dean Greygoose
Ground: The New Croft, Chalkstone Way, Haverhill, Suffolk CB9 0BW **(T)** 01440 702 137
Capacity: 3,000 **Seats:** 200 **Covered:** 200 **Midweek Matchday:** Tuesday **Clubhouse:** Yes

Colours(change): All red. (All blue).
Previous Names: None.
Previous Leagues: East Anglian. Essex & Suffolk Border.
Records:
Senior Honours: Essex & Suffolk Border League Champions 1947-48, 62-63, 63-64.
Eastern Counties League Cup 1964-65, League Champions 78-79. Suffolk Senior Cup 1995-96.

10 YEAR RECORD

04-05	05-06	06-07	07-08	08-09	09-10	10-11	11-12	12-13	13-14
EC1 5	EC1 8	EC1 2	ECP 10	ECP 21	ECP 12	ECP 8	ECP 14	ECP 10	ECP 7

IPSWICH WANDERERS

Founded: 1983 Nickname: Wanderers

Secretary: Paul Crickmore **(T)** 07577 745 778 **(E)** iwfc@hotmail.co.uk
Chairman: Terry Fenwick **Manager:** Glenn Read **Prog Ed:** Nick Pope
Ground: SEH Sports Centre, Humber Doucy Lane, Ipswich IP4 3NR **(T)** 01473 728 581
Capacity: **Seats:** **Covered:** **Midweek Matchday:** Wednesday **Clubhouse:**

Colours(change): Blue & white/blue/white (All orange)
Previous Names: Loadwell Ipswich 1983-89
Previous Leagues:
Records: **Att:** 335 v Woodbridge, Eastern Counties League 1993-94.
Senior Honours: Eastern Counties Div.1 Champions 1997-98, 04-05. Suffolk Senior Cup 2012-13.

10 YEAR RECORD

04-05	05-06	06-07	07-08	08-09	09-10	10-11	11-12	12-13	13-14
EC1 1	ECP 7	ECP 10	ECP 22	EC1 17	EC1 17	EC1 10	EC1 12	EC1 4	EC1 3

KIRKLEY & PAKEFIELD

Founded: 1886 Nickname: The Kirks

Secretary: Mike Guymer **(T)** 07826 520 988 **(E)** mikeguymer@yahoo.co.uk
Chairman: Robert Jenkerson **Manager:** Jamie Godbold
Ground: K. & P. Community Sports & S. Club, Walmer Rd, Lowestoft NR33 7LE **(T)** 01502 513 549
Capacity: 2,000 **Seats:** 150 **Covered:** 150 **Midweek Matchday:** Tuesday **Clubhouse:** Yes **Shop:** Yes

Colours(change): Royal blue & white/royal blue/royal blue (All maroon).
Previous Names: Kirkley. Kirkley & Waveney 1929-33. Merged with Pakefield in 2007.
Previous Leagues: Norfolk & Suffolk. Anglian Combination.
Records: **Att:** 1,125 v Lowestoft Town. **Goalscorer:** Barry Dale - 241. **Apps:** Barry Dale - 495.
Senior Honours: Suffolk Senior Cup 1900-01, 01-02, 24-25, 00-01, 01-02. Anglian Combination League 2001-02, 02-03.

10 YEAR RECORD

04-05	05-06	06-07	07-08	08-09	09-10	10-11	11-12	12-13	13-14
EC1 3	ECP 14	ECP 7	ECP 6	ECP 6	ECP 4	ECP 12	ECP 13	ECP 12	ECP 12

MILDENHALL TOWN

Founded: 1898 Nickname: The Hall

Secretary: Brian Hensby **(T)** 07932 043 261 **(E)** bhensby@talktalk.net
Chairman: Martin Tuck **Manager:** Christian Appleford **Prog Ed:** Frank Marshall
Ground: Recreation Way, Mildenhall, Suffolk IP28 7HG **(T)** 01638 713 449
Capacity: 2,00 **Seats:** 50 **Covered:** 200 **Midweek Matchday:** Tuesday **Clubhouse:** Yes **Shop:** Yes

Colours(change): Amber/black/black. (Red & white/white/red).
Previous Names: None
Previous Leagues: Bury & District. Cambridgeshire. Cambridgeshire Premier.
Records: **Att:** 450 v Derby County, Friendly, July 2001.
Senior Honours:

10 YEAR RECORD

04-05	05-06	06-07	07-08	08-09	09-10	10-11	11-12	12-13	13-14
ECP 6	ECP 5	ECP 2	ECP 5	ECP 11	ECP 6	ECP 5	ECP 7	ECP 7	ECP 10

NEWMARKET TOWN

Founded: 1877 Nickname: The Jockeys

Secretary: Elaine Jeakins **(T)** 07801 815 682 **(E)** elaine.jeakins@ntlworld.com
Chairman: John Olive **Manager:** Kevin Grainger
Ground: Town Ground, Cricket Field Road, Off Cheveley Rd, Newmarket CB8 8BT **(T)** 01638 663 637
Capacity: 2,750 **Seats:** 144 **Covered:** 250 **Midweek Matchday:** Tuesday **Clubhouse:** Yes **Shop:** Yes

Colours(change): Yellow/blue/yellow (Blue/blue/yellow)
Previous Names: None
Previous Leagues: Bury Senior. Ipswich Senior. Essex & Suffolk B. United Counties.
Records: **Att:** 2,701 v Abbey United (now Cambridge Utd) FA Cup, 01.10.49.
Senior Honours: Suffolk Senior Cup 1934-35, 93-94. Suffolk Premier Cup 1993-94, 94-95, 96-97.
Eastern Counties League Division 1 2008-09.

10 YEAR RECORD

04-05	05-06	06-07	07-08	08-09	09-10	10-11	11-12	12-13	13-14
ECP 13	ECP 17	ECP 12	ECP 21	EC1 1	ECP 16	ECP 19	ECP 20	EC1 2	ECP 9

NORWICH UNITED

Founded: 1903 Nickname: Planters

Secretary: Keith Cutmore **(T)** 07788 437 515 **(E)** secretary.nufc@hotmail.co.uk
Chairman: John Hilditch **Manager:** Damian Hilton **Prog Ed:** Barnes Print
Ground: Plantation Park, Blofield, Norwich NR13 4PL **(T)** 01603 716 963
Capacity: 3,000 **Seats:** 100 **Covered:** 1,000 **Midweek Matchday:** Tuesday **Clubhouse:** Yes **Shop:** Yes

Colours(change): Yellow & blue/blue/blue. (All grey)
Previous Names: Poringland & District > 1987
Previous Leagues: Norwich & District. Anglian Combination
Records: **Att:** 401 v Wroxham, Eastern Co. Lge, 1991-92. **Goalscorer:** M. Money. **Apps:** Tim Sayer.
Senior Honours: Anglian Combination Senior Cup 1983-84. Eastern Counties League Division One 1990-91, 01-02.

10 YEAR RECORD

04-05	05-06	06-07	07-08	08-09	09-10	10-11	11-12	12-13	13-14
ECP 14	ECP 20	ECP 16	ECP 15	ECP 19	ECP 15	ECP 6	ECP 9	ECP 13	ECP 6

STANWAY ROVERS

Founded: 1956 Nickname: Rovers

Secretary: Kevin Mather **(T)** 07846 927 510 **(E)** kev.mather@hotmail.com
Chairman: Roy Brett **Manager:** Angelo Harrop
Ground: Hawthorns, New Farm Road, Stanway, Colchester CO3 0PJ **(T)** 01206 578 187
Capacity: 1,500 **Seats:** 100 **Covered:** 250 **Midweek Matchday:** Wednesday **Clubhouse:** Yes **Shop:** Yes

Colours(change): Amber/black/black. (All white).
Previous Names: None.
Previous Leagues: Colchester & East Essex. Essex & Suffolk Border.
Records: **Att:** 210 v Harwich & P, Eastern Co. Lge Div.1, 2004.
Senior Honours: Eastern Counties League Division 1 Champions 2005-06, League Cup 2008-09.

10 YEAR RECORD

04-05	05-06	06-07	07-08	08-09	09-10	10-11	11-12	12-13	13-14
EC1 6	EC1 1	ECP 14	ECP 7	ECP 9	ECP 5	ECP 7	ECP 5	ECP 9	ECP 13

THETFORD TOWN
Founded: 1883 Nickname:

Secretary: Jackie Skipp **(T)** 07919 998 579 **(E)** jackieskipp@live.co.uk
Chairman: Mick Bailey **Manager:** Mark Scott **Prog Ed:** Barnes Print
Ground: Recreation Ground, Mundford Road, Thetford, Norfolk IP24 1NB **(T)** 01842 766 120
Capacity: **Seats:** Yes **Covered:** Yes **Midweek Matchday:** Tuesday **Clubhouse:** Yes

Colours(change): Claret & blue/claret/claret (All sky blue)
Previous Names: None
Previous Leagues: Founder member of Eastern Counties League
Records: **Att:** 394 v Diss Town, Norfolk Senior Cup, 1991.
Senior Honours: Norfolk Senior Cup 1947-48, 90-91. Norfolk & Suffolk League 1954-55.

10 YEAR RECORD

04-05	05-06	06-07	07-08	08-09	09-10	10-11	11-12	12-13	13-14
EC1 19	EC1 22	EC1 11	EC1 13	EC1 16	EC1 11	EC1 5	EC1 2	ECP 19	ECP 16

WALSHAM-LE-WILLOWS
Founded: 1888 Nickname: The Willows

Secretary: Gordon Ross **(T)** 07742 111 892 **(E)** gordonaross@aol.com
Chairman: Mike Powles **Manager:** Paul Smith
Ground: The Meadow, Summer Road, Walsham-le-Willows IP31 3AH **(T)** 01359 259 298
Capacity: **Seats:** 100 **Covered:** 100 **Midweek Matchday:** Wednesday **Clubhouse:** Yes

Colours(change): Yellow/red/yellow (Sky blue & white/black/sky blue)
Previous Names: None
Previous Leagues: Bury & District. Suffolk & Ipswich.
Records:
Senior Honours: Suffolk & Ipswich Senior League Champions 2001-02, 02-03. Suffolk Senior Cup 2005-06.
Eastern Counties League Division 1 Champions 2006-07.

10 YEAR RECORD

04-05	05-06	06-07	07-08	08-09	09-10	10-11	11-12	12-13	13-14
EC1 4	EC1 5	EC1 1	ECP 16	ECP 10	ECP 13	ECP 17	ECP 17	ECP 6	ECP 8

WHITTON UNITED
Founded: 1926 Nickname:

Secretary: Phil Pemberton **(T)** 07429 116 538 **(E)** pemby64@hotmail.com
Chairman: Mark Richards **Manager:** Paul Bugg
Ground: King George V Playing Fields, Old Norwich Road, Ipswich IP1 6LE **(T)** 01473 464 030
Capacity: **Seats:** **Covered:** **Midweek Matchday:** Tuesday **Clubhouse:**

Colours(change): Green and white stripes/green/green (All orange)
Previous Names:
Previous Leagues:
Records: **Att:** 528 v Ipswich Town, 29.11.95.
Senior Honours: Suffolk & Ipswich League 1946-47, 47-48, 65-66, 67-68, 91-92, 92-93. Suffolk Senior Cup 1958-59, 62-63, 92-93.
Suffolk Premier Cup 2011-12. Eastern counties Division One 2013-14.

10 YEAR RECORD

04-05	05-06	06-07	07-08	08-09	09-10	10-11	11-12	12-13	13-14
EC1 14	EC1 6	EC1 8	EC1 3	ECP dnf	EC1 10	EC1 2	EC1 3	EC1 7	EC1 1

WIVENHOE TOWN
Founded: 1925 Nickname: The Dragons

Secretary: Lorraine Stevens **(T)** 07565 364 019 **(E)** lorraine.rogers@btopenworld.com
Chairman: Mo Osman **Manager:** Mo Osman
Ground: Broad Lane, Elmstead Road, Wivenhoe CO7 7HA **(T)**
Capacity: 2876 **Seats:** 161 **Covered:** 1300 **Midweek Matchday:** Tuesday **Clubhouse:** Yes **Shop:** Yes

Colours(change): Blue & white/blue/blue (Red/black/black)
Previous Names: Wivenhoe Rangers.
Previous Leagues: Brightlingsea & District, Colchester & East Essex. Essex & Suffolk Border, Essex Senior, Isthmian
Records: **Att:** 1,912 v Runcorn, FA Trophy, 1st Round, Feb. 1990. **Goalscorer:** (258 in 350 games). **Apps:** Keith Bain (538).
Senior Honours: Isthmian Division 2 North 1987-88. Division 1 1989-90. Essex Senior Trophy 1987-88.

10 YEAR RECORD

04-05	05-06	06-07	07-08	08-09	09-10	10-11	11-12	12-13	13-14
SthE 5	SthE 6	Isth1N 11	Isth1N 22	ECP 17	ECP 20	ECP 20	ECP 19	ECP 18	ECP 19

DIVISION ONE

A.F.C. SUDBURY RESERVES

Founded: 1999 Nickname: AFC

Secretary: David Webb **(T)** 07885 327 510 **(E)** dave-afc@supanet.com
Chairman: **Manager:** Danny Laws **Prog Ed:** Darren Theobald
Ground: The Mel Group Stadium, King's Marsh Brundon Lane, Sudbury CO10 7HN **(T)** 01787 376 213
Colours(change): Yellow/blue/yellow (All red)

ADDITIONAL INFORMATION:

BRAINTREE TOWN RESERVES

Founded: Nickname:

Secretary: Paul Tyler **(T)** 07769 978 142 **(E)** paulstyler@hotmail.co.uk
Chairman: Lee Harding **Manager:** Mark Sansom **Prog Ed:** Mark Sansom
Ground: Stoneylands Stadium, New Road, Long Melford, Sudbury CO10 9JY **(T)** 01787 312 187
Colours(change): Orange/blue/blue (White/orange/orange)

ADDITIONAL INFORMATION:

CORNARD UNITED

Founded: 1964 Nickname: Ards

Secretary: Mark Hoskin **(T)** 07806 570 599 **(E)** markhoskin68@gmail.com
Chairman: **Manager:** Mark Hoskin
Ground: Backhouse Lane, Great Cornard, Sudbury, Suffolk CO10 0NL **(T)** 07806 570 599
Colours(change): Blue & white/blue/blue (Gold & black/black/black)

ADDITIONAL INFORMATION:
Record Att: 400 v Colchester United 1997. **Goalscorer:** Andy Smiles. **Apps:** Keith Featherstone.
Honours: Essex & Suffolk Border League Champions 1988-89. Eastern Counties Div. 1 1989-90. Suffolk Senior Cup 89-90.

DEBENHAM LC

Founded: 1991 Nickname: The Hornets

Secretary: Dan Snell **(T)** 07840 246 837 **(E)** snelly1992@hotmail.co.uk
Chairman: Pip Alden **Manager:** Stuart Reavell **Prog Ed:** Martyn Clarke
Ground: Debenham Leisure Centre, Gracechurch Street, Debenham IP14 6BL **(T)** 01728 861 101 **Capacity:** 1,000
Colours(change): Yellow/black/yellow. (All navy blue).

ADDITIONAL INFORMATION: Record Att: 400. **Goalscorer:** Lee Briggs. **Apps:** Steve Nelson.
Previous Name: Debenham Angels > 2005.
Previous League: Suffolk & Ipswich > 2005.

DEREHAM TOWN RESERVES

Founded: Nickname:

Secretary: Ray Bayles **(T)** 07769 644 740 **(E)** ray.bayles@ntlworld.com
Chairman: Simon Barnes **Manager:** Garth Good **Prog Ed:** Barnes Print
Ground: Aldiss Park, Norwich Road, Dereham, Norfolk NR20 3PX **(T)** 01362 690 460
Colours(change): Black & white stripes/black/black (Red/white/white)

ADDITIONAL INFORMATION:

DOWNHAM TOWN

Founded: 1881 Nickname: Town

Secretary: George Dickson **(T)** 07545 181 242 **(E)** george.dickson@me.com
Chairman: Sandra Calvert **Manager:** Mark Reeve **Prog Ed:** Barnes Print
Ground: Memorial Field, Lynn Road, Downham Market PE38 9AU **(T)**
Colours(change): Red/black/red (All blue)

ADDITIONAL INFORMATION:
Record Att: 325 v Wells Town, Norfolk Senior Cup, 1998-99. **Honours:** Peterborough Senior Cup 1962, 63, 67, 72, 87. Peterborough League 1963, 74, 79, 87, 88. Norfolk Senior Cup 1964, 66.

GREAT YARMOUTH TOWN

Founded: 1897 Nickname:

Secretary: Len Beresford **(T)** 07873 861 983 **(E)** lenberesfordgyfc@hotmail.com
Chairman: Stephen Brierley **Manager:** Ricci Butler **Prog Ed:** Nathan Smith
Ground: The Wellesley, Sandown Road, Great Yarmouth NR30 1EY **(T)** 07873 861 983 **Capacity:** 3,600
Colours(change): Yellow/black/yellow (Light blue/white/light blue)

ADDITIONAL INFORMATION:
Record Att: 8,944 v Crystal Palace FA Cup R1 52-53. **Goalscorer:** Gordon South - 298 (1927-47). **Apps:** Mark Vincent - 700 (84-05).
Honours: Eastern Counties League Champions 1968-69, Division 1 2009-10. Norfolk Senior Cup (x 12)

HALSTEAD TOWN
Founded: 1879 Nickname: The Town

Secretary: Steve Webber **(T)** 07848 822 802 **(E)** halsteadtownfc@aol.com
Chairman: Jimmy Holder **Manager:** Mark Benterman **Prog Ed:** Barnes Print
Ground: Rosemary Lane, Broton Industrial Estate, Halstead, Essex CO9 1HR **(T)** 01787 472 082
Colours(change): Black & white stripes/white/black (Red & white stripes/red/red)

ADDITIONAL INFORMATION:
Record Att: 4,000 v Walthamstowe Avenue, Essex Senior Cup 1949.
Honours: Eastern Counties Champions 1994-95, 95-96. Div.1 2002-03. Essex Senior Trophy 1994-95, 96-97.

HAVERHILL BOROUGH
Founded: 2011 Nickname:

Secretary: Ben Cowling **(T)** 07904 685 010 **(E)** bencow_144@hotmail.com
Chairman: Barry Geoghegan **Manager:** Ben Cowling
Ground: The New Croft, Chalkestone Way, Haverhill, Suffolk CB9 0BW **(T)** 01440 702 137 **Capacity:** 3,000
Colours(change): Navy blue/navy blue/red (Grey/grey/white)

ADDITIONAL INFORMATION:
Previous Names: Haverhill Sports Association > 2013.
Previous Leagues: Essex & Suffolk Border > 2013.

KING'S LYNN RESERVES
Founded: Nickname:

Secretary: Norman Cesar **(T)** 07887 373 956 **(E)** ncesar1947@yahoo.co.uk
Chairman: Keith Chapman **Manager:** Jonathan Hawes
Ground: The Walks, Tennyson Road, King's Lynn PE30 5PB. **(T)** 01553 760 060 **Capacity:** 8,200
Colours(change): Yellow/blue/yellow. (Turquoise/black/turquoise).

ADDITIONAL INFORMATION:

LEISTON RESERVES
Founded: Nickname:

Secretary: David Rees **(T)** 07977 782 559 **(E)** gagrees@aol.com
Chairman: Andy Crisp
Ground: The LTAA, Victory Road, Leiston, Suffolk IP16 4DZ **(T)** 01728 830 308
Colours(change): Blue/white/red (All red)

ADDITIONAL INFORMATION:

LONG MELFORD
Founded: 1868 Nickname: The Villagers

Secretary: Richard Powell **(T)** 07897 751 298 **(E)** richard.j.powell@hotmail.co.uk
Chairman: Colin Woodhouse **Manager:** Jules Mumford **Prog Ed:** Andy Cussans
Ground: Stoneylands Stadium, New Road, Long Melford, Suffolk CO10 9JY **(T)** 01787 312 187
Colours(change): Black & white stripes/black/black (Navy/white/red)

ADDITIONAL INFORMATION:
Honours: Essex & Suffolk Border Champions x5. Suffolk Senior Cup x8.

MARCH TOWN UNITED
Founded: 1885 Nickname: Hares

Secretary: Raymond Bennett **(T)** 07944 721 312 **(E)** r.bennett639@btinternet.com
Chairman: Phil White **Manager:** Chris Bartlett Gary Wesley
Ground: GER Sports Ground, Robin Goodfellow Lane, March, Cambs PE15 8HS **(T)** 01354 653 073
Colours(change): Amber/black/black (All blue)

ADDITIONAL INFORMATION:
Record Att: 7,500 v King's Lynn, FA Cup 1956.
Honours: United Counties League 1953-54. Eastern Counties 1987-88.

NEEDHAM MARKET RESERVES
Founded: 1919 Nickname: The Marketmen

Secretary: Mark Easlea **(T)** 07795 456 502 **(E)** m.easlea@sky.com
Chairman: Keith Nunn **Manager:** Kevin Horlock
Ground: Bloomfields, Quinton Road, Needham Market IP6 8DA. **(T)** 01449 721 000 **Capacity:** 1,000
Colours(change): Red/black/red (All white)

ADDITIONAL INFORMATION:

SAFFRON WALDEN TOWN

Founded: 1872 Nickname: The Bloods

Secretary: Andy Player **(T)** 07818 725 727 **(E)** andyplayer135@hotmail.com
Chairman: **Manager:** Stuart Wardley **Prog Ed:** Jim Duvall
Ground: 1 Catons Lane, Saffron Walden, Essex CB10 2DU **(T)** 01799 520 980
Colours(change): Red & black stripes/black/black (Blue & white stripes/blue/blue)

ADDITIONAL INFORMATION:
Record Goalscorer: Alec Ramsey - 192. **Apps:** Les Page - 538. **Honours:** Essex Senior League 1973-74, 99-00.
Eastern Counties 1982-83. Essex Senior Challenge Trophy 1982-83, 83-84, 84-85.
Previous Lge: Eastern Counties > 2011. Folded in 2011 reformed for 2012-13 season.

STOWMARKET TOWN

Founded: 1883 Nickname: Gold and Blacks

Secretary: Neil Sharp **(T)** 07747 774 030 **(E)** footballsecretary@stowmarkettownfc.co.uk
Chairman: Neil Sharp **Manager:** Rick Andrews **Prog Ed:** Alex Moss
Ground: Greens Meadow, Bury Road, Stowmarket, Suffolk IP14 1JQ **(T)** 01449 612 533
Colours(change): Gold & black/black/black (All red)

ADDITIONAL INFORMATION:
Previous League: Essex & Suffolk Border. **Record Att:** 1,200 v Ipswich Town, friendly, July 1994.
Honours: Suffolk Senior Cup x10

SWAFFHAM TOWN

Founded: 1892 Nickname: Pedlars

Secretary: Ray Ewart **(T)** 07990 526 744 **(E)** rayewart@aol.com
Chairman: Wayne Hardy **Manager:** Paul Hunt **Prog Ed:** Andy Black
Ground: Shoemakers Lane, Swaffham, Norfolk PE37 7NT **(T)** 01760 722 700
Colours(change): Black & white stripes/black/black (All red)

ADDITIONAL INFORMATION:
Record Att: 250 v Downham Town, Eastern Counties League Cup, 03.09.91.
Honours: Eastern Counties Division 1 2000-01.

TEAM BURY

Founded: 2005 Nickname:

Secretary: Ross Wilding **(T)** 07971 199 810 **(E)** ross.wilding@wsc.ac.uk
Chairman: John Hall **Manager:** Ross Wilding **Prog Ed:** Ross Wilding
Ground: Bury Town FC, Ram Meadow, Cotton Lane, Bury St Edmunds IP33 1XP **(T)** 01284 754 721
Colours(change): All blue (All red)

ADDITIONAL INFORMATION:

WOODBRIDGE TOWN

Founded: 1885 Nickname: The Woodpeckers

Secretary: Terry Fryatt **(T)** 07803 073 558 **(E)** tfryatt6@btinternet.com
Chairman: John Beecroft **Manager:** Lee Elliston
Ground: Notcutts Park, Fynn Road, Woodbridge IP12 4LS **(T)** 01394 385 308 **Capacity:** 3,000
Colours(change): Black & white stripes/black/black. (All red).

ADDITIONAL INFORMATION: Att: 3,000 v Arsenal, for the opening of the floodlights, 02.10.90.
Suffolk Senior Cup 1885, 77-78, 92-93, 93-94.
Ipswich & District Senior Champions 1912-13. Suffolk & Ipswich Senior 1988-89.

GROUND DIRECTIONS

BRANTHAM ATHLETIC - Brantham Leisure Centre CO11 1RZ - 01206 392 506
Turn off the A12 heading towards East Bergholt, stay on the B1070 through East Bergholt and go straight across the roundabout with the A137. Turn left immediately at the T-junction and follow this road around the sharp curve to the right and turn right immediately before the Village Hall. Follow this road around the sharp left hand turn and the Social Club and the car park are on the right.

DISS TOWN - Brewers Green Lane IP22 4QP - 01379 651 223
Off B1066 Diss -Thetford road near Roydon school. One and a half miles from Diss (BR).

ELY CITY - Unwin Sports Ground CB6 2SH - 01353 662 035
Follow signs for Kings Lynn/Downham Market as you approach Ely. Don't go into the city centre. After the Little Chef roundabout (junction of A10/A142) continue for approx half a mile until the next roundabout. Turn left for Little Downham (the B1411). There is also a sign for a Golf Course. The Golf Course is part of a Sports Complex which includes the football club. After turning left at the roundabout take another left after only about 50 metres into the Sports Complex entrance. The football club is at the end of the drive past the rugby club and tennis courts.

FC CLACTON - Rush Green Bowl CO16 7BQ - 01255 432 590
Leave the A12 at junction 29, then at roundabout take the 1st exit, then merge onto the A120 (sign posted Clacton, Harwich). Branch left, then merge onto the A133 (sign posted Clacton). Continue along the A133 following signs to Clacton until St Johns Roundabout (tiled Welcome to Clacton sign) take the 4th exit onto St Johns Rd - B1027 (sign posted St Osyth) Entering Clacton On Sea B1027 (fire station on left). B1027 At second mini-roundabout turn left onto Cloes Lane (Budgens on right). Continue down Cloes Lane for about 1/2 mile, passing St.Clares School on your right, at traffic lights, turn right onto Rush Green Rd. Rush Green Bowl will then appear on the right after 1/4 mile.

FAKENHAM TOWN - Clipbush Pk, Clipbush Lane NR21 8SW - 01328 855 859
Corner of A148 & Clipbush Lane.

FELIXSTOWE & WALTON - Town Ground, Dellwood Ave IP11 9HT - 01394 282 917
The A12 meets the A14 (Felixstowe to M1/M6 trunk road) at Copdock interchange, just to the South of Ipswich. For Felixstowe take the A14 heading east over the Orwell Bridge. Follow the A14, for approx. 14 miles until you come to a large roundabout with a large water tower on your right, take the 1st exit off the roundabout, which is straight on. Take the first exit at the next roundabout, straight ahead again. At the next roundabout take the fourth exit onto Beatrice Avenue, take the first left into Dellwood Avenue. The ground is 100 yards down on the left behind tall wooden fencing.

GODMANCHESTER ROVERS - Bearscroft Lane PE29 2LQ - 07774 830 507
From A14 turn off for Godmanchester. Take A1198 towards Wood Green Animal Shelter, Bearscroft Lane is half mile from A14 on the left.

GORLESTON - Emerald Park, Woodfarm Lane NR31 9AQ - 01493 602 802
On Magdalen Estate follow signs to Crematorium, turn left and follow road to ground.

HADLEIGH UNITED - Millfield, Tinkers Lane IP7 5NG - 01473 822 165
On reaching Hadleigh High Street turn into Duke Street (right next to Library), continue on for approximately 150 metres and take left turn into narrow lane immediately after going over small bridge, continue to end of the lane where you will find the entrance to club car park.

HAVERHILL ROVERS - The New Croft, Chalkstone Way CB9 0LD - 01440 702 137
Take the A143 in to Haverhill and, at the roundabout by Tesco, turn left and then right in the one in front of the store. Carry on over the next roundabout past Aldi on the left and past the Sports Centre, Cricket Club and garage on the left. Just after the Workspace Office Solutions building take a right towards the town centre (towards Parking (South). The drive way into Hamlet Croft is a small turning on the left just after Croft Lane (look for the sign for Tudor Close).

IPSWICH WANDERERS - SEH Sports Centre IP4 3NR 01473 728 581

KIRKLEY & PAKEFIELD - K & P Community & Sports Club, Walmer Road, NR33 7LE - 01502 513 549.
From A12 to Lowestoft town centre and go over roundabout at Teamways Garage and past Teamways Pub. Take next left into Walmer Road.

MILDENHALL TOWN - Recreation Way, Mildenhall, Suffolk IP28 7HG - 01638 713449 (club)
Next to swimming pool and car park a quarter of a mile from town centre.

NEWMARKET TOWN - Town Ground, Cricket Field Road CB8 8BG - 01638 663 637 (club).
Four hundred yards from Newmarket BR.Turn right into Green Road and right at cross roads into new Cheveley Rd. Ground is at top on left.

NORWICH UNITED - Plantation Park, Blofield, Norwich, Norfolk NR13 4PL - 01603 716963 - Off the A47.

STANWAY ROVERS - `Hawthorns', New Farm Road CO3 0PG - 01206 578 187
Leave A12 at Jct 26 to A1124. Turn right(from London)or left from Ipswich onto Essex Yeomanry Way. A1124 towards Colchester 1st right into Villa Rd,then left into Chaple Rd, and left into New Farm Rd. Ground 400 yds on left.Nearest BR station is Colchester North.

THETFORD TOWN - Recreation Ground, Munford Road IP24 1NB - 01842 766 120
Off bypass (A11) at A143 junction - ground 800 yards next to sports ground.

WALSHAM LE WILLOWS - Walsham Sports Club, Summer Road IP31 3AH 01359 259 298
From Bury - Diss road (A143) turn off down Summer Lane in Walsham-le-Willows and ground is on the right.

WHITTON UNITED - King George V Playing Fields IP1 6LE - 01473 464 030
Turn off A14, junction A1156 approx 3 miles west of A12/A14 junction

WIVENHOE TOWN - Broad Lane, Elmstead Road CO7 7HA - 01206 825 380
The ground is situated off the B1027 to the north of Wivenhoe.

DIVISION ONE

AFC SUDBURY RESERVES - The Mel Group Stadium, King's Marsh Brundon Lane, Sudbury CO10 7HN
From Colchester, Bury St Edmunds and Ipswich: Enter Sudbury and follow signs for Halstead/Chelmsford. Go aross the river bridge and go under the old rail bridge, then turn right at the traffic lights (Kings Head) into Bulmer Road and the first right again into Brundon Lane. The road narrows before reaching ground on the right hand side.

BRAINTREE TOWN RESERVES - See Long Melford.

CORNARD UNITED - Blackhouse Lane CO10 0NL - 07811 096 382
Left off roundabout on A134 coming from Ipswich/Colchester into Sudbury, follow signs for Country Park - ground is immediately opposite along Blackhouse Lane.

DEBENHAM LC - Debenham Leisure Centre IP14 6BL - 01728 861 101
Approach Ipswich along the A14. Turn left at junction 51 onto the A140 signposted towards Norwich. After approx 4 miles turn right towards Mickfield and follow the road into Debenham turning left into Gracechurch Street. Debenham Leisure Centre is approx 1 mile on the right hand side.

DEREHAM TOWN - Aldiss Park, Norwich Road, Dereham, Norfolk NR20 3PX - 01362 690 460

DOWNHAM TOWN - Memorial Field, Lynn Road PE38 9QE - 01366 388 424
One and a quarter miles from Downham Market (BR) - continue to town clock, turn left and ground is three quarters of a mile down Lynn Road.

GREAT YARMOUTH TOWN - The Wellesley, Sandown Road NR30 1EY - 01493 656 099
Just off Marine Parade 200 yards north of the Britannia Pier. Half a mile from the BR station.

HALSTEAD TOWN - Rosemary Lane CO9 1HR - 01787 472 082
From A1311 Chelmsford to Braintree road follow signs to Halstead.

HAVERHILL BOROUGH - See Haverhill Rovers.

KING'S LYNN RESERVES - The Walks, Tennyson Road, King's Lynn PE30 5PB - 01553 760 060
At the roundabout, at the junction of A47 and the A17, follow the A47, signposted King's Lynn and Norwich. Travel along the dual carriageway for approx. one and a half miles branching off left, following the signs for Town Centre, onto the Hardwick roundabout. Take the first exit, following the signs for Town Centre, travel through two sets of traffic lights until reaching a further set of traffic lights at the Southgates roundabout. Take the fourth exit onto Vancouver Avenue, and travel for approx. 300 metres, going straight across a mini roundabout, The Walks is a further 200 metres along on the left hand side, with car parking outside the ground. The changing rooms and hospitality suite are located at the rear of the main stand.

LEISTON RESERVES - The LTAA, Victory Road, Leiston, Suffolk IP16 4DZ
Take junction 28 off the M25, take the A12/A1023 exit to Chelmsford/Romford/Brentwood, keep left at the fork, follow signs for Chelmsford/A12 (E) and merge onto A12, at the roundabout, take the 3rd exit onto the A14 ramp, merge onto A14, at junction 58, exit toward A12, keep left at the fork, follow signs for Lowestoft/Woodbridge/A12 (N) and merge onto A12, go through 7 roundabouts, turn right onto A1094, turn left onto Snape Rd/B1069, continue to follow B1069, turn left onto Victory Rd, ground will be on the left.

LONG MELFORD - Stoneylands Stadium CO10 9JY - 01787 312 187
Turn down St Catherine Road off Hall St (Bury-Sudbury road) and then turn left into New Road.

MARCH TOWN UNITED - GER Sports Ground PE15 8HS - 01354 653 073
5 mins from town centre, 10 mins from BR station.

NEEDHAM MARKET RESERVES - Bloomfields, Quinton Road, Needham Market IP6 8DA.

SAFFRON WALDEN TOWN - Catons Lane CB10 2DU - 01799 522 789
Into Castle Street off Saffron-W High St. Then left at T jct and 1st left by Victory Pub.

STOWMARKET TOWN - Greens Meadow, Bury Road IP14 1JQ - 01449 612 533
About 800 yards from Stowmarket station (BR).Turn right at lights and head out of town over roundabout into Bury Road, Ground is on the right.

SWAFFHAM TOWN - Shoemakers Lane PE37 7NT - 01760 722 700

TEAM BURY - Ram Meadow, Cotton Lane IP33 1XP - 01284 754 721

WOODBRIDGE TOWN - Notcutts Park, Seckford Hall Road IP12 4DA - 01394 385 308
From Lowestoft turn left into Woodbridge at last roundabout (or first roundabout from Ipswich). Take first turning left and first left again. Drive to ground at end of road on left.

ESSEX SENIOR LEAGUE

Sponsored by: No sponsor
Founded: 1971
Recent Champions:
2009: Romford
2010: Witham Town
2011: Enfield 1893
2012: Witham Town
2013: Burnham Ramblers
essexseniorfootballleague.moonfruit.com

		P	W	D	L	F	A	GD	Pts
1	(P) Great Wakering Rovers	38	29	5	4	112	40	72	92
2	Haringey Borough	38	29	4	5	103	31	72	91
3	Enfield 1893	38	28	5	5	102	39	63	89
4	Tower Hamlets	38	24	7	7	73	48	25	79
5	FC Romania	38	21	9	8	82	56	26	72
6	Sawbridgeworth Town	38	22	5	11	87	59	28	71
7	Takeley	38	17	5	16	64	72	-8	56
8	Basildon United	37	16	7	14	85	69	16	55
9	Hullbridge Sports	38	15	8	15	51	51	0	53
10	Clapton	38	14	8	16	54	54	0	50
11	Eton Manor	38	12	12	14	56	72	-16	48
12	Barking	38	13	7	18	61	60	1	46
13	Sporting Bengal United	38	12	8	18	74	99	-25	44
14	Bowers & Pitsea	38	11	10	17	60	72	-12	43
15	London APSA	38	10	8	20	53	70	-17	38
16	Ilford	38	9	7	22	50	86	-36	34
17	Stansted	38	8	8	22	50	87	-37	32
18	Greenhouse London	37	5	12	20	43	85	-42	27
19	Southend Manor	38	6	9	23	38	81	-43	27
20	London Bari	38	3	6	29	29	96	-67	15

LEAGUE CHALLENGE CUP

ROUND 1

Stansted	v	Sporting Bengal United	2-4
Barking	v	Haringey Borough	1-4
Clapton	v	Great Wakering Rovers	1-1 1-3p
Hullbridge Sports	v	Basildon United	0-2

ROUND 2

Sporting Bengal United	v	Haringey Borough	2-0
Ilford (Ilford reinstated)	v	London Bari	1-2
London APSA	v	Sawbridgeworth Town	2-1
Basildon United	v	Southend Manor	3-2
Enfield 1893	v	FC Romania	6-1
Great Wakering Rovers	v	Eton Manor	3-3 3-2p
Takeley	v	Bowers & Pitsea	3-1
Greenhouse London	v	Tower Hamlets	0-2

QUARTER FINALS

Sporting Bengal United	v	Ilford	5-2
London APSA	v	Basildon United	0-2
Enfield 1893	v	Great Wakering Rovers	0-2
Takeley	v	Tower Hamlets	0-0 4-2p

SEMI FINALS

Sporting Bengal United	v	Basildon United	2-1
Great Wakering Rovers	v	Takeley	2-2, 4-2p

FINAL

Great Wakering Rovers	v	Sporting Bengal United	1-0

	1	2	3	4	5	6	7	8	9	10	11	12	13	14	15	16	17	18	19	20
1 Barking		1–2	4–0	1–3	4–0	5–0	0–3	2–2	3–3	1–2	1–2	0–3	2–4	4–0	2–1	3–0	1–2	2–2	3–4	1–2
2 Basildon United	6–1		2–0	2–0	1–3	2–2	2–2	1–4	2–0	1–2	1–0	7–1	3–3	5–0	1–2	1–1	8–5	2–0	2–3	1–2
3 Bowers & Pitsea	0–2	3–1		0–0	2–2	1–2	0–3	2–5	2–2	1–5	3–0	3–3	2–2	2–0	0–1	2–4	4–1	2–2	3–0	5–1
4 Clapton	1–0	1–0	0–1		1–1	2–1	1–3	1–0	2–2	1–1	3–1	4–0	5–0	2–1	0–3	2–0	0–1	2–2	2–0	2–3
5 Enfield 1893	1–0	1–0	2–0	4–0		2–0	5–3	2–1	1–0	1–2	2–0	5–2	2–1	7–0	3–0	5–0	4–3	4–1	5–0	4–1
6 Eton Manor	0–0	5–1	1–1	3–1	1–4		1–4	1–1	0–0	0–4	0–0	0–3	1–1	3–0	1–1	1–1	5–2	4–1	2–3	0–5
7 FC Romania	2–1	3–3	3–2	4–2	2–1	3–0		2–4	4–2	0–0	1–3	1–0	1–3	2–0	1–2	3–2	2–3	1–0	5–1	1–1
8 Great Wakering Rovers	3–1	1–1	7–2	2–1	2–2	6–1	2–0		5–0	2–1	1–0	6–0	4–1	6–1	4–0	2–1	3–2	5–0	4–0	2–0
9 Greenhouse London	1–2	HW	1–0	3–2	2–5	1–2	1–1	0–2		1–2	1–3	1–1	0–4	1–1	1–6	2–1	1–1	2–5	1–1	1–3
10 Haringey Borough	2–0	6–0	4–1	2–1	2–0	2–1	1–2	4–2	3–0		3–1	3–2	2–0	4–1	2–0	5–0	3–0	5–0	3–0	3–0
11 Hullbridge Sports	1–1	1–2	3–2	0–0	3–2	0–0	1–2	0–1	2–0	1–5		0–1	2–1	5–2	2–1	0–0	1–0	2–1	1–1	2–0
12 Ilford	0–1	3–5	2–1	1–1	0–2	1–2	0–2	1–3	4–0	0–2	0–4		1–0	2–0	0–2	3–3	2–2	3–1	0–1	0–3
13 London APSA	1–1	1–2	0–2	1–2	1–1	0–1	0–2	3–1	2–2	3–2	1–2	3–1		1–1	1–4	0–2	4–2	1–1	3–1	1–2
14 London Bari	1–2	1–4	0–2	0–2	0–1	2–3	3–3	0–2	0–1	0–2	1–1	0–1	3–1		0–4	0–0	2–1	0–2	0–1	2–3
15 Sawbridgeworth Town	2–1	3–2	1–1	3–1	0–2	6–3	5–2	0–1	4–3	3–1	0–2	2–2	4–2	5–1		3–2	2–2	3–2	2–1	1–1
16 Southend Manor	0–4	1–0	0–1	2–1	1–4	0–0	1–4	0–2	1–2	0–0	1–1	4–1	0–1	4–0	1–7		0–3	0–2	0–2	0–2
17 Sporting Bengal United	1–2	2–2	2–5	3–2	0–6	2–1	1–1	2–6	2–2	0–7	3–1	1–1	0–1	2–1	4–0	6–2		3–1	2–7	1–2
18 Stansted	0–0	0–6	1–1	1–2	1–2	1–3	1–1	2–4	3–1	1–3	2–1	4–1	2–1	0–1	2–1	1–1	2–6		1–3	0–3
19 Takeley	0–2	2–3	2–0	2–1	0–3	1–2	0–0	1–2	0–0	2–2	2–1	4–2	3–0	3–2	0–2	3–1	5–1	3–2		1–4
20 Tower Hamlets	3–0	3–1	1–1	0–0	0–1	2–1	1–3	2–2	3–2	2–1	3–1	3–2	1–0	2–2	2–1	2–1	0–0	2–0	3–1	

ESSEX SENIOR - STEP 5

	Reserve Division East	P	W	D	L	F	A	GD	Pts
1	Canvey Island Reserves	16	13	1	2	53	19	34	40
2	Thurrock Reserves	16	10	4	2	43	21	22	34
3	East Thurrock United Reserves	16	9	3	4	40	17	23	30
4	Southend Manor Reserves	16	9	1	6	35	27	8	28
5	Tilbury Reserves	16	8	3	5	37	28	9	27
6	Burnham Ramblers Reserves	16	4	5	7	33	32	1	17
7	Hullbridge Sports Reserves	16	4	3	9	24	47	-23	15
8	Great Wakering Rovers Res.	16	2	3	11	19	49	-30	9
9	Bowers & Pitsea Reserves	16	1	1	14	21	65	-44	4

	Reserve Division West	P	W	D	L	F	A	GD	Pts
1	Barking Reserves	14	10	2	2	31	12	19	32
2	Chelmsford City Reserves	14	9	2	3	50	20	30	29
3	Romford Reserves	14	9	2	3	35	21	14	29
4	AFC Hornchurch Res. (-3)	14	8	2	4	25	18	7	23
5	Takeley Reserves	14	6	1	7	29	43	-14	19
6	Sawbridgeworth Town Reserves	14	5	3	6	30	31	-1	18
7	London APSA Reserves	14	2	2	10	16	32	-16	8
8	Clapton Reserves	14	0	0	14	12	51	-39	0

GORDON BRASTED MEMORIAL CUP

ROUND 1

Great Wakering Rovers	v	Sporting Bengal United	10-2
Basildon United	v	London Bari	3-0
Tower Hamlets	v	Clapton	0-3
Enfield 1893	v	Bowers & Pitsea	2-1

ROUND 2

Haringey Borough	v	Great Wakering Rovers	4-0
Basildon United	v	Takeley	0-1
Eton Manor	v	Clapton	4-1
FC Romania	v	London APSA	0-1
Hullbridge Sports	v	Ilford	6-0
Greenhouse London	v	Enfield 1893	1-3
Sawbridgeworth Town	v	Stansted	4-3
Southend Manor	v	Barking	3-1

QUARTER FINALS

Haringey Borough	v	Takeley	3-1
Eton Manor	v	London APSA	1-2
Hullbridge Sports	v	Enfield 1893	HW
Sawbridgeworth	v	Southend Manor	4-0

SEMI FINALS

Hullbridge Sports	v	Sawbridgeworth Town	2-0
Haringey Borough	v	London APSA	4-2

FINAL

Haringey Borough	v	Hullbridge Sports	0-1

CLUB MOVEMENTS

Premier Division - In: Newham (NC - formerly London APSA). Waltham Forest (R - Isthmian Div.1 North).

Out: Great Wakering Rovers (P - Isthmian Div.1 North). London APSA (NC - Newham).

BARKING
Founded: 1880 Nickname: The Blues

Secretary: John Bryant **(T)** **(E)** barlexbryant@btinternet.com
Chairman: Rob O'Brien **Manager:** Mick O'Shea **Prog Ed:** Ashley Hanson
Ground: Mayesbrook Park, Lodge Avenue, Dagenham RM8 2JR **(T)** 0776 458 7112
Capacity: 2,500 **Seats:** 200 **Covered:** 600 **Midweek Matchday:** Tuesday **Clubhouse:** Yes **Shop:** Yes

Colours(change): All blue.
Previous Names: Barking Rov. Barking Woodville. Barking Working Lads Institute, Barking Institute. Barking T. Barking & East Ham U.
Previous Leagues: South Essex, London, Athenian. Isthmian. Southern.
Records: **Att:** 1,972 v Aldershot, FA Cup 2nd Rnd, 1978. **Goalscorer:** Neville Fox - 241 (65-73). **Apps:** Bob Makin - 566.
Senior Honours: Essex Senior Cup 1893-94, 95-96, 1919-20, 45-46, 62-63, 69-70, 89-90. London Senior Cup 1911-12, 20-21, 26-27, 78-79.

10 YEAR RECORD

04-05	05-06	06-07	07-08	08-09	09-10	10-11	11-12	12-13	13-14
SthE 6	SthE 5	ESen 6	ESen 9	ESen 12	ESen 8	ESen 6	ESen 7	ESen 6	ESen 12

BASILDON UNITED
Founded: 1963 Nickname: The Bees

Secretary: Richard Mann **(T)** 07527 743 535 **(E)**
Chairman: Dave Maxwell **Manager:** Colin Cook **Prog Ed:** Richard Mann
Ground: The Stadium, Gardiners Close, Basildon SS14 3AW **(T)** 01268 520 268
Capacity: 2,000 **Seats:** 400 **Covered:** 1,000 **Midweek Matchday:** Wednesday **Clubhouse:** Yes **Shop:** No

Colours(change): Yellow & black
Previous Names: Armada Sports.
Previous Leagues: Grays & Thurrock. Greater London. Essex Senior. Athenian. Isthmian.
Records: **Att:** 4,000 v West Ham, ground opening 11.08.70.
Senior Honours: Isthmian League Division 2 Champions 1983-84.

10 YEAR RECORD

04-05	05-06	06-07	07-08	08-09	09-10	10-11	11-12	12-13	13-14
ESen 7	ESen 11	ESen 10	ESen 16	ESen 8	ESen 12	ESen 12	ESen 18	ESen 13	ESen 8

BOWERS & PITSEA
Founded: 1946 Nickname:

Secretary: Lee Stevens **(T)** 07910 626 727 **(E)** lee-stevens@sky.com
Chairman: Barry Hubbard **Manager:** Rob Small **Prog Ed:** Lee Stevens
Ground: Len Salmon Stadium, Crown Avenue, Pitsea, Basildon SS13 2BE **(T)** 01268 581 977
Capacity: 2,000 **Seats:** 200 **Covered:** 1,000 **Midweek Matchday:** Wednesday **Clubhouse:** Yes **Shop:** Yes

Colours(change): All claret. (All sky blue).
Previous Names: Bowers United > 2004.
Previous Leagues: Thurrock & Thameside Combination. Olympian.
Records: **Att:** 1,800 v Billericay Town, FA Vase. **Most goals in a season:** David Hope - 50 1998-99.
Senior Honours: Essex Senior 1980-81, 98-99.

10 YEAR RECORD

04-05	05-06	06-07	07-08	08-09	09-10	10-11	11-12	12-13	13-14
ESen 10	ESen 15	ESen 4	ESen 7	ESen 11	ESen 17	ESen 14	ESen 15	ESen 19	ESen 14

CLAPTON
Founded: 1878 Nickname: Tons

Secretary: Shirley Doyle **(T)** 0798 358 8883 **(E)** ShirleyDoyle@claptonfc.com
Chairman: John Murray Smith **Manager:** Mike Walther
Ground: The Old Spotted Dog, Upton Lane, Forest Gate E7 9NU **(T)** 0794 400 9386
Capacity: 2,000 **Seats:** 100 **Covered:** 180 **Midweek Matchday:** Tuesday **Clubhouse:** Yes **Shop:** No

Colours(change): Red & white
Previous Names: None
Previous Leagues: Southern (founder member). London. Isthmian (founder member).
Records: **Att:** 12,000 v Tottenham Hotspur, FA Cup, 1898-99. First English club to play on the continent, beating a Belgian XI in 1890.
Senior Honours: Isthmian League Champions 1910-11, 22-23, Division 2 1982-83. Essex Senior Cup (x 4).

10 YEAR RECORD

04-05	05-06	06-07	07-08	08-09	09-10	10-11	11-12	12-13	13-14
Isth2 16	Isth2 16	ESen 14	ESen 11	ESen 16	ESen 16	ESen 17	ESen 17	ESen 18	ESen 10

ENFIELD 1893 FC

Founded: 1893 Nickname:

Secretary: Mark Wiggs **(T)** 0795 764 7820 **(E)** enfieldfc@ntlworld.com
Chairman: Steve Whittington **Manager:** Paul Norris
Ground: The Harlow Arena, Elizabeth Way, Harlow, Essex CM19 5BE **(T)** 07957 647 820
Capacity: **Seats:** **Covered:** **Midweek Matchday:** **Clubhouse:** Yes

Colours(change): Blue & white
Previous Names: Enfield Spartans > 1900. Enfield > 2007.
Previous Leagues: Tottenham & District, North Middlesex, London, Athenian, Isthmian, Alliance, Southern
Records: **Att:** 10,000 v Spurs, floodlight opening at Southbury Rd., 10.10.62. **Goals:** Tommy Lawrence - 191 (1959-64). **Apps:** Andy Pape - 643 (85-92 93-99)
Senior Honours: FA Trophy 1981-82, 87-88. Alliance League 1982-83, 85-86. FA Amateur Cup 1966-67, 69-70. Essex Senior League 2010-11.

10 YEAR RECORD

04-05	05-06	06-07	07-08	08-09	09-10	10-11	11-12	12-13	13-14
Isth2 2	SthE 16	Isth1N 13	ESen 2	ESen 2	ESen 4	ESen 1	ESen 7	ESen 9	ESen 3

ETON MANOR

Founded: 1901 Nickname: The Manor

Secretary: Alex Lee (General Manager) **(T)** **(E)**
Chairman: Reg Curtis **Manager:** Kieren King **Prog Ed:** Reg Curtis
Ground: Waltham Abbey FC, Capershotts, Sewardstone Road, Waltham Abbey EN9 1LU **(T)** 01992 711 287
Capacity: 2,500 **Seats:** 200 **Covered:** 600 **Midweek Matchday:** Monday **Clubhouse:** Yes

Colours(change): Sky blue & navy
Previous Names: Wildernes Leyton.
Previous Leagues: London. Greater London. Metropolitan.
Records: **Att:** 600 v Leyton Orient, opening of floodlights. **Goalscorer:** Dave Sams.
Senior Honours:

10 YEAR RECORD

04-05	05-06	06-07	07-08	08-09	09-10	10-11	11-12	12-13	13-14
ESen 12	ESen 13	ESen 11	ESen 4	ESen 6	ESen 15	ESen 8	ESen 14	ESen 5	ESen 11

F.C. ROMANIA

Founded: 2006 Nickname:

Secretary: Emil Vintila **(T)** 07907 944 409 **(E)** emilvintila17@yahoo.co.uk
Chairman: Ion Vintila **Manager:** Ion Vintila
Ground: Cheshunt FC, Theobalds Lane, Cheshunt, Herts EN8 8RU **(T)** 01992 625 793
Capacity: 3,500 **Seats:** 424 **Covered:** 600 **Midweek Matchday:** **Clubhouse:** Yes

Colours(change): Yellow/blue/yellow (All orange)
Previous Names: None
Previous Leagues: Middlesex County 2006-13.
Records:
Senior Honours:

10 YEAR RECORD

04-05	05-06	06-07	07-08	08-09	09-10	10-11	11-12	12-13	13-14
							MidxP 2	MidxP 2	ESen 5

GREENHOUSE LONDON

Founded: 2000 Nickname:

Secretary: Rosie Garnett **(T)** **(E)** rosie.garnett@greenhousecharity.org
Chairman: Trevor Duberry **Prog Ed:** Shane Dorsett
Ground: Haringey Boro' FC, Coles Park, White Hart Lane N17 7JP **(T)**
Capacity: **Seats:** **Covered:** **Midweek Matchday:** Wednesday **Clubhouse:** Yes **Shop:** No

Colours(change): All red
Previous Names: Mauritius Sports merged with Walthamstow Avenue & Pennant 2007. Mauritius Sports Association 2009-11. Haringey & Waltham Development 2011-13
Previous Leagues: London Intermediate 2001-03. Middlesex County 2003-2007.
Records:
Senior Honours:

10 YEAR RECORD

04-05	05-06	06-07	07-08	08-09	09-10	10-11	11-12	12-13	13-14
			ESen 13	ESen 15	ESen 18	ESen 11	ESen 12	ESen 8	ESen 18

HARINGEY BOROUGH

Founded: 1907 Nickname: Borough

Secretary: John Bacon **(T)** 07979 050 190 **(E)** baconjw@hotmail.com
Chairman: Aki Achillea **Manager:** Tom Loizu **Prog Ed:** John Bacon
Ground: Coles Park, White Hart Lane, Tottenham, London N17 7JP **(T)** 0208 889 1415 (Matchday)
Capacity: 2,500 **Seats:** 280 **Covered:** yes **Midweek Matchday:** **Clubhouse:** Yes **Shop:** No

Colours(change): Green
Previous Names: Tufnell Park 1907
Previous Leagues: London, Isthmian, Spartan, Delphian, Athenian, Spartan South Midlands > 2013.
Records: **Att:** 400
Senior Honours: London Senior Cup 1912-13, 90-91, Athenian League 1913-14

10 YEAR RECORD

04-05	05-06	06-07	07-08	08-09	09-10	10-11	11-12	12-13	13-14
SSM P 18	SSM P 19	SSM P 21	SSM1 2	SSM P 18	SSM P 15	SSM P 8	SSM P 5	SSM P 9	ESen 2

HULLBRIDGE SPORTS

Founded: 1945 Nickname:

Secretary: Mrs Beryl Petre **(T)** 01702 230 630 **(E)** beryl@petre1942.fsnet.co.uk
Chairman: Andrew Burgess **Prog Ed:** Beryl Petre
Ground: Lower Road, Hullbridge, Hockley Essex SS5 6BJ **(T)** 01702 230 420
Capacity: 1,500 **Seats:** 60 **Covered:** 60 **Midweek Matchday:** Tuesday **Clubhouse:** Yes **Shop:** No

Colours(change): Royal blue & white stripes/royal/royal.
Previous Names: None
Previous Leagues: Southend & District. Southend Alliance.
Records: **Att:** 800 v Blackburn Rovers, FA Youth Cup 1999-00.
Senior Honours:

10 YEAR RECORD

04-05	05-06	06-07	07-08	08-09	09-10	10-11	11-12	12-13	13-14
ESen 15	ESen 14	ESen 12	ESen 14	ESen 9	ESen 11	ESen 9	ESen 11	ESen 15	ESen 9

ILFORD

Founded: 1987 Nickname: The Foxes

Secretary: Marion Chilvers **(T)** 07710 285571 **(E)** rogerchilvers@aol.com
Chairman: Roger Chilvers **Manager:** Martin Haywood **Prog Ed:** Len Llewellyn
Ground: Cricklefield Stadium, 486 High Road, Ilford, Essex IG1 1UE **(T)** 020 8514 8352
Capacity: 3,500 **Seats:** 216 **Covered:** Yes **Midweek Matchday:** **Clubhouse:** Yes **Shop:** No

Colours(change): Blue and white hoops/blue/blue (All red)
Previous Names: Reformed as Ilford in 1987 after the original club merged with Leytonstone in 1980.
Previous Leagues: Spartan 1987-94, Essex Senior 1996-2004, Isthmian 2004-05, 2006-13, Southern 2005-06.
Records: Not known
Senior Honours: Isthmian League Division Two 2004-05.

10 YEAR RECORD

04-05	05-06	06-07	07-08	08-09	09-10	10-11	11-12	12-13	13-14
Isth2 1	SthE 21	Isth1N 21	Isth1N 21	Isth1N 17	Isth1N 20	Isth1N 20	Isth1N 20	Isth1N 22	ESen 16

LONDON BARI

Founded: 1995 Nickname:

Secretary: Malin Hagerberg (Publicity M'ger) **(T)** 02076 840 793 **(E)**
Chairman: Kashka Anthony Ray **Manager:** Christopher Davis-Emokpae
Ground: The Old Spotted Dog, Upton Lane, Forest Gate E7 9NP **(T)** 02076 840 793
Capacity: 2,000 **Seats:** 100 **Covered:** 180 **Midweek Matchday:** **Clubhouse:** Yes

Colours(change): All red
Previous Names: Bari FC.
Previous Leagues: South Essex 1995-98. Asian League. Essex Sunday Corinthian League > 2012.
Records:
Senior Honours:

10 YEAR RECORD

04-05	05-06	06-07	07-08	08-09	09-10	10-11	11-12	12-13	13-14
							EsxSC 1	ESen 10	ESen 20

NEWHAM

Founded: 1993 Nickname:

Secretary: Zabir Bashir **(T)** 07956 660 699 **(E)** zabirbashir23@hotmail.com

Chairman: Zulfi Ali **Manager:** Zak Hussein

Ground: Terrence McMillan Stadium, Maybury Road, London E13 8RZ **(T)**

Capacity: 2000 **Seats:** **Covered:** **Midweek Matchday:** **Clubhouse:**

Colours(change): All blue
Previous Names: Ahle Sunnah. London APSA > 2014
Previous Leagues: Asian League.
Records:
Senior Honours:

10 YEAR RECORD

04-05	05-06	06-07	07-08	08-09	09-10	10-11	11-12	12-13	13-14
ESen 13	ESen 9	ESen 13	ESen 17	ESen 14	ESen 13	ESen 10	ESen 13	ESen 16	ESen 15

SAWBRIDGEWORTH TOWN

Founded: 1890 Nickname: Robins

Secretary: Lesley Atkins **(T)** **(E)** sawbosec@hotmail.com

Chairman: Steve Day **Manager:** Pete Wickham

Ground: Crofters End, West Road, Sawbridgeworth CM21 0DE **(T)** 01279 722 039

Capacity: 2,500 **Seats:** 175 **Covered:** 300 **Midweek Matchday:** Tuesday **Clubhouse:** Yes **Shop:** No

Colours(change): Red & black
Previous Names: Sawbridgeworth > 1976.
Previous Leagues: Stortford. Spartan. Herts County. Essex Olympian.
Records: **Att:** 610 v Bishops Stortford.
Senior Honours:

10 YEAR RECORD

04-05	05-06	06-07	07-08	08-09	09-10	10-11	11-12	12-13	13-14
ESen 8	ESen 6	ESen 8	ESen 12	ESen 13	ESen 10	ESen 16	ESen 6	ESen 14	ESen 6

SOUTHEND MANOR

Founded: 1955 Nickname: The Manor

Secretary: Rik Moran **(T)** 01702 615 577 **(E)** rikjmoran@gmail.com

Chairman: Steven Robinson **Manager:** Wayne Seal

Ground: The Arena, Southchurch Pk, Lifstan Way, Southend SS1 2TH **(T)** 01702 615 577

Capacity: 2,000 **Seats:** 500 **Covered:** 700 **Midweek Matchday:** Tuesday **Clubhouse:** Yes **Shop:** No

Colours(change): Yellow & black
Previous Names: None
Previous Leagues: Southend Borough Combination. Southend & District Alliance.
Records: **Att:** 1,521 v Southend United, opening floodlights, 22.07.91.
Senior Honours: Essex Senior Division One 1987-88. Essex Senior League 1990-91.
Essex Senior League Cup 1987-88, 89-90, 2000-01. Essex Senior Trophy 1992-93.

10 YEAR RECORD

04-05	05-06	06-07	07-08	08-09	09-10	10-11	11-12	12-13	13-14
ESen 6	ESen 10	ESen 9	ESen 6	ESen 4	ESen 7	ESen 5	ESen 2	ESen 7	ESen 19

SPORTING BENGAL UNITED

Founded: 1996 Nickname: Bengal Tigers

Secretary: Khayrul Alam **(T)** 0207 392 2126 **(E)** bfauk@btconnect.com

Chairman: Aroz Miah **Manager:** Mamun Chowdhury

Ground: Mile End Stadium, Rhodeswell Rd, Off Burdett Rd E14 4TW **(T)** 020 8980 1885

Capacity: **Seats:** Yes **Covered:** **Midweek Matchday:** Wednesday **Clubhouse:**

Colours(change): All royal blue
Previous Names: None.
Previous Leagues: Asian League. London Intermediate, Kent 2003-11.
Records: **Att:** 4,235 v Touring Phalco Mohammedan S.C.
Senior Honours:

10 YEAR RECORD

04-05	05-06	06-07	07-08	08-09	09-10	10-11	11-12	12-13	13-14
Kent P 14	Kent P 15	Kent P 17	Kent P 17	Kent P 17	Kent P 15	Kent P 15	ESen 10	ESen 11	ESen 13

STANSTED

Founded: 1902 Nickname: Blues

Secretary: Tom Williams **(T)** 07921 403 842 **(E)** stanstedfc@yahoo.co.uk
Chairman: Glyn Warwick **Manager:** Paul Attfield
Ground: Hargrave Park, Cambridge Road, Stansted CM24 8BY **(T)** 07921 403 842
Capacity: 2,000 **Seats:** 200 **Covered:** 400 **Midweek Matchday:** Tuesday **Clubhouse:** Yes **Shop:** No

Colours(change): All royal blue
Previous Names: None.
Previous Leagues: Spartan. London. Herts County.
Records: **Att:** 828 v Whickham, FA Vase, 1983-84.
Senior Honours:

10 YEAR RECORD

04-05	05-06	06-07	07-08	08-09	09-10	10-11	11-12	12-13	13-14
ESen 11	ESen 16	ESen 16	ESen 10	ESen 10	ESen 1	ESen 2	ESen 16	ESen 17	ESen 17

TAKELEY

Founded: 1903 Nickname:

Secretary: Mick Rabey **(T)** 07831 845 466 **(E)** Takeleyfc@mail.com
Chairman: Pat Curran **Manager:** Duncan Easley
Ground: Station Road, Takeley, Bishop's Stortford CM22 6QA **(T)** 01279 870 404
Capacity: **Seats:** Yes **Covered:** Yes **Midweek Matchday:** Tuesday **Clubhouse:** Yes

Colours(change): All royal blue with white trim. (All red with white trim).
Previous Names: None.
Previous Leagues: Essex Intermediate/Olympian.
Records:
Senior Honours: Essex Olympian League 2001-02.

10 YEAR RECORD

04-05	05-06	06-07	07-08	08-09	09-10	10-11	11-12	12-13	13-14
EssxO 8	EssxO 9	EssxO 3	EssxO 2	ESen 3	ESen 6	ESen 13	ESen 3	ESen 3	ESen 7

TOWER HAMLETS

Founded: 2000 Nickname: Green Army

Secretary: Adam Richardson **(T)** 07535 858 493 **(E)** thfcsecretary@hotmail.com
Chairman: Mohammed Nural Hoque
Ground: Mile End Stadium, Rhodeswell Rd, Poplar E14 7TW **(T)** 020 8980 1885
Capacity: 2,000 **Seats:** Yes **Covered:** Yes **Midweek Matchday:** Wednesday **Clubhouse:**

Colours(change): Red & black
Previous Names: Bethnal Green United 2000-2013.
Previous Leagues: Middlesex 2000-09.
Records:
Senior Honours:

10 YEAR RECORD

04-05	05-06	06-07	07-08	08-09	09-10	10-11	11-12	12-13	13-14
MidxP 7			MidxP 8	MidxP 1	ESen 5	ESen 4	ESen 9	ESen 12	ESen 4

WALTHAM FOREST

Founded: 1964 Nickname: The Stags

Secretary: Tony Brazier **(T)** 0771 564 0171 **(E)** bjmapbr@ntlworld.com
Chairman: Turgut Esendagli **Manager:** Turgut Esendagli **Prog Ed:** Andrzej Perkins
Ground: Wadham Lodge, Kitchener Road, Walthamstow E17 4JP **(T)** 02085 272 444
Capacity: 3,500 **Seats:** 216 **Covered:** Yes **Midweek Matchday:** Tuesday **Clubhouse:** Yes

Colours(change): White/blue/blue (Orange/black/orange)
Previous Names: Pennant 1964-88. Walthamstow Pennant 1988-95. Merged with Leyton to form Leyton Pennant 1995-2003.
Previous Leagues: Isthmian 2003-04, 06-14. Southern 2004-06.
Records:
Senior Honours: Essex Senior Cup 2005-06.

10 YEAR RECORD

04-05	05-06	06-07	07-08	08-09	09-10	10-11	11-12	12-13	13-14
SthE 9	SthE 8	Isth1N 8	Isth1N 19	Isth1N 20	Isth1N 16	Isth1N 21	Isth1N 17	Isth1N 18	Isth1N 23

HELLENIC LEAGUE

Sponsored by: Uhlsport
Founded: 1953
Recent Champions:
2009: Hungerford Town
2010: Almondsbury Town
2011: Wantage Town
2012: Oxford City Nomads
2013: Marlow
hellenicleague.co.uk

PREMIER DIVISION	P	W	D	L	F	A	GD	Pts
1 (P) Wantage Town	38	30	3	5	103	40	63	93
2 Ardley United	38	28	7	3	100	32	68	91
3 Ascot United	38	23	9	6	101	34	67	78
4 Highmoor Ibis	38	23	8	7	77	42	35	76
5 Binfield	38	21	6	11	74	50	24	69
6 Kidlington	38	20	6	12	75	61	14	66
7 Highworth Town	38	18	7	13	74	60	14	61
8 Flackwell Heath	38	17	9	12	83	50	33	60
9 Oxford City Nomads	38	18	5	15	97	67	30	59
10 Thame United	38	15	10	13	64	56	8	55
11 Reading Town	38	16	6	16	54	53	1	54
12 Brimscombe & Thrupp	38	16	4	18	68	70	-2	52
13 Bracknell Town	38	15	5	18	59	65	-6	50
14 Wootton Bassett Town	38	11	12	15	60	60	0	45
15 Shrivenham	38	13	4	21	77	86	-9	43
16 Cheltenham Saracens	38	12	3	23	54	101	-47	39
17 Abingdon United	38	8	4	26	45	102	-57	28
18 Holyport	38	6	5	27	42	114	-72	23
19 Newbury	38	5	7	26	60	113	-53	22
20 (R) Abingdon Town	38	2	6	30	31	142	-111	12

LEAGUE CHALLENGE CUP

ROUND 1

Ardley United	v	Malmesbury Victoria	8-0
Ascot United	v	Newbury	7-1
Bracknell Town	v	Binfield	2-2 4-5p
Brimscombe & Thrupp	v	North Leigh United	4-2
Carterton	v	Didcot Town	2-0
Chalfont Wasps	v	Easington Sports	0-2
Clanfield	v	Abingdon United	2-3
Cricklade Town	v	Cheltenham Saracens	AW
Headington Amateurs	v	Purton	0-2
Highworth Town	v	Oxford City Nomads	3-1
Hook Norton	v	Kidlington	2-4
Lydney Town	v	Wootton Bassett Town	5-2
Maidenhead United	v	Holyport	5-4
Milton United	v	Thame United	1-0
Old Woodstock Town	v	Abingdon Town	1-4
Reading Town	v	Highmoor Ibis	0-2
Shrivenham	v	Wokingham & Emmbrook	3-0
Tuffley Rovers	v	Chinnor	3-0
Wantage Town	v	Fairford Town	4-2
Woodley Town	v	Tytherington Rocks	1-3

ROUND 2

AFC Hinksey	v	Burnham	2-0
Ascot United	v	Kidlington	4-0
Beverstock	v	Purton	1-3
Easington Sports	v	Abingdon Town	3-1
Finchampstead	v	Flackwell Heath	3-5
Highmoor Ibis	v	Tytherington Rocks	2-4
Letcombe	v	Cirencester Town Dev.	1-5
Lydney Town	v	Shortwood United Reserves	1-3
Milton United	v	Cheltenham Saracens	1-1 7-6
Tuffley Rovers	v	Wantage Town	2-3
Carterton	v	Abingdon United	0-4
New College Swindon	v	Rayners Lane	1-3
Penn & Tylers Green	v	Ardley United	0-2
Brimscombe & Thrupp	v	Highworth Town	0-1
Shrivenham	v	Maidenhead United	4-3
Henley Town	v	Binfield	0-1

ROUND 3

AFC Hinksey	v	Abingdon United	3-3, 2-3p
Ardley United	v	Cirencester Town Dev.	2-0
Easington Sports	v	Rayners Lane	2-3
Flackwell Heath	v	Highworth Town	1-1, 4-3p
Milton United	v	Shortwood United Reserves	0-1
Purton	v	Ascot United	1-4
Shrivenham	v	Wantage Town	0-1
Tytherington Rocks	v	Binfield	2-0

PREMIER DIVISION	1	2	3	4	5	6	7	8	9	10	11	12	13	14	15	16	17	18	19	20
1 Abingdon Town		0–1	1–5	1–1	1–5	1–1	1–3	0–3	1–4	1–1	1–4	1–3	1–4	1–1	2–1	1–1	1–4	0–7	1–5	0–5
2 Abingdon United	2–0		1–4	0–5	0–3	1–4	0–4	1–4	0–5	1–3	2–6	1–2	1–1	2–5	0–2	2–3	3–2	2–2	0–3	4–3
3 Ardley United	1–1	4–0		2–2	1–0	3–1	3–0	2–1	3–0	2–0	4–4	5–1	2–0	5–1	4–1	2–1	3–2	2–0	3–0	1–1
4 Ascot United	10–0	4–1	0–1		1–0	3–1	1–1	3–1	3–0	2–2	2–2	6–0	0–1	3–1	3–1	1–2	2–0	4–0	1–2	1–1
5 Binfield	7–0	3–2	0–3	0–1		2–2	0–1	8–1	1–0	2–1	1–0	2–0	3–1	3–2	3–2	2–3	2–1	1–1	2–1	1–0
6 Bracknell Town	2–0	1–2	1–2	0–5	0–2		1–0	2–1	2–0	1–2	2–0	2–2	0–2	3–3	0–2	4–0	3–2	0–4	0–1	4–1
7 Brimscombe & Thrupp	5–3	0–1	0–6	2–4	2–3	2–1		2–0	2–1	1–2	3–4	2–0	0–5	4–0	1–2	3–2	1–4	2–4	3–4	0–1
8 Cheltenham Saracens	2–1	2–1	0–6	1–5	2–1	1–3	1–2		0–5	0–4	2–1	4–0	4–3	2–1	3–1	1–3	2–1	3–3	1–6	2–1
9 Flackwell Heath	3–0	3–0	3–1	0–4	1–1	0–0	0–3	2–2		2–2	4–0	6–2	9–0	3–2	4–1	1–0	5–3	0–2	1–0	1–1
10 Highmoor Ibis	5–0	3–1	2–1	1–1	2–1	3–2	1–0	2–0	1–0		3–0	3–0	1–2	0–0	2–1	1–0	2–1	0–1	1–2	2–2
11 Highworth Town	5–0	1–0	1–1	0–2	1–1	1–0	1–2	2–0	4–3	1–1		7–0	3–2	4–0	0–2	1–0	2–3	1–0	2–4	1–1
12 Holyport	5–2	1–1	1–3	0–4	2–3	1–4	0–3	0–0	1–4	0–2	1–2		2–6	3–2	2–3	0–1	3–2	1–4	0–6	0–0
13 Kidlington	1–0	3–0	0–0	2–0	1–1	3–0	3–2	3–1	1–1	3–2	1–2	2–0		4–2	1–4	2–1	2–3	1–1	0–1	2–3
14 Newbury	3–4	3–1	0–4	2–4	3–4	0–3	0–2	2–1	1–7	2–3	3–2	3–3	0–1		3–2	1–2	4–5	1–1	1–1	2–2
15 Oxford City Nomads	8–0	0–0	4–3	2–2	0–1	4–5	2–2	12–0	2–0	1–4	4–1	5–1	2–2	9–1		0–5	4–2	1–2	0–4	2–0
16 Reading Town	1–0	1–0	0–2	1–1	2–3	3–0	0–0	1–0	1–3	0–1	0–0	2–0	0–1	2–1	0–3		1–2	1–0	0–3	2–1
17 Shrivenham	7–1	3–4	0–2	1–4	5–0	3–1	4–4	3–2	1–1	1–5	1–3	0–3	2–0	2–1	1–1	1–4		0–1	1–1	1–2
18 Thame United	3–0	4–2	1–1	0–3	2–1	0–1	1–2	3–1	0–0	3–4	0–2	2–0	1–3	3–1	3–2	2–2	1–2		0–3	0–0
19 Wantage Town	10–2	3–2	0–1	2–1	1–1	3–1	2–1	4–3	1–0	2–1	3–1	3–0	3–2	5–1	0–3	3–2	2–1	4–0		1–0
20 Wootton Bassett Town	3–1	2–3	1–2	0–2	1–0	0–1	2–1	1–0	1–1	2–2	1–2	6–2	3–4	3–1	0–1	4–4	3–0	2–2	0–4	

HELLENIC LEAGUE - STEP 5/6

DIVISION ONE EAST	P	W	D	L	F	A	GD	Pts
1 (P) Milton United	26	18	4	4	61	22	39	58
2 Wokingham & Emmbrook	26	16	5	5	66	45	21	53
3 AFC Hinksey	25	16	3	6	72	32	40	51
4 Headington Amateurs	26	15	6	5	54	35	19	51
5 Penn & Tylers Green	26	13	4	9	63	48	15	43
6 Chalfont Wasps	25	13	2	10	49	40	9	41
7 Henley Town	26	11	3	12	52	53	-1	36
8 Chinnor	26	10	5	11	54	42	12	35
9 Rayners Lane	26	10	5	11	48	52	-4	35
10 Burnham	26	11	1	14	39	58	-19	34
11 Maidenhead United	26	8	7	11	46	55	-9	31
12 Didcot Town	26	7	2	17	44	69	-25	23
13 Finchampstead	26	5	1	20	45	61	-16	16
14 Woodley Town	26	3	2	21	22	103	-81	11

DIVISION ONE WEST	P	W	D	L	F	A	GD	Pts
1 Tytherington Rocks	28	20	6	2	76	22	54	66
2 Lydney Town	28	19	4	5	78	26	52	61
3 Shortwood United	28	18	3	7	79	36	43	57
4 Fairford Town	28	15	6	7	69	39	30	51
5 Clanfield	28	15	2	11	52	37	15	47
6 Tuffley Rovers	28	14	4	10	50	45	5	46
7 Purton	28	14	2	12	60	48	12	44
8 North Leigh United	28	13	4	11	71	54	17	43
9 Easington Sports	28	12	7	9	50	48	2	40
10 Hook Norton	28	11	6	11	43	43	0	39
11 New College Swindon	28	8	7	13	36	55	-19	31
12 Malmesbury Victoria	28	8	5	15	37	59	-22	29
13 Carterton	28	6	3	19	38	82	-44	21
14 Old Woodstock Town	28	2	5	21	23	83	-60	11
15 Letcombe	28	2	2	24	20	105	-85	8

LEAGUE CHALLENGE CUP continued...

QUARTER FINALS

Abingdon United	v	Wantage Town	3-5
Shortwood United Res.	v	Highworth Town	1-2
Ardley United	v	Tytherington Rocks	1-0
Ascot United	v	Rayners Lane	4-0

SEMI FINALS

Ascot United	v	Wantage Town	3-2
Ardley United	v	Highworth Town	2-1

FINAL

Ardley United	v	Ascot United	1-2

DIVISION ONE EAST	1	2	3	4	5	6	7	8	9	10	11	12	13	14
1 AFC Hinksey		7–2		3–1	3–0	2–0	0–1	7–3	3–3	0–1	2–1	3–1	0–2	9–0
2 Burnham Reserves	1–2		2–5	0–3	2–0	1–0	0–4	4–0	0–2	3–0	0–2	3–4	4–2	3–2
3 Chalfont Wasps	0–3	1–0		4–3	5–1	3–1	3–1	3–1	1–3	1–0	1–2	0–1	1–3	2–0
4 Chinnor	0–1	2–1	3–0		3–0	2–0	1–4	3–2	6–1	0–2	2–3	0–2	1–1	4–0
5 Didcot Town Reserves	3–2	3–0	0–3	2–2		2–6	1–2	1–1	3–2	2–3	1–0	3–1	5–4	8–2
6 Finchampstead	3–6	2–3	3–1	0–3	4–1		1–3	0–2	0–0	0–3	1–2	2–3	2–3	8–0
7 Headington Amateurs	1–1	3–0	2–0	4–4	1–0	2–1		2–0	6–1	1–2	6–3	0–0	2–1	1–1
8 Henley Town	4–2	0–1	2–3	3–0	3–2	4–2	1–2		1–3	2–2	2–1	2–1	4–5	2–1
9 Maidenhead United Reserves	0–2	2–3	1–1	1–0	6–1	2–1	4–1	1–4		1–1	4–6	3–2	1–1	0–0
10 Milton United	1–0	0–1	1–1	0–0	3–0	2–1	5–1	3–0	4–1		1–0	1–0	7–0	5–2
11 Penn & Tylers Green	1–3	4–1	0–3	3–2	1–0	4–3	2–2	0–0	2–0	2–6		3–3	6–0	3–0
12 Rayners Lane	0–6	2–2	2–1	2–2	6–4	0–2	1–1	2–3	2–1	0–1	3–1		1–3	3–1
13 Wokingham & Emmbrook	2–2	6–0	5–1	3–0	2–0	4–1	2–0	2–0	2–2	1–0	2–2	3–1		3–1
14 Woodley Town	1–3	0–2	0–5	0–7	2–1	3–1	0–1	0–6	2–1	2–7	0–9	1–5	1–4	

DIVISION ONE WEST	1	2	3	4	5	6	7	8	9	10	11	12	13	14	15
1 Carterton		0–7	0–1	0–8	3–4	7–0	2–1	2–3	3–1	5–2	1–1	1–3	0–3	1–2	1–4
2 Clanfield	2–0		2–1	2–1	1–2	1–0	0–4	1–0	1–1	2–0	6–3	6–1	1–4	1–2	2–1
3 Easington Sports	2–0	1–0		2–3	1–1	5–0	2–2	3–3	3–3	4–1	3–3	0–1	1–5	3–2	1–4
4 Fairford Town	5–1	4–0	4–1		3–0	1–1	1–2	2–3	1–1	4–0	2–0	1–3	0–3	3–2	2–2
5 Hook Norton	3–1	1–1	0–3	0–0		4–1	1–2	2–0	1–3	3–1	2–2	2–1	1–2	1–2	0–1
6 Letcombe	1–2	0–4	0–1	2–3	1–4		1–4	2–3	2–0	0–1	4–1	0–7	0–6	0–2	0–2
7 Lydney Town	5–1	0–1	5–2	2–0	0–0	5–0		7–0	5–1	3–1	7–3	2–1	1–1	5–1	2–0
8 Malmesbury Victoria	4–0	0–3	0–1	0–2	1–4	1–1	0–1		1–1	3–3	2–0	4–0	0–4	0–3	0–4
9 New College Swindon	1–1	3–1	0–1	0–3	0–1	3–1	0–2	1–1		2–1	2–0	2–1	1–2	2–0	0–3
10 North Leigh United	4–1	3–2	2–1	1–2	3–0	11–0	3–1	2–4	5–1		6–0	6–2	3–2	2–2	3–3
11 Old Woodstock Town	3–0	0–2	0–0	0–3	0–4	2–0	1–5	0–1	3–3	0–2		0–1	1–5	0–1	0–5
12 Purton	2–3	0–1	0–2	5–2	2–0	6–1	1–1	4–2	2–0	2–0	5–0		4–0	1–3	1–1
13 Shortwood United Res.	1–1	2–1	4–1	4–4	4–0	6–1	0–4	2–0	3–1	1–2	6–0	5–0		1–2	0–1
14 Tuffley Rovers	4–1	2–1	1–2	0–3	1–1	4–0	1–0	2–1	1–3	3–3	4–0	0–2	1–3		1–1
15 Tytherington Rocks	5–0	1–0	2–2	2–2	3–1	9–1	1–0	2–0	6–0	1–0	1–0	3–2	4–0	4–1	

CLUB MOVEMENTS

Premier Division - In: Milton United (P). Thatcham Town (Southern Div.1 S&W).
Out: Abingdon Town (R - North Berkshire). Wantage Town (P - Southern Div.1 S&W).
Division One East - In: Brackley Town Development (N). Easington Sports (S - Div.1 West). Old Woodstock Town (S - Div.1 West).
Out: AFC Hinksey (F). Maidenhead United Reserves (F). Milton United (P).
Division One West - In: Cirencester Town Development (P). Longelevens (P - Gloucestershire County).
Wantage Town Reserves (P). **Out:** Easington Sports (S - Div.1 East). Malmesbury Victoria (W - joined Wiltshire County).
Old Woodstock Town (S - Div.1 West).

ABINGDON UNITED
Founded: 1946 Nickname: The U's

Secretary: John Blackmore **(T)** 07747 615 691 **(E)** secretaryaufc@virginmedia.com
Chairman: Mrs Deborah Blackmore **Manager:** Andy Zoldan **Prog Ed:** Bill Fletcher
Ground: The North Court, Northcourt Road, Abingdon OX14 1PL **(T)** 01235 203 203
Capacity: 2,000 **Seats:** 158 **Covered:** 258 **Midweek Matchday:** Tuesday **Clubhouse:** Yes

Colours(change): All yellow
Previous Names: None
Previous Leagues: North Berkshire 1949-58, Hellenic 1958-2006
Records: **Att:** 2,500 in 2007.
Senior Honours: Hellenic League Division 1 1981-82, League Cup 1965-66. Berks & Bucks Senior Trophy x2.

10 YEAR RECORD

04-05	05-06	06-07	07-08	08-09	09-10	10-11	11-12	12-13	13-14
Hel P 5	Hel P 3	Hel P 18	Sthsw 16	Sthsw 15	Sthsw 14	Sthsw 16	Sthsw 18	Sthsw 20	Hel P 17

ARDLEY UNITED
Founded: 1945 Nickname:

Secretary: Norman Stacey **(T)** 07711 009 198 **(E)** ardley.house@virgin.net
Chairman: Norman Stacey **Manager:** Kevin Brock **Prog Ed:** Peter Sawyer
Ground: The Playing Fields, Oxford Road, Ardley OX27 7NZ **(T)** 07711 009 198
Capacity: 1,000 **Seats:** 100 **Covered:** 200 **Midweek Matchday:** Tuesday **Clubhouse:** Yes **Shop:** No

Colours(change): Sky blue/navy blue/sky blue
Previous Names: None
Previous Leagues: Oxford Senior.
Records: **Att:** 670 v Oxford United July 2013.
Senior Honours: Hellenic League Division One 1996-97, 97-98.

10 YEAR RECORD

04-05	05-06	06-07	07-08	08-09	09-10	10-11	11-12	12-13	13-14
Hel P 18	Hel P 10	Hel P 4	Hel P 13	Hel P 5	Hel P 7	Hel P 3	Hel P 3	Hel P 5	Hel P 2

ASCOT UNITED
Founded: 1965 Nickname: Yellaman

Secretary: Mark Gittoes **(T)** 07798 701995 **(E)** mark.gittoes@ascotunited.net
Chairman: Mike Harrison **Manager:** Jeff Lamb **Prog Ed:** Ian Watson
Ground: Ascot Racecourse, Car Park 10, Winkfield Rd, Ascot SL5 7RA **(T)** 01344 291 107
Capacity: **Seats:** **Covered:** **Midweek Matchday:** Tuesday **Clubhouse:** Yes

Colours(change): Yellow & blue/blue/yellow
Previous Names: None.
Previous Leagues: Reading Senior.
Records: **Att:** 1,149 - 19/08/2011.
Senior Honours:

10 YEAR RECORD

04-05	05-06	06-07	07-08	08-09	09-10	10-11	11-12	12-13	13-14
ReadS 3	ReadS 4	ReadS 1	Hel1E 4	Hel1E 2	Hel P 15	Hel P 12	Hel P 14	Hel P 7	Hel P 3

BINFIELD
Founded: 1892 Nickname: Moles

Secretary: Rob Challis **(T)** 07515 336 989 **(E)** robchallis@binfieldfc.com
Chairman: Bob Bacon **Manager:** Mark Tallentire **Prog Ed:** Colin Byers
Ground: Stubbs Lane off Hill Farm Lane, Binfield RG42 5NR **(T)** 01344 860 822
Capacity: **Seats:** yes **Covered:** yes **Midweek Matchday:** Monday **Clubhouse:** Yes

Colours(change): All red.
Previous Names: None.
Previous Leagues: Ascot & District. Great Western Combination. Reading & Dist. Chiltonian.
Records: **Att:** 1000+ Great Western Combination.
Senior Honours: Hellenic League Division 1 East 2008-09.

10 YEAR RECORD

04-05	05-06	06-07	07-08	08-09	09-10	10-11	11-12	12-13	13-14
Hel1E 5	Hel1E 8	Hel1E 11	Hel1E 9	Hel1E 1	Hel P 8	Hel P 2	Hel P 8	Hel P 3	Hel P 5

BRACKNELL TOWN
Founded: 1896 Nickname: The Robins

Secretary: Darrell Freeland **(T)** 07712 473 142 **(E)** darrell_freeland@hotmail.com
Chairman: Chris Day **Manager:** Ed Carpenter **Prog Ed:** Rob Scully
Ground: Larges Lane Bracknell RG12 9AN **(T)** 01344 412 305
Capacity: 2,500 **Seats:** 190 **Covered:** 400 **Midweek Matchday:** Tuesday **Clubhouse:** Yes **Shop:** Yes

Colours(change): Red and white hoops/red/red
Previous Names: None
Previous Leagues: Great Western Comb., Surrey Senior 1963-70, London Spartan 1970-75, Isthmian 1984-2004, Southern 2004-10
Records: **Att:** 2,500 v Newquay - FA Amateur Cup 1971. **Goalscorer:** Justin Day. **Apps:** James Woodcock.
Senior Honours:

10 YEAR RECORD

04-05	05-06	06-07	07-08	08-09	09-10	10-11	11-12	12-13	13-14
SthW 20	SthW 19	Sthsw 19	Sthsw 20	Sthsw	Sthsw 22	Hel P 16	Hel P 21	Hel1E 5	Hel P 13

BRIMSCOMBE & THRUPP
Founded: 1886 Nickname: Lilywhites

Secretary: Allan Boulton **(T)** 07850 471 331 **(E)** allanboulton1@sky.com
Chairman: Clive Baker **Manager:** Mike Green **Prog Ed:** Bon Hill
Ground: 'The Meadow', London Road, Brimscombe Stroud, Gloucestershire GL5 2SH **(T)** 07833 231 464
Capacity: **Seats:** **Covered:** **Midweek Matchday:** Tuesday **Clubhouse:** Yes

Colours(change): White/blue/blue.
Previous Names: Brimscombe AFC 1886- late 1970s. Brimscombe and Thrupp merged.
Previous Leagues: Gloucestershire County
Records:
Senior Honours: Gloucestershire County League 2010-11. Hellenic League Div.1 West 2012-13.

10 YEAR RECORD

04-05	05-06	06-07	07-08	08-09	09-10	10-11	11-12	12-13	13-14
					GlCo 5	GlCo 1	Hel1W 4	Hel1W 1	Hel P 12

CHELTENHAM SARACENS
Founded: 1964 Nickname: Sara's

Secretary: Bob Attwood **(T)** 07778 502 539 **(E)** bobattwood@tiscali.co.uk
Chairman: Brian Dix **Prog Ed:** Bob Attwood
Ground: Petersfield Park, Tewkesbury Road GL51 9DY **(T)** 01242 584 134
Capacity: **Seats:** Yes **Covered:** Yes **Midweek Matchday:** Wednesday **Clubhouse:** Yes

Colours(change): All navy blue
Previous Names:
Previous Leagues:
Records: **Att:** 327 v Harrow Hill 31/08/2003.
Senior Honours: Glouscestershire Senior Cup 1991-92. Hellenic League Division 1 1999-2000.

10 YEAR RECORD

04-05	05-06	06-07	07-08	08-09	09-10	10-11	11-12	12-13	13-14
Hel1W 6	Hel1E 8	Hel1W 6	Hel1W 5	Hel1W 12	Hel1W 4	Hel1W 3	Hel P 15	Hel P 11	Hel P 16

FLACKWELL HEATH
Founded: 1907 Nickname: Heath

Secretary: Jo Parsons **(T)** 07984 199 878 **(E)** joparsons19@sky.com
Chairman: Terry Glynn **Manager:** Graham Malcolm Chris Parsons
Ground: Wilks Park, Magpie Lane, Heath End Rd, Flackwell Hth HP10 9EA. **(T)** 01628 523 892
Capacity: 2,000 **Seats:** 150 **Covered:** Yes **Midweek Matchday:** Tuesday **Clubhouse:** Yes **Shop:** No

Colours(change): All red.
Previous Names: None.
Previous Leagues: Great Western Combination. Hellenic. Isthmian.
Records: **Att:** 1,500 v Oxford United, charity match, 1966. **Goalscorer:** Tony Wood. **Apps:** Lee Elliott.
Senior Honours:

10 YEAR RECORD

04-05	05-06	06-07	07-08	08-09	09-10	10-11	11-12	12-13	13-14
Isth2 9	Isth2 4	Isth1N 22	Hel P 9	Hel P 16	Hel P 4	Hel P 8	Hel P 4	Hel P 10	Hel P 8

HIGHMOOR-IBIS

Founded: 2001 | Nickname: Mighty Moor

Secretary: Chris Gallimore **(T)** 07717 154 435 **(E)** chris.gallimore@sjpp.co.uk
Chairman: Martin Law **Manager:** Marcus Richardson **Prog Ed:** Martin Law
Ground: Palmer Park Stadium, Wokingham Road, Reading RG6 1LF **(T)** 0118 901 5080
Capacity: **Seats:** **Covered:** **Midweek Matchday:** Monday **Clubhouse:**

Colours(change): All blue
Previous Names: Highmoor and Ibis merged to form today's club in 2001.
Previous Leagues: Reading > 2011.
Records:
Senior Honours: Reading League Senior Division 2003-04, 10-11.

10 YEAR RECORD

04-05	05-06	06-07	07-08	08-09	09-10	10-11	11-12	12-13	13-14
ReadS 4	ReadS 3	ReadS 2	ReadS 6	ReadS 2	ReadS 4	ReadS 1	Hel1E 2	Hel P 12	Hel P 4

HIGHWORTH TOWN

Founded: 1893 | Nickname: Worthians

Secretary: Fraser Haines **(T)** 07939 032 451 **(E)** fraserhaines@btinternet.com
Chairman: Rohan Haines **Manager:** John Fisher **Prog Ed:** Mike Markham
Ground: Elm Recreation Ground, Highworth SN6 7DD **(T)** 01793 766 263
Capacity: 2,000 **Seats:** 150 **Covered:** 250 **Midweek Matchday:** Tuesday **Clubhouse:** Yes **Shop:** No

Colours(change): Red/black/black.
Previous Names: None.
Previous Leagues: Swindon & District. Wiltshire.
Records: **Att:** 2,000 v QPR, opening of floodlights. **Goalscorer:** Kevin Higgs. **Apps:** Rod Haines.
Senior Honours: Hellenic League Champions 2004-05.

10 YEAR RECORD

04-05	05-06	06-07	07-08	08-09	09-10	10-11	11-12	12-13	13-14
Hel P 1	Hel P 12	Hel P 15	Hel P 6	Hel P 6	Hel P 9	Hel P 4	Hel P 6	Hel P 16	Hel P 11

HOLYPORT

Founded: 1934 | Nickname: The Villagers

Secretary: Lyn Davies **(T)** 07824 605 731 **(E)** Lyn.davies@rbwm.gov.uk
Chairman: Tony Andrews **Manager:** Martin Kenealy **Prog Ed:** Richard Tyrell
Ground: Summerleaze Village SL6 8SP **(T)** 07515 789 415
Capacity: **Seats:** **Covered:** **Midweek Matchday:** Tuesday **Clubhouse:** Yes

Colours(change): Claret/green/claret
Previous Names: None
Previous Leagues: None
Records: **Att:** 218 v Eton Wick, 2006. **Goalscorer:** Jamie Handscomb - 78. **Apps:** Sam Jones - 216.
Senior Honours: Norfolkian Senior Cup 1999-2000. Hellenic League Division One East 2010-11.

10 YEAR RECORD

04-05	05-06	06-07	07-08	08-09	09-10	10-11	11-12	12-13	13-14
Hel1E 15	Hel1E 14	Hel1E 9	Hel1E 7	Hel1E 5	Hel1E 3	Hel1E 1	Hel P 13	Hel P 14	Hel P 18

KIDLINGTON

Founded: 1909 | Nickname:

Secretary: David Platt **(T)** 07956 531 185 **(E)** dplatt45@hotmail.co.uk
Chairman: TBA **Manager:** Martin Wilkinson **Prog Ed:** Donna Conelly
Ground: Yarnton Road, Kidlington, Oxford OX5 1AT **(T)** 01865 849 777
Capacity: **Seats:** Yes **Covered:** Yes **Midweek Matchday:** Tuesday **Clubhouse:** Yes **Shop:** No

Colours(change): All green
Previous Names: None.
Previous Leagues: Oxford Senior.
Records: **Att:** 2,500 v Showbiz XI, 1973.
Senior Honours:

10 YEAR RECORD

04-05	05-06	06-07	07-08	08-09	09-10	10-11	11-12	12-13	13-14
Hel1W 3	Hel P 20	Hel P 9	Hel P 15	Hel P 9	Hel P 11	Hel P 7	Hel P 18	Hel P 13	Hel P 6

MILTON UNITED

Founded: 1909 Nickname: Miltonians

Secretary: Lee Chapple **(T)** **(E)** milton.united.fc@hotmail.co.uk
Chairman: Andy Burchette **Manager:** Paul Bedwell **Prog Ed:** Tom McCabe
Ground: Potash Lane, Milton Heights, OX13 6AG **(T)** 01235 832 999
Capacity: **Seats:** **Covered:** **Midweek Matchday:** Monday **Clubhouse:** Yes

Colours(change): Claret & sky/claret & sky/claret
Previous Names:
Previous Leagues:
Records: **Att:** 608 Carterton v Didcot Town, League Cup Final, 07.05.05. **Goalscorer:** Nigel Mott.
Senior Honours: Hellenic League 1990-91. Division One East 2013-14.

10 YEAR RECORD

04-05	05-06	06-07	07-08	08-09	09-10	10-11	11-12	12-13	13-14
Hel P 13	Hel P 11	Hel P 7	Hel P 7	Hel P 21	Hel1E 7	Hel1E 4	Hel1E 14	Hel1E 14	Hel1E 1

NEWBURY

Founded: 1887 Nickname: The Town

Secretary: Knut Riemann **(T)** 07855 031 000 **(E)** kriemann@yahoo.com
Chairman: Keith Moss **Manager:** Callum Wilmoth **Prog Ed:** Luciano Marigliano
Ground: Faraday Road, Newbury RG14 2AD **(T)** 01635 41031
Capacity: **Seats:** **Covered:** **Midweek Matchday:** Tuesday **Clubhouse:** Yes

Colours(change): Amber & black/black/amber & black
Previous Names: Old London Apprentice > 2005. O L A Newbury 2005-2007.
Previous Leagues: Reading Senior > 2008.
Records: **Att:** 246 v Kintbury Rangers 27/12/2008.
Senior Honours: Hellenic League 1978-79, 80-81, Division One East 2011-12. Athenian League 1982-83.

10 YEAR RECORD

04-05	05-06	06-07	07-08	08-09	09-10	10-11	11-12	12-13	13-14
Read2 1	Read1 4	Read1 1	ReadS 2	Hel1E 3	Hel1E 16	Hel1E 3	Hel1E 1	Hel P 15	Hel P 19

OXFORD CITY NOMADS

Founded: 1936 Nickname: The Nomads

Secretary: Colin Taylor **(T)** 07817 885 396 **(E)** ctoxford@btinternet.com
Chairman: Richard Lawrence **Manager:** Chris Fontaine **Prog Ed:** Colin Taylor
Ground: Court Place Farm Stadium, Marsh Lane, Marston OX3 0NQ **(T)** 01865 744 493
Capacity: 3,000 **Seats:** 300 **Covered:** 400 **Midweek Matchday:** Wednesday **Clubhouse:** Yes **Shop:** Yes

Colours(change): Blue & white hoops/blue/blue.
Previous Names: Quarry Nomads > 2005.
Previous Leagues: Chiltonian.
Records: **Att:** 334 v Headington Amateurs, 25.08.03.
Senior Honours: Hellenic League Premier Division 2011-12.

10 YEAR RECORD

04-05	05-06	06-07	07-08	08-09	09-10	10-11	11-12	12-13	13-14
Hel1W 15	Hel1E 11	Hel1E 12	Hel1W 9	Hel1W 3	Hel P 10	Hel P 17	Hel P 1	Hel P 4	Hel P 9

READING TOWN

Founded: 1966 Nickname: Town

Secretary: Richard Grey **(T)** 07759 126 850 **(E)** richardigrey@aol.com
Chairman: Kevin Brandstatter **Manager:** Colin Millard **Prog Ed:** David Wright
Ground: Reading Town Sports Ground, Scours Lane, Reading RG30 6AY **(T)** 0118 945 3555
Capacity: 2000 **Seats:** 120 **Covered:** 200 **Midweek Matchday:** Tuesday **Clubhouse:** Yes **Shop:** No

Colours(change): Red & black stripes/black/black
Previous Names: Lower Burghfield, XI Utd, Vincents Utd, Reading Garage, ITS Reading T.
Previous Leagues: Chiltonian Lge. Combined Counties.
Records: **Att:** 1067 v AFC Wimbledon, Combined Counties 03.05.03.
Senior Honours:

10 YEAR RECORD

04-05	05-06	06-07	07-08	08-09	09-10	10-11	11-12	12-13	13-14
CCP 19	CCP 10	CCP 9	CCP 13	Hel P 8	Hel P 3	Hel P 13	Hel P 7	Hel P 17	Hel P 11

SHRIVENHAM

Founded: 1900 Nickname: Shrivy

Secretary: Andy Timbrell **(T)** 07999 133 439 **(E)** timbrell.andrew63@btopenworld.com
Chairman: James Dore **Manager:** Sam Collier **Prog Ed:** Matty Hirst
Ground: The Recreation Ground, Barrington Park, Shrivenham SN6 8BJ **(T)** 07767 371 414
Capacity: **Seats:** **Covered:** **Midweek Matchday:** Wednesday **Clubhouse:** Yes

Colours(change): Blue & white hoops/blue/blue.
Previous Names: None.
Previous Leagues: North Berkshire.
Records: **Att:** 800 v Aston Villa, 21.05.2000.
Senior Honours: Hellenic Division One West 2004-05.

10 YEAR RECORD

04-05	05-06	06-07	07-08	08-09	09-10	10-11	11-12	12-13	13-14
Hel1W 1	Hel P 8	Hel P 10	Hel P 8	Hel P 18	Hel P 16	Hel P 20	Hel P 16	Hel P 19	Hel P 15

THAME UNITED

Founded: 1883 Nickname: Red Kites

Secretary: Jake Collinge **(T)** 07753 502 955 **(E)** jake@jcpc.org.uk
Chairman: Jake Collinge **Manager:** Mark West **Prog Ed:** Jake Collinge
Ground: The ASM Stadium, Meadow View Pk, Tythrop Wa, Thame, Oxon, OX9 3RN **(T)** 01844 214 401
Capacity: 2,500 **Seats:** Yes **Covered:** Yes **Midweek Matchday:** Tuesday **Clubhouse:** Yes

Colours(change): Red & black/black/red & black.
Previous Names: Thame F.C.
Previous Leagues: Oxon Senior. Hellenic. South Midlands. Isthmian. Southern.
Records: **Att:** 1,382 v Oxford United Jan 2011. **Goalscorer:** Not known. **Apps:** Steve Mayhew.
Senior Honours: Isthmian Division 2 1994-95.

10 YEAR RECORD

04-05	05-06	06-07	07-08	08-09	09-10	10-11	11-12	12-13	13-14
SthW 11	SthW 22	Hel P 20	Hel1E 10	Hel1E 9	Hel1E 1	Hel P 10	Hel P 9	Hel P 9	Hel P 10

THATCHAM TOWN

Founded: 1895 Nickname: Kingfishers

Secretary: Ron renton **(T)** 07561 149 558 **(E)** ron.renton@btinternet.com
Chairman: Eric Bailey **Manager:** Gareth Thomas **Prog Ed:** Andy Morris
Ground: Waterside Park, Crookham Hill, Thatcham, Berks RG18 4QR **(T)** 01635 862 016
Capacity: 3,000 **Seats:** 300 **Covered:** 300 **Midweek Matchday:** Tuesday **Clubhouse:** Yes **Shop:** Yes

Colours(change): Blue and white stripes/blue/blue
Previous Names: Not known
Previous Leagues: Hellenic 1974-82, Athenian 1982-84, London Spartan 1984-86, Wessex 1986-2006. Southern 2006-14.
Records: 1,400 v Aldershot - FA Vase
Senior Honours: Hellenic League 1974-75. Wessex League 1995-96.

10 YEAR RECORD

04-05	05-06	06-07	07-08	08-09	09-10	10-11	11-12	12-13	13-14
Wex1 3	Wex1 2	Sthsw 6	Sthsw 15	Sthsw 6	Sthsw 12	Sthsw 5	Sthsw 8	SthC 17	Sthsw 19

WOOTTON BASSETT TOWN

Founded: 1882 Nickname: Bassett

Secretary: Ian Thomas **(T)** 07714 718 122 **(E)** ian.thomas@wbtfc.co.uk
Chairman: Andy Walduck **Manager:** Paul Braithwaite **Prog Ed:** Mark Smedley
Ground: Cirencester Town FC, Corinium Stadium Kingshill, Cirencester, Glos. GL7 1HS **(T)** 01793 853 880
Capacity: 4,500 **Seats:** 550 **Covered:** 1,250 **Midweek Matchday:** Wednesday **Clubhouse:** Yes **Shop:** No

Colours(change): Blue/blue/yellow.
Previous Names: None.
Previous Leagues: Wiltshire.
Records: **Record Att:** 2,103 v Swindon Town, July 1991. **Goalscorer:** Brian 'Tony' Ewing. **Apps:** Steve Thomas.
Senior Honours: **Previous Leagues:** Wiltshire.

10 YEAR RECORD

04-05	05-06	06-07	07-08	08-09	09-10	10-11	11-12	12-13	13-14
Hel P 21	Hel1W 5	Hel1W 11	Hel1W 15	Hel1W 4	Hel1W 2	Hel P 15	Hel1W 5	Hel1W 2	Hel P 14

BRACKLEY TOWN DEVELOPMENT

Founded: Nickname: The Saints

Secretary: Patrick Ashby **(T)** 07969 825 636 **(E)** pat.ashby55@btinternet.com
Chairman: Francis Oliver **Manager:** Nick Johnson **Prog Ed:** Matthew Wise
Ground: St James Park, Churchill Way, Brackley, Northamptonshire, NN13 8EJ **(T)** 01280 704 077
Colours(change): Red & white/red/red

ADDITIONAL INFORMATION:

BURNHAM RESERVES

Founded: Nickname: The Blues

Secretary: Gary Reeves **(T)** 07919 415 141 **(E)** burnhamfcsec@aol.com
Chairman: Gary Reeves **Manager:** Merv Lloyd
Ground: The Gore, Wymers Wood Road, Burnham, Slough SL1 8JG **(T)** 01628 668 654
Colours(change): Blue & white/blue/blue

ADDITIONAL INFORMATION:

CHALFONT WASPS

Founded: 1922 Nickname: The Stingers

Secretary: Bob Cakebread **(T)** 07895 094 579 **(E)** robert.cakebread@btinternet.com
Chairman: Steve Waddington **Manager:** Matt Brion **Prog Ed:** Alan Yeomans
Ground: Crossleys, Bowstridge Lane Chalfont, St Giles HP8 4QN **(T)** 01494 875 050
Colours(change): Yellow and black stripes/black/black

ADDITIONAL INFORMATION:
Record Att: 82 v Didcot Town 17/12/2005.
Honours: Hellenic League Division 1 East 2007-08.

CHINNOR

Founded: 1971 Nickname:

Secretary: Richard Carr **(T)** 07786 115 089 **(E)** rjcarr5@btinternet.com
Chairman: Fred Saulsbury **Manager:** David Ridgley **Prog Ed:** Frank Byrne
Ground: Station Road, Chinnor, Oxon OX39 4PV **(T)** 01844 352 579
Colours(change): Yellow/black/yellow

ADDITIONAL INFORMATION:
Previous League: Oxfordshire Senior.
Record Att: 306 v Oxford Quarry Nomads, 29.08.2005.

DIDCOT TOWN RESERVES

Founded: 1907 Nickname: Railwaymen

Secretary: Jacquelyn Chalk **(T)** 07872 317 845 **(E)** jacquelyn-dtfc@virginmedia.com
Chairman: John Bailey **Manager:** Mark Janes & Neal McDermaid **Prog Ed:** Steve Clare
Ground: Loop Meadow Stadium, Bowmont Water, Didcot OX11 7GA **(T)** 01235 813 138 **Capacity:** 5,000
Colours(change): Red & white/white/red

ADDITIONAL INFORMATION:
Previous League: Hellenic Reserves.

EASINGTON SPORTS

Founded: 1946 Nickname: The Clan

Secretary: Angela Clives **(T)** 07815 325 905 **(E)** aclives@btinternet.com
Chairman: Phil Lines **Manager:** Craig Pearman **Prog Ed:** Richard Meadows
Ground: Addison Road, Banbury OX16 9DH **(T)** 01295 257 006
Colours(change): Red & white/black/black, red & white

ADDITIONAL INFORMATION:
Record Att: 258 v Hook Norton.
Hnours: Oxfordshire Senior League 1957-58, 58-59. Division 1 1965-66. Oxfordshire Senior Ben Turner Trophy 1970-71.

FINCHAMPSTEAD

Founded: 1952 Nickname: Finches

Secretary: Nick Markman **(T)** 07793 866 324 **(E)** njm826@btinternet.com
Chairman: Richard Laugharne **Manager:** Jon Laugharne **Prog Ed:** Richard Laugharne
Ground: Memorial Park The Village, Finchampstead RG40 4JR **(T)** 0118 9732 890
Colours(change): Red & black/black/black

ADDITIONAL INFORMATION:
Record Att: 425 v Sandhurst, 1958-59.
Honours: Chiltonian League 1987-88. Reading Senior Challenge Cup 1986-87. Hellenic League Division 1 East 2001-02.

HEADINGTON AMATEURS

Founded: 1949 Nickname: A's

Secretary: Donald Light **(T)** 07764 943 778 **(E)** donald.light@ntlworld.com
Chairman: Donald Light **Manager:** Matty Jacob & Keith Jones **Prog Ed:** Donald Light
Ground: The Pavillion, Barton Recreation Ground, Oxford OX3 9LA **(T)** 01865 762 974
Colours(change): All red

ADDITIONAL INFORMATION:
Record Att: 250 v Newport AFC, 1991. **Goalscorer:** Tony Penge. **Apps:** Kent Drackett.
Honours: Oxfordshire Senior League 1972-73, 73-74, 75-76, 76-77, Division 1 1968-69. Hellenic League Division One West 2010-11.

HENLEY TOWN

Founded: 1871 Nickname: Lillywhites

Secretary: Tony Kingston **(T)** 07712 139 592 **(E)** kingstontony6@gmail.com
Chairman: Kim Chapman **Manager:** Craig Hiscock & Craig Sumner **Prog Ed:** Tony Kingston
Ground: The Triangle Ground, Mill Lane, Henley RG9 4HB **(T)** 07758 376 369
Colours(change): Red & white/red/red

ADDITIONAL INFORMATION: Att: 2000+ v Reading, 1922. **Goalscorer:** M. Turner.
Hellenic League Div.1 1963-64, 67-68, Div.1 East 2000-01. Chiltonian League Division 1 1987-88. Premier 1999-00.

OLD WOODSTOCK TOWN

Founded: 1998 Nickname:

Secretary: Ian Whelan **(T)** 07827 894 869 **(E)** ian.whelan@lucyswitchgear.com
Chairman: Ted Saxton **Manager:** Ben Sadler **Prog Ed:** Andy Meaden
Ground: New Road, Woodstock OX20 1PD **(T)** 07748 152 243 **Capacity:** 1,000
Colours(change): Red/red/white

ADDITIONAL INFORMATION:
Previous Names: Woodstock Town (1911) and Old Woodstock (1920) merged in 1998 to form today's club.
Record Att: 258 v Kidlington, 27.08.01.
Honours: Oxfordshire Senior League 1998-99.

PENN & TYLERS GREEN

Founded: 1905 Nickname:

Secretary: Andrea Latta **(T)** 07904 538 868 **(E)** hsvlatta1955@yahoo.co.uk
Chairman: Tony Hurst **Manager:** Giovanni Sepede **Prog Ed:** James Keating
Ground: French School Meadows, Elm Road, Penn, Bucks HP10 8LF **(T)** 01494 815 346
Colours(change): Blue & white stripes/blue/blue

ADDITIONAL INFORMATION:
Previous League: Chiltonian (Founder member).
Record Att: 125 v Chalfont Wasps, August 2000.

RAYNERS LANE

Founded: 1933 Nickname: The Lane

Secretary: Tony Pratt **(T)** 01895 233 853 **(E)** richard.mitchell@tesco.net
Chairman: Martin Noblett **Manager:** Mick Bradshaw **Prog Ed:** Richard Mitchell
Ground: Tithe Farm Social Club, Rayners Lane, South Harrow HA2 0XH **(T)** 0208 868 8724
Colours(change): Yellow/green/yellow

ADDITIONAL INFORMATION:
Record Att: 550 v Wealdstone 1983.
Honours: Hellenic League Division 1 1982-83, Division One West 2012-13.

WOKINGHAM & EMMBROOK

Founded: 2004 Nickname: Satsumas

Secretary: Neil Van Den Dungan **(T)** 07429 442 019 **(E)** neil.van.den.dungen@nike.com
Chairman: Graham Tabor **Manager:** Dan Bateman **Prog Ed:** Alex Woodrow
Ground: Emmbrook Sports & Social Club Lowther Road, Wokingham. RG41 1JB **(T)** 0118 9780209
Colours(change): Orange/black/black.

ADDITIONAL INFORMATION: Record Att: 305 v Binfield, 25.03.2005.
Honours: Reading Senior 2008-09, 11-12, 12-13.

WOODLEY TOWN

Founded: 1904 Nickname: Town

Secretary: John Mailer **(T)** 07883 341 628 **(E)** john_mailer@hotmail.co.uk
Chairman: Mark Rozzier **Manager:** Damien Marshall **Prog Ed:** Mark Beaven
Ground: Scours Lane, Reading, Berkshire, RG30 6AY **(T)** 0118 9453 555
Colours(change): All navy blue

ADDITIONAL INFORMATION:
Previous League: Reading.
Honours: Reading Football League Senior Division 2008-09. Berkshire Trophy Centre Senior Cup 2008-09.

CARTERTON

Founded: 1922 Nickname:

Secretary: Nick Truman **(T)** 07918 690 985 **(E)** nicktruman@hotmail.com
Chairman: Tom Amer **Manager:** Mark Moss **Prog Ed:** Tom Amer
Ground: Kilkenny Lane, Carterton, Oxfordshire OX18 1DY. **(T)** 01993 842 410 **Capacity:** 1,500
Colours(change): Blue/blue/yellow

ADDITIONAL INFORMATION: Record Att: 650 v Swindon Town, July 2001. **Goalscorer:** Phil Rodney.

CIRENCESTER TOWN DEVELOPMENT

Founded: 2011 Nickname: Centurions

Secretary: Scott Griffin **(T)** 07968 338 106 **(E)** scott.griffin@cirentownfc.plus.com
Chairman: Steve Abbley **Manager:** Clive Messenger **Prog Ed:** Scott Griffin
Ground: Corinium Stadium, Kingshill Lane, Cirencester Glos GL7 1HS **(T)** 01285 654 543
Colours(change): Red & black stripes/black/red.

ADDITIONAL INFORMATION:

CLANFIELD

Founded: 1890 Nickname: Robins

Secretary: John Osborne **(T)** 01993 771 631 **(E)** john_osborne6@sky.com
Chairman: John Osborne **Manager:** Peter Osborne **Prog Ed:** Trevor Cuss
Ground: Radcot Road, Clanfield OX18 2ST **(T)** 01367 810 314
Colours(change): All red

ADDITIONAL INFORMATION:
Record Att: 197 v Kidlington August 2002.
Honours: Hellenic League Division 1 1969-70.

FAIRFORD TOWN

Founded: 1891 Nickname: Town

Secretary: William Beach **(T)** 07919 940 909 **(E)** wbeach007@btinternet.com
Chairman: Mike Tanner **Manager:** Gareth Davies
Ground: Cinder Lane, London Road, Fairford GL7 4AX **(T)** 01285 712 071 **Capacity:** 2,000
Colours(change): All red.

ADDITIONAL INFORMATION: Att: 1,525 v Coventry City, friendly, July 2000. **Goalscorer:** Pat Toomey.

HOOK NORTON

Founded: 1898 Nickname: Hooky

Secretary: Michael Barlow **(T)** 07766 554 980 **(E)** michael.barlow@hancocks-legal.co.uk
Chairman: Michael Barlow **Manager:** Joe Davies **Prog Ed:** Alan White
Ground: The Bourne, Hook Norton OX15 5PB **(T)** 01608 737 132
Colours(change): Royal blue/royal blue/white

ADDITIONAL INFORMATION:
Record Att: 244 v Banbury United, 12/12/98.
Honours: Oxfordshire Senior League 1999-00, 00-01. Hellenic League Division 1 West 2001-02.

LETCOMBE

Founded: 1910 Nickname: Brooksiders

Secretary: Des Williams **(T)** 07765 144 985 **(E)** deswilliams45@btinternet.com
Chairman: Dennis Stock **Manager:** Stuart Wright **Prog Ed:** Russell Stock
Ground: Bassett Road, Letcombe Regis OX12 9JU **(T)** 07765 144 985
Colours(change): All purple

ADDITIONAL INFORMATION:
Record Att: 203 v Old Woodstock Town, 29/08/04.
Honours: North Berkshire League Division One 1989-90. Chiltonian League Division One 1990-91.

LONGLEVENS AFC

Founded: Nickname: Levens

Secretary: Andrew Davis **(T)** 07739 966 967 **(E)** bodrumdavis@hotmail.com
Chairman: Chris Bishop **Manager:** James French
Ground: Saw Mills End, Corinium Avenue, Gloucester GL4 3DG **(T)** 01452 530388 (CH)
Colours(change): Red & black/black/red

ADDITIONAL INFORMATION:
Previous League: Gloucestershire County > 2014.
League Honours: Gloucestershire County 2013-14.

LYDNEY TOWN

Founded: 1911 Nickname: The Town

Secretary: Roger Sansom **(T)** 07887 842 125 **(E)** rogersansom@outlook.com
Chairman: Ashley Hancock **Manager:** Mark Lee **Prog Ed:** Roger Sansom
Ground: Lydney Recreation Ground, Swan Road, Lydney GL15 5RU **(T)** 01594 844 523
Colours(change): Black & white stripes/black/black

ADDITIONAL INFORMATION:
Record Att: 375 v Ellwood, 05.11.05.
Honours: Gloucestershire County League 2005-06. Hellenic League Division 1 West 2006-07.

NEW COLLEGE ACADEMY

Founded: 1984 Nickname: College

Secretary: Mark Cosnett **(T)** 07846 204 174 **(E)** newcollegeswinfcsec@yahoo.co.uk
Chairman: Ian Howell **Manager:** Mark Teasdale **Prog Ed:** Mark Csonett
Ground: Sumpermarine RFC Sports & Social, Supermarine Rd, South Marston SN3 4BZ **(T)** 01793 824 828
Colours(change): All royal blue

ADDITIONAL INFORMATION: Previous League: Wiltshire > 2011.

NORTH LEIGH RESERVES

Founded: 1908 Nickname: The Millers

Secretary: Keith Huxley **(T)** 07775 818 066 **(E)** huxley893@btinternet.com
Chairman: Peter King **Manager:** Paul Lewis
Ground: Eynsham Hall Park Sports Ground OX29 6PN. **(T)** 07775 818 066 **Capacity:** 2,000
Colours(change): Yellow/black/yellow

ADDITIONAL INFORMATION:
Previous Leagues: Hellenic Reserves.

PURTON

Founded: 1923 Nickname: The Reds

Secretary: Alan Eastwood **(T)** 07950 889 177 **(E)** alan.eastwood83@ntlworld.com
Chairman: Alan Eastwood **Manager:** Justin Miller **Prog Ed:** Alan Eastwood
Ground: The Red House, Purton SN5 4DY **(T)** 01793 770 262 (MD)
Colours(change): All red

ADDITIONAL INFORMATION:
Honours: Wiltshire League 1945-46, 46-47, 47-48. Wiltshire County League 1985-86. Hellenic League Division 1 1995-96, Division 1 West 2003-04. Wiltshire Senior Cup 1938-39, 48-49, 50-51, 54-55, 87-88, 88-89, 94-95.

SHORTWOOD UNITED RESERVES

Founded: Nickname: The Wood

Secretary: Mark Webb **(T)** 07792 323 784 **(E)** squish.shortwoodfc@live.co.uk
Chairman: Peter Webb **Manager:** Paul Meredith
Ground: Meadowbank, Shortwood, Nailsworth GL6 0SJ **(T)** 01453 833 936
Colours(change): Red & white/red & white/black

ADDITIONAL INFORMATION:
Previous League: Gloucestershire Northern Senior.
Honours: Gloucestershire Northern Senior League 2011-12. Hellenic Division 2 West 2012-13.

TUFFLEY ROVERS

Founded: Nickname:

Secretary: Neil Spiller **(T)** 07545 492 261 **(E)** admin@tuffleyroversfc.co.uk
Chairman: Neil Brinkworth **Manager:** Warren Evans **Prog Ed:** Neil Spiller
Ground: Glevum Park Lower Tuffley Lane, Tuffley, Gloucester GL2 5DT **(T)** 07708 361 808 **Capacity:** 1,000
Colours(change): All claret

ADDITIONAL INFORMATION:
Previous League: Gloucestershire County.

TYTHERINGTON ROCKS

Founded: 1896 Nickname: The Rocks

Secretary: Graham Shipp **(T)** 07811 318 424 **(E)** tramar1618@btinternet.com
Chairman: Ted Travell **Manager:** Lukasz Cabaj **Prog Ed:** Mark Brown
Ground: Hardwicke Playing Field, Tytherington Glos GL12 8UJ **(T)** 07837 555 776
Colours(change): Amber & black/black/black

ADDITIONAL INFORMATION:
Previous League: Gloucestershire County.
Record Att: 424 v Winterbourne United, 26/08/2007.

WANTAGE TOWN RESERVES

Founded: Nickname: The Alfredians

Secretary: John Culley (T) 07522 418 760 (E) john_clly@yahoo.co.uk
Chairman: Tony Woodward **Manager:** Nick Rowe **Prog Ed:** Tony Woodward
Ground: Alfredian Park Manor Road, Wantage OX12 8DW (T) 01235 764 781
Colours(change): Green & white/white/green

ADDITIONAL INFORMATION:

DIVISION TWO EAST	P	W	D	L	F	A	GD	Pts
1 Binfield Reserves	22	17	4	1	74	28	46	55
2 Bracknell Town Reserves	22	15	3	4	82	25	57	48
3 Penn & Tylers Green Reserves	22	14	0	8	61	53	8	42
4 Thame United Reserves	22	12	3	7	42	31	11	39
5 Ascot United 'Dev'	22	11	2	9	41	31	10	35
6 Finchampstead Reserves	22	10	2	10	43	54	-11	32
7 Holyport Reserves	22	9	2	11	51	62	-11	29
8 Rayners Lane Reserves	22	8	2	12	40	46	-6	26
9 Wokingham & Emmbrook Res.	22	7	2	13	32	48	-16	20
10 Chinnor Reserves	22	5	4	13	31	55	-24	19
11 Chalfont Wasps Reserves	22	5	3	14	36	59	-23	18
12 Henley Town Reserves	22	4	3	15	24	65	-41	15

DIVISION TWO WEST	P	W	D	L	F	A	GD	Pts
1 (P) Cirencester Town 'Dev'	22	15	6	1	76	30	46	51
2 (P) Wantage Town Reserves	22	16	3	3	55	19	36	51
3 Wootton Bassett Town Res.	22	13	5	4	47	22	25	44
4 Oxford City Nomads 'Dev'	22	14	1	7	75	33	42	43
5 Hook Norton Reserves	22	11	5	6	42	26	16	38
6 Brimscombe & Thrupp Reserves	22	10	5	7	53	43	10	35
7 Beversbrook	22	8	3	11	35	59	-24	27
8 Shrivenham Reserves	22	6	4	12	32	62	-30	22
9 Highworth Town Reserves	22	6	2	14	30	58	-28	20
10 Old Woodstock Town Reserves	22	4	2	16	22	73	-51	14
11 Cheltenham Saracens Reserves	22	4	4	14	24	39	-15	13
12 Fairford Town Reserves	22	3	4	15	27	54	-27	13

GROUND DIRECTIONS

PREMIER DIVISION

ABINGDON UNITED - The North Court, Northcourt Road, Abingdon OX14 1PL - 01235 203 203
From the north – Leave A34 at Abingdon north turning. Ground on right at first set of traffic lights.
From the south – Enter Town Centre, leave north on A4183 (Oxford Road).
Ground on left after one mile.

ARDLEY UNITED - The Playing Fields OX27 7NZ - 07711 009 198
From M40 Junction 10 take B430 towards Middleton Stoney the ground is on the right hand side after mile. From Oxford take B430 through Weston-on-the-Green & Middleton Stoney then on the left hand side after passing Church in village.

ASCOT UNITED - Ascot Racecourse SL5 7RA - 07798 701 995
From Ascot High Street, with Ascot Racecourse on the left, follow the A329 to the mini-roundabout, at the end of the High Street, turn left on Winkfield Rd, go through road underpass and take the first right (signposted Car Park 7&8). Follow the track past the Ascot United welcome sign, through gates into the large car park and the ground is approx. 600m further on.

BINFIELD - Hill Farm Lane RG42 5NR - 01344 860 822
From M4 Junction 10 take A329 signposted Wokingham & Binfield, at roundabout take 1st exit. Go through 1st set of traffic lights, turn left at 2nd set opposite Travel Lodge. Follow road through village over two mini-roundabouts, at 'T' junction with church in front of you turn right. Take left filter road after 150 yards into Stubbs Lane. Ground is on left at end of short lane.

BRACKNELL TOWN - Larges Lane Bracknell RG12 9AN - 01344 412 305
Leave M4 at J10, take A329M signposted Wokingham & Bracknell. Follow road for 5 miles, over roundabout, pass Southern industrial estate (Waitrose etc.) on right to a 2nd roundabout with traffic lights; take 2nd exit and follow signposts for M3. At next roundabout take 1st exit. At next roundabout take 3rd exit, Church Road dual carriageway. This brings you to another roundabout with Bracknell & Wokingham college on right and Old Manor PH on left, take 5th exit for Ascot - A329. Go down hill on dual carriageway, London Road to next roundabout take 4th exit back up the dual carriageway, London Road, Larges Lane last left turn before reaching roundabout again. Ground 200 yards on right.

BRIMSCOMBE & THRUPP - 'The Meadow', London Road, Brimscombe Stroud, Gloucestershire GL5 2SH - 07833 231 464
9 miles north of Cirencester on A419. 2 miles south of Stroud on A419.

CHELTENHAM SARACENS - PETERSFIELD PARK GL51 9DY - 01242 584 134
Follow directions into Cheltenham following signs for railway station. At Station roundabout take Gloucester Road, in a Northerly direction for approx 2 miles. Turn left at lights past Tesco entrance onto Tewkesbury Rd, follow road past 'The Range' store over railway bridge. Take 1st left and then 1st left again, then left into service road into car park.

FLACKWELL HEATH - Wilks Park, Magpie Lane HP10 9EA - 01628 523 892
Junction 4 of M40 Follow signs A404 (High Wycombe) Turn right at traffic lights halfway down Marlow Hill, signposted Flackwell Heath. Ground three (3) miles on left.

HIGHMOOR - IBIS - Palmer Park Stadium, Wokingham Road, Reading RG6 1LF - 01189 375 080
From A4 (Also indicated as London Road Reading) At the KIngs Road/A 329 Junction turn into the A329 the Palmer Park ground is approx. 300 metres on the left.

HIGHWORTH TOWN - Elm Recreation Ground SN6 7DD - 01793 766 263
Enter Town on A361, turn into The Green by Veterinary Surgery, Ground and Car Park 100 yards on left.

HOLYPORT - Summerleaze Village SL6 8SP - 07702 369 708
From the A4 Maidenhead take the B4447 towards Cookham after mile turn right into Ray Mill Road West, at the T-junction turn left into Blackamoor Lane. As road bends sharply you will see the entrance to the ground on left, signposted Holyport FC. Please observe speed limit down track to the ground.

KIDLINGTON - Yarnton Road OX5 1AT - 01865 841 526
From Kidlington Roundabout take A4260 into Kidlington. After 3rd set of traffic lights take 2nd left into Yarnton Road. Ground 300 yards on left, just past Morton Avenue.

MILTON UNITED - Potash Lane OX13 6AG - 01235 832 999
Exit A34 at Milton, 10 miles south of Oxford & 12 miles north of junction 13 of M4. Take A4130 towards Wantage approximately 200 metres turn 1st left then right into Milton Hill. Ground 400 metres on the left.

NEWBURY - Faraday Road RG14 2AD - 01635 41031
Leave M4 at junction 13 taking Newbury road. Take A4 towards Thatcham, then take 1st right by 'Topp Tiles' into Faraday Road, ground is at end of road.

OXFORD CITY NOMADS - Court Place Farm Stadium OX3 0NQ - 01865 744 493
From South: From Newbury travel along the A34 towards Oxford turn onto Ring Road heading towards London (East). Follow Ring Road over 5 roundabouts to the Green Road roundabout signposted London, M40 East. Go straight over towards Banbury. A fly-over is visible, turn left onto the slip road and follow road to Court Place Farm Stadium on left. From North: At the North Oxford roundabout, travel towards London M40 on the Eastern by-pass, turn off at the flyover, the ground is visible to the left as you go over bridge.

READING TOWN - Scours Lane RG30 6AY - 0118 945 3555
Leave M4 at junction 12 and take A4 towards Reading. Turn left at 1st lights go through Tilehurst Centre turn right into Norcot Road then left into Oxford Road and 1st right into Scours Lane.

SHRIVENHAM - The Recreation Ground SN6 8BJ - 07767 371 414
Shrivenham village is signposted off A420 Oxford to Swindon road, six miles east of Swindon, four miles west of Faringdon. Drive through village turn into Highworth Road, ground is on right, car park on left.

THAME UNITED - The ASM Stadium, Meadow View Park, Tythrop Wa, Thame, Oxon, OX9 3RN 01844 214 401. From the west: At the Oxford Road roundabout on the edge of Thame take the first left (sign posted Aylesbury) and follow the by-pass. At the next roundabout take the third exit on to Tythrop Way. The ground is 200 yards on the left.

From the east: Leave the M40 at Junction 6 and follow the signposts to Thame. On arriving in Thame, take the first right on to Wenman Road (B4012). Stay on the B4012 as it by-passes Thame, going straight over two roundabouts. The ground is on the right, directly off the by-pass, approximately half a mile after you pass Chinnor Rugby Club.

THATCHAM TOWN - Waterside Park, Crookham Hill, Thatcham RG18 4QR - 01635 862 016
From North, follow A34/A339 towards Newbury. Then follow A4 signposted Thatcham, continue on A4 through Thatcham until you come to a roundabout with a signpost to the Railway Station off to the right (Pipers Way). Continue to the station and go over the level crossing, ground is approximately 250m on left.

From West leave the M4 at junction 13 then follow the directions above. From the East, leave the M4 at junction 12 and follow A4 towards Newbury/Thatcham then follow directions above to the Railway station.

WOOTTON BASSETT - Cirencester Town FC, Corinium Stadium Kingshill, Cirencester, Glos. GL7 1HS - 01793 853 880
Leave bypass at Burford Road roundabout. Aim for Stow, turn right at traffic lights, then right again at next junction, first left into Kingshill Lane. Ground 500 yards on right.

DIVISION 1 EAST

BRACKLEY TOWN RESERVES - St James Park, Churchill Way, Brackley, Northamptonshire, NN13 8EJ - 01280 704 077
Take A43 from Northampton or Oxford, or A422 from Banbury to large roundabout south of town. Take exit marked Brackley (South) and follow towards the town (Tesco store on left). Pass the Locomotive public house and take first turning right, signposted Football Club, into Churchill Way - road leads into Club car park.

BURNHAM RESERVES - The Gore, Wymers Wood Road, Burnham, Slough SL1 8JG 01628 668 654
Approximately 2 miles from the M4 junction 7 and 5 miles from the M40 junction 2. From M40 take A355 to A4 signposted Maidenhead. From M4 take A4 towards Maidenhead until you reach roundabout with Sainsbury Superstore on left. Turn right into Lent Rise Road. Travel approximately 1½ miles over two double roundabouts, 100 yards after second double roundabout fork right into Wymers Wood Road. Ground entrance on right.

CHALFONT WASPS - Crossleys Bowstridge Lane HP8 4QN - 01494 875 050
A413 to Chalfont St Giles, follow signposts for village centre. Bowstridge Lane is 400 yards on left immediately after the shops. Crossleys is 400 yards along Bowstridge Lane on the right. Ground is directly ahead.

CHINNOR - Station Road OX39 4PV - 01844 352 579
Leave M40 at junction 6 and follow B4009 sign posted Princes Risborough. After 3 miles enter Chinnor and turn left at Crown PH roundabout. Ground is 400 yards on right.

DIDCOT TOWN RESERVES - Loop Meadow Stadium OX11 7GA - 01235 813 138
From A34 take A4130 towards Didcot, at first roundabout take first exit, at next roundabout take third exit, then straight across next two roundabouts, at 5th roundabout turn right into Avon Way, ground is on the left. Also footpath direct from Didcot Railway Station.

EASINGTON SPORTS - Addison Road OX16 9DH - 01295 257 006
From North/South M40- Leave M40 at J11, follow A422 to Banbury, 2nd r'about take A4260 to Adderbury. Go through three sets of traffic lights, at top of hill at T-junc' turn left. Take 3rd right into Addison Rd. From South West A361 – Entering Banbury take 1st right turning into Springfield Av after 'The Easington' PH. Follow road, take T-junc' right into Grange Rd, 1st right into Addison Rd. Ground on left at end of road.

FINCHAMPSTEAD - Memorial Park, The Village RG40 4JR - 0118 973 2890
A321 from Wokingham, then fork right onto B3016. At the Greyhound Public House turn right onto the B3348. The ground is 200 yards on the right.

HEADINGTON AM' - Barton Recreation Ground OX3 9LA - 01865 760 489
A40 from London take last exit at Headington Roundabout. A40 from Witney take first exit. Take first left after leaving roundabout into North Way. Follow North Way to end where road merges to become Barton Village Road. Ground at bottom of hill on left.

HENLEY TOWN - The Triangle Ground RG9 4HB - 01491 411 083
From Henley Town Centre take the A4155 towards Reading. Mill Lane is approximately one mile from the Town Centre on the left immediately before the Jet Garage. From M4 Junction 11 head towards Reading on the A33 inner distribution road then follow A4155 signed to Henley, turn right into Mill Lane after the Jet Garage. Ground & Car Park on the left over the Railway Bridge.

OLD WOODSTOCK TOWN - New Road, Woodstock OX20 1PD - 07748 152 243
A44 from Oxford, turn right opposite The Crown into Hensington Road. After half a mile road bends to right, take 1st turning right into New Road. Ground on left.

PENN & TYLERS GREEN - French School Meadows HP10 8LF - 01494 815 346
From West - 'M40 to High Wycombe leave at J4. Follow A404 to Amersham, via Wycombe. Stay on A404 up the hill past railway station approx. 3 miles at Hazlemere Crossroads turn right onto the B474 signposted to Penn and Beaconsfield. Continue for approx. one mile go past three new houses on left, turn into Elm Road, the ground is on the left. From East -Leave M40 at Junction 2 and take the road signed Beaconsfield. From Beaconsfield follow the road through Penn towards Hazlemere, pass the pond on green and entrance to ground is on the right had side of road before the hill.

RAYNERS LANE - Tithe Farm Social Club HA2 0XH - 0208 868 8724
From A40 Polish War Memorial turn left into A4180 (West End Road), approx. 500 metres turn right into Station Approach, at traffic lights turn right into Victoria Road. At next roundabout continue straight on to traffic lights at junction with Alexandra Avenue (Matrix Bar & Restaurant on left). Continue straight on over traffic lights and take second turning on left into Rayners Lane. Ground is approximately half a mile on the left.

WOKINGHAM & EMMB' - Emmbrook Sports & Social Club Lowther Rd, Wokingham. RG41 1JB 0118 9780 209
From M4 – exit J10 – take left slip road signposted Reading . After 100 yds exit to Winnersh Triangle /Earley . As you approach traffic lights go through both sets bearing right towards Earley/Winnersh / Wokingham . Continue to next set of traffic lights and keep left bearing left under Railway Bridge . Keep left and bear left at next set of traffic lights to Winnersh/Wokingham on A329 –Reading Road . Continue straight ahead to traffic lights – go straight ahead continuing on A329 –Reading Road passing Sainsbury's on your right . Continue through next lights, under bridge and past BP garage on the left . Once past the garage take next left into Old Forest Road . Go over the bridge to next turn on the right hand side into Lowther Road and immediately right into the Emmbrook Sports and Social Club.

WOODLEY TOWN - Scours Lane, Reading, Berkshire, RG30 6AY - 0118 9453 555
Come off J12 of the M4 head along the A4 towards Reading, take a left onto Langley Hill and follow it all the way up onto Park Lane, continue onto School Road past the Tilehurst shops and then down onto Kentwood Hill. At the bottom of the hill take a right onto the Oxford Road towards Reading and just past the Waitrose Shop you need to take a left into an industrial estate and under the railway bridge and the ground will be in front of you to your right.

DIVISION 1 WEST

CARTERTON - Kilkenny Lane OX18 1DY - 01993 842 410

Leave A40 follow B4477 for Carterton continue along Monahan Way turning right at roundabout, at traffic lights turn right onto Upavon Way. At next set of lights turn right onto B4020 to Burford. Take 2nd right into Swinbrook Road carry onto Kilkenny Lane, a single-track road). Ground & car park 200 metres on left hand side.

CIRENCESTER TOWN DEV. - Corinium Stadium, Kingshill Lane, Cirencester Glos GL7 1HS - 01285 654 543

Leave bypass at Burford Road roundabout. Aim for Stow, turn right at traffic lights, then right again at next junction, first left into Kingshill Lane. Ground 500 yards on right.

CLANFIELD - Radcot Road OX18 2ST - 01367 810 314

Situated on A4095 at southern end of village, 8 miles west of Witney and 4 miles east of Faringdon.

FAIRFORD TOWN - Cinder Lane London Road GL7 4AX - 01285 712 071

Take A417 from Lechlade, turn left down Cinder Lane 150 yards after 40 mph sign. From Cirencester take Lechlade Road, turn right down Cinder Lane 400 yards after passing the Railway Inn.

HOOK NORTON - The Bourne OX15 5PB - 01608 737 132

From Oxford – A44 to junction with A361 turn right, take 1st left to a 'T' junction, turn right & enter village, after 30 MPH turn left then 1st right into 'The Bourne', take 1st left into ground.

LETCOMBE - Bassett Road OX12 9JU - 07765 144 985

Take the B4507 from Wantage (Sign posted White Horse). Turn left after half a mile to Letcombe Regis. Ground on Far side of Village, on the right hand side of road.

LONGLEVENS AFC - Saw Mills End, Corinium Avenue, Gloucester GL4 3DG - 01452 530388 (Clubhouse)

From South: From M5 Gloucester exit junction 11a, and bear left onto A417. At roundabout take 2nd exit continue on A417 for ½ mile. At next roundabout take 2nd exit (look for coroners court sign) for ½ mile then turn left on Sawmills End (Ibis Hotel). Ground is on the left just past hotel.
From North: From M5 Gloucester exit junction 11, at roundabout take third exit onto A40 for approx 2 miles. At roundabout take 2nd exit (A417) for 1 mile. At roundabout take 3rd exit (look for coroners court sign) for ½ mile then turn left on Sawmills End (Ibis Hotel). Ground is on the left just past hotel.

LYDNEY TOWN - Lydney Recreation Ground GL15 5RU - 01594 844 523

From Gloucester – take Lydney road off A48 down Highfield Hill and into the town centre. Take 1st left into Swan Road after 2nd set of pelican lights. From Chepstow – at by-pass roundabout take Lydney road. Go over railway crossing then take 2nd right into Swan Road.

NEW COLLEGE SWINDON - Supermarine RFC Sports & Social Supermarine Road South Marston Swindon SN3 4BZ - 01793 824 828

From M5 Junction 11a, take the A417 to Cirencester, then A419 Swindon. At the A361 junction by Honda Factory take road to Highworth. After one mile Club is on 4th roundabout.
From M4 Junction 15, take A419 towards Swindon Cirencester, take A361, then as above .
From A420 Swindon take A419 to Cirencester, near Honda factory take A361, then as above.

NORTH LEIGH RESERVES - Eynsham Hall Park Sports Ground OX29 6PN - 07775 818 066

Ground situated on A4095 Witney to Woodstock road, three miles east of Witney. Entrance 300 yards east of main park entrance.

PURTON - The Red House SN5 4DY - 01793 770 262 MD

Red House is near Village Hall Square; Purton is well signposted from all directions, situated on the B4041 Wootton Bassett to Cricklade Road, NW of Swindon.

SHORTWOOD UNITED RESERVES - Meadowbank, Shortwood, Nailsworth GL6 0SJ 01453 833 936

When entering Nailsworth from Stroud turn right at mini roundabout, when coming from Cirencester go straight over roundabout, and when from Bath turn left at mini roundabout.
Proceed up Spring Hill 30 yards turn left at Raffles Wine Warehouse, straight through town turn left at Brittannia Pub carry on for 1 mile until you come to Shortwood village you will see sign post on fork in the road keep to the left follow on for quarter of a mile ground opposite church.

TUFFLEY ROVERS - Glevum Park Lower Tuffley Lane, Tuffley, Gloucester GL2 5DT - 07708 361 808

From the motorway junction 12 of the M5 motorway head towards Gloucester for a short distance on the B4008 down to a roundabout. At this roundabout take the second exit A38 towards Gloucester. After 1/2 mile you will reach another roundabout with a Holiday Inn on your right. Take the first exit continuing along the A38 on towards Gloucester until you reach a large traffic light junction at the end of the dual carriageway (approx 1.5 miles). At these lights continue straight over ignoring sign for Tuffley to the right. Once through this first set of lights keep to the right and keep in the right filter lane to the next lights. Turn right here and head towards City Centre and Historic Docks along the Old Bristol Road. Just after the newly shaped road straightens along the old road take the turning right in to Lower Tuffley Lane. Continue along Lower Tuffley Lane almost to the end and the entrance to the ground is on the left through a gateway directly after the commercial premises of Marshall Langston and opposite a large transport depot.

TYTHERINGTON ROCKS - Hardwicke Playing Field GL12 8UJ - 07837 555 776

From M5 Junction 14 take A38 for Bristol. Tytherington turn-off is approximately three (3) miles. Enter village, ground is signposted.

WANTAGE TOWN RESERVES - Alfredian Park Manor Road, Wantage OX12 8DW - 01235 764 781

Proceed to Market Square. Take road at southeast corner (Newbury Street signposted to Hungerford). Continue for approximately a quarter of a mile take right turning into the ground. Clearly marked “Wantage Town FC”.

Longlevens FC - Gloucestershire County Champions 2013-14.

2013-14 champions - Hollands & Blair. Photo: Alan Coomes

2013-14 - Crockenhill. Photo: Alan Coomes

KENT INVICTA LEAGUE

Sponsored by: Pain & Glory Sports
Founded: 2011

Recent Champions
2012: Bly Spartans
2013: Phoenix Sports

		P	W	D	L	F	A	GD	Pts
1	Hollands & Blair	28	25	1	2	123	23	100	76
2	Lydd Town	28	20	6	2	68	20	48	66
3	Sutton Athletic	28	15	7	6	70	29	41	52
4	Fleet Leisure	28	17	1	10	71	38	33	52
5	Orpington	28	15	7	6	52	30	22	52
6	Bearsted	28	16	3	9	75	37	38	51
7	Rusthall	28	16	3	9	70	54	16	51
8	Bridon Ropes	28	12	4	12	59	52	7	40
9	Seven Acre & Sidcup	28	11	4	13	58	64	-6	37
10	Glebe	28	11	2	15	52	53	-1	35
11	Kent Football United	28	8	9	11	60	57	3	33
12	Eltham Palace	28	6	3	19	26	66	-40	21
13	Lewisham Borough	28	5	2	21	34	102	-68	17
14	Meridian VP	28	4	4	20	31	85	-54	16
15	Crockenhill	28	1	0	27	20	159	-139	3

CHALLENGE TROPHY

ROUND 1

Eltham Palace	v	Brodon Ropes	0-1
Bridon Ropes	v	Eltham Palace	5-0
Lewisham Borough	v	Glebe	2-0
Glebe	v	Lewisham Borough	2-2
Seven Acre & Sidcup	v	Orpington	2-0
Orpington	v	Seven Acre & Sidcup	2-1
Bearsted	v	Kent Football United	1-3
Kent Football United	v	Bearsted	3-1
Crockenhill	v	Fleet Leisure	0-7
Fleet Leisure	v	Crockenhill	7-1
Lydd Town	v	Hollands & Blair	2-3
Hollands & Blair	v	Lydd Town	4-1
Sutton Athletic	v	Rusthall	5-0
Rusthall	v	Sutton Athletic	2-0
Meridian			Bye

QUARTER FINALS

Meridian VP	v	Lewisham Borough	4-2
Lewisham Borough	v	Meridian VP	4-0
Seven Acre & Sidcup	v	Fleet Leisure	2-3
Fleet Leisure	v	Seven Acre & Sidcup	7-1
Kent Football United	v	Bridon Ropes	2-3
Bridon Ropes	v	Kent Football United	5-0
Sutton Athletic	v	Hollands & Blair	0-1
Hollands & Blair	v	Sutton Athletic	3-6

SEMI FINALS

Lewisham Borough	v	Fleet Leisure	3-4
Fleet Leisure	v	Lewisham Borough	5-0
Bridon Ropes	v	Sutton Athletic	1-2
Sutton Athletic	v	Bridon Ropes	4-0

FINAL

Fleet Leisure	v	Sutton Athletic	0-3

		1	2	3	4	5	6	7	8	9	10	11	12	13	14	15
1	Bearsted		2–0	10–0	1–0	2–0	2–2	2–3	2–1	8–0	0–1	3–0	1–0	3–2	1–2	0–1
2	Bridon Ropes	1–4		6–2	1–2	1–1	2–1	1–5	2–2	5–1	1–0	3–0	2–2	3–1	2–1	0–4
3	Crockenhill	0–8	1–7		3–0	2–4	1–5	0–15	0–12	0–6	0–9	1–3	3–4	0–4	0–2	0–9
4	Eltham Palace	0–3	0–4	3–1		1–3	0–1	0–2	1–1	0–3	0–0	0–1	1–6	1–4	2–3	0–3
5	Fleet Leisure	1–2	3–1	5–0	3–1		3–2	0–2	3–0	7–0	3–0	2–1	1–2	2–3	3–1	2–1
6	Glebe	5–4	1–2	5–0	3–0	0–1		0–5	1–3	4–0	1–3	1–0	1–3	0–1	3–2	1–3
7	Hollands & Blair	5–2	4–1	13–0	6–0	3–2	2–1		1–0	3–0	1–2	3–1	0–1	3–1	3–1	2–1
8	Kent Football United	2–1	0–2	5–0	2–3	0–2	1–1	1–12		5–0	0–2	3–3	2–0	4–1	3–3	2–2
9	Lewisham Borough	3–2	0–5	6–4	0–3	0–6	1–2	1–4	1–1		0–3	3–2	1–1	0–1	3–8	0–1
10	Lydd Town	2–1	3–2	4–0	1–1	2–1	3–0	1–1	4–0	2–0		6–0	2–1	5–1	2–2	1–1
11	Meridian VP	1–2	0–0	2–1	1–3	0–5	0–4	0–3	1–5	6–4	1–4		0–2	2–8	1–2	0–4
12	Orpington	1–1	3–2	5–0	0–1	2–1	1–0	0–5	4–1	3–0	0–1	1–1		1–1	1–1	0–0
13	Rusthall	2–5	3–2	2–1	2–0	4–5	3–2	1–5	2–1	8–0	0–0	3–0	1–3		4–2	1–1
14	Seven Acre & Sidcup	2–3	2–1	2–0	5–1	3–1	3–4	0–6	1–1	2–1	1–3	6–1	0–4	1–3		0–3
15	Sutton Athletic	0–0	3–0	3–0	3–2	2–1	4–1	3–5	2–2	6–0	1–2	3–3	0–1	2–3	4–0	

CLUB MOVEMENTS

Premier Division - In: Gravesham Borough (NC - formerly Fleet Leisure).

Sheppey United (P - Kent County - NC - formerly Sheppey & Sheerness United).

Out: Fleet Leisure (NC - Gravesham Borough).

2013-14 - Eltham Palace. Photo: Alan Coomes

2013-14 - Fleet Leisure (now Gravesham Borough). Photo: Alan Coomes.

BEARSTED

Founded: 1895 Nickname:

Secretary: Roy Benton **(T)** 07849 809 875 **(E)** benton951@aol.com
Chairman: **Manager:** Kevin Stevens **Prog Ed:** Janine Harris
Ground: Otham Sports Club, Honey Lane, Otham, Maidstone ME15 8RG **(T)** 07860 360 280
Colours(change): White/blue/blue (All yellow)

ADDITIONAL INFORMATION:
Previous League: Kent County > 2011.

BRIDON ROPES

Founded: 1935 Nickname:

Secretary: Richard Clements **(T)** 07884 457 852 **(E)** rich.clements@live.co.uk
Chairman: Clive Smith **Manager:** Gary Lisney
Ground: Meridian Sports & Social Club, Charlton Park Lane, Charlton, London SE7 8QS **(T)** 0208 8561923
Colours(change): Blue & white/blue/blue (All red)

ADDITIONAL INFORMATION:
Previous Lge: Kent County > 2011.

CROCKENHILL

Founded: 1946 Nickname:

Secretary: Steve Cullen **(T)** 07702 886 966 **(E)** steve.cullen@virgin.net
Chairman: **Prog Ed:** Alan Curnick
Ground: Wested Meadow Ground, Eynesford Road, Crockenhill, Kent BR8 8EJ **(T)** 01322 666 767
Colours(change): Red & white/black/black (All blue)

ADDITIONAL INFORMATION:
Previous Lge: Kent County > 2011.

ELTHAM PALACE

Founded: 1961 Nickname:

Secretary: Neil Proctor **(T)** 07796 698 666 **(E)** neilproctor@live.co.uk
Chairman: Neil Proctor **Manager:** Walt Noriega
Ground: Green Court Sports Club, Green Court Rd, Crockenhill, Kent BR8 8HF **(T)** 07796 698 666
Colours(change): All yellow with blue trim (black & white/black/white)

ADDITIONAL INFORMATION:

GLEBE

Founded: 2013 Nickname:

Secretary: Nikola Curtis **(T)** 07875 036 907 **(E)** nikola.curtis@ntlworld.com
Chairman: Rocky McMillan **Prog Ed:** Rocky McMillan
Ground: Holmesdale FC, Oakley Road, Bromley, Kent BR2 8HG **(T)** 07903 274 178
Colours(change): Red & black/black/black (White/red/red)

ADDITIONAL INFORMATION:

GRAVESHAM BOROUGH

Founded: 1927 Nickname:

Secretary: Dave Hughes **(T)** 07725 961 273 **(E)** fleetleisurefc@aol.com
Chairman: **Prog Ed:** Dave Hughes
Ground: Rochester United FC, Rede Court Road, Strood, Kent ME2 3TU **(T)** 01634 710 577
Colours(change): All red (Yellow/black/yellow)

ADDITIONAL INFORMATION:
Previous Name: Beauwater FC. Fleet Leisure > 2014.
Previous League: Kent County > 2013.

HOLLANDS & BLAIR

Founded: 1970 Nickname: Blair

Secretary: Laurence Plummer **(T)** 07540 841 799 **(E)** laurence.plummer@btinternet.com
Chairman: Barry Peirce **Manager:** Paul Piggott **Prog Ed:** Richard Day
Ground: Star Meadow Sports Club, Darland Avenue, Gillingham, Kent ME7 3AN **(T)** 01634 573839
Colours(change): All red (Yellow & blue)

ADDITIONAL INFORMATION:
Previous Lge: Kent County > 2011.
Honours: Kent County 2010-11. Kent Invicta 2013-14.

2013-14 - Glebe. Photo: Alan Coomes

2013-14 - Lewisham Borough. Photo: Alan Coomes.

KENT FOOTBALL UNITED

Founded: 2010 Nickname:

Secretary: Samuel MacNeil **(T)** 07885 749 267 **(E)** kentelitefc@hotmail.co.uk
Chairman: Samuel MacNeil
Ground: Glentworth Sports Club, Lowfield Street, Dartford, Kent DA1 1JB **(T)** 07860 654 558
Colours(change): Blue & white/blue/blue (Yellow & black/black/black)

ADDITIONAL INFORMATION:

LEWISHAM BOROUGH

Founded: 2003 Nickname: The Boro

Secretary: Ray Simpson **(T)** 07958 946 236 **(E)** grancan_jamaica@yahoo.co.uk
Chairman: Ray Simpson **Manager:** Kevin Harris **Prog Ed:** Ray Simpson
Ground: Ladywell Arena, Silvermere Road, Catford, London SE6 4QX **(T)** 0208 314 1986
Colours(change): All royal blue (All yellow)

ADDITIONAL INFORMATION:
Previous Lge: Kent county > 2011.

LYDD TOWN

Founded: 1885 Nickname:

Secretary: Bruce Marchant **(T)** 01303 275 403 **(E)** brucemarchant@hotmail.com
Chairman: **Manager:** Dave Smith **Prog Ed:** Dave Johncock
Ground: The Lindsey Field, Dengemarsh Road, Lydd, Kent TN29 9JH **(T)** 01797 321 904
Colours(change): Green & red/green/red (Blue & white stripes/blue/blue)

ADDITIONAL INFORMATION:
Previous Lge: Kent County > 2011.

MERIDIAN VP

Founded: 1995 Nickname:

Secretary: Dwinder Tamna **(T)** 07977 274 179 **(E)** dtamna@meridianfc.co.uk
Chairman: Dwinder Tamna **Manager:** Dwinder Tamna &Richard Dimmock **Prog Ed:** Dwinder Tamna
Ground: Meridian Sports & Social Club, 110 Charlton Park Lane, London SE7 8QS **(T)** 0208 856 1923
Colours(change): All sky blue (All red)

ADDITIONAL INFORMATION:
Previous Lge: Kent County > 2011.
Previous Name: Meridan 1995-2013.

ORPINGTON

Founded: 1939 Nickname:

Secretary: Paul Wade **(T)** 07940 027 897 **(E)** paul.wade@virgin.net
Chairman: Jeff Cockburn **Manager:** Byron Beard **Prog Ed:** Phil Alder
Ground: Green Court Road, Crockenhill, Kent BR8 8HJ **(T)** 07940 355 595
Colours(change): Amber/black/amber (All blue)

ADDITIONAL INFORMATION:
Previous Lge: Kent County > 2011.

RUSTHALL

Founded: 1890 Nickname:

Secretary: Jason Plunkett **(T)** 01892 571 970 **(E)** plunkettjase@sky.com
Chairman: Ben Martin **Manager:** Gary Sharman **Prog Ed:** Richard Smith
Ground: Jockey Farm, Nellington Road, Rusthall, Tunbridge Wells, Kent TN4 8SH **(T)** 07865 396 299
Colours(change): Green & white stripes/green/green (Blue & black/black/black)

ADDITIONAL INFORMATION:
Previous Lge: Kent County > 2011.

SEVEN ACRE & SIDCUP

Founded: 1900 Nickname:

Secretary: Lee Hill **(T)** 07834 583 395 **(E)** lhsasfc@gmail.com
Chairman: Steve Reader **Manager:** Lee Hill **Prog Ed:** John Brand
Ground: Seven Acre & Sidcup FC, Bayliss Avenue, Thamesmead, London SE28 8NJ **(T)** 07834 583 395
Colours(change): Red & black/black/black (Green/black/black)

ADDITIONAL INFORMATION:
Previous Lge: Kent County > 2011.

SHEPPEY UNITED

Founded: 1890 Nickname:

Secretary: Jonathon Longhurst **(T)** 07713 065 099 **(E)** jonl@bond-group.co.uk
Chairman: Matthew Smith **Manager:** Kevin Hake **Prog Ed:** Sam Searle
Ground: Holm Park, Queenborough Road ME12 3DB **(T)** 01795 669 547
Colours(change): Red & white stripes/blacl/black (Yellow/royal blue/royal blue)

ADDITIONAL INFORMATION:
Previous Name: Sheppey & Sheerness United.
Previous League: Kent County > 2014.

SUTTON ATHLETIC

Founded: 1898 Nickname:

Secretary: Guy Eldridge **(T)** 07778 053 433 **(E)** guy.eldridge@btconnect.com
Chairman: Micky Kelleher **Manager:** Ben Young **Prog Ed:** John Ball
Ground: The Pavillion Lower Road, Sports Ground, Lower Road, Hextable, Kent BR8 7RZ **(T)** 07788 446 495
Colours(change): Green & white/green/green (Black & white/black/white)

ADDITIONAL INFORMATION:
Previous League: Kent County > 2011.
Previous Names: Sutton United > 2012.

2013-14 - Seven Acre & Sidcup. Photo: Alan Coomes.

MIDLAND FOOTBALL LEAGUE

Formed in 2014 after the merger of the
Midland Football Alliance (1994) and the Midland Football Combination (1927)

MIDLAND FOOTBALL COMBINATION 2013-14

Recent Champions:

2009: Loughborough University. 2010: Heath Hayes. 2011: Heather St. Johns.
2012: Continental Star. 2013: Walsall Wood

PREMIER DIVISION	P	W	D	L	F	A	GD	Pts
1 Brocton	34	25	6	3	100	49	51	81
2 Bromsgrove Sporting	34	23	3	8	92	35	57	72
3 Nuneaton Griff	34	20	4	10	96	75	21	64
4 Bolehall Swifts	34	18	6	10	73	50	23	60
5 Atherstone Town	34	18	6	10	75	55	20	60
6 Studley	34	16	8	10	64	54	10	56
7 Lichfield City	34	13	11	10	52	50	2	50
8 Stafford Town	34	14	8	12	56	57	-1	50
9 Alvis Sporting Club	34	14	8	12	69	79	-10	50
10 Southam United	34	14	5	15	62	80	-18	47
11 Littleton	34	14	4	16	74	60	14	46
12 Racing Club Warwick	34	11	7	16	60	63	-3	40
13 Earlswood Town	34	11	4	19	47	66	-19	37
14 Blackwood	34	11	4	19	49	74	-25	37
15 Pershore Town	34	10	3	21	57	80	-23	33
16 Coventry Copsewood (-1pt)	34	8	10	16	54	77	-23	33
17 Pilkington XXX	34	6	8	20	53	77	-24	26
18 Pelsall Villa	34	5	5	24	41	93	-52	20

Feb 2014 - Castle Vale JKS withdrew - record expunged.

DIVISION ONE	P	W	D	L	F	A	GD	Pts
1 Cadbury Athletic	28	21	4	3	93	26	67	67
2 Fairfield Villa	28	17	5	6	67	33	34	56
3 Sutton United	28	16	7	5	68	32	36	55
4 Aston	28	18	1	9	62	43	19	55
5 Phoenix United (-3)	28	17	5	6	73	44	29	53
6 Chelmsley Town	28	13	5	10	45	48	-3	44
7 Hampton	28	12	7	9	53	49	4	43
8 Feckenham	28	11	6	11	49	50	-1	39
9 West Midlands Police	28	8	8	12	46	59	-13	32
10 Shirley Town	28	10	2	16	36	59	-23	32
11 Knowle	28	8	6	14	29	47	-18	30
12 Barnt Green Spartak	28	7	6	15	43	53	-10	27
13 Droitwich Spa	28	7	4	17	46	71	-25	25
14 FC Glades Sporting (-3)	28	5	4	19	35	73	-38	16
15 Coton Green	28	2	6	20	22	80	-58	12

PREMIER DIVISION	1	2	3	4	5	6	7	8	9	10	11	12	13	14	15	16	17	18
1 Atherstone Town		4-0	0-1	3-2	1-0	3-0	6-2	1-2	4-2	0-1	1-0	3-1	3-0	3-1	3-1	2-1	0-1	0-3
2 Blackwood	3-0		2-2	1-1	1-4	3-2	2-1	2-5	2-2	3-5	1-4	1-1	3-3	1-1	2-1	0-1	2-1	1-0
3 Bolehall Swifts	1-2	2-1		1-0	0-0	3-0	0-3	1-3	1-0	3-0	1-2	0-2	1-2	3-2	3-0	1-1	2-1	1-1
4 Brocton	1-4	5-0	4-3		2-3	5-3	4-3	1-0	2-1	0-2	0-1	1-0	1-1	4-1	5-0	2-1	1-1	2-2
5 Bromsgrove Sporting	2-2	4-3	1-1	3-2		5-1	2-0	3-3	4-1	1-3	0-4	3-0	0-2	5-0	5-2	2-1	1-0	0-4
6 Castle Vale JKS	1-1	3-2	0-1	2-5	0-2		2-2	0-2	0-2	1-3	3-5	2-1	2-2	2-2	3-0	1-2	1-2	1-5
7 Coventry Copsewood	1-1	4-2	3-1	1-3	3-3	2-2		1-1	2-1	1-1	0-3	3-1	2-1	5-0	4-2	1-1	0-4	0-2
8 Earlswood Town	6-1	4-0	1-3	1-1	1-0	1-0	2-2		1-3	1-1	2-2	5-1	4-1	4-0	2-1	3-0	3-1	4-0
9 Lichfield City	1-4	0-0	4-3	0-1	2-0	2-1	1-0	3-2		1-2	2-1	2-1	2-1	3-1	5-2	1-2	3-3	0-3
10 Littleton	1-1	1-1	2-0	1-1	0-3	5-1	3-1	2-2	4-2		3-0	5-0	1-1	2-2	5-1	3-0	1-0	2-3
11 Nuneaton Griff	1-2	3-1	3-1	1-4	3-1	6-1	1-1	4-3	4-1	1-0		3-1	2-0	1-2	1-0	1-4	1-5	0-1
12 Pelsall Villa	2-1	2-1	0-2	0-5	2-3	4-0	1-1	2-4	0-3	1-0	1-2		3-3	4-2	0-2	2-4	0-3	1-2
13 Pershore Town	3-1	4-2	0-5	3-1	2-2	1-0	1-2	1-3	1-1	0-1	2-2	2-0		4-0	2-2	3-3	0-0	1-2
14 Pilkington XXX	2-1	1-0	1-3	0-4	0-5	1-5	0-1	1-1	1-5	5-3	2-5	0-1	3-3		3-2	2-3	1-5	1-3
15 Racing Club Warwick	2-3	2-2	1-2	2-0	2-1	4-0	0-2	1-5	2-2	0-7	1-2	1-2	0-4	3-1		0-2	1-1	1-3
16 Southam United	4-0	3-2	1-2	2-2	4-1	5-2	0-2	1-1	4-3	0-3	2-1	3-1	5-1	1-3	3-2		2-3	1-1
17 Stafford Town	2-2	6-0	2-2	1-3	1-2	3-2	0-2	3-2	2-5	0-1	4-1	1-1	5-1	5-3	5-0	1-0		0-4
18 Walsall Wood	1-0	1-0	4-0	3-1	1-2	2-2	1-0	3-2	1-2	2-1	0-0	2-0	5-0	2-1	2-1	4-2	2-1	

MIDLAND FOOTBALL LEAGUE - STEP 5/6/7

DIVISION TWO	P	W	D	L	F	A	GD	Pts
1 Kenilworth Town KH	30	22	3	5	90	48	42	69
2 Coventry United	30	22	2	6	105	33	72	68
3 Paget Rangers	30	20	6	4	98	33	65	66
4 Badsey Rangers	30	16	7	7	69	39	30	55
5 Rostance Edwards	30	15	6	9	72	59	13	51
6 Leamington Hibernian	30	14	7	9	48	40	8	49
7 Alcester Town (-3pts)	30	15	4	11	79	71	8	46
8 Barton United	30	13	4	13	48	65	-17	43
9 Polesworth	30	12	6	12	59	90	-31	42
10 Perrywood	30	12	4	14	58	50	8	40
11 Enville Athletic	30	10	3	17	59	62	-3	33
12 Austrey Rangers	30	10	3	17	55	64	-9	33
13 Northfield Town	30	9	6	15	45	63	-18	33
14 FC Stratford	30	6	3	21	43	92	-49	21
15 Burntwood Town (-3)	30	5	4	21	54	102	-48	16
16 Inkberrow	30	2	6	22	39	110	-71	12

RESERVE DIVISION ONE	P	W	D	L	F	A	GD	Pts
1 Loughborough Dynamo Res.	16	13	1	2	67	25	42	40
2 Quorn Reserves	16	12	0	4	63	28	35	36
3 Lichfield City Reserves	16	8	3	5	39	29	10	27
4 Evesham United Reserves	16	7	5	4	30	24	6	26
5 Barwell Reserves	16	6	4	6	33	30	3	22
6 Redditch United Reserves	16	5	2	9	29	41	-12	17
7 Coalville Town Reserves	16	5	1	10	18	36	-18	16
8 Gresley Reserves	16	3	3	10	23	37	-14	12
9 Atherstone Town Reserves	16	3	1	12	22	74	-52	10

RESERVE DIVISION TWO	P	W	D	L	F	A	GD	Pts
1 Bolehall Swifts Reserves	20	13	3	4	61	24	37	42
2 Knowle Reserves	20	12	2	6	51	28	23	38
3 Alvechurch Reserves	20	10	5	5	38	21	17	35
4 Brocton Reserves	20	10	4	6	40	30	10	34
5 Fairfield Villa Reserves	20	10	4	6	46	38	8	34
6 Sutton United Reserves	20	10	3	7	40	36	4	33
7 Cadbury Athletic Reserves	20	8	2	10	37	56	-19	26
8 Pelsall Villa Reserves (-6)	20	8	1	11	46	41	5	19
9 Continental Star Reserves	20	4	4	12	24	60	-36	16
12 Droitwich Spa Reserves	20	2	7	11	21	52	-31	13
11 Racing Club Warwick Res. (-6)	20	3	5	12	36	54	-18	8

LES JAMES CHALLENGE CUP

PRELIMINARY ROUND

Leamington Hibernian	v	Coventry United	2-6
Droitwich Spa	v	Polesworth	2-3
Barton United	v	Burntwood Town	2-0
Sutton United	v	Rugeley Rangers	3-1
Inkberrow	v	Paget Rangers	1-6
FC Stratford	v	Austrey Rangers	2-1
Kenilworth Town KH	v	Perrywood	4-2
Barnt Green Spartak	v	Enville Athletic	2-1
Badsey Rangers	v	Northfield Town	4-0

ROUND 1

Alcester Town	v	Rostance Edwards	2-5
Fairfield Villa	v	Coton Green	3-2
Knowle	v	Coventry United	1-2
Polesworth	v	Feckenham	1-2 aet
Barton United	v	Sutton United	2-4
Paget Rangers	v	West Midlands Police	0-4
FC Stratford	v	Kenilworth Town KH	1-4
FC Glades Sporting	v	Chelmsley Town	4-6
Shirley Town	v	Barnt Green Spartak	1-2
Badsey Rangers	v	Phoenix United	3-1

ROUND 2

Rostance Edwards	v	Fairfield Villa	1-1, 4-5p
Southam United	v	Littleton	6-3
Coventry United	v	Brocton	0-1
Feckenham	v	Coventry Copsewood	0-1
Stafford Town	v	Studley	2-1
Pilkington XXX	v	Castle Vale JKS	0-0, 3-1p
Lichfield City	v	Pershore Town	0-3
Sutton United	v	Bolehall Swifts	1-3 aet
Alvis Sporting Club	v	West Midlands Police	2-1
Nuneaton Griff	v	Pelsall Villa	2-1
Cadbury Athletic	v	Kenilworth Town KH	8-0
Bromsgrove Rovers	v	Aston	3-1
Hampton	v	Atherstone Town	2-3
Racing Club Warwick	v	Chelmsley Town	1-3
Barnt Green Spartak	v	Blackwood	2-4
Badsey Rangers	v	Earlswood Town	2-3

ROUND 3

Fairfield Villa	v	Southam United	2-3 aet
Brocton	v	Coventry Copsewood	3-3, 5-4p
Stafford Town	v	Pilkington XXX	6-4
Pershore Town	v	Bolehill Swifts	1-4
Alvis Sporting Club	v	Nuneaton Griff	3-1
Cadbury Athletic	v	Bromsgrove Sporting	1-2
Atherstone United	v	Chelmsley Town	1-0
Blackwood	v	Earlswood Town	4-0

QUARTER FINALS

Blackwood	v	Stafford Town	0-2
Alvis Sporting Club	v	Bromsgrove Sporting	0-5
Atherstone Town	v	Brocton	4-1
Bolehall Swifts	v	Southam United	1-1, 4-2p

SEMI-FINALS

Atherstone Town	v	Bolehall Swifts	4-1
Stafford Town	v	Bromsgrove Sporting	5-3

FINAL

Stafford Town	v	Atherstone Town	2-1

MIDLAND FOOTBALL ALLIANCE 2013-14

Recent Champions:

2009: Market Drayton Town. 2010: Barwell. 2011: Coalville Town.
2012: Gresley. 2013: Stratford Town

		P	W	D	L	F	A	GD	Pts
1	(P) Tividale	42	28	11	3	86	34	52	95
2	Boldmere St. Michaels	42	25	8	9	94	55	39	83
3	Highgate United	42	23	10	9	96	60	36	79
4	Coleshill Town	42	23	9	10	94	47	47	78
5	Quorn	42	23	8	11	91	48	43	77
6	Walsall Wood	42	20	11	11	70	43	27	71
7	Coventry Sphinx	42	19	10	13	77	73	4	67
8	AFC Wulfrunians	42	18	11	13	89	76	13	65
9	Causeway United	42	19	7	16	88	75	13	64
10	Stourport Swifts	42	18	9	15	72	61	11	63
11	Tipton Town	42	17	12	13	80	70	10	63
12	Westfields	42	17	10	15	84	70	14	61
13	Alvechurch	42	17	7	18	68	72	-4	58
14	Kirby Muxloe	42	16	8	18	64	70	-6	56
15	Loughborough University	42	14	10	18	82	86	-4	52
16	Shepshed Dynamo	42	12	9	21	73	82	-9	45
17	Continental Star	42	12	4	26	59	99	-40	40
18	Heath Hayes	42	9	11	22	54	92	-38	38
19	Dunkirk	42	9	9	24	56	99	-43	36
20	Rocester	42	7	9	26	43	95	-52	30
21	Heather St. John's	42	7	9	26	56	116	-60	30
22	Gornal Athletic (-14)	42	8	10	24	53	106	-53	20

LEAGUE CUP

ROUND 1

Alvechurch	v	Boldmere St Michaels	0-0 1-3p
Causeway United	v	Tividale	2-1
Dunkirk	v	Shepshed Dynamo	1-0
Gornal Athletic	v	Stourport Swifts	1-4
Loughborough University	v	Kirby Muxloe	2-0
Walsall Wood	v	Continental Star	5-3

ROUND 2

Coleshill Town	v	Boldmere St Michaels	3-4
Dunkirk	v	Heather St John's	3-1
Highgate United	v	Coventry Sphinx	1-0
Loughborough University	v	Quorn	0-1
Rocester	v	Tipton Town	2-3
Stourport Swifts	v	AFC Wulfrunians	1-0
Walsall Wood	v	Heath Hayes	4-1
Westfields	v	Causeway United	2-0

QUARTER FINALS

Boldmere St Michaels	v	Highgate United	0-2
Dunkirk	v	Quorn	0-2
Tipton Town	v	Walsall Wood	2-0
Westfields	v	Stourport Swifts	0-5

SEMI FINALS

Highgate United	v	Tipton Town	0-0
Tipton Town	v	Highgate Town	0-0, 3-1p
Quorn	v	Westfields	1-2
Westfields	v	Quorn	1-3

FINAL

Quorn	v	Tipton Town	1-0

		1	2	3	4	5	6	7	8	9	10	11	12	13	14	15	16	17	18	19	20	21	22
1	AFC Wulfrunians		2–1	4–2	0–2	1–2	3–2	1–3	4–1	1–1	3–1	2–1	1–3	5–2	2–1	1–1	5–1	3–0	2–1	1–3	0–3	1–4	1–1
2	Alvechurch	1–3		2–4	2–3	1–3	5–3	1–2	3–2	1–2	3–1	3–1	3–0	2–0	2–2	1–1	3–2	1–0	2–0	4–4	0–1	0–0	0–0
3	Boldmere St. Michaels	5–2	2–0		4–1	1–0	3–2	2–1	2–0	6–1	3–0	4–2	2–2	4–0	2–1	3–0	3–0	1–2	0–0	3–2	0–0	3–0	2–1
4	Causeway United	1–1	2–1	2–2		1–0	2–1	4–2	6–1	4–1	8–1	2–3	1–0	3–1	1–3	1–6	2–1	3–1	0–3	2–1	0–2	2–2	0–4
5	Coleshill Town	1–5	0–2	3–0	3–0		3–0	1–1	4–0	2–0	2–1	6–1	2–3	4–0	5–0	3–0	0–0	2–0	3–3	3–1	1–1	0–0	1–1
6	Continental Star	2–4	0–1	2–0	2–0	0–4		0–1	2–0	2–4	4–3	4–0	1–2	1–0	2–4	2–5	3–2	4–1	2–1	1–1	2–3	0–3	1–4
7	Coventry Sphinx	1–3	3–1	1–1	2–2	0–6	4–1		5–2	3–2	1–1	2–2	1–0	4–2	4–2	0–2	3–0	2–0	1–1	2–0	1–2	1–0	3–1
8	Dunkirk	2–2	0–2	3–2	1–0	1–1	0–0	0–1		3–2	3–2	3–0	2–3	3–0	3–1	0–7	1–1	3–5	2–2	2–3	1–1	0–4	1–3
9	Gornal Athletic	1–2	2–0	1–0	0–9	0–4	0–0	3–3	0–0		1–2	1–2	0–4	1–1	3–1	0–0	2–3	1–6	1–3	5–1	2–3	0–1	0–3
10	Heath Hayes	3–2	2–2	3–1	2–1	1–2	0–2	3–1	1–4	3–2		0–1	3–3	0–1	2–2	1–2	0–0	1–4	1–1	2–1	0–2	1–1	3–1
11	Heather St. John's	1–1	2–6	1–3	1–2	1–0	1–3	3–3	3–3	4–0	2–2		0–0	1–6	1–1	1–4	2–4	4–2	0–3	2–1	0–4	0–1	1–1
12	Highgate United	3–3	3–0	2–3	2–2	4–4	6–1	1–3	3–1	4–1	4–0	1–1		2–2	3–0	2–1	5–0	2–1	2–0	2–3	1–1	2–1	2–0
13	Kirby Muxloe	1–2	2–0	1–2	4 1	3–1	1–0	3–0	2–0	1–1	0–0	2–1	1–2		3–0	0–4	3–0	2–2	3–2	0–2	2–3	0–1	2–1
14	Loughborough University	2–2	2–2	3–1	2–1	6–4	9–2	3–1	1–2	1–2	1–1	3–1	0–2	0–2		2–4	3–0	2–1	1–1	3–3	1–2	2–2	1–3
15	Quorn	6–1	4–0	1–1	2–4	2–1	2–0	4–0	3–2	5–0	4–0	2–1	1–0	1–1	1–3		2–0	0–0	3–0	2–1	0–3	0–1	4–0
16	Rocester	0–7	0–2	0–5	1–5	1–4	4–2	1–2	3–0	3–3	2–1	4–1	2–3	0–1	1–2	1–1		0–0	1–2	0–1	0–0	0–0	1–2
17	Shepshed Dynamo	1–0	3–2	1–2	2–1	1–4	1–1	1–2	1–1	2–2	0–1	6–2	0–2	4–0	2–2	3–1	2–3		2–2	0–0	1–3	1–0	4–5
18	Stourport Swifts	2–2	1–2	1–2	2–2	1–2	3–0	2–1	5–0	2–1	3–1	4–0	1–2	0–4	2–1	3–0	3–0	4–1		2–0	2–1	0–2	2–1
19	Tipton Town	0–0	5–1	2–6	2–2	0–0	1–2	2–0	3–2	2–0	4–2	4–0	2–0	4–1	4–1	2–2	1–1	2–5	1–0		1–1	1–2	3–2
20	Tividale	2–1	2–0	1–1	1–0	3–0	2–0	2–2	1–0	6–0	3–1	3–1	5–3	1–1	1–0	1–0	2–0	3–2	5–0	0–2		1–1	1–1
21	Walsall Wood	2–2	1–2	3–0	3–1	0–1	1–0	2–1	1–0	0–1	1–1	6–1	4–4	3–1	1–2	2–0	2–0	3–0	1–2	2–2	1–3		0–2
22	Westfields	3–1	0–1	1–1	0–2	0–2	5–0	3–3	4–1	3–3	4–0	4–3	0–2	2–2	2–5	0–1	4–0	3–2	3–0	2–2	2–1	2–5	

CLUB MOVEMENTS

Premier Division - Out: Tividale (P - Northern Premier Div.1S). **Division One - In:** Uttoxter Town (P - Staffordshire County).

A.F.C. WULFRUNIANS — Founded: 2005 — Nickname:

Secretary: Ian Davies **(T)** 07989 953 738 **(E)** jaki.davies1512@btinternet.com
Chairman: David Pointon
Ground: Castlecroft Stadium, Castlecroft Road, Wolverhampton WV3 8NA **(T)** 01902 761410
Capacity: **Seats:** Yes **Covered:** Yes **Midweek Matchday:** **Clubhouse:** Yes

Colours(change): Red/black/red
Previous Names: None
Previous Leagues: West Midlands (Regional). Midland Alliance 2013-14.
Records:
Senior Honours: West Midlands (Regional) League Division Two 2005-06, Premier Division 2008-09, 12-13.

10 YEAR RECORD

04-05	05-06	06-07	07-08	08-09	09-10	10-11	11-12	12-13	13-14
	WM2 1	WM1 2	WMP 6	WMP 1	WMP 3	WMP 3	WMP 5	WMP 1	MidAl 8

ALVECHURCH — Founded: 1929 — Nickname: The Church

Secretary: Stephen Denny **(T)** 07710 012 733 **(E)** alvechurchfc@btinternet.com
Chairman: Richard Thorndike
Ground: Lye Meadow, Redditch Road, Alvechurch B48 7RS **(T)** 0121 445 2929
Capacity: 3,000 **Seats:** 100 **Covered:** 300 **Midweek Matchday:** Tuesday **Clubhouse:** Yes No

Colours(change): Yellow/black/black.
Previous Names: Alvechurch FC >1992. Re-formed in 1994.
Previous Leagues: Midland Combination. Midland Alliance > 2014.
Records:
Senior Honours: Since 1994: Midland Combination Premier 2002-03. Worcestershire Senior Urn 03-04, 04-05, 12-13.

10 YEAR RECORD

04-05	05-06	06-07	07-08	08-09	09-10	10-11	11-12	12-13	13-14
MidAl 15	MidAl 14	MidAl 10	MidAl 14	MidAl 10	MidAl 7	MidAl 20	MidAl 13	MidAl 11	MidAl 13

BASFORD UNITED — Founded: 1900 — Nickname: None

Secretary: Neil McGowan **(T)** 07817 941 136 **(E)** neilmcgowan@basfordunitedfc.co.uk
Chairman: Chris Munroe **Prog Ed:** Chris Munroe
Ground: Greenwich Avenue, off Bagnall Road, Basford, Nottingham NG6 0LD **(T)** 07803 890 446
Capacity: **Seats:** **Covered:** Yes **Midweek Matchday:** **Clubhouse:** Yes

Colours(change): Amber/black & amber/amber
Previous Names: None
Previous Leagues: Notts Alliance > 2011. Central Midlands 2011-12. East Midlands Counties 2012-13. Northern Counties East 2013-14.
Records:
Senior Honours: Notts Alliance Division One 1997-98. Central Midlands Southern 2011-12. East Midland Counties 2012-13.

10 YEAR RECORD

04-05	05-06	06-07	07-08	08-09	09-10	10-11	11-12	12-13	13-14
		NottS 3	NottS 5	NottS 3	NottS 2	NottS 2	CMSth 1	EMC 1	NCEP 5

BOLDMERE ST. MICHAELS — Founded: 1883 — Nickname: The Mikes

Secretary: Rob Paterson **(T)** 07528 177 046 **(E)** paterson_r3@sky.com
Chairman: Keith Fielding
Ground: Trevor Brown Memorial Ground, Church Road, Boldmere B73 5RY **(T)** 0121 373 4435
Capacity: 2,500 **Seats:** 230 **Covered:** 400 **Midweek Matchday:** Tuesday **Clubhouse:** Yes

Colours(change): White/black/black
Previous Names: None.
Previous Leagues: West Midlands (Regional). Midland Combination. Midland Alliance > 2014.
Records:
Senior Honours: AFA Senior Cup 1947-48. Midland Combination Premier 1985-86, 88-89, 89-90.

10 YEAR RECORD

04-05	05-06	06-07	07-08	08-09	09-10	10-11	11-12	12-13	13-14
MidAl 10	MidAl 10	MidAl 7	MidAl 4	MidAl 4	MidAl 6	MidAl 3	MidAl 12	MidAl 9	MidAl 2

BROCTON

Founded: 1937 Nickname:

Secretary: Terry Homer **(T)** 07791 841 774 **(E)** terryhomer@yahoo.co.uk
Chairman: Brian Townsend
Ground: Silkmore Lane Sports Grd, Silkmore Lane, Stafford, Staffordshire ST17 4JH **(T)**
Capacity: **Seats:** 100 **Covered:** 100 **Midweek Matchday:** **Clubhouse:** Yes

Colours(change): Green & white/white/green
Previous Names: None
Previous Leagues: Rugeley & Dist 1946-48. Cannock Chase. Staffs Co. Staffs Sen./Mid Lge 1991-94/1994-2003. Midland Combination > 2014.
Records:
Senior Honours: Midland Combination Premier 2013-14.

10 YEAR RECORD

04-05	05-06	06-07	07-08	08-09	09-10	10-11	11-12	12-13	13-14
MCmP 7	MCmP 12	MCmP 15	MCmP 9	MCmP 16	MCmP 7	MCmP 8	MCmP 6	MCmP 5	MCmP 1

CAUSEWAY UNITED

Founded: 1957 Nickname:

Secretary: Frank Webb **(T)** 07977 599 847 **(E)**
Chairman: Carl Burley
Ground: Halesowen Town FC, The Grove, Old Hawne Lane, Halesowen B63 3TB **(T)** 0121 550 9433
Capacity: **Seats:** **Covered:** **Midweek Matchday:** Tuesday **Clubhouse:** Yes

Colours(change): All blue. (All white).
Previous Names: None.
Previous Leagues: West Midlands (Regional). Midland Alliance > 2014.
Records: **Att:** 150. **Apps:** Malcolm Power - 300+
Senior Honours:

10 YEAR RECORD

04-05	05-06	06-07	07-08	08-09	09-10	10-11	11-12	12-13	13-14
MidAl 16	MidAl 19	MidAl 17	MidAl 6	MidAl 9	MidAl 12	MidAl 10	MidAl 7	MidAl 17	MidAl 9

COLESHILL TOWN

Founded: 1894 Nickname:

Secretary: David Brown **(T)** 07799 075 828 **(E)** dave.brown@skanska.co.uk
Chairman: Paul Billing **Prog Ed:** David Brown
Ground: Pack Meadow, Packington Lane, Coleshill B46 3JQ **(T)** 01675 463 259
Capacity: **Seats:** **Covered:** **Midweek Matchday:** Tuesday **Clubhouse:** Yes

Colours(change): White/blue/blue (All red)
Previous Names: None.
Previous Leagues: Midland Combination. Midland Alliance 2008-2014.
Records:
Senior Honours: Midland Combination Division Two 1969-70. Premier 07-08.

10 YEAR RECORD

04-05	05-06	06-07	07-08	08-09	09-10	10-11	11-12	12-13	13-14
MCmP 9	MCmP 11	MCmP 4	MCmP 1	MidAl 11	MidAl 8	MidAl 12	MidAl 16	MidAl 15	MidAl 4

CONTINENTAL STAR

Founded: 1973 Nickname:

Secretary: Keith John **(T)** 07956 429 046 **(E)** keith.john6@hotmail.co.uk
Chairman: Keith John
Ground: Rushall Olympic FC, Dales Lane, Rushall, Walsall, West Midlands WS4 1LJ **(T)** 01922 641 021
Capacity: **Seats:** **Covered:** **Midweek Matchday:** **Clubhouse:**

Colours(change): Yellow/blue/blue (Red/black/white)
Previous Names: Handsworth Continental Star 2001-02.
Previous Leagues: Midland Combination 1993-2012. Midland Alliance 2012-14.
Records:
Senior Honours: Midland Combination Division 2 1995-96, Premier Division 2011-12.

10 YEAR RECORD

04-05	05-06	06-07	07-08	08-09	09-10	10-11	11-12	12-13	13-14
MCmP 20	MCmP 22	MCmP 19	MCmP 18	MCmP 17	MCmP 14	MCmP 11	MCmP 1	MidAl 16	MidAl 17

COVENTRY SPHINX

Founded: 1946 Nickname: Sphinx

Secretary: Jackie McGowan **(T)** 07843 477 799 **(E)** jackie.mcgowan@coventrysphinx.co.uk
Chairman: Dannie Cahill
Ground: Sphinx Spts & Social Club, Sphinx Drive, Coventry CV3 1WA **(T)** 02476 451 361
Capacity: **Seats:** Yes **Covered:** Yes **Midweek Matchday:** Tuesday **Clubhouse:** Yes

Colours(change): Sky blue & white stripe/navy/navy (All red).
Previous Names: Sphinx > 1995.
Previous Leagues: Midland Combination. Midland Alliance 2007-14.
Records:
Senior Honours: Midland Combination Premier 2006-07.

10 YEAR RECORD

04-05	05-06	06-07	07-08	08-09	09-10	10-11	11-12	12-13	13-14
MCmP 2	MCmP 2	MCmP 1	MidAl 19	MidAl 7	MidAl 9	MidAl 16	MidAl 3	MidAl 14	MidAl 7

DUNKIRK

Founded: 1946 Nickname: The Boatmen

Secretary: Steve Throssell **(T)** 07903 322 446 **(E)** philipallen1982@hotmail.co.uk
Chairman: David Johnson
Ground: Ron Steel Spts Ground, Lenton Lane, Clifton Bridge, Nottingham NG7 2SA **(T)** 0115 985 0803
Capacity: 1,500 **Seats:** 150 **Covered:** 150 **Midweek Matchday:** Tuesday **Clubhouse:** Yes

Colours(change): Red/black/black (All yellow)
Previous Names: None
Previous Leagues: Notts Amateur 1946-75, Notts All. 1975-95, Central Midlands 1995-2008, East Midlands Counties 2008-10. Mid All. 2010-14
Records:
Senior Honours: Notts Amateur League 1973-75. Central Midlands League Supreme Division 2004-05. East Midlands Counties 2009-10

10 YEAR RECORD

04-05	05-06	06-07	07-08	08-09	09-10	10-11	11-12	12-13	13-14
CM Su 1	CM Su 8	CM Su 6	CM Su 4	EMC 5	EMC 1	MidAl 8	MidAl 18	MidAl 10	MidAl 19

HEATH HAYES

Founded: 1964 Nickname:

Secretary: Kathlyn Davies **(T)** 07969 203 063 **(E)** kathlyndavies@aol.com
Chairman: Craig Brotherton
Ground: Coppice Colliery Grd, Newlands Lane, Heath Hayes, Cannock, WS12 3HH **(T)** 07969 203 063
Capacity: **Seats:** Yes **Covered:** Yes **Midweek Matchday:** Tuesday **Clubhouse:** Yes

Colours(change): Blue & white stripes/blue/white (Yellow/black/yellow)
Previous Names:
Previous Leagues: Staffordshire County, West Midlands, Midland Combination 2006-10. Midland Alliance 2010-14.
Records:
Senior Honours: Staffordshire County League Division 1 1977-78. West Midlands League Division 1 North 1998-99.
Midland Combination Premier Division 2009-10.

10 YEAR RECORD

04-05	05-06	06-07	07-08	08-09	09-10	10-11	11-12	12-13	13-14
WMP 6	WMP 13	MCmP 8	MCmP 10	MCmP 10	MCmP 1	MidAl 11	MidAl 14	MidAl 18	MidAl 18

KIRKBY MUXLOE

Founded: 1910 Nickname:

Secretary: Philip Moloney **(T)** 07775 992 778 **(E)** pmoloney1@hotmail.com
Chairman: Les Warren
Ground: Kirby Muxloe Sports Club, Ratby Lane LE9 2AQ **(T)** 0116 239 2301
Capacity: **Seats:** **Covered:** Yes **Midweek Matchday:** Tuesday **Clubhouse:** Yes

Colours(change): All royal blue (All orange)
Previous Names:
Previous Leagues: Leicester Mutual. Leicester City. Leicestershire Senior. East Midlands Counties 2008-09. Midland Alliance 2009-14.
Records:
Senior Honours: Leicestershire Co. Cup 2006-07. Leicestershire Senior Champions 2007-08.
East Midlands Counties Champions 2008-09.

10 YEAR RECORD

04-05	05-06	06-07	07-08	08-09	09-10	10-11	11-12	12-13	13-14
LeicS 4	LeicS 8	LeicS 2	LeicS 1	EMC 1	MidAl 10	MidAl 9	MidAl 11	MidAl 12	MidAl 14

LONG EATON UNITED

Founded: 1956 Nickname: Blues

Secretary: Jim Fairley **(T)** **(E)** jim@longeatonutd.co.uk
Chairman: Jim Fairley
Ground: Grange Park, Station Rd, Long Eaton, Derbys NG10 2EG **(T)** 0115 973 5700
Capacity: 1,500 **Seats:** 450 **Covered:** 500 **Midweek Matchday:** Tuesday **Clubhouse:** Yes **Shop:** No

Colours(change): All blue. (All red).
Previous Names:
Previous Leagues: Central Alliance 1956-61, Mid Co Football Lge 1961-82, NCE 1982-89, 2002-14. Central Midlands 1989-2002
Records: **Att:** 2,019 v Burton Albion FA Cup 1973
Senior Honours: Derbyshire Senior Cup 1964-65, 75-76. Northern Counties East Div1S 1984-85. League Cup 2008-09.

10 YEAR RECORD

04-05	05-06	06-07	07-08	08-09	09-10	10-11	11-12	12-13	13-14
NCEP 12	NCEP 19	NCEP 11	NCEP 12	NCEP 2	NCEP 10	NCEP 12	NCEP 15	NCEP 12	NCEP 11

LOUGHBOROUGH UNIVERSITY

Founded: 1920 Nickname:

Secretary: Margaret Folwell **(T)** 01509 226 127 (Office Hrs) **(E)** secretary@loughboroughfootball.co.uk
Chairman: Stuart McLaren
Ground: Loughborough Uni Stadium, Holywell Sports Complex, Holywell Park LE11 3TU **(T)** 01509 228 774
Capacity: **Seats:** Yes **Covered:** Yes **Midweek Matchday:** **Clubhouse:** Yes

Colours(change): Purple/purple/grey. (All white).
Previous Names: None
Previous Leagues: Leicestershire Senior. Midland Combination. Midland Alliance 2009-14.
Records:
Senior Honours: Midland Combination 2008-09.

10 YEAR RECORD

04-05	05-06	06-07	07-08	08-09	09-10	10-11	11-12	12-13	13-14
			MCmP 4	MCmP 1	MidAl 13	MidAl 4	MidAl 5	MidAl 4	MidAl 15

LYE TOWN

Founded: 1930 Nickname:

Secretary: Yvonne Bignell **(T)** 07921 662 837 **(E)**
Chairman: Brian Blakemore
Ground: Sports Ground, Stourbridge Road, Lye, Stourbridge, West Mids DY9 7DH **(T)** 01384 422 672
Capacity: **Seats:** **Covered:** **Midweek Matchday:** **Clubhouse:** Yes

Colours(change): Blue/blue/white
Previous Names:
Previous Leagues: Worcestershire Combination 1931-39. Birmingham & Dist/West Midlands (Regional) 1947-62/1962-2014.
Records:
Senior Honours: West Midlands (Regional) 2013-14.
Worcestershire Senior Urn 2013-14.

10 YEAR RECORD

04-05	05-06	06-07	07-08	08-09	09-10	10-11	11-12	12-13	13-14
WMP 8	WMP 6	WMP 8	WMP 10	WMP 11	WMP 19	WMP 11	WMP 15	WMP 2	WMP 1

QUORN

Founded: 1924 Nickname: Reds

Secretary: Reg Molloy **(T)** 07729 173 333 **(E)** k.molloy@ntlworld.com
Chairman: Stuart Turner **Manager:** Tommy Brookbanks **Prog Ed:** Malcolm Unwin
Ground: Farley Way Stadium, Farley Way, Quorn, Leicestershire LE12 8RB **(T)** 01509 620 232
Capacity: 1,550 **Seats:** 350 **Covered:** 250 **Midweek Matchday:** **Clubhouse:** Yes

Colours(change): All red (Yellow/blue/blue)
Previous Names: Quorn Methodists
Previous Leagues: Leicestershire Senior, Midland Alliance > 2007. NPL 2007-2012. United Counties 2012-13. Midland Alliance 2013-14.
Records: Not known
Senior Honours: Leicestershire Senior Cup 1940, 1952, 1954.
Leicestershire Senior League 2000-01

10 YEAR RECORD

04-05	05-06	06-07	07-08	08-09	09-10	10-11	11-12	12-13	13-14
MidAl 4	MidAl 7	MidAl 3	NP 1 12	NP1S 12	NP1S 20	NP1S 15	NP1S 21	UCL P 7	MidAl 5

ROCESTER

Founded: 1876 Nickname: Romans

Secretary: Barry Smith **(T)** 07770 762 825 **(E)** rocesterfc@btinternet.com
Chairman: Ian Cruddas **Prog Ed:** Barry Smith
Ground: Hillsfield, Mill Street, Rocester, Uttoxeter ST14 5JX **(T)** 01889 591 301
Capacity: 4,000 **Seats:** 230 **Covered:** 500 **Midweek Matchday:** Tuesday **Clubhouse:** Yes **Shop:** Yes

Colours(change): Amber/black/black. (All royal blue).
Previous Names: None.
Previous Leagues: Staffs Sen. (Founder Member). W.Mids (Reg). Mid.All (FM) Southern. NPL. Midland Alliance 2005-14.
Records: **Apps:** Peter Swanwick 1962-82.
Senior Honours: Staffordshire Senior 1985-86, 86-87. West Mids (Regional) Div.1 87-88. Midland Alliance 1998-99, 2003-04.

10 YEAR RECORD

04-05	05-06	06-07	07-08	08-09	09-10	10-11	11-12	12-13	13-14
NPL 1 22	MidAl 22	MidAl 12	MidAl 5	MidAl 20	MidAl 16	MidAl 14	MidAl 6	MidAl 13	MidAl 20

SHEPSHED DYNAMO

Founded: 1994 Nickname: Dynamo

Secretary: Danny Pole **(T)** 07866 500 187 **(E)** secretary@shepsheddynamo.co.uk
Chairman: Mick Sloan
Ground: The Dovecote, Butt Hole Lane, Shepshed, Leicestershire LE12 9BN **(T)** 01509 650 992
Capacity: 2,050 **Seats:** 570 **Covered:** 400 **Midweek Matchday:** **Clubhouse:** Yes **Shop:** Yes

Colours(change): Black and white stripes/black/black (All yellow)
Previous Names: Shepshed Albion/Charterhouse > 1994
Previous Leagues: Leics Sen 1907-16,19-27,46-50,51-81, Mid Co 81-82,N.C.E. 82-83,Sth 83-88,96-04,N.P.L.88-93,04-12,Mid Com 93-94,Mid All 94-95,13-14. UCL 12-13.
Records: 2,500 v Leicester City - Friendly 1996-97
Senior Honours: Midland Counties League 1981-82, League Cup 81-82. Northern Counties East 1982-83, League Cup 82-83. Midland Alliance 1995-96. Leicestershire Senior Cup x7

10 YEAR RECORD

04-05	05-06	06-07	07-08	08-09	09-10	10-11	11-12	12-13	13-14
NP 1 15	NP 1 10	NP 1 20	NP 1 15	NP1S 8	NP1S 17	NP1S 21	NP1S 22	UCL P 9	MidAl 16

STOURPORT SWIFTS

Founded: 1882 Nickname: Swifts

Secretary: Laura McDonald **(T)** 07793 768 793 **(E)** Lmacca65@hotmail.com
Chairman: Chris Reynolds
Ground: Walshes Meadow, Harold Davis Drive, Stourport on Severn DY13 0AA **(T)** 01299 825 188
Capacity: 2,000 **Seats:** 250 **Covered:** 150 **Midweek Matchday:** **Clubhouse:** Yes **Shop:** Yes

Colours(change): Gold & black/black/black (All blue)
Previous Names: None
Previous Leagues: Kidderminster/Worcestershire/West Midlands (Regional) > 1998, Midland Alliance 1998-2001, 12-14, Southern 2001-12.
Records: 2,000
Senior Honours: Midland Alliance 2000-01

10 YEAR RECORD

04-05	05-06	06-07	07-08	08-09	09-10	10-11	11-12	12-13	13-14
SthW 14	SthW 20	SthM 22	SthM 17	SthM 16	SthM 17	Sthsw 17	Sthsw 21	MidAl 5	MidAl 10

TIPTON TOWN

Founded: 1948 Nickname:

Secretary: Ann Wheale **(T)** 07535 975 142 **(E)** b.wheale@sky.com
Chairman: Matthew Danks
Ground: Tipton Sports Academy, Wednesbury Oak Road, Tipton DY4 0BS **(T)** 0121 502 5534
Capacity: 1,000 **Seats:** 200 **Covered:** 400 **Midweek Matchday:** Wednesday **Clubhouse:** Yes

Colours(change): Black & white stripes/black/red. (All orange).
Previous Names: None.
Previous Leagues: West Midlands (Regional). Midland Alliance 2005-14.
Records: **Att:** 1,100 v Wolves, 01.08.88.
Senior Honours: Wednesbury Senior Cup 1975-76, 76-77, 80-81, 95-96. West Midlands (Regional) Div.1 83-84. Prem 04-05.

10 YEAR RECORD

04-05	05-06	06-07	07-08	08-09	09-10	10-11	11-12	12-13	13-14
WestP 1	MidAl 11	MidAl 5	MidAl 9	MidAl 5	MidAl 4	MidAl 2	MidAl 9	MidAl 6	MidAl 11

WALSALL WOOD

Founded: 1907 Nickname:

Secretary: Ivor Osborne **(T)** 07583 175 664 **(E)** ivorjosborne@talktalk.net

Chairman: Andy Roper

Ground: Oak Park, Lichfield Road, Walsall Wood, Walsall WS9 9NP **(T)**

Capacity: **Seats:** Yes **Covered:** Yes **Midweek Matchday:** **Clubhouse:** Yes

Colours(change): All red (All sky blue)

Previous Names: Walsall Borough (formed when Walsall Wood & Walsall Sportsco merged) 1982-96.

Previous Leagues: Midland Combinataion 1986-92, 2006-13. Staffordshire Senior 1992-93. West Midlands 1993-2006. Mid Alliance 2013-14.

Records:

Senior Honours: Worcestershire/Midland Combination 1951-52, 2012-13.

10 YEAR RECORD

04-05	05-06	06-07	07-08	08-09	09-10	10-11	11-12	12-13	13-14
WM1 6	WM1 4	MidCo 12	MidCo 11	MidCo 7	MidCo 6	MidCo 9	MidCo 14	MidCo 1	MidAl 6

WESTFIELDS

Founded: 1966 Nickname: The Fields

Secretary: Andrew Morris **(T)** 07860 410 548 **(E)** andrew@andrew-morris.co.uk

Chairman: John Morgan **Manager:** Sean Edwards **Prog Ed:** Andrew Morris

Ground: Allpay Park, Widemarsh Common, Hereford HR4 9NA **(T)** 07860 410 548

Capacity: 2,000 **Seats:** 150 **Covered:** 150 **Midweek Matchday:** Tuesday **Clubhouse:** Yes **Shop:** Yes

Colours(change): All Maroon & sky blue/sky blue/sky blue (All white)

Previous Names: None.

Previous Leagues: Herefordshire Sunday. Worcester & Dist. West Midlands (Regional). Midland Alliance > 2014.

Records: **Att:** 590 v Hereford United, Hereford Senior Invitation Cup Final 2012. **Goalscorer:** Paul Burton. **Apps:** Jon Pugh.

Senior Honours: Hereford Senior Cup 1985-86, 88-89, 91-92, 95-96, 01-02, 02-03, 04-05, 05-06, 07-08, 11-12, 12-13.
West Midlands (Regional) Premier 2002-03.

10 YEAR RECORD

04-05	05-06	06-07	07-08	08-09	09-10	10-11	11-12	12-13	13-14
MidAl 6	MidAl 20	MidAl 16	MidAl 11	MidAl 17	MidAl 5	MidAl 6	MidAl 2	MidAl 2	MidAl 12

GROUND DIRECTIONS - PREMIER DIVISION

AFC WULFRUNIANS - Castlecroft Stadium, Castlecroft Road, Wolverhampton, WV3 8N - 01902-761 410

Follow A454 (signposted Bridgnorth) and turn left at Mermaid Pub onto Windmill Lane. Turn right onto Castlecroft Avenue. Ground is straight across past Wightwick Cricket Ground.

ALVECHURCH - Lye Meadow, Redditch Rd., Alvechurch, B48 7RS - 0121-445 2929

M42 Junction 2. Take A441 towards Redditch. At first roundabout turn right onto A4120 signposted Alvechurch. Ground approx 1km on right. Car park entrance on right before ground.

BASFORD UNITED - Greenwich Avenue, Basford, Nottingham, NG6 0LE. Tel: (07803) 890446.

From M1 Junction 26 - Follow A610 to Nottingham for 1.3 miles, passing over one roundabout. Turn left at the second roundabout by the Gateway Hotel onto Cinderhill Road following signpost to Bulwell. After a quarter of mile turn right into Bagnall Road, and a further half a mile turn left into Greenwich Avenue, the entrance to the ground is straight ahead. From the north (A60) - Entering Nottingham via the A60, turn right onto the B6004 Oxclose Lane (signposted to Basford). After 2.2 miles, pass over the level crossing and continue onto David Lane. After a quarter of a mile turn right onto Bagnall Road and a further quarter of a mile turn right into Greenwich Avenue, the entrance to the ground is straight ahead. From the south (A52) - Entering Nottingham via the A52, continue along the Ring Road A6514 following signs to Mansfield for approximately two miles, until the junction with the A610 is reached. Turn left onto the A610 (signposted to M1). After 0.8 miles turn right on to Stockhill Lane (B6004). Continue along Stockhill Lane for a third of a mile, turning left at the mini roundabout into Mill Street and then turning left into Bagnall Road. After a quarter of a mile turn right into Greenwich Avenue, the entrance to the ground is straight ahead.

BOLDMERE ST. MICHAELS - The Trevor Brown Memorial Ground, Church Road, Boldmere, Sutton Coldfield B73 5RY - 0121-384 7531

A38(M) from M6 junction 6 and A5127 from Birmingham to Yenton Traffic Lights. Left on A452 Chester Road, then 6th.right into Church Road.

From M6 junction 5 A452 Brownhills to Yenton Traffic Lights. Straight on then 6th right into Church Road.

BROCTON - Ground: Silkmore Lane Sports Ground, Silkmore Lane , Stafford , Staffordshire , ST17 4JH
From M6 J13 take A449 towards Stafford for 1.5 miles until reaching traffic lights by Esso petrol station. Turn right at lights into Rickescote Road, follow road round over railway bridge to mini island, at island bear left into Silkmore Lane. At next mini island take 4th exit for entrance to ground. From Lichfield/Rugeley. After passing Staffs Police HQ at Baswick go downhill past BMW garage and pub to large island, take 1st exit into Silkmore Lane, at next mini island take 2nd exit into ground entrance. Do not turn into Lancaster Road or Silkmore Crescent as directed by Sat Navs.

CAUSEWAY UNITED - War Memorial Athletic Ground, High Street, Amblecote, Stourbridge, West Midlands, DY8 4HN - 01384-394040
From Stourbridge Ring Road take A491 towards Wolverhampton. Ground is on left within 300 yards immediately after 1st set of traffic lights and opposite the Royal Oak public house.

COLESHILL TOWN - Pack Meadow, Packington Lane, Coleshill, B46 3JQ - 01675 463 259
From M6 Junction 4 take A446 signposted Lichfield. Straight over 1st roundabout then immediately turn right across dual carriageway onto B4117 signposted Coleshill. After school on right, turn right into Packington Lane. Ground is ½ mile on left.

CONTINENTAL STAR - Rushall Olympic F.C. Dales Lane, Rushall, Walsall WS4 1LJ 01922 641 021
From M6 Junction 7 head North on Birmingham Road/A34 towards Chapel Lane. At the roundabout take the 2nd exit onto Broadway N/A4148. At the roundabout take the 1st exit onto Birmingham Road. At the roundabout take the 2nd exit onto Springhill Road. At the roundabout take the 1st exit onto Ablewell Street. Turn left onto Town Hill. Keep right at the fork. Turn right onto Upper Rushall Street. Continue onto Lower Rushall Street. Continue onto Lichfield Street/A461. Go through 1 roundabout. Turn right onto Daw End Lane/B4154. Continue to follow B4154. Turn right into Rushall Olympic Football Club.

COVENTRY SPHINX - Sphinx Drive, Off Siddeley Avenue, Coventry, CV3 1WA - 02476 451 361
From M6. Leave M6 at Junction 3 and take A444 towards Coventry. Continue to Binley Road (6 roundabouts) and turn left on A428 Binley Road towards Binley. Pass a row of shops on left and Bulls Head public house on right. After the Bulls Head, turn 1st right into Biggin Hall Crescent. Then take the 5th left turn into Siddeley Avenue. Take 1st left into Sphinx Drive and the ground is at the end.
From M42 & A45. Follow A45 towards Coventry and take A4114 Coventry at Coventry Hill Hotel. At roundabout take 2nd exit to next roundabout and take 3rd exit onto Holyhead Road. After approx 2.5 miles you will come to Coventry Ring Road where you turn left and then get over to your right onto the ring road. Continue on Ring Road and leave at Junction 3 signposted M69 and Football Stadium. Follow signs for A428 Binley until you see Bulls Head public house on your right. Then follow the above instructions.

DUNKIRK - The Ron Steel Sports Ground, Lenton Lane, Clifton Bridge, Nottingham, NG7 2SA 0115 985 0803
From M1 Junction 24 take A453 towards Nottingham, through Clifton and join A52 onto Clifton Bridge. Get in middle lane down the slip road onto the island under the flyover signposted Industrial Estate. Take immediate 1st left and 1st left again onto Lenton Lane. Follow the road past Greenwood Meadows and the ground is 200 yards on the right.

HEATH HAYES - Coppice Colliery Ground, Newlands Lane, Heath Hayes, Cannock, Staffordshire, WS12 3HH - 07969 203 063
From M6 Junction 11 take the A4601 towards Cannock and at the 1st island turn right onto the A460 signposted Rugeley/Cannock Business Parks. At the double island (A5) go straight on still on A460 and over two islands. At the 3rd island, turn right onto A5190 signposted Lichfield. Pass Texaco garage on the right and take the next right turn into Newlands Lane. Entrance to the ground is 50 yards down the lane on the left under the barrier.

KIRBY MUXLOE - Kirby Muxloe Sports Club, Ratby Lane, Kirby Muxloe, Leics, LE9 2AQ 0116 239 3201
Leave M1 at Junction 21a and follow signs to Kirby Muxloe. Road goes round and back over Motorway and down hill to a roundabout. Go straight on to mini roundabout and straight on to Ratby Lane. Entrance is next to last house on the right.

LONG EATON UNITED - Grange Park, Station Road, Long Eaton, NG10 2EG. Tel: (0115) 973 5700.
M1 Junc 25, take A52 towards Nottingham, to island by Bardills Garden Centre, right onto B6003. Approx 2 miles to end of road to T-junction. At traffic lights, turn right A453 and take 2nd left into Station Road. Entrance on left down un-named road opposite disused car park next to Grange School.

LOUGHBOROUGH UNIVERSITY - Loughborough University Stadium, Holywell Sports Complex, Holywell Park, Loughborough, Leics, LE11 3TU - 01509 228 774
From M42/A42 exit at Junction 13 and take the A512 towards Loughborough. After crossing Junction 23 of the M1 travel approx 3/4 mile to first traffic island. Turn right into University (LE11 3QF Red Building is on your right). Keep straight on at both small islands. Bear left into large spectator car park, entrance on left hand side. Please note that there is limited parking at Stadium for Officials/Team Coach/Cars.

LYE TOWN - Sports Ground, Stourbridge Road, Lye, Stourbridge, West Mids DY9 7DH
Tel: 01384-422672

Situated on A458 Birmingham to Stourbridge RoadFrom M5 Junction 3, take road marked Kidderminster, as far as lights at the bottom of Hagley Hill. Turn right, then take the third turning off the first island. Carry straight on at the next island. Turn left at Lights/Crossroads, onto the A458. Ground approximately 400 yards on the left hand side.

QUORN - Farley Way, Quorn, Leicestershire, LE12 8RB - 01509 620 232

Exit Junction 21A of M1 Motorway onto A46. Proceed towards Loughborough on A6. Approx 2 miles from Loughborough turn left at island. After 200 yards turn left at traffic lights. Ground on left.

ROCESTR - Hillsfield, Mill Street, Rocester, Uttoxeter, Staffordshire ST14 5JX - 01889 591 301

From Uttoxeter take the B5030, signposted Ashbourne/Alton Towers After 3 miles turn right opposite the JCB factory over humpback bridge into Rocester village. Turn right at mini island into Mill Street, ground is 500 yards on the left immediately past the JCB Academy.

SHEPSHED DYNAMO - The Dovecote Stadium, Butthole lane, Shepshed, Leicestershire, LE12 9BN - 01509 650 992

From Junction 23 of M1 motorway take the A512 towards Ashby. Turn right at first set of lights and after approx 1 mile take 2nd exit at mini roundabout (after petrol station). Carry on for half mile over speed humps. Butthole Lane is opposite the Black Swan Public House.

STOURPORT SWIFTS - Walshes Meadow, Harold Davies Drive, Stourport on Severn, Worcs, DY13 0AA - 01299 825 188

Follw the one way system through Stourport Town Centre signposted 'Sports Centre'. Go over the river bridge and turn first left into Harold Davies Drive. Ground is at the rear of the Sports Centre.

TIPTON TOWN - Tipton Sports Academy, Wednesbury Oak Road, Tipton, West Mids, DY4 0BS - 0121 502 5534

From M6 junction 9 take A461 through Wednesbury Town Centre to Ockerhill Island. Follow signs taking a full right turn towards Bilston (A4098). In ½ mile turn left at traffic lights (A4037). Ground 100 yards on left. Use 2nd Entrance.

From M5 junction 2 take A4123 for about 3 miles until you reach Burnt Tree Island. Take second exit towards Wolverhampton and continue to next set of traffic lights. Turn right A4037 and continue for 3 miles. Pass ASDA supermarket and ground is 100 yards on the right. Use 1st Entrance.

WALSALL WOOD - Oak Park, Lichfield Road, Walsall Wood, Staffordshire, WS9 9NP- 07583 175 664

From North- Leave M6 at Junction 12 and take A5 until big island just outside Brownhills (next island after 'The Turn' pub on left). Take A452 Chester Road North through Brownhills High Street to traffic lights at Shire Oak (Pub at junction on right hand side). Turn right onto A461 towards Walsall, go to next set of traffic lights, cross over and turn right immediately onto Oak Park Leisure Centre Car park (rear of Kentucky Fried Chicken). Proceed diagonally over car park and follow road round to ground entrance.

From South using M5/M6 motorways- M5 North past Junction 1 onto M6 North. Leave at Junction 9 (Wednesbury turn off) and take A4148 to Walsall. Proceed for about 2 miles over several islands until going down a hill alongside the Arboretum. At big island at bottom, turn right onto A461 for Lichfield. Take A461 for about 4 miles and go through Walsall Wood village (after Barons Court Hotel on right) up the hill after village, Oak Park is on the left opposite Fitness First. Turn left and go diagonally across Oak Park Leisure Centre car park. Follow road round to ground entrance.

WESTFIELDS - 'Allpay park', Widemarsh Common, Grandstand Road., Hereford, HR4 9NA 07860 410 548

On reaching the outskirts of Hereford from Worcester, continue along A4103, over roundabout signposted Holmer and Leisure Centre. Proceed for 1 mile to large roundabout by the "Starting Gate Inn" and turn left towards Hereford. Proceed for ½ mile, past Hereford Leisure Centre and at mini roundabout, turn right. Proceed 150 yards and bear left around the Common, in front of Cricket Pavilion and immediately turn right into the driveway for allpay.park.

ALVIS SPORTING CLUB
Founded: 1928 Nickname:

Secretary: Nicola Rynolds **(T)** 07962 322 838 **(E)** nicola541@btinternet.com
Chairman: Don Corrigan
Ground: Gypsy Lane, Kenilworth, CV8 1FN **(T)** 07962 322 838
Colours(change): Sky blue/navy/sky blue

ADDITIONAL INFORMATION: Previous Leagues: Midland Combination > 2014.
Honours: Midland Combination Division One 2012-13.

ATHERSTONE TOWN
Founded: 2004 Nickname: The Adders

Secretary: Graham Read **(T)** 01908 211 166 **(E)** grahamgdr777@aol.com
Chairman: Robert Weale
Ground: Sheepy Road, Atherston, Warwickshire CV9 3AD **(T)** 01827 717 829
Colours(change): Red and white stripes/black/black

ADDITIONAL INFORMATION:
Previous Leagues: Midland Combination 2004-06, 2011-14. Midland Alliance 2006-08, 11-12. Southern 2008-11.
Honours: Midland Combination Division 1 2004-05, Premier Division 2005-06. Midland Alliance 2007-08.

BOLEHILL SWIFTS
Founded: 1953 Nickname:

Secretary: Philip Crowley **(T)** 07702 786 722 **(E)** bolehallswifts.philcrowley@hotmail.co.uk
Chairman: Les Fitzpatrick
Ground: Rene Road, Bolehall, Tamworth, Staffordshire B77 3NN **(T)** 07702 786 722
Colours(change): All yellow.

ADDITIONAL INFORMATION: Previous Leagues: Midland Combination > 2014.
Honours: Midland Combination Division 2 1984-85.

BROMSGROVE SPORTING
Founded: 2009 Nickname: The Rouslers

Secretary: David Stephens **(T)** 07955 121 966 **(E)** dave@bromsgrovesporting.co.uk
Chairman: John Teece
Ground: The Victoria Ground, Birmingham Road, Bromsgrove, Worcs, B61 0DR **(T)** 01527 876949 **Capacity:** 4,893
Colours(change): Red & white stripes/blue/blue

ADDITIONAL INFORMATION: Previous Leagues: Midland Combination > 2014.

CADBURY ATHLETIC
Founded: 1994 Nickname:

Secretary: Jon Slater **(T)** 07786 321 986 **(E)** jon.slater@hotmail.com
Chairman: John Peckham
Ground: Alvechurch FC, Lye Meadow, Redditch Road, Alvechurch, Worcs B48 7RS **(T)** 07725 868 328
Colours(change): Purple/purple/white

ADDITIONAL INFORMATION:

COVENTRY COPSEWOOD
Founded: 1923 Nickname:

Secretary: David Wilson **(T)** 07884 585 440 **(E)** davide.wilson@hotmail.co.uk
Chairman: Robert Abercrombie
Ground: Copsewood Sports & Social Club, Allard Way, Binley, Coventry CV3 1JP **(T)** 07884 585 440
Colours(change): All blue

ADDITIONAL INFORMATION: Previous Leagues: Midland Combination > 2014.
Previous Names: G.P.T. Coventry > 2000, Coventry Marconi > 2005.
Honours: Midland Combination Challenge Cup 2006-07.

HEATHER ST. JOHN'S
Founded: 1949 Nickname:

Secretary: Adrian Rock **(T)** 07952 633 331 **(E)** adrianrock@hotmail.co.uk
Chairman: Paul Harrison
Ground: St John's Park, Ravenstone Rd, Heather LE67 2QJ **(T)** 01530 263 986
Colours(change): All royal blue (All red)

ADDITIONAL INFORMATION: Previous Leagues: Midland Combination > 2011. Midland Alliance 2011-14.
Honours: Midland Combination 2010-11.

HIGHGATE UNITED

Founded: 1948 Nickname: Red or Gate

Secretary: Paul Davis **(T)** 07527 941 993 **(E)** jimmymerry777@gmail.com
Chairman: Gary Bishop **Manager:** Mark Burge
Ground: The Coppice, Tythe Barn Lane, Shirley Solihull B90 1PH **(T)** 07591 172 318
Colours(change): All red (White/black/black)

ADDITIONAL INFORMATION: Not known
Midland Combination Premier 1972-73, 73-74, 74-75.

HINCKLEY AFC

Founded: 2014 Nickname:

Secretary: Stephen Jelfs **(T)** 07720 299 313 **(E)** secretary@hinckleyafc.org.uk
Chairman: Gary Hancox
Ground: St. John's Park, Ravenstone Road, Heather, Leicestershire, LE67 2QJ **(T)** 01530 263 986
Colours(change): Red & blue/blue & red/blue

ADDITIONAL INFORMATION:

LICHFIELD CITY

Founded: 1970 Nickname:

Secretary: Michael Tyler **(T)** 07756 521 301 **(E)** tylermick1954@hotmail.co.uk
Chairman: Darren Leaver
Ground: Brownsfield Park, Brownsfield Road, Lichfield, Staffs, WS13 6AY **(T)**
Colours(change): Blue with white V/blue/blue

ADDITIONAL INFORMATION: Previous Leagues: Midland Combination > 2014.

LITTLETON

Founded: 1890 Nickname:

Secretary: Mrs M Brighton **(T)** 01386 832 906 **(E)** mbrighton1@hotmail.co.uk
Chairman: Colin Emms
Ground: 5 Acres, Pebworth Road, North Littleton, Evesham, Worcs, WR11 8QL **(T)** 07765 224 290
Colours(change): Red/white/red

ADDITIONAL INFORMATION: Previous Leagues: Midland Combination > 2014.

NUNEATON GRIFF

Founded: 1972 Nickname:

Secretary: Peter Kemp **(T)** 07944 457 250 **(E)** nuneatongriff@sky.com
Chairman: John Gore
Ground: The Pingles Stadium, Avenue Road, Nuneaton, Warwickshire CV11 4LX **(T)** 07944 457 250
Colours(change): Blue & white stripes/blue/blue

ADDITIONAL INFORMATION: Previous Leagues: Midland Combination > 2014.
Honours: Midland Combination Premier Division 1999-2000, 00-01.

PELSALL VILLA

Founded: 1898 Nickname:

Secretary: Shaun Mason **(T)** 07779 111 023 **(E)** shaunmason1967@yahoo.co.uk
Chairman: Shaun Mason
Ground: The Bush Ground, Walsall Road, Walsall, West Midlands WS3 4BP **(T)** 07504 981 141
Colours(change): Red & black stripes/black/black

ADDITIONAL INFORMATION: Previous Leagues: Midland Combination > 2014.

PERSHORE TOWN

Founded: 1988 Nickname:

Secretary: Jane Conway **(T)** 07841 377 788 **(E)** jane.chamberlain@homecall.co.uk
Chairman: Ken Tallis
Ground: King George V Playing Field, King George's Way, Pershore WR10 1QU **(T)** 07841 377 788
Colours(change): Blue & white/blue/blue

ADDITIONAL INFORMATION:
Previous Leagues: Midland Alliance (Founder members). Midland Combination > 2014.
Honours: Midland Combination Division 2 1989-90, Premier 1993-94.

PILKINGTON XXX

Founded: 2002 Nickname:

Secretary: Ms Kim Holland **(T)** 07432 784 340 **(E)** pilkingtonxxx@gmail.com
Chairman: Darren McGinley
Ground: TSA Sports Ground, Eckersall Road, Kings Norton, Birmingham B38 8SR **(T)** 07525 844 853
Colours(change): Red & navy/red/navy

ADDITIONAL INFORMATION: Previous Leagues: Midland Combination > 2014.
Previous Name: Burman Hi-Ton > 2002.
Honours: Midland Combination Division 2 2001-02.

RACING CLUB WARWICK

Founded: 1919 Nickname: Racers

Secretary: Pat Murphy **(T)** 07926 188 553 **(E)** pja.murphy@hotmail.co.uk
Chairman: Andrew Cowlard
Ground: Townsend Meadow, Hampton Road, Warwick, Warwickshire CV34 6JP **(T)** 01926 495 786
Colours(change): Amber & gold/black/black

ADDITIONAL INFORMATION: Previous Leagues: Midland Combination > 2014.
Record Att: 1,280 v Leamington FC, Midland All.26/12/2005. **Goalscorer:** Steve Edgington - 200. **Apps:** Steve Cooper - 600+
Honours: Midland Combination Premier Division 1987-88.

SOUTHAM UNITED

Founded: 1905 Nickname:

Secretary: Charles Hill **(T)** 07802 949 781 **(E)** charles@southamunitedfc.com
Chairman: Charles Hill
Ground: Banbury Road, Southam, Warwickshire CV47 2BJ **(T)** 07802 949 781
Colours(change): Yellow/blue/blue

ADDITIONAL INFORMATION: Previous Leagues: Midland Combination > 2014.
Honours: Midland Combination Division 3 1980-81.

STAFFORD TOWN

Founded: 1976 Nickname:

Secretary: David Howard **(T)** 07789 110 923 **(E)** staffordtown@hotmail.co.uk
Chairman: Gordon Evans
Ground: Evans Park, Riverway, Stafford ST16 3TH **(T)** 07789 110 923
Colours(change): All red

ADDITIONAL INFORMATION:
Previous Leagues: Midland Combination 1977-84, 2012-14. Staffordshire 1984-93. West Midlands (Regional) 1993-2012.
Previous Names: Stafford > 1981.

STUDLEY

Founded: 1971 Nickname: Bees

Secretary: Bob Fletcher **(T)** 07745 310 077 **(E)** bobtheat@hotmail.co.uk
Chairman: Barry Cromwell
Ground: The Beehive, Abbeyfields Drive, Studley B80 7BE **(T)** 01527 853 817 **Capacity:** 1,500
Colours(change): Sky blue/navy/sky blue

ADDITIONAL INFORMATION: Previous Names: Studley BKL > 2002.
Previous Leagues: Redditch & Sth Warwicks Sunday Combination. Midland Combination 2013-14. Midland Alliance > 2013.
Record Att: 810 v Leamington 2003-04. Goalscorer: Brian Powell. Apps: Lee Adams - 523.
Honours: Midland Combination Div.1 1991-92. Worcestershire FA Senior Urn 00-01,01-02, 02-03.

UTTOXETER TOWN

Founded: 1983 Nickname:

Secretary: Graham Shenton **(T)** 07984 582 252 **(E)** graham.shenton@vodafone.com
Chairman: Graham Shenton
Ground: Oldfields Sports Ground, Springfield Road, Uttoxeter, ST14 7JX **(T)** 01889 564 347
Colours(change): Yellow/navy/navy

ADDITIONAL INFORMATION: Previous Leagues: Staffordshire County Senior > 2014.
League Honours: Staffordshire Senior Division One 2012-13.

GROUND DIRECTIONS - DIVISION ONE

ALVIS SPORTING CLUB - The Pavilion, Copsewood Sports & Social Club, Allard Way, Binley, Coventry, CV3 1JP

M6 South: Leave at junction 2 and follow A4600 signs for City Centre. Go over 3 roundabouts and past 1 set of traffic lights, on reaching the 2nd set of traffic lights with Coventry Oak pub on left, turn left down Hipswell Highway. Follow road for 1 mile and reach another set of lights (Fire Station is on left and Mill Pool pub is on right). Go over lights and the ground is 300 yards on the left.

Alvis Sporting Club From M40: Follow A46 signs to Coventry and Leicester, stay on this road until very end, you then reach a roundabout with a flyover, go round the roundabout following M69 signs. This road takes you past Asda and you reach a set of traffic lights with a roundabout. Take 2nd left turn off the roundabout, again following M69 signs, This is Allard Way and takes you past Matalan on left, Go under railway bridge and ground is 400 yards on the right. A45 from Birmingham Direction: Follow A45 until reaching a slip road signposted A46, this slip road has the Festival Pub on left side of it. It is after a roundabout with big Peugeot car showroom on left. Go down slip road and take 2nd exit. , this is another slip road leading to A46, signposted B4114 Coventry. Follow road until reaching roundabout with a flyover, and then follow as M40 directions above

ATHERSTONE TOWN - Sheepy Road, Atherston, Warwickshire CV9 3AD - 01827 717 829

Take M42 towards Atherstone. Exit at Junction 10. Travel southbound on A5 towards Nuneaton for approximately 4 miles. At third roundabout take first exit to Holly Lane Industrial Estate. Over railway bridge (Aldi HQ on left). At the next roundabout turn right onto Rowlands Way. Ground is 300 yards on the right. Car park and street parking in Rowlands Way.

BOLEHILL SWIFTS - Rene Road, Bolehall, Tamworth, Staffordshire B77 3NN

Exit M42 at Junction 10, take A5 towards Tamworth, exit A5 at 2nd exit (Glascote & Amington Industrial Estate). Turn right onto Marlborough Way, at next island turn left (B5000), turn right into Argyle Street (opposite chip shop). At T-junction, turn left into Amington Road, drive over the canal bridge, and turn 2nd right into Leedham Avenue. Take right fork into Rene Road. Club is situated 150 yards on right immediately after school.

BROMSGROVE SPORTING - The Victoria Ground, Birmingham Road, Bromsgrove, Worcs, B61 0DR

From M5 J4 take A38 to Bromsgrove, after island at M42 J1, take 1st right at Traffic Lights (signposted Bromsgrove North). Ground is 1000 metres on right (opposite Tesco Garage). From M42 J1, follow above directions from islands.

CADBURY ATHLETIC - Cadbury Recreation Ground, Bournville Lane, Birmingham, B30 1LA

From M5 Junction 4: Take A38 to Birmingham, turn right at Selly Oak lights (A4040), travel 1 mile down Oak Tree Lane/Linden Road to Bournville Lane, turn left, the ground is on the left. From M42 Junction 2: Take A441 to Birmingham through Kings Norton to Cotteridge, take Watford Road (A4040) for 1 mile to Bourneville Lane, and turn right, ground on left. From Birmingham City Centre: Take A38 Bristol Road to Selly Oak Lights, turn left, travel 1 mile down Oak Tree Lane/Linden Road to Bournville Lane, turn left, ground on right. Note: All routes in the South of Birmingham are well signposted for “Cadbury World”. Following these will lead to our ground. (A-Z Page 105 2E)

COVENTRY COPSEWOOD - Copsewood Sports & Social Club, Allard Way, Binley , Coventry , West Midlands , CV3 1HQ

M6 South: Leave at junction 2 and follow A4600 signs for City Centre. Go over 3 roundabouts and past 1 set of traffic lights, on reaching the 2nd set of traffic lights with Coventry Oak pub on left, turn left down Hipswell Highway. Follow road for 1 mile and reach another set of lights (Fire Station is on left and Mill Pool pub is on right). Go over lights and the ground is 300 yards on the left. From M40: Follow A46 signs to Coventry and Leicester, stay on this road until very end, you then reach a roundabout with a flyover, go round the roundabout following M69 signs. This road takes you past Asda and you reach a set of traffic lights with a roundabout. Take 2nd left turn off the roundabout, again following M69 signs, This is Allard Way and takes you past Matalan on left, Go under railway bridge and ground is 400 yards on the right. A45 from Birmingham Direction: Follow A45 until reaching a slip road signposted A46, this slip road has the Festival Pub on left side of it. It is after a roundabout with big Peugeot car showroom on left. Go down slip road and take 2nd exit. , this is another slip road leading to A46, signposted B4114 Coventry. Follow road until reaching roundabout with a flyover, and then follow as M40 directions above.

EARLSWOOD TOWN - The Victoria Ground, Birmingham Road, Bromsgrove, Worcs, B61 0DR

From M5 J4 take A38 to Bromsgrove, after island at M42 J1, take 1st right at Traffic Lights (signposted Bromsgrove North). Ground is 1000 metres on right (opposite Tesco Garage). From M42 J1, follow above directions from islands.

HEATHER ST. JOHN'S - St. John's Park, Ravenstone Road, Heather LE67 2QJ - 01530 263 986

Exit M42 at Junction 11. Take the road towards Measham, pass the Car Auctions and go over the traffic lights. At 2nd mini island take 2nd exit onto Leicester Road. After approximately 3 miles you will enter Heather. At T junction turn left. At mini island take 2nd exit onto Ravenstone Road and go up the hill. Ground is 200 metres on the left.

HIGHGATE UNITED - The Coppice, Tythe Barn Lane, Shirley, Solihull, B90 1PH - 0121 744 4194

From M42 Junction 4 take A34 towards Birmingham. Go to far end of Shirley Village and turn left into Haslucks Green Road. Take the left hand fork by the Colebrook pub and go past Shirley Station and the Drawbridge pub. At 'T' junction turn left and go over railway bridge. Turn left into Tythe Barn Lane and the ground is the 2nd entrance on the right approx 200 yards down the lane.

HINCKLEY AFC - St. John's Park, Ravenstone Road, Heather, Leicestershire, LE67 2QJ - 01530 263986

Exit M42 at Junction 11. Take the road towards Measham, pass the Car Auctions and go over the traffic lights. At 2nd mini island take 2nd exit onto Leicester Road. After approximately 3 miles you will enter Heather. At T junction turn left. At mini island take 2nd exit onto Ravenstone Road and go up the hill. Ground is 200 metres on the left.

LICHFIELD CITY - Brownsfield Park, Brownsfield Road , Lichfield , Staffordshire , WS13 6AY

From M42 J10, follow A5 towards Brownhills, or J9 and follow A446 to Lichfield, then follow signs for A38 Lichfield/Derby. From Swinfen Roundabout take 3rd exit for A38 north and then take next off A38 onto A5192 (Cappers Lane). Follow A5192 through 2 islands onto Eastern Avenue. The Ground is on the right at the top of the hill next to Norgreen factory. From M6 J12, follow A5 towards Lichfield then A38 to Lichfield Derby, then follow instructions as above.

LITTLETON - Five Acres, Pebworth Road, North Littleton , Evesham , Worcestershire , WR11 8QL

Get on A46 and aim for Bidford-on-Avon, leave A46 at Bidford roundabout and follow signs for B439 (Bidford 0.5 miles). Come to roundabout in Bidford and take exit B4085 (Cleeve Prior), over a very narrow bridge controlled by traffic lights, straight over crossroads following sign to Honeybourne Broadway. Straight on for approx. 3 miles signpost right turn for the Littletons at crossroads, the ground is 1.25 miles on the right.

NUNEATON GRIFF - The Pingles Stadium, Avenue Road , Nuneaton , Warwickshire , CV11 4LX

From M5, M42 & M6: Take M6 south to junction 3 and leave by turning left onto A444 (Nuneaton). Stay on A444 through Bermuda Park, McDonalds and George Eliot Hospital roundabouts until reaching large roundabout with footbridge over road. Carry straight on (2nd exit) and downhill, taking right hand lane. At bottom of hill you reach Coton Arches Island, take 2nd exit (A4252 Avenue Road) and travel 1/2 mile to Cedar Tree Pub traffic lights, turn left into Stadium car park service road. It is unsuitable for coaches to turn around in. From A5: Travel south following signs for Nuneaton. After passing through Atherstone travel for 2 1/2 miles until junction with A444. At this junction (Royal Red Gate Pub) turn right at staggered junction and continue on A444 through Caldecote and Weddington into Nuneaton. Join one-way system at Graziers Arms by turning left and immediately take right hand lane for 300 yards and follow A444 for Coventry. At Third Island turn left on to dual carriageway (Coton Road) for 1/2 mile and turn left at Coton Arches island on to A4252 (Avenue Road) then as above.

PELSALL VILLA - The Bush Ground, Walsall Road , Walsall , West Midlands , WS3 4BP

Leave M6 at junction 7 sign-posted A34 Birmingham. Take A34 towards Walsall to 1st Island, turn right (marked Ring Road) across 3 islands. At large island at the bottom of the hill, take last exit marked Lichfield. Up hill and across next island to traffic lights, continue to next set of lights and turn left (B4154 Pelsall). Go over Railway Bridge to Old Bush Public House, the ground is next to the public house signposted Pelsall Cricket Club. From Birmingham East: Follow A452 from Spitfire Island then follow signs towards Brownhills. At the traffic lights at the Shire Oak P.H, turn left onto A461 (Walsall) and pass the entrance to Walsall Wood FC. At the traffic lights in Shelfield (The Spring Cottage PH) turn right (signposted Pelsall). At the next set of traffic lights turn left, the Bush is approx 400 yards on left. From: Coventry: Take A45 to Stonebridge Island, turn right onto A452 but then keep to the right following A446 (signposted Lichfield). Follow the A446 to Bassett's Pole Island. Take the 3rd exit onto A38 (Lichfield). Leave the A38 at sliproad for the A5 and take the 2nd exit at the island. Follow the A5 over next 2 islands and at Muckley Corner turn left (inside lane) to join A461. Go straight on at the traffic lights and follow directions as above.

PERSHORE TOWN - King George V Playing Field, King George's Way , Pershore WR10 1QU

M5 Junction 7, take B4080 (formerly A44) to Pershore. On entering the town turn left at 2nd set of traffic lights (signposted Leisure Centre). The ground is 300 yards on the left hand side.

PILKINGTON XXX - Triplex Sports, Eckersall Road, Kings Norton , Birmingham B38 8SR

From Cotteridge A441 through and past Kings Norton Station, 150 yards turn right across dual carriageway at petrol station, approximately 300 yards there is a sharp bend, turn right. Ground is on right.

RACING CLUB WARWICK - Hampton Road , Warwick , Warwickshire , CV34 6JP

M40 Junction 15, signposted Warwick. At roundabout with traffic lights take A429 to Warwick. Follow this road for 1/2 mile and you will come to houses on your left. Take the 2nd turn on the left into Shakespeare Avenue. Follow to T-junction. Turn right into Hampton Road. Entrance to ground is 50 yards on left.

SOUTHAM UNITED - Banbury Road , Southam , Warwickshire , CV47 2BJ

From Birmingham: M40 Junction 12, exit to A4451 to Southam. Approximately 6 1/2 miles to an island in Southam, turn right, at 2nd island turn right again, ground is 100 yards on right. From Coventry: take A423 Banbury Road; the ground is approximately 12 1/2 miles from Coventry

STAFFORD TOWN - Evans Park, Riverway, Stafford ST16 3TH

From M6 junction 13, take A449 towards Stafford for 1½ miles until reaching traffic lights by an Esso petrol station. Turn right at the lights into Rickerscote Road, follow the road round over railway bridge to a mini island. At the island bear left into Silkmore Lane, after approximately 600 yards take the 2nd exit at the mini island and carry on until a large island, take the 2nd exit towards Stafford town centre (A34 Lichfield Road). Go over the railway bridge with Alstrom factory on the left hand side. Straight on at 1st set of traffic lights, then bear left at next set of lights (A518 Uttoxeter) and follow road round with B&Q and Argos on your left hand side. At the roundabout (with KFC and Pizza Hut in front of you) take the 2nd exit (A518 Uttoxeter) and follow to traffic lights. Go straight over lights into Riverway, the ground entrance is approximately 80 yards on the right hand side. Follow the driveway behind the cricket pavilion to the stadium entrance.

STUDLEY - The Beehive, Abbeyfields Drive, Studley, B80 7BF

Leave M42 at junction 3 (Redditch A435) and turn towards Redditch. Follow dual carriageway to the end. Stay on A435 and go straight on at island. Pass 'The Boot' public house and after 550 yards turn left into Abbeyfields Drive. The ground is on the right.

UTTOXETER - Oldfields Sports Club Springfield Road Uttoxeter Staffordshire ST14 7JX - 01889 564347

MIDLAND LEAGUE DIVISION TWO CONSTITUTION 2014-15

			2012-13
1	ASTON	Coleshill Town FC, Pack Meadow, Packington Lane, Coleshill, Warwickshire, B46 3JQ	MidC1
2	BARNT GREEN SPARTAK	TSA Sports Ground, Eckersall Road, Kings Norton, Birmingham, B38 8SR	MidC1
3	CHELMSLEY TOWN	The Pavilion, Coleshill Road, Marston Green, Birmingham, B37 7HW	MidC1
4	COTON GREEN	New Mill Lane, Fazeley, Tamworth, B78 3RX	MidC1
5	COVENTRY UNITED	The Alan Higgs Centre, Allard Way, Coventry, CV3 1HW	MidC2
6	DROITWICH SPA	King George Playing Fields, Briar Mill, Droitwich, WR9 0RZ	MidC1
7	EARLSWOOD TOWN	The Pavilions, Malthouse Lane, Earlswood, Solihull, B94 5DX	MidCP
8	FAIRFIELD VILLA	Recreation Ground, Stourbridge Road, Fairfield, Bromsgrove, Worcs, B61 9LZ	MidC1
9	FC GLADES SPORTING	The Pavilions, Malthouse Lane, Earlswood, Solihull, B94 5DX	MidC1
10	FECKENHAM	Studley Sports & Social Club, Eldorado Close, Studley, Warwickshire, B80 7HP	MidC1
11	HAMPTON	Hampton Sports Club, Field Lane, Solihull, B91 2RT	MidC1
12	KENILWORTH TOWN K.H.	Gypsy Lane, Kenilworth, CV8 1FN	MidC2
13	KNOWLE	The Robins Nest, Hampton Road, Knowle, Solihull, B93 0NX	MidC1
14	PAGET RANGERS	Trevor Brown Memorial Ground, Church Road, Great Barr, Birmingham, B73 5RY	MidC2
15	PHOENIX UNITED	Vale Stadium, Farnborough Road, Castle Vale, Birmingham, B35 7BE	MidC1
16	SUTTON UNITED	Hollyfield Road, Sutton Coldfield, B75 7SE	MidC1

MIDLAND LEAGUE DIVISION THREE CONSTITUTION 2014-15

			2012-13
1	ALCESTER TOWN	Old Stratford Road, Oversley Green, Alcester, Warwickshire, B49 6LN	MidC2
2	AUSTREY RANGERS	Austrey Fields, Garborough Lane, off Newton Lane, Austrey, Warwickshire, CV9 3EG	MidC2
3	BADSEY RANGERS	Badsey Recreation Ground, Sands Lane, Badsey, Evesham, Worcs, WR11 7EZ	MidC2
4	BARTON UNITED	Holland Sports Club, Efflinch Lane, Barton Under Needwood, Staffordshire, DE13 8ET	MidC2
5	BOLDMERE SPORTS & S.F.	Boldmere Sports and Social Club, 323 Boldmere Road, Boldmere, B73 5HQ	
6	BURTWOOD TOWN	Coppynook Playing Fields, Hospital Road, Hammerwich, WS7 0EJ	MidC2
7	ENVILLE ATHLETIC	Hall Drive, Enville, Stourbridge, West Midlands, DY7 5HB	MidC2
8	FC STRATFORD	Stratford Town FC, Knights Lane, Tiddington, Stratford upon Avon, CV37 7BZ	MidC2
9	INKBERROW	Recreation Ground, Sands Road, Inkberrow, Worcestershire, WR7 4PX	MidC2
10	LEAMINGTON HIBERNIAN	Bishops Tachbrook Sports and S.C, The Meadow, Kingsley Rd, Leamington Spa, CV33 9RR	MidC2
11	NORTHFIELD TOWN	Shenley Lane Community Association, 472 Shenley Lane, Selly Oak, Birmingham, B29 4HZ	MidC2
12	PERRYWOOD	Neel Park, Droitwich Road, Perdiswell, Worcester, WR3 7SN	MidC2
13	POLESWORTH	North Warwickshire Sports & Social Club, Hermitage Hill, Polesworth, Tamworth, Staffs, B78 1HT	MidC2
14	REDDITCH BOROUGH	Valley Stadium, Bromsgrove Road, Redditch, Worcestershire, B97 4RN	
15	ROSTANCE EDWARDS	Grosvenor Park, Somerfield Road, Walsall, WS3 2EH	MidC2
16	SMITHSWOOD FIRS	Mackadown Lane. Sheldon, Birmingham, B33 0JT	Birm&Dist

NORTH WEST COUNTIES LEAGUE

Sponsored by: Vodkat
Founded: 1982
Recent Champions:
2009: AFC Fylde.
2010: Newcastle Town.
2011: New Mills.
2012: Ramsbottom United.
2013: Padiham.
nwcfl.com

PREMIER DIVISION	P	W	D	L	F	A	GD	Pts
1 (P) Norton United	42	32	4	6	101	38	63	100
2 Runcorn Linnets	42	29	8	5	103	39	64	95
3 Glossop North End	42	25	8	9	73	33	40	83
4 Maine Road	42	24	9	9	85	42	43	81
5 Runcorn Town	42	25	4	13	87	45	42	79
6 Ashton Athletic	42	23	5	14	78	50	28	74
7 AFC Liverpool	42	21	7	14	88	54	34	70
8 Bootle	42	21	7	14	87	57	30	70
9 Colne	42	20	4	18	71	67	4	64
10 Congleton Town	42	17	9	16	58	58	0	60
11 Stockport Sports	42	15	12	15	64	69	-5	57
12 West Didsbury & Chorlton	42	15	8	19	52	66	-14	53
13 AFC Blackpool	42	14	7	21	60	87	-27	49
14 Winsford United	42	15	3	24	57	83	-26	48
15 Silsden	42	13	8	21	52	70	-18	47
16 Barnoldswick Town	42	12	7	23	59	89	-30	43
17 St Helens Town	42	11	10	21	55	89	-34	43
18 Alsager Town	42	11	7	24	57	85	-28	40
19 Squires Gate	42	12	4	26	51	89	-38	40
20 Abbey Hey	42	9	13	20	47	86	-39	40
21 Bacup & Rossendale Borough	42	9	12	21	38	68	-30	39
22 (R) Wigan Robin Park	42	7	8	27	53	112	-59	29

LEAGUE CHALLENGE CUP FINAL

ROUND 1

1874 Northwich	v	Hanley Town	3-2 aet
Atherton Collieries	v	Cheadle	4-0
Atherton LR	v	AFC Darwen	1-2
Daisy Hill	v	Irlam	0-4
Formby	v	Nelson	4-0
Holker Old Boys	v	Leek CSOB	2-0
Northwich Flixton Villa	v	Eccleshall @ Eccleshall	4-5 aet
Oldham Boro	v	Chadderton @ Chadderton	1-2
Rochdale Town	v	Widnes Vikings	3-0

ROUND 2

Abbey Hey	v	Eccleshall	4-0
AFC Darwen	v	Colne	4-2
Atherton Collieries	v	Bacup & Rossendale Boro'	
Bootle	v	Norton United	3-0
Chadderton	v	Ashton Athletic	0-1
Congleton Town	v	Ashton Town	2-0
Glossop North End	v	Maine Road	0-2
Irlam	v	Runcorn Town	1-5
Rochdale Town	v	Holker Old Boys	3-2
Runcorn Linnets	v	Barnoldswick Town	1-0
Silsden	v	Formby	1-4 aet
Squires Gate	v	1874 Northwich	1-5
St Helens Town	v	Alsager Town	1-2
West Didsbury & Chorlton	v	AFC Liverpool	1-5
Wigan Robin Park	v	AFC Blackpool	2-3
Winsford United	v	Stockport Sports	3-1

ROUND 3

1874 Northwich	v	Formby	1-0
AFC Blackpool	v	AFC Liverpool	1-0
Alsager Town	v	Runcorn Linnets	0-1
Bootle	v	Abbey Hey	0-1
Congleton Town	v	Ashton Athletic	1-1 aet
(R) Ashton Athletic	v	Congleton Town	2-1
Maine Road	v	Winsford United	3-0
Rochdale Town	v	Atherton C. or Bacup	3-0
Runcorn Town	v	AFC Darwen	5-0

QUARTER FINALS

1874 Northwich	v	Abbey Hey	2-1
Maine Road	v	AFC Blackpool	4-0
Rochdale Town	v	Runcron Town	3-1
Runcorn Linnets	v	Ashton Athletic	0-2

SEMI-FINALS

Main Road	v	1874 Northwich	3-1
1874 Northwich	v	Maine Road	0-3
Rochdale Town	v	Ashton Athletic	1-3
Ashton Athletic	v	Rochdale Town	3-1

FINAL

Ashton Athletic	v	Maine Road	1-0

PREMIER DIVISION	1	2	3	4	5	6	7	8	9	10	11	12	13	14	15	16	17	18	19	20	21	22
1 Abbey Hey		0–2	2–2	4–2	2–0	1–1	1–1	0–4	1–4	0–0	1–3	2–2	2–1	1–2	1–3	2–1	0–3	1–1	0–3	2–1	0–1	2–1
2 A.F.C. Blackpool	3–3		0–2	1–1	1–0	4–1	1–3	0–3	3–0	1–1	1–1	0–2	2–4	1–2	1–4	2–2	2–0	4–2	2–1	0–4	3–2	2–6
3 A.F.C. Liverpool	4–0	2–4		5–1	1–1	4–0	2–0	3–0	4–2	1–0	0–2	1–2	2–3	2–3	0–4	3–1	2–1	3–0	1–1	2–2	6–0	1–2
4 Alsager Town	1–3	0–1	2–1		2–3	3–0	2–0	1–4	0–4	1–2	1–2	0–3	0–2	0–3	0–0	1–2	1–1	1–2	2–3	2–0	3–2	2–1
5 Ashton Athletic	3–1	6–1	0–1	3–0		0–0	3–0	1–0	1–0	0–1	2–1	1–2	2–0	1–0	1–3	1–1	1–2	6–2	2–1	2–2	4–0	6–2
6 Bacup & Rossendale Borough	0–0	0–0	1–2	1–1	0–2		0–2	0–1	1–2	1–1	2–0	1–2	0–4	1–3	0–2	3–0	3–0	3–2	0–1	0–1	1–2	1–4
7 Barnoldswick Town	3–1	1–2	2–1	1–1	1–2	1–1		2–3	1–0	1–1	0–2	2–3	1–1	1–5	0–2	2–1	4–0	1–2	1–2	5–2	2–2	2–1
8 Bootle	5–0	2–1	0–1	2–0	1–0	0–0	4–0		4–0	2–0	3–1	2–1	0–4	2–1	2–2	2–0	2–4	1–2	2–2	5–0	5–0	0–1
9 Colne	2–0	2–0	0–4	4–3	1–0	1–1	1–2	2–1		2–1	0–0	0–1	0–1	1–6	0–3	3–1	4–0	7–0	3–2	0–4	3–1	5–1
10 Congleton Town	3–1	4–2	1–0	2–3	3–2	0–1	3–1	2–1	3–1		0–2	3–3	0–2	0–4	4–2	2–1	0–2	1–0	2–3	3–1	1–1	3–0
11 Glossop North End	0–0	3–1	2–1	4–1	1–2	2–0	2–0	2–1	1–1	3–2		0–1	0–1	1–1	1–0	3–0	5–1	2–3	0–3	1–0	5–0	5–0
12 Maine Road	3–0	3–1	0–1	2–0	2–0	1–0	7–0	0–0	3–0	2–0	1–1		2–2	0–0	2–1	1–2	1–2	6–0	1–1	5–1	1–1	3–0
13 Norton United	2–0	2–0	3–1	4–2	1–2	4–0	4–0	2–1	2–1	3–1	0–1	3–0		0–2	4–1	2–0	4–2	2–1	2–1	1–0	5–1	2–1
14 Runcorn Linnets	7–1	4–0	1–3	4–2	4–0	1–1	3–1	3–1	3–4	1–1	2–1	2–2	1–5		4–0	1–0	3–0	1–1	2–1	0–0	3–2	2–1
15 Runcorn Town	1–3	1–2	4–1	0–3	2–1	4–1	4–1	4–1	1–2	3–0	0–0	4–1	1–2	0–1		3–0	2–0	2–0	3–1	0–1	1–1	1–0
16 Silsden	2–2	4–1	3–1	3–2	0–1	1–2	3–1	0–2	1–3	0–0	0–1	1–3	1–0	1–1	0–4		5–1	1–0	2–2	2–0	1–0	2–1
17 Squires Gate	2–2	1–3	1–1	1–2	0–1	3–3	4–0	1–4	2–1	0–2	0–1	1–2	1–2	0–4	0–1	3–2		3–0	1–2	1–0	0–2	2–1
18 St Helens Town	2–1	1–1	1–1	0–3	2–6	1–1	1–1	1–2	0–1	1–1	0–2	0–5	3–3	0–3	0–3	2–0	5–0		2–2	3–0	4–1	0–2
19 Stockport Sports	1–1	2–1	1–4	2–1	0–3	0–2	0–3	5–5	1–0	0–2	0–0	2–1	1–3	0–3	1–2	1–1	3–0	1–1		2–3	1–1	2–1
20 West Didsbury & Chorlton	2–0	2–0	1–3	0–0	1–1	0–1	3–2	4–3	1–1	1–0	1–3	0–2	0–0	0–2	1–0	2–0	2–1	1–2	2–2		1–0	1–2
21 Wigan Robin Park	1–1	3–1	0–8	2–3	2–4	4–1	3–2	3–3	0–2	1–2	0–3	3–1	1–5	0–1	1–5	1–1	2–3	1–4	0–2	3–4		1–3
22 Winsford United	1–2	0–2	0–0	1–1	3–1	1–2	3–5	1–1	2–1	1–0	0–3	1–0	0–4	0–4	0–4	2–3	2–1	2–1	1–2	2–0	3–1	

NORTH WEST COUNTIES LEAGUE - STEP 5/6

	DIVISION ONE	P	W	D	L	F	A	GD	Pts
1	(P) Nelson	36	29	2	5	135	51	84	89
2	Formby	36	26	6	4	97	37	60	84
3	(P) 1874 Northwich	36	26	6	4	79	28	51	84
4	Hanley Town	36	23	4	9	86	55	31	73
5	Atherton Collieries	36	19	9	8	100	62	38	66
6	Holker Old Boys	36	17	9	10	80	60	20	60
7	Rochdale Town	36	17	4	15	95	78	17	55
8	Atherton LR	36	17	3	16	66	66	0	54
9	AFC Darwen (-1pt)	36	15	7	14	64	64	0	51
10	Irlam	36	14	8	14	53	64	-11	50
11	Cheadle Town (-3pts)	36	14	7	15	65	74	-9	46
12	Ashton Town	36	11	11	14	57	61	-4	44
13	Chadderton (-3pts)	36	12	8	16	58	71	-13	41
14	Widnes Vikings (-1pt)	36	9	9	18	58	84	-26	35
15	Leek CSOB	36	8	5	23	55	93	-38	29
16	Oldham Boro	36	7	7	22	45	90	-45	28
17	Eccleshall	36	7	5	24	43	78	-35	26
18	Daisy Hill	36	6	4	26	43	103	-60	22
19	Northwich Flixton Villa (-3pts)	36	6	4	26	48	108	-60	19

	RESERVE DIVISION	P	W	D	L	F	A	GD	Pts
1	Glossop North End Reserves	16	11	2	3	49	23	26	35
2	New Mills Reserves	16	11	1	4	53	26	27	34
3	Cheadle Town Reserves	16	8	2	6	39	37	2	26
4	Irlam Reserves	16	6	5	5	31	29	2	23
5	Padiham Reserves	16	6	2	8	29	31	-2	20
6	AFC Darwen Reserves	16	6	2	8	27	33	-6	20
7	West Didsbury & Chorlton Res.	16	6	2	8	28	44	-16	20
8	Barnoldswick Town Reserves	16	3	5	8	31	43	-12	14
9	Silsden Reserves	16	3	3	10	34	55	-21	12

DIVISION ONE	1	2	3	4	5	6	7	8	9	10	11	12	13	14	15	16	17	18	19
1 1874 Northwich		4–1	1–0	1–1	3–0	3–0	4–0	3–0	2–1	0–1	4–2	6–0	0–0	1–0	1–3	1–0	1–1	2–1	4–0
2 A.F.C. Darwen	1–4		1–0	3–3	1–3	3–0	1–1	2–0	3–2	2–5	1–2	4–2	2–1	5–2	1–3	5–0	2–3	0–0	1–0
3 Ashton Town	0–5	0–1		1–3	1–2	0–0	4–1	2–2	4–3	2–2	0–1	0–0	1–1	4–0	1–2	1–2	4–1	2–2	2–1
4 Atherton Collieries	0–1	2–2	2–1		0–0	3–1	6–2	5–0	6–0	2–2	2–2	2–3	4–2	4–0	2–1	3–3	3–1	2–4	5–1
5 Atherton Laburnum Rovers	1–3	1–3	3–1	3–1		2–1	4–1	1–2	2–0	1–3	4–3	3–1	2–0	1–6	2–3	5–1	0–1	0–5	2–0
6 Chadderton	1–3	3–0	3–1	1–2	3–2		1–2	1–0	4–1	0–2	0–1	1–1	2–2	3–2	1–7	6–3	4–1	0–3	2–2
7 Cheadle Town	2–2	0–4	1–1	2–2	1–1	2–0		5–1	3–1	1–4	1–4	4–1	4–2	0–0	2–3	1–2	2–0	1–0	5–2
8 Daisy Hill	2–3	1–4	2–2	3–1	1–2	0–0	0–2		2–1	1–3	1–7	2–3	0–2	2–3	3–4	4–1	3–5	2–1	1–1
9 Eccleshall	0–2	2–1	0–1	1–2	2–1	1–3	1–3	1–2		2–3	1–2	2–2	0–1	1–0	1–6	2–1	2–0	1–1	1–1
10 Formby	0–0	2–0	0–1	1–0	3–0	1–0	3–0	7–1	4–0		2–1	2–2	4–1	7–3	1–3	2–0	3–1	2–1	1–2
11 Hanley Town	1–2	1–4	0–3	1–5	2–1	2–2	5–3	3–0	1–0	1–1		2–3	3–0	4–0	3–0	2–1	3–0	1–0	3–2
12 Holker Old Boys	0–1	4–0	0–1	2–2	1–1	4–1	4–1	4–1	2–3	0–1	1–1		2–1	5–1	1–2	2–0	4–1	6–3	3–1
13 Irlam	1–1	2–0	1–1	1–3	1–2	3–1	1–0	3–1	2–1	1–1	0–3	2–2		0–3	0–2	4–1	1–1	3–2	1–0
14 Leek County School Old Boys	1–2	0–0	0–1	1–3	2–6	1–4	3–3	3–1	2–2	1–5	0–2	1–3	1–2		0–4	6–1	6–1	1–3	1–1
15 Nelson	3–1	4–0	5–1	4–2	5–1	2–2	2–1	8–0	1–0	0–4	3–4	3–2	2–5	7–0		2–2	8–4	6–1	8–1
16 Northwich Flixton Villa	0–1	1–2	4–4	2–5	0–4	2–3	3–1	2–1	1–0	0–6	5–1	0–3	2–4	0–2	0–3		0–1	3–4	1–5
17 Oldham Boro	0–1	0–0	3–4	0–2	2–1	0–1	1–2	2–1	1–1	2–3	1–3	2–2	0–1	2–1	0–6	2–2		0–2	2–2
18 Rochdale Town	4–3	4–2	3–2	8–6	1–2	6–2	0–2	2–0	4–5	4–2	0–5	2–3	7–0	2–0	1–4	7–2	4–1		2–2
19 Widnes Vikings	0–3	2–2	3–3	1–4	2–0	1–1	1–3	4–0	2–1	1–4	2–4	0–2	3–1	1–2	0–6	3–0	5–2	3–1	

CLUB MOVEMENTS

Premier Division - In: 1874 Northwich (P). Nelson (P).

Out: Norton United (P - Northern Premier Div.1 South). Wigan Robin Park (R).

Division One - In: Barnton (P - Cheshire League Div.1). Cammell Laird (Resigned from Northern Premier Div.1 North). Litherland Remyca (P - Liverpool County Premier). Wigan Robin Park (R). Widnes (NC - from Widnes Vikings)

Out: 1894 Northwich (P). Formby (F). Leek CSOB (W - now SCSL Div.1). Nelson (P). Widnes Vikings (NC - to Widnes)

1874 NORTHWICH

Founded: 2012 Nickname:

Secretary: Vicki England **(T)** **(E)**

Chairman: Paul Stockton **Manager:** Ian Street **Prog Ed:** Andy Dignum

Ground: Winsford United FC, Wharton Road, Winsford, Cheshire CW7 3AE **(T)** 01606 558 447

Capacity: 6,000 **Seats:** Seats **Covered:** Yes **Midweek Matchday:** Tuesday **Clubhouse:** Yes

Colours(change): Green/black/green & white (All claret with sky blue trim)
Previous Names: None
Previous Leagues: None
Records: 541 v Formby 28/09/2013
Senior Honours:

10 YEAR RECORD

04-05	05-06	06-07	07-08	08-09	09-10	10-11	11-12	12-13	13-14
									NWC1 3

A.F.C. BLACKPOOL

Founded: 1947 Nickname: Mechs

Secretary: William Singleton **(T)** 01253 761 721 **(E)**

Chairman: Henry Baldwin **Manager:** Stuart Parker **Prog Ed:** David Tebbett

Ground: Mechanics Ground, Jepson Way, Common Edge Road, Blackpool, FY4 5DY **(T)** 01253 761 721

Capacity: 2,000 **Seats:** 250 **Covered:** 1,700 **Midweek Matchday:** Tuesday **Clubhouse:** Yes **Shop:** Yes

Colours(change): All tangerine (White/navy blue/navy blue & tangerine)
Previous Names: Blackpool Mechanics. **Previous Ground:** Stanley Park 1947-49.
Previous Leagues: Fylde, Blackpool & Fylde Combination, West Lancashire, Lancashire Combination 1962-68.
Records: **Att:** 4,300 v FC United of Manchester, 18/02/2006 at Blackpool FC.
Senior Honours: Lancashire County FA Shield 1957/58, 1960/61. West Lancashire League 1960/61, 61/62.
North West Counties League Division Three 1985/86, Division One 2010-11.

10 YEAR RECORD

04-05	05-06	06-07	07-08	08-09	09-10	10-11	11-12	12-13	13-14
NWC2 10	NWC2 9	NWC1 13	NWC1 9	NWC1 15	NWC1 15	NWC1 1	NWCP 9	NWCP 10	NWCP 13

A.F.C. LIVERPOOL

Founded: 2008 Nickname: Reds

Secretary: Wayne McDonald **(T)** **(E)**

Chairman: Chris Stirrup **Manager:** Paul Moore **Prog Ed:** Paul Smith

Ground: The Arriva Stadium (Marine FC), College Road, Crosby, Liverpool L23 3AS **(T)** 0151 924 1743 or 0151 286 9101

Capacity: 3,185 **Seats:** 400 **Covered:** 1,400 **Midweek Matchday:** Wednesday **Clubhouse:** Yes **Shop:** Yes

Colours(change): All red (Yellow/black/yellow)
Previous Names: None
Previous Leagues: None
Records: **Att:** 604 v Wigan Robin Park 06/09/2008.
Senior Honours: North West Counties Trophy 2008-09, 09-10.

10 YEAR RECORD

04-05	05-06	06-07	07-08	08-09	09-10	10-11	11-12	12-13	13-14
				NWC1 4	NWC1 5	NWC1 4	NWCP 19	NWCP 11	NWCP 7

ABBEY HEY

Founded: 1902 Nickname:

Secretary: Tony McAllister **(T)** 0161 231 7147 **(E)**

Chairman: James Whittaker **Manager:** Luke Gibson **Prog Ed:** Gordon Lester

Ground: The Abbey Stadium, Goredale Avenue, Gorton, Manchester M18 7HD **(T)** 0161 231 7147

Capacity: **Seats:** Yes **Covered:** Yes **Midweek Matchday:** Tuesday **Clubhouse:** Yes

Colours(change): Red/black/red (Blue/white/blue)
Previous Names:
Previous Leagues: Manchester Amateur, South East Lancashire, Manchester.
Records: 985 v FC United of Manchester, March 2006.
Senior Honours: Manchester League 1981-82, 88-89, 88-89, 91-92, 93-94, 94-95.

10 YEAR RECORD

04-05	05-06	06-07	07-08	08-09	09-10	10-11	11-12	12-13	13-14
NWC1 14	NWC1 11	NWC1 17	NWC1 17	NWCP 21	NWCP 22	NWC1 15	NWC1 3	NWC1 2	NWCP 20

ALSAGER TOWN

Founded: 1968 Nickname: The Bullets

Secretary: Chris Robinson **(T)** 07888 750 532 **(E)**
Chairman: Terry Greer **Manager:** Phil Parkinson **Prog Ed:** John Shenton
Ground: The LAW Training Stadium, Woodland Court, Alsager ST7 2DP **(T)** 07888 750532
Capacity: 3,000 **Seats:** 250 **Covered:** 1,000 **Midweek Matchday:** Tuesday **Clubhouse:** Yes **Shop:** Yes

Colours(change): White & black/white/white. (All red).
Previous Names: Alsager FC (Merger of Alsager Institute & Alsager Utd) in 1965.
Previous Leagues: Crewe. Mid Cheshire. Northern Premier.
Records: **Att:** 606 v Whitley Bay - 14.11.2009. **Goalscorer:** Gareth Rowe. **Apps:** Wayne Brotherton.
Senior Honours: Leek Cup 2001-02

10 YEAR RECORD

04-05	05-06	06-07	07-08	08-09	09-10	10-11	11-12	12-13	13-14
NWC1 7	NWC1 3	NP1S 16	NP1S 14	NWCP 7	NWCP 18	NWCP 20	NWCP 13	NWCP 15	NWCP 18

ASHTON ATHLETIC

Founded: 1968 Nickname:

Secretary: Alan Greenhalgh **(T)** 01942 716 360 **(E)**
Chairman: Jimmy Whyte **Manager:** Jay Foulds **Prog Ed:** Alan Greenhalgh
Ground: Brockstedes Park, Downall Green, Ashton in Markerfield WN4 0NR **(T)** 01942 716 360
Capacity: 600 **Seats:** 100 **Covered:** 300 **Midweek Matchday:** Tuesday **Clubhouse:** Yes

Colours(change): All yellow. (All maroon).
Previous Names: None.
Previous Leagues: Lancashire Combination, Manchester Amateur League
Records: **Att:** 168 v Runcorn Linnets 20014. **Apps:** Steve Rothwell - 50+
Senior Honours: Atherton Charity Cup 2006-07, 07-08, 08-09.

10 YEAR RECORD

04-05	05-06	06-07	07-08	08-09	09-10	10-11	11-12	12-13	13-14
Manc 10	Manc 4	NWC2 16	NWC2 3	NWCP 6	NWCP 21	NWCP 22	NWCP 14	NWCP 20	NWCP 6

BACUP & ROSSENDALE BOROUGH

Founded: 1878 Nickname: The Boro

Secretary: Natalie Peters **(T)** 01706 878 655 **(E)** commercial@barbfc.co.uk
Chairman: Brent Peters **Manager:** Brent Peters **Prog Ed:** Michael Carr
Ground: Brian Boys Stadium, Cowtoot Lane, Blackthorn, Bacup, OL13 8EE **(T)** 01706 878 655
Capacity: 3,000 **Seats:** 500 **Covered:** 1,000 **Midweek Matchday:** Wednesday **Clubhouse:** Yes

Colours(change): White with black trim/black/black. (Yellow with royal blue trim/royal blue/yellow).
Previous Names: Bacup FC. Bacup Borough > 2013.
Previous Leagues: Lancashire Combination 1903-82
Records: **Att:** 4,980 v Nelson 1947 **Goalscorer:** Jimmy Clarke
Senior Honours: North West Counties League Division Two 2002-03, Challenge Cup 2003-04.

10 YEAR RECORD

04-05	05-06	06-07	07-08	08-09	09-10	10-11	11-12	12-13	13-14
NWC1 9	NWC1 17	NWC1 15	NWC1 18	NWCP 8	NWCP 12	NWCP 11	NWCP 17	NWCP 17	NWCP 21

BARNOLDSWICK TOWN

Founded: 1972 Nickname:

Secretary: Lynn James **(T)** **(E)**
Chairman: Ian James **Manager:** Stuart Airdrie **Prog Ed:** Peter Naylor
Ground: Silentnight Stadium, West Close Road, Barnoldswick, Colne, BB18 5LJ **(T)** 01282 815 817
Capacity: **Seats:** Yes **Covered:** Yes **Midweek Matchday:** Tuesday **Clubhouse:** Yes

Colours(change): Yellow & Royal Blue/royal blue/royal blue (All red)
Previous Names: Today's club formed after the merger of Barnoldswick United and Barnoldswick Park Rovers in 2003
Previous Leagues: Craven, East Lancashire, West Lancashire.
Records: **Att:** 334 v Spennymoor, FA Vase, 2011-12.
Senior Honours: West Lancashire Division 1 1998-99

10 YEAR RECORD

04-05	05-06	06-07	07-08	08-09	09-10	10-11	11-12	12-13	13-14
WLaP 15	WLaP 15	WLaP 13	WLaP 10	WLaP 6	NWC1 2	NWCP 7	NWCP 4	NWCP 9	NWCP 16

BOOTLE

Founded: 1954 Nickname:

Secretary: Joe Doran **(T)** 0151 531 0665 **(E)**
Chairman: Bobby Capstick **Manager:** Joe Doran **Prog Ed:** Dave Miley Junior
Ground: Delta Taxi Stadium, Vestey Rd, Off Bridle Road, Bootle L30 1NY **(T)** 0151 525 4796
Capacity: **Seats:** **Covered:** Yes **Midweek Matchday:** Tuesday **Clubhouse:** Yes

Colours(change): All blue. (Yellow/black & yellow/black).
Previous Names: Langton Dock 1953 - 1973.
Previous Leagues: Liverpool Shipping. Lancashire Combination. Cheshire. Liverpool County Combination >2006.
Records: **Att:** 1,078 v Everton Reserves, Liverpool Senior Cup Feb 2010.
Senior Honours: Liverpool County Champions 1964-65, 65-66, 67-68, 68-69, 69-70, 70-71, 71-72, 72-73, 73-74. North West Counties Div.1 Champions 2008-09

10 YEAR RECORD

04-05	05-06	06-07	07-08	08-09	09-10	10-11	11-12	12-13	13-14
Liv 12	Liv 3	NWC2 10	NWC2 6	NWC1 1	NWCP 3	NWCP 6	NWCP 3	NWCP 3	NWCP 8

COLNE

Founded: 1996 Nickname:

Secretary: Edward Lambert **(T)** 01282 862 545 **(E)**
Chairman: Shaun O'Neill **Manager:** Steve Cunningham **Prog Ed:** Ray Davies
Ground: The XLCR Stadium, Harrison Drive, Colne, Lancashire. BB8 9SL **(T)** 01282 862 545
Capacity: 1,800 **Seats:** 160 **Covered:** 1,000 **Midweek Matchday:** Tuesday **Clubhouse:** Yes **Shop:** Yes

Colours(change): All Red. (White/black/black).
Previous Names: None
Previous Leagues: None
Records: **Att:** 1,742 v AFC Sudbury F.A. Vase SF 2004 **Goalscorer:** Geoff Payton **App:** Richard Walton
Senior Honours: BEP Cup Winners 1996-97 North West Counties League Division Two 2003-04.

10 YEAR RECORD

04-05	05-06	06-07	07-08	08-09	09-10	10-11	11-12	12-13	13-14
NWC1 10	NWC1 9	NWC1 11	NWC1 5	NWCP 18	NWCP 8	NWCP 5	NWCP 8	NWCP 8	NWCP 9

CONGLETON TOWN

Founded: 1901 Nickname: Bears

Secretary: Ken Mead **(T)** 01260 278 152 **(E)**
Chairman: Peter Evans **Manager:** Jim Vince **Prog Ed:** Ken Mead
Ground: Ivy Gardens, Booth Street, Crescent Road, Congleton, Cheshire CW12 4DG **(T)** 01260 274 460
Capacity: 5,000 **Seats:** 250 **Covered:** 1,200 **Midweek Matchday:** Tuesday **Clubhouse:** Yes **Shop:** Yes

Colours(change): Black & white/black/black. (Black & yellow/yellow/yellow).
Previous Names: Congleton Hornets
Previous Leagues: Crew & District, North Staffs, Macclesfield, Cheshire , Mid Cheshire, NW Co, NPL
Records: **Att:** 6,800 v Macclesfield, Cheshire Lge1953-54 **Goalscorer:** Mick Bidde 150+ **App:** Ray Clack 600+ Graham Harrison 600+
Senior Honours: Cheshire Senior Cup 1920-21, 37-38.

10 YEAR RECORD

04-05	05-06	06-07	07-08	08-09	09-10	10-11	11-12	12-13	13-14
NWC1 19	NWC1 12	NWC1 10	NWC1 9	NWCP 4	NWCP 5	NWCP 8	NWCP 11	NWCP 7	NWCP 10

GLOSSOP NORTH END

Founded: 1886 Nickname: Hillmen

Secretary: Peter Hammond **(T)** **(E)**
Chairman: David Atkinson **Manager:** Chris Willcox Neil Rimmer
Ground: Surrey Street, Glossop, Derbys SK13 7AJ **(T)** 01457 855 469
Capacity: 2,374 **Seats:** 209 **Covered:** 509 **Midweek Matchday:** Tuesday **Clubhouse:** Yes **Shop:** Yes

Colours(change): All blue (Orange/black/orange).
Previous Names: Glossop North End1886-1896 and Glossop FC 1898-1992. Reformed in 1992.
Previous Leagues: The Football League. Cheshire County. Manchester. Lancashire Comb.
Records: **Att:** 10,736 v Preston North End F.A. Cup 1913-1914
Senior Honours: Manchester League 1927-28. Derbyshire Senior Cup 2000-01.

10 YEAR RECORD

04-05	05-06	06-07	07-08	08-09	09-10	10-11	11-12	12-13	13-14
NWC1 13	NWC1 16	NWC1 9	NWC1 7	NWCP 5	NWCP 7	NWCP 14	NWCP 6	NWCP 13	NWCP 3

MAINE ROAD

Founded: 1955 Nickname: Blues

Secretary: Derek Barber **(T)** 0161 431 8243 **(E)**

Chairman: Ron Meredith **Prog Ed:** Jeff Newman

Ground: Brantingham Road, Chorlton-cum-Hardy M21 0TT **(T)** 0161 861 0344

Capacity: 2,000 **Seats:** 200 **Covered:** 700 **Midweek Matchday:** Monday **Clubhouse:** Yes

Colours(change): All sky blue. (Red & black stripes/black/white).
Previous Names: City Supporters Rusholme 1955-late sixties.
Previous Leagues: Rusholme Sunday 1955-66, Manchester Amateur Sunday 1966-72 & Manchester 1972-87.
Records: **Att:** 3,125 v FC United Manchester, NWC Div.1, 04.11.06, at Stalybridge Celtic.
Senior Honours: Manchester Premier League 1982-83, 83-84, 84-85, 85-86. North West Counties Division Two 1989-90, Challenge Cup 07-08.

10 YEAR RECORD

04-05	05-06	06-07	07-08	08-09	09-10	10-11	11-12	12-13	13-14
NWC1 8	NWC1 10	NWC1 6	NWC1 4	NWCP 13	NWCP 6	NWCP 13	NWCP 18	NWCP 2	NWCP 4

NELSON

Founded: 1883 Nickname: Admirals

Secretary: Rauf Abdul Khan **(T)** **(E)**

Chairman: Fayyaz Ahmed **Manager:** Mark Fell **Prog Ed:** Shuaid Khan

Ground: Little Wembley, Lomeshaye Way, Nelson, Lancs BB9 7BN. **(T)** 01282 787 752

Capacity: 1500 **Seats:** 150 **Covered:** 200 **Midweek Matchday:** Tuesday **Clubhouse:** Yes **Shop:** Yes

Colours(change): All blue. (White/black/black).
Previous Names: Reformed in 2011.
Previous Leagues: Since 1946: Lancs Comb 1946-82. NW Counties 1982-88, 92-2010. West Lancs 1988-92.
Records: **Att:** 14,143 v Bradford Park Avenue, Div.3 North, 10.04.26.
Senior Honours: Football League Division Three North 1922-23.
North West Counties Division One 2013-14.

10 YEAR RECORD

04-05	05-06	06-07	07-08	08-09	09-10	10-11	11-12	12-13	13-14
NWC2 6	NWC2 3	NWC1 20	NWC1 20	NWCP 17	NWCP 17		NWC1 15	NWC1 10	NWC1 1

RUNCORN LINNETS

Founded: 2006 Nickname: Linnets

Secretary: Lynn Johnston **(T)** 01606 43008 **(E)**

Chairman: Derek Greenwood **Manager:** Joey Dunn **Prog Ed:** Jon Urquhart

Ground: Millbank Linnets Stadium, Murdishaw Ave, Runcorn, Cheshire WA7 6HP **(T)** 07050 801733 (Clubline)

Capacity: **Seats:** Yes **Covered:** Yes **Midweek Matchday:** Tuesday **Clubhouse:** Yes

Colours(change): Yellow & green/green/yellow & green. (Blue & white/white/blue)
Previous Names: None
Previous Leagues: None.
Records: **Att:** 1,037 v Witton Albion, pre season friendly July 2010
Senior Honours: NWCFL Challenge Cup 2012-13.

10 YEAR RECORD

04-05	05-06	06-07	07-08	08-09	09-10	10-11	11-12	12-13	13-14
		NWC2 2	NWC1 12	NWCP 11	NWCP 11	NWCP 12	NWCP 5	NWCP 6	NWCP 2

RUNCORN TOWN

Founded: 1967 Nickname:

Secretary: Linda Young **(T)** 01928 590 508 **(E)**

Chairman: Tony Riley **Manager:** Simon Burton **Prog Ed:** Paul Watson

Ground: Pavilions Sports Complex, Sandy Lane, Weston Point, Runcorn WA7 4EX **(T)** 01928 590 508

Capacity: **Seats:** Yes **Covered:** Yes **Midweek Matchday:** Monday **Clubhouse:** Yes

Colours(change): All royal blue (All green)
Previous Names: Mond Rangers 1967-2005 (Amalgamated with ICI Weston 1974-75).
Previous Leagues: Runcorn Sunday 1967-73, Warrington & District 1973-84, West Cheshire 1984-10.
Records: **Att:** 665 v Runcorn Linnets, NWCL Premier April 2013.
Senior Honours: West Cheshire League Division Two 2006-07. Runcorn Senior Cup 2004-05, 05-06, 07-08.

10 YEAR RECORD

04-05	05-06	06-07	07-08	08-09	09-10	10-11	11-12	12-13	13-14
WCh2 2	WCh1 15	WCh2 1	WCh1 3	WCh1 4	WCh1 3	NWC1 2	NWCP 2	NWCP 4	NWCP 5

SILSDEN

Founded: 1904 Nickname:

Secretary: John Barclay **(T)** 01535 656213 **(E)**

Chairman: Sean McNulty **Manager:** Andy Geary **Prog Ed:** Peter Hanson

Ground: Keighley Road, Keighley Road, Silsden, BD20 0EH **(T)**

Capacity: **Seats:** Yes **Covered:** Yes **Midweek Matchday:** Wednesday **Clubhouse:** Yes

Colours(change): All red (Royal blue & white stripes/white/white).
Previous Names: Reformed in 1980.
Previous Leagues: Craven & District. West Riding County Amateur.
Records: **Att:** 1,564 v FC United of Manchester- March 2007
Senior Honours:

10 YEAR RECORD

04-05	05-06	06-07	07-08	08-09	09-10	10-11	11-12	12-13	13-14
NWC2 2	NWC1 14	NWC1 14	NWC1 11	NWCP 9	NWCP 14	NWCP 16	NWCP 12	NWCP 18	NWCP 15

SQUIRES GATE

Founded: 1948 Nickname:

Secretary: John Maguire **(T)** 01253 348 512 **(E)**

Chairman: Stuart Hopwood **Manager:** Dave McCann **Prog Ed:** Albert Cooper

Ground: School Road, Marton, Blackpool, Lancs FY4 5DS **(T)** 01253 348 512

Capacity: 1,000 **Seats:** 100 **Covered:** Yes **Midweek Matchday:** Tuesday **Clubhouse:** Yes

Colours(change): All blue. (All red)
Previous Names: Squires Gate British Legion FC >1953.
Previous Leagues: Blackpool & District Amateur 1958-61. West Lancashire 1961-91.
Records: **Att:** 600 v Everton, friendly 1995.
Senior Honours:

10 YEAR RECORD

04-05	05-06	06-07	07-08	08-09	09-10	10-11	11-12	12-13	13-14
NWC1 17	NWC1 13	NWC1 18	NWC1 6	NWCP 10	NWCP 13	NWCP 9	NWCP 16	NWCP 21	NWCP 19

ST HELENS TOWN

Founded: 1946 Nickname: Town

Secretary: Jeff Voller **(T)** 0151 222 2963 **(E)**

Chairman: John McKiernan **Manager:** Ian Price **Prog Ed:** Jeff Voller

Ground: Ashton Athletic FC, Downall Green, Ashton in Makerfield WN4 0NR **(T)** 01942 716 360

Capacity: 600 **Seats:** 100 **Covered:** 300 **Midweek Matchday:** Tuesday **Clubhouse:** Yes

Colours(change): Red & white stripes/red/red & white (Sky blue/navy/navy).
Previous Names: St Helen's Town formed in 1903 folded in 1923.
Previous Leagues: Liverpool Co Comb 1946-49 Lancs Comb 49-75, Chesh Co. 75-82
Records: **Att:** 8,500 v Manchester City 27/04/50. **Goalscorer:** S. Pennington. **App:** Alan Wellens
Senior Honours: Lancashire Combination 1971-72 . FA Vase 1986-87.

10 YEAR RECORD

04-05	05-06	06-07	07-08	08-09	09-10	10-11	11-12	12-13	13-14
NWC1 3	NWC1 8	NWC1 19	NWC1 14	NWCP 16	NWCP 9	NWCP 17	NWCP 21	NWCP 19	NWCP 17

STOCKPORT SPORTS

Founded: 1970 Nickname: The Saxons

Secretary: Chris Culkin **(T)** **(E)**

Chairman: Wayne Ashworth **Manager:** Asa Crowe **Prog Ed:** Rob Clarke

Ground: Stockport Sports Village, Lambeth Grove, Woodley SK6 1QX **(T)**

Capacity: 2,300 **Seats:** 300 **Covered:** Yes **Midweek Matchday:** Tuesday **Clubhouse:** Yes

Colours(change): White/navy/white (All maroon)
Previous Names: Woodley Athletic. Woodley Sports > 2012.
Previous Leagues: Lancashire and Cheshire, Manchester, North West Counties
Records: 1,500 v Stockport County
Senior Honours: North West Counties League Division 2 1999-2000.
Cheshire Senior Cup 2003-04.

10 YEAR RECORD

04-05	05-06	06-07	07-08	08-09	09-10	10-11	11-12	12-13	13-14
NP 1 11	NP 1 4	NP 1 10	NP1N 17	NP1N 13	NP1N 19	NP1N 11	NP1N 8	NWCP 16	NWCP 11

WEST DIDSBURY & CHORLTON

Founded: 1908 Nickname: West

Secretary: Rob Turley **(T)** 07891 298 441 **(E)**
Chairman: Glyn Meacher **Prog Ed:** John Churchman
Ground: The Recreation Ground, End of Brookburn Road, Chorlton, Manchester M21 8FF **(T)** 07891 298 441
Capacity: **Seats:** Yes **Covered:** Yes **Midweek Matchday:** Tuesday **Clubhouse:** Yes

Colours(change): White with black trim/black/black (All sky blue)
Previous Names: Christ Church AFC 1908-1920. West Didsbury AFC 1920-2003.
Previous Leagues: Manchester Alliance pre 1920. Lancashire & Cheshire Amateur 1920-2006. Manchester 2006-2012.
Records: 230 v Altrincham pre-season July 2003.
Senior Honours: Manchester League Division One 2010-11. NWCL Division One Trophy 2012-13.

10 YEAR RECORD

04-05	05-06	06-07	07-08	08-09	09-10	10-11	11-12	12-13	13-14
						Manc1 1	MancP 7	NCE1 3	NWCP 12

WINSFORD UNITED

Founded: 1883 Nickname: Blues

Secretary: Robert Astles **(T)** 01606 558 447 **(E)**
Chairman: Mark Loveless **Manager:** Rob Byrne **Prog Ed:** Robert Astles
Ground: The Barton Stadium, Kingsway, Winsford, Cheshire CW7 3AE **(T)** 01606 558 447
Capacity: 6,000 **Seats:** 250 **Covered:** 5,000 **Midweek Matchday:** Tuesday **Clubhouse:** Yes **Shop:** Yes

Colours(change): Navy & royal blue/royal blue/royal blue (All black & yellow).
Previous Names: Over Wanderers 1883-1887
Previous Leagues: The Combination 1902-04. Cheshire County 1919-40, 47-82. N.P.L. 1987-01
Records: **Att:** 8,000 v Witton Albion, 1947. **Goalscorer:** Graham Smith 66 **Apps:** Edward Harrop 400
Senior Honours: Cheshire League 1920-21, 76-77. Cheshire Senior Cup 1958-59, 79-80, 92-93.
North West Counties League Division Two 2006-07.

10 YEAR RECORD

04-05	05-06	06-07	07-08	08-09	09-10	10-11	11-12	12-13	13-14
NWC2 3	NWC2 4	NWC2 1	NWC1 10	NWCP 19	NWCP 19	NWCP 3	NWCP 7	NWCP 5	NWCP 14

A.F.C. DARWEN
Founded: 2009 (reformed) Nickname:

Secretary: Sarah Hindle **(T)** **(E)**
Chairman: Wayne Wild **Manager:** Kenny Langford **Prog Ed:** Steve Hart
Ground: Anchor Ground, Anchor Road, Darwen, Lancs, BB3 0BB. **(T)** 01254 776 193
Colours(change): All red (All navy & yellow)

ADDITIONAL INFORMATION: Original club founded in 1875.
Previous Leagues: West Lancashire. Football Alliance. Football League. Lancashire Combination. Cheshire League.
Record Att: 14,000 v Blackburn Rovers 1882.
Honours: Lancashire League 1902. North West Counties League Cup 1983. North West Alliance Cup 1996.

ASHTON TOWN
Founded: 1962 Nickname:

Secretary: Stephen Ochwat **(T)** **(E)**
Chairman: Mark Hayes **Manager:** John Brownrigg **Prog Ed:** Billy Bristow
Ground: The AM Property Group Std, Edge Green St, Ashton-in-Makerfield, Wigan, WN4 8SL **(T)** 01942 701 483
Colours(change): Red & white stripes/red/red (Yellow/green/yellow)

ADDITIONAL INFORMATION:
Record Att: 1,865 v FC United of Manchester 2007.
Honours: Warrington League Guardian Cup.

ATHERTON COLLIERIES
Founded: 1916 Nickname: The Colts

Secretary: Emil Anderson **(T)** **(E)**
Chairman: Paul Gregory **Manager:** Steve Pilling **Prog Ed:** Joseph Gibbons
Ground: Alder Street, Atherton, Greater Manchester M46 9EY **(T)** 07968 548 056
Colours(change): Black & white stripes/black/black (All blue)

ADDITIONAL INFORMATION:
Record Att: 3,300 in Lancashire Combination 1920's.
Honours: North West Counties League Division 3 1986-87.

ATHERTON L.R.
Founded: 1956 Nickname: The Panthers

Secretary: Ronnie Wilcox **(T)** **(E)**
Chairman: Jane Wilcock **Manager:** Michael Clegg **Prog Ed:** Jeff Gorse
Ground: Crilly Park, Spa Road, Atherton, Manchester M46 9JX **(T)** 01942883950/07921579532 **Capacity:** 3,000
Colours(change): Royal blue & yellow/royal blue/yellow (White/navy blue/white).

ADDITIONAL INFORMATION: **Record Att:** 2,300 v Aldershot Town F.A. Vase Q-Final replay 93-94. **Goalscorer:** Shaun Parker **App:** Jim Evans
Honours: North West Counties League 1992-93, 93-94. Champions Trophy 1992-93, 93-94.

BARNTON
Founded: 1946 Nickname:

Secretary: Ken Stevenson **(T)** **(E)**
Chairman: Ian Ross **Manager:** Andy Burgess **Prog Ed:** Ken Stevenson
Ground: Tonwfield, Townfield Lane, Barnton, Cheshire CW8 4LH **(T)** 07709 585 644
Colours(change): White & black stripes/white/white (All orange)

ADDITIONAL INFORMATION: **Previous Leagues:** Mid-Cheshire. Cheshire. **Record Att:** 260 v Bramwell, 25/04/98.
League Honours: Mid-Cheshire 1979-80, 82-83, 88-89, 96-97, 97-98, 98-99, 99-2000, 2000-01, 01-02, 02-03, 04-05.
Cheshire Division Two 2012-13. **FA/County Cups:** Cheshire Amateur Cup 1948-49, 68-69, 2001-02, 03-04.
Cheshire Senior Cup 1980-81. Mid-Cheshire Challenge Cup 2013-14.

CAMMELL LAIRD
Founded: 1907 Nickname: Lairds

Secretary: Anthony R Woods **(T)** 07931 761 429 **(E)** toddywood@hotmail.com
Chairman: Frank Games Tony Sullivan
Ground: MBS Stadium, St Peter's Road, Rock Ferry, Birkenhead CH42 1PY **(T)** 0151 645 3121 **Capacity:** 2,000
Colours(change): All royal blue (Red & black/red/black)

ADDITIONAL INFORMATION: **Record Att:** 1,700 v Harwich & Parkeston - FA Vase 5th Round 1990-91
Honours: North West Counties League Division 2, League Cup and Trophy 2004-05, Division 1 2005-06.
West Cheshire League x19 (Most recently 2000-01). Cheshire Amateur Cup x11.
Wirral Senior Cup.

CHADDERTON
Founded: 1947 Nickname: Chaddy

Secretary: David Shepherd **(T)** 0161 624 9733 **(E)**
Chairman: Bob Sopel **Manager:** Steve Patterson & Mark Cook **Prog Ed:** Bob Sopel
Ground: Andrew Street, Chadderton, Oldham, Greater Manchester OL9 0JT **(T)** 07506 104 005
Colours(change): All red & black (All orange)

ADDITIONAL INFORMATION:
Record Att: 2,352 v FC United of Manchester 2006.
Honours: Gilgryst Cup 1969-70. Umbro International Cup 1999-00.

CHEADLE TOWN
Founded: 1961 Nickname:

Secretary: Stuart Crawford **(T)** **(E)**
Chairman: Chris Davies **Manager:** Steve Brokenbrow **Prog Ed:** Stuart Crawford
Ground: Park Road Stadium, Cheadle, Cheshire, SK8 2AN **(T)** 0161 428 2510
Colours(change): All green (Gold & dark blue/dark blue/dark blue).

ADDITIONAL INFORMATION:
Record Att: 3,377 v FC United of Manchester (At Stockport County). **Goalscorer:** Peter Tilley. **Apps:** John McArdle.
Honours: Manchester Division One 1979-80.

DAISY HILL
Founded: 1894 Nickname:

Secretary: Robert Naylor **(T)** 01942 818 544 **(E)**
Chairman: Graham Follows **Manager:** Craig Thomas **Prog Ed:** Craig Thomas
Ground: New Sirs, St James Street, Westhoughton, Bolton, BL5 2EB **(T)** 01942 818 544
Colours(change): All royal blue (All red)

ADDITIONAL INFORMATION:
Reformed in 1952.
Record Att: 2,000 v Horwich RMI, Westhoughton Charity Cup Final 1979-80. **Goalscorer & Apps:** Alan Roscoe 300gls, 450app
Honours: Bolton Combination Premier Division 1962-63, 72-73, 75-76, 77-78.

ECCLESHALL
Founded: 1971 Nickname:

Secretary: Jim tunney **(T)** **(E)**
Chairman: Andy Mapperson **Manager:** Shaun Hollinshead **Prog Ed:** Richard Marsh
Ground: Pershall Park, Chester Road, Eccleshall, ST21 6NE **(T)** 01785 851 351 (MD)
Colours(change): Navy & sky blue/navy/navy (All maroon)

ADDITIONAL INFORMATION:
Record Att: 2,011 v FC United of Manchester November 2005.
Honours: Midland League 1990, 2002-03.

HANLEY TOWN
Founded: 1966 Nickname:

Secretary: Roy Penhallurick **(T)** **(E)**
Chairman: Paul Legge **Manager:** Dave Price **Prog Ed:** Kelsey Stair
Ground: Abbey Lane, Bucknall, Stoke-on-Trent, Staffordshire ST2 9AJ **(T)** 07599 397 053
Colours(change): All blue (Red/black & white/white)

ADDITIONAL INFORMATION:
Previous Leagues: Staffordshire County Senior.
Record: Att: 1,000.
Honours: Staffordshire County Senior League 2012-13.

HOLKER OLD BOYS
Founded: 1936 Nickname: Cobs

Secretary: John Adams **(T)** 01229 828 176 **(E)**
Chairman: Dick John **Manager:** Gary Fawcett **Prog Ed:** Dave Smith
Ground: Rakesmoor, Rakesmoor Lane, Hawcoat, Barrow-in-Furness, LA14 4QB **(T)** 01229 828 176
Colours(change): Green & white/green/green & white (All blue)

ADDITIONAL INFORMATION:
Record Att: 2,303 v FC United of Manchester FA Cup at Craven Park 2005-06. **Goalscorer:** Dave Conlin.
Honours: West Lancashire League 1986-87.

IRLAM
Founded: 1969 Nickname:

Secretary: Warren Dodd **(T)** 07718 756402/07969 946277 **(E)**
Chairman: Ron Parker **Manager:** Steve Nixon **Prog Ed:** Warren Dodd
Ground: Silver Street, Irlam, Manchester M44 6HR **(T)** 07718756402~07969946277
Colours(change): All blue (Red/black/black)

ADDITIONAL INFORMATION:
Previous Name: Mitchell Shackleton. **Previous League:** Manchester Amateur. Manchester.
Record Att: 1,600 v Hallam FA Vase.

LITHERLAND REMYCA
Founded: 1959 Nickname:

Secretary: Dave Evans **(T)** **(E)**
Chairman: Don Rimmer **Manager:** Dave Abraham **Prog Ed:** Gary Langley
Ground: Litherland Sports Park, Boundary Road, Litherland, Liverpool L21 7LA **(T)** 0151 288 6288
Colours(change): Red/black/red (All orange)

ADDITIONAL INFORMATION: **Previous Leagues:** I Zingari. Liverpool County.
League Honours: Zingari Premier Division 1987-88, 93-94, 94-95, 95-96, Division Two 2005-06.
Liverpool County Division Two 2006-07.
FA/County Cups: Lancashire Amateur Cup 1990-91.

NORTHWICH FLIXTON VILLA

Founded: 2005 Nickname:

Secretary: Shannon Rushe **(T)** **(E)**
Chairman: Andrew Fetherston **Manager:** Wale Ajet **Prog Ed:** Noel McCourt
Ground: Valley Road, Flixton Manchester M41 8RQ **(T)** 0161 748 2903
Colours(change): Green & white/white/green (Yellow/blue/blue).

ADDITIONAL INFORMATION: Previous Name: Northwich Villa 2005-13.
Previous Lge: Cheshire 2005-11. **Record Att:** 149 v Northwich Victoria 2009.
League honours: Cheshire League Division One 2008-09, Division One Cup 2009-10.
FA/County Cups: Mid-Cheshire Cup 2010-11.

OLDHAM BORO

Founded: 1964 Nickname:

Secretary: Charlotte Mills **(T)** **(E)**
Chairman: Mark Kilgannon **Manager:** Tony Mills **Prog Ed:** Russ Gratton
Ground: Seel Park (Mossley FC), Market Street, Mossley OL5 0ES **(T)**
Colours(change): Orange/black/black (Blue & black/black/black)

ADDITIONAL INFORMATION: Previous Leagues: Lancashire Combination. Manchester Amateur.
Record Att: 1,767 v FC United of Manchester 2006.
League honours: North West Counties Division Two 1997-98.

ROCHDALE TOWN

Founded: 1924 Nickname:

Secretary: Deborah Hibbert **(T)** 01706 527103 **(E)**
Chairman: Mark Canning **Manager:** Mark Canning **Prog Ed:** Deborah Hibbert
Ground: Mayfield Sports Centre, Keswick Street, Castleton, Rochdale OL11 3AG **(T)** 01706 527 103
Colours(change): Blue & black/white/blue (White/blue/white).

ADDITIONAL INFORMATION: Previous Leagues: Rochdale Alliance. Manchester League.
Record Att: 2,473 v FC United of Manchester (at Radcliffe Borough).
League honours: Manchester Division One 1986-87.

WIDNES

Founded: 2003 Nickname:

Secretary: Bill Morley **(T)** **(E)**
Chairman: David Day **Manager:** Steve Hill **Prog Ed:** Bill Morley
Ground: Select Security Stadium, Lower House Lane, Widnes, Cheshire WA8 7DZ **(T)** 0151 510 6000
Colours(change): White/black/white (All royal blue)

ADDITIONAL INFORMATION: Previous Names: Formed as Dragons AFC in 2003. Widnes Dragons > 2012. Widnes Vikings 2012-14.
Previous Leagues: West Cheshire League.

WIGAN ROBIN PARK

Founded: 2005 Nickname: Robins

Secretary: Taffy Roberts **(T)** 01942 404 950 **(E)**
Chairman: Darryl Picton **Manager:** John Neafcy **Prog Ed:** Margaret Wood
Ground: Robin Park Arena, Loire Drive, Robin Park, Wigan, WN5 0UH **(T)** 01942 404 950
Colours(change): Red & white/red/red (Blue & white/blue/blue)

ADDITIONAL INFORMATION: Record Att: 298 v AFC Liverpool 31/03/09.
League Honours: Manchester Premier 2007-08. North West Counties Division One 2011-12.

GROUND DIRECTIONS

1874 NORTHWICH - The Barton Stadium, Kingsway, Winsford, Cheshire. CW7 3AE. 01606 558447
From M6 junction 18, follow A54 through Middlewich for approx 3 miles, bear right at roundabout at Winsford Railway Station, follow road for approx 1 mile, turn right into Kingsway, ground is on the right.

AFC BLACKPOOL-Mechanics Ground, Jepson Way, Common Edge Road, Blackpool, Lancashire FY4 5DY. 01253 761721
M6 to M55, exit at junction 4. At roundabout turn left along A583 to traffic lights, turn right into Whitehill Road, to traffic lights (2 miles). Go straight across the main road into Jepson Way, ground at top.

AFC LIVERPOOL-Valerie Park, Eaton Street, Prescot, Merseyside, L34 6ND. 0151 430 0507
From North: M6 to Junction 26, onto M58 to Junction 3. Follow A570 to junction with A580 (East Lancs Road). (Approach junction in right hand lane of the two lanes going straight on). Cross A580 and take first road on right (Bleak Hill Road). Follow this road through to Prescot (2 miles). At traffic lights turn right, straight on at large roundabout (do not follow route onto Prescot by-pass) and right at next lights. 100 yards turn right at Hope and Anchor pub into Hope Street. Club will be in sight at bottom of road. From South: M6 to Junction 21a (M62 junction 10). Follow M62 towards Liverpool, to junction 7. Follow A57 to Rainhill and Prescot. Through traffic lights at Fusilier pub, 100 yards turn right at Hope and Anchor pub (as above). From East: Follow M62 as described in 'From South' or A580 East Lancs Road to Junction with A570 (Rainford by-pass), turn left and take first right. Follow route as 'From North'

ABBEY HEY-The Abbey Stadium, Goredale Avenue, Gorton, Manchester M18 7HD. 0161 231 7147
M60 to junction 24, take A57 to Manchester City Centre for approx 1 mile, at first set of major traffic lights (MacDonalds on right) pass through for approx 300yards, turn left immediatley before overhead railway bridge (A.H.F.C. sign) into Woodland Avenue. Take first right, pass under railway bridge, turn first left into Goredale Avenue.

ALSAGER TOWN-The Town Ground, Woodland Court, Alsager, Staffs, ST7 2DP 01270 882336
M6 to Junction16, A500 towards Stoke, leave A500 at 2nd exit (A34 to Congleton) at 2nd set of traffic lights on A34 turn left for Alsager, turn right opposite Caradon/Twyfords Factory (500 Yards), into Moorhouse Ave, West Grove mile on right. No available parking within the ground.
ASHTON ATHLETIC-Brocstedes Park, Downall Green, Ashton in Makerfield. WN4 0NR. 01942 716360
M6 northbound to junction 25, follow the slip road to the island and turn right A49, proceed for approx 0.50 mile turning right into Soughers Lane. At the T junction turn right into Downall Green Road and go over the motorway bridge passing a church on your right. Turn 2nd right into Booths Brow Road and turn 2nd right again into Brocstedes Road which is a narrow street. After 200 yards turn right down a shale road into the car park and ground.
From The North: M6 southbound to junction 24, proceed on to the slip road keeping in the right hand lane, turn right go over the motorway bridge and immediately re-enter the M6 Northbound for approximately 100 yards. Leave at junction 25,Follow the slip road to the island and turn right A49, proceed for approx 0.50 mile turning right into Soughers Lane. At the T junction turn right into Downall Green Road and go over the motorway bridge passing a church on your right. Turn 2nd right into Booths Brow Road and turn 2nd right again into Brocstedes Road which is a narrow street. After 200 yards turn right down a shale road into the car park and ground.
BACUP BOROUGH-Brian Boys Stadium, Cowtoot Lane, Blackthorn, Bacup, Lancashire. OL13 8EE. 01706 878655
From M62, take M66 onto A681, through Rawtenstall to Bacup Town Centre, turn left onto the A671 towards Burnley, after approx. 300 yards turn right immediately before the Irwell Inn climbing Cooper Street, turn right into Blackthorn Lane, then first left into Cowtoot Lane to ground.
BARNOLDSWICK TOWN-Silentnight Stadium, West Close Road, Barnoldswick, Colne, BB18 5EW. 01282 815817
ravelling from Blackburn to Colne on M65 to end, straight on at roundabout onto Vivary Way onto North Valley Road. Through two sets of traffic lights to roundabout, turn left to Barnoldswick. Straight on till you come to roundabout in Kelbrook turn left to Barnoldswick.On entering Barnoldswick straight ahead at traffic lights, straight ahead at mini roundabout. Travel through built up area past Fosters Arms pub on left set back. Take first right onto Greenberfield Lane, travel 50 yards take middle single track (signposted) travel to bottom of track and bare right to car park at rear of ground.
Travelling from Barrow on A59 from Gisburn towards Skipton turn right at Barnoldswick signpost. Travel approx 2 miles taking 1st left onto Greenberfield Lane, travel 50 yards take middle single track (signposted) travel to bottom of track bare right to car park at rear of ground.
If using a SatNav use postcode BB18 5LJ.
BOOTLE-Delta Taxi Stadium, Vestey Road, off Bridle Road, Bootle, L30 4UN. 0151 525 4796 or 07852 742790
At Liverpool end of M57and M58 follow signs for Liverpool (A59 (S)), for 1 1/2 miles. At Aintree racecourse on left and Aintree Train Station on right ,turn right at lights into Park Lane. Turn left at second set of lights into Bridle Road. After 200 yards turn left at lights into Vestey Estate , ground 200 yards.
COLNE-The XLCR Stadium, Harrison Drive, Colne, Lancashire. BB8 9SL. 01282 862545
Follow M65 to end of motorway. Turn left and follow signs for Skipton and Keighley, continue to roundabout, take 1st left up Harrison Drive, across small roundabout, follow road to ground.
CONGLETON TOWN-Booth Street, off Crescent Road, Congleton, Cheshire, CW12 4DG. 01260 274460
On approach to Congleton from M6, past Waggon & Horses Pub, at 1st roundabout 2nd exit, past fire station, 2nd right into Booth Street. Ground at top of road.
GLOSSOP NORTH END-Surrey Street, Glossop, Derbyshire. SK13 7AJ. 01457 855469
A57 to Glossop, turn left at traffic lights (near Tesco sign), Glossopbrook Road. Follow road to top of hill. Ground on right.
MAINE ROAD-Brantingham Road, Chorlton-cum-Hardy, Manchester. M21 0TT. 0161 861 0344
M60 to junction 7, A56 towards Manchester. At traffic island follow signs for Manchester United, Lancs CC, turn right at next set of traffic lights signposted A5145 (Chorlton-cum-Hardy/Stockport), through next set of traffic lights. Take left fork at Y junction (traffic lights) onto A6010 (Wilbraham Road) to Chorlton. Through traffic lights (ignore pedestrian lights) for approx 1 mile. Left at next traffic lights into Withington Road, first left into Brantingham Road. Ground 300 yards on left. From North: M60 clockwise to junction 5 onto A5103 towards Manchester Centre for approx 2 miles, turn left at traffic lights (Wilbraham Road) A6010, then right at 2nd set of lights (Withington Road), first left into Brantingham Road. Ground 300 yards on left.
NELSON-Victoria Park, Lomeshaye Way, Nelson, Lancs BB9 7BN. 01282 613 820
M65 to Junction 13. Take first left (A6068 Fence), 2nd left (B6249 Nelson), the 2nd right, signposted Lomeshaye Village, to ground.
RUNCORN LINNETS-Millbank Linnets Stadium, Murdishaw Ave, Runcorn, Cheshire. WA7 6HP. 07050 801733 (Clubline)
orth East-M56 junction 12 take A557 Widnes/Northwich. At Roundabout take 1st Exit onto A557 heading Frodsham A56, go through 1 roundabout. Turn left at Chester Rd/A56, turn left at Chester Rd/A533. At the r'about, take the 2nd exit onto Murdishaw Ave. Destination on the Right. Head West on M56 towards Exit 11. At junction 11, take the A56 exit to Preston Brook/Daresbury. At the roundabout take the 1st exit onto Chester Rd/A56 heading to Preston Brook/Daresbury. Continue to follow Chester Rd, go through 2 roundabouts.At the roundabout take the 2nd exit onto Murdishaw Ave. Destination on the right.
RUNCORN TOWN-Pavilions Sports Complex, Sandy Lane, Weston Point, Runcorn, Cheshire WA7 4EX. 01928 590 508
M56 J12. Head towards Liverpool. Come off at 4th exit (Runcorn Docks), turn left at the top of slip road, left at T-Junction, then left into Pavilions. M62 J7. Head towards Runcorn. When crossing Runcorn Bridge, stay in the right hand lane. Follow road around and come off at second exit (Runcorn Docks). Turn right at the top of slip road, left at T-Junction, then left into Pavilions.
SILSDEN-Keighley Road, Silsden, BD20 0EH
A629 Skipton to Keighley road, take A6034, ground in on the left after the golf driving range.
SQUIRES GATE-School Road, Marton, Blackpool, FY4 5DS. 01253 798583
From M55: At the end of the M55 (J4), continue along dual carriageway (A5230), and bear left at major roundabout, staying on A5230. At second traffic lights, turn left onto B5261. After passing Shovels pub on left, turn left at lights, and first car park is on left after approx 50 yards. Parking is also available down the lane leading to the Club, on your left, after another 40 yards. If both these are full, parking is also available on the Shovels car park, or on the car park adjacent to the playing fields (turn right at the lights after passing the pub).
ST HELENS TOWN - Ashton Athletic FC, Downall Green, Ashton in Makerfield WN4 0NR. 01942 716 360
From South: M6 to junction 25, turn right onto A49, after 1/2 mile turn right into Soughers Lane, at T junction turn right into Downall Green Road, pass over M6 and turn 2nd right into Boothbrow Road, turn 2nd right in Brocstedes Road.
STOCKPORT SPORTS-Lambeth Grove, Woodley, Stockport, Cheshire SK6 1QX
Take exit 25 toward BREDBURY. At the roundabout, take the 2nd exit onto Ashton Rd (A560). Turn slight left-Continue on A560. Turn right at Lower Bents Lane. Continue on School Brow (B6104). Turn slight left at Stockport Rd (B6104). Turn right at Green Lane.
WEST DIDSBURY & CHORLTON-The Recreation Ground, End of Brookburn Road, Chorlton, Manchester M21 8FF-07891 298441
From the M60 take junction 5 onto Princess Road towards city centre. Turn left at Christie Fields offices/Premier Inn onto Barlow Moor Road and continue past Chorlton Park to Chorlton bus station. Turn left into Beech Road, then 2nd left into Reynard Road and continue past the Chorltonville sign passing over 5 speed ramps as far as Brookburn Primary School. Turn left into Brookburn Road and continue to the end of the cul de sac, through the gateway and down the tarmac access which leads into the ground. From Stretford follow Edge Lane and turn right into St Clements Road at church. Continue through Chorlton Green and pass graveyard on left and then Bowling Green PH. Go past school and turn immediately right and continue to end of Brookburn Road as above. There is car parking within the grounds of the club, but restricted access for coaches.

Premier Division continued...

WINSFORD UNITED-The Barton Stadium, Kingsway, Winsford, Cheshire. CW7 3AE. 01606 558447
From M6 junction 18, follow A54 through Middlewich for approx 3 miles, bear right at roundabout at Winsford Railway Station, follow road for approx 1 mile, turn right into Kingsway, ground is on the right.

DIVISION ONE

AFC DARWEN-Anchor Ground, Anchor Road, Darwen, Lancs, BB3 0BB. 07989-744584
Leave M65 at Junction 4. At traffic lights turn left onto A666 (signposted Darwen). After approx ? mile turn left between Anchor Car Sales and the Anchor Pub. Bare right and ground 200 yards on left.

ASHTON TOWN-Edge Green Street, Ashton-in-Makerfield, Wigan, Greater Manchester. WN4 8SL. 01942 701483
M6 to Junction 23, A49 to Ashton-in-Makerfield. Turn right at the traffic lights onto the A58 towards Bolton. After approx. three quarters of a mile, turn right into Golbourne Road. After 200 yards turn right into Edge Green Street. Ground at bottom of street.

ATHERTON COLLIERIES-Alder Street, Atherton, Greater Manchester. M46 9EY. 07968 548056
M61 to junction 5, follow sign for Westhoughton, turn left onto A6, turn right onto A579 (Newbrook Road/Bolton Road) into Atherton. At first set of traffic lights turn left into High Street, then second left into Alder Street to ground.

ATHERTON L.R.-Crilly Park, Spa Road, Atherton, Greater Manchester. M46 9XG. 01942 883950
M61 to Junction 5, follow signs for Westhoughton, turn left onto A6, turn right at first lights into Newbrook Road, then turn right into Upton Road, passing Atherton Central Station. Turn left into Springfield Road and left again into Hillside Road into Spa Road and ground.

BARNTON - Tonwfield, Townfield Lane, Barnton, Cheshire CW8 4LH 07709 585 644
Turn off the A533 (Northwich to Runcorn) at the Beech Tree Inn (Barnton Village) into Beech Lane. Turn right at the 'T' junction with Townfield Lane - the ground is 200 yards on the left signed Memorial Hall. Note parking restrictions well signed.

CAMMELL LAIRD - MBS Stadium, St Peter's Road, Rock Ferry, Birkenhead CH42 1PY 0151 645 3121
From Chester: M563/A41 towards Birkenhead, at New ferry signpost take the B5136 towards New ferry, approx 1 mile, turn right at traffic island into Proctor Road, ground at the bottom of Proctor Road. From Liverpool: Take the Birkenhead Tunnel, A41 for approx 1 mile, take the B5136 signposted New Ferry / Rock Ferry at big round-a-bout. Follow until the 2nd set of traffic lights, turn left, then first right into St Peters Road, ground at the bottom of the road on the left.

CHADDERTON-Andrew Street, Chadderton, Oldham, Greater Manchester OL9 0JT. 0161 624 9733
M62 to junction 20, following A627(M) towards Manchester. Motorway becomes a dual carriageway, turn left at first major traffic lights (A699) Middleton Road, then second left into Burnley Street, Andrew Street at the end.

CHEADLE TOWN-Park Road Stadium, Cheadle, Cheshire, SK8 2AN. 0161 428 2510
M60 to junction 2 (formerly M63 junction 11), follow A560 to Cheadle. Go through first main set of traffic lights and then first left after shops into Park Road. Ground at end of road.

DAISY HILL-New Sirs, St James Street, Westhoughton, Bolton, BL5 2EB. 01942 818 544.
M61 to junction 5, A58 (Snydale Way/Park Road) for one and a half mile, left into Leigh Road (B5235) for 1 mile to Daisy Hill. Turn right into village 200 yards after mini roundabout, then left between church and school into St James Street. Ground 250 yards on left.

ECCLESHALL-Pershall Park, Chester Road, Eccleshall, ST21 6NE. 01785-851351 (Match Days Only)
M6 to junction 14 then A5013 to Eccleshall, right at mini-roundabout and then left at next mini-roundabout into High Street B5026, ground 1 mile on right.
M6 to junction 15, then A519 to Eccleshall right at mini-roundabout to High Street B5026, ground 1 mile on right.

HANLEY TOWN - Abbey Lane, Bucknall, Stoke-on-Trent, Staffordshire ST2 8AJ.

HOLKER OLD BOYS-Rakesmoor, Rakesmoor Lane, Hawcoat, Barrow-in-Furness, Cumbria. LA14 4QB. 01229 828176
M6 to junction 36. Take the A590 all the way to Barrow-in-Furness. At the borough boundary continue along the A590. After 1? miles you will pass the Kimberley Clark paper mill on your right. Immediately after passing the paper mill turn left into Bank Lane, signposted "Barrow Golf Club" on the left hand side of the A590 and "Hawcoat yard on the right hand side of the A590. Follow this road to the T- junction at the top of the hill outside the Golf Club. Turn left here into Rakesmoor Lane the ground is 200 yds. down the road on the right. *Please be advised that Rakesmoor Lane beyond the ground is a single-track road and as such is unsuitable for coaches. It is not possible to turn a coach into the ground when approaching from that direction.*

IRLAM-Irlam Football Club, Silver Street, Irlam, Manchester M44 6HR. 07718 756402/07969 946277
From Peel Green Roundabout (M60 Junction 11), take A57 to Irlam, and then B5320 into Lower Irlam. After passing Morsons Project, turn right into Silver Street, at Nags Head Pub. The ground is situated at the bottom of Silver Street on the right hand side.

LITHERLAND REMYCA.- Litherland Sports Park, Boundary Road, Litherland, Liverpool L21 7LA. 0151 288 6288.
End of M57/M58 ALONG Dunningsbridge Road towards Docks, Turn Right at Junction of Bootle Golf Course on the Right hand side into Boundary Road, 2nd turning on the left into sports park.

NORTHWICH FLIXTON VILLA-Valley Road, Flixton, Manchester M41 8RQ-0161 748 2903
Leave M60 junction 10, take the B5214, signposted Urmston, at the second roundabout take third exit, take right only lane on the exit in Davyhulme Road, follow this road to Valley Road, just after the left hand bend after 1 1/2 miles. The ground is at the other end of the road.

OLDHAM BORO - Atherton Collieries FC, Alder Street, Atherton M46 9EY
See Atherton Collieries above.

ROCHDALE TOWN - Mayfield Sports Centre, Keswick Street, Castleton, Rochdale. OL11 3AG. 01706 527 103
M62 to junction 20, follow A627M towards Rochdale. Keep right on A627M and turn right at traffic lights at BMW Garage go to next roundabout, take 2nd exit into Queensway towards Castleton and through the Industrial Estate. Turn Right at traffic lights into Manchester Road, A664. Go past Castleton Rail station and turn left at Fairwell Inn, into Keswick St, go through new housing estate to ground --- Rochdale Town FC ground is next to Castlehawk Golf Club.

WIDNES VIKINGS - Select Security Stadium, Lower House Lane, Widnes, Cheshire WA8 7DZ. 0151 510 6000
From the M62 - Exit at Junction 7, take A568 dual carriageway towards Widnes (Following brown signs to Halton Stadium). Keep right after junction onto Ashley Way (A562). Take 2nd exit off roundabout (McDonald's on the right). Take 2nd exit off mini-roundabout into Lowerhouse Lane.
From Runcorn & the South: Cross Widnes/Runcorn Bridge (A533). Follow signs to Widnes (A562). At roundabout take 3rd exit towards Widnes Town Centre. Take first left following brown signs to Halton Stadium(McDonald's on the right). Take 2nd exit off mini-roundabout into Lowerhouse Lane.

WIGAN ROBIN PARK-Robin Park Arena, Loire Drive, Robin Park, Wigan, WN5 0UH. 01942 404 950
M6 J25 take road into Wigan and follow signs for the DW Stadium (Wigan Athletic) Ground is next to stadium, behind Wickes DIY store on the retail park.

NORTHERN COUNTIES EAST LEAGUE

Sponsored by: Toolstation
Founded: 1982
Recent Champions:
2009: Mickleover Sports
2010: Bridlington Town
2011: Farsley
2012: Retford United
2013: Scarborough Athletic
ncel.org.uk

PREMIER DIVISION	P	W	D	L	F	A	GD	Pts
1 (P) Brighouse Town	44	32	5	7	138	50	88	101
2 Tadcaster Albion	44	29	10	5	116	48	68	97
3 Barton Town Old Boys	44	29	6	9	124	52	72	93
4 Worksop Parramore	44	29	5	10	105	53	52	92
5 Basford United	44	26	6	12	97	57	40	84
6 Albion Sports	44	25	5	14	109	77	32	80
7 Pickering Town	44	25	4	15	126	78	48	79
8 Heanor Town	44	24	5	15	113	81	32	77
9 Retford United	44	22	10	12	95	52	43	76
10 Athersley Recreation	44	23	7	14	103	73	30	76
11 Long Eaton United	44	23	3	18	77	64	13	72
12 Bridlington Town	44	21	8	15	100	82	18	71
13 Thackley	44	22	4	18	92	83	9	70
14 Garforth Town	44	19	7	18	85	70	15	64
15 Maltby Main (-12pts)	44	19	3	22	88	87	1	48
16 Glasshoughton Welfare	44	14	6	24	59	98	-39	48
17 Staveley Miners Welfare (-1pt)	44	13	6	25	79	98	-19	44
18 Armthorpe Welfare	44	11	7	26	59	97	-38	40
19 Parkgate	44	10	9	25	57	86	-29	39
20 Liversedge	44	10	6	28	58	115	-57	36
21 Nostell Miners Welfare	44	6	4	34	46	134	-88	22
22 (R) Winterton Rangers	44	5	6	33	35	139	-104	21
23 (R) Lincoln Moorlands Railway	44	2	2	40	27	214	-187	8

LEAGUE CUP

PRELIMINARY ROUND

Rossington Main	v	Louth Town	4-3
Selby Town	v	Clipstone	2-1
Teversal	v	Dinnington Town	4-1
Appleby Frodingham	v	Hemsworth Miners Welfare	2-3
Cleethorpes Town	v	Hallam	3-1
Pontefract Collieries	v	Shirebrook Town	1-3

ROUND 1

AFC Emley	v	Teversal	3-2
Dronfield Town	v	Shaw Lane Aquaforce	2-1
Bottesford Town	v	Hall Road Rangers	1-2
Shirebrook Town	v	Worsbrough Bridge Athletic	1-2 aet
Hemsworth Miners Welfare	v	Grimsby Borough	0-0 4-2p
Rossington Main	v	Knaresborough Town	0-6
Yorkshire Amateur	v	Selby Town	2-3 aet
Eccleshill United	v	Cleethorpes Town	20/11

ROUND 2

Glasshoughton Welfare	v	Tadcaster Albion	2-4
Garforth Town	v	Hall Road Rangers	4-2
AFC Emley	v	Retford United	1-2
Hemsworth Miners Welfare	v	Knaresborough Town	1-2
Lincoln Moorlands Railway	v	Winterton Rangers	2-5
Liversedge	v	Dronfield Town	3-5
Armthorpe Welfare	v	Thackley	0-2
Parkgate	v	Heanor Town	0-8
Pickering Town	v	Worsbrough Bridge Ath.	2-1 aet
Selby Town	v	Maltby Main	2-2, 4-2p
Nostell Miners Welfare	v	Staveley Miners Welfare	4-0
Albion Sports	v	Eccleshill or Cleethorpes	1-3
Basford United	v	Brighouse Town	1-3
Worksop Parramore	v	Barton Town Old Boys	3-1
Bridlington Town	v	Athersley Recreation	2-0

ROUND 3

Eccleshill United	v	Tadcaster Albion	2-1
Brighouse Town	v	Long Eaton United	2-2, 9-10p
Brindlington Town	v	Worksop Parramore	1-0
Garforth Town	v	Knaresborough Town	0-2
Heanor Town	v	Thackley	4-1
Nostell Miners Welfare	v	Selby Town	2-1
Pickering Town	v	Dronfield Town	4-2
Winterton Rangers	v	Retford United	0-4

QUARTER FINALS

Pickering Town	v	Long Eaton United	1-2
Retford United	v	Heanor Town	0-2
Nostell Miners Welfare	v	Eccleshill United	0-1
Bridlington Town	v	Knaresborough Town	0-1

SEMI FINALS

Long Eaton United	v	Knaresborough Town	0-1
Heanor Town	v	Eccleshill United	3-4

FINAL

Eccleshill United	v	Knaresborough Town	2-2, 2-4p

PREMIER DIVISION	1	2	3	4	5	6	7	8	9	10	11	12	13	14	15	16	17	18	19	20	21	22	23
1 Albion Sports		8–1	5–2	1–1	1–3	3–3	2–5	3–2	1–1	3–2	6–1	3–2	2–3	2–3	4–1	2–0	3–2	0–3	6–2	1–1	1–5	4–0	0–2
2 Armthorpe Welfare	0–4		1–2	3–2	2–1	0–3	1–5	1–2	1–1	1–3	4–1	1–1	1–2	2–0	2–1	2–3	2–6	0–0	2–0	0–1	2–0	3–1	2–3
3 Athersley Recreation	1–0	2–0		1–3	0–4	3–3	2–3	0–1	5–2	3–2	8–1	2–2	4–1	4–6	6–2	1–0	1–1	0–2	0–0	0–1	2–4	2–1	1–2
4 Barton Town Old Boys	2–3	4–0	1–2		1–1	2–1	2–1	2–0	3–2	4–0	5–0	5–0	2–0	2–0	2–0	0–0	4–0	1–0	2–0	2–2	4–0	8–0	2–4
5 Basford United	2–1	3–1	3–1	0–2		3–1	1–0	2–1	0–1	5–1	7–0	0–0	2–0	0–5	3–2	4–2	1–1	2–2	4–1	5–3	4–1	1–0	1–0
6 Bridlington Town	0–4	2–0	3–2	2–1	0–7		2–6	3–0	3–2	5–0	10–0	3–3	1–2	2–0	7–2	0–0	0–1	1–2	4–0	0–4	2–1	1–1	0–2
7 Brighouse Town	3–4	4–1	2–2	1–1	2–1	0–1		4–1	3–1	0–0	4–0	3–0	3–1	2–0	2–0	4–0	3–2	2–0	2–2	8–1	4–2	9–1	5–2
8 Garforth Town	1–1	0–2	1–2	1–4	1–1	5–2	2–3		1–2	1–3	6–2	2–2	3–2	3–0	2–0	3–2	3–5	2–2	2–0	0–0	1–2	1–0	1–1
9 Glasshoughton Welfare	1–2	1–0	0–2	0–6	2–3	0–2	1–3	3–3		1–2	3–0	2–0	0–3	3–3	6–1	0–2	1–2	1–6	2–0	0–2	0–3	3–1	0–2
10 Heanor Town	2–1	3–1	2–2	4–0	0–3	2–1	1–0	2–1	1–3		6–0	5–0	4–3	1–1	4–2	2–0	5–2	1–1	1–2	1–3	4–3	5–0	0–3
11 Lincoln Moorlands Railway	0–4	0–4	0–4	1–6	0–2	2–4	0–9	0–5	1–1	1–8		0–2	0–2	1–3	1–2	0–4	0–6	0–6	0–8	1–8	1–6	0–2	2–1
12 Liversedge	4–5	3–2	0–4	3–1	0–1	0–3	1–5	0–4	1–3	1–4	4–3		0–4	1–4	1–1	2–1	1–3	0–3	3–5	0–4	1–2	2–0	1–7
13 Long Eaton United	3–1	1–0	0–2	1–3	2–3	1–1	0–4	0–2	7–0	1–1	6–0	3–1		1–3	2–1	2–0	2–1	0–1	1–0	0–1	3–2	2–0	0–1
14 Maltby Main	0–2	6–0	5–1	1–5	3–1	1–3	0–2	1–0	1–2	4–2	6–2	0–3	0–2		3–1	2–1	1–2	0–3	2–1	1–2	1–4	2–1	1–3
15 Nostell Miners Welfare	1–2	0–0	0–6	1–4	0–6	4–2	0–2	2–0	2–4	4–9	1–0	1–0	0–1	1–5		0–1	0–4	0–5	2–2	0–5	2–0	0–2	2–4
16 Parkgate	3–1	2–2	1–4	2–6	3–1	3–4	3–0	1–3	0–0	1–5	1–2	0–1	0–0	0–3	2–0		0–4	2–1	3–1	2–2	2–2	2–2	1–3
17 Pickering Town	0–3	3–0	3–2	2–6	2–2	1–2	1–3	0–2	6–0	3–0	11–0	0–4	0–3	6–1	3–0	2–1		2–1	6–2	0–4	7–2	7–1	3–1
18 Retford United	5–1	1–1	2–3	5–1	1–0	1–0	2–5	2–1	1–2	0–4	5–0	2–0	0–1	2–0	6–1	1–1	2–1		1–4	1–1	0–1	4–0	0–0
19 Staveley Miners Welfare	0–2	1–1	0–4	1–3	2–0	3–3	2–4	2–4	1–0	2–5	5–1	8–2	1–2	3–1	2–0	1–0	2–4	3–2		2–4	1–3	4–0	0–3
20 Tadcaster Albion	0–1	4–1	2–2	2–1	5–0	2–2	1–3	4–1	0–1	2–0	6–0	2–0	4–1	2–0	4–1	4–3	5–0	1–1	1–1		2–0	6–0	1–0
21 Thackley	1–2	3–2	0–2	2–3	2–1	1–2	1–1	0–1	1–0	2–1	8–1	2–1	5–2	3–2	3–1	4–2	1–1	2–5	1–0	2–2		2–0	0–3
22 Winterton Rangers	1–3	0–4	0–2	0–3	0–3	2–4	0–3	0–7	3–1	1–5	1–1	1–5	1–4	1–5	1–1	2–0	1–8	1–1	2–1	2–3	1–2		1–1
23 Worksop Parramore	2–1	4–3	1–2	2–2	2–0	3–2	2–1	0–2	8–0	4–0	4–1	1–0	3–0	2–2	4–3	1–0	0–2	3–4	3–1	1–2	3–1	4–0	

DIVISION ONE	P	W	D	L	F	A	GD	Pts
1 (P) Cleethorpes Town	42	28	7	7	104	50	54	91
2 (P) Shaw Lane Aquaforce	42	27	6	9	125	45	80	87
3 Bottesford Town	42	24	12	6	101	43	58	84
4 Eccleshill United	42	24	9	9	94	51	43	81
5 Shirebrook Town	42	22	10	10	90	46	44	76
6 Knaresborough Town	42	23	7	12	92	52	40	76
7 Clipstone	42	22	10	10	88	63	25	76
8 AFC Emley	42	21	11	10	85	65	20	74
9 Pontefract Collieries	42	20	13	9	96	58	38	73
10 Worsbrough Bridge Athletic	42	20	13	9	94	62	32	73
11 Hall Road Rangers	42	17	7	18	94	89	5	58
12 Selby Town (-3pts)	42	19	3	20	77	86	-9	57
13 Rossington Main	42	18	3	21	65	89	-24	57
14 Dronfield Town	42	13	12	17	71	85	-14	51
15 Teversal	42	14	8	20	76	91	-15	50
16 Grimsby Borough (-3pts)	42	15	4	23	73	98	-25	46
17 Hemsworth Miners Welfare	42	12	9	21	61	79	-18	45
18 Dinnington Town	42	12	4	26	59	111	-52	40
19 Yorkshire Amateur	42	11	5	26	59	99	-40	38
20 Hallam	42	6	11	25	58	99	-41	29
21 Louth Town	42	6	2	34	49	136	-87	20
22 (R) Appleby Frodingham	42	3	4	35	50	164	-114	13

DIVISION ONE	1	2	3	4	5	6	7	8	9	10	11	12	13	14	15	16	17	18	19	20	21	22
1 AFC Emley		4–1	3–3	2–0	2–2	2–4	1–0	2–5	7–2	2–1	4–3	1–0	2–0	2–1	2–2	1–1	0–1	3–2	1–1	2–3	1–1	2–2
2 Appleby Frodingham	0–4		0–7	1–3	2–2	2–3	1–3	0–2	0–4	1–5	5–6	0–3	0–4	3–1	2–2	0–2	1–5	0–3	2–9	0–1	1–6	0–2
3 Bottesford Town	4–0	3–2		3–0	0–1	3–2	1–1	1–0	2–0	4–0	3–1	3–1	1–0	6–0	4–1	0–0	0–2	1–2	2–1	2–2	2–0	6–0
4 Cleethorpes Town	3–1	7–1	0–3		2–1	8–0	5–0	0–2	2–1	6–1	4–1	3–3	1–2	2–0	4–4	0–1	4–2	3–2	2–1	3–0	1–0	9–1
5 Clipstone Welfare	3–4	1–0	0–0	0–2		1–1	2–0	2–4	2–1	2–1	4–0	2–1	1–3	4–1	1–3	3–1	2–0	0–3	2–0	3–3	5–1	1–0
6 Dinnington Town	0–2	7–3	1–7	0–2	0–1		0–1	1–4	1–2	2–6	0–0	0–0	0–2	4–1	2–3	1–2	0–2	1–0	0–3	1–0	2–2	3–0
7 Dronfield Town	2–2	2–1	3–3	1–3	1–1	0–3		2–2	4–0	2–1	3–1	1–2	2–2	1–1	1–1	1–2	6–2	1–6	0–1	2–0	2–2	0–3
8 Eccleshill United	2–2	3–3	3–0	1–2	3–3	2–1	2–0		2–3	2–0	4–4	1–0	1–3	5–0	2–2	2–1	4–0	0–2	1–1	0–2	2–2	3–1
9 Grimsby Borough	1–2	1–2	3–0	1–1	3–2	2–3	1–3	0–2		1–3	0–2	3–2	2–1	3–2	2–4	5–1	4–2	0–4	1–1	3–0	1–2	1–0
10 Hall Road Rangers	0–3	2–2	2–2	1–3	3–5	5–2	2–3	0–1	3–1		8–3	5–2	1–1	2–0	3–2	6–1	4–2	1–3	1–4	1–1	3–1	2–3
11 Hallam	0–2	5–0	2–2	1–1	1–2	0–1	2–2	0–4	1–1	1–2		2–1	0–2	1–2	1–1	3–1	1–3	0–4	0–2	1–1	2–2	2–3
12 Hemsworth Miners Welfare	1–0	1–2	0–0	0–1	1–1	1–2	2–2	0–4	2–3	2–2	5–2		1–4	2–1	0–4	0–3	1–3	1–3	1–1	2–5	0–1	6–0
13 Knaresborough Town	2–1	9–1	0–2	2–2	1–4	4–0	4–1	0–0	2–1	4–0	2–1	1–2		3–1	1–3	0–2	3–1	0–1	1–2	4–0	1–2	0–0
14 Louth Town	0–1	2–0	1–2	1–3	1–3	4–3	1–3	0–4	0–5	0–3	2–1	0–1	2–5		2–7	4–1	3–1	1–3	0–6	3–11	0–4	1–1
15 Pontefract Collieries	1–3	5–1	1–1	4–0	2–1	5–0	1–1	0–2	3–1	3–0	1–0	0–1	0–1	2–1		6–1	1–1	0–1	3–0	2–0	2–1	3–1
16 Rossington Main	2–0	2–1	1–2	2–3	2–5	4–0	3–2	1–7	4–1	1–1	3–2	2–0	2–4	2–0	3–2		0–2	0–4	0–2	2–1	2–3	1–0
17 Selby Town	2–2	4–3	4–3	1–2	0–2	3–2	3–1	0–1	2–1	0–2	4–0	1–3	1–0	4–2	3–3	1–3		3–1	4–2	1–3	1–4	3–1
18 Shaw Lane Aquaforce	0–2	2–0	1–1	1–1	3–4	9–0	1–3	2–0	13–0	4–2	2–0	3–3	2–2	11–2	1–1	4–1	4–0		2–1	7–2	1–2	2–1
19 Shirebrook Town	2–1	12–0	0–4	1–2	1–1	2–1	4–1	2–1	1–1	3–0	2–0	4–1	2–2	3–2	0–0	2–0	2–0	1–2		3–1	1–2	2–0
20 Teversal	1–2	5–2	0–4	0–3	2–1	1–3	4–3	0–1	4–3	1–3	1–1	1–2	1–2	5–3	1–1	2–1	2–0	0–4	0–0		1–1	5–0
21 Worsbrough Bridge Athletic	1–1	4–0	2–2	0–0	3–3	7–2	1–2	4–0	4–1	0–3	3–3	2–2	2–3	2–0	1–0	4–1	3–2	1–0	1–1	4–1		1–3
22 Yorkshire Amateur	3–4	6–4	0–2	0–1	1–2	3–0	5–2	2–3	0–3	3–3	0–1	0–2	1–5	1–0	4–5	2–0	0–1	0–0	0–1	5–2	1–5	

CLUB MOVEMENTS

Premier Division - In: Cleethorpes Town (P). Handsworth Parramore (NC - from Worksop Parramore). Shaw Lane Aquaforce (P). Wakefield (R - Northern Premier Div.1 North). Worksop Town (formerly Northern Premier Prem Div.).

Out: Basford United (S - Midland League). Brighouse Town (P - Northern Premier Div.1 North). Lincoln Moorlands Railway (R). Long Eaton (S - Midland League). Worksop Parramore (NC - to Handsworth Parramore). Winterton Rangers (R).

Division One - In: AFC Mansfield (P - Central Midlands North). Lincoln Moorlands Railway (R). Penistone Church (P - Sheffield County League). Winterton Rangers (R).

Out: Appleby Frodingham (R - Central Midlands North). Cleethorpes Town (P). Dinnington Town (F). Shaw Lane Aquaforce (P).

ALBION SPORTS

Founded: 1974 Nickname: Lions

Secretary: Jaj Singh **(T)** **(E)** info@albionsports.co.uk
Chairman: Kultar Singh **Manager:** Kulwinder Singh Sandhu **Prog Ed:** Peter Cusack
Ground: Throstle Nest, Newlands, Farsley, Leeds, LS28 5BE. **(T)** 0113 255 7292
Capacity: 3,500 **Seats:** 1,750 **Covered:** 1,750 **Midweek Matchday:** Wednesday **Clubhouse:** n/a

Colours(change): Yellow/royal blue/royal blue (All red)
Previous Names:
Previous Leagues: Bradford Amateur Sunday 1974-2007. West Riding County Amateur 2007-11.
Records:
Senior Honours: Northern Counties East Division One 2012-13.

10 YEAR RECORD

04-05	05-06	06-07	07-08	08-09	09-10	10-11	11-12	12-13	13-14
							NCE1 4	NCE1 1	NCEP 6

ARMTHORPE WELFARE

Founded: 1926 Nickname: Wellie

Secretary: Craig Trewick **(T)** **(E)** armthorpe.welfare@hotmail.co.uk
Chairman: Steve Taylor **Manager:** Brian Johnston **Prog Ed:** Phil Wiffen
Ground: Welfare Ground, Church Street, Armthorpe, Doncaster DN3 3AG **(T)** 07775 797 013 (Match days only)
Capacity: 2,500 **Seats:** 250 **Covered:** 400 **Midweek Matchday:** Tuesday **Clubhouse:** No **Shop:** No

Colours(change): All royal blue (All red)
Previous Names:
Previous Leagues: Doncaster Senior 1976-83.
Records: **Att:** 2,000 v Doncaster R Charity Match 1985-86. **Goalscorer:** Martin Johnson. **App:** Gary Leighton. **Win:** 10-0. **Defeat:** 1-7
Senior Honours: West Riding Challenge Cup 1981-82, 82-83. Northern Counties East Division 1 Central 1984-85.

10 YEAR RECORD

04-05	05-06	06-07	07-08	08-09	09-10	10-11	11-12	12-13	13-14
NCEP 18	NCEP 10	NCEP 13	NCEP 9	NCEP 15	NCEP 3	NCEP 13	NCEP 13	NCEP 20	NCEP 18

ATHERSLEY RECREATION

Founded: 1979 Nickname: Penguins

Secretary: Peter Goodlad **(T)** **(E)** petegoodlad@yahoo.co.uk
Chairman: Dennis Hirst **Manager:** Peter Goodlad **Prog Ed:** Jamie Wallman
Ground: Sheerien Park, Ollerton Road, Athersley North, Barnsley, S71 3DP **(T)** 07910 121 070
Capacity: 2,000 **Seats:** 150 **Covered:** 420 **Midweek Matchday:** Tuesday **Clubhouse:** No **Shop:** Yes

Colours(change): White & black/black/black (All orange)
Previous Names:
Previous Leagues: Sheffield & Hallamshire County Senior 1997-2012.
Records:
Senior Honours: Sheffield & Hallamshire County Senior Division Two 1997-98, Premier Division 1999-2000, 03-04, 04-05, 06-07, 08-09, 11-12

10 YEAR RECORD

04-05	05-06	06-07	07-08	08-09	09-10	10-11	11-12	12-13	13-14
SHSP 1	SHSP 2	SHSP 1	SHSP 2	SHSP 1	SHSP 2	SHSP 2	SHSP 1	NCE1 2	NCEP 10

BARTON TOWN OLD BOYS

Founded: 1995 Nickname: Swans

Secretary: Peter Mitchell **(T)** 01652 635 838 **(E)** bartontown@gmail.com
Chairman: Richard Nicholls **Manager:** Dave Anderson **Prog Ed:** David Paylor
Ground: The Euronics Ground, Marsh Lane, Barton-on-Humber **(T)** 01652 661 871
Capacity: 3,000 **Seats:** 240 **Covered:** 540 **Midweek Matchday:** Tuesday **Clubhouse:** Yes **Shop:** No

Colours(change): Sky blue/navy blue/sky blue (Orange/black/orange)
Previous Names:
Previous Leagues: Lincolnshire 1995-2000, Humber (Founder member) 2000-01, Central Midlands 2001-07.
Records:
Senior Honours: Lincolnshire League 1996-97. Central Midlands League Supreme Division 2005-06.

10 YEAR RECORD

04-05	05-06	06-07	07-08	08-09	09-10	10-11	11-12	12-13	13-14
CM Su 4	CM Su 1	CM Su 2	NCE1 9	NCE1 5	NCE1 6	NCE1 2	NCEP 11	NCEP 8	NCEP 3

BRIDLINGTON TOWN

Founded: 1918 Nickname: Seasiders

Secretary: Gavin Branton **(T)** **(E)** gavinbranton@yahoo.co.uk
Chairman: Peter Smurthwaite **Manager:** Gary Allanson **Prog Ed:** Dom Taylor & Joe Gillott
Ground: Neil Hudgell Law Stadium, Queensgate, Bridlington YO16 7LN **(T)** 01262 606 879
Capacity: 3,000 **Seats:** 500 **Covered:** 500 **Midweek Matchday:** Tuesday **Clubhouse:** Yes **Shop:** Yes

Colours(change): All red (All white).
Previous Names: Original Bridlington Town folded in 1994. Greyhound FC changed to Bridlington Town.
Previous Leagues: Yorkshire 1924-39, 59-82, NCEL 1982-90, 99-2003, Northern Premier 1990-94, 2003-08
Records: **Att:** 1,006 v FC Utd of Manchester, NPLD1N, 03.11.07. **Goalscorer:** Neil Grimson. **Apps:** Neil Grimson - 200+ (1987-97).
Senior Honours: FA Vase 1992-93. Northern Counties East 2002-03, 2009-10, Division 1 1992-93.
ERCFA Senior Cup 1921,22,23,31,53,57,61,65,67,70,72,89,93,05

10 YEAR RECORD

04-05	05-06	06-07	07-08	08-09	09-10	10-11	11-12	12-13	13-14
NP P 20	NP 1 11	NP 1 24	NP1N 18	NCEP 4	NCEP 1	NCEP 3	NCEP 2	NCEP 3	NCEP 12

CLEETHORPES TOWN

Founded: 1998 Nickname: The Owls

Secretary: Jevon Southam **(T)** **(E)** jevon.southam@yahoo.com
Chairman: David Patterson **Manager:** Marcus Newell **Prog Ed:** Craig Kendall
Ground: The Bradley Football Development Centre Bradley Road, Grimsby, DN37 0AG **(T)**
Capacity: 1,000 **Seats:** 180 **Covered:** 200 **Midweek Matchday:** Wednesday **Clubhouse:** Yes

Colours(change): Blue & black/black/blue (Red & black/white/red)
Previous Names: LSS Lucarlys 1998-2008.
Previous Leagues: Lincolnshire 2003-05, 10-12. Central Midlands 2005-06. Humber Premier 2006-09.
Records:
Senior Honours: Lincolnshire League 2011-12. Northern Counties East Division One 2013-14.

10 YEAR RECORD

04-05	05-06	06-07	07-08	08-09	09-10	10-11	11-12	12-13	13-14
Lincs 4	CM P 4	Humb 3	Humb 10	Humb 9	Humb dnf	Lincs 3	Lincs 1	NCE1 4	NCE1 1

GARFORTH TOWN

Founded: 1964 Nickname: The Miners

Secretary: Paul Bracewell **(T)** **(E)** enquiries@garforthtown.net
Chairman: Brian Close **Manager:** Graham Nicholas **Prog Ed:** Chris Mather
Ground: Cedar Ridge, Garforth, Leeds LS25 2PF **(T)** 0113 287 7145
Capacity: 3,000 **Seats:** 278 **Covered:** 200 **Midweek Matchday:** Tuesday **Clubhouse:** Yes **Shop:** No

Colours(change): Yellow & blue/blue/blue (Purple/white/black)
Previous Names: Garforth Miners 1964-85
Previous Leagues: Leeds Sunday Comb. 1972-76, West Yorkshire 1976-78, Yorkshire 1978-82, NCE 1982-2007. Northern Premier 2007-13.
Records: 2,428 v Chester, NPL Div.1 North, 29/04/2011
Senior Honours: Northern Counties East Division 1 1997-98

10 YEAR RECORD

04-05	05-06	06-07	07-08	08-09	09-10	10-11	11-12	12-13	13-14
NCE1 2	NCEP 10	NCEP 4	NP1N 10	NP1N 16	NP1N 20	NP1N 13	NP1N 5	NP1N 22	NCEP 14

GLASSHOUGHTON WELFARE

Founded: 1964 Nickname: Welfare or Blues

Secretary: Frank MacLachlan **(T)** 07710 586 447 **(E)** frank.maclachlan@btinternet.com
Chairman: Phil Riding **Manager:** John Mills **Prog Ed:** Nigel Lea
Ground: Glasshoughton Centre, Leeds Road, Glasshoughton, Castleford WF10 4PF **(T)** 01977 511 234
Capacity: 2,000 **Seats:** 0 **Covered:** 250 **Midweek Matchday:** Tuesday **Clubhouse:** Yes **Shop:** Yes

Colours(change): Royal blue & white/blue/blue (Green & white/white/white)
Previous Names:
Previous Leagues: West Yorkshire.
Records: **Att:** 350 v Ossett Albion, Presidents Cup 1998. **Win:** 8-1. **Defeat:** 0-8.
Senior Honours: West Riding County Cup 1993-94.

10 YEAR RECORD

04-05	05-06	06-07	07-08	08-09	09-10	10-11	11-12	12-13	13-14
NCEP 11	NCEP 16	NCEP 16	NCEP 20	NCE1 19	NCE1 13	NCE1 7	NCE1 2	NCEP 16	NCEP 16

HANDSWORTH PARRAMORE

Founded: 1936 Nickname: Amber Parras

Secretary: Max Ross **(T)** **(E)**
Chairman: Pete Whitehead **Manager:** Russell Eagle **Prog Ed:** Paul Hill
Ground: The Windsor Foodservice Stadium, Sandy Land, Worksop S80 1UJ **(T)** 01909 479 955
Capacity: 2,500 **Seats:** 200 **Covered:** 750 **Midweek Matchday:** Tuesday **Clubhouse:** Yes **Shop:** No

Colours(change): Amber & black/black/black (All sky blue)
Previous Names: Parramore Sports > 2010. Sheffield Parramore 2010-2011. Worksop Parramore 2011-14.
Previous Leagues: Sheffield & Hallam County Senior 1985-2008. Central Midlands 2008-11
Records:
Senior Honours: Central Midland League Supreme Division 2010-11.

10 YEAR RECORD

04-05	05-06	06-07	07-08	08-09	09-10	10-11	11-12	12-13	13-14
SHS1 12	SHS1 6	SHS1 13	SHS1 5	CM P 4	CM Su 8	CM Su 1	NCE1 3	NCEP 7	NCEP 4

HEANOR TOWN

Founded: 1883 Nickname: The Lions

Secretary: Amanda Jones **(T)** **(E)** heanortownfc@hotmail.co.uk
Chairman: Geoff Clarence **Manager:** Glen Clarence **Prog Ed:** Tony Squires
Ground: The Town Ground, Mayfield Avenue, Heanor DE75 7EN **(T)** 01773 713 742
Capacity: 2,700 **Seats:** 100 **Covered:** 1,000 **Midweek Matchday:** Tuesday **Clubhouse:** Yes

Colours(change): White/black/white (Red/white/red)
Previous Names: None
Previous Leagues: Midland 1961-72. Central Midlands 1986-2008. East Midlands Counties 2008-12.
Records:
Senior Honours: East Midlands Counties 2011-12.

10 YEAR RECORD

04-05	05-06	06-07	07-08	08-09	09-10	10-11	11-12	12-13	13-14
CM Su 19	CM Su 6	CM Su 14	CM Su 11	EMC 12	EMC 7	EMC 3	EMC 1	NCEP 11	NCEP 8

LIVERSEDGE

Founded: 1910 Nickname: Sedge

Secretary: John Bryan Oakes **(T)** 01274 683 327 **(E)** bryan@bryanoakes.orangehome.co.uk
Chairman: Vacant **Manager:** David Thompson **Prog Ed:** Andrew Taylor
Ground: Clayborn Ground, Quaker Lane, Hightown Road, Cleckheaton WF15 8DF **(T)** 01274 862 108
Capacity: 2,000 **Seats:** 250 **Covered:** 750 **Midweek Matchday:** Tuesday **Clubhouse:** Yes **Shop:** Yes

Colours(change): Sky blue & navy/navy/navy (All red).
Previous Names:
Previous Leagues: Spen Valley, West Riding Co. Amateur 1922-72, Yorkshire 1972-82
Records: **Att:** 986 v Thackley **Goalscorer:** Denis Charlesworth **App:** Barry Palmer
Senior Honours: Northern Counties East League Cup 2005-06.

10 YEAR RECORD

04-05	05-06	06-07	07-08	08-09	09-10	10-11	11-12	12-13	13-14
NCEP 6	NCEP 2	NCEP 12	NCEP 4	NCEP 14	NCEP 9	NCEP 17	NCEP 14	NCEP 15	NCEP 20

MALTBY MAIN

Founded: 1916 Nickname: Miners

Secretary: John Mills **(T)** 01709 813 609 **(E)** john_mills_@hotmail.co.uk
Chairman: Mark Ducker **Manager:** Mick Norbury **Prog Ed:** Nick Dunhill
Ground: Muglet Lane, Maltby, Rotherham S66 7JQ. **(T)** 07795 693 683
Capacity: 2,000 **Seats:** 150 **Covered:** 300 **Midweek Matchday:** Wednesday **Clubhouse:** No **Shop:** No

Colours(change): Red/black/black (All blue)
Previous Names: Maltby Miners Welfare 1970-96
Previous Leagues: Sheffield Co Senior. Yorkshire League 1973-82
Records: **Att:** 1,500 v Sheffield Weds (friendly) 1991-92
Senior Honours: Sheffield & Hallamshire Senior Cup1977-78

10 YEAR RECORD

04-05	05-06	06-07	07-08	08-09	09-10	10-11	11-12	12-13	13-14
NCEP 19	NCEP 18	NCEP 10	NCEP 18	NCEP 12	NCEP 16	NCEP 11	NCEP 18	NCEP 14	NCEP 15

NOSTELL MINERS WELFARE

Founded: 1928 Nickname: The Welfare

Secretary: Granville Marshall **(T)** 01924 864 462 **(E)** nostwellmwfc@hotmail.com
Chairman: Granville Marshall **Manager:** Darren Holmes **Prog Ed:** Malcolm Lamb
Ground: The Welfare Grd, Crofton Co. Centre, Middle Lane, New Crofton WF4 1LB **(T)** 01924 866 010
Capacity: 1500 **Seats:** 100 **Covered:** 200 **Midweek Matchday:** Tuesday **Clubhouse:** Yes

Colours(change): Yellow/black/black. (All blue).
Previous Names:
Previous Leagues: Wakefield 1950-66, 69-82, West Yorkshire 1966-68, 82-2006
Records:
Senior Honours: West Yorkshire Premier Division 2004-05

10 YEAR RECORD

04-05	05-06	06-07	07-08	08-09	09-10	10-11	11-12	12-13	13-14
WYkP 1	WYkP 3	NCE1 4	NCE1 5	NCEP 13	NCEP 18	NCEP 9	NCEP 17	NCEP 18	NCEP 21

PARKGATE

Founded: 1969 Nickname: The Steelmen

Secretary: Bruce Bickerdike **(T)** **(E)** secretary@parkgatefc.co.uk
Chairman: Albert Dudill **Manager:** Steve Adams **Prog Ed:** Dave Platts
Ground: Roundwood Sports Complex, Green Lane, Rawmarsh, S62 6LA **(T)** 01709 826 600
Capacity: 1,000 **Seats:** 300 **Covered:** 300 **Midweek Matchday:** Tuesday **Clubhouse:** Yes **Shop:** No

Colours(change): All Red & White. (All blue).
Previous Names: BSC Parkgate (1982-86) RES Parkgate (pre 1994)
Previous Leagues: BIR County Senior. Yorkshire 1974-82.
Records: **Att:** v Worksop 1982
Senior Honours: N.C.E. Division One 2006-07. Wilkinson Sword Trophy 2006-07.

10 YEAR RECORD

04-05	05-06	06-07	07-08	08-09	09-10	10-11	11-12	12-13	13-14
NCE1 12	NCE1 6	NCE1 1	NCEP 8	NCEP 11	NCEP 14	NCEP 2	NCEP 7	NCEP 9	NCEP 19

PICKERING TOWN

Founded: 1888 Nickname: Pikes

Secretary: Stephen Chapman **(T)** **(E)** usherso8@btinternet.com
Chairman: Keith Usher **Manager:** Mitch Cook **Prog Ed:** Peter Dickinson
Ground: Recreation Club, off Mill Lane, Malton Road, Pickering YO18 7DB **(T)** 01751 473 317
Capacity: 2,000 **Seats:** 200 **Covered:** 500 **Midweek Matchday:** Tuesday **Clubhouse:** Yes **Shop:** Yes

Colours(change): All blue. (All yellow).
Previous Names:
Previous Leagues: Beckett, York & District, Scarborough & District, Yorkshire 1972-1982
Records: **Att:** 1,412 v Notts County (friendly) in August 1991
Senior Honours: N.C.E. Div 2 1987-88. North Riding Cup 1990-91. Wilkinson Sword Trophy 2000-01. North Riding Senior Cup 2012-13.

10 YEAR RECORD

04-05	05-06	06-07	07-08	08-09	09-10	10-11	11-12	12-13	13-14
NCEP 5	NCEP 6	NCEP 9	NCEP 3	NCEP 9	NCEP 7	NCEP 7	NCEP 12	NCEP 5	NCEP 7

RETFORD UNITED

Founded: 1987 Nickname: The Badgers

Secretary: Annie Knight **(T)** **(E)** retfordunited@sky.com
Chairman: Daniel Keeton **Manager:** Paul Ward **Prog Ed:** Jon Knight
Ground: Cannon Park, Leverton Road, Retford, Notts DN22 6QF **(T)** 01777 710 300
Capacity: 2,000 **Seats:** 150 **Covered:** 200 **Midweek Matchday:** Tuesday **Clubhouse:** Yes **Shop:** Yes

Colours(change): Black and white/black/black (All orange)
Previous Names:
Previous Leagues: Gainsborough & Dist, Nottinghamshire Alliance > 2001, Central Midlands 2001-04, Northern Counties East 2004-07
Records: 1,527 v Doncaster Rovers - Friendly July 2006. **Goalscorer:** Steve Hardy - 272 (1987-97). **Apps:** Andy Powell - 126 (1990-95)
Senior Honours: Notts All. Div.1 2000-01. Central Mids Div.1 01-02, Supreme Division 03-04, Lge Cup 01-02, 03-04, Floodlit Cup 03-04.
N.C.E. Prem. Division 06-07, 11-12, N.P.L. Div.1S 07-08, 08-09. Notts Sen. Cup 08-09.

10 YEAR RECORD

04-05	05-06	06-07	07-08	08-09	09-10	10-11	11-12	12-13	13-14
NCE1 8	NCE1 2	NCEP 1	NP1S 1	NP1S 1	NP P 6	NP P 22	NCEP 1	NCEP 4	NCEP 9

SHAW LANE AQUAFORCE

Founded: 1991 | Nickname: The Ducks

Secretary: David Exley **(T)** **(E)** dave.exley50@hotmail.co.uk

Chairman: Craig Wood **Manager:** Craig Elliot **Prog Ed:** Karen Parton

Ground: Shaw Lane, Barnsley, S70 6HZ **(T)** 01226 203 509

Capacity: **Seats:** **Covered:** **Midweek Matchday:** **Clubhouse:**

Colours(change): Blue & white/blue/blue (Yellow/black/black)
Previous Names: Worsborough Common 1991-2011. Aqua Force Barnsley 2011-2012.
Previous Leagues: Sheffield & Hallamshire County 2011-13.
Records:
Senior Honours: Sheffield & Hallamshire County Senior League 2012-13.

10 YEAR RECORD

04-05	05-06	06-07	07-08	08-09	09-10	10-11	11-12	12-13	13-14
		SHS1 4	SHS1 7	SHS1 4	SHS1 8	SHS1 9	SHS1 2	SHSP 1	NCE1 2

STAVELEY MINERS WELFARE

Founded: 1989 | Nickname: The Welfare

Secretary: Ele Reaney **(T)** 01246 471 441 **(E)** staveleyed@hotmail.co.uk

Chairman: Terry Damms **Manager:** James Colliver **Prog Ed:** Ele Reaney

Ground: Inkersall Road, Staveley, Chesterfield, S43 3JL **(T)** 01246 471 441

Capacity: 5,000 **Seats:** 220 **Covered:** 400 **Midweek Matchday:** Wednesday **Clubhouse:** Yes **Shop:** Yes

Colours(change): Blue & white/blue/blue (All yellow)
Previous Names: None
Previous Leagues: Chesterfield & District Amateur 1989-91. County Senior 1991-93.
Records: 910 v Chesterfield, Friendly, 20/07/2011. **Goalscorer:** Ryan Damms - 102. **Apps:** Shane Turner.
Senior Honours: County Senior League Division 3 1991-92, Division 2 1992-93. N.C.E. Division One 2010-11.

10 YEAR RECORD

04-05	05-06	06-07	07-08	08-09	09-10	10-11	11-12	12-13	13-14
NCE1 9	NCE1 10	NCE1 6	NCE1 8	NCE1 4	NCE1 4	NCE1 1	NCEP 5	NCEP 13	NCEP 17

TADCASTER ALBION

Founded: 1892 | Nickname: The Brewers

Secretary: Howard Clarke **(T)** **(E)** sandra.clarke1@tiscali.co.uk

Chairman: Matthew Gore **Manager:** Paul Marshall **Prog Ed:** Mark Murphy & Karen Faughey

Ground: i2i Stadium, Ings Lane, Tadcaster LS24 9AY **(T)** 07518 820 730 or 07949 452 054

Capacity: 1,500 **Seats:** 150 **Covered:** 400 **Midweek Matchday:** Tuesday **Clubhouse:** Yes **Shop:** No

Colours(change): All yellow, blue & white (All white, blue & yellow)
Previous Names: None
Previous Leagues: York, Harrogate, Yorkshire 1973-82.
Records: **Att:** 1,200 v Winterton FA Vase 4th Round 1996-7
Senior Honours: Northern Counties East Division 1 2009-10.

10 YEAR RECORD

04-05	05-06	06-07	07-08	08-09	09-10	10-11	11-12	12-13	13-14
NCE1 6	NCE1 3	NCE1 7	NCE1 12	NCE1 17	NCE1 1	NCEP 4	NCEP 8	NCEP 6	NCEP 2

THACKLEY

Founded: 1930 | Nickname: Dennyboys

Secretary: Mark Holstead **(T)** **(E)** john_thackleyafc@yahoo.co.uk

Chairman: Philip Woollias **Manager:** Andy Patterson **Prog Ed:** John McCreery

Ground: Dennyfield, Ainsbury Avenue, Thackley, Bradford BD10 0TL **(T)** 01274 615 571

Capacity: 3000 **Seats:** 300 **Covered:** 600 **Midweek Matchday:** Tuesday **Clubhouse:** Yes **Shop:** No

Colours(change): Red/white/red. (White/black/white).
Previous Names: Thackley Wesleyians 1930-39
Previous Leagues: Bradford Am, W. Riding Co. Am., West Yorks, Yorks 1967-82
Records: **Att:** 1,500 v Leeds United 1983
Senior Honours: W. Riding County Cup 1963-64, 66-67, 73-74, 74-75. Bradford & District Senior Cup (x13).

10 YEAR RECORD

04-05	05-06	06-07	07-08	08-09	09-10	10-11	11-12	12-13	13-14
NCEP 8	NCEP 9	NCEP 18	NCEP 16	NCEP 7	NCEP 4	NCEP 8	NCEP 10	NCEP 10	NCEP 13

WORKSOP TOWN

Founded: 1861 Nickname: Tigers

Secretary: Paul Stacey **(T)** **(E)** wtfcsecretary@gmail.com

Chairman: Ian Smith **Manager:** Mark Shaw **Prog Ed:** Steve Jarvis

Ground: The Windsor Foodservice Stadium, off Sandy Lane, Worksop S80 1UJ **(T)** 01909 479 955

Capacity: 2,500 **Seats:** 200 **Covered:** 750 **Midweek Matchday:** Wednesday **Clubhouse:** Yes **Shop:** Yes

Colours(change): Amber with black/black/amber (White with black/white/white)

Previous Names: Not known

Previous Leagues: Central All.1947-49, 60-61, Midland Co. 1949-60, 61-68, 69-74, Northern Premier 1968-69, 74-2004, 2007-14, Conf. 2004-07

Records: 8,171 v Chesterfield - FA Cup 1925 (Central Avenue)

Senior Honours: Sheffield Senior Cup 1923-24, 52-53, 54-55, 65-66, 69-70,72-73, 81-82, 84-85, 94-95, 96-97, 2002-03, 11-12.
Northern Premier League President's Cup 1985-86, 96-97, Chairman's Cup 2001-02.

10 YEAR RECORD

04-05	05-06	06-07	07-08	08-09	09-10	10-11	11-12	12-13	13-14
Conf N 17	Conf N 9	Conf N 21	NP P 9	NP P 17	NP P 18	NP P 7	NP P 15	NP P 9	NP P 4

A.F.C. EMLEY
Founded: 2005 Nickname: Pewits

Secretary: Andrew Painten **(T)** **(E)** office@afcemley.co.uk
Chairman: Terry Higgins **Manager:** Darren Hepworth **Prog Ed:** Dan Brownhill
Ground: The Welfare Ground, Off Upper Lane, Emley, nr Huddersfield, HD8 9RE. **(T)** 01924 849 392 **Capacity:** 2,000
Colours(change): Claret & sky blue/sky blue/claret (Green/black/green)

ADDITIONAL INFORMATION:
Previous League: West Yorkshire 2005-06.

AFC MANSFIELD
Founded: 2012 Nickname: The Bulls

Secretary: Andrew Saunders **(T)** **(E)**
Chairman: Steve Hymas **Manager:** Micky Taylor **Prog Ed:** Peter Craggs
Ground: Forest Town Stadium, Clipstone Road West, Forest Town, Mansfield NG19 0EE **(T)** 07973 491 739
Colours(change): Red/black/black (Yellow/blueblue)

ADDITIONAL INFORMATION:
Previous League: Central Midlands North 2012-14.
League honours: Central Midlands North 2013-14.

BOTTESFORD TOWN
Founded: 1974 Nickname: The Poachers

Secretary: Tony Dixon **(T)** **(E)** anthony.reeve3@ntlworld.com
Chairman: Tony Reeve **Manager:** John Corbett **Prog Ed:** Liz Gray
Ground: Birch Park, Ontario Road, Bottesford, Scunthorpe, DN17 2TQ **(T)** 01724 871 883 **Capacity:** 1,000
Colours(change): All blue & yellow (Green & black/black/black & green)

ADDITIONAL INFORMATION:
Previous Leagues: Lincolnshire 1974-2000. Central Midlands 2000-07.
Honours: Lincolnshire League 1989-90, 90-91, 91-92. Central Midlands League Supreme Division 2006-07.

CLIPSTONE
Founded: 1928 Nickname: The Cobras

Secretary: Les Graham **(T)** **(E)** clipstonefc@yahoo.co.uk
Chairman: Brett Marshall **Manager:** Chris Millington **Prog Ed:** Kevin Clarke
Ground: Worksop Van Hire Stad, Clipstone Rd East, Clipstone Village, Mansfield, NG21 9AB. **(T)** 01623 423 730 **Capacity:** 500
Colours(change): Black & white/black/black (All red)

ADDITIONAL INFORMATION:
Previous Names: Clipstone Welfare.
League honours: Central Midlands League 1993-94, 96-97.

DRONFIELD TOWN
Founded: 1998 Nickname: None

Secretary: Darren Bradwell **(T)** **(E)** dronfieldtownfc@yahoo.co.uk
Chairman: Patrick Williams **Manager:** Craig Butler **Prog Ed:** Michael Payne
Ground: Stonelow Playing Fields, Stonelow Road, Dronfield, S18 2DA **(T)** **Capacity:** 500
Colours(change): Red & black/black with red/red & black (Royal blue/white/royal blue)

ADDITIONAL INFORMATION:
Previous Leagues: Central Midlands > 2013.
League honours: Hope Valley B Division 2001-02, A Division 2002-03, Premiership 2003-04.
Midland Regional Alliance Division One 2005-06, Premier 2007-08. Central Midlands North 2012-13.

ECCLESHILL UNITED
Founded: 1948 Nickname: The Eagles

Secretary: Adrian Benson **(T)** **(E)**
Chairman: Adrian Benson **Manager:** Lee Duxbury **Prog Ed:** Paul Everett
Ground: The Rapid Solicitors Stadium, Kingsway, Wrose, Bradford, BD2 1PN **(T)** 01274 615 739 **Capacity:** 2,225
Colours(change): Blue & white/blue/blue & red (All fuschia).

ADDITIONAL INFORMATION:
Record Att: 715 v Bradford City 1996-97. **Win:** 10-1. **Defeat:** 0-6.
Honours: Bradford Senior Cup 1985-86. Northern Counties East Division 1 1996-97.

GRIMSBY BOROUGH
Founded: 2003 Nickname: The Wilderness Boys

Secretary: Nigel Fanthorpe **(T)** **(E)** nigelfanthorpe@hotmail.co.uk
Chairman: Vacant **Manager:** Steve Newby & Nigel Fanthorpe **Prog Ed:** Brian Sylvester
Ground: The Bradley Football Development Centre, Bradley Road, Grimsby, DN37 0AG **(T)** 07890 318 054 **Capacity:** 1,000
Colours(change): Blue/blue/white (All yellow)

ADDITIONAL INFORMATION:
Previous League: Central Midlands 2004-08.
FA/County Cups: Lincolnshire Junior Cup 2007-08.

HALL ROAD RANGERS
Founded: 1959 Nickname: Rangers

Secretary: Alan Chaplin **(T)** **(E)** hallroadrangers@live.co.uk
Chairman: Darren Sunley **Manager:** Lee Hastings **Prog Ed:** Mike Harker
Ground: Dene Park, Dene Close, Beverley Road, Dunswell HU6 0AA **(T)** 01482 850 101 **Capacity:** 1,200
Colours(change): Blue & white/blue/blue (Red/black/black)

ADDITIONAL INFORMATION: App:1,200 v Manchester City Aug 93 **Goalscorer:** G James **App:** G James
East Riding Senior Cup 1972-73, 93-94. N.C.E. Division Two 1990-91.

HALLAM (SECOND OLDEST CLUB IN THE WORLD)
Founded: 1860 Nickname: Countrymen

Secretary: Kevin Scott **(T)** **(E)** theclub@hallamfc.co.uk
Chairman: Chris Taylor **Manager:** Steve Toyne & Mark Ramsden **Prog Ed:** Wayne Rutledge
Ground: Sandygate Road, Crosspool, Sheffield S10 5SE **(T)** 0114 230 9484 **Capacity:** 1,000
Colours(change): All blue (All yellow).

ADDITIONAL INFORMATION: Att: 2,000 v Hendon F.A. Amateur Cup. **Goalscorer:** A Stainrod 46. **App:** P. Ellis 500+. **Win:** 7-0 x2. **Defeat:** 0-7.
Honours: Northern Counties East League Cup 2003-04.
Previous League: Yorkshire 1952-82.

HEMSWORTH MINERS WELFARE
Founded: 1981 Nickname: Wells

Secretary: Phillip Crapper **(T)** 01977 614 723 **(E)** acracknell@naue.co.uk
Chairman: Tony Benson **Manager:** Wayne Benn **Prog Ed:** Anthony Crapper
Ground: Fitzwilliam Stadium, Wakefield Road, Fitzwilliam, Pontefract, WF9 5AJ **(T)** 01977 614 997 **Capacity:** 2,000
Colours(change): Cyan blue/navy/navy (All white)

ADDITIONAL INFORMATION:
Previous League: West Riding County Amateur 1995-2008.
Record Att: 505 v Kinsley Boys, 2007. **Goalscorer:** Paul Crapper - Total 375 - In a season 52. **Apps:** Paul Crapper - 809.

KNARESBOROUGH TOWN
Founded: 1902 Nickname: None

Secretary: Clare Rudzinski **(T)** **(E)** knaresboroughtownafc@gmail.com
Chairman: Terry Hewlett **Manager:** Brian Davey **Prog Ed:** Daniel Rudzinski
Ground: Manse Lane, Knaresborough, HG5 8LF **(T)** 01423 548 896 **Capacity:** 1,000
Colours(change): Red/black/red (Yellow & black stripes/black/yellow)

ADDITIONAL INFORMATION:
Previous Leagues: West Yorkshire 1971. Harrogate & District 1971-93. West Yorkshire 1993-2012.
Honours: West Yorkshire League Premier Division 2008-09.

LINCOLN MOORLANDS RAILWAY
Founded: 1989 Nickname: The Moors

Secretary: Mark Hodds **(T)** **(E)** mhodds@btinternet.com
Chairman: Peter Tute **Manager:** Damon Parkinson **Prog Ed:** Mark Hodds
Ground: Moorland Sports Ground, Newark Road, Lincoln LN6 8RT **(T)** 01522 874 111
Colours(change): All maroon (All yellow)

ADDITIONAL INFORMATION:
League honours: Central Midlands Supreme 1999-00.
FA/County Cups: Lincolnshire Senior Cup 2006-07.

LOUTH TOWN
Founded: 2007 Nickname: The White Wolves

Secretary: Richard Hill **(T)** **(E)** ltfcsecretary@gmail.com
Chairman: Stephen Clark **Manager:** Paul Walden **Prog Ed:** Daniel Turner
Ground: The Park Avenue Stadium, Park Avenue, Louth, LN11 8BY **(T)** 01507 601 123 **Capacity:** 1,500
Colours(change): White/black/white & black (All orange)

ADDITIONAL INFORMATION:
Previous League: Central Midlands 2007-10.
League honours: Central Midlands League Premier Division 2008-09, Supreme Division 2009-10.

PENISTON CHURCH
Founded: 1906 Nickname: None

Secretary: David Hampshire **(T)** **(E)** penistonechurchfc@gmail.com
Chairman: Scott Fairbank **Manager:** Ian Richards **Prog Ed:** Andy Green
Ground: Church View Road, Penistone, Sheffield S36 6AT **(T)**
Colours(change): Black & white/black/black (Light blue /navy blue/light blue)

ADDITIONAL INFORMATION:
Previous Leagues: Sheffield & Hallamshire County Senior 1990-2014.

PONTEFRACT COLLIERIES

Founded: 1958 Nickname: Colls

Secretary: Trevor Waddington **(T)** **(E)**
Chairman: Guy Nottingham **Manager:** Nicky Handley & Duncan Bray **Prog Ed:** Patrick Monaghan
Ground: The Beechnut Lane Stadium, Skinner Lane, Pontefract, WF8 4QE **(T)** 01977 600 818 **Capacity:** 1,200
Colours(change): Blue & white/blue & white/blue (Claret & sky blue/claret & sky blue/claret)

ADDITIONAL INFORMATION:
Previous League: West Yorkshire 1958-79. Yorkshire 1979-82.
Record Att: 1,000 v Hull City, floodlight opening 1987.
League honours: Northern Counties East League Division One 1983-84, 95-96.

ROSSINGTON MAIN

Founded: 1919 Nickname: The Colliery

Secretary: Gerald Parsons **(T)** **(E)** g-parsons2@sky.com
Chairman: Carl Stokes **Manager:** Steve Brennan **Prog Ed:** Peter Murden
Ground: Welfare Ground, Oxford Street, Rossington, Doncaster, DN11 0TE **(T)** 01302 865 524 (MD) **Capacity:** 2,000
Colours(change): All blue (All red)

ADDITIONAL INFORMATION:
Record Att: 1,243 v Doncaster Rovers 09/07/2013. **Goalscorer:** Lee Holmes - 115+. **Apps:** Dave Holvey - 250.
League honours: Central Midlands League Premier Division 1984-85.

SELBY TOWN

Founded: 1919 Nickname: The Robins

Secretary: Thomas Arkley **(T)** 07830 218 657 **(E)** toonarkley@yahoo.co.uk
Chairman: Ralph Pearse **Manager:** Dave Ricardo
Ground: The Rigid Group Stadium, Richard Street, Scott Road, Selby YO8 0DB **(T)** 01757 210 900 **Capacity:** 5,000
Colours(change): All red (All blue).

ADDITIONAL INFORMATION: Att: 7,000 v Bradford PA FA Cup1st Round 1953-54
League honours: Yorkshire League 1934-35, 35-36, 52-53, 53-54. Northern Counties East Division One 1995-96.

SHIREBROOK TOWN

Founded: 1985 Nickname: None

Secretary: Aimee Radford **(T)** 01623 742 535 **(E)** aimeeradford@yahoo.co.uk
Chairman: Dan Marsh **Manager:** Mark Camm & Danny Bacon
Ground: Shirebrook Spts and So C, Langwith Road, Shirebrook, Mansfield, NG20 8TF **(T)** 01623 742 535 **Capacity:** 2,000
Colours(change): Red/black/black (All white)

ADDITIONAL INFORMATION:
Record Goalscorer: Craig Charlesworth - 345. **Apps:** Martin Rowbottom - 384.
League honours: Central Midlands League Supreme Division 2000-01, 01-02. Northern Counties East Division One 2003-04.

TEVERSAL

Founded: 1918 Nickname: Tevie Boys

Secretary: Kevin Newton **(T)** 07711 358 060 **(E)** enquiries@teversalfc.co.uk
Chairman: Peter Cockerill **Prog Ed:** Kevin Newton
Ground: Teversal Grange Spts and So.Centre, Carnarvon St, Teversal, NG17 3HJ **(T)** 07711 358 060 **Capacity:** 2,000
Colours(change): Red/black/black (All royal blue)

ADDITIONAL INFORMATION:
Previous Name: Teversal Grange. **Previous League:** Central Midlands 2000-05.
Honours: Central Midlands League 2004-05.

WINTERTON RANGERS

Founded: 1930 Nickname: Rangers

Secretary: Mark Fowler **(T)** 07775 907 606 **(E)** wrfc@talktalk.net
Chairman: David Crowder **Manager:** Darren Waring **Prog Ed:** WayneTurtle,MartynGirdham
Ground: West Street, Winterton, Scunthorpe DN15 9QF. **(T)** 01724 732 628 **Capacity:** 3,000
Colours(change): All blue. (All red).

ADDITIONAL INFORMATION: Att: 1,200 v Sheffield United, flood lights switch on, October 1978.
NCE Premier 2007-08.

WORSBROUGH BRIDGE ATHLETIC

Founded: 1923 Nickname: The Briggers

Secretary: Charlie Wyatt **(T)** 01226 284 452 **(E)** crw@wyatts.adsl24.co.uk
Chairman: John Cooper **Manager:** Dave Mace **Prog Ed:** Charlie Wyatt
Ground: Park Road, Worsbrough Bridge, Barnsley, S70 5LJ **(T)** 01226 284 452 **Capacity:** 2,000
Colours(change): Red/black/red (Yellow/green/green)

ADDITIONAL INFORMATION: Previous Leagues: Barnsley 1952-61. County Senior 1962-70. Yorkshire 1971-82.
Record Att: 1,603 v Blyth Spatans, FA Amateur Cup 1971.
League honours: Barnsley League Division One 1952-53, 58-59, 59-60. County Senior League Division One 1965-66, 69-70.

YORKSHIRE AMATEUR

Founded: 1918 Nickname: Ammers

Secretary: Jeni French **(T)** **(E)** william.ellis5@virginmedia.com
Chairman: Jeni French **Manager:** Phil Harding & Lincoln Richards **Prog Ed:** Tony Dean
Ground: Bracken Edge, Roxholme Road, Leeds, LS8 4DZ (Sat. Nav. LS7 4JG) **(T)** 0113 289 2886 **Capacity:** 1,550
Colours(change): White/navy/red (All royal blue)

ADDITIONAL INFORMATION: Previous Leagues: Yorkshire 1920-24, 30-82.
Record Att: 4,000 v Wimbledon, FA Amateur Cup Quarter Final 1932.
League honours: Yorkshire League 1931-32, Division Two 1958-59, Division Three 1977-78.
FA/County Cups: West Riding Cup x3. Leeds & District Senior Cup.

GROUND DIRECTIONS

ALBION SPORTS-Throstle Nest, Newlands, Farsley, Leeds, LS28 5BE. Tel: 0113 255 7292
Come off the M606 at the roundabout. Take fourth exit onto Rooley Lane which is the A6177, continue to follow A6177 through two roundabouts then turn right onto Leeds Road A647. Continue to follow A647, go through roundabout. At next roundabout, take second exit onto Bradford Road B6157. Follow for ½ mile before turning left onto New Street then turn right onto Newlands. Ground on left.

ARMTHORPE WELFARE-Welfare Ground, Church Street, Armthorpe, Doncaster, DN3 3AG. Tel: (01302) 842795-Match days only
From the north, turn left at main roundabout in the centre of Doncaster and straight across at next roundabout on to Wheatley Hall Road. Turn right on to Wentworth Road, go to top of hill towards the Hospital on to Armthorpe Road. From the south, take the M18 to J4 on to the A630. At 2nd roundabout, turn left and proceed to next roundabout, then turn right. Ground 400 yards on left behind Netto.

ATHERSLEY RECREATION-Sheerien Park, Ollerton Road, Athersley North, Barnsley, S71 3DP. Tel: 07910 121070
From North: M1 J38. Go down slip road, round roundabout and back under motorway. Take first left onto Haigh Lane, go to top of the hill and, at T-junction, turn right. At next T-junction, turn left onto Shaw Lane and go to bottom of hill. At T-junction of A61, turn right to Barnsley, go through first set of traffic lights and take first left onto Newstead Road. Follow to second roundabout and turn right onto Ollerton Road. Follow to second turn on left-do not take it but go past and entrance is between houses 123-125 Ollerton Road. Follow drive into ground.

BARTON TOWN OLD BOYS-The Euronics Ground, Marsh Lane, Barton-on-Humber. Tel: (01652) 635838
Approaching from the South on A15, Barton is the last exit before the Humber Bridge. Follow the A1077 into the town. Turn right at the mini roundabout at the bottom of the hill into Holydyke. Take second left onto George Street and then into King Street. Marsh Lane is opposite the junction of King Street and High Street. The ground is at the end of Marsh Lane, on the right, immediately after the cricket ground.

BRIDLINGTON TOWN-Queensgate Stadium, Queensgate, Bridlington, East Yorkshire, YO16 7LN. Tel: (01262) 606879
From South (Hull, Beeford, Barmston): Approach Bridlington on the A165, passing golf course on right and Broadacres Pub, Kingsmead Estate on left. Straight through traffic lights to roundabout by B&Q. Turn right. At traffic lights turn left and over the railway bridge. At roundabout bear left and carry on heading north up Quay Road. After traffic lights turn right into Queensgate. Ground is 800 yards up the road on the right.
From South and West (Driffield, Hull, York): Approach Bridlington on A614. (This was formally the A166). Straight on at traffic lights (Hospital on right) and follow the road round the bend. At roundabout straight across to mini roundabout and bear right (second exit). Follow road around to right and to traffic lights. Straight on. At next traffic lights (just after Kwikfit) turn left into Queensgate. Ground is 800 yards up the road on the right.
From North (Scarborough): Approach Bridlington (Esso garage on right) at roundabout turn left then at mini roundabout second exit. Follow road around to right and to traffic lights. Straight on. At next traffic lights (just after Kwikfit) turn left into Queensgate. Ground is 800 yards up the road on the right.

CLEETHORPES TOWN-The Bradley Football Development Centre, Bradley Road, Grimsby, DN37 0AG
Head East along the M180/A180. Exit at the Great Coates Interchange. Travel back over motorway to first Roundabout. Take first exit and follow for two miles to Trawl Pub Roundabout. Take second exit, follow for two miles to Bradley Roundabout. Take second exit on to Bradley Road. The ground is approximately 500 yards on the left.

GARFORTH TOWN - Cedar Ridge, Garforth, Leeds LS25 2PF. Tel: 0113 287 7145
From North: travel south on A1 and join M1. Turn off at 1st junc (47). From South: M1 to junc 47. From Leeds area: join M1 at junc 44 or 46 and turn off at junc 47. From West: M62 to junc 29, join M1 and off at junc 47. From junc 47: take turning signe 'Garforth' (A642). Approx. 200 yds turn left into housing estate opposite White House. (Cedar Ridge). Stadium at end of lane. From the South (alternative): A1, turn off on to A63 signposted 'Leeds' immediately after 'Boot & Shoe' Public House. At 1st roundabout turn right on to A656 and follow to next roundabout. Take 1st left on to A642 (Garforth) and follow from M1 junc 47.

GLASSHOUGHTON WELFARE-The Glasshoughton Centre, Leeds Rd, Glasshoughton, Castleford, WF10 4PF. Tel: (01977) 511234
Leave the M62 J32, signposted Castleford/Pontefract (A639). At the bottom of the slip road take the A656, taking carer to pick up the middle lane for Castleford. After approx. 1/4 mile, bear left at the first roundabout and, after a further 1/4 mile, left at the next roundabout on to Leeds Road. Ground is then 200 yards on the right.

HANDSWORTH PARRAMORE-The Windsor Foodservice Stadium, Sandy Land, Worksop S80 1TJ. Tel: 01909 479 955
From either the A1 or M1 J31, take the A57 towards Worksop. After approximately 7 miles, look out for the A60/Sandy Lane turnoff at the roundabout. Continue over two mini-roundabouts for ¾mile then turn left into the retail park and left again into the stadium car park.

HEANOR TOWN-Mayfield Avenue, Heanor DE75 7EN-01773 713 742
From M1: J26, take A610 Ripley Road to end of dual carriageway then take A608 to Heanor via Langley Mill. At traffic lights at top of long hill take left lane signed Ilkeston. First right into Mundy Street, second left onto Godfrey Street. Ground on left where road forks. From A608 Derby: Enter town and see Tesco on left. Turn right at roundabout to the Market Place. Turn right at end of square and at crossroads right again onto Mundy Street. Then left into Godfrey Street and ground on left where road forks.

LIVERSEDGE-Clayborn Ground, Quaker Lane, Hightown Road, Cleckheaton, WF15 8DF. Tel: (01274) 682108
M62 J26, A638 into Cleckheaton, right at lights on corner of Memorial Park, through next lights and under railway bridge, first left (Hightown Rd) and Quaker Lane is approx 1/4 mile on left and leads to ground. From M1 J40, A638 thru Dewsbury and Heckmondwike to Cleckheaton, left at Memorial Park lights then as above. Buses 218 & 220 (Leeds-Huddersfield) pass top of Quaker Lane.

MALTBY MAIN-Muglet Lane, Maltby, Rotherham, S66 7JQ. Tel: (07795) 693683
Exit M18 at Junc 1 with A631. Two miles into Maltby, right at traffic lights at Queens Hotel corner on to B6427 Muglet Lane. Ground 3/4 mile on left.

NOSTELL MINERS WELFARE-The Welfare Ground, Crofton Community Centre, Middle Lane, New Crofton, Wakefield, WF4 1LB. Tel: (01924) 866010
M1 J39, head towards Wakefield (A638), Denby Dale road. Leave Wakefield on the A638 (Doncaster Rd), towards Wakefield Trinity Ground. Continue on this road for another 2 miles, you will pass the Red Beck Motel on your right. Go under the bridge and turn right opposite the Public house 'Crofton Arms'. Follow road through Crofton village (1 1/4 miles). Turn left at 'Slipper' public house, then right onto Middle Lane, follow road round to reach Crofton Community Centre.

PARKGATE-Roundwood Sports Complex, Green Lane, Rawmarsh, Rotherham, S62 6LA. Tel: (01709) 826600
From Rotherham A633 to Rawmarsh. From Doncaster A630 to Conisbrough, then A6023 through Swinton to Rawmarsh. Grd at Green Lane-right from Rotherham, left from Conisbrough at the Crown Inn. Ground 800yds on right.

PICKERING TOWN-Recreation Club, off Mill Lane, Malton Rd, Pickering, YO18 7DB. Tel: (01751) 473317
A169 from Malton. On entering Pickering, take 1st left past Police Station and BP garage into Mill Lane, ground 200 yds on right.

RETFORD UNITED - Cannon Park, Leverton Road, Retford, Notts DN22 6QF. Tel: (01777) 869 468 / 710 300
Leave the A1 at Ranby and follow the A620 towards Retford. Go past Ranby prison and go straight on at the next 2 mini roundabouts. At the 3rd roundabout take the 3rd exit signposted Gainsborough. Passing Morrisons on the left, go through the traffic lights and move into the right hand lane. Turn right at the traffic lights. Turn left at the traffic lights by the Broken Wheel Public House into Leverton Road. Go past the Masons Arms Public House and go over 2 hump backed bridges. The ground is signposted and is on the right.

SHAW LANE AQUAFORCE - Shaw Lane, Barnsley, S70 6HZ. Tel: 01226 203 509
Leave the M1 at J37 and take the A628 (Barnsley). Use left hand lane and proceed through traffic lights. Take second right (Shaw Lane). The ground is 100m on the right.

STAVELEY MINERS WELFARE-Inkersall Road, Staveley, Chesterfield, S43 3JL. Tel: (01246) 471441
M1 J30 follow A619 Chesterfield. Staveley is 3 miles from J30. Turn left at GK Garage in Staveley town centre into Inkersall Road. Ground is 200 yards on right at side of Speedwell Rooms.

TADCASTER ALBION-2inspire Park, Ings Lane, Tadcaster, LS24 9AY
From West Riding and South Yorks-Turn right off A659 at John Smith's Brewery Clock. From East Riding-Turn left off A659 after passing over river bridge and pelican crossing (New Street).

NORTHERN COUNTIES EAST LEAGUE - STEP 5/6

THACKLEY-Dennyfield, Ainsbury Avenue, Thackley, Bradford, BD10 0TL. Tel: (01274) 615571
On main Leeds/Keighley A657 road, turn off at Thackley corner which is 2 miles from Shipley traffic lights and 1 mile from Greengates lights. Ainsbury Avenue bears to the right 200yds down the hill. Ground is 200yds along Ainsbury Avenue on the right.

WORKSOP TOWN -The Windsor Foodservice Stadium, off Sandy Lane, Worksop S80 1UJ. Tel: (01909) 479 955
From either the A1 or M1 J31, take the A57 towards Worksop. After approximately 7 miles, look out for the A60/Sandy Lane turnoff at the roundabout. Continue over two mini-roundabouts for ¾mile then turn left into the retail park and left again into the stadium car park.

DIVISION ONE

A.F.C. EMLEY-The Welfare Ground, Off Upper Lane, Emley, nr Huddersfield, HD8 9RE. Tel: 01924 849392 or 07702 712287
From M1 J38: Travel on road signposted to Huddersfield through the village of Bretton to the first roundabout. Take first exit off this roundabout signposted Denby Dale. After approximately one mile turn right at road signposted Emley. After 2 miles enter the village of Emley. Entrance to ground is opposite a white bollard in centre of road. (Narrow entrance).
From M1 J39: Travel on road signposted toward Denby Dale. Travel for approximately 3 miles up hill to first roundabout. Take 2nd exit and follow directions as above.

A.F.C. MANSFIELD - Forest Town Stadium, Clipstone Road West, Forest Town, Mansfield NG19 0EE. Tel: 07973 491 739
The ground is situated approximately 3 miles to the north east of Mansfield town centre and sits on the B6030 Clipstone Road West. Pedestrian access can be gained via gates on Clipstone Road West with vehicle access via Main Avenue and then the 2nd right, turning into Second Avenue.

BOTTESFORD TOWN-Birch Park, Ontario Road, Bottesford, Scunthorpe, DN17 2TQ. Tel: (01724) 871883
Exit M180 via M181-Scunthorpe. At circle (Berkeley Hotel), turn right into Scotter Road. At circle (Asda) straight ahead, 2nd left into South Park road then on to Sunningdale Road, turn right into Goodwood Road, Birch Park at end (right turn). Please note that Goodwood Road is not suitable for large vehicles. Instead, take 2nd right off Sunningdale Road which is Quebec Road, then 2nd right which is Ontario Road down to the bottom and ground is on the left.

CLIPSTONE - The Lido Ground, Clipstone Road East, Clipstone Village, Mansfield, NG21 9AB. Tel: 01623 423730
From M1 J29, take exit signposted A617 Mansfield. At next roundabout, take third exit continuing on the A617. Keep going straight on until you get to the Mansfield ring road with Riley's snooker hall on your right and a miner's statue on your left. Follow the road round underneath a pedestrian bridge and take the next left onto the A6191 (Ratcliffe Gate). After around half a mile, turn left onto the B6030 (Carter Lane). Follow the B6030 for about 3 miles, go straight on at a roundabout and the ground will be on your left.

DRONFIELD TOWN - Stonelow Playing Fields, Stonelow Road, Dronfield, S18 2DA
From South: At M1 J29, 2nd exit A617 Chesterfield. At roundabout, take 4th exit (A61 Sheffield), then 2nd and 3rd exits at next roundabouts to stay on A61. Leave at first slip road signed Sheepbridge/Unstone. Right towards Unstone/Dronfield. Go across 1st mini roundabout, then right and immediate left at next mini roundabout onto Green Lane. Up hill, 2nd right onto Stonelow Road and 1st right onto Shireoaks. From North: At M1 J30, 3rd exit towards Renishaw. Through Renishaw and Eckington then right for Coal Aston. Left at first mini roundabout, keep on Green Lane, down steep hill and left onto Stonelow Road then take 1st right onto Shireoaks.

ECCLESHILL UNITED-The Smith Butler Stadium, Kingsway, Wrose, Bradford, BD2 1PN. Tel: (01274) 615739
M62 J26 onto M606, right onto Bradford Ring Road A6177, left on to A650 for Bradford at 2nd roundabout. A650 Bradford Inner Ring Road onto Canal Rd, branch right at Staples (Dixons Car showrooms on right), fork left after 30mph sign to junction with Wrose Road, across junction-continuation of Kings Rd, first left onto Kingsway. Ground is 200 yards on right.

GRIMSBY BOROUGH-Grimsby Community Stadium, Bradley Road, Grimsby, DN37 0AG
Head South East on the A180 to the Great Coates turn off come back over the A180 and follow for 1/2 mile to the roundabout, take first exit follow over one mini roundabout and through one set of traffic lights until you come to the Trawl Pub roundabout, take the second exit onto Littlecoates road and follow over one mini roundabout to the second roundabout and take the second exit onto Bradley Road. The ground is approx 800 yards on your left with car and coach parking facilities.

HALL ROAD RANGERS-Dene Park, Dene Close, Beverley Road, Dunswell, nr Hull, HU6 0AA. Tel: (01482) 850101
M62 to A63, turn left before Humber Bridge onto A164 to Beverley, after approx. 5 miles turn right onto A1079. In 2 miles, turn left at large roundabout to ground 20 yards on right.

HALLAM-Sandygate, Sandygate Road, Crosspool, Sheffield, S10 5SE. Tel: (0114) 230 9484
A57 Sheffield to Glossop Rd, left at Crosspool shopping area signed Lodge Moor on to Sandygate Rd. Ground half mile on left opposite Plough Inn. 51 bus from Crucible Theatre.

HEMSWORTH MINERS WELFARE-Fitzwilliam Stadium, Wakefield Road, Fitzwilliam, Pontefract, WF9 5AJ. Tel: (01977) 614997
From East/West: M62 to J32 towards Pontefract then follow A628 towards Hemsworth. At Ackworth roundabout (Stoneacre Suzuki Garage), take a right on to the A638 Wakefield Road. Travel half a mile to next roundabout then take first exit. Travel one mile to crossroads and turn left into Fitzwilliam. Pass a row of shops on your right and turn left after the bus shelter before an iron bridge. To ground. **From North**: A1 South to M62 then follow above directions. **From South:** A1(M) North to A638 Wakefield Road. Travel to Ackworth Roundabout (Stoneacre Suzuki Garage) and go straight across and follow the A638 to the next roundabout. Take first exit then to crossroads. Turn left into Fitzwilliam and pass row of shops on your right. Turn left after bus shelter before iron bridge and carry on to the ground. Alternative: M1 to J32 then take M18 to A1(M).

KNARESBOROUGH TOWN-Manse Lane, Manse Lane, Knaresborough, HG5 8LF. Tel: 01423 548896
From West/South Leeds Area: A658 or A61 towards Harrogate. Join A658 southern bypass towards York. At roundabout with B6164, turn left to Knaresborough. Turn left at second roundabout and travel over river bridge. Manse Lane is first on right alongside garage; From East Leeds Area: A58 or A1 to Wetherby. Join B6164 to Knaresborough then as above. From East on A59 from A1: Turn right at first roundabout. Manse Lane is first turn left after speed restriction sign.

LINCOLN MOORLANDS RAILWAY-Lincoln Moorlands Railway Sports Ground, Newark Road, Lincoln, LN6 8RT. Tel: (01522) 874111
From North: A1 to Markham Moor. Take A57 until Lincoln by-pass. At Carholme Roundabout take 3rd. exit towards Lincoln South. Travel 1.7 miles to Skellingthorpe Roundabout and take 2nd. Exit towards Lincoln South. Travel 1.6 miles to Doddington Roundabout and take 1st. exit B1190 towards Lincoln South. Travel 2.1 miles until T-Junction. Turn left onto A1434 and travel 0.4 mile. Entrance to ground is on left immediately after Chancery Close. From Newark: A46 to Lincoln by-pass. At roundabout take last exit onto A1434 towards Lincoln. Travel for 3.1 miles, entrance to ground on left immediately after Chancery Close signposted 'Moorlands Railway Club'.

LOUTH TOWN-The Park Avenue Stadium, Park Avenue, Louth, LN11 8BY. Tel: 07891 965531
Enter Louth from the A16 onto North Home Road. Go 1/2 mile and follow the road as it bends to the right to become Newbridge Hill. At the junction, turn right onto Ramsgate. At the mini roundabout next to Morrisons, turn left onto Eastgate. Go 1/2 mile down Eastgate and turn right into Park Avenue just past the fire station.

PENISTON CHURCH - Church View Road, Penistone, Sheffield S36 6AT. Tel: (01977) 600818
From North: Leave M1 at J37, take 3rd exit A628 Manchester. After ½ mile take 2nd exit A628 Manchester. After approx 4 mile take 2nd exit A628 Manchester then at traffic lights turn left to Penistone Town Centre. On entering town centre after pelican crossing take 1st left Victoria Street then 2nd left. Ground is on your right. From South: Leave M1 at J35A at roundabout take 2nd exit A616 Manchester. At next roundabout take 2nd exit A616 Manchester then take 1st exit signed Penistone, Huddersfield A629. Follow this road through Wortley, Thurgoland and then take B6462 then travel under 3 railway bridges. Turn sharp left after 3rd bridge and follow road to the right onto Church View Road. Ground is approx 600 yards on left.

PONTEFRACT COLLIERIES-Skinner Lane, Pontefract, WF8 4QE. Tel: (01977) 600818
M62 jct32 (Xscape) towards Pontefract. Left at lights after roundabout for park entrance and retail park. Traffic through town should follow racecourse signs through lights to roundabout and back to lights.

ROSSINGTON MAIN-Welfare Ground, Oxford Street, Rossington, Doncaster, DN11 0TE. Tel: (01302) 865524 (Matchdays only)
Enter Rossington and go over the railway crossings. Passing the Welfare Club, Oxford Street is the next road on the right. The ground is at the bottom of Oxford Street.

SELBY TOWN-The Selby Times Stadium, Richard St, Scott Rd, Selby, YO8 4BN. Tel: (01757) 210900
From Leeds, left at main traffic lights in Selby down Scott Rd, then 1st left into Richard St. From Doncaster, go straight across main traffic lights into Scott Rd then 1st left. From York, right at main traffic lights into Scott Rd and 1st left.

SHIREBROOK TOWN-Shirebrook Staff Sports and Social Club, Langwith Road, Shirebrook, Mansfield, Notts, NG20 8TF. Tel: (01623) 742535
Depart M1 at Junction 29, at roundabout take A617 towards Mansfield (for 3.5 miles), at next roundabout take 2nd Exit B6407 Common Lane towards Shirebrook (or 1.8 miles), go straight on at next roundabout (for 300 yards), at staggered crossroads turn right onto Main Street (for 1.1 miles), at T Junction turn right (for 100 yards), take the first road on your left (Langwith Road). The ground is 400 yards on the right.

TEVERSAL-Teversal Grange Sports and Social Centre, Carnarvon Street, Teversal, Sutton-in-Ashfield, NG17 3HJ. Tel: (07773) 922539
From North: Travel South on the M1 to junction 29 take the A6175 to Heath and Holmewood. Travel through Holmewood, and at the roundabout take the B6039 to Hardstaff and Tibshelf. At the T-junction in Tibshelf (pub on your left) turn left onto B6014 travelling over the motorway into Teversal. Follow the road passing the Carnarvon Arms pub and under a bridge, take 2nd left onto Coppywood Close, travel to the top and following the road round with the ground at the top.
From South: From the M1 junction 28, take the A38 to Mansfield. Travel through a number of sets of traffic lights and after passing the Kings Mill Reservoir you will come to a major junction (King & Miller Pub and McDonalds on your left). Travel straight on taking the A6075 towards Mansfield Woodhouse, at the next set of traffic lights turn left onto the B6014 to Stanton Hill. You will come to a roundabout with a Kwik Save on your left, continue on the B6014 towards Tibshelf. Take the second right onto Coppywood Close, travel to the top and following the road round with the ground at the top.

WINTERTON RANGERS-West Street, Winterton, Scunthorpe, DN15 9QF. Tel: (01724) 732628
From Scunthorpe-Take A1077 Barton-on-Humber for 5 miles. On entering Winterton take 3rd right (Eastgate), 3rd left (Northlands Rd) and 1st Right (West St). Ground 200 yards on left.

WORSBOROUGH BRIDGE ATHLETIC-Park Road, Worsbrough Bridge, Barnsley, S70 5LJ. Tel: (01226) 284452
On the A61, Barnsley-Sheffield road two miles south of Barnsley, 2 miles from M1 J36 opposite Blackburns Bridge.

YORKSHIRE AMATEUR-Bracken Edge, Roxholme Road, Leeds, LS8 4DZ. Tel: (0113) 262 4093
From South-M1 to Leeds, then A58 to Wetherby Road to Fforde Green Hotel, left at lights and proceed to Sycamore Avenue (on right). From East-A1 to Boot & Shoe Inn then to Shaftesbury Hotel, turn right into Harehills Lane, then to Sycamore Avenue.

NORTHERN LEAGUE

Sponsored by: Ebac
Founded: 1889
Recent Champions:
2009: Newcastle Benfield
2010: Spennymoor Town
2011: Spennymoor Town
2012: Spennymoor Town
2013: Darlington 1883
northernleague.org

DIVISION ONE	P	W	D	L	F	A	GD	Pts
1 (P) Spennymoor Town	44	30	10	4	117	38	79	100
2 Celtic Nation FC	44	28	11	5	107	41	66	95
3 Shildon	44	27	10	7	109	45	64	91
4 Guisborough Town	44	26	7	11	100	61	39	85
5 West Auckland Town	44	23	15	6	86	58	28	84
6 Ashington	44	24	5	15	94	60	34	77
7 Dunston UTS	44	20	13	11	84	55	29	73
8 Bishop Auckland	44	18	14	12	82	54	28	68
9 Durham City	44	18	14	12	85	59	26	68
10 Whitley Bay	44	21	4	19	92	73	19	67
11 Consett	44	19	9	16	110	83	27	66
12 Billingham Synthonia	44	20	5	19	86	83	3	65
13 Penrith	44	17	10	17	90	88	2	61
14 Newcastle Benfield	44	14	14	16	85	59	26	56
15 Crook Town	44	16	8	20	90	111	-21	56
16 Marske United	44	14	10	20	64	88	-24	52
17 Morpeth Town	44	13	10	21	73	78	-5	49
18 Newton Aycliffe	44	14	7	23	80	106	-26	49
19 Sunderland RCA	44	12	8	24	57	93	-36	44
20 Bedlington Terriers	44	11	10	23	52	99	-47	43
21 (R) Team Northumbria	44	10	7	27	60	109	-49	37
22 (R) Hebburn Town	44	4	7	33	43	124	-81	19
23 (R) Billingham Town	44	2	2	40	26	207	-181	8

LEAGUE CUP

ROUND 1

Seaham Red Star	v	Crook Town	1-2
Thornaby	v	Bedlington Terriers	5-4
Washington	v	Jarrow Roofing BCA	3-2
Billingham Synthonia	v	Ashington	1-3
Morpeth Town	v	Sunderland RCA	7-1
North Shields	v	Shildon	1-0
Stokesley Sports Club	v	Marske United	1-1 5-6p
West Allotment Celtic	v	Ryton & Crawcrook Albion	1-0
Norton & Stockton Ancients	v	Brandon United	1-2
Consett	v	Chester-Le-Street	5-4
Whitley Bay	v	Willington	2-0
Newton Aycliffe	v	Team Northumbria	0-1
West Auckland Town	v	Birtley Town	3-1

ROUND 2

Heaton Stannington	v	Team Northumbria	2-3 aet
Alnwick Town	v	North Shields	1-3
Ashington	v	Thornaby	3-3, 5-3p
Billingham Town	v	Brandon United	1-2
Bishop Auckland	v	Durham City	2-1
Marske United	v	South Shields	3-1
Washington	v	Whitley Bay	0-1
West Auckland Town	v	Darlington RA	3-3, 4-3p
Whickham	v	Penrith	2-0
Crook Town	v	Whitehaven	1-3
Dunston UTS	v	Hebburn Town	4-3
Esh Winning	v	Tow Law Town	0-1
Morpeth Town	v	Celtic Nation FC	0-4
Newcastle Benfield	v	Guisborough Town	1-2 aet
West Allotment Celtic	v	Northallerton Town	5-3
Spennymoor Town	v	Consett	5-2

ROUND 3

Whickham	v	Tow Law Town	1-4
Ashington	v	Celtic Nation FC	2-0
Bishop Auckland	v	Team Northumbria	3-1
Guisborough Town	v	Spennymoor Town	3-2 aet
Marske United	v	West Allotment Celtic	2-0
Whitehaven	v	Dunston UTS	3-1
Brandon United	v	North Shields	1-0
West Auckland Town	v	Whitley Bay	0-1

QUARTER FINALS

Marske United	v	Guisborough Town	4-1
Brandon United	v	Whitehaven	0-2
Whitley Bay	v	Bishop Auckland	3-2
Tow Law Town	v	Ashington	1-3

SEMI FINALS

Ashington	v	Marske United	1-4
Whitehaven	v	Whitley Bay	2-3

FINAL

Marske United	v	Whitley Bay	2-1 aet

DIVISION ONE	1	2	3	4	5	6	7	8	9	10	11	12	13	14	15	16	17	18	19	20	21	22	23
1 Ashington		0-1	3-1	3-1	1-2	4-0	1-1	7-3	4-0	1-1	0-4	3-1	0-2	0-0	3-0	4-0	2-1	0-2	2-3	4-0	4-1	5-1	2-1
2 Bedlington Terriers	0-3		0-1	3-1	0-3	1-4	0-1	3-4	1-2	3-2	0-3	2-1	1-1	1-0	0-7	2-3	0-0	0-2	1-2	2-4	1-0	0-2	0-3
3 Billingham Synthonia	2-1	4-0		4-0	0-3	1-5	2-0	6-1	1-3	1-1	1-3	5-1	3-3	2-1	2-1	3-2	5-0	1-5	1-3	1-1	3-0	0-2	6-2
4 Billingham Town	1-8	0-5	0-3		2-6	1-2	0-4	1-4	1-2	0-3	1-3	2-1	2-3	1-0	0-9	1-6	4-5	0-8	0-7	2-4	0-2	0-2	0-5
5 Bishop Auckland	0-2	3-1	4-0	6-0		1-0	3-2	8-1	2-0	0-0	1-2	1-1	0-0	2-1	0-0	0-2	4-2	2-3	1-1	1-2	3-0	4-0	1-2
6 Celtic Nation FC	2-0	0-0	1-1	11-0	1-1		4-4	4-0	1-0	0-0	3-1	2-0	5-0	3-0	1-0	3-0	3-0	4-3	3-3	1-1	2-1	1-2	3-0
7 Consett	3-2	10-2	4-3	8-0	3-0	1-2		4-3	0-0	0-1	1-5	3-0	7-1	1-2	1-1	4-1	2-2	0-2	2-1	3-4	4-1	2-5	2-2
8 Crook Town	2-1	2-2	1-0	6-1	3-1	1-4	2-2		4-3	1-2	3-2	3-1	1-4	2-0	3-0	3-3	1-2	4-2	0-4	3-1	2-2	4-5	3-0
9 Dunston UTS	1-1	2-2	0-0	6-0	1-2	1-1	1-1	3-2		2-0	2-0	2-0	2-0	5-0	2-2	4-0	5-2	1-1	0-2	1-1	4-1	1-1	0-5
10 Durham City	2-3	6-1	0-2	5-0	0-2	0-1	3-4	1-0	1-1		2-1	9-3	4-1	1-1	1-1	4-1	3-2	2-3	1-3	3-0	2-0	1-1	1-0
11 Guisborough Town	1-1	3-0	2-1	5-1	2-2	2-3	2-5	4-2	1-2	1-1		3-0	1-0	2-2	2-1	3-1	4-3	0-0	3-0	2-1	2-0	3-4	3-1
12 Hebburn Town	1-2	1-2	0-2	0-0	1-1	0-6	0-4	2-2	0-5	3-5	1-1		1-0	1-4	1-3	5-2	0-2	0-0	1-3	0-1	2-3	0-2	2-6
13 Marske United	0-1	1-1	0-2	0-0	1-1	0-4	3-1	3-2	3-1	0-0	0-4	2-1		3-1	2-2	5-1	1-3	1-2	0-1	3-2	5-1	2-2	3-2
14 Morpeth Town	0-3	1-1	5-2	9-0	0-0	0-1	3-5	3-1	0-2	2-1	0-1	4-0	1-2		1-1	2-1	1-6	0-4	1-4	5-0	7-2	3-1	2-0
15 Newcastle Benfield	2-0	3-0	5-1	5-0	2-2	3-1	1-2	6-1	0-0	1-1	1-2	0-1	4-0	2-1		4-2	2-2	0-3	2-2	2-2	4-0	0-0	3-2
16 Newton Aycliffe	3-4	1-2	4-0	3-0	0-0	0-2	1-1	3-3	0-3	1-5	4-3	3-1	3-2	1-1	4-2		3-3	1-1	0-1	2-1	1-2	4-1	3-1
17 Penrith	3-0	2-2	1-3	5-1	4-2	2-2	2-0	1-0	0-0	3-1	1-2	4-3	2-2	3-4	2-0	2-4		0-3	2-2	5-1	2-2	4-1	2-3
18 Shildon	2-3	3-0	6-2	7-0	4-0	1-1	4-2	0-2	1-0	2-3	2-3	6-0	2-1	1-1	1-0	3-0	1-0		1-1	4-0	2-0	0-0	1-1
19 Spennymoor Town	4-0	5-1	3-1	10-0	1-1	3-0	1-0	5-0	2-0	2-2	1-0	1-0	4-1	1-1	1-0	5-0	4-0	4-2		3-0	4-1	1-1	3-1
20 Sunderland RCA	1-2	1-3	2-4	3-1	0-4	0-3	4-1	1-2	0-1	0-0	0-3	5-3	2-0	0-0	2-0	0-4	0-1	1-2	1-1		3-0	0-2	2-1
21 Team Northumbria	1-3	1-1	2-1	5-0	1-1	0-2	2-5	2-1	3-5	0-2	2-2	1-1	0-2	3-1	2-1	4-1	1-2	2-4	0-4	3-1		0-3	3-4
22 West Auckland Town	2-1	1-1	2-1	6-0	1-0	2-2	2-0	1-1	5-3	1-1	3-2	1-2	3-1	3-2	1-1	3-0	2-0	1-1	3-1	0-0	2-2		1-1
23 Whitley Bay	1-0	0-3	0-1	5-1	4-1	0-3	2-0	1-1	1-5	4-1	1-2	6-0	5-0	2-0	2-1	3-1	2-0	1-2	1-0	5-2	3-1	0-2	

NORTHERN LEAGUE - STEP 5/6

DIVISION TWO	P	W	D	L	F	A	GD	Pts
1 (P) North Shields	42	31	7	4	141	33	108	100
2 (P) West Allotment Celtic	42	27	9	6	96	58	38	90
3 (P) Jarrow Roofing BCA	42	26	8	8	118	63	55	86
4 Seaham Red Star	42	27	7	8	99	45	54	85
5 Heaton Stannington	42	25	6	11	88	59	29	81
6 Norton & Stockton Ancients	42	20	9	13	83	66	17	69
7 Northallerton Town	42	19	9	14	84	67	17	66
8 Whickham	42	19	7	16	86	63	23	64
9 Washington	42	19	5	18	92	98	-6	62
10 Tow Law Town	42	17	8	17	91	82	9	59
11 Chester-Le-Street	42	15	13	14	66	72	-6	58
12 Darlington RA	42	15	11	16	81	76	5	56
13 Birtley Town	42	16	8	18	64	74	-10	56
14 Thornaby	42	16	6	20	85	84	1	54
15 Willington	42	14	8	20	64	86	-22	50
16 (R) Whitehaven	42	14	7	21	69	94	-25	49
17 South Shields	42	11	15	16	62	88	-26	48
18 Alnwick Town	42	10	9	23	65	99	-34	39
19 Brandon United	42	9	7	26	61	101	-40	34
20 Stokesley Sports Club	42	8	9	25	61	99	-38	33
21 Ryton & Crawcrook Albion	42	7	7	28	45	106	-61	28
22 Esh Winning	42	8	3	31	50	138	-88	27

J.R. CLEATOR CUP
(League champions v League Cup winners)

Whitley Bay	v	Spennymoor Town	1-4

ERNSET ARMSTRONG MEMORIAL CUP

ROUND 1

Darlington RA	v	Seaham Red Star	2-0
Tow Law Town	v	Stokesley Sports Club	3-0
Washington	v	Whickham	2-1
Alnwick Town	v	Norton & Stockton Ancients	0-1
Birtley Town	v	Jarrow Roofing BCA	2-4
Willington	v	West Allotment Celtic	4-1

ROUND 2

Chester-Le-Street	v	Thornaby	2-3 aet
South Shields	v	Northallerton Town	2-6
Washington	v	Tow Law Town	2-1
Jarrow Roofing BCA	v	Norton & Stockton Ancients	4-3 aet
Whitehaven	v	Ryton & Crawcrook Albion	2-4
North Shields	v	Esh Winning	2-0
Willington	v	Darlington RA	2-3*
Willington	v	Darlington RA	1-3
Heaton Stannington	v	Brandon United	2-1

**Match abandoned after 45 mins*

QUARTER FINALS

Jarrow Roofing BCA	v	Northallerton Town	2-1
Darlington RA	v	North Shields	2-3
Heaton Stannington	v	Thornaby	1-0
Washington	v	Ryton & Crawcrook Albion	1-0

SEMI FINALS

Washington	v	Heaton Stannington	3-2
North Shields	v	Jarrow Roofing BCA	1-2 aet

FINAL

Jarrow Roofing BCA	v	Washington	1-0

DIVISION TWO	1	2	3	4	5	6	7	8	9	10	11	12	13	14	15	16	17	18	19	20	21	22
1 Alnwick Town		0-0	5-1	1-1	1-0	4-2	0-2	3-4	2-6	1-0	1-1	3-0	2-6	1-1	1-1	1-3	2-3	1-4	0-4	0-1	0-2	2-2
2 Birtley Town	5-2		2-1	3-1	1-1	4-0	1-3	1-4	1-2	1-3	0-1	2-0	1-2	3-1	2-1	4-0	2-2	2-1	0-0	6-2	1-1	2-4
3 Brandon United	1-4	9-0		0-1	2-4	1-1	1-1	0-4	0-5	0-1	1-5	3-1	0-2	1-1	1-1	3-5	0-3	7-0	1-2	1-1	1-5	3-0
4 Chester-Le-Street	3-1	3-0	0-0		2-1	2-0	2-1	0-2	2-1	4-2	1-1	1-1	1-6	2-2	0-0	3-0	0-3	0-5	0-0	2-1	1-1	3-0
5 Darlington RA	2-1	1-2	2-3	2-0		10-2	2-0	3-3	2-1	1-2	0-0	2-2	2-1	3-3	4-1	2-3	4-3	2-3	0-4	0-3	6-0	2-2
6 Esh Winning	2-2	3-1	1-2	1-4	1-5		2-5	0-3	0-6	1-5	3-2	3-1	1-2	1-2	3-1	0-3	2-4	1-5	1-3	3-6	4-1	0-2
7 Heaton Stannington	4-2	3-0	5-1	1-3	1-3	1-0		4-3	0-0	2-1	1-1	1-1	1-2	2-0	0-1	2-1	1-0	6-1	3-2	2-1	4-2	2-1
8 Jarrow Roofing BCA	3-0	1-1	2-0	5-1	1-0	10-0	1-0		1-2	4-2	3-1	4-0	3-1	4-2	1-1	2-1	2-4	3-3	0-2	4-3	2-1	1-3
9 North Shields	3-0	0-0	6-0	3-0	5-1	5-0	3-1	1-0		2-2	3-2	6-1	0-1	4-3	5-0	2-0	1-1	8-0	3-0	5-1	10-0	4-1
10 Northallerton Town	1-4	3-2	4-0	2-4	1-1	6-0	1-2	1-1	1-3		2-1	2-1	3-0	4-0	2-2	3-2	4-2	2-0	1-3	1-1	4-2	3-3
11 Norton & Stockton Ancients	4-1	2-0	1-0	3-2	3-0	7-0	1-1	2-3	1-2	2-1		5-0	0-5	2-2	3-2	1-0	2-1	0-2	3-3	0-3	3-2	2-1
12 Ryton & Crawcrook Albion	1-2	0-1	4-1	2-2	0-1	2-0	0-4	1-4	1-4	0-3	2-1		0-1	1-2	1-4	0-2	2-0	1-7	2-4	1-1	2-1	3-4
13 Seaham Red Star	5-0	4-2	1-2	3-1	1-1	1-0	1-2	1-1	3-0	1-1	2-1	3-0		5-0	2-0	5-2	3-0	4-1	2-2	1-2	1-0	3-0
14 South Shields	0-3	2-1	1-1	4-3	3-3	2-3	0-2	1-5	1-3	2-2	1-0	2-4	1-1		2-1	1-1	4-3	1-2	2-2	1-1	2-1	0-0
15 Stokesley Sports Club	2-1	0-1	3-0	2-3	1-2	1-2	2-4	3-6	3-3	2-1	0-1	2-2	0-1	1-3		3-1	1-2	3-1	2-2	0-3	2-2	3-5
16 Thornaby	2-2	2-0	3-1	1-1	3-0	3-0	4-5	1-1	1-4	1-2	2-2	0-1	4-0	1-2	4-2		6-3	2-4	3-1	3-1	5-0	3-1
17 Tow Law Town	3-1	2-3	1-3	1-1	5-0	2-0	2-2	1-3	0-0	3-1	3-5	1-1	2-3	1-1	5-0	4-2		3-0	3-4	2-2	1-3	2-1
18 Washington	1-2	2-2	4-3	3-1	0-3	4-3	3-1	4-2	0-9	3-0	1-4	4-0	1-1	1-1	5-1	4-2	2-3		2-3	0-5	3-1	0-0
19 West Allotment Celtic	5-3	2-1	2-1	2-2	2-1	1-1	0-1	3-5	0-0	3-0	5-0	2-1	2-1	3-2	3-2	2-1	3-2	1-0		3-1	2-0	3-0
20 Whickham	3-0	0-1	4-1	1-1	2-0	4-0	2-0	3-3	0-1	0-2	0-1	4-1	2-3	0-1	4-1	4-0	2-0	1-0	2-3		1-2	2-5
21 Whitehaven	4-2	1-2	1-3	2-1	1-1	1-0	4-3	2-1	0-4	0-0	3-5	2-1	1-1	4-0	4-1	1-1	2-3	3-2	3-1	2-3		0-1
22 Willington	1-1	2-0	2-1	2-1	1-1	2-3	1-2	0-3	0-6	0-2	1-1	5-0	0-7	2-0	1-2	4-1	1-2	0-4	0-2	0-3	3-1	

CLUB MOVEMENTS

Premier Division - In: Jarrow Roofing BCA (P). North shields (P). West Allotment Celtic (P).

Out: Billingham Town (R). Hebburn Town (R). Spennymoor Town (P - Northern Premier Div.1 North). Team Northumbria (R).

Division One - In: Billingham Town (R). Hebburn Town (R). Ryhope CW (P - Wearside). Team Northumbria (R).

Out: Jarrow Roofing BCA (P). North shields (P). West Allotment Celtic (P). Whitehaven (R - Wearside - due to ground grading).

ASHINGTON

Founded: 1883 Nickname: The Colliers

Secretary: Brian Robson **(T)** 07843 661 686 **(E)** brian.robson@piramal.com
Chairman: Ian Lavery **Prog Ed:** Ian Jobson
Ground: Woodhorn Lane, Ashington NE63 9FW **(T)** 01670 811 991
Capacity: **Seats:** **Covered:** **Midweek Matchday:** Tuesday **Clubhouse:** Yes **Shop:** Yes

Colours(change): Black & White stripes/black/black.
Previous Names: None
Previous Leagues: Northern Alliance, Football League, N. Eastern, Midland, Northern Counties, Wearside, N.P.L.
Records: **Att:** 13,199 v Rochdale FA Cup 2nd round 1950
Senior Honours: Northern League Div.2 Champions 2000-01, 03-04.

10 YEAR RECORD

04-05	05-06	06-07	07-08	08-09	09-10	10-11	11-12	12-13	13-14
NL 1 10	NL 1 16	NL 1 19	NL 1 17	NL 1 16	NL 1 6	NL 1 8	NL 1 5	NL 1 7	NL 1 6

BEDLINGTON TERRIERS COMM.

Founded: 1949 Nickname: Terriers

Secretary: Jim Anderson **(T)** 07929 272 647 **(E)** nbsfc@blueyonder.co.uk
Chairman: Ronan Liddane **Prog Ed:** Terry Brown
Ground: Doctor Pit Welfare Park, Park Road, Bedlington NE22 5AT **(T)** 07514 412 137
Capacity: 3,000 **Seats:** 300 **Covered:** 500 **Midweek Matchday:** Wednesday **Clubhouse:** Yes

Colours(change): Red with white trim/red/red.
Previous Names: Bedlington Mechanics 1949-53 Bedlington United 1961-65
Previous Leagues: Northern Alliance
Records: **Att:** 2,400 v Colchester United FA Cup 1st round **Goalscorer:** John Milner
Senior Honours: Northern Lge Div 1: 97-98, 98-99, 99-00, 2000-01, 01-02. Northumberland Senior Cup 1996-97, 97-98, 2001-02,03-04.

10 YEAR RECORD

04-05	05-06	06-07	07-08	08-09	09-10	10-11	11-12	12-13	13-14
NL 1 3	NL 1 2	NL 1 20	NL 1 15	NL 1 14	NL 1 7	NL 1 9	NL 1 7	NL 1 15	NL 1 20

BILLINGHAM SYNTHONIA

Founded: 1923 Nickname: Synners

Secretary: Graham Craggs **(T)** 07702 530 335 **(E)** graham.craggs@gb.abb.com
Chairman: Stuart Coleby **Prog Ed:** Graeme Goodman
Ground: The Stadium, Central Ave, Billingham, Cleveland TS23 1LR **(T)** 01642 532 348
Capacity: 1,970 **Seats:** 370 **Covered:** 370 **Midweek Matchday:** Wednesday **Clubhouse:** Yes **Shop:** Yes

Colours(change): Green & white quarters/white/white
Previous Names: Billingham Synthonia Recreation
Previous Leagues: Teesside 1923-the war
Records: **Att:** 4,200 v Bishop Auckland 1958 **Goalscorer:** Tony Hetherington **App:** Andy Harbron
Senior Honours: Northern Lge 1956-57, 88-89, 89-90, 95-96. Div.2 86-87.

10 YEAR RECORD

04-05	05-06	06-07	07-08	08-09	09-10	10-11	11-12	12-13	13-14
NL 1 2	NL 1 7	NL 1 14	NL 1 9	NL 1 15	NL 1 12	NL 1 12	NL 1 11	NL 1 12	NL 1 20

BISHOP AUCKLAND

Founded: 1886 Nickname:

Secretary: John Stubbs **(T)** 07726 694 672 **(E)** johnstubbsuk@btinternet.com
Chairman: Richard Tremewan **Prog Ed:** John Stubbs
Ground: Heritage Park, Bishop Auckland, Co. Durham DL14 9AE **(T)** 01388 604 605
Capacity: 2,004 **Seats:** 250 **Covered:** 722 **Midweek Matchday:** Tuesday **Clubhouse:** Yes **Shop:** No

Colours(change): Light & dark blue/blue/light & dark blue
Previous Names: Auckland Town 1889-1893
Previous Leagues: Northern Alliance 1890-91, Northern League 1893-1988, Northern Premier 1988-2006
Records: **Att:** 17,000 v Coventry City FA Cup 2nd round 1952 **App:** Bob Hardisty
Senior Honours: (Post War) Northern League 1949-50, 50-51, 51-52, 53-54, 54-55, 55-56, 66-67, 84-85, 85-86 (18th Nth Lge title). Durham Challenge Cup 2012-13.

10 YEAR RECORD

04-05	05-06	06-07	07-08	08-09	09-10	10-11	11-12	12-13	13-14
NP P 19	NP 1 22	NL 1 16	NL 1 20	NL 1 18	NL 1 13	NL 1 14	NL 1 8	NL 1 6	NL 1 8

CELTIC NATION

Founded: 2005 Nickname:

Secretary: Michael Linden **(T)** 07717 103 666 **(E)** linden146@btinternet.com

Chairman: Stephen Skinner **Prog Ed:** David Bradley

Ground: Gillford Park Railway Club, Off Pettrill Bank Rd, Carlisle, Cumbria CA1 3AF **(T)** 01228 545 115

Capacity: **Seats:** Yes **Covered:** Yes **Midweek Matchday:** Tuesday **Clubhouse:**

Colours(change): Green & white hoops/green/green & white hoops

Previous Names: Gillford Park Spartans > 2005. Gillford Park 2005-12.

Previous Leagues: Northern Alliance 2005-09.

Records:

Senior Honours: Northern Alliance Division 1 2006-07, Premier Division 2008-09, Challenge Cup 2008-09.

10 YEAR RECORD

04-05	05-06	06-07	07-08	08-09	09-10	10-11	11-12	12-13	13-14
	NAI 2 2	NAI 1 1	NAI P 3	NAI P 2	NL 2 11	NL 2 11	NL 2 2	NL 1 10	NL 1 2

CONSETT

Founded: 1899 Nickname: Steelman

Secretary: David Pyke **(T)** 07889 419 268 **(E)** david_pyke@hotmail.co.uk

Chairman: Frank Bell **Prog Ed:** Gary Welford

Ground: Belle Vue Park, Ashdale Road, Consett, DH8 7BF **(T)** 01207 588 886

Capacity: 4,000 **Seats:** 400 **Covered:** 1000 **Midweek Matchday:** Tuesday **Clubhouse:** Yes **Shop:** No

Colours(change): All Red

Previous Names: None

Previous Leagues: N.All 1919-26, 35-37, N.E.C. 26-35, 37-58, 62-64, Midland 58-60, N.Co. 60-62, Wearside 64-70

Records: **Att:** 7000 v Sunderland Reserves, first match at Belle Vue 1950

Senior Honours: Norh Eastern Lg 39-40 Div 2 26-27, Northern Counties Lg 61-62, Northern Leageu Div.2 1988-89, 05-06.

10 YEAR RECORD

04-05	05-06	06-07	07-08	08-09	09-10	10-11	11-12	12-13	13-14
NL 1 19	NL 2 1	NL 1 4	NL 1 2	NL 1 2	NL 1 10	NL 1 2	NL 1 15	NL 1 9	NL 1 11

CROOK TOWN

Founded: 1889 Nickname: Black & Ambers

Secretary: Ian Todd **(T)** 07941 459 755 **(E)** iantodd147@gmail.com

Chairman: Ian Hirst **Prog Ed:** Ian Todd

Ground: The Sir Tom Cowie Millfield, West Road, Crook, Co.Durham DL15 9PW **(T)** 01388 762 959

Capacity: **Seats:** **Covered:** **Midweek Matchday:** **Clubhouse:**

Colours(change): Amber/black/amber

Previous Names: Crook C.W.

Previous Leagues: Durham Central 1941-45.

Records:

Senior Honours: FA Amateur Cup 1900-01, 53-54, 58-59, 61-62, 63-64. Northern League x5 Div.2 2012-13, League Cup x3. Durham Challenge Cup x4. Durham Benefit Bowl x6. Ernest Armstrong Memorial Trophy 1997.

10 YEAR RECORD

04-05	05-06	06-07	07-08	08-09	09-10	10-11	11-12	12-13	13-14
NL 2 7	NL 2 5	NL 2 14	NL 2 14	NL 2 9	NL 2 13	NL 2 12	NL 2 10	NL 2 1	NL 1 15

DUNSTON UTS

Founded: 1975 Nickname: The Fed

Secretary: Bill Montague **(T)** 07981 194 756 **(E)** w.montague@sky.com

Chairman: Malcolm James **Prog Ed:** Bill Montague

Ground: UTS Stadium, Wellington Rd, Dunston, Gateshead NE11 9JL **(T)** 0191 493 2935

Capacity: 2,000 **Seats:** 120 **Covered:** 400 **Midweek Matchday:** Wednesday **Clubhouse:** Yes **Shop:** No

Colours(change): All Blue with white trim/blue/blue

Previous Names: Dunston Federation Brewery > 2007. Dunston Federation > 2009.

Previous Leagues: Northern Amateur & Wearside league

Records: **Att:** 1,550 v Sunderland Shipowners Cup Final 01.04.88 **Goalscorer:** Paul King **App:** Paul Dixon

Senior Honours: Wearside League 1988-89, 89-90. Northern League Div.2 92-93. Div.1 2003-04, 04-05. FA Vase 2011-12.

10 YEAR RECORD

04-05	05-06	06-07	07-08	08-09	09-10	10-11	11-12	12-13	13-14
NL 1 1	NL 1 3	NL 1 7	NL 1 6	NL 1 6	NL 1 4	NL 1 7	NL 1 3	NL 1 5	NL 1 7

DURHAM CITY

Founded: 1949 Nickname: City

Secretary: Kevin Hewitt **(T)** 07897 611 640 **(E)** hewittkd@fsmail.net
Chairman: Olivier Bernard **Prog Ed:** Josh Fisk
Ground: The Durham UTS Arena, New Ferens Park, Belmont Ind.Est. DH1 1GG **(T)** 0191 386 9616
Capacity: 2,700 **Seats:** 270 **Covered:** 750 **Midweek Matchday:** Tuesday **Clubhouse:** Yes **Shop:** No

Colours(change): Yellow/blue/blue
Previous Names: Original club founded in 1918 disbanded in 1938 and reformed in 1949
Previous Leagues: Victory 1918-19, North Eastern 1919-21, 28-38, Football League 1921-28, Wearside 1938-39, 50-51, Northern 1951-2008. NPL 2008-12.
Records: 2,750 v Whitley Bay - FA Vase Semi-final 2001-02
Senior Honours: Northern League 1994-95, 2007-08. Northern Premier League Division 1 North 2008-09, Chairman's Cup 2008-09.

10 YEAR RECORD

04-05	05-06	06-07	07-08	08-09	09-10	10-11	11-12	12-13	13-14
NL 1 6	NL 1 11	NL 1 8	NL 1 1	NP1N 1	NP P 20	NP1N 17	NP1N 9	NL 1 14	NL 1 9

GUISBOROUGH TOWN

Founded: 1973 Nickname: Priorymen

Secretary: Keith Smeltzer **(T)** 07811 850 388 **(E)** keithsmeltzer@hotmail.co.uk
Chairman: Don Cowan **Prog Ed:** Danny Clark
Ground: King George V Ground, Howlbeck Road, Guisborough TS14 6LE **(T)** 01287 636 925
Capacity: **Seats:** Yes **Covered:** Yes **Midweek Matchday:** Wednesday **Clubhouse:** Yes

Colours(change): Red & white stripes/black/red
Previous Names: None
Previous Leagues: Northern Counties East 1982-85.
Records: **Att:** 3,112 v Hungerford FA Vase Semi-final. **Goalscorer:** Mark Davis 341. **Apps:** Mark Davis 587.
Senior Honours: Northern Alliance 1979-80. Northern League Cup 1987-88. Nth Riding Sen Cup 1989-90, 90-91, 91-92, 92-93, 94-95

10 YEAR RECORD

04-05	05-06	06-07	07-08	08-09	09-10	10-11	11-12	12-13	13-14
NL 1 21	NL 1 19	NL 2 9	NL 2 12	NL 2 7	NL 2 5	NL 2 2	NL 1 16	NL 1 11	NL 1 4

JARROW ROOFING BOLDON C.A.

Founded: 1987 Nickname: Roofing

Secretary: David Ramsey **(T)** 07791 707 363 **(E)** secretary@jarrowroofingfc.co.uk
Chairman: Richard McLoughlin **Prog Ed:** Andrew Hudson
Ground: Boldon CA Sports Ground, New Road, Boldon Colliery NE35 9DZ **(T)** 07714 525 549
Capacity: 3,500 **Seats:** 150 **Covered:** 800 **Midweek Matchday:** Tuesday **Clubhouse:** Yes

Colours(change): All blue and yellow
Previous Names:
Previous Leagues: S. Tyneside Senior 1987-88, Tyneside Am. 1988-91, Wearside 1991-96
Records: **Att:** 500 v South Shields **Goalscorer:** Mick Hales **App:** Paul Chow
Senior Honours:

10 YEAR RECORD

04-05	05-06	06-07	07-08	08-09	09-10	10-11	11-12	12-13	13-14
NL 1 12	NL 1 15	NL 1 15	NL 1 22	NL 2 16	NL 2 3	NL 1 19	NL 1 20	NL 2 4	NL 2 3

MARSKE UNITED

Founded: 1956 Nickname: The Seasiders

Secretary: Les Holtby **(T)** 07804 150 880 **(E)** admin@marskeunitedfc.com
Chairman: Peter Collinson **Prog Ed:** Moss Holtby
Ground: GER Stad., Mount Pleasant Avenue, Marske by the Sea, Redcar TS11 7BW **(T)** 01642 471 091
Capacity: **Seats:** Yes **Covered:** Yes **Midweek Matchday:** Tuesday **Clubhouse:** Yes

Colours(change): Yellow/blue/blue
Previous Names: None
Previous Leagues: Wearside 1985-97.
Records: **Defeat:** 3-9. **Goalscorer:** Chris Morgan 169. **Apps:** Mike Kinnair 583.
Senior Honours: Teesside League 1980-81, 84-85. Wearside League 1995-96. North Riding Senior Cup 1994-95.
North Riding County Cup 1980-81, 85-86.

10 YEAR RECORD

04-05	05-06	06-07	07-08	08-09	09-10	10-11	11-12	12-13	13-14
NL 2 15	NL 2 10	NL 2 5	NL 2 8	NL 2 5	NL 2 4	NL 2 3	NL 1 18	NL 1 19	NL 1 16

MORPETH TOWN

Founded: 1909 Nickname: Highwaymen

Secretary: David McMeekan **(T)** 07425 135 301 **(E)** drmcmeekan@yahoo.co.uk
Chairman: Ken Beattie **Prog Ed:** David McMeekan
Ground: Craik Park, Morpeth Common, Morpeth, Northumberland, NE61 2YX **(T)** 07425 135 301
Capacity: **Seats:** Yes **Covered:** Yes **Midweek Matchday:** Wednesday **Clubhouse:** Yes

Colours(change): Amber & black stripes/black/black
Previous Names: None
Previous Leagues: Northern Alliance > 1994.
Records:
Senior Honours: Northern Alliance 1983-84, 93-94, Northern League Division 2 1995-96. Northumberland Senior Cup 2006-07.

10 YEAR RECORD

04-05		05-06		06-07		07-08		08-09		09-10		10-11		11-12		12-13		13-14	
NL 1	13	NL 1	6	NL 1	10	NL 1	8	NL 1	12	NL 1	21	NL 2	20	NL 2	4	NL 2	3	NL 1	17

NEWCASTLE BENFIELD

Founded: 1988 Nickname: The Lions

Secretary: Gary Thompson **(T)** 07816 918 261 **(E)** gctwnphg@gmail.com
Chairman: Jimmy Rowe **Prog Ed:** Ian Cusack
Ground: Sam Smiths Park, Benfield Road, Walkergate NE6 4NU **(T)** 07816 918 261
Capacity: 2,000 **Seats:** 150 **Covered:** 250 **Midweek Matchday:** Wednesday **Clubhouse:** Yes **Shop:** No

Colours(change): Blue & white hoops/blue/blue
Previous Names: Heaton Corner House. Newcastle Benfield Saints.
Previous Leagues: Northern Alliance 1988-2003
Records:
Senior Honours: Northern Alliance Div 2 Champions 1989-90, Div 1 1994-95, 2002-03.
Northern League Cup 2006-07. Northern League Champions 2008-09.

10 YEAR RECORD

04-05		05-06		06-07		07-08		08-09		09-10		10-11		11-12		12-13		13-14	
NL 1	4	NL 1	9	NL 1	5	NL 1	4	NL 1	1	NL 1	5	NL 1	4	NL 1	12	NL 1	21	NL 1	14

NEWTON AYCLIFFE

Founded: 1965 Nickname: Aycliffe

Secretary: Stephen Cunliffe **(T)** 07872 985 501 **(E)** stecunliffe@aol.com
Chairman: Alan Oliver **Prog Ed:** Stephen Cunkiffe
Ground: Moore Lane Park, Moore Lane, Newton Aycliffe, Co. Durham DL5 5AG **(T)** 01325 312 768
Capacity: **Seats:** Yes **Covered:** Yes **Midweek Matchday:** Wednesday **Clubhouse:** Yes

Colours(change): All blue
Previous Names: None
Previous Leagues: Wearside 1984-94, 2008-09. Durham Alliance > 2008.
Records: **Att:** 520 v Teesside Athletic (Sunderland Shipwoners Final) 2008-09.
Senior Honours: Darlington & District Division 'A' 2004-05. Durham Alliance League 2007-08. Wearside League 2008-09.
Northern League Division Two 2010-11.

10 YEAR RECORD

04-05		05-06		06-07		07-08		08-09		09-10		10-11		11-12		12-13		13-14	
DaD'A'	1					DuAl	1	Wear	1	NL 2	9	NL 2	1	NL 1	9	NL 1	17	NL 1	18

NORTH SHIELDS

Founded: 1992 Nickname: Robins

Secretary: David Thompson **(T)** 07969 239 476 **(E)** nsfc.dt@gmail.com
Chairman: Alan Matthews **Prog Ed:** Mark Scott
Ground: Daren Persson Staduim, Ralph Gardner Park, West Percy Rd, Chirton, North **(T)** 07759 766 732
Capacity: **Seats:** **Covered:** **Midweek Matchday:** **Clubhouse:**

Colours(change): All red
Previous Names: Preston Colliery > 1928, North Shields Athletic 1995-99.
Previous Leagues: Wearside.
Records:
Senior Honours: FA Amateur Cup 1968-69, N.C.E. Prem Div 91-92, Lge Cup 90-91. Wearside League 1998-99, 01-02, 03-04.
Northern League Division Two 2013-14.

10 YEAR RECORD

04-05		05-06		06-07		07-08		08-09		09-10		10-11		11-12		12-13		13-14	
NL 2	11	NL 2	12	NL 2	18	NL 2	17	NL 2	15	NL 2	6	NL 2	4	NL 2	8	NL 2	8	NL 2	1

PENRITH

Founded: 1894 Nickname: Blues

Secretary: Ian White **(T)** 07960 958 367 **(E)** ianwhite77@hotmail.com
Chairman: Mark Forster **Prog Ed:** Brian Kirkbride
Ground: The Stadium, Frenchfield Park, Frenchfield, Penrith CA11 8UA **(T)** 01768 865 990
Capacity: 4,000 **Seats:** 200 **Covered:** 1,000 **Midweek Matchday:** Tuesday **Clubhouse:** Yes **Shop:** No

Colours(change): Blue/white/blue.
Previous Names: Penrith FC. Penrith Town.
Previous Leagues: Carlisle & Dist. Northern 1942-82. NWC 1982-87, 90-97. NPL 1987-90.
Records: 2,100 v Chester 1981
Senior Honours: Northern League Division 2 Champions 2002-03, 07-08.

10 YEAR RECORD

04-05	05-06	06-07	07-08	08-09	09-10	10-11	11-12	12-13	13-14
NL 2 8	NL 2 4	NL 2 7	NL 2 1	NL 1 7	NL 1 14	NL 1 17	NL 1 19	NL 1 13	NL 1 13

SHILDON

Founded: 1890 Nickname: Railwaymen

Secretary: Gareth Howe **(T)** 07976 822 453 **(E)** gareth.howe3@btopenworld.com
Chairman: Brian Burn **Prog Ed:** Archie MacKay
Ground: Dean Street, Shildon, Co. Durham DL4 1HA **(T)** 01388 773 877
Capacity: 4,000 **Seats:** 480 **Covered:** 1000 **Midweek Matchday:** Wednesday **Clubhouse:** Yes **Shop:** No

Colours(change): All red
Previous Names: Shildon Athletic > 1923.
Previous Leagues: Auckland & Dist 1892-86, Wear Valley 1896-97, Northern 1903-07, North Eastern 1907-32
Records: **Att:** 11,000 v Ferryhill Athletic, Durham Senior Cup 1922 **Goalscorer:** Jack Downing 61 (1936-7) **App:** Bryan Dale
Senior Honours: Durham Amateur Cup 1901-02, 02-03, Durham Challenge Cup 1907-08, 25-26, 71-72,
Northern League Champions 1933-34, 34-35, 35-36,36-37, 39-40, Div 2 2001-02.

10 YEAR RECORD

04-05	05-06	06-07	07-08	08-09	09-10	10-11	11-12	12-13	13-14
NL 1 11	NL 1 18	NL 1 9	NL 1 5	NL 1 8	NL 1 2	NL 1 5	NL 1 10	NL 1 8	NL 1 3

SUNDERLAND RYHOPE C.A.

Founded: 1961 Nickname:

Secretary: Rob Jones **(T)** 07932 951 842 **(E)** Robert-jones10@live.co.uk
Chairman: Graham Defty **Prog Ed:** Colin Wilson
Ground: Meadow Park, Beachbrooke, Stockton Rd, Ryhope, Sunderland SR2 0NZ **(T)** 0191 523 6555
Capacity: 2,000 **Seats:** 150 **Covered:** 200 **Midweek Matchday:** Wednesday **Clubhouse:** Yes

Colours(change): Red & white/black/red
Previous Names: Ryhope Community Ass. FC
Previous Leagues: S.C. Vaux: Tyne & Wear, NorthEastern Am a Ryhope CA N Alliance.>82
Records: Not Known
Senior Honours: Northern Alliance League Cup 1981.

10 YEAR RECORD

04-05	05-06	06-07	07-08	08-09	09-10	10-11	11-12	12-13	13-14
NL 2 16	NL 2 17	NL 2 19	NL 2 4	NL 2 4	NL 2 2	NL 1 13	NL 1 4	NL 1 22	NL 1 19

WEST ALLOTMENT CELTIC

Founded: 1928 Nickname:

Secretary: Ted Ilderton **(T)** 07795 246 245 **(E)** tedilderton@gmail.com
Chairman: Roland Mather **Prog Ed:** Craig Dobson
Ground: Whitley Park, Whitley Road, Benton NE12 9FA **(T)** 07795 246 245
Capacity: **Seats:** **Covered:** **Midweek Matchday:** Monday **Clubhouse:**

Colours(change): Green & white hoops/green/green
Previous Names:
Previous Leagues: Tynemouth & District. Northern Amateur. Northern Alliance.
Records: **Att:** 510 v Cray Wanderers FA Vase 2004
Senior Honours: Northern Am. 1956-57, 57-58, 58-59, 59-60, 81-82, 82-83, Div 2: 38-39.
Northern Alliance: 1986-87, 90-91, 91-92, 97-98, 98-99, 99-2000, 01-02, 03-04. Northern League Div 2 2004-05

10 YEAR RECORD

04-05	05-06	06-07	07-08	08-09	09-10	10-11	11-12	12-13	13-14
NL 2 1	NL 1 13	NL 1 18	NL 1 13	NL 1 9	NL 1 15	NL 1 20	NL 2 7	NL 2 7	NL 2 2

WEST AUCKLAND TOWN

Founded: 1893 Nickname: West

Secretary: Allen Bayles **(T)** 07894 329 005 **(E)** allenbayles@hotmail.co.uk
Chairman: Jim Palfreyman **Prog Ed:** Michael Bainbridge
Ground: Darlington Road, West Auckland, Co. Durham DL14 9HU **(T)** 07800 796 630
Capacity: 3,000 **Seats:** 250 **Covered:** 250 **Midweek Matchday:** Tuesday **Clubhouse:** Yes **Shop:** No

Colours(change): Yellow/black/yellow
Previous Names: Auckland St Helens. St Helens. West Auckland.
Previous Leagues: Auck&D.,Wear Val,Sth D'ham All.Mid D'ham, Nth Lge 1919-20.Palantine 20-24.Sth D'ham 27-28.Gaunless Val 33-34
Records: **Att:** 6,000 v Dulwich Hamlet FA Amateur Cup 1958-59
Senior Honours: Sir Thomas Lipton Trophy 1909, 1911, Northern League 1959-60, 60-61. Div 2 1990-91. League Cup 1958-59, 62-63, Durham Challenge Cup 1964-65

10 YEAR RECORD

04-05	05-06	06-07	07-08	08-09	09-10	10-11	11-12	12-13	13-14
NL 1 17	NL 1 5	NL 1 6	NL 1 16	NL 1 20	NL 1 16	NL 1 6	NL 1 2	NL 1 4	NL 1 5

WHITLEY BAY

Founded: 1897 Nickname: The Bay

Secretary: Derek Breakwell **(T)** 07889 888 187 **(E)** dbreakwell@hotmail.co.uk
Chairman: Paul McIlduff **Prog Ed:** Julian Tyley
Ground: Hillheads Park, Rink Way, Whitley Bay, NE25 8HR **(T)** 0191 291 3637
Capacity: 4,500 **Seats:** 450 **Covered:** 650 **Midweek Matchday:** Tuesday **Clubhouse:** Yes **Shop:** Yes

Colours(change): Blue & white stripes/blue/blue
Previous Names: Whitley Bay Athletic 1950-58
Previous Leagues: Tyneside 1909-10, Northern All. 1950-55, N. Eastern 1955-58, Northern 1958-88 N.P.L. 1988-00
Records: 7,301 v Hendon, FA Amateur Cup 1965.
Senior Honours: Northern Alliance 1952-53, 53-54. Northern League 1964-65, 65-66, 06-07. NPL Div 1 1990-91, FA Vase 2001-02, 08-09, 09-10, 10-11.

10 YEAR RECORD

04-05	05-06	06-07	07-08	08-09	09-10	10-11	11-12	12-13	13-14
NL 1 5	NL 1 10	NL 1 1	NL 1 3	NL 1 3	NL 1 3	NL 1 3	NL 1 6	NL 1 3	NL 1 10

ALNWICK TOWN

Founded: 1879 Nickname:

Secretary: Cyril Cox **(T)** 07811 555 363 **(E)** uk2usa@hotmail.co.uk
Chairman: Tommy McKie **Prog Ed:** Michael Cook
Ground: St. Jame's Park, Weavers Way, Alnwick, Northumberland NE66 1BG **(T)** 01665 603 162
Colours(change): Black & white stripes/black/black

ADDITIONAL INFORMATION: Previous Names: Alnwick Utd Services 1879-1900, Alnwick Utd Juniors 1900-1936.
Previous Lge: Northern Alliance 1935-82, 2007-11. Northern League 1982-2007.
League honours: Nothern Alliance title 9 times.

BILLINGHAM TOWN

Founded: 1967 Nickname: Billy Town

Secretary: Peter Martin **(T)** 07873 794 768 **(E)** peterwlmartin@hotmail.com
Chairman: Peter Martin **Prog Ed:** Peter Martin
Ground: Bedford Terrace, Billingham, Cleveland TS23 4AE **(T)** 07873 794 768 **Capacity:** 3,000
Colours(change): All blue

ADDITIONAL INFORMATION: Att: 1,500 v Man City FA Youth Cup 1985 **Goalscorer:** Paul Rowntree 396 **App:** Paul Rowntree 505
Durham Cup 1976-77, 77-78, 2003-04

BIRTLEY TOWN

Founded: 1993 Nickname: The Hoops

Secretary: Trevor Armstrong **(T)** 07958 540 389 **(E)** trevellen1@sky.com
Chairman: John Heslington **Prog Ed:** Andrew Walker
Ground: Birtley Sports Complex, Durham Road, Birtley DH3 2TB **(T)** 07958 540 389
Colours(change): Green & white hoops/green/green

ADDITIONAL INFORMATION:
Previous League: Wearside 1993-2007.
Honours: Wearside League 2002-03, 06-07, Division 2 1994-95, League Cup 1998, 2002, 2006.

BRANDON UNITED

Founded: 1968 Nickname: United

Secretary: Barry Ross **(T)** 07717 673 090 **(E)** kayowe48@gmail.com
Chairman: David Bussey **Prog Ed:** Dean Johnson
Ground: Welfare Park, Rear Commercial Street, Brandon DH7 7PL **(T)** 07717 673 090
Colours(change): All red

ADDITIONAL INFORMATION: Previous League: Wearside 1981-83. **Record Att:** 2,500 F.A. Sunday Cup Seim-final.
Record: Goalscorer: Tommy Holden. **Apps:** Derek Charlton 1977-86. **Honours:** F.A. Sunday Cup 1975-76.
Northern Alliance Division 2 1977-78, 78-79. Northern League 2002-03, Division 2 1984-85, 99-2000.

CHESTER-LE-STREET TOWN

Founded: 1972 Nickname: Cestrians

Secretary: Lenny Lauchlan **(T)** 07807 419 872 **(E)** l.w.lauchlan@durham.ac.uk
Chairman: Joe Burlison **Prog Ed:** Keith Greener
Ground: Moor Park, Chester Moor, Chester-le-Street, Co.Durham DH2 3RW **(T)** 07972 419 275
Colours(change): Blue & white hoops/white/white with blue trim

ADDITIONAL INFORMATION: Previous Name: Garden Farm 1972-78. **Previous League:** Wearside 1977-83.
Record Att: 893 v Fleetwood FA Vase 1985 **App:** Colin Wake 361.
Honours: Washington League 1975-6 Wearside League1980-81, Northern League Div 2 1983-84, 97-98.

DARLINGTON R.A.

Founded: 1993 Nickname:

Secretary: Alan Hamilton **(T)** 07872 324 808 **(E)** nobbydarlo@ntlworld.com
Chairman: Doug Hawman **Prog Ed:** Alan Hamilton
Ground: Brinkburn Road, Darlington, Co. Durham DL3 9LF **(T)** 01325 468 125
Colours(change): All red

ADDITIONAL INFORMATION:
Previous League: Darlington & District 1993-99.
Honours: Auckland & District League 2000-01. Wearside League 2004-05.

ESH WINNING

Founded: 1885 Nickname: Stags

Secretary: Michael Young **(T)** 07837 205 732 **(E)** michael.young86@btinternet.com
Chairman: Charles Ryan **Prog Ed:** Michael Young
Ground: West Terrace, Waterhouse, Durham DH7 9BQ **(T)** 0191 373 3872 **Capacity:** 3,500
Colours(change): Yellow/green/green

ADDITIONAL INFORMATION:
Record Att: 5,000 v Newcastle Utd Res. 1910 & Bishop Auckland 1921 **Goalscorer:** Alan Dodsworth 250+ **App:** Neil McLeary - 194.
League honours: Northern League Champions 1912-13.

HEATON STANNINGTON

Founded: 1910 Nickname: The Stan

Secretary: Geoff Walker **(T)** 07932 252 981 **(E)** geoffwalker51@yahoo.com
Chairman: Bill Pitt **Prog Ed:** Kevin Mochrie
Ground: Grounsell Park, Newton Road, High Heaton, Newcastle upon Tyne NE7 7HP **(T)** 0191 281 9230
Colours(change): Black & white stripes/black/black & white hoops

ADDITIONAL INFORMATION:
Previous Leagues: Northern Alliance >2013.
Honours: Northern Alliance 2011-12, 12-13.

HEBBURN TOWN

Founded: 1912 Nickname: Hornets

Secretary: Tom Derrick **(T)** 07981 456 653 **(E)** tomderrick39@hotmail.com
Chairman: Bill Laffey **Prog Ed:** Richard Bainbridge
Ground: Hebburn Sports & Social, Victoria Rd West, Hebburn, Tyne&Wear NE31 1UN **(T)** 0191 483 5101
Colours(change): Yellow & black stripes/black/black

ADDITIONAL INFORMATION: Att: 503 v Darwen FA Cup Prelim replay 07/09/1991, **Win:** 10-1. **Defeat:** 3-10.
Tyneside League 1938-39, Northern Combination 1943-44, Wearside League 1966-67.

NORTHALLERTON TOWN

Founded: 1994 Nickname: Town

Secretary: Lesley Clark **(T)** 07891 595 267 **(E)** lesleyclark05@yahoo.co.uk
Chairman: Les Hood
Ground: The Calvert Stadium, Ainderby Road, Northallerton DL7 8HA **(T)** 01609 778 337
Colours(change): Black & white stripes/black/black & white

ADDITIONAL INFORMATION: Previous Name: Northallerton FC 1994. **Previous League:** Harrogate & District.
Record Att: 695 v Farnborough Town FA Trophy 3rd Round 20/02/1993.
Honours: Northern League Division 2 1996-97, League Cup 1993-94.

NORTON & STOCKTON ANCIENTS

Founded: 1959 Nickname: Ancients

Secretary: Glenn Youngman **(T)** 07984 258 608 **(E)** cfs_ifa@hotmail.com
Chairman: Michael Mulligan **Prog Ed:** Michael Mulligan
Ground: Norton (Teesside) Sports Complex, Station Rd, Norton TS20 1PE **(T)** 01642 554 031 **Capacity:** 2,000
Colours(change): Amber & black/black & amber/black

ADDITIONAL INFORMATION: Att: 1,430 v Middlesbrough, Friendly 1988.
Northern League Cup 1982-83.

RYHOPE COLLIERY WELFARE

Founded: Nickname:

Secretary: Dougie Bennison **(T)** 07515 066 344 **(E)** dougie.benison@btinternet.com
Chairman: Darren Norton
Ground: Ryhope Recreation Park, Ryhope Street, Ryhope, Sunderland SR2 0AB **(T)**
Colours(change): Red & white stripes/black/red

ADDITIONAL INFORMATION: Previous Names: Vaux Ryhope 1988-92.
Previous League: Wearside > 2012, 2013-14. Northern League 2012-13.
League honours: Wearside League 1927-28, 61-62, 62-63, 63-64, 65-66, 2010-11, 11-12.
FA/County Cups: Durham Challenge Cup 1977-78.

RYTON & CRAWCROOK ALBION

Founded: 1970 Nickname:

Secretary: Stevie Carter **(T)** 07939 573 108 **(E)** racafc@outlook.com
Chairman: Richard Hands **Prog Ed:** Chris Holt
Ground: Kingsley Park, Stannerford Road, Crawcrook NE40 3SN **(T)** 0191 413 4448 **Capacity:** 2,000
Colours(change): Blue & black stripes/black/blue

ADDITIONAL INFORMATION: Att: 1,100 v Newcastle United 1998
Northern Alliance Division 1 Champions 1996-97.

SEAHAM RED STAR

Founded: 1973 Nickname: The Star

Secretary: Dave Copeland **(T)** 07834 473 001 **(E)** davidcopelandc@aol.com
Chairman: Joe Scollen **Prog Ed:** Dave Copeland
Ground: Seaham Town Park, Stockton Road, Seaham. Co.Durham SR7 0HY **(T)**
Colours(change): Red & white stripes/red with white flash/red with white turnover

ADDITIONAL INFORMATION: Previous Name: Seaham Colliery Welfare Red Star 1978-87. **Previous League:** Wearside 1979-83.
Record Att: 1,500 v Guisborough. **App:** Michael Whitfield.
Honours: Durham Challenge Cup 1979-80, Wearside League & League Cup 1981-82, Northern League Cup 1992-93.

SOUTH SHIELDS

Founded: 1974 Nickname: Mariners

Secretary: Philip Reay **(T)** 07506 641 815 **(E)** philipreay@rocketmail.com
Chairman: Gary Crutwell **Prog Ed:** Philip Reay
Ground: Eden Lane, Peterlee SR8 5ND **(T)** 07506 641 815
Colours(change): Claret & blue/white/white

ADDITIONAL INFORMATION: Att:1,500 v Spennymoor, Durham Challenge Cup Final 1994-95.
Northern Alliance 1974-75, 75-76, Wearside League 1976-77, 92-93, 94-95.
Monkwearmouth Charity Cup 1986-87.

STOKESLEY SPORTS CLUB

Founded: 1920 Nickname:

Secretary: Peter Grainge **(T)** 07712 883 874 **(E)** peterssc@hotmail.co.uk
Chairman: Tim Allison **Prog Ed:** Tim Allison
Ground: Stokesley Sports Club, Broughton Road, Stokesley TS9 5JQ **(T)** 01642 710 051
Colours(change): Black & red/black/black

ADDITIONAL INFORMATION:
Stokesley & District League 1975-76. Northern League Division Two 2009-10.

TEAM NORTHUMBRIA

Founded: 1999 Nickname:

Secretary: Adam Castling **(T)** 07970 478 723 **(E)** adam.castling@northumbria.ac.uk
Chairman: Colin Stromsoy **Prog Ed:** Adam Castling
Ground: Coach Lane, Benton, Newcastle upon Tyne NE7 7XA **(T)** 0191 215 6575
Colours(change): All red

ADDITIONAL INFORMATION:
Northern Alliance Premier 2005-06. Northern League Division Two 2011-12.

THORNABY

Founded: 1980 Nickname:

Secretary: Trevor Wing **(T)** 07860 780 446 **(E)** trevor.wing10@btinternet.com
Chairman: Laurence Lyons **Prog Ed:** Trevor Wing
Ground: Teesdale Park, Acklam Road, Thornaby, Stockton on Tees TS17 7JU **(T)** 01642 672 896
Colours(change): All blue

ADDITIONAL INFORMATION: Previous Names: Stockton Cricket Club 1965-1980, Stockton 1980-99 and Thornaby-on-Tees 1999-2000
Previous League: Wearside 1981-85. **Records Att:** 3,000 v Middlesbrough friendly Aug 1986 **App:** Michael Watson
Honours: North Riding County Cup, 1985-86, Northern Lge Div 2 1987-88, 91-92

TOW LAW TOWN

Founded: 1890 Nickname: Lawyers

Secretary: Steve Moralee **(T)** 07810 238 731 **(E)** stephen.moralee@btinternet.com
Chairman: Sandra Gordon **Prog Ed:** John Dixon
Ground: Ironworks Ground, Tow Law, Bishop Auckland DL13 4EQ **(T)** 01388 731 443 **Capacity:** 6,000
Colours(change): Black & white stripes/black/black

ADDITIONAL INFORMATION: 5,500 v Mansfield Town FA Cup 1967.
Northern League Champions 1923-24, 24-25, 94-95. League Cup 73-74.

WASHINGTON

Founded: 1949 Nickname: Mechanics

Secretary: Barry Spendley **(T)** 07810 536 964 **(E)** Derek.Armstrong1@ntlworld.com
Chairman: Derek Armstrong **Prog Ed:** Bob Goodwin
Ground: Nissan Sports Complex, Washington Road Sunderland SR5 3NS **(T)** 07810530964~07761325797
Colours(change): All red

ADDITIONAL INFORMATION:
Previous Names: Washington Mechanics, Washington Ikeda Hoover. **Previous League:** Wearside.
Record Att: 3,800 v Bradford Park Avenue FA Cup 1970.
Honours: Washington Amateur: 1956-57,57-58, 58-59,59-60,61-62,62-63, League Cup: 1955-56, 58-59, 60-61, 64-65.

WHICKHAM

Founded: 1944 Nickname:

Secretary: Les Dixon **(T)** 07974 308 162 **(E)** Whickhamfcsecretary@hotmail.co.uk
Chairman: Brian McCartney **Prog Ed:** Mick Tucker
Ground: Glebe Sports Club, Rectory Lane, Whickham NE11 9NQ **(T)** 0191 4200 186
Colours(change): Black & white stripes/black/black

ADDITIONAL INFORMATION: Record Att: 3,165 v Windsor & Eton FA Vase SF 1981.
Honours: FA Vase 1980-81, Wearside Lge 77-78, 87-88, Sunderland Shipowners Cup 77-78, 80-81,
Northern Comb 69-70, 72-73, 73-74 Lge Cup 60-61, 73-74

WILLINGTON

Founded: 1906 Nickname:

Secretary: Geoff Siddle **(T)** 07532 341 105 **(E)** siddle403@btinternet.com
Chairman: Robert Nichols **Manager:** Robert Lee **Prog Ed:** Geoff Siddle
Ground: Hall Lane, Willington, Co. Durham DL15 0QG **(T)** 01388 745 912 **Capacity:** 7,000
Colours(change): Blue & white/blue/blue & white

ADDITIONAL INFORMATION:
Previous Leagues: Northern League. Wearside > 2013.
Records (Lge/Cup post 1939): Goalscorer: Brett Cummings - 150, 1992-08. Apps: Brett Cummings - 407, 1992-08.
Honours: Northern League 1913-14, 25-26, 29-30. FA Amateur Cup 1949-50.

GROUND DIRECTIONS

ALNWICK TOWN- M1, at exit 32, take slip road left for M18 toward The North / Doncaster / Hull, at exit 2, take slip road left for A1(M) toward the North, keep straight onto A1 / Doncaster by Pass, keep straight onto A1(M), take slip road for A1(M) / Aberford by Pass, road name changes to A1 / Leeming Lane, keep straight onto A1(M), keep left onto A1, take slip road left for A1068 toward Alnwick / Alnmouth, at roundabout, take 1st exit onto Willowburn Avenue, turn left, and then immediately turn left onto St James Estate, ground is on the right.

ASHINGTON-Leave the A1 at the junction with the A19 north of Newcastle. Go along the A19 eastwards untio the next roundabout . Here take the second left (A189) signposted to Bedlington and Ashington. Continue along A189 until reach Woodhorn roundabout, turn left onto A197. Turn left at first roundabout. Just before the hospital car park entrance, turn right. Ground is on left.

BEDLINGTON TERRIERS-From the A1:- Take the Seaton Burn turn off and at the roundabout take the second turn off (A1088).
At the next roundabout, take the first turnoff to pass Aesica on the left. Straight over at the next roundabout.
You will go down a dip, over a bridge and back up the other side, do not turn off, continue on the same road until you come into Bedlington. At the top of the bank there is a roundabout outside the Red Lion pub, go straight over. Down the hill there is another roundabout at the Netto shop, take the second turnoff (turning right). Follow the road past the Police station and Law courts and the road bends sharply to the left. Continue around the corner, take the second right. The ground is at the top of the street.

BILLINGHAM SYNTHONIA-Leave A19 onto A1027 sign posted towards Billingham. Continue straight ahead over a couple of roundabouts, and you will be on Central Avenue. The ground is on left opposite an empty office block.

BILLINGHAM TOWN-Leave A19 on A1027 signed Billingham. Turn left at third roundabout, into Cowpen Lane. Go over a railway bridge, then first left into Warwick Crescent, then first left again into Bedford Terrace (follow one-way signs) to the ground.

BIRTLEY TOWN-Leave A1(M) at Angel of the North and follow signs to Birtley (A167). Continue along main road through town. Go past Komatsu factory on right and then after approx 200 yards turn right into an unmarked side road. Ground is directly in front of you.

BISHOP AUCKLAND-NORTH: From junction 60 of the A1 follow the A689 to Bishop Auckland. Go straight across the next 2 roundabouts. At the 3rd roundabout turn left onto the A688 and straight across the next 2 roundabouts. At the following roundabout turn left at Aldi and then go straight across at the next roundabout. The stadium is 200 yards on your right. **SOUTH:** From junction 58 from the A1, take the A68 towards Bishop Auckland. At the West Auckland by-pass, turn right at the roundabout. Go straight across at the next roundabout and the stadium is located 500 yards on your left.

BRANDON UNITED-Leave A1 on A690, go through Durham and continue on A690. Once at 'Langley Moor' (you go under a railway bridge), turn right at the "Lord Boyne" pub. After 100 yards take the next left. Go up the road for approx half a mile, and turn right at the newsagents. Take the next left, and Brandon's ground is up a small track.

CELTIC NATION-Take junction 42 off the M6 and then the A6 into Carlisle. After 1.75 miles take left turn into Petterill Bank Road (junction is at traffic lights). After half a mile turn right onto track immediately before railway bridge. This leads you to the ground.

CHESTER LE STREET-Leave A1M at junction 63 and take the A167 towards Chester Le Street and Durtham. Keep going along this road for a couple of miles. You will go under a railway bridge, and as the road begins to climb, you will see the Chester Moor pub on your left. Turn into the pub and the ground is accessed along a track at the rear of the pub car park.

CONSETT-Take the A692 from the east into Consett. On the edge of the town, the A692 takes a left at a roundabout. Continue along the A692 for approx 100 yards, before turning right into Leadgate Road. Go along here for approx .25 mile, and turn right into Ashdale Road. There is a road sign for the Leisure Centre pointing into Ashdale Road. The ground is approx 200 yards along Ashdale Road on your right.

CROOK TOWN-Leave the A1 at Junction 62, and take the A690 towards Durham. Keep on this road through Durham, Meadowfield, Willington and Helmington Row. When you arrive in Crook town centre keep going straight ahead, as the A690 becomes the A689. The ground is situated on this road on your right, approximately 300 yards from the town centre.

DARLINGTON RAILWAY ATHLETIC-Leave A1(M) at junction 58 and follow the A68 into Darlington. Continue along the road until you see the Brown Trout public house on your right. Turn left at this point into Brinkburn Road, and the ground is 100 yards along on the left.

DUNSTON U.T.S.-From south take Dunston/Whickham exit off A1M. Turn right at top of slip road into Dunston Road and head down the bank. As the road veers left, the road becomes Wellington Road, and the ground is situated on your left.

DURHAM CITY-Leave the A1M at J62 (signed Durham City) At the top of the slip road turn left. After about 1/2 mile bear left (signed Belmont + Dragonville). At the top of the slip road turn left.
At traffic lights turn left then take the 2nd left, the stadium is on your right.

ESH WINNING-Leave the A1 at Junction 62, and take the A690 towards Durham. Keep on this road through Durham. Once you start to head down a bank on the A690, you will come to a roundabout. Take the right turn onto the B6302, which will be signposted towards Ushaw Moor. Keep on this road though Ushaw Moor (there is a staggered crossroads to negotiate), and carry on the B6302 into Esh Winning. Keep on going as the ground is not in Esh Winning, but the next village along, Waterhouses. When the road takes a sharp left you will see a track continuing straight ahead. The ground is along this track.

GUISBOROUGH TOWN-Turn off the A19 into the A174, then come off at the second junction, turning right onto the A172. Follow this round until roundabout with A1043, take left exit to join the A1043. Take right at next roundabout to join the A171. At second roundabout turn right into Middlesbrough Road (will be signposted towards Guisborough) then take left turning at traffic lights into Park Lane. Take first left into Howlbeck Road, and the ground is at the end of the road.

HEATON STANNINGTON - Grounsell Park, Newton Road, High Heaton, Newcastle upon Tyne NE7 7HP. Tel: 0191 281 9230

HEBBURN TOWN-Leave A1M on A194(M) (junction 65) and follow signs for Tyne Tunnel. Continue until fourth roundabout and turn left on to B1306 (Hebburn, Mill Lane). Right at traffic lights into Victoria Road. Ground 200 yards long this road on the left.

HORDEN C.W.-Take A19 to Peterlee turn off (B1320). Follow main road into Peterlee then through on the same road, following signs to Horden (B1320). At T-junction, turn left into Sunderland Road, at lights, (A1086) and then right into South Terrace. Ground is at bottom of South Terrace.

JARROW ROOFING-From south take A19 and follow signs for Tyne Tunnel. Turn right at junction marked Boldon Colliery (Testo Roundabout) on to the A184. Turn left at the next r'about, into the B1293, and head towards Asda. At second r'about, turn right at end of retail park. At the r'about at the entrance to Asda, take the "10 to" exit, and you will pass a large brick building on you right, known as The Shack. Turn right into the car park after this building, and at the far end of the car park there is a small lane that leads off left. Roofers ground is at the end of this track.

MARSKE UNITED -Leave A19 and join Parkway (A174) to Marske until Quarry Lane r'about. Take exit (A1085) into Marske. Take the next right after you pass under a railway, into Meadow Rd. Take the next left into Southfield Rd and the entrance is on your left shortly before a T-junc.

MORPETH TOWN-From south. Turn off the A1 onto A197, sign posted Morpeth. Turn left at sign pointing Belsay (B6524). Take right turn just before bridge under the A1. Ground is signposted and up a small track is on the right.

NEWCASTLE BENFIELD-Take the A1058 from either the Tyne Tunnel or central Newcastle. Turn off this road at the junction with Benfield Road. Turn south at this junction, and the Crosslings building will be on your left. Ground is around 400 metres on left, by taking the first turning after passing railway bridge. The ground is 100 yards along this road.

NEWTON AYCLIFFE-From North, leave the A1at junction 60, and travel west along the A689 towards Bishop Auckland. At the roundabout, turn left to join A167. Travel along here for a couple of miles, and at first traffic lights and turn right onto B6443 (Central Avenue). At first roundabout (Tesco's) turn left into Shafto Way then 3rd left into Gunn Way then right into Moore Lane.

NORTHALLERTON TOWN-Leave A1 at Leeming Bar (A684) and follow signs to Northallerton. Approaching the town take the left turn B1333, signed Romanby. Ground is on left after 50 yards in Romanby.

NORTH SHIELDS-Continue north on the A19 after Tyne Tunnel. Take right exit at roundabout onto the A1058. At next roundabout take third exit at Billy Mill, signed to North Shields. At roundabout with A193, turn right, then take second left into Silkey's Lane. Ground is 100 yards on left.

NORTON & STOCKTON ANCIENTS -Leave A19 at Stockton/Norton turn off (A1027) and follow signs to Norton. At the roundabout at the top of the bank take a right turn onto the B1274. Take the next right into Station Road. Ground entrance is on left of road in a large sports complex, the entrance to which is just before the railway crossing. The ground a 200 yards along this track.

PENRITH-Turn off M6 at junction 40 then onto dual carriageway to Appleby and Scotch Corner. Take the A686 (signposted Alston), for approximately half a mile. Then take a right turn (opposite Carleton Road), and follow the track running parallel with the A66. Turn left into the sports complex and follow the road to the far end.

RYHOPE CW - From the A1 exit onto A168 toward A19/Thirsk/Teesside. Continue onto A19. Take the A1018 ramp to Sunderland. At the roundabout, take the 2nd exit onto Stockton Rd/A1018. Continue to follow Stockton Road. Go through 2 roundabouts. Slight left onto Ryhope Street S/B1286. Ground will be on the left.

RYTON & CRAWCROOK ALBION-Leave the A1 at the south side of the River Tyne (A694). At the roundabout take the A695 (sign posted Blaydon). At Blaydon take the B6317 through Ryton to reach Crawcrook. Turn right at the traffic lights (sign posted Ryton/Clara Vale). Kingsley Park is situated approximately 500 meters on the right.

SEAHAM RED STAR-Leave A19 on B1404 slip road. Follow signs to Seaham/Ryhope. Turn right at traffic lights on to the B1285. Then left at Red Star social club approximately 200 yards after the traffic lights. There is a car park at the next roundabout behid their social club The ground is a short walk at the top of the park.

SHILDON-Leave A1M at junction 58. Follow A68 signed Bishop Auckland, turn right at roundabout onto A6072. At Shildon turn right at second roundabout (onto B6282) , then left into Byerley Rd (still the B6282). Right at Timothy Hackworth pub into Main St., then at the top of the bank, left into Dean Street.

SOUTH SHIELDS- Turn off the A19 onto the B1320 (Burnhope Way), go over the first roundabout then at the next roundabout turn left onto Essington Way, then turn right onto Yoden Road as signposted 'Community Facility' and proceed and turn right onto Robson Avenue again as indicated with a signpost to 'Community Facility' and on to Eden Lane to the ground.

STOKESLEY SPORTS CLUB-Turn off A19 onto A174 (Teesport/Redcar). Take third exit onto A172 (Whitby/Stokesley). Turn right and keep on A172 to Stokesley. In Stokesley bear left at first roundabout, still keeping on the A172. At next roundabout go straight across into Broughton Road (Second exit-B1257). Ground is 100 yards on left-hand side.

SUNDERLAND R.C.A.-From the A19, leave at the junction with the A690, but on that roundabout take the B1286 through Doxford Park. Continue along this road for some time (there are number of roundabouts), but there are signposts to Ryhope along this road. You will eventually come to a T-junction at the end of the B1286, and turn right onto the A1018. After 200 yards you will come to another roundabout, here take a right turn. Then take the next right into a new housing estate. There is a board at the entrance pointing you to Meadow Park, the home of R.C.A. The ground is at the far end of the estate.

TEAM NORTHUMBRIA-Take the A1058 from either the A19 or central Newcastle. Turn off this road at the junction with Benfield Road. Turn north at large Crosslings warehouse into Red Hall Drive, this then becomes Coach Lane. The ground is on the right just past Newcastle University halls of residence.

THORNABY-Turn off A19 onto A1130 and head towards Thornaby. Continue along Acklam Road for about half a mile. Ground is signposted from the main road- on the right up a track between houses after half a mile.

TOW LAW TOWN-Leave the A1 at junction 58 and turn on to A68. Follow signs for Tow Law/Corbridge. Ground is at far end of Tow Law on the left side. The ground is situated on Ironworks Road, which is the first left after a sharp left hand bend on the A68 in Tow Law.

WASHINGTON-Leave the A19 on slip road marked "Nissan Offices" as you pass Sunderland travelling north. This is the A1290. Continue to follow "Nissan Offices" signs. Left at traffic lights, then right at roundabout into complex. Ground is at far end of the plant.

WEST ALLOTMENT CELTIC-Continue on the A19 north after Tyne Tunnel until A191 exit. Take left exit marked Gosforth & Newcastle. A191 for three miles. The ground, The Blue Flames Sports Ground is on left.

WEST AUCKLAND TOWN-Leave A1 at junction 58 on to the A68. Follow signs to W. Auckland/Corbridge. On entering village, ground is behind factory on left side. Ground is up a track on the left side of road next to Oakley Grange Farm.

WHICKHAM-From A1M take the A692 junction, and travel in the direction signed to Consett. At top of the back the road forks left towards Consett, but you should take the right fork along the B6317 to Whickham. Follow this road for 1.5 miles, left turn into Rectory Lane (B6316). Take first right into Holme Avenue, and then first left. The ground is at top of lane. More car parking can be found further along Rectory Lane, take the next right. Walk past the cricket pitch to access the football club.

WHITLEY BAY-Leave the A19 on the A191, and turn eastwards towards Whitely Bay. Continue along New York Road (A191) which then becomes Rake Lane (A191). Pass hospital on right & then into Shields Rd. and Hillheads Rd (both A191). Ground is to the right, floodlights can be seen from miles away! It is next to an ice rink.

WILLINGTON - Hall Lane, Willington, Co. Durham DL15 0QG. Tel: 01388 745 912

SOUTH WEST PENINSULA LEAGUE

Sponsored by: Carlsberg
Founded: 2007
Recent Champions:
2009: Bodmin Town
2010: Buckland Athletic
2011: Buckland Athletic
2012: Bodmin Town
2013: Bodmin Town
swpleague.co.uk

PREMIER DIVISION	P	W	D	L	F	A	GD	Pts
1 Plymouth Parkway	38	29	3	6	121	33	88	90
2 Exmouth Town	38	26	8	4	85	28	57	86
3 Saltash United	38	27	4	7	104	33	71	85
4 Ivybridge Town	38	24	5	9	98	60	38	77
5 Godolphin Atlantic	38	23	6	9	75	50	25	75
6 Withridge	38	23	4	11	83	49	34	73
7 Bodmin Town	38	22	7	9	75	41	34	73
8 Launceston	38	22	5	11	92	61	31	71
9 St Austell	38	20	8	10	99	58	41	68
10 Torpoint Athletic	38	17	8	13	70	56	14	59
11 Newquay	38	15	4	19	78	91	-13	49
12 Elburton Villa	38	14	6	18	64	92	-28	48
13 St Blazey	38	14	4	20	72	72	0	46
14 Camelford	38	14	4	20	59	79	-20	46
15 Bovey Tracey	38	13	7	18	62	95	-33	46
16 Falmouth Town	38	8	5	25	46	84	-38	29
17 Elmore	38	6	8	24	62	110	-48	26
18 Cullompton Rangers	38	4	6	28	45	117	-72	18
19 (R) Tavistock	38	2	5	31	34	107	-73	11
20 (R) Liskeard Athletic	38	1	5	32	32	140	-108	8

THROGMORTON CUP

ROUND 1			
Axminster Town	v	Appledore	1-5
Bovey Tracey	v	Holsworthy	6-1
Bude Town	v	University of Exeter	1-5
Callington Town	v	Foxhole Stars	8-1
Crediton United	v	Exwick Villa	2-1
Exmouth Town	v	Budleigh Salterton	0-2
Galmpton United	v	Totnes & Dartington	3-2
Godolphin Atlantic	v	St Dennis	4-0
Liskeard Athletic	v	Okehampton Argyle	6-2
Liverton United	v	Plymstock United	2-1
Mousehole	v	Helston Athletic	3-1
Penryn Athletic	v	Porthleven	0-2
Penzance	v	Newquay	4-2
Perranporth	v	Ivybridge Town	1-3
Sidmouth Town	v	Cullompton Rangers	1-2
Sticker	v	Newton Abbot Spurs	3-2
Stoke Gabriel	v	Truro City	1-0
Teignmouth	v	Dobwalls	4-2
Torpoint Athletic	v	Wadebridge Town	2-1
Vospers Oak Villa	v	Alphington	6-2
ROUND 2			
Appledore	v	Budleigh Salterton	3-1
Bodmin Town	v	Camelford	3-1
Bovey Tracey	v	Torpoint Athletic	1-2
Crediton United	v	Elmore	1-4
Cullompton Rangers	v	Witheridge	1-4
Elburton Villa	v	Stoke Gabriel	1-3
Falmouth Town	v	St Blazey	0-1
Godolphin Atlantic	v	Callington Town	4-0
Liskeard Athletic	v	Vospers Oak Villa	3-6
Mousehole	v	Porthleven	5-2
Plymouth Parkway	v	Tavistock	7-2
Saltash United	v	Galmpton United	5-1
St Austell	v	Penzance 0 (96)	3
Sticker	v	Liverton United	7-3
Teignmouth	v	Launceston	3-3 4-1p
University of Exeter	v	Ivybridge Town	1-3
ROUND 3			
Appledore	v	Bodmin Town	0-2
Mousehole	v	Stoke Gabriel	1-1 HW on pens
Saltash United	v	Elmore	6-0
St Austell	v	Ivybridge Town	4-1
St Blazey	v	Teignmouth	1-1 AW on pens
Sticker	v	Godolphin Atlantic	0-3
Torpoint Athletic	v	Witheridge	1-0
Vospers Oak Villa	v	Plymouth Parkway	1-7
QUARTER FINALS			
Godolphin Atlantic	v	Teignmouth	3-2
Mousehole	v	Saltash United	2-1
Plymouth Parkway	v	Bodmin Town	3-1
Torpoint Athletic	v	St Austell	0-1
SEMI FINALS			
Godolphin Atlantic	v	Plymouth Parkway	1-3
Mousehole	v	St Austell	2-3
FINAL			
Plymouth Parkway	v	St Austell	2-0

PREMIER DIVISION	1	2	3	4	5	6	7	8	9	10	11	12	13	14	15	16	17	18	19	20
1 AFC St Austell		1-2	2-2	4-1	4-4	2-2	4-0	1-2	1-0	1-2	5-3	4-2	8-0	6-0	2-4	1-0	3-2	4-1	4-4	3-2
2 Bodmin Town	4-1		1-1	0-1	3-2	6-0	0-0	0-2	5-1	0-1	2-4	1-0	6-1	2-1	1-0	0-0	4-2	3-2	4-3	1-2
3 Bovey Tracey	1-5	0-4		2-1	3-1	3-4	1-4	2-4	2-3	2-0	3-1	2-2	3-2	1-0	0-1	0-6	2-2	1-0	5-0	0-7
4 Camelford	2-2	0-1	2-5		7-0	2-1	1-0	0-2	3-2	1-3	0-6	1-6	2-0	1-2	0-4	0-2	4-2	0-3	0-4	1-3
5 Cullompton Rangers	0-3	1-2	1-1	1-6		2-3	1-0	1-3	4-0	1-1	0-5	2-5	0-0	5-1	0-5	2-5	0-6	2-0	1-2	1-2
6 Elburton Villa	0-7	1-5	0-0	1-1	4-3		5-2	1-6	2-1	1-4	3-4	0-4	3-2	2-0	1-3	0-2	1-0	2-0	1-0	2-4
7 Elmore	0-0	0-1	3-1	0-2	1-0	4-6		0-4	0-3	3-5	1-4	0-2	0-1	1-3	2-6	2-6	1-3	5-1	3-7	1-2
8 Exmouth Town	2-1	0-0	2-0	1-0	6-0	2-1	3-1		3-0	2-0	2-2	1-1	4-0	0-2	0-0	1-0	3-2	5-0	1-0	0-0
9 Falmouth Town	0-3	1-2	1-2	0-1	1-1	1-1	4-4	1-1		0-5	1-2	1-2	2-1	2-3	2-5	1-3	0-1	2-0	1-2	0-2
10 Godolphin Atlantic	2-0	2-0	4-1	3-1	4-2	0-0	6-1	1-0	2-0		1-1	0-4	3-1	1-1	1-0	0-2	3-2	2-0	1-1	2-0
11 Ivybridge Town	0-1	2-2	3-1	0-1	5-0	4-1	5-2	1-3	4-0	3-1		4-2	3-0	3-2	0-4	2-0	2-1	3-1	2-1	0-5
12 Launceston	3-4	1-2	2-0	1-1	6-3	2-1	2-2	0-1	0-1	3-1	3-2		4-0	2-0	0-2	1-0	2-1	2-0	2-0	4-0
13 Liskeard Athletic	1-2	2-3	3-4	0-4	2-2	1-5	1-3	3-7	1-4	0-3	0-0	1-4		1-3	0-5	1-2	0-5	2-2	0-5	2-5
14 Newquay	1-6	2-1	11-0	5-1	3-0	4-2	8-3	0-5	1-3	2-3	3-4	2-3	3-2		0-5	0-5	0-2	4-2	2-2	0-2
15 Plymouth Parkway	3-1	0-1	2-2	3-0	2-1	2-1	0-0	3-1	6-2	6-0	0-2	6-0	8-0	6-1		3-0	2-1	4-2	2-0	3-2
16 Saltash United	3-0	0-0	4-1	5-2	6-0	4-0	1-1	0-0	5-0	3-1	3-2	3-2	6-0	2-0	2-1		8-1	3-0	0-2	1-0
17 St Blazey	0-1	0-0	1-3	1-3	3-1	1-2	3-3	0-1	1-0	2-0	2-3	3-4	4-0	1-1	2-1	3-7		4-2	2-1	1-2
18 Tavistock	0-0	0-5	0-2	1-6	2-0	2-2	2-2	1-4	1-4	2-4	3-5	1-3	1-1	1-2	0-5	0-2	0-1		0-2	0-2
19 Torpoint Athletic	2-2	2-0	3-2	3-0	1-0	1-0	2-5	2-0	1-1	0-0	0-0	5-3	4-0	2-2	1-2	0-3	0-3	4-1		1-0
20 Witheridge	1-0	2-1	3-1	0-0	4-0	1-2	4-2	1-1	1-0	1-3	0-2	3-3	8-0	1-3	2-7	3-0	2-1	3-0	1-0	

DIVISION ONE EAST	P	W	D	L	F	A	Pts	
1 (P) Stoke Gabriel	30	23	5	2	100	21	79	74
2 Teignmouth	30	19	7	4	81	38	43	64
3 Galmpton United	30	19	5	6	78	50	28	62
4 Exwick Town	30	17	6	7	82	51	31	57
5 Totnes & Dartington	30	13	6	11	71	65	6	45
6 Crediton United	30	12	6	12	60	59	1	42
7 Exeter University	30	12	5	13	58	56	2	41
8 Alphington	30	11	7	12	64	71	-7	40
9 Budleigh Salterton	30	11	6	13	64	60	4	39
10 Appledore	30	10	6	14	53	49	4	36
11 Newton Abbot Spurs	30	10	5	15	55	54	1	35
12 Axminster Town	30	8	7	15	52	68	-16	31
13 Sidmouth Town	30	7	8	15	41	58	-17	29
14 Okehampton Argyle	30	7	7	16	47	79	-32	28
15 Liverton United	30	7	4	19	43	119	-76	25
16 Plymstock United	30	6	6	18	40	91	-51	24

DIVISION ONE WEST	P	W	D	L	F	A	GD	Pts
1 (P) Callington Town	29	24	1	4	83	40	43	73
2 Mousehole	29	23	0	6	68	40	28	69
3 Helston Athletic	30	20	1	9	101	50	51	61
4 Sticker	30	17	4	9	85	51	34	55
5 Penryn Athletic	30	16	6	8	68	43	25	54
6 Truro City Reserves	30	17	1	12	76	60	16	52
7 Wadebridge Town	29	15	4	10	75	48	27	49
8 Dobwalls	30	15	2	13	63	54	9	47
9 St Dennis	30	14	3	13	71	63	8	45
10 Vospers Oak Villa	29	12	6	11	57	59	-2	42
11 Porthleven	30	8	7	15	54	70	-16	31
12 Perranporth	30	7	4	19	46	68	-22	25
13 Bude Town	30	6	5	19	43	78	-35	23
14 Penzance	30	6	5	19	41	87	-46	23
15 Holsworthy	30	7	0	23	37	101	-64	21
16 Foxhole Stars	30	6	1	23	27	83	-56	19

DIVISION ONE EAST	1	2	3	4	5	6	7	8	9	10	11	12	13	14	15	16
1 Alphington		1-0	3-1	3-3	2-2	2-0	1-4	1-3	0-4	2-1	2-2	3-4	0-2	3-3	1-1	0-0
2 Appledore	4-3		2-2	1-1	1-1	5-1	2-3	1-1	3-2	5-0	1-2	1-1	0-3	0-2	2-2	3-0
3 Axminster Town	3-1	3-4		2-2	5-4	0-3	1-2	1-2	1-1	1-1	5-3	3-2	0-4	1-2	1-1	3-1
4 Budleigh Salterton	1-2	3-2	2-0		2-1	1-1	2-2	5-0	2-0	2-0	2-3	0-1	0-3	1-2	1-3	0-4
5 Crediton United	3-1	3-1	4-1	3-2		1-1	1-3	2-2	3-1	1-4	4-0	2-0	0-2	4-6	2-1	4-2
6 Exwick Villa	1-3	2-1	2-1	3-1	3-3		2-1	4-3	4-0	2-1	4-1	4-2	3-3	2-3	4-3	3-5
7 Galmpton United	1-8	3-1	1-0	4-3	2-1	2-4		2-0	4-1	2-0	6-3	3-0	0-0	1-4	4-0	5-0
8 Liverton United	6-2	0-5	1-7	1-5	3-3	1-10	1-2		2-1	1-4	3-0	2-1	1-4	1-5	0-7	1-2
9 Newton Abbot Spurs	2-3	1-2	5-1	1-3	1-0	1-1	1-0	4-0		4-1	1-3	2-1	0-0	2-2	2-3	1-6
10 Okehampton Argyle	2-6	1-2	2-2	0-1	1-0	4-3	2-2	6-0	0-6		3-0	3-1	3-8	0-1	2-2	2-2
11 Plymstock United	2-4	1-0	3-3	3-3	2-0	0-7	1-1	0-4	2-4	1-1		0-1	0-4	0-5	1-7	1-4
12 Sidmouth Town	1-1	1-3	2-0	3-1	6-1	0-1	1-5	1-1	0-4	2-2	0-0		1-4	1-3	2-3	1-0
13 Stoke Gabriel	3-0	1-0	2-1	5-2	3-0	1-0	3-1	23-0	1-0	8-0	3-1	3-2		0-0	0-1	1-1
14 Teignmouth	7-2	2-1	0-1	3-2	0-3	0-3	1-1	5-0	1-1	4-0	3-1	1-1	4-0		7-0	1-4
15 Totnes & Dartington	1-3	1-0	5-0	3-6	0-2	1-1	3-4	2-1	4-2	4-1	6-3	1-1	0-4	2-4		1-3
16 University of Exeter	4-1	2-0	1-2	1-5	1-2	1-3	3-7	4-2	1-0	4-0	0-1	1-1	0-2	0-0	1-3	

DIVISION ONE WEST	1	2	3	4	5	6	7	8	9	10	11	12	13	14	15	16
1 Bude Town		2-4	0-1	3-1	3-3	2-1	0-1	1-3	1-2	2-2	1-2	0-4	2-4	0-2	5-6	1-2
2 Callington Town	3-0		3-2	4-0	5-1	3-1	4-0	3-2	1-0	4-1	5-2	6-2	4-3	0-4	1-0	4-1
3 Dobwalls	1-3	0-0		5-0	5-4	4-1	1-4	1-3	3-0	3-0	1-2	2-1	1-3	2-3	4-1	2-3
4 Foxhole Stars	0-1	0-3	1-3		0-5	2-1	2-3	1-2	2-1	0-3	2-1	2-1	1-2	0-2	4-3	2-2
5 Helston Athletic	2-0	5-1	2-3	5-1		9-0	2-3	1-2	2-1	3-0	4-1	4-2	5-3	4-1	6-2	0-1
6 Holsworthy	3-5	1-4	0-6	2-1	5-7		1-4	0-3	0-3	0-2	2-1	2-1	1-2	0-5	1-0	1-3
7 Mousehole	6-1	2-0	3-0	4-0	2-1	5-0		1-0	2-0	1-0	3-2	1-0	2-0	4-3	0-2	2-1
8 Penryn Athletic	7-1	2-3	5-2	3-1	1-4	2-0	2-0		2-2	1-1	4-1	0-3	2-3	2-0	0-2	4-2
9 Penzance	1-2	1-6	0-2	3-0	1-4	4-2	2-3	2-6		6-4	1-1	1-3	1-1	1-6	2-1	1-1
10 Perranporth	5-2	0-2	0-2	1-0	1-4	5-0	1-3	2-1	2-2		1-1	1-2	0-4	0-2	1-2	3-4
11 Porthleven	1-1	1-2	0-2	4-0	0-1	0-1	2-3	2-2	5-3	1-0		1-3	3-3	5-1	2-3	3-2
12 St Dennis	2-1	1-2	3-0	1-2	1-6	1-3	4-1	1-1	7-0	5-3	4-4		1-4	6-3	4-2	1-0
13 Sticker	5-1	2-3	4-0	3-0	1-3	8-1	2-1	1-1	4-0	3-0	8-0	0-3		1-3	5-1	2-2
14 Truro City Reserves	1-1	2-4	4-3	3-2	2-1	2-4	2-3	0-2	4-0	2-1	3-1	4-1	2-1		5-1	2-3
15 Vospers Oak Villa	1-1	1-0	1-1	2-0	1-0	3-0	3-0	2-2	3-0	1-3	2-2	2-2	6-1	3-2		1-4
16 Wadebridge Town	2-0	2-3	0-1	7-0	1-3	4-3	4-1	0-1	7-0	5-3	2-3	5-1	1-2	4-1	1-1	

CLUB MOVEMENTS

Premier Division - In: Callington Town (P). Stoke Gabriel (P).

Out: Liskeard Athletic (R). Tavistock (R).

Division One East - In: Brixham (P - South Devon League). St Martins (P - Devon & Exeter League). Tavistock (R).

Out: Stoke Gabriel (P).

Division One West - In: Illogan (P - Cornwall Combination). Liskeard Athletic (R). Millbrook (P - East Cornwall League).

Out: Callington Town (P). Foxhole Stars (W). Truro City Reserves (W).

BODMIN TOWN
Founded: 1896 Nickname:

Secretary: Nick Giles **(T)** **(E)** nickgiles@live.co.uk
Chairman: James Chapman **Manager:** Darren Gilbert
Ground: Priory Park, Bodmin, Cornwall PL31 2AE **(T)** 01208 78165
Colours(change): Yellow & black (All white)

ADDITIONAL INFORMATION:
Previous League: South Western.
Honours: South Western League 1990-91, 93-94, 2005-06. South West Peninsula Premier Division 2007-08, 08-09, 11-12, 12-13. Cornwall Senior Cup 2011-12, 12-13.

BOVEY TRACEY
Founded: 1950 Nickname: Moorlanders

Secretary: Steve Cooney **(T)** **(E)** steve.cooney@hotmail.co.uk
Chairman: Peter Horrell **Manager:** Shaun Hayward
Ground: Western Counties Roofing (Mill Marsh Pk), Ashburton Rd, Bovey TQ13 9FF **(T)** 01626 833 896
Colours(change): All red (All green)

ADDITIONAL INFORMATION:
Previous League: South Devon.
Honours: Herald Cup 1960-61. South Devon League Premier Division 2007-08.

CALLINGTON
Founded: 1989 Nickname: The Pasty Men

Secretary: Nick Smith **(T)** **(E)** womble1954@me.com
Chairman: Andrew Long **Manager:** Lee Beer
Ground: Ginsters Marshfield Parc PL17 7DR **(T)** 01579 382 647
Colours(change): Red & black (Yellow & black)

ADDITIONAL INFORMATION:
Previous League: South Western.
League honours: South West Peninsula Division One West 2013-14.

CAMELFORD
Founded: 1893 Nickname: Camels

Secretary: Hilary Kent **(T)** **(E)** hilarykent@camelfordfc.fsnet.co.uk
Chairman: Ollie Rowe **Manager:** Reg Hambly
Ground: Trefew Park, PL32 9TS **(T)**
Colours(change): White & blue (Blue & white)

ADDITIONAL INFORMATION:
Honours: South West Peninsula Division One West 2010-11.

CULLOMPTON RANGERS
Founded: 1945 Nickname: The Cully

Secretary: Alan Slark **(T)** **(E)** alanslark1@tiscali.co.uk
Chairman: Debbie Whiteway **Manager:** Jamie Ward
Ground: Speeds Meadow, Cullompton EX15 1DW **(T)** 01884 33090
Colours(change): Red & black (Yellow & blue)

ADDITIONAL INFORMATION:
Previous League: Devon County 1992-2007.

ELBURTON VILLA
Founded: 1982 Nickname: The Villa

Secretary: Nick Pope **(T)** **(E)** pope.n@sky.com
Chairman: Dave Winters **Manager:** Nick Pope
Ground: Haye Road, Elburton, Plymouth PL9 8HS **(T)** 01752 480 025
Colours(change): Red & white stripes/black (Blue & white)

ADDITIONAL INFORMATION:
Previous League: Devon County 1992-2007.

ELMORE
Founded: 1947 Nickname: Eagles

Secretary: Keith Humphreys **(T)** **(E)** keith_humphreys@sky.com
Chairman: Julian (Jed) Hewitt **Manager:** Pete Buckingham & Clive Jones
Ground: Horsdon Park, Heathcoat Way, Tiverton, Devon EX16 6DB **(T)** 01884 252 341
Colours(change): All green (All red)

ADDITIONAL INFORMATION:
Previous League: Western League > 2013.
Record Att: 1,713 v Tiverton Town Friday April 14th 1995. **Apps:** P Webber. **Win:** 17-0. **Defeat:** 2-7.
Honours: East Devon Senior Cup 1972-73, 75-76. Devon Senior Cup 1987-88.

EXMOUTH TOWN

Founded: 1933 Nickname: The Town

Secretary: Brian Barnden **(T)** **(E)** brian7645@btinternet.com
Chairman: Bob Chamberlain **Manager:** Richard Pears
Ground: King George V, Exmouth EX8 3EE **(T)** 01395 263 348
Colours(change): All royal blue (All red)

ADDITIONAL INFORMATION:
Previous League: Devon & Exeter League > 2007.
Honours: South West Peninsula Division 1 East 2012-13.

FALMOUTH TOWN

Founded: 1949 Nickname: The Ambers

Secretary: Wayne Pascoe **(T)** **(E)** pascoerichard@hotmail.com
Chairman: Vacant **Manager:** John Dent
Ground: Bickland Park, Bickland Water Road, Falmouth TR11 4PB **(T)** 01326 375 156
Colours(change): Amber & black (All blue)

ADDITIONAL INFORMATION:
Honours: South Western League 1961-62, 65-66, 67-68, 70-71, 71-72, 72-73, 73-74, 85-86, 86-87, 88-89, 89-90, 91-92, 96-97, 99-2000. Western League 1974-75, 75-76, 76-77, 77-78. Cornwall Combination 1983-84.

GODOLPHIN ATLANTIC AFC

Founded: 1980 Nickname: G Army

Secretary: Margaret Ashwood **(T)** **(E)** godolphin.arms@btconnect.com
Chairman: Tania Semmens **Manager:** Derek Martin
Ground: Godolphin Way, Cornwall TR7 3BU **(T)**
Colours(change): Sky blue & white (Maroon & black)

ADDITIONAL INFORMATION:
Previous League: East Cornwall Premier > 2008.
Honours: South West Peninsula Div.1 West 2012-13.

IVYBRIDGE TOWN

Founded: 1925 Nickname: The Ivys

Secretary: Paul Cocks **(T)** **(E)** secretary@ivybridgefc.com
Chairman: Dave Graddon **Manager:** Nicky Marker
Ground: Erme Valley, Ermington Road, Ivybridge PL21 9ES **(T)** 01752 896 686
Colours(change): Green & black (Yellow & blue)

ADDITIONAL INFORMATION:
Previous League: Devon County.
Honours: Devon County League 2005-06.

LAUNCESTON

Founded: 1891 Nickname: The Clarets

Secretary: Keith Ellacott **(T)** **(E)** launcestonfc@aol.com
Chairman: Alan Bradley **Manager:** Leigh Cooper
Ground: Pennygillam Ind. Est., Launceston PL15 7ED **(T)** 01566 773 279
Colours(change): All claret (Sky blue & black)

ADDITIONAL INFORMATION:
Previous League: South Western.
Honours: South Western League 1995-96.

NEWQUAY

Founded: 1890 Nickname: The Peppermints

Secretary: Jason Pratt **(T)** **(E)** pra.family@btinternet.com
Chairman: Peter Butterley
Ground: Mount Wise TR7 2BU **(T)** 01637 872 935
Colours(change): Red & white (Blue & yellow)

ADDITIONAL INFORMATION:
League honours: South West Peninsula Division One West 2011-12.

PLYMOUTH PARKWAY AFC

Founded: 1988 Nickname: The Parkway

Secretary: Genny Turner **(T)** **(E)** gennyt@sky.com
Chairman: James Parsons **Manager:** Wayne Hillson
Ground: Bolitho Park, St Peters Road, Manadon, Plymouth PL5 3JH **(T)**
Colours(change): Yellow & blue (Grey & white)

ADDITIONAL INFORMATION:
Previous Name: Ex-Air Flyers Plymouth.
Previous League: South Western 1998-2007.
League honours: South West Peninsula Premier Division 2013-14. **Cups:** Throgmorton Cup 2010-11, 2013-14.

SALTASH UNITED
Founded: 1945 Nickname: The Ashes

Secretary: Luke Ranford **(T)** **(E)** luke.ranford@googlemail.com
Chairman: Bill Wakeham **Manager:** Martin Burgess
Ground: Kimberley Stadium, Callington Road, Saltash PL12 6DX **(T)** 01752 845 746
Colours(change): Red & white stripes & black (Blue & black)

ADDITIONAL INFORMATION:
Previous League: South Western 2006-07.
Honours: South Western League 1953-54, 75-76. Western League Division 1 1976-77, Premier 1984-85, 86-87, 88-89.

ST. AUSTELL
Founded: 1890 Nickname: The Lily Whites

Secretary: Peter Beard **(T)** **(E)** peterbeard45@gmail.com
Chairman: James Hutchings **Manager:** Phil Lafferty
Ground: Poltair Park, Trevarthian Road, St Austell PL25 4LR **(T)** 01726 66099
Colours(change): All white (Yellow & blue)

ADDITIONAL INFORMATION:
Previous League: South Western 1951-2007.

ST. BLAZEY
Founded: 1896 Nickname: The Green & Blacks

Secretary: Martin Richards **(T)** **(E)** marty.rich60@talktalk.net
Chairman: Martin Richards **Manager:** Bobby Oaten
Ground: Blaise Park, Station Road, St Blazey PL24 2ND **(T)** 01725 814 110 **Capacity:** 3,000
Colours(change): Green & black (Blue & white)

ADDITIONAL INFORMATION:
Previous League: South Western 1951-2007.
League honours: South Western Lge 1954-55, 57-58, 62-63, 63-64, 80-81, 82-83, 98-99, 2000-01, 01-02, 02-03, 03-04, 04-05, 06-07.

STOKE GABRIEL
Founded: 1905 Nickname: The Railwaymen

Secretary: Mike Calf (Acting) **(T)** **(E)** michael.calf@btinternet.com
Chairman: Mike Calf **Manager:** Gary Fisher
Ground: G J Churchward Memorial TQ9 6RR **(T)** 01803 782 913
Colours(change): Maroon & blue (Yellow & green)

ADDITIONAL INFORMATION:
Previous Leagues: Devon County > 2007.
League honours: South West Peninsula Division One East 2013-14.

TORPOINT ATHLETIC
Founded: 1887 Nickname: The Point

Secretary: Robbie Morris **(T)** **(E)** robbietafc81@live.co.uk
Chairman: Paul Whitworth **Manager:** Bradley Yeo
Ground: The Mill, Mill Lane, Carbeile Road, Torpoint PL11 2RE **(T)** 01752 812 889
Colours(change): Yellow & black (All white)

ADDITIONAL INFORMATION:
Previous League: South Western 1962-2007.
Honours: South Western League 1964-65, 66-67.

WITHERIDGE
Founded: 1920 Nickname: The Withy

Secretary: Chris Cole **(T)** **(E)** chriscole128@hotmail.com
Chairman: Andre Pike **Manager:** Chris Vinnecombe
Ground: Edge Down Park, Fore Street, Witheridge EX16 8AH **(T)** 01884 861 511
Colours(change): All blue (Orange & blue)

ADDITIONAL INFORMATION:
Previous League: Devon County 2006-07.

DIVISION ONE EAST CONSTITUTION 2014-15

	Club	Ground	Tel
1	ALPHINGTON	The Chronicles, Church Road, Alphington, Exeter EX2 8SW	01392 279 556
2	APPLEDORE	Marshford, Churchill Way, Appledore EX39 1PA	01237 475 015
3	AXMINSTER TOWN	Tiger Way EX13 5HN	
4	BRIXHAM AFC	Wall Park Road TQ5 9UE	
5	BUDLEIGH SALTERTON	Greenway Lane, Budleigh Salterton EX9 6SG	01395 443 850
6	CREDITON UNITED	Lords Meadow, Commercial Road, Crediton EX17 1ER	01363 774 671
7	EXWICK VILLA	Foxhayes, Exwick, Exter EX4 2BQ	
8	GALMPTON UNITED AFC	War Memorial Playing Field, Greenway Road, Galmpton, Brixham TQ5 0LN	
9	LIVERTON UNITED	Halford TQ12 6JF	
10	NEWTON ABBOT SPURS	Recreation Ground, Marsh Road, Newton Abbot TQ12 2AR	01626 365 343
11	OKEHAMPTON ARGYLE	Simmons Park, Mill Road, Okehampton EX20 1PR	01837 53997
12	PLYMSTOCK UNITED	Dean Cross, Dean Cross Road, Plymstock PL9 7AZ	01752 406 776
13	SIDMOUTH TOWN	Manstone Recreation Ground, Manstone Lane, Sidmouth EX10 9TF	01395 577 087
14	ST. MARTINS AFC	Minster Park EX6 8AT	
15	TAVISTOCK AFC	Langsford Park PL19 8JR	01822 614 447
16	TEIGNMOUTH	Coombe Valley, Coombe Lane, Teignmouth TQ14 9EX	01626 776 688
17	TOTNES & DARTINGTON SC	Foxhole Sports Ground, Dartington TQ9 6EB	
18	UNIVERSITY OF EXETER	University Sports Ground, Topsham Road, Topsham EX3 0LY	01392 879 542

DIVISION ONE WEST CONSTITUTION 2014-15

	Club	Ground	Tel
1	BUDE TOWN	Broadclose Park EX23 8DR	
2	DOBWALLS	Lantoom Park, Duloe Road, Dobwalls PL14 4LU	07721 689 380
3	HELSTON ATHLETIC	Kellaway Park, Clodgy Lane, Helston TR13 8PJ	01326 573 742
4	HOLSWORTHY AFC	Upcott Field, North Road, Holsworthy EX22 6HF	01409 254 295
5	ILLOGAN RBL	Oxland Parc TR16 4DG	01209 216 488
6	LISKEARD ATHLETIC	Lux Park PL14 3HZ	01579 342 665
7	MILLBROOK AFC	Jenkins Park PL10 1EN	01752 822 113
8	MOUSEHOLE	Trungle Parc, Paul, Penzance TR19 6UG	01736 731 518
9	PENRYN ATHLETIC	Kernick, Kernick Road, Penryn TR10 9EW	01326 375 182
10	PENZANCE	Penlee Park, Alexandra Place, Penzance TR18 4NE	01736 361 964
11	PERRANPORTH	Ponsmere Valley, Budnick Estate, Perranporth TR6 0DB	
12	PORTHLEVEN	Gala Parc, Mill Lane, Porthleven TR13 9LQ	01326 569 655
13	ST. DENNIS	Boscawen Park, St Dennis PL26 8DW	01726 822 635
14	STICKER	Burngullow Park PL26 7EN	01726 71003
15	VOSPERS OAK VILLA	Weston Mill, Ferndale Road, Weston Mill, Plymouth PL2 2EL	01752 363 352
16	WADEBRIDGE TOWN	Bodieve Park, Bodieve Road, Wadebridge PL27 6EA	01208 812 537

GROUND DIRECTIONS-PREMIER DIVISION

BODMIN TOWN-Priory Park, Bodmin, Cornwall PL31 2AE. Tel: 01208 781 65.
Situated in Priory Park through main car park. Use football car park on Saturdays.

BOVEY TRACEY-Western Counties Roofing (Mill Marsh Park), Ashburton Road, Bovey Tracey TQ13 9FF. Tel: 01626 832 780.
Coming off the A38 East or Westbound at Drumbridges take the Bovey Tracey turn-off, straight through the lights at Heathfield. Next roundabout take 2nd exit, next roundabout take 3rd exit, then left, 35 yards, follow road to bottom of drive then enter through gate.

CALLINGTON - Ginsters Marshfield Parc PL17 7DR. Tel: 01579 382 647.
Ground is in the grounds of Callington Community College which is a quarter of a mile from the town centre.

CAMELFORD-Trefrew Park PL32 9TS.
From the South drive into Camelford up Victoria Road for 300 yards, turn left into Oakwood Rise. Follow road around for approximately 300 yards. Entrance is on the right up the lane. From the North as you enter Camelford turn right into Oakwood Rise then as above.

CULLOMPTON RANGERS-Speeds Meadow, Cullompton EX15 1DW. Tel: 01884 33090.
Leave M5 at junction 28, left at Town Centre, at Meadow Lane turn left past Sports Centre, at end of road turn right, then in 100 yards turn left into ground at end of lane.

ELBURTON VILLA-Haye Road, Elburton, Plymouth PL9 8NS. Tel: 01752 480 025.
From Plymouth City Centre take A379 Kingsbridge Road. At third roundabout turn left into Haye Road (signposted Saltram House). Ground 50 yards on left.

ELMORE -Horsdon Park, Heathcoat Way, Tiverton, Devon EX16 6DB. Tel: 01884 252 341.
From M5 leave at Junction 27 towards Tiverton on the A373. After approx 6 miles take the exit signed "Tiverton & Industrial Estate" Ground is then 350 meters on your right.

EXMOUTH TOWN -King George V, Exmouth EX8 3EE. Tel: 01395 263348.
From Junction 30 of M5 take te A376 to Exmouth, on entering the town the ground is on your right, before the railway station.

FALMOUTH TOWN-Bickland Park, Bickland Water Road, Falmouth TR11 4PB. Tel: 01326 375 156.
Take Penryn by-pass from Asda roundabout. Leave by-pass at Hillhead roundabout, take first right and follow industrial estate signs. Ground 1/2 mile on the left.

GODOLPHIN ATLENTIC -Godlphin Way TR7 3BU.
Off Henver Road turn into Godolphin Way and ground is then first entrance on the left.

SOUTH WEST PENINSULA LEAGUE - STEP 6/7

IVYBRIDGE TOWN-Erme Valley, Ermington Road, Ivybridge. Tel: 01752 896 686.

From Plymouth-leave A38 at Ivybridge and follow signs towards Ermington. Ground is immediately next to South Devon Tennis Centre. From Exeter-leave A38 at Ivybridge. Ground is in front of you at the end of the slip road.

LAUNCESTON-Pennygillam, Pennygillam Ind. Est., Launceston PL15 7ED. Tel: 01566 773 279.

Leave A30 onto Pennygillam roundabout, turn into Pennygillam Industrial Estate. Ground is 400 yards on the left.

NEWQUAY AFC-Mount Wise TR7 2BU

From link road turn right onto Mount Wise, just past traffic lights turn Right into Clevedon Road.

PLYMOUTH PARKWAY-Bolitho Park, St Peters Road, Manadon, Plymouth PL5 3OZ.

From Cornwall/Exeter exit at the Manadon/Tavistock junction off the Plymouth Parkway (A38), off roundabout into St Peters Road. Entrance is one mile on the right.

SALTASH UNITED-Ground: Kimberley Stadium, Callington Road, Saltash PL12 6DX. Tel: 01752 845 746.

At the top of Town Centre fork right at mini-roundabout. Ground is situated 400m ahead on the left-hand side next to Leisure Centre and Police Station.

ST AUSTELL-Poltair Park, Trevarthian Road, St Austell PL25 4LR Tel: 07966 130 158

Near Poltair School and St Austell Brewery (5 minutes from St Austell Rail Station).

ST BLAZEY-Blaise Park, Station Road, St Blazey PL24 2ND. Tel: 01725 814 110.

A390 from Lostwithiel to St Austell. At village of St Blazey turn left at traffic lights by Church/Cornish Arms pub into Station Road. Ground is 200 yards on the left.

LISKEARD ATHLETIC-Lux Park Sport Association, Coldstyle Road, Lux Park, Liskeard PL14 2HZ. Tel: 01579 342 665.

From the Parade (middle of town) turn left at the monument, then first right following signs for Leisure Centre at Lux Park.

STOKE GABRIEL - G J Churchward Memorial TQ9 6RR. Tel: 01803 782 913.

At Tweenaway Cross turn Right, after quarter of a mile turn Left at the Parkers Arms Inn. After approx 1 mile ground entrance is signposted on your right, before the village itself.

TORPOINT ATHLETIC-The Mill, Mill Lane, Carbeile Road, Torpoint PL11 2NA. Tel: 01752 812 889.

Take turning at Carbeile Inn onto Carbeille Road and first turning on the right into Mill Lane.

WITHERIDGE-Edge Down Park, Fore Street, Witheridge EX16 8AH. Tel: 01884 861 511.

B3137 Tiverton to Witheridge, on entering the village football pitch is on the right-hand side before the Fire Station and School.

SOUTHERN COUNTIES LEAGUE

Founded: As the Kent League in 1966

Recent Champions:
2009: VCD Athletic
2010: Faversham Town
2011: Hythe Town
2012: Herne Bay
2013: Erith & Belvedere
scefl.com

PREMIER DIVISION	P	W	D	L	F	A	GD	Pts
1 (P) Whyteleafe	32	26	2	4	111	35	76	80
2 Ashford United	32	22	3	7	72	37	35	69
3 Erith Town	32	21	4	7	67	43	24	67
4 Tunbridge Wells	32	20	5	7	90	47	43	65
5 Corinthian	32	16	10	6	60	41	19	58
6 Phoenix Sports	32	17	5	10	70	49	21	56
7 Cray Valley PM	32	14	8	10	64	50	14	50
8 Beckenham Town	32	15	4	13	76	58	18	49
9 Greenwich Borough	32	15	2	15	71	63	8	47
10 Holmesdale	32	13	5	14	48	64	-16	44
11 Lordswood	32	13	3	16	49	79	-30	42
12 Canterbury City	32	9	5	18	41	63	-22	32
13 Deal Town	32	9	2	21	46	82	-36	29
14 Fisher	32	7	7	18	45	77	-32	28
15 Rochester United	32	7	6	19	43	75	-32	27
16 Sevenoaks Town	32	5	5	22	44	84	-40	20
17 Woodstock Sports	32	3	4	25	31	81	-50	13

LEAGUE CUP

PRELIMINARY ROUND (2 LEGS)

Rochester United	v	Woodstock Sports	3-1
Woodstock Sports	v	Rochester United	1-1

ROUND 1

Beckenham Town	v	Sevenoaks Town	6-2
Sevenoaks Town	v	Beckenham Town	
Erith Town	v	Holmesdale	2-2
Holmesdale	v	ErithTown	3-5
Corinthian	v	Greenwich Borough	3-2
Greenwich Borough	v	Corinthian	1-4
Rochester United	v	Fisher	1-3
Fisher	v	Rochester United	
Ashford United	v	Tunbridge Wells	4-0
Tunbridge Wells	v	Ashford United	2-3
Canterbury City	v	Lordswood	1-0
Lordswood	v	CanterburyCity	1-3
Cray Valley PM	v	Deal Town	5-1
Deal Town	v	Cray ValleyPM	2-3
Phoenix Sports	v	Whyteleafe	3-2
Whyteleafe	v	Phoenix Sports	0-4

QUARTER FINALS

Ashford United	v	Erith Town	0-1
Erith Town	v	Ashford United	4-4
Corinthian	v	Phoenix Sports	3-1
Phoenix Sports	v	Corinthian	1-0
Cray Valley PM	v	Beckenham Town	3-1
Beckenham Town	v	Cray Valley PM	5-0
Fisher	v	Canterbury city	3-2
Canterbury City	v	Fisher	1-1

SEMI FINALS

Corinthian	v	Erith Town	4-1
Erith Town	v	Corinthian	1-1
Fisher	v	Beckenham town	4-3
Beckenham Town	v	Fisher	3-0

FINAL

Beckenham Town	v	Corinthian	2-0

PREMIER DIVISION	1	2	3	4	5	6	7	8	9	10	11	12	13	14	15	16	17
1 Ashford United		3–0	2–0	1–0	1–1	4–2	0–2	4–1	1–0	2–0	1–2	0–2	2–0	4–2	1–0	2–1	3–1
2 Beckenham Town	4–2		4–3	2–2	2–3	3–2	0–3	1–1	4–3	6–0	1–1	2–2	5–0	4–2	2–3	1–2	4–0
3 Canterbury City	1–4	0–2		2–1	1–2	2–0	0–2	1–1	1–4	1–1	5–2	0–2	1–2	1–0	0–0	0–4	3–1
4 Corinthian	1–0	2–0	2–0		1–1	4–1	1–0	3–1	3–2	1–1	3–4	0–0	1–1	3–0	1–1	1–0	4–1
5 Cray Valley Paper Mills	0–2	1–3	3–2	1–1		0–1	3–4	3–0	0–0	5–1	1–2	2–2	2–0	0–3	1–1	2–2	4–0
6 Deal Town	1–4	3–2	1–0	1–2	2–5		1–3	4–5	0–4	2–5	3–0	3–2	0–2	4–0	1–2	3–7	1–0
7 Erith Town	1–1	1–0	3–1	2–2	3–1	0–0		2–1	3–0	3–2	4–3	2–1	2–1	4–0	2–3	0–3	1–0
8 Fisher	2–2	0–5	2–1	1–2	1–1	1–2	1–2		1–0	1–4	2–2	1–3	1–2	5–1	2–2	0–4	2–1
9 Greenwich Borough	0–2	0–4	3–0	5–2	5–1	1–3	0–1	1–0		1–2	3–3	1–7	5–3	7–3	3–1	2–3	4–0
10 Holmesdale	2–4	1–0	0–0	1–4	0–3	2–0	2–0	3–1	2–3		0–1	1–0	1–3	2–0	1–2	0–7	3–2
11 Lordswood	1–3	4–3	1–2	1–3	0–4	4–1	3–2	3–2	1–3	1–3		0–1	0–4	0–1	0–1	0–7	2–1
12 Phoenix Sports	4–3	3–0	3–3	3–2	1–0	2–2	0–1	4–1	1–3	3–0	0–2		2–1	4–1	1–3	1–3	5–0
13 Rochester United	0–4	2–3	1–4	1–2	1–3	2–1	1–6	2–3	3–1	1–1	0–1	1–2		2–2	1–2	1–3	1–1
14 Sevenoaks Town	0–4	0–1	0–2	1–1	2–3	2–0	4–2	1–1	0–2	1–2	2–3	2–3	1–1		1–5	3–0	2–3
15 Tunbridge Wells	2–3	3–1	6–1	2–4	0–5	6–0	4–0	3–0	5–1	2–2	7–1	3–1	8–0	5–2		2–3	2–0
16 Whyteleafe	2–0	4–1	3–1	3–0	6–2	3–1	3–5	7–2	2–0	3–0	3–0	5–1	2–2	4–0	6–1		4–0
17 Woodstock Sports	2–3	2–6	1–2	1–1	0–1	3–0	1–1	1–2	1–4	1–3	0–1	1–4	3–1	2–2	0–3	1–2	

CLUB MOVEMENTS

Premier Division - In: Crowborough Athletic (S - Sussex County League). Croydon (S - Combined Counties League). Erith & Belvedere (R - Isthmian Div.1 North). Lingfield (S - Sussex County League).
Out: Whyteleafe (P - Isthmian Division One North).

2013-14 - Ashford United. Photo: Alan Coomes.

2013-14 - Cray Valley. Photo: Alan Coomes.

ASHFORD UNITED

Founded: 1930 Nickname: The Nuts&Bolts

Secretary: Mary Hallybone **(T)** 07597 615 556 **(E)** mary.hallybone@yahoo.co.uk
Chairman: Derek Pestridge **Prog Ed:** Dave Read
Ground: The Homelands, Ashford Road TN26 1NJ **(T)** 01233 611 838
Capacity: **Seats:** Yes **Covered:** Yes **Midweek Matchday:** Tuesday **Clubhouse:** Yes

Colours(change): Green & white (Yellow & green)
Previous Names: Ashford Town 1930-2010.
Previous Leagues: Kent Invicta >2013
Records: **Att:** @ Homelands - 3,363 v Fulham, FAC 1st Rnd 1994. **Goalscorer:** Dave Arter - 192. **Apps:** Peter McRobert - 765.
Senior Honours: Kent League 1948-49. Kent Senior Cup 1958-59, 62-63, 92-93, 95-96.

10 YEAR RECORD

04-05	05-06	06-07	07-08	08-09	09-10	10-11	11-12	12-13	13-14
Isth1 20	Isth1 21	Isth1S 18	Isth1S 8	Isth1S 7	Isth1S 20		K_lv 5	K_lv 3	SCE 2

BECKENHAM TOWN

Founded: 1887 Nickname: Reds

Secretary: Peter Palmer **(T)** 07774 728 758 **(E)** peterpalmer3@sky.com
Chairman: Jason Huntley **Manager:** Jason Huntley **Prog Ed:** Peter Palmer
Ground: Eden Park Avenue, Beckenham Kent BR3 3JL **(T)** 07774 728 758
Capacity: 4,000 **Seats:** 120 **Covered:** 120 **Midweek Matchday:** Tuesday **Clubhouse:** Yes **Shop:** Yes

Colours(change): All red (All blue).
Previous Names: Stanhope Rovers.
Previous Leagues: South East London Amateur. Metropolitan. London Spartan.
Records: **Att:** 720 v Berkhamsted, FA Cup 1994-95. **Goalscorer:** Ricky Bennett. **Apps:** Lee Fabian - 985.
Senior Honours:

10 YEAR RECORD

04-05	05-06	06-07	07-08	08-09	09-10	10-11	11-12	12-13	13-14
Kent P 10	Kent P 2	Kent P 11	Kent P 3	Kent P 15	Kent P 4	Kent P 10	Kent P 6	Kent P 11	SCE 8

CANTERBURY CITY

Founded: 1904 Nickname:

Secretary: John Barlow **(T)** 07852 188 194 **(E)** jonjo@almonry.freeserve.co.uk
Chairman: Tim Clarke **Manager:** Ada Gower **Prog Ed:** John Fabre
Ground: Herne Bay FC, Winch's Field, Standley Gardens, Heren Bay CT6 5SG **(T)**
Capacity: 3,000 **Seats:** 200 **Covered:** 1,500 **Midweek Matchday:** Wednesday **Clubhouse:** Yes **Shop:** Yes

Colours(change): All burgundy (All green)
Previous Names:
Previous Leagues: Kent 1947-59, 94-01, Metropolitan 1959-60, Southern 1960-61, 94, Kent County 2007-11.
Records:
Senior Honours: Kent County League Division One East 2007-08, 08-09.

10 YEAR RECORD

04-05	05-06	06-07	07-08	08-09	09-10	10-11	11-12	12-13	13-14
			KC1E 1	KC1E 1	KC P 5	KC P 2	Kent P 9	Kent P 9	SCE 12

CORINTHIAN

Founded: 1972 Nickname:

Secretary: Sue Billings **(T)** 07734 855 554 **(E)** corinthians@billingsgroup.com
Chairman: R J Billings **Manager:** James Collins
Ground: Gay Dawn Farm, Valley Road, Longfield DA3 8LY **(T)** 01474 573 118
Capacity: **Seats:** **Covered:** **Midweek Matchday:** Tuesday **Clubhouse:** Yes

Colours(change): Green & white hoops/white (Yellow/green/green)
Previous Names: Welling United Reserves > 2009.
Previous Leagues: Southern 1985-91.
Records:
Senior Honours:

10 YEAR RECORD

04-05	05-06	06-07	07-08	08-09	09-10	10-11	11-12	12-13	13-14
				Kent 2 6	Kent P 14	Kent P 12	Kent P 7	Kent P 4	SCE 5

2013-14 - Fisher. Photo: Alan Coomes.

2013-14 - Greenwich Borough. Photo: Alan Coomes.

CRAY VALLEY PAPER MILLS

Founded: 1919 Nickname: Millers

Secretary: Dave Wilson **(T)** 07715 961 886 **(E)** wilson433@ntlworld.com
Chairman: Frank May **Manager:** Paul Gross **Prog Ed:** Dave Wilson
Ground: Badgers Sports, Middle Park Avenue, Eltham SE9 5HT **(T)**
Capacity: **Seats:** **Covered:** **Midweek Matchday:** Wednesday **Clubhouse:**

Colours(change): Green/black/black (All sky blue).
Previous Names: None
Previous Leagues: Spartan 1991-97, Spartan South Midlands 1997-98, London Intermediate 1998-01, Kent County 2001-11.
Records:
Senior Honours: Kent County League Premier Division 2004-05.

10 YEAR RECORD

04-05	05-06	06-07	07-08	08-09	09-10	10-11	11-12	12-13	13-14
KC P 1		KC P 7	KC P 9	KC P 5	KC P 6	KC P 3	Kent P 11	Kent P 8	SCE 7

CROWBOROUGH ATHLETIC

Founded: 1894 Nickname: The Crows

Secretary: Eric Gillett **(T)** 07879 434467 **(E)** emgillett@hotmail.co.uk
Chairman: Tony Bowen **Manager:** Sean Muggeridge & Simon Colbran **Prog Ed:** Malcolm Boyes
Ground: Crowborough Co. Stadium, Alderbrook Rec, Fermor Road, TN6 3DJ **(T)** 07879 434 467
Capacity: 2,000 **Seats:** **Covered:** 150 **Midweek Matchday:** Tuesday **Clubhouse:**

Colours(change): All blue (All red).
Previous Names:
Previous Leagues: Sussex County 1974-2008. Isthmian 2008-09. Sussex County 2009-14.
Records:
Senior Honours: Sussex County Division One 2007-08. League Cup 2006-07.

10 YEAR RECORD

04-05	05-06	06-07	07-08	08-09	09-10	10-11	11-12	12-13	13-14
SxC2 1	SxC1 6	SxC1 4	SxC1 1	Isth1S 22	SxC1 18	SxC1 12	SxC1 13	SxC1 15	SxC1 5

CROYDON

Founded: 1953 Nickname: The Trams

Secretary: Ms Shazia Ahmed **(T)** 07966 428 151 **(E)** shazia.croydonfc@outlook.com
Chairman: Dickson Gill **Prog Ed:** Simon Hawkins
Ground: Croydon Sports Arena, Albert Road, South Norwood SE25 4QL **(T)** 02086 545 524 (CH - 0208 654 8555)
Capacity: 8,000 **Seats:** 500 **Covered:** 1,000 **Midweek Matchday:** Wednesday **Clubhouse:** Yes **Shop:** Yes

Colours(change): Sky & navy blue/sky & navy/sky (Yellow & purple/yellow & purple/yellow)
Previous Names: Croydon Amateurs 1953-73.
Previous Leagues: Surrey Senior 1953-63. Spartan 1963-64. Athenian 1964-74. Isthmian1974- 2006. Kent 2006-09. Combined Counties 2009-14.
Records: **Att:**1,600 v Dorking,Surrey Sen Lge Charity Final 05/54. **G'scorer:**Fred Morris - 147 (59-64). **Apps:**Alec Jackson - 452(77-88)
Senior Honours: Surrey Senior League Cup 1960-61, 62-63. Surrey Senior Charity Cup 1962-63. Spartan Lg 1963-64. Athenian Div.2 1965-66. Surrey Senior Cup 1981-82. Isthmian League Division One 1999-00. London Senior Cup 2001-02. Kent Lge Charity Shield 09.

10 YEAR RECORD

04-05	05-06	06-07	07-08	08-09	09-10	10-11	11-12	12-13	13-14
Isth1 22	Isth2 10	Kent P 3	Kent P 12	Kent P 9	CCP 16	CCP 20	CCP 16	CCP 14	CCP 13

DEAL TOWN

Founded: 1908 Nickname: Town

Secretary: Jackie Mapstone **(T)** **(E)** Jackiemapstone@hotmail.co.uk
Chairman: Derek Hares **Prog Ed:** Colin Adams
Ground: Charles Sports Ground, St Leonards Road, Deal. CT14 9BB **(T)** 01304 375 623
Capacity: 2,500 **Seats:** 180 **Covered:** 180 **Midweek Matchday:** Tuesday **Clubhouse:** Yes **Shop:** Yes

Colours(change): Black & white/black/black (All red).
Previous Names: Deal Cinque Ports FC > 1920
Previous Leagues: Thanet. East Kent. Kent. Aetolian. Southern. Greater London.
Records: **Att:** 2,495 v Newcastle Town, FA Vase S-F, 26.03.2000.
Senior Honours:

10 YEAR RECORD

04-05	05-06	06-07	07-08	08-09	09-10	10-11	11-12	12-13	13-14
Kent P 13	Kent P 9	Kent P 8	Kent P 9	Kent P 12	Kent P 9	Kent P 11	Kent P 15	Kent P 12	SCE 13

2013-14 - Holmesdale. Photo: Alan Coomes.

2013-14 - Phoenix Sports. Photo: Alan Coomes.

ERITH & BELVEDERE

Founded: 1922 Nickname: Deres

Secretary: Adam Peters **(T)** 07984 090 805 **(E)** clubsec_erithandbelvederefc@live.com
Chairman: John McFadden **Manager:** Matt Longhurst **Prog Ed:** Brian Spurrell / Martin Tarrant
Ground: Welling FC, Park View Road, Welling, DA16 1SY **(T)** 07984 090 805
Capacity: 4,000 **Seats:** 1,070 **Covered:** 1,000 **Midweek Matchday:** Tuesday **Clubhouse:** Yes **Shop:** Yes

Colours(change): Blue & white quarters/blue/blue. (Red & white quarters/red/red)
Previous Names: Belvedere & District FC (Formed 1918 restructured 1922)
Previous Leagues: Kent. London. Corinthian. Athenian. Southern. Kent League 2005-13. Isthmian 2013-14.
Records: 5,573 v Crook C.W., FA Amateur Cup 19/02/1949
Senior Honours: Kent League 1981-82, 2012-13. London Senior Cup 1944-45.

10 YEAR RECORD

04-05		05-06		06-07		07-08		08-09		09-10		10-11		11-12		12-13		13-14	
SthE	21	Kent P	4	Kent P	7	Kent P	7	Kent P	8	Kent P	12	Kent P	5	Kent P	2	Kent P	1	Isth1N	24

ERITH TOWN

Founded: 1959 Nickname: The Dockers

Secretary: Paul Carter **(T)** 07863 347 587 **(E)** fixtures@erithtown.co.uk
Chairman: Ian Birrell **Manager:** Simon Austin **Prog Ed:** Ian Birrell
Ground: Badger Sports, Middle Park Avenue, Eltham, London SE9 5HT **(T)**
Capacity: 1,450 **Seats:** 1,006 **Covered:** 1,066 **Midweek Matchday:** Monday **Clubhouse:** Yes **Shop:** No

Colours(change): Red & black/black/black. (Yellow & black/white/white).
Previous Names: Woolwich Town 1959-89 and 1990-97.
Previous Leagues: London Metropolitan Sunday. London Spartan.
Records: **Att:** 325 v Charlton Athletic, friendly. **Goalscorer:** Dean Bowey.
Senior Honours:

10 YEAR RECORD

04-05		05-06		06-07		07-08		08-09		09-10		10-11		11-12		12-13		13-14	
Kent P	15	Kent P	14	Kent P	14	Kent P	5	Kent P	7	Kent P	12	Kent P	8	Kent P	4	Kent P	3	SCE	3

FISHER

Founded: 1908 Nickname: The Fish

Secretary: Dan York **(T)** 07719 632 635 **(E)** dan@fisherfc.co.uk
Chairman: Ben Westmancott **Manager:** Billy Walton **Prog Ed:** Jevon Hall
Ground: Dulwich Hamlet FC, Edgar Kail Way, East Dulwich SE22 8BD **(T)**
Capacity: 3,000 **Seats:** 500 **Covered:** 1,000 **Midweek Matchday:** Monday **Clubhouse:** Yes **Shop:** Yes

Colours(change): Black & white/black/black. (Orange/orange/black).
Previous Names: Fisher Athletic. Reformed as Fisher F.C. in 2009.
Previous Leagues: Parthenon, Kent Amateur, London Spartan, Southern, Isthmian, Conference.
Records: **Att:** 4,283 v Barnet Conference 04/05/1991. **Goalscorer:** Paul Shinners - 205. **Apps:** Dennis Sharp - 720.
Senior Honours: Southern League Southern Division 1982-83, Premier 86-87, Eastern 2004-05. Kent Senior Cup 1983-84. Isthmian League Cup 2005-06.

10 YEAR RECORD

04-05		05-06		06-07		07-08		08-09		09-10		10-11		11-12		12-13		13-14	
SthE	1	Isth P	3	Conf S	10	Conf S	4	Conf S	22	Kent P	13	Kent P	16	Kent P	10	Kent P	14	SCE	14

GREENWICH BOROUGH

Founded: 1928 Nickname: Boro

Secretary: Norman Neal **(T)** 07958 077 958 **(E)** norman.neal@ntlworld.com
Chairman: Perry Skinner **Manager:** Ian Jenkins **Prog Ed:** Patrick Mahony
Ground: Holmesdale FC, 68 Oakley Road, Bromley, Kent BR2 8HQ **(T)**
Capacity: **Seats:** **Covered:** **Midweek Matchday:** Wednesday **Clubhouse:** Yes **Shop:** No

Colours(change): Red & black/black/black. (Blue & black/black/black).
Previous Names: Woolwich Borough Council Athletic FC.
Previous Leagues: South London Alliance. Kent Amateur. London Spartan.
Records: **Att:** 2,000 v Charlton Athletic, turning on of floodlights, 1978.
Senior Honours: Kent League 86-87, 87-88.

10 YEAR RECORD

04-05		05-06		06-07		07-08		08-09		09-10		10-11		11-12		12-13		13-14	
Kent P	9	Kent P	13	Kent P	5	Kent P	8	Kent P	3	Kent P	5	Kent P	4	Kent P	16	Kent P	15	SCE	9

HOLMESDALE

Founded: 1956 Nickname:

Secretary: Ross Mitchell **(T)** 07875 730 862 **(E)** secretary@holmesdalefc.co.uk
Chairman: Mark Harris **Manager:** John-Paul Collier **Prog Ed:** Mark Harris
Ground: Holmesdale Sp.& Soc.Club, 68 Oakley Rd, Bromley BR2 8HQ **(T)** 020 8462 4440
Capacity: **Seats:** **Covered:** **Midweek Matchday:** Tuesday **Clubhouse:** Yes **Shop:** Yes

Colours(change): Green & yellow/green/yellow. (All blue).
Previous Names: None.
Previous Leagues: Thornton Heath & Dist. Surrey Inter. Surrey South Eastern. Kent County.
Records: **Goals:** M Barnett - 410 (in 429 apps).
Senior Honours:

10 YEAR RECORD

04-05	05-06	06-07	07-08	08-09	09-10	10-11	11-12	12-13	13-14
KC1W 8	KC1W 1	KC P 1	Kent P 15	Kent P 5	Kent P 10	Kent P 14	Kent P 13	Kent P 16	SCE 10

LINGFIELD

Founded: 1893 Nickname:

Secretary: Caroline Dean **(T)** 07958 540 211 **(E)** caroline.dean.2@googlemail.com
Chairman: Bill Blenkin **Manager:** David 'Dixie' Dean **Prog Ed:** David Antino
Ground: Sports Pavillion, Godstone Road, Lingfield, Surrey RH7 6BT **(T)** 01342 834 269
Capacity: 1,000+ **Seats:** Yes **Covered:** Yes **Midweek Matchday:** Tuesday **Clubhouse:** Yes **Shop:** No

Colours(change): Red & Yellow/red or black/yellow. (Blue & white/blue or black/blue)
Previous Names: None.
Previous Leagues: Redhill. Surrey Intermediate. Combined Counties. Mid Sussex. Sussex County > 2014.
Records:
Senior Honours:

10 YEAR RECORD

04-05	05-06	06-07	07-08	08-09	09-10	10-11	11-12	12-13	13-14
SxC3 3	SxC3 2	SxC2 10	SxC2 2	SxC1 8	SxC1 10	SxC1 11	SxC1 7	SxC1 6	SxC1 15

LORDSWOOD

Founded: 1968 Nickname: Lords

Secretary: Steve Lewis **(T)** 07968 429 941 **(E)** slew1953@hotmail.co.uk
Chairman: Ron Constantine **Manager:** Jason Lillis **Prog Ed:** Paul Caulfield
Ground: Martyn Grove, Northdane Way, Walderslade, ME5 8YE **(T)** 01634 669 138
Capacity: 600 **Seats:** 123 **Covered:** 123 **Midweek Matchday:** Tuesday **Clubhouse:** Yes **Shop:** No

Colours(change): Orange/black/orange (Grey/grey/blue).
Previous Names: None.
Previous Leagues: Rochester & Dist. Kent County.
Records:
Senior Honours:

10 YEAR RECORD

04-05	05-06	06-07	07-08	08-09	09-10	10-11	11-12	12-13	13-14
Kent P 16	Kent P 8	Kent P 13	Kent P 16	Kent P 16	Kent P 16	Kent P 13	Kent P 12	Kent P 5	SCE 11

PHOENIX SPORTS

Founded: 1935 Nickname:

Secretary: Alf Levy **(T)** 07795 182 927 **(E)** senior@phoenixsportsclub.org
Chairman: Andrew Mortlock **Manager:** Steve O'Boyle & Tony Beckingham **Prog Ed:** Alf Levy
Ground: Phoenix Sports Ground, Mayplace Road East, Barnehurst, Kent DA7 6JT **(T)** 01322 526 159
Capacity: **Seats:** **Covered:** **Midweek Matchday:** Wednesday **Clubhouse:**

Colours(change): Green/black/black (All red)
Previous Names:
Previous Leagues: Spartan League. Kent County > 2011. Kent Invicta 2011-13.
Records:
Senior Honours: Kent County Division Two West 2004-05, Division One West 2007-08. Kent Invicta League 2012-13.

10 YEAR RECORD

04-05	05-06	06-07	07-08	08-09	09-10	10-11	11-12	12-13	13-14
KC2W 1	KC1W 3	KC1W 5	KC1W 1	KC P 8	KC P 4	KC P 5	K_lv 2	K_lv 1	SCE 6

ROCHESTER UNITED

Founded: 1982 Nickname:

Secretary: Tony Wheeler **(T)** 07775 735 543 **(E)** tony.wheelerrufc@yahoo.co.uk
Chairman: David Archer **Manager:** Matt Hume
Ground: Rochester United Sports Ground, Rede Court Road, Strood, Kent ME2 3TU **(T)** 01634 710577
Capacity: **Seats:** **Covered:** **Midweek Matchday:** Tuesday **Clubhouse:**

Colours(change): Red/black/black (Grey/grey/red)
Previous Names: Templars. Bly Spartans.
Previous Leagues: Kent County > 2011. Founder Members of Kent Invicta 2011-12.
Records:
Senior Honours: Kent County League Division One West 2007-08. Kent Invicta League 2011-12.

10 YEAR RECORD

04-05	05-06	06-07	07-08	08-09	09-10	10-11	11-12	12-13	13-14
KC1W 3	KC1W 10	KC1W 2	KC1W 1	KC P 10	KC P 12	KC P 15	K_Iv 1	Kent P 13	SCE 15

SEVENOAKS TOWN

Founded: 1883 Nickname: Town

Secretary: Eddie Diplock **(T)** 07876 444 274 **(E)** paul@stjfc.org.uk
Chairman: Paul Lansdale **Manager:** Micky Collins **Prog Ed:** Ian Murphy
Ground: Greatness Park, Seal Road, Sevenoaks TN14 5BL **(T)** 01732 741 987
Capacity: 2,000 **Seats:** 110 **Covered:** 200 **Midweek Matchday:** Wednesday **Clubhouse:**

Colours(change): Blue & black/black/black (Green & white/green/green).
Previous Names: None.
Previous Leagues: Sevenoaks League. Kent Amateur/County.
Records:
Senior Honours:

10 YEAR RECORD

04-05	05-06	06-07	07-08	08-09	09-10	10-11	11-12	12-13	13-14
Kent P 11	Kent P 16	Kent P 10	Kent P 11	Kent P 14	Kent P 6	Kent P 7	Kent P 14	Kent P 17	SCE 16

TUNBRIDGE WELLS

Founded: 1886 Nickname: The Wells

Secretary: Phill Allcorn **(T)** 07900 243 508 **(E)** secretary@twfcexec.com
Chairman: Clive Maynard **Manager:** Martin Larkin
Ground: Culverden Stadium, Culverden Down, Tunbridge Wells TN4 9SG **(T)** 01892 520 517
Capacity: 3,750 **Seats:** 250 **Covered:** 1,000 **Midweek Matchday:** Tuesday **Clubhouse:** Yes **Shop:** No

Colours(change): All red (White/black/white)
Previous Names: None.
Previous Leagues: Isthminan. London Spartan.
Records: **Att:** 1,754 v Hadleigh United, FA Vase SF 1st Leg 2012-13. **Goalscorer:** John Wingate - 151. **Apps:** Tony Atkins - 410.
Senior Honours: Kent Senior Trophy 2012-13.

10 YEAR RECORD

04-05	05-06	06-07	07-08	08-09	09-10	10-11	11-12	12-13	13-14
Kent P 7	Kent P 10	Kent P 15	Kent P 10	Kent P 10	Kent P 7	Kent P 6	Kent P 5	Kent P 7	SCE 4

WOODSTOCK SPORTS

Founded: 1927 Nickname: Sports

Secretary: Colin Page **(T)** 07970 549 355 **(E)** wsfc.secretary@gmx.co.uk
Chairman: Ron Welling **Manager:** Lee Hockey **Prog Ed:** Mike Wood
Ground: The WE Mannin Stadium, Woodstock Park, Broadoak Rd, Sittingbourne ME9 8AG **(T)** 07970 549 355
Capacity: 3,000 **Seats:** 200 **Covered:** 1,500 **Midweek Matchday:** Wednesday **Clubhouse:** Yes **Shop:** Yes

Colours(change): All blue (All red).
Previous Names: Amalgamated with Teynham & Lynsted in 1998, Norton Sports 1998-2011.
Previous Leagues: Kent County.
Records:
Senior Honours:

10 YEAR RECORD

04-05	05-06	06-07	07-08	08-09	09-10	10-11	11-12	12-13	13-14
KC1E 1		KC P 3	KC P 1	Kent P 11	Kent P 11	Kent P 9	Kent P 8	Kent P 10	SCE 17

SPARTAN SOUTH MIDLANDS LEAGUE

Sponsored by: Molten
Founded: 1998
Recent Champions:
2009: Biggleswade Town
2010: Aylesbury United
2011: Chalfont St Peter
2012: Royston Town
2013: Dunstable Town
ssmfl.org

PREMIER DIVISION	P	W	D	L	F	A	GD	Pts
1 (P) Hanwell Town	42	35	6	1	127	36	91	111
2 Ampthill Town	42	31	4	7	124	46	78	97
3 Colney Heath	42	26	10	6	92	36	56	88
4 St Margaretsbury	42	26	7	9	86	50	36	85
5 Berkhamsted	42	26	6	10	111	58	53	84
6 Hoddesdon Town	42	24	6	12	88	62	26	78
7 London Colney	42	22	6	14	88	64	24	72
8 Cockfosters	42	16	10	16	69	62	7	58
9 AFC Dunstable	42	15	13	14	74	69	5	58
10 Tring Athletic	42	16	10	16	71	70	1	58
11 Hillingdon Borough	42	17	7	18	90	91	-1	58
12 Holmer Green	42	16	8	18	85	87	-2	56
13 Hadley	42	14	10	18	52	67	-15	52
14 Harefield United	42	14	8	20	85	82	3	50
15 London Tigers	42	14	7	21	70	75	-5	49
16 Hertford Town	42	15	4	23	76	94	-18	49
17 Biggleswade United	42	11	14	17	65	76	-11	47
18 Oxhey Jets	42	13	8	21	74	99	-25	47
19 Stotfold	42	14	5	23	49	91	-42	47
20 Leverstock Green	42	10	4	28	57	117	-60	34
21 (R) Hatfield Town	42	3	5	34	42	152	-110	14
22 (R) London Lions	42	3	4	35	38	129	-91	13

PREMIER DIVISION CUP

ROUND 1			
Hillingdon Borough	v	Biggleswade United	0-4
London Colney	v	London Lions	7-0
Holmer Green	v	Hertford Town	5-2
Oxhey Jets	v	Berkhamsted	1-6
Tring Athletic	v	St Margaretsbury	2-3
London Tigers	v	Leverstock Green	1-3
ROUND 2			
Stotfold	v	London Colney	0-7
Hadley	v	Leverstock Green	4-2
Holmer Green	v	Colney Heath	1-0
Cockfosters	v	Harefield United	3-0
Biggleswade United	v	St Margaretsbury	3-1
Berkhamsted	v	AFC Dunstable	4-1
Hanwell Town	v	Ampthill Town	0-2
Hatfield Town	v	Hoddesdon Town	0-7
QUARTER FINALS			
Berkhamsted	v	Hoddesdon Town	4-2
London Colney	v	Cockfosters	7-1
Ampthill Town	v	Hadley	1-0
Biggleswade United	v	Holmer Green	2-3
SEMI FINALS			
Berkhamsted	v	London Colney	4-4, 5-4p
Holmer Green	v	Ampthill Town	2-5
FINAL			
Berkhamsted	v	Ampthill Town	2-2, 4-5p

CHALLENGE TROPHY

ROUND 1			
Arlesey Town Reserves	v	Hatfield Town	2-3
Southall	v	The 16 FC (Luton)	5-1
Stotfold	v	Caddington	HW
Hadley	v	Oxhey Jets	6-1
Harpenden Town	v	Hertford Town	2-5
Wolverton Town	v	Grendon Rangers	3-2
Baldock Town	v	Codicote	2-3
Old Bradwell United	v	Stony Stratford Town	2-1
Kentish Town	v	Cockfosters	1-2
Crawley Green	v	Colney Heath	3-2
Amersham Town	v	Langford	1-2
Pitstone & Ivinghoe	v	AFC Dunstable	4-5
Aston Clinton	v	New Bradwell St Peter	0-4
Biggleswade United	v	Hanwell Town	1-2
Chesham United Reserves	v	Wodson Park	2-1
Brimsdown	v	Harefield United	0-5

PREMIER DIVISION	1	2	3	4	5	6	7	8	9	10	11	12	13	14	15	16	17	18	19	20	21	22
1 AFC Dunstable		0–1	2–2	1–2	1–1	0–3	1–2	0–0	2–0	1–0	1–1	1–1	0–4	1–5	4–1	3–0	3–1	2–2	1–3	2–2	3–0	2–0
2 Ampthill Town	3–0		0–2	5–1	2–0	5–4	3–0	0–0	1–1	4–1	3–0	8–3	2–0	2–1	5–1	3–1	7–0	4–2	5–0	0–1	6–2	1–4
3 Berkhamsted	2–1	2–1		5–4	1–3	0–1	1–0	0–1	3–1	9–1	4–2	4–2	3–2	2–4	5–0	4–0	1–0	3–0	5–0	1–1	4–0	1–0
4 Biggleswade United	1–5	1–4	2–2		1–1	0–2	1–1	1–2	2–2	5–1	1–0	2–1	2–2	4–1	1–3	1–1	HW	1–1	0–0	2–1	1–1	0–0
5 Cockfosters	2–2	1–3	2–1	2–1		2–1	1–1	2–6	1–0	2–0	3–0	1–0	1–2	2–2	3–1	1–1	3–1	1–3	0–0	0–3	0–1	1–2
6 Colney Heath	4–0	1–0	3–0	2–1	1–1		1–2	1–2	3–1	1–1	3–1	4–1	1–0	2–1	4–0	0–2	4–0	1–0	0–0	3–0	1–1	2–0
7 Hadley	3–0	0–4	1–1	1–1	2–2	1–4		0–0	3–3	2–0	2–1	1–5	2–2	2–1	0–3	1–0	4–0	2–1	0–2	1–1	1–2	2–1
8 Hanwell Town	4–1	2–0	3–0	3–2	2–0	1–1	2–1		3–0	4–0	2–1	4–0	3–1	2–0	10–0	4–1	2–1	4–3	7–2	4–1	4–0	3–1
9 Harefield United	2–3	2–3	0–2	2–1	1–1	1–2	5–3	1–1		8–0	3–6	2–4	2–3	1–5	4–1	5–1	1–1	3–1	3–0	2–3	4–0	2–2
10 Hatfield Town	3–3	1–4	0–11	1–4	1–2	2–6	1–2	0–5	0–2		0–2	3–3	1–5	1–2	1–3	0–6	0–5	1–2	2–4	0–4	2–1	2–2
11 Hertford Town	1–4	3–8	0–2	3–1	3–2	0–2	2–1	0–2	3–2	2–4		2–3	1–2	2–1	1–2	4–3	3–2	3–3	0–3	1–3	2–1	1–1
12 Hillingdon Borough	1–1	1–4	3–0	3–1	1–0	3–3	4–2	1–4	0–3	5–0	0–4		2–3	2–0	4–1	3–3	2–1	3–1	3–2	0–1	2–3	2–4
13 Hoddesdon Town	1–1	4–2	2–4	2–1	2–1	0–4	1–0	1–3	1–2	2–2	0–1	3–2		4–0	1–0	0–2	4–0	1–2	2–1	3–2	3–1	2–1
14 Holmer Green	5–2	0–5	3–0	3–3	0–3	0–4	1–0	1–2	2–1	2–1	1–1	3–3	1–3		6–0	1–3	6–0	2–2	3–2	1–4	1–0	3–3
15 Leverstock Green	0–5	0–1	3–3	1–1	3–2	1–5	2–0	1–2	0–2	3–0	2–1	1–3	2–2	2–3		3–8	2–1	0–0	1–3	1–2	1–2	1–2
16 London Colney	0–0	1–2	1–2	3–0	0–2	3–0	2–0	2–1	3–0	4–2	2–1	2–1	0–1	6–3	2–1		1–0	1–2	3–1	4–1	1–2	4–4
17 London Lions	2–4	1–5	2–2	0–5	1–11	1–4	0–1	1–7	1–3	3–4	0–5	1–5	2–6	1–1	2–1	0–2		0–2	2–2	0–2	0–2	0–1
18 London Tigers	1–2	0–2	1–3	0–2	0–2	0–0	3–2	4–5	2–1	8–1	0–2	1–3	2–5	5–2	2–0	0–0	1–3		2–0	1–2	1–2	4–0
19 Oxhey Jets	0–5	0–0	2–6	4–1	1–2	0–2	0–2	0–4	1–1	3–1	9–5	1–1	1–0	2–4	3–1	3–2	3–2	0–1		2–4	6–5	1–1
20 St Margaretsbury	2–0	0–2	0–2	1–1	2–1	1–1	2–0	2–2	3–1	2–0	3–0	3–1	1–1	1–0	8–3	0–1	1–0	2–0	3–2		5–1	4–0
21 Stotfold	1–1	1–1	0–4	2–0	2–1	1–1	0–1	1–3	2–1	2–0	0–4	2–1	0–2	0–3	0–3	1–4	1–0	0–4	4–3	1–2		1–2
22 Tring Athletic	0–3	1–3	4–2	1–3	4–0	0–0	0–0	1–2	3–4	2–1	3–1	1–2	1–3	1–1	3–2	1–2	5–0	2–0	3–2	2–0	2–0	

DIVISION ONE	P	W	D	L	F	A	GD	Pts
1 (P) Sun Postal Sports	38	30	3	5	120	39	81	93
2 (P) Kings Langley	38	27	5	6	133	31	102	86
3 Bedford	38	26	8	4	108	32	76	86
4 Welwyn Garden City	38	24	3	11	118	52	66	75
5 Crawley Green	38	22	7	9	79	48	31	73
6 FC Broxbourne Borough	38	20	7	11	65	48	17	67
7 Baldock Town	38	19	8	11	82	54	28	65
8 Harpenden Town	38	17	9	12	88	79	9	60
9 Winslow United	38	18	5	15	85	55	30	59
10 Codicote	38	16	11	11	75	59	16	59
11 Southall	38	16	11	11	66	53	13	59
12 Chesham United Reserves	38	14	10	14	67	74	-7	52
13 Buckingham Athletic	38	16	3	19	67	77	-10	51
14 Risborough Rangers	38	11	10	17	53	59	-6	43
15 Kentish Town	38	10	5	23	49	99	-50	35
16 Amersham Town	38	8	4	26	41	88	-47	28
17 Wodson Park	38	6	8	24	41	107	-66	26
18 Stony Stratford Town	38	7	1	30	41	146	-105	22
19 Langford	38	5	4	29	41	140	-99	19
20 Arlesey Town Reserves	38	2	10	26	38	117	-79	16

DIVISION ONE CUP

ROUND 1

Stony Stratford Town	v	Risborough Rangers	2-4
Southall	v	FC Broxbourne Borough	2-1
Codicote	v	Bedford	1-1 4-3p
Kentish Town	v	Harpenden Town	4-2

ROUND 2

Risborough	v	Crawley Green	2-0
Langford	v	Buckingham Athletic	4-2
Sun Postal Sports	v	Arlesey Town Reserves	2-3
Southall	v	Chesham United Reserves	1-3
Welwyn Garden City	v	Winslow United	0-2
Kings Langley	v	Wodson Park	7-1
Amersham Town	v	Baldock Town	1-3
Codicote	v	Kentish Town	1-4

QUARTER FINALS

Chesham United Reserves	v	Langford	3-1
Baldock Town	v	Kings Langley	1-2
Risborough Rangers	v	Winslow United	2-1
Arlesey Town Reserves	v	Kentish Town	0-1

SEMI FINALS

Risborough Rangers	v	Kentish Town	4-0
Chesham United Reserves	v	Kings Langley	2-5

FINAL

Kings Langley	v	Risborough Rangers	3-0

CHALLENGE TROPHY continued...

Leverstock Green	v	St Margaretsbury	1-5
Totternhoe	v	Mursley United	1-0
FC Broxbourne Borough	v	Ampthill Town	3-1
Kings Langley	v	Buckingham Athletic	8-1
Hales Leys United	v	Welwyn Garden City	2-6
Risborough Rangers	v	Hillingdon Borough	3-5
Sun Postal Sports	v	Berkhamsted	2-3
London Tigers	v	London Colney	0-4
Bedford	v	Tring Athletic	1-1 3-4p

ROUND 2

Crawley Green	v	Hertford Town	2-1
Hanwell Town	v	St Margaretsbury	2-1
Tring Athletic	v	Hoddesdon Town	3-3, 4-5p
Chesham United Reserves	v	AFC Dunstable	5-2
Stotfold	v	Tring Corinthians	3-0
New Bradwell St Peter	v	Southall	1-3
Langford	v	London Lions	2-1
London Colney	v	Hillingdon Borough	3-2
Hadley	v	Cockfosters	0-2
Welwyn Garden City	v	Codicote	4-4, 3-4p
Hatfield Town	v	Willen	AW
Holmer Green	v	Berkhamsted	0-3
Kent Athletic	v	Kings Langley	0-6
Totternhoe	v	Harefield United	1-0
Wolverton Town	v	FC Broxbourne Borough	3-7
Winslow United	v	Old Bradwell United	1-0

ROUND 3

Langford	v	Winslow United	0-1
Stotfold	v	Totternhoe	3-2
Kings Langley	v	FC Broxbourne Borough	1-0
Cockfosters	v	Crawley Green	3-0
Hoddesdon Town	v	Chesham United Res.	2-2, 4-3p
Berkhamsted	v	Hanwell Town	4-2
London Colney	v	Southall	2-0
Codicote	v	Willen	4-0

QUARTER FINALS

Cockfosters	v	Codicote	2-1
London Colney	v	Berkhamsted	1-3
Hoddesdon Town	v	Winslow United	5-0
Kings Langley	v	Stotfold	1-2

SEMI FINALS

Berkhamsted	v	Stotfold	1-3
Hoddesdon Town	v	Cockfosters	1-3

FINAL

Stotfold	v	Cockfosters	1-2

DIVISION ONE	1	2	3	4	5	6	7	8	9	10	11	12	13	14	15	16	17	18	19	20
1 Amersham Town		2–0	1–2	0–1	1–1	2–3	1–2	0–1	1–2	1–3	0–1	2–4	1–0	0–0	0–3	6–1	1–4	1–3	2–5	0–3
2 Arlesey Town Reserves	0–2		1–5	0–5	1–2	2–4	3–3	0–1	1–6	2–4	1–5	0–0	0–3	3–3	0–0	3–1	2–5	1–6	0–1	2–2
3 Baldock Town	1–2	3–0		2–2	1–1	7–0	1–3	1–0	2–1	1–1	3–0	1–2	2–2	1–0	5–3	5–1	0–2	1–2	2–1	7–0
4 Bedford	8–1	1–0	1–5		1–1	4–0	2–0	0–1	4–0	3–0	5–0	3–3	6–0	2–2	2–0	6–0	0–0	3–2	2–1	8–0
5 Broxbourne Borough	3–1	2–0	4–1	1–2		2–1	0–1	1–1	4–0	0–4	1–0	2–1	4–2	1–0	2–1	3–0	1–3	1–0	2–1	1–3
6 Buckingham Athletic	1–1	1–1	2–1	4–3	4–0		4–1	0–1	0–2	5–2	1–0	0–1	3–0	1–3	1–3	4–1	1–2	4–2	1–3	2–1
7 Chesham United Reserves	3–1	2–3	0–0	2–0	2–0	1–1		1–1	3–2	2–6	1–3	0–3	5–0	0–2	4–0	2–1	1–1	1–1	1–1	0–0
8 Codicote	1–1	2–2	0–1	1–2	1–1	1–4	8–3		2–2	1–1	2–2	0–4	6–1	3–0	1–3	6–0	0–3	0–2	2–1	5–0
9 Crawley Green	7–0	4–0	3–1	1–1	3–0	0–2	2–0	1–0		0–0	3–1	3–2	4–0	1–0	1–3	3–1	2–1	1 0	1–1	2–2
10 Harpenden Town	3–0	3–1	2–2	0–7	2–4	3–2	2–1	3–5	1–1		7–0	1–2	3–1	4–1	4–0	4–0	0–4	2–2	2–0	1–1
11 Kentish Town	3–0	1–1	1–2	0–4	1–1	2–0	0–4	1–3	0–0	1–0		2–6		1–2	0–4	3–4	0–1	0–9	3–2	3–4
12 Kings Langley	4–0	5–0	4–1	1–1	3–1	6–2	5–1	6–0	1–2	11–1	8–0		1–1	3–0	0–0	4–0	0–1	1–0	2–0	7–0
13 Langford	0–2	1–1	2–3	0–2	1–3	1–3	2–5	3–6	1–3	2–4	1–4	0–8		2–6	1–4	4–1	0–6	1–7	1–0	1–1
14 Risborough Rangers	1–0	4–1	2–2	0–1	0–0	1–3	2–3	1–3	1–2	0–0	0–2	0–1	9–1		0–0	2–1	0–2	1–0	1–1	5–1
15 Southall	0–1	0–0	0–0	0–2	3–0	2–0	2–2	1–1	0–4	1–1	5–2	1–3	8–0	0–0		2–0	4–2	0–3	2–2	3–1
16 Stony Stratford Town	2–1	7–2	0–2	1–4	0–9	3–1	2–3	1–1	3–0	0–7	1–3	0–10	2–1	0–3	1–2		0–5	0–4	1–3	2–1
17 Sun Postal Sports	3–0	3–1	3–0	1–4	1–3	3–1	4–1	0–0	1–0	4–0	3–2	2–1	8–1	5–0	5–2	10–0		5–2	2–1	6–2
18 Welwyn Garden City	2–0	9–1	2–1	1–3	1–2	3–0	3–1	3–1	3–4	7–3	5–1	3–2	3–1	4–0	2–2	10–1	4–1		0–3	4–0
19 Winslow United	6–2	3–0	3–5	1–1	HW	4–0	4–1	1–4	1–0	4–1	5–1	0–2	6–0	3 0	0–1	5–1	1–3	1–2		6–1
20 Wodson Park	1–4	6–2	0–2	0–2	0–1	2–1	1–1	2–3	1–3	0–3	0–0	0–6	0–3	1–1	0–1	2–1	1–5	1–2	0–1	

SPARTAN SOUTH MIDLANDS LEAGUE - STEP 5/6/7

DIVISION TWO	P	W	D	L	F	A	GD	Pts
1 Hale Leys United	26	22	2	2	93	26	67	68
2 Kent Athletic	26	17	5	4	69	32	37	56
3 Mursley United	26	17	5	4	60	28	32	56
4 The 61 FC (Luton)	26	15	4	7	55	39	16	49
5 Pitstone & Ivinghoe	26	11	5	10	51	50	1	38
6 Totternhoe	26	10	6	10	45	41	4	36
7 Aston Clinton	26	11	2	13	45	54	-9	35
8 Old Bradwell United	26	10	3	13	57	57	0	33
9 Grendon Rangers	26	9	3	14	30	51	-21	30
10 Wolverton Town	26	8	5	13	47	60	-13	29
11 Tring Corinthians	26	7	7	12	36	54	-18	28
12 New Bradwell St Peter	26	7	4	15	45	70	-25	25
13 Brimsdown	26	4	5	17	35	58	-23	17
14 Willen	26	4	4	18	37	85	-48	16

DIVISION TWO CUP

ROUND 1

Totternhoe	v	Tring Corinthians	1-2
Pitstone & Ivinghoe	v	Mursley United	3-2
Kent Athletic	v	Risborough Rangers	0-6
Hale Leys Utd	v	Caddington	8-3
Wolverton Town	v	The 61 FC (Luton)	2-3
Old Bradwell United	v	Broxbourne Borough	0-1

QUARTER FINALS

Hale Leys Utd	v	The 61 FC (Luton)	5-3
Aston Clinton	v	Aylesbury Reserves	8-1
Pitstone & Ivinghoe	v	Broxbourne Borough	2-1
Risborough Rangers	v	Tring Corinthians	4-2

SEMI FINALS

Aston Clinton	v	Hale Leys Utd	2-1
Pitstone & Ivinghoe	v	Risborough Rangers	1-2

FINAL

Aston Clinton	v	Risborough Rangers	2-0

DIVISION TWO	1	2	3	4	5	6	7	8	9	10	11	12	13	14
1 Aston Clinton		HW	2-0	1-6	1-4	3-1	3-0	4-3	1-2	1-3	2-2	3-5	4-1	3-0
2 Brimsdown	1-3		0-2	1-6	1-1	0-0	5-1	1-4	2-3	0-2	1-2	2-2	5-1	3-3
3 Grendon Rangers	1-0	0-3		1-2	1-3	1-3	2-2	1-0	0-3	1-1	1-0	2-2	1-3	1-3
4 Hale Leys United	2-0	4-2	4-0		1-5	1-1	4-0	4-0	10-2	5-0	4-0	3-1	6-0	3-1
5 Kent Athletic	2-1	2-0	4-1	0-1		1-2	5-1	3-0	2-1	1-1	2-2	2-1	2-1	4-0
6 Mursley United	2-0	2-0	3-0	0-1	6-1		6-0	5-2	2-1	2-2	1-0	2-2	2-0	1-0
7 New Bradwell St Peter	1-2	3-2	2-1	0-4	2-1	0-4		2-0	2-2	1-2	2-1	0-1	2-3	2-2
8 Old Bradwell United	7-2	4-0	3-1	2-3	0-1	3-1	4-4		1-0	0-4	4-0	1-2	0-0	3-2
9 Pitstone & Ivinghoe	4-0	2-1	1-3	2-3	2-2	2-2	3-2	6-2		0-2	0-1	0-1	3-1	3-2
10 The 61 FC (Luton)	2-1	2-0	2-0	3-2	2-2	0-1	6-3	4-1	1-3		3-2	4-2	3-1	0-2
11 Totternhoe	1-1	3-0	1-2	0-2	1-3	4-0	3-2	0-0	2-2	3-2		5-0	2-2	2-0
12 Tring Corinthians	1-2	2-2	0-1	0-4	1-5	0-2	2-0	2-1	1-2	1-3	0-3		0-0	4-4
13 Willen	1-4	2-3	2-3	3-3	1-8	3-6	1-7	2-4	3-1	2-1	2-5	0-2		2-3
14 Wolverton Town	2-1	2-0	2-3	1-5	1-3	1-3	1-4	3-8	1-1	2-0	3-0	1-1	5-0	

RESERVE DIVISION ONE	P	W	D	L	F	A	GD	Pts
1 St Margaretsbury Reserves	26	18	4	4	64	25	39	58
2 Hoddesdon Town Reserves	26	18	3	5	64	20	44	57
3 Cockfosters Reserves	26	16	4	6	65	32	33	52
4 London Colney Reserves	26	15	7	4	52	30	22	52
5 Holmer Green Reserves	26	13	1	12	40	48	-8	40
6 Hadley Reserves	26	12	3	11	60	51	9	39
7 Oxhey Jets Reserves	26	9	6	11	50	54	-4	33
8 Baldock Town Reserves	26	9	5	12	43	57	-14	32
9 AFC Dunstable Reserves	26	9	2	15	65	69	-4	29
10 Kent Athletic Reserves	26	7	8	11	33	51	-18	29
11 Risborough Rangers Reserves	26	8	3	15	39	44	-5	27
12 Kings Langley Reserves	26	7	4	15	36	57	-21	25
13 London Lions Reserves	26	7	2	17	28	48	-20	23
14 The 61 FC (Luton) Reserves	26	7	2	17	23	76	-53	23

RESERVE DIVISION TWO	P	W	D	L	F	A	GD	Pts
1 Crawley Green Reserves (-3pts)	22	18	3	1	65	16	49	54
2 Totternhoe Reserves	22	15	1	6	41	24	17	46
3 Sun Postal Sports Reserves (-3pts)	22	14	3	5	57	27	30	42
4 Wodson Park Reserves	22	11	3	8	29	30	-1	36
5 Wolverton Town Reserves	22	9	2	11	36	42	-6	29
6 Mursley United Reserves	22	8	5	9	42	55	-13	29
7 Winslow United Reserves	22	7	3	12	33	43	-10	24
8 Buckingham Athletic Reserves	22	6	5	11	38	37	1	23
9 Stony Stratford Town Reserves	22	7	2	13	38	39	-1	23
10 Langford Reserves	22	6	5	11	38	47	-9	23
11 Aston Clinton Reserves	22	6	4	12	28	62	-34	22
12 Old Bradwell United Reserves	22	6	2	14	31	54	-23	20

CLUB MOVEMENTS

Premier Division - In: Kings Langley (P). Sun Postal Sports (P). Wembley (S - Combined Counties).
Out: Hanwell Town (P - Southern Div.1 Central). Hatfield Town (R). London Lions (R).

Division One - In: Bush Hill Rangers (P - Herts Senior County). Edgware Town (N). Hatfield Town (R). London Lions (R).
Out: Kentish Town (W). Kings Langley (P). Sun Postal Sports (P).

Division Two - In: Clean Slate (P - North Bucks & District Intermediate League).
Ealing Town (Merger of AFC Hillgate and Aym Higher - from Middlesex County Div.2).

Out: N/A

A.F.C. DUNSTABLE

Founded: 1981 Nickname: Od's

Secretary: Craig Renfrew **(T)** 07976 192 530 **(E)** renfrewcraig@aol.com
Chairman: Simon Bullard **Manager:** Steve Heath **Prog Ed:** Craig Renfrew
Ground: Dunstable Town FC, Creasey Park, Creasey Pk Dr, Brewers Hill Road, LU6 1BB **(T)** 01582 891 433
Capacity: 3,200 **Seats:** 350 **Covered:** 1,000 **Midweek Matchday:** **Clubhouse:** Yes **Shop:** Yes

Colours(change): Royal blue/royal blue/white (All red)
Previous Names: Old Dunstablians 1981- 2004.
Previous Leagues:
Records:
Senior Honours: Spartan South Midlands Division Two 2003-04, 06-07, Premier Division 2012-13.

10 YEAR RECORD

04-05	05-06	06-07	07-08	08-09	09-10	10-11	11-12	12-13	13-14
SSM2 6	SSM2 2	SSM2 1	SSM2 4	SSM2 3	SSM1 5	SSM1 2	SSM P 3	SSM P 8	SSM P 9

AMPTHILL TOWN

Founded: 1881 Nickname:

Secretary: Eric Turner **(T)** 07866 336 421 **(E)** ericturner789@btinternet.com
Chairman: Lee Roberts **Manager:** Derwayne Stupple **Prog Ed:** Eric Turner
Ground: Ampthill Park, Woburn Street, Ampthill MK45 2HX **(T)** 01525 404 440
Capacity: **Seats:** Yes **Covered:** Yes **Midweek Matchday:** **Clubhouse:** Yes

Colours(change): Yellow/blue/blue (Blue/yellow/yellow)
Previous Names: None
Previous Leagues: United Counties 1965.
Records:
Senior Honours:

10 YEAR RECORD

04-05	05-06	06-07	07-08	08-09	09-10	10-11	11-12	12-13	13-14
SSM1 17	SSM1 16	SSM1 4	SSM1 7	SSM1 15	SSM1 13	SSM1 16	SSM1 2	SSM P 5	SSM P 2

BERKHAMSTED

Founded: 2009 Nickname: Comrades

Secretary: Keith Hicks **(T)** 07767 430 087 **(E)** keithhicks@btinternet.com
Chairman: Steve Davis **Manager:** Mick Vipond **Prog Ed:** Grant Hastie
Ground: Broadwater, Lower Kings Road, Berkhamsted HP4 2AL **(T)** 01442 865 977
Capacity: 2,500 **Seats:** 170 **Covered:** 350 **Midweek Matchday:** **Clubhouse:** Yes **Shop:** Yes

Colours(change): Yellow/blue/blue (White/black/black)
Previous Names: None
Previous Leagues:
Records:
Senior Honours: Spartan South Midlands League Division 1 2009-10, 10-11.

10 YEAR RECORD

04-05	05-06	06-07	07-08	08-09	09-10	10-11	11-12	12-13	13-14
					SSM1 1	SSM1 1	SSM P 7	SSM P 11	SSM P 5

BIGGLESWADE UNITED

Founded: 1929 Nickname:

Secretary: Tracey James **(T)** 07714 661 827 **(E)** tracey.james58@btinternet.com
Chairman: Chris Lewis **Manager:** Mick Reardon **Prog Ed:** Tracey James
Ground: Second Meadow, Fairfield Rd, Biggleswade, Beds SG18 0BS **(T)** 07714 661 827
Capacity: 2,000 **Seats:** 30 **Covered:** 130 **Midweek Matchday:** Wednesday **Clubhouse:** Yes **Shop:** No

Colours(change): Red/navy/red (Sky blue/navy/navy)
Previous Names: None
Previous Leagues: Beds & District and Midland. Herts County.
Records: **Att:** 250 v Biggleswade Town
Senior Honours: Spartan South Midlands Division One 1996-97, Premier Division 2008-09. Hunts FA Premier Cup 1998-99. Beds Senior Trophy 2003-04. Beds Senior Cup 2001-02.

10 YEAR RECORD

04-05	05-06	06-07	07-08	08-09	09-10	10-11	11-12	12-13	13-14
SSM1 3	SSM P 9	SSM P 14	SSM P 18	SSM P 1	SSM P 20	SSM P 20	SSM P 19	SSM P 18	SSM P 17

COCKFOSTERS

Founded: 1921 Nickname: Fosters

Secretary: Graham Bint (T) 07729 709 926 (E) graham.bint@ntlworld.com
Chairman: Roy Syrett **Manager:** Mick Roche **Prog Ed:** Alan Simmons
Ground: Cockfosters Sports Ground, Chalk Lane, Cockfosters, Herts EN4 9JG (T) 0208 449 5833
Capacity: **Seats:** Yes **Covered:** Yes **Midweek Matchday:** **Clubhouse:**

Colours(change): All red (White/blue/blue)
Previous Names: Cockfosters Athletic 1921-68.
Previous Leagues: Barnet 1921-30s. Wood Green 1930s-46. Northern Suburban Int. 1946-66. Hertfordshire County 1966-1991. Spartan 1991-97.
Records: 408 v Saffron Walden.
Senior Honours: London Interim Cup 1970-71, 89. Herts Sen Co Lge 1978-79, 80-81, 83-84. Aubrey Cup 1978-79, 84-85. Herts Interm Cup 1978-79.

10 YEAR RECORD

04-05	05-06	06-07	07-08	08-09	09-10	10-11	11-12	12-13	13-14
SSM1 8	SSM1 8	SSM1 2	SSM1 17	SSM1 19	SSM1 11	SSM1 15	SSM1 9	SSM1 2	SSM P 8

COLNEY HEATH

Founded: 1907 Nickname: Magpies

Secretary: Martin Marlborough (T) 07960 155 463 (E) m.marlborough@stalbans.gov.uk
Chairman: Martin Marlborough **Manager:** Wesley Awad **Prog Ed:** Martin Marlborough
Ground: The Recreation Ground, High St, Colney Heath, St Albans AL4 0NP (T) 01727 824 325
Capacity: **Seats:** **Covered:** **Midweek Matchday:** **Clubhouse:** Yes

Colours(change): Black & white stripes/black/black & white (Yellow/blue/yellow)
Previous Names: None
Previous Leagues: Herts Senior County League 1953-2000
Records:
Senior Honours: Herts County League Div 2 Champions 1953-54 Div 1 A 55-56, Prem 58-99, 99-00, Div 1 88-89, Spartan South Midlands Div 1 2005-06 , SSML Cup 05-06

10 YEAR RECORD

04-05	05-06	06-07	07-08	08-09	09-10	10-11	11-12	12-13	13-14
SSM1 5	SSM1 1	SSM P 16	SSM P 15	SSM P 12	SSM P 5	SSM P 5	SSM P 8	SSM P 13	SSM P 3

HADLEY

Founded: 1882 Nickname:

Secretary: Bob Henderson (T) 07748 267 295 (E) gensecretary@hadleyfc.com
Chairman: Guy Slee **Manager:** Micky Hazard **Prog Ed:** Guy Slee
Ground: Potters Bar Town FC, Watkins Rise (off The Walk), Potters Bar EN6 1QB (T) 01707 654 833
Capacity: 2,000 **Seats:** 150 **Covered:** 250 **Midweek Matchday:** **Clubhouse:** Yes **Shop:** Yes

Colours(change): Red/black/black (Black & white stripes/white/white)
Previous Names: None
Previous Leagues: Barnet & Dist. 1922-57, Nth Suburban 57-70, Mid Herts 70-77, Herts Sen. 77-85, 99-2007, Sth Olym. 85-99, W Herts 2007-08.
Records:
Senior Honours: Hertfordshire Senior County League Division 3 1977-78, Division 1 2001-02, Premier 2003-04, 04-05. West Hertfordshire League 2007-08. Aubrey Cup 2005-06.

10 YEAR RECORD

04-05	05-06	06-07	07-08	08-09	09-10	10-11	11-12	12-13	13-14
HertP 1	HertP 3	HertP 2	WHert 1	SSM2 2	SSM1 2	SSM P 14	SSM P 15	SSM P 12	SSM P 13

HAREFIELD UNITED

Founded: 1868 Nickname: Hares

Secretary: Glenn Bellis (T) 07973 563 282 (E) glennbellis@btconnect.com
Chairman: Gamboor Dhaliwal **Manager:** Phil Granville **Prog Ed:** Keith Ronald
Ground: Preston Park, Breakespeare Road North, Harefield, UB9 6NE (T) 01895 823 474
Capacity: 1,200 **Seats:** 150 **Covered:** Yes **Midweek Matchday:** Tuesday **Clubhouse:** Yes **Shop:** No

Colours(change): Red/black/red (White/red/black)
Previous Names: None
Previous Leagues: Uxbridge & District, Great Western Comb, Panthernon, Middlesex, Athenian & Isthmian.
Records: Att: 430 v Bashley FA Vase
Senior Honours: Middlesex Premier Cup 1985-86

10 YEAR RECORD

04-05	05-06	06-07	07-08	08-09	09-10	10-11	11-12	12-13	13-14
SSM P 5	SSM P 4	SSM P 2	SSM P 5	SSM P 2	SSM P 6	SSM P 21	SSM P 18	SSM P 10	SSM P 14

HERTFORD TOWN

Founded: 1908 — Nickname: The Blues

Secretary: Sylvia Sinclair **(T)** 07740 871 378 **(E)** sylviasinclair@hotmail.com
Chairman: Peter Sinclair **Manager:** Paul Halsey **Prog Ed:** Matt Harris
Ground: Hertingfordbury Park, West Street, Hertford, SG13 8EZ **(T)** 01992 583 716
Capacity: 6,500 **Seats:** 200 **Covered:** 1,500 **Midweek Matchday:** Tuesday **Clubhouse:** Yes **Shop:** Yes

Colours(change): All blue (Red/black/black)
Previous Names: None
Previous Leagues: Herts Co. Spartan. Delphian 59-63. Athenian 63-72. Eastern Co 72-73.
Records: **Att:** 5,000 v Kingstonian FA Am Cup 2nd Round 55-56 **App:** Robbie Burns
Senior Honours: Herts Senior Cup 66-67 East Anglian Cup 62-63, 69-70

10 YEAR RECORD

04-05	05-06	06-07	07-08	08-09	09-10	10-11	11-12	12-13	13-14
Isth2 4	Isth2 13	SSM P 3	SSM P 4	SSM P 10	SSM P 16	SSM P 9	SSM P 16	SSM P 17	SSM P 16

HILLINGDON BOROUGH

Founded: 19190 — Nickname: Boro

Secretary: Graham Smith **(T)** 01895 673 181 **(E)** jackieandgraham@talktalk.net
Chairman: Mick Harris **Manager:** Jason O'Connor **Prog Ed:** Oliver Chalk
Ground: Middlesex Stadium, Breakspear Rd, Ruislip HA4 7SB **(T)** 01895 639 544
Capacity: 1,500 **Seats:** 150 **Covered:** 150 **Midweek Matchday:** **Clubhouse:** Yes

Colours(change): White/royal blue/royal blue (Maroon or Navy blue/black or yellow/maroon or navy blue)
Previous Names: Yiewsley. Bromley Park Rangers.
Previous Leagues: Southern 1964-84, 2006-08. South Midlands 1990-2006. Isthmian 2008-09.
Records:
Senior Honours: South Midlands Cup 1996-97.

10 YEAR RECORD

04-05	05-06	06-07	07-08	08-09	09-10	10-11	11-12	12-13	13-14
SSM P 6	SSM P 2	SthW 16	SthW 13	Isth1N 22	SSM P 18	SSM P 16	SSM P 10	SSM P 19	SSM P 11

HODDESDON TOWN

Founded: 1879 — Nickname: Lilywhites

Secretary: Jane Sinden **(T)** 01767 631 297 & fax **(E)** janedsinden@fsmail.net
Chairman: Roger Merton **Manager:** Neil Conner **Prog Ed:** Jane Sinden
Ground: The Stewart Edwards Stadium, Lowfield, Park View Hoddesdon EN11 8PX **(T)** 01992 463 133
Capacity: **Seats:** **Covered:** **Midweek Matchday:** **Clubhouse:**

Colours(change): White/black/black (All blue)
Previous Names: None
Previous Leagues: Hertfordshire County 1920-25. Spartan 1963-75. London Spartan 1975-77. Athenian 1977-84.
Records:
Senior Honours: **(FA Comps & League):** FA Vase 1974-75 (1st Winners).
Spartan League Champions 1970-71, Division 1 1935-36, Division 2 'B' 1927-28

10 YEAR RECORD

04-05	05-06	06-07	07-08	08-09	09-10	10-11	11-12	12-13	13-14
SSM P 20	SSM1 7	SSM1 5	SSM1 3	SSM1 5	SSM1 4	SSM1 9	SSM1 3	SSM1 3	SSM P 6

HOLMER GREEN

Founded: 1908 — Nickname:

Secretary: Matt Brades **(T)** 01494 716 114 **(E)** brades@badgerway.plus.com
Chairman: Rob Shed **Manager:** Chris Allen **Prog Ed:** John Anderson
Ground: Airedale Park, Watchet Lane, Holmer Green, Bucks HP15 6UF **(T)** 01494 711 485
Capacity: 1,000 **Seats:** 25 **Covered:** yes **Midweek Matchday:** Tuesday **Clubhouse:** Yes

Colours(change): Green & white hoops/green/green (All red)
Previous Names: None
Previous Leagues: Chesham 1908-38, Wycombe Combination 1984-95, Chiltonian 1995-98.
Records:
Senior Honours: Spartan South Midlands Senior 1995-96, 98-99, Division 1 2009-10.

10 YEAR RECORD

04-05	05-06	06-07	07-08	08-09	09-10	10-11	11-12	12-13	13-14
SSM P 13	SSM P 7	SSM P 19	SSM P 20	SSM P 20	SSM1 1	SSM P 17	SSM P 20	SSM P 22	SSM P 12

KINGS LANGLEY

Founded: 1886 Nickname:

Secretary: Andy Mackness **(T)** 07976 692801 **(E)** andymackness@yahoo.co.uk
Chairman: Derry Edgar **Manager:** Ritchie Hanlon & Paul Hughes **Prog Ed:** Roy Mitchard
Ground: Gaywood Park, Hempstead Road, Kings Langley Herts WD4 8BS **(T)** 07976 692 801
Capacity: **Seats:** **Covered:** **Midweek Matchday:** **Clubhouse:** Yes

Colours(change): Black & white/black/black (Yellow/white/white)
Previous Names: None
Previous Leagues: Hertfordshire County 1946-52, 55-2001. Parthenon 1952-55.
Records:
Senior Honours: Hertfordshrie County 1949-50, 51-52, 65-66, 66-67, Division One 1975-76. Spartan South Midlands Division Two 2007-08.

10 YEAR RECORD

04-05	05-06	06-07	07-08	08-09	09-10	10-11	11-12	12-13	13-14
SSM2 10	SSM2 6	SSM2 2	SSM2 1	SSM1 2	SSM1 7	SSM1 3	SSM1 4	SSM1 6	SSM1 2

LEVERSTOCK GREEN

Founded: 1895 Nickname: The Green

Secretary: Brian Barter **(T)** 07982 072 783 **(E)** b.barter@btopenworld.com
Chairman: Brian Barter **Manager:** Dene Gardner **Prog Ed:** Brian Barter
Ground: Pancake Lane, Leverstock Green, Hemel Hempstead, Herts HP2 4NQ **(T)** 01442 246 280
Capacity: 1,500 **Seats:** 50 **Covered:** 100 **Midweek Matchday:** Tuesday **Clubhouse:** Yes **Shop:** No

Colours(change): White/green/green (Yellow/blue/blue)
Previous Names: None
Previous Leagues: West Herts (pre 1950) & Herts County 50-91
Records: **Att:** 1,000 **App:** Jonnie Wallace
Senior Honours: South Midlands Senior Division 1996-97.

10 YEAR RECORD

04-05	05-06	06-07	07-08	08-09	09-10	10-11	11-12	12-13	13-14
SSM P 14	SSM P 6	SSM P 5	SSM P 7	SSM P 6	SSM P 10	SSM P 4	SSM P 11	SSM P 15	SSM P 20

LONDON COLNEY

Founded: 1907 Nickname: Blueboys

Secretary: Dave Brock **(T)** 07508 035 835 **(E)** davebrock42@hotmail.com
Chairman: Tony Clafton **Manager:** James Nicholls **Prog Ed:** Johnny Armitt
Ground: Cotlandswick Playing Fields, London Colney, Herts AL2 1DW **(T)** 01727 822132
Capacity: **Seats:** Yes **Covered:** Yes **Midweek Matchday:** **Clubhouse:** Yes

Colours(change): All royal blue (All red)
Previous Names:
Previous Leagues: Herts Senior 1955-93.
Records: 300 v St Albans City Hertfordshire Senior Cup 1998-99.
Senior Honours: Herts Senior League 1956-57, 59-60, 86-87, 88-89. 89-90.
South Midlands Senior Division 1994-95. Spartan South Midlands Premier Division 2001-02, Division One 2011-12.

10 YEAR RECORD

04-05	05-06	06-07	07-08	08-09	09-10	10-11	11-12	12-13	13-14
SSM P 11	SSM P 14	SSM P 10	SSM P 22	SSM1 9	SSM1 3	SSM1 5	SSM1 1	SSM P 7	SSM P 7

LONDON TIGERS

Founded: 2006 Nickname: Tigers

Secretary: Mick Wilkins **(T)** 07802 212 787 **(E)** wilki1@aol.com
Chairman: Mesba Ahmed **Manager:** Armand Kavaja **Prog Ed:** Armand Kavaja
Ground: Avenue Park, Western Avenue, Perivale, Greenford UB6 8GA **(T)** 020 7289 3395 (10am-6pm)
Capacity: **Seats:** **Covered:** **Midweek Matchday:** **Clubhouse:**

Colours(change): Orange/black/black (Yellow/blue/blue)
Previous Names: Kingsbury Town and London Tigers merged in 2006. Kingsbury London Tigers 2006-11.
Previous Leagues: None
Records:
Senior Honours:

10 YEAR RECORD

04-05	05-06	06-07	07-08	08-09	09-10	10-11	11-12	12-13	13-14
		SSM P 13	SSM P 14	SSM P 5	SSM P 8	SSM P 12	SSM P 14	SSM P 20	SSM P 15

OXHEY JETS

Founded: Nickname: Jets

Secretary: David Fuller **(T)** 07786 627 659 **(E)** d.g.fuller@ntlworld.com
Chairman: Phil Andrews **Manager:** Wayne Gladdy **Prog Ed:** David Fuller
Ground: Boundary Stadium, Altham Way, South Oxhey, Watford WD19 6FW **(T)** 020 8421 6277
Capacity: 1,000 **Seats:** 100 **Covered:** 100 **Midweek Matchday:** Wednesday **Clubhouse:** Yes **Shop:** No

Colours(change): All royal blue (All green)
Previous Names: None
Previous Leagues: Herts Senior County
Records: **Att:** 257 v Barnet Herts Senior Cup 05-06 **App:** Ian Holdon
Senior Honours: Herts Senior County Premier 2000-01, 01-02, 02-03. SSML Div 1 Champions 2004-2005, Herts Senior Centenary Trophy 2004-2005

10 YEAR RECORD

04-05	05-06	06-07	07-08	08-09	09-10	10-11	11-12	12-13	13-14
SSM1 1	SSM P 13	SSM P 7	SSM P 19	SSM P 13	SSM P 11	SSM P 19	SSM P 17	SSM P 3	SSM P 18

ST MARGARETSBURY

Founded: 1894 Nickname: Athletic

Secretary: Richard Palette **(T)** 07721 679 681 **(E)** SMFCsecretary@aol.com
Chairman: Gary Stock **Manager:** Gavin Kelsey **Prog Ed:** Gary Stock
Ground: Recreation Ground, Station Road, St Margarets SG12 8EH **(T)** 01920 870 473
Capacity: 1,000 **Seats:** 60 **Covered:** 60 **Midweek Matchday:** Tuesday **Clubhouse:** Yes **Shop:** No

Colours(change): Red & black stripes/black/black (Yellow/blue/yellow)
Previous Names: Stanstead Abbots > 1962
Previous Leagues: East Herts, Hertford & District, Waltham & District, 47-48 Herts Co. 48-92
Records: **Att:** 450 v Stafford Rangers FA Cup 2001-02
Senior Honours: Spartan Lg 95-96 Herts Senior Centenary Trophy 92-93, Herts Charity Shield 97-98

10 YEAR RECORD

04-05	05-06	06-07	07-08	08-09	09-10	10-11	11-12	12-13	13-14
SSM P 7	SSM P 12	SSM P 15	SSM P 11	SSM P 14	SSM P 14	SSM P 18	SSM P 12	SSM P 4	SSM P 4

STOTFOLD

Founded: 1946 Nickname: The Eagles

Secretary: Julie Longhurst **(T)** 07752 430 493 **(E)** julie.longhurst46@virginmedia.com
Chairman: Phil Pateman **Manager:** Steve Young **Prog Ed:** Phil Pateman
Ground: Roker Park, The Green, Stotfold, Hitchin, Herts SG5 4AN **(T)** 01462 730 765
Capacity: 5,000 **Seats:** 300 **Covered:** 300 **Midweek Matchday:** Tuesday **Clubhouse:** Yes

Colours(change): Amber/black/black. (All blue).
Previous Names: None
Previous Leagues: Biggleswade & Dist, Norths Herts & South Midlands, United Counties > 2010
Records: **Att:**1,000 **Goalscorer:** Roy Boon **Apps:** Roy Boon & Dave Chellew
Senior Honours: S. Midlands League 1980-81. Bedfordshire Senior Cup 1964-65, 93-94. Bedfordshire Premier Cup 1981-82, 98-99. United Counties League 2007-08.

10 YEAR RECORD

04-05	05-06	06-07	07-08	08-09	09-10	10-11	11-12	12-13	13-14
UCL P 9	UCL P 11	UCL P 19	UCL P 1	UCL P 2	UCL P 7	SSM P 13	SSM P 9	SSM P 14	SSM P 19

SUN POSTAL SPORTS

Founded: 1898 Nickname:

Secretary: Steve Woolner **(T)** 07713 886 621 **(E)** seniorfootball@sunpostal.co.uk
Chairman: Martin Sills **Manager:** Paul Hobbs **Prog Ed:** Kevin Affleck
Ground: Sun Postal Sports Club, Bellmountwood Avenue, Watford, Herts WD17 3BN **(T)** 01923 227 453
Capacity: **Seats:** **Covered:** **Midweek Matchday:** **Clubhouse:** Yes

Colours(change): Yellow/royal blue/royal blue (Orange/black/black)
Previous Names: Sun Engraving FC 1898-1935. Sun Sports 1935-95.
Previous Leagues: Watford & District. Hertfordshire Senior County 1935-2003.
Records:
Senior Honours: Spartan South Midlands Division One 2013-14.

10 YEAR RECORD

04-05	05-06	06-07	07-08	08-09	09-10	10-11	11-12	12-13	13-14
SSM1 13	SSM1 9	SSM1 13	SSM1 17	SSM1 20	SSM1 14	SSM1 11	SSM1 22	SSM1 17	SSM1 1

TRING ATHLETIC

Founded: 1958 Nickname: Athletic

Secretary: Bob Winter **(T)** 07979 816 528 **(E)** robert.winter2007@ntlworld.com
Chairman: Mick Eldridge **Manager:** Julian Robinson **Prog Ed:** Barry Simmons
Ground: Grass Roots Stadium, Pendley Sports Centre, Cow Lane, Tring HP23 5NT **(T)** 01442 891 144
Capacity: 1,233 **Seats:** 150 **Covered:** 100+ **Midweek Matchday:** Tuesday **Clubhouse:** Yes **Shop:** Yes

Colours(change): Red/black/black (Yellow/green/green)
Previous Names: None
Previous Leagues: West Herts 58-88
Records: **Goalscorer:** Andy Humphreys - 209 **App:** Mark Boniface - 642
Senior Honours: Spartan South Midlands Senior Division 1999-00

10 YEAR RECORD

04-05	05-06	06-07	07-08	08-09	09-10	10-11	11-12	12-13	13-14
SSM P 4	SSM P 10	SSM P 11	SSM P 10	SSM P 8	SSM P 3	SSM P 2	SSM P 6	SSM P 22	SSM P 10

WEMBLEY

Founded: 1946 Nickname: The Lions

Secretary: Mrs Jean Gumm **(T)** 07876 125 784 **(E)** wembleyfc@aol.com
Chairman: Brian Gumm **Manager:** Ian Bates **Prog Ed:** Richard Markiewicz
Ground: Vale Farm, Watford Road, Sudbury, Wembley HA0 3HG. **(T)** 0208 904 8169
Capacity: 2450 **Seats:** 350 **Covered:** 950 **Midweek Matchday:** Tuesday **Clubhouse:** Yes **Shop:** No

Colours(change): Red & white/red/red (All blue)
Previous Names: None
Previous Leagues: Middlesex Lge. Spartan. Delphian. Corinthian. Athenian. Isthmian.
Records: **Att:** 2654 v Wealdstone, FA Amateur Cup 1952-53. **Goals:** Bill Handraham (105). **Apps:** Spud Murphy (505).
Senior Honours:

10 YEAR RECORD

04-05	05-06	06-07	07-08	08-09	09-10	10-11	11-12	12-13	13-14
Isth2 13	Isth2 11	CCP 3	CCP 14	CCP 17	CCP 15	CCP 14	CCP 10	CCP 15	CCP 9

DIVISION ONE

AMERSHAM TOWN

Founded: Nickname:

Secretary: John Phillips **(T)** 01923 805 322 **(E)** jp_ammo@yahoo.co.uk
Chairman: Simon Damery **Manager:** Daniel Madden **Prog Ed:** Michael Gahagan
Ground: Spratleys Meadow, School Lane, Amersham, Bucks HP7 0EL **(T)** No telephone
Colours(change): Black & white stripes/black/black (All yellow)

ADDITIONAL INFORMATION:

ARLESEY TOWN RESERVES

Founded: Nickname:

Secretary: Chris Sterry **(T)** 07540 201 473 **(E)** chris.sterry@ntlworld.com
Chairman: Manny Cohen **Manager:** Keith Coughlin **Prog Ed:** Jason Marshall
Ground: The Armadillo Stadium, Hitchen Road, Arlesey, Beds. SG15 6RS **(T)** 01462 734 504
Colours(change): Light blue/dark blue/dark blue (Yellow/black/black)

ADDITIONAL INFORMATION:
Previous League: Bedfordshire County >2013.

BALDOCK TOWN

Founded: Nickname:

Secretary: Lee Rusbridge **(T)** 07981 789 037 **(E)** leeboy0483@hotmail.com
Chairman: Graham Kingham **Manager:** Scott Grant **Prog Ed:** Ross Graham
Ground: Hitchen Town FC, Top Field, Fishponds Road, Hitchen, SG5 1NU. **(T)** 01462 459 028
Colours(change): All red (All navy blue)

ADDITIONAL INFORMATION:
Previous League: Hertfordshire Senior County > 2013.

BEDFORD

Founded: 1957 Nickname:

Secretary: Paolo Riccio **(T)** 07868 370 464 **(E)** paolo.riccio@ntlworld.com
Chairman: Lui La Mura **Manager:** Luigi Rocco **Prog Ed:** Paul Warne
Ground: McMullen Park, Meadow Lane, Cardington, Bedford, MK44 3SB **(T)** 07831 594 444
Colours(change): Black & white stripes/black/black (All maroon)

ADDITIONAL INFORMATION:
Previous League: United Counties 1970-80.
Record Att: (at Fairhill) 1,500 v Bedford Town-South Mids Div 1 1992 **Apps:** Simon Fordham - 418
Honours: Bedfordshire Senior Trophy 2012-13.

BROXBOURNE BOROUGH

Founded: 1959 Nickname:

Secretary: Michelle Luker **(T)** 07932 014 154 **(E)** chell.luker@gmail.com
Chairman: John Murphy **Manager:** Mark Beals **Prog Ed:** Graham Dodd
Ground: Broxbourne Borougn V & E Club, Goffs Lane, Cheshunt, Herts EN7 5QN **(T)** 01992 624 281 **Capacity:** 500
Colours(change): All Blue. (All yellow)

ADDITIONAL INFORMATION: Record Att: 120 **Goalscorer:** Wayne Morris **App:** Brian Boehmer

BUCKINGHAM ATHELTIC

Founded: Nickname:

Secretary: Colin Howkins **(T)** 07751 659 769 **(E)** colin@thehowkins.co.uk
Chairman: Tony Checkley **Manager:** Damien Wiffin **Prog Ed:** Matt Walker
Ground: Stratford Fields, Stratford Road, Buckingham MK18 1NY **(T)** 01280 816 945 (MD)
Colours(change): Sky blue/navy blue/navy blue (Yellow/black/yellow)

ADDITIONAL INFORMATION:

BURGESS HILL RANGERS

Founded: Nickname:

Secretary: Tolga Huseyin **(T)** 07956 470 127 **(E)** tolga@bushhillrangers.com
Chairman: Sonar Mustafa **Manager:** Sonar Mustafa **Prog Ed:** Osman Cannur
Ground: Goldsdown Stadium, Goldsdown Road, Enfield Middlesex EN3 7RP **(T)** 0208 804 5491
Colours(change): Blue/yellow/yellow (Yellow/blue/blue)

ADDITIONAL INFORMATION:

CHESHAM UNITED RESERVES

Founded: Nickname:

Secretary: Alan Lagden **(T)** 01494 782 022 **(E)** alan.lagden@sky.com
Chairman: Brian McCarthy **Manager:** Paul Burgess **Prog Ed:** Steve Doman
Ground: The Meadow, Amy Lane, Chesham, Bucks HP5 1NE **(T)** 01494 783 964
Colours(change): All claret (Yellow/black/yellow)

ADDITIONAL INFORMATION:

CODICOTE

Founded: 1913 Nickname:

Secretary: Ian Moody **(T)** 07980 920 674 **(E)** codicote.fc@hotmail.co.uk
Chairman: James Bundy **Manager:** Liam Errington **Prog Ed:** James Bundy
Ground: Gosling Sports Park, Stanborough Road, Welwyn Garden City Herts AL8 6XE **(T)** 01707 331 056
Colours(change): All red (White/black/white)

ADDITIONAL INFORMATION:
Previous Leagues: Hertfordshire County 1913-27, 1993-2012. North Hertfordshire 1927-93.
Honours: North Herts League Division One 1929-30, 1974-75, Division Two 1968-69, Premier Division 1977-78.
Herts Senior County League 2011-12.

CRAWLEY GREEN

Founded: 1988 Nickname:

Secretary: Eddie Downey **(T)** 07956 107 477 **(E)** eddied@thamesideltd.co.uk
Chairman: Alan Clark **Manager:** Mark Smith **Prog Ed:** Alan Clark
Ground: Barton Rovers FC, Sharpenhoe Road, Barton Le Cay, Beds MK45 4SD **(T)** 01582 882 398
Colours(change): All maroon (Sky blue/navy/sky blue)

ADDITIONAL INFORMATION:

EDGWARE TOWN

Founded: Nickname:

Secretary: Daren Bloor **(T)** 07773 312 110 **(E)** secretary@edgwaretown.co.uk
Chairman: Antony Manzi **Manager:** Antony Manzi **Prog Ed:** David Nocher
Ground: Silver Jubilee Park, Townsend Lane, London NW9 7NE **(T)** 0208 205 1645
Colours(change): Green & white/white/green (Yellow/blue/blue)

ADDITIONAL INFORMATION:

HARPENDEN TOWN

Founded: 1891 Nickname: Town

Secretary: Steve Fakes **(T)** 07734 700 226 **(E)** smf_2001@yahoo.co.uk
Chairman: Steve Fakes **Manager:** Danny Plumb **Prog Ed:** Roman Motyczak
Ground: Rothamstead Park, Amenbury Lane, Harpenden AL5 2EF **(T)** 07734700226/07702 604771
Colours(change): Yellow/navy blue/navy blue (Red/red/black)

ADDITIONAL INFORMATION:
Previous Name: Harpenden FC 1891-1908. **Previous League:** Hertfordshire County.
Honours: South Midlands League x2. Hertfordshire Junior Cup x5.

HATFIELD TOWN

Founded: 1886 Nickname: Blueboys

Secretary: Joanne Maloney **(T)** 07725 071 014 **(E)** secretary@hatfieldtownfc.co.uk
Chairman: Chris Maloney **Manager:** Ashley Purser **Prog Ed:** Tom Bailey
Ground: Gosling Sport Park, Stanborough Rd, Welwyn Garden City, Herts AL8 6XE **(T)** 01707 384 300 **Capacity:** 1,500
Colours(change): All royal blue (Orange/black/black).

ADDITIONAL INFORMATION:
Herts Senior Champions 2007-08

LANGFORD

Founded: 1908 Nickname: Reds

Secretary: Ian Chessum **(T)** 07749 102 060 **(E)** ianchessum@hotmail.com
Chairman: Ian Chessum **Manager:** Phil Childs **Prog Ed:** Ian Chessum
Ground: Forde Park, Langford Road, Henlow, Beds SG16 6AF **(T)** 01462 816 106 **Capacity:** 2,000
Colours(change): All red. (All blue).

ADDITIONAL INFORMATION: **Record Att:** 450 v QPR 75th Anniversary 1985

LONDON LIONS

Founded: 1995 Nickname: Lions

Secretary: Basil Wein **(T)** 07970 661 990 **(E)** basilw@londonlions.com
Chairman: Basil Wein **Manager:** Tony Gold **Prog Ed:** Dan Jacobs
Ground: Hemel Hemstead FC, Vauxhall Road, Hemel Hempstead, HP2 4HW **(T)** 01442 259 777
Colours(change): All blue (All red)

ADDITIONAL INFORMATION:
Hertfordshire Senior County Premier Division 2009-10. Spartan South Midlands Division One 2012-13.

RISBOROUGH RANGERS

Founded: Nickname:

Secretary: Nick Bishop **(T)** 07855 958 236 **(E)** nick@lloydlatchford.co.uk
Chairman: Richard Woodward **Manager:** Bob Rayner **Prog Ed:** Richard Woodward
Ground: " Windsors" Horsenden Lane, Princes Risborough. Bucks HP27 9NE **(T)** 07849 843632 (MD only)
Colours(change): All red (White/black/white)

ADDITIONAL INFORMATION:

SOUTHALL

Founded: 1871 Nickname:

Secretary: Aman Singh Jaswal **(T)** 07957 168 370 **(E)** apnayouth@gmail.com
Chairman: Channa Singh **Manager:** Colin Brown **Prog Ed:** Maninder Khunkhan
Ground: Hanwell Town FC, Perivale Lane, Perivale, Greenford, Middlesex UB6 8TL **(T)** 0208 998 1701
Colours(change): Red & white/black/black (White & blue/blue/white)

ADDITIONAL INFORMATION:
Previous Names: Southall Athletic.

STONY STRATFORD TOWN

Founded: 1898 Nickname:

Secretary: Steven Sartain **(T)** 07901 664 000 **(E)** steve.sartain456@btinternet.com
Chairman: Philip Smith **Manager:** Anthony Lands **Prog Ed:** Annette Way
Ground: Ostlers Lane, Stony Stratford, Milton Keynes MK11 1AR **(T)** 07914 012 709
Colours(change): Sky blue/navy/sky (Yellow/black/yellow)

ADDITIONAL INFORMATION:
Previous League: Northampton Combination.
Record Att: 476 v Aston Villa U21 1996.

WELWYN GARDEN CITY

Founded: 1921 Nickname: Citizens

Secretary: Karen Browne **(T)** 07876 232 670 **(E)** kazzie.browne@gmail.com
Chairman: Ollie Croft **Manager:** Adam Fisher **Prog Ed:** Karen Browne
Ground: Herns Way, Welwyn Garden City, Herts AL7 1TA **(T)** 01707 329 358
Colours(change): Claret/claret/sky blue (Orange/black/orange)

ADDITIONAL INFORMATION:
Previous League: Metropolitan & Greater London.
Honours: South Midlands League 1973-74, Division 1 1981-82.

WINSLOW UNITED

Founded: 1891 Nickname:

Secretary: Andy Setterfield **(T)** 07703 117 443 **(E)** andysetterfield@gmail.com
Chairman: Colin O'Dell **Manager:** Perry Mercer **Prog Ed:** Gareth Robins
Ground: The Recreation Ground, Elmfields Gate, Winslow, Bucks MK18 3JG **(T)** 01296 713 057
Colours(change): Yellow/blue/yellow (Orange/orange/black)

ADDITIONAL INFORMATION:

WODSON PARK

Founded: Nickname:

Secretary: Lee Cook **(T)** 07778 192 960 **(E)** lee.cook@wodsonmail.co.uk
Chairman: Lee Cook **Manager:** Simon Riddle **Prog Ed:** Lee Cook
Ground: Ware FC, Wadesmill Road, Herts SG12 0UQ **(T)** 01920 870 091
Colours(change): Sky & navy blue stripes/navy blue/navy blue (All red)

ADDITIONAL INFORMATION:

SPARTAN SOUTH MIDLANDS DIVISION TWO CONSTITUTION 2014-15

	Club	Ground	Tel
1	ASTON CLINTON	Green Park, Staplebridge Road, Aston Clinton, Bucks HP22 5NE	07707 685 148
2	BRIMSDOWN	Goldsdown Stadium, Goldsdown Road, Enfield, EN3 7RP	0208 804 5491
3	CLEANSLATE	Ampthill Town FC, Woburn Road, Ampthill MK45 2HX	01525 404 440
4	EALING TOWN	Avenue Park, Western Avenue, Greenford, Middlesex UB6 8GA	07715 845 203
5	GRENDON RANGERS	The Village Hall, Main Street, Grendon Underwood, Aylesbury, Bucks. HP18 0SP	07979 470 734 (Sec)
6	HALE LEYS UNITED	Fairford Leys Pitch, Andrews Way, Aylesbury, Bucks. HP17 8QQ	07731 444 652
7	KENT ATHLETIC	Kent Social Club, Tenby Drive, Luton, LU4 9BN	01582 582 723
8	MURSLEY UNITED	The Playing Field, Station Road, Mursley MK17 0SA	07852 229 126
9	NEW BRADWELL ST PETER	Recreation Ground, Bradwell Road, Bradville, Milton Keynes MK13 7AD	01908 313 835
10	OLD BRADWELL UNITED	Abbey Road, Bradwell Village, Milton Keynes, MK13 9AR	07840 583 309
11	PITSTONE AND IVINGHOE	Pitstone Recreation Ground, Vicarage Road, Pitstone LU7 9EY	01296 661 271 (match days)
12	THE 61 FC (LUTON)	Kingsway Ground, Beverley Road, Luton LU4 8EU	07749 531 492
13	TOTTERNHOE	Tptternhoe Recreation Ground, Dunstable Road, Totternhoe, Beds LU6 1QP	01582 606 738
14	TRING CORINTHIANS	Tring Corinthians FC, Icknield Way, Tring, Herts HP23 5HJ	07886 528 214
15	WILLEN	Willen Playing Fields, Portland Drive, Milton Keynes, MK15 9JP	07855 830 229
16	WOLVERTON TOWN	The New Park, Field Lane, Greenleys, Milton Keynes MK12 6AZ	01908 220 218

GROUND DIRECTIONS-PREMIER & DIVISION ONE

AFC DUNSTABLE - Creasey Park Stadium, Creasey Park Drive, Brewers Hill Road, Dunstable, Beds LU6 1BB Tel 01582 667555

From the South: When travelling north on the A5, go straight across the lights in the centre of Dunstable. Turn left at the next main set of lights into Brewers Hill Road. You will immediately pass the Fire Station on your left. Carry on until you hit the first roundabout. Go over the roundabout and take the immediate right into Creasey Park Drive. *From North:* When travelling south on the A5, go through the chalk cutting and over the first set of traffic lights. At the next set of lights turn right into Brewers Hill Road. Go over the roundabout and take the immediate right into Creasey Park Drive. Public Transport: Creasey Park is well served by buses. Arriva and Centrebus services from Luton, Houghton Regis Leighton Buzzard and Aylesbury all stop at the bottom of Brewers Hill Road. Some 24 services stop directly opposite Creasey Park Drive in Weatherby.

AMERSHAM TOWN - Spratleys Meadow, School Lane, Amersham, Bucks HP7 No telephone

From London, take the A413 towards Aylesbury. At the first roundabout in Amersham where the A413 turns left, keep straight on. Then carry on straight over the next four roundabouts to Amersham Old Town. At the western end of the Old Town turn right into right into Mill Lane. At the top of Mill Lane turn left into School Lane. Ground is 100 yards on the left.

AMPTHILL TOWN - Ampthill Park, Woburn Street, Ampthill Tel: 01525 404440.

From the South, leave M1 at junction 12 Toddington. Turn right as signposted until you meet the junction with the Ampthill bypass. Go straight across until you meet a mini-roundabout at the town centre. Turn left into Woburn Street. The ground is about half a mile on the right, just past a lay-by. From the North, leave the M1 at J13 and turn left. At first set of traffic lights, turn right onto A507 Ridgmont bypass. Continue until you see the right-hand turning signposted for Ampthill. Ground is about a mile on the left, opposite the rugby ground.

ARLESEY TOWN RESERVES - The Armadillo Stadium, Hitchen Road, Arlesey, Beds. SG15 6RS Tel 01462 734 504

From junction 10 on the A1(M) follow the A507 towards Shefford. At the 3rd roundabout turn left signposted Arlesey station. Follow the road for 1.5 miles through village, ground is on the left.

From M1 North, junction 13 follow A507 to Clophill. Continue straight over roundabout through Shefford & Henlow to roundabout signposted Arlesey station, then as above.

From M1 junction 10, take A1081 Airport Way onto A505 Hitchin Road towards Hitchen. Turn left onto A600 Bedford Road past Hitchin Town FC, turn right at 2nd roundabout to Ickleford. Go through village and bear left to Arlesey, ground is on the right.

BALDOCK TOWN - Hitchen Town FC, Top Field, Fishponds Road, Hitchen, SG5 1NU. Tel 01462 459 028

Exit A1(M) at junction 8 (Stevenage North & Hitchen). Take the A602 towards Hitchen, go over two roundabouts and through the lights on the one-way system following the signs for Bedford (A600). There is a large open green to the right. At the next roundabout, turn right into Fishponds Road and the ground is about 100 yards on the left.

From the M1 junction 10 (Luton South & Airport) follow the A505 signposted Hitchin.On entering Hitchin, turn left at the first large roundabout and follow signs for Bedford A600. At the next roundabout turn right into Fishponds Road and ground is on the left.

BEDFORD FC - McMullen Park, Meadow Lane, Cardington, Bedford, MK44 3SB. Tel 01234 831024

From the M1 Junction 13: take the A421 on to the Bedford Bypass, take the third exit onto the A603, the ground is 250 yards on the left. From the A1 at Sandy: take A603 to Bedford. The ground is on the right just before you reach the Bedford Bypass.

BERKHAMSTED - Broadwater, Lower Kings Road, Berkhamsted HP4 2AL Tel 01442 865977

Exit A41 onto A416. Go straight over the town centre traffic lights into Lower Kings Road. Go over the canal bridge and take first left into Broadwater. Follow the road to the left, going parallel to the canal. The ground is on the right hand side, sandwiched between the canal and the railway.

BIGGLESWADE UNITED - Second Meadow, Fairfield Road, Biggleswade SG18 0BS Tel 01767 316270

From A1 south take second roundabout (Sainsbury's NOT Homebase). Cross the river bridge and then take second left into Sun Street then take first left into Fairfield Road and travel to the very end and into lane. From A1 north, take first roundabout (Sainsbury's) and follow previous instructions.

BROXBOURNE BOROUGH - Broxbourne Borougn V & E Club, Goffs Lane, Cheshunt, Herts EN7 5QN Tel 01992 624 281

From M25 junction 25, take A10 north towards Cheshunt. At first roundabout take first exit onto B198 (Cuffey & Goffs Oak) At the second roundabout take third exit into Goffs Lane. Ground is on the immediate right.

BUCKINGHAM ATHLETIC - Stratford Fields, Stratford Road, Buckingham MK18 1NY Tel: 01280 816945 (match days & opening hours only)

From Oxford, Aylesbury or Bletchley: take the Buckingham ring road to the roundabout where the A422 from Stony Stratford/Deanshanger meet-turn left, towards town centre. The ground is situated on the left behind fir trees at the bottom of the hill where 30mph begins (opposite a recently-built block of luxury apartments). From Milton Keynes: Up A5 then (A422) to Buckingham-straight across roundabout towards the town centre-ground location as above. From M1: come off at junction 13 and follow A421 straight through, turning right where it meets the Buckingham ring road – then follow as above, turning left at the next-but-one roundabout.

BURGESS HILL RANGERS - Goldsdown Stadium, Goldsdown Road, Enfield Middlesex EN3 7RP Tel: 0208 804 5491

M25 junction 25, then head south on the A10. Turn left at the second set of traffic lights into Caterhatch Lane. At the end of the road, turn right at the roundabout into Hertford Road. At the next mini roundabout turn left into Green Street. At the next mini roundabout turn left into Goldsdown Road and the ground is directly ahead.

CHESHAM UNITED RESERVES - The Meadow, Amy Lane, Chesham, Bucks HP5 1NE Tel 01494 783964

Take J20 off the M25 to the A41 Aylesbury/Hemel follow this road for about 7 miles, your turn off is after the Service Station, the turn off is for Berkhamsted/Chesham, take the right hand lane in the slip road to the A416 to Chesham. Follow this road through Ashley Green (being careful of the speed trap) past the college on your left, when you get to the bottom of the hill take a left turn at the mini roundabout. Follow the road for about 1.5 miles, go straight over the next two roundabouts, then get in to the left lane to take the first exit from the next roundabout, you will pass a pub called the Red Lion on your right shortly after this. Follow the road to a mini roundabout; take the right exit going past two petrol stations either side of the road. Ground is on the third exit off the next roundabout. See club website for other routes.

COCKFOSTERS - Cockfosters Sports Ground, Chalk Lane, Cockfosters, Herts EN4 9JG Tel: 020 8449 5833

Leaving the M25 motorway at junction 24 (Potters Bar), take the A111 signposted to Cockfosters. The ground is situated approximately 2 miles from the motorway on the right immediately before Cockfosters Underground Station. VEHICLE DRIVERS PLEASE BE AWARE THAT THE YELLOW LINES & PARKING RESTRICTIONS IN CHALK LANE ARE STRICTLY ENFORCED UP TO 6.30PM INCLUDING SATURDAYS

CODICOTE - Gosling Sports Park, Stanborough Road, Welwyn Garden City Herts AL8 6XR Tel 01707 331056

From A1 (M), take A414 towards Hertford/Welwyn Garden City. At the roundabout take the first exit onto the A6129, leading to Stanborough/ Wheathampstead. At the next roundabout take the second exit onto the A6129 Stanborough Road. At the next roundabout take the third exit into Gosling Sports Park.

COLNEY HEATH - The Recreation Ground, High Street, Colney Heath, St Albans, Herts AL4 0NS Tel 01727 826188

From the A1, leave at junction 3 and follow A414 St. Albans. At long roundabout take the left into the village and ground is just past the school on left after 400 yards.

From the M25, leave at junction 22 and follow B556 Colney Heath. On entering the village turn left at Queens Head PH (roundabout) and follow High Street for ½ mile. The ground is on the right just before the school.

From M1 going south; leave at junction 7. At Park Street roundabout follow A414 Hatfield. Continue on A414 past London Colney. Enter Colney Heath coming round the long roundabout and into village. The ground is past the school on the left after 400 yards.

CRAWLEY GREEN - Barton Rovers FC, Sharpenhoe Road, Barton Le Cay, Beds MK45 4SD Tel 01582 882398

From M1 J12, turn right from South turn left from North, onto the A5120. After approximately 1.5 miles, take the second turning on the right signposted Harlington and Barton. Follow the road through Sharpenhoe to Barton. At mini-roundabout turn right and after about 400 yards, turn right into the ground. Ground entrance is in Luton Road.

EDGWARE TOWN - Silver Jubilee Park, Townsend Lane, London NW9 7NE Tel: 0208 205 1645

From Edgware tube station, turn left onto Station Road and then left onto Edgware Road. Go South for about two miles on Edgware Road, turn right onto Kingsbury Road. Turn first left onto Townsend Lane down to the bottom of the hill and then turn left into the park through the park barriers..

HADLEY - Potters Bar Town FC, Parkfield Stadium, Watkins Rise (off The Walk), Potters Bar EN6 1QB Tel 01707 654833

From M25, exit at junction 24 towards Potters Bar along Southgate Road A111. Turn right at first set of traffic lights into High Street A1000. After the petrol station on the left and pedestrian crossing, take the first left into The Walk. After 200 yards, turn right into Watkins Rise. The ground is at the end on the right. Nearest BR Station: Potters Bar. PLEASE NOTE: do not park in the Mayfair Lodge Home car park opposite the ground. Offenders will be clamped.

HAREFIELD UNITED - Preston Park, Breakspear Road North, Harefield, Middlesex, UB9 6NE Tel: 01895 823474.

From the M25 at Junction 16 turn left. At the roundabout turn right towards Denham and at the next roundabout turn left then right at the end of the road. Turn left by the Pub and follow the road over the canal and into the village. Go straight across the roundabout into Breakspear Road and the ground is approximately 800 metres on the right.

HARPENDEN TOWN - Rothamstead Park, Amenbury Lane, Harpenden AL5 2EF Tel: 07968 120032

Approaching Harpenden from St. Albans, turn left into Leyton Road at mini-roundabout by the Silver Cup and Fire Station. Coming from Luton, go through the town and as you leave (just past The George) turn right into Leyton Road. Turn left in Amenbury Lane and then left into car park after 300 yards. Entrance to the Club is up the pathway, diagonally across the car park in the far corner from the entrance. This is a pay-and-display car park up to 6.30pm.

HATFIELD TOWN - Gosling Sports Park, Stanborough Road, Welwyn Garden City, Herts AL8 6XE Tel 01707 384300

From A1 (M) junction 4, take A414 towards Hertford/Welwyn Garden City. At the roundabout take the 1st exit onto the A6129, heading to Stanborough/Wheathampstead. At the next roundabout take the 2nd exit onto the A6129 Stanborough Road. At the next roundabout take the 3rd exit into Gosling Sports Park.

HERTFORD TOWN - Hertingfordbury Park, West Street, Hertford, Herts SG13 8EZ Tel 01992 583716

From the A1 follow the A414 to Hertford until you see Gates Ford Dealership on the right. At next roundabout double back and immediately past Gates (now on your left) turn left into West Street. This is a narrow road and when it bears left, turn right and go down the hill and over a bridge to the ground. From the A10 follow the A414 until you see Gates.

HILLINGDON BOROUGH - Middlesex Stadium, Breakspear Road, Ruislip, Middlesex HA4 7SB Tel 01895 639544

From M40/A40 eastbound, leave the A40 at the Swakeleys roundabout, exit is sign-posted Ickenham & Ruislip and take the B467. At the second mini-roundabout turn left into Breakspear Road South. After approx 1 mile, turn right into Breakspear Road by the Breakspear Arms PH. The ground is a further 1/2 mile on the left-hand side.

HODDESDON TOWN - Stewart Edwards Stadium, Lowfield, Park View, Hoddesdon, Herts, EN11 8PU Tel: 01992 463133

For SatNav users, please key in EN11 8PX, which will take you to Park Road, directly opposite the ground

From the A10, take Hoddesdon turnoff (A1170). Follow the slip road to the roundabout at the bottom of the hill and then turn right into Amwell Street. Take the first right, at the church, into Pauls Lane. Follow the road round to left which becomes Taveners Way. At the mini-roundabout opposite the Iceland store, turn right into Brocket Road. At T junction turn left into Park View and the ground is 200 yards on the right.

HOLMER GREEN - Airedale Park, Watchet Lane, Holmer Green, Bucks HP15 6UF Tel 01494 711485

From Amersham on A404 High Wycombe Road. After approx 2 miles turn right into Sheepcote Dell Road. Continue until end of road at Bat & Ball pub. Turn right, then immediately left. Continue approx 1/2 mile until double mini-roundabouts. Turn left in front of the Mandarin Duck restaurant into Airedale Park 150 yards on the right

KINGS LANGLEY - Gaywood Park, Hempstead Road, Kings Langley Herts WD4 8BS Tel: 07976 692801

From M25 leave at junction 20. Take A4251 to Kings Langley. Go through the village. The ground is approximately 1/2 mile on the right.

LANGFORD - Forde Park, Langford Road, Henlow, Beds SG16 6AG Tel: 01462 816106.

From West along A57 to Henlow then north on A6001. Ground at north end of Henlow

From North and East, leave A1 at Langford water tower then into Langford. Turn left at Boot Restaurant. Follow A6001 round to the left. Club is 1/2 mile away.

LEVERSTOCK GREEN - Pancake Lane, Leverstock Green, Hemel Hempstead, Herts Tel: 01442 246280.

From M1 at Junction 8, Follow A414 to second roundabout turn left along Leverstock Green Way. Pancake Lane is on the left 300 yards past the Leather Bottle Public House. Ground is 300 yards on left. All visitors are requested to park inside the ground.

LONDON COLNEY - Cotlandswick Playing Fields, London Colney, Herts AL2 1DW Tel: 01727 822132.

From M25 J22, follow the A1081 signposted to St Albans. At London Colney roundabout take A414, signposted Hemel Hempstead/Watford. There is a hidden turn into the ground after approximately 500 metres (just after lay-by) signposted Sports Ground and London Colney FC. Follow the ground around between the Rugby and Irish clubs to ground entrance.

LONDON LIONS - Hemel Hemstead FC, Vauxhall Road, Homel Hempstead, HP2 4HW Tel 01442 259 777

From M1 motorway exit at junction 8 onto the A414 towards Hemel Hempstead.After the second roundabout, get into the outside lane and turn right onto Leverstock Green Road. At mini roundabout, turn left into Vauxhall Road, at next mini roundabout, take the second exit into the ground.

SPARTAN SOUTH MIDLANDS LEAGUE - STEP 5/6/7

LONDON TIGERS - Avenue Park, Western Avenue, Perivale, Greenford, Middlesex UB6 8GA Tel 020 7289 3395 (10am-6pm) – out of hours please call 07949 189191

Exit junction 16 of the M25 onto the A40 (M) towards London. After you pass the Target roundabout there will be a sharp left turn at the 200yard marker for the Greenford slip road from the A40 into Avenue Park, just past the overhead footbridge. If coming from Central London or Hangar Lane, drive up to the Target roundabout and do a U-turn onto the eastbound carriageway and turn left into Avenue Park after the footbridge. The nearest Tube station is Greenford on the Central Line, which is a 10-minute walk.

OXHEY JETS - Boundary Stadium, Altham Way (off Little Oxhey Lane), South Oxhey, Watford WD19 6FW Tel: 020 8421 6277

From Bushey + Oxhey Station, take Pinner Road (A4008) and continue along Oxhey Lane towards Harrow. At the traffic lights turn right into Little Oxhey Lane. Altham Way is on left just after crossing a narrow railway bridge. Please park in the large swimming pool car park marked "Jets overflow parking" to avoid either blocking in cars, or being blocked in.

RISBOROUGH RANGERS - " Windsors" Horsenden Lane, Princes Risborough. Bucks HP27 9NE Tel 07849 843632 (MD only)

On entering Prices Risborough from Aylesbury, turn left at first roundabout. At the second roundabout turn right. Go pass Esso petrol station on left hand side. After approximately 400 yards take the right fork. Take second turn on left (Picts Lane). At junction turn right over the railway bridge and then immediately right again. Ground is approximately 200 yards on the right hand side.

SOUTHALL - Hanwell Town FC, Perivale Lane, Perivale, Greenford, Middlesex UB6 8TL Tel 020 8998 1701

From West, junction 16 M25 and follow A40 (M) towards London. Go over the Greenford flyover and get into the nearside lane signposted Ealing & Perivale. Exit and turn right across the A40. The ground is immediately on the left. Turn left into Perivale Lane and the entrance is 200 yards on the left. Nearest railway station is Perivale (London Underground – Central Line).

ST. MARGARETSBURY - Recreation Ground, Station Road, St. Margarets, Herts SG12 8EH Tel: 01920 870473

A10 to Cambridge. Exit at A414 Harlow & Chelmsford. Proceed 400 yards to Amwell roundabout and take 3rd exit (B181) to Stanstead Abbotts. Ground is 1/2 mile on the right-hand side.

STONY STRATFORD TOWN - Ostlers Lane, Stony Stratford, Milton Keynes MK11 1AR Tel: 07914 012709

From Dunstable on the A5 heading north: On approaching Bletchley continue on the main A5 trunk road signposted to Towcester & Hinckley. Continue to the very end of dual carriageway, where you will meet a main roundabout. This is where the main A5 intersects with the A508 to Northampton. At this roundabout take first exit, this is the old (single carriageway) A5. Follow the main road, straight through the traffic lights, over the river bridge and take the second turning right into Ostlers Lane. The ground is approx 200yds on the right.

From Buckingham on the A422: Continue on the A422, straight on at the first roundabout (pedestrian footbridge overhead). Continue on until you meet the next roundabout and take the last exit (the old single carriageway A5). Then proceed as above.

STOTFOLD - Roker Park, The Green, Stotfold, Hitchin, Herts SG5 4AN Tel 01462 730765

At A1 junction 10, take the A507 to Stotfold and right into town. Proceed along High Street and at traffic lights turn right (from Hitchin – straight over traffic lights) towards Astwick Turn right at the Crown pub into The Green. The ground is set back from The Green on the left.

SUN POSTAL SPORTS - Sun Postal Sports Club, Bellmountwood Avenue, Watford, Herts WD17 3BM Tel: 01923 227453

From Watford town centre take the A411 (Hempstead Road) away from the Town Hall towards Hemel Hempstead. At 2nd set of traffic lights turn left into Langley Way. At the next roundabout, where there is a parade of shops on the left and the "Essex Arms" on the right, take the third exit into Cassiobury Drive. Then take the first turn left into Bellmountwood Avenue then at the left hand bend turn right into the Club entrance.

TRING ATHLETIC - The Grass Roots Stadium, Pendley Sports Centre, Cow Lane, Tring, Herts HP23 5NT. Tel: 01442 891144

From M25 take A41 to Aylesbury. At roundabout at junction take last exit sign-posted Berkhamsted. Turn next left into Cow Lane. Stadium is on the right at end of Cow Lane.

WELWYN GARDEN CITY - Herns Way, Welwyn Garden City, Herts AL7 1TA Tel: 01707 329358

Best Route to the Ground: From A1 (M) follow Welwyn Garden City signpost A1000. Take second exit off one-way system, sign-posted Panshanger. Ground is 400 yards on left.

WEMBLEY - Vale Farm, Watford Road HA0 3AG - 0208 904 8169

From Sudbury Town Station 400 yards along Watford Road.

WINSLOW UNITED - The Recreation Ground, Elmfields Gate, Winslow, Bucks MK18 3JG Tel 01296 713057

Best Route to the Ground: A413 from Aylesbury to Winslow, turn right from High Street into Elmfields Gate. Ground is100 yards on left. A421 Milton Keynes to Buckingham, turn left through Great Horwood to Winslow. Turn left from High Street into Elmfields Gate. PLEASE PARK IN PUBLIC CAR PARK OPPOSITE GROUND IF POSSIBLE.

WODSON PARK - Ware FC, Wadesmill Road, Herts SG12 0UQ Tel 01920 463247

From the South: leave the M25 at junction 25 and take the A10 north past Cheshunt and Hoddesdon. After crossing the Lea Valley with Ware below and to your right, leave the A10 at the junction for the A1170 (signposted for Wadesmill and Thundridge). The slip road comes off the A10 onto a roundabout. Turn left (first exit) onto Wadesmill Road (A1170) and come back over the A10 to a second roundabout. Go straight over and take the first turn on the left into Wodson Park Sports Centre. The football ground is on the far left of the car park. From the North: Leave the A10 at the Ware North turn off (A1170). The slip road takes you to a roundabout. Turn right (3rd exit) into Wadesmill Road and take the first left into Wodson Park Sports Centre.

SUSSEX COUNTY LEAGUE

Sponsored by: No sponsor
Founded: 1920
Recent Champions:
2009: Eastbourne United Association
2010: Whitehawk. 2011: Crawley Down
2012: Three Bridges. 2013: Peacehaven & Telscombe
scfl.org.uk

DIVISION ONE	P	W	D	L	F	A	GD	Pts
1 East Preston	38	30	6	2	92	23	69	96
2 (P) East Grinstead Town	38	24	7	7	84	39	45	79
3 Littlehampton Town	38	24	5	9	85	41	44	77
4 Horsham YMCA	38	22	10	6	110	45	65	76
5 Crowborough Athletic	38	21	7	10	69	41	28	70
6 Hassocks	38	17	9	12	72	65	7	60
7 Pagham	38	16	10	12	66	57	9	58
8 Dorking Wanderers	38	16	7	15	68	63	5	55
9 Ringmer	38	16	5	17	61	64	-3	53
10 St Francis Rangers	38	15	6	17	66	68	-2	51
11 Chichester City	38	14	9	15	53	65	-12	51
12 Arundel	38	15	5	18	58	68	-10	50
13 Newhaven	38	13	10	15	67	63	4	49
14 Shoreham	38	12	8	18	65	82	-17	44
15 Lingfield	38	12	6	20	70	88	-18	42
16 Hailsham Town	38	13	3	22	63	91	-28	42
17 Selsey	38	12	5	21	45	76	-31	41
18 Lancing (-6pts)	38	12	8	18	55	80	-25	38
19 Rye United	38	6	8	24	38	45	-7	26
20 (R) Worthing United	38	2	2	34	22	145	-123	8

Rye United withdrew 21/03/14 - all outstanding fixtures were awarded to opponents

DIVISION TWO	P	W	D	L	F	A	GD	Pts
1 (P) Eastbourne United AFC	32	23	5	4	99	34	65	74
2 (P) Broadbridge Heath	32	21	9	2	85	21	64	72
3 (P) Loxwood	32	22	4	6	98	52	46	70
4 Little Common	32	19	4	9	86	61	25	61
5 Haywards Heath Town	32	15	11	6	73	55	18	56
6 Wick & Barnham United	32	15	7	10	64	47	17	52
7 Mile Oak (-1pt)	32	14	10	8	55	44	11	51
8 Bexhill United	32	12	9	11	57	43	14	45
9 Westfield (-3pts)	32	12	5	15	55	50	5	38
10 AFC Uckfield	32	10	8	14	55	62	-7	38
11 Steyning Town	32	10	8	14	53	68	-15	38
12 Oakwood	32	11	5	16	57	82	-25	38
13 Saltdean United	32	10	3	19	53	101	-48	33
14 Midhurst & Easebourne	32	9	1	22	35	81	-46	28
15 Storrington	32	7	5	20	50	74	-24	26
16 Rustington	32	7	3	22	40	76	-36	24
17 Seaford Town	32	4	5	23	31	95	-64	17

LEAGUE CUP

ROUND 1

Wick & Barnham	v	Steyning Town	3-1
Haywards Heath Town	v	Loxwood	1-0
Saltdean United	v	Rustington	6-2
Storrington	v	Bexhill United	3-3 4-2p
Oakwood	v	Seaford Town	3-1

ROUND 2

Wick & Barnham	v	Worthing United	3-4
Pagham	v	Haywards Heath Town	5-0
Crowborough Athletic	v	Chichester City	3-3 4-2p
Arundel	v	Westfield	4-3
Dorking Wanderers	v	Lingfield	4-3
Ringmer	v	Saltdean United	3-0
Eastbourne United	v	Storrington	2-3
Newhaven	v	AFC Uckfield	3-0
East Grinstead Town	v	Hassocks	2-1
Horsham YMCA	v	Mile Oak	4-1
Oakwood	v	Shoreham	0-7
Hailsham Town	v	Littlehampton Town	1-5
East Preston	v	Midhurst & Easebourne	HW
Selsey	v	Broadbridge Heath	1-0
St Francis Rangers	v	Rye United	1-1 5-4p
Little Common	v	Lancing	1-2

ROUND 3

Worthing United	v	Pagham	0-9
Crowborough Athletic	v	Arundel	4-3
Dorking Wanderers	v	Ringmer	1-4
Storrington	v	Newhaven	0-1
East Grinstead Town	v	Horsham YMCA	0-1
Shoreham	v	Littlehampton Town	2-2 3-4p
East Preston	v	Selsey	1-1 4-3p
St Francis Rangers	v	Lancing	2-1

QUARTER FINALS

Pagham	v	Crowborough Athletic	
Ringmer	v	Newhaven	2-1 aet
Horsham YMCA	v	Littlehampton Town	1-2
East Preston	v	St Francis Rangers	3-0

SEMI FINALS

Crowborough Athletic	v	Ringmer	3-0
East Preston	v	Littlehampton Town	2-1

FINAL

Crowborough Athletic	v	East Preston	0-1

DIVISION ONE	1	2	3	4	5	6	7	8	9	10	11	12	13	14	15	16	17	18	19	20
1 Arundel		3-1	0-3	0-2	0-0	0-5	4-1	3-1	0-2	1-2	1-5	0-4	1-0	1-0	1-2	2-2	0-1	3-2	3-1	3-1
2 Chichester City	2-0		1-1	2-2	1-3	3-0	3-1	1-1	2-2	1-1	4-1	1-1	2-2	1-0	1-0	HW	3-1	2-1	1-2	1-0
3 Crowborough Athletic	3-0	1-0		2-1	2-3	0-3	2-1	4-0	1-0	1-1	4-0	0-1	1-0	4-2	3-0	2-1	1-2	1-1	3-4	3-0
4 Dorking Wanderers	2-2	3-1	1-2		2-0	0-3	3-1	1-2	2-0	0-0	1-1	5-2	1-1	0-3	1-4	HW	3-0	3-1	2-0	4-1
5 East Grinstead Town	2-0	3-0	3-0	3-0		0-3	3-0	1-1	0-0	4-2	1-0	1-6	4-1	4-1	4-2	HW	1-1	4-1	3-0	8-0
6 East Preston	3-1	4-0	1-1	3-0	0-2		1-0	5-0	1-1	6-0	3-1	3-2	2-0	2-1	2-0	HW	4-0	1-0	2-1	2-0
7 Hailsham Town	0-3	4-0	2-2	5-3	0-3	3-3		2-1	1-2	1-2	1-3	1-2	4-3	0-2	3-2	2-4	1-3	3-2	3-2	5-0
8 Hassocks	2-1	2-2	1-0	1-0	2-2	0-4	6-1		1-1	2-1	3-1	2-1	1-1	6-1	2-5	2-1	5-0	5-1	0-2	3-0
9 Horsham YMCA	3-2	2-1	2-1	4-2	1-4	1-1	9-0	5-0		5-0	4-3	3-3	5-1	5-1	2-1	0-0	2-1	6-3	0-0	6-0
10 Lancing	1-4	1-0	1-6	1-2	2-0	1-5	0-2	1-3	0-6		1-1	1-6	2-2	1-2	4-0	4-1	2-0	1-2	2-3	4-1
11 Lingfield	1-3	2-1	3-2	1-1	0-2	1-4	4-5	0-1	3-1	2-3		0-0	0-6	4-3	0-2	HW	3-1	4-5	2-5	3-1
12 Littlehampton Town	2-0	7-0	0-0	2-1	3-0	0-0	3-1	1-0	3-2	2-0	1-4		3-1	0-2	4-2	HW	0-1	0-3	2-1	10-1
13 Newhaven	0-0	3-4	0-2	2-5	3-1	1-1	3-2	3-0	0-3	1-1	4-1	0-1		2-1	0-0	3-2	5-1	2-2	1-2	8-0
14 Pagham	2-2	3-0	1-1	2-1	3-2	1-2	2-2	3-3	2-2	1-0	2-0	0-2	1-1		2-2	1-0	3-0	4-0	4-2	3-1
15 Ringmer	1-3	4-1	2-0	1-3	0-3	0-2	2-0	2-1	2-0	2-3	2-1	1-4	1-2	0-0		1-2	2-1	3-2	1-0	4-0
16 Rye United	AW	0-2	AW	1-1	1-3	AW	AW	1-4	1-3	0-0	3-3	2-0	AW	2-2	AW		3-1	AW	5-4	AW
17 Selsey	0-2	2-1	1-3	2-1	0-0	1-4	0-2	2-1	1-1	0-3	3-2	1-2	1-3	2-0	1-1	HW		1-2	6-0	1-1
18 Shoreham	5-3	1-3	0-2	5-1	0-2	0-3	2-1	3-3	1-4	3-3	1-1	0-2	0-1	0-1	1-1	1-1	4-2		2-1	3-3
19 St Francis Rangers	4-0	1-1	1-2	1-3	1-1	0-1	2-1	1-1	0-4	2-1	2-4	1-0	2-0	0-0	3-2	2-2	5-0	1-3		5-0
20 Worthing United	0-6	0-3	1-3	1-5	0-4	1-3	0-1	1-3	0-11	0-2	1-5	0-3	3-1	0-4	2-4	2-3	0-4	0-2	0-2	

SUSSEX COUNTY LEAGUE - STEP 5/6/7

DIVISION THREE	P	W	D	L	F	A	GD	Pts
1 Langney Wanderers	20	16	2	2	64	20	44	50
2 Ferring	20	12	5	3	44	20	24	41
3 Roffey	20	10	3	7	37	30	7	33
4 Uckfield Town	20	10	3	7	35	30	5	33
5 Sidlesham	20	9	3	8	35	31	4	30
6 Ifield	20	9	2	9	45	47	-2	29
7 Hurstpierpoint	20	9	1	10	29	42	-13	28
8 Clymping	20	6	4	10	23	33	-10	22
9 Southwick	20	6	2	12	31	42	-11	20
10 Rottingdean Village	20	4	3	13	28	49	-21	15
11 Billinghurst	20	4	2	14	29	56	-27	14

RESERVE DIVISION EAST	P	W	D	L	F	A	GD	Pts
1 Haywards Heath Town Reserves	20	13	5	2	47	22	25	44
2 Newhaven Reserves	20	13	3	4	54	26	28	42
3 Westfields Reserves	20	12	5	3	41	25	16	41
4 Little Common Reserves	20	12	2	6	50	32	18	38
5 Lancing Reserves	20	10	5	5	43	21	22	35
6 Hailsham Town Reserves	20	11	1	8	37	25	12	34
7 AFC Uckfield Reserves	20	7	2	11	36	39	-3	23
8 Southwick Reserves	20	5	6	9	35	53	-18	21
9 Seaford Town Reserves (-1pt)	20	5	2	13	18	39	-21	16
10 Bexhill United Reserves	20	5	0	15	23	47	-24	15
11 Hurstpierpoint Reserves	20	1	1	18	23	78	-55	4

RESERVE PREMIER	P	W	D	L	F	A	GD	Pts
1 Saltdean United Reserves	22	18	1	3	55	16	39	55
2 Hassocks Reserves	22	15	3	4	67	33	34	48
3 Eastbourne Town Reserves	22	13	2	7	37	32	5	41
4 Shoreham Reserves	22	10	3	9	49	42	7	33
5 Pagham Reserves	22	10	2	10	45	47	-2	32
6 Steyning Town Reserves	22	9	3	10	44	49	-5	30
7 Mile Oak Reserves	22	8	5	9	40	41	-1	29
8 Ringmer Reserves	22	8	4	10	43	41	2	28
9 St Francis Rangers Reserves	22	7	1	14	26	63	-37	22
10 Eastbourne United AFC Reserves	22	6	3	13	43	47	-4	21
11 Selsey Reserves	22	6	3	13	34	56	-22	21
12 Littlehampton Town Res. (-1pt)	22	5	4	13	47	63	-16	18

RESERVE DIVISION WEST	P	W	D	L	F	A	GD	Pts
1 Broadbridge Heath Reserves	22	18	2	2	83	24	59	56
2 Arundel Reserves	22	15	2	5	61	31	30	47
3 Roffey Reserves	22	14	2	6	57	33	24	44
4 Loxwood Reserves	22	13	2	7	56	40	16	41
5 Wick & Barnham United Reserves	22	11	3	8	63	58	5	36
6 Sidlesham Reserves	22	10	4	8	52	45	7	34
7 Storrington Reserves	22	9	2	11	53	60	-7	29
8 Ferring Reserves	22	9	2	11	45	60	-15	29
9 Clymping Reserves	22	6	4	12	41	60	-19	22
10 Rustington Reserves	22	5	2	15	26	50	-24	17
11 Worthing United Reserves	22	5	2	15	38	74	-36	17
12 Midhurst & Easebourne Reserves	22	3	1	18	35	75	-40	10

DIVISION TWO	1	2	3	4	5	6	7	8	9	10	11	12	13	14	15	16	17
1 AFC Uckfield		0–2	4–0	1–2	1–1	1–4	2–3	3–3	0–2	4–2	1–1	6–0	2–0	2–0	0–0	2–5	2–2
2 Bexhill United	2–2		1–2	3–2	0–0	5–1	1–5	5–0	0–0	1–1	3–0	4–0	3–0	2–2	4–2	0–1	0–1
3 Broadbridge Heath	2–0	2–2		2–2	2–2	0–2	3–0	4–0	3–0	3–0	2–0	4–1	3–0	4–1	6–0	1–0	2–0
4 Eastbourne United Association	3–2	1–0	0–1		4–0	3–0	1–1	4–0	0–3	2–0	6–1	7–0	4–0	9–0	2–1	6–1	3–2
5 Haywards Heath Town	1–1	1–0	1–1	3–4		2–2	3–4	4–2	2–0	2–3	3–2	6–1	3–3	1–1	5–3	1–1	3–1
6 Little Common	7–2	1–0	2–2	2–2	4–2		4–2	2–0	4–2	1–3	2–1	5–0	6–1	4–6	6–2	1–0	3–4
7 Loxwood	3–1	5–4	0–1	2–5	3–1	6–3		3–2	5–2	4–1	5–2	2–0	10–0	1–1	2–0	2–0	1–0
8 Midhurst & Easebourne	1–2	0–2	1–5	0–4	1–4	0–1	2–1		3–1	0–3	1–0	4–0	1–4	0–2	1–5	2–1	0–1
9 Mile Oak	1–1	4–3	0–0	2–2	2–4	0–0	2–2	2–0		2–1	0–2	5–0	2–1	4–0	1–0	1–1	3–3
10 Oakwood	1–4	1–1	0–5	0–3	2–2	5–4	2–4	3–0	0–5		2–1	4–3	2–4	2–1	3–2	0–3	2–4
11 Rustington	1–0	0–1	0–6	2–2	0–1	2–1	3–5	1–2	1–3	0–3		3–0	6–0	2–1	4–4	0–1	1–3
12 Saltdean United	3–0	2–2	0–5	0–4	3–3	3–1	0–5	6–1	1–2	5–2	1–0		5–2	1–4	4–4	5–3	1–3
13 Seaford Town	4–1	0–2	0–6	0–2	1–2	1–2	0–4	1–2	0–0	2–2	2–1	1–2		2–3	0–2	1–5	0–2
14 Steyning Town	2–3	1–3	1–1	1–4	2–3	0–2	3–2	0–3	1–1	2–2	5–0	4–1	1–1		1–0	1–2	2–1
15 Storrington	2–3	3–0	0–6	0–2	0–3	0–1	1–1	2–0	0–1	2–3	2–3	3–1	2–0	3–1		1–2	1–1
16 Westfield	1–2	0–0	0–0	0–1	1–3	1–4	0–1	4–1	1–2	3–1	2–0	1–2	7–0	1–2	4–3		3–3
17 Wick & Barnham United	1–0	3–1	1–1	4–3	0–1	3–4	2–4	1–2	3–0	3–1	6–0	1–2	0–0	1–1	3–0	1–0	

DIVISION THREE	1	2	3	4	5	6	7	8	9	10	11
1 Billingshurst		2-3	1-3	6-2	1-3	2-7	1-1	3-5	2-0	4-1	1-2
2 Clymping	1-1		2-2	0-3	0-2	0-1	2-3	4-1	2-0	1-0	2-3
3 Ferring	6-0	0-0		1-1	4-1	1-1	2-2	HW	1-0	4-1	2-1
4 Hurstpierpoint	1-0	1-0	1-6		3-0	0-3	6-1	3-0	1-3	0-5	2-1
5 Ifield	6-1	2-1	2-3	1-2		1-1	3-4	5-0	5-3	3-2	1-0
6 Langney Wanderers	5-1	2-0	2-0	5-1	4-1		3-0	4-2	2-3	4-2	3-1
7 Roffey	3-0	4-0	0-2	3-0	2-0	2-1		2-2	1-2	3-0	0-1
8 Rottingdean Village	2-3	1-2	1-3	2-0	2-2	0-4	2-3		0-2	0-2	3-3
9 Sidlesham	1-0	1-1	1-0	1-2	8-2	0-3	1-0	1-3		1-1	0-0
10 Southwick	2-0	1-2	1-0	1-0	3-5	2-3	1-3	1-2	0-6		1-1
11 Uckfield Town	2-0	3-0	2-4	3-0	3-0	1-6	1-0	2-0	5-1	0-4	

CLUB MOVEMENTS

Division One - In: Broadbridge Heath (P). Crawley Down (R - Isthmian Div.1 South). Eastbourne Town (R - Isthmian Div.1 South). Eastbourne United (P). Loxwood Plaistow (P).
Out: Crowborough (S - Southern Counties East League). East Grinstead (P - Isthmian Div.1 South).
Lingfield (S - Southern Counties East League). Rye United (W). Worthing United (R).
Division Two - In: AFC Uckfield Town (Formed by the merger of AFC Uckfield and Uckfield Town). Worthing United (R).
Out: AFC Uckfield (now part of AFC Uckfield Town after merger with Uckfield Town).
Broadbridge Heath (P). Eastbourne United (P). Loxwood Plaistow (P).
Division Three - In: Bosham - (P - West Sussex). Burgess Hill & Hurst Albion (Formed by the merger of Hurstpierpoint and Burgess Hill). **Out:** Hurstpierpoint (now part of Burgess Hill & Hurst Albion after merger with Burgess Hill).Uckfield Town (now part of AFC Uckfield Town after merger with AFC Uckfield).

ARUNDEL

Founded: 1889 Nickname: Mulletts

Secretary: Kathy Wilson **(T)** 07778 783 294 **(E)** kathymwilson@btinternet.com
Chairman: Bob Marchant **Prog Ed:** Kathy Wilson
Ground: Mill Road, Arundel, W. Sussex BN18 9QQ **(T)** 01903 882 548
Capacity: 2,200 **Seats:** 100 **Covered:** 200 **Midweek Matchday:** Tuesday **Clubhouse:** Yes **Shop:** No

Colours(change): Red/white/red (All Blue)
Previous Names:
Previous Leagues: West Sussex
Records: **Att:** 2,200 v Chichester (League) 1967-68 **Goalscorer:** Paul J Bennett **App:** 537 Paul Bennett (Goalkeeper)
Senior Honours: Sussex County Champions 1957-58, 58-59, 86-87.

10 YEAR RECORD

04-05	05-06	06-07	07-08	08-09	09-10	10-11	11-12	12-13	13-14
SxC1 9	SxC1 7	SxC1 3	SxC1 3	SxC1 2	SxC1 12	SxC1 9	SxC1 17	SxC1 14	SxC1 12

BROADBRIDGE HEATH

Founded: 1919 Nickname:

Secretary: Andrew Crisp **(T)** 07501 057 654 **(E)** crispandy@hotmail.com
Chairman: Keith Soane
Ground: Broadbridge Leisure Centre, Wickhurst Lane Broadbridge Heath Horsham RH12 **(T)** 01403 211 311
Capacity: **Seats:** **Covered:** **Midweek Matchday:** **Clubhouse:**

Colours(change): All blue (White/red/red)
Previous Names: None
Previous Leagues: Horsham & District >1971. West Sussex 1971-79. Southern Counties Combination 1979-83.
Records:
Senior Honours:

10 YEAR RECORD

04-05	05-06	06-07	07-08	08-09	09-10	10-11	11-12	12-13	13-14
SxC2 12	SxC2 11	SxC2 17	SxC2 17	SxC2 9	SxC2 14	SxC2 6	SxC2 5	SxC2 6	SxC2 2

CHICHESTER CITY

Founded: 2000 Nickname: Chi

Secretary: Michael Maiden **(T)** 07971 818 761 **(E)** michael.maiden@virgin.net
Chairman: Mike Madden
Ground: Oaklands Way, Chichester, W Sussex PO19 6AR **(T)** 01243 533 368
Capacity: 2,000 **Seats:** none **Covered:** 200 **Midweek Matchday:** Tuesday **Clubhouse:** Yes **Shop:** Yes

Colours(change): White/green/green (Orange/black/black)
Previous Names: Chichester FC (pre 1948), Chichester City 1948-2000. Merged with Portfield in 2000, Chicester City Utd 2000-08
Previous Leagues:
Records:
Senior Honours: Sussex County Division One 2003-04.

10 YEAR RECORD

04-05	05-06	06-07	07-08	08-09	09-10	10-11	11-12	12-13	13-14
SxC1 16	SxC1 8	SxC1 11	SxC1 16	SxC1 7	SxC1 3	SxC1 14	SxC1 20	SxC1 19	SxC1 11

CRAWLEY DOWN GATWICK

Founded: 1993 Nickname: The Anvils

Secretary: Richard Munn **(T)** 07909 578 134 **(E)** richardmunn@hotmail.co.uk
Chairman: Brian Suckling
Ground: The Haven Sportsfield, Hophurst Lane, Crawley Down RH10 4LJ **(T)** 01342 717 140
Capacity: 1,000 **Seats:** **Covered:** 50 **Midweek Matchday:** **Clubhouse:** Yes

Colours(change): All Red (All green)
Previous Names: Crawley Down United > 1993. Crawley Down Village > 1999. Crawley Down > 2012.
Previous Leagues: Mid Sussex, Sussex County > 2011. Isthmian 2011-14.
Records: 404 v East Grinstead Town 96
Senior Honours: Sussex County Division One 2010-11.

10 YEAR RECORD

04-05	05-06	06-07	07-08	08-09	09-10	10-11	11-12	12-13	13-14
SxC2 10	SxC2 5	SxC2 16	SxC2 6	SxC2 3	SxC1 8	SxC1 1	Isth1S 16	Isth1S 13	Isth1S 23

DORKING WANDERERS Founded: Nickname:

Secretary: Becky Flemming **(T)** 07889 751 566 **(E)** beckysecretary@dorkingwanderersfc.com
Chairman: Marc White
Ground: West Humble Playing Fields, London Road, Dorking, Surrey **(T)** 07841 671 825
Capacity: **Seats:** **Covered:** **Midweek Matchday:** **Clubhouse:**

Colours(change): Blue & black stripes/black/black (All red).
Previous Names:
Previous Leagues:
Records:
Senior Honours: Sussex County League Division Three 2010-11.

10 YEAR RECORD

04-05	05-06	06-07	07-08	08-09	09-10	10-11	11-12	12-13	13-14
						SxC3 1	SxC2 3	SxC1 20	SxC1 8

EAST PRESTON Founded: 1966 Nickname:

Secretary: Keith Freeman **(T)** 07986 596 913 **(E)** keweia@btinternet.com
Chairman: Sharon Savage
Ground: Roundstone Recreation Ground, Lashmar Road, East Preston BN16 1ES **(T)** 01903 776 026
Capacity: **Seats:** **Covered:** **Midweek Matchday:** **Clubhouse:**

Colours(change): White/black/black (All blue)
Previous Names:
Previous Leagues:
Records:
Senior Honours: Sussex County League Division Three 1983-84, Division Two 1997-98, 2011-12, Division One 2013-14.

10 YEAR RECORD

04-05	05-06	06-07	07-08	08-09	09-10	10-11	11-12	12-13	13-14
SxC1 11	SxC1 16	SxC1 10	SxC1 4	SxC1 18	SxC2 14	SxC2 14	SxC2 1	SxC1 3	SxC1 1

EASTBOURNE TOWN Founded: 1881 Nickname: Town

Secretary: Mark Potter **(T)** 07720 846 857 **(E)** markpotter@eastbournera.fsnet.co.uk
Chairman: David Jenkins
Ground: The Saffrons, Compton Place Road, Eastbourne BN21 1EA **(T)** 01323 724 328
Capacity: 3,000 **Seats:** 200 **Covered:** Yes **Midweek Matchday:** **Clubhouse:** Yes **Shop:** No

Colours(change): Blue & yellow/blue/blue (Red/yellow/red)
Previous Names: Devonshire Park 1881-89
Previous Leagues: Southern Amateur 1907-46, Corinthian 1960-63, Athenian 1963-76, Sussex County 1976-2007. Isthmian 2007-14.
Records: 7,378 v Hastings United - 1953
Senior Honours: Sussex County League 1976-77, Sussex Senior Cup x12.
Sussex RUR Charity Cup x3. AFA Senior Cup x2.

10 YEAR RECORD

04-05	05-06	06-07	07-08	08-09	09-10	10-11	11-12	12-13	13-14
SxC1 10	SxC1 5	SxC1 1	Isth1S 19	Isth1S 13	Isth1S 22	Isth1S 18	Isth1S 14	Isth1S 11	Isth1S 24

EASTBOURNE UNITED ASSOCIATION Founded: 1894 Nickname: The U's

Secretary: Brian Dowling **(T)** 07507 225 450 **(E)** brian.dowling@btinternet.com
Chairman: Les Aisbitt
Ground: The Oval, Channel View Road, Eastbourne, BN22 7LN **(T)** 01323 726 989
Capacity: 3,000 **Seats:** 160 **Covered:** 160 **Midweek Matchday:** Tuesday **Clubhouse:** Yes **Shop:** Yes

Colours(change): White/black/black (All maroon).
Previous Names: Eastbourne Old Comrades, Eastbourne United (merged with Shinewater Assoc in 2000)
Previous Leagues: Metropolitan 1956-64, Athenian 64-77, Isthmian 77-92
Records: **Att:** 11,000 at Lynchmore
Senior Honours: Sussex County Division Two 2013-14.

10 YEAR RECORD

04-05	05-06	06-07	07-08	08-09	09-10	10-11	11-12	12-13	13-14
SxC1 5	SxC1 14	SxC1 7	SxC1 11	SxC1 1	SxC1 6	SxC1 20	SxC2 6	SxC2 4	SxC2 1

HAILSHAM TOWN

Founded: 1885 Nickname: The Stringers

Secretary: Lorraine Maris **(T)** 07748 926 070 **(E)** lozzamaris@aol.com
Chairman: Peter Coleman
Ground: The Beaconfield, Western Road, Hailsham BN27 3JF **(T)** 01323 840 446
Capacity: 2,000 **Seats:** none **Covered:** 100 **Midweek Matchday:** Tuesday **Clubhouse:** Yes

Colours(change): Yellow/green/green (All light blue)
Previous Names: Hailsham.
Previous Leagues: East Sussex, Southern Combination
Records: **Att:** 1350 v Hungerford T. FA Vase Feb 89 **Goalscorer:** Howard Stephens 51 **App:** Phil Comber 713
Senior Honours:

10 YEAR RECORD

04-05	05-06	06-07	07-08	08-09	09-10	10-11	11-12	12-13	13-14
SxC1 12	SxC1 10	SxC1 6	SxC1 13	SxC1 15	SxC1 19	SxC1 16	SxC2 2	SxC1 12	SxC1 16

HASSOCKS

Founded: 1902 Nickname: The Robins

Secretary: Sarah John **(T)** 07703 346 208 **(E)** sarahajohn@btinternet.com
Chairman: Phil Brotherton
Ground: The Beacon, Brighton Road, Hassocks BN6 9NA **(T)** 01273 846 040
Capacity: 1,800 **Seats:** 270 **Covered:** 100 **Midweek Matchday:** Tuesday **Clubhouse:** Yes **Shop:** No

Colours(change): All Red. (Yellow/black/yellow)
Previous Names:
Previous Leagues: Mid Sussex, Brighton & Hove & Dist and Southern Counties Comb
Records: **Att:** 610 v Burgess Hill Town **Goalscorer:** Pat Harding 43
Senior Honours:

10 YEAR RECORD

04-05	05-06	06-07	07-08	08-09	09-10	10-11	11-12	12-13	13-14
SxC1 8	SxC1 9	SxC1 5	SxC1 7	SxC1 16	SxC1 14	SxC1 6	SxC1 4	SxC1 7	SxC1 6

HORSHAM YMCA

Founded: 1898 Nickname: YM's

Secretary: Andy Flack **(T)** 07775 857 392 **(E)** andy.flack@horsham.gov.uk
Chairman: Mick Browning
Ground: Goring Mead, Horsham, West Sussex RH13 5BP **(T)** 01403 252 689
Capacity: 1,575 **Seats:** 150 **Covered:** 200 **Midweek Matchday:** **Clubhouse:** Yes **Shop:** No

Colours(change): White/black/red (All blue)
Previous Names:
Previous Leagues: Horsham & District, Brighton & Hove, Mid Sussex, Sussex County > 2006, Isthmian 2006-11.
Records: 950 v Chelmsford City - FA Cup 2000
Senior Honours: Sussex League 2004-05, 05-06.
John O'Hara Cup 2001-02.

10 YEAR RECORD

04-05	05-06	06-07	07-08	08-09	09-10	10-11	11-12	12-13	13-14
SxC1 1	SxC1 1	Isth1S 9	Isth1S 21	SxC1 3	Isth1S 11	Isth1S 22	SxC1 16	SxC1 10	SxC1 4

LANCING

Founded: 1941 Nickname:

Secretary: John Rea **(T)** 07598 301 296 **(E)** john.rea62@yahoo.com
Chairman: Martin Gander
Ground: Culver Road, Lancing, West Sussex BN15 9AX **(T)** 01903 767 285
Capacity: **Seats:** **Covered:** **Midweek Matchday:** **Clubhouse:** Yes

Colours(change): Yellow/blue/yellow (All light blue)
Previous Names: Lancing Athletic
Previous Leagues: Brighton & Hove & District.
Records:
Senior Honours: Brighton League 1946-47, 47-48.

10 YEAR RECORD

04-05	05-06	06-07	07-08	08-09	09-10	10-11	11-12	12-13	13-14
SxC2 13	SxC2 12	SxC2 14	SxC2 12	SxC2 9	SxC2 11	SxC2 2	SxC1 2	SxC1 13	SxC1 18

LITTLEHAMPTON TOWN

Founded: 1896 Nickname: Golds

Secretary: Paul Cox **(T)** 07771 623 224 **(E)** cox121@yahoo.com
Chairman: Robert McAlees
Ground: Sportsfield, St Flora's Road, Littlehampton BN17 6BD **(T)** 01903 716 390
Capacity: **Seats:** **Covered:** **Midweek Matchday:** **Clubhouse:**

Colours(change): Yellow/black/black (All white)
Previous Names: Littlehampton 1896-1938.
Previous Leagues: None
Records: Lost in the FAC Prelim v Tunbridge W. 15-16 on pens after 40 kicks had been taken - At the time a European record and one short of the World record.
Senior Honours: Sussex County Division Two 2003-04, 12-13.

10 YEAR RECORD

04-05	05-06	06-07	07-08	08-09	09-10	10-11	11-12	12-13	13-14
SxC1 4	SxC1 4	SxC1 20	SxC2 8	SxC2 14	SxC2 12	SxC2 11	SxC2 4	SxC2 1	SxC1 3

LOXWOOD

Founded: Nickname:

Secretary: George Read **(T)** 07791 766 857 **(E)** thomasread00@btinternet.com
Chairman: Barry Hunter
Ground: Loxwood Sports Ass., Plaistow Road, Loxwood RH14 0RQ **(T)** 07791 766 857
Capacity: **Seats:** **Covered:** **Midweek Matchday:** **Clubhouse:**

Colours(change): Black & white/black/white (All red)
Previous Names:
Previous Leagues: West Sussex > 2006.
Records:
Senior Honours: Sussex County League Division Three 2007-08.

10 YEAR RECORD

04-05	05-06	06-07	07-08	08-09	09-10	10-11	11-12	12-13	13-14
		SxC3 7	SxC3 1	SxC2 10	SxC2 5	SxC2 6	SxC2 5	SxC2 9	SxC2 3

NEWHAVEN

Founded: 1887 Nickname:

Secretary: Martin Garry **(T)** 07768 508 011 **(E)** martin.garry@premierfoods.co.uk
Chairman: Andrew Lloyd
Ground: Fort Road Newhaven East Sussex BN9 9DA **(T)** 01273 513 940
Capacity: **Seats:** Yes **Covered:** Yes **Midweek Matchday:** **Clubhouse:** Yes

Colours(change): All red & yellow (All blue)
Previous Names: None
Previous Leagues: None
Records:
Senior Honours: Sussex County League Division One 1953-54, 73-74, Division Two 1971-72, 90-91, Division Three 2011-12.

10 YEAR RECORD

04-05	05-06	06-07	07-08	08-09	09-10	10-11	11-12	12-13	13-14
SxC3 11	SxC3 4	SxC3 9	SxC3 5	SxC3 4	SxC3 9	SxC3 7	SxC3 1	SxC2 2	SxC1 13

PAGHAM

Founded: 1903 Nickname: The Lions

Secretary: Marc Hilton **(T)** 07771 810 757 **(E)** marcmhilton@live.co.uk
Chairman: Tony Shea
Ground: Nyetimber Lane, Pagham, W Sussex PO21 3JY **(T)** 01243 266 112
Capacity: 2,000 **Seats:** 200 **Covered:** 200 **Midweek Matchday:** **Clubhouse:** Yes **Shop:** No

Colours(change): White/black/black (All green)
Previous Names: None
Previous Leagues: Chichester 1903-50, West Sussex 50-69
Records: **Att:** 1,200 v Bognor 1971 **Goalscorer:** Dick De Luca **App:** Graham Peach
Senior Honours: Sussex County Division Two 1978-79, 86-87, 2006-07. Division One 80-81, 87-88, 88-89.

10 YEAR RECORD

04-05	05-06	06-07	07-08	08-09	09-10	10-11	11-12	12-13	13-14
SxC1 19	SxC2 13	SxC2 1	SxC1 9	SxC1 11	SxC1 17	SxC1 4	SxC1 6	SxC1 5	SxC1 7

RINGMER

Founded: 1906 Nickname: Blues

Secretary: Sally Crouch **(T)** 07510 109 509 **(E)** sallycrouch@ringmerfc.co.uk
Chairman: Bob Munnery
Ground: Caburn Ground, Anchor Field, Ringmer BN8 5QN **(T)** 01273 812 738
Capacity: 1,000 **Seats:** 100 **Covered:** Yes **Midweek Matchday:** Tuesday **Clubhouse:** Yes **Shop:** Yes

Colours(change): Navy & light blue/navy/navy. (Yellow/yellow/red).
Previous Names: None.
Previous Leagues: Brighton.
Records: 1,350 v Southwick, Sussex County League, 1970-71.
Senior Honours: Sussex County Division Two 1968-69. Division One 1970-71. Sussex Senior Cup 1972-73.

10 YEAR RECORD

04-05	05-06	06-07	07-08	08-09	09-10	10-11	11-12	12-13	13-14
SxC1 6	SxC1 2	SxC1 9	SxC1 10	SxC1 9	SxC1 13	SxC1 10	SxC1 15	SxC1 9	SxC1 9

SELSEY

Founded: 1903 Nickname: Blues

Secretary: Gordon Weller **(T)** 07852 954 042 **(E)** g.weller1@btinternet.com
Chairman: David Lee **Prog Ed:** Gordon Weller
Ground: High Street Ground, Selsey, Chichester, PO20 0QG **(T)** 01243 603 420
Capacity: 1,000 **Seats:** 25 **Covered:** 98 **Midweek Matchday:** Tuesday **Clubhouse:** Yes **Shop:** No

Colours(change): All blue (All yellow).
Previous Names: None
Previous Leagues: Chichester & District, West Sussex.
Records: **Att:** 750-800 v Chichester or Portfield 1950's
Senior Honours: Sussex County Division Two 1963-64, 75-76.

10 YEAR RECORD

04-05	05-06	06-07	07-08	08-09	09-10	10-11	11-12	12-13	13-14
SxC2 14	SxC2 2	SxC1 8	SxC1 15	SxC1 10	SxC1 11	SxC1 17	SxC1 12	SxC1 18	SxC1 17

SHOREHAM

Founded: 1892 Nickname: Musselmen

Secretary: Clive Harman **(T)** 07761 054 431 **(E)** clive.harman.1966@btinternet.com
Chairman: Stuart Slaney
Ground: Middle Road, Shoreham-by-Sea, W Sussex, BN43 6LT **(T)** 01273 454 261
Capacity: 1,500 **Seats:** 150 **Covered:** 700 **Midweek Matchday:** **Clubhouse:** Yes **Shop:** No

Colours(change): All blue (All red).
Previous Names: None.
Previous Leagues: West Sussex.
Records: **Att:** 1,342 v Wimbledon
Senior Honours: Sussex County Division One 1951-52, 52-53, 77-78. Division Two 61-62, 76-77, 93-94. John O'Hara League Cup 2007-08.

10 YEAR RECORD

04-05	05-06	06-07	07-08	08-09	09-10	10-11	11-12	12-13	13-14
SxC2 3	SxC1 13	SxC1 13	SxC1 12	SxC1 6	SxC1 9	SxC1 18	SxC1 18	SxC1 17	SxC1 14

ST. FRANCIS RANGERS

Founded: 2002 Nickname: Saints/Rangers

Secretary: John Goss **(T)** 07748 705 240 **(E)** j.goss462@btinternet.com
Chairman: John Goss **Prog Ed:** John Goss
Ground: Cowell Ground, Princess Royal Hospital, Lewes Rd, Haywards Hth RH16 4EX **(T)** 01444 474 021
Capacity: 1,000 **Seats:** None **Covered:** 100 **Midweek Matchday:** Tuesday **Clubhouse:** Yes **Shop:** No

Colours(change): Black & white/black/black (Green & white/green/green)
Previous Names: Formed when Ansty Rangers & St Francis merged 2002.
Previous Leagues: None
Records:
Senior Honours:

10 YEAR RECORD

04-05	05-06	06-07	07-08	08-09	09-10	10-11	11-12	12-13	13-14
SxC2 4	SxC2 3	SxC2 2	SxC1 14	SxC1 12	SxC1 16	SxC1 19	SxC1 19	SxC1 11	SxC1 10

A.F.C. UCKFIELD TOWN
Founded: 1988 Nickname: The Oaks

Secretary: Mark O'Hara **(T)** 07710 901 701 **(E)** mso@hydraplc.com
Chairman: Tom Parker
Ground: The Oaks, Old Eastbourne Road, Uckfield TN22 5QL **(T)** 01825 890 905
Colours(change): Red & black/black/black (All light blue)

ADDITIONAL INFORMATION:
Sussex County League Division 2 League Cup 2004-05, Division Two 2010-11.

BEXHILL UNITED
Founded: Nickname:

Secretary: Mrs Tracy Aston **(T)** 07791 368 049 **(E)** tracyaston21@aol.com
Chairman: Bill Harrison **Prog Ed:** Mrs Tracy Aston
Ground: The Polegrove, Brockley Road, Bexhill on Sea TN39 3EX **(T)** 07791 368 049
Colours(change): White & black/black/black (Blue & yellow/blue/blue)

ADDITIONAL INFORMATION:

HAYWARDS HEATH TOWN
Founded: 1888 Nickname:

Secretary: Tony Sim **(T)** 01444 453 754 **(E)**
Chairman: Mick Cottingham
Ground: Hanbury Park Stadium, Haywards Heath RH16 4GL **(T)** 01444 412 837
Colours(change): All blue (All yellow)

ADDITIONAL INFORMATION:
Honours: Sussex County League 1949-50, 69-70. Sussex Senior Cup 1957-58.

LITTLE COMMON
Founded: 1966 Nickname:

Secretary: Daniel Eldridge **(T)** 07759 125 252 **(E)** danieleldridge11@btinternet.com
Chairman: Ken Cherry
Ground: Little Common Recreation Ground, Green Lane, Bexhill on Sea TN39 4PH **(T)** 01424 845 861
Colours(change): Claret & blue/claret/claret (Yellow/blue/blue)

ADDITIONAL INFORMATION:
Previous Name: Albion United > 1986. **Previous League:** East Sussex 1994-2005.
Honours: East Sussex League 1975-76, 76-77, 2004-05.

MIDHURST & EASEBOURNE
Founded: Nickname:

Secretary: Ted Dummer MBE **(T)** 01730 813 887 **(E)** acs@harrisonrenwick.com
Chairman: Darren Chiverton **Prog Ed:** Ted Dummer MBE
Ground: Rotherfield, Dodsley Lane, Easebourne, Midhurst GU29 9BE **(T)** 01730 816 557
Colours(change): All blue (Orange/blue/orange)

ADDITIONAL INFORMATION:
Previous League: West Sussex 1999-2002.
Honours: Sussex County League Division 2 Cup 1988-89, Division 3 Cup 2002-03.

MILE OAK
Founded: 1960 Nickname: The Oak

Secretary: Chris Tew **(T)** 07733 323 453 **(E)** chris_tew@lineone.net
Chairman: Leslie Hamilton
Ground: Mile Oak Recreation Ground, Chalky Road, Portslade BN41 2YU **(T)** 01273 423 854
Colours(change): Orange & black/black/black (All green)

ADDITIONAL INFORMATION:
Previous League: Brighton & Hove District.
Honours: Brighton & Hove District 1980-81. Sussex County League Division 2.

OAKWOOD
Founded: 1962 Nickname:

Secretary: Madeleine Williams **(T)** 07873 875 994 **(E)** peteandmad@blueyonder.co.uk
Chairman: Stuart Lovegrove
Ground: Tinsley Lane, Three Bridges, Crawley RH10 8AJ **(T)** 01293 515 742
Colours(change): Red & black/black/black (Blue/white/white)

ADDITIONAL INFORMATION:
Previous League: Southern Counties Combination 1980-84.
Honours: Sussex County Division 2 Cup 1989-90.

RUSTINGTON

Founded: Nickname:

Secretary: Kevin Short **(T)** 07739 145 186 **(E)** kevinshort@carleasing.co.uk
Chairman: John Virgoe
Ground: Recreation Ground, Jubilee Avenue, Rustington BN16 3NB **(T)** 01903 770 495
Colours(change): All blue (White & blue/white/white)

ADDITIONAL INFORMATION:
Honours: Sussex County League Division 3 2006-07.

SALTDEAN UNITED

Founded: 1966 Nickname:

Secretary: Iain Feilding **(T)** 07880 870 886 **(E)** secretary@saltdeanunitedfc.co.uk
Chairman: Robert Thomas
Ground: Hill Park, Coombe Vale Saltdean Brighton East Sussex BN2 8HJ **(T)** 01273 309 898
Colours(change): Red & black/black/black (All yellow)

ADDITIONAL INFORMATION:
Previous Leagues: Brighton > 1984.

SEAFORD TOWN

Founded: Nickname:

Secretary: John Smith **(T)** 07940 511 504 **(E)** johnsmithn@btinternet.com
Chairman: Bob Thomsett
Ground: The Crouch, Bramber Road, Seaford BN25 1AG **(T)** 01323 892 221
Colours(change): All red (Blue/yellow/blue)

ADDITIONAL INFORMATION:
Honours: Sussex County League Division Two 2005-06.

STEYNING TOWN

Founded: Nickname:

Secretary: David Kennett **(T)** 07585 601 213 **(E)** diddy.kennett1@btinternet.com
Chairman: Richard Woodbridge
Ground: The Shooting Field, Steyning, West Sussex BN44 3RQ **(T)** 01903 814 601
Colours(change): Red & white/red/red (All yellow)

ADDITIONAL INFORMATION:
Honours: Sussex County League Division 2 1977-78, Division 1 1984-85, 85-86, League Cup 1978-79, 83-84, 85-86.

STORRINGTON

Founded: 1920 Nickname:

Secretary: Keith Dalmon **(T)** 07889 367 956 **(E)** keithdalmon@btinternet.com
Chairman: Stan Rhodie
Ground: Recreation Ground, Pulborough Road, Storrington RH20 4HJ **(T)** 01903 745 860
Colours(change): All blue (All red)

ADDITIONAL INFORMATION:
Honours: Sussex County League Division 2 Cup 1979, Division 3 Cup 1998, Division 3 2005.
Vernon Wentworth Cup 1998, 2003.

WESTFIELD

Founded: 1927 Nickname:

Secretary: Gill Attewell **(T)** 07928 176 658 **(E)** gillattewell@gmail.com
Chairman: Graham Drinkwater **Prog Ed:** Gill Attewell
Ground: The Parish Field, Main Road, Westfield TN35 4SB **(T)** 01424 751 011
Colours(change): Yellow/green/green (All blue)

ADDITIONAL INFORMATION:
Previous League: East Sussex 1971-97.
Honours: East Sussex 1977-78, League Cup 77-78. Hastings Senior Cup 2007-08.

WICK & BARNFIELD UNITED

Founded: 2013 Nickname:

Secretary: Terry Gaunt **(T)** 07782 165 919 **(E)** coxsteven1@aol.com
Chairman: Keith Croft
Ground: Crabtree Park, Coomes Way, Wick, Littlehampton, W Sussex BN17 7LS **(T)** 01903 713 535 **Capacity:** 1,000
Colours(change): Red & blue/red/red (White & black/black/white).

ADDITIONAL INFORMATION:
Previous Name: Barnfield FC merged with Wick June 2013.

WORTHING UNITED

Founded: 1952 Nickname:

Secretary: Mark Sanderson **(T)** 07968 856 183 **(E)** helsnmark@aol.com
Chairman: Steve Taylor
Ground: The Robert Albon Memorial Ground, Lyons Way BN14 9JF **(T)** 01903 234 466
Colours(change): Sky blue & whites/blue/sky blue (Red & black/black/red)

ADDITIONAL INFORMATION:
Previous Names: Wigmore Athletic 1952-88. Amalgamated with Southdown to form Worthing United in 1988.
League Honours: Sussex County Division Two 1973-74, Division Three 1989-90.

SUSSEX COUNTY DIVISION THREE CONSTITUTION 2014-15

	Club	Ground	Telephone
1	BILLINGHURST	Jubilee Field, Three Bridges Road Three Bridges Sussex RH10 1LQ	01293 442 000
2	BOSHAM	Recreation Ground, Walton Lane, Bosham, West Sussex PO18 8QF	01243 681 279
3	BURGESS HILL & HURST ALBION	Fairfield Recreation Ground, Cuckfield Road, Hurstpierpoint BN6 9SD	01273 834 783
4	CLYMPING	Clymping Village Hall, Clymping, Littlehampton BN17 5GW	07951 196 784
5	FERRING	The Glebelands, Ferring, West Sussex BN12 5JL	01903 243 618
6	IFIELD	Edwards Sports & Social Club, Ifield Green, Rusper Road, Crawley	01293 420 598
7	LANGNEY WANDERERS	Shinewater Lane Playing Field, off Lavender Close, Milfoil Drive in north Langney, Eastbourne BN23 8DQ	
8	ROFFEY	Bartholomew Way, Horsham RH12 5JL	
9	ROTTINGDEAN VILLAGE	Rottingdean Sports Centre, Falmer Road, Rottingdean BN2 7DA	01273 306 436
10	SIDLESHAM	Recreation Ground, Selsey Road Sidlesham Nr Chichester PO20 7RD	01243 641538
11	SOUTHWICK	Old Barn Way, Southwick BN42 4NT	01273 701 010

GROUND DIRECTIONS

ARUNDEL-Mill Road, Arundel, West Sussex BN18 9QQ-01903 882 548

A27 from Worthing to Arundel over Railway Bridge to roundabout . Second exit into Queen Street to town centre and turn right over bridge. Car park leading to ground 100 yards on right.

BROADBRIDGE HEATH-Wickhurst Lane, Broadbridge Heath, Horsham RH12 3YS-01403 211 311

Alongside A24, Horsham north/south bypass. From the A24 Horsham Bypass, at the large roundabout/underpass take the Broadbridge Heath Bypass towards Guildford and then at the first roundabout turn left into Wickhurst Lane.

CHICHESTER CITY-Oaklands Park, Oaklands Way, Chichester PO19 6AR-07845 105 822

Half a mile north of the city centre, adjacent to festival theatre. Turn into Northgate car park and entrance to the ground is next to the Chichester Rackets Club.

CRAWLEY DOWN GATWICK -The Haven Sportsfield, Hophurst Lane, Crawley Down RH10 4LJ - 01342 717 140

From the North: Turn off the M23 at Junction 10 signposted East Grinstead At the roundabout at the Copthorne Hotel, take the 2nd exit, signed A264 East Grinstead. At the next roundabout (Duke's Head) take the 3rd exit, B2028 south, toward Turners Hill After approx. 1 mile turn left into Sandy Lane. (just after entering the 30mph zone and a telephone box in the layby on the right). At the end of Sandy Lane (war memorial on the right), turn left signed Felbridge. After a couple of bends the Haven Centre is on your left. From the East: Travel through East Grinstead on the A22 until the Junction with the A264 at the Felbridge Traffic lights. Turn left (Sign posted Crawley) and after 100 Meters take the Left Fork towards Crawley Down. Approx 1.5 Miles Haven Centre on Right. From the South: Travel North through Turners Hill on the B2028 after approx 2 Miles take the 2nd turning on your right (Vicarage Road). This is a Right fork and is sited just after passing over a small bridge. Follow Vicarage Road for approx 1/2 Mile past Junction with Sandy Lane and The Haven Centre is 200 Meters on your left.

DORKING WANDERERS- West Humble Playing Fields, London Road, Dorking.

Take A24 to Dorking at roundabout stay on A24 to Leatherhead. Go past Denbies Vineyard on left. At end of vineyard take 2nd turning on the left straight into the playing field.

EAST PRESTON - Roundstone Recreation Ground, Lashmar Road, East Preston, West Sussex BN16 1ES - 01903 776026

From Worthing proceed west for six miles on A259 to The Roundstone PH. From the roundabout, take the first exit, signposted East Preston. Turn left over the railway crossing. Turn left soon afterwards, and then first right into Roundstone Drive. Turn left into Lashmar Road and the approach road to the ground is on the right.

EASTBOURNE TOWN - The Saffrons, Compton Place Road, Eastbourne BN21 1EA - 01323 724 328

Come into Eastbourne following the signs for Eastbourne Railway Station. When arriving at the railway station mini-roundabout turn right into Grove Road, (opposite from the station) and carry on past the Police Station and Town Hall (the large clock building.) Go straight over at the junction past the Caffyns car showroom (you can see the ground on your right), then take the first right turn into Compton Place Road and the entrance to The Saffrons car park is 100 yards on the right.

EASTBOURNE UNITED AFC-The Oval, Channel View Ropad, Eastbourne, East Sussex BN22 7LN-011323 726989

From A22 follow signs to Eastbourne East seafront. Turn left onto seafront and left again into Channel View Road at Princess Park & ground is first right.

HAILSHAM TOWN-The Beaconsfield, Western Road, Hailsham, East Sussex BN27 3DN-01323 840446

A22 to Arlington Road, turn east, then left into South Road- left into Diplocks Way until Daltons. Four miles from Polegate BR (Brighton-Eastbourne line).

HASSOCKS-The Beacon, Brighton Rd., Hassocks BN6 9NA-01273 846040

Off A273 Pyecombe Road to Burgess Hill. Ground is 300 yards south of Stonepound crossroads (B2116) to Hurstpeirpoint or Hassocks.

HORSHAM YMCA-Gorings Mead, Horsham, West Sussex RH13 5BP-01403 252 689

From the east, take A281 (Brighton Road) and the ground is on the left and sign posted opposite Gorings Mead.

LANCING-Culver Road, Lancing, West Sussex BN15 9AX. -01903 767 285.

From A27 turn south at Lancing Manor roundabout into Grinstead Lane, 3rd turning on right North Farm Rd. Turn left then immedlately. right into Culver Rd. From railway station take 3rd turning on left heading north.

LITTLEHAMPTON TOWN-The Sportsfield, St Flora's Road, Littlehampton BN17 6BD-01903 716 390

Leave A259 at Waterford Business Park and turn into Horsham Road. After Shell Garage turn left into St. Floras Road. Ground is at the end of road on the left.

LOXWOOD-Loxwood Sports Association, Plaistow Road, Loxwood RH14 0SX-01404 753 185

Leave A272 between Billinghurst and Wisborough Green and join the B2133 for 3.4 miles. On entering Loxwood Village take 1st left into Plaistow Road, ground situated 100 yards on the left.

NEWHAVEN-Fort Road Recreation Ground, Newhaven, East Sussex BN9 9EE. -01273 513 940.

From A259, follow the one way system around the town of Newhaven. Turn left into South Road (pass the Police Station) which becomes Fort Road. The ground is visible on the right just past a small parade of shops and before the approach road to Newhaven Fort. Postcode for Sat-nav users: BN9 9DA

PAGHAM-Nyetimber Lane, Pagham, West Sussex PO21 3JY-01243 266 112

Turn off A27 Chichester by-pass (signposted A259 Pagham). Ground in village of Nyetimber. Three miles from Bognor (BR). Buses 260 & 240

RINGMER-Caburn Ground, Anchor Field, Ringmer-01273 812 738

From Lewes road turn right into Springett Avenue, opposite Ringmer village

SELSEY-High Street Ground, Selsey, Chichester, West Sussex-01243 603420

Through Selsey High Street to fire station. Take turning into car park alongside the station. Entrance is in the far corner. Regular buses from Chichester.

SHOREHAM-Middle Road, Shoreham-by-Sea, West Sussex BN43 6LT-01273 454 261

From Shoreham (BR) go east over level crossing, up Dolphin Road. Ground is 150 yards on right.

ST FRANCIS RANGERS-The Princess Royal Hospital, Lewes Road, Haywards Heath, RH16 4EX Tel No: 01444 474 021 and social club 01444 441 881

Enter through the main hospital entrance on the Lewes Road and follow signs to Sports Complex.

DIVISION TWO

AFC UCKFIELD TOWN-The Oaks, Old Eastbourne Road, Uckfield, East Sussex TN22 5QL-07847 662 337

Next to Rajdutt Restaurant on Old Eastbourne Road, south of Uckfield town centre.

BEXHILL UNITED-The Polegrove, Brockley Road, Bexhill-on-Sea, East Sussex TN39 3EX-07815 425 682.

A27 to Little Common then fourth exit off roundabout to Cooden Beach. Left and follow to end, turn right into Brockby Road. Ground at bottom of hill on the right.

HAYWARDS HEATH TOWN-Hanbury Park Stadium, Haywards Heath RH16 3PX-01444 412 837.

A272 to Haywards Heath town centre. At Sussex roundabout, north on B2708 (Hazelgrove Road) take first right into New England Road, then the 4th right (Allen Road) leads to ground.

LITTLE COMMON-Little Common Spts Pavilion, Little Common Rec., Green Lane, Bexhill-on-Sea, TN39 4PH-01424 845 861.

From the west take the A259, at Little Common roundabout take second exit into Peartree Lane and then left into Little Common Recreation Ground car park.

MIDHURST & EASEBOURNE-Rotherfield, Dodsley Lane, Easebourne, Midhurst, W. Sussex GU29 9BE-01730 816 557.

Ground one mile out of Midhurst on London Road (A286) opposite Texaco Garage. Ample car parking.

MILE OAK-Mile Oak Recreation Ground, Chalky Road, Portslade-01273 423 854.

From A27 (Brighton Bypass) leave at A293 exit. Right at first roundabout. Ground 1 mile on right. Parking in the Sports Centre opposite the ground (park) entrance.

SUSSEX COUNTY LEAGUE - STEP 5/6/7

OAKWOOD-Tinsley Lane, Three Bridges, Crawley RH10 8AJ-01293 515 742.

From the South on M23, take junction 10 exit left onto A2011, next roundabout take fourth exit right, next roundabout second exit, take first right into Tinsley Lane. Ground entrance 100 metres on left.

RUSTINGTON-Recreation Ground, Jubilee Avenue, Rustington, West Sussex BN16 3NB-01903 770 495.

From the East follow A259 past Sainsburys. Left at next roundabout on to B2187 over Windmill Bridge. Straight on at roundabout, first right, then first left into Woodlands Avenue. Car park is 80 yards on your right, next to the Village hall. From the West proceed to Watersmead roundabout with Bodyshop on your left. Take B2187 half a mile, past BP garage, take third right into Albert Road, then first right into Woodlands Avenue.

SALTDEAN UNITED-Hill Park, Coombe Vale, Saltdean, Brighton BN2 8HJ-01273 309 898.

A259 coast road east from Brighton to Saltdean Lido, left into Arundel Drive West, and Saltdean Vale to bridle path at beginning of Combe Vale. Club 200yds along track.

SEAFORD TOWN-The Crouch, Bramber Road, Seaford BN25 1AG-01323 892 221.

A259 to Seaford. At mini roundabout by station, turn left (coming from Newhaven) or RIGHT (from Eastbourne). At end of Church Street, across junction, then left at end. After 500m turn left up Ashurst Road Bramber Road is at the top.

STEYNING TOWN-The Shooting Field, Steyning, W. Sussex BN44 3RP. -01903 812 228.

Entering Steyning from the west. Take 1st left in the High St (Tanyard Lane) Follow into Shooting Field estate, ground is 4th turn on the left. Entering Steyning from the east. From the High St., turn right into Church St.. Turn left by Church into Shooting Field estate. NB Coaches MUST park in Church Street Car Park.

STORRINGTON-Recreation Ground, Pulborough Road, Storrington RH20 4HJ-01903 745 860.

A24 right at roundabout at Washington. Four miles to Storrington through village. Third exit at roundabout and second right into Spearbridge Road.

WESTFIELD-The Parish Field, Main Road, Westfield TN35 4SB-01483 751 011.

From Hastings take the A21, turning right onto the A28 towards Ashford. Travel through Westfield, and the ground is located off Westfield Lane on the left.

WICK & BARNHAM UNITED -Crabtree Park, Coomes Way, Wick, Littlehampton, West Sussex BN17 7LS Tel No: 01903 713 535

A27 to Crossbush.A284 towards Littlehampton. After one mile over level crossing left into Coomes Way next to Locomotive pub. Ground at end.

WORTHING UNITED-The Robert Albion Memorial Ground, Lyons Way, Worthing BN14 9JF. 01903 234 466.

From the West past Hill Barn roundabout to second set of traffic lights, turn left into Lyons Way. From East first set of traffic lights at end of Sompting bypass, turn right into Lyons Way.

DIVISION THREE

BILLINGHURST-Jubilee Field, Three Bridges Road Three Bridges Sussex RH10 1LQ-01293 442 000

Heading towards Crawley past Three Bridges railway station on the left, take the 2nd right into Three Bridges Road, and then 1st left 75 yards down. The ground is down Jubilee Walk (80 yards)opposite the Plough Inn.

BOSHAM -Recreation Ground, Walton Lane, Bosham, West Sussex PO18 8QF - 01243 681 279.

From Chichester take the A259 towards Emsworth/Portsmouth. On reaching Bosham, turn left at the Swan Public House roundabout half a mile to the T junction, turn left. Car park 50 yards on Left.

BURGESS HILL & HURST ALBION -Fairfield Rec. Ground, Cuckfield Road, BN6 9SD-01273 834 783.

At Hurstpierpoint crossroads, go north into Cuckfield Road (B2117) for 1km. Ground entrance between houses nos.158 & 160.

CLYMPING-Clymping Village Hall, Clymping, Littelhampton BN17 5GW-07951 196 784.

Follow A259 west of Littlehampton. Just over the Bridge, on the right hand side before the small roundabout.

FERRING-The Glebelands, Ferring, West Sussex BN12 5JL

To Ferring main shops, turn right into Greystoke Road.

IFIELD-Edwards Sports & Social Club, Ifield Green, Rusper Road, Crawley. -01293 420 598.

From A23 Crawley by-pass going north, left at roundabout signed Charlwood. Third left into Ifield Green, first right past Royal Oak (PH) into Rusper Road.

LANGNEY WANDERERS - Shinewater Lane Playing Field, off Lavender Close, Milfoil Drive in north Langney, Eastbourne, East Sussex BN23 8DQ.

ROFFEY-Bartholomew Way, Horsham RH12 5JL.

A24 heading South, turn left at Rusper roundabout. Take first left into Lemmington Way. Take left at T junction into Bartholomew Way.

ROTTINGDEAN VILLAGE-Rottingdean Sports Centre, Falmer Road, Rottingdean BN2 7DA. -01273 306 436

After leaving the Rottingdean Village one way system go past Bazehill Road and the entrance to the ground is next on the right.

SIDLESHAM

SOUTHWICK-Old Barn Way, off Manor Hall Way, Southwick, Brighton BN42 4NT-01273 701 010

A27 from Brighton take first left after Southwick sign to Leisure Centre. Ground adjacent. Five minutes walk from Fishergate or Southwick stations.

UNITED COUNTIES LEAGUE

Sponsored by: ChromaSport & Trophies
Founded: 1895
Recent Champions:
2009: Stewarts & Lloyds Corby
2010: Daventry Town
2011: St Neots Town
2012: Long Buckby
2013: Holbeach United
nwcfl.co.uk

PREMIER DIVISION	P	W	D	L	F	A	GD	Pts
1 (P) Spalding United	36	32	1	3	122	22	100	97
2 Huntingdon Town	36	26	7	3	105	39	66	85
3 AFC Rushden & Diamonds	36	26	3	7	88	35	53	81
4 Deeping Rangers	36	23	6	7	113	45	68	75
5 Cogenhoe United	36	23	6	7	77	35	42	75
6 Yaxley	36	21	5	10	72	41	31	68
7 Wisbech Town	36	17	5	14	77	61	16	56
8 Wellingborough Town	36	15	7	14	63	54	9	52
9 Peterborough Northern Star	36	12	11	13	53	58	-5	47
10 Desborough Town	36	13	7	16	53	72	-19	46
11 Holbeach United	36	13	5	18	65	70	-5	44
12 AFC Kempston Rovers	36	11	11	14	67	86	-19	44
13 Sleaford Town	36	10	6	20	53	75	-22	36
14 Boston Town	36	8	10	18	42	68	-26	34
15 Northampton Sileby Rangers	36	7	7	22	42	98	-56	28
16 Newport Pagnell Town	36	7	6	23	41	85	-44	27
17 Harborough Town	36	7	5	24	29	81	-52	26
18 Long Buckby AFC (-6pts)	36	7	9	20	46	89	-43	24
19 (R) Stewarts & Lloyds Corby	36	3	5	28	27	121	-94	14

LEAGUE CUP

PRELIMINARY ROUND

Wisbech Town	v	Northampton ON Chenecks	4-1
AFC Kempston Rovers	v	Blackstones	4-1
Spalding United	v	Olney Town	3-0
Holbeach United	v	Peterborough Northern Star	1-2
Burton Park Wanderers	v	Thrapston Town	2-1
Newport Pagnell Town	v	Desborough Town	1-1 3-2p
Northampton Sileby Ranger	v	Sleaford Town	2-1
Bourne Town	v	Yaxley	2-1
Harborough Town	v	Raunds Town	0-1 aet
Harrowby United	v	Deeping Rangers	0-4

ROUND 1

Wisbech Town	v	Eynesbury Rovers	4-3
AFC Rushden & Diamonds	v	Huntingdon Town	2-3
Rothwell Corinthians	v	Bugbrooke St Michaels	2-0
AFC Kempston Rovers	v	Long Buckby AFC	1-0
Spalding United	v	Peterborough Northern Star	5-0
Boston Town	v	Burton Park Wanderers	5-3
Woodford United	v	Newport Pagnell Town	3-1
Potton United	v	Northampton Sileby Ranger	2-0
Stewarts & Lloyds Corby	v	Cogenhoe United	0-1
Lutterworth Athletic	v	Bourne Town	2-1
Buckingham Town	v	Wellingborough Town	0-5
Raunds Town	v	Northampton Spencer	1-4
Deeping Rangers	v	Peterborough Sports	7-0
Wellingborough Whitworth			Bye
Irchester United	v	Rushden & Higham United	2-1
Oadby Town	v	St Neots Town Saints	3-1

PREMIER DIVISION	1	2	3	4	5	6	7	8	9	10	11	12	13	14	15	16	17	18	19
1 AFC Kempston Rovers		1–3	1–1	2–3	0–3	4–3	4–1	5–3	3–8	1–0	1–1	6–2	2–2	2–0	1–8	4–4	1–1	1–1	1–1
2 AFC Rushden & Diamonds	3–0		1–0	4–2	1–2	1–2	3–1	3–1	1–2	4–1	2–1	4–0	2–3	5–1	1–2	3–0	4–1	2–1	1–0
3 Boston Town	1–2	2–1		1–3	2–2	1–1	5–1	0–2	0–5	0–1	0–0	4–0	1–2	2–1	0–3	1–0	0–1	1–0	0–4
4 Cogenhoe United	2–1	0–0	1–0		0–0	3–1	4–0	1–0	2–1	1–2	3–2	6–1	1–2	2–1	2–5	1–0	0–0	6–1	3–0
5 Deeping Rangers	6–3	2–3	1–1	0–2		5–1	2–0	4–0	1–1	6–1	4–0	3–1	1–1	2–0	1–2	4–0	3–0	4–1	2–2
6 Desborough Town	1–1	0–2	2–0	0–2	1–8		2–0	2–1	1–1	3–2	1–3	2–0	0–1	2–1	2–6	2–4	2–3	3–0	2–4
7 Harborough Town	1–0	0–6	1–3	1–2	1–2	0–2		2–2	0–4	1–1	1–0	0–2	2–1	1–0	0–4	1–0	0–2	0–3	0–2
8 Holbeach United	3–0	1–3	2–2	0–1	2–3	2–1	3–2		2–3	5–0	3–1	5–2	1–1	5–0	0–5	3–0	4–2	0–4	0–3
9 Huntingdon Town	6–2	1–0	2–1	1–1	2–1	1–1	3–0	2–1		5–1	3–0	3–2	4–0	2–1	2–0	8–1	2–3	3–2	1–0
10 Long Buckby	3–3	0–1	1–0	0–3	2–7	0–0	2–0	1–4	1–2		6–1	1–1	1–1	1–3	0–5	4–4	1–1	5–1	0–2
11 Newport Pagnell Town	0–1	1–2	0–0	0–4	3–8	3–3	1–1	4–1	0–2	3–2		1–0	3–2	0–1	0–3	0–0	1–0	1–2	2–3
12 Northampton Sileby Rangers	1–2	1–7	2–1	2–1	0–7	2–4	3–2	1–1	2–2	3–0	3–0		0–4	2–2	0–6	1–1	0–5	1–3	0–3
13 Peterborough Northern Star	0–0	1–1	3–2	2–0	0–4	1–2	0–0	2–3	3–2	0–0	3–0	1–1		2–3	0–2	3–2	1–1	0–4	0–1
14 Sleaford Town	1–2	1–2	1–1	0–0	2–8	1–1	2–3	2–0	2–3	3–3	4–2	2–1	3–3		1–2	3–0	3–1	2–4	0–3
15 Spalding United	4–2	1–2	12–0	1–0	3–0	3–0	4–0	2–0	1–2	2–0	4–0	3–1	2–0	3–0		4–0	1–0	2–0	2–1
16 Stewarts & Lloyds Corby	1–6	0–3	0–4	1–9	1–3	0–1	1–3	1–1	0–9	1–2	0–5	1–0	0–2	0–2	0–7		2–1	1–6	0–3
17 Wellingborough Town	3–0	1–4	6–2	1–2	2–1	1–2	2–2	2–1	1–1	6–0	3–1	1–1	3–2	1–0	2–3	1–0		1–3	1–2
18 Wisbech Town	4–1	1–1	1–1	1–1	1–2	3–0	2–0	0–2	0–4	4–1	3–1	4–1	2–1	3–4	1–1	7–0	1–3		1–3
19 Yaxley	1–1	1–2	2–2	1–3	3–1	2–0	2–1	3–1	2–2	2–0	6–0	0–2	2–3	1–0	1–4	4–1	1–0	1–2	

UNITED COUNTIES LEAGUE - STEP 5/6

DIVISION ONE	P	W	D	L	F	A	GD	Pts
1 (P) Oadby Town	42	34	7	1	159	37	122	109
2 (P) Eynesbury Rovers	42	31	5	6	118	41	77	98
3 (P) Harrowby United	42	28	8	6	115	53	62	92
4 Northampton Spencer	42	23	10	9	82	42	40	79
5 Lutterworth Athletic (-3pts)	42	25	3	14	90	65	25	75
6 Northampton ON Chenecks	42	21	10	11	90	64	26	73
7 Olney Town (-3pts)	42	20	7	15	86	68	18	64
8 Burton Park Wanderers	42	18	10	14	78	61	17	64
9 St Neots Town Saints	42	17	10	15	81	66	15	61
10 Potton United	42	18	7	17	82	78	4	61
11 Buckingham Town	42	18	7	17	59	76	-17	61
12 Raunds Town	42	15	13	14	60	59	1	58
13 Thrapston Town	42	16	9	17	81	84	-3	57
14 Rushden and Higham United	42	13	12	17	65	60	5	51
15 Rothwell Corinthians	42	12	9	21	68	88	-20	45
16 Peterborough Sports	42	11	11	20	82	82	0	44
17 Wellingborough Whitworth	42	12	8	22	78	89	-11	44
18 Bugbrooke St Michaels	42	13	3	26	75	102	-27	42
19 Irchester United	42	11	9	22	49	87	-38	42
20 Blackstones	42	12	5	25	66	102	-36	41
21 Bourne Town	42	8	7	27	66	126	-60	31
22 Woodford United	42	1	0	41	23	223	-200	3

RESERVE DIVISION	P	W	D	L	F	A	GD	Pts
1 Cogenhoe United Reserves	38	34	3	1	150	27	123	105
2 Peterborough Northern Star Reserves	38	31	4	3	122	34	88	97
3 Eynesbury Rovers Reserves	38	22	9	7	89	65	24	75
4 Oadby Town Reserves (-6pts)	38	22	9	7	90	55	35	69
5 Bugbrooke St Michaels Reserves	38	19	5	14	82	65	17	62
6 Rothwell Corinthians Reserves	38	18	5	15	80	62	18	59
7 Desborough Town Reserves	38	18	3	17	89	86	3	57
8 Harborough Town Reserves	38	18	2	18	96	77	19	56
9 Northampton ON Chenecks Res.(-1pt)	38	14	13	11	72	73	-1	54
10 Wellingborough Whitworth Reserves	38	17	2	19	80	106	-26	53
11 Huntingdon Town Reserves	38	15	6	17	85	88	-3	51
12 Bourne Town Reserves	38	14	3	21	72	82	-10	45
13 Rushden and Higham United Res.	38	14	3	21	70	106	-36	45
14 Irchester United Reserves (-3pts)	38	14	4	20	70	85	-15	43
15 Thrapston Town Reserves	38	12	7	19	66	84	-18	43
16 Northampton Spencer Reserves	38	12	5	21	64	81	-17	41
17 Stewarts & Lloyds Corby Reserves	38	11	7	20	67	95	-28	40
18 Olney Town Reserves	38	10	7	21	68	87	-19	37
19 Long Buckby AFC Reserves	38	8	3	27	45	108	-63	27
20 Raunds Town Reserves	38	6	2	30	46	137	-91	20

DIVISION ONE	1	2	3	4	5	6	7	8	9	10	11	12	13	14	15	16	17	18	19	20	21	22
1 Blackstones		1–1	3–1	0–2	0–5	1–4	2–4	1–2	2–0	0–4	0–2	0–2	1–2	3–3	0–3	3–1	1–2	2–1	2–3	1–4	5–3	1–2
2 Bourne Town	5–5		4–2	0–1	0–0	0–2	0–3	5–3	1–3	1–3	2–5	2–4	3–3	2–6	0–2	2–2	1–2	0–0	2–3	1–1	3–5	4–2
3 Buckingham Town	3–0	4–0		1–0	2–0	0–3	0–3	2–1	1–2	2–2	0–3	2–4	2–1	0–2	1–4	1–1	2–0	1–1	3–1	2–1	0–0	2–0
4 Bugbrooke St Michaels	5–2	0–5	3–4		1–2	2–1	1–3	2–1	2–3	3–1	1–2	1–8	1–2	1–5	2–1	2–3	3–3	1–4	3–0	1–2	3–0	7–1
5 Burton Park Wanderers	0–1	4–2	0–1	1–0		1–1	2–3	2–1	3–1	1–1	0–0	3–2	3–1	1–0	2–4	1–1	0–1	0–3	4–4	2–2	0–1	4–1
6 Eynesbury Rovers	7–1	4–0	1–1	2–0	0–1		2–2	2–0	2–1	4–1	3–2	1–2	2–0	2–1	4–1	4–1	5–1	3–0	5–0	2–0	3–1	6–0
7 Harrowby United	5–1	6–2	7–2	5–0	1–0	0–2		2–2	1–2	1–1	0–1	2–2	4–3	5–2	3–1	4–1	2–1	1–1	0–0	2–1	4–1	4–0
8 Irchester United	0–3	1–2	0–2	1–1	2–1	1–4	0–1		1–4	3–3	0–3	2–2	2–1	4–2	2–3	0–4	1–1	2–1	0–1	2–1	1–1	1–0
9 Lutterworth Athletic	4–1	3–1	2–1	3–1	0–2	1–3	1–4	2–3		5–1	1–2	3–6	0–4	0–0	3–1	2–1	2–0	2–2	3–0	0–1	2–0	8–0
10 Northampton ON Chenecks	2–1	1–2	2–1	3–2	0–1	4–1	0–2	2–0	2–1		1–1	0–1	0–2	1–0	3–2	3–2	2–2	1–1	2–0	1–1	2–0	6–0
11 Northampton Spencer	2–0	2–0	4–0	2–0	0–2	1–3	1–3	1–1	5–1	0–2		0–1	3–0	1–1	1–0	1–0	4–2	0–0	5–0	2–0	1–0	3–1
12 Oadby Town	2–2	10–0	9–1	6–2	8–0	3–0	1–1	9–0	4–0	6–1	3–0		4–0	2–1	5–1	2–0	3–0	2–2	1–1	5–1	2–0	3–0
13 Olney Town	2–4	3–1	0–2	3–2	1–0	0–5	2–0	1–2	1–2	2–0	1–3	2–3		2–2	3–1	2–2	1–1	2–1	1–0	5–1	1–3	7–0
14 Peterborough Sports	0–2	1–0	3–0	2–4	3–2	1–2	1–2	1–2	0–3	3–3	2–4	1–4	2–3		2–2	3–2	2–2	0–0	1–3	5–1	1–1	9–0
15 Potton United	2–0	5–3	4–1	0–2	1–3	2–2	2–2	2–0	1–2	3–4	1–0	2–5	1–1	3–0		2–2	2–1	1–3	0–3	2–1	3–1	4–1
16 Raunds Town	2–1	4–1	0–0	2–0	0–0	0–4	0–1	1–0	1–2	0–3	2–1	0–0	0–0	1–1	1–0		2–1	2–1	1–1	2–1	2–1	1–0
17 Rothwell Corinthians	3–4	4–1	1–2	4–2	0–4	0–0	6–2	1–1	1–4	0–6	1–1	0–2	2–2	1–3	0–2	0–3		6–3	0–2	1–4	1–2	4–1
18 Rushden & Higham United	1–0	1–0	1–2	5–3	1–1	0–1	1–4	3–1	0–1	2–2	2–2	2–0	0–3	3–2	1–1	2–0	0–1		0–2	0–2	1–2	5–0
19 St Neots Town Saints	1–3	6–2	0–2	2–2	6–2	2–1	3–6	2–0	0–0	1–3	1–1	0–1	0–1	0–0	6–1	1–1	1–2	2–1		0–0	3–0	5–0
20 Thrapston Town	4–0	7–1	1–1	3–0	2–2	2–5	2–1	3–0	0–4	2–1	1–1	0–8	1–6	5–1	0–3	2–2	0–3	0–4	2–1		2–2	10–1
21 Wellingborough Whitworth	1–1	0–1	2–1	2–1	2–3	3–7	0–3	2–2	2–3	2–3	3–3	1–2	1–3	3–2	2–2	3–1	1–0	0–1	2–6	1–2		16–0
22 Woodford United	0–5	2–3	0–1	2–5	0–13	1–3	0–6	0–1	1–4	0–7	0–6	2–8	1–6	0–5	0–4	0–6	2–6	0–6	0–8	0–5	2–5	

LEAGUE CUP continued...

ROUND 2

Wisbech Town	v	Huntingdon Town	1-2
Rothwell Corinthians	v	AFC Kempston Rovers	1-1, 5-4p
Spalding United	v	Boston Town	2-3
Woodford United	v	Potton United	1-3
Cogenhoe United	v	Lutterworth Athletic	1-1, 2-3p
Wellingborough Town	v	Northampton Spencer	2-1
Deeping Rangers	v	Wellingborough Whitworth	9-1
Ischester United	v	Oadby Town	0-5

QUARTER FINALS

Huntingdon Town	v	Rothwell Corinthians	2-0
Boston Town	v	Potton United	3-0
Lutterworth Athletic	v	Wellingborough Town	1-4
Deeping Rangers	v	Oadby Town	5-1

SEMI FINALS

Huntingdon Town	v	Boston Town	5-0
Wellingborough Town	v	Deeping Rangers	0-5

FINAL

Huntingdon Town	v	Deeping Rangers	5-4 aet

CLUB MOVEMENTS

Premier Division - In: Eynesbury Rovers (P). Harrowby United (P). Oadby Town (P).
Thurnby Nirvana (P - East Midland Counties).
Out: Spalding United (P - Northern Premier Div.1 South). Stewarts & Lloyds Corby (R).

Division One - In: Stewarts & Lloyds Corby (R).
Out: Eynesbury Rovers (P). Harrowby United (P). Oadby Town (P).

A.F.C. KEMPSTON ROVERS

Founded: 1884 Nickname: Walnut Boys

Secretary: Kevin Howlett **(T)** 07721 849 671 **(E)** howlett.home@btinternet.com
Chairman: Russell Shreeves **Prog Ed:** Mark Kennett
Ground: Hillgrounds Leisure, Hillgrounds Road, Kempston, Bedford MK42 8SZ **(T)** 01234 852 346
Capacity: 2,000 **Seats:** 100 **Covered:** 250 **Midweek Matchday:** Tuesday **Clubhouse:** Yes

Colours(change): Red & white stripes/black/black
Previous Names: Kempston Rovers > 2004.
Previous Leagues: South Midlands 1927-53
Records:
Senior Honours: U.C.L. Prem. 1973-74, Div 1 1957-58, 85-86, Div 2 1955-56, KO Cup 1955-56, 57-58, 59-60, 74-75, 76-77. UCL Division One 2010-11. Beds Senior Cup 1908-09, 37-38, 76-77, 91-92. Hinchingbrooke Cup 2010-11.

10 YEAR RECORD

04-05	05-06	06-07	07-08	08-09	09-10	10-11	11-12	12-13	13-14
UCL 1 16	UCL 1 4	UCL 1 3	UCL P 12	UCL 1 5	UCL 1 5	UCL 1 1	UCL P 10	UCL P 17	UCL P 12

A.F.C. RUSHDEN & DIAMONDS

Founded: 2011 Nickname:

Secretary: Miss Stephanie Webb **(T)** 07753 752 908 **(E)** secretary@afcdiamonds.com
Chairman: Ralph Burditt **Manager:** Andy Peaks **Prog Ed:** Miss Stephanie Webb
Ground: The Dog and Duck, London Road, Wellingborough, Northants NN8 2DP **(T)** 01933 441 388
Capacity: **Seats:** Yes **Covered:** Yes **Midweek Matchday:** **Clubhouse:** Yes

Colours(change): White with red & blue trim/royal blue/white (Yellow with black trim/yellow/yellow)
Previous Names: None
Previous Leagues: None
Records:
Senior Honours: None

10 YEAR RECORD

04-05	05-06	06-07	07-08	08-09	09-10	10-11	11-12	12-13	13-14
								UCL 1 2	UCL P 3

BOSTON TOWN

Founded: 1964 Nickname: Poachers

Secretary: Edward Graves **(T)** 07963 418 434 **(E)** btfcsec@hotmail.co.uk
Chairman: Mick Vines **Manager:** Nathon Collins **Prog Ed:** Eddie Graves
Ground: Tattershall Road, Boston, Lincs PE21 9LR **(T)** 01205 365 470
Capacity: 6,000 **Seats:** 450 **Covered:** 950 **Midweek Matchday:** Tuesday **Clubhouse:** Yes

Colours(change): Blue & white stripes/blue/blue
Previous Names: Boston > 1994
Previous Leagues: Lincs, Central Alliance, Eastern co, Midland N. Co. E, C. Mids
Records: **Att:** 2,700 v Boston United FA Cup 1970. **Goalscorer:** Gary Bull 57 during 2006-07 season.
Senior Honours: Midland League 1974-75, 78-79, 80-81. Central Midlands 88-89. United Counties League 1994-95, 2000-01.

10 YEAR RECORD

04-05	05-06	06-07	07-08	08-09	09-10	10-11	11-12	12-13	13-14
UCL P 11	UCL P 6	UCL P 2	UCL P 6	UCL P 5	UCL P 5	UCL P 7	UCL P 14	UCL P 10	UCL P 14

COGENHOE UNITED

Founded: 1958 Nickname: Cooks

Secretary: Lewis Sander **(T)** 07835 951 091 **(E)** secretary@cogenhoeunited.co.uk
Chairman: Derek Wright **Prog Ed:** Brian Kempster
Ground: Compton Park, Brafield Road, Cogenhoe NN7 1ND **(T)** 01604 890 521
Capacity: 5,000 **Seats:** 100 **Covered:** 200 **Midweek Matchday:** Tuesday **Clubhouse:** Yes **Shop:** No

Colours(change): Blue/blue/white
Previous Names:
Previous Leagues: Central Northants Comb, prem 67-84
Records: **Att:** 1,000 Charity game 90 **Goalscorer & Appearances:** Tony Smith
Senior Honours: United Counties League 2004-05. Buckingham Charity Cup 2010-11.

10 YEAR RECORD

04-05	05-06	06-07	07-08	08-09	09-10	10-11	11-12	12-13	13-14
UCL P 1	UCL P 5	UCL P 5	UCL P 9	UCL P 9	UCL P 8	UCL P 15	UCL P 12	UCL P 8	UCL P 5

DEEPING RANGERS

Founded: 1964 Nickname: Rangers

Secretary: TBC **(T)** **(E)**

Chairman: Kevin Davenport **Manager:** Tuncay Korkmaz **Prog Ed:** Robin Crowson

Ground: Deeping Sports Club, Outgang Road, Market Deeping, PE6 8LQ **(T)** 01778 344 701

Capacity: 1,000 **Seats:** 180 **Covered:** 250 **Midweek Matchday:** Tuesday **Clubhouse:** Yes

Colours(change): Claret & blue/blue/claret.
Previous Names: None
Previous Leagues: Peterborough & District 1966 - 1999.
Records:
Senior Honours: Lincs Sen Cup, B Cup, Peterborough FA Cup (3). UCL Premier Champions 2006-07

10 YEAR RECORD

04-05	05-06	06-07	07-08	08-09	09-10	10-11	11-12	12-13	13-14
UCL P 12	UCL P 20	UCL P 1	UCL P 7	UCL P 4	UCL P 4	UCL P 14	UCL P 4	UCL P 5	UCL P 4

DESBOROUGH TOWN

Founded: 1896 Nickname: Ar Tam

Secretary: John Lee **(T)** 01536 760 002 **(E)** johnlee@froggerycottage85.fsnet.co.uk

Chairman: Ernie Parsons **Manager:** Ian Walker **Prog Ed:** John Lee

Ground: Waterworks Field, Braybrooke Rd, Desborough NN14 2LJ **(T)** 01536 761 350

Capacity: 8,000 **Seats:** 250 **Covered:** 500 **Midweek Matchday:** Tuesday **Clubhouse:** Yes

Colours(change): All royal blue
Previous Names: None
Previous Leagues: None
Records: **Att:** 8,000 v Kettering Town
Senior Honours: N'hants/Utd Co. Champs 1900-01, 01-02, 06-07, 20-21, 23-24, 24-25, 27-28, 48-49, 66-67. Lge C 77-78, 00-01, 07-08.
N'hants Sen C 1910-11, 13-14, 28-29, 51-52. Northants Senior Cup 1910-11, 13-14, 28-29, 51-52.

10 YEAR RECORD

04-05	05-06	06-07	07-08	08-09	09-10	10-11	11-12	12-13	13-14
UCL P 10	UCL P 18	UCL P 14	UCL P 3	UCL P 11	UCL P 18	UCL P 19	UCL P 16	UCL P 11	UCL P 10

EYNESBURY ROVERS

Founded: 1897 Nickname: Rovers

Secretary: Catherine Watts **(T)** 07787 567 338 **(E)** cathywatts17@hotmail.com

Chairman: Brian Barnes **Manager:** Martin Field & Matt Plumb **Prog Ed:** Graham Mills

Ground: Alfred Hall Memorial Ground, Hall Road, Eynesbury, St Neots PE19 2SF **(T)** 07938 511 581uc

Capacity: **Seats:** **Covered:** **Midweek Matchday:** **Clubhouse:**

Colours(change): Royal & white stripes/royal/royal
Previous Names: None
Previous Leagues: United Counties 1946-52. Eastern Counties 1952-63.
Records: **Att:** 5,000 v Fulham 1953 (Stanley Matthews guested for Eynesbury).
Senior Honours: United Counties Division 1 1976-77.
Huntingdonshire Senior Cup x11. Huntingdonshire Premier Cup 1950-51, 90-91, 95-96.

10 YEAR RECORD

04-05	05-06	06-07	07-08	08-09	09-10	10-11	11-12	12-13	13-14
UCL 1 11	UCL 1 7	UCL 1 10	UCL 1 13	UCL 1 7	UCL 1 3	UCL 1 6	UCL 1 6	UCL 1 3	UCL 1 2

HARBOROUGH TOWN

Founded: 1976 Nickname:

Secretary: Pauline Winston **(T)** 07446 415 329 **(E)** p.winston2402@btinternet.com

Chairman: Andrew Winston **Prog Ed:** Gary Wainwright

Ground: Bowden's Park, Northampton Road, Market Harborough, Leics. LE16 9HF **(T)** 01858 467 339

Capacity: **Seats:** Yes **Covered:** Yes **Midweek Matchday:** Tuesday **Clubhouse:** Yes

Colours(change): Yellow & black stripes/black/yellow & black
Previous Names:
Previous Leagues: Northants Combination
Records:
Senior Honours: Northants Combination 2009-10.

10 YEAR RECORD

04-05	05-06	06-07	07-08	08-09	09-10	10-11	11-12	12-13	13-14
					NhCo 1	UCL 1 17	UCL 1 2	UCL P 19	UCL P 17

HARROWBY UNITED

Founded: 1949 Nickname: The Arrows

Secretary: Michael Atter **(T)** 07742 077 474 **(E)** mjproperty@fsmail.net
Chairman: Ian Weatherstone **Manager:** Mark Fardell & Jason Harrison **Prog Ed:** Craig Whyley
Ground: Harrowby Lane Playing Fields, Harrowby Lane, Grantham, Lincs NG31 9QY **(T)** 01476 401 201
Capacity: **Seats:** **Covered:** **Midweek Matchday:** **Clubhouse:**

Colours(change): Red/black/black
Previous Names: Harrowby United 1949-2009. Grantham Rangers 2009-2010. Reformed as Harrowby United in 2012.
Previous Leagues: Grantham 1949-66, 2006-07. Central Alliance. East Midlands Regional. UCL 1990-06. Lincolnshire 2007-08. C.Mids 2007-10.
Records:
Senior Honours: United Counties Division One 1991-92.
Lincolnshire Junior Cup 2011-12.

10 YEAR RECORD

04-05	05-06	06-07	07-08	08-09	09-10	10-11	11-12	12-13	13-14
UCL P 5	UCL P 22		Lincs 16	CM Su 17	CM Su 18			UCL 1 6	UCL 1 3

HOLBEACH UNITED

Founded: 1929 Nickname: Tigers

Secretary: Karl Fawcett **(T)** 07955 947 606 **(E)** holbeachunitedfc@yahoo.co.uk
Chairman: Dave Dougill **Manager:** John Chand **Prog Ed:** Jamie Hiller
Ground: Carters Park, Park Road, Holbeach, Lincs PE12 7EE **(T)** 01406 424 761
Capacity: 4,000 **Seats:** 200 **Covered:** 450 **Midweek Matchday:** Tuesday **Clubhouse:** Yes **Shop:** No

Colours(change): Yellow with black trim/black/yellow (All blue or White with red trim/red/white)
Previous Names:
Previous Leagues: Peterborough U Co L 46-55, Eastern 55-62, Midland Co 62-63
Records: **Att:** 4,094 v Wisbech 1954
Senior Honours: United Counties League 1989-90, 02-03, 12-13. Lincs Sen A Cup (4), Senior Cup B 57-58
Lincolnshire Senior Trophy 2011-12, 12-13.

10 YEAR RECORD

04-05	05-06	06-07	07-08	08-09	09-10	10-11	11-12	12-13	13-14
UCL P 3	UCL P 17	UCL P 11	UCL P 11	UCL P 16	UCL P 16	UCL P 17	UCL P 6	UCL P 1	UCL P 11

HUNTINGDON TOWN

Founded: 1995 Nickname:

Secretary: Russell Yezek **(T)** 07974 664 818 **(E)** russell.yezek@ntlworld.com
Chairman: Paul Hunt **Manager:** Seb Hayes **Prog Ed:** Gemmy Beeny
Ground: Jubilee Park, Kings Ripton Road,, Huntingdon, Cambridgeshire PE28 2NR **(T)** 07974 664 818
Capacity: **Seats:** **Covered:** **Midweek Matchday:** **Clubhouse:**

Colours(change): Red & black stripes/red/red & black.(Red/red/red & black)
Previous Names:
Previous Leagues: Cambridgeshire.
Records:
Senior Honours: Cambridgeshire Div.1B 1999-2000. Hunts. Junior Cup 1999-00, 2000-01, 01-02. Hunts Scott Gatty Cup 2001-02.
United Counties League Division One 2011-12.

10 YEAR RECORD

04-05	05-06	06-07	07-08	08-09	09-10	10-11	11-12	12-13	13-14
UCL 1 14	UCL 1 12	UCL 1 14	UCL 1 4	UCL 1 14	UCL 1 8	UCL 1 5	UCL 1 1	UCL P 4	UCL P 2

LONG BUCKBY AFC

Founded: 1937 Nickname: Bucks

Secretary: Dave Austin **(T)** 07701 723 477 **(E)** lbafc.dja@gmail.com
Chairman: Dave Austin
Ground: Station Road, Long Buckby NN6 7QA **(T)** 07749 393 045
Capacity: 1,000 **Seats:** 200 **Covered:** 200 **Midweek Matchday:** Tuesday **Clubhouse:** Yes **Shop:** No

Colours(change): All maroon (All yellow)
Previous Names: Long Buckby Nomads
Previous Leagues: Rugby & District Central, Northants Combination pre 68
Records: **Att:** 750 v Kettering Town
Senior Honours: United Counties League Div.2 1970-71, 71-72, Premier Division 2011-12. Northants Senior Cup 2008-09. Munsell Cup 2009.

10 YEAR RECORD

04-05	05-06	06-07	07-08	08-09	09-10	10-11	11-12	12-13	13-14
UCL P 8	UCL P 21	UCL P 12	UCL P 2	UCL P 8	UCL P 3	UCL P 4	UCL P 1	UCL P 16	UCL P 18

NEWPORT PAGNELL TOWN

Founded: 1963 Nickname: Swans

Secretary: Mrs Pauline Wooldridge **(T)** 07966 441 992 **(E)** julieandsteveh1@sky.com
Chairman: Mike Stanton **Prog Ed:** Ben Sharpe
Ground: Willen Road, Newport Pagnell MK16 0DF **(T)** 01908 611 993
Capacity: 2,000 **Seats:** 100 **Covered:** 100 **Midweek Matchday:** Tuesday **Clubhouse:** Yes **Shop:** No

Colours(change): White & green hoops/white/white
Previous Names: Newport Pagnell Wanderers > 1972.
Previous Leagues: North Bucks 1963-71. South Midlands 1971-73.
Records:
Senior Honours: United Counties League Div.1 1981-82, 2001-02. Bucks & Berks Intermediate Cup 2001-02. Berks & Bucks Senior Trophy 2009-10, 10-11.

10 YEAR RECORD

04-05	05-06	06-07	07-08	08-09	09-10	10-11	11-12	12-13	13-14
UCL P 18	UCL P 15	UCL P 7	UCL P 15	UCL P 3	UCL P 6	UCL P 3	UCL P 5	UCL P 6	UCL P 16

NORTHAMPTON SILEBY RANGERS

Founded: 1968 Nickname: Sileby

Secretary: Dave King **(T)** 07783 150 082 **(E)** david@djbattams.f2s.com
Chairman: Robert Clarke **Manager:** Daren Young **Prog Ed:** Dave Battams
Ground: Fernie Fields Sports Ground, Moulton, Northampton NN3 7BD **(T)** 01604 670366
Capacity: **Seats:** Yes **Covered:** Yes **Midweek Matchday:** Wednesday **Clubhouse:** Yes

Colours(change): Red/black/red (All navy blue)
Previous Names: Northampton Vanaid > 2000.
Previous Leagues: Northampton League > 1993.
Records: **Att:** 78.
Senior Honours: Northampton Town League 1988-89 89-90. UCL Div 1 1993-94, 2002-03, 04-05, 12-13.

10 YEAR RECORD

04-05	05-06	06-07	07-08	08-09	09-10	10-11	11-12	12-13	13-14
UCL 1 1	UCL 1 13	UCL 1 12	UCL 1 12	UCL 1 3	UCL 1 9	UCL 1 9	UCL 1 16	UCL 1 1	UCL P 15

OADBY TOWN

Founded: 1937 Nickname: The Poachers

Secretary: Rob Farrar **(T)** 07833 431 945 **(E)** robfarrar@btinternet.com
Chairman: Brian Fletcher-Warington **Manager:** Steve Walker **Prog Ed:** Books Indesign
Ground: Freeway Park, Wigston Road, Oadby LE2 5QG **(T)** 01162 715 728
Capacity: 5,000 **Seats:** 224 **Covered:** 224 **Midweek Matchday:** Tuesday **Clubhouse:** Yes **Shop:** Yes

Colours(change): White & red/red/red (All blue or all orange)
Previous Names: Oadby Imperial > 1951.
Previous Leagues: Leicestershire Senior. Midland Alliance > 2011. East Midlands Counties 2011-12.
Records:
Senior Honours: Leicestershire Senior Div.2 1951-52. Prem 63-64, 67-68, 68-69, 72-73, 94-95, 96-97, 97-98, 98-99. Midland Alliance 99-00. United Counties Division One 2013-14.

10 YEAR RECORD

04-05	05-06	06-07	07-08	08-09	09-10	10-11	11-12	12-13	13-14
MidAl 7	MidAl 18	MidAl 11	MidAl 17	MidAl 19	MidAl 14	MidAl 22	EMC 3	UCL 1 4	UCL 1 1

PETERBOROUGH NORTHERN STAR

Founded: 1900 Nickname:

Secretary: Glen Harper **(T)** 07884 288 756 **(E)** ghdjfc@hotmail.com
Chairman: Tony Zirpolo **Prog Ed:** Rodney Payne
Ground: Chestnut Ave, Dogsthorpe, Eye, Peterborough, Cambs PE1 4PE **(T)** 01733 552 416
Capacity: 1,500 **Seats:** none **Covered:** yes **Midweek Matchday:** Wednesday **Clubhouse:** Yes

Colours(change): Black & white stripes/black/black
Previous Names: Eye Utd >2005
Previous Leagues: Peterborough Lge >2003
Records:
Senior Honours: Peterborough League 2002-03. Hinchingbrooke Cup 2009-10. United Counties League Division One 2008-09. UCL Knock-out Cup 2010-11.

10 YEAR RECORD

04-05	05-06	06-07	07-08	08-09	09-10	10-11	11-12	12-13	13-14
UCL 1 4	UCL 1 9	UCL 1 5	UCL 1 2	UCL 1 1	UCL 1 2	UCL P 6	UCL P 7	UCL P 13	UCL P 9

SLEAFORD TOWN

Founded: 1968 Nickname: Town

Secretary: Ms Jenny O'Rourke **(T)** 07777 604 325 **(E)** jennyorourke@btinternet.com
Chairman: Brian Rowland **Manager:** Kris Jones **Prog Ed:** Kris Jones
Ground: Eslaforde Park, Boston Road, Sleaford, Lincs NG34 9GH **(T)** 01529 415 951
Capacity: **Seats:** 88 **Covered:** 88 **Midweek Matchday:** Tuesday **Clubhouse:** Yes

Colours(change): Green/black/green
Previous Names:
Previous Leagues: Lincolnshire
Records:
Senior Honours: United Counties League Division One 2005-06.

10 YEAR RECORD

04-05	05-06	06-07	07-08	08-09	09-10	10-11	11-12	12-13	13-14
UCL 1 6	UCL 1 1	UCL 1 2	UCL P 14	UCL P 15	UCL P 9	UCL P 18	UCL P 19	UCL P 18	UCL P 13

THURNBY NIRVANA

Founded: 2008 Nickname:

Secretary: Zak Hajat **(T)** 07811 843 136 **(E)** nirvanafc@hotmail.com
Chairman: Kirk Master **Manager:** Damion Qualiey **Prog Ed:** Bookindesign
Ground: Dakyn Road, Thurnby Lodge, Leicester LE5 2ED **(T)** 0116 243 3308
Capacity: **Seats:** **Covered:** Yes **Midweek Matchday:** **Clubhouse:**

Colours(change): All green (All red)
Previous Names: Thurnby Rangers and Leicester Nirvana merged to form today's club in 2008.
Previous Leagues: Leicestershire Senior. East Midland Counties > 2014
Records:
Senior Honours: Leicestershire Senior Premier Division 2004-05. East Midland Counties 2013-14.

10 YEAR RECORD

04-05	05-06	06-07	07-08	08-09	09-10	10-11	11-12	12-13	13-14
LeicS 1	LeicS 4	LeicS 5	LeicS 18	LeicS 6	LeicS 3	EMC 9	EMC 7	EMC 3	EMC 1

WELLINGBOROUGH TOWN

Founded: 2004 Nickname: Doughboys

Secretary: Mick Walden **(T)** 07817 841 752 **(E)** mwalden@dsl.pipex.com
Chairman: Martin Potton **Manager:** Ben Watts **Prog Ed:** Neil Morris
Ground: The Dog & Duck, London Road, Wellingborough NN8 2DP **(T)** 01933 441 388
Capacity: **Seats:** Yes **Covered:** Yes **Midweek Matchday:** Tuesday **Clubhouse:** Yes

Colours(change): Yellow/royal blue/royal blue. (Red & black stripes/black/black)
Previous Names: Original team (Formed 1867) folded in 2002 reforming in 2004
Previous Leagues: Metropolitan. Southern.
Records:
Senior Honours: United Counties League 1964-65.

10 YEAR RECORD

04-05	05-06	06-07	07-08	08-09	09-10	10-11	11-12	12-13	13-14
	UCL 1 2	UCL P 3	UCL P 10	UCL P 18	UCL P 11	UCL P 5	UCL P 8	UCL P 15	UCL P 8

WISBECH TOWN

Founded: 1920 Nickname: Fenmen

Secretary: Gavin Clarey **(T)** 07919 100 060 **(E)** gavclarey@hotmail.co.uk
Chairman: Barry Carter **Manager:** Dick Creasey **Prog Ed:** Spencer Larham
Ground: The Fenland Stadium, Lynn Road, Wisbech PE14 7AL **(T)** 01945 581 511
Capacity: **Seats:** 118 **Covered:** Yes **Midweek Matchday:** Tuesday **Clubhouse:** Yes

Colours(change): All red. (Yellow/green/yellow).
Previous Names: None
Previous Leagues: Peterborough 1920-35. UCL 1935-50. EC 1950-52, 70-97, 2003-13. Midland 1952-58. Southern 1958-70, 97-2002.
Records: **Att:** 8,044 v Peterborough Utd, Midland Lge 25/08/1957 **Goalscorer:** Bert Titmarsh - 246 (1931-37) **Apps:** Jamie Brighty - 731
Senior Honours: United Counties League Champions 1946-47, 47-48. Southern League Division 1 1961-62.
Eastern Counties League 1971-72, 76-77, 90-91, League Cup 2010-11. East Anglian Cup 1987-88.

10 YEAR RECORD

04-05	05-06	06-07	07-08	08-09	09-10	10-11	11-12	12-13	13-14
ECP 16	ECP 4	ECP 11	ECP 12	ECP 16	ECP 11	ECP 4	ECP 4	ECP 2	UCL P 7

YAXLEY

Founded: 1900 Nickname: The Cuckoos

Secretary: Mrs Sandra Cole **(T)** 07847 123 898 **(E)** sandracole22@ntlworld.com

Chairman: Alan Andrews **Manager:** Brett Whaley **Prog Ed:** Jeff Lenton

Ground: Leading Drove, Holme Road, Yaxley, Peterborough PE7 3NA **(T)** 01733 244 928

Capacity: 1,000 **Seats:** 150 **Covered:** yes **Midweek Matchday:** Tuesday **Clubhouse:** Yes **Shop:** Yes

Colours(change): All blue (All red).
Previous Names: Yaxley Rovers.
Previous Leagues: Peterborough & Dist., Hunts & West Anglia
Records: **Goalscorer:** Ricky Hailstone 16
Senior Honours: United Counties League Division One 1996-97. Hunts Senior Cup (7), UCL Cup 2005-2006

10 YEAR RECORD

04-05	05-06	06-07	07-08	08-09	09-10	10-11	11-12	12-13	13-14
UCL P 4	UCL P 7	UCL P 15	UCL P 16	UCL P 14	UCL P 19	UCL P 16	UCL P 18	UCL P 12	UCL P 6

Eynesbury Rovers with the United Counties Division One Runners-up Pennant and medals.
Photo: Gordon Whittington.

BLACKSTONES

Founded: 1920 Nickname: Stones

Secretary: Ian MacGillivray **(T)** 07749 620 825 **(E)** imacgilli@aol.com
Chairman: Gary Peace **Prog Ed:** Ian MacGillivray
Ground: Lincoln Road, Stamford, Lincs PE9 1SH **(T)** 01780 757 835 **Capacity:** 1,000
Colours(change): White & black/maroon/sky blue (Black & green stripes/black/black)

ADDITIONAL INFORMATION: Record Att: 700 v Glinton
Honours: Lincolnshire Senior Cup A 1992-93, 2003-04. Lincolnshire Senior Trophy 2010-11.

BOURNE TOWN

Founded: 1883 Nickname: Wakes

Secretary: Rob Lambert **(T)** 07933 511 514 **(E)** roblambert51@gmail.com
Chairman: Darren Munton & Steve Elger **Prog Ed:** Rob Lambert
Ground: Abbey Lawn, Abbey Road, Bourne, Lincs PE10 9EN **(T)** 07598 815 357
Colours(change): Red/red/red & black

ADDITIONAL INFORMATION:
Record Att: FA Trophy 1970 **Goalscorer:** David Scotney.
U.C.L. Champions 1968-69, 69-70, 71-72, 90-91. Lincolnshire Senior A Cup 1971-72, 2005-06.

BUCKINGHAM TOWN

Founded: 1883 Nickname: Robins

Secretary: Darren Seaton **(T)** 07808 792 486 **(E)** djrseaton@hotmail.com
Chairman: Vince Hyde **Manager:** Chris Robson **Prog Ed:** Darren Seaton
Ground: Irish Centre, Manor Fields, Bletchley, Milton Keynes MK2 2HX **(T)** 01908 375 978
Colours(change): All red (Yellow/blue/blue)

ADDITIONAL INFORMATION:
Paid: £7,000 to Wealdstone for Steve Jenkins 1992 Received: £1,000 from Kettering Town for Terry Shrieves.
Honours: Southern League Southern Division 1990-91. U.C.L. 1983-84, 85-86. Berks & Bucks Senior Cup 1983-84.

BUGBROOKE ST MICHAELS

Founded: 1929 Nickname: Badgers

Secretary: Graham Connew **(T)** 07799 492 280 **(E)** graybags05@btinternet.com
Chairman: Kevin Gardner **Manager:** Colin Cooper **Prog Ed:** Mrs Debbie Preston
Ground: Birds Close, Gayton Road, Bugbrooke NN7 3RW **(T)** 01604 830 707
Colours(change): White/black/black (Yellow & blue/blue/blue)

ADDITIONAL INFORMATION:
Record Att: 1,156. **Golascorer:** Vince Thomas. **Apps:** Jimmy Nord.
Honours: Northants Junior Cup 1989-90, 2011-12, Central Northants Comb. x6. U.C.L. Division 1 Champions 1998-99.

BURTON PARK WANDERERS

Founded: 1961 Nickname: The Wanderers

Secretary: Dave Borrett **(T)** 07794 959 915 **(E)** daveborrett66@gmail.com
Chairman: Steve Harding **Manager:** Jimmy Simpson **Prog Ed:** Mrs Sam Gordon
Ground: Burton Park, Polwell Lane, Burton Latimer, Northants NN15 5PS **(T)** 07980 013 506
Colours(change): Blue & black stripes/black/black

ADDITIONAL INFORMATION:
Record Att: 253 v Rothwell, May 1989.

IRCHESTER UNITED

Founded: 1883 Nickname: The Romans

Secretary: Glynn Cotter **(T)** 07802 728 736 **(E)** glynn.cotter@btinternet.com
Chairman: Geoff Cotter **Manager:** Steve Sargent **Prog Ed:** Geoff Cotter
Ground: Alfred Street, Irchester NN29 7DR **(T)** 01933 312 877 **Capacity:** 1,000
Colours(change): All blue (All red)

ADDITIONAL INFORMATION:
Northants Lge Div 2 1930-31, 31-32, Rushden & District Lge (9), Northants Jnr Cup 1929-30, 33-34, 48-49, 75-76.
United Counties League Division 1 2009-10.

LUTTERWORTH ATHLETIC

Founded: 1983 Nickname:

Secretary: Lee English **(T)** 07545 432 200 **(E)** mike622@btinternet.com
Chairman: Mick English **Manager:** Lee English & Mike English **Prog Ed:** Eddy Robinson
Ground: Hall Park, Hall Lane, Bitteswell, Lutterworth LE17 4LN **(T)** 07545 432 200
Colours(change): Green & white hoops/white/white (Yellow & black horizontal stripes/black/yellow)

ADDITIONAL INFORMATION:
Previous League: Leicestershire Senior > 2012. East Midlands Counties 2012-13.

NORTHAMPTON O.N. CHENECKS
Founded: 1946 Nickname:

Secretary: Bryan Lewin **(T)** 07920 108 300 **(E)** cytringan@tesco.net
Chairman: Eddie Slinn **Manager:** Graham Cottle **Prog Ed:** Gina Cottle
Ground: Old Northamptonians Sports Ground,Billing Road,Northampton NN1 5RX **(T)** 01604 634 045
Colours(change): White/blue/blue

ADDITIONAL INFORMATION:
Honours: U.C.L. Div 1 1977-78, 79-80. Northants Junior Cup 2009-10.

NORTHAMPTON SPENCER
Founded: 1936 Nickname: Millers

Secretary: Nick Hillery **(T)** 07894 150 853 **(E)**
Chairman: Graham Wrighting **Manager:** Ben Stone **Prog Ed:** Andy Goldsmith
Ground: Kingsthorpe Mill, Studand Road, Northampton NN2 6NE **(T)** 01604 718 898 **Capacity:** 2,000
Colours(change): Green & yellow/green/yellow

ADDITIONAL INFORMATION: Record Att: 800 v Nottingham Forest 1993 **App;** P. Jelley 622 1984-2002
Honours: United Counties League Division One 1984-85. Premier 1991-92. Northants Senior Cup Winners 2005-06.

OLNEY TOWN
Founded: 1903 Nickname: The Nurserymen

Secretary: Andrew Baldwin **(T)** 07932 141 623 **(E)** andew@abaldwin.go-plus.net
Chairman: Paul Tough **Prog Ed:** Paul Tough
Ground: Recreation Ground, East Street, Olney, Bucks MK46 4DW **(T)** 01234 712 227
Colours(change): All green

ADDITIONAL INFORMATION:
Previous League: Rushden & District.
Honours: U.C.L. Div 1 1972-73. Berks & Bucks Intermediate Cup 1992-93.

PETERBOROUGH SPORTS
Founded: 1908 Nickname:

Secretary: John Robinson **(T)** 07894 445 991 **(E)**
Chairman: Stephen Cooper **Manager:** Chris Plummer **Prog Ed:** Stephen Cooper
Ground: 651 Lincoln Road, Peterborough PE1 3HA **(T)** 01733 567 835
Colours(change): All navy blue

ADDITIONAL INFORMATION:
Previous Names: Brotherhoods Engineering Works. Bearings Direct during 1990s.
Previous Leagues: Peterborough & District >2013.

POTTON UNITED
Founded: 1943 Nickname: Royals

Secretary: Mrs Bev Strong **(T)** 07703 442 565 **(E)** bev.strong@tiscali.co.uk
Chairman: Alan Riley **Manager:** Darren Staniforth **Prog Ed:** Mrs Bev Strong
Ground: The Hollow, Bigglewade Road, Potton, Beds SG19 2LU **(T)** 01767 261 100
Colours(change): All blue (Red/black/red)

ADDITIONAL INFORMATION:
Record Att: 470 v Hastings Town, FA Vase 1989.
Honours: U.C.L. 1986-87, 88-89, Div.1 2003-04. Beds Senior Cup x5. Huntingdonshire Premier Cup x4. E.Anglian Cup 1996-97

RAUNDS TOWN
Founded: 1946 Nickname: Shopmates

Secretary: Dave Jones **(T)** 07763 492 184 **(E)** david.jones180@ntlworld.com
Chairman: Mrs Lesley Jones **Prog Ed:** Dave Jones
Ground: Kiln Park, London Rd, Raunds, Northants NN9 6EQ **(T)** 01933 623 351 **Capacity:** 3,000
Colours(change): Red & black stripes/black/black

ADDITIONAL INFORMATION: Record Att: 1500 v Crystal Palace 1991 **Goalscorer:** Shaun Keeble. **App:** Martin Lewis - 355
Honours: Northants Senior Cup 1990-91.

ROTHWELL CORINTHIANS
Founded: 1934 Nickname: Corinthians

Secretary: Mark Budworth **(T)** 07730 416 960 **(E)** mbudworth@budworthhardcastle.com
Chairman: Mick Whittemore **Prog Ed:** David Rhinds
Ground: Sergeants Lawn, Desborough Road, Rothwell, NN14 6JQ **(T)** 01536 711 706
Colours(change): Red & black stripes/black/black (Blue & black stripes/black/black or Black & red/black/black).

ADDITIONAL INFORMATION:

RUSHDEN & HIGHAM UNITED

Founded: Formed: 2007 Nickname:

Secretary: Ms Jo Griffiths **(T)** 07792 902 390 **(E)** griffy05@hotmail.co.uk
Chairman: Ian Lockhart **Manager:** Ady Mann **Prog Ed:** Ms Jo Griffiths
Ground: Hayden Road, Rushden, Northants NN10 0HX **(T)** 01933 410 036
Colours(change): Orange/orange/black

ADDITIONAL INFORMATION:
Club was formed after the merger of Rushden Rangers and Higham Town.

ST NEOTS TOWN SAINTS

Founded: Nickname:

Secretary: Marian Izzard **(T)** 07989 546 466 **(E)** marfrador@yahoo.co.uk
Chairman: Colin Parker **Manager:** Andy Davis **Prog Ed:** Mark Davis
Ground: Rowley Park, Kester Way, St Neots, cambridgshire PE19 6SN **(T)** 01480 470 012
Colours(change): All blue (All red)

ADDITIONAL INFORMATION:

STEWARTS & LLOYDS CORBY

Founded: 1935 Nickname: The Foundrymen

Secretary: John Davies **(T)** 07588 018 397 **(E)** foundrychairman@hotmail.co.uk
Chairman: John Davies **Manager:** Barry Britton **Prog Ed:** John Davies
Ground: Recreation Ground, Occupation Road, Corby NN17 1EH **(T)** 01536 401 497 **Capacity:** 1,500
Colours(change): White & grey/grey/grey

ADDITIONAL INFORMATION: Goalscorer: Joey Martin 46
United Counties League Division One 1973-74, 74-75, Premier 85-86, 08-09.

THRAPSTON TOWN

Founded: 1960 Nickname: Venturas

Secretary: Mrs Cathy Stevens **(T)** 07972 355 880 **(E)** cathy.stevens@uwclub.net
Chairman: Bruce Stevens **Manager:** Richard Scott **Prog Ed:** Kevin O'Brien
Ground: Chancery Lane, Thrapston, Northants NN14 4JL **(T)** 01832 732 470 **Capacity:** 1,000
Colours(change): All royal blue (Red/black/red)

ADDITIONAL INFORMATION:
Honours: Kettering Amateur League 1970-71, 72-73, 73-74, 77-78. Northants Junior Cup 1987-88, 98-99, 03-04.

WELLINGBOROUGH WHITWORTH

Founded: 1973 Nickname: Flourmen

Secretary: Julian Souster **(T)** 07825 632 545 **(E)** whitworthfc@yahoo.co.uk
Chairman: Martin Goodes **Prog Ed:** Julian Souster
Ground: London Road, Wellingborough, Northants NN8 2DP **(T)** 07825 632 545
Colours(change): Red & black stripes/black/red (Black & white stripes/black/black)

ADDITIONAL INFORMATION:
Previous Name: Whitworths. **Previous League:** East Midlands Alliance > 1985.
Honours: Rushden & District League 1976-77. Northants Junior Cup 1996. U.C.L. Division One 2006-07.

WOODFORD UNITED

Founded: 1946 Nickname: Reds

Secretary: Andrew Worrall **(T)** 07500 067 734 **(E)** andy.worrall@engel.at
Chairman: Mrs Yvonne Worrall **Manager:** Adam Knight **Prog Ed:** Andrew Worrall
Ground: Byfield Road, Woodford Halse, Daventry, Northants NN11 3QR **(T)** 01327 263 734 **Capacity:** 3,000
Colours(change): All red

ADDITIONAL INFORMATION: 1,500 v Stockport County
United Counties League Division 2 1973-74, Premier Division 2005-06.

GROUND DIRECTIONS

AFC KEMPSTON ROVERS - Take A421 Bedford by pass turning as indicated to Kempston onto A5140 Woburn Road. At roundabout turn left into St John's Street then right into Bedford Road. After the shops and park on the left turn immediately left into Hillgrounds Road. Ground is past the swimming pool on right hand side.

AFC RUSHDEN & DIAMONDS - Leave A.45 at Wellingborough turn-off, pass Tesco's Store on left-hand side, up to roundabout. Take first exit to town centre. Ground is 300 yards on right-hand side. Entry just past the Dog & Duck public house adjacent to entry to Whitworths ground.

BLACKSTONES FC - From Stamford Centre take A6121 towards Bourne. Turn left into Lincoln Road. Ground on the right hand side. Go into town on A16 from Spalding. Turn left at roundabout into Liquor Pond Street becoming Queen Street over railway crossing along Sleaford Road. Turn right into Carlton Road then right at crossroads into Fydell Street. Over railway crossing and river take 2nd left (sharp turn) into Tattershall Road. Continue over railway crossing, ground on left.

BOSTON TOWN - Go into town on A16 from Spalding. Turn left at roundabout into Liquor Pond Street becoming Queen Street over railway crossing along Sleaford Road. Turn right into Carlton Road then right at crossroads into Fydell Street. Over railway crossing and river take 2nd left (sharp turn) into Tattershall Road. Continue over railway crossing, ground on left.

BOURNE TOWN - From Town Centre turn east on A151 towards Spalding into Abbey Road. Ground approximately half a mile on right.

BUCKINGHAM TOWN - Take A413 out of Buckingham and continue on that road until entering Winslow. As you enter Winslow there is a garage on the right hand side. Take the 1st turn right past the garage (Avenue Road) and then the 1st turn right again into Park Road. Entrance at end of road through the blue gates. Bear left into the car park..

BUGBROOKE ST MICHAELS - At M1 Junction 16 take A45 to Northampton. At first roundabout follow signs to Bugbrooke. Go straight through village, ground entrance immediately past last house on the left.

BURTON PARK WANDERERS - From A14 take J10 towards Burton Latimer, at Alpro roundabout turn right, then straight over roundabout next to Versalift then right at Morrisions. Follow the round around the top of Morrisions continue until you are past the small Alumasc building on the left.

Entrance to ground is next left.

COGENHOE UNITED - From A45 Northampton Ring Road turn as indicated to Billing/Cogenhoe. Go over River Nene and up hill ignoring first turning on left to Cogenhoe. Take next left and ground is on right hand side.

DEEPING RANGERS - From Town Centre head north on B1524 towards Bourne. Turn right onto Towngate East at Towngate Tavern Pub. Go straight over mini roundabout onto Outgang Road. Ground 1/4 mile on left. From A16 by pass at roundabout with the A15 Bourne Road turn towards Deeping then left into Northfields Road, then left into Towngate/Outgang Road. Ground 1/4 mile on left.

DESBOROUGH TOWN - Take exit 3 marked Desborough off the A14 and follow bypass for 2 miles. At roundabout turn right and ground is 200 yards on the left hand side.

EYNESBURY ROVERS - From the A1 take the A428 towards Cambridge. Turn left at the Tesco roundabout and continue on Barford Road for half a mile going straight on at 4 roundabouts. Turn left into Hardwick Road and left into Hall Road. Ground at end of road

HARBOROUGH TOWN - Half a mile south of Market Harborough on the A508. 4 miles north of the A14 junction 2 towards Market Harborough turn left towards Leisure Centre, but keep left passed inflatable dome on the right, then through large car park, club house straight in front, with parking area.

HARROWBY UNITED - From A1 take B6403, go past roundabout, past Ancaster turn and take road for Harrowby. Follow the road into Grantham, ground on right opposite Cherry Tree public house.

HOLBEACH UNITED - Approaching Town Centre traffic lights from Spalding Direction take Second Left, or from Kings Lynn direction take sharp right, into Park Road. Ground is 300 yards on the left.

HUNTINGDON TOWN - At the A1 Brampton Hut roundabout, follow signs for A14 East until reaching the Spittals Interchange roundabout, Follow the A141 towards St Ives/March and go over 3 roundabouts. Take next left turn at traffic lights towards Kings Ripton and the ground is on the left.

IRCHESTER UNITED - From A509 Wellingborough/Newport Pagnell Road turn into Gidsy Lane to Irchester. Turn left into Wollaston Road B659. Alfred Street is on left hand side with the ground at the end.

LONG BUCKBY AFC - From the Village Centre turn into Station Road. Ground on left hand side. Parking is available in South Close adjacent to the Rugby Club (do NOT park "half on half off" the pavement outside the ground)

LUTTERWORTH ATHLETIC - http://www.pitchero.com/clubs/lutterworthathleticfootballclub/location

NEWPORT PAGNELL TOWN - From the A422 Newport Pagnell by pass turn into Marsh End Road, then first right into Willen Road.

NORTHAMPTON ON CHENECKS - Leave A45 at exit marked Bedford A428 and Town Centre. Take exit into Rushmere Road marked Abington, Kingsthorpe and County Cricket. At first set of lights turn left into Billing Road, sports ground 250 yards on the right.

NORTHAMPTON SILEBY RANGERS - Approach from A43 (Kettering): From large roundabout with traffic lights, take the A5076 Talavera Way exit, signpostedto Market Harborough, Moulton Park and Kingsthorpe. The entrance to the ground is about a quarter of a mile on the left. Approach from A45: Take exit to A43 Ring Road / Kettering / Corby. Go straight over 1 roundabout to large roundabout with traffic lights. Then follow directions above.

NORTHAMPTON SPENCER - The ground is in Kingsthorpe area of Northampton on A508, Market Harborough road out of Town. Look for W Grose's garage (Vauxhall) and turn left at traffic lights into Thornton Rd, then first right into Studlands Rd. Follow to bottom of hill and onto track between allotments. Ground is after a right turn at end of track.

OADBY TOWN - Greene King Park, Wigston Road, Oadby, Leicestershire LE2 5QG - 01162 715728

OLNEY TOWN - From the North enter via A509 Warrington Road then turn left into Midland Road and immediately right into East Street. Ground on left hand side after Fire Station. From Milton Keynes: Follow the A509 into Olney, over river bridge, 200 metres past the Swan Bistro and public house and take the first turning right onto the market square immediately before the traffic lights), follow road to the right onto a one way system into East Street. Follow East Street for 500 metres, the ootball Club is on the right hand side, car park entrance being the immediately following right turn.

PETERBOROUGH NORTHERN STAR - From A1 turn on to A1139 Fletton Parkway. Follow signs for A47 Wisbech. Exit at Junction 7 (near Perkins Engines Site). At top of slip road turn left into Eastfield Road. At Traffic lights turn right into Newark Avenue and then first right in to Eastern Avenue. Take 2nd left in to Chestnut Avenue and the club is on the right behind steel Palisade Fencing

PETERBOROUGH SPORTS - From the North - Come in on the A15 Southbound and cross the large A47 Roundabout just past Morrison's on your right. ***Take the left hand slip road at a set of traffic lights after approximately 400 yards and turn right at the T-Junction after 50 yards. The entrance to the ground is approx 400 yards down on your left in front of a church and before a zebra crossing where there is a sign to the health centre. If journeying from the East take the turning from the A47 signposted City Centre and follow instructions from *** above. If journeying from the South or West come in via the A47 and take the exit signposted City Centre. You go straight on at this roundabout (back up alongside A47) and then take the 3rd (right) at the large roundabout with the A15 and follow instructions from *** above.

POTTON UNITED - From Sandy, take B1042 into Potton. Head towards Potton Town Centre and take right turn towards Biggleswade (B1040). The ground is on left hand side at foot of hill

RAUNDS TOWN - From North, East or West, take A14 J13 and follow A45 signs to Raunds. Turn left at roundabout by BP garage. From South follow A45 towards Thrapston. Turn right at roundabout by BP garage. Ground on left.

ROTHWELL CORINTHIANS - A14 to Rothwell. Take B669 towards Desborough. Ground on right at rear of cricket field opposite last houses on the left. Parking on verge or in adjacent field if gate open. Access to ground via footpath.

RUSHDEN AND HIGHAM UNITED - From A6/A45 Junction take Higham/Rushden bypass. At third roundabout turn right, then turn right immediately after the school. From Bedford (A6) take bypass and turn left at first roundabout then turn right immediately after the school

SHEPSHED DYNAMO - The Dovecote Stadium Butt Hole Lane Shepshed Leicestershire LE12 9BN - 01509 650992

SLEAFORD TOWN - 15 Sleaford By-pass, roundabout to A17 Holdingham Roundabout third exit towards Boston on A17 Take second exit of A17 towards Sleaford ground is 1 mile on right hand side before you enter Sleaford

SPALDING UNITED - Follow signs to Spalding Town Centre. From the north drive south down Pinchbeck Road towards Spalding. At traffic lights turn right into Kings Road. At the next set of lights turn left into Winfrey Avenue. The Ground is on the left. From the south follow signs to The Railway station and Bus Stations. The Ground is opposite the Bus Station on Winfrey Avenue. There is parking outside the ground in a pay and display car park.

ST NEOTS TOWN SAINTS - From both the A1 and the Cambridge side of the A428 into Loves Farm St Neots, follow Kester Road until you reach the stadium.

STEWARTS & LLOYDS CORBY - From the Oundle/Weldon Road turn at roundabout into A6086 Lloyds Road and continue to roundabout. Take second exit going over railway line along Rockingham Road. Continue over speed bumps then turn left into Occupation Road and first right into Cannock Road. Ground is beyond the British Steel Club and Rugby pitch.

THRAPSTON TOWN - Exit A14 at A605 roundabout, travel towards Peterborough till 1st roundabout (approx 700 metres).Take first exit into Thrapston. AT traffic lights turn into Oundle Road adjacent to Masons Arms Pub. Turn left into Devere Road and ground at bottom of hill.

THURNBY NIRVANA - From M1 - Exit at Jct 22 (A50/A511 to Leicester/Coalville). Follow A50 to Leicester, until you reach signs for A563 (Glenfirth Way). Go over flyover (Troon Way), after the Tesco Hamilton roundabout, turn left onto Scraptoft Lane. Take first right on to Thurncourt Road, turn right on to Daykn Road. Entrance 300m on the left.

WELLINGBOROUGH TOWN - Leave A.45 at Wellingborough turn-off, pass Tesco's Store on left-hand side, up to roundabout. Take first exit to town centre. Ground is 300 yards on right-hand side. Entry just past the Dog & Duck public house adjacent to entry to Whitworths ground.

WELLINGBOROUGH WHITWORTH - Leave A45 by pass and go past Tescos etc. Turn left at roundabout then turn right immediately after Dog and Duck pub and go through 2nd gate down to the ground .

WISBECH TOWN - From A1 follow signs for Wisbech (A47). At the outskirts of Wisbech, take 2nd exit off roundabout, signposted A47. After 1.5 miles, go straight over at the next roundabout. At next roundabout (another 3.1 miles on, Total Garage on right) take first exit (signposted B198 West Walton/Walsoken). Cross over next roundabout (which is new, so not marked on some maps and sat navs) and follow road for just over a mile. The entrance to the stadium is on the right via the right turn lane.

WOODFORD UNITED - A361 Daventry to Banbury Road. Turn left in Byfield. Follow road to Woodford Halse. Ground on left just past industrial estate.

YAXLEY - Leave A1 at Norman Cross and travel towards Peterborough. Turn off A15 at traffic lights. Bear immediately right and go past cemetery. At bottom of hill turn right into Main Street then left into Holme Road. After short distance go over small bridge and turn left between a bungalow and house into Leading Drove. Ground on left hand side.

WESSEX LEAGUE

Sponsored by: Sydenhams

Founded: 1986

Recent Champions:
2008: AFC Totton. 2009: Poole Town. 2010: Poole Town.
2011: Poole Town. 2012: Winchester City. 2013: Blackfield & Langley.

wessexleague.co.uk

PREMIER DIVISION	P	W	D	L	F	A	GD	Pts
1 (P) Sholing	42	33	5	4	134	29	105	104
2 Alresford Town	42	31	4	7	125	52	73	97
3 Folland Sports (-3pts)	42	27	7	8	100	48	52	85
4 Newport (IOW)	42	25	9	8	105	47	58	84
5 Winchester City	42	25	6	11	93	41	52	81
6 Blackfield & Langley	42	23	9	10	81	57	24	78
7 Bemerton Heath Harlequins	42	22	5	15	99	65	34	71
8 AFC Portchester (-6pts)	42	21	13	8	86	43	43	70
9 Moneyfields (-6pts)	42	21	10	11	75	53	22	67
10 Fareham Town	42	18	8	16	78	81	-3	62
11 Brockenhurst	42	17	8	17	72	82	-10	59
12 Hamworthy United	42	16	9	17	78	78	0	57
13 Whitchurch United	42	16	7	19	57	69	-12	55
14 Lymington Town	42	15	5	22	71	99	-28	50
15 Bournemouth	42	12	7	23	66	89	-23	43
16 Christchurch	42	11	7	24	56	112	-56	40
17 Horndean	42	10	7	25	55	95	-40	37
18 Totton & Eling	42	12	0	30	54	117	-63	36
19 Verwood Town	42	8	10	24	45	78	-33	34
20 Fawley	42	7	9	26	49	108	-59	30
21 (R) Downton	42	6	8	28	49	121	-72	26
22 (R) Romsey Town	42	6	7	29	43	107	-64	24

DIVISION ONE	P	W	D	L	F	A	GD	Pts
1 (P) Petersfield Town	30	23	5	2	118	36	82	74
2 (P) Andover Town	30	23	4	3	108	28	80	73
3 Cowes Sports	30	22	3	5	84	36	48	69
4 Hythe & Dibden	30	19	5	6	85	37	48	62
5 Tadley Calleva	30	15	7	8	64	43	21	52
6 Team Solent (-3pts)	30	16	5	9	82	51	31	50
7 United Services Portsmouth	30	14	5	11	61	53	8	47
8 Pewsey Vale	30	14	4	12	59	52	7	46
9 Laverstock & Ford	30	12	2	16	46	54	-8	38
10 Amesbury Town	30	12	2	16	56	66	-10	38
11 New Milton Town	30	10	2	18	69	71	-2	32
12 Fleet Spurs	30	8	3	19	50	79	-29	27
13 Ringwood Town	30	7	1	22	41	104	-63	22
14 Hayling United (-1pt)	30	6	4	20	47	106	-59	21
15 Andover New Street	30	7	0	23	33	111	-78	21
16 East Cowes Victoria	30	4	4	22	32	108	-76	16

Stockbridge withdrew - record expunged.

PREMIER DIVISION	1	2	3	4	5	6	7	8	9	10	11	12	13	14	15	16	17	18	19	20	21	22
1 AFC Portchester		0-2	3-0	1-1	2-0	3-0	2-0	6-0	3-2	4-2	0-2	1-3	1-0	4-0	2-0	2-2	4-0	1-1	7-0	2-2	1-1	0-3
2 Alresford Town	2-2		5-3	5-1	2-2	3-0	7-1	3-2	1-4	4-0	6-1	4-0	2-2	4-2	3-2	5-1	2-0	2-3	4-1	1-0	3-0	3-0
3 Bemerton Heath Harlequins	2-1	1-5		2-1	6-0	3-0	5-1	3-1	4-2	1-1	1-3	4-0	3-3	1-1	0-1	0-2	2-1	2-2	8-0	1-1	2-3	0-1
4 Blackfield & Langley	0-0	3-4	2-1		3-1	1-0	2-2	2-2	2-0	0-2	3-0	2-0	2-0	1-2	1-1	1-0	2-1	3-1	1-0	2-1	2-1	0-0
5 Bournemouth	1-1	1-2	2-3	2-2		2-0	0-3	3-1	2-3	3-1	0-6	0-1	4-2	1-2	2-2	2-4	3-0	1-0	2-1	1-0	5-1	3-4
6 Brockenhurst	1-3	0-2	1-0	4-1	1-3		3-1	4-3	4-2	1-2	2-2	2-5	2-1	3-3	0-3	0-0	4-1	2-0	3-0	2-1	4-0	3-2
7 Christchurch	2-3	0-2	1-5	0-1	4-2	2-2		1-1	1-1	2-1	1-2	0-2	2-1	2-5	1-1	0-2	4-2	0-3	3-1	5-2	3-1	0-2
8 Downton	3-3	1-3	1-3	1-3	3-2	3-3	1-2		2-3	2-1	1-2	2-0	0-3	3-1	1-1	2-3	2-3	0-3	0-3	0-3	0-3	0-4
9 Fareham Town	1-1	1-3	2-1	1-3	2-1	0-2	3-2	6-0		2-0	1-0	1-1	2-1	5-0	2-3	4-4	2-2	1-1	5-4	4-0	1-0	1-1
10 Fawley	0-3	0-7	1-3	1-3	2-2	4-2	2-1	0-2	1-0		1-3	1-0	1-2	0-4	1-2	0-5	2-4	2-2	3-1	2-2	0-3	0-7
11 Folland Sports	1-1	1-0	0-2	5-0	4-1	0-0	4-0	4-0	5-1	3-2		3-1	3-0	2-0	2-1	2-3	3-1	1-2	5-1	1-0	1-1	2-0
12 Hamworthy United	1-2	0-2	3-2	2-3	2-1	2-0	4-0	4-0	0-0	3-2	1-1		1-2	2-2	1-1	2-2	8-1	0-4	3-2	3-0	2-2	1-4
13 Horndean	0-1	2-1	2-3	0-5	1-0	2-3	4-5	1-1	5-2	3-3	0-1	1-2		2-2	2-2	1-3	1-1	0-5	1-2	2-0	4-2	1-3
14 Lymington Town	0-2	2-3	1-3	2-3	4-1	2-2	1-0	4-2	3-0	4-1	1-6	2-4	1-0		0-2	0-2	2-1	0-4	2-1	2-3	1-3	1-5
15 Moneyfields	1-0	3-1	4-3	4-2	2-0	1-2	1-1	0-0	3-0	1-1	0-3	4-2	5-0	4-2		1-2	1-0	0-3	3-2	3-1	0-1	1-2
16 Newport (IOW)	1-1	4-0	3-0	2-1	2-2	1-4	12-0	7-0	2-1	2-2	0-1	5-1	3-0	4-0	2-1		3-1	0-2	1-2	2-0	1-1	0-2
17 Romsey Town	0-4	0-3	1-3	0-6	1-1	4-2	0-1	2-4	0-2	1-1	2-2	1-5	3-0	1-3	0-1	0-4		0-3	0-2	1-1	1-2	0-2
18 Sholing	1-0	4-0	2-1	3-2	1-0	5-0	8-0	12-1	6-0	3-0	2-3	4-0	9-0	5-1	3-1	1-1	5-0		2-0	4-1	4-1	2-1
19 Totton & Eling	1-6	0-4	0-1	1-5	2-0	4-2	4-1	1-0	0-1	4-2	0-3	3-2	0-1	1-3	2-4	0-4	1-2	0-3		5-3	1-4	0-4
20 Verwood Town	2-2	0-5	1-5	0-0	1-3	0-1	1-1	1-1	1-3	1-1	2-1	2-1	1-0	3-1	0-3	1-2	0-0	0-1	5-0		0-1	1-0
21 Whitchurch United	0-1	0-3	0-4	0-1	1-4	1-1	3-0	3-0	0-4	4-0	2-2	2-2	0-2	1-2	0-1	1-0	2-1	1-2	0-1	2-1		2-1
22 Winchester City	2-0	2-2	0-2	2-2	4-0	4-0	3-0	2-0	6-0	2-0	5-4	1-1	3-0	2-0	0-0	0-2	2-3	0-3	4-0	1-0	0-1	

LEAGUE CUP

ROUND 1

Bournemouth	v	Ringwood Town	4-1
Romsey Town	v	Pewsey Vale	3-1
Stockbridge	v	Lymington Town	2-3
Andover New Street	v	East Cowes Victoria	2-3
Sholing	v	United Services Portsmouth	9-0
Amesbury Town	v	Hamworthy United	2-3
Fleet Spurs	v	Team Solent	1-8

ROUND 2

Blackfield & Langley	v	Laverstock & Ford	3-0
Fawley	v	Christchurch	2-4 aet
Alresford Town	v	Downton	4-1
Bournemouth	v	Hythe & Dibden	1-2 aet
Folland Sports	v	AFC Porchester	2-0
Romsey Town	v	Moneyfields	0-1
Lymington Town	v	Brockenhurst	1-3
Totton & Eling	v	Petersfield Town	1-4
East Cowes Victoria	v	Winchester City	0-4
Sholing	v	Tadley Calleva	6-1
Hayling United	v	Fareham Town	AW
Bemerton Heath Harlequins	v	Hamworthy United	2-0
Whitchurch United	v	Horndean	3-0
Verwood Town	v	Cowes Sports	0-2
New Milton Town	v	Andover Town	1-2
Team Solent	v	Newport (IOW)	1-2

ROUND 3

Blackfield & Langley	v	Christchurch	3-0
Alresford Town	v	Hythe & Dibden	6-1
Folland Sports	v	Moneyfields	0-2
Brockenhurst	v	Petersfield Town	1-2 aet
Winchester City	v	Sholing	4-5
Fareham Town	v	Bemerton Heath Harlequins	0-3
Whitchurch United	v	Cowes Sports	5-0
Andover Town	v	Newport (IOW)	2-4

QUARTER FINALS

Blackfield & Langley	v	Alresford Town	0-2
Moneyfields	v	Petersfield Town	3-4
Sholing	v	Bemerton Heath Harlequins	7-0
Whitchurch United	v	Newport (IOW)	1-0

SEMI FINALS

Sholing	v	Alresford Town	0-2
Peterfield Town	v	Whitchurch United	3-2

FINAL

Alresford Town	v	Petersfield Town	7-2

DIVISION ONE	1	2	3	4	5	6	7	8	9	10	11	12	13	14	15	16
1 Amesbury Town		6-2	2-3	0-0	4-2	4-1	3-0	5-2	1-0	1-3	1-5	1-3	4-1	1-5	0-2	1-2
2 Andover New Street	2-1		0-2	0-4	3-1	2-1	0-6	1-4	1-0	0-3	2-6	2-3	0-3	0-2	1-5	2-3
3 Andover Town	4-0	3-2		3-0	11-0	3-0	7-1	3-0	7-0	2-0	1-1	2-0	7-0	1-1	4-0	2-1
4 Cowes Sports	4-3	4-1	3-2		6-1	3-2	5-2	5-0	4-0	1-2	2-4	3-0	4-1	4-0	1-2	1-0
5 East Cowes Victoria	1-4	0-3	1-3	0-3		2-1	2-2	1-4	1-1	0-5	0-3	2-5	5-1	1-3	1-6	1-1
6 Fleet Spurs	0-1	5-0	2-4	0-4	1-0		4-0	2-2	1-3	3-2	1-2	1-1	4-1	1-0	0-4	2-0
7 Hayling United	2-3	1-2	0-8	2-2	2-0	4-3		0-1	0-5	2-2	0-6	2-3	5-1	2-5	1-3	0-0
8 Hythe & Dibden	5-0	7-0	2-2	1-2	5-0	3-0	8-2		5-0	2-0	2-2	2-2	4-0	3-0	2-1	2-0
9 Laverstock & Ford	1-0	4-0	0-3	1-0	2-0	4-0	2-1	1-3		4-0	2-5	1-2	4-1	0-5	3-0	1-2
10 New Milton Town	1-2	6-3	0-2	1-3	6-0	10-2	7-1	0-3	3-2		2-4	3-2	1-2	2-3	1-2	1-4
11 Petersfield Town	3-0	14-0	0-4	2-3	5-0	6-3	2-0	3-1	2-1	5-0		3-0	10-1	0-0	4-4	5-0
12 Pewsey Vale	5-1	2-0	4-1	0-1	1-3	2-1	1-2	0-1	1-0	3-1	2-5		6-2	1-3	1-3	0-1
13 Ringwood Town	1-1	3-1	1-7	1-4	3-5	3-1	1-3	0-5	0-1	2-1	1-2	3-4		0-2	0-5	4-1
14 Tadley Calleva	0-4	0-1	3-3	1-1	1-1	4-1	9-1	2-2	1-0	3-1	1-3	1-1	2-1		3-0	2-0
15 Team Solent	4-1	3-2	3-2	2-4	9-1	1-3	6-1	0-3	2-2	5-2	1-1	1-1	1-2	5-1		1-1
16 United Services Portsmouth	2-1	9-0	1-2	2-3	4-0	4-4	5-2	3-1	3-1	3-3	1-5	0-3	4-1	2-1	2-1	

CLUB MOVEMENTS

Premier Division - In: Andover Town (P). Petersfield Town (P).

Out: Downton (R). Romsey Town (R). Sholing (P - Southern League Div.1 South & West).

Division One - In: Downton (R). Romsey Town (R).

Out: Andover Town (P). Hayling United (WN). Petersfield Town (P). Stocksbridge (WS).

A.F.C. PORTCHESTER
Founded: 1971 Nickname:

Secretary: Jason Brooker **(T)** 07972 165 077 **(E)** secretary@afcportchester.co.uk
Chairman: Paul Kelly **Prog Ed:** Rob McGinn
Ground: Wicor Recreation Ground Cranleigh Road Portchester Hampshire PO16 9DP **(T)** 01329 233 833 (Clubhouse)
Capacity: **Seats:** **Covered:** **Midweek Matchday:** Tuesday **Clubhouse:** Yes

Colours(change): Tangerine/black/tangerine (All blue)
Previous Names: Loyds Sports 1971-73. Colourvison Rangers 1973-76. Wilcor Mill 1976-2003.
Previous Leagues: City of Portsmouth Sunday. Portsmouth & District >1998. Hampshire 1998-2004.
Records:
Senior Honours: Hampshire League Division One 2001-02.

10 YEAR RECORD

04-05	05-06	06-07	07-08	08-09	09-10	10-11	11-12	12-13	13-14
Wex3 14	Wex3 11	Wex2 4	Wex1 14	Wex1 19	Wex1 6	Wex1 3	Wex1 2	WexP 15	WexP 8

ALRESFORD TOWN
Founded: 1898 Nickname: The Magpies

Secretary: Keith Curtis **(T)** 07703 346 672 **(E)** secretary.alresfordtownfc@gmail.com
Chairman: Trevor Ingram **Prog Ed:** Gregory Boughton
Ground: Arlebury Park, The Avenue, Alresford, Hants SO24 9EP **(T)** 01962 735 100 or 07703 346 672
Capacity: **Seats:** Yes **Covered:** Yes **Midweek Matchday:** Tuesday **Clubhouse:** Yes

Colours(change): Black & white stripes/black/black & white. (Yellow & blue/blue/yellow & blue)
Previous Names:
Previous Leagues: Winchester League, North Hants league, Hampshire League
Records:
Senior Honours: Winchester League Division Two & One
Hampshire Senior Cup 2012-13.

10 YEAR RECORD

04-05	05-06	06-07	07-08	08-09	09-10	10-11	11-12	12-13	13-14
Wex2 10	Wex2 20	Wex1 2	WexP 21	WexP 18	WexP 17	WexP 15	WexP 15	WexP 2	WexP 2

ANDOVER TOWN
Founded: 2013 Nickname:

Secretary: Barbara Paddock **(T)** 07795 6824 032 **(E)** lawrence.blair@sparsholt.ac.uk
Chairman: Lawrence Blair **Manager:** Neil Benson **Prog Ed:** Lawrence Blair
Ground: Portway Stadium, West Portway, Portway Industrial Estate, Andover AP10 3LF **(T)**
Capacity: **Seats:** **Covered:** **Midweek Matchday:** **Clubhouse:**

Colours(change): All blue (All orange)
Previous Names: None
Previous Leagues: None
Records:
Senior Honours: None

10 YEAR RECORD

04-05	05-06	06-07	07-08	08-09	09-10	10-11	11-12	12-13	13-14
									Wex1 2

BEMERTON HEATH HARLEQUINS
Founded: 1989 Nickname: Quins

Secretary: Andy Hardwick **(T)** 07561 164 068 **(E)** secretarybhhfc@hotmail.com
Chairman: Steve Slade **Prog Ed:** Steve Brooks
Ground: The Clubhouse, Western Way, Bemerton Heath Salisbury SP2 9DT **(T)** 01722 331 925
Capacity: 2,100 **Seats:** 250 **Covered:** 350 **Midweek Matchday:** Tuesday **Clubhouse:** Yes **Shop:** No

Colours(change): Black & white quarters/black/black & white (All orange)
Previous Names: Bemerton Athletic, Moon FC & Bemerton Boys merged in 1989
Previous Leagues: Salisbury & Wilts Comb, Salisbury & Andover Sunday
Records: **Att:**1,118 v Aldershot Town **App:** Keith Richardson
Senior Honours: Wiltshire Senior Cup 1992-93. Wessex League Cup 2009-10.

10 YEAR RECORD

04-05	05-06	06-07	07-08	08-09	09-10	10-11	11-12	12-13	13-14
Wex1 14	Wex1 14	WexP 11	WexP 13	WexP 12	WexP 3	WexP 2	WexP 2	WexP 5	WexP 7

BLACKFIELD & LANGLEY

Founded: 1935 Nickname:

Secretary: Claire Sinclair **(T)** 07990 518 710 **(E)** bandlfc@hotmail.com

Chairman: Owen Lightfoot

Ground: Gang Warily Rec., Newlands Rd, Southampton, SO45 1GA **(T)** 02380 893 603

Capacity: 2,500 **Seats:** 180 **Covered:** nil **Midweek Matchday:** Tuesday **Clubhouse:** Yes

Colours(change): Green & white/white/green & white (All maroon).
Previous Names:
Previous Leagues: Southampton Senior. Hampshire.
Records: **Att:** 240
Senior Honours: Hampshire League 1987-88, Division Two 1984-85, Southampton Senior Cup (4).
Wessex League Premier Division 2012-13.

10 YEAR RECORD

04-05	05-06	06-07	07-08	08-09	09-10	10-11	11-12	12-13	13-14
Wex2 7	Wex2 14	Wex1 16	Wex1 10	Wex1 2	WexP 8	WexP 14	WexP 16	WexP 1	WexP 6

BOURNEMOUTH

Founded: 1875 Nickname: Poppies

Secretary: Mike Robins **(T)** 07947 687 808 **(E)** bournemouthpoppiesfc@gmail.com

Chairman: Bob Corbin **Prog Ed:** Mike Robins

Ground: Victoria Park, Namu Road, Winton, Bournemouth BH9 2RA **(T)** 01202 515 123

Capacity: 3,000 **Seats:** 205 **Covered:** 205 **Midweek Matchday:** Tuesday **Clubhouse:** Yes **Shop:** Yes

Colours(change): All Red (Yellow & blue/blue/blue)
Previous Names: Bournemouth Rovers, Bournemouth Wanderers, Bournemouth Dean Park
Previous Leagues: Hampshire
Records: Goalscorer (since 1990) Darren McBride 95 (111+26 games) Apps (since 1990) Mark Dancer 358 (318+40 games)
Senior Honours: Wessex League Cup Winners: 2011.

10 YEAR RECORD

04-05	05-06	06-07	07-08	08-09	09-10	10-11	11-12	12-13	13-14
Wex1 11	Wex1 7	WexP 5	WexP 5	WexP 15	WexP 4	WexP 5	WexP 9	WexP 13	WexP 15

BROCKENHURST

Founded: 1898 Nickname: The Badgers

Secretary: Pete Lynes **(T)** 07908 109 696 **(E)** peter.m.lynes@btopenworld.com

Chairman: Pete Lynes **Prog Ed:** Ian Claxton

Ground: Grigg Lane, Brockenhurst, Hants SO42 7RE **(T)** 01590 623 544

Capacity: 2,000 **Seats:** 200 **Covered:** 300 **Midweek Matchday:** Wednesday **Clubhouse:** Yes

Colours(change): Blue & white/blue/blue. (Green & white/green/green).
Previous Names:
Previous Leagues: Hampshire
Records: **Att:** 1,104 v St Albans City
Senior Honours: Hampshire League 1975-76. Wessex League Division One 2012-13.

10 YEAR RECORD

04-05	05-06	06-07	07-08	08-09	09-10	10-11	11-12	12-13	13-14
Wex1 18	Wex1 21	WexP 13	WexP 6	WexP 5	WexP 13			Wex1 1	WexP 11

CHRISTCHURCH

Founded: 1885 Nickname: Priory

Secretary: Ian Harley **(T)** 07900 133 954 **(E)** secretary@christchurchfc.co.uk

Chairman: Mark Duffy **Prog Ed:** Mark Duffy

Ground: Hurn Bridge S.C, Avon Causeway, Christchurch BH23 6DY **(T)** 01202 473 792

Capacity: 1,200 **Seats:** 215 **Covered:** 265 **Midweek Matchday:** Wednesday **Clubhouse:** Yes

Colours(change): All Blue (All yellow)
Previous Names:
Previous Leagues: Hampshire
Records: **App:** John Haynes
Senior Honours: Hants Jnr Cup (3), Hants Intermediate Cup 86-87, Bournemouth Senior Cup (5)

10 YEAR RECORD

04-05	05-06	06-07	07-08	08-09	09-10	10-11	11-12	12-13	13-14
Wex1 17	Wex1 10	WexP 14	WexP 16	WexP 7	WexP 5	WexP 6	WexP 3	WexP 3	WexP 16

FAREHAM TOWN

Founded: 1946 Nickname: The Robins

Secretary: Paul Procter **(T)** 07445 805 122 **(E)** farehamtnfc@gmail.com
Chairman: Nick Ralls **Prog Ed:** Neil Stock
Ground: Cams Alders, Palmerston Drive, Fareham, Hants PO14 1BJ **(T)** 07445 805 122
Capacity: 2,000 **Seats:** 450 **Covered:** 500 **Midweek Matchday:** Tuesday **Clubhouse:** Yes **Shop:** Yes

Colours(change): Red & black/black/red (All blue)
Previous Names: None
Previous Leagues: Portsmouth, Hampshire & Southern
Records: **Att:** 2,015 v Spurs (friendly 1985)
Senior Honours: Hampshire Senior Cup 1957, 1963, 1968, 1993. Hampshire League Champions.

10 YEAR RECORD

04-05	05-06	06-07	07-08	08-09	09-10	10-11	11-12	12-13	13-14
Wex1 16	Wex1 9	WexP 8	WexP 8	WexP 10	WexP 6	WexP 8	WexP 12	WexP 9	WexP 10

FAWLEY

Founded: 1923 Nickname:

Secretary: Kevin Mitchell **(T)** 07836 259 682 **(E)** fawleysecretary@hotmail.co.uk
Chairman: Kevin Mitchell **Prog Ed:** Kevin Mitchell
Ground: Waterside Spts & Soc. club, 179 Long Lane, Holbury, Soto, SO45 2PA **(T)** 02380 893 750 (Club)
Capacity: **Seats:** **Covered:** **Midweek Matchday:** Wednesday **Clubhouse:** Yes

Colours(change): All Blue (Red/white/red)
Previous Names: Esso Fawley > 2002
Previous Leagues: Hampshire Premier > 2004.
Records:
Senior Honours:

10 YEAR RECORD

04-05	05-06	06-07	07-08	08-09	09-10	10-11	11-12	12-13	13-14
Wex2 21	Wex2 7	Wex1 5	Wex1 6	Wex1 9	Wex1 2	WexP 20	WexP 19	WexP 17	WexP 20

FOLLAND SPORTS

Founded: 1938 Nickname:

Secretary: Adrian Harris **(T)** 07774 962 813 **(E)** follandsportsfc@hotmail.co.uk
Chairman: Adrian Stremel **Prog Ed:** Adrian Harris
Ground: Folland Park, Kings Ave, Hamble, Southampton SO31 4NF **(T)** 02380 452 173
Capacity: 1,000 **Seats:** 150 **Covered:** 150 **Midweek Matchday:** Tuesday **Clubhouse:** Yes **Shop:** No

Colours(change): Claret/sky blue/claret (White/red/red)
Previous Names: Folland Sports (pre 1990), Aerostructures SSC 1990-97, Hamble ASSC 1997-2011. GE Hamble 2011-13.
Previous Leagues:
Records:
Senior Honours: Southampton Senior Cup 1984-85, 86-87, 91-92. Wessex League Division 1 2009-10.

10 YEAR RECORD

04-05	05-06	06-07	07-08	08-09	09-10	10-11	11-12	12-13	13-14
Wex1 21	Wex1 15	WexP 20	WexP 17	WexP 21	Wex1 1	WexP 12	WexP 5	WexP 7	WexP 3

HAMWORTHY UNITED

Founded: 1926 Nickname: The Hammers

Secretary: Peter Gallop **(T)** 07925 062 545 **(E)** ham-utd-fc-secretary@hotmail.co.uk
Chairman: Mark Bartlett **Prog Ed:** Stuart Tanner
Ground: The County Ground, Blandford Close, Hamworthy, Poole, BH15 4BF **(T)** 01202 674 974
Capacity: 2,000 **Seats:** **Covered:** **Midweek Matchday:** Tuesday **Clubhouse:** Yes **Shop:** No

Colours(change): Maroon & sky blue/maroon/maroon (Yellow & black/black/yellow)
Previous Names: Hamworthy St. Michael merged with Trinidad Old Boys 1926
Previous Leagues: Dorset Premier
Records:
Senior Honours: Dorset Premier League 2002-03, 03-04.

10 YEAR RECORD

04-05	05-06	06-07	07-08	08-09	09-10	10-11	11-12	12-13	13-14
Wex1 15	Wex1 6	WexP 15	WexP 10	WexP 8	WexP 16	WexP 9	WexP 7	WexP 10	WexP 12

HORNDEAN

Founded: 1887 Nickname:

Secretary: Michael Austin **(T)** 07983 969 644 **(E)** horndeanfc1887@yahoo.co.uk
Chairman: David Sagar **Prog Ed:** Michael Austin
Ground: Five Heads Park Five Heads Road Horndean Hampshire PO8 9NZ **(T)** 02392 591 363
Capacity: **Seats:** **Covered:** **Midweek Matchday:** Tuesday **Clubhouse:**

Colours(change): All red (All pale blue)
Previous Names:
Previous Leagues: Hampshire 1972-86, 1995-2004. Wessex 1986-95
Records: **Att:** 1,560 v Waterlooville, Victory Cup, April 1971. **Goalscorer:** Frank Bryson 348 (including 83 during the 1931-32 season)
Senior Honours:

10 YEAR RECORD

04-05	05-06	06-07	07-08	08-09	09-10	10-11	11-12	12-13	13-14
Wex2 9	Wex2 6	WexP 16	WexP 11	WexP 22	Wex1 12	Wex1 2	WexP 17	WexP 11	WexP 17

LYMINGTON TOWN

Founded: 1876 Nickname:

Secretary: Barry Torah **(T)** 07849 646 234 **(E)** Secretary.lymingtontownfc@yahoo.com
Chairman: George Shaw **Prog Ed:** Barry Torah
Ground: The Sports Ground, Southampton Road, Lymington SO41 9ZG **(T)**
Capacity: 3,000 **Seats:** 200 **Covered:** 300 **Midweek Matchday:** Tuesday **Clubhouse:** Yes

Colours(change): Red/black/black (Yellow/blue/yellow)
Previous Names: None
Previous Leagues: Hampshire.
Records:
Senior Honours: Wessex League Cup 2006-07.

10 YEAR RECORD

04-05	05-06	06-07	07-08	08-09	09-10	10-11	11-12	12-13	13-14
Wex2 1	Wex1 17	WexP 12	WexP 20	WexP 18	WexP 20	WexP 11	WexP 14	WexP 19	WexP 14

MONEYFIELDS

Founded: 1987 Nickname: Moneys

Secretary: Wayne Dalton **(T)** 07766 250 812 **(E)** secretary@moneyfieldsfc.co.uk
Chairman: Paul Gregory **Prog Ed:** David Hayter
Ground: Moneyfields Sports Ground, Moneyfield Ave, Copnor, P'mouth PO3 6LA **(T)** 02392 665 260
Capacity: 1,500 **Seats:** 150 **Covered:** 150 **Midweek Matchday:** Tuesday **Clubhouse:** Yes **Shop:** Yes

Colours(change): Yellow/navy/navy (All white).
Previous Names: Portsmouth Civil Service
Previous Leagues: Portsmouth. Hampshire.
Records: **Att:** 250 v Fareham, WexD1 05-06 **Goalscorer:** Lee Mould 86 **App:** Matt Lafferty - 229 **Win:** 9-0v Blackfield & Langley 01-02.
Senior Honours: Portsmouth Premier Champions 1990-91, 91-92. Senior Cup 1990-91.
Hampshire Division Three 1991-92, Division Two 1992-93, Division One 1996-97.

10 YEAR RECORD

04-05	05-06	06-07	07-08	08-09	09-10	10-11	11-12	12-13	13-14
Wex1 10	Wex1 11	WexP 7	WexP 7	WexP 3	WexP 12	WexP 7	WexP 4	WexP 4	WexP 9

NEWPORT (I.O.W.)

Founded: 1888 Nickname: The Port

Secretary: John Simpkins **(T)** 07771 964 704 **(E)** secretary.newport.iwfc@gmail.com
Chairman: Paul Phelps **Prog Ed:** Chris Davis
Ground: St George's Park, St George's Way, Newport PO30 2QH **(T)** 01983 525 027
Capacity: 5,000 **Seats:** 300 **Covered:** 1,000 **Midweek Matchday:** Tuesday **Clubhouse:** Yes **Shop:** Yes

Colours(change): Yellow/blue/yellow. (All white)
Previous Names:
Previous Leagues: I.O.W. 1896-28. Hants 28-86. Wessex 86-90.
Records: **Att:** 2,270 v Portsmouth (friendly) 07.07.2001. **Goalscorer:** Roy Grilfillan - 220 1951-57. **Apps:** Jeff Austin - 540 1969-87.
Senior Honours: Southern League Eastern Division 2000-01. Hants Senior Cup (x8). I.O.W. Cup (34)

10 YEAR RECORD

04-05	05-06	06-07	07-08	08-09	09-10	10-11	11-12	12-13	13-14
Isth1 18	Isth1 22	SthS 20	SthS 22	WexP 6	WexP 9	WexP 10	WexP 13	WexP 6	WexP 4

PETERSFIELD TOWN

Founded: Nickname:

Secretary: Mark Nicoll **(T)** 07949 328 240 **(E)** m.nicoll1@ntlworld.com
Chairman: Tim Scott **Prog Ed:** David Burley
Ground: Love Lane, Petersfield, Hampshire GU31 4BW **(T)** 01730 233 416
Capacity: **Seats:** **Covered:** **Midweek Matchday:** Tuesday **Clubhouse:** Yes

Colours(change): Red & black stripes/black/black (All green)
Previous Names: Petersfield United folded in 1993. Petersfield Town reformed 1993 to join Wessex League.
Previous Leagues: Hampshire 1980-84. Isthmian 1984-93.
Records:
Senior Honours:

10 YEAR RECORD

04-05	05-06	06-07	07-08	08-09	09-10	10-11	11-12	12-13	13-14
Wex2 5	Wex2 15	Wex1 17	Wex1 8	Wex1 4	Wex1 8	Wex1 11	Wex1 12	Wex1 6	Wex1 1

TOTTON & ELING

Founded: 1925 Nickname:

Secretary: Chas Wood **(T)** 07501 797 723 **(E)** sectottonandeling@btinternet.com
Chairman: Angus Steel **Prog Ed:** Andy Tipp
Ground: Millers Park,Little Tesrwood Farm Salisbury Road Totton SO40 2RW **(T)** 07501 797 723
Capacity: **Seats:** Yes **Covered:** Yes **Midweek Matchday:** Tuesday **Clubhouse:** Yes

Colours(change): Red/black/black (Yellow/blue/blue)
Previous Names: BAT Sports > 2007
Previous Leagues: Hampshire.
Records: 2,763 v AFC Wimbledon, FA Vase (game switched to AFC Wimbedon).
Senior Honours: Hampshire Champions 1987-88, 88-89. Wessex Division 1 2008-09.

10 YEAR RECORD

04-05	05-06	06-07	07-08	08-09	09-10	10-11	11-12	12-13	13-14
Wex1 9	Wex1 18	Wex2 5	Wex1 5	Wex1 1	WexP 7	WexP 18	WexP 11	WexP 12	WexP 18

VERWOOD TOWN

Founded: 1920 Nickname:

Secretary: Nigel Watts **(T)** 07517 077 566 **(E)** secretary@vtfc.co.uk
Chairman: Steve Jefferis **Prog Ed:** Dan Scott
Ground: Potterne Park Potterne Way Verwood Dorset BH21 6RS **(T)** 01202 814 007
Capacity: **Seats:** Yes **Covered:** Yes **Midweek Matchday:** Wednesday **Clubhouse:**

Colours(change): Red/black/red (Yellow/blue/yellow)
Previous Names:
Previous Leagues: Hampshire
Records:
Senior Honours: Wessex League Division One 2011-12.

10 YEAR RECORD

04-05	05-06	06-07	07-08	08-09	09-10	10-11	11-12	12-13	13-14
Wex3 16	Wex3 3	Wex1 6	Wex1 4	Wex1 13	Wex1 7	Wex1 9	Wex1 1	WexP 14	WexP 19

WHITCHURCH UNITED

Founded: 1903 Nickname:

Secretary: Cara Lewis **(T)** 07788 535 359 **(E)** secretarywufc@gmail.com
Chairman: Brian Jackman **Prog Ed:** John Rutledge
Ground: Longmeadow Winchester Road Whitchurch Hampshire RG28 7RB **(T)** 01256 892 493
Capacity: **Seats:** **Covered:** Yes **Midweek Matchday:** Wednesday **Clubhouse:** Yes

Colours(change): Red & white stripes/black/red (Maroon & sky blue/maroon/maroon)
Previous Names: None
Previous Leagues: Hampshire >1992, 1994-95. Wessex 1992-94.
Records:
Senior Honours: Hampshire League Division Two 1989-90.

10 YEAR RECORD

04-05	05-06	06-07	07-08	08-09	09-10	10-11	11-12	12-13	13-14
Wex2 12	Wex2 22	Wex2 12	Wex1 17	Wex1 6	Wex1 10	Wex1 7	Wex1 8	Wex1 2	WexP 13

WINCHESTER CITY

Founded: 1884 **Nickname:** The Capitals

Secretary: Martin Moody **(T)** 07768 848 905 **(E)** secretary.wcfc@gmail.com

Chairman: Paul Murray **Prog Ed:** Andy Hadlington

Ground: The City Ground, Hillier Way, Winchester SO23 7SR **(T)** 07768 848 905

Capacity: 2,500 **Seats:** 200 **Covered:** 275 **Midweek Matchday:** Tuesday **Clubhouse:** Yes **Shop:** Yes

Colours(change): Red & black stripes/red/red (Blue & black stripes/blue/blue)
Previous Names: None
Previous Leagues: Hampshire 1898-71, 73-03. Southern 1971-73, 2006-09, 2012-13. Wessex 2003-06. 2009-12.
Records: 1,818 v Bideford, FA Vase Semi-final.
Senior Honours: Hants Senior Cup 1932, 2005. Southampton Senior Cup 2000-01.
Hampshire Premier Division 2002-03. Wessex Division One 2003-04, 05-06, Premier Division 2011-12. FA Vase 2004.

10 YEAR RECORD

04-05	05-06	06-07	07-08	08-09	09-10	10-11	11-12	12-13	13-14
Wex1 2	Wex1 1	SthW 13	SthW 17	SthW 22	WexP 11	WexP 3	WexP 1	SthC 22	WexP 5

Click Back in Time!

Over 37 years of publishing the Non-League Club Directory has filled a room full of information and photographs covering the game we know and love.

What we intend, over time, is to create a website that shares with you everything we have accumulated, which we hope will bring back some fond memories of season's gone by.

A unique look back at how the game has evolved since the 1940s will also make for interesting reading, including league tables from season's gone by.

Log on to **www.non-leagueclubdirectory.co.uk** today and see how many faces from teams gone by you recognise

AMESBURY TOWN

Founded: 1904 Nickname:

Secretary: Arthur Mundy **(T)** 07791 148 594 **(E)** amesburytownfc@gmail.com
Chairman: Jason Cameron **Prog Ed:** Mark Hilton
Ground: Bonnymead Park Recreation Road Amesbury SP4 7BB **(T)** 01980 623 489
Colours(change): All blue (All yellow)

ADDITIONAL INFORMATION:
Previous Name: Amesbury FC. **Previous League:** Hampshire.
Record Att: 625 - 1997.

ANDOVER NEW STREET

Founded: 1895 Nickname:

Secretary: Lucy Harfield **(T)** 07786 152 277 **(E)** andovernewstreetfc@hotmail.co.uk
Chairman: Martin Tobin **Prog Ed:** Jimmy Wilson
Ground: Foxcotte Park Charlton Andover Hampshire SP11 0HS **(T)** 01264 358 358
Colours(change): Green & black/black/black (Yellow/blue/white)

ADDITIONAL INFORMATION:
Record Att: 240.
Honours: Trophyman Cup 2003-04.

COWES SPORTS

Founded: 1881 Nickname: Yachtsmen

Secretary: Glynn M Skinner **(T)** 07854 889 446 **(E)** csfcsecretary@yahoo.com
Chairman: Ian Lee **Prog Ed:** Peter Jeffery
Ground: Westwood Park Reynolds Close off Park Rd Cowes Isle of Wight PO31 7NT **(T)** 01983 718 277
Colours(change): Blue & White stripes/black/blue (Red/white/red)

ADDITIONAL INFORMATION:
Previous League: Hampshire > 1994.
Honours: Hampshire League 1993-94.

DOWNTON

Founded: 1905 Nickname: The Robins

Secretary: Brian Ford **(T)** 07743 538984 **(E)** info@downtonfc.com
Chairman: Colin Stainer **Prog Ed:** Mark Smith
Ground: Brian Whitehead Sports Ground Wick Lane Downton Wiltshire SP5 3NF **(T)** 01725 512 162
Colours(change): Red/white/red (Yellow/blue/yellow)

ADDITIONAL INFORMATION: **Att:** 55 v AFC Bournemouth - Friendly.
Wiltshire Senior Cup 1979-80, 80-81. Wiltshire Junior Cup 1949-50. Wessex League Cup 1995-96.
Wessex League Division One 2010-11.

EAST COWES VICTORIA ATHLETIC

Founded: Nickname:

Secretary: Darren Dyer **(T)** 07725 128 701 **(E)** ecvafc@outlook.com
Chairman: Kenny Adams **Prog Ed:** Darren Dyer
Ground: Beatrice Avenue Whippingham East Cowes Isle of Wight PO32 6PA **(T)** 01983 297 165
Colours(change): Red & white/black/black (Orange & white/white/orange)

ADDITIONAL INFORMATION:

FLEET SPURS

Founded: Nickname:

Secretary: Phil Blakey **(T)** 07941 225 579 **(E)** wessex@fleetspurs.co.uk
Chairman: Bryan Sheppard **Prog Ed:** Bryan Sheppard
Ground: Kennels Lane Southwood Farnborough Hampshire, GU14 0ST **(T)**
Colours(change): Blue with red trim/red/blue (Yellow/black/yellow)

ADDITIONAL INFORMATION:

HYTHE & DIBDEN

Founded: Nickname:

Secretary: Scott Johnston **(T)** 07825 550 624 **(E)** hythedibdenfc@aol.com
Chairman: Dave Cox **Prog Ed:** Scott Johnston
Ground: Clayfield, Claypit Lane, Dibden SO45 5TN **(T)** 07769 951 982
Colours(change): Green & white/white/green (All blue)

ADDITIONAL INFORMATION:

LAVERSTOCK & FORD

Founded: 1956 Nickname:

Secretary: Matthew McMahon **(T)** 07795 665 731 **(E)** sec.laverstockandfordfc@gmail.com
Chairman: John Pike **Prog Ed:** Andrew Wykes
Ground: The Dell, Church Road, Laverstock, Salisbury, Wilts SP1 1QX **(T)** 01722 327 401
Colours(change): Green & white hoops/green/green (Yellow/blue/white)

ADDITIONAL INFORMATION:

NEW MILTON TOWN

Founded: 2007 Nickname: The Linnets

Secretary: Ian Claxton **(T)** 01425 271 865 **(E)** newmiltontown@yahoo.co.uk
Chairman: John Breaker **Prog Ed:** Ian Claxton
Ground: Fawcett Fields, Christchurch Road, New Milton, BH25 6QB **(T)** 01425 628 191 **Capacity:** 3,000
Colours(change): Maroon & blue stripes/blue/blue (Orange/red/red)

ADDITIONAL INFORMATION:
Honours: Wessex League 1998-99, 04-05.

PEWSEY VALE

Founded: 1948 Nickname:

Secretary: Julie Wootton **(T)** 01672 911 797 **(E)** pewseyvalefc@hotmail.co.uk
Chairman: Alan Ritchie **Prog Ed:** Julie Wootton
Ground: Recreation Ground, Kings Corne,r Ball Road, Pewsey SN9 5BS **(T)** 01672 5629 090
Colours(change): White/navy/navy (All yellow)

ADDITIONAL INFORMATION:
Previous League: Wiltshire.

RINGWOOD TOWN

Founded: 1879 Nickname:

Secretary: Aubrey Hodder **(T)** 07754 460 501 **(E)** ringwoodtownfc@live.co.uk
Chairman: Phil King **Prog Ed:** Phil King
Ground: The Canotec Stadium Long Lane Ringwood Hampshire BH24 3BX **(T)** 01425 473 448
Colours(change): All red (Blue/blue/black)

ADDITIONAL INFORMATION:

ROMSEY TOWN

Founded: 1886 Nickname:

Secretary: Clare Crossland **(T)** 07864 877 274 **(E)** romseytownfc@gmail.com
Chairman: Ken Jacobs **Prog Ed:** Cameron Melling
Ground: The Bypass Ground, South Front, Romsey, SO51 8GJ **(T)** 01794 516 691
Colours(change): White & black/black/black. (Blue/white/blue).

ADDITIONAL INFORMATION:
Wessex League Champions 1989-90.

TADLEY CALLEVA

Founded: Nickname:

Secretary: Steve Blackburn **(T)** 07787 501 028 **(E)** tadleycallevafc@sky.com
Chairman: Sandy Russell **Prog Ed:** Andy Russell
Ground: Barlows Park Silchester Road Tadley Hampshire RG26 3PX **(T)** 07787 501 028
Colours(change): Yellow & black/black/yellow (Burgundy & blue/burgundy/blue)

ADDITIONAL INFORMATION:

TEAM SOLENT

Founded: Nickname:

Secretary: Adam Kelly **(T)** 07917 415 304 **(E)** secretary.teamsolent@solent.ac.uk
Chairman: Bill Moore **Prog Ed:** Izzy Jansen
Ground: Test Park, Lower Broomhill Road, Southampton SO16 9BP **(T)**
Colours(change): All red (Yellow/black/black).

ADDITIONAL INFORMATION:
Previous Lge: Hampshire > 2011.

UNITED SERVICES PORTSMOUTH

Founded: 1962 Nickname:

Secretary: Bob Brady (T) 07887 541 782 (E) usportsmouthfc@hotmail.co.uk
Chairman: Richard Stephenson Lt. RN **Prog Ed:** Charlie Read
Ground: Victory Stadium HMS Temeraire Burnaby Road Portsmouth PO1 2HB (T) 02392 573 041 (Gr'sman)
Colours(change): Royal blue & red stripes/royal blue/royal blue (Red & white/red/red)

ADDITIONAL INFORMATION:
Previous Name: Portsmouth Royal Navy 1962-2005.
Honours: Hampshire League Division Two 1967-68, 77-78, 80-81. Portsmouth Senior Cup 2011-12.

GROUND DIRECTIONS

AFC PORTCHESTER - Wicor Recreation Ground Cranleigh Road Portchester Hampshire PO16 9DP 07798 734678 (M)
Leave the M27 at Junction 11 and follow the signs to Portchester into Portchester Road. Carry on for approx 1 mile at the large roundabout, take the 3rd exit into Cornaway Lane and at the 'T' junction turn right in Cranleigh Road and follow the road to the end. Postcode for Satellite Navigation systems PO16 9DP

ALRESFORD TOWN FC - Arlebury Park The Avenue Alresford Hampshire SO24 9EP 01962 735 100
Alresford is situated on the A31 between Winchester and Alton. Arlebury Park is on the main avenue into Alresford opposite Perins School.
Postcode for Satellite Navigation systems SO24 9EP

AMESBURY TOWN FC - Bonnymead Park Recreation Road Amesbury SP4 7BB 01980 623489
From Salisbury take A345 to Amesbury, turn left just past the bus station and proceed through the one way system, when road splits with Friar Tuck Café and Lloyds Bank on left turn left and follow road over the river bridge and when road bears sharp right turn left into Recreation Road.
From A303 at Countess Roundabout go into Amesbury, straight over traffic lights, at mini-roundabout turn right into one way system and follow directions as above.
Postcode for Satellite Navigation systems SP4 7BB

ANDOVER NEW STREET FC - Foxcotte Park Charlton Andover Hampshire SP11 0HS 01264 358358 Weekends from Midday, Evenings from 1900 hrs
From Basingstoke follow the A303 to Weyhill roundabout. At roundabout turn right and 2nd roundabout turn left on to A342. Approx 1/2 mile turn right into Short Lane, continue into Harroway Lane to the 'T' junction at the top. Turn right into Foxcotte Lane and continue for about 3/4 mile then turn left, this still Foxcotte Lane, to the top some 3/4 mile to the roundabout straight across into Foxcotte Park. Postcode for Satellite Navigation systems SP11 0TA.

ANDOVER TOWN - Portway Stadium,Portway Industrial Estate, Andover AP10 3LF
Leave A303 at Junction for A342 . If from the East cross back over A303. At large roundabout take A342 across the face of the Premier Hotel. First right into the Portway Industrial Estate then follow the one way system and after the road swings right at the bottom of the hill the ground is on the left.

BEMERTON HEATH HARLEQUINS FC - The Clubhouse Western Way Bemerton Heath Salisbury Wiltshire SP2 9DT 01722 331925 (Club) 331218 (Office)
Turn off the A36 Salisbury to Bristol road at Skew Bridge (right turn if coming out of Salisbury), 1st left into Pembroke Road for 1/2 mile, 2nd left along Western Way – Ground is 1/4 mile at the end of the road. 40 minutes walk fro Salisbury railway station. Bus service 51 or 52 from the city centre.
Postcode for Satellite Navigation systems SP2 9DP

BLACKFIELD & LANGLEY FC - Gang Warily Community and Recreation Centre Newlands Road Fawley Southampton SO45 1GA 02380 893 603
Leave M27 at Junction 2 signposted A326 to Fawley. Head South along A326 through several roundabouts. Pass the Holbury P/H on your right at roundabout take the right fork signposted Lepe and Fawley.At the 1st set of traffic lights turn left then turn left into the ground, approx 200 yards. There is a sign at the traffic lights indicating Blackfield & Langley FC. Postcode for Satellite Navigation systems SO45 1GA

BOURNEMOUTH FC - Victoria Park Namu Road Winton Bournemouth Dorset BH9 2RA 01202 515 123
From the North and East – A338 from Ringwood. Take the 3rd exit signed A3060 Wimborne, going under the road you've just left. Stay on this road passing Castlepoint Shopping Centre (on your right), then the Broadway Hotel on your right, keep straight ahead passing the Horse & Jockey on your left, keep to the nearside lane. At roundabout take the 1st exit marked A347, pass Redhill Common on your right and the fire station on your left: continue on the A347 turning left at the filter with the pub – The Ensbury Park Hotel – immediately in front of you. 1st left into Victoria Avenue, and then third right into Namu Road, turning right at the end into the lane for the ground entrance.
From the West – A35 from Poole. Take the A3049 Dorset Way passing Tower Park (which is hidden from view) on your right, at the next roundabout take the second exit, and then the first exit at the next roundabout, taking up a position in the outside lane. At the next roundabout (with a pub called the Miller and Carter Steakhouse on your right) take the third exit, Wallisdown Road A3049. Go through the shopping area of Wallisdown across two roundabouts and at the third one take the first exit, you will see the ground on your right as you approach the pelican crossing. Turn right into Victoria Avenue, then third right into Namu Road, turning right at the end into the lane for the ground entrance. Postcode for Satellite Navigation systems BH9 2RA

BROCKENHURST FC - Grigg Lane Brockenhurst Hampshire SO42 7RE 01590 623544
Leave the M27 at Junction 1 and take the A337 to Lyndhurst. From Lyndhurst take the A337 signposted Brockenhurst, turn right at Careys Manor Hotel into Grigg Lane. Ground situated 200 yards on the right. Postcode for Satellite Navigation systems SO42 7RE

CHRISTCHURCH FC - Hurn Bridge Sports Club Avon Causeway Hurn Christchurc Dorset BH23 6DY 01202 473 792
A338 from Ringwood turn off at sign for Bournemouth International Airport (Hurn) on left. At T junction turn right, continue through traffic lights, at the small roundabout in Hurn turn right away from the Airport, exit signed Sopley and 100 yards on the right is Hurn Bridge Sports Ground. Postcode for Sat. Nav. systems BH23 6DY

COWES SPORTS FC - Westwood Park Reynolds Close off Park Road Cowes Isle of Wight PO31 7NT 01983 293 793
Turn left out of the Cowes pontoon, 1st right up Park Road approx 1/2 mile take the 4th right into Reynolds Close. Postcode for Sat. Nav. systems PO31 7NT

DOWNTON FC - Brian Whitehead Sports Ground Wick Lane Downton Wiltshire SP5 3NF 01725 512 162
The ground is situated 6 miles south of Salisbury on the A338 to Bournemouth. In the village – sign to the Leisure Centre (to west) – this is Wick Lane – football pitch and Club approx 1/4 mile on the left. Postcode for Satellite Navigation systems SP5 3NF

EAST COWES VICTORIA FC - Beatrice Avenue Whippingham East Cowes Isle of Wight PO32 6PA 01983 297 165
From East Cowes ferry terminal follow Well Road into York Avenue until reaching Prince of Wells PH, turn at the next right into Crossways Road then turn left into Beatrice Avenue, from Fishbourne follow signs to East Cowes and Whippingham Church, ground is 200 yards from the church on Beatrice Avenue.
Postcode for Satellite Navigation systems PO32 6PA

FAREHAM TOWN FC - Cams Alders Football Stadium Cams Alders Palmerston Drive Fareham Hampshire PO14 1BJ 07930 853 235 (Club)
Leave the M27 at Junction 11. Follow signs A32 Fareham – Gosport. Pass under the viaduct with Fareham Creek on your left, straight over at the roundabout then fork right – B3385 sign posted Lee-on-Solent. Over the railway bridge, Newgate Lane and turn immediately first right into Palmerston Business Park, follow the road to the ground. Postcode for Satellite Navigation systems PO14 1BJ

FAWLEY AFC - Waterside Sports and Social Club 179-182 Long Lane Holbury Southampton Hampshire SO45 2PA 02380 893750 (Club) 896621 (Office)
Leave the M27 at Junction 2 and follow the A326 to Fawley/Beaulieu. Head south for approx 7 miles. The Club is situated on the right hand side 2/3 mile after crossing the Hardley roundabout. The Club is positioned directly behind the service road on the right hand side. Postcode for Satellite Navigation systems SO45 2PA

FLEET SPURS FC - Kennels Lane Southwood Farnborough Hampshire, GU14 0ST
From the M3 Junction 4A take the A327 towards Farnborough/Cove. Left at the roundabout, over the railway line, left at the next roundabout Kennels Lane is on the right opposite the Nokia building, entrance is 100 yards on the left. Postcode for Satellite Navigation systems GU14 0ST

FOLLAND SPORTS - Folland Park Kings Avenue Hamble-Le-Rice Southampton Hampshire SO31 4NF 02380 452 173
Leave the M27 at Junction 8 and take the turning for Southampton East At the Windhover roundabout take the exit for Hamble (B3397) Hamble Lane, proceed for 3 miles. Upon entering Hamble the ground is on the right via Kings Avenue, opposite the Harrier P/H. Postcode for Satellite Navigation systems SO31 4NF

HAMWORTHY UNITED FC - The County Ground Blandford Close Hamworthy Poole Dorset BH15 4BF 01202 674 974
From M27 to Cadnam – follow A31 to Ringwood – A347/A348 Ferndown - Bearcross – follow on this road until you pass the Mountbatten Arms on your left – turn right at next roundabout onto the A3049 and follow the signs to Dorchester and Poole. Continue on this dual carriageway over the flyover to the next roundabout – straight across and take the 2nd exit left off the dual carriageway to Upton / Hamworthy – go straight across 2 mini roundabouts and continue to Hamworthy passing the Co-op store on your left – then turn left at the 2nd set of traffic lights into Blandford Close. Postcode for Satellite Navigation systems BH15 4BF

HORNDEAN FC - Five Heads Park Five Heads Road Horndean Hampshire PO8 9NZ 02392 591 363
Leave A3(M) at Junction 2 and follow signs to Cowplain. Take the slip road passing Morrisons store on the right crossing over the mini roundabout then continue to the set of traffic lights ensuring you are in the right hand lane signed Horndean. Turn right at these traffic lights and continue on for approximately 400 yards until you reach the Colonial Bar on your left, next junction on your left after the Colonial Bar is Five Heads Road, turn left into Five Heads Road and the ground is approx 1/4 mile along this road. Postcode for Satellite Navigation systems PO8 9NZ

HYTHE & DIBDEN FC - Clayfield, Claypit Lane, Dibden SO45 5TN 07769 951 982
Postcode for Satellite Navigation systems SO45 5TN

LAVERSTOCK & FORD FC - The Dell Church Road Laverstock Salisbury Wiltshire SP1 1QX 01722 327 401
From Southampton – At the end of the carriageway from Southampton (A36) turn right at traffic lights for the Park & Ride by the Tesco store. Turn left at the traffic lights over the narrow bridge then take the next turning into Manor Farm Road. Take the next turning right into Laverstock Road, (do not turn left under the railway bridge). Keep left into Laverstock village, past the Church and the Club is situated on the left hand side directly opposite the Chinese takeaway and shop.
From Bournemouth – Follow the A36 to Southampton past Salisbury College and straight across the Tesco roundabout take left at traffic lights into the Park & Ride (take the corner slowly, the road goes back on itself) then follow directions as above. Postcode for Satellite Navigation systems SP1 1QX

LYMINGTON TOWN FC - The Sports Ground Southampton Road Lymington Hampshire SO41 9ZG 01590 671 305 (Club)
From the North & East – Leave the M27 at Junction 1 (Cadnam/New Forest) and proceed via Lyndhurst then Brockenhurst on the A337. On the outskirts of Lymington proceed through main set of traffic lights with Royal Quarter Housing Development and the Police Station on your right hand side. Continue for just another 250 metres and turn left immediately into St Thomas's Park with he ground in front of you.
Alternatively, turn left at the traffic lights into Avenue Road then first right, Oberland Court, with the Lymington Bowling Club facing you.
If travelling from the direction of Christchurch & New Milton using the A337 pass the White Hart P/H on the outskirts of Pennington and proceed down and up Stanford Hill. Passing the Waitrose Supermarket on your left hand side, the ground is situated immediately on your right hand side sign posted St Thomas Park.
Postcode for Satellite Navigation systems SO41 9ZG

MONEYFIELDS FC - Moneyfields Sports Ground Moneyfield Avenue Copnor Portsmouth Hampshire PO3 6LA 02392 665 260 (Club) 07766 250 812 (M)
Leave the A27 from the West and East at the Southsea turn off (A2030). Head down the Eastern Road and turn right into Tangiers Road at the fourth set of traffic lights – continue along this road until you pass the school and shops on your left and take the next right into Folkestone Road carrying on through to Martins Road and the Moneyfields Sports & Social Club is directly in front of you. Postcode for Satellite Navigation systems PO3 6LA

NEW MILTON TOWN FC - Fawcett Fields Christchurch Road New Milton Hampshire BH25 6QB 01425 628 191
Leave the M27 at Junction 2 and follow the signs to Lyndhurst. Carry on this road over four roundabouts and take the next slip road.At the traffic lights turn right to Lyndhurst. Go around the one way system and follow the signs to Christchurch (A35). After 10 miles at the Cat and Fiddle Public House turn left and continue towards the Chewton Glen Hotel. First exit at roundabout A337 to New Milton.The ground is one mile on the left. Postcode for Sat. Nav. systems BH25 6QB

NEWPORT (IOW) FC LTD. - St Georges Park St Georges Way Newport Isle of Wight PO30 2QH 01983 525 027 (Club)
From the Fishbourne Car Ferry Terminal take the A3054 towards Newport. At the large roundabout in the town centre take the A3020 towards Sandown, under the footbridge then 1st exit off the next roundabout. The ground is 200 yards on the left. Postcode for Satellite Navigation systems PO30 2QH

PETERSFIELD TOWN FC - Love Lane Petersfield Hampshire GU31 4BW 01730 233 416
Off circulatory one-way system in the town centre. Approx 10 minutes walk from Petersfield train station. Postcode for Satellite Navigation systems GU31 4BW

PEWSEY VALE FC - Recreation Ground Kings Corner Ball Road Pewsey 01672 562 900
From Pewsey's King Alfred statue, take the B3087 Burbage Road for 100 yards and then turn right into the Co-op car park, park in top right hand corner next to the bowls and tennis club and then walk through to the ground. Postcode for Satellite Navigation systems SN9 5BS

RINGWOOD TOWN FC - The Canotec Stadium Long Lane Ringwood Hampshire BH24 3BX 01425 473 448
Travel to Ringwood via the A31 (M27). From Ringwood town centre travel 1 mile on the B3347 towards Christchurch. At the Texaco petrol station turn into Moortown Lane and after 200 yards turn right into Long Lane. The ground is situated 250 yards on your left. Postcode for Satellite Navigation systems BH24 3BX

ROMSEY TOWN FC - The Bypass Ground South Front Romsey Hampshire SO51 8GJ
The ground is situated on the south of the town on the A27/A3090 roundabout (Romsey by pass), adjacent to the Romsey Rapids and Broadlands Estate.
Postcode for Satellite Navigation systems SO51 8GJ

TADLEY CALLEVA FC - Barlows Park Silchester Road Tadley Hampshire RG26 3PX

From M3 Basingstoke Junction 6 take the A340 to Tadley, travel through Tadley and at the main traffic lights turn right into Silchester Road, proceed for 0.5 mile then turn left into the car park. Postcode for Satellite Navigation systems RG26 3PX

TEAM SOLENT - Test Park, Lower Broomhill Road, Southampton SO16 9QZ

Leave the M27 at junction 3 for M271. Take the first slip road off the M271 and then first exit off the roundabout on to Lower Broomhill Road. Carry on to the next roundabout and take the last exit, (coming back on yourself) into Redbridge lane and the entrance to Test Park is approx. 500m on right.

From City centre take the Millbrook road to the M271, first slip road off on to roundabout, 3rd exit on to Lower Broomhill Way and then as above.

Postcode for Satellite Navigation systems SO16 9QZ

TOTTON & ELING FC - Millers Park,Little Tesrwood Farm Salisbury Road Totton SO40 2RW 07445 523 103

Leave M27 at Junction.2 and take A326 exit signposted Totton/Fawley. Almost immediately leave A326 onto slip road signposted Totton Town Centre which will meet the A36 (Salisbury Road). Turn left on to A36 and proceed for approx. three quarters of a mile and the ground entrance is on the left just before the Calmore Roundabout

UNITED SERVICES PORTSMOUTH FC - Victory Stadium HMS Temeraire Burnaby Road Portsmouth Hampshire PO1 2HB

02392 724235 (Clubhouse) 02392 725315 (Office)

Leave the M27 at Junction 12 and join the M275 to Portsmouth. Follow the signs to Gunwharf, turn right at the traffic lights into Park Road then left at the next set of lights into Burnaby Road and the entrance is at the end of this road on the right.via HMS Temeraire.

NB Car parking in HMS Temeraire is for Senior Club and Match Officials only on the production of a current Sydenhams League (Wessex) pass. Free car parking for players and supporters is at the Portsmouth University Nuffield car park opposite the Registry Public House – follow Anglesea Road and signs for Southsea/Ferry Terminals, go under railway bridge past lights, keeping US Rogby Stadium on your right into Hampshire Terrace and keeping right, LOOP back into Anglesey Road, go through pedestrian lights and then immediately left into the car park. From car park turn right past pedestrian lights into Cambridge Road, then right into Burnaby Road. Postcode for Satellite Navigation systems PO1 2HB

VERWOOD TOWN FC - POTTERNE PARK POTTERNE WAY VERWOOD DORSET BH21 6RS 01202 814 007

Turn off the A31 at Verwood/Matchams junctions just West of Ringwood Town centre exit (immediately after garage if coming from the East) to join the B3081. Follow the B3081 through the forest for approximately 4 miles coming into Verwood itself. At the second set of traffic lights turn left into Black Hill. At the roundabout take the 1st exit left into Newtown Road. At the end of Newtown Road turn left and then 1st left into Potterne Way. Note: Along Black Hill on the left you will pass Bradfords Building Merchants and the entrance to the Verwood Sports & Social Club where post match refreshments are made available.

Postcode for Satellite Navigation systems BH21 6RS

WHITCHURCH UNITED FC - Longmeadow Winchester Road Whitchurch Hampshire RG28 7RB 01256 892 493

From the South – take the A34 (North), 2 miles north of Bullington Cross take the Whitchurch exit. Head for Whitchurch Town Centre. The ground is 500 yards on your right. Postcode for Satellite Navigation systems RG28 7RB

WINCHESTER CITY - The City Ground, Hillier Way, Winchester SO23 7SR 07768 848 905

From Junction 9 on the M3 take the A33/A34 for one mile then follow A33 for a further mile.

Take the first left into Kings Worthy and follow the road for about three miles. When you enter the 30mph zone take the second left, first right, then left into Hillier Way, Ground is on the right.

WEST MIDLANDS (REGIONAL) LEAGUE

Sponsored by: No sponsor
Founded: 1889
Recent Champions:
2009: AFC Wulfrunians
2010: Ellesmere Rangers
2011: Tividale
2012: Gornal Athletic
2013: AFC Wulfrunians

PREMIER DIVISION	P	W	D	L	F	A	GD	Pts
1 (P) Lye Town	42	31	8	3	141	39	102	101
2 Pegasus Juniors	42	32	4	6	127	44	83	100
3 W'Ton Casuals	42	31	5	6	128	68	60	98
4 Shawbury United	42	30	7	5	139	50	89	97
5 Black Country Rangers (-3pts)	42	29	2	11	120	58	62	86
6 Sporting Khalsa	42	26	4	12	130	63	67	82
7 Bewdley Town	42	20	5	17	94	75	19	65
8 Dudley Town	42	19	6	17	101	87	14	63
9 Cradley Town	42	19	5	18	89	87	2	62
10 Wellington	41	18	8	15	85	87	-2	62
11 Ellesmere Rangers	42	18	7	17	91	87	4	61
12 Smethwick Rangers	42	16	5	21	87	100	-13	53
13 Wellington Amateurs	42	15	6	21	78	88	-10	51
14 Malvern Town	42	16	3	23	74	95	-21	51
15 Wednesfield	41	14	8	19	72	78	-6	50
16 Bilston Town (2007)	42	13	4	25	77	107	-30	43
17 Dudley Sports	42	11	10	21	64	107	-43	43
18 Wolverhampton Sporting Com.	42	10	7	25	54	97	-43	37
19 Shifnal Town (-1pt)	42	9	6	27	49	104	-55	32
20 Willenhall Town	42	7	7	28	50	133	-83	28
21 (R) Bustleholme	42	6	8	28	57	152	-95	26
22 (R) Bromyard Town	42	7	3	32	40	141	-101	24

Bartley Green withdrew - record expunged.

DIVISION ONE	P	W	D	L	F	A	GD	Pts
1 (P) AFC Bridgnorth	30	26	3	1	117	18	99	81
2 (P) Haughmond	30	22	4	4	89	33	56	70
3 Bartestree	30	18	7	5	80	36	44	61
4 Wem Town	30	17	3	10	91	59	32	54
5 Penncroft	30	12	9	9	78	73	5	45
6 Hanwood United (-3pts)	30	15	1	14	68	64	4	43
7 Wyrley	30	13	4	13	70	69	1	43
8 Stone Old Alleynians	30	10	8	12	54	50	4	38
9 Gornal Athletic Res	30	10	8	12	62	71	-9	38
10 Hereford Lads Club	30	12	2	16	58	68	-10	38
11 Trysull	30	9	8	13	63	68	-5	35
12 Shenstone Pathfinders	30	9	6	15	47	68	-21	33
13 Ledbury Town	30	9	4	17	60	89	-29	31
14 St Martins	30	8	4	18	48	96	-48	28
15 (R) Mahal	30	7	3	20	47	93	-46	24
16 (R) Wolverhampton United	30	5	2	23	29	106	-77	17

DIVISION TWO	P	W	D	L	F	A	GD	Pts
1 (P) AFC Ludlow	26	17	3	6	91	28	63	54
2 (P) Team Dudley	26	17	3	6	83	39	44	54
3 (P) Worcester Raiders	26	16	2	8	107	77	30	50
4 Penkridge Town	26	15	5	6	75	56	19	50
5 (P) Wrens Nest	25	14	5	6	64	40	24	47
6 Newport Town	26	11	7	8	80	57	23	40
7 Wolverhampton Sp. Com. Res (-3pts)	26	13	4	9	53	73	-20	40
8 Malvern Rangers (-4pts)	26	13	3	10	85	66	19	38
9 Warstone Wanderers	25	11	4	10	65	58	7	37
10 F C Stafford	26	11	3	12	77	53	24	36
11 Sikh Hunters (-3pts)	26	9	2	15	55	85	-30	26
12 Red Star Alma	26	4	4	18	31	94	-63	16
13 Wyrley Reserves	26	2	5	19	29	83	-54	11
14 Bilbrook	26	2	2	22	32	118	-86	8

PREMIER DIVISION	1	2	3	4	5	6	7	8	9	10	11	12	13	14	15	16	17	18	19	20	21	22
1 Bewdley Town		4-2	0-6	0-1	6-0	4-1	6-0	1-2	2-0	3-2	0-0	0-1	0-0	3-1	2-4	5-2	6-1	3-0	1-1	0-3	1-4	3-1
2 Bilston Town (2007)	2-2		1-3	6-1	6-1	0-3	2-1	1-4	3-2	1-2	1-3	2-4	1-2	3-2	1-4	0-4	0-2	2-0	1-4	3-0	2-0	1-1
3 Black Country Rangers	4-2	3-2		5-0	5-0	3-0	2-3	5-1	1-3	1-3	0-2	1-2	1-0	5-0	3-2	4-1	0-2	3-2	6-1	3-1	4-1	4-1
4 Bromyard Town	1-2	1-3	1-8		2-1	2-4	1-3	1-5	2-4	0-3	3-1	0-2	1-1	1-0	1-2	0-8	1-5	0-3	1-1	3-6	0-5	1-5
5 Bustleholme	1-3	3-3	1-1	1-1		3-3	2-5	0-5	1-7	1-7	3-1	0-5	2-8	3-1	0-5	2-2	2-5	3-1	1-3	1-1	0-2	5-4
6 Cradley Town	2-0	1-0	1-3	2-1	5-0		3-2	2-4	3-2	2-3	2-0	3-1	0-4	4-1	4-1	1-1	1-5	2-2	1-1	1-2	7-0	2-0
7 Dudley Sports	1-6	2-1	2-2	3-4	3-4	2-3		1-0	2-1	0-0	1-2	0-2	1-2	2-0	0-5	1-10	0-1	3-3	1-2	1-1	1-2	2-1
8 Dudley Town	4-4	4-0	1-2	3-0	5-0	2-2	5-1		1-5	2-2	2-2	1-3	1-2	0-2	6-2	2-1	2-3	2-0	0-5	0-3	3-1	6-1
9 Ellesmere Rangers	1-6	0-1	0-2	3-1	4-1	1-0	2-2	2-1		1-2	1-2	2-4	1-1	2-0	1-3	2-0	6-6	0-0	2-3	3-0	1-0	3-0
10 Lye Town	4-2	5-2	2-0	3-0	6-0	3-0	8-0	9-2	2-1		5-0	1-1	3-1	7-0	4-0	2-1	1-1	6-0	4-1	3-1	2-0	7-0
11 Malvern Town	2-1	2-1	2-5	3-1	4-1	2-1	3-0	9-1	1-2	2-0		0-3	1-3	0-0	4-0	2-6	3-6	3-1	1-8	2-5	1-3	3-1
12 Pegasus Juniors	2-1	7-3	2-4	6-0	4-1	3-0	6-1	2-1	8-0	1-0	1-0		0-2	4-0	1-4	2-0	4-0	4-1	3-1	2-2	2-2	7-0
13 Shawbury United	2-0	4-0	4-0	8-1	8-1	4-1	2-2	3-2	6-1	3-4	4-2	5-2		2-1	5-2	1-2	0-3	6-0	6-1	2-1	3-1	6-0
14 Shifnal Town	0-1	2-1	1-2	1-3	2-2	1-2	3-4	0-3	2-2	1-7	3-1	2-1	1-7		0-3	0-4	3-2	1-0	0-1	2-2	5-1	0-0
15 Smethwick Rangers	3-0	1-1	0-5	5-0	2-1	2-1	1-0	1-1	2-5	1-2	3-1	2-3	3-5	1-4		1-6	2-2	2-3	0-3	0-2	2-2	1-3
16 Sporting Khalsa	3-1	2-0	3-1	8-0	2-1	3-2	2-3	1-2	5-1	0-0	4-0	0-5	0-3	4-0	6-1		0-3	3-1	3-3	2-1	4-1	5-2
17 Wednesfield	3-0	4-5	5-3	4-0	4-2	2-4	4-0	2-1	2-0	2-2	4-0	1-4	0-0	3-1	3-2	2-1		3-2	4-0	4-2	2-1	5-3
18 Wellington	0-1	2-3	0-3	1-0	4-2	2-5	0-0	4-1	1-3	1-1	2-1	0-1	2-2	2-1	2-4	1-2	0-3		2-1	3-3	0-2	2-1
19 Wellington Amateurs	0-3	2-0	0-2	2-1	0-2	5-1	1-1	0-2	3-3	1-3	3-2	0-1	0-0	2-4	1-1	1-2	1-2	1-3		1-2	1-3	2-3
20 Willenhall Town	5-1	7-2	1-0	0-1	2-1	3-0	2-2	1-6	1-6	0-6	2-1	0-8	3-4	1-1	2-0	2-4	1-3	4-1	1-0		1-0	4-0
21 Wolverhampton Casuals	2-4	5-0	2-4	2-1	4-0	5-3	0-0	1-1	3-4	2-2	2-1	0-2	0-2	4-0	1-5	1-5	2-4	4-0	0-2	3-4		2-2
22 Woverhampton Sporting Community	1-4	1-8	0-1	3-0	1-1	2-4	0-5	0-4	1-1	1-3	0-2	1-1	2-6	2-0	3-2	0-8	0-6	2-0	0-3	1-1	0-2	

DIVISION ONE	1	2	3	4	5	6	7	8	9	10	11	12	13	14	15	16
1 AFC Bridgnorth		0-0	6-0	3-0	1-1	4-0	4-1	5-0	6-1	4-0	7-0	4-0	5-0	7-0	5-1	2-1
2 Bartestree	1-1		4-0	3-1	3-2	0-2	0-0	5-0	3-0	3-0	5-0	0-2	6-1	3-1	1-2	9-2
3 Gornal Athletic Reserves	2-5	2-4		1-2	0-6	3-1	1-0	5-2	5-5	4-0	4-1	3-1	1-1	2-0	3-4	2-2
4 Hanwood United	2-3	1-3	2-0		1-2	0-3	9-0	4-1	3-3	0-1	5-4	1-3	1-3	4-2	2-1	2-3
5 Haughmond	1-3	1-1	3-0	3-0		2-0	6-2	3-0	2-0	2-2	4-1	3-2	3-0	5-0	3-1	1-2
6 Hereford Lads Club	1-4	0-1	1-1	0-2	2-5		1-2	6-1	1-3	3-1	10-1	2-2	0-2	1-0	1-4	0-5
7 Ledbury Town	0-4	1-3	6-1	5-2	1-1	6-2		2-4	3-3	2-1	1-2	0-3	2-1	4-1	2-1	2-3
8 Mahal	1-3	2-6	1-1	1-3	1-4	3-1	4-4		1-3	0-1	0-4	1-1	3-1	1-3	2-0	0-5
9 Penncroft	0-1	4-0	2-5	5-1	2-6	1-4	8-3	5-1		2-2	3-5	2-1	1-1	3-2	5-3	4-0
10 Shenstone Pathfinders	1-4	1-2	3-3	1-3	0-2	1-3	3-1	3-1	2-2		4-1	2-3	3-2	4-1	1-2	3-1
11 St Martins	1-8	0-4	3-1	1-2	3-7	3-2	2-0	2-1	2-2	0-1		0-0	1-1	0-2	1-5	2-0
12 Stone Old Alleynians	0-1	1-1	2-1	1-2	0-1	1-2	1-3	2-3	4-1	4-2	4-1		2-3	3-3	2-1	2-2
13 Trysull	0-4	2-2	2-2	2-4	1-2	0-1	7-1	2-4	2-2	6-2	4-4	1-1		5-1	1-2	3-2
14 Wem Town	0-5	0-1	0-3	3-1	1-6	1-3	3-1	0-7	0-1	1-1	1-0	0-4	1-4		0-10	0-3
15 Wolverhampton United	3-2	4-3	2-2	1-5	3-1	6-1	4-2	5-1	2-2	1-1	4-0	3-1	2-3	10-2		1-3
16 Wyrley	0-6	3-3	0-4	2-3	0-1	3-4	4-3	4-0	2-3	5-0	4-3	1-1	3-2	4-0	1-3	

DIVISION TWO	1	2	3	4	5	6	7	8	9	10	11	12	13	14
1 AFC Ludlow		8-1	1-1	13-1	0-2	1-3	5-0	4-0	2-1	10-0	1-3	2-4	0-1	5-0
2 Bilbrook	2-5		2-0	1-5	0-7	2-4	0-1	2-4	1-9	1-5	1-6	2-3	2-2	3-1
3 FC Stafford	0-2	10-1		2-4	2-3	2-4	5-0	5-1	1-3	0-1	4-3	6-1	1-3	8-1
4 Malvern Rangers	1-5	8-0	1-2		1-0	5-4	8-0	7-0	2-2	5-1	0-1	1-8	3-3	7-0
5 Newport Town	3-0	2-2	2-4	3-1		1-1	3-5	1-4	0-2	7-0	2-2	4-4	5-2	6-1
6 Penkridge Town	0-2	8-1	4-2	1-0	3-3		5-0	3-1	2-2	1-1	4-1	2-4	2-1	3-2
7 Red Star Alma	0-6	2-1	3-3	2-2	1-7	1-2		2-4	1-4	1-1	1-4	0-7	0-2	3-1
8 Sikh Hunters	0-1	5-1	1-5	4-2	1-4	4-5	4-2		2-5	1-2	2-1	4-8	1-1	4-1
9 Team Dudley	0-4	4-1	3-1	0-1	1-1	1-2	6-2	9-2		3-2	2-1	5-3	3-0	3-0
10 Warstone Wanderers	2-2	3-1	3-2	1-5	1-5	6-2	3-1	2-1	1-6		2-2	2-1	0-9	1-0
11 Wolverhamptonton Sporting Community Reserves	0-2	4-1	2-2	3-5	4-2	6-3	6-0	1-0	1-5	1-3		3-5	0-1	3-3
12 Worcester Raiders	2-7	8-2	1-5	4-3	8-2	2-2	2-1	9-2	4-2	3-5	5-1		2-6	4-2
13 Wrens Nest	0-0	3-1	2-1	4-1	5-3	5-1	1-0	1-2	2-1	1-4	1-3	5-2		4-2
14 Wyrley Reserves	1-3	1-0	1-3	2-6	2-2	0-4	2-2	1-1	0-1	2-1	2-3	1-3	0-0	

CLUB MOVEMENTS

Premier Division - In: AFC Bridgnorth (P). Haughmond (P).

Out: Bromyard Town (R). Bustlehome (R). Lye Town (P - Midlands Football League).

Division One - In: AFC Ludlow (P). Bromyard Town (R). Bustlehome (R). Team Dudley (P). Worcester Riders (P). Wrens Nest (P).

Out: AFC Bridgnorth (P). Haughmond (P). Mahal (R). Wolverhampton United (R).

Division Two - In: Darlaston Town (N). Gornal Colts (N - former junior team). Kington Town (P - Hereford County). Malvern Town Reserves (Worcester & District). Oakengates Athletic (P - Mercian Regional Football League Premier). Mahal (R). Tipton Youth (N - former junior team). Wolverhampton United (R).

Out: AFC Ludlow (P). Team Dudley (P). Worcester Raiders (P). Wrens Nest (P).

AFC BRIDGNORTH

Founded: 2013 Nickname:

Secretary: Steve Groome **(T)** 07748 302 650 **(E)**
Chairman: Stan Parkes
Ground: Crown Meadow, Innage Lane, Bridgnorth. WV16 4HS **(T)** 07748 302 650
Colours(change): All blue

ADDITIONAL INFORMATION:

BEWDLEY TOWN

Founded: 1978 Nickname:

Secretary: Steve Godfrey **(T)** 07739 626 169 **(E)** stevegodfrey09@gmail.com
Chairman: Geoff Edwards
Ground: Ribbesford Meadows, Ribbesford, Bewdley, Worcs DY12 2TJ **(T)** 07739 626 169
Colours(change): Royal blue with yellow trim/royal blue/royal blue

ADDITIONAL INFORMATION:
Honours: Worcestershire Senior Urn 2011-12.

BILSTON TOWN COMMUNITY

Founded: 2007 Nickname:

Secretary: Paul lloyd **(T)** 07949 315 489 **(E)** paulelloyd@hotmail.co.uk
Chairman: Graham Hodson
Ground: Queen Street Stadium, Queen Street, Bilston WV14 7EX **(T)** 07725 816 043
Colours(change): Orange/orange/white

ADDITIONAL INFORMATION:

BLACK COUNTRY RANGERS

Founded: 1996 Nickname:

Secretary: Andy Harris **(T)** 07891 128 896 **(E)** blackcountryrangers@hotmail.co.uk
Chairman: Paul Garner
Ground: Cradley Town F C, Beeches View Avenue, Cradley, Halesowen B63 2HB **(T)** 07746 231 195
Colours(change): All red.

ADDITIONAL INFORMATION:
Honours: West Midlands (Regional) Division One 2010-11.

CRADLEY TOWN

Founded: 1948 Nickname:

Secretary: David Attwood **(T)** 07708 659 636 **(E)** d.attwood@sky.com
Chairman: Trevor Thomas
Ground: The Beeches, Beeches View Avenue, Cradley, Halesowen B63 2HB **(T)** 07746 231 195
Colours(change): All red

ADDITIONAL INFORMATION:

DUDLEY SPORTS

Founded: 1978 Nickname:

Secretary: John Lewis **(T)** 07737 099 385 **(E)** kath-john.lewis@blueyonder.co.uk
Chairman: Ashley Forrest
Ground: Hillcrest Avenue, Brierley Hill, West Mids DY5 3QH **(T)** 01384 826 420
Colours(change): Green & white/green/green & white

ADDITIONAL INFORMATION:

DUDLEY TOWN

Founded: 1893 Nickname:

Secretary: David Ferrier **(T)** 07986 549 675 **(E)** davef.dtfc@blueyonder.co.uk
Chairman: Stephen Austin
Ground: The Dell Stadium, Bryce Road, Brierley Hill, West Mids DY5 4NE **(T)** 01384 812 800
Colours(change): Red/black/red & black

ADDITIONAL INFORMATION:

ELLESMERE RANGERS

Founded: 1969 Nickname: The Rangers

Secretary: John Edge **(T)** 07947 864 357 **(E)** john.edge2@homecall.co.uk
Chairman: Neil Williams
Ground: Beech Grove, Ellesmere, Shropshire SY12 0BT **(T)** 07947 864 357 **Capacity:** 1250
Colours(change): Sky blue/navy/navy

ADDITIONAL INFORMATION:
Previous Leagues: West Midlands > 20120. Midland Alliance 2010-2013.
Honours: West Midlands League Premier Division 2009-10.

GORNAL ATHLETIC

Founded: 1945 Nickname:

Secretary: Kevin Williams **(T)** 07762 585 149 **(E)** k.williams880@btinternet.com
Chairman: Kevin Williams
Ground: Garden Walk Stadium, Garden Walk, Lower Gornal, Dudley DY3 2NR **(T)** 01384 358 398
Colours(change): Yellow/green/green

ADDITIONAL INFORMATION:
West Midlands (Regional) Division One South 2003-04, Premier Division 2011-12.

HAUGHMOND

Founded: 1980 Nickname:

Secretary: Vicky Jenks **(T)** 07971 506 077 **(E)** vicky.jenks@btinternet.com
Chairman: William Gough
Ground: Sundorne Sports Village, Sundorne Road, Shrewsbury. SY1 4RQ **(T)** 01743 256 260
Colours(change): White/black/black

ADDITIONAL INFORMATION:

MALVERN TOWN

Founded: 1947 Nickname:

Secretary: Margaret Scott **(T)** 07944 110 402 **(E)** marg@malverntown.co.uk
Chairman: Richard Bond
Ground: Langland Stadium, Lamgland Avenue, Malvern WR14 2QE **(T)** 01684 574 068 **Capacity:** 2,500
Colours(change): White/white/blue

ADDITIONAL INFORMATION: Records: Att: 1,221 v Worcester City FA Cup. **Goals:** Graham Buffery. **Apps:** Nick Clayton.
Honours: Worcestershire Senior Urn (x7). Midland Combination Division One 1955-56.

PEGASUS JUNIORS

Founded: 1955 Nickname: The Redmen

Secretary: Nik Marsh **(T)** 07816 121 248 **(E)** nikmarsh1982@gmail.com
Chairman: Chris Wells
Ground: Old School Lane, Hereford HR1 1EX **(T)** 07980 465 995 **Capacity:** 1,000
Colours(change): Red & white/white/red

ADDITIONAL INFORMATION: Att: 1,400 v Newport AFC, 1989-90.
Honours: Worcestershire Senior Urn 85-86. Hellenic Div.1 Champions 84-85, 98-99.
Previous Lge: Hellenic > 2011.

SHAWBURY UNITED

Founded: 1992 Nickname:

Secretary: David Martin **(T)** 07739 915 089 **(E)** daibando161274@aol.com
Chairman: Chris Kirkup
Ground: Butler Sports Ground, Bowensfield, Wem, Shrewsbury SY4 5AP **(T)** 01939 233 287
Colours(change): Black & white/black/black

ADDITIONAL INFORMATION:
Honours: Shropshire Challenge Cup 2012-13.

SHIFNAL TOWN

Founded: 1964 Nickname:

Secretary: Derek Groucott **(T)** 07910 120 512 **(E)** carolderek2@blueyonder.co.uk
Chairman: Dean Craven
Ground: Phoenix Park, Coppice Green Lane, Shifnal, Shrops TF11 8PB **(T)** 01952 463 257
Colours(change): Red & white stripes/black/black

ADDITIONAL INFORMATION:
Honours: West Midlands (Regional) League Premier Division 2006-07.

SMETHWICK RANGERS
Founded: 1977 Nickname:

Secretary: Darshan Ram **(T)** 07983 625 385 **(E)** darshan.ram@federalmogul.com
Chairman: Ajaib Garcha
Ground: Hillcrest Avenue, Brierley Hill, West Mids. DY5 3QH **(T)** 01384 826 420
Colours(change): Blue/blue/gold

ADDITIONAL INFORMATION:
Previous Name: AFC Smethwick.
Honours: West Midlands Division One 2012-13.

SPORTING KHALSA
Founded: 1991 Nickname:

Secretary: Parmjit Singh Gill **(T)** 07976 606 132 **(E)** parm@sportingkhalsa.com
Chairman: Rajinder Singh Gill
Ground: Aspray Arena, Noose Lane, Willenhall WV13 3BB **(T)** 01902 219 208
Colours(change): Yellow/blue/yellow.

ADDITIONAL INFORMATION:

WEDNESFIELD
Founded: 1961 Nickname:

Secretary: Ronald Brown **(T)** 07528 589 508 **(E)** wedfc@gmail.com
Chairman: David Saville
Ground: Cottage Ground, Amos Lane, Wednesfield WV11 1ND **(T)**
Colours(change): Red & white stripes/black/black

ADDITIONAL INFORMATION:

WELLINGTON
Founded: 1968 Nickname:

Secretary: Michael Perkins **(T)** 07842 186 643 **(E)** perkins@haworth13.freeserve.co.uk
Chairman: Phillip Smith
Ground: Wellington Playing Field, Wellington, Hereford HR4 8AZ **(T)** 07842 186 643 (MD)
Colours(change): All orange

ADDITIONAL INFORMATION:

WELLINGTON AMATEURS
Founded: 1950 Nickname:

Secretary: Dave Gregory **(T)** 07976 829 927 **(E)** dave.gregory@ppmedia.co.uk
Chairman: Dave Gregory
Ground: Wickes Stadium, School grove, Oakengates, telford, Shrops TF2 6BQ **(T)**
Colours(change): Red/black/black

ADDITIONAL INFORMATION:

WILLENHALL TOWN
Founded: 1953 Nickname: The Lockmen

Secretary: Simon Hall **(T)** 07901 560 691 **(E)** chairperson@wtfcofficial.co.uk
Chairman: Simon Hall
Ground: Long Lane Park, Long Lane, Essington, Wolverhampton. WV11 2AA **(T)** 01922 406 604
Colours(change): All red

ADDITIONAL INFORMATION:
Previous Leagues: Staffs Co, West Mids 1975-78, 1991-94, Southern 1982-91, 2005-08, Midland All. 1994-2004, 2010-12, N.P.L 2004-05, 2008-10.
Honours: Staffs County Premier 1974-75. West Mids Division 1 1975-76, Premier 77-78. Southern League Midland Division 1983-84.

WOLVERHAMPTON CASUALS
Founded: 1899 Nickname:

Secretary: Michael Green **(T)** 07870 737 229 **(E)** wtoncasualsfc@aol.com
Chairman: Garath Deacon
Ground: Brinsford Stadium, Brinsford Lane, Wolverhampton WV10 7PR **(T)** 01902 783 214
Colours(change): All green

ADDITIONAL INFORMATION:

WOLVERHAMPTON SPORTING COMMUNITY Founded: 2001 Nickname:

Secretary: Paul Wood **(T)** 01902 403 422 **(E)** wolvessporting@yahoo.co.uk
Chairman: John Quarry
Ground: Wednesfield F C, Cottage Ground, Amos Lane, Wednesfield. WV11 1ND **(T)** 01902 735 506
Colours(change): Orange & black/black/black

ADDITIONAL INFORMATION:
Previous Name: Heath Town Rangers 2001-10.

WEST MIDLANDS (REGIONAL) LEAGUE DIVISION ONE CONSTITUTION 2014-15

	Club	Ground	Telephone
1	AFC LUDLOW	Showtime Security Stadium, Burway Lane, Bromfield Road, Ludlow SY8 2BN	01584 876 000
2	BARTESTREE	Bartestree Playing Fields, Bartestree, Hereford HR1 4BY	07712 193 838
3	BROMYARD TOWN	Delahay Meadow, Stourport Road, Bromyard HR7 4NT	07885 849 948
4	BUSTLEHOLME	Tipton Town F C, Wednesbury Oak Road, Tipton, West Mid. B71 1PJ	07836 265 300
5	HANWOOD UNITED	Hanwood Recreation Ground, Hanwood SY5 8LD	01743 861 276
6	HEREFORD LADS CLUB	Hereford Lads Club, Wide Marsh Common, Hereford HR4 9NA	01432 267 127
7	LEDBURY TOWN	Ledbury Town FC., New Street, Ledbury. HR8 2EL	01531 631 463
8	PENNCROFT	Aldersley Leisure Village, Aldersley Road, Wolverhampton WV6 9NW	07738 185 458
9	SHENSTONE PATHFINDER	Shenston Pavilion Club, Birmingham Road, Shenstone WS14 0LR	07917 372 398
10	ST MARTINS	The Venue, Burma Road, Parkhall, Oswestry, Shrops. SY11 8AS	01691 684 840
11	STONE OLD ALLEYNIANS	Springbank Park, Yarnfield Lane, Yarnfield ST15 0NF	01785 761 891
12	TEAM DUDLEY	The Dell Stadium, Bryce Road, Brierley Hill DY5 4NE	07960 181 530
13	TRYSULL	Wolverhampton Casuals FC, Brinsford Road, Coven Heath, Wolverhampton WV10 7PR	07870 737 229
14	WEM TOWN	Butler Sports Centre, Bowens Field, Wem SY4 5AP	07905 443 209
15	WORCESTER RAIDERS	Claines Lane, Worcestershire WR3 7SS	07845 553 400 (MD)
16	WRENS NEST	Handrahan Sports Stadium, Mile Flat, Wallheath DY6 0AX	07963 935 601
17	WYRLEY	Wyrley Juniors FC, Long Lane, Essington, Wolverhampton. WS6 6AT	01922 478 339

WEST MIDLANDS (REGIONAL) LEAGUE DIVISION TWO CONSTITUTION 2014-15

	Club	Ground	Telephone
1	AFC WORCESTER OLYMPIC	Claines Lane, Worcester WR3 7SS	07929 347 966 (MD)
2	BARTLEY GREEN ILLEY	Illey Lane, Halesowen, West Midlands B62 0HE	07967 630 644
3	BILBROOK	Pendeford Lane, off Wobaston Road, Wolverhampton WV9 5HQ	07966 226 638 (Sec)
4	DARLASTON TOWN (1874)	Bentley Road South, Walsall, West Midlands WV10 8LN	07722 562 849
5	FC STAFFORD	Rowley Park Stadium, (3G surface) Averill Road, Stafford. ST17 9XX	01785 251 060
6	GORNAL COLTS	Long Lane Park, Essington, Wolverhampton WV11 2AA	07899 960 806
7	KINGTON TOWN	Mill Street, Kington, Herefordshire HR5 3AL	01544 231 007
8	MAHAL	Hadley Stadium, Wilson Road, Smethwick B68 9JW	0121 434 4848
9	MALVERN TOWN RES.	Langland Stadium, Langland Avenue, Malvern WR14 2EQ	01684 574 068
10	NEWPORT TOWN	Shuker Field, Audley Avenue, Newport, Shropshire TF10 7SG	07837 192 397 (MD)
11	OAKENGATES ATHLETIC	Doseley Road, Dawley, Telford, Shropshire TF4 3AB	07810 871 660
12	POWICK RANGERS	Malvern Vale Community Centre, Swineyard Road, Malvern Worcestershire WR14 1GU	07958 176 937 (MD)
13	RED STAR ALMA	Bentley Youth FC, Bentley Road South, Walsall WV10 8LN	07722 562 849
14	SIKH HUNTERS	Aston University Recreation Centre, Birmingham Road, Walsall B43 7AJ	07875 356 273 (Sec)
15	TIPTON YOUTH AFC	Coneygree Road, Tipton, West Midlands DY4 8XF	0845 352 7237
16	WARSTONES WANDERERS	Aldersley Leisure Village, Aldersley Road, Aldersley, Wolverhampton WV6 9NW	07738 185 458
17	WOLVERHAMPTON UNITED	Prestwood Road West, Wednesfield WV11 1HN	07774 299 623
18	WRLEY RESERVES	Wyrley Juniors FC, Long Lane, Essington, Wolverhampton. WS6 6AT	07899 960 806 (MD)

GROUND DIRECTIONS - PREMIER DIVISION

AFC BRIDGNORTH - Crown Meadow, Innage Lane, Bridgnorth. WV16 4HL Tel: 01746 763 001

Follow signs for Shrewsbury A458 over River Bridge on bypass. At next island turn right (Town Centre). At ?T? Junction turn right, first left into Victoria Road. Turn right at crossroads by Woodberry Down. Follow road round to right. Club is on the right 300 yards from crossroads.

BEWDLEY TOWN - Ribbesford Meadows, Ribbesford, Bewdley, Worcs. DY12 2TJ Tel: 07739-626169

From Kidderminster follow signs to Bewdley on A456 past West Midlands Safari Park and follow signs to Town Centre at next Island. Go over River Bridge into Town and turn left at side of Church (High Street). Stay on this road for 1 ½ miles. Entrance to ground is on left.

BILSTON TOWN COMMUNITY - Queen Street, Bilston WV14 7EX Tel: 07949 315 489

From M6 Junction 10 take A454 to Wolverhampton then pick up A563 to Bilston. Turn left at 2nd roundabout and left at mini roundabout by the ambulance station. under the by-pass bridge and first left into Queens Street. Ground is 500 yards on left

BLACK COUNTRY RANGERS - see Cradley Town F C. Tel: 07746-231195/01384-569658

CRADLEY TOWN - The Beeches, Beeches View Avenue, Cradley, Halesowen, West Mids. B63 2HB Tel: 07799-363467

From M5 Junction 3 take A456 Manor Way (SP Kidderminster). Straight on at first island, turn right (second exit) at second island into Hagley Road (B4183). Pass Foxhunt Inn on left and turn third (careful some might say second!!) left into Rosemary Road. Straight on into Lansdowne Road/Dunstall Road and turn left at T-junction into HuntingtreeRoad/Lutley Mill Road.

Left again at next T-junction into Stourbridge Road (A458) and immediately left again into Beecher Road East.

First left into Abbey Road and after 250 yards swing right up along Meres Road. Take first left into Hedgefield Grove go straight to the end where the ground entrance is almost opposite in Beeches View Avenue between house numbers 48 and 50.

DUDLEY SPORTS - Hillcrest Avenue, Brierley Hill, West Mids. DY5 3QH Tel: 01384-826420

The Ground is situated in Brierley Hill, just off A461. It can be approached from Stourbridge off the Ring Road to Amblecote, turning right at third set of traffic lights or from Dudley passing through Brierley Hill Town centre. A – Z ref, 4H, page 67.

DUDLEY TOWN - The Dell Stadium, Bryce Road, Brierley Hill, West Mids. DY5 4NE Tel: 01384-812943

From M5 Junction 4 follow signs for Stourbridge. From the Ring Road, take A491 sign posted Wolverhampton.

At the second set of lights, turn right onto Brettle Lane A461. After approx 6 miles you will approach Brierley Hill High Street.

Turn left at lights onto bank Street. You will see Civic hall and Police Station. Carry on over small bridge and at next set of traffic lights you will see Bryce Road and Stadium is on your left. A-Z Birmingham 5F 93 A-Z West Midlands 5B 88

ELLESMERE RANGERS - Beech Grove, Ellesmere, Shropshire, SY12 0BT - 07947 864 357

Follow A5 Wellington and take A495 to Ellesmere. On Approaching Ellesmere, straight over at roundabout, then turn left into housing estate opposite Lakelands School. At crossroads, turn left and the 1st right down the lane to Beech Grove Playing Fields.

GORNAL ATHLETIC - Lower Gornal, Dudley, West Midlands DY3 2NR Tel: 07762 585 149

From Dudley, take A459 to Sedgley, past the Fire Station. Turn left at the Green Dragon Public House, on the B4175 (Jews Lane). Follow the road until you come to the Old Bull's Head Pub, turn left into Redhall Road. Take the second left to Garden Walk.

From Wolverhampton, use A449 past Wombourne. Turn left at Himley House lights. (B4176) Over next set of major traffic lights at Bull Street. Second left into Central Drive. Left into Bank Road. Follow road round to the Ground.

HAUGHMOND - Shrewsbury Sports Village, Sundorne Road, Shrewsbury. SY1 4RQ Tel: 07785 531 754

M54 - Continue on M54, this then merges to the A5. At first roundabout, take second exit signed A49. Continue to next mini-roundabout, take first exit. Go straight over next mini-roundabout - Sundorne Road. Next mini-roundabout, take first exit. This is the Sports Village.

MALVERN TOWN - Langland Stadium, Langland Avenue, Malvern. WR14 2QE Tel: 01684-574068

Leave M5 at Junction 7 and turn towards Worcester. Turn left at next roundabout onto A4440 towards Malvern. Straight over next two roundabouts and take left slip road onto A449 at next roundabout. When approaching Malvern, turn left onto B4208 signposted Welland. Straight over three roundabouts and then take the third left into Orford Way. Take the third left into Langland Avenue. Ground is 300 yards on left.

WEST MIDLANDS LEAGUE - STEP 6/7

PEGASUS JUNIORS - Old School Lane, Hereford. HR1 1EX Tel: 07980-465995

Approach City on A4103 from Worcester. At roundabout on outskirts take 2nd exit (A4103) over railway bridge, traffic light controlled. Take 2nd turning on left into Old School Lane. Ground entrance 150 metres on left.

Approach City on A49 from Leominster. On City outskirts take 1st exit at roundabout – Roman Road. First turning on right is Old School Lane. Ground entrance 150 metres on left.

SHAWBURY UNITED - Butler Sports Ground, Bowensfield, Wem, Shrewsbury. SY4 5AP Tel: 01939-233287

From the A5 Shrewsbury by-pass, take the A49 heading towards Whitchurch. Go through the villages of Hadnall & Preston Brockhurst and then take a left turn at crossroads onto the B5063 sign posted Wem. At next junction turn right under Railway Bridge on to the B5476 into Mill Street. At next Junction by Church turn right into High Street, take the next left after pedestrian crossing into New Street and then next left by the Public House into Pyms Road. Take the 2nd left into Bowens Field and ground is 100 yards straight ahead.

SHIFNAL TOWN - Phoenix Park, Coppice Green Lane, Shifnal, Shrops. TF11 8PB Tel: 01952-463257

From M54 junction 3, take A41 towards Newport and Whitchurch. Take first left signposted Shifnal. As you enter Shifnal, take first turning on right signposted football stadium. The ground is approximately 500 yards on left past Idsall School.

If travelling along A464 Wolverhampton Road to Shifnal. On entering Shifnal, just under the railway bridge and before the traffic lights turn right and sharp right again along Aston Street. Continue along this street until sharp right hand bend. Take left turn and then sharp right along Coppice Green Lane. Ground is approximately 500 yards on left past Idsall School.

SMETHWICK RANGERS - Hillcrest Avenue, Brierley Hill, West Mids. DY5 3QH Tel: 01384-826420

The Ground is situated in Brierley Hill, just off A461. It can be approached from Stourbridge off the Ring Road to Amblecote, turning right at third set of traffic lights or from Dudley passing through Brierley Hill Town centre.

A – Z ref, 4H, page 67.

SPORTING KHALSA - Aspray Arena, Noose Lane, Willenhall. WV13 3BB Tel: 09102-219208

From M6 junction 10, take 2nd exit onto A454 to Wolverhampton/Dudley A463. Take the A454 exit towards Wolverhampton. At Keyway junction take 2nd exit onto the Keyway A454 and continue on A454 going through one roundabout. At next traffic lights make a u turn at Nechells Lane. Turn left into Noose Lane and over roundabout. Ground is located on your left.

WEDNESFIELD - Cottage Ground, Amos Lane, Wednesfield. WV11 1ND

Going south, leave M6 at Junction 11 onto A460 towards Wolverhampton. After approx. 3 miles turn left at the Millhouse Public House into Pear Tree Lane. Continue on across mini-island into Knowle Lane. At Red Lion Public House continue across mini-island into Long Knowle Lane. Continue across mini-island into Amos Lane. Ground is about ½ mile along on left hand side.

Going north, leave M6 at Junction 10A onto M54. Leave M54 at Junction 1 onto A460 towards Wolverhampton. Turn left at Millhouse Public House and continue as above.

WELLINGTON - Wellington Playing Field, Wellington, Hereford. HR4 8AZ

The Ground is situated in Wellington, behind School and opposite the Church. Wellington is 8 miles South of Leominster or 6 miles North of Hereford on the A49. At the Hereford end of the dual carriageway take the turn for Wellington.

WELLINGTON AMATEURS - Wickes Stadium, School Grove, Oakengates, Telford, Shrops. TF2 6BQ

From M54 take Junction 5. At roundabout take first left onto Rampart Way. At traffic lights take the first left onto A442 (Eastern Primary). Leave A442 at next junction. At roundabout (Greyhound Interchange), take the second exit onto B5061 (Holyhead Road). Just after red brick Church on right, turn right onto Vicar Street. Take the next left into School Grove. Continue to the end of the street and proceed up the slope onto the Car Park.

WILLENHALL TOWN - Long Lane Park, Long Lane, Essington, Wolverhampton. WV11 2AA - Tel: 01922-406604

From Junction 11 of the M6, take the A462 (Warstones Road) towards Willenhall. Continue straight over the roundabout and then take your second left into Broad Lane. Take your first left into Long Lane. Ground is situated on the left, about halfway down Long Lane.

WOLVERHAMPTON CASUALS - Brinsford Stadium, Brinsford Lane, Wolverhampton. WV10 7PR Tel: 01902-783214

Turn onto M54 off M6 Northbound. Take Junction 2 and turn right onto A449 to Stafford. Go to next island and come back on yourself towards M54. Brinsford Lane is approximately ½ mile from island on left.

Ground is 200 yards on left in Brinsford Lane.

WOLVERHAMPTON SPORTING C. - Wednesfield F C, Cottage Ground, Amos Lane, Wednesfield WV11 1ND Tel: 01902-735506

Going south, leave M6 at Junction 11 onto A460 towards Wolverhampton. After approx. 3 miles turn left at the Millhouse Public House into Pear Tree Lane. Continue on across mini-island into Knowle Lane. At Red Lion Public House continue across mini-island into Long Knowle Lane. Continue across mini-island into Amos Lane. Ground is about ½ mile along on left hand side.

Going north, leave M6 at Junction 10A onto M54. Leave M54 at Junction 1 onto A460 towards Wolverhampton. Turn left at Millhouse Public House and continue as above.

WESTERN LEAGUE

Sponsored by: Toolstation
Founded: 1892
Recent Champions:
2009: Bitton
2010: Bideford
2011: Larkhall Athletic
2012: Merthyr Town
2013: Bishop Sutton
toolstationleague.com

LES PHILLIPS CUP

FINAL

Cribbs v Larkhall Athletic 0-2

Played at Hallen FC

PREMIER DIVISION	P	W	D	L	F	A	GD	Pts
1 (P) Larkhall Athletic	40	34	5	1	114	33	81	107
2 Bristol Manor Farm	40	26	8	6	104	32	72	86
3 Gillingham Town	40	23	7	10	87	47	40	76
4 Odd Down (Bath)	40	22	8	10	76	45	31	74
5 Street	40	21	5	14	75	65	10	68
6 Bitton	40	19	8	13	75	58	17	65
7 Melksham Town	40	20	5	15	74	67	7	65
8 Willand Rovers	40	18	6	16	69	63	6	60
9 Sherborne Town	40	18	5	17	74	70	4	59
10 Brislington	40	16	11	13	61	59	2	59
11 Buckland Athletic	40	16	10	14	72	51	21	58
12 Bridport	40	15	8	17	78	81	-3	53
13 Cadbury Heath	40	15	5	20	77	80	-3	50
14 Longwell Green Sports	40	11	14	15	52	69	-17	47
15 Hallen	40	11	11	18	55	75	-20	44
16 Slimbridge	40	12	7	21	53	70	-17	43
17 Winterbourne United (-3pts)	40	13	6	21	77	104	-27	42
18 Ilfracombe Town	40	10	3	27	47	93	-46	33
19 Bishop Sutton	40	8	8	24	47	92	-45	32
20 (R) Radstock Town (-3pts)	40	10	4	26	51	110	-59	31
21 (R) Hengrove Athletic	40	8	4	28	33	87	-54	28

DIVISION ONE	P	W	D	L	F	A	GD	Pts
1 (P) Bradford Town	42	32	6	4	143	43	100	102
2 (P) Shepton Mallet	42	26	11	5	113	52	61	89
3 Barnstaple Town	42	26	5	11	102	62	40	83
4 Wincanton Town	42	23	8	11	116	70	46	77
5 Cribbs	42	23	8	11	89	61	28	77
6 Welton Rovers	42	21	11	10	82	56	26	74
7 Corsham Town	42	20	10	12	62	71	-9	70
8 Wellington	42	18	10	14	65	64	1	64
9 Almondsbury UWE	42	19	7	16	77	77	0	64
10 Chippenham Park	42	19	6	17	64	72	-8	63
11 Devizes Town (-4pts)	42	19	7	16	71	72	-1	60
12 Roman Glass St George	42	16	5	21	78	91	-13	53
13 Calne Town	42	14	10	18	74	70	4	52
14 Ashton and Backwell United	42	15	7	20	49	63	-14	52
15 Chard Town	42	14	9	19	56	58	-2	51
16 Wells City	42	14	8	20	63	75	-12	50
17 Cheddar	42	12	9	21	66	92	-26	45
18 Warminster Town	42	11	9	22	54	88	-34	42
19 Keynsham Town	42	12	6	24	56	94	-38	42
20 Westbury United	42	11	8	23	50	75	-25	41
21 Oldland Abbotonians	42	5	10	27	54	104	-50	25
22 Portishead Town	42	5	4	33	34	108	-74	19

PREMIER DIVISION	1	2	3	4	5	6	7	8	9	10	11	12	13	14	15	16	17	18	19	20	21
1 Bishop Sutton		4-0	3-3	1-1	0-1	1-6	1-4	2-3	0-1	3-0	2-0	0-2	3-3	1-3	1-0	0-4	0-3	2-2	3-6	0-2	1-7
2 Bitton	5-0		1-2	3-1	3-1	2-2	2-0	3-0	1-1	0-0	6-0	0-3	2-2	3-2	0-0	1-0	4-1	0-0	3-4	2-3	1-0
3 Bridport	3-1	3-4		2-0	0-3	0-1	4-3	2-3	1-1	5-2	2-1	3-4	4-0	2-6	0-2	2-1	1-2	1-1	0-3	2-3	1-2
4 Brislington	2-0	1-2	2-1		0-0	1-1	1-1	1-0	2-2	3-0	0-2	1-5	1-0	2-3	1-2	2-0	0-0	3-1	3-1	1-2	3-2
5 Bristol Manor Farm	1-1	0-0	3-2	1-0		1-0	3-3	1-2	0-1	3-1	3-1	1-1	6-0	6-0	2-3	10-2	3-1	2-2	1-0	4-0	2-0
6 Buckland Athletic	0-0	2-0	3-3	1-1	1-1		2-1	0-1	1-1	4-0	1-2	0-2	0-0	1-2	3-1	7-0	0-2	2-0	1-3	1-1	3-2
7 Cadbury Heath	0-4	0-4	2-2	1-2	1-2	0-2		2-1	1-3	4-1	1-1	1-3	2-2	2-3	2-1	2-0	3-0	3-1	3-5	2-0	5-1
8 Gillingham Town	2-0	9-2	1-2	2-3	1-1	4-0	6-1		3-0	2-0	6-0	2-2	0-0	1-2	2-2	2-2	2-0	2-0	0-1	2-1	6-2
9 Hallen	1-2	0-4	0-0	1-0	0-3	1-2	4-2	2-2		1-1	1-0	1-1	1-2	2-0	2-4	3-5	0-3	0-2	0-2	5-2	3-3
10 Hengrove Athletic	3-0	0-1	1-2	0-2	0-3	2-0	3-2	2-3	1-3		3-1	0-3	2-0	2-2	0-1	1-1	1-0	0-1	0-1	0-3	1-0
11 Ilfracombe Town	1-3	1-2	2-4	2-4	2-0	0-5	1-3	1-3	3-1	1-0		1-1	1-4	0-1	1-2	4-0	2-0	0-3	1-2	2-0	1-2
12 Larkhall Athletic	5-1	0-3	4-1	3-1	2-0	2-1	2-1	3-0	4-1	5-0	7-0		4-1	3-0	1-0	6-1	2-1	4-1	3-1	3-2	3-0
13 Longwell Green Sports	0-0	2-0	1-3	1-1	0-2	3-1	1-5	0-2	3-0	3-1	0-2	0-4		1-1	0-2	4-2	1-3	2-0	1-1	1-1	1-1
14 Melksham Town	2-2	1-0	1-2	1-1	1-5	2-3	1-3	1-3	2-0	6-0	1-0	0-1	3-1		1-3	2-1	4-2	3-1	2-1	0-0	7-0
15 Odd Down (Bath)	3-0	3-1	4-2	0-1	0-2	3-2	0-1	0-0	2-1	3-0	6-3	0-0	1-1	1-0		2-0	0-1	1-2	1-0	1-1	3-0
16 Radstock Town	4-1	2-0	0-3	1-3	0-8	3-2	0-4	0-2	1-1	2-0	2-1	0-3	0-3	2-3	1-7		0-3	2-1	1-2	3-1	2-2
17 Sherborne Town	2-0	4-1	2-1	5-1	1-2	1-1	3-1	3-2	1-2	2-0	2-2	3-4	1-1	0-1	4-2	0-3		0-3	1-2	1-5	7-4
18 Slimbridge	2-4	0-0	1-2	2-2	0-4	0-3	1-0	3-0	1-3	2-1	4-0	2-3	3-1	2-3	1-2	1-0	0-1		0-2	0-1	1-4
19 Street	3-0	1-5	3-3	1-0	0-2	0-3	0-2	0-2	3-3	2-1	1-0	0-1	2-2	3-0	2-5	4-0	2-2	1-3		3-2	4-3
20 Willand Rovers	1-0	3-1	2-0	3-4	0-6	2-1	2-1	0-1	1-0	6-0	1-3	1-2	0-2	1-0	1-1	4-2	1-2	2-2	2-0		5-0
21 Winterbourne United	1-0	0-3	2-2	3-3	0-5	0-3	5-2	0-2	4-2	1-3	4-1	1-3	1-2	3-1	2-2	3-1	6-4	4-1	0-3	2-1	

DIVISION ONE	1	2	3	4	5	6	7	8	9	10	11	12	13	14	15	16	17	18	19	20	21	22
1 Almondsbury UWE		3-1	1-6	0-3	1-1	0-2	1-2	3-0	0-0	4-1	5-2	0-2	3-1	3-1	2-1	3-3	4-2	1-2	0-3	2-3	4-3	2-1
2 Ashton & Backwell United	1-0		1-2	0-5	2-1	0-1	2-2	0-1	2-0	2-3	2-1	1-2	1-1	2-0	1-1	2-3	0-0	1-0	2-1	0-3	1-1	1-0
3 Barnstaple Town	4-3	2-0		2-2	4-2	1-2	3-3	0-1	8-1	1-1	2-0	3-1	4-3	3-1	0-3	2-2	4-1	2-0	4-2	4-1	2-1	1-0
4 Bradford Town	7-0	5-1	2-1		4-1	3-1	2-1	4-0	3-5	7-1	0-1	1-0	5-3	11-1	6-0	1-1	2-2	3-0	5-2	1-1	1-0	3-1
5 Calne Town	0-0	0-0	0-2	3-2		2-1	0-0	0-2	0-2	2-4	1-3	2-2	2-0	6-0	1-1	0-3	4-0	2-1	2-0	5-1	1-1	0-1
6 Chard Town	2-2	1-1	0-1	1-2	3-1		1-2	1-1	2-0	0-1	2-0	3-1	1-2	1-0	1-2	2-2	2-1	1-1	2-1	1-0	5-3	0-1
7 Cheddar	0-2	1-5	1-2	1-4	1-3	2-2		1-0	2-3	2-4	1-2	2-0	2-0	4-0	3-0	2-4	1-2	0-1	1-0	3-1	2-0	0-3
8 Chippenham Park	2-1	0-1	1-2	0-2	3-4	2-0	2-0		3-0	3-2	4-1	0-2	1-2	1-0	3-1	3-2	3-3	1-0	2-5	0-0	1-5	1-4
9 Corsham Town	1-2	2-1	1-0	0-5	1-1	2-0	1-1	3-0		3-1	2-2	4-3	2-1	2-1	1-0	0-4	3-3	0-1	0-0	1-1	0-0	3-2
10 Cribbs	4-1	7-3	1-0	1-3	2-2	1-1	4-1	2-2	1-2		2-0	1-0	1-0	3-1	5-1	2-2	3-1	5-1	2-0	0-1	3-1	3-1
11 Devizes Town	1-4	1-0	0-3	0-3	0-3	2-1	4-3	3-1	2-1	1-1		4-1	1-1	1-0	4-0	0-1	1-0	2-2	5-0	2-2	1-1	0-3
12 Keynsham Town	1-3	3-1	1-6	0-1	1-6	0-3	1-1	2-2	2-4	0-1	2-2		0-3	6-4	4-3	1-4	2-1	1-3	2-1	0-5	2-0	2-5
13 Oldland Abbotonians	1-2	1-2	1-3	3-7	3-1	0-0	3-3	0-2	0-1	0-4	3-5	1-1		1-1	1-5	1-3	2-3	1-2	2-2	0-2	1-2	2-4
14 Portishead Town	0-3	1-0	2-1	1-6	0-1	0-3	3-3	1-2	1-2	1-2	0-4	0-2	2-2		0-1	0-4	0-1	3-2	0-1	1-3	0-2	1-1
15 Roman Glass St George	4-2	1-0	4-6	0-3	3-2	3-1	4-0	2-1	1-1	0-3	0-3	0-2	1-2	2-0		2-3	1-2	1-0	2-3	1-2	2-3	2-4
16 Shepton Mallet	4-1	2-0	2-3	1-3	3-2	2-0	5-2	5-1	3-1	2-0	3-0	2-0	4-0	3-1	2-4		4-0	2-3	3-0	1-1	5-0	1-1
17 Warminster Town	1-3	0-1	2-1	0-7	1-3	1-0	2-3	1-1	1-2	0-2	2-4	2-1	3-2	1-0	2-0	1-1		2-2	0-2	0-2	2-0	2-3
18 Wellington	0-0	0-2	2-0	1-1	3-2	2-2	4-2	1-2	0-2	1-0	0-2	3-1	1-1	0-2	4-4	2-2	2-1		3-2	3-1	3-1	2-2
19 Wells City	0-0	0-2	5-1	0-2	2-0	2-0	1-1	1-4	1-1	1-1	2-1	2-0	4-2	1-3	3-5	2-2	1-0	0-1		1-1	2-0	4-3
20 Welton Rovers	3-1	3-0	2-1	3-3	1-1	2-1	3-0	3-1	0-1	3-2	1-2	3-0	2-0	6-0	2-4	1-1	3-3	1-0	2-1		1-0	3-3
21 Westbury United	0-2	0-3	1-3	0-2	1-0	4-2	1-2	1-2	6-0	1-1	2-1	0-1	0-0	2-1	0-3	0-3	1-1	0-2	2-0	3-2		0-0
22 Wincanton Town	2-3	2-1	2-2	3-1	5-4	2-1	7-2	1-2	4-1	3-1	5-0	1-1	9-1	3-0	3-3	2-4	5-2	3-4	4-2	2-1	5-1	

CLUB MOVEMENTS

Premier Division - In: Bradford Town (P). Shepton Mallet (P).

Out: Hengrove Athletic (R). Larkhall Athletic (P - Southern South & West). Radstock Town (R).

Division One - In: Hengrove Athletic (R). Radstock Town (R)..

Out: Bradford Town (P). Shepton Mallet (P).

BISHOP SUTTON

Founded: 1977 Nickname: Bishops

Secretary: Malcolm Hunt **(T)** 07799 623 901 **(E)** bishopsuttonafcsecretary@hotmail.co.uk
Chairman: George Williams **Manager:** Lee Smith
Ground: Lakeview, Wick Road, Bishops Sutton, Bristol BS39 5XN. **(T)** 01275 333 097
Capacity: 1,500 **Seats:** 100 **Covered:** 200 **Midweek Matchday:** Monday **Clubhouse:** Yes **Shop:** No

Colours(change): All blue (All yellow)
Previous Names:
Previous Leagues: Weston & District (youth), Bristol & Avon, Somerset Senior >1991
Records: **Att:** 400 v Bristol City
Senior Honours: Somerset Junior Cup 1980-81. Western League Division One 1997-98, Premier Division 2012-13.

10 YEAR RECORD

04-05	05-06	06-07	07-08	08-09	09-10	10-11	11-12	12-13	13-14
WestP 18	WestP 16	WestP 21	WestP 19	WestP 15	WestP 4	WestP 5	WestP 6	WestP 1	WestP 19

BITTON

Founded: 1922 Nickname: The Ton

Secretary: Mark Tilling **(T)** 07446 183 295 **(E)** bittonafc@gmail.com
Chairman: Shawn Evans **Manager:** Paul Britton
Ground: Rapid Solicitors Ground, Bath Road, Bitton, Bristol BS30 6HX. **(T)** 01179 323 222
Capacity: 1,000 **Seats:** 48 **Covered:** 200 **Midweek Matchday:** Tuesday **Clubhouse:** Yes **Shop:** No

Colours(change): Red & white/black/black (Yellow/green/yellow)
Previous Names:
Previous Leagues: Avon Premier Combination, Gloucestershire County
Records: **Goalscorer:** A. Cole
Senior Honours: Somerset Senior Cup 1992-93. Les Phillips Cup 2007-08. Western League Premier Division 2008-09.

10 YEAR RECORD

04-05	05-06	06-07	07-08	08-09	09-10	10-11	11-12	12-13	13-14
WestP 8	WestP 8	WestP 8	WestP 7	WestP 1	WestP 8	WestP 2	WestP 2	WestP 7	WestP 6

BRADFORD TOWN

Founded: 1992 Nickname:

Secretary: Nikki Akers **(T)** 07866 693 167 **(E)** bradfordtownfc@gmail.com
Chairman: Les Stevens **Manager:** Paul Shanley
Ground: Bradford Sports & Social Club, Trowbridge Rd, Bradford on Avon BA15 1EE **(T)** 07801 499 168
Capacity: **Seats:** **Covered:** **Midweek Matchday:** Wednesday **Clubhouse:** Yes

Colours(change): Blue & white/blue/blue (All yellow)
Previous Names:
Previous Leagues: Wiltshire Senior > 2005.
Records:
Senior Honours: Western League Division One 2013-14.

10 YEAR RECORD

04-05	05-06	06-07	07-08	08-09	09-10	10-11	11-12	12-13	13-14
	West1 10	West1 17	West1 13	West1 3	West1 4	West1 6	West1 5	West1 3	West1 1

BRIDPORT

Founded: 1885 Nickname: Bees

Secretary: Chris Tozer **(T)** 07500 064 317 **(E)** sevie@tiscali.co.uk
Chairman: Adrian Scadding **Manager:** Trevor Senior
Ground: St Mary's Field, Bridport, Dorset DT6 5LN **(T)** 01308 423 834
Capacity: **Seats:** **Covered:** **Midweek Matchday:** Tuesday **Clubhouse:** Yes

Colours(change): Red/black/black (All yellow)
Previous Names:
Previous Leagues: Dorset Combination 1984-89.
Records: **Att:** 1,150 v Exeter City 1981.
Senior Honours: Dorset Senior Cup x8. Dorset Senior Amateur Cup x6.

10 YEAR RECORD

04-05	05-06	06-07	07-08	08-09	09-10	10-11	11-12	12-13	13-14
WestP 19	West1 6	West1 11	West1 18	West1 13	West1 10	West1 3	WestP 14	WestP 14	WestP 12

BRISLINGTON

Founded: 1956 Nickname: Bris

Secretary: Kevin Jacobs **(T)** 07976 724 202 **(E)** kevinjacobs1@hotmail.co.uk
Chairman: Phil Rex **Manager:** Jeff Meacham
Ground: Ironmould Lane, Brislington, Bristol BS4 4TZ **(T)** 01179 774 030
Capacity: 2,000 **Seats:** 144 **Covered:** 1,500 **Midweek Matchday:** Tuesday **Clubhouse:** Yes **Shop:** No

Colours(change): Red & black/black/black. (All yellow)
Previous Names:
Previous Leagues: Somerset Senior until 1991
Records:
Senior Honours: Somerset Senior League 1988-89. Somerset Premier Cup 1992-93. Western League Division One 1994-95.

10 YEAR RECORD

04-05	05-06	06-07	07-08	08-09	09-10	10-11	11-12	12-13	13-14
WestP 10	WestP 10	WestP 17	WestP 13	WestP 10	WestP 9	WestP 15	WestP 7	WestP 2	WestP 10

BRISTOL MANOR FARM

Founded: 1964 Nickname: The Farm

Secretary: Andy Radford **(T)** 07747 038 423 **(E)** andy@bristolmanorfarm.com
Chairman: Geoff Sellek **Manager:** Lee Lashenko
Ground: The Creek, Portway, Sea Mills, Bristol BS9 2HS **(T)** 0117 968 3571
Capacity: 2,000 **Seats:** 98 **Covered:** 350 **Midweek Matchday:** Tuesday **Clubhouse:** Yes **Shop:** No

Colours(change): Red/black/black (All yellow)
Previous Names:
Previous Leagues: Bristol Suburban 64-69, Somerset Senior 69-77
Records: **Att;** 500 v Portway **App:** M. Baird
Senior Honours: Glos Trophy 1987-88, Glos Am. Cup 1989-90. Western League Division One 1982-83.

10 YEAR RECORD

04-05	05-06	06-07	07-08	08-09	09-10	10-11	11-12	12-13	13-14
WestP 7	WestP 3	WestP 12	WestP 16	WestP 5	WestP 7	WestP 7	WestP 8	WestP 18	WestP 2

BUCKLAND ATHLETIC

Founded: 1977 Nickname: The Bucks

Secretary: Christine Holmes **(T)** 07856 525 730 **(E)** phardingham@virginmedia.com
Chairman: Roy Holmes **Manager:** Adam Castle
Ground: Homers Heath, South Quarry, Kingskerswell Road, Newton Abbot TQ12 5JU **(T)** 01626 361 020
Capacity: **Seats:** Yes **Covered:** Yes **Midweek Matchday:** Wednesday **Clubhouse:** Yes

Colours(change): All yellow (All blue)
Previous Names:
Previous Leagues: Devon County League 2000-07. South West Pininsula.
Records:
Senior Honours: South West Peninsula League Premier Division 2009-10, 10-11. Throgmorton Cup 2009-10.

10 YEAR RECORD

04-05	05-06	06-07	07-08	08-09	09-10	10-11	11-12	12-13	13-14
Devon 8	Devon 7	Devon 13	SWPP 14	SWPP 3	SWPP 1	SWPP 1	SWPP 2	WestP 10	WestP 11

CADBURY HEATH

Founded: Nickname:

Secretary: Martin Painter **(T)** 07971 399 268 **(E)** martinbristol1955@hotmail.com
Chairman: Steve Plenty **Manager:** Andy Black
Ground: Springfield, Cadbury Heath Road, Bristol BS30 8BX **(T)** 07971 399 268
Capacity: **Seats:** **Covered:** **Midweek Matchday:** Wednesday **Clubhouse:** Yes

Colours(change): Red & white/red/red (Yellow/blue/blue)
Previous Names:
Previous Leagues: Gloucestershire County 1968-75, 80-2000. Midland Combination 1975-77.
Records:
Senior Honours: Gloucestershire County League 1998-99. Western League Division One 2011-12.

10 YEAR RECORD

04-05	05-06	06-07	07-08	08-09	09-10	10-11	11-12	12-13	13-14
West1 13	West1 14	West1 9	West1 5	West1 4	West1 11	West1 4	West1 1	WestP 4	WestP 13

GILLINGHAM TOWN

Founded: 1879 Nickname:

Secretary: Terry Lucas **(T)** 07873 587 455 **(E)** terrylucas@sky.com
Chairman: Dave Graham **Manager:** Kevan Davis
Ground: Hardings Lane, Gillingham, Dorset SP8 4HX **(T)** 01747 823 673
Capacity: **Seats:** **Covered:** **Midweek Matchday:** Tuesday **Clubhouse:** Yes

Colours(change): All tangerine (Sky blue/navy/navy)
Previous Names:
Previous Leagues: Dorset Premier 1970-2008.
Records:
Senior Honours:

10 YEAR RECORD

04-05	05-06	06-07	07-08	08-09	09-10	10-11	11-12	12-13	13-14
Dor P 5	Dor P 4	Dor P 9	Dor P 2	Dor P 12	Dor P 3	Dor P 7	West1 3	WestP 3	WestP 3

HALLEN

Founded: 1949 Nickname:

Secretary: Richard Stokes **(T)** 07791 492 640 **(E)** sinbad88@hotmail.co.uk
Chairman: Barrie Phillips **Manager:** Paul Owen
Ground: Hallen Centre, Moorhouse Lane, Hallen Bristol BS10 7RU **(T)** 01179 505 559
Capacity: 2,000 **Seats:** 200 **Covered:** 200 **Midweek Matchday:** Tuesday **Clubhouse:** Yes

Colours(change): Blue/black/blue (All orange)
Previous Names: Lawrence Weston Ath, Lawrence Weston Hallen
Previous Leagues: Gloucestershire County, Hellenic
Records: **Att:** 803 v Bristol Rovers 1997
Senior Honours: Gloucestershire Co. Lge 1988-89, 92-93. Western Division One 2003-04.

10 YEAR RECORD

04-05	05-06	06-07	07-08	08-09	09-10	10-11	11-12	12-13	13-14
WestP 4	WestP 9	WestP 9	WestP 15	WestP 9	WestP 12	WestP 16	WestP 4	WestP 9	WestP 15

ILFRACOMBE TOWN

Founded: 1902 Nickname: Bluebirds

Secretary: Tony Alcock **(T)** 07973 469 673 **(E)** afalcock@aol.com
Chairman: M. Hayne **Manager:** Tom Bulley
Ground: Marlborough Park, Ilfracombe, Devon EX34 8PD **(T)** 01271 865 939
Capacity: 2,000 **Seats:** 60 **Covered:** 450 **Midweek Matchday:** Tuesday **Clubhouse:** Yes

Colours(change): All blue (All red)
Previous Names:
Previous Leagues: North Devon, East Devon Premier, Exeter & District, Western,
Records: **Att:** 3,000 v Bristol City **Goalscorer:** Kevin Squire **App:** Bob Hancock 459
Senior Honours: East Devon Premier League, North Devon Senior League, North Devon Premier League.

10 YEAR RECORD

04-05	05-06	06-07	07-08	08-09	09-10	10-11	11-12	12-13	13-14
West1 8	West1 4	West1 3	WestP 8	WestP 14	WestP 3	WestP 3	WestP 11	WestP 16	WestP 18

LONGWELL GREEN SPORTS

Founded: 1966 Nickname: The Green

Secretary: David Heal **(T)** 07917 778 463 **(E)** dave@monaghanhardware.co.uk
Chairman: John Gibbs **Manager:** Gary Powell
Ground: Longwell Green Com. Centre, Shellards Road BS30 9AD **(T)** 01179 323 722
Capacity: 1,000 **Seats:** Yes **Covered:** 100 **Midweek Matchday:** Tuesday **Clubhouse:** Yes **Shop:** Yes

Colours(change): Blue & white/black/black (Yellow/blue/blue)
Previous Names: None
Previous Leagues: Gloucestershire County.
Records: **Att:** 500 v Mangotsfield 2005
Senior Honours:

10 YEAR RECORD

04-05	05-06	06-07	07-08	08-09	09-10	10-11	11-12	12-13	13-14
GlCo 2	West1 12	West1 8	West1 8	West1 2	WestP 11	WestP 17	WestP 13	WestP 15	WestP 14

MELKSHAM TOWN

Founded: 1876 | Nickname: Town

Secretary: Mark Jeffery **(T)** 07739 905 575 **(E)** markmtfc@virginmedia.com

Chairman: Dave Wiltshire **Manager:** Darren Perrin

Ground: The Conigre, Market Place, Melksham, Wiltshire SN12 6ES **(T)** 01225 702 843

Capacity: **Seats:** Yes **Covered:** Yes **Midweek Matchday:** Monday **Clubhouse:** Yes

Colours(change): Yellow/black/yellow (All red)
Previous Names: Melksham > 1951.
Previous Leagues:
Records: **Att:** 2,821 v Trowbridge Town, FA Cup 1957-58.
Senior Honours: Western League Division 1 1979-80, 96-97. Wiltshire Shield x6. Wiltshire Senior Cup x5 Most recently 2012-13.

10 YEAR RECORD

04-05	05-06	06-07	07-08	08-09	09-10	10-11	11-12	12-13	13-14
WestP 14	WestP 14	WestP 5	WestP 11	WestP 11	WestP 19	WestP 8	West1 2	WestP 13	WestP 7

ODD DOWN (BATH)

Founded: 1901 | Nickname: The Down

Secretary: Lorraine Brown **(T)** 07734 924 435 **(E)** lorainebrown@btinternet.com

Chairman: Dave Loxton **Manager:** Ray Johnston

Ground: Lew Hill Memorial Ground, Combe Hay Lane, Odd Down BA2 8PA **(T)** 01225 832 491

Capacity: 1,000 **Seats:** 160 **Covered:** 250 **Midweek Matchday:** Tuesday **Clubhouse:** Yes **Shop:** No

Colours(change): Blue/blue/white (All red)
Previous Names:
Previous Leagues: Wilts Premier, Bath & District & Somerset Senior
Records: **App:** Steve Fuller 475 **Goalscorer:** Joe Matano 104
Senior Honours:

10 YEAR RECORD

04-05	05-06	06-07	07-08	08-09	09-10	10-11	11-12	12-13	13-14
WestP 13	WestP 15	WestP 11	WestP 21	West1 19	West1 2	WestP 8	WestP 9	WestP 8	WestP 4

SHEPTON MALLET

Founded: 1986 | Nickname:

Secretary: Gary Banfield **(T)** 07762 880 705 **(E)** gkrkb@tiscali.co.uk

Chairman: John Hugill **Manager:** Andrew Jones

Ground: Playing Fields, Old Wells Road, West Shepton, Shepton Mallet BA4 5XN **(T)** 01749 344 609

Capacity: 2,500 **Seats:** 120 **Covered:** Yes **Midweek Matchday:** Tuesday **Clubhouse:** Yes

Colours(change): Black & white/black/black & white (Yellow & blue/blue/yellow & blue)
Previous Names:
Previous Leagues: Somerset Senior.
Records: **Att:** 274 v Chippenham Town FA Cup 2000-01.
Senior Honours: Somerset Senior League 2000-01.
Somerset Senior Cup 1997-98.

10 YEAR RECORD

04-05	05-06	06-07	07-08	08-09	09-10	10-11	11-12	12-13	13-14
West1 20	West1 20	West1 20	West1 11	West1 17	West1 17	West1 14	West1 16	West1 7	West1 2

SHERBORNE TOWN

Founded: 1894 | Nickname:

Secretary: Colin Goodland **(T)** 07929 090 612 **(E)** colingoodland@live.co.uk

Chairman: Steve Paradise **Manager:** Jamie Manley

Ground: Raleigh Grove, Terrace Playing Field, Sherborne DT9 5NS **(T)** 01935 816 110

Capacity: **Seats:** Yes **Covered:** Yes **Midweek Matchday:** Wednesday **Clubhouse:** Yes

Colours(change): Black & white/black/white (Green/white/black).
Previous Names:
Previous Leagues: Dorset Premier
Records: **Att:** 1,000 v Eastleigh, Andy Shephard Memorial match 27.07.03.
Senior Honours: Dorset Premier League 1981-82, Dorset Senior Cup 2003-04.
Western League Division One 2012-13.

10 YEAR RECORD

04-05	05-06	06-07	07-08	08-09	09-10	10-11	11-12	12-13	13-14
Dor P 6	Dor P 2	West1 4	West1 2	WestP 12	WestP 18	WestP 14	WestP 17	West1 1	WestP 9

SLIMBRIDGE

Founded: 1899 Nickname: The Swans

Secretary: Colin Gay **(T)** 07702 070 229 **(E)** colin.hamish@icloud.com
Chairman: John Mack **Manager:** Leon Sterling
Ground: Wisloe Road, Cambridge, Glos GL2 7AF **(T)** 07702 070 229
Capacity: **Seats:** Yes **Covered:** Yes **Midweek Matchday:** Tuesday **Clubhouse:** Yes **Shop:** Yes

Colours(change): Blue/blue/white.
Previous Names: None
Previous Leagues: Stroud & District. Gloucester Northern. Gloucestershire County. Hellenic >2013.
Records: Since 2002-03. **Att:** 525 v Shortwood United, Hellenic Prem. 24.08.03. **Goals:** Julian Freeman - 79 (from 122 apps.).
Senior Honours: Gloucester Northern League 2007-08. Gloucestershire County League 2008-09.

10 YEAR RECORD

04-05	05-06	06-07	07-08	08-09	09-10	10-11	11-12	12-13	13-14
Hel P 4	Hel P 5	Hel P 1	GlN1 1	GlCo 1	Hel1W 1	Hel P 5	Hel P 5	Hel P 6	WestP 16

STREET

Founded: 1880 Nickname: The Cobblers

Secretary: James Vickery **(T)** 07792 866 367 **(E)** streetfootballclub@outlook.com
Chairman: John Stevens **Manager:** Dan Badman
Ground: The Tannery Ground, Middlebrooks, Street BA16 0TA **(T)** 01458 445 987
Capacity: 2,000 **Seats:** 120 **Covered:** 25 **Midweek Matchday:** Tuesday **Clubhouse:** Yes

Colours(change): Green & white/green/green (All red)
Previous Names: None
Previous Leagues: Somerset Senior.
Records: **Att;** 4,300 v Yeovil Town FA Cup 47
Senior Honours: Somerset Senior League 1996-97.

10 YEAR RECORD

04-05	05-06	06-07	07-08	08-09	09-10	10-11	11-12	12-13	13-14
West1 7	West1 3	WLaP 19	WestP 18	WestP 13	WestP 6	WestP 13	WestP 10	WestP 6	WestP 5

WILLAND ROVERS

Founded: 1946 Nickname: Rovers

Secretary: Dom Clark **(T)** 07546 561 212 **(E)** domclarkwillandrovers@gmail.com
Chairman: Mike Mitchell **Manager:** Scott Rogers
Ground: Silver Street, Willand, Collumpton, Devon EX15 2RG **(T)** 01884 33885
Capacity: 2,000 **Seats:** 75 **Covered:** 150 **Midweek Matchday:** Wednesday **Clubhouse:** Yes

Colours(change): White/white/black (Yellow/blue/yellow)
Previous Names: None.
Previous Leagues: Devon County.
Records: **Att:** 650 v Newton Abbot 1992-3 **Goalscorer:** Paul Foreman
Senior Honours: Devon County League 1998-99, 00-01, Western League Division One 2004-05, Les Phillips Cup 2006-07.

10 YEAR RECORD

04-05	05-06	06-07	07-08	08-09	09-10	10-11	11-12	12-13	13-14
West1 1	WestP 6	WestP 6	WestP 3	WestP 3	WestP 2	WestP 4	WestP 5	WestP 11	WestP 8

WINTERBOURNE UNITED

Founded: 1911 Nickname: The Bourne

Secretary: Geoff Endicott **(T)** 07778 678 823 **(E)** g.endicott@btopenworld.com
Chairman: Robyn Maggs **Manager:** David Wilson & Dave Hemmings
Ground: Oakland Park, Alomondsbury, Bristol BS32 4AG **(T)** 07976 255 666
Capacity: **Seats:** **Covered:** **Midweek Matchday:** Wednesday **Clubhouse:** Yes

Colours(change): White & red (Red & black)
Previous Names: Winterbourne Wasps 1911-1918
Previous Leagues: Bristol & Suburban >1950. Bristol & District 1950-68. Bristol Premier Combination 1968-92. Gloucestershire County 1992-2001. Hellenic 2001-12.
Records: **Att:** 229 v Malmesbury Victoria, 29/08/2004.
Senior Honours: Gloucestershire County League 2000-01. Hellenic League Division 1 West 2005-06, 07-08.

10 YEAR RECORD

04-05	05-06	06-07	07-08	08-09	09-10	10-11	11-12	12-13	13-14
Hel1W 9	Hel1W 1	Hel1W 10	Hel1W 1	Hel1W 7	Hel1W 13	Hel1W 10	Hel1W 3	WestP 12	WestP 17

PREMIER DIVISION GROUND DIRECTIONS

BISHOP SUTTON - Lakeview, Wick Road, Bishop Sutton BS39 5XN 01275 333097 - On main A368 Bath to Weston-Super-Mare road at rear of Butchers Arms Public House.

BITTON - Recreation Ground, Bath Road, Bitton, Bristol BS30 6HX 0117 932 3222 - From M4 leave at Junction 18. Take A46 towards Bath, at first roundabout take A420 for Wick / Bridgeyate. On approach to Bridgeyate turn left at mini-roundabout onto A4175 and follow for 2.2 miles, then turn left for Bath on A431. The ground is 100 yards on the right.

From Bath take A431, go through Kelston and Bitton village. Ground is on the left. From Chippenham take A420 to Bristol and turn left at mini-roundabout onto A4175 and follow as above.

BRADFORD TOWN - Bradford Sports & Social Club, Trowbridge Road, Bradford on Avon, Wiltshire BA15 1EW 01225 866 649 - From Bath or Melksham on entering Bradford on Avon follow the signs for A363 to Trowbridge. The ground is after a mini roundabout and behind a stone wall on the right hand side. From Trowbridge, follow A363 to Bradford-on-Avon. The ground is just past shop on right, behind stone wall on left.

BRIDPORT - St Marys Field, Bridport, Dorset DT6 5LN 01308 423 834 - Follow Bridport by-pass in any direction to the Crown Inn roundabout. Take exit to town centre, at first set of traffic lights (Morrisons) turn left. Ground is 200 yards on the right.

BRISLINGTON - Ironmould Lane, Brislington, Bristol BS4 4TZ 0117 977 4030 - On A4 Bristol to Bath road, about 500 yards on Bath side of Park & Ride. Opposite the Wyevale Garden Centre.

BRISTOL MANOR FARM - The Creek, Portway, Sea Mills, Bristol BS9 2HS 0117 968 3571 - Leaving M5 at Junction 18, take A4 marked Bristol. U-turn on dual carriageway by Bristol and West Sports Ground and then ground is half-mile on left hand side

BUCKLAND ATHLETIC - Homers Heath, Kingskerwell Road, Newton Abbot TQ12 5JU - 01626 361020 - From Plymouth : Take the exit off the A38 marked Newton Abbot. Travel for approx 5 miles until you come to a roundabout. Turn left and head downhill towards another Roundabout. Turn right & drive for approx 800 yards. Go straight across the B&Q R/bout. Travel along the avenue, and at the top end of this road, turn left and head towards the train Station. Go past the station, go over the railway and get into the right hand lane. At the 2nd set of traffic lights turn right. Go under the railway and follow this road to the next mini roundabout. Go straight across. Go up the hill and down the other side. The ground is situated on the right hand side, opposite Combined linen services. **From Exeter:** Take the A380 signposted Torquay and travel along this road until you reach Penn Inn roundabout. Take the right hand lane and follow the road around which takes you into the left lane and towards the town centre. Take the 1st left and you are now on the main road towards Decoy. The same directions then apply as above. Coaches will not be able to go through the tunnel at Decoy. Please phone for these directions.

CADBURY HEATH - Springfield, Cadbury Heath Road, Bristol BS30 8BX 0117 967 5731 (social club) - M5-M4-M32 Exit 1 follow signs for ring road, exit roundabout for Cadbury Heath left, 100m mini roundabout straight across, 400m mini roundabout turn right into Tower Road North, 150m turn right into Cadbury Heath Road, ground 50m on right via Cadbury Heath Social Club car park.

GILLINGHAM TOWN - Hardings Lane, Gillingham, Dorset SP8 4HX 01747 823 673 - Proceed to middle of town to the High Street. Hardings Lane is a turning off of the High Street, at the Shaftesbury or Southern end of the High Street.

HALLEN - Hallen Centre, Moorhouse Lane, Hallen, Bristol BS10 7RU 0117 950 5559 - From Junction 17 M5 follow A4018 towards Bristol. At third roundabout turn right into Crow Lane. Proceed to T junction - turn right and right again at mini roundabout by Henbury Lodge Hotel. At next mini roundabout turn left into Avonmouth Way. Continue for 1.5 miles into Hallen village. At crossroads turn left into Moorhouse Lane

ILFRACOMBE TOWN - Marlborough Park, Ilfracombe, Devon EX34 8PD 01271 865 939 - Take A361 for Ilfracombe and in town take first right after traffic lights. Follow Marlborough Road to top and ground is on the left.

LONGWELL GREEN SPORTS - Longwell Green Community Centre, Shellards Road, Longwell Green BS30 9DW 0117 932 3722 - Leave Junction 1 M32 follow signs for Ring Road (A4174). At Kingsfield roundabout turn into Marsham Way. At first set of traffic lights turn left into Woodward Drive. Continue to min roundabout and turn right into Parkway Road and continue to Shellards Road. Ground is situated to the rear of the Community Centre.

MELKSHAM TOWN - The Conigre, Market Place, Melksham, Wiltshire SN12 6ES 01225 702 843 - Turn into Market Place car park and then left into grounds of Cooper Avon Tyres Sports & Social Club (Melksham House) Ground situated at end of drive.

ODD DOWN - Lew Hill, Memorial Ground, Combe Hay Lane, Odd Down, Bath BA2 8AP 01225 832 491 - Situated behind Odd Down Park & Ride on main A367 Bath to Exeter road.

SHEPTON MALLET - Playing Fields, Old Wells Road, West Shepton, Shepton Mallet BA4 5XN - 01749 344 609 - From the town take B3136 (Glastonbury Road) for approximately 1/2 mile. Turn right at junction of Old Wells Road near King William Public House. Approximately 300 yards up the Old Wells Road turn left into the playing fields.

SHERBORNE TOWN - Raleigh Grove, The Terrace Playing Field, Sherborne, Dorset DT9 5NS 01935 816 110 - From Yeovil take A30 - marked Sherborne. On entering town turn right at traffic lights, over next traffic lights and at the next junction turn right. Go over bridge, take second left marked 'Terrace Pling Fields' Turn into car park, football club car park is situated in the far right-hand corner.

SLIMBRIDGE - Wisloe Road, Cambridge. GL2 7AF 07702 070 229 - From the A38 take the A4135 to Dursley. The ground is 100 yards on the left.

STREET - The Tannery Field, Middlebrooks, Street, Somerset BA16 0TA 01458 445 987 - Ground is signposted from both ends of A39 and B3151.

WILLAND ROVERS - Silver Street, Willand, Cullompton, Devon EX15 2RG 01884 33885 - Leave M5 Junction 27 and take first left at roundabout. Follow signs to Willand. After passing Halfway House pub on right, go straight over mini-roundabout (signposted to Cullompton) ground is 400 metres on left hand side

WINTERBOURNE UNITED - Oaklands Park, Almondsbury, Bristol BS32 4AG - 01454 612220 - From M4 (West) leave at junction 20 to M5 (Sth West). Leave immediately at junction 16 (A38 Thornbury), turn right onto A38, then first left 100 yards from junction, in front of Motorway Police HQ, Ground next door. Signposted from A38 'Gloucestershire FA HQ'.

ALMONDSBURY U.W.E. Founded: Nickname:

Secretary: Douglas Coles **(T)** 07748 655 399 **(E)** doug2004.coles@blueyonder.co.uk
Chairman: Mike Blessing **Manager:** John Black
Ground: The Field, Almondsbury, Bristol BS32 4AA **(T)** 01454 612 240
Colours(change): Green & white/green/green (All yellow)

ADDITIONAL INFORMATION:

ASHTON & BACKWELL UNITED Founded: 2010 Nickname:

Secretary: Ted Roylance **(T)** 07508 205 729 **(E)** ted.roylance@btinternet.com
Chairman: Jim Biggins **Manager:** Richard Coombes
Ground: The Lancer Scott Stadium, West Town Road, Backwell. BS48 3HQ **(T)** 01275 461 273
Colours(change): Maroon/navy/navy (Sky blue & white & maroon)

ADDITIONAL INFORMATION:
Previous Names: Formed when Backwell United merged with the Senior and Youth section of Ashton Boys FC.

BARNSTAPLE TOWN Founded: 1906 Nickname: Barum

Secretary: Jane Huxtable **(T)** 07773 668 461 **(E)** jane@barnstapletownfc.com
Chairman: Jasmine Chesters **Manager:** Barry Yeo
Ground: Mill Road, Barnstaple, North Devon EX31 1JQ **(T)** 01271 343 469 **Capacity:** 5,000
Colours(change): All red. (All cyan)

ADDITIONAL INFORMATION: Att: 6,200 v Bournemouth FA Cup 1st Round 51-52 **App:** Ian Pope
Western Champions 1952-53, 79-80, Devon Pro Cup (12), Devon Senior Cup 1992-93.
Western League Division One 1993-94.

CALNE TOWN Founded: 1886 Nickname: Lilywhites

Secretary: Wayne McLaughlin **(T)** 07795 833 702 **(E)** wmm498@msn.com
Chairman: Simon Gardner (Vice) **Manager:** Simon Gardner
Ground: Bremhill View, Calne, Wiltshire SN11 9EE **(T)** 07795 833 702
Colours(change): Black & white/black/black (All blue)

ADDITIONAL INFORMATION:
Record Att: 1,100 v Swindon, friendly 1987. **Goalscorer:** Robbie Lardner. **Apps:** Gary Swallow - 259.
Honours: Wiltshire Senior Cup x4 Most recently 2011-12.

CHARD TOWN Founded: Nickname: The Robins

Secretary: Ian Hallett **(T)** 01308 868 795 **(E)** ian.hallett2010@btinternet.com
Chairman: Richard Allen **Manager:** Adam Fricker
Ground: Denning Sports Field, Zembard Lane, Chard, Somerset TA20 1JL **(T)** 01460 61402
Colours(change): All red (White/blue/blue)

ADDITIONAL INFORMATION:
Honours: Somerset Senior League 1949-50, 53-54, 59-60, 67-68, 69-70. Somerset Senior Cup 1952-53, 66-67.
South West Counties Cup 1988-89.

CHEDDAR Founded: 1892 Nickname: The Cheesemen

Secretary: Bruce Harvey **(T)** 07500 908 538 **(E)** harvs360@hotmail.co.uk
Chairman: Simon Brooks **Manager:** Jared Greenhalgh
Ground: Bowdens Park, Draycott Road, Cheddar BS27 3RL **(T)** 01934 707 271
Colours(change): Yellow/black/yellow (All blue)

ADDITIONAL INFORMATION:
Previous Leagues: Cheddar Valley. Weston Super Mare & District. Somerset Senior > 2012.
Honours: Cheddar Valley League 1910-11. Somerset Senior League Premier Division 2011-12.

CHIPPENHAM PARK Founded: Nickname:

Secretary: Jane Blackmore **(T)** 07879 400 501 **(E)** jane@thornburysurfacing.co.uk
Chairman: Damien Coulter **Manager:** Dave Ferris
Ground: Hardenhuish Park, Bristol Road, Chippenham. SN14 6LR **(T)** 01249 650 400
Colours(change): All blue (All yellow)

ADDITIONAL INFORMATION:
Previous League: Wiltshire > 2013.

CORSHAM TOWN
Founded: 1884 Nickname:

Secretary: Richard Taylor **(T)** 07944 183 973 **(E)** richtaylor_ctfc@hotmail.com
Chairman: Ken Baldwin **Manager:** Trevor Rawlings
Ground: Southbank Ground, Lacock Road, Corsham SN13 9HS **(T)** 07963 030 652 **Capacity:** 1,500
Colours(change): Red & white/red/red (Yellow & blue/blue/yellow)

ADDITIONAL INFORMATION: Att: 550 v Newport Co. FA Cup **App:** Craig Chaplin
Wiltshire Senior Cup 1975-76, 96-97, 04-05. Western Premier Division 2006-07.

CRIBBS
Founded: 1958 Nickname:

Secretary: Simon Hartley **(T)** 07970 744 063 **(E)** welshwizard1973@aol.com
Chairman: Dave Nelson **Manager:** Gavin Tufton
Ground: The Lawns, Station Road, Henbury, Bristol BS10 7TB **(T)** 0117 950 2303
Colours(change): Blue/blue/red (Red/red/white)

ADDITIONAL INFORMATION:
Previous Leagues: Gloucestershire County > 2012.
Honours: Gloucester County League 2011-12.

DEVIZES TOWN
Founded: 1885 Nickname:

Secretary: Neil Fautley **(T)** 07891 341 344 **(E)** neil@hallmarkflooring.co.uk
Chairman: Shaun Moffat **Manager:** Darren Walters & Justin Webster
Ground: Nursteed Road, Devizes, Wiltshire SN10 3DX **(T)** 01380 722 817
Colours(change): Red & white/black/black (All blue)

ADDITIONAL INFORMATION:
Honours: Western League Division One 1999-2000. Wiltshire Senior Cup x14.

HENGROVE ATHLETIC
Founded: 1948 Nickname: The Grove

Secretary: Graham Whitaker **(T)** 07970 848 285 **(E)** graham.whitaker1@btinternet.com
Chairman: Nigel Gray **Manager:** Jamie Hillman
Ground: Norton Lane, Whitchurch, Bristol BS14 9TB **(T)** 07973 864 537
Colours(change): All green (All sky blue)

ADDITIONAL INFORMATION:
Somerset County League Premier Division 2005-06. Somerset Senior Cup 1979-80.

KEYNSHAM TOWN
Founded: 1895 Nickname: K's

Secretary: Julian French **(T)** 07814 609 853 **(E)** julian.french@friendslifeservices.co.uk
Chairman: Malcolm Trainer **Manager:** Steve Cains
Ground: AJN Stadium, Bristol Road, Keynsham BS31 2BE **(T)** 0117 986 5878
Colours(change): Gold/black/gold (All green)

ADDITIONAL INFORMATION:
Previous League: Somerset Senior.
Honours: Somerset Senior Cup 1951-52, 57-58, 2002-03.

OLDLAND ABBOTONIANS
Founded: 1910 Nickname: The O's

Secretary: Martin McConachie **(T)** 07432 614 494 **(E)** secretary@oldlandfootball.com
Chairman: Robert Clarke **Manager:** Dale Dempsey
Ground: Aitchison Playing Field, Castle Road, Oldland Common, Bristol BS30 9SZ **(T)** 01179 328 263
Colours(change): Blue & white/blue/blue (All yellow)

ADDITIONAL INFORMATION:
Previous League: Somerset County.
Honours: Les Phillips Cup 2008-09.

PORTISHEAD TOWN
Founded: 1910 Nickname: Posset

Secretary: Jean Harrison **(T)** 07969 045 310 **(E)** Jemaha@mypostoffice.co.uk
Chairman: Adrian Green **Manager:** Dave Hewitt
Ground: Bristol Road, Portishead, Bristol BS20 6QG **(T)** 01275 817 600
Colours(change): White/black/black (All red)

ADDITIONAL INFORMATION:
Previous League: Somerset County.
Honours: Somerset County League 2004-05.

RADSTOCK TOWN

Founded: 1895 Nickname:

Secretary: Simon Wilkinson **(T)** 07557 276 619 **(E)** rtfc@hotmail.co.uk
Chairman: Mike Hibbard **Manager:** Lloyd Edgell
Ground: Southfields Recreation Ground, Southfields, Radstock BA3 2NZ **(T)** 01761 435 004 **Capacity:** 1,250
Colours(change): Red/white/red (All sky blue)

ADDITIONAL INFORMATION:

ROMAN GLASS ST GEORGE

Founded: Nickname:

Secretary: Emily Baldwin **(T)** 07708 277 592 **(E)** emilyjaynebaldwin@blueyonder.co.uk
Chairman: Roger Hudd **Manager:** Bob Johnson
Ground: Oaklands Park, Gloucester Road, Alomndsbury BS32 4AG **(T)** 01454 612 220
Colours(change): White/black/white (All red)

ADDITIONAL INFORMATION:
Previous League: Gloucestershire County.
Honours: Gloucestershire County League 2006-07.

WARMINSTER TOWN

Founded: 1878 Nickname:

Secretary: Chris Robbins **(T)** 07738 783 619 **(E)** Chrisjrobbins@virginmedia.com
Chairman: Pete Russell **Manager:** Derek Graham & Andrew Crabtree
Ground: Weymouth Street, Warminster BA12 9NS **(T)** 01985 217 828
Colours(change): Red & black/red & black/red (Light blue/dark blue/light blue)

ADDITIONAL INFORMATION:
Previous Leagues: Wiltshire County > 1930, 1945-83, 2002-06. Western League 1930-39, 83-2002. Wessex 2006-12.

WELLINGTON

Founded: 1892 Nickname: Wellie

Secretary: David Derrick **(T)** 07927 623 946 **(E)** david230275@googlemail.com
Chairman: Mike Hall **Manager:** Mike Hawes
Ground: Wellington Playing Field, North Street, Wellington TA21 8NE **(T)** 01823 664 810 **Capacity:** 3,000
Colours(change): Orange/black/orange (Claret/blue/claret)

ADDITIONAL INFORMATION: Record Goalscorer: Ken Jones

WELLS CITY

Founded: 1890 Nickname:

Secretary: David Green **(T)** 07584 045 238 **(E)** daveg55@hotmail.co.uk
Chairman: Steve Loxton **Manager:** Sam Andrews
Ground: Athletic Ground, Rowdens Road, Wells, Somerset BA5 1TU **(T)** 01749 679 971
Colours(change): All blue (All yellow)

ADDITIONAL INFORMATION:
Western League Division One 2009-10.

WELTON ROVERS

Founded: 1887 Nickname: Rovers

Secretary: Malcolm Price **(T)** 07970 791 644 **(E)** malcolm@weltonr.plus.com
Chairman: Stuart Minall **Manager:** Nick Beaverstock
Ground: West Clewes, North Road, Midsomer Norton, Bath BA3 2QD **(T)** 02762 412 097 **Capacity:** 2,400
Colours(change): Green & white/green/green (Yellow/blue/yellow).

ADDITIONAL INFORMATION: Att: 2,000 v Bromley FA Am Cup 1963 **Goalscorer:** Ian Henderson 51
Somerset Senior Cup (10). Somerset Premier Cup 2009-10.

WESTBURY UNITED

Founded: 1921 Nickname: White Horsemen

Secretary: Roger Arnold **(T)** 07584 318 302 **(E)** rogerarnold33@hotmail.com
Chairman: Paul Brickley **Manager:** Adam Collington
Ground: Meadow Lane, Westbury, Wiltshire BA13 3QA **(T)** 01373 823 409
Colours(change): Green & white/green/green (Blue & red/blue/blue)

ADDITIONAL INFORMATION:
Record Att: 4,000 v Llanelli FA Cup 1st Round 1937 & v Walthamstow Avenue FA Cup 1937.
Honours: Wiltshire League 1934-35, 37-38, 38-39, 49-50, 50-51, 55-56. Western League Div.1 1991-92. Wilts Senior Cup x4.

WINCANTON TOWN

Founded: Nickname:

Secretary: Mike Hatcher **(T)** 07734 567 464 **(E)** mike831hatcher@gmail.com
Chairman: Andy Stewart **Manager:** Paul Down
Ground: Wincanton Sports Ground, Moor Lane, Wincanton. BA9 9EJ **(T)** 01963 31815
Colours(change): Yellow/black/black (All grey)

ADDITIONAL INFORMATION:
Previous League: Dorset Premier >2013.

DIVISION ONE GROUND DIRECTIONS

ALMONDSBURY UWE - The Field, Almondsbury, Bristol BS34 4AA 01454 612 240 - Exit M5 at Junction 16. Arriving from the south take the left exit lane. Turn left at lights and ground is 150m on right hand side. Arriving from east take right hand lane on slip road. Take 3rd exit and ground is 150m on right hand side.
ASHTON & BACKWELL UNITED - Backwell Recreation Ground, West Town Road, Backwell. BS48 3HQ - 07916 120 382 - Off the main A370 in Backwell, travelling from Bristol the entrance is on the right, apprximately 500 metres after the crossroads. Travelling from Weston Super Mare the entrance to the ground is on the left approximately 500 metrs past the New Inn Pub and Restaurant.
BARNSTAPLE TOWN - Mill Road, Barnstaple, North Devon EX31 1JQ 01271 343469 - From M5 South, exit junction 27, take A361 to Barnstaple, in town take A361 for Ilfracombe, then first left over bridge is Mill Road.
CALNE TOWN - Bremhill View, Calne, Wiltshire SN11 9EE - Take A4 to Calne from Chippenham, on approaching Calne turn left at the first roundabout on to A3102 Calne bypass. At the next roundabout turn right, next left and then right and right again.
CHARD TOWN - Dening Sports Field, Zembard Lane, Chard, Somerset TA20 1JL 01460 61402 - From A30 High Street, follow Swimming Pool/Sports Centre signs via Helliers road. Turn right into Crimchard, turn left into Zembard Lane. Ground is on right hand side.
CHEDDAR - Bowdens Park, Draycott Road, Cheddar BS27 3RL - 01934 707 271 - FROM WELLS: Take the A371 (Weston Super Mare) through Draycott and Bowdens Park is on your left about half a mile past Cheddar Garden Centre (if you get to the church you've gone too far). FROM WESTON: Head towards Wells on the A371 and go through the village of Cheddar. The church is on your right as you come out of the village and Bowdens Park is 200 yards past the church on your right hand side.
CHIPPENHAM PARK - Hardenhuish Park, Bristol Road, Chippenham. SN14 6LR 01249 650 400 - Exit 17 from M4. Follow A350 towards Chippenham for three miles to first roundabout, take second exit (A350); follow road to third roundabout (junction with A420). Turn left and follow signs to town centre. Ground is 1km on left hand side adjacent to pedestrian controlled traffic lights. Car/Coach park located adjacent to traffic lights.
CORSHAM TOWN - Southbank, Lacock Road, Corsham, Wiltshire SN13 9HS 01249 715609 - A4 into Corsham, at Hare and Hounds Roundabout take the Melksham Road B3353 until the War Memorial, then Lacock Road. Ground a half a mile on the right side.
CRIBBS - The Lawns, Station Road, Henbury, Bristol BS10 7TB - 0117 950 2303 - From M5 J17 follow signs to Bristol West & Clifton on the A4018 dual carriageway cross two roundabouts, at 3rd roundabout take fourth exit and follow signs to M5, take 1st turning left after car dealers, ground straight ahead.
DEVIZES TOWN - Nursteed Road, Devizes, Wiltshire SN10 3DX 01380 722 817 - Leave Devizes on A342 for Andover. Ground is on the right hand side opposite Eastleigh Road.
HENGROVE ATHLETIC - Norton Lane, Whitchurch, Bristol BS14 0BT 01275 832 894 - Take A37 from Bristol through Whitchurch village past Maes Knoll pub, over hump bridge taking next turning on right, which is Norton Lane. Ground is immediately after Garden Centre.
KEYNSHAM TOWN - Crown Field, Bristol Road, Keynsham BS31 2DZ 0117 986 5876 - On A4175 off the Bristol to Bath A4. On left immediately after 30mph sign.
OLDLAND ABBOTONIANS - Aitchison Playing Field, Castle Road, Oldland Common, Bristol BS30 9PP 0117 932 8263 - Exit M4 at Jct19 to M32. Exit M32 at Jct 1after 400 yds and take 1st exit from roundabout for A4174. Straight over traffic lights to next roundabout continuing on A4174. Go over five roundabouts for approximately 4.8 miles. At next roundabout take 1st exit to Deanery Road (A420) and continue for 0.9 miles to Griffin Public house and turn right into Bath Road (A4175) . Continue for 1.3 miles to Oldland Common High Street and look for Dolphin Public House. Turning for Castle Street is next left between Chinese Chip Shop and Post Office. Ground is at the end of Castle Road.
PORTISHEAD - Bristol Road, Portishead, Bristol BS20 6QG 01275 817 600 - Leave M5 at Junction 19 and take road to Portishead. At outskirts of town take 1st exit from small roundabout signposted Clevedon and Police H.Q. Ground is 150 yds along road on left by bus stop.
RADSTOCK TOWN - Southfields Recreation Ground, Southfields, Radstock BA3 2NZ 01761 435 004 - The town of Radstock is situated 15 miles south east of Bristol and 8 miles southwest of Bath on the A367. At the double roundabout in Radstock town centre take the A362 towards Frome. The ground is on the right hand bend, third turning. Turn right into Southfield, ground is 200 yards ahead.
ROMAN GLASS ST GEORGE - Oaklands Park, Gloucester Road, Almondsbury BS32 4AG 07708 277592 - Exit M5 at Junction 16. Arriving from the south take the left exit lane. Turn left at lights and ground is 100m on left hand side. Arriving from east take right hand lane on slip road. Take 3rd exit nd ground is 100m on left hand side.
WARMINSTER TOWN - Weymouth Street, Warminster, BA12 9NS - 01454 612220 - A36 from Salisbury, head for town centre, turn left at traffic lights in the town centre signposted A350 Shaftesbury. Club is situated approx. 400 yards on left hand side at top of Weymouth Street.
WELLINGTON - The Playing Field, North Street, Wellington, Somerset TA21 8NA 01749 679 971 - Leave the M5 motorway at Junction 26 and follow directions to Wellington. At town centre traffic lights take turning into North Street. Take the next left adjacent to the Fire Station and signposted 'Car Park'. The ground is in the corner of the car park.
WELLS CITY - Athletic Ground, Rowdens Road, Wells, Somerset BA5 1TU 01749 679 971 - From North & Southwest - Follow A39 to Strawberry Way to roundabout, follow A371 East Somerset Way and take right turn into Rowdens Road. Ground is on left. From East - Follow A371 from Shepton Mallet. After approximately 5 miles on East Somerset Way take left turn into Rowdens Road. Ground is on left.
WELTON ROVERS - West Clewes, North Road, Midsomer Norton BA3 2QD 01761 412 097 - The ground is on the main A362 in Midsomer Norton.
WESTBURY UNITED - Meadow Lane, Westbury, Wiltshire BA13 3AF 01373 823 409 - From town centre proceed along Station Road towards rail station. At double mini roundabout turn right. Ground is 300 metres on left hand side opposite Fire Station.
WINCANTON TOWN - Wincanton Sports Ground, Moor Lane, Wincanton. BA9 9EJ - 01963 31815 - Travelling to Wincanton on the A357 via Sturminster Newton turn right at the roundabout after passing under the A303 into Laurence Hill and follow the road across three further roundabouts into Southgate Road. Traffic from the A303 will also enter Southgate Road when following the signs to the town. At the junction turn right in the direction of Buckhorn Weston going under the A303 again before entering Moor Lane. Wincanton Sports Centre is on the left.

ALMARY GREEN ANGLIAN COMBINATION

Sponsored by: Almary Green
Founded: 1964
Recent Champions:
2009: Kirby Muxloe SC
2010: Blofield United
2011: Cromer Town
2012: Cromer Town
2013: Acle United
angliancombination.org.uk

PREMIER DIVISION	P	W	D	L	F	A	GD	Pts
1 Acle United	30	20	4	6	83	33	50	64
2 Spixworth	30	18	5	7	65	36	29	59
3 Blofield United (-1)	30	18	4	8	71	41	30	57
4 Dersingham Rovers	30	16	6	8	61	38	23	54
5 Kirkley & Pakefield Reserves	30	15	8	7	52	46	6	53
6 Mattishall	30	15	5	10	79	57	22	50
7 Cromer Town (-2)	30	15	6	9	56	53	3	49
8 Reepham Town	30	13	5	12	57	52	5	44
9 Norwich CEYMS	30	13	5	12	47	45	2	44
10 St Andrews	30	11	7	12	52	45	7	40
11 Wroxham Reserves	30	9	4	17	48	56	-8	31
12 Caister	30	9	4	17	48	62	-14	31
13 Sheringham	30	8	5	17	35	92	-57	29
14 Wymondham Town	30	7	4	19	29	64	-35	25
15 (R) Loddon United	30	8	1	21	38	76	-38	25
16 (R) Beccles Town	30	5	7	18	30	55	-25	22

MUMMERY CUP
(Premier and Division One Clubs)

ROUND 1

Dersingham Rovers	v	Blofield United	2-0
Acle United	v	Kirkley & Pakefield Reserves	0-1
North Walsham Town	v	Caister	1-2
Cromer Town	v	Wroxham Reserves	3-1
Foulsham	v	Aylsham	0-5
Mundford	v	Stalham Town	1-1, 3-4p
Sheringham	v	Harleston Town	2-2, 2-4p
Loddon United	v	Poringland Wanderers	AW
Holt United	v	Wymondham Town	1-3
Norwich CEYMS	v	Long Stratton	3-1
Spixworth	v	Hellesdon	3-1
Hempnall	-	Bye	
Mattishall	v	Beccles Town	4-3
Reepham Town	v	Corton	4-1
Hindringham	v	St Andrews	2-2, 7-6p
Bradenham Wanderers	v	Horsford United	2-3

ROUND 2

Dersingham Rovers	v	Kirkley & Pakefield Reserves	4-3
Caister	v	Cromer Town	5-3
Aylsham	v	Stalham Town	2-3 aet
Harleston Town	v	Poringland Wanderers	4-2 aet
Wymondham Town	v	Norwich CEYMS	0-2
Spixworth	v	Hempnall	7-0
Mattishall	v	Reepham Town	7-0
Hindringham	v	Horsford United	4-2

QUARTER FINALS

Dersingham Rovers	v	Caister	HW
Stalham Town	v	Harleston Town	1-0
Norwich CEYMS	v	Spixworth	0-1
Mattishall	v	Hindringham	3-1

SEMI FINALS

Dersingham Rovers	v	Stalham Town	3-1
Spixworth	v	Mattishall	1-3

FINAL

Dersingham Rovers	v	Mattishall	1-2 aet

CYRIL BALLYN TROPHY
(Division Two, Three, Four, Five and Six first teams and external league reserve sides)

FINAL

Bungay Town	v	Waveney	3-0

DON FROST CUP

(Premier Division champions v Mummery Cup holders)

Acle United	v	Spixworth	0-1

CS MORLEY CUP
(Anglian Combination reserve teams)

FINAL

Gayton United	v	Watton United Reserves	1-2

PREMIER DIVISION	1	2	3	4	5	6	7	8	9	10	11	12	13	14	15	16
1 Acle United		3-1	0-3	1-2	3-0	1-1	3-2	2-1	6-1	2-1	3-0	1-1	3-0	2-0	2-0	2-0
2 Beccles Town	0-3		1-3	3-1	1-2	1-2	1-1	0-1	1-1	2-3	1-1	0-2	0-4	2-4	2-1	3-0
3 Blofield United	0-4	2-1		0-0	2-2	2-2	3-1	4-0	1-2	2-1	2-2	7-2	0-1	6-1	2-1	2 1
4 Caister	0-6	2-0	1-3		3-6	0 0	3-4	0-4	3-2	1-3	5-2	9-0	1-2	0-3	1-2	1-0
5 Cromer Town	2-0	6-2	3-2	3-2		0-5	0-0	2-1	3-2	1-0	3-2	1-1	2-1	2-1	2-2	0-0
6 Dersingham Rovers	2-0	1-1	3-1	3-0	2-2		1-2	2-0	2-6	2-3	3-1	6-0	4-1	0-1	3-0	3-2
7 Kirkley & Pakefield Reserves	1-1	2-0	3-1	0-2	4-2	1-0		2-0	0-1	2-1	2-1	3-3	0-8	3-3	2-1	1-1
8 Loddon United	1-7	1-2	1-4	2-1	1-0	0-3	0-3		1-4	1-4	0-1	5-2	1-3	1-4	1-5	2-0
9 Mattishall	5-1	2-1	1-2	3-0	2-4	2-2	2-2	7-1		2-2	1-3	5-1	0-4	3-0	6-1	3-2
10 Norwich CEYMS	1-3	1-0	1-3	3-1	2-1	3-1	2-2	3-1	2-0		2-1	0-2	0-0	1-1	1-2	0-1
11 Reepham Town	4-2	2-0	1-4	0-0	1-3	2-1	1-2	3-2	0-4	1-1		7-0	1-3	3-2	7-1	3-1
12 Sheringham	0-8	1-1	1-3	0-5	3-0	0-1	0-1	2-5	3-2	0-2	3-1		2-1	0-3	0-6	0-1
13 Spixworth	1-2	2-1	1-0	2-0	2-0	5-1	2-1	2-1	3-3	4-1	0-0	0-0		3-2	0-2	4-0
14 St Andrews	1-1	0-0	0-1	2-0	4-2	0-1	0-1	2-0	2-3	0-1	1-2	7-2	2-2		3-2	2-0
15 Wroxham Res	1-4	1-1	0-1	1-1	0-1	0-1	2-1	1-2	4-0	3-0	0-1	1-2	2-3	1-1		0-1
16 Wymondham Town	1-7	0-1	0-5	2-3	2-1	1-3	1-3	1-1	0-4	3-2	0-3	0-2	4-1	0-0	4-2	

ANGLIAN COMBINATION PREMIER DIVISION CONSTITUTION 2014-15

	Club	Ground	Phone
1	ACLE UNITED	Bridewell Lane, Acle, Norwich NR13 3RA	01493 752989
2	BLOFIELD UNITED	Old Yarmouth Road, Blofield, Norwich NR13 4LE	07748 863203
3	CAISTER	Caister Playing Fields, off Allendale Road, Caister-on-Sea NR30 5ES	07852 212210
4	CROMER TOWN	Cabbell Park, Mill Road, Cromer NR27 0AD	07940 092131
5	DERSINGHAM ROVERS	Behind Feathers Hotel, Manor Road, Dersingham, King's Lynn PE31 6LN	01485 542707
6	HARLESTON TOWN	Wilderness Lane, Harleston IP20 9DD	07887 781603
7	KIRKLEY & PAKEFIELD RESERVES	Kirkley & Pakefield Comm. Centre, Walmer Road, Lowestoft NR33 7LE	01502 513549
8	LONG STRATTON	Long Stratton Playing Field, Long Stratton, Manor Road NR15 2XR	07806 792840
9	MATTISHALL	Mattishall Playing Fields, South Green, Mattishall, Norwich NR20 3JY	01362 850246
10	NORWICH CEYMS	Hilltops Sports Centre, Main Road, Swardeston, Norwich NR14 8DU	01508 578826
11	REEPHAM TOWN	Stimpsons Piece, Station Road, Reepham NR10 4LJ	07887 442470
12	SHERINGHAM	Recreation Ground, Weybourne Road, Sheringham NR26 8WD	01263 824804
13	SPIXWORTH	Spixworth Village Hall, Crostick Lane, Spixworth, Norwich NR10 3NQ	01603 898092
14	ST ANDREWS	Thorpe Recreation Ground, Laundry Lane, Thorpe St Andrew, Norwich NR7 0XQ	01603 300316
15	WROXHAM RESERVES	Trafford Park, Skinners Lane, Wroxham NR12 8SJ	01603 783538
16	WYMONDHAM TOWN	Kings Head Meadow, Back Lane, Wymondham NR18 0LB	01953 607326

In: Harleston Town (P). Long Stratton (P).

Out: Beccles Town (R). Loddon United (R).

DIVISION ONE	P	W	D	L	F	A	GD	Pts
1 (P) Long Stratton	28	19	6	3	63	23	40	63
2 (P) Harleston Town	28	18	7	3	76	35	41	61
3 North Walsham Town	28	16	4	8	89	52	37	52
4 Foulsham	28	14	10	4	72	40	32	52
5 Bradenham Wanderers	28	13	7	8	62	41	21	46
6 Hellesdon	28	14	3	11	74	54	20	45
7 Horsford United	28	11	7	10	54	51	3	40
8 Aylsham	28	10	8	10	52	47	5	38
9 Stalham Town	28	10	5	13	47	45	2	35
10 Holt United	28	10	4	14	53	69	-16	34
11 Hindringham	28	9	4	15	40	56	-16	31
12 Poringland Wanderers	28	8	3	17	48	67	-19	27
13 Corton	28	7	4	17	44	94	-50	25
14 Hempnall	28	6	3	19	39	85	-46	21
15 (R) Mundford	28	6	3	19	31	85	-54	21

DIVISION TWO	P	W	D	L	F	A	GD	Pts
1 (P) Scole United	30	23	3	4	113	24	89	72
2 (P) Mulbarton Wanderers	30	22	4	4	105	34	71	70
3 Bungay Town	30	22	3	5	85	23	62	69
4 Sprowston Athletic	30	21	5	4	107	36	71	68
5 Wells Town	30	17	3	10	74	53	21	54
6 UEA (-2)	30	15	6	9	67	30	37	49
7 Attleborough Town	30	15	4	11	66	49	17	49
8 Hoveton Wherrymen	30	14	7	9	60	56	4	49
9 Martham	30	12	5	13	52	53	-1	41
10 Beccles Caxton	30	12	2	16	61	79	-18	38
11 East Harling	30	10	3	17	71	68	3	33
12 Thetford Rovers (-1)	30	9	2	19	50	69	-19	28
13 Sprowston Wanderers (-1)	30	9	2	19	27	75	-48	28
14 Acle United Reserves (-2)	30	6	3	21	32	67	-35	19
15 (R) Hemsby	30	6	1	23	53	121	-68	19
16 (R) Brandon Town	30	0	1	29	16	202	-186	1

DIVISION THREE	P	W	D	L	F	A	GD	Pts
1 (P) Waveney	26	21	2	3	84	17	67	65
2 (P) Caister Reserves	26	18	4	4	79	29	50	58
3 (P) Marlingford	26	18	1	7	77	42	35	55
4 Freethorpe	26	14	7	5	65	46	19	49
5 Swaffham Town Reserves	26	13	3	10	68	36	32	42
6 Thorpe Village	26	13	3	10	54	38	16	42
7 Easton	26	10	7	9	50	42	8	37
8 South Walsham (-1)	26	10	6	10	69	57	12	35
9 North Walsham Town Reserves	26	9	4	13	53	53	0	31
10 Costessey Sports	26	7	4	15	47	71	-24	25
11 Loddon United Reserves (-1)	26	7	3	16	34	79	-45	23
12 Blofield United Reserves	26	7	2	17	38	94	-56	23
13 Downham Town Reserves (-2)	26	6	5	15	38	68	-30	21
14 (R) Hempnall Reserves	26	3	1	22	22	106	-84	10

DIVISION FOUR	P	W	D	L	F	A	GD	Pts
1 (P) Fakenham Town Reserves	26	19	5	2	89	27	62	62
2 (P) Mattishall Reserves	26	20	1	5	89	34	55	61
3 (P) Norwich CEYMS Reserves	26	18	5	3	81	27	54	59
4 (P) Yelverton	26	16	4	6	68	37	31	52
5 Sheringham Reserves (-2)	26	16	3	7	52	29	23	49
6 Long Stratton Reserves	26	14	5	7	46	29	17	47
7 Buxton	26	13	4	9	53	54	-1	43
8 Redgrave Rangers	26	9	5	12	34	52	-18	32
9 Bungay Town Reserves	26	10	0	16	57	67	-10	30
10 Sprowston Athletic Reserves	26	8	3	15	50	91	-41	27
11 Horsford United Reserves	26	7	3	16	44	58	-14	24
12 Stalham Town Reserves (-3)	26	4	5	17	23	52	-29	14
13 Wymondham Town Reserves (-2)	26	3	1	22	20	91	-71	8
14 (R) Newton Flotman (-1)	26	2	2	22	28	86	-58	7

DIVISION FIVE	P	W	D	L	F	A	GD	Pts
1 (P) Redgate Rangers	28	24	2	2	102	22	80	74
2 (P) Hingham Athletic	28	21	4	3	104	31	73	67
3 (P) Watton United Reserves	28	20	4	4	104	42	62	64
4 (P) Feltwell United	28	19	6	3	80	38	42	63
5 (P) Hindringham Reserves (-2)	28	14	5	9	57	47	10	45
6 (P) St Andrews Reserves	28	13	5	10	52	48	4	44
7 Beccles Town Reserves (-1)	28	12	4	12	47	59	-12	39
8 Bradenham Wanderers Reserves	28	11	3	14	63	63	0	36
9 Poringland Wanderers Reserves	28	10	4	14	49	72	-23	34
10 Aylsham Reserves	28	7	6	15	38	76	-38	27
11 Harleston Town Reserves (-2)	28	6	8	14	41	71	-30	24
12 Attleborough Town Reserves	28	7	3	18	29	74	-45	24
13 Holt United Reserves (-2)	28	7	3	18	33	53	-20	22
14 (W) Thorpe Rovers (-4)	28	5	4	19	27	69	-42	15
15 (R) Mundford Reserves (-4)	28	2	3	23	19	80	-61	5

DIVISION SIX	P	W	D	L	F	A	GD	Pts
1 (P) Mulbarton Wanderers Reserves	28	23	2	3	100	28	72	71
2 (P) Gayton United	28	21	2	5	104	38	66	65
3 (P) Earsham	28	20	3	5	75	35	40	63
4 (P) Hellesdon Reserves	28	18	1	9	71	41	30	55
5 (P) Foulsham Reserves	28	17	2	9	101	53	48	53
6 (P) Dersingham Rovers Reserves	28	16	3	9	72	43	29	51
7 (P) Reepham Town Reserves	28	13	4	11	59	56	3	43
8 Corton Seltic	28	13	2	13	73	70	3	41
9 Easton Reserves (-1)	28	12	4	12	43	65	-22	39
10 Scole United Reserves	28	10	6	12	62	64	-2	36
11 Thorpe Village Reserves (-1)	28	10	1	17	53	80	-27	30
12 Thetford Town Reserves (-1)	28	6	7	15	42	80	-38	24
13 East Harling Reserves	28	6	0	22	35	90	-55	18
14 Freethorpe Reserves	28	4	0	24	32	113	-81	12
15 Martham Reserves (-1)	28	1	3	24	22	88	-66	5

Joining Division Six in 2014-15:

Costessey Sports Reserves (Norwich & Dist.D3).
Necton (Central & South Norfolk Div.2).
South Walsham Reserves (Norwich & Dist.D3).
Thetford Rovers Reserves. UEA Reserves (Norwich & Dist.D1).
Waveney Reserves (Lowestoft & Dist.Div1).
Wells Town Reserves (NW Norfolk D2).

BEDFORDSHIRE COUNTY LEAGUE

Sponsored by: No sponsor
Founded: 1904
Recent Champions:
2009: Caldecote
2010: Blunham
2011: Blunham
2012: Shefford Town & Campton
2013: Caldecote
bedfordshirefootballleague.co.uk

PREMIER DIVISION	P	W	D	L	F	A	GD	Pts
1 AFC Oakley Sports M&DH	26	17	4	5	56	23	33	55
2 AFC Kempston Town & Bedford College	26	16	5	5	48	33	15	53
3 Shillington	26	12	5	9	53	39	14	41
4 Wilstead	26	12	5	9	65	64	1	41
5 Renhold United	26	10	8	8	63	58	5	38
6 Marston Shelton Rovers	26	11	2	13	66	50	16	35
7 Lidlington United Sports	26	9	6	11	37	41	-4	33
8 Ickwell & Old Warden (-3)	26	10	5	11	52	44	8	32
9 Wootton Blue Cross (-3)	25	9	8	8	44	46	-2	32
10 Pavenham	26	9	3	14	43	53	-10	30
11 Shefford Town & Campton	26	8	5	13	61	66	-5	29
12 Sharnbrook (-3)	25	9	4	12	51	74	-23	28
13 Flitwick Town	26	7	6	13	51	62	-11	27
14 Caldecote (-3)	26	8	2	16	41	78	-37	23

DIVISION ONE	P	W	D	L	F	A	GD	Pts
1 (P) AFC Turvey	22	15	2	5	58	31	27	47
2 (P) Eastcotts AFC	22	14	4	4	33	21	12	46
3 Marabese Ceramics	22	14	3	5	63	26	37	45
4 (P) Sandy	22	12	4	6	50	34	16	40
5 Sundon Park Rangers	22	12	1	9	50	34	16	37
6 Henlow	22	11	3	8	59	52	7	36
7 Woburn Lions	22	9	2	11	47	58	-11	29
8 Shefford Town & Campton Reserves	22	9	1	12	42	48	-6	28
9 Elstow Abbey	22	8	2	12	45	47	-2	26
10 Brickhill Tigers	22	7	3	12	34	47	-13	24
11 Bedford SA	22	7	1	14	30	55	-25	22
12 (R) Bromham United	22	1	0	21	16	74	-58	3

BRITANNIA CUP

ROUND 1

Renhold United	v	Ickwell & Old Warden	4-4, 5-4p
Wooton Blue Cross	v	Lidlington United Sports	3-2
Marston Shelton Rovers	v	AFC Oakley M&DH	2-1
Pavenham	v	Shefford Town & Campton	1-4
AFC Kempston Town & B.C.	-	Bye	
Shillington	v	Flitwick Town	1-1, 3-4p
Shambrook	-	Bye	
Wilstead	v	Caldecote	2-1

QUARTER FINALS

Renhold United	v	Wootton Blue Cross	1-2
Marston Shelton Rovers	v	Shefford Town & Campton	1-2 aet
AFC Kempston Town & B.C.	v	Flitwick Town	1-0
Shambrook	v	Wilstead	1-3

SEMI FINALS

AFC Kempston Town & B.C.	v	Wilstead	0-1
Wooton Blue Cross	v	Shefford Town & Campton	AW

FINAL

Shefford Town & Campton	v	Wilstead	2-0

DIVISION TWO	P	W	D	L	F	A	GD	Pts
1 (P) AFC Oakley Sports M&DH Res.	24	18	2	4	80	29	51	56
2 (P) Cranfield United	24	17	2	5	78	30	48	53
3 (P) Queens Park Crescents	24	15	4	5	60	33	27	49
4 (P) Clifton	24	14	3	7	51	37	14	45
5 (P) Potton Town	24	14	2	8	62	51	11	44
6 (P) Great Barford	24	12	4	8	64	46	18	40
7 Kings AFC	24	10	5	9	57	63	-6	35
8 Potton United Reserves	24	9	2	13	42	42	0	29
9 Co-op Sports	24	7	5	12	42	56	-14	26
10 AFC Kempston Tn & Bedford Coll Res.	24	7	3	14	43	61	-18	24
11 AFC Harlington	24	5	6	13	42	59	-17	21
12 Riseley Sports	24	4	2	18	33	79	-46	14
13 Renhold United Reserves	24	3	2	19	32	100	-68	11

PREMIER DIVISION	1	2	3	4	5	6	7	8	9	10	11	12	13	14
1 AFC Kempston Town & Bedford College		2-1	3-0	2-1	1-1	0-2	1-0	1-0	2-2	2-1	2-0	4-2	4-1	2-0
2 AFC Oakley Sports M&DH	0-1		5-1	1-1	4 0	1 0	2 0	2-0	3-3	2-1	5-1	1-0	1-1	1-1
3 Caldecote	5-6	0-1		1-2	3-2	2-1	3-2	0-0	0-4	1-0	4-5	3-2	1-2	1-0
4 Flitwick Town	1-1	1-3	1-2		2-0	2-0	2-3	2-3	4-5	1-1	3-3	0-4	4-5	3-1
5 Ickwell & Old Warden	2-2	0-1	4-0	1-1		5-1	3-1	2-1	1-0	1-1	3-0	5-1	0-1	1-1
6 Lidlington United Sports	0-0	0-2	4-1	1-2	2-1		0-4	0-1	1-1	2-3	2-1	2-2	4-1	0-1
7 Marston Shelton Rovers	1-2	0-6	6-0	4-4	1-2	1-3		0-0	3-0	10-0	3-1	3-1	3-0	7-3
8 Pavenham	3-1	0-3	7-1	3-0	2-1	0-1	1-3		1-3	1-2	3-5	0-1	4-5	2-1
9 Renhold United	1-0	2-1	3-2	2-4	3-4	3-3	1-0	2-3		3-2	2-2	2-6	2-2	6-3
10 Sharnbrook	3-1	1-3	3-3	4-3	4-3	1-3	4-2	3-6	1-6		4-3	2-1	3-5	V-V
11 Shefford Town & Campton	2-1	1-2	2-3	1-3	3-1	2-4	2-5	9-0	3-2	4-1		0-2	1-2	2-2
12 Shillington	1-2	2-1	2-1	4-0	5-1	0-0	2-1	3-1	2-0	2-3	2-2		3-1	2-2
13 Wilstead	1-2	3-4	6-2	5-3	1-7	3-0	5-2	1-0	2-2	4-1	4-4	1-1		2-3
14 Wootton Blue Cross	2-3	1-0	5-1	2-1	2-1	1-1	2-1	1-1	3-3	2-2	1-2	1-0	3-1	

BEDFORDSHIRE COUNTY PREMIER DIVISION CONSTITUTION 2014-15

	Club	Ground
1	AFC KEMPSTON & BEDFORD COLLEGE	Hillgrounds Road, Kempston, Bedford MK42 8SZ
2	AFC OAKLEY SPORTS M&DH	Oakley Village Sports Centre, Oakley, Bedford MK43 7RU
3	AFC TURVEY	The Stonefields, Grove Road, Turvey MK43 8EA
4	CALDECOTE	The Playing Fields, Harvey Close, Upper Caldecote SG18 9BQ
5	EASTCOTTS AFC	Wootton Blue Cross FC, Weston Park, Bedford Road, Wootton MK43 9JT
6	FLITWICK TOWN	FOOTBALL TURF (3G) Redborne Upper School (North Site), Flitwick Road, Ampthill, Beds MK45 2NU
7	ICKWELL & OLD WARDEN	Ickwell Green, Ickwell, Bedfordshire SG18 9EE
8	LEA SPORTS PSG	Greenfields, Bury Road, Shillington SG5 3NX
9	LEIGHTON UNITED SPORTS	Hurst Grove, Lidlington, Bedfordshire MK43 0SB
10	MARSTON SHELTON ROVERS	Bedford Road, Marston Moretaine, Bedford MK43 0LE
11	PAVENHAM	Pavenham Playing Field, Pavenham, Bedfordshire MK43 7PE
12	RENHOLD UNITED	Renhold Playing Fields, Renhold, Bedford MK41 0LR
13	SANDY	Bedford Road, Sandy SG19 1EL
14	SHARNBROOK	Playing Fields, Lodge Road, Sharnbrook MK44 1JP
15	SHEFFORD TOWN & CAMPTON	Campton Playing Field, Rectory Road, Campton, Bedfordshire SG17 5PF
16	WILSTEAD	Jubilee Playing Fields, Bedford Road, Wilstead MK45 3HE
17	WOOTTON BLUE CROSS	Weston Park, Bedford Rd., Wootton MK43 9JT

In: AFC Turvey (P). Eastcotts AFC (P). Lea Sports PSG (NC - from Shillington). Sandy (P).
Out: AFC Biggleswade (F). Shillington (NC - to Lea Sports PSG).

Additional Changes from 2013-14 season (outside of regular promotion/relegation)
In: Division Three: Bedford United - (NC - from Bedford Panthers).
Division Four: Caldecote U20, FC Serbia Bedford, Lea Sports PSG Reserves, Moggerhanger United Reserves, Westoning U20, White Eagles.
Out: Division One: Woburn Lions (F). **Division Two:** Co-op Sports (F), Kings AFC (F). Potton United Reserves (S - UCL).
Division Three: AFC Bush (W). Bedford Panthers (NC - to Bedford United).

DIVISION THREE	P	W	D	L	F	A	GD	Pts
1 (P) Meltis Albion	24	20	1	3	73	32	41	61
2 (P) Stevington	24	15	2	7	67	35	32	47
3 (P) Westoning	24	14	3	7	73	46	27	45
4 (P) Bedford Panthers	24	13	3	8	81	48	33	42
5 (P) Elstow Abbey Reserves	24	13	0	11	72	50	22	39
6 (P) Kempston Hammers Sports	24	11	3	10	37	38	-1	36
7 (P) Kempston Athletic	24	10	4	10	57	77	-20	34
8 Marston Shelton Rovers Reserves	24	10	3	11	61	68	-7	33
9 Kempston Con Club Sports	24	9	3	12	52	70	-18	30
10 Wilstead Reserves	24	8	2	14	55	70	-15	26
11 Clifton Reserves	24	6	4	14	45	74	-29	22
12 (R) Ickwell & Old Warden Res.	24	6	1	17	47	82	-35	19
13 AFC Bush	24	5	3	16	49	79	-30	18

DIVISION FOUR	P	W	D	L	F	A	GD	Pts
1 (P) Meltis Albion Reserves	26	21	3	2	97	33	64	66
2 (P) FC Houghton Saturday	26	20	3	3	97	35	62	63
3 (P) Clapham Sports	26	16	5	5	96	42	54	53
4 (P) Wootton Village	26	15	3	8	79	44	35	48
5 (P) Sandy Reserves	26	14	3	9	56	49	7	45
6 (P) Moggerhanger United	26	12	2	12	79	61	18	38
7 (P) Flitwick Town Reserves	26	12	2	12	67	66	1	38
8 Cranfield United Reserves	26	11	3	12	61	69	-8	36
9 Mid Beds Tigers	26	10	1	15	57	98	-41	31
10 Bedford Park Rangers	26	9	2	15	73	81	-8	29
11 Dinamo Flitwick	26	9	1	16	62	91	-29	28
12 Atletico Europa	26	7	3	16	53	83	-30	24
13 Caldecote A	26	6	0	20	41	99	-58	18
14 Shefford Town & Campton A	26	4	1	21	42	109	-67	13

CENTENARY CUP

FINAL
Henlow v Sundon Park Rangers 2-1

JUBILEE CUP

FINAL
Great Barford v Queens Park Crescents 1-1, 3-1p

WATSON SHIELD

FINAL
Meltis Albion v Stevington 0-3

CAMBRIDGESHIRE COUNTY LEAGUE

Sponsored by: Kershaw Mechanical Services Ltd
Founded: 1891
Recent Champions:
2009: Fulbourn Institute
2010: Fulbourn Institute
2011: Lakenheath
2012: Linton Granta
2013: Great Shelford

PREMIER DIVISION	P	W	D	L	F	A	GD	Pts
1 Over Sports	32	23	7	2	94	33	61	76
2 Great Shelford	32	21	6	5	75	29	46	69
3 Foxton	32	19	5	8	82	40	42	62
4 Sawston United	32	17	8	7	84	52	32	59
5 Lakenheath	32	18	4	10	76	60	16	58
6 Hardwick	32	16	5	11	64	47	17	53
7 West Wratting	32	14	6	12	76	71	5	48
8 Wisbech St Mary	32	12	5	15	38	55	-17	41
9 Eaton Socon	32	11	7	14	47	65	-18	40
10 Cottenham United	32	11	3	18	45	64	-19	36
11 Fulbourn Institute	32	10	5	17	56	69	-13	35
12 Linton Granta	32	9	6	17	51	70	-19	33
13 Cambridge University Press	32	10	3	19	49	78	-29	33
14 Soham Town Rangers Reserves	32	10	2	20	51	69	-18	32
15 Cambridge City Reserves (-3)	32	9	8	15	54	74	-20	32
16 Brampton	32	9	5	18	49	82	-33	32
17 (R) Soham United	32	6	9	17	54	87	-33	27

PREMIER DIVISION CUP

ROUND 1

Cambridge City Reserves	v	West Wratting	1-3
Cottenham United	v	Soham United	8-2

ROUND 2

Over Sports	v	Eaton Socon	2-0
Hardwick	v	Fulbourn Institute	4-1
Cambridge University Press	v	Foxton	4-3
Wisbech St Mary	v	Linton Granta	2-4
Soham Town Rangers Reserves	v	Brampton	2-1
West Wratting	v	Waterbeach	HW
Cottenham United	v	Sawston United	4-2
Lakenheath	v	Great Shelford	0-2

QUARTER FINALS

Over Sports	v	Hardwick	4-0
Cambridge University Press	v	Linton Granta	3-1
Soham Town Rangers Reserves	v	West Wratting	2-3
Cottenham United	v	Great Shelford	2-2, 2-4p

SEMI FINALS

Over Sports	v	Cambridge University Press	3-1
West Wratting	v	Great Shelford	3-2

FINAL

Over Sports	v	West Wratting	2-1

PREMIER DIVISION	1	2	3	4	5	6	7	8	9	10	11	12	13	14	15	16	17
1 Brampton		2-1	3-1	2-2	1-1	1-5	0-4	0-2	1-2	5-1	3-1	2-2	2-5	1-0	3-3	1-2	1-1
2 Cambridge City Reserves	5-2		5-2	1-3	2-2	0-8	3-2	1-0	2-1	1-2	4-0	3-3	2-1	3-3	0-4	3-3	2-3
3 Cambridge University Press	2-3	0-2		0-2	2-1	1-0	3-4	1-8	2-1	2-3	2-1	2-5	2-8	2-1	0-0	0-3	1-3
4 Cottenham United	1-3	1-0	2-1		3-4	3-2	4-1	1-0	1-2	0-3	1-3	0-3	2-2	1-3	2-3	1-2	2-0
5 Eaton Socon	1-3	1-0	2-2	1-0		0-6	0-2	0-2	1-3	0-2	2-2	1-0	0-3	4-1	2-0	3-1	2-0
6 Foxton	5-1	1-0	2-0	5-0	5-2		3-0	2-6	3-1	2-4	0-1	3-3	3-3	4-0	2-1	3-1	0-1
7 Fulbourn Institute	2-1	0-2	2-5	2-1	3-3	1-2		1-2	0-1	6-1	5-0	0-1	3-0	3-2	2-2	2-3	0-1
8 Great Shelford	1-0	2-1	0-0	2-1	3-0	2-2	7-2		1-0	3-0	4-0	0-0	1-3	1-0	1-1	6-2	4-0
9 Hardwick	8-0	3-0	2-1	1-2	2-2	3-0	3-3	0-1		4-1	2-1	0-3	2-3	2-1	3-1	3-3	2-0
10 Lakenheath	3-2	6-0	4-2	4-0	2-1	0-3	0-0	3-0	2-1		4-0	1-2	2-2	4-2	4-1	2-5	1-3
11 Linton Granta	1-0	3-3	1-3	2-4	1-2	1-1	3-1	1-2	1-1	4-2		2-5	2-3	3-0	1-3	1-1	5-0
12 Over Sports	5-0	6-1	5-0	3-2	6-0	1-0	2-0	3-1	1-1	3-3	3-0		1-1	5-1	5-2	4-0	1-2
13 Sawston United	7-2	3-1	1-0	0-0	0-3	0-2	7-0	1-1	0-1	3-1	3-2	0-1		3-0	5-5	3-2	4-3
14 Soham Town Rangers Reserves	1-0	2-1	2-3	1-3	2-1	1-2	2-1	0-2	4-1	1-4	0-2	0-2	1-4		0-0	3-1	4-1
15 Soham United	3-2	3-3	1-5	4-0	2-3	1-4	1-1	1-7	1-3	1-1	2-3	1-3	1-3	0-8		1-4	2-1
16 West Wratting	3-0	2-2	1-0	2-0	4-2	1-2	1-3	2-2	3-5	1-2	3-2	4-5	2-2	3-0	5-3		6-1
17 Wisbech St Mary	1-2	0-0	0-2	2-0	0-0	0-0	3-0	0-1	2-0	0-4	1-1	0-2	2-1	2-5	1-0	4-0	

CAMBRIDGESHIRE COUNTY PREMIER DIVISION CONSTITUTION 2014-15

1	BRAMPTON	Thrapston Road Playing Fields, Brampton, Huntingdon PE28 4TB
2	CAMBRIDGE CITY RESERVES	Cottenham Village College, High Street, Cottenham, Cambridge, Cambridgeshire CB24 8UA
3	CAMBRIDGE UNIVERSITY PRESS	CUP Sports Ground, Shaftesbury Road, Cambridge CB2 2BS
4	CHERRY HINTON	Recreation Ground, High Street, Cherry Hinton Cambridge CB1 9HZ
5	COTTENHAM UNITED	King George V Playing Field, Lamb Lane, Cottenham, Cambridge CB4 8TB
6	EATON SOCON	River Road, Eaton Ford, St Neots PE19 3AU
7	FOXTON	Hardman Road, off High Street, Foxton CB22 6RP
8	FULBOURN INSTITUTE	Fulbourn Recreation, Home End, Fulbourn CB21 5HS
9	GAMLINGAY UNITED	Gamlingay Community Centre, Stocks Lane, Gamlingay, Cambridgeshire SG19 3JR
10	GREAT SHELFORD	Recreation Ground, Woollards Lane, Great Shelford CB2 5LZ
11	HARDWICK	Egremont Road, Hardwick, Cambridge CB3 7XR
12	LAKENHEATH	The Pit, Wings Road, Lakenheath IP27 9HN
13	LINTON GRANTA	Recreation Ground, Meadow Lane, Linton, Cambridge CB21 6HX
14	OVER SPORTS	Over Recreation Ground, The Doles, Over, Cambridge CB4 5NW
15	SAWSTON UNITED	Spicers Sports Ground, New Road, Sawston CB22 4BW
16	SOHAM TOWN RANGERS RESERVES	Soham Town Rangers FC, Julius Martin Lane, Soham, Ely CB7 5EQ
17	WEST WRATTING	Recreation Ground, Bull Lane, West Wratting CB21 5NJ
18	WISBECH ST MARY	Wisbech St Mary Playing Fields , Station Road, Wisbech St Mary, Wisbech PE13 4RT

In: Cherry Hinton (P). Gamlingay United (P).
Out: Soham United (R).

CAMBRIDGESHIRE COUNTY LEAGUE - STEP 7

SENIOR DIVISION A	P	W	D	L	F	A	GD	Pts
1 (P) Gamlingay United	28	17	8	3	83	47	36	59
2 (P) Cherry Hinton	28	16	8	4	81	40	41	56
3 Fenstanton	28	15	5	8	65	45	20	50
4 Hemingfords United (-3)	28	16	3	9	59	40	19	48
5 Royston Town A	28	14	5	9	52	43	9	47
6 Hundon	28	13	7	8	62	45	17	46
7 Great Paxton	28	11	7	10	63	44	19	40
8 Milton	28	10	7	11	51	52	-1	37
9 West Row Gunners	28	11	4	13	54	63	-9	37
10 Chatteris Town (-3)	28	10	5	13	38	46	-8	32
11 Ely City Reserves (-6)	28	8	10	10	43	56	-13	28
12 Girton United	28	6	7	15	50	72	-22	25
13 Comberton United	28	7	4	17	39	67	-28	25
14 Cambridge University Press Res. (-3)	28	6	6	16	43	71	-28	21
15 Fulbourn Institute Reserves	28	5	4	19	34	86	-52	19

SENIOR DIVISION B	P	W	D	L	F	A	GD	Pts
1 Fowlmere	28	20	4	4	96	36	60	64
2 Somersham Town	28	18	5	5	72	36	36	59
3 Bluntisham Rangers	28	16	8	4	87	44	43	56
4 Witchford 96	28	15	6	7	80	43	37	51
5 Sawston Rovers	28	14	6	8	67	48	19	48
6 Outwell Swifts	28	13	5	10	59	60	-1	44
7 Lakenheath Reserves	28	12	6	10	57	55	2	42
8 Wimblington	28	12	4	12	74	72	2	40
9 Hardwick Reserves	28	11	4	13	60	64	-4	37
10 Needingworth United (-1)	28	11	3	14	71	70	1	35
11 West Wratting Reserves	28	8	6	14	47	59	-12	30
12 Longstanton	28	7	6	15	49	69	-20	27
13 Hemingfords United Reserves	28	5	7	16	48	81	-33	22
14 Swavesey Institute (-1)	28	4	8	16	42	103	-61	19
15 St Ives Rangers (-12)	28	4	2	22	27	96	-69	2

WILLIAM COCKELL CUP

FINAL
Fenstanton v Great Paxton 4-0

PERCY OLDHAM CUP

FINAL
Sawston Rovers v Witchford 96 3-4

DIVISION ONE A	P	W	D	L	F	A	GD	Pts
1 Barrington	24	19	1	4	58	18	40	58
2 Orwell	24	18	3	3	83	32	51	57
3 Ashdon Villa	24	15	7	2	52	22	30	52
4 Sawston United Reserves	24	16	0	8	45	37	8	48
5 Whittlesford United	24	14	3	7	49	34	15	45
6 Fulbourn Sports & Social Club	24	12	2	10	57	40	17	38
7 Bassingbourn	24	9	3	12	42	43	-1	30
8 Linton Granta Reserves	24	8	2	14	40	56	-16	26
9 Haverhill Rovers Reserves	24	7	5	12	37	54	-17	26
10 Duxford United	24	5	2	17	39	67	-28	17
11 Castle Camps (-3)	24	5	4	15	44	66	-22	16
12 Great Chishill (-3)	24	5	3	16	35	69	-34	15
13 Balsham	24	4	3	17	36	79	-43	15

DIVISION ONE B	P	W	D	L	F	A	GD	Pts
1 Godmanchester Rovers Reserves	24	19	2	3	90	21	69	59
2 Doddington United	24	19	2	3	77	26	51	59
3 Burwell Swifts	24	19	1	4	70	28	42	58
4 Bar Hill Saturday	24	13	5	6	64	41	23	44
5 Bottisham & Lode	24	11	1	12	44	53	-9	34
6 Manea United	24	9	3	12	47	49	-2	30
7 Huntingdon United	24	10	0	14	60	80	-20	30
8 Eaton Socon Reserves	24	9	2	13	46	61	-15	29
9 Buckden	24	8	4	12	49	62	-13	28
10 Littleport Town	24	9	1	14	45	66	-21	28
11 Milton Reserves	24	7	2	15	45	73	-28	23
12 March Town United Reserves	24	5	2	17	28	60	-32	17
13 Chatteris Town Reserves	24	4	3	17	23	68	-45	15

DIVISION TWO A	P	W	D	L	F	A	GD	Pts
1 Haverhill Borough Reserves	24	21	1	2	88	16	72	64
2 Great Chesterford	24	18	2	4	68	45	23	56
3 Saffron Rangers	24	15	6	3	68	28	40	51
4 Papworth	24	14	3	7	73	44	29	45
5 Fowlmere Reserves	24	13	3	8	61	44	17	42
6 Gransden	24	10	3	11	63	59	4	33
7 Meldreth	24	10	3	11	47	54	-7	33
8 City Life	24	9	3	12	41	56	-15	30
9 Thaxted Rangers (-3)	24	9	3	12	42	50	-8	27
10 Steeple Bumpstead	24	6	4	14	46	61	-15	22
11 Abington United	24	5	1	18	41	89	-48	16
12 Great Shelford Reserves (-6)	24	7	0	17	47	62	-15	15
13 Cambourne Rovers	24	2	2	20	33	110	-77	8

DIVISION TWO B	P	W	D	L	F	A	GD	Pts
1 Wisbech St Mary Reserves	22	18	2	2	90	28	62	56
2 Elsworth Sports	22	16	2	4	60	33	27	50
3 Over Sports Reserves	22	13	4	5	69	35	34	43
4 Exning Athletic	22	14	0	8	49	36	13	42
5 Fordham	22	12	4	6	66	32	34	40
6 Brampton Reserves	22	12	4	6	54	43	11	40
7 Isleham United	22	10	3	9	49	43	6	33
8 Mepal Sports	22	7	3	12	37	50	-13	24
9 March Rangers	22	5	1	16	24	58	-34	16
10 Sutton United (-6)	22	6	1	15	42	62	-20	13
11 Bluntisham Rangers Reserves	22	4	0	18	26	58	-32	12
12 Cottenham United Reserves	22	3	0	19	25	113	-88	9

DIVISION ONE PLAY-OFF

Godmanchester Rovers Reserves 0-0, 6-5p Barrington

DIVISION TWO PLAY-OFF

Haverhill Borough Reserves 2-0 Wisbech St Mary Reserves

DIVISION THREE A	P	W	D	L	F	A	GD	Pts
1 Thurlow Royal Exchange	24	21	2	1	116	28	88	65
2 Cherry Hinton Reserves	24	20	2	2	105	29	76	62
3 Debden	24	17	3	4	103	39	64	54
4 Eynesbury Rovers A	24	15	2	7	74	47	27	47
5 Great Paxton Reserves	24	13	3	8	74	60	14	42
6 Steeple Morden	24	11	3	10	73	63	10	36
7 Burwell Swifts Reserves (-3)	24	9	1	14	61	56	5	25
8 Eaton Socon A	24	7	3	14	44	77	-33	24
9 Hundon Reserves	24	7	2	15	40	76	-36	23
10 Hardwick A (-6)	24	8	4	12	50	58	-8	22
11 Wilbraham	24	6	1	17	28	79	-51	19
12 Comberton United Reserves (-6)	24	6	0	18	36	106	-70	12
13 Bottisham & Lode Reserves	24	3	0	21	41	127	-86	9

DIVISION THREE B	P	W	D	L	F	A	GD	Pts
1 Red Lodge	24	21	0	3	101	20	81	63
2 Wisbech St Mary A	24	18	3	3	83	41	42	57
3 Little Downham Swifts	24	17	2	5	92	49	43	53
4 Alconbury	24	16	2	6	70	40	30	50
5 Mildenhall United	24	14	3	7	82	73	9	45
6 Willingham Wolves	24	14	1	9	78	44	34	43
7 Stretham Hotspurs	24	13	2	9	71	64	7	41
8 Fenstanton Reserves	24	7	2	15	58	70	-12	23
9 Soham United Reserves (-3)	24	7	3	14	70	90	-20	21
10 Estover Park	24	6	3	15	42	71	-29	21
11 Benwick Athletic	24	5	2	17	41	70	-29	17
12 Wimblington Reserves	24	3	3	18	42	98	-56	12
13 Hemingfords United A	24	2	0	22	28	128	-100	6

DIVISION THREE PLAY-OFF

Thurlow Royal Exchange 2-4 Red Lodge

DIVISION FOUR A	P	W	D	L	F	A	GD	Pts
1 Little Paxton	24	19	1	4	92	27	65	58
2 Bar Hill Saturday Reserves	24	18	1	5	86	42	44	55
3 Litlington Athletic	24	17	2	5	72	33	39	53
4 Melbourn	24	16	2	6	72	43	29	50
5 Saffron Crocus	24	15	3	6	41	25	16	48
6 Gamlingay United Reserves	24	13	3	8	63	35	28	42
7 Linton Granta A	24	7	5	12	45	66	-21	26
8 Glemsford & Cavendish United	24	7	3	14	48	74	-26	24
9 Cambridge Ambassadors	24	6	5	13	34	60	-26	23
10 Foxton Reserves	24	6	3	15	44	78	-34	21
11 Therfield & Kelshall (-6)	24	7	3	14	31	53	-22	18
12 Duxford United Reserves	24	4	4	16	31	70	-39	16
13 West Wratting A (-3)	24	3	1	20	27	80	-53	7

DIVISION FOUR B	P	W	D	L	F	A	GD	Pts
1 Houghton & Wyton	24	21	1	2	107	18	89	64
2 Ely Crusaders	24	20	2	2	108	22	86	62
3 The Eagle	24	17	2	5	66	32	34	53
4 Wisbech St Mary B	24	13	3	8	59	55	4	42
5 Waterbeach (-3)	24	13	1	10	51	50	1	37
6 Gorefield Athletic (-6)	24	12	3	9	55	28	27	33
7 Earith United	24	9	1	14	47	72	-25	28
8 Littleport Town Reserves	24	8	3	13	36	61	-25	27
9 Mepal Sports Reserves	24	7	3	14	39	89	-50	24
10 Milton A	24	7	2	15	54	73	-19	23
11 Doddington United Reserves	24	6	4	14	49	62	-13	22
12 Haddenham Rovers	24	6	3	15	36	74	-38	21
13 Chatteris Town A (-3)	24	2	2	20	32	103	-71	5

DIVISION FOUR PLAY-OFF

Little Paxton 2-4 Houghton & Wyton

DIVISION FIVE A	P	W	D	L	F	A	GD	Pts
1 Whittlesford United Reserves	20	17	3	0	65	24	41	54
2 Clare Town	20	13	3	4	80	29	51	42
3 Sawston Rovers Reserves	20	12	3	5	65	33	32	39
4 Kedington United	20	12	2	6	68	42	26	38
5 Saffron Dynamos	20	9	3	8	52	45	7	30
6 Thurlow Royal Exchange Reserves	20	8	5	7	57	53	4	29
7 Saffron Rangers Reserves	20	5	6	9	47	59	-12	21
8 Bottisham & Lode A	20	6	1	13	42	77	-35	19
9 Balsham Reserves	20	5	2	13	40	61	-21	17
10 “Sawston United “”A””	20	4	3	13	33	86	-53	15
11 Finchingfield (-3)	20	2	3	15	25	65	-40	6

DIVISION FIVE B	P	W	D	L	F	A	GD	Pts
1 Alconbury Reserves	22	17	2	3	89	17	72	53
2 Offord United	22	17	2	3	79	16	63	53
3 Papworth Reserves	22	12	5	5	56	41	15	41
4 Mott MacDonald	22	12	3	7	62	48	14	39
5 Barrington Reserves	22	12	0	10	50	48	2	36
6 Histon Hornets	22	11	2	9	69	43	26	35
7 Bassingbourn Reserves	22	9	1	12	57	62	-5	28
8 Haslingfield	22	7	3	12	42	79	-37	24
9 Buckden Reserves	22	7	2	13	39	57	-18	23
10 Little Paxton Reserves	22	6	0	16	34	82	-48	18
11 Steeple Morden Reserves	22	6	0	16	33	87	-54	18
12 Gransden Reserves	22	4	4	14	32	62	-30	16

DIVISION FIVE C	P	W	D	L	F	A	GD	Pts
1 Lakenheath Casuals	20	17	0	3	68	20	48	51
2 Isleham Warriors	20	14	2	4	49	33	16	44
3 Waterbeach Colts Old Boys	20	13	1	6	59	29	30	40
4 Isleham Wanderers	20	10	2	8	53	36	17	32
5 Isleham United Reserves	20	10	2	8	39	33	6	32
6 Red Lodge Reserves	20	8	2	10	37	44	-7	26
7 Witchford 96 Reserves (-3)	20	8	3	9	42	35	7	24
8 Burwell Tigers	20	6	5	9	37	40	-3	23
9 Barton Mills	20	6	2	12	30	51	-21	20
10 Swavesey Institute Reserves	20	4	2	14	29	71	-42	14
11 “Cottenham United “”A””	20	3	1	16	28	79	-51	10

DIVISION FIVE D	P	W	D	L	F	A	GD	Pts
1 Chatteris Fen Tigers	24	18	2	4	92	37	55	56
2 Outwell Swifts Reserves	24	18	2	4	78	35	43	56
3 Upwell Town	24	17	1	6	87	35	52	52
4 Wisbech St Mary C	24	15	5	4	70	36	34	50
5 March Saracens	24	16	1	7	94	48	46	49
6 Coldham United	24	13	3	8	73	49	24	42
7 Manea United Reserves	24	13	2	9	94	53	41	41
8 Benwick Athletic Reserves	24	10	2	12	34	58	-24	32
9 Wimblington A	24	9	1	14	59	66	-7	28
10 Walsoken United	24	6	2	16	38	71	-33	20
11 Doddington United A	24	4	0	20	19	110	-91	12
12 March Rangers Reserves (-6)	24	3	1	20	33	113	-80	4
13 Gorefield Athletic Reserves (-6)	24	3	0	21	28	88	-60	3

CENTRAL MIDLANDS LEAGUE

Sponsored by: Windsor Foodservice
Founded: 1971
Recent Champions:
2009: Radcliffe Olympic
2010: Louth Town
2011: Sheffield Parramore
2012: (N) Westella & Willerby (S) Basford United
2013: (N) Dronfield Town (S) Sutton Town AFC

NORTH DIVISION	P	W	D	L	F	A	GD	Pts
1 (P) AFC Mansfield	32	28	2	2	145	24	121	86
2 Westella Hanson	32	27	1	4	114	56	58	82
3 Thorne Colliery	32	22	3	7	76	43	33	69
4 Harworth Colliery Inst.	32	19	4	9	78	47	31	61
5 Newark Town	32	17	2	13	77	62	15	53
6 Clay Cross Town	32	17	2	13	68	64	4	53
7 Kinsley Boys	32	14	6	12	71	66	5	48
8 Ollerton Town	32	15	2	15	73	66	7	47
9 Phoenix	32	14	3	15	74	84	-10	45
10 Glapwell	32	11	6	15	50	76	-26	39
11 Sherwood Colliery	32	11	4	17	63	67	-4	37
12 Bentley Colliery	32	11	4	17	69	81	-12	37
13 Brodsworth Welfare	32	10	4	18	57	75	-18	34
14 Easington United	32	9	5	18	54	77	-23	32
15 Thoresby CW	32	8	4	20	45	69	-24	28
16 Askern	32	4	13	15	55	78	-23	25
17 Welbeck Welfare	32	2	1	29	29	163	-134	7

SOUTH DIVISION	P	W	D	L	F	A	GD	Pts
1 Clifton All Whites	32	23	4	5	89	43	46	73
2 (P) South Normanton Athletic	32	22	3	7	92	43	49	69
3 Bulwell	32	20	7	5	82	48	34	67
4 Bilborough Pelican	32	16	7	9	79	56	23	55
5 Allenton Utd	32	16	6	10	80	58	22	54
6 Southwell City	32	16	6	10	65	65	0	54
7 Real Utd	32	16	5	11	79	70	9	53
8 Pinxton	32	13	12	7	69	48	21	51
9 Mickleover RBL	32	16	3	13	66	52	14	51
10 Belper Utd	32	14	7	11	70	53	17	49
11 Swanwick Pentrich Road	32	13	6	13	58	59	-1	45
12 Mickleover Royals	32	12	4	16	60	70	-10	40
13 Hucknall Town	32	6	11	15	52	59	-7	29
14 Holbrook St Michaels	32	5	8	19	42	71	-29	23
15 Blidworth Welfare	32	5	7	20	30	95	-65	22
16 Linby Colliery	32	4	9	19	40	76	-36	21
17 Calverton MW	32	1	3	28	24	111	-87	6

Barrowby withdrew - results expunged.

LEAGUE CHALLENGE CUP

ROUND 1
Round 1

Real United	v	Calverton MW	5-1
Swanwick Pentrich Road	v	Barrowby	5-1
Thoresby CW	v	Kinsley Boys	AW

ROUND 2

Ollerton Town	v	Real United	2-4
Pinxton	v	Bentley Colliery	HW
Phoenix	v	Thorne Colliery	0-3
Clay Cross Town	v	Welbeck Welfare	4-0
Southwell City	v	Westella	2-3
Blidworth Welfare	v	Mickleover RBL	0-1
Askern	v	Sherwood Colliery	1-6
Clifton All Whites	v	Hucknall Town	3-0
Holbrook St Michaels	v	Easington United	1-3
Glapwell	v	Belper United	0-2
Swanwick Pentrich Road	v	Bulwell	1-0
Bilborough Pelican	v	Allenton United	4-5
Mickleover Royals	v	AFC Mansfield	1-4
Newark Town	v	Linby Colliery	2-3
South Normanton Athletic	v	Kinsley Boys	3-0
Brodsworth Welfare	v	Harworth CI	0-5

ROUND 3

Real United	v	Pinxton	4-2
Thorne Colliery	v	Clay Cross Town	3-0
Westella	v	Mickleover RBL	1-0
Sherwood Colliery	v	Clifton All Whites	2-5
Easington United	v	Belper United	1-4
Swanwick Pentrich Road	v	Allenton United	8-0
AFC Mansfield	v	Linby Colliery	2-1
South Normanton Athletic	v	Harworth CI	1-0

QUARTER FINALS

Real United	v	Thorne Colliery	2-5
Westella	v	Clifton All Whites	1-2
Belper United	v	Swanwick Pentrich Road	1-1, 4-2p
AFC Mansfield	v	South Normanton Athletic	2-1

SEMI FINALS

Thorne Colliery	v	Clifton All Whites	1-0
Belper United	v	AFC Mansfield	2-7

FINAL

Thorne Colliery	v	AFC Mansfield	1-2

NORTH DIVISION	1	2	3	4	5	6	7	8	9	10	11	12	13	14	15	16	17
1 AFC Mansfield		6-1	0-0	5-0	8-3	4-0	10-0	5-0	2-1	5-1	4-0	5-0	4-3	8-0	1-0	5-0	6-0
2 Askern	0-0		0-0	2-3	1-5	2-3	1-2	4-0	1-2	0-4	2-2	3-2	1-1	1-1	1-1	2-0	1-5
3 Bentley Colliery	3-8	3-3		2-1	2-3	1-2	2-2	0-4	3-1	4-6	0-5	0-1	2-4	3-0	1-2	4-0	2-4
4 Brodsworth Welfare	1-3	3-2	1-4		0-1	3-0	2-0	3-2	2-2	1-2	2-3	3-0	1-2	2-2	0-2	8-0	2-6
5 Clay Cross Town	3-7	1-1	0-2	5-0		2-0	1-3	1-0	2-5	0-2	1-4	2-0	4-1	3-1	0-2	5-1	2-3
6 Easington Utd	1-2	3-3	1-4	3-1	2-1		1-5	2-3	H-W	2-5	4-1	0-2	2-2	0-2	3-7	9-1	4-5
7 Glapwell	0-4	2-2	3-1	0-1	2-1	5-1		1-1	1-2	1-3	0-3	2-6	2-1	1-1	A-W	2-1	1-5
8 Harworth CI	0-3	3-1	2-1	4-1	1-2	2-0	2-2		2-0	2-0	3-4	7-1	1-0	2-1	2-1	6-1	2-3
9 Kinsley Boys	0-6	3-3	4-2	1-1	2-2	5-1	2-5	0-3		5-1	3-1	3-3	3-1	2-1	2-1	2-0	1-2
10 Newark Town	0-6	1-1	5-0	4-1	2-3	0-1	2-0	2-3	1-1		4-2	1-2	3-0	2-0	0-4	7-1	0-2
11 Ollerton Town	2-1	5-1	2-6	1-2	1-3	3-2	4-0	1-1	4-0	3-4		1-3	3-2	H-W	1-2	6-0	2-4
12 Phoenix	0-7	6-4	2-5	4-3	2-3	2-2	3-4	0-5	0-6	0-1	7-0		2-2	1-3	3-2	6-1	1-5
13 Sherwood Colliery	0-3	3-1	2-4	3-1	1-2	1-1	6-1	1-2	2-1	0-1	1-0	1-2		4-3	1-2	5-1	3-4
14 Thoresby CW	0-6	1-0	3-1	2-2	A-W	0-3	1-2	1-4	0-2	4-1	0-1	0-1	2-1		2-3	7-2	1-4
15 Thorne Colliery	1-4	2-2	4-2	3-1	2-0	1-0	2-0	1-1	6-1	3-1	1-0	H-W	4-1	3-2		7-0	2-1
16 Welbeck	1-5	1-5	1-4	1-4	2-5	1-0	1-1	0-7	2-8	1-9	0-6	1-8	1-4	2-3	5-4		0-9
17 Westella Hanson	3-2	4-3	5-1	4-1	4-2	1-1	3-0	4-1	5-1	4-2	3-2	2-4	3-4	2-1	5-1	H-W	

SOUTH DIVISION	1	2	3	4	5	6	7	8	9	10	11	12	13	14	15	16	17
1 Allenton Utd		1-1	1-3	2-1	3-8	4-0	1-2	2-2	2-2	3-2	3-0	3-1	2-2	4-3	1-3	3-5	2-2
2 Belper Utd	2-1		1-1	0-2	1-1	4-1	2-4	7-0	3-1	3-2	3-0	2-2	3-1	5-2	1-3	2-3	1-3
3 Bilborough Pelican	4-3	2-2		8-1	2-2	5-1	0-2	5-1	4-0	4-1	2-1	1-0	2-2	1-2	0-2	5-2	2-2
4 Blidworth Welfare	1-4	1-3	1-2		0-2	2-1	0-6	3-1	0-3	2-2	2-5	H-W	1-1	2-2	1-2	0-4	0-4
5 Bulwell	0-3	4-2	4-1	11-0		4-2	2-1	3-1	1-1	1-1	1-0	3-2	1-5	0-1	3-2	2-0	0-0
6 Calverton MW	1-4	0-4	1-4	2-0	0-3		1-3	0-0	0-6	0-0	0-4	0-5	0-1	3-4	0-7	1-3	2-2
7 Clifton All Whites	1-4	2-1	3-1	5-1	3-1	6-1		2-1	2-1	3-1	2-2	5-4	3-2	2-6	4-2	7-0	3-2
8 Holbrook St Michaels	0-3	3-0	0-3	1-1	0-5	3-1	0-1		1-1	1-2	3-2	2-3	2-2	1-1	2-3	1-1	0-1
9 Hucknall Town	0-4	3-6	7-1	1-1	0-1	3-0	0-0	1-1		1-1	2-4	1-2	4-4	1-0	2-2	0-2	1-1
10 Linby Colliery	0-3	0-2	2-2	1-1	1-3	3-2	1-4	1-0	0-2		1-4	1-2	3-3	0-3	0-4	4-2	1-2
11 Mickleover RBL	0-0	0-3	0-2	6-0	1-3	1-0	1-2	3-1	2-0	3-1		2-1	1-0	5-1	3-1	1-2	3-5
12 Mickleover Royals	2-4	0-0	0-4	5-2	1-1	4-0	3-1	1-5	3-2	4-0	3-1		1-4	0-5	2-3	2-3	1-0
13 Pinxton	3-2	4-0	5-0	2-2	1-3	4-1	0-0	2-0	1-0	2-2	2-2	1-1		5-1	1-0	2-3	1-0
14 Real Utd	1-3	1-1	2-2	4-0	4-5	3-0	0-6	3-2	3-2	3-1	1-3	3-4	3-2		0-3	2-2	3-0
15 South Normanton Athletic	3-2	2-1	3-0	3-2	6-0	6-0	0-0	3-1	2-0	4-3	3-1	6-1	1-2	2-4		3-0	1-2
16 Southwell City	2-1	3-1	0-5	2-0	2-3	4-1	2-1	1-3	1-1	1-1	2-4	1-0	2-2	2-3	1-1		3-2
17 Swanwick Pentrich Road	1-2	0-3	2-1	A-W	1-1	5-2	0-3	4-3	4-3	2-1	0-1	4-0	2-0	1-5	3-6	1-4	

CENTRAL MIDLANDS NORTHERN DIVISION CONSTITUTION 2014-15

	Club	Ground	Telephone
1	APPLEBY FRODINGHAM	Brumby Hall Sports Ground, Ashby Road, Scunthorpe, DN16 1AA	01724 402134
2	ASKERN	Welfare Sports Ground, Manor Way, Doncaster Road, Askern, DN6 0AJ	
3	BENTLEY COLLIERY WELFARE	Bentley Miners Welfare , The Avenue, Bentley , Doncaster DN5 0PN	01302 874420
4	BILSTHORPE	Eakring Road, Bilsthorpe, Newark, Nottinghamshire NG22 8QW	07986 284762
5	BRODSWORTH WELFARE AFC	Welfare Road, Woodlands, Doncaster DN6	07967 708430
6	CLAY CROSS TOWN	Mill Lane, Holmgate, Clay Cross, Chesterfield	07980 354522
7	DINNINGTON TOWN	Phoenix Park, 131 Laughton Road, Dinnington, Nr Sheffield S25 2PP	07854 722 465
8	EASINGTON UNITED	Low Farm, Beak Street, Easington, Hull HU12 0TT	None
9	FC BOLSOVER	Bolsover Sports and Social Club	07790 968 631
10	GLAPWELL (2011)	Hall Corner, Glapwell, Chesterfield, Derbyshire S44 5P	07870 195684
11	HARWORTH COLLIERY INSTITUTE	Recreation Ground, Scrooby Road, Bircotes, Doncaster DN11 8JT	01302 750614
12	KINSLEY BOYS	Kinsley Playing Fields	
13	NEWARK TOWN	Collingham FC, Station Road, Collingham NG23 7RA	01636 892303
14	OLLERTON TOWN	The Lane, Walesby Lane, New Ollerton, Newark NG22 9UX	None
15	PHOENIX SPORTS & SOCIAL	Phoenix Sports Complex, Bawtry Road, Brinsworth, Rotherham S60 5PA	01709 363864
16	SHERWOOD COLLIERY	Debdale Lane, Mansfield Woodhouse, Mansfield, Nottinghamshire NG19 7N	07813 718302
17	THORNE COLLIERY	Moorends Welfare, Grange Road, Moorends, Thorne, Doncaster DN8 4LU	07855 545221
18	THORESBY COLLIERY WELFARE	Thoresby Colliery Spts Ground, Fourth Avenue, Edwinstowe NG21 9NS	07802 417987
19	WELBECK WELFARE	Elkesley Road, Meden Vale, Mansfield, Nottinghamshire NG20 9P	07791 155891
20	WESTELLA HANSON	Blackburn Leisure Social Club, Prescott Avenue, Brough HU15 1BB	01482 667353

In: Appleby Fordingham (R - Northern Counties East Div.1). Bilsthorpe (N). FC Bolsover (N). Dinnington Town (R - Northern Counties East Div.1).

Out: AFC Mansfield (P - Northern Counties East Div.1).

CENTRAL MIDLANDS SOUTHERN DIVISION CONSTITUTION 2014-15

	Club	Ground	Telephone
1	BELPER UNITED	Alton Manor, Nailers Way, Belper DE56 0HT	None
2	BILBOROUGH PELICAN	Brian Wakefield Sports Ground, Trentside Lane,Old Lenton Lane, Nottingham NG7 2SA	0115 929 4728
3	BLIDWORTH WELFARE	Blidworth Welfare Miners SC, Mansfield Road, Blidworth, Mansfield NG21 0LR	01623 793361
4	BULWELL	Mill Street Playing Field, off Greenwich Avenue, Basford, Nottingham NG6 0LD	
5	CALVERTON MINERS WELFARE	Calverton Miners Welfare, Hollinwood Lane, Calverton NG14 6NR	0115 965 4390
6	CLIFTON ALL WHITES	Green Lane, Clifton, Nottingham NG11 9AY	0115 921 5401
7	EASTWOOD COMMUNITY	Corination Park, Chewton Street, Eastwood NG16 3HB	
8	HARROWBY SAINTS	Environcom Stadium, Dickens Road, Grantham NG31 9QY	01476 590 822
9	HOLBROOK ST MICHAELS	Mackney Road, Holbrook, Belper, Derbyshire DE56 0T	07885 499358
10	HUCKNALL TOWN AFC	Watnall Road, Hucknall, Nottingham, Nottinghamshire NG15 6E	07535 124295
11	HUCKNALL ROLLS ROYCE	Watnall road, Hucknall, Nottinghamshire NG15	
12	LINBY COLLIERY	Church Lane, Linby, Nottinghamshire NG15 8A	07932 591068
13	MICKLEOVER ROYAL BRITISH LEGION	Mickleover RBL, Poppyfields Drive, Mickleover, Derby DE3 9GQ	01332 513548
14	MICKLEOVER ROYALS	Station Road, Micleover, Derby, Derbyshire DE3 9F	01332 736356
15	PINXTON	Welfare Ground, Wharf Road, Pinxton NG16 6LG	07989 324249
16	REAL UNITED	Grove Farm, Lenton Lane, Nottingham NG7 2SA	None
17	SOUTHWELL CITY	War Memorial Recreation Ground, Bishop's Drive, Southwell NG25 0JP	01636 814386
18	SWANWICK PENTRICH ROAD	Highfield Road, Swanwick, Alfreton, Derbyshire DE55 1BW	

In: Eastwood Community (N). Harrowby Saints (N - formerly Grantham Town U18s). Hucknall Rolls Royce (S - Nottinghamshire Senior).

Out: Allention United (F). Barrowby (WS). South Normanton Athletic (P - East Midlands Counties).

CHESHIRE LEAGUE

Sponsored by: No sponsor
Founded: 1919
Recent Champions:
2009: Woodley
2010: Club AZ
2011: Greenalls Padgate St Oswalds
2012: Knutsford
2013: Knutsford

PREMIER DIVISION	P	W	D	L	F	A	GD	Pts
1 Garswood United	30	20	5	5	70	25	45	65
2 Eagle Sports	30	18	7	5	56	28	28	61
3 Whaley Bridge	30	18	6	6	72	28	44	60
4 Rudheath Social	30	19	3	8	66	38	28	60
5 (P) Barnton	30	17	6	7	92	48	44	57
6 Knutsford	30	16	8	6	65	33	32	56
7 Crewe	30	16	3	11	67	41	26	51
8 Rylands	30	15	4	11	60	40	20	49
9 Greenalls Padgate St Oswalds	30	13	6	11	57	59	-2	45
10 Linotype Cheadle HN	30	13	4	13	67	56	11	43
11 Gamesley	30	11	6	13	44	46	-2	39
12 Billinge FC	30	8	5	17	41	71	-30	29
13 Styal	30	7	5	18	34	65	-31	26
14 Denton Town FC	30	4	4	22	34	111	-77	16
15 Pilkington	30	3	5	22	37	94	-57	14
16 (R) Middlewich Town	30	3	1	26	28	107	-79	10

DIVISION ONE	P	W	D	L	F	A	GD	Pts
1 (P) Poynton (-3)	30	23	5	2	88	31	57	71
2 (P) Sandbach United	30	21	1	8	92	44	48	64
3 Congleton Vale	30	18	5	7	75	46	29	59
4 Malpas	30	18	3	9	84	56	28	57
5 Warrington Town Reserve	30	17	4	9	84	60	24	55
6 Lostock Gralam	30	16	3	11	73	58	15	51
7 Tarporley Victoria	30	13	5	12	69	56	13	44
8 Daten	30	13	5	12	49	55	-6	44
9 Penlake	30	13	3	14	73	83	-10	42
10 Golborne Sports	30	12	5	13	50	60	-10	41
11 Grappenhall Sports FC	30	12	4	14	63	71	-8	40
12 Maine Road Reserves	30	10	2	18	52	62	-10	32
13 Egerton	30	9	4	17	58	83	-25	31
14 Moore United FC	30	7	1	22	40	80	-40	22
15 Sale Town (-3)	30	6	2	22	61	107	-46	17
16 (R) Barnton Wanderers	30	3	6	21	36	95	-59	15

DIVISION ONE CUP

ROUND 1

Linotype Cheadle HN	v	Billinge	3-2 aet
Greenalls Padgate St Oswa	v	Crewe	4-2
Garswood United	v	Rudheath Social	3-0
Gamesley	v	Knutsford	3-4
Barnton	v	Pilkington	5-2 aet
Rylands	v	Middlewich Town	2-0
Styal	v	Whaley Bridge	1-2
Denton Town	v	Eagle Sports	1-3

QUARTER FINALS

Linotype Cheadle HN	v	Greenalls Padgate St Oswa	AW
Garswood United	v	Knutsford	1-0
Barnton	v	Rylands	3-4 aet
Whaley Bridge	v	Eagle Sports	3-1

SEMI FINALS

Greenalls Padgate St Oswa	v	Garswood United	0-2
Rylands	v	Whaley Bridge	1-0

FINAL

Garswood United v Rylands 4-1

MEMORIAL CUP

FINAL

Knutsford v Eagle Sports 3-2

DIVISION TWO CHALLENGE CUP

FINAL

Lostock Gralam v Malpas 0-2

RESERVES CHALLENGE CUP

FINAL

Denton Town Reserves v Whaley Bridge Reserves 0-2

RESERVE DIVISION	P	W	D	L	F	A	Pts	
1 Greenalls Padgate ST O Reserves	32	24	2	6	111	45	66	74
2 Whaley Bridge Reserves	32	22	6	4	91	41	50	72
3 Barnton Reserves	32	23	2	7	101	52	49	71
4 Billinge Reserves	32	19	6	7	99	61	38	63
5 Styal Reserves	32	19	1	12	108	69	39	58
6 Garswood United Reserves	32	18	2	12	88	72	16	56
7 Linotype Cheadle HN Reserves	32	16	6	10	89	64	25	54
8 Rylands Reserves	32	13	8	11	65	71	-6	47
9 Grappenhall Sports Reserves	32	12	8	12	59	63	-4	44
10 Eagle Sports Reserves	32	13	3	16	71	74	-3	42
11 Poynton Reserves	32	10	9	13	63	57	6	39
12 Daten Reserves	32	10	5	17	67	87	-20	35
13 Gamesley Reserves	32	9	6	17	64	90	-26	33
14 Middlewich Town Reserves	32	9	4	19	55	90	-35	31
15 Pilkington Reserves	32	6	6	20	50	112	-62	24
16 Denton Town Reserves (-7)	32	6	2	24	51	121	-70	13
17 Egerton Reserves	32	2	6	24	42	105	-63	12

DIVISION ONE	1	2	3	4	5	6	7	8	9	10	11	12	13	14	15	16
1 Barnton		3-3	4-1	4-2	1-2	1-2	1-2	6-0	2-2	3-2	7-0	3-3	1-0	1-0	1-0	3-2
2 Billinge FC	2-5		1-0	0-1	1-1	1-1	1-5	2-4	1-3	3-1	4-2	1-1	0-3	0-4	2-1	0-0
3 Crewe	0-2	1-3		4-0	1-2	5-0	1-0	4-1	2-1	1-3	6-1	11-2	1-2	2-1	2-0	2-3
4 Denton Town	0-11	2-0	1-4		1-3	0-3	1-3	1-5	0-6	4-4	3-2	3-0	1-6	2-6	1-1	2-3
Denton Town (both games v Rudheath played at Denton)													1-1			
5 Eagle Sports	4-3	0-1	1-1	7-2		1-2	1-1	2-0	1-1	1-0	5-0	2-1	1-0	1-0	2-0	2-0
6 Gamesley	1-3	2-0	1-1	5-2	0-2		1-1	1-1	1-1	2-3	4-0	4-0	1-0	3-2	4-0	0-5
7 Garswood United	3-2	6-1	2-1	3-0	0-0	3-0		3-1	1-2	2-0	5-1	1-0	2-0	2-2	1-0	0-2
8 Greenalls Padgate St Oswalds	1-1	2-1	0-0	3-0	2-1	3-1	2-1		1-1	2-2	7-1	4-2	0-2	5-2	2-1	0-7
9 Knutsford	2-2	4-0	1-3	4-0	0-1	3-0	2-1	3-0		0-2	4-0	3-2	3-2	1-1	4-1	0-2
10 Linotype Cheadle HN	3-3	5-1	2-0	4-0	2-1	0-3	0-1	3-2	1-3		5-1	6-1	2-4	0-2	3-4	2-0
11 Middlewich Town	1-4	2-4	0-3	4-0	1-3	0-0	0-6	1-3	1-5	1-4		3-2	0-2	1-0	1-2	0-4
12 Pilkington	1-4	3-1	1-2	2-2	1-3	3-2	0-3	3-3	0-1	0-5	1-0		0-2	2-3	2-4	0-2
13 Rudheath Social	4-2	3-0	2-1	-	3-4	1-0	1-6	2-1	2-0	5-1	1-0	4-1		1-1	3-1	2-2
14 Rylands	1-3	3-1	2-3	3-1	2-1	1-0	0-1	0-1	1-1	3-0	7-1	4-1	0-3		1-0	2-1
15 Styal	0-6	0-4	2-3	5-1	0-0	2-0	0-3	1-0	1-3	0-0	4-2	2-2	1-5	1-4		0-0
16 Whaley Bridge	4-0	3-2	0-1	5-0	1-1	1-0	2-2	4-1	1-1	3-2	2-1	6-0	4-0	0-2	3-0	

CHESHIRE LEAGUE PREMIER DIVISION CONSTITUTION 2014-15

	Club	Ground	Telephone
1	BILLINGE	Billinge Comm. Spts/Soccer Cte , Carrmill Road , Billinge WN5 7TX	01744 893 533
2	CREWE	Cumberland Arena, Thomas Street, Crewe CW1 2BD	
3	DENTON TOWN	Whittles Park, Heather Lea, Denton M34 6EJ	
4	EAGLE SPORTS	Eagle Sports Club, Thornton Road, Great Sankey, Warrington WA5 2SZ	
5	GAMESLEY	Melandra Park, Melandra Castle Road, Gamesley, Glossop SK13 6UQ	
6	GARSWOOD UNITED	The Wooders, Simms Lane End, Garswood Road, Garswood, Ashton-in-Makerfield WN4 0XH	
7	GREENALLS PADGATE ST OSWALDS	Carlsberg Tetley Social Club, Long Lane, Warrington WA2 8PU	
8	KNUTSFORD	Manchester Road, Knutsford WA16 0NT	
9	LINOTYPE & CHEADLE HN	The Heath, Norbreck Avenue, Cheadle, Stockport SK8 2ET	
10	PILKINGTON	Ruskin Drive, Dentons Green, St Helens WA10 6RP	
11	POYNTON	Poynton Sports Club, London Road North, Poynton, Cheshire SK12 1AG	
12	RUDHEATH SOCIAL	Griffiths Park, Middlewich Road, Rudheath, Northwich, Cheshir CW9 7DR	
13	RYLANDS	Rylands Recreation Club, Gorsey Lane, Warrington WA2 7RZ	
14	SANDBACH UNITED	Hind Heath Road, Sandbach, Cheshire CW113LZ	01270 768 389
15	STYAL	Altrincham Road, Styal, Wilmslow SK9 4JE	
16	WHALEY BRIDGE	Horwich Park, Park Road, Whaley Bridge, High Peak SK23 7DJ	

In: Poyton (P). Sandbach United (P).

Out: Barnton (P - North West Counties Div.1). Middlewich Town (R).

DORSET PREMIER LEAGUE

Sponsored by: BeSpoke Teamwear
Founded: 1957
Recent Champions:
2009: Portland United
2010: Hamworthy Recreation
2011: Hamworthy Recreation
2012: Westland Sports
2013: Portland United

		P	W	D	L	F	A	GD	Pts
1	Portland United	32	22	5	5	97	37	60	71
2	Weymouth Reserves	32	19	7	6	78	40	38	64
3	Merley Cobham Sports	32	19	5	8	74	37	37	62
4	Hamworthy Recreation	32	17	5	10	100	46	54	56
5	Wareham Rangers	32	14	8	10	68	56	12	50
6	Mere Town	32	14	7	11	75	56	19	49
7	Swanage Town & Herston (-3)	32	15	5	12	68	66	2	47
8	Bridport Reserves	32	13	4	15	73	61	12	43
9	Tintinhull	32	11	7	14	56	55	1	40
10	Blandford United	32	12	4	16	49	70	-21	40
11	Sherborne Town Reserves	32	10	8	14	57	69	-12	38
12	Holt United	32	10	7	15	43	61	-18	37
13	Parley Sports	32	9	10	13	59	79	-20	37
14	Shaftesbury Town (-3)	32	11	7	14	54	74	-20	37
15	Cranborne	32	9	7	16	46	89	-43	34
16	Poole Borough	32	6	8	18	53	94	-41	26
17	Hamworthy United Reserves (-8)	32	7	4	21	47	107	-60	16

LEAGUE CUP

PRELIMINARY ROUND

Sherborne Town Reserves	v	Mere Town	1-2

ROUND 1

Blandford United	v	Bridport Reserves	1-2
Hamworthy Recreation	v	Merley Cobham Sports	2-0
Parley Sports	v	Weymouth Res	3-4
Poole Borough	v	Holt United	3-1
Portland United (w/o)	v	Shaftesbury Town	
Mere Town	v	Hamworthy United Reserves	2-1
Swanage Town & Herston	v	Cranborne	0-4
Wareham Rangers	v	Tintinhull	3-4

QUARTER FINALS

Bridport Reserves	v	Portland United	0-2
Hamworthy Recreation	v	Cranborne	4-0
Mere Town	v	Poole Borough	4-1
Tintinhull	v	Parley Sports	4-2

SEMI FINALS

Mere Town	v	Portland United	1-2
Tintinhull	v	Hamworthy Recreation	1-3

FINAL

Hamworthy Recreation	v	Portland United	0-0, 5-4p

		1	2	3	4	5	6	7	8	9	10	11	12	13	14	15	16	17
1	Blandford United		1-0	4-2	1-9	4-2	1-0	1-3	1-4	2-1	2-0	3-0	1-3	4-3	1-5	1-1	2-3	0-1
2	Bridport Reserves	4-3		2-4	4-3	9-2	1-1	1-2	1-1	9-2	4-0	0-1	4-4	3-1	1-0	2-1	2-2	1-2
3	Cranborne	0-1	3-0		1-4	3-1	1-2	2-2	0-6	2-2	0-4	3-2	3-1	3-3	0-2	2-1	2-4	1-1
4	Hamworthy Recreation	4-1	1-0	8-0		1-1	3-0	2-3	1-2	7-2	4-3	2-5	2-3	11-1	3-0	1-1	0-2	3-0
5	Hamworthy United Reserves	1-0	1-6	1-1	2-8		3-1	1-8	0-5	4-4	2-2	1-7	3-2	3-2	0-1	0-3	2-1	0-5
6	Holt United	2-2	0-4	2-1	1-3	3-0		4-0	2-2	3-1	2-2	0-5	0-1	2-2	3-3	1-0	0-3	1-0
7	Mere Town	0-0	6-1	0-2	2-2	0-1	0-1		2-0	3-1	6-0	3-4	2-2	0-4	7-3	2-0	3-0	7-2
8	Merley Cobham Sports	3-1	0-2	2-2	1-0	1-0	4-1	1-2		3-1	7-1	1-2	5-0	2-0	2-0	2-1	2-2	0-1
9	Parley Sports	0-2	4-3	1-1	3-2	1-0	1-0	2-2	0-4		3-1	1-1	1-1	1-2	5-0	2-1	3-3	2-2
10	Poole Borough	1-0	5-1	2-0	0-4	5-3	2-1	2-2	1-2	0-2		3-3	3-4	2-2	0-3	3-3	1-4	1-6
11	Portland United	4-1	2-0	9-0	1-1	6-1	2-1	3-2	4-1	2-0	6-1		7-0	3-0	2-5	3-0	0-1	1-0
12	Shaftesbury Town	1-2	1-0	3-0	0-3	0-6	2-2	1-1	2-1	4-0	1-0	0-3		2-2	2-3	6-1	1-1	3-2
13	Sherborne Town Reserves	3-1	2-0	1-4	0-3	4-1	0-2	4-0	3-2	6-4	1-1	0-0	4-1		1-3	2-1	0-1	0-2
14	Swanage Town & Herston	2-2	2-1	0-2	3-2	2-1	0-1	4-2	1-3	2-2	3-0	0-4	6-1	2-2		3-2	2-2	1-3
15	Tintinhull	2-0	0-2	7-1	2-2	3-2	6-2	0-2	0-1	2-2	5-2	2-2	1-0	1-0	4-3		2-1	0-0
16	Wareham Rangers	1-4	1-3	5-0	1-0	4-1	3-1	4-1	1-2	2-3	5-2	0-3	3-2	1-1	0-3	2-3		4-4
17	Weymouth Reserves	5-0	3-2	6-0	0-1	5-1	3-1	1-0	2-2	3-2	3-3	4-0	2-0	3-1	5-1	1-0	1-1	

DORSET PREMIER LEAGUE CONSTITUTION 2014-15

1	BLANDFORD UNITED	Recreation Ground, Park Road, Blandford Forum DT11 7DB	07932 414524 (Sec)
2	BRIDPORT RESERVES	St Marys Field, Skilling Hill Road, Bridport DT6 5LA	01308 423 834
3	CRANBORNE	Recreation Ground, Penny's Lane, Cranborne, Wimborne BH21 5QE	01725 517 440
4	HAMWORTHY RECREATION	Hamworthy Rec. Club, Magna Road, Canford Magna, Wimborne BH21 3AE	01202 881 922
5	HAMWORTHY UNITED RESERVES	The County Ground, Blandford Close, Hamworthy, Poole BH15 4BF	01202 674 974
6	MERE TOWN	Duchy Manor, Springfield Road, Mere, BA12 6EW	07725 021 587 (Sec)
7	MERLEY COBHAM SPORTS	Cobham Sports & Social Club, Merley House Lane, Wimborne BH21 3AA	01202 885 773
8	PARLEY SPORTS	Parley Sports Club, Christchurch Road, West Parley BH22 8SQ	01202 573 345
9	POOLE BOROUGH	Turlin Moor Recreation Ground, Hamworthy, Poole BH21 5XX	07872 167 221
10	PORTLAND UNITED	New Grove Corner, Grove Road, Portland DT5 1DP	01305 861 489
11	SHAFTESBURY TOWN	Cockrams, Coppice Street, Shaftesbury SP7 8PF	01747 852 990
12	SHERBORNE TOWN RESERVES	Raleigh Grove, The Terrace Playing Fields, Sherborne DT9 5NS	01935 816 110
13	SWANAGE TOWN & HERSTON	Day's Park, off De Moulham Road, Swanage BH19 2JW	01929 424 673
15	TINTINHULL	Tintinhull Playing Fields, Montacute Road, Tintinhull, Yeovil BA22 8QD	07525 137759 (Sec)
16	WAREHAM RANGERS	Purbeck Sports Centre, Worgret Road, Wareham, Dorset BH20 4PH	01929 556 454
17	WESTLAND SPORTS	Alvington Development Centre, Alvington Lane, Yeovil, BA22 8UX	07977 102799
18	WEYMOUTH RESERVES	Bob Lucas Stadium, Radipole Lane, Weymouth DT4 9XJ	01305 785 558

In: Westland Sports (P - Dorset Senior League).
Out: Holt United (W).

ESSEX & SUFFOLK BORDER LEAGUE

Sponsored by: Kent Blaxill Building Products
Founded: 1911
Recent Champions:
2009: West Bergholt
2010: Gas Recreation
2011: Brightlingsea Regent
2012: West Bergholt
2013: Gas Recreation

LEAGUE CUP

QUARTER FINALS			
Barnston AFC	v	Holland FC	1-3
White Notley	v	Alresford Colne Rangers	2-5
Mersea Island	v	Harwich & Parkeston	1-6
Little Oakley	v	Great Bentley	3-0
SEMI FINALS			
Holland FC	v	Harwich & Parkeston	AW
Little Oakley	v	Alresford Colne Rangers	0-5
FINAL			
Alresford Colne Rangers	v	Harwich & Parkeston	0-1

PREMIER DIVISION	P	W	D	L	F	A	GD	Pts
1 Gas Recreation (-3)	30	24	3	3	100	30	70	72
2 West Bergholt	30	21	6	3	95	37	58	69
3 Harwich & Parkeston	30	21	3	6	87	30	57	66
4 Tollesbury	30	19	6	5	81	37	44	63
5 University of Essex	30	14	4	12	58	44	14	46
6 Holland FC	30	12	9	9	58	43	15	45
7 Little Oakley	30	13	6	11	63	49	14	45
8 Alresford Colne Rangers	30	14	2	14	48	54	-6	44
9 White Notley	30	11	7	12	65	70	-5	40
10 Coggeshall Town	30	11	5	14	52	56	-4	38
11 Barnston AFC	30	7	7	16	38	76	-38	28
12 Tiptree Jobserve	30	8	3	19	45	71	-26	27
13 Lawford Lads	30	8	3	19	47	82	-35	27
14 Earls Colne	30	7	6	17	35	74	-39	27
15 Great Bentley (-3)	30	6	6	18	39	100	-61	27
16 (R) Dedham Old Boys	30	2	8	20	24	82	-58	14

DIVISION ONE	P	W	D	L	F	A	GD	Pts
1 Alresford Colne Rangers Reserves	26	18	4	4	89	44	45	58
2 West Bergholt Reserves (-3)	26	15	8	3	73	34	39	50
3 Little Oakley Reserves	26	14	6	6	72	40	32	48
4 (P) Boxted Lodgers	26	13	8	5	61	43	18	47
5 Hedinghams United	26	13	3	10	57	38	19	42
6 Clacton United	26	12	4	10	46	51	-5	40
7 Kirby Athletic	26	11	5	10	78	71	7	38
8 Mersea Island	26	9	6	11	34	44	-10	33
9 Bradfield Rovers (+3)	26	9	3	14	49	65	-16	33
10 Wormingford Wanderers	26	9	5	12	61	47	14	32
11 Gosfield United	26	8	6	12	39	42	-3	30
12 Hatfield Peverel	26	9	3	14	52	64	-12	30
13 (W) Rayne	26	8	3	15	41	54	-13	27
14 (W) Panfield Bell	26	2	0	24	28	143	-115	6

PREMIER DIVISION	1	2	3	4	5	6	7	8	9	10	11	12	13	14	15	16
1 Alresford Colne Rangers		3-1	1-0	3-0	5-3	2-0	5-2	0-3	3-1	0-1	1-1	2-1	0-3	2-7	0-0	3-1
2 Barnston AFC	0-2		2-1	4-1	1-2	0-3	0-0	2-1	0-1	3-3	0-4	4-2	0-0	0-3	0-2	1-8
3 Coggeshall Town	2-1	2-1		6-2	1-2	0-3	4-0	2-3	0-0	1-1	2-1	1-0	1-3	3-5	0-5	0-0
4 Dedham Old Boys	2-4	1-3	1-1		1-1	0-5	1-1	0-3	0-2	2-0	0-6	2-5	0-1	1-4	0-2	0-0
5 Earls Colne	1-0	1-1	2-6	1-1		0-5	2-3	1-2	1-1	3-1	0-0	0-3	1-2	1-0	0-3	1-0
6 Gas Recreation	2-1	6-0	4-1	2-1	2-1		11-0	0-1	2-0	4-0	2-1	3-0	2-0	1-3	4-4	3-0
7 Great Bentley	3-1	2-4	2-6	1-1	3-1	HW		3-2	0-3	2-1	3-3	0-3	2-3	1-1	0-4	2-2
8 Harwich & Parkeston	0-1	9-0	5-0	5-0	5-0	2-2	4-0		4-3	3-1	3-0	5-1	4-0	2-1	3-1	2-2
9 Holland FC	3-0	2-1	4-1	1-1	3-1	2-3	5-1	2-2		1-2	4-0	3-3	1-1	2-3	2-4	4-0
10 Lawford Lads	7-1	6-2	1-4	2-0	3-3	2-4	1-0	0-5	0-2		0-2	0-3	1-2	1-4	1-5	0-2
11 Little Oakley	4-0	1-1	0-2	2-0	3-1	2-4	5-2	1-2	3-1	5-0		4-0	1-2	1-5	3-2	4-5
12 Tiptree Jobserve	1-0	1-1	0-3	0-2	1-2	0-3	3-0	1-3	4-0	3-2	1-2		0-2	0-1	3-3	1-4
13 Tollesbury	1-2	2-2	3-0	6-1	4-1	3-5	8-0	2-1	1-1	6-1	0-0	4-1		4-1	3-2	12-1
14 University of Essex	1-0	3-1	1-1	1-1	4-1	0-1	3-1	0-2	0-2	1-2	0-2	2-1	0-1		2-4	1-1
15 West Bergholt	3-1	3-1	1-0	5-2	5-0	2-2	3-0	3-1	0-0	9-2	0-0	5-3	4-1	2-0		6-1
16 White Notley	0-4	1-2	2-1	5-0	5-1	1-4	2-4	1-0	2-2	0-5	6-2	8-0	1-1	2-1	2-3	

ESSEX & SUFFOLK BORDER LEAGUE PREMIER DIVISION CONSTITUTION 2014-15

1	ALRESFORD COLNE RANGERS	Ford Lane, Alresford, Colchester CO7 8AU	07896 54 122
2	BARNSTON	High Easter Road Barnston CM6 1LZ	07813 200 189
3	BOXTED LODGERS	Cage Lane Boxted	07766 202 577
4	COGGESHALL TOWN	The Crops, West Street, Coggeshall CO6 1NS	01376 562 843
5	EARLS COLNE	Green Farm Meadow, Halstead Road, Earls Colne, Colchester CO6 2NG	01787 223 584
6	GAS RECREATION	Bromley Road, Colchester CO4 3JE	01206 860 383
7	GREAT BENTLEY	The Green, Heckfords Road, Great Bentley, Colchester CO7 8LY	01206 251 532
8	HARWICH & PARKESTON	The Royal Oak, Main Road, Dovercourt, Harwich CO12 4AA	01255 503 643
9	HOLLAND	Eastcliff Sports Ground, Dulwich Road, Holland-on-Sea CO15 5HP	07833 467 395
10	LAWFORD LADS	School Lane, Lawford, Manningtree CO11 2JA	01206 397 211
11	LITTLE OAKLEY	War Memorial Club Ground, Harwich Road, Little Oakley, Harwich CO12 5ED	01255 880 370
12	TIPTREE JOBSERVE	Florence Park, Grange Road, Tiptree, Colchester CO5 0UH	None
13	TOLLESBURY	EShrub End Community and Sports Centre, Boadicea Way, Colchester	01621 869 358
14	UNIVERSITY OF ESSEX	University Essex Sports Centre, Wivenhoe Park, Colchester CO4 3SQ	01206 873 250
15	WEST BERGHOLT	Lorkin Daniel Field, Lexden Road, West Bergholt, Colchester CO6 3BW	01206 241 525
16	WHITE NOTLEY	Oak Farm, Faulkbourne, Witham CM8 1SF	01376 519864

In: Boxted Lodgers (P).

Out: Dedham Old Boys (R).

ESSEX & SUFFOLK BORDER LEAGUE - STEP 7

DIVISION TWO	P	W	D	L	F	A	GD	Pts
1 (P) Gas Recreation Reserves	22	17	3	2	95	26	69	54
2 (W) Harwich & Parkeston Reserves	22	15	3	4	76	27	49	48
3 (P) University of Essex Reserves (-3)	22	17	0	5	76	28	48	48
4 (E) Colne Engaine	22	13	6	3	57	18	39	45
5 (P) Coggeshall Town Reserves (-3)	22	13	4	5	53	39	14	40
6 (P) Holland FC Reserves (+3)	22	7	3	12	44	67	-23	27
7 (P) Barnston AFC Reserves (+6)	22	5	2	15	34	77	-43	23
8 Great Bentley Reserves	22	7	1	14	36	78	-42	22
9 Boxted Lodgers Reserves	22	6	1	15	32	57	-25	19
10 Earls Colne Reserves	22	5	3	14	33	60	-27	18
11 Tiptree Jobserve Reserves (-3)	22	5	5	12	33	56	-23	17
12 Dedham Old Boys Reserves	22	4	5	13	31	67	-36	17

DIVISION THREE	P	W	D	L	F	A	GD	Pts
1 (P) Team Brantham	24	18	2	4	82	31	51	56
2 (P) FC Clacton Reserves (-3)	24	17	3	4	89	24	65	51
3 (W) Bures United (-4)	24	15	4	5	93	33	60	45
4 (W) White Notley Reserves	24	12	1	11	70	57	13	37
5 (P) Bradfield Rovers Reserves (+3)	24	10	1	13	44	81	-37	34
6 (P) Gosfield United Reserves (+3)	24	8	3	13	45	60	-15	30
7 (P) Hatfield Peverel Reserves	24	7	2	14	34	55	-21	23
8 (P) Lawford Lads Reserves (+2)	24	5	5	13	28	49	-21	22
9 (P) Mersea Island Reserves	24	3	3	18	22	117	-95	12

Also joining Division Two for the 2014-15 season:
Cinque Port (P - Colchester & East Essex Prem.)
Horkesley (P - Colchester & East Essex Prem.)
Kelvedon Social (P - Colchester & East Essex Prem.)
Tiptree Perrywood (P - Colchester & East Essex Div.3.)
Weeley Athletic (N)

ESSEX OLYMPIAN LEAGUE

Sponsored by: ProKit UK
Founded: 1966
Recent Champions:
2009: Harold Wood Athletic
2010: Harold Wood Athletic
2011: Kelvedon Hatch
2012: Frenford Senior
2013: Frenford Senior

PREMIER DIVISION		P	W	D	L	F	A	GD	Pts
1	Southminster St. Leonards	26	18	5	3	53	20	33	59
2	Kelvedon Hatch	26	17	4	5	61	29	32	55
3	Frenford Senior (+3)	26	16	4	6	50	27	23	55
4	Rayleigh Town	26	14	5	7	44	34	10	47
5	Buckhurst Hill (-9)	26	16	3	7	54	43	11	42
6	Bishops Stortford Swifts (+3)	26	11	6	9	58	49	9	42
7	Newbury Forest	26	11	4	11	46	48	-2	37
8	Hannakins Farm	26	11	2	13	43	45	-2	35
9	Wadham Lodge	26	9	5	12	43	41	2	32
10	May & Baker E.C.	26	9	3	14	41	54	-13	30
11	Harold Wood Athletic	26	9	2	15	43	56	-13	29
12	Manford Way	26	8	2	16	42	61	-19	26
13	(R) White Ensign (+3)	26	6	4	16	34	58	-24	25
14	(R) Harold Hill	26	2	1	23	37	84	-47	7

SENIOR CUP

ROUND 1

Shenfield AFC	v	Frenford Senior	1-5
Upminster	v	Broomfield	6-1
Snaresbrook	v	Westhamians	1-3
Runwell Hospital	v	Old Southendian	1-2
Ramsden Scotia	v	Rochford Town	2-5
Canning Town	v	Buckhurst Hill	3-4
Basildon Town	v	Hutton	6-1
Leytonstone United	v	Benfleet	1-5
Wadham Lodge	v	Manford Way	5-2
Roydon	v	Galleywood	0-2
LOASS	v	Epping	4-4, 4-2p
Old Chelmsfordians	v	Sungate	2-0
Rayleigh Town	v	Forest Glade	7-0
May & Baker E.C.	v	Kelvedon Hatch	3-7
Toby	v	Newham United	5-1
Ryan FC	v	Hannakins Farm	4-2

ROUND 2

Leigh Ramblers	v	Frenford Senior	2-1
Catholic United	v	Upminster	2-3
White Ensign	v	Westhamians	1-2
Debden Sports	v	Old Southendian	0-1
Rochford Town	v	Buckhurst Hill	2-1
Bishops Stortford Swifts	v	Basildon Town	7-6
Old Barkabbeyans	v	Southminster St. Leonards	0-3
Benfleet	v	Wadham Lodge	0-3
Newbury Forest	v	Galleywood	3-4
LOASS	v	Springfield	0-2

PREMIER DIVISION	1	2	3	4	5	6	7	8	9	10	11	12	13	14
1 Bishops Stortford Swifts		2-3	2-1	5-1	6-1	3-1	1-1	4-2	2-1	4-0	1-4	2-3	1-2	3-1
2 Buckhurst Hill	3-3		1-1	4-3	2-1	2-1	2-3	3-1	1-3	2-1	3-0	1-1	3-0	3-1
3 Frenford Senior	3-2	2-3		2-0	3-2	2-2	2-1	3-0	0-1	1-0	0-1	0-2	4-1	6-0
4 Hannakins Farm	3-1	2-3	0-2		3-3	2-0	1-2	1-3	2-1	1-0	0-1	0-0	2-0	2-0
5 Harold Hill	1-2	0-2	0-1	3-6		2-3	0-2	0-1	4-3	2-4	2-3	2-4	1-2	1-4
6 Harold Wood Athletic	1-2	5-2	1-2	1-3	5-2		4-1	3-1	3-0	1-1	0-1	0-1	1-5	2-0
7 Kelvedon Hatch	3-2	4-0	1-1	3-1	6-1	2-1		3-0	4-1	4-2	1-0	3-0	6-0	3-3
8 Manford Way	2-2	1-2	1-4	1-2	4-2	7-2	1-2		1-3	2-4	2-4	0-1	0-3	3-1
9 May & Baker E.C.	3-3	1-2	1-4	2-1	1-5	0-2	1-0	2-3		3-4	2-1	2-3	2-1	1-1
10 Newbury Forest	0-2	1-0	0-1	3-2	2-1	7-0	3-2	0-2	1-1		2-2	2-1	3-1	2-1
11 Rayleigh Town	3-0	3-2	1-2	2-1	1-0	2-1	1-2	6-1	1-0	4-2		0-0	1-1	0-0
12 Southminster St. Leonards	2-2	2-0	3-1	2-0	2-0	2-0	1-0	3-1	4-1	1-1	6-0		3-1	1-0
13 Wadham Lodge	1-1	1-2	0-0	0-2	6-0	4-1	0-0	0-1	1-2	3-0	1-1	1-0		7-2
14 White Ensign	3-0	0-3	1-2	1-2	6-1	0-2	0-2	1-1	0-3	4-1	2-1	0-5	2-1	

ESSEX OLYMPIAN LEAGUE PREMIER DIVISION CONSTITUTION 2014-15

1	BISHOP'S STORTFORD SWIFTS	Silver Leys, Hadham Road (A1250), Bishop's Stortford CM23 2QE	07500 901 621
2	BUCKHURST HILL	Roding Lane, Buckhurst Hill IG9 6BJ	020 8504 1189
3	FRENFORD SENIOR	Frenford Clubs, The Drive, Ilford, Essex, IG1 3PS	020 8518 0992
4	HANNAKINS FARM	Hannakins Farm Community Centre, Rosebay Avenue, Billericay CM12 0SY	01277 630 851
5	HAROLD WOOD ATHLETIC	Harold Wood Recreation Park, Harold View, Harold Wood RM3 0LX	01708 375 698
6	KELVEDON HATCH	New Hall, School Road, Kelvedon Hatch, Brentwood CM15 0DH	07774 129 867
7	MANFORD WAY	London Marathon Sports Ground, Forest Road, Hainault IG6 3HJ	0208 500 3486
8	MAY & BAKER CLUB	May & Baker Spts/Soc. Club, Dagenham Road, Dagenham RM7 0QX	0208 919 2156
9	NEWBURY FOREST	Oakside Stadium, Station Road, Barkingside, IG6 1NB	0208 550 3611
10	NEWHAM UNITED	Cave Road, Plaistow E13 9DX	07939 788 048
11	RAYLEIGH TOWN	Rayleigh Town Sports/Soc. Club, London Road, Rayleigh SS6 9DT	01268 784 001
12	SOUTHMINSTER ST LEONARDS	King George V Playing Fields, Station Road, Southminster CM0 7EW	07718 869 883
13	SPRINGFIELD	Springfield Hall Park, Arun Close, Springfield CM1 7QE	01245 492 441
14	WADHAM LODGE	Wadham Lodge Sports Ground, Kitchener Road, Walthamstow E17 4JP	0208 527 2444

In: Newham United (P). Springfield (P).

Out: Harold Hill (R). White Ensign (R).

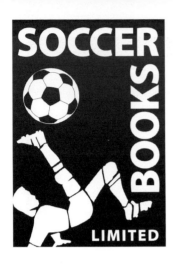

SENIOR CHALLENGE CUP (Premier Champions v Senior Cup Holders)

FINAL

Frenford Senior	v	Kelvedon Hatch	1-0

DIVISION ONE	P	W	D	L	F	A	GD	Pts
1 (P) Newham United	22	14	1	7	65	37	28	43
2 (P) Springfield	22	13	2	7	51	29	22	41
3 Hutton	22	13	2	7	66	52	14	41
4 Leigh Ramblers	22	13	2	7	53	41	12	41
5 Galleywood	22	11	4	7	49	35	14	37
6 Old Southendian	22	11	2	9	48	45	3	35
7 Canning Town	22	9	7	6	53	35	18	34
8 Old Chelmsfordians	22	7	4	11	39	42	-3	25
9 Westhamians	22	7	3	12	33	64	-31	24
10 Herongate Athletic	22	6	2	14	32	63	-31	20
11 (R) Benfleet	22	6	2	14	31	64	-33	20
12 (R) Old Barkabbeyans	22	6	1	15	43	56	-13	19

DIVISION TWO	P	W	D	L	F	A	GD	Pts
1 (P) Ongar Town	20	15	3	2	60	32	28	48
2 (P) Shenfield A.F.C. (+3)	20	13	1	6	54	25	29	43
3 Basildon Town	20	12	1	7	48	42	6	37
4 Runwell Hospital	20	11	2	7	50	34	16	35
5 Toby	20	9	4	7	47	39	8	31
6 Debden Sports	20	8	3	9	46	45	1	27
7 Lakeside (-6)	20	11	0	9	42	51	-9	27
8 Roydon (+3)	20	6	3	11	29	41	-12	24
9 Ryan F.C.	20	6	3	11	37	52	-15	21
10 (R) Upminster	20	6	2	12	29	46	-17	20
11 (R) Broomfield	20	1	2	17	29	64	-35	5

DIVISION THREE	P	W	D	L	F	A	GD	Pts
1 (P) Rochford Town	20	15	3	2	82	35	47	48
2 (P) Snaresbrook	20	13	2	5	64	34	30	41
3 Alemite Athletic	20	12	2	6	65	43	22	38
4 (P) LOASS	20	10	5	5	43	31	12	35
5 Ramsden Scotia	20	9	5	6	45	38	7	32
6 Sungate	20	9	3	8	50	46	4	30
7 Catholic United	20	9	2	9	45	41	4	29
8 Stambridge United	20	7	3	10	29	43	-14	24
9 Epping	20	7	2	11	48	50	-2	23
10 Forest Glade	20	2	5	13	28	58	-30	11
11 Leytonstone United	20	0	2	18	16	96	-80	2

Joining Division Three for 2014-15:
East Londoners (P - Ilford & District).
FC Hamlets (P - Essex Business Houses) (NC - to FC Hamlets POAPC.
Southend Sports (P - Southend Borough Combination).

RESERVES DIVISION ONE	P	W	D	L	F	A	GD	Pts
1 Frenford Senior	22	15	5	2	61	27	34	50
2 Manford Way	22	15	5	2	53	36	17	50
3 Harold Wood Athletic	22	14	5	3	54	27	27	47
4 White Ensign	22	11	5	6	49	29	20	38
5 Rayleigh Town	22	11	4	7	40	30	10	37
6 Canning Town	22	10	2	10	30	39	-9	32
7 May & Baker E.C.	22	6	7	9	30	30	0	25
8 Kelvedon Hatch	22	6	6	10	36	41	-5	24
9 Hutton	22	5	5	12	22	43	-21	20
10 Old Chelmsfordians	22	4	4	14	33	51	-18	16
11 (R) Southminster St. Leonards	22	4	4	14	24	55	-31	16
12 (R) Debden Sports	22	4	2	16	26	50	-24	14

SENIOR CUP continued...

Old Chelmsfordians	v	Alemite Athletic	1-2
Stambridge United	v	Rayleigh Town	2-4
Herongate Athletic	v	Kelvedon Hatch	0-2
Toby	v	Harold Wood Athletic	2-3
Ongar Town	v	Harold Hill	5-2 aet
Lakeside	v	Ryan FC	2-3

ROUND 3

Leigh Ramblers	v	Upminster	8-0
Westhamians	v	Old Southendian	2-1 aet
Rochford Town	v	Bishops Stortford Swifts	1-6
Southminster St Leonards	v	Wadham Lodge	3-0
Galleywood	v	Springfield	0-0, 5-4p
Alemite Athletic	v	Rayleigh Town	2-7
Kelvedon Hatch	v	Harold Wood Athletic	2-1
Ongar Town	v	Ryan FC	1-2

QUARTER FINALS

Leigh Ramblers	v	Westhamians	7-1
Bishops Stortford Swifts	v	Southminster St. Leonards	1-2
Galleywood	v	Rayleigh Town	1-1, 3-4p
Kelvedon Hatch	v	Ryan FC	3-0

SEMI FINALS

Leigh Ramblers	v	Southminster St. Leonards	1-4
Rayleigh Town	v	Kelvedon Hatch	2-0

FINAL

Southminster St Leonards	v	Rayleigh Town	0-0, 1-4p

RESERVES DIVISION TWO	P	W	D	L	F	A	GD	Pts
1 (P) Runwell Hospital	22	14	3	5	52	31	21	45
2 (P) Old Barkabbeyans	22	13	4	5	57	40	17	43
3 (P) Stambridge United	22	13	3	6	45	28	17	42
4 (P) Old Southendian (+2)	22	10	6	6	56	46	10	38
5 Catholic United	22	11	4	7	62	40	22	37
6 Springfield	22	10	6	6	49	42	7	36
7 Galleywood (+3)	22	8	4	10	39	55	-16	31
8 Upminster	21	8	6	7	64	50	14	30
9 Benfleet (-1)	22	7	4	11	38	58	-20	24
10 Buckhurst Hill (-3)	22	7	1	14	43	31	12	19
11 Herongate Athletic	21	3	3	15	28	66	-38	12
12 Westhamians	22	2	6	14	33	79	-46	12

RESERVES DIVISION THREE	P	W	D	L	F	A	GD	Pts
1 Ramsden Scotia	20	16	1	3	54	12	42	49
2 (P) Basildon Town	20	12	2	6	38	27	11	38
3 (P) Toby	20	10	4	6	38	32	6	34
4 (P) Sungate	20	10	4	6	41	43	-2	34
5 Ryan F.C.	20	10	3	7	48	36	12	33
6 (P) Leigh Ramblers	20	8	3	9	44	39	5	27
7 (P) Shenfield A.F.C.	20	8	3	9	42	52	-10	27
8 (P) Newham United	20	7	3	10	40	38	2	24
9 Leytonstone United (+3)	20	4	4	12	31	51	-20	19
10 Broomfield	20	5	3	12	24	42	-18	18
11 (P) Harold Hill (-3)	20	4	2	14	23	51	-28	11

LEAGUE CHAMPIONS - LONGLEVENS FOOTBALL CLUB...
Back Row – L to R – Tim Hall (Assistant Manager), Nick Humphries, Jake Ellmore, Adam Hughes, Mark Harris,Jake Underwood, Dave Rich, Adam Phillips, Ellis Sausman, Luke Kavanagh, Brad Barnard, James French (Manager).
Middle Row – L to R – Shaun O'Connor, Craig Martin (Captain), Craig Beaton, Ryan Dunn, Brad Martin.
Front Row – L to R – Craig Martin (Captain), Luke Kavanagh, Ed Smyllie, Dave Rich, Adam Phillips.

...and the same club this time celebrating their Les James League Cup success!
Back Row: - James French (Manager), Ryan Dunn, Dave Merrick, Mark Harris, Brad Martin, Scott Goodhall, Shaun O'Connor, Jake Ellmore, Ellis Sausman, Brad Barnard, Jake Underwood, Lee Blackmore, Bill Davis (Club President), Craig Beaton, Tim Hall (Assistant Manager).
Front Row: - Craig Martin (Captain), Luke Kavanagh, Ed Smyllie, Dave Rich, Adam Phillips.

GLOUCESTERSHIRE COUNTY LEAGUE

Sponsored by: David Wilson Homes
Founded: 1968
Recent Champions:
2009: Slimbridge
2010: Thornbury Town
2011: Brimscombe and Thrupp
2012: Cribbs Friends Life
2013: Longlevens

		P	W	D	L	F	A	GD	Pts
1	(P) Longlevens	34	26	5	3	105	32	73	83
2	Gala Wilton	34	20	6	8	85	45	40	66
3	Bristol Telephones	34	19	8	7	91	66	25	65
4	Kings Stanley	34	18	10	6	72	41	31	64
5	Southmead CS Athletic (-3)	34	18	6	10	68	59	9	57
6	Patchway Town	34	14	12	8	58	47	11	54
7	Frampton United	34	15	7	12	64	48	16	52
8	Ellwood	34	13	9	12	50	59	-9	48
9	Rockleaze Rangers	34	12	5	17	52	62	-10	41
10	Chipping Sodbury Town	34	11	7	16	67	67	0	40
11	Kingswood	34	11	7	16	56	61	-5	40
12	Henbury (-3)	34	12	7	15	47	62	-15	40
13	Hanham Athletic	34	9	9	16	53	77	-24	36
14	Bishops Cleeve Reserves (-3)	34	10	8	16	65	90	-25	35
15	Bristol Academy	34	10	5	19	60	87	-27	35
16	Thornbury Town	34	9	6	19	47	67	-20	33
17	Yate Town Res	34	7	7	20	51	82	-31	28
18	Berkeley Town	34	8	4	22	47	86	-39	28

LES JAMES LEAGUE CUP

PRELIMINARY ROUND

Bishops Cleeve Reserves	v	Gala Wilton	AW
Hanham Athletic	v	Bristol Telephones	2-0

FIRST ROUND

Frampton United	v	Bristol Academy	2-2, 2-4p
Berkeley Town	v	Rockleaze Rangers	2-3
Patchway Town	v	Yate Town Reserves	0-0, 5-4p
Thornbury Town	v	Chipping Sodbury Town	0-3
Southmead CS Athletic	v	Ellwood	2-3
Kingswood	v	Longlevens	1-4
Kings Stanley	v	Gala Wilton	2-2, 3-0p
Hanham Athletic	v	Henbury	0-3

QUARTER FINALS

Bristol Academy	v	Rockleaze Rangers	2-3
Patchway Town	v	Henbury	2-1
Chipping Sodbury Town	v	Ellwood	6-1
Longlevens	v	Kings Stanley	3-0

SEMI FINALS

Rockleaze Rangers	v	Patchway Town	1-0
Ellwood	v	Longleven	1-3

FINAL

Longlevens	v	Rockleaze Rangers	3-0

(At Kingswood Football Club) *Attendance 136*

		1	2	3	4	5	6	7	8	9	10	11	12	13	14	15	16	17	18
1	Berkeley Town		3-5	1-1	1-4	2-6	0-4	1-5	0-1	2-2	0-1	0-2	1-2	1-9	1-4	1-2	1-2	3-3	2-1
2	Bishops Cleeve Reserves	1-4		4-0	2-2	1-0	2-2	4-2	0-1	0-0	3-3	1-4	2-4	1-7	2-2	4-1	1-2	2-1	6-3
3	Bristol Academy	2-4	2-3		3-3	2-3	3-1	2-1	2-5	3-5	3-1	1-1	5-3	3-1	2-4	0-5	1-2	4-1	2-1
4	Bristol Telephones	4-0	3-0	1-3		1-1	4-0	3-2	5-3	1-3	3-4	4-1	2-1	1-5	7-3	2-1	5-0	4-0	0-3
5	Chipping Sodbury Town	1-2	9-3	3-0	1-4		4-2	0-5	2-1	7-1	1-3	1-1	2-2	1-2	1-6	1-2	2-3	4-0	2-2
6	Ellwood	1-3	3-0	3-1	2-2	5-2		0-1	2-1	1-1	3-1	0-5	1-0	3-2	0-0	5-3	2-1	2-0	2-2
7	Frampton United	2-1	3-0	3-2	2-2	2-1	4-0		0-1	1-1	4-0	1-2	2-0	0-2	1-1	3-2	1-3	1-2	5-0
8	Gala Wilton	5-2	3-0	1-2	5-0	5-1	3-0	0-0		5-0	1-0	3-2	2-2	0-6	1-1	0-1	0-1	4-1	4-1
9	Hanham Athletic	0-2	2-1	3-5	1-1	0-4	0-0	3-2	0-1		2-0	4-2	1-2	1-2	2-3	1-3	2-4	3-1	4-2
10	Henbury	0-1	5-1	2-0	0-1	0-0	4-1	0-2	0-3	2-3		1-3	3-2	0-5	2-2	2-1	2-2	1-1	1-0
11	Kings Stanley	2-0	3-3	6-0	1-2	2-0	1-1	2-2	1-0	2-1	2-0		4-2	0-3	3-0	1-1	3-1	1-1	3-1
12	Kingswood	2-0	1-1	1-1	1-2	2-1	0-1	1-1	3-4	5-2	0-1	0-3		0-0	0-0	4-1	1-4	1-2	5-1
13	Longlevens	4-2	2-0	2-1	1-1	1-1	2-1	5-1	1-1	6-3	3-0	3-0	2-1		3-2	4-0	8-1	2-1	2-1
14	Patchway Town	1-0	0-4	1-1	4-0	1-0	1-1	2-3	3-3	2-1	2-2	0-0	3-0	1-0		1-0	1-2	1-1	1-0
15	Rockleaze Rangers	3-2	1-2	2-1	0-2	1-0	3-0	0-0	1-7	0-0	4-0	2-2	1-3	2-2	1-2		1-2	2-1	3-2
16	Southmead CS Athletic	1-2	5-1	3-1	3-3	2-2	3-0	1-2	2-2	1-1	1-2	0-2	2-3	1-2	1-0	1-0		4-2	2-1
17	Thornbury Town	1-0	3-1	4-1	7-8	0-1	0-1	1-0	0-4	4-0	0-2	2-2	1-2	0-1	1-3	1-0	0-0		1-2
18	Yate Town Reserves	2-2	4-4	3-0	2-4	1-2	0-0	3-0	3-5	0-0	2-2	0-3	2-0	0-5	1-0	3-2	2-5	0-3	

GLOUCESTERSHIRE COUNTY LEAGUE CONSTITUTION 2014-15

1	AEK BOCO	True Clarity Pavilion, Greenbank Road, Hanham, Bristol BS15 3RZ	0117 9477331
2	BERKELEY TOWN	Station Road, Berkeley GL13 9AJ	07807 781269
3	BISHOPS CLEEVE RESERVES	Kayte Lane, Southam, Cheltenham GL52 3PD	01242 676166
4	BRISTOL TELEPHONES	BTRA Sports Ground, Stockwood Lane, Stockwood, Bristol BS14 8SJ	01275 891 776
5	CHELTENHAM CIVIL SERVICE	Civil Service Sports Ground, Tewkesbury Road, Uckington, Cheltenham GL51 9SL	01242 680 424
6	CHIPPING SODBURY TOWN	The Ridings, Wickwar Road, Chipping Sodbury, Bristol BS37 6BQ	07787 522100
7	ELLWOOD	Bromley Road, Ellwood, Coleford GL16 7LY	01594 832927
8	FRAMPTON UNITED	The Bell Field, Bridge Road, Frampton on Severn, Gloucestershire GL2 7HA	07817 486933
9	GALA WILTON	The Gala Club, Fairmile Gardens, Tewkesbury Road, Longford, Glou GL2 9EB	01452 524 447
10	HANHAM ATHLETIC	The Playing Fields Pavilion, 16 Vicarage Road, Hanham, Bristol BS15 3AH	0117 9678291
11	HENBURY	Arnell Drive Playing Field, Lorain Walk, Henbury, Bristol BS10 7AS	0117 959 0475
12	KINGS STANLEY	Marling Close, Broad Street, Kings Stanley, Stonehouse GL10 3PN	01453 828975
13	KINGSWOOD	Kingswood PF, Wickwar Road, Kingswood, Wotton-under-Edge GL12 8RF	07971 682091
14	PATCHWAY TOWN	Scott Park, Coniston Road, Patchway, Bristol BS34 5JR	0117 949 3952
15	ROCKLEAZE RANGERS	Coombe Dingle Sport Complex, Coombe Dingle, Bristol BS9 2BJ	0117 962 6718
16	SOUTHMEAD CS ATHLETIC	Pen Park Sports Pavillion, Jarratts Road, Bristol BS10 6WF	0117 9508362
17	THORNBURY TOWN	Mundy Playing Fields, Kington Lane, Thornbury BS35 1NA	01454 413645
18	YATE TOWN RESERVES	Lodge Road, Yate, Bristol BS37 7LE	Club: 01454 228103

In: AEK Boco (P - Bristol Premier Combination). Cheltenham Civil Service (P - Gloucester Northern Senior League).
Out: Longlevens (P - Hellenic). Bristol Academy (W).

HAMPSHIRE PREMIER LEAGUE

Sponsored by: Puma Engineering
Founded: 2007
Recent Champions:
2009: Colden Common.2010: Colden Common.
2011: Liphook United
2012: Liphook United
2013: Locks Heath

SENIOR DIVISION	P	W	D	L	F	A	GD	Pts
1 Baffins Milton Rovers	32	23	7	2	87	28	59	76
2 Locks Heath	32	19	8	5	77	39	38	65
3 Headley United	32	17	8	7	74	44	30	58
4 Winchester Castle	32	18	4	10	67	47	20	58
5 Overton United	32	17	4	11	71	61	10	55
6 Liphook United	32	16	6	10	83	62	21	54
7 Clanfield	32	16	5	11	77	56	21	53
8 Colden Common	32	14	6	12	66	60	6	48
9 Paulsgrove	32	14	5	13	73	61	12	47
10 AFC Aldermaston	32	13	7	12	71	65	6	46
11 Otterbourne	32	14	3	15	64	56	8	45
12 AFC Stoneham	32	12	4	16	60	73	-13	40
13 Hedge End Rangers	32	9	8	15	53	66	-13	35
14 Fleetlands	32	8	4	20	50	106	-56	28
15 QK Southampton	32	6	6	20	49	87	-38	24
16 Liss Athletic	32	6	4	22	49	80	-31	22
17 Bournemouth Sports	32	4	3	25	33	113	-80	15

SENIOR CUP

ROUND 1

AFC Aldermaston	v	Upham	5-1
Andover Lions	v	Bournemouth Sports	2-1
Broughton	v	QK Southampton	1-3
Bush Hill	v	Fleetlands	6-4
Durley	v	Colden Common	2-4
Hamble Club	v	Liss Athletic	4-2
Headley United	v	Hedge End Rangers	2-1
Infinity	v	Four Marks	5-1
Locks Heath	v	Winchester Castle	3-2
Lyndhurst	v	Baffins Milton Rovers	0-4
Michelmarsh & Timsbury	v	Liphook United	2-5

ROUND 2

Clanfield	v	Baffins Milton Rovers	0-4
AFC Stoneham	v	Overton United	1-2
Headley United	v	Infinity	2-0
Liphook United	v	AFC Aldermaston	1-2
Locks Heath	v	Andover Lions	1-2
Otterbourne	v	Hamble Club	0-2
QK Southampton	v	Colden Common	0-3
Paulsgrove	v	Fleetlands	5-1

QUARTER FINALS

Andover Lions	v	Colden Common	1-2
Headley United	v	Hamble Club	1-5
Paulsgrove	v	Overton United	0-2
Baffins Milton Rovers	v	AFC Aldermaston	2-1

SEMI FINALS

Colden Common	v	Hamble Club	2-1
Baffins Milton Rovers	v	Overton United	5-0

FINAL

Baffins Milton Rovers	v	Colden Common	4-0

SENIOR DIVISION	1	2	3	4	5	6	7	8	9	10	11	12	13	14	15	16	17
1 AFC Aldermaston		7-1	2-2	1-0	1-5	1-1	6-3	0-1	1-0	3-4	2-1	1-1	4-1	1-2	0-1	2-2	1-4
2 AFC Stoneham	4-0		0-2	6-1	0-7	2-5	4-0	1-0	1-5	2-0	2-4	3-3	1-5	1-2	2-2	0-1	0-2
3 Baffins Milton Rovers	5-1	5-1		8-0	1-1	0-3	4-0	5-0	5-2	4-2	3-3	0-2	1-0	1-1	2-2	3-0	1-0
4 Bournemouth Sports	4-4	0-4	0-4		2-0	1-7	0-3	0-4	1-1	1-5	1-4	0-1	1-3	1-2	4-1	2-1	1-3
5 Clanfield	0-3	3-1	1-1	5-0		3-0	11-4	3-5	2-1	2-2	1-1	2-1	5-2	2-1	3-0	2-1	0-3
6 Colden Common	1-4	1-1	0-3	2-1	2-1		3-1	1-2	0-3	3-1	0-1	3-2	2-1	2-5	0-1	5-2	1-2
7 Fleetlands	1-2	1-6	0-4	4-2	1-5	0-3		3-3	1-1	5-1	2-0	2-2	2-1	2-1	3-1	1-3	0-3
8 Headley United	2-1	0-2	1-1	3-0	4-0	1-1	6-0		4-1	2-0	4-2	1-2	0-0	4-2	1-1	2-2	2-2
9 Hedge End Rangers	1-4	2-2	1-2	1-0	2-1	2-1	3-1	0-2		2-2	4-3	2-5	0-3	1-4	1-2	2-2	1-3
10 Liphook United	5-1	2-1	0-2	6-0	5-1	0-0	4-1	2-2	3-3		1-0	2-4	4-2	2-3	2-2	5-1	2-0
11 Liss Athletic	2-5	1-2	2-3	1-2	2-5	3-5	1-2	0-3	0-3	2-3		2-2	0-4	0-2	1-3	1-2	1-3
12 Locks Heath	2-2	2-1	0-1	5-1	2-0	2-3	2-0	4-1	3-0	5-0	1-1		3-2	2-2	2-2	3-0	1-0
13 Otterbourne	3-0	2-0	0-3	7-3	1-1	2-2	3-2	4-0	2-0	0-4	1-2	0-2		1-2	4-1	3-1	2-4
14 Overton United	2-4	1-4	1-5	5-0	0-1	5-3	4-0	1-2	1-1	3-1	2-0	1-5	3-1		2-1	3-0	3-3
15 Paulsgrove	3-1	7-1	1-2	7-0	2-0	3-1	9-1	1-7	0-3	1-2	1-4	1-2	3-0	1-0		4-1	5-2
16 QK Southampton	0-5	0-3	0-2	3-3	4-2	2-3	3-3	1-5	2-2	1-6	2-3	2-4	0-2	7-1	3-2		0-2
17 Winchester Castle	1-1	0-1	1-2	2-1	1-2	2-2	5-1	1-0	3-2	3-5	4-1	1-0	0-2	2-4	4-2	1-0	

HAMPSHIRE PREMIER LEAGUE SENIOR DIVISION CONSTITUTION 2014-15

1	AFC STONEHAM	Jubilee Park, Chestnut Avenue, Eastleigh SO50 9PF	
2	BAFFINS MILTON ROVERS	Langstone Harbour Sports Ground, Eastern Road, Portsmouth PO3 5LY	
3	BUSH HILL	Mansel Park, Evenlode Road, Millbrook, Southampton SO16 9LT	
4	CLANFIELD	Peel Park, Chalton Lane, Clanfield, Waterlooville PO8 0RJ	07765 238 231
5	COLDEN COMMON	Colden Common Rec., Main Road, Colden Common, Winchester SO21 1RP	01962 712 365
6	FLEETLANDS	DARA Fleetlands, Lederle Lane, Gosport PO13 0AA	01329 239 723
7	HAMBLE CLUB	Shell Mex Ground, Hamble Lane, Hamble-le-Rice, Southampton SO31 4QJ	07818 204 400
8	HEADLEY UNITED	Headley Playing Fields, Mill Lane, Headley, Bordon, GU35 0PD	
9	HEDGE END RANGERS	Norman Rodaway Rec Ground, Heathouse Lane, Hedge End, Southampton SO30 0LE	
10	LIPHOOK UNITED	Recreation Ground, London Road, Liphook GU30 7AN	
11	LISS ATHLETIC	Newman Collard Playing Fields Liss GU33 7LH	01730 894 022
12	LOCKS HEATH	Locksheath Rec, 419 Warsash Rd, Titchfield Common, Fareham PO14 4JX	
13	OTTERBOURNE	Oakwood Park, Oakwood Avenue, Otterbourne SO21 2ED	01962 714 681
14	OVERTON UNITED	Overton Recreation Centre, Bridge Street, Overton RG25 3HD	01256 770 561
15	PAULSGROVE	Paulsgrove Social Club, Marsden Road, Paulsgrove, Portsmouth PO6 4JB	02392 324 102
16	QK SOUTHAMPTON	Lordshill Recreation Centre, Redbridge Lane, Lordshill, Southampton SO16 0XN	
17	STOCKBRIDGE	Stockbridge Recreation Ground, High Street, Stockbridge SO20 6EU	
18	WINCHESTER CASTLE	Hants Co. Council Spts Ground, Petersfield Rd (A31),Chilcombe, Winchester SO23 8ZB	

In: Bush Hill (P). Hamble Club (P). Stockbridge (resigned from Wessex Div.1 during 2013-14).
Out: AFC Aldermaston (W - now playing in the Thames Valley Premier League, formerly Reading Senior).
Bournemouth Sports (W - now playing in Bournemouth Hayward Saturday League).

HERTS SENIOR COUNTY LEAGUE

Sponsored by: HertSavers Credit Union
Founded: 1898 reformed 1935
Recent Champions:
2009: Metropolitan Police Bushey
2010: London Lions
2011: Hinton
2012: Baldock Town
2013: Metropolitan Police Bushey

PREMIER DIVISION	P	W	D	L	F	A	GD	Pts
1 Bedmond Sports & S.C.	30	23	1	6	87	42	45	70
2 Belstone	30	21	3	6	105	41	64	66
3 Whitwell	30	20	3	7	71	34	37	63
4 (P) Bush Hill Rangers	30	17	5	8	70	38	32	56
5 Standon & Puckeridge	30	15	5	10	74	66	8	50
6 Letchworth Garden City Eagles	30	13	3	14	71	72	-1	42
7 Sarratt	30	12	6	12	66	80	-14	42
8 Wormley Rovers	30	11	8	11	58	51	7	41
9 Cuffley	30	11	8	11	63	65	-2	41
10 Bushey Sports Club	30	11	5	14	71	64	7	38
11 Chipperfield Corinthians	30	11	5	14	50	63	-13	38
12 Sandridge Rovers	30	10	5	15	43	59	-16	35
13 Bovingdon	30	9	3	18	47	88	-41	30
14 Mill End Sports	30	8	4	18	39	63	-24	28
15 (R) Hinton	30	6	4	20	50	86	-36	22
16 (R) Knebworth	30	5	6	19	51	104	-53	21

DIVISION ONE	P	W	D	L	F	A	GD	Pts
1 (P) Hatfield Social	24	20	3	1	70	22	48	63
2 (P) Lemsford	24	15	5	4	72	37	35	50
3 (P) Hertford Heath	24	14	3	7	55	32	23	45
4 Evergreen	24	13	6	5	75	53	22	45
5 Bushey Rangers	24	12	8	4	69	38	31	44
6 Kimpton Rovers	24	10	5	9	51	58	-7	35
7 AFC Hatfield Town	24	9	2	13	48	62	-14	29
8 Welwyn Garden City Reserves	24	7	5	12	46	55	-9	26
9 Buntingford Town	23	6	4	13	37	40	-3	22
10 Codicote Sports	21	7	1	13	38	70	-32	22
11 Cheshunt Ambers	23	7	0	16	35	63	-28	21
12 Old Parmiterians	22	6	2	14	37	65	-28	20
13 Harvesters	23	3	2	18	28	66	-38	11

AUBERY CUP

ROUND 1

Old Parmiterians	v	Bush Hill Rangers	1-8
Hatfield Social	v	Buntingford Town	2-0
Tansley	v	Codicote Sports	4-1
Cheshunt Ambers	v	Evergreen	1-6
Panshanger	v	Bushey Rangers	2-0
Hinton	v	Sarratt	2-3
AFC Hatfield	v	Bedmond Sports and Social Club	4-6
Standon and Puckeridge	v	Cuffley	3-0
Belstone	v	Wormley Rovers	1-3
Bovingdon	v	Whitwell	4-1
Knebworth	v	Mill End Sports	3-1
Lemsford	v	Harvesters 2012	4-1
Hertford Heath	v	Letchworth Garden City Eagles	1-5
Hatfield Town 1886	v	Kimpton Rovers	0-3
Welwyn Garden City Reserves	v	Sandridge Rovers	3-2
Chipperfield Corinthians	v	Bushey SC	3-4

ROUND 2

Sarratt	v	Bedmond Sports and Social Club	0-2
Welwyn Garden City Reserves	v	Standon and Puckeridge	0-2
Evergreen	v	Bush Hill Rangers	2-1
Hatfield Social	v	Tansley	2-1
Panshanger	v	Bushey SC	0-7
Wormley Rovers	v	Kimpton Rovers	5-6 aet
Lemsford	v	Letchworth Garden City Eagles	1-4
Knebworth	v	Bovingdon	0-5

QUARTER FINAL

Hatfield Social	v	Bedmond Sports and Social Club	2-3
Bovingdon	v	Letchworth Garden City Eagles	1-3
Standon and Puckeridge	v	Kimpton Rovers	3-1
Evergreen	v	Bushey SC	5-3 aet

SEMI FINAL

Standon and Puckeridge	v	Letchworth Garden City Eagles	4-1
Bedmond Sports and Social Club	v	Evergreen	1-3

FINAL

Evergreen	v	Standon and Puckeridge	0-4

PREMIER DIVISION	1	2	3	4	5	6	7	8	9	10	11	12	13	14	15	16
1 Bedmond Sports and Social Club		2-1	1-2	1-3	3-2	1-1	2-1	7-1	5-2	10-1	4-1	1-0	4-1	6-2	HW	2-1
2 Belstone	1-4		3-1	4-5	2-0	5-2	3-0	2-2	12-0	4-1	3-0	5-0	3-3	4-1	1-2	5-1
3 Bovingdon	2-5	0-4		1-0	1-0	1-3	2-4	5-3	5-1	1-6	1-0	3-2	1-2	1-7	0-5	0-3
4 Bush Hill Rangers	1-2	6-3	1-1		5-0	2-2	1-1	3-1	2-0	2-1	0-1	2-2	7-0	0-3	1-0	2-1
5 Bushey SC	1-2	1-6	2-2	1-0		4-1	4-3	2-3	3-1	2-2	3-0	5-0	2-2	5-0	4-4	1-3
6 Chipperfield Corinthians	1-2	0 3	3-2	2-2	3-3		2-4	0-0	5-3	5-1	2-1	1-2	3-2	1-0	1-2	2-1
7 Cuffley	1-2	1-7	1-3	2-3	0-1	0-3		1-3	4-4	4-2	1-1	5-2	1-0	0-4	2-1	3-1
8 Hinton	0-3	3-6	3-2	0-4	0-4	3-1	2-2		2-3	1-4	0-4	0-0	3-6	1-2	1-2	1-2
9 Knebworth	1-4	0-4	3-3	3-2	1-8	1-2	2-2	2-6		3-4	3-1	0-1	3-4	3-3	1-2	0-3
10 Letchworth Garden City Eagles	3-0	0-2	7-0	2-5	3-5	4-0	1-4	3-0	1-2		4-3	3-0	4-2	1-1	0-1	3-3
11 Mill End Sports	5-3	1-1	6-2	0-1	2-1	2-0	0-3	0-4	1-4	1-3		0-1	1-4	4-1	1-2	1-1
12 Sandridge Rovers	0-2	0-1	3-0	0-3	2-0	0-2	3-3	4-1	4-1	1-2	0-1		2-1	3-1	1-3	2-2
13 Sarratt	2-1	1-2	3-2	0-4	4-2	2-0	1-4	4-3	2-2	3-2	2-0	1-4		1-2	3-0	1-1
14 Standon and Puckeridge	2-4	1-5	3-2	0-3	3-2	4-0	2-2	4-1	5-1	3-2	2-0	6-2	4-4		3-1	3-1
15 Whitwell	2-0	1-0	4-0	HW	3-2	3-1	1-1	2-1	3-0	4-0	6-0	1-1	9-1	5-1		0-2
16 Wormley Rovers	1-4	2-3	0-1	4 0	3-1	3-1	2-3	2-1	1-1	0-1	1-1	3-1	4-4	1-1	5-2	

HERTS SENIOR COUNTY LEAGUE - STEP 7

RESERVE NORTH & EAST	P	W	D	L	F	A	GD	Pts
1 Cuffley Reserves	22	18	2	2	83	26	57	56
2 FC Broxbourne Borough U23s	22	18	0	4	61	21	40	54
3 Bush Hill Rangers Res.	21	14	3	4	59	37	22	45
4 Buntingford Town Res.	22	9	8	5	46	39	7	35
5 Wormley YFC	22	9	4	9	54	42	12	31
6 Hertford Heath Reserves	22	9	3	10	38	46	-8	30
7 St Ippolyts	22	9	2	11	64	89	-25	29
8 Letchworth Garden City Eagles Res.	22	7	4	11	41	59	-18	25
9 Wormley Rovers Res.	22	7	2	13	42	55	-13	23
10 Standon and Puckeridge Res.	21	6	1	14	52	61	-9	19
11 Hinton Reserves	22	5	3	14	39	71	-32	18
12 Baldock Town 'A'	22	3	2	17	32	65	-33	11

RESERVES CUP

FINAL

Cuffley Reserves	v	Bushey SC Reserves	1-6

RESERVE SOUTH & WEST	P	W	D	L	F	A	GD	Pts
1 Bedmond Sports and S. C. Res.	20	15	2	3	57	25	+32	47
2 Sarratt Reserves	20	13	2	5	50	34	+16	41
3 Bushey SC Reserves	20	11	3	6	78	40	+38	36
4 Sandridge Rovers Res.	20	11	3	6	55	34	+21	36
5 Bovingdon Reserves	20	11	2	7	51	34	+17	35
6 Chipperfield Corinthians Res.	20	9	2	9	37	45	-8	29
7 Knebworth Reserves	20	7	2	11	28	39	-11	23
8 Mill End Sports Reserves	20	6	4	10	66	64	+2	22
9 Kimpton Rovers Reserves	20	5	4	11	37	61	-24	19
10 Evergreen Reserves	20	5	2	13	37	83	-46	17
11 Lemsford Reserves	20	3	2	15	27	64	-37	11

HERTS SENIOR COUNTY PREMIER DIVISION CONSTITUTION 2014-15

	Club	Ground	Phone
1	BEDMOND SPORTS & SOCIAL	Toms Lane Recreation Ground, Toms Lane, Bedmond, Abbots Langley WD5 0RB	01923 267 991
2	BELSTONE	The Medburn Ground, Watling Street, Radlett WD6 3AB	020 8207 2395
3	BOVINGDON	Green Lane, Bovingdon, Hemel Hempstead HP3 0LA	01442 832628
4	BUSHEY SPORTS CLUB	Met Police Sports Club, Aldenham Road, Bushey, Watford WD2 3TR	01923 243947
5	BUSH HILL RANGERS	Goldsdown Road, Brimsdown, Enfield, Middlesex EN3 7R	020 8804 5491
6	CHIPPERFIELD CORINTHIANS	Queens Street, Chipperfield, Kings Langley WD4 9BT	01923 269554
7	CUFFLEY	King George's Playing Fields, Northaw Road East, Cuffley EN6 4LU	07815 174434
8	HATFIELD SOCIAL		
9	HERTFORD HEATH		
10	LEMSFORD		
11	LETCHWORTH GARDEN CITY EAGLES	Pixmore Playing Fields, Ledgers Lane, Baldock Road, Letchworth SG6 2EN	07855 337175
12	MILL END SPORTS	King George V Playing Fields, Penn Road, Mill End, Rickmansworth WD3 8QX	01923 776892
13	SANDRIDGE ROVERS	Spencer Recreation Ground, Sandridge, St Albans AL4 9DD	01727 835506
14	SARRATT	King George V Playing Fields, George V Way, Sarratt WD3 6AU	07711 618028
15	STANDON & PUCKERIDGE	Station Road, Standon, Ware SG11 1QT	01920 823460
16	WHITWELL	King George V Recreation Grnd, Bradway, Whitwell SG4 8BE	07796 111970
17	WORMLEY ROVERS	Wormley Sports Club, Church Lane, Wormley EN10 7QF	01992 460650

In: Hatfield Social (P). Hertford Heath (P). Lemsford (P).
Out: Bush Hill Rangers (P - Spartan South Midlands Division One). Hinton (R). Knebworth (R).

Bedmond Sports spray the champagne after collecting the Herts Senior County League Premier Division silverware. Photo: Gordon Whittington.

Standon & Puckeridge 2013-14 Aubrey Cup winners. Photo: Gordon Whittington.

HUMBER PREMIER LEAGUE

Sponsored by: No sponsor
Founded: 2000
Recent Champions:
2009: Chalk Lane
2010: Reckitts
2011: Sculcoates Amateurs
2012: Reckitts AFC
2013: Beverley Town

PREMIER DIVISION	P	W	D	L	F	A	GD	Pts
1 Beverley Town	28	25	2	1	90	18	72	77
2 Reckitts AFC	28	22	2	4	78	26	52	68
3 Sculcoates Amateurs	28	17	6	5	89	42	47	57
4 Chalk Lane	28	17	3	8	70	41	29	54
5 Crown FC	28	15	4	9	75	47	28	49
6 Goole United	28	13	7	8	77	55	22	46
7 Hessle Rangers	28	12	4	12	80	72	8	40
8 North Cave	28	10	9	9	50	52	-2	39
9 Pocklington Town	28	11	1	16	52	65	-13	34
10 Scarborough Athletic Reserves	28	10	3	15	50	76	-26	33
11 Hornsea Town (-3)	28	8	5	15	36	61	-25	26
12 Bridlington Sports Club	28	6	4	18	43	94	-51	22
13 St. Andrews	28	7	1	20	51	103	-52	22
14 Hedon Rangers	28	6	3	19	36	64	-28	21
15 Westella & Willerby	28	4	0	24	34	95	-61	12

DIVISION ONE	P	W	D	L	F	A	GD	Pts
1 Wawne United	26	19	3	4	111	47	64	60
2 East Riding Rangers	26	14	7	5	54	40	14	49
3 Brandesburton	26	15	3	8	82	57	25	48
4 Rapid Solicitors	26	14	5	7	86	56	30	47
5 Driffield Evening Institute	26	13	6	7	75	57	18	45
6 South Cave	26	12	6	8	70	57	13	42
7 Hessle United FC	26	9	7	10	69	72	-3	34
8 Little Weighton	26	10	4	12	61	64	-3	34
9 North Ferriby Athletic (-3)	26	10	5	11	58	65	-7	32
10 Howden AFC	26	9	3	14	52	62	-10	30
11 Pinefleet Wolfreton	26	6	6	14	52	88	-36	24
12 Driffield JFC	26	6	5	15	51	80	-29	23
13 Long Riston	26	6	4	16	53	93	-40	22
14 Hessle Sporting Club	26	6	2	18	45	81	-36	20

LEAGUE CUP

ROUND 1

St. Andrews	v	Withernsea AFC	9-1
Little Weighton	v	Reckitts AFC	1-7
Hessle United	v	Westella & Willerby	3-5
Malet Lambert YC	v	Wawne United	2-1
Chalk Lane	v	Hessie Sporting Club	1-3
North Ferriby Athletic	v	Pinefleet Wolfreton	6-2 aet
Hessle Rangers	v	Goole United	1-2
Brandesburton	v	Long Riston	4-3 aet
Crown FC	v	Driffield JFC	4-0
Bridlington Sports Club	v	Beverley Town	3-7 aet
Sculcoates Amateurs	v	Howden AFC	5-0
North Cave	v	South Cave	3-0
Rapid Solicitors	v	Pocklington Town	1-5
Scarborough Athletic Reserves	v	Hedon Rangers	2-2, 5-4p
East Riding Rangers	v	Driffield Evening Institute	1-2

ROUND TWO

St. Andrews	v	Reckitts AFC	0-6
Westella & Willerby	v	Malet Lambert YC	5-2
Hessle Sporting Club	v	North Ferriby Athletic	4-0
Goole United	v	Brandesburton	0-2
Crown FC	v	Hornsea Town	3-0
Beverley Town	v	Sculcoates Amateurs	1-1, 3-4p
North Cave	v	Pocklington Town	2-3
Scarborough Athletic Reserves	v	Driffield Evening Institute	0-4

QUARTER FINALS

Reckitts AFC	v	Westella & Willerby	0-0, 3-4p
Hessle Sporting Club	v	Brandesburton	4-1
Crown FC	v	Sculcoates Amateurs	AW
Pockington Town	v	Driffield Evening Institute	2-1

SEMI-FINALS

Westella & Willerby	v	Hessie Sporting Club	3-1
Sculcoates Amateurs	v	Pocklington Town	5-0

FINAL

Westella & Willerby	v	Sculcoates Amateurs	0-5

PREMIER DIVISION	1	2	3	4	5	6	7	8	9	10	11	12	13	14	15
1 Beverley Town		9-0	1-1	4-1	6-0	1-0	3-0	7-2	2-0	2-0	0-1	5-0	0-0	2-0	5-1
2 Bridlington Sports Club	1-5		1-8	4-4	0-3	6-2	3-1	0-1	2-1	0-1	2-4	1-5	1-10	6-2	1-0
3 Chalk Lane	1-4	3-1		2-6	2-1	4-0	4-1	1-0	0-0	2-1	1-2	3-1	2-3	8-1	3-1
4 Crown FC	0-3	2-0	4-1		4-1	4-1	1-2	3-0	1-1	2-4	0-2	6-2	2-3	5-1	10-0
5 Goole United	3-4	2-1	1-3	1-0		2-2	6-2	1-4	1-1	2-0	1-1	6-0	0-0	1-3	6-2
6 Hedon Rangers	0-2	3-3	0-1	1-5	1-2		0-3	1-2	3-4	1-0	1-2	1-0	0-3	2-1	2-1
7 Hessle Rangers	1-3	2-0	1-5	5-0	7-9	2-2		8-0	2-2	8-2	1-8	6-0	3-3	5-4	3-1
8 Hornsea Town	0-2	1-1	0-1	2-2	2-2	1-0	1-0		0-3	5-0	1-3	2-2	2-3	0-1	3-1
9 North Cave	0-2	3-3	0-2	0-0	1-1	0-5	2-2	2-1		1-0	1-4	2-0	4-6	5-4	1-0
10 Pocklington Town	1-3	1-0	2-2	1-2	2-6	3-1	1-3	2-3	0-1		0-2	5-1	1-3	4-2	4-0
11 Reckitts AFC	0-1	7-0	2-1	2-0	2-3	3-2	2-1	2-0	5-0	3-1		2-0	2-2	4-0	6-0
12 Scarborough Athletic Reserves	0-5	5-1	5-1	0-1	3-2	3-1	2-3	1-1	2-1	1-2	3-2		1-6	2-2	1-0
13 Sculcoates Amateurs	2-3	5-1	0-1	1-3	1-1	2-1	3-1	4-0	1-1	3-4	2-0	7-1		4-1	2-4
14 St. Andrews	1-3	3-2	0-7	2-4	1-6	2-3	4-3	3-2	3-6	4-5	0-1	0-5	0-7		3-1
15 Westella & Willerby	2-3	1-2	2-0	1-3	0-7	2-0	1-4	5-0	0-7	2-5	2-4	2-4	2-3	0-3	

2013-14 - Snodland Town. Photo: Alan Coomes.

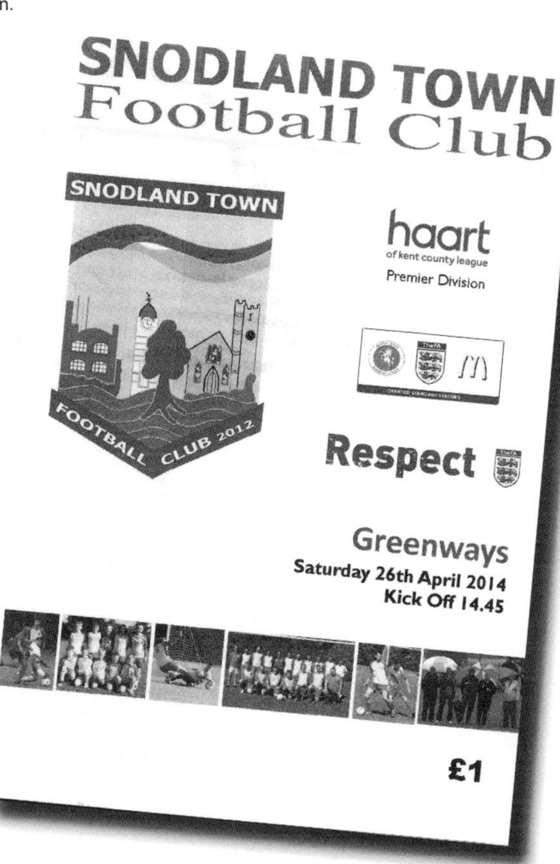

KENT COUNTY LEAGUE

Sponsored by: NRG
Founded: 1922
Recent Champions:
2009: Hollands & Blair
2010: Stansfield O & B Club
2011: Hollands & Blair
2012: Bromley Green
2013: Hildenborough Athletic

PREMIER DIVISION	P	W	D	L	F	A	GD	Pts
1 Metrogas	28	20	5	3	72	30	42	65
2 (P) Sheppey & Sheerness Utd	28	21	1	6	88	28	60	64
3 APM Contrast	28	20	1	7	71	29	42	61
4 Snodland Town	28	18	3	7	68	38	30	57
5 Greenways	28	17	2	9	79	41	38	53
6 Stansfeld O&B Club	28	15	5	8	78	47	31	50
7 Erith 147 Sports	28	14	5	9	59	49	10	47
8 Hildenborough Athletic	28	10	5	13	54	56	-2	38
9 Staplehurst Monarchs Utd	28	11	1	16	63	75	-12	34
10 Bredhurst Juniors	28	8	7	13	44	68	-24	31
11 Fleetdown Utd.	28	7	5	16	34	58	-24	26
12 Tudor Sports (-3)	28	7	5	16	38	80	-42	23
13 Chipstead (-1)	28	6	5	17	44	87	-43	22
14 (R) Bromley Green	28	6	3	19	35	54	-19	21
15 (R) Farnborough OB Guild	28	2	3	23	29	116	-87	9

Rolveden record expunged.

DIVISION ONE EAST	P	W	D	L	F	A	GD	Pts
1 (P) Guru Nanak	20	15	4	1	79	28	51	49
2 (P) Borden Village	20	13	3	4	50	29	21	42
3 Sevenoaks	20	10	6	4	52	33	19	36
4 Kennington	20	10	0	10	39	48	-9	30
5 New Romney	20	8	3	9	33	35	-2	27
6 Otford Utd	20	7	5	8	42	33	9	26
7 Park Regis (-3)	20	8	4	8	48	39	9	25
8 Hollands & Blair Reserves (-3)	20	7	7	6	42	34	8	25
9 Malgo (-1)	20	6	3	11	34	58	-24	20
10 (R) Deal Town Rangers (-1)	20	3	5	12	32	62	-30	13
11 N.K. Aces (-1)	20	1	4	15	24	76	-52	6

DIVISION ONE WEST	P	W	D	L	F	A	GD	Pts
1 (P) Holland Sports	22	16	3	3	59	31	28	51
2 Peckham Town	22	15	2	5	61	25	36	47
3 Long Lane	22	14	2	6	58	48	10	44
4 Bexlians	22	13	4	5	57	42	15	43
5 Coney Hall	22	9	3	10	45	47	-2	30
6 Belvedere (-1)	21	9	3	9	42	45	-3	29
7 AFC Mottingham	22	9	1	12	47	53	-6	28
8 Halls AFC	22	6	4	12	38	52	-14	22
9 Ide Hill	22	5	6	11	33	42	-9	21
10 Forest Hill Park	22	6	3	13	39	54	-15	21
11 Bexley	21	5	6	10	36	54	-18	21
12 AFC Sevenoaks	22	4	3	15	48	70	-22	15

BILL MANKLOW INTER REGIONAL CHALLENGE CUP

ROUND 1

Milton & Fulston United	v	Bexlians	AW
Halls AFC	v	N.K. Aces	6-0
Stansfeld O&B Club	v	Kennington	HW
Peckham Town	v	Sheppey & Sheerness United	4-1
Ide Hill	v	Otford United	4-3
Farnborough Old Boys Guild	v	Long Lane	4-5
Greenways	v	Tudor Sports	3-2

ROUND 2

Belvedere	v	Peckham Town	2-3
Halls AFC	v	Stansfeld O&B Club	2-3
Borden Village	v	Greenways	2-1
Ide Hill	v	Coney Hall	1-4
Erith 147 Sports	v	Bredhurst Juniors	3-3, 4-3p
Park Regis	v	A.P.M. Contrast	2-4
Staplehurst Monarchs United	v	Long Lane	4-2
Snodland Town	v	Bexlians	3-1
Holland Sports	v	Hildenborough Athletic	1-5
Bromley Green	v	New Romney	0-1
Chipstead	v	Bexley	0-2
AFC Mottingham	v	Malgo	5-4
AFC Sevenoaks	v	Deal Town Rangers	3-0
Sevenoaks	v	Metrogas	0-1
Forest Hill Park	v	Hollands & Blair Reserves	1-3
Fleetdown United	v	Guru Nanak	1-2

ROUND 3

Guru Nanak	v	New Romney	2-1
Erith 147 Sports	v	Hildenborough Athletic	1-2
Coney Hall	v	Metrogas	2-1
Staplehurst Monarchs United	v	AFC Sevenoaks	2-5
Bexley	v	AFC Mottingham	1-1, 0-3p
Stansfeld O&B Club	v	Peckham Town	2-1
APM Contrast	v	Hollands & Blair Reserves	2-1
Snodland Town	v	Borden Village	0-4

QUARTER FINALS

Guru Nanak	v	Hildenborough Athletic	3-2
Coney Hall	v	AFC Sevenoaks	0-0, 7-6p
AFC Mottingham	v	Stansfeld O&B Club	2-7
APM Contrast	v	Borden Village	0-2

SEMI FINALS

Guru Nanak	v	Coney Hall	0-3
Stansfeld O&B Club	v	Borden Village	2-3

FINAL

Coney Hall	v	Borden Village	1-0

PREMIER DIVISION	1	2	3	4	5	6	7	8	9	10	11	12	13	14	15
1 A.P.M. Contrast		1-2	2-0	4-1	5-0	7-1	2-0	3-2	1-0	3-0	0-2	2-0	0-0	1-2	3-0
2 Bredhurst Juniors	0-6		2-0	3-2	1-4	3-3	3-0	3-4	4-4	0-5	1-3	1-2	2-2	1-4	3-2
3 Bromley Green	1-2	2-0		0-2	0-2	0-0	0-2	1-2	2-4	0-0	1-4	5-1	0-2	2-3	1-1
4 Chipstead	0-3	1-1	6-3		1-1	1-0	2-1	0-9	1-1	0-1	2-3	1-4	1-5	0-8	2-4
5 Erith 147 Sports	1-4	1-1	1 0	2-4		2-1	1-0	5-3	1-1	1-3	3-1	0-1	2-0	3-2	2-3
6 Farnborough OB Guild	0-2	0-1	0-3	4-4	0-9		2-3	1-9	0-8	0-2	1-6	2-5	2-0	4-8	3-2
7 Fleetdown Utd.	0-3	4-1	0-4	1-1	0-0	4-0		1-1	1-2	1-2	0-2	2-0	2-3	3-1	1-1
8 Greenways	3-2	1-3	3-2	1-0	1-1	5-0	3-0		2-1	1-3	2-0	0-2	2-4	6-1	7-1
9 Hildenborough Athletic	1-4	2-1	0-1	6-3	1-2	4-2	3-1	1-0		1-4	0-4	2-4	2-5	5-2	0-1
10 Metrogas	1-0	2-1	3-0	3-0	3-1	9-3	6-1	1-0	1-1		3-0	4-2	2-1	3-0	4-1
11 Sheppey & Sheerness Utd	5-2	3-0	2-0	4-1	7-0	7-0	3-1	0-1	2-0	1-1		1-0	5-1	7-0	9-0
12 Snodland Town	2-3	5-0	3-0	3-1	3-1	3-0	0-0	2-1	2-0	3-3	4-3		1-1	3-1	9-1
13 Stansfeld O&B Club	4-1	2-2	3-0	6-1	2-6	4-0	8-1	2-3	3-1	5-2	0-1	1-2		3-3	3-1
14 Staplehurst Mon Utd.	1-4	1-2	4-3	3-4	1-3	3-0	4-1	1-3	1-2	2-0	0-1	1-0	1-6		3-1
15 Tudor Sports	0-1	2-2	0-4	3-2	0-4	2-0	0 3	0-4	1-1	1-1	4-2	1-2	1-2	4-2	

KENT COUNTY LEAGUE PREMIER DIVISION CONSTITUTION 2014-15

	Club	Ground	Phone
1	APM CONTRAST	Otham Sports Club, Honey Lane, Otham, Maidstone, Kent ME15 8RG	07860 360 280
2	BORDEN VILLAGE	Borden Playstool, Wises Lane, Borden, Sittingbourne Kent ME9 8LP	07921 912 209
3	BREDHURST JUNIORS	Upchurch Cricket Club, Hollywell Lane, Upchurch, Kent ME9 7HN	07939 547 353
4	CHIPSTEAD	Chipstead Rec, Chevening Road, Chipstead, Sevenoaks TN13 2SA	07753 603 944 or 07843 078689
5	ERITH '147 SPORTS	STC Sports Ground, Ivor Grove, New Eltham SE9 2AJ	0208 858 2057
6	FLEETDOWN UNITED	Heath Lane Open Space, Heath Lane (Lower), Dartford DA1 2QH	01322 273 848
7	GREENWAYS	Elite Venue, (formerly known as the AEI), Dunkirk Close, Gravesend, Kent DA12 5ND	01474 323 817
8	GURU NANAK	Guru Nanak Sports Ground, Khalsa Avenue (Off Trinity Road), Gravesend DA12 1LU	07956 514 264
9	HILDENBOROUGH ATHLETIC	Racecourse Sports Ground, The Slade, Tonbridge TN9 1DS (SatNav: TN9 1HR)	07595 386 657
10	HOLLAND SPORTS	Holland Sports & Social Club, The Pavilion, Mill Lane, Hurst Green Surrey RH8 9DG	01883 716 529
11	METROGAS	Marathon Playing Fields, Forty Foot Way, Avery Hill Road, New Eltham SE9 2EX	020 8859 1579
12	SNODLAND TOWN	Potyns Field, Paddlesworth Road, Snodland ME6 5DL	07894 488 451
13	STANSFELD O & B CLUB	Metrogas Sports Grd, Marathon PF, Forty Foot Way, Avery Hill Rd, New Eltham SE9 2EX	020 8859 1579
14	STAPLEHURST & MONARCHS UNITED	Jubilee Sports Ground, Headcorn Road, Staplehurst TN12 0DS	01580 892 292
15	TUDOR SPORTS	STC Sports Ground, Ivor Grove, New Eltham SE9 2AJ	0208 850 2057

In: Borden Village (P). Guru Nanak (P). Holland Sports (P).

Out: Bromley Green (R). Farnborough Old Boys Guild (R). Sheppey & Sheerness United (P - Kent Invicta - NC to Sheppey United).

DIVISION TWO EAST	P	W	D	L	F	A	GD	Pts
1 (P) East Kent College	20	15	4	1	63	12	51	49
2 (P) Faversham Strike Force	20	15	2	3	91	24	67	47
3 APM Contrast Reserves	20	14	3	3	66	25	41	45
4 Lydd Town Reserves	20	12	4	4	70	34	36	40
5 Deal Town Reserves	20	10	1	9	49	49	0	31
6 Woodstock Park	20	9	2	9	44	48	-4	29
7 Larkfield & New Hythe W (-3)	20	10	0	10	49	33	16	27
8 Tenterden Town (-3)	20	6	2	12	32	61	-29	17
9 Platt United	20	4	1	15	25	87	-62	13
10 Bearsted Reserves (-1)	20	4	1	15	32	57	-25	12
11 Hawkenbury (-1)	20	1	0	19	14	105	-91	2

DIVISION TWO WEST	P	W	D	L	F	A	GD	Pts
1 (P) Phoenix Sports Reserves	22	15	4	3	58	29	29	49
2 (P) Halstead United	22	15	2	5	62	36	26	47
3 (P) Blackheath United	22	14	3	5	56	35	21	45
4 Bexley Borough	22	14	1	7	78	48	30	43
5 Sutton Athletic Reserves	22	13	2	7	55	33	22	41
6 Old Roan	22	10	1	11	63	59	4	31
7 Greenways Reserves	22	9	3	10	46	64	-18	30
8 Fleetdown Utd. Reserves	22	6	6	10	41	51	-10	24
9 Old Bromleians (-1)	22	6	4	12	42	48	-6	21
10 Dulwich Village	22	6	3	13	50	59	-9	21
11 New Park	22	6	2	14	35	72	-37	20
12 (R) Seven Acre & Sidcup Res. (-1)	22	1	3	18	27	79	-52	5

LES LECKIE CUP

SEMI FINALS

Guru Nanak	v	Coney Hall	0-3
Stansfeld Oxford & Bermon	v	Borden Village	2-3

FINAL

Coney Hall	v	Borden Village	1-0

BARRY BUNDOCK WEST KENT SHIELD

SEMI FINALS

FC Elmstead	v	Farnborough O.B. Guildford	2-1
Old Roan	v	Stansfeld O&B Club Res.	1-0

FINAL

FC Elmstead	v	Old Roan	2-1

DIVISION THREE EAST	P	W	D	L	F	A	GD	Pts
1 (P) Hawkinge Town	18	13	4	1	55	20	35	43
2 (P) South Darenth	18	12	0	6	48	26	22	36
3 Sheppey Utd Reserves	18	10	1	7	34	26	8	31
4 Little Sharsted	18	9	2	7	48	35	13	29
5 Guru Nanak Reserves	18	8	4	6	48	50	-2	28
6 Borden Village Reserves	18	7	5	6	34	33	1	26
7 Bromley Green Reserves	18	5	5	8	22	41	-19	20
8 New Romney Reserves (-1)	18	5	5	8	18	26	-8	19
9 Kennington Reserves (-3)	18	4	3	11	28	54	-26	12
10 Staplehurst Monarchs. Utd Res. (-1)	18	1	3	14	22	46	-24	5

DIVISION THREE WEST	P	W	D	L	F	A	GD	PTS
1 (P) Stansfeld O&B Club Reserves	20	15	2	3	67	24	43	47
2 (P) FC Elmstead	20	14	3	3	59	22	37	45
3 (P) Long Lane Reserves	20	14	2	4	60	33	27	44
4 Farnborough O B Guild Reserves	20	14	2	4	53	31	22	44
5 Metrogas Reserves (-1)	20	9	1	10	44	38	6	27
6 Club Langley	20	7	3	10	44	48	-4	24
7 Bexlians Reserves	20	7	2	11	31	36	-5	23
8 Hildenborough Athletic Reserves (-1)	20	7	3	10	37	53	-16	23
9 Tudor Sports Reserves (-4)	20	7	4	9	38	46	-8	21
10 Orpington Reserves	20	2	3	15	34	67	-33	9
11 Meridian VP Reserves (-1)	20	1	1	18	18	87	-69	3

Metrogas FC
Premier Division Champions

FC Elmstead
Barry Bundock West Kent Challenge Shield Winners

Holland Sports FC
Division One West Champions

Kent County Football League Leading Goalscorer
2013-14
Daniel Bradshaw - Sheppey & Sheerness United

East Kent College FC
Division Two East Champions
Les Leckie Cup Winners
Kent FA Junior Cup - Group A Winners

League Sponsors with Peter Shilton at
Annual Presentation Dinner 2014

Faversham Strike Force FC
Fair Play Award Winners 2013-14

University of Kent FC Under 21's
Under 21 Development League Champions

Derek Peck
Referee Long Service Award
Martyn Staveley
Referee of the Year 2013-14

Richard Chesson - Little Sharsted FC
Secretary of the Year 2013-14

Luke Williams and Liam Morris
East Kent College FC
Aford Awards Manager of the Year 2013-14

Adam Luscombe - Platt United FC
League Personality of the Year 2013-14

LEICESTERSHIRE SENIOR LEAGUE

Sponsored by: Everards Brewery
Founded: 1919
Recent Champions:
2009: Anstey Nomads
2010: Thurmaston Town
2011: Ashby Ivanhoe
2012: Rothley Imperial
2013: Rothley Imperial

PREMIER DIVISION	P	W	D	L	F	A	GD	Pts
1 Allexton & New Parks	32	20	7	5	87	33	54	67
2 Melton Mowbray	32	21	4	7	104	55	49	67
3 (P) Ashby Ivanhoe	32	21	4	7	82	34	48	67
4 Birstall United	32	20	5	7	77	42	35	65
5 FC GNG	32	20	2	10	92	52	40	62
6 Friar Lane & Epworth	32	18	5	9	91	50	41	59
7 Sileby Town	32	15	11	6	72	39	33	56
8 Caterpillar (-3)	32	16	6	10	80	66	14	51
9 Desford	32	13	6	13	62	59	3	45
10 Kirby Muxloe Reserves	32	13	5	14	49	64	-15	44
11 Shepshed Dynamo Reserves	32	10	6	16	71	77	-6	36
12 Cottesmore Amateurs (-3)	32	11	4	17	55	69	-14	34
13 Saffron Dynamo	32	8	4	20	46	89	-43	28
14 Earl Shilton Albion	32	8	1	23	56	97	-41	25
15 Rothley Imperial (-6)	32	10	1	21	55	100	-45	25
16 Dunton & Broughton Rangers	32	6	3	23	36	93	-57	21
17 (R) Highfield Rangers	32	4	2	26	24	120	-96	14

DIVISION ONE	P	W	D	L	F	A	GD	Pts
1 (P) Blaby & Whetstone Athletic Res.	32	25	4	3	82	34	48	79
2 (P) Houghton Rangers	32	24	2	6	107	35	72	74
3 (P) St Andrews Reserves	32	23	4	5	96	51	45	73
4 (P) Barlestone St Giles	32	20	4	8	72	44	28	64
5 FC Khalsa (-3)	32	20	2	10	92	56	36	59
6 Lutterworth Town	32	16	5	11	75	58	17	53
7 Anstey Town	32	16	3	13	65	57	8	51
8 Asfordby Amateurs (-6)	32	16	5	11	58	55	3	47
9 Ratby Sports	32	13	6	13	75	69	6	45
10 Croxton Kerrial Dons	32	13	3	16	67	71	-4	42
11 Heather St Johns Reserves (-3)	31	9	6	16	56	78	-22	30
12 Thurnby Nirvana Reserves	30	9	3	18	57	83	-26	30
13 Lutterworth Athletic Reserves (-6)	32	10	3	19	53	68	-15	27
14 Anstey Nomads Reserves (-1)	32	6	9	17	39	72	-33	26
15 Hathern	32	5	5	22	38	80	-42	20
16 Ellistown & Ibstock United Reserves (-3)	32	4	3	25	33	125	-92	12
17 Barrow Town Reserves (-12)	31	6	3	22	51	80	-29	9

BEACON BITTER CUP

PRELIMINARY ROUND

Blaby & Whetstone A.Res.	v	Anstey Nomads Reserves	3-1
Melton Mowbray	v	Shepshed Dynamo Res.	1-2

ROUND 1

Allexton & New Parks	v	Highfield Rangers	4-2
Anstey Town	v	Ellistown & Ibstock United Res.	2-0
Asfordby Amateurs	v	Heather St Johns Reserves	2-1
Ashby Ivanhoe	v	Rothley Imperial	9-0
Croxton Kerrial Dons	v	St Andrews Reserves	3-2
Desford	v	Cottesmore Amateurs	2-0
Dunton & Broughton R.	v	Birstall United	2-4
FC GNG	v	Saffron Dynamo	2-2, 4-2p
Hathern	v	Blaby & Whetstone A.Res.	1-4
Houghton Rangers	v	Barlestone St Giles	1-1, 1-4p
Kirby Muxloe Reserves	v	Earl Shilton Albion	7-0
Lutterworth Athletic Res.	v	FC Khalsa	5-3
Lutterworth Town	v	Ratby Sports	5-4
Shepshed Dynamo Res.	v	Friar Lane & Epworth	5-2
Sileby Town	v	Caterpillar	2-2, 4-2p
Thurnby Nirvana Res.	v	Barrow Town Reserves	4-6

ROUND 2

Alexton & New Parks	v	Kirby Muxloe Reserves	1-2
Ashby Ivanhoe	v	Desford	3-0
Barlestone St Giles	v	Blaby & Whetstone Ath. Res.	0-0, 6-7p
Barrow Town Reserves	v	Croxton Kerrial Dons	2-5
Lutterworth Athletic Res.	v	Asfordby Amateurs	2-3
Lutterworth Town	v	Anstey Town	1-1, 4-1p
Shepshed Dynamoe Res.	v	Birstall United	2-0
Sileby Town	v	FC GNG	2-1

QUARTER FINALS

Ashfordby Amateurs	v	Ashby Ivanhoe	0-0, 4-3p
Blaby & Whetstone A.Res.	v	Shepshed Dynamoe Res.	1-0
Lutterworth Town	v	Kirby Muxloe Reserves	3-0
Sileby Town	v	Croxton Kerrial Dons	1-2

SEMI FINALS

Ashfordby Amateurs	v	Croxton Kerrial Dons	0-1
Blaby & Whetstone A.Res.	v	Lutterworth Town	2-0

FINAL

Croxton Kerrial Dons	v	Blaby & Whetstone A.Res.	3-0

PREMIER DIVISION	1	2	3	4	5	6	7	8	9	10	11	12	13	14	15	16	17
1 Allexton & New Parks		1-1	2-1	5-0	4-0	3-2	3-1	6-0	1-2	3-1	3-0	3-1	3-3	4-1	7-2	3-0	1-1
2 Ashby Ivanhoe	1-1		2-2	7-0	2-1	1-4	9-0	1-2	3-1	3-2	5-0	6-0	1-0	2-0	2-3	0-2	1-0
3 Birstall United	3-2	2-2		0-1	2-1	2-0	2-0	3-1	3-1	5-2	2-0	2-1	2-5	6-1	4-1	3-2	1-1
4 Caterpillar	0-4	1-4	1-3		3-0	1-1	2-1	4-1	5-3	0-0	4-1	5-0	1-4	7-2	4-1	3-1	2-2
5 Cottesmore Amateurs	2-1	1-0	1-3	4-2		2-1	0-1	3-1	3-0	1-1	4-0	0-0	0-5	10-0	1-2	0-3	1-2
6 Desford	1-2	0-2	2-2	2-2	5-1		1-3	2-0	0-5	1-4	2-0	4-1	2-1	0-3	1-1	5-2	2-3
7 Dunton & Broughton Rangers	0-1	0-3	0-3	2-2	2-4	1-2		2-1	0-5	1-4	1-0	1-2	1-5	1-2	2-2	2-2	0-5
8 Earl Shilton Albion	0-2	1-3	0-4	0-4	5-1	3-5	5-3		1-3	1-3	5-2	1-3	5-3	2-3	1-3	2-3	1-2
9 FC GNG	2-1	4-3	3-2	3-2	1-2	5-2	4-2	3-2		1-0	7-0	5-0	3-5	2-1	5-1	1-1	4-0
10 Friar Lane & Epworth	1-1	1-2	4-1	4-2	5-2	2-5	6-2	2-0	2-2		7-0	2-1	2-1	5-1	5-0	7-1	2-2
11 Highfield Rangers	0-1	0-2	0-4	1-5	3-2	0-4	0-1	1-1	0-7	1-5		4-1	0-9	5-3	0-1	0-12	1-3
12 Kirby Muxloe Reserves	0-3	0-3	0-4	0-1	1-3	3-1	2-0	4-1	3-0	3-2	2-1		2-0	2-2	3-0	3-0	2-2
13 Melton Mowbray	2-2	2-1	3-1	5-3	1-0	1-0	6-2	8-0	0-1	3-2	3-0	2-2		4-2	3-2	4-2	2-2
14 Rothley Imperial	3-2	1-2	2-1	0-3	5-0	1-2	2-1	1-6	0-5	0-2	6-1	1-4	4-5		0-2	3-6	2-1
15 Saffron Dynamo	0-7	1-4	0-0	4-6	2-2	1-2	3-0	3-5	3-2	1-3	0-1	1-2	0-2	0-3		2-1	1-5
16 Shepshed Dynamo Reserves	1-4	0-1	1-2	1-4	2-2	0-0	2-3	0-2	3-2	1-2	6-0	1-1	4-3	5-0	5-3		1-1
17 Sileby Town	1-1	1-3	0-2	0-0	4-1	1-1	3-0	7-0	1-0	2-1	2-2	3-0	3-4	2-0	1-0	9-0	

LEICESTERSHIRE SENIOR LEAGUE PREMIER DIVISION CONSTITUTION 2014-15

	Club	Ground	Phone
1	ALLEXTON & NEW PARKS	Glenfield Road, Leicester LE3 6D	07413 679783
2	BARLESTONE ST GILES	Barton Road, Barlestone, Nuneaton CV13 0EP	01455 291 392
3	BIRSTALL UNITED	Meadow Lane, Birstall LE4 4FN	0116 267 1230
4	BLABY & WHETSTONE ATH. RES.	Warwick Road, Whetstone, Leicestershire LE8 6LW	01162 286 852
5	CATERPILLAR SPORTS	Peckleton Lane, Desford, Leicester LE9 9JT	07856 179485
6	COTTESMORE AMATEURS	Rogues Park, Main Street, Cottesmore, Oakham LE15 4DH	01572 813486
7	DESFORD	Sport in Desford, Peckleton Lane, Desford, Leicester LE9 9JU	01455 828786
8	DUNTON & BROUGHTON RANGERS	Station Road, Dunton Bassett LE17 5LF	07780 957479
9	EARL SHILTON ALBION	Stoneycroft Park, New Street, Earl Shilton LE9 7FR	01455 844277
10	FRIAR LANE & EPWORTH	Knighton Lane East, Aylestone Park, Leicester LE2 6FT	0116 283 3629
11	GNG	Nanpantan Sports Ground, Nanpantan Road, Loughborough LE11 3YD	01509 237148
12	HOUGHTON RANGERS	Houghton Playing Fields, Weir Lane, Houghton on the Hill, Leicester LE7 9GR	n/a
13	KIRBY MUXLOE SC RESERVES	Ratby Lane, Kirby Muxloe, Leicester LE9 9AQ	0116 239 3201
14	MELTON MOWBRAY	All England Sports Ground, Saxby Road, Melton Mowbray LE13 1BP	07977 266729
15	ROTHLEY IMPERIAL	Loughborough Road, Mountsorrell, Leicester LE7 7NH	0116 292 0538
16	SAFFRON DYNAMO	Cambridge Road, Whetstone LE8 3LG	07957 151630
17	SILEBY TOWN	Memorial Park, Seagrave Road, Sileby, Loughborough LE12 7TP	07708 231563/07860 842046
18	ST ANDREWS RESERVES	Canal Street, Aylestone Road, Leicester LE2 8LX	01162 839 298

In: Barlestone St Giles (P). Blaby & Whetstone Athletic Reserves (P). Houghton Rangers (P). St Andrews Reserves (P).

Out: Ashby Ivanhoe (P - East Midlands League). Highfield Rangers (R). Shepshed Dynamo Reserves (W).

LIVERPOOL COUNTY PREMIER LEAGUE

Sponsored by: No sponsor

Founded: 2006

Recent Champions:

2009: Waterloo Dock

2010: Waterloo Dock

2011: Waterloo Dock

2012: Aigburth Peoples Hall

2013: West Everton Xaviers

PREMIER DIVISION	P	W	D	L	F	A	GD	Pts
1 Aigburth Peoples Hall	26	23	1	2	88	28	60	70
2 Waterloo Dock	26	19	6	1	79	25	54	63
3 Page Celtic (-3)	26	16	3	7	67	42	25	48
4 Old Xaverians (+3)	26	14	2	10	60	44	16	47
5 (P) Litherland REMYCA	26	13	4	9	58	49	9	43
6 LN Warbreck	26	14	1	11	61	61	0	43
7 East Villa	26	12	6	8	69	46	23	42
8 West Everton Xaviers	26	11	5	10	55	59	-4	38
9 Pinewoods	26	8	4	14	65	86	-21	28
10 South Sefton Borough	26	7	5	14	35	50	-15	26
11 Red Rum	26	5	4	17	45	85	-40	19
12 ROMA	26	5	4	17	27	76	-49	19
13 Kingsley United	26	5	2	19	32	46	-14	17
14 Stoneycroft	26	4	5	17	25	69	-44	17

ZINGARI CUP

ROUND 1

Roma	v	Waterloo Dock	2-5
South Sefton Borough	v	Litherland REMYCA	0-4
Allerton	v	West Everton Xaviers	AW
Old Xaverians	v	LN Warbreck	2-2, 4-3p
Aigburth Peoples Hall	v	Page Celtic	2-2, 5-3p
Kingsley United	v	East Villa	4-7
Red Rum	v	Stoneycroft	9-5

QUARTER FINALS

Waterloo Dock	v	Pinewoods	4-2
Litherland REMYCA	v	West Everton Xaviers	2-5
LN Warbeck	v	Aigburth Peoples Hall	1-3
East Villa	v	Red Rum	4-2

SEMI FINALS

Waterloo Dock	v	West Everton Xaviers	2-0
Aigburth Peoples Hall	v	East Villa	3-0

FINAL

Waterloo Dock	v	Aigburth Peoples Hall	2-2, 2-4p

GEORGE MAHON CUP

ROUND 1

Quarry Bank Old Boys	v	Cheshire Lines	3-2
KCFC	v	Salisbury Athletic	1-2
Eli Lilly	v	Warbreck	4-4, 4-6p
Walton Community	v	Aintree Villa	2-3

ROUND 2

Litherland REMYCA	v	Page Celtic	0-2
Copperas Hill	v	Lucas Sports	3-2
Byron	v	South Sefton Borough	AW
Old Holts	v	Waterloo Grammar School	0-3
Salisbury Athletic	v	West Everton Xaviers	1-4
Alder	-	Bye	
Lower Breck	v	Waterloo Dock	0-6
Kingsley United	v	Aigburth Peoples Hall	AW
Collegiate Old Boys	v	BRNESC	6-0
Warbreck	v	Red Rum	AW
Old Xaverians	v	Aintree Villa	4-2

PREMIER DIVISION	1	2	3	4	5	6	7	8	9	10	11	12	13	14
1 Aigburth Peoples Hall		2-0	3-1	4-1	2-0	4-2	4-0	5-2	3-2	4-1	3-2	6-2	A-W	5-2
2 East Villa	1-3		4-2	1-5	1-2	0-2	1-4	5-0	8-0	3-1	1-1	1-1	2-2	2-0
3 Kingsley United	0-2	A-W		A-W	A-W	2-1	0-3	0-4	2-4	A-W	2-2	2-1	0-2	A-W
4 Litherland REMYCA	1-2	1-3	4-1		6-0	2-3	1-1	2-2	3-3	5-0	0-1	3-1	1-5	1-1
5 LN Warbreck	2-5	3-6	1-2	A-W		3-3	4-2	3-5	3-2	2-1	1-2	9-2	0-5	4-1
6 Old Xaverians	0-1	2-1	H-W	1-2	1-3		1-3	1-3	8-1	4-2	1-0	1-2	2-1	1-2
7 Page Celtic	0-3	2-5	1-0	4-0	0-2	3-2		3-1	4-5	5-0	3-1	3-0	2-3	5-2
8 Pinewoods	2-2	3-8	6-3	4-5	2-4	1-6	3-4		7-3	4-3	4-1	1-2	1-11	1-3
9 Red Rum	3-4	A-W	4-3	1-4	H-W	3-4	2-4	0-5		A-W	0-0	4-1	2-6	1-3
10 ROMA	2-7	0-0	0-4	2-5	1-3	1-3	1-6	3-0	1-1		2-2	1-0	1-4	2-5
11 South Sefton Borough	0-4	2-2	H-W	2-3	2-3	3-5	0-4	2-0	5-0	3-0		A-W	1-3	0-3
12 Stoneycroft	0-6	0-8	H-W	1-2	2-4	2-3	1-1	2-2	1-1	0-1	1-2		0-2	1-1
13 Waterloo Dock	1-0	4-2	3-3	3-1	7-1	1-1	0-0	3-0	H-W	1-1	3-0	3-1		2-2
14 West Everton Xaviers	1-4	4-4	1-5	3-0	1-4	1-3	1-3	2-2	6-3	5-0	2-1	2-1	1-4	

DIVISION ONE	P	W	D	L	F	A	GD	Pts
1 (P) Liver Academy (-3)	24	20	3	1	74	28	46	60
2 (P) Collegiate Old Boys	24	16	4	4	61	29	32	52
3 (P) Byron	24	13	7	4	75	50	25	46
4 (P) Lower Breck	24	12	5	7	41	35	6	41
5 Wood Street	24	9	7	8	64	56	8	34
6 Alumni	24	9	4	11	64	56	8	31
7 Waterloo Grammar School O. B. (+3)	24	8	4	12	50	48	2	31
8 Alder	24	6	10	8	46	45	1	28
9 Copperas Hill	24	7	6	11	52	64	-12	27
10 Edge Hill Boys Club Old Boys	24	7	3	14	34	44	-10	24
11 Old Xaverians Reserves	24	6	4	14	40	57	-17	22
12 BRNESC	24	7	1	16	27	73	-46	22
13 Lucas Sports	24	5	4	15	39	82	-43	19

DIVISION TWO	P	W	D	L	F	A	GD	Pts
1 (P) Litherland REMYCA Reserves	20	14	4	2	73	20	53	46
2 (P) Cheshire Lines (-1)	20	12	4	4	48	26	22	39
3 (P) Walton Community (-3)	20	12	5	3	61	33	28	38
4 Salisbury Athletic	20	12	1	7	59	47	12	37
5 Warbreck	20	10	4	6	64	48	16	34
6 Eli Lilly (3)	20	8	3	9	41	46	-5	30
7 KCFC (-3)	20	7	3	10	32	32	0	21
8 Alder Reserves (-5)	20	8	2	10	31	54	-23	21
9 East Villa Reserves (+2)	20	5	3	12	44	59	-15	20
10 Aintree Villa	20	4	1	15	39	80	-41	13
11 Old Xaverians A	20	2	2	16	33	85	-52	8

GEORGE MAHON CUP

Round 2 continued..

Edge Hill Boys Club Old Boys	v	Stoneycroft	3-3, 5-4p
LN Warbeck	v	Liver Academy	6-2
Alumni	v	Pinewoods	3-4
East Villa	v	Allerton	HW
Wood Street	v	ROMA	1-0

ROUND 3

Page Celtic	v	Copperas Hill	6-1
South Sefton Borough	v	Waterloo Grammar School	0-2
West Everton Xaviers	v	Alder	AW
Waterloo Dock	v	Aigburth Peoples Hall	0-0, 4-3p
Collegiate Old Boys	v	Red Rum	3-2
Old Xaverians	v	Edge Hill Boys Club Old Boys	3-0
LN Warbreck	v	Pinewoods	5-2
East Villa	v	Wood Street	3-1

QUARTER FINALS

Page Celtic	v	Waterloo Grammar School	4-0
Alder	v	Waterloo Dock	0-7
Collegiate Old Boys	v	Old Xaverians	2-0
LN Warbreck	v	East Villa	6-3

SEMI FINALS

Page Celtic	v	Waterloo Dock	4-1
Collegiate Old Boys	v	LN Warbreck	0-1 (aet)

FINAL

Page Celtic	v	LN Warbreck	4-2

LIVERPOOL COUNTY PREMIER LEAGUE PREMIER DIVISION CONSTITUTION 2014-15

1	AIGBURTH PEOPLE'S HALL	Cheshire Lines FC, Southmead Road, Allerton, Liverpool L19 5NB	07446 916 999
2	BYROM	LCFA 3G Pitch, Walton Hall Avenue, Liverpool L4 9XP	07799 077 256
3	COLLEGIATE OLD BOYS	Heron Eccles Ground, Abbotshey Road, Liverpool L18 7JT	07796 965 064
4	EAST VILLA	Heron Eccles Ground, Abbotshey Road, Liverpool L18 7JT	0151 270 20635
5	LIVER ACADEMY	Flinders Street, Kirkdale, Liverpool L5 7QY	07818 415 817
6	LOWER BRECK	Liverpool Soccer Centre, Walton Hall Park, Liverpool L4 9XP	
7	OLD XAVERIANS	St Francis Xaviers College, Beconsfield Road, Liverpool L25 6EG	07799 148866
8	PAGE CELTIC	Lord Derby Memorial Ground, Seel Road, Huyton, Liverpool L36 6DG	0151 525 3668
9	RED RUM	Croxteth Comm. Comp. School, Parkstile Lane, Liverpool L11 0BD	07402 944 999
10	ROMA	LCFA 3G Pitch, Walton Hall Avenue, Liverpool L4 9XP	07932 834 100
11	SOUTH SEFTON BOROUGH	Mill Dam Field behind the Punch Bowl Pub, Bridges Lane, Sefton L29 7WA	07979 375 574
12	STONEYCROFT	Maiden Lane Playing Fields, Maiden Lane, Liverpool L13 9AN	07900 915 722
13	WARBRECK	LCFA 3G Pitch, Walton Hall Avenue, Liverpool L4 9XP	0151 523 4488 Ext 102
14	WATERLOO DOCK	Edinburgh Park, Townsend Lane, Liverpool L6 0BB	07411 724 356
15	WEST EVERTON XAVERIANS	Flinders St Playing fields, Commercial Road, Kirkdale, Liverpool L5 7QY	07932 033 476

In: Byron (P). Collegiate Old Boys (P). Liver Academy (P). Lower Breck (P). Warbreck (NC from Liverpool North Warbreck).

Out: Allerton (WN). Kingsley United (W). Litherland REMYCA (P - North West Counties). Liverpool North Warbreck (NC to Warbreck). Pinewoods (W).

MANCHESTER LEAGUE

Sponsored by: FBT Europe
Founded: 1893
Recent Champions:
2009: Gregorians
2010: AVRO
2011: AVRO
2012: Hindsford
2013: Hindsford

PREMIER DIVISION	P	W	D	L	F	A	GD	Pts
1 Hindsford	28	15	8	5	58	43	15	53
2 AFC Monton	28	16	3	9	78	57	21	51
3 Royton Town	28	15	5	8	83	67	16	50
4 Prestwich Heys	28	15	4	9	72	50	22	49
5 Dukinfield Town	28	14	5	9	71	46	25	47
6 Stockport Georgians	28	14	5	9	50	46	4	47
7 Walshaw Sports	28	12	7	9	64	49	15	43
8 Wythenshawe Amateurs	28	11	9	8	42	46	-4	42
9 AVRO	28	11	6	11	52	58	-6	39
10 Manchester Gregorians	28	10	7	11	45	49	-4	37
11 Springhead	28	9	5	14	53	55	-2	32
12 East Manchester	28	9	5	14	50	65	-15	32
13 Rochdale SH	28	9	4	15	58	64	-6	31
14 (R) Old Alts	28	8	5	15	32	47	-15	29
15 Wythenshawe Town	28	1	4	23	26	92	-66	7

GILGRYST CUP

ROUND 1

Hindsford	v	AVRO	1-0
Springhead	v	Wythenshawe Amateurs	1-4
Walshaw Sports	v	Dukinfield	3-0
Rochdale Sacred Heart	v	Prestwich Heys	1-2
AFC Monton	v	Old Alts	HW
Manchester Gregorians	-	Bye	
Royton Town	v	Stockport Georgians	1-2
East Manchester	v	Wythenshawe Town	2-0

QUATER FINALS

Hindsford	v	Wythenshawe Amateurs	4-1
Walshaw Sports	v	Prestwich Heys	2-1
AFC Monton	v	Manchester Gregorians	3-3, 3-4p
Stockport Georgians	v	East Manchester	5-1

SEMI FINALS

Hindsford	v	Walshaw Sports	2-1
AFC Monton	v	Stockport Georgians	1-0

FINAL

Hindsford	v	AFC Monton	2-0

DIVISION ONE	P	W	D	L	F	A	GD	Pts
1 (P) Chapel Town	22	15	1	6	61	29	32	46
2 (P) Atherton Town	22	15	1	6	52	23	29	46
3 (P) Elton Vale	22	14	3	5	70	40	30	45
4 Beechfield United	22	11	2	9	52	43	9	35
5 Irlam Steel	22	11	2	9	57	52	5	35
6 Leigh Athletic	22	9	7	6	68	51	17	34
7 Heywood St James	22	9	5	8	57	67	-10	32
8 Breightmet United	22	8	2	12	46	49	-3	26
9 Uppermill	22	8	2	12	47	51	-4	26
10 Hollinwood (-6)	22	9	5	8	50	61	-11	26
11 Chadderton Reserves	22	5	2	15	39	75	-36	17
12 Wilmslow Albion	22	1	2	19	24	82	-58	5

DIVISION TWO	P	W	D	L	F	A	GD	Pts
1 Rochdale SH Reserves	26	17	4	5	92	38	54	55
2 Walshaw Reserves	26	16	4	6	80	48	32	52
3 Springhead Reserves	26	14	9	3	78	44	34	51
4 Prestwich Heys Reserves (-3)	26	15	4	7	64	39	25	46
5 Hindsford Reserves	26	10	8	8	71	71	0	38
6 Hollinwood Reserves	26	11	3	12	80	89	-9	36
7 AVRO Reserves	26	10	5	11	62	71	-9	35
8 Wythenshawe Ams Reserves	26	9	6	11	55	50	5	33
9 Stockport G Reserves	26	7	11	8	55	56	-1	32
10 Manchester Gregorians Reserves	26	8	6	12	63	84	-21	30
11 E Manchester Reserves	26	7	7	12	58	74	-16	28
12 Irlam Steel Reserves	26	8	4	14	55	74	-19	28
13 Wythenshawe T Reserves	26	4	7	15	34	72	-38	19
14 Old Alts Reserves	26	4	6	16	56	93	-37	18

PREMIER DIVISION	1	2	3	4	5	6	7	8	9	10	11	12	13	14	15
1 AFC Monton		1-2	3-1	2-2	9-4	4-3	3-3	2-3	4-1	3-2	2-0	3-0	3-3	3-2	4-1
2 AVRO	1-2		2-2	2-2	3-3	0-0	2-1	0-5	2-1	2-4	3-1	2-2	2-5	1-3	4-0
3 Dukinfield Town	4-2	4-4		1-0	2-0	2-3	0-1	2-3	6-0	5-0	3-0	3-2	3-1	2-2	6-0
4 East Manchester	2-6	0-3	3-0		3-1	0-1	2-3	2-2	3-0	2-5	2-4	0-1	5-4	1-2	1-0
5 Hindsford	2-1	0-1	0-0	0-0		1-1	0-0	2-0	1-1	3-4	2-1	3-0	2-1	2-0	5-1
6 Manchester Gregorians	2-4	2-1	4-3	1-2	1-3		1-0	2-3	2-3	0-3	1-0	1-1	0-1	1-1	2-2
7 Old Alts	0-1	0-1	0-2	0-2	1-2	1-0		0-2	1-2	3-3	2-0	3-3	1-2	1-3	4-1
8 Prestwich Heys	2-3	6-0	2-3	2-0	3-4	2-0	1-2		3-2	1-2	2-1	2-3	1-6	1-1	3-0
9 Rochdale Sacred Heart	4-2	1-3	1-3	7-1	2-3	1-3	8-1	1-1		2-2	1-3	2-1	2-1	0-1	2-2
10 Royton Town	6-2	1-5	3-2	3-6	4-4	2-3	3-0	3-5	2-0		1-0	2-2	2-2	3-4	4-1
11 Springhead	2-0	2-1	2-2	3-4	2-2	1-2	0-0	4-5	6-3	2-4		5-1	2-5	1-0	3-1
12 Stockport Georgians	2-1	3-1	1-0	3-0	0-1	4-4	0-2	1-3	2-1	4-1	2-0		2-0	0-1	2-1
13 Walshaw Sports	2-5	3-0	4-2	4-2	1-3	2-0	1-0	1-1	4-1	3-4	1-1	1-2		1-1	3-0
14 Wythenshawe Amateurs	1-0	3-2	1-3	1-1	0-1	1-1	2-1	2-1	0-5	0-5	2-2	2-3	2-2		3-1
15 Wythenshawe Town	0-3	1-2	2-5	4-2	1-4	1-4	0-1	1-7	1-4	1-5	1-5	1-3	0-0	1-1	

DIVISION THREE	P	W	D	L	F	A	GD	Pts
1 Royton T Reserves	20	15	4	1	77	25	52	49
2 AFC Monton Reserves	20	11	3	6	54	31	23	36
3 Elton Vale Reserves	20	10	5	5	61	43	18	35
4 Dukinfied Town Reserves	20	10	3	7	50	31	19	33
5 Beechfield United Reserves	20	8	8	4	50	32	18	32
6 Breightmet Utd Reserves	20	8	4	8	45	45	0	28
7 Uppermill Reserves	20	7	4	9	46	45	1	25
8 Leigh Ath Reserves	20	6	5	9	42	50	-8	23
9 Chapel Town Reserves	20	6	4	10	44	72	-28	22
10 Atherton Town Reserves	20	6	3	11	37	59	-22	21
11 Wilmslow Alb Reserves	20	1	1	18	18	91	-73	4

DIVISION FOUR	P	W	D	L	F	A	GD	Pts
1 AVRO A	24	16	5	3	97	47	50	53
2 Walshaw SC A	24	15	5	4	88	52	36	50
3 Elton Vale A	24	11	4	9	69	61	8	37
4 Dukinfield Town A	24	9	5	10	63	68	-5	32
5 Royton Town A	24	7	4	13	53	84	-31	25
6 Springhead A. (-1)	24	5	9	10	61	70	-9	23
7 Atherton Town A	24	3	4	17	41	90	-49	13

MURRAY SHIELD

ROUND 1			
Leigh Athletic	v	AFC Bury	AW
Heywood St James	-	Bye	
Elton Vale	v	Uppermill	5-3
Chadderton Reserves	-	Bye	
Wilmslow Albion	v	Atherton Town	3-4 aet
Chapel Town	v	Irlam Steel	2-1
Beechfield United	-	Bye	
Hollinwood	v	Breightmet United	0-2
QUARTER FINALS			
AFC Bury	v	Heywood St James	HW
Elton Vale	v	Chadderton Reserves	3-1
Atherton Town	v	Chapel Town	5-1
Beechfield United	v	Breightmet United	1-4
SEMI FINALS			
AFC Bury	v	Elton Vale	AW
Atherton Town	v	Breightmet United	2-1
FINAL			
Elton Vale	v	Atherton Town	3-1

MANCHESTER LEAGUE PREMIER DIVISION CONSTITUTION 2014-15

1 AFC MONTON	Off Worlsey Road, Winton, Salford M30 8J	07836 321193
2 AVRO	Lancaster Club, Broadway, Failsworth, Oldham M35 0DX	0161 681 3083
3 ATHERTON TOWN	Howe Bridge sports centre, Eckersley Fold Lane, Atherton M46 0RQ	
4 CHAPEL TOWN	Rowton Park, Chapel-en-le-Frith, High Peak SK23 0ND	
5 DUKINFIELD TOWN	Woodhams Park, Birch Lane, Dukinfield SK16 5AP	0161 343 4529
6 EAST MANCHESTER	Wright Robinson Sports College, Abbey Hey Lane, Gorton M18 8RL	0161 370 5121
7 ELTON VALE	Elton Vale Sports Club, Elton Vale Road, Bury BL8 2RZ	
8 HINDSFORD	Squires Lane, Tyldesley M29 8JF	None
9 MANCHESTER GREGORIANS	MCFC, Platt Lane Complex, Yew Tree Road, Fallowfield M14 7UU	07740 585459
10 PRESTWICH HEYS	Sandgate Road, Whitefield M45 6WG	0161 773 8888
11 ROCHDALE SACRED HEART	Fox Park, Belfield Mill Lane, Rochdale OL16 2UB	
12 ROYTON TOWN	Crompton Cricket Club Complex, Christine Street, Shaw, Oldham OL2 7SF	01706 847421
13 SPRINGHEAD	Ashfield Crescent PF, St John Street, Lees, Oldham OL4 4DG	0161 627 0260
14 STOCKPORT GEORGIANS	Cromley Road, Woodsmoor, Stockport SK2 7DT	0161 483 6581
15 WALSHAW SPORTS CLUB	Walshaw Sports Club, Sycamore Road, Tottington, Bury BL8 3EG	01204 882448
16 WYTHENSHAWE AMATEUR	Longley Lane, Northenden, Wythenshawe M22 4LA	0161 998 7268

In: Dukinfield Town (P). Pennington (P). Rochdale Sacred Heart (P).

Out: Old Altrinchamians (R). Pennington (W - reformed for 2014-15 in Div.1). Wythenshawe Town (S - Cheshire League).

MIDDLESEX COUNTY LEAGUE

Sponsored by: Cherry Red Books
Founded: 1984
Recent Champions:
2009: Bethnal Green United
2010: Interwood
2011: Willesden Constantine
2012: Interwood
2013: British Airways

PREMIER DIVISION	P	W	D	L	F	A	GD	Pts
1 Sporting Hackney	30	21	5	4	89	35	54	68
2 Kensington Dragons	30	19	8	3	79	44	35	65
3 Interwood	30	19	6	5	81	39	42	63
4 Cricklewood Wanderers	30	17	5	8	86	55	31	56
5 FC Assyria	30	16	3	11	60	52	8	51
6 Broadfields United	30	13	5	12	55	49	6	44
7 British Airways (-3)	30	12	8	10	65	60	5	41
8 Indian Gymkhana Club	30	11	7	12	59	53	6	40
9 West Essex	30	10	8	12	72	63	9	38
10 AFC Hayes Reserves	30	9	11	10	58	68	-10	38
11 FC Deportivo Galicia	30	12	2	16	61	79	-18	38
12 Hillingdon	30	10	6	14	64	62	2	36
13 Kilburn	30	8	4	18	72	108	-36	28
14 Singh Sabha Slough	30	6	8	16	52	78	-26	26
15 (R) Hounslow Wanderers	30	6	4	20	47	101	-54	22
16 (R) Sloane	30	5	2	23	45	99	-54	17

ALEC SMITH PREMIER DIVISION CUP

ROUND 1

Hounslow Wanderers	v	Sporting Hackney	1-4
Kensington Dragons	v	Interwood	0-0, 2-4p
AFC Hayes Reserves	v	Sloane	7-1
West Essex	v	British Airways	1-0
FC Assyria	v	Broadfields United	2-1
Indian Gymkhana Club	v	Cricklewood Wanderers	2-0
FC Deportivo Galicia	v	Kilburn	3-4
Hillingdon	v	Singh Sabha Slough	1-2

QUARTER FINALS

AFC Hayes Reserves	v	Interwood	1-4
West Essex	v	Indian Gymkhana Club	4-2
Singh Sabha Slough	v	Sporting Hackney	1-3
FC Assyria	v	Kilburn	5-4

SEMI FINALS

Sporting Hackney	v	West Essex	2-3
FC Assyria	v	Interwood	0-0, 3-5p

FINAL

West Essex	v	Interwood	1-0

PREMIER DIVISION	1	2	3	4	5	6	7	8	9	10	11	12	13	14	15	16
1 AFC Hayes Reserves		0-0	2-1	3-5	2-4	4-1	1-1	0-0	3-3	1-6	1-2	2-3	1-1	2-1	1-3	1-4
2 British Airways	2-2		1-1	3-4	3-1	3-2	3-2	1-4	1-0	1-3	2-3	0-1	4-0	7-2	1-2	5-3
3 Broadfields United	2-2	3-3		2-0	3-2	3-1	1-3	3-0	3-2	2-4	0-1	4-2	1-1	1-2	1-2	0-0
4 Cricklewood Wanderers	2-2	4-2	2-4		2-1	4-2	3-0	10-2	1-0	0-0	2-3	5-1	4-1	2-1	2-2	1-1
5 FC Assyria	1-1	1-3	2-4	1-0		4-1	1-0	4-2	2-4	AW	2-1	4-2	4-3	4-1	0-3	2-0
6 FC Deportivo Galicia	3-1	1-2	3-2	1-2	0-2		3-2	5-0	2-5	0-5	4-3	2-4	4-4	3-1	3-0	0-6
7 Hillingdon	1-2	2-2	1-2	4-2	2-3	0-2		2-0	2-3	3-4	1-2	9-4	2-1	4-2	4-2	1-1
8 Hounslow Wanderers	1-3	2-5	0-3	1-4	0-2	1-1	2-3		1-5	2-5	2-3	4-1	5-4	4-2	1-10	3-2
9 Indian Gymkhana Club	0-4	0-1	1-0	0-1	3-0	2-3	2-2	2-1		2-0	0-3	2-2	2-2	4-0	2-4	2-2
10 Interwood	10-2	HW	4-1	4-2	0-0	5-1	1-1	0-2	HW		4-5	5-1	1-1	2-0	0-3	6-2
11 Kensington Dragons	2-2	7-1	3-0	3-3	1-1	3-2	1-2	3-2	2-2	1-0		6-3	1-1	2-2	3-1	1-0
12 Kilburn	3-4	3-3	3-1	1-2	0-4	4-5	3-3	5-2	3-5	2-2	0-4		1-6	8-3	2-5	1-5
13 Singh Sabha Slough	1-4	2-3	0-2	2-1	1-2	0-2	2-1	2-2	1-1	1-2	1-6	3-2		6-1	1-3	1-0
14 Sloane	2-5	3-1	1-3	2-4	4-5	2-1	2-3	1-1	2-0	2-6	0-1	0-1	3-1		0-7	2-5
15 Sporting Hackney	3-0	0-0	HW	4-3	HW	1-2	3-2	5-0	2-0	0-0	1-1	6-2	7-1	3-1		6-1
16 West Essex	0-0	2-2	1-2	2-9	6-1	4-1	2-1	5-0	3-5	1-2	2-2	2-4	6-1	3-0	1-1	

MIDDLESEX COUNTY LEAGUE PREMIER DIVISION CONSTITUTION 2014-15

1	AFC HAYES RESERVES	Brook House FC, Farm Park, Kingshill Avenue, Hayes UB4 8DD	020 8845 0110
2	BRITISH AIRWAYS	Crane Lodge Road, Cranford TW5 9PQ	07779 638 080
3	BROADFIELDS UNITED	Harefield United, Preston Park, Breakspear Road North, Harefield UB9 6NE	07944 370 116
4	C.B. HOUNSLOW UNITED RESERVES	Osterley Sports Club, Tentelow Lane, Norwood Green UB2 4LW	020 8569 5345
5	CRICKLEWOOD WANDERERS	Vale Farm Sports Centre, Watford Road, North Wembley, London HA0 3HE	07931 595 564
6	FC ASSYRIA	Northolt Rugby Club, Cayton Road, Greenford UB6 8B	020 8813 1701
7	FC DEPORTIVO GALICIA	Osterley Sports Club, Tentelow Lane, Osterley, Southall UB2 4LW	07956 300 681
8	HILLINGDON	Brunel Uni. Sports Complex, Kingston Park, Kingston Lane, Hillingdon UB8 3PW	07831 177 307
9	INDIAN GYMKHANA	Indian Gymkhana Club, Thornbury Avenue, Osterley TW7 4NQ	020 8568 4009
10	INTERWOOD	Wadham Lodge, Kitchener Road, Walthamstow, London E17 4JP	020 8527 2444
11	KENSINGTON DRAGONS	Osterley Sports Club, Tentelow Lane, Norwood Green, Middlesex UB2 4LW	07940 858 265
12	KILBURN	Osterley Sports Club, Tentelow Lane, Norwood Green, Middlesex UB2 4LW	07931 807 928
13	LPOSSA	LPR Club (LPOSSA), 136 Greenford Road, Harrow, Middlesex HA1 3QL	020 8423 5838
14	SINGH SABHA SLOUGH	The Falcon Sports Centre, Stoke Poges Centre, Slough SL1 3LW	07917 773 727
15	SOUTH KILBURN	Vale Farm, Watford Road, North Wembley HA0 3HE	07595 256 309
16	SPORTING HACKNEY	Hackney Marshes, Homerton Road, Hackney, London E9 5PF	07970 191 573
17	TOOTING & MITCHAM WANDERERS	Whyteleafe FC, Chruch Road, Whyteleafe, Surrey CR3 0AR	020 8660 5491
18	WEST ESSEX	Hackney Marshes, Homerton Road, Hackney, London E9 5PF	07956 557 438

In: C.B. Hounslow United Reserves (P). LPOSSA (P). South Kilburn (Combined Counties Div.1).
Tooting & Mitcham Wanderers (P - Surrey South Eastern Combination Intermediate Div.2).
Out: Hounslow Rangers (R). Sloane (R).

DIVISION ONE CENTRAL & EAST	P	W	D	L	F	A	GD	Pts
1 Pearscroft United	22	16	4	2	74	28	46	52
2 London Elite	22	14	5	3	59	21	38	47
3 FFC Haringey	22	13	3	6	68	33	35	42
4 St Lawrence	22	9	6	7	37	32	5	33
5 Stonewall	22	10	3	9	44	40	4	33
6 Chiswick	22	9	4	9	47	57	-10	31
7 Fire United Christian	22	9	3	10	50	49	1	30
8 The Wilberforce Wanderers	22	9	1	12	43	61	-18	28
9 AFC Wembley	22	7	6	9	42	34	8	27
10 Supreme Athletic (-3)	22	9	0	13	39	41	-2	24
11 J-GAIA	22	4	3	15	39	75	-36	15
12 (R) Edmonton Rangers	22	3	2	17	29	100	-71	11

DIVISION ONE WEST	P	W	D	L	F	A	GD	Pts
1 (P) LPOSSA	22	19	1	2	99	24	75	58
2 Kodak (Harrow)	22	14	2	6	47	34	13	44
3 Pitshanger Dynamo	22	14	1	7	71	31	40	43
4 Bedfont Sports	21	12	3	6	56	31	25	39
5 Imperial College Old Boys	22	11	2	9	41	33	8	35
6 (P) C.B. Hounslow United Reserves	22	10	3	9	40	46	-6	33
7 Brentham	22	8	3	11	43	75	-32	27
8 Hillingdon Abbots	22	6	5	11	25	50	-25	23
9 Southall Utd	22	5	5	12	26	41	-15	20
10 Wembley Park	22	5	2	15	30	66	-36	17
11 AFC Southall	20	5	0	15	29	72	-43	15
12 West London Saracens (-9)	21	6	3	12	37	41	-4	12

DIVISION TWO	P	W	D	L	F	A	GD	Pts
1 (P-1W) Heston Bombers	22	16	2	4	55	23	32	50
2 (P-1CE) Greens United	22	16	1	5	79	50	29	49
3 (P-1CE) AFC Hillgate	22	15	0	6	96	38	58	45
4 Mile End Park Rangers	22	13	3	5	54	42	12	42
5 Paddington Elite	22	13	1	7	56	34	22	40
6 Club Santacruzense de Londres	22	10	7	5	72	44	28	37
7 FC Staines	22	7	3	12	34	69	-35	24
8 Aym Higher	22	7	2	12	31	58	-27	23
9 Tokyngton Manor	22	7	1	14	60	78	-18	22
10 British Airways 3rds	22	6	3	13	71	88	-17	21
11 South Acton	22	6	2	14	46	77	-31	20
12 Laleham Casuals	22	1	1	20	28	81	-53	4

MCFL COMBINATION	P	W	D	L	F	A	GD	Pts
1 Hillingdon Reserves	22	18	2	2	69	31	38	56
2 Larkspur Rovers	22	18	1	3	102	31	71	55
3 Victoria	22	17	1	4	84	34	50	52
4 LPOSSA Reserves	22	16	2	4	73	31	42	50
5 AFC Heathrow	22	11	2	9	57	71	-14	35
6 Wembley Park Reserves	22	8	2	12	53	69	-16	26
7 St Lawrence Reserves	22	7	4	11	37	48	-11	25
8 Hounslow Wanderers Reserves	22	7	1	14	33	51	-18	22
9 C.B. Hounslow United Social	22	6	2	14	28	63	-35	20
10 Hayes & Hanwell	22	6	1	15	31	45	-14	19
11 Centenary Park	22	4	6	12	42	65	-23	18
12 Moditown	22	1	2	19	25	95	-70	5

SENIOR RESERVE DIVISION	P	W	D	L	F	A	GD	Pts
1 Broadfields United Reserves	16	12	2	2	64	23	41	38
2 Kensington Dragons Reserves	16	12	2	2	51	28	23	38
3 British Airways Reserves	16	9	2	5	47	26	21	29
4 Indian Gymkhana Club Reserves	16	9	2	5	40	30	10	29
5 Sporting Hackney Reserves	16	8	2	6	52	28	24	26
6 Pitshanger Dynamo Reserves	16	6	3	7	40	42	-2	21
7 C.B. Hounslow United Social Reserves	16	3	3	10	21	56	-35	12
8 Brentham Reserves	16	2	1	13	20	55	-35	7
9 Fire United Christian Reserves	16	1	3	12	20	67	-47	6

SENIOR OPEN CUP

PRELIMINARY ROUND

AFC Southall	v	Hillingdon Abbots	1-3

ROUND 1

Chiswick	v	Brentham	5-0
Kodak (Harrow)	v	Hillingdon Abbots	4-1
Stonewall	v	Hillingdon	4-1
Supreme Athletic	v	Pitshanger Dynamo	3-3, 6-5p
Edmonton Rangers	v	West London Saracens	2-5
Imperial College Old Boys	v	Cricklewood Wanderers	0-3
West Essex	v	Wembley Park	5-0
C.B. Hounslow United Reserves	v	Stedfast (WITHDRAWN)	3-4

ROUND 2

St Lawrence	v	Broadfields United	3-4
J-GAIA	v	Kilburn	AW
FC Assyria	v	London Elite	2-2, 3-5p
Hounslow Wanderers	v	Chiswick	5-4
Pearscroft United	v	Interwood	2-2, 5-6p
FC Deportivo Galicia	v	Cricklewood Wanderers	4-8
AFC Hayes Reserves	v	AFC Wembley	1-2
Indian Gymkhana Club	v	The Wilberforce Wanderers	1-2
Stonewall	v	Sporting Hackney	0-3
Singh Sabha Slough	v	Bedfont Sports	5-3
LPOSSA	v	Supreme Athletic	3-1
Fire United Christian	v	Sloane	2-1
West End	v	Kensington Dragons	3-2
FFC Haringey	v	West Essex	3-1
Southall Utd	v	Kodak (Harrow)	1-6
Stedfast	v	West London Saracens	1-2

ROUND 3

LPOSSA	v	FFC Haringey	4-2
The Wilberforce Wanderers	v	Singh Sabha Slough	2-1
Cricklewood Wanderers	v	Hounslow Wanderers	8-6
Interwood	v	Fire United Christian	8-1
Kodak (Harrow)	v	West London Saracens	3-1
Sporting Hackney	v	AFC Wembley	5-2
West End	v	Broadfields United	5-1
Kilburn	v	London Elite	2-6

QUARTER FINALS

LPOSSA	v	Interwood	3-2
Sporting Hackney	v	West End	2-1
Kodak (Harrow)	v	Cricklewood Wanderers	2-1
London Elite	v	The Wilberforce Wanderers	4-3

SEMI FINALS

Sporting Hackney	v	LPOSSA	2-0
Kodak (Harrow)	v	London Elite	0-0, 1-2p

FINAL

Sporting Hackney	v	London Elite	3-2

NORTH BERKSHIRE LEAGUE

Sponsored by: No sponsor
Founded: 1909
Recent Champions:
2009: Saxton Rovers
2010: Saxton Rovers
2011: Lambourn Sports
2012: Crowmarsh Gifford
2013: Saxton Rovers
nbfl.co.uk

DIVISION ONE	P	W	D	L	F	A	GD	Pts
1 Kintbury Rangers (+6)	16	10	5	1	50	17	33	41
2 Ardington & Lockinge (+3)	17	10	6	1	38	21	17	39
3 Dorchester	18	11	5	2	46	30	16	38
4 Long Wittenham Athletic	18	8	2	8	33	29	4	26
5 Berinsfield	18	7	5	6	48	45	3	26
6 Saxton Rovers	18	7	3	8	33	34	-1	24
7 Faringdon Town	18	6	6	6	32	36	-4	24
8 Harwell International	15	3	2	10	19	34	-15	11
9 Wallingford Town	18	3	2	13	27	55	-28	11
10 Crowmarsh Gifford	18	2	4	12	23	48	-25	10

Wootton & Dry Sandford withdrew - records expunged.

NORTH BERKS CUP

ROUND 1

Kennington Athletic	v	Grove Rangers	6-3
Appleton Stars	v	Didcot Eagles	1-11
Hagbourne United	v	Burghclere FC	0-2

ROUND 2

Ardington & Lockinge	v	Bension Lions	5-0
Berinsfield	-	Bye	
Dorchester	v	Kennington Athletic	8-0
Didcot Eagles	v	Wallingford Town	4-2
Crowmarsh Gifford	-	Bye	
Faringdon Town	-	Bye	
Drayton	v	Westminster	5-4
Hanney United	v	East Hendred	4-3
Harwell International	v	Long Wittenham Athletic	0-4
Wootton & Dry Sandford	-	Bye	
Marcham	v	Stanford-in-the-Vale	0-1
Saxton Rovers	-	Bye	
Coleshill United	v	Burghclere FC	2-10
Steventon	v	Sutton Courtenay	2-4
Kintbury Rangers	v	Radley	5-2
Lambourn Sports	-	Bye	

ROUND 3

Ardington & Lockinge	v	Berinsfield	2-1
Dorchester	v	Didcot Eagles	10-0
Crowmarsh Gifford	v	Faringdon Town	0-4
Drayton	v	Hanney United	4-2
Long Wittenham Athletic	v	Wootton & Dry Sandford	HW
Stanford-in-the-Vale	v	Saxton Rovers	1-5
Burghclere FC	v	Sutton Courtenay	3-0
Kintbury Rangers	v	Lambourn Sports	HW

QUARTER FINALS

Ardington & Lockinge	v	Dorchester	0-1
Faringdon Town	v	Drayton	1-2
Long Wittenham Athletic	v	Saxton Rovers	3-0
Burghclere FC	v	Kintbury Rangers	0-2

SEMI FINALS

Dorchester	v	Drayton	1-0
Long Wittenham Athletic	v	Kintbury Rangers	2-1

FINAL

Dorchester	v	Long Wittenham Athletic	1-2

DIVISION ONE	1	2	3	4	5	6	7	8	9	10
1 Ardington & Lockinge		3-4	3-2	1-1	1-0	HW	0-0	3-1	5-1	5-1
2 Berinsfield	4-4		1-1	2-7	4-0	1-0	1-5	3-1	3-0	6-2
3 Crowmarsh Gifford	1-3	3-3		2-7	3-1	3-0	0-5	AW	1-3	0-4
4 Dorchester	1-1	2-2	4-2		6-4	HW	0-4	3-2	2-2	3-2
5 Faringdon Town	0-0	4-2	0-0	0-0		3-1	0-4	2-1	2-2	2-2
6 Harwell International	1-2	0-6	3-0	1-3	1-5		C-C	2-2	2-4	4-1
7 Kintbury Rangers	2-3	4-4	2-2	1-0	2-2	HW		4-1	3-1	4-1
8 Long Wittenham Athletic	1-2	2-1	4-0	2-3	0-1	2-0	1-1		3-2	3-0
9 Saxton Rovers	0-1	2-0	3-2	1-2	5-2	1-1	1-2	1-2		2-1
10 Wallingford Town	1-1	5-1	2-1	1-2	2-4	1-3	0-7	1-5	0-2	

NORTH BERKSHIRE LEAGUE DIVISION ONE CONSTITUTION 2014-15

1	ABINGDON TOWN	Culham Road, Abingdon OX14 3HP	01235 521 684
2	ARDINGTON & LOCKINGE	White Road (Off Well Street), Ardington, Oxfordshire OX12 8QB	07989 526 959
3	BERINSFIELD	Lay Avenue, Berinsfield OX10 7N	07983 399 992
4	CROWMARSH GIFFORD	Crowmarsh Recreation Ground, Crowmarsh Gifford, Wallingford OX10 8EB	07825 711 578
5	DORCHESTER	Drayton Road, Dorchester	07800 705 516
6	DRAYTON	Recreation Ground, Lockway, Drayton OX14 4LF	01235 531 425
7	FARINGDON TOWN	Tucker Park, Park Road, Faringdon SN7 7DP	01367 241 759
8	KINTBURY RANGERS	Inkpen Road, Kintbury, Hungerford RG17 9TY	07771 636 594
9	LONG WITTENHAM ATHLETIC	Bodkins Sports Field, East End of Village, Long Wittenham	01865 407 202
10	SAXTON ROVERS	Recreation Ground, Caldecott Road, Abingdon OX14 5HR	07752 390 039
11	WALLINGFORD TOWN	Wallingford Sports Park , Hithercroft Road , Wallingford OX10 9RB	07973 736 386
12	WATLINGTON TOWN	Recreation Ground, Shirburn Road, Watlington, Oxfordshire OX49 5BZ	07785 336 277

In: Abingdon Town (Hellenic Premier). Drayton (P). Watlington Town (S - Oxford Senior).
Out: Harwell International (W). Wootton & Dry Sandford (WS).

DIVISION TWO	P	W	D	L	F	A	GD	Pts
1 Abingdon United Reserves	20	17	3	0	69	17	52	54
2 Wantage Town 'A'	20	15	3	2	61	14	47	48
3 (P) Drayton	20	13	2	5	70	40	30	41
4 East Hendred	20	10	2	8	47	32	15	32
5 Steventon	20	8	3	9	40	53	-13	27
6 Marcham	20	8	2	10	45	46	-1	26
7 Radley	20	7	4	9	43	41	2	25
8 Faringdon Town Reserves	20	7	4	9	37	43	-6	25
9 Coleshill United	20	6	4	10	47	54	-7	22
10 Saxton Rovers Reserves	20	3	1	16	20	77	-57	10
11 Sutton Courtenay	20	2	0	18	19	81	-62	6

DIVISION THREE	P	W	D	L	F	A	GD	Pts
1 (P) Burghclere FC (+3)	19	15	1	3	53	23	30	49
2 (P) Kintbury Reserves	20	13	3	4	56	28	28	42
3 (P) Stanford-in-the-Vale	20	13	2	5	60	21	39	41
4 (P) Westminster	20	12	1	7	39	34	5	37
5 Hanney United (-3)	20	12	1	7	44	28	16	34
6 Benson Lions	20	9	2	9	40	44	-4	29
7 Blewbury	20	8	3	9	40	37	3	27
8 Hungerford Town Swifts	20	8	1	11	36	40	-4	25
9 Dorchester Reserves (+3)	19	5	1	13	19	57	-38	19
10 Clanfield 85 Reserves	20	2	2	16	20	70	-50	8
11 Milton United Reserves	18	1	3	14	29	54	-25	6

DIVISION FOUR	P	W	D	L	F	A	GD	Pts
1 (P) Turnpike Sports	20	17	2	1	94	17	77	53
2 (P) Grove Rangers	20	11	5	4	60	35	25	38
3 Benson AFC	20	12	2	6	62	38	24	38
4 East Hendred Reserves	20	10	2	8	52	51	1	32
5 Kennington Athletic	20	10	2	8	46	56	-10	32
6 Berinsfield Reserves	20	7	4	9	68	58	10	25
7 Long Wittenham Reserves	20	8	1	11	49	65	-16	25
8 Faringdon Town A	20	7	2	11	32	56	-24	23
9 Drayton Reserves	20	6	2	12	44	70	-26	20
10 Ardington Reserves	20	6	1	13	47	70	-23	19
11 Hagbourne United	20	4	1	15	28	66	-38	13

DIVISION FIVE	P	W	D	L	F	A	GD	Pts
1 (P) Uffington United	16	12	1	3	77	30	47	37
2 (P) Stanford-in-the-Vale Res.	16	12	0	4	50	34	16	36
3 (P) Steventon Reserves	16	9	2	5	48	30	18	29
4 Wallingford Town Reserves	16	9	1	6	68	35	33	28
5 Didcot Eagles	16	8	1	7	71	50	21	25
6 Hagbourne Utd. Reserves	16	7	0	9	34	48	-14	21
7 Challow FC	16	6	1	9	47	52	-5	19
8 Grove Rangers Reserves	16	5	2	9	41	58	-17	17
9 Appleton Stars	16	0	0	16	18	117	-99	0

NORTH BERKS CHARITY SHIELD

ROUND 1

Didcot Eagles	v	Bension Lions	2-2, 5-4p
Hagbourne United	v	Radley	0-5
Burghclere FC	v	Westminster	4-2
Challow FC	v	Appleton Stars	3-2
Steventon	v	Hanney United	3-2
Milton United Reserves	v	Stanford-in-the-Vale	4-1
Benson AFC	v	Grove Rangers	3-2
Marcham	v	Blewbury	0-1
Drayton	v	Clanfield 85 Reserves	2-1
Wantage Town 'A'	v	Kennington Athletic	8-0

ROUND 2

Didcot Eagles	v	Radley	1-12
Burghclere FC	v	Challow FC	9-1
Lambourn Sports	-	Bye	
Coleshill United	v	Ardington & Lockinge	0-9
Steventon	v	Wallingford Town	4-6
Faringdon Town	-	Bye	
Milton United Reserves	v	Benson AFC	1-2
Crowmarsh Gifford	-	Bye	
Saxton Rovers	-	Bye	
Blewbury	v	East Hendred	1-2
Long Wittenham Athletic	v	Kintbury Rangers	2-7
Abingdon United Reserves	v	Harwell International	3-1
Berinsfield	-	Bye	
Dorchester	v	Sutton Courtenay	HW
Wootton & Dry Sandford	-	Bye	
Drayton	v	Wantage Town 'A'	0-4

ROUND 3

Radley	v	Burghclere FC	0-1
Lambourn Sports	v	Ardington & Lockinge	AW
Wallingford Town	v	Faringdon Town	3-4
Benson AFC	v	Crowmarsh Gifford	2-5
Saxton Rovers	v	East Hendred	1-2
Kintbury Rangers	v	Abingdon United Reserves	3-1
Berinsfield	v	Dorchester	1-2
Wootton & Dry Sandford	v	Wantage Town 'A'	AW

QUARTER FINALS

Burghclere FC	v	Ardington & Lockinge	1-3
Faringdon Town	v	Crowmarsh Gifford	6-1
East Hendred	v	Kintbury Rangers	1-3
Dorchester	v	Wantage Town 'A'	1-2

SEMI FINALS

Ardington & Lockinge	v	Faringdon Town	1-0
Kintbury Rangers	v	Wantage Town 'A'	3-2

FINAL

Ardington & Lockinge	v	Kintbury Rangers	3-5

WAR MEMORIAL TROPHY

FINAL

Westminster	v	East Hendred	2-0

LEAGUE CUP

FINAL

Faringdon Town A	v	Wallingford Town Reserves	1-2

AG KINGHAM CUP

FINAL

Wallingford Town Reserves	v	Berinsfield Reserves	7-2

NAIRNE PAUL TROPHY

FINAL

Kintbury Reserves	v	Saxton Rovers Reserves	1-2

NORTHAMPTONSHIRE COMBINATION

Sponsored by: MDH Teamwear
Founded: N/K
Recent Champions:
2009: Harpole
2010: Harborough Town
2011: Brixworth All Saints
2012: Harpole
2013: Harpole
northantscombination.co.uk

PREMIER DIVISION	P	W	D	L	F	A	GD	Pts
1 Brixworth All Saints	28	21	2	5	64	24	40	65
2 Stanion Redstar	28	20	4	4	93	41	52	64
3 Weldon United	28	16	8	4	70	36	34	56
4 Welford Victoria	28	17	4	7	72	31	41	55
5 James King Blisworth	28	17	4	7	82	48	34	55
6 Harpole	28	14	6	8	64	41	23	48
7 Earls Barton United (-3)	28	14	4	10	60	43	17	43
8 Kettering Nomads	28	12	6	10	55	53	2	42
9 Moulton (-3)	28	10	5	13	67	68	-1	32
10 Milton	28	7	9	12	40	41	-1	30
11 Ringstead Rangers (-3)	28	7	7	14	38	64	-26	25
12 Roade (-3)	28	7	6	15	37	45	-8	24
13 Corby DGL Locos	28	7	2	19	49	79	-30	23
14 Corby S&L Khalsa	28	3	3	22	35	100	-65	12
15 (R) Corby Pegasus (-3)	28	1	4	23	17	129	-112	4

PREMIER DIVISION CUP

ROUND 1

Stanion Redstar	v	Milton	3-0
Corby S&L Khalsa	-	Bye	
Welford Victoria	v	Weldon United	3-2 aet
Earls Barton United	v	Ringstead Rangers	1-1, 1-4p
Corby DGL Locos	v	James King Blisworth	0-3
Roade	v	Kettering Nomads	2-0
Moulton	v	Brixworth All Saints	0-1
Corby Pegasus	v	Harpole	0-7

QUARTER FINALS

Stanion Redstar	v	Corby S&L Khalsa	2-0
Welford Victoria	v	Ringstead Rangers	2-0
James King Blisworth	v	Roade	3-0
Brixworth All Saints	v	Harpole	3-2

SEMI FINALS

Stanion Redstar	v	Welford Victoria	0-1 aet
James King Blisworth	v	Brixworth All Saints	1-0

FINAL

Welford Victoria	v	James King Blisworth	1-2 aet

PREMIER DIVISION	1	2	3	4	5	6	7	8	9	10	11	12	13	14	15
1 Brixworth All Saints		4-0	7-0	3-1	3-1	2-0	0-2	0-2	1-0	H-W	4-0	3-0	1-2	2-1	0-0
2 Corby DGL Locos	0-1		3-3	6-0	4-5	3-2	1-3	2-3	2-3	4-0	3-4	1-3	0-5	3-0	0-6
3 Corby Pegasus	0-5	2-3		0-4	0-2	1-8	1-5	0-3	1-0	1-3	0-2	1-1	2-11	0-7	0-4
4 Corby S&L Khalsa	0-3	3-0	4-1		1-6	1-5	0-4	1-3	1-6	2-5	0-2	0-3	1-4	1-2	1-2
5 Earls Barton United	1-2	3-2	10-0	2-0		0-1	1-3	5-0	1-0	2-1	2-0	0-0	1-1	1-2	1-1
6 Harpole	1-3	4-0	8-1	5-1	4-0		0-3	0-1	1-1	3-3	4-0	3-2	2-0	0-3	2-0
7 James King Blisworth	0-5	4-1	9-0	3-1	2-3	2-2		3-3	0-0	5-2	3-1	3-1	6-3	2-2	0-1
8 Kettering Nomads	1-3	5-2	4-0	4-1	2-2	0-1	1-2		2-1	3-3	6-1	2-1	1-2	2-2	1-0
9 Milton	1-1	1-1	1-1	0-0	0-1	5-1	1-3	1-1		6-3	1-1	1-0	0-2	0-0	1-2
10 Moulton	0-1	4-0	4-1	3-3	2-1	0-1	5-3	3-1	3-2		6-1	1-1	1-6	2-3	1-3
11 Ringstead Rangers	1-3	3-1	1-1	2-2	3-2	0-1	3-2	2-2	1-2	2-2		1-5	1-2	1-2	2-1
12 Roade	2-3	0-1	H-W	5-1	2-3	1-1	1-3	1-0	0-1	1-3	0-0		1-4	1-2	0-2
13 Stanion Redstar	3-0	1-4	7-0	5-1	4-0	2-2	3-2	7-1	5-3	3-2	3-2	0-3		1-1	1-1
14 Weldon United	4-2	3-0	7-0	6-3	3-0	2-2	4-2	2-0	4-1	4-3	1-1	1-1	1-3		0-0
15 Welford Victoria	1-2	4-2	6-0	10-1	0-4	4-0	2-3	5-1	2-1	5-2	3-0	4-1	1-3	2-1	

NORTHANTS COMBINATION PREMIER DIVISION CONSTITUTION 2014-15

	Club	Ground	Tel
1	BRIXWORTH ALL SAINTS	St Davids Close, off Froxhill Crescent, Brixworth NN6 9EA	01604 880073
2	CORBY DGL LOCOMOTIVES	Cottingham Road, Corby, Northants NN17 1TD	-
3	CORBY EAGLES	Kingswood Community Centre, Alberta Close, Corby, Northants.NN18 9HU	-
4	CORBY S&L KHALSA	Corby Rugby Club, Rockingham Road, Corby NN17 1AE	01536 204466
5	EARLS BARTON UNITED	The Grange, Northampton Road, Earls Barton, Northants NN6 0HA	-
6	GRETTON	Gretton Recreation Ground, Kirby Road, Gretton, Northants. NN17 3DB	-
7	HARPOLE	Playing Field, Larkhall Lane, Harpole NN7 4DP	-
8	JAMES KING BLISWORTH	Blisworth Playing Field, Courteenhall Road, Blisworth NN7 3DD	07974 006484
9	KETTERING NOMADS	Orlingbury Road, Isham, Nr Kettering, Northants. NN14 1HY	-
10	MILTON	Collingtree Road, Milton Malsor, Northampton NN7 3AU	-
11	MOULTON	Brunting Road, Moulton, Northampton NN3 7QF	01604 492675
12	RINGSTEAD RANGERS	Gladstone Street, Ringstead NN14 4DE	-
13	ROADE	Connolly Way, Hyde Road, Roade NN7 2LU	01604 862814
14	STANION REDSTAR	Village Hall, Brigstock Road, Stanion, Corby NN14 1BX	-
15	WELDON UNITED	Oundle Road, Weldon NN17 3JT	-
16	WELFORD VICTORIA	Welford Sports Field, Newlands Road, Welford NN6 6HR	-

In: Corby Eagles (P). Gretton (P).
Out: Corby Pegasus (R).

DIVISION ONE	P	W	D	L	F	A	GD	Pts
1 (P) Corby Eagles	28	24	1	3	130	33	97	73
2 (P) Gretton	28	22	1	5	102	52	50	67
3 Corby Grampian	28	15	6	7	73	44	29	51
4 Wootton St George (-3)	28	15	4	9	82	54	28	46
5 Clipston	28	14	3	11	64	70	-6	45
6 Wollaston Victoria	28	11	10	7	69	50	19	43
7 Heyford Athletic	28	11	5	12	72	73	-1	38
8 Burton United	28	10	6	12	62	57	5	36
9 Corby Strip Mills	28	11	3	14	55	65	-10	36
10 Kettering Orchard Park	28	10	4	14	57	64	-7	34
11 Wellingborough Old Grammarians	28	8	7	13	41	66	-25	31
12 Wilby	28	8	5	15	47	101	-54	29
13 Medbourne	28	7	6	15	56	81	-25	27
14 Stanwick Rovers	28	7	5	16	45	72	-27	26
15 (R) Walgrave Amber	28	3	2	23	45	118	-73	11

DIVISION TWO	P	W	D	L	F	A	GD	Pts
1 (P) Weedon	28	26	0	2	119	46	73	78
2 (P) Daventry Drayton Grange	28	24	1	3	122	25	97	73
3 (P) Corby Ravens	28	19	4	5	92	42	50	61
4 Finedon Volta	28	20	0	8	67	47	20	60
5 West Haddon Albion	28	10	5	13	52	59	-7	35
6 FC Higham (-6)	28	11	7	10	68	62	6	34
7 Higham Ferrers (-6)	28	12	4	12	57	58	-1	34
8 Kettering Park Rovers	28	12	2	14	67	89	-22	32
9 Northampton SPA	28	8	6	14	56	77	-21	30
10 Spratton	28	8	5	15	39	72	-33	29
11 Borough Alliance	28	7	6	15	43	68	-25	27
12 Great Doddington (-3)	28	8	3	17	50	82	-32	24
13 Grange Park Rangers (-3)	28	6	8	14	58	77	-19	23
14 Higham Town	28	6	3	19	43	80	-37	21
15 FC Titchmarsh	28	4	4	20	49	98	-49	16

DIVISION THREE	P	W	D	L	F	A	GD	Pts
1 (P) Wellingborough Rising Sun	28	25	2	1	131	29	102	77
2 (P) AFC Corby Shamrock	28	24	0	4	145	44	101	72
3 (P) Kislingbury	28	18	5	5	88	48	40	59
4 Kettering PL United	28	16	4	8	76	46	30	52
5 Northampton Mereway (-9)	28	18	4	6	98	57	41	49
6 Wellingborough Gleneagles	28	15	2	11	92	47	45	47
7 AFC Rothwell	28	14	1	13	60	55	5	43
8 Desborough & Rothwell United	28	11	8	9	68	53	15	41
9 Wellingborough Aztecs	28	11	5	12	61	58	3	38
10 Corby Kingswood (-3)	28	9	2	17	65	87	-22	26
11 Northampton AFC Obelisk	28	7	3	18	46	92	-46	24
12 Corby United	28	6	5	17	47	91	-44	23
13 Kettering Ise Lodge	28	6	4	18	49	97	-48	22
14 Corby Hellenic Fisher	28	5	3	20	58	133	-75	18
15 Irthlingborough Rangers	28	1	0	27	30	177	-147	3

RESERVE PREMIER DIVISION	P	W	D	L	F	A	GD	Pts
1 Stanion Redstar Reserves	24	21	0	3	90	30	60	63
2 Corby DGL Locos Reserves	24	15	2	7	68	43	25	47
3 Weldon United Reserves	24	14	3	7	64	32	32	45
4 Moulton Reserves	24	13	4	7	50	55	-5	43
5 Roade Reserves (-3)	24	14	2	8	54	46	8	41
6 Kettering Nomads Reserves (-3)	24	13	1	10	69	49	20	37
7 Brixworth All Saints Reserves	24	11	3	10	64	55	9	36
8 Bugbrooke St Michaels 'A' (-3)	24	10	1	13	48	58	-10	28
9 James King Blisworth Reserves (-9)	24	11	2	11	59	46	13	26
10 Ringstead Rangers Reserves (-3)	24	6	7	11	38	55	-17	22
11 Harpole Reserves (-9)	24	6	6	12	32	53	-21	15
12 (R) Milton Reserves	24	1	6	17	32	72	-40	9
13 (R) Corby Pegasus Reserves	24	1	3	20	30	104	-74	6

RESERVE DIVISION ONE	P	W	D	L	F	A	GD	Pts
1 (P) Weldon United 'A'	20	16	2	2	50	26	24	50
2 (P) Wollaston Victoria Reserves	20	13	4	3	58	33	25	43
3 (P) Corby Grampian Reserves	20	11	3	6	57	32	25	36
4 Earls Barton United Reserves (-3)	20	11	3	6	46	31	15	33
5 Medbourne Reserves	20	9	4	7	33	34	-1	31
6 Wellingborough Old Grammarians Res.	20	7	3	10	39	44	-5	24
7 Wootton St George Reserves (-3)	20	8	2	10	53	46	7	23
8 Wilby Reserves (-3)	20	6	6	8	51	51	0	21
9 Welford Victoria Reserves	20	6	3	11	28	45	-17	21
10 (R) Kettering Orchard Park Res (-3)	20	5	1	14	34	68	-34	13
11 (R) Heyford Athletic Reserves (-3)	20	2	1	17	25	64	-39	4

RESERVE DIVISION TWO	P	W	D	L	F	A	GD	Pts
1 (P) Weedon Reserves	22	19	0	3	96	30	66	57
2 (P) Gretton Reserves (-3)	22	19	2	1	126	23	103	56
3 (P) Corby Eagles Reserves	22	14	6	2	105	28	77	48
4 (P) Spratton Reserves	22	14	2	6	70	48	22	44
5 Bugbrooke St Michaels 'B' (-9)	22	14	2	6	71	30	41	35
6 West Haddon Albion Reserves (-3)	22	9	1	12	41	63	-22	25
7 Finedon Volta Reserves (-3)	22	8	2	12	38	59	-21	23
8 Stanwick Rovers Reserves (-3)	22	8	2	12	43	69	-26	23
9 Higham Town Reserves	22	4	3	15	24	77	-53	15
10 Corby Strip Mills Reserves (-3)	22	5	1	16	25	92	-67	13
11 FC Titchmarsh Reserves (-12)	22	5	3	14	48	82	-34	6
12 Corby Hellenic Fisher Reserves	22	0	2	20	20	106	-86	2

NORTHERN ALLIANCE

Sponsored by: Pin Point Recruitment
Founded: 1890
Recent Champions:
2009: Walker Central
2010: Harraby Catholic Club
2011: Heaton Stannington
2012: Heaton Stannington
2013: Heaton Stannington

PREMIER DIVISION	P	W	D	L	F	A	GD	Pts
1 Blyth Town	28	19	5	4	95	27	68	62
2 Carlisle City	28	16	6	6	57	33	24	54
3 Killingworth Station	28	17	2	9	61	57	4	53
4 Walker Central	28	15	6	7	54	38	16	51
5 Red House Farm FC	28	15	4	9	56	43	13	49
6 Stocksfield	28	15	4	9	62	51	11	49
7 Shankhouse (-3)	28	13	6	9	62	44	18	42
8 Whitley Bay A (-3)	28	13	4	11	65	38	27	40
9 Wallington	28	11	6	11	57	58	-1	39
10 Northbank Carlisle	28	8	8	12	45	59	-14	32
11 Seaton Delaval Amateurs (-3)	28	9	5	14	45	53	-8	29
12 Ashington Colliers	28	8	3	17	36	55	-19	27
13 Gateshead Rutherford	28	5	6	17	38	91	-53	21
14 Hebburn Reyrolle (-3)	28	5	5	18	48	94	-46	17
15 (R) Percy Main Amateurs	28	4	4	20	29	69	-40	16

CHALLENGE CUP

ROUND 1

Northbank Carlisle	v	Gateshead Rutherford	0-1
Percy Main Amateurs	v	Hebburn Reyrolle	3-2
Red House Farm	v	Seaton Delaval Amateurs	4-1 aet
Walker Central	v	Ashington Colliers	2-1
Whitley Bay A	v	Killingworth Station	2-1
Stocksfield	v	Shankhouse	3-0
Carlisle City	v	Blyth Town	1-0
Ashington Colliers	v	Blyth Town	2-3

QUARTER FINALS

Carlisle City	v	Wallington	0-4
Walker Central	v	Gateshead Rutherford	3-0
Whitley Bay A	v	Percy Main Amateurs	2-1
Stocksfield	v	Red House Farm	2-3

SEMI FINALS

Walker Central	v	Red House Farm	0-0, 3-1p
Wallington	v	Whitley Bay A	2-1

FINAL

Walker Central	v	Wallington	1-3

PREMIER DIVISION	1	2	3	4	5	6	7	8	9	10	11	12	13	14	15
1 Ashington Colliers		2-1	2-1	1-2	3-0	0-1	1-0	0-1	2-1	2-0	1-5	3-4	1-2	1-1	1-2
2 Blyth Town	0-0		2-2	10-0	8-0	7-2	7-1	2-0	1-1	2-2	1-0	3-1	2-0	1-3	1-0
3 Carlisle City	2-0	3-1		2-0	5-3	3-1	1-1	3-1	1-2	3-2	2-1	7-1	2-1	5-1	1-1
4 Gateshead Rutherford	3-1	1-5	0-0		3-0	0-4	1-3	2-2	1-3	2-1	0-5	3-2	1-2	3-3	1-4
5 Hebburn Reyrolle	2-2	1-8	0-1	3-3		0-1	4-0	3-1	2-2	0-4	3-5	1-2	3-5	4-1	3-14
6 Killingworth Station	4-3	1-4	2-0	4-3	2-5		4-3	3-2	1-3	3-1	4-1	2-3	1-1	0-5	1-1
7 Northbank Carlisle	6-1	0-4	1-4	7-1	2-2	0-4		3-2	1-3	1-1	2-4	1-0	0-0	1-1	2-1
8 Percy Main Amateurs	3-1	2-3	0-1	3-2	0-1	1-3	3-3		0-2	1-2	2-4	2-2	0-2	1-0	0-4
9 Red House Farm FC	1-0	3-2	2-0	1-1	5-0	2-3	3-1	3-1		1-0	3-3	2-1	4-3	1-4	0-1
10 Seaton Delaval Amateurs	3-1	2-7	3-2	6-2	1-1	0-2	1-0	1-1	2-1		0-3	2-0	2-2	1-2	1-3
11 Shankhouse	3-0	0-0	0-1	6-1	2-1	0-1	0-2	2-0	1-5	2-1		1-2	3-2	2-2	1-1
12 Stocksfield	3-0	0-4	1-0	5-0	3-0	1-3	0-0	5-0	2-1	4-3	3-3		4-1	2-2	1-0
13 Walker Central	2-1	0-1	1-1	3-0	3-0	4-1	3-3	2-0	3-0	1-0	1-1	5-3		2-1	1-0
14 Wallington	1-4	0-5	2-2	4-1	3-2	2-0	0-1	4-0	4-1	4-2	3-1	1-4	1-2		2-7
15 Whitley Bay A	1-2	0-3	1-2	1-1	5-4	2-3	3-0	6-0	2-0	0-1	0-3	1-3	2-0	2-0	

NORTHERN ALLIANCE PREMIER DIVISION CONSTITUTION 2014-15

	Club	Ground	Phone
1	ASHINGTON COLLIERS	Ashington FC, Hirst Welfare, Alexandra Road, Ashington NE63 9HF	07745 344502
2	BLYTH TOWN	South Newsham Playing Fields, Blyth NE24 3PP	07730 058814
3	CARLISLE CITY	Sheepmount Sports Complex, Sheepmount, Carlisle CA3 8XL	07739 478547
4	GATESHEAD RUTHERFORD	Farnacres, Beggarswood Park, Coach Road, Lobley Hill, Gateshead NE11 0HH	07882 544585
5	HEBBURN REYROLLE	Hebburn Sports Ground, 16 South Drive, Hebburn NE31 1ZX	0191 483 5101
6	KILLINGWORTH SPORTING	West Moor Community Centre, Benton Lane, West Moor, Newcastle NE12 7NP	07789 900159
7	NORTH SHIELDS ATHLETIC	John Spence Community High School, Preston Road, North Shields, Tyne & Wear NE29 9PU	
8	NORTHBANK CARLISLE	Sheepmount Sports Complex, Sheepmount, Carlisle CA3 8XL	07761 416331
9	RED HOUSE FARM	Kingston Park Road, Newcastle-upon-Tyne NE3 2HY	07809 627368
10	SEATON DELAVAL AMATEURS	Wheatridge Park, Seaton Delaval, Whitley Bay NE25 0QH	07527 289744
11	SHANKHOUSE	Action Park, Dudley NE23 7HY	07908 969412
12	STOCKSFIELD	Stocksfield Sports Ground, Main Road, Stocksfield NE43 7NN	07867 782589
13	WALKER CENTRAL	Monkchester Green, Walker, Newcastle-upon-Tyne NE6 2LJ	07449 309210
14	WALLINGTON	Oakford Park, Scots Gap, Morpeth NE61 4EJ	07793 596474
15	WHICKHAM SPORTING CLUB	Rose Avenue, Whickham, Tyne and Wear NE16 4NA	
16	WHITLEY BAY A	Hillheads Park, Rink Way, off Hillheads Road, Whitley Bay NE25 8HR	0191 291 3636

In: North Shields Athletic (P). Whickham Sporting Club (formerly Gateshead Redheugh) (P).
Out: Percy Main Amateurs (R).

DIVISION ONE	P	W	D	L	F	A	GD	Pts
1 (P) North Shields Athletic	28	20	4	4	93	43	50	64
2 (P) Gateshead Redheugh 1957 (-3)	28	19	1	8	94	47	47	55
3 Cramlington Town	28	17	3	8	67	48	19	54
4 Newcastle Chemfica (IND)	28	15	7	6	71	40	31	52
5 Birtley St Josephs	28	13	7	8	73	56	17	46
6 Gosforth Bohemians	28	13	4	11	55	48	7	43
7 Newcastle University (-3)	28	12	6	10	71	52	19	39
8 Wooler	28	10	7	11	54	68	-14	37
9 Ponteland United	28	9	8	11	45	66	-21	35
10 Bedlington Terriers Reserves	28	9	5	14	55	61	-6	32
11 Cullercoats	28	9	4	15	47	62	-15	31
12 Hexham	28	9	3	16	47	71	-24	30
13 New Fordley	28	8	5	15	56	82	-26	29
14 Heddon (-3)	28	7	2	19	45	98	-53	20
15 (R) Willington Quay Saints	28	5	4	19	39	70	-31	19

DIVISION TWO	P	W	D	L	F	A	GD	Pts
1 (P) Blyth Isabella	28	21	3	4	112	49	63	66
2 (P) AFC Newbiggin	28	20	4	4	89	35	54	64
3 (P) Wallsend Boys Club	28	19	3	6	75	33	42	60
4 Longbenton	28	18	4	6	89	41	48	58
5 Grainger Park Boys Club	28	16	2	10	77	66	11	50
6 Gateshead Leam Rangers	28	14	5	9	74	36	38	47
7 Alnwick Town Reserves	28	14	4	10	63	64	-1	46
8 Whitburn Athletic	28	9	9	10	52	58	-6	36
9 High Howdon Social Club	28	10	4	14	59	69	-10	34
10 Newcastle Benfield Reserves (-3)	28	11	3	14	66	69	-3	33
11 Seaton Burn	28	7	9	12	40	58	-18	30
12 Wideopen and District	28	6	4	18	40	84	-44	22
13 West Allotment Celtic A	28	7	1	20	47	93	-46	22
14 Swalwell (-3)	28	5	4	19	38	91	-53	16
15 Cramlington United (-3)	28	1	5	22	32	107	-75	5

COMBINATION CUP

ROUND 1

Cramlington Town	v	Bedlington Terriers Reserves	3-1
Cullercoats	v	Newcastle Unisversity	0-2
Heddon	v	Gosforth Bohemians	0-11
New Fordley	v	Birtley St Josephs	0-3
Newcastle Chemfica (IND)	v	Hexham	3-1
North Shields Athletic	v	Willington Quay Saints	5-2
Wooler	v	Ponteland United	4-2 aet

QUARTER FINALS

Birtley St Josephs	v	Wooler	4-0
Gateshead Redheugh 1957	v	Newcastle Unisversity	3-1
Gosforth Bohemians	v	Cramlington Town	4-0
Newcastle Chemfica (IND)	v	North Shields Athletic	4-0

SEMI FINALS

Gateshead Redheugh 1957	v	Newcastle Chemfica Ind	2-3
Gosforth Bohemians	v	Birtley St Josephs	2-3

FINAL

Birtley St Josephs	v	Newcastle Chemfica Ind	0-1

GEORGE DOBBIN LEAGUE CUP

ROUND 1

Ashington Colliers	v	Blyth Isabella	2-1
Birtley St Josephs	v	AFC Newbiggin	4-2
Carlisle City	v	Northbank Carlisle	0-1
Grainger Park B C	v	Willington Quay Saints	0-4
New Fordley	v	Cullercoats	4-2
North Shields Athletic	v	Swalwell	6-2
Percy Main Amateurs	v	Longbenton	0-2
Red House Farm	v	Wideopen and District	6-0
Shankhouse	v	West Allotment Celtic A	2-1
Stocksfield	v	Cramlington Town	4-0
Wallington	v	High Howdon S C	2-0
Wallsend Boys Club	v	Seaton Delaval Amateurs	4-4, 5-4p
Whitburn Athletic	v	Newcastle Chemfica Ind	1-2
Bedlington Terriers Reserves	v	Newcastle Benfield Reserves	4-5 aet
Alnwick Town Reserves	v	Ponteland United	3-5
Seaton Delaval Amateurs	v	New Fordley	10-1

ROUND 2

Ashington Colliers	v	Whitley Bay A	2-1
Birtley St Josephs	v	Killingworth Station	1-0
Cramlington Town	v	Hexham	6-1
Gateshead Redheugh 1957	v	Wallington	4-2
Gateshead Rutherford	v	Wallsend Boys Club	3-7 aet
Gosforth Bohemians	v	New Fordley	1-6
Hebburn Reyrolle	v	Longbenton	4-3
Newcastle University	v	Blyth Town	1-6
North Shields Athletic	v	Seaton Burn	4-1
Ponteland United	v	Red House Farm	1-0
Shankhouse	v	Willington Quay Saints	4-0
Stocksfield	v	Newcastle Benfield Reserves	3-4
Wooler	v	Newcastle Chemfica Ind	0-3
Northbank Carlisle	v	Heddon	8-1
Ponteland United	v	Shankhouse	3-1
Seaton Delaval Amateurs	v	Northbank Carlisle	2-1

ROUND 3

Cramlington Town	v	Blyth Town	2-6 aet
Gateshead Redheugh 1957	v	Birtley St Josephs	3-1
Hebburn Reyrolle	v	Ponteland United	5-2
Newcastle Chemfica (IND)	v	Northbank Carlisle	2-1
North Shields Athletic	v	New Fordley	4-2
Shankhouse	v	Ashington Colliers	2-2, 4-3p
Walker Central	v	Wallsend Boys Club	5-4
Newcastle Benfield Reserves	v	Gateshead Leam Rangers	4-3

QUARTER FINALS

Hebburn Reyrolle	v	Blyth Town	0-11
Newcastle Chemfica (IND)	v	Gateshead Redheugh 1957	6-4
North Shields Athletic	v	Walker Central	3-1
Shankhouse	v	Newcastle Benfield Reserves	3-0

SEMI FINALS

North Shields Athletic	v	Newcastle Chemfica Ind	2-2 aet
Blyth Town	v	Shankhouse	0-1

FINAL

Newcastle Chemfica (IND)	v	Shankhouse	1-3

NOTTINGHAMSHIRE SENIOR LEAGUE

Sponsored by: Precision
Founded: 2004
Recent Champions:
2009: Bilborough Pelican
2010: Clifton FC
2011: Boots Athletic
2012: Bulwell FC
2013: Bulwell FC

SENIOR DIVISION	P	W	D	L	F	A	GD	Pts
1 Selston	32	24	4	4	101	42	59	76
2 Kimberley Miners Welfare	32	23	3	6	90	47	43	72
3 Hucknall Rolls Leisure	32	21	6	5	94	41	53	69
4 Beeston AFC	32	18	5	9	91	60	31	59
5 Wollaton	32	18	4	10	81	55	26	58
6 Cotgrave	32	18	3	11	74	67	7	57
7 Awsworth Villa	32	15	5	12	69	60	9	50
8 Magdala Amateurs	32	14	4	14	81	71	10	46
9 FC Cavaliers	32	13	6	13	66	74	-8	45
10 Attenborough	32	12	6	14	59	58	1	42
11 Boots Athletic	32	10	10	12	60	65	-5	40
12 Ruddington Village	32	11	7	14	64	75	-11	40
13 Keyworth United	32	10	2	20	57	83	-26	32
14 Burton Joyce	32	8	6	18	69	93	-24	30
15 Bilborough Town	32	6	5	21	40	85	-45	23
16 Sandhurst (-6)	32	6	4	22	40	101	-61	16
17 (R) Nottingham United	32	3	4	25	45	104	-59	13

SENIOR CUP

ROUND 1

Ashland Rovers	v	Magdala Amateurs	3-4
Bingham Town	v	Underwood Villa	3-2
Awsworth Villa	v	Beeston AFC	1-4
Boots Athletic	v	Netherfield Albion	2-1
Selston	v	Ruddington Village	4-5
Kimberley Miners Welfare	v	FC Samba	1-0
Burton Joyce	v	Attenborough	2-4
Keyworth United	v	Moorgreen	1-2 aet
Cotgrave	v	Gedling Southbank	1-0
Newark Flowserve	v	Hucknall Rolls Leisure	1-4
Clifton AFC	v	Greyfriars	AW
Bilborough Town	v	Nottingham United	4-1
Wollaton	v	FC Cavaliers	2-0
Nottinghamshire	v	Kirton Brickworks	0-4

ROUND 2

Magdala Amateurs	v	West Bridgford	4-2
Bingham Town	v	Beeston AFC	5-0
Boots Athletic	v	Ruddington Village	4-2
Kimberley Miners Welfare	v	Attenborough	2-1 aet
Moorgreen	v	Cotgrave	4-0
Hucknall Rolls Leisure	v	Sandhurst	6-0
Greyfriars	v	Bilborough Town	1-0
Wollaton	v	Kirton Brickworks	3-1

QUARTER FINALS

Magdala Amateurs	v	Bingham Town	3-2
Boots Athletic	v	Kimberley Miners Welfare	4-0
Moorgreen	v	Hucknall Rolls Leisure	1-2
Greyfriars	v	Wollaton	1-2

SEMI FINALS

Magdala Amateurs	v	Boots Athletic	0-1
Hucknall Rolls Leisure	v	Wollaton	1-0

FINAL

Boots Athletic	v	Hucknall Rolls Leisure	2-3 aet

PREMIER DIVISION	1	2	3	4	5	6	7	8	9	10	11	12	13	14	15	16	17
1 Attenborough		2-1	1-5	2-0	1-1	2-0	1-1	3-0	0-3	2-0	3-3	3-4	1-2	1-2	1-3	1-1	1-0
2 Awsworth Villa	H-W		2-2	1-1	0-3	3-1	6-2	4-3	1-3	1-3	1-2	1-0	0-0	4-0	2-2	0-1	2-3
3 Beeston AFC	1-2	0-2		2-2	3-1	3-0	2-0	4-4	3-3	3-0	1-2	4-0	11-4	5-2	1-1	1-3	4-2
4 Bilborough Town	3-1	0-1	2-4		2-2	2-1	2-4	0-7	3-4	1-3	0-5	0-4	4-1	5-2	2-0	4-6	1-3
5 Boots Athletic	2-2	2-2	3-6	3-0		0-1	1-3	2-2	2-3	0-3	3-5	3-3	3-0	2-2	1-0	0-1	2-1
6 Burton Joyce	3-3	3-10	3-2	4-0	1-3		1-1	3-3	1-1	4-3	3-1	4-5	5-3	1-2	1-0	3-3	3-4
7 Cotgrave	3-2	6-1	5-1	1-0	2-0	4-2		2-0	1-3	2-1	0-3	3-2	6-3	3-3	2-1	0-4	3-2
8 FC Cavaliers	3-1	1-6	1-2	0-2	3-4	4-2	0-3		0-0	4-3	2-0	2-1	5-2	4-3	3-1	1-4	1-6
9 Hucknall Rolls Leisure	4-1	4-1	1-3	4-1	2-0	4-1	3-1	6-0		3-2	1-1	0-3	9-1	4-0	8-1	3-2	0-0
10 Keyworth United	1-7	4-2	1-5	1-1	2-3	4-2	3-5	1-2	1-4		2-4	0-2	2-1	3-2	3-2	0-1	0-0
11 Kimberley Miners Welfare	1-3	2-1	5-1	1-0	0-0	4-2	1-0	1-0	4-3	3-2		2-1	5-1	3-2	2-0	2-3	7-0
12 Magdala Amateurs	3-2	1-4	0-4	5-1	3-3	6-3	4-0	1-1	1-3	0-3	1-2		3-2	3-3	9-0	2-4	6-2
13 Nottingham United	0-2	1-2	A-W	0-0	3-3	2-4	1-2	0-1	1-3	A-W	2-0	3-4		0-2	5-4	1-1	0-6
14 Ruddington Village	2-1	0-2	1-2	2-0	0-1	2-2	4-1	4-2	0-0	5-3	1-4	2-0	4-3		5-2	1-4	2-4
15 Sandhurst	0-1	1-3	0-6	2-1	2-4	5-3	2-1	0-3	0-3	4-2	1-9	0-4	4-1	1-1		1-1	0-4
16 Selston	6-2	7-2	4-0	3-0	4-2	2-1	5-3	1-2	4-2	6-0	2-4	4-0	4-1	3-1	3-0		4-1
17 Wollaton	0-4	0-1	3-0	6-0	3-1	2-1	3-4	2-2	1-0	2-1	5-2	3-0	4-1	2-2	6-0	1-0	

NOTTINGHAMSHIRE SENIOR LEAGUE SENIOR DIVISION CONSTITUTION 2014-15

1	ATTENBOROUGH	Nottingham University Grounds, University Boulevard, Nottingham	07799 105593
2	AWSWORTH VILLA	The Shilo, Attewell Road, Awsworth, Nottingham NG16 2SY	07792 509159
3	BEESTON AFC	Hetley Pearson Rec. Grd, Cartwright Way, Queens Road, Beeston NG9 1RL	07976 943699
4	BILBOROUGH TOWN	Basil Russell Park, Maple Drive, Nuthall, Nottingham	07403 231039
5	BINGHAM TOWN	Butt Field, Bingham, Nottingham NG13 8GG	
6	BOOTS ATHLETIC	Trent Vale Road, Beeston Rylands, Nottingham. NG91ND	07904 409689
7	BURTON JOYCE	The Poplars, Station Road, Burton Joyce, Nottingham, NG14 5AN	07738 879266
8	COTGRAVE	Woodview, Cotgrave Welfare, Woodview, Cotgrave, Nottingham	07751 114989
9	FC CAVALIERS	Carrington Sports Ground, Mansfield Road, Carrington, Nottingham	07527 801634
10	KEYWORTH UNITED	Platt Lane Sports Complex, Platt Lane, Keyworth, Nottingham	07867 676421
11	KIRTON BRICKWORKS	The Station Road Ground, Station Road, Kirton, Ollerton, Nottinghamshire NG22 9LG	
12	MAGDALA AMATEURS	ROKO Health Club, Wilford Lane, West Bridgford, Nottingham, NG2 7RN	07816 962429
13	RUDDINGTON VILLAGE	Elms Park, Ruddington, Nottingham	07545 388439
14	SANDHURST	Walesby Sports & Social Club, Forest Lane, Walesby, Nottingham, NG22 9PF	07780 661646
15	SELSTON	Selston Parish Hall, Mansfield Road, Selston, Nottingham, NG16 6EE	07532 183393
16	WEST BRIDGFORD	Regatta Way Sports Ground, Regatta Way, Gamston, West Bridgford, Nottingham NG2 5AT	
17	WOLLATON	Wollaton Sports Association, 753 Wollaton Road, Wollaton, NG8 2AN	07986 584736

In: Bingham Town (P). Kirton Brickworks (P). West Bridgford (P). **Out:** Hucknall Rolls Leisure (S - Central Midlands South). Kimberley Miners Welfare (P - East Midlands Counties). Nottingham United (R).

DIVISION ONE	P	W	D	L	F	A	GD	Pts
1 (P) Kirton Brickworks	28	19	5	4	84	43	41	62
2 (P) West Bridgford	28	20	2	6	84	44	40	62
3 (P) Bingham Town	28	17	7	4	63	32	31	58
4 Southwell City Reserves	28	14	8	6	71	50	21	50
5 Netherfield Albion	28	15	4	9	72	56	16	49
6 Underwood Villa	28	13	6	9	70	48	22	45
7 Radcliffe Olympic Reserves	28	13	3	12	58	55	3	42
8 Hucknall Rolls Leisure Reserves	28	12	6	10	55	60	-5	42
9 Ruddington Village Reserves	28	11	2	15	73	73	0	35
10 Linby Colliery Welfare Reserves	28	9	6	13	59	58	1	33
11 Wollaton Reserves	28	9	4	15	36	58	-22	31
12 Awsworth Villa Reserves	28	8	4	16	54	77	-23	28
13 Gedling Southbank	28	6	8	14	33	53	-20	26
14 Magdala Amateurs Reserves	28	5	4	19	36	86	-50	19
15 Nottinghamshire	28	3	3	22	32	87	-55	12

DIVISION TWO	P	W	D	L	F	A	GD	Pts
1 (P) Moorgreen	18	14	2	2	65	21	44	44
2 (P) Ashland Rovers	18	14	1	3	69	26	43	43
3 (P) Newark Flowserve	18	12	0	6	63	32	31	36
4 (P) Kimberley Miners Welfare Res	18	11	3	4	40	31	9	36
5 FC Samba	18	8	1	9	45	39	6	25
6 Greyfriars	18	7	3	8	41	39	2	24
7 Underwood Villa Reserves	18	7	0	11	41	51	-10	21
8 Nottinghamshire Reserves	18	6	1	11	35	55	-20	19
9 Bilborough Town Reserves	18	4	2	12	44	70	-26	14
10 Sandhurst Reserves	18	0	1	17	10	89	-79	1

OXFORDSHIRE SENIOR LEAGUE

Sponsored by: No sponsor
Founded: N/K
Recent Champions:
2009: Garsington
2010: Adderbury Park
2011: Hinksey
2012: Oxford University Press
2013: Riverside

PREMIER DIVISION	P	W	D	L	F	A	GD	Pts
1 Oakley	24	18	3	3	60	13	47	57
2 Mansfield Road	24	15	3	6	55	41	14	48
3 Freeland	24	14	4	6	57	21	36	46
4 OUP	24	12	4	8	55	31	24	40
5 Riverside	24	11	7	6	57	53	4	40
6 Bletchingdon	24	11	6	7	48	35	13	39
7 Horspath	24	12	3	9	51	47	4	39
8 Stonesfield	24	11	3	10	39	40	-1	36
9 Marston Saints	24	7	5	12	30	43	-13	26
10 Adderbury Park	24	7	4	13	43	56	-13	25
11 Chalgrove	24	6	5	13	38	56	-18	23
12 Launton Sports	24	4	5	15	37	55	-18	17
13 Garsington	24	1	2	21	23	102	-79	5

PRESIDENTS CUP

ROUND 1

Broughton & NN	v	North Oxford	6-1
Oakley	v	Oxford Irish	HW
Middleton Cheney	v	Freeland	1-0
Chalgrove	v	Enstone	16-0
Kidlington OB	v	Launton Sports	1-4
Garsington	v	Adderbury Park	1-3
Bletchingdon	v	OUP	0-1
Marston Saints	v	Kidlington Reserves	2-3
Mansfield Road	v	Northway	5-1
Riverside	v	Horspath	7-1
Stonesfield	v	Eynsham	3-0
Watlington	v	Yarnton	0-1

ROUND 2

OUP	v	Kidlington Reserves	1-2
Oakley	v	Broughton & NN	4-1
Charlton	v	Middleton Cheney	3-1
Riverside	v	Stonesfield	3-2
Chalgrove	v	Launton Sports	3-1

QUARTER FINALS

Yarnton	v	Kidlington Reserves	0-2
Chalgrove	v	Charlton	3-0
Mansfield Road	v	Adderbury Park	3-1
Roverside	v	Oakley	AW

SEMI FINALS

Oakley	v	Kidlington Reserves	4-2
Chalgrove	v	Mansfield Road	2-2, 4-1p

FINAL

Mansfield Road	v	Oakley	0-3

PREMIER DIVISION	1	2	3	4	5	6	7	8	9	10	11	12	13
1 Adderbury Park		1-2	3-1	1-4	4-2	2-2	2-2	0-4	2-0	1-3	1-2	1-5	4-0
2 Bletchingdon	3-1		1-1	0-2	HW	1-3	2-2	1-1	2-0	0-2	1-1	6-1	0-0
3 Chalgrove	2-2	3-6		2-1	5-1	1-3	2-2	3-5	0-0	0-7	1-3	2-3	0-1
4 Freeland	7-0	1-0	2-3		3-1	6-1	3-0	1-2	1-1	1-0	1-3	1-1	0-0
5 Garsington	1-6	1-4	2-1	0-9		1-3	1-6	0-2	1-2	0-3	1-7	1-1	3-4
6 Horspath	3-2	0-1	2-0	0-2	7-2		2-3	3-4	2-1	0-2	1-0	4-3	2-1
7 Launton Sports	0-1	1-4	2-3	1-3	3-3	2-4		1-3	0-1	1-2	4-0	3-5	1-0
8 Mansfield Rd	4-3	1-1	2-0	0-4	6-0	2-0	1-1		1-0	0-6	1-2	4-1	1-2
9 Marston Saints	3-2	0-3	1-2	2-3	2-0	1-2	2-1	1-4		2-2	1-0	3-5	3-2
10 Oakley	3-1	2-1	2-0	1-2	5-1	2-1	3-0	5-1	1-0		0-0	0-0	2-0
11 OUP	1-2	3-1	2-2	1-0	12-0	4-2	3-0	1-2	0-0	0-1		3-1	4-2
12 Riverside	1-1	6-2	3-1	0-0	3-0	3-3	2-1	4-2	3-3	0-6	2-1		2-4
13 Stonesfield	1-0	2-6	0-3	1-0	4-1	1-1	3-0	1-2	4-1	1-0	4-2	1-2	

DIVISION ONE		P	W	D	L	F	A	GD	Pts
1	Kidlington Reserves	18	14	2	2	59	24	35	44
2	Eynsham	18	11	5	2	57	32	25	38
3	Broughton & NN	18	12	1	5	39	27	12	37
4	Middleton Cheney	18	10	5	3	40	21	19	35
5	Charlton	18	9	3	6	38	29	9	30
6	Watlington	18	6	5	7	39	44	-5	23
7	Yarnton	18	6	2	10	39	46	-7	20
8	Kidlington OB	18	3	4	11	28	49	-21	13
9	North Oxford	18	1	4	13	22	53	-31	7
10	Northway	18	1	3	14	29	65	-36	6

DIVISION TWO		P	W	D	L	F	A	GD	Pts
1	Middleton Cheney Reserves	16	12	2	2	53	16	37	38
2	Freeland Reserves	16	8	1	7	38	33	5	25
3	Bletchingdon Reserves	16	8	1	7	33	30	3	25
4	Marston Saints Reserves	16	7	3	6	21	31	-10	24
5	Adderbury Park Reserves	16	5	5	6	33	30	3	20
6	Mansfield Rd Reserves	16	6	2	8	39	39	0	20
7	Stonesfield Reserves	16	5	5	6	28	39	-11	20
8	OUP Reserves	16	5	3	8	38	51	-13	18
9	Eynsham Reserves	10	4	2	10	26	40	-14	14

DIVISION THREE		P	W	D	L	F	A	GD	Pts
1	Oakley Reserves	14	10	2	2	42	16	26	32
2	North Oxford Reserves	14	8	2	4	32	23	9	26
3	Horspath Reserves	14	8	0	6	40	28	12	24
4	Yarnton Reserves	14	6	1	7	33	34	-1	19
5	Launton Sports Reserves	14	6	1	7	30	33	-3	19
6	Broughton & NN Reserves	14	5	2	7	23	28	-5	17
7	Charlton Reserves	14	3	4	7	22	34	-12	13
8	Watlington Reserves	14	3	2	9	18	44	-26	11

PETERBOROUGH & DISTRICT LEAGUE

Sponsored by: ChromaSport
Founded: 1902
Recent Champions:
2009: Ramsey Town
2010: Rutland Rangers
2011: Ramsey Town
2012: Pinchbeck United
2013: Moulton Harrox

PREMIER DIVISION	P	W	D	L	F	A	GD	Pts
1 Kings Lynn Town Reserves	32	26	4	2	115	34	81	82
2 Netherton United	32	25	3	4	127	28	99	78
3 Whittlesey United	32	20	9	3	75	32	43	69
4 Peterborough ICA Sports	32	20	6	6	92	33	59	66
5 Uppingham Town	32	20	6	6	75	44	31	66
6 Moulton Harrox	32	19	5	8	99	44	55	62
7 Riverside	32	16	6	10	78	68	10	54
8 Leverington Sports	32	12	4	16	63	78	-15	40
9 Sawtry	32	10	5	17	56	72	-16	35
10 Coates Athletic	32	10	5	17	49	75	-26	35
11 Oakham United (-2)	32	11	4	17	48	82	-34	35
12 Stilton United	32	9	6	17	46	74	-28	33
13 Deeping Rangers Reserves (+4)	32	5	12	15	49	71	-22	31
14 Crowland Town (+2)	32	6	9	17	48	85	-37	29
15 Pinchbeck United	32	4	10	18	39	93	-54	22
16 Ramsey Town (-2)	32	6	3	23	38	98	-60	19
17 (R) Whittlesey Blue Star (-1)	32	2	5	25	29	115	-86	10

Parsons Grove (F) - record expunged.

PREMIER SHIELD

ROUND 1

Whittlesey United	v	Deeping Rangers Reserves	0-4
Netherton United	v	Whittlesey Blue Star	9-0
Leverington Sports	v	Crowland Town	0-1
Riverside	v	Parson Drove 92	1-0
Coates Athletic	v	Oakham United	7-1
Stilton United	v	Uppingham Town	0-4
Peterborough ICA Sports	v	Pinchbeck United	3-2
Sawtry	v	Kings Lynn Reserves	1-2

QUARTER FINALS

Deeping Rangers Reserves	v	Netherton United	0-6
Crowland Town	v	Riverside	3-2
Coates Athletic	v	Uppingham Town	0-1
Peterborough ICA Sports	v	Kings Lynn Reserves	1-2

SEMI FINALS

Netherton United	v	Crowland Town	8-0
Uppingham Town	v	Kings Lynn Reserves	1-5

FINAL

Netherton United	v	Kings Lynn Reserves	2-2, 11-10p

PREMIER DIVISION	1	2	3	4	5	6	7	8	9	10	11	12	13	14	15	16	17
1 Coates Athletic		1-1	3-3	3-4	0-3	0-2	1-7	4-0	3-2	2-0	4-1	1-3	2-1	0-1	1-1	7-2	0-4
2 Crowland Town	3-3		1-1	1-1	1-5	1-5	1-3	4-2	0-5	2-2	0-1	1-4	1-2	2-2	2-4	4-0	3-5
3 Deeping Rangers Reserves	4-1	0-0		2-5	1-5	0-0	1-2	0-0	0-0	1-2	1-1	2-4	2-1	2-4	1-3	0-0	1-1
4 Kings Lynn Town Reserves	5-1	4-2	1-0		9-2	3-2	2-1	2-1	2-0	4-0	7-0	4-0	7-0	4-0	2-0	6-0	2-2
5 Leverington Sports	1-2	3-1	3-6	2-5		0-2	0-1	4-2	1-2	2-2	3-1	4-2	3-6	3-1	0-3	2-2	0-3
6 Moulton Harrox	4-1	4-1	1-5	4-2	6-0		3-5	7-2	4-2	2-2	6-1	1-2	7-1	3-0	5-1	6-1	1-1
7 Netherton United	2-0	10-0	1-1	3-1	3-2	1-0		6-0	2-2	10-0	4-0	8-0	6-1	7-1	6-0	6-0	4-1
8 Oakham United	8-1	3-2	1-0	1-6	1-0	2-1	0-3		0-2	1-1	1-0	3-3	0-7	0-2	0-1	3-0	0-3
9 Peterborough ICA Sports	4-0	2-0	7-0	1-3	5-2	0-0	2-1	8-2		9-0	5-0	1-1	3-0	2-0	0-2	4-0	1-0
10 Pinchbeck United	1-0	0-1	4-4	1-6	1-3	0-6	0-3	2-2	1-1		2-3	2-3	2-3	4-1	0-4	1-1	1-1
11 Ramsey Town	1-3	3-4	1-4	1-3	2-1	0-1	0-7	0-3	1-5	0-1		2-4	3-2	3-2	1-5	2-2	1-3
12 Riverside	1-0	1-1	3-1	2-6	1-2	2-1	3-0	1-2	3-3	4-3	2-0		2-2	2-3	2-4	6-2	0-1
13 Sawtry	1-1	0-1	4-0	0-0	2-0	1-2	2-3	1-2	0-3	5-2	2-1	2-4		1-2	1-2	1-0	2-5
14 Stilton United	1-2	3-1	1-1	0-4	3-3	0-4	1-4	5-0	1-2	1-1	1-1	2-6	2-0		0-1	3-1	0-2
15 Uppingham Town	1-0	3-3	3-2	0-1	1-1	3-3	2-1	2-0	2-4	2-1	3-0	3-0	0-0	4-2		8-0	0-0
16 Whittlesey Blue Star	0-1	1-2	3-2	1-3	1-2	0-3	0-6	1-5	0-5	2-0	3-5	0-6	3-4	1-1	2-5		0-2
17 Whittlesey United	3-1	2-1	5-1	1-1	0-1	4-3	1-1	3-1	2-0	4-0	4-2	1-1	1-1	3-0	3-2	4-0	

DIVISION ONE	P	W	D	L	F	A	GD	Pts
1 (P) Thorney	30	27	3	0	118	26	92	84
2 (P) Langtoft United	30	20	6	4	77	28	49	66
3 (P) Holbeach United Reserves	30	20	5	5	89	37	52	65
4 AFC Stanground	30	18	5	7	101	56	45	59
5 (P) Peterborough Sports Reserves (-4)	30	17	5	8	89	53	36	52
6 Ketton	30	15	6	9	66	46	20	51
7 Long Sutton Athletic	30	14	5	11	63	73	-10	47
8 Ryhall United	30	14	4	12	71	55	16	46
9 Netherton United Reserves	30	11	2	17	79	84	-5	35
10 Warboys Town	30	9	6	15	50	67	-17	33
11 Kings Cliffe	30	8	8	14	46	73	-27	32
12 Sutton Bridge United	30	9	4	17	65	80	-15	31
13 Moulton Harrox Reserves	30	7	7	16	50	80	-30	28
14 Peterborough ICA Sports Reserves (-1)	30	7	4	19	40	101	-61	24
15 (P) Stamford Belvedere	30	5	3	22	32	88	-56	18
16 Farcet United	30	2	1	27	39	128	-89	7

DIVISION TWO	P	W	D	L	F	A	GD	Pts
1 (P) Baston	28	19	4	5	70	31	39	61
2 (P) Langtoft United Reserves	28	18	4	6	72	42	30	58
3 Leverington Sports Reserves (+4)	28	13	7	8	60	36	24	50
4 (P) Oundle Town	28	15	4	9	90	57	33	49
5 Peterborough ICA Sports 'A' (-1)	28	15	5	8	87	56	31	49
6 Crowland Town Reserves	28	12	8	8	60	44	16	47
7 Peterborough Rovers Post Office FC (-1)	28	15	3	10	65	52	13	47
8 Whittlesey United Reserves (-2)	28	14	4	10	69	43	26	44
9 Coates Athletic Reserves	28	10	9	9	66	66	0	39
10 Gedney Hill	28	9	10	9	79	69	10	37
11 Guyhirn	28	10	3	15	63	72	-9	33
12 Pinchbeck United Reserves (-1)	28	9	7	12	57	68	-11	33
13 Oakham United Reserves (+2)	28	3	6	19	34	105	-71	17
14 (R) Ramsey Town Reserves (-1)	28	1	8	19	26	105	-79	10
15 (R - D4) Long Sutton Athletic Res (-6)	28	3	6	19	28	80	-52	9

DIVISION THREE	P	W	D	L	F	A	GD	Pts
1 (P) Wittering	24	19	3	2	109	48	61	60
2 (P) Netherton United 'A'	24	17	3	4	84	39	45	54
3 (P) Thorney Reserves	24	13	6	5	69	50	19	45
4 (P) Ketton Reserves	24	12	2	10	69	52	17	38
5 (P) Parkway Eagles (+3)	24	10	3	11	38	42	-4	36
6 (P) Parkside	24	11	2	11	71	63	8	35
7 (P) Sawtry Reserves	24	10	4	10	59	58	1	34
8 Riverside Reserves	24	8	5	11	62	64	-2	29
9 Uppingham Town Reserves	24	8	5	11	46	53	-7	29
10 Stilton United Reserves	24	9	2	13	40	67	-27	29
11 Ryhall United Reserves (-5)	24	8	5	11	53	73	-20	24
12 Farcet United Reserves	24	5	2	17	33	72	-39	17
13 Kings Cliffe Reserves	24	3	4	17	21	73	-52	13

DIVISION FOUR	P	W	D	L	F	A	GD	Pts
1 (P) Spalding Town (+2)	24	20	3	1	95	20	75	65
2 (P) Glinton United	24	20	3	1	69	18	51	63
3 (P) Hampton Sport (+2)	24	16	6	2	119	32	87	56
4 (P) Baston Reserves (+4)	24	12	6	6	62	37	25	46
5 (P) Tydd St Mary (+4)	24	9	6	9	52	49	3	37
6 (P) Peterborough Sports 'A' (-2)	24	10	5	9	69	52	17	33
7 AFC Peterborough	24	8	3	13	51	73	-22	27
8 Warboys Town Reserves (-1)	24	7	6	11	42	80	-38	26
9 Stamford Belvedere Reserves (-3)	24	8	3	13	42	56	-14	24
10 Pinchbeck United 'A' (+1)	24	5	6	13	31	64	-33	22
11 Sutton Bridge United Reserves (-6)	24	6	5	13	44	89	-45	17
12 Leverington Sports 'A' (-1)	24	3	3	18	33	70	-37	11
13 (R) Ryhall United A (-6)	24	3	3	18	41	110	-69	6

DIVISION FIVE	P	W	D	L	F	A	GD	Pts
1 (P) Bretton North End	24	18	2	4	125	42	83	56
2 (P) Powerleague FC	24	17	3	4	140	44	96	54
3 (P) Oundle Town Reserves (+2)	24	16	3	5	108	44	64	53
4 (P) Eye United	24	16	2	6	97	41	56	50
5 Peterborough ICA Sports 'B'	24	15	3	6	92	45	47	48
6 (P) Rutland DR (+2)	24	13	5	6	82	48	34	46
7 (P) Thorpe Wood Rangers (+2)	24	12	2	10	74	61	13	40
8 (P) Huntingdon Sun (+2)	24	10	3	11	74	64	10	35
9 Tydd St Mary Reserves (-2)	24	9	1	14	76	97	-21	26
10 Parkside Reserves	24	6	1	17	63	130	-67	19
11 Whaplode Drove	24	5	1	18	52	120	-68	16
12 Gaultree	24	1	5	18	24	170	-146	8
13 Parkway Eagles Reserves (-6)	24	0	5	19	27	128	-101	-1

PETERBOROUGH & DISTRICT LEAGUE PREMIER DIVISION CONSTITUTION 2014-15

	Club	Ground	Phone
1	COATES ATHLETIC	Feldale Field, Drybread Rd PE7 1XL & Manor Field, Station Rd, Whittesey PE17 1UA	07934 304 103
2	CROWLAND TOWN	Snowden Field, Thorney Road, Crowland PE6 0AL	07908 185 284
3	DEEPING RANGERS RESERVES	Outgang Road, Towngate East, Market Deeping PE6 8LQ	07977 971 796
4	HOLBEACH UNITED RESERVES	Carters Park, Park Road, Holbeach Spalding PE12 7EE	07714 018 695
5	LANGTOFT UNITED	Manor Way, Sports Ground, Langtoft, Peterborough PE6 9LP	07768 650 507
6	LEVERINGTON SPORTS	Church Road, Leverington, Wisbech PE13 5DE	07933 208 468
7	MOULTON HARROX	Broad Lane, Moulton, Spalding PE12 6PN	07730 770 407
8	NETHERTON UNITED	The Grange, Mayors Walk, Peterborough PE3 9TT	07808 774 302
9	OAKHAM UNITED	Barleythorpe, Oakham, Rutland LE15 7EE	01572 756 781
10	PETERBOROUGH ICA SPORTS	Ringwood, South Bretton PE3 9SH	07827 446 844
11	PETERBOROUGH SPORTS RES.	651 Lincoln Road, Peterborough PE1 3HR	07894 445 991
12	PINCHBECK UNITED	Glebe Playing Fields, Knight Street, Pinchbeck, Spalding PE11 3RB	07730 466 579
13	RAMSEY TOWN	Cricketfield Lane, Ramsey, Huntingdon PE26 1BG	07876 240 731
14	RIVERSIDE ROVERS	City of Peterborough Academy, Reeves Way, Peterborough PE1 5LQ	07876 631 685
15	SAWTRY	Greenfields, Straight Drove, Sawtry, Cambridgeshire PE28 5XE	07719 641 431
16	STILTON UNITED	Yaxley FC, Leading Drove, Holme Road, Yaxley PE7 3NA	07756 778 154
17	THORNEY	The Park, Tavistock Close, Thorney PE6 0SJ	07743 296 505
18	UPPINGHAM TOWN	Todds Piece, North Street East, Uppingham LE15 9QL	07787 573 700

In: Holbeach United Reserves (P). Langtoft United (P). Peterborough Sports Reserves (P). Thorney (P).
Out: Kings Lynn Town Reserves (P - Eastern Counties Div.1). Parsons Grove (F - Jan 2014). Whittlesey Blue Star (R). Whittlesey United (Merged with Coates Athletic).

NON
LEAGUE DAY
06.09.14
Support your
LOCAL
FOOTBALL CLUB
nonleagueday.co.uk

SHEFFIELD & HALLAMSHIRE SENIOR LEAGUE

Sponsored by: Windsor Food Services
Founded: N/K
Recent Champions:
2009: Athersley Recreation
2010: Sheffield Reserves
2011: Swallownest Miners Welfare
2012: Athersley Recreation
2013: Shaw Lane Aqua Force Barnsley

PREMIER DIVISION	P	W	D	L	F	A	GD	Pts
1 Handsworth FC	26	21	1	4	70	24	46	64
2 Oughtibridge WMSC	26	18	4	4	56	30	26	58
3 Houghton Main	26	16	3	7	57	40	17	51
4 Penistone Church	26	15	3	8	59	35	24	48
5 Swallownest Miners Welfare	26	12	4	10	49	40	9	40
6 Athersley Recreation Reserves	26	11	4	11	51	50	1	37
7 Millmoor Juniors	26	11	4	11	46	53	-7	37
8 Stocksbridge Park Steels Reserves	26	10	6	10	59	45	14	36
9 Swinton Athletic	26	10	0	16	43	42	1	30
10 Wombwell Main	26	8	4	14	42	70	-28	28
11 Frecheville CA FC	26	6	8	12	36	55	-19	26
12 Everest	26	7	3	16	37	52	-15	24
13 (R) Ecclesfield Red Rose	26	6	5	15	34	59	-25	23
14 (R) High Green Villa	26	4	5	17	29	73	-44	17

DIVISION ONE	P	W	D	L	F	A	GD	Pts
1 (P) Jubilee Sports	26	16	5	5	66	35	31	53
2 (P) Joker FC (Sat)	26	16	4	6	67	44	23	52
3 (P) Wickersley	26	15	6	5	62	41	21	51
4 Millmoor Juniors Reserves	26	14	2	10	74	72	2	44
5 Rotherham Town FC	26	13	4	9	72	50	22	43
6 Penistone Church Reserves	26	13	4	9	71	49	22	43
7 Silkstone United	26	12	7	7	61	48	13	43
8 Thorncliffe	26	10	5	11	64	61	3	35
9 Sheffield Athletic	26	11	1	14	58	62	-4	34
10 Hallam FC Reserves	26	9	5	12	61	73	-12	32
11 South Kirkby Colliery	26	8	4	14	52	61	-9	28
12 Thorpe Hesley	26	7	5	14	43	62	-19	26
13 Sheffield Bankers	26	6	2	18	50	72	-22	20
14 Davy FC	26	4	2	20	47	118	-71	14

DIVISION TWO	P	W	D	L	F	A	GD	Pts
1 (P) North Gawber Colliery	26	20	5	1	93	23	70	65
2 (P) Kingstone United FC	26	17	3	6	81	43	38	54
3 (P) AFC Dronfield NC	26	14	4	8	71	54	17	46
4 Sheffield Lane Top	26	12	7	7	54	46	8	43
5 Bawtry Town FC	26	10	9	7	69	62	7	39
6 Caribbean Sports	26	11	4	11	48	52	-4	37
7 Maltby Main Reserves	26	11	3	12	65	81	-16	36
8 Sheffield FC Reserves	26	10	5	11	54	45	9	35
9 Worsbrough Bridge Athletic Reserves	26	9	5	12	49	54	-5	32
10 Bramley Sunnyside	26	10	2	14	57	72	-15	32
11 Boynton Sports (-1)	26	9	2	15	58	77	-19	28
12 New Bohemians	26	6	7	13	53	65	-12	25
13 Kiveton Park	26	5	8	13	32	53	-21	23
14 Frecheville CAFC Reserves	26	5	2	19	32	89	-57	17

LEAGUE CUP

ROUND 1

Bramley Sunnyside	v	Silkstone United	1-2
Davy FC	v	Sheffield FC Reserves	1-4
Everest	v	Penistone Church Reserves	4-1
Handsworth FC	v	Stocksbridge Park Steels Reserves	3-1
Houghton Main	v	Swallownest MW U21	4-1
Jubilee Sports	v	Frecheville CA FC	5-2
Maltby Main Reserves	v	Davy U21	5-2
Millmoor Juniors Reserves	v	North Gawber Colliery U21	5-1
New Bohemians	v	Sheffield Lane Top	2-3
North Gawber Colliery	v	Caribbean Sports	5-3
Rotherham Town FC	v	Bawtry Town U21	4-1
Shaw Lane Aqua Force U21	v	Sheffield Athletic	2-2, 3-4p
South Kirkby Colliery	v	Houghton Main U21	5-0
Swinton Athletic U21	v	Joker FC (Sat)	3-0
Valley Knights U21	v	Millmoor Juniors	0-10
Wombwell Main	v	Thorncliffe	8-5

ROUND 2

Kiveton Park	v	Sheffield FC Reserves	1-3
AFC Dronfield NC	v	Ecclesfield Red Rose	4-3
Athersley Recreation Reserves	v	Rotherham Town FC	3-2
Frecheville CAFC Reserves	v	Hallam FC Reserves	2-3
High Green Villa	v	South Kirkby Colliery	2-0
Jubilee Sports	v	Millmoor Juniors U21	9-1
Maltby Main Reserves	v	Penistone Church	0-6
Millmoor Juniors Reserves	v	Houghton Main	1-2
North Gawber Colliery	v	Thorpe Hesley	7-0
Sheffield Athletic	v	Handsworth FC	1-5
Sheffield Bankers (awarded to Sheffield Bankers)	v	Swallownest Miners Welfare	1-4
Sheffield Lane Top	v	Millmoor Juniors	1-5
Silkstone United	v	Swinton Athletic	0-4
Treeton Terriers U21	v	Worsbrough Bridge Athletic Reserves	1-3
Wickersley	v	Kingstone United FC	2-4
Wombwell Main	v	Everest	2-0

ROUND 3

Handsworth FC	v	Sheffield FC Reserves	2-1
Kingstone United FC	v	High Green Villa	5-1
Millmoor Juniors	v	Houghton Main	1-3
North Gawber Colliery	v	Jubilee Sports	3-2
Sheffield Bankers	v	Wombwell Main	4-3
Swinton Athletic	v	Athersley Recreation Reserves	0-1
Worsbrough Bridge Athletic Reserves	v	Penistone Church	0-2
Hallam FC Reserves	v	AFC Dronfield NC	4-2

QUARTER FINALS

Houghton Main	v	Hallam FC Reserves	8-0
Penistone Church	v	Athersley Recreation Reserves	3-1
Sheffield Bankers	v	North Gawber Colliery	4-1
Handsworth FC	v	Kingstone United FC	8-1

SEMI FINALS

Penistone Church	v	Sheffield Bankers	4-2
Handsworth FC	v	Houghton Main U21	1-5

FINAL

Houghton Main	v	Penistone Church	1-3

PREMIER DIVISION	1	2	3	4	5	6	7	8	9	10	11	12	13	14
1 Athersley Recreation Reserves		3-2	1-2	1-1	0-3	4-0	0-2	4-1	1-1	2-1	1-4	3-1	3-2	1-2
2 Ecclesfield Red Rose	3-3		0 3	1-1	2-4	0-3	1-1	1-2	1-3	1-3	0-4	1-3	1-2	0-3
3 Everest	3-0	1-2		3-4	1-3	4-0	1-3	2-0	0-3	3-4	2-4	1-3	4-0	1-1
4 Frecheville CA FC	4-4	2-2	0-0		1-3	1-1	2-0	3-1	0-2	0-0	2-6	1-2	0-2	1-1
5 Handsworth FC	3-1	4-0	3-0	3-1		4-1	1-2	2-0	3-0	1-3	1-1	2-1	2-1	3-1
6 High Green Villa	0-5	1-3	1-0	1-3	0-3		1-4	1-2	2-2	1-5	2-3	2-2	2-1	1-1
7 Houghton Main	4-0	2-0	3-1	2-0	2-6	2-1		5-3	3-0	0-1	1-0	4-0	1-3	2-1
8 Millmoor Juniors	1-0	1-2	1-0	3-0	0-1	1-0	4-2		1-3	3-2	0-0	2-2	3-2	6-2
9 Oughtibridge WMSC	2-1	3-1	1-0	3-0	1-0	5-1	1-0	2-2		1-2	2-1	0-1	2-0	3-2
10 Penistone Church	0-4	0-2	5-0	1-2	3-0	3-3	0-1	2-2	4-6		2-0	1-0	0-2	4-0
11 Stocksbridge Park Steels Reserves	0-2	0-1	2-2	3-4	1-5	6-0	3-3	6-1	2-2	0-1		1-1	0-4	3-2
12 Swallownest Miners Welfare	2-3	1-0	5-0	5-1	1-2	2-0	4-4	4-0	1-3	1-3	3-2		2-0	1-0
13 Swinton Athletic	2-3	2-3	3-0	2-0	0-1	1-2	5-0	5-0	0-2	0-3	0-4	2-0		1-2
14 Wombwell Main	4-1	4-4	0-3	3-2	0-7	6-2	1-4	0-6	1-3	0-6	1-3	2-1	2-1	

SOMERSET COUNTY LEAGUE

Sponsored by: Errea

Founded: 1890

Recent Champions:

2009: Bridgwater Town Reserves

2010: Bridgwater Town Reserves

2011: Shirehampton

2012: Nailsea United

2013: Nailsea United

PREMIER DIVISION	P	W	D	L	F	A	GD	Pts
1 Nailsea United	34	26	3	5	108	60	48	81
2 Clutton	34	25	4	5	95	40	55	79
3 Watchet Town	34	24	2	8	89	47	42	74
4 Fry Club	34	22	6	6	91	38	53	72
5 Shirehampton	34	20	4	10	95	51	44	64
6 Minehead	34	17	5	12	70	53	17	56
7 Berrow	34	15	5	14	67	65	2	50
8 Stockwood Green	34	16	1	17	67	67	0	49
9 Cutters Friday	34	14	6	14	74	75	-1	48
10 Bishops Lydeard	34	12	5	17	58	61	-3	41
11 Bridgwater Town Reserves	34	11	7	16	57	76	-19	40
12 Nailsea Town	34	12	4	18	55	76	-21	40
13 Ilminster Town	34	10	4	20	50	79	-29	34
14 Odd Down Reserves	34	11	1	22	45	80	-35	34
15 Yatton Athletic	34	8	9	17	57	79	-22	33
16 (R) Street Reserves	34	9	4	21	40	78	-38	31
17 (R) Langford Rov. 2000 (-3)	34	8	6	20	62	91	-29	27
18 (R) Weston St Johns	34	7	2	25	39	103	-64	23

ERREA PREMIER/FIRST DIVISION CUP

ROUND 1

Shirehampton	v	Burnham United	6-2
Street Reserves	v	Stockwood Green	3-2
Odd Down Reserves	v	Saltford	3-2
Bishops Lydeard	v	Dundry Athletic	2-1

Round 2

Clevedon United	v	Middlezoy Rovers	1-4
Frome Collegians	v	Nailsea Town	3-1
Brislington Reserves	v	Shirehampton	4-3
Street Reserves	v	Cutters Friday	3-4
Shepton Mallet Reserves	v	Minehead	3-2
Castle Cary	v	St George Easton in Gorda	3-2
Ilminster Town	v	Yatton Athletic	3-0
Westfield	v	Odd Down Reserves	2-1
Watchet Town	v	Bishops Lydeard	5-4
Congresbury	v	Keynsham Town Reserves	5-3
Clutton	v	Bridgwater Town Reserves	4-1
Nailsea United	v	Purnell Sports	6-1
Banwell	v	Larkhall Athletic Reserves	2-3
Wrington Redhill	v	Broad Plain House	0-3
Fry Club	v	Weston St Johns	4-2
Langford Rovers 2000	v	Berrow	2-1

PREMIER DIVISION	1	2	3	4	5	6	7	8	9	10	11	12	13	14	15	16	17	18
1 Berrow		2-1	1-0	1-3	3-1	0-1	2-4	4-4	5-1	3-2	4-1	1-0	3-3	3-1	2-2	1-4	0-2	3-2
2 Bishops Lydeard	1-1		3-1	2-2	3-2	1-2	3-0	2-0	0-2	3-0	2-3	1-0	2-2	1-2	0-0	1-2	0-2	2-0
3 Bridgwater Town Reserves	4-0	1-0		0-3	1-1	1-4	1-1	2-1	0-6	3-0	4-4	3-1	1-4	1-0	3-0	1-2	4-1	1-1
4 Clutton	3-1	6-2	2-1		2-0	3-2	3-1	2-1	5-1	3-1	4-2	0-2	1-3	4-1	3-1	2-0	4-0	3-0
5 Cutters Friday	0-3	4-3	6-2	1-2		2-2	1-1	2-1	1-1	2-0	3-3	8-2	2-10	6-4	4-0	1-0	5-0	1-4
6 Fry Club	1-0	0-0	1-2	4-2	5-1		7-0	5-0	2-2	2-0	2-4	4-0	0-1	3-2	1-0	5-1	2-1	3-1
7 Ilminster Town	0-4	1-0	0-0	0-2	1-3	1-3		0-4	2-1	3-2	2-4	1-2	2-0	2-0	1-3	2-4	6-0	4-1
8 Langford Rovers 2000	1-2	5-2	2-4	2-4	1-2	2-2	3-3		0-1	6-2	2-7	1-1	2-2	1-3	1-6	2-3	2-1	2-1
9 Minehead	2-1	4-2	7-1	0-0	3-2	1-2	2-0	2-1		2-0	0-2	4-0	1-2	3-1	4-2	0-2	2-3	1-1
10 Nailsea Town	3-1	3-2	1-0	2-4	4-1	1-1	1-0	2-1	1-1		3-1	1-4	1-0	2-4	3-1	1-10	4-0	1-1
11 Nailsea United	4-3	2-0	2-2	3-1	2-0	2-0	2-1	7-0	6-3	5-4		5-3	4-1	0-1	2-1	4-2	3-1	3-1
12 Odd Down Reserves	2-3	2-4	2-1	0-3	1-6	0-4	1-2	1-2	2-0	1-0	1-2		0-4	1-2	3-1	2-1	2-1	2-3
13 Shirehampton	2-0	5-2	6-1	1-1	0-2	2-3	5-0	4-5	0-3	3-2	1-3	4-0		5-1	3-0	2-0	5-1	0-1
14 Stockwood Green	3-1	1-2	3-0	1-3	0-0	3-1	6-2	5-3	1-2	1-0	1-4	1-2	2-3		4-0	3-1	2-0	4-2
15 Street Res	1-3	0-4	2-2	0-3	4-0	0-5	2-1	1-0	0-5	0-2	0-5	2-0	0-1	2-0		1-3	3-2	1-2
16 Watchet Town	3-1	4-0	3-2	2-1	4-0	1-1	3-1	4-1	3-0	2-0	4-1	3-1	3-1	2-1	4-1		3-1	2-1
17 Weston St Johns	3-5	0-5	1-4	0-9	1-0	1-8	3-2	1-2	1-0	0-1	0-2	0-4	1-2	1-3	1-2	3-3		2-0
18 Yatton Athletic	0-0	0-2	5-3	2-2	2-4	0-3	1-3	1-1	2-3	5-5	3-4	2-0	1-8	4-0	1-1	2-1	4-4	

SOMERSET COUNTY LEAGUE PREMIER DIVISION CONSTITUTION 2014-15

1	BERROW	Red Road Playing Fields, Berrow, Burnham-on-Sea TA8 2LY	07714 122 050
2	BISHOPS LYDEARD	Darby Way, Bishops Lydeard TA4 3BE	07771 506 613
3	BRIDGWATER TOWN RESEVES	Fairfax Park, College Way, Bath Road, Bridgwater TA6 4TZ	01278 446 899
4	BROAD PLAIN HOUSE	Broad Plain FC, Creswike Road, Knowle	
5	CLUTTON	Warwick Fields, Upper Bristol Road , Behind Warwick Arms, Clutton, Nr Bristol BS39 5TA	
6	CUTTERS FRIDAY	The Cutters Club, Stockwood Lane, Stockwood, Bristol BS14 8SJ	01275 839 830
7	FROME COLLEGIANS	Selwood Middle School, Berkley Road, Frome, Somerset BA11 2EF	
8	FRY CLUB	Cadbury's, Somerdale, Keynsham, Bristol BS31 2AU	0117 9376 500
9	ILMINSTER TOWN	Recreation Ground, Ilminster TA19 0EF	07875 378 663
10	MINEHEAD	Recreation Ground, Irnham Road, Minehead TA24 5DP	01643 704 989
11	NAILSEA TOWN	Fryth Way, Pound Lane, Nailsea BS48 2AS	07763 925 811
12	NAILSEA UNITED	Grove Sports Ground, Old Church, Nailsea BS48 4ND	01275 856 892
13	ODD DOWN RESERVES	Lew Hill Memorial Ground, Combe Hay Lane, Odd Down, Bath BA2 8PH	01225 832 491
14	SHIREHAMPTON	Recreation Ground, Penpole Lane, Shirehampton, Bristol BS11 0EA	0117 923 5461
15	STOCKWOOD GREEN	Hursley Lane, Woolard Lane, Whitchurch, Bristol BS14 0QY	01275 891 300
16	WATCHET TOWN	Memorial Ground, Doniford Road, Watchet TA23 0TG	01984 631 041
17	WRINGTON REDHILL	The Recreation Field, Silver Street, Wrington, Bristol BS40 5QN	07918 192 544
18	YATTON ATHLETIC	Hangstones Playing Fields, Stowey Road, Yatton, North Somerset BS49 4HS	

In: Broad Plain House (P). Frome Collegians (P). Wrington Redhill (P).
Out: Langford Rovers 2000 (R-D1W). Street Reserves (R-D1W). Weston St Johns (R-D1W)

DIVISION ONE	P	W	D	L	F	A	GD	Pts
1 (P) Broad Plain House	34	21	9	4	98	45	53	72
2 (P) Wrington Redhill	34	20	11	3	111	36	75	71
3 (P) Frome Collegians	34	20	9	5	95	36	59	69
4 Middlezoy Rovers	34	20	6	8	85	57	28	66
5 Westfield FC	34	20	5	9	93	46	47	65
6 Dundry Athletic (-3)	34	20	8	6	94	60	34	65
7 Brislington Reserves	34	19	6	9	69	53	16	63
8 Larkhall Athletic Reserves	34	19	4	11	87	55	32	61
9 Clevedon United	34	14	8	12	78	77	1	50
10 Congresbury	34	11	8	15	65	73	-8	41
11 Keynsham Town Reserves	34	9	7	18	64	81	-17	34
12 St George Easton in Gordano	34	9	7	18	62	90	-28	34
13 Burnham United	34	9	7	18	61	95	-34	34
14 Saltford	34	6	13	15	46	85	-39	31
15 Castle Cary	34	6	7	21	45	79	-34	25
16 Shepton Mallet Reserves	34	6	7	21	31	104	-73	25
17 Banwell	34	5	9	20	53	92	-39	24
18 Purnells Sports FC (-3)	34	5	3	26	29	102	-73	15

DIVISION TWO EAST	P	W	D	L	F	A	GD	Pts
1 (P-D1E) Long Ashton	30	21	5	4	90	34	56	68
2 (P-D1E) Welton Rovers Reserves	30	20	5	5	84	37	47	65
3 (P-D1E) Chilcompton Sports	30	19	5	6	83	40	43	62
4 (P-D1E) Timsbury Athletic	30	17	10	3	66	31	35	61
5 (P-D1E) Peasedown Athletic	30	14	11	5	62	37	25	53
6 Bishop Sutton Reserves (-8)	30	17	4	9	63	47	16	47
7 Imperial FC	30	13	5	12	62	51	11	44
8 Chew Magna (-1)	30	12	5	13	53	56	-3	40
9 Fry Club Reserves	30	11	5	14	47	49	-2	38
10 Tunley Athletic	30	10	5	15	52	71	-19	35
11 Ashton and Backwell United Reserves (-1)	30	7	8	15	55	75	-20	28
12 Radstock Town Reserves (-7)	30	9	6	15	63	60	3	26
13 Hengrove Athletic Reserves	30	7	5	18	42	79	-37	26
14 Cutters Friday Reserves	30	6	6	18	40	93	-53	24
15 Stockwood Green Reserves (-3)	30	6	6	18	39	74	-35	21
16 Farrington Gurney (-2)	30	3	5	22	25	92	-67	12

PREMIER/FIRST DIVISION CUP continued...

Round 3

Middlezoy Rovers	v	Frome Collegians	4-2
Brislington Reserves	v	Cutters Friday	2-3
Shepton Mallet Reserves	v	Castle Cary	0-2
Ilminster Town	v	Westtfield	1-2
Watchet Town	v	Congresbury	4-1
Clutton	v	Nailsea Town	1-2
Larkhall Athletic Reserves	v	Broad Plain House	0-2
Fry Club	v	Langford Rovers 2000	6-0

Quarter Finals

Middlezoy Rovers	v	Cutters Friday	1-3
Castle Cary	v	Westtfield	0-2
Watchet Town	v	Nailsea Town	2-1
Broad Plain House	v	Fry Club	1-2

Semi Finals

Cutters Friday	v	Westtfield	1-1, 3-4p
Watchet Town	v	Fry Club	5-0

Final

Westfield	v	Watchet Town	3-0

DIVISION TWO CUP

FINAL

Well City Reserves	v	Bishop Sutton Reserves	4-0

DIVISION TWO WEST	P	W	D	L	F	A	GD	Pts
1 (P-D1W) Cleeve West Town	32	25	4	3	97	25	72	79
2 (P-D1W) Wells City Reserves	31	19	7	5	96	42	54	64
3 (P-D1W) Glastonbury FC	32	18	9	5	75	30	45	63
4 (P-D1W) Staplegrove	32	19	6	7	91	49	42	63
5 (P-D1W) Portishead Town Reserves	32	19	6	7	80	46	34	63
6 Winscombe	32	16	10	6	63	36	27	58
7 Uphill Castle (-3)	32	16	8	8	80	44	36	53
8 North Curry	31	15	6	10	81	48	33	51
9 Combe St Nicholas (-3)	32	15	6	11	75	42	33	48
10 Worle	32	14	4	14	64	60	4	46
11 Nailsea United Reserves	32	11	4	17	50	66	-16	37
12 Kewstoke Lions (-3)	32	10	5	17	44	72	-28	32
13 Cheddar Reserves (-2)	32	9	3	20	45	67	-22	28
14 Nailsea Town Reserves (-3)	32	6	7	19	48	69	-21	22
15 Burnham United Reserves	32	5	3	24	38	128	-90	18
16 Churchill Club 70 (-4)	32	4	3	25	28	116	-88	11
17 Weston St Johns Reserves	32	2	5	25	30	145	-115	11

STAFFORDSHIRE COUNTY SENIOR LEAGUE

Sponsored by: No sponsor
Founded: 1957
Recent Champions:
2009: Foley
2010: Stretton Eagles
2011: Ball Haye Green
2012: Hanley Town
2013: Hanley Town

PREMIER DIVISION	P	W	D	L	F	A	GD	Pts
1 Wolstanton United	32	24	5	3	101	23	78	77
2 (P) Uttoxeter Town	32	23	5	4	112	40	72	74
3 Ball Haye Green	29	15	10	4	63	34	29	55
4 Norton United	32	15	9	8	58	57	1	54
5 Redgate Clayton	31	16	4	11	71	52	19	52
6 Audley	31	13	10	8	51	32	19	49
7 Abbey Hulton United	32	14	5	13	69	64	5	47
8 Newcastle Town	31	12	6	13	51	60	-9	42
9 Cheadle Town	32	11	8	13	52	52	0	41
10 Kidsgrove Athletic	32	12	5	15	45	62	-17	41
11 Eccleshall AFC	32	9	7	16	58	93	-35	34
12 Hilton Harriers	30	9	6	15	62	80	-18	33
13 AFC Hanley Town	32	8	8	16	53	67	-14	32
14 Florence	32	8	7	17	59	80	-21	31
15 AFC Leek Town	30	9	4	17	50	83	-33	31
16 (R) Keele University	30	7	4	19	47	86	-39	25
17 Alsager Town	32	4	11	17	57	94	-37	23

DIVISION ONE	P	W	D	L	F	A	GD	Pts
1 (P) MMU	32	26	4	2	97	38	59	78
2 Stapenhill Reserves	32	23	4	5	91	40	51	73
3 Bradwell	32	19	6	7	80	51	29	63
4 Knypersley Vics	32	18	6	8	78	51	27	60
5 (P) Brereton Social	32	18	6	8	70	45	25	60
6 Silverdale Athletic	32	17	3	12	76	56	20	54
7 Ashbourne	32	15	5	12	70	59	11	50
8 Cheadle Smu	32	14	5	13	58	57	1	47
9 Congleton Athletic	32	13	4	15	56	59	-3	43
10 Betley	32	11	5	16	66	71	-5	38
11 Redgate Clayton Reserves	32	10	7	15	62	76	-14	37
12 Milton United	32	10	5	17	51	73	-22	35
13 Foley	32	9	6	17	40	59	-19	33
14 Hall Heath	32	7	8	17	76	106	-30	29
15 Abbey Hulton United Reserves	32	7	6	19	46	65	-19	27
16 Norton United "A"	32	7	2	23	60	106	-46	23
17 Sandbach United Reserves	32	4	6	22	47	112	-65	18

DIVISION TWO	P	W	D	L	F	A	GD	Pts
1 (P) Featherstone	26	20	3	3	97	32	65	63
2 (P) Uttoxter Town Reserves	26	20	2	4	66	28	38	62
3 (P) Hawkins Sports	26	18	6	2	87	35	52	35
4 Longton AG	26	18	2	6	106	43	63	56
5 Stone Old Alleynians Reserves	26	14	2	10	74	61	13	44
6 Whittington	26	13	3	10	87	46	41	42
7 Leek CSOB Reserves	26	12	5	9	52	45	7	41
8 Milton United Reserves	26	11	4	11	40	45	-5	37
9 Cheadle Town Reserves	26	10	2	14	45	67	-22	32
10 Longton	26	8	0	18	40	82	-42	24
11 Hilton Harriers Reserves	26	7	2	17	52	75	-23	23
12 Betley Reserves	26	6	2	18	46	90	-44	20
13 The LA	26	6	2	18	38	82	-44	20
14 Tunstall Town	26	1	1	24	24	123	-99	4

STAFFS COUNTY SENIOR LEAGUE PREMIER DIVISION CONSTITUTION 2014-15

	Club	Ground
1	AFC HANLEY TOWN	Abbey Lane, Bucknall, Stoke-on-Trent ST2 8AU
2	AFC LEEK TOWN	Ball Haye Green WMC, Ball Haye Green, Leek ST13 6BH
3	ABBEY HULTON UNITED	Birches Head Road, Abbey Hulton, Stoke-on-Trent ST2 8DD
4	ALSAGER TOWN RESERVES	Law Training Stadium, Wood Park, Alsager ST7 2DP
5	AUDLEY & DISTRICT	Town Fields, Old Road, Bignall, Stoke-on-Trent ST7 8QH
6	BALL HAYE GREEN	Ball Haye Green WMC, Ball Haye Green, Leek ST13 6BH
7	BRERETON SOCIAL	Brereton Sports and Social Club, Armitage Lane, Rugeley, Staffordshire WS15 1ED
8	CHEADLE TOWN	Thorley Drive, Cheadle, Staffordshire. ST10 1SA
9	ECCLESHALL AFC	Pershall Park, Chester Road, Eccleshall ST21 6NE
10	FLORENCE	Florence Sports & Social, Lightwood Road, Longton, Stoke-on-Trent ST7 4JS
11	HILTON HARRIERS ATHLETIC	The Mease, Hilton, Derbyshire, DE65 5LS
12	KIDSGROVE ATHLETIC RESERVES	The Seddon Stadium, Hollinwood Road, Kidsgrove, Stoke-on-Trent ST7 1DQ
13	MMU CHESHIRE	Sandbach, Cheshire East CW11 3LZ
14	NEWCASTLE TOWN RESERVES	The Aspire Stadium, Buckmaster Avenue, Clayton, Newcastle-under-Lyme ST5 3BX
15	NORTON UNITED	The Autonet Insurance Stadium, Community Drive, Smallthorne, Stoke-on-Trent ST6 1QF
16	REDGATE CLAYTON	Clayton Community Centre, Northwood Lane, Clayton, Newcastle-under-Lyme ST5 4BN
17	WOLSTANTON UNITED	Bradwell Community Centre, Riceyman Road, Bradwell, Newcastle-under-Lyme ST5 8LD

In: Brereton Social (P). MMU Cheshire (P).
Out: Keele University (R). Uttoxeter Town (P - Midland Division 1).

SUFFOLK & IPSWICH LEAGUE

Sponsored by: TouchlineSIL
Founded: 1896
Recent Champions:
2009: Grundisburgh
2010: Old Newton United
2011: Grundisburgh
2012: Woodbridge Athletic
2013: Ipswich Valley Rangers

SENIOR DIVISION	P	W	D	L	F	A	GD	Pts
1 Achilles	30	23	3	4	89	41	48	72
2 Grundisburgh	30	22	3	5	94	41	53	69
3 Ipswich Valley Rangers	30	18	4	8	76	40	36	58
4 Crane Sports	30	18	2	10	91	61	30	56
5 Capel Plough	30	16	2	12	53	44	9	50
6 Wickham Market	30	15	1	14	58	62	-4	46
7 Haughley United	30	12	4	14	52	49	3	40
8 East Bergholt United	30	12	3	15	49	52	-3	39
9 Wenhaston United	30	12	1	17	57	66	-9	37
10 Felixstowe Harpers United	30	10	6	14	46	55	-9	36
11 Leiston St Margarets	30	9	7	14	59	83	-24	34
12 Melton St Audrys	30	9	5	16	41	66	-25	32
13 Stanton	30	9	5	16	55	81	-26	32
14 Westerfield United	30	8	7	15	42	62	-20	31
15 (R) Old Newton United	30	8	7	15	48	77	-29	31
16 (R) Coplestonians	30	7	4	19	36	66	-30	25

DIVISION ONE	P	W	D	L	F	A	GD	Pts
1 (P) Bramford United	26	23	2	1	107	24	83	71
2 (P) Claydon	26	19	1	6	72	43	29	58
3 Framlingham Town	26	18	4	4	57	30	27	58
4 Henley Athletic	26	18	3	5	72	35	37	57
5 Sporting 87	26	15	3	8	57	45	12	48
6 Ipswich Exiles	26	13	1	12	48	47	1	40
7 Trimley Athletic	26	9	6	11	40	39	1	33
8 Mendlesham	26	10	0	16	47	59	-12	30
9 St Johns	26	8	5	13	40	52	-12	29
10 AFC Crowley	26	8	2	16	38	69	-31	26
11 Parkside United	26	7	3	16	44	58	-14	24
12 Ipswich Athletic	26	7	3	16	39	69	-30	24
13 (R) Saxmundham Sports	26	4	3	19	23	75	-52	15
14 (R) Ransomes Sports (-3)	26	4	2	20	29	68	-39	11

BOB COLEMAN CUP

ROUND 1

AFC Hoxne	v	Barham Athletic	2-3
Aldeburgh Town	v	AFC Elmsett	HW
Bacton United 89	v	Shotley	2-1
Bartons	v	Adhara	6-3
Bildeston Rangers	v	Stowupland Falcons	4-3
Boxford Rovers	v	Benhall St Mary	0-3
Chantry Grasshoppers	v	Thurston	5-6
Cockfield United	v	Bramford Road Old Boys	8-1
Coddenham	v	Waterside	0-6
Halesworth Town	v	Mendlesham	0-6
Kesgrave Kestrels	v	Willis	4-1
Parkside United	v	Witnesham Wasps	1-2
Salvation Army	v	Claydon	0-5
Sizewell Associates	v	Cedars Park	1-2
Sporting 87	v	Woolverstone United	15-1
Sproughton Sports	v	Stonham Aspal	1-2
Sproughton United	v	Elmswell	0-11
St Clements Hospital	v	Ufford Sports	2-2, 5-6p
Stradbroke United	v	Somersham	0-10
Tacket Street BBOB	v	Tattingstone United	0-3
Trimley Red Devils	v	Great Blakenham	2-1
Walsham Le Willows 'A'	v	AFC Titans	8-3

ROUND 2

Bacton United 89	v	Claydon	3-3, 3-1
Barham Athletic	v	Benhall St Mary	2-3
Bartons	v	Aldeburgh Town	4-2
Cedars Park	v	Tattingstone United	4-1
Cockfield United	v	Bildeston Rangers	2-4
Framlingham Town	v	Somersham	4-2
Henley Athletic	v	Thurston	6-0
Ipswich Athletic	v	Sporting 87	6-2
Ipswich Exiles	v	Stonham Aspal	4-1
Mendlesham	v	Bramford United	3-6
St Johns	v	Saxmundham Sports	3-0
Trimley Athletic	v	Elmswell	3-2
Trimley Red Devils	v	Kesgrave Kestrels	5-1
Ufford Sports	v	Ransomes Sports	0-5
Walsham Le Willows 'A'	v	Stow United	1-5
Witnesham Wasps	v	Waterside	2-0

ROUND 3

Achilles	v	Grundisburgh	1-1, 2-4p
Bacton United 89	v	Leiston St Margarets	2-4
Benhall St Mary	v	East Bergholt United	1-4
Cedars Park	v	Crane Sports	AW
Coplestonians	v	Witnesham Wasps	8-0
Felixstowe Harpers United	v	Henley Athletic	0-1
Haughley United	v	Old Newton United	2-1
Ipswich Athletic	v	Framlingham Town	0-6
Ipswich Exiles	v	Bildeston Rangers	5-4
Ipswich Valley Rangers	v	Westerfield United	3-0
Melton St Audrys	v	Bartons	HW
Ransomes Sports	v	Stanton	0-3
St Johns	v	Stow United	0-2
Trimley Red Devils	v	Trimley Athletic	5-1
Wenhaston United	v	Capel Plough	3-2
Wickham Market	v	Bramford United	1-3

SENIOR DIVISION	1	2	3	4	5	6	7	8	9	10	11	12	13	14	15	16
1 Achilles		3-0	3-2	2-2	0-1	6-0	3-1	2-2	3-1	5-2	5-0	3-2	3-3	2-1	2-0	1-3
2 Capel Plough	0-2		1-0	0-2	3-0	2-1	0-1	2-0	2-0	2-1	2-3	1-3	7-4	0-3	2-2	2-1
3 Coplestonians	0-2	0-3		0-4	0-3	0-1	2-3	0-2	1-1	2-3	0-3	1-1	1-0	2-3	2-1	0-1
4 Crane Sports	4-5	4-3	2-0		4-0	0-2	1-6	5-2	4-0	3-5	0-2	2-0	5-0	4-1	4-2	4-0
5 East Bergholt United	1-3	2-1	0-1	2-4		0-0	2-3	2-1	1-1	1-1	1-2	3-1	2-1	5-1	2-3	2-4
6 Felixstowe Harpers United	0-5	1-4	0-2	2-1	1-2		5-0	1-1	2-2	2-2	1-0	2-2	5-0	3-2	1-2	1-2
7 Grundisburgh	4-1	0-1	4-3	1-1	3-1	3-1		2-4	1-0	4-1	7-0	5-0	3-0	3-2	5-1	4-1
8 Haughley United	2-3	0-1	1-1	2-0	2-0	4-2	0-1		1-4	0-1	2-2	3-0	1-0	4-2	4-1	1-3
9 Ipswich Valley Rangers	0-3	3-1	3-1	3-0	2-0	1-0	5-1	3-0		6-1	5-0	1-2	1-1	6-2	2-0	3-1
10 Leiston St Margarets	3-1	0-2	3-3	4-3	1-5	2-1	0-8	4-3	2-3		2-0	4-4	1-6	2-2	1-1	1-3
11 Melton St Audrys	0-4	1-1	5-2	4-3	1-2	1-2	1-1	3-2	1-4	2-1		0-1	3-3	1-3	1-1	1-2
12 Old Newton United	2-6	1-3	3-4	3-6	2-1	2-2	1-4	0-2	0-5	3-3	2-1		5-3	1-0	1-1	1-2
13 Stanton	1-2	2-1	1-2	3-7	2-4	1-2	2-4	1-0	2-1	5-3	1-0	1-1		2-0	3-2	5-1
14 Wenhaston United	2-4	1-2	3-0	2-3	2-1	2-1	1-5	1-3	2-4	1-0	4-1	2-1	4-0		0-1	3-0
15 Westerfield United	0-1	2-1	5-2	2-4	2-0	2-4	1-1	0-3	3-2	1-5	0-2	1-2	2-2	1-2		1-1
16 Wickham Market	2-4	1-3	1-2	3-5	0-3	2-0	0-0	2-0	2-4	1-0	2-0	5-1	8-0	4-3	0-1	

DIVISION TWO	P	W	D	L	F	A	GD	Pts
1 (P) Benhall St Mary	26	19	3	4	80	18	62	60
2 (P) Somersham	26	18	3	5	85	38	47	57
3 AFC Hoxne	26	16	7	3	75	31	44	55
4 Bacton United 89	26	18	1	7	72	31	41	55
5 Stowupland Falcons	26	16	4	6	58	32	26	52
6 Bildeston Rangers (-3)	26	15	4	7	91	55	36	46
7 Trimley Red Devils	26	12	3	11	49	51	-2	39
8 Aldeburgh Town	26	11	2	13	49	54	-5	35
9 Cedars Park	26	10	5	11	49	55	-6	35
10 Stonham Aspal	26	6	3	17	31	77	-46	21
11 Salvation Army	26	5	6	15	39	90	-51	21
12 Bartons	26	5	4	17	41	73	-32	19
13 (R) Cockfield United (-3)	26	5	3	18	40	72	-32	15
14 (R) Sproughton Sports	26	0	4	22	27	109	-82	4

DIVISION THREE	P	W	D	L	F	A	GD	Pts
1 (P) Adhara (-4)	24	20	3	1	101	22	79	59
2 AFC Hoxne Reserves	23	16	2	5	84	26	58	50
3 (P) Boxford Rovers	24	14	4	6	68	32	36	46
4 Ufford Sports	24	13	3	8	74	51	23	42
5 Walsham Le Willows 'A'	24	13	3	8	59	47	12	42
6 Elmswell	24	12	3	9	72	53	19	39
7 Tacket Street BBOB	24	12	3	9	55	50	5	39
8 Bramford Road Old Boys	24	10	6	8	51	63	-12	36
9 Thurston (-1)	24	7	5	12	47	67	-20	25
10 Halesworth Town	24	6	2	16	39	71	-32	20
11 Coplestonians 'A' (-3)	24	6	4	14	38	56	-18	19
12 Willis	24	3	0	21	22	90	-68	9
13 (R) Trimley Red Devils Reserves (-3)	23	3	2	18	19	101	-82	8

DIVISION FOUR	P	W	D	L	F	A	GD	Pts
1 (P) Barham Athletic	26	23	3	0	103	18	85	72
2 (P) Waterside (-3)	26	20	2	4	120	39	81	59
3 (P) Witnesham Wasps	26	18	5	3	96	31	65	59
4 St Clements Hospital	26	17	3	6	94	34	60	54
5 Bacton United 89 Reserves	25	14	3	8	60	45	15	45
6 Somersham Reserves	26	12	3	11	63	53	10	39
7 Stonham Aspal Reserves	26	11	3	12	62	59	3	36
8 Tattingstone United (-6)	26	13	2	11	62	49	13	35
9 Coddenham (-1)	26	9	3	14	71	94	-23	29
10 Cedars Park Reserves (-1)	26	8	3	15	53	72	-19	26
11 Woolverstone United (-2)	26	6	1	19	35	102	-67	17
12 Cockfield United Reserves (-1)	26	5	1	20	38	101	-63	15
13 (R) Stradbroke United (-1)	26	4	3	19	33	133	-100	14
14 (R) Felixstowe Harpers United 'A' (-1)	25	3	1	21	21	81	-60	9

DIVISION FIVE	P	W	D	L	F	A	GD	Pts
1 (P) Shotley	26	25	0	1	150	21	129	75
2 (P) Stowupland Falcons Reserves	26	20	3	3	100	27	73	63
3 (P) Aldeburgh Town Reserves	26	13	3	10	72	44	28	42
4 East Bergholt United 'A'	26	13	1	12	69	75	-6	40
5 Benhall St Mary Reserves	26	12	3	11	56	54	2	39
6 Sproughton United	26	12	4	10	56	69	-13	39
7 Kesgrave Kestrels	26	12	2	12	52	55	-3	38
8 Halesworth Town Reserves	26	9	7	10	51	61	-10	34
9 Elmswell Reserves	26	9	4	13	67	72	-5	31
10 Old Newton United 'A'	26	9	5	12	63	78	-15	31
11 Bramford Road Old Boys Reserves	26	10	1	15	70	91	-21	28
12 Sizewell Associates	26	7	5	14	48	75	-27	26
13 (R) Witnesham Wasps Reserves	26	7	4	15	47	88	-41	25
14 (R) Tattingstone United Reserves	26	2	2	22	34	125	-91	8

BOB COLEMAN CUP

ROUND 4

Crane Sports	v	East Bergholt United	0-4
Framlingham Town	v	Melton St Audrys	3-2
Haughley United	v	Coplestonians	0-2
Henley Athletic	v	Stanton	4-1
Ipswich Exiles	v	Bramford United	3-2
Leiston St Margarets	v	Grundisburgh	0-3
Trimley Red Devils	v	Stow United	1-5
Wenhaston United	v	Ipswich Valley Rangers	0-2

QUARTER FINALS

Coplestonians	v	East Bergholt United	2-2, 2-3
Framlingham Town	v	Ipswich Valley Rangers	1-2
Grundisburgh	v	Stow United	3-2
Henley Athletic	v	Ipswich Exiles	0-1

SEMI FINALS

Grundisburgh	v	Ipswich Valley Rangers	2-0
Ipswich Exiles	v	East Bergholt United	2-3

FINAL

East Bergholt United	v	Grundisburgh	0-2

DIVISION SIX	P	W	D	L	F	A	GD	Pts
1 (P) Chantry Grasshoppers	22	17	3	2	112	48	64	54
2 (P) Bildeston Rangers Reserves	22	15	1	6	81	47	34	46
3 (P) Stowupland Falcons 'A'	22	13	4	5	61	34	27	43
4 (P) Ufford Sports Reserves	22	12	2	8	74	59	15	38
5 Sporting 87 'A' (-6)	21	13	2	6	73	45	28	35
6 Bacton United 89 'A'	22	9	5	8	69	60	9	32
7 AFC Titans	22	7	5	10	50	66	-16	26
8 Kesgrave Kestrels Reserves	22	7	4	11	50	61	-11	25
9 Sproughton Sports Reserves (-1)	22	6	2	14	47	98	-51	19
10 Salvation Army Reserves (-4)	22	6	2	14	57	71	-14	16
11 AFC Elmsett (-3)	21	5	2	14	49	89	-40	14
12 Stonham Aspal 'A' (-3)	22	4	2	16	38	83	-45	11

INTERMEDIATE A	P	W	D	L	F	A	GD	Pts
1 Crane Sports Reserves	26	20	2	4	102	22	80	62
2 Achilles Reserves	26	19	4	3	76	19	57	61
3 Coplestonians Reserves	26	19	3	4	107	46	61	60
4 Old Newton United Reserves	26	19	3	4	85	45	40	60
5 Felixstowe Harpers United Reserves	26	14	6	6	80	56	24	48
6 East Bergholt United Reserves	26	12	3	11	82	54	28	39
7 Grundisburgh Reserves	26	11	4	11	74	56	18	37
8 Wenhaston United Reserves	26	10	6	10	53	58	-5	36
9 Ipswich Valley Rangers Reserves	25	8	3	14	49	79	-30	27
10 Westerfield United Reserves	26	7	3	16	57	78	-21	24
11 Melton St Audrys Reserves (-1)	26	5	6	15	46	78	-32	20
12 (R) Haughley United Res. (-2)	26	6	3	17	40	97	-57	19
13 (R) Ransomes Sports Res. (-2)	26	4	3	19	39	94	-55	13
14 (W) AFC Crowley Reserves (-5)	25	1	3	21	18	126	-108	1

INTERMEDIATE B	P	W	D	L	F	A	GD	Pts
1 (P) Stanton Reserves	24	18	2	4	60	22	38	56
2 (P) St Johns Reserves (-2)	26	18	3	5	81	50	31	55
3 Bramford United Reserves	26	16	3	7	84	45	39	51
4 Claydon Reserves	26	14	4	8	61	33	28	46
5 Henley Athletic Reserves	25	12	5	8	66	53	13	41
6 Sporting 87 Reserves	26	12	4	10	65	53	12	40
7 Wickham Market Reserves (-1)	26	12	3	11	55	54	1	38
8 Mendlesham Reserves	25	8	6	11	54	74	-20	30
9 Trimley Athletic Reserves	26	9	2	15	40	70	-30	29
10 Capel Plough Reserves (-1)	25	7	4	14	48	57	-9	24
11 Ipswich Exiles Reserves	26	7	3	16	44	70	-26	24
12 (R) Leiston St Margarets Res.	26	6	5	15	45	68	-23	23
13 (R) Framlingham Town Res. (-1)	25	7	3	15	53	88	-35	23
14 (R) Saxmundham Sports Res. (-5)	24	7	3	14	43	62	-19	19

SUFFOLK & IPSWICH LEAGUE SENIOR DIVISION CONSTITUTION 2014-15

	Club	Ground	Telephone
1	ACHILLES	Pauls Social Club, Salmet Close, Ipswich IP2 9BA	01473 604 874
2	BRAMFORD UNITED	Acton Road Playing Field, Bramford, Ipswich IP8 4HU	01473 240 425
3	CAPEL PLOUGH	Friars, Capel St Mary, Ipswich IP9 2XS	07816 662 514
4	CLAYDON	Blue Circle Ground, Great Blakenham Ipswich IP6 0JZ	07731 473 958
5	CRANE SPORTS	Gresham Sports & Social Club, Tuddenham Road, Ipswich IP4 3QJ	01473 250 816
6	EAST BERGHOLT UNITED	Gandish Road, East Bergholt, Colchester CO7 6TP	07778 679 967
7	FELIXSTOWE HARPERS UNITED	Trimley Sports & Social Club, High Road, Trimley St Martin, Felixstowe IP11 0QH	01394 275 240
8	GRUNDISBURGH	The Playing Field, Ipswich Road, Grundisburgh, Woodbridge IP13 6TJ	07974 947 221
9	HAUGHLEY UNITED	King George VI Playing Field, Green Road, Haughley IP14 3JY	01449 673 460
10	IPSWICH VALLEY RANGERS	Gainsborough Sports Centre, 5 Braziers Wood, Ipswich IP3 0SP	01473 433 644
11	LEISTON ST MARGARETS	Junction Meadow, Abbey Road, Leiston IP16 4RD	01728 831 239
12	MELTON ST AUDRYS	St Audrys Sports & Social Club, Lodge Farm Lane, Melton, Woodbridge IP12 1LX	01394 389 505
13	STANTON	Stanton Recreation Ground, Old Bury Road, Stanton, Bury St Edmunds IP31 2BX	07515 898 412
14	WENHASTON UNITED	Wenhaston Playing Field, Hall Road, Wenhaston IP19 9EP	07769 613 793
15	WESTERFIELD UNITED	Rushmere Sports Centre, The Street, Rushmere St Andrew, Ipswich IP5 1DE	01473 272 525
16	WICKHAM MARKET	The Playing Field, Wickham Market IP13 0HE	01728 747 303

In: Bramford United (P). Claydon (P). **Out:** Coplestonians (R). Old Newton United (R).

SURREY ELITE INTERMEDIATE LEAGUE

Sponsored by: No Sponsor
Founded: 2008
Recent Champions:
2009: Eversley
2010: Epsom Eagles
2011: Spelthorne Sports
2012: Epsom Athletic
2013: Yateley Green

INTERMEDIATE DIVISION	P	W	D	L	F	A	GD	Pts
1 N P L	30	20	7	3	85	39	46	67
2 Battersea Ironsides	30	22	0	8	84	50	34	66
3 Abbey Rangers (-1)	30	17	9	4	55	35	20	59
4 Yateley United	30	16	7	7	60	41	19	55
5 Horsley (+2)	30	14	8	8	64	38	26	52
6 Ripley Village	30	15	5	10	64	53	11	50
7 Tooting Bec	30	13	9	8	65	47	18	48
8 Virginia Water (-3)	30	16	2	12	74	55	19	47
9 AFC Cubo (+3)	30	11	6	13	51	62	-11	42
10 Merrow	30	10	6	14	60	63	-3	36
11 Reigate Priory (+2)	30	9	6	15	48	76	-28	35
12 Old Farnboronians	30	11	1	18	53	76	-23	34
13 Warlingham	30	10	3	17	63	65	-2	33
14 Bookham (-1)	30	7	7	16	44	67	-23	27
15 Puretown	30	7	3	20	36	73	-37	24
16 Coulsdon Town	30	1	3	26	22	88	-66	6

INTERMEDIATE LEAGUE CHALLENGE CUP

ROUND 1			
Abbey Rangers	v	Pureton	3-0
Ripley Village	v	Warlingham	1-1, 3-4p
Bookham	v	Reigate Priory	7-1
Merrow	v	Old Farnboronians	4-6
Horsley	v	Battersea Ironsides	0-1
Tooting Bec	v	N P L	1-5
AFC Cubo	v	Coulsdon Town	3-2
Virginia Water	v	Yateley United	2-3
Quarter Finals			
Old Farnboronians	v	Bookham	1-2
Yateley United	v	Battersea Ironsides	0-2
Warlingham	v	N P L	AW
Abbey Rangers	v	AFC Cubo	3-0
Semi Finals			
N P L	v	Bookham	2-1
Battersea Ironsides	v	Abbey Rangers	0-1
Final			
Abbey Rangers	v	N P L	2-1

INTERMEDIATE DIVISION	1	2	3	4	5	6	7	8	9	10	11	12	13	14	15	16
1 Abbey Rangers		HW	0-3	5-1	0-0	1-2	3-0	1-1	4-1	1-1	3-3	1-0	3-1	3-2	HW	2-0
2 AFC Cubo	2-2		1-4	4-3	5-1	AW	3-2	1-4	2-1	1-1	1-3	2-1	1-2	0-3	2-1	1-1
3 Battersea Ironsides	3-2	5-2		4-1	3-0	0-2	3-2	4-0	HW	5-1	6-5	4-1	1-2	4-3	3-1	0-4
4 Bookham	0-2	3-1	1-5		AW	1-1	0-2	0-4	2-1	2-0	2-1	2-0	2-3	1-3	4-4	0-1
5 Coulsdon Town	AW	0-2	AW	0-3		AW	1-1	0-5	2-4	0-1	AW	1-7	2-3	3-5	1-6	3-7
6 Horsley	2-4	1-1	4-1	2-2	9-3		1-2	2-2	2-3	4-1	5-0	0-1	1-1	4-4	0-0	1-0
7 Merrow	0-3	1-2	2-0	3-0	8-2	0-8		3-4	3-1	2-1	2-3	2-4	2-1	2-0	1-2	1-4
8 N P L	2-2	2-0	4-2	7-2	HW	0-0	1-1		4-0	3-1	3-3	4-0	2-6	3-1	2-1	6-0
9 Old Farnboronians	1-2	3-4	2-4	3-1	3-1	0-3	1-1	1-4		2-1	2-1	3-4	3-1	2-4	2-1	2-1
10 Puretown	1-2	1-6	2-3	1-3	HW	0-4	5-3	1-6	1-3		2-0	1-3	2-6	0-4	1-2	1-2
11 Reigate Priory	0-1	1-2	0-4	2-2	2-1	2-1	2-2	1-1	0-5	0-2		3-2	2-1	0-3	4-2	2-3
12 Ripley Village	1-1	5-1	3-2	2-0	0-0	0-1	3-3	2-3	4-1	2-0	3-2		1-0	4-2	1-3	3-2
13 Tooting Bec	3-3	2-2	0-2	2-2	2-1	1-2	1-1	2-0	8-1	2-2	4-1	1-1		2-2	3-0	1-1
14 Virginia Water	4-0	4-1	1-2	HW	HW	3-2	0-6	0-1	4-1	1-0	9-2	0-3	1-2		3-1	0-2
15 Warlingham	0-3	4-0	0-5	3-3	7-0	4-0	2-1	2-4	5-1	1-3	1-2	6-1	1-2	1-6		1-2
16 Yateley United	1-1	1-1	4-2	1-1	5-0	1-0	2-1	0-3	2-0	0-2	1-1	2-2	2-0	3-2	5-1	

SURREY ELITE INTERMEDIATE LEAGUE INTERMEDIATE DIVISION CONSTITUTION 2014-15

1	ABBEY RANGERS	Addlestone Moor, Addlestone Moor Road, Addlestone KT15 2QH	01932 442 962
2	AFC CUBO	Barn Elms Sports Ground, Queen Elizabeth Walk, Barnes SW13 0DG	020 8876 9873
3	AFC SPELTHORNE SPORTS	296 Staines Road West, Ahford Common, Ashford TW15 1RY	
4	BALHAM	Wimbledon Extension, Off Robin Hood Way, Kingston Vale SW15	
5	BATTERSEA IRONSIDES	Battersea Ironsides S&S Club, Burntwood Lane, Earlsfield SW17 0AW	020 8874 9913
6	HORSLEY	Toms Field, Long Reach, West Horsley KT14 6PG	01483 282 516
7	MERROW	The Urnfield, Downside Road, Guildford, Surrey, GU4 8PH	n/a
8	NPL	NPL Sports Club, Queens Road, Teddington, TW11 0LW	n/a
9	OLD FARNBORONIANS	Cody S&S Club, Armstrong Way, The Fairway, Farnborough GU14 0LP	01252 543 009
10	PROJECT CLAPHAM	Denning Mews, Clapham, SW12 8QT	07921 639 136
11	REIGATE PRIORY	Reigate Priory Cricket Club, off Park Lane, Reigate RH2 8JX	01737 240 872
12	RIPLEY VILLAGE	The Green, Ripley, Woking GU23 6AN	01483 225 484
13	TOOTING BEC	Raynes Park Sports Ground, Taunton Avenue SW20 0BH	n/a
14	VIRGINIA WATER	The Timbers, Crown Road, Virginia Water GU25 4HS	01344 843 811
15	WARLINGHAM	Verdayne Sports Ground, Warlingham, Surrey	020 8660 5491
16	YATELEY UNITED	Chandlers Lane, Yateley, Hampshire GU46 7SZ	n/a

In: AFC Spelthorne Sports (P - Surrey County Intermediate League (Western) Prem). Balham (P - Surrey South Eastern Combination Intermediate Div.1). Project Clapham (P - Surrey South Eastern Combination Intermediate Div.1).
Out: Bookham (R - Surrey South Eastern Combination Intermediate Div.1). Puretown. Coulsdon Town.

TEESSIDE LEAGUE

Sponsored by: Jack Hatfield Sports
Founded: 1891
Recent Champions: 2009: BEADS FC. 2010: BEADS FC. 2011: Grangetown Boys Club. 2012: Richmond Town. 2013: Endeavor

DIVISION ONE	P	W	D	L	F	A	GD	Pts
1 Whinney Banks Youth & CC	24	20	3	1	110	36	74	63
2 Acklam Steelworks	24	20	2	2	105	27	78	62
3 Northallerton Town Reserves	24	14	5	5	93	51	42	47
4 Thornaby Dubliners	24	13	4	7	64	46	18	43
5 Grangetown Boys Club	24	11	4	9	71	64	7	37
6 Beechwood, Eastside & DS	24	10	5	9	58	46	12	35
7 Fishburn Park	24	9	4	11	58	62	-4	31
8 Lingdale	24	10	0	14	74	72	2	30
9 Richmond Mavericks	24	8	5	11	52	74	-22	29
10 Redcar Newmarket	24	8	2	14	47	66	-19	26
11 Great Ayton United	24	5	5	14	34	79	-45	20
12 Nunthorpe Athletic	24	5	2	17	36	94	-58	17
13 North Ormesby	24	2	1	21	36	121	-85	7

DIVISION TWO	P	W	D	L	F	A	GD	Pts
1 (P) Thirsk Falcons	22	16	3	3	82	27	55	51
2 (P) Stockton West End	22	15	2	5	101	41	60	47
3 (P) New Marske	22	14	3	5	62	36	26	45
4 Loftus Athletic	22	12	3	7	61	49	12	39
5 Guisborough Globe	22	10	6	6	52	42	10	36
6 Billingham Synthonia Reserves	22	12	0	10	57	52	5	36
7 Richmond Town Reserves	22	10	2	10	44	46	-2	32
8 Yarm	22	8	2	12	37	53	-16	26
9 Cargo Fleet	22	7	1	14	45	88	-43	22
10 Kader	22	6	2	14	39	65	-26	20
11 St Mary's College	22	5	4	13	41	70	-29	19
12 Billingham T Intermediates	22	2	2	18	36	88	-52	8

Billingham Athletic record expunged

DIVISION ONE	1	2	3	4	5	6	7	8	9	10	11	12	13
1 Acklam Steelworks		4-3	2-0	8-1	3-0	10-3	6-0	5-0	9-1	4-2	4-0	1-2	1-2
2 BEADS	1-4		0-1	0-0	4-2	4-2	6-1	1-3	4-0	2-3	6-2	1-2	3-3
3 Fishburn Park	0-2	2-2		4-1	4-1	1-6	6-3	0-3	6-2	0-1	3-1	5-1	4-3
4 Grangetown BC	1-3	3-2	5-2		3-2	8-6	3-2	1-2	1-3	3-0	2-2	3-5	2-4
5 Great Ayton United	0-8	2-1	3-3	3-3		1-7	4-0	2-2	4-0	1-5	0-2	3-3	0-1
6 Lingdale	0-3	1-3	5-2	2-3	1-2		3-0	1-2	7-1	3-1	1-3	0-2	1-5
7 North Ormesby	1-3	2-3	1-4	0-10	1-2	2-8		3-13	2-2	1-3	3-2	3-4	1-12
8 Northallerton Town Reserves	2-6	1-1	6-2	3-3	11-0	5-3	3-4		7-0	3-1	6-3	1-1	3-3
9 Nunthorpe Athletic	0-5	0-4	2-2	3-8	2-0	2-4	4-1	1-2		0-2	4-0	0-3	2-7
10 Redcar Newmarket	2-7	1-2	3-2	1-3	1-1	4-3	4-2	2-4	2-3		2-4	2-2	3-6
11 Richmond Mavericks	1-1	2-2	3-3	2-4	4-1	1-2	5-2	1-8	5-2	2-1		3-3	0-9
12 Thornaby Dubliners	3-4	1-2	3-1	2-0	3-0	0-3	8-1	3-1	3-2	4-0	1-2		1-3
13 Whinney Banks YCC	2-2	4-1	3-1	3-0	7-0	7-2	3-0	4-2	6-0	4-1	4-2	5-4	

TEESSIDE LEAGUE DIVISION ONE CONSTITUTION 2014-15

	Club	Ground
1	BEADS FC	Beechwood & Easterside Social Club, Marton Road, Middlesbrough TS4 3PP
2	FISHBURN PARK	Eskdale School, Broomfield Park, Whitby, N Yorkshire YO22 4EB
3	GRANGETOWN BOYS CLUB	Grangetown Youth & Community Centre 1,Trunk Road, Grangetown, Middlesbrough TS6 7HP
4	GREAT AYTON UNITED	Great Ayton Sports Club, Leven Park, Easby Lane, Great Ayton, Middlesbrough TS9 6JJ
5	LINGDALE FC	The Track, Lingdale Playing Field, Lingdale TS12 3DW
6	NEW MARSKE	New Marske Social Club, Gurney Street, New Marske, Redcar TS11 8AN
7	NORTH ORMESBY	Unity City Academy, Ormesby Road, Middlesbrough TS3 7AL
8	NORTHALLERTON TOWN	Regencey Stadium, Ainderby Road, Romanby, Northallerton DL7 8HA
9	NUNTHORPE ATHLETIC	Nunthorpe Recreation Club, Guisborough Road, Nunthorpe, Middlesbrough TS7 0LE
10	REDCAR NEWMARKET	Rye Hill School, Redcar Lane, Redcar TS10 2HN
11	RICHMOND MAVERICKS	Richmond School, Darlington Road, Richmond DL10 7BQ
12	STOCKTON WEST END	North Shore Health Academy, Talbot Street, Stockton TS20 2AY
13	THIRSK FALCONS	Flatts Playimg Fields, Chapel Street, Thirsk
14	THORNABY DUBLINERS	Harold Wilson Sports Complex, Bader Avenue, Thornaby TS17 8PH
15	WHINNEY BANKS YCC	Outwood Academy, Hall Drive, Middlesbrough TS5 7JX

In: New Marske (P). Stockton West End (P). Thirsk Falcons (P).
Out: Acklam Steelworks (E). Hemlington Smithy (W).

THAMES VALLEY PREMIER LEAGUE

Formerly the Reading Football League > 2014
Founded: 1988
Recent Champions:
2009: Woodley Town
2010: Reading YMCA
2011: Highmoor Ibis
2012: South Reading
2013: Reading YMCA

SENIOR DIVISION	P	W	D	L	F	A	GD	Pts
1 Highmoor Ibis Reserves	22	16	2	4	55	24	31	50
2 Reading YMCA	22	15	4	3	70	25	45	49
3 Marlow United	22	14	2	6	62	25	37	44
4 Woodcote Stoke Row	22	12	1	9	53	46	7	37
5 Sandhurst Devels	22	9	2	11	41	42	-1	29
6 Taplow United	22	9	2	11	39	47	-8	29
7 Mortimer	22	8	4	10	31	45	-14	28
8 Cookham Dean	22	7	6	9	34	36	-2	27
9 Rotherfield United	22	8	3	11	23	36	-13	27
10 Bracknell Rovers	22	7	2	13	35	60	-25	23
11 (R) Frilsham & Yattendon	22	5	3	14	34	68	-34	18
12 Wraysbury Village (-3)	22	4	5	13	30	53	-23	14
Newbury FC Reserves (F)								

SENIOR CUP

ROUND 1

Unity	v	Wraysbury Village	3-0
Frilsham & Yattendon	v	Woodcote Stoke Row	2-3
Newbury FC	v	Sandhurst Devels	AW
Highmoor Ibis Reserves	v	Reading YMCA	2-3
Mortimer	v	Barton Rovers	HW

ROUND 2

Unity	v	Rotherfield United	0-1
Woodcote Stoke Row	v	Bracknell Rovers	4-0
Hurst	v	AFC Corinthians	2-1
Woodley Town Reserves	v	Westwood United	0-5
Cookham Dean	v	Marlow United	1-2
R.E.M.E. Arborfield	v	Taplow United	0-1
Ashridge Park	v	Sandhurst Devels	3-4
Reading YMCA	v	Mortimer	3-1

QUARTER FINALS

Rotherfield United	v	Woodcote Stoke Row	2-2, 3-5p
Hurst	v	Westwood United	0-2
Marlow United	v	Taplow United	1-1, 4-5
Sandhurst Devels	v	Reading YMCA	1-3

SEMI FINALS

Woodcote Stoke Row	v	Westwood United	4-1
Taplow United	v	Reading YMCA	2-5

FINAL

Woodcote Stoke Row	v	Reading YMCA	4-7

SENIOR DIVISION	1	2	3	4	5	6	7	8	9	10	11	12
1 Bracknell Rovers		2-1	3-1	1-2	0-2	1-2	3-2	3-2	0-3	2-3	2-5	2-2
2 Cookham Dean	3-0		1-1	1-3	0-3	4-0	0-0	1-1	3-1	1-0	1-2	H-W
3 Frilsham & Yattendon	3-2	2-2		0-2	4-1	2-3	2-6	0-1	4-3	1-2	4-1	1-3
4 Highmoor Ibis Reserves	6-0	6-4	2-1		2-1	5-0	1-3	2-3	2-0	4-0	6-1	H-W
5 Marlow United	6-0	0-2	10-0	1-1		5-0	1-2	3-0	2-2	1-3	2-1	H-W
6 Mortimer	3-3	2-1	1-1	0-2	1-2		1-1	0-0	3-2	3-1	0-3	1-2
7 Reading YMCA	6-1	3-1	7-0	2-3	2-4	2-0		3-0	5-0	0-0	6-0	7-1
8 Rotherfield United	3-2	0-1	2-3	1-0	1-0	0-1	1-2		2-0	0-1	2-1	0-0
9 Sandhurst Devels	0-3	1-1	5-0	1-2	1-2	3-2	2-3	3-0		3-1	3-2	3-0
10 Taplow United	4-1	4-2	2-0	2-0	0-3	2-4	2-4	4-0	0-2		2-4	3-3
11 Woodcote Stoke Row	0-1	3-2	5-1	1-1	3-4	2-1	0-2	5-2	4-1	4-2		3-0
12 Wraysbury Village	1-3	2-2	4-3	1-3	0-9	1-3	2-2	1-2	1-2	5-1	1-3	

THAMES VALLEY PREMIER LEAGUE SENIOR DIVISION CONSTITUTION 2014-15

1	AFC ALDERMASTON	AWE, Aldermaston, Berkshire RG7 4PR	
2	BRACKNELL ROVERS	John Nike Stadium, Bagshot Road, Bracknell, Berkshire RG12 9SE	07584 161621
3	COOKHAM DEAN	Alfred Major Roo Ground, Hillcrest Avenue, Cookham Rise , Maidenhead SL6 9NB	01628 819423
4	HIGHMOOR-IBIS RESERVES	Palmer Park Stadium, Wokingham Road, Reading RG6 1LF	01189 375 080
5	HURST	Cantley Park, Wokingham	
6	MARLOW UNITED	Bisham Abbey National Sports Centre, Abbey Way, Marlow, Bucks SL7 1RR	None
7	MORTIMER	Alfred Palmer Memorial PF, West End Road, Mortimer, Reading RG7 3TW	07770860301
8	READING YMCA	Padworth Village Hall, Padworth, Reading, Berkshire RG7 4HY	07917 571835
9	ROTHERFIELD UNITED	Bishopswood Sports Ground, Horsepond Rd, Gallowstree Common RG4 9BT	0845 094 1206
10	SANDHURST DEVELS	Sandhurst Memorial Ground, York Town Road, Sandhurst GU47 9BJ	07799067751
11	TAPLOW UNITED	Stanley Jones Field, Berry Hill, Taplow SL6 0DA	01628 621745
12	UNITY	Cintra Park, Cintra Avenue, Reading RG2 7AU	
13	WOODCOTE & STOKE ROW	Woodcote Recreation Ground, Woodcote, Reading RG8 0QY	0118 9471376
14	WRAYSBURY VILLAGE	Wraysbury village	

In: AFC Aldermaston (S - Hampshire League). Hurst (P). Unity (P).
Out: Frilsham & Yattendon (R). Newbury FC Reserves (F - Sept 2013).

THAMES VALLEY LEAGUE - STEP 7

DIVISION ONE	P	W	D	L	F	A	GD	Pts
1 (P) Unity (-4)	18	14	3	1	40	18	22	41
2 Westwood United	18	12	3	3	60	18	42	39
3 (P) Hurst	18	11	1	6	47	33	14	34
4 R.E.M.E Arborfield (-3)	18	10	0	8	32	23	9	27
5 AFC Corinthians (-3)	18	8	2	8	36	31	5	23
6 Woodley Town Reserves	18	6	3	9	27	40	-13	21
7 Highmoor Ibis ""A""	18	6	2	10	28	40	-12	20
8 Ashridge Park	18	5	1	12	29	46	-17	16
9 Sandhurst Devels Reserves	18	4	3	11	17	44	-27	15
10 Cookham Dean Reserves (-3)	18	3	4	11	19	42	-23	10

DIVISION TWO	P	W	D	L	F	A	GD	Pts
1 (P) Sonning	21	16	4	1	62	23	39	52
2 (P) Woodley Hammers	22	14	5	3	86	40	46	47
3 (P) Winnersh Rangers	22	12	3	7	61	44	17	39
4 Reading YMCA Rapids	22	11	5	6	53	37	16	38
5 Wargrave	21	10	3	8	49	38	11	33
6 Taplow United Reserves	22	10	3	9	43	54	-11	33
7 Pinewood	22	9	4	9	49	42	7	31
8 Berkshire United (-3)	22	10	3	9	75	73	2	30
9 Goring United	22	5	4	13	28	56	-28	19
10 Mortimer Reserves	22	5	3	14	35	50	-15	18
11 Westwood United Reserves	22	4	3	15	31	59	-28	15
12 (R) Woodley Town ""A""	22	4	2	16	30	86	-56	14

DIVISION THREE	P	W	D	L	F	A	GD	Pts
1 (P) Compton	16	13	1	2	59	12	47	40
2 (P) Eldon Celtic (-3)	16	12	3	1	53	29	24	36
3 (P) Wokingham & Emmbrook "A"	16	10	0	6	40	25	15	30
4 Baughurst AFC	16	9	2	5	29	24	5	29
5 Marlow United Reserves (-1)	16	8	3	5	35	18	17	26
6 Twyford & Ruscombe	16	4	5	7	30	29	1	17
7 Woodcote Stoke Row Res	16	3	2	11	17	38	-21	11
8 Theale	16	2	1	13	12	55	-43	7
9 (R) Goring Utd Reserves	16	2	1	13	22	67	-45	7

DIVISION FOUR	P	W	D	L	F	A	GD	Pts
1 (P) White Eagles	18	16	0	2	82	18	64	48
2 (P) Barkham Athletic	18	14	1	3	98	39	59	43
3 (P) S.R.C.C.	18	12	2	4	57	30	27	38
4 Unity Reserves (-3)	18	10	2	6	50	23	27	29
5 Rotherfield United Reserves	18	9	2	7	40	30	10	29
6 Woodley Hammers Reserves	18	8	1	9	39	37	2	25
7 AFC Corinthians Reserves	18	6	2	10	50	82	-32	20
8 "Sonning ""A""	18	4	1	13	34	78	-44	13
9 Hurst Reserves	18	3	0	15	27	76	-49	9
10 (R) Sonning Sports	18	2	1	15	18	82	-64	7

DIVISION FIVE	P	W	D	L	F	A	GD	Pts
1 (P) Shinfield	18	15	0	3	65	19	46	45
2 (P) Highmoor Ibis ""B""	18	13	0	5	66	32	34	39
3 (P) Wargrave Reserves	18	11	2	5	68	34	34	35
4 Bracknell Rovers Reserves	18	10	2	6	37	38	-1	32
5 Woodley Town ""B""	18	9	4	5	31	29	2	31
6 Baughurst AFC Reserves (-3)	18	9	0	9	47	42	5	24
7 FC Reading Dons	18	8	0	10	38	41	-3	24
8 AFC Corinthians ""A""	18	5	1	12	24	45	-21	16
9 Taplow United ""A""	18	3	0	15	14	70	-56	9
10 The Hop Leaf	18	2	1	15	24	64	-40	7

INTERMEDIATE CUP (FROM THE QUARTER FINALS)

QUARTER FINALS

Pinewood	v	Woodley Hammers	1-3
Sonning	v	Woodley Town A	4-0
Eldon Celtic	v	Wargrave	4-3
Reading YMCA Rapids	v	Compton	0-4

SEMI FINALS

Woodley Hammers	v	Sonning	4-1
Eldon Celtic	v	Compton	3-1

FINAL

Woodley Hammers	v	Eldon Celtic	4-0

WEARSIDE LEAGUE

Sponsored by: No Sponsor
Founded: 1892
Recent Champions:
2009: Newton Aycliffe
2010: Ryhope Colliery Welfare
2011: Ryhope Colliery Welfare
2012: Stockton Town
2013: Stockton Town

		P	W	D	L	F	A	GD	Pts
1	Stockton Town	38	34	2	2	129	28	101	104
2	(P) Ryhope CW	38	30	5	3	132	26	106	95
3	Redcar Athletic	38	27	3	8	103	54	49	84
4	Cleator Moor Celtic	38	25	4	9	100	47	53	79
5	Richmond Town	38	22	8	8	108	55	53	74
6	Easington Colliery AFC	38	19	3	16	104	76	28	60
7	Seaton Carew	38	17	6	15	90	78	12	57
8	Silksworth Colliery Welfare	38	16	7	15	64	64	0	55
9	Sunderland West End	38	16	7	15	71	82	-11	55
10	Jarrow	38	15	7	16	75	82	-7	52
11	Horden CW	38	16	4	18	78	90	-12	52
12	Ashbrooke Belford House	38	14	7	17	94	98	-4	49
13	Annfield Plain	38	13	7	18	73	92	-19	46
14	Wolviston	38	12	9	17	67	70	-3	45
15	Harton and Westoe CW	38	10	9	19	67	111	-44	39
16	Prudhoe Town	38	9	7	22	60	109	-49	34
17	Hartlepool	38	8	4	26	58	109	-51	28
18	Coxhoe Athletic	38	6	7	25	47	118	-71	25
19	Boldon CA	38	7	3	28	35	120	-85	24
20	Gateshead Leam Rangers	38	4	11	23	48	94	-46	23

LEAGUE CUP

FINAL
Ashbrooke Belford House v Redcar Athletic 3-2

MONKWEARMOUTH CHARITY CUP

FINAL
Ryhope CW v Stockton Town 2-0

SUNDERLAND SHIPOWNERS CUP

FINAL
Easington Colliery AFC v Ashbrooke Belford House 5-3

	1	2	3	4	5	6	7	8	9	10	11	12	13	14	15	16	17	18	19	20
1 Annfield Plain		2-3	5-2	1-4	3-0	0-2	2-1	6-1	2-3	2-3	0-4	6-1	1-2	2-2	0-1	3-2	2-1	0-4	2-2	2-3
2 Ashbrooke Belford House	3-2		1-2	5-3	4-0	1-2	1-1	5-1	2-6	10-3	0-3	1-1	1-7	1-5	1-3	6-1	5-1	0-2	1-2	3-2
3 Boldon CA	0-2	0-3		1-6	3-2	2-1	2-2	1-5	1-1	0-2	4-3	1-3	1-2	3-6	0-5	0-4	0-4	0-4	0-2	0-6
4 Cleator Moor Celtic	5-1	3-0	4-0		5-0	4-1	0-0	2-1	6-0	7-0	2-1	3-1	3-1	1-0	2-5	2-0	1-0	1-1	1-1	1-4
5 Coxhoe Athletic	0-2	0-0	0-3	0-3		1-7	3-2	4-3	1-1	2-5	4-1	5-1	2-2	1-4	1-4	1-4	2-1	2-7	1-2	0-6
6 Easington Colliery AFC	5-1	1-2	1-0	0-3	8-0		3-1	7-0	0-2	3-0	3-4	10-0	3-2	2-2	0-2	2-1	2-2	3-2	1-3	0-3
7 Gateshead Leam Rangers	0-1	1-5	1-1	2-3	1-1	3-4		3-2	1-1	1-2	1-2	1-1	0-2	0-3	1-3	2-1	0-1	1-5	1-1	4-3
8 Hartlepool	1-1	2-3	4-2	1-3	1-0	1-4	3-1		1-1	3-3	0-2	2-3	1-2	1-4	0-1	2-1	1-2	1-4	0-2	1-1
9 Harton and Westoe CW	1-1	6-6	4-0	0-3	2-2	0-5	5-3	2-5		2-4	0-3	1-2	2-2	2-3	1-4	3-3	0-2	2-3	3-1	2-5
10 Horden CW	2-3	2-2	1-2	2-5	5-0	1-6	3-0	2-1	10-2		2-1	3-0	1-3	0-2	1-1	5-2	1-2	0-3	3-0	1-1
11 Jarrow	1-1	4-2	5-1	2-2	3-1	1-4	6-0	3-0	0-1	0-2		5-0	2-3	2-2	0-4	2-2	3-2	0-4	3-3	1-1
12 Prudhoe Town	3-3	2-2	6-1	1-2	3-2	3-3	4-1	2-4	4-5	5-1	1-2		1-6	2-0	0-3	2-4	1-2	0-2	1-2	1-1
13 Redcar Athletic	2-6	2-1	4-0	1-0	2-1	3-1	3-2	5-1	1-2	3-1	5-1	0-0		5-2	0-1	1-3	6-0	0-3	3-2	4-0
14 Richmond Town	6-0	5-1	4-0	3-0	5-1	3-5	4-0	5-0	3-1	3-1	5-1	6-0	0-4		1-1	1-2	1-1	1-4	0-0	1-2
15 Ryhope CW	5-0	2-2	3-0	3-0	7-1	6-1	1-1	6-0	6-0	2-0	3-0	6-0	0-1	1-1		2-0	1-3	0-2	7-0	6-1
16 Seaton Carew	3-0	2-4	1-0	4-2	2-1	4-2	3-3	6-0	4-0	2-4	1-1	5-0	3-5	1-2	1-4		3-1	0-5	1-5	2-2
17 Silksworth Colliery Welfare	2-2	4-2	2-0	0-2	2-2	4-0	2-1	6-1	2-1	2-0	1-1	2-0	2-3	0-0	2-6	1-4		1-5	4-1	0-0
18 Stockton Town	6-1	3-0	7-0	2-1	3-0	4-1	3-0	1-0	8-0	3-0	6-0	3-2	1-0	6-2	1-5	1-1	2-0		2-0	3-1
19 Sunderland West End	5-3	5-4	1-2	1-3	0-2	2-1	2-3	3-2	1-0	1-2	5-1	3-2	2-4	2-6	0-6	1-1	1-0	2-3		2-2
20 Wolviston	0-1	5-1	3-0	0-3	1-1	3-0	2-2	0-5	1-2	3-0	1-2	0-1	1-2	0-4	0-5	1-3	1-0	0-1	1-3	

WEARSIDE LEAGUE CONSTITUTION 2014-15

1	ANNFIELD PLAIN	Derwent Park , West Road , Annfield Plain DH9 8PZ	07833 366 056
2	ASHBROOKE BELFORD HOUSE	Silksworth Park, Blind Lane, Silksworth, Sunderland SR3 1AX	07505 503873
3	BOLDON COMMUNITY ASSOCIATION	Boldon Welfare, New Road, Boldon Colliery NE35 9DS	0191 536 4180 (Cricket Club)
4	CLEATOR MOOR CELTIC	Celtic Club, Birks Road, Cleator Moor CA25 5HR	01946 812476
5	COXHOE ATHLETIC	Beechfield Park, Coxhoe DH6 4SD	07956 159916
6	DARLINGTON CLEVELAND BRIDGE	Eastbourne Sports Complex, Bourne Avenue, Darlington DL1 1LJ	01325 243177/243188
7	EASINGTON COLLIERY AFC	Easington Welfare Park SR8 3JJ	07720 611905
8	GATESHEAD LEAM RANGERS	Dawdon Welfare Park, Green Drive, Dawdon, Seaham SR7 7XL	07859 000402
9	HARTLEPOOL	Grayfields Enclose, Jesmond Gardens, Hartlepool TS24 8QS	01429 299428
10	HARTON AND WESTOE	Harton Colliery Welfare, Boldon Lane. NE34 ONA	07847 271495
11	JARROW	Perth Green Community Assoc., Inverness Road, Jarrow NE32 4AQ	0191 489 3743
12	PRUDHOE TOWN	Kimberley Park, Broomhouse Road, Prudhoe NE42 5EH	01661 835900
13	REDCAR ATHLETIC	Green Lane, Redcar TS10 3RW	07854 935380
14	RICHMOND TOWN	Earls Orchard Playing Field. DL10 4RH	07970 789526
15	SEATON CAREW	Hornby Park, Elizabeth Way, Seaton Carew. TS25 2AZ	07877 077515
16	SILKSWORTH RANGERS	Silksworth Park, Blind Lane, Silksworth, Sunderland SR3 1AX	07423 014566
17	STOCKTON TOWN	Bishopton Road West, Stockton-on-Tees TS19 0QD	07832 967008
18	SUNDERLAND WEST END	Ford Quarry, Keelmans Lane, Pennywell, Sunderland	07812 439248
19	WHITEHAVEN	Focus Scaffolding Sports Complex, Coach Road, Whitehaven, CA28 9DB	01946 692 211
20	WOLVISTON	Metcalfe Park, Wynyard Road, Wolviston, Billingham TS22 5NE	07768 321651

In: Whitehaven (R - Northern League Div.2).
Out: Ryhope C.W. (R - Northern League Div.2).

WEST CHESHIRE LEAGUE

Sponsored by: Carlsberg
Founded: 1892
Recent Champions:
2009: West Kirby
2010: Cammell Laird Reserves
2011: West Kirby
2012: Ashville
2013: Maghull

DIVISION ONE	P	W	D	L	F	A	GD	Pts
1 Maghull	30	25	1	4	83	32	51	76
2 Hale	30	19	4	7	92	45	47	61
3 Ashville	30	17	4	9	53	38	15	55
4 South Liverpool	30	16	6	8	75	55	20	54
5 Chester Nomads	30	13	5	12	53	49	4	44
6 Mallaby	30	13	3	14	49	41	8	42
7 Cammell Laird Reserves	30	12	6	12	66	63	3	42
8 Mossley Hill Athletic	30	12	5	13	46	48	-2	41
9 Newton	30	11	8	11	47	50	-3	41
10 Vauxhall Motors	30	12	4	14	54	49	5	40
11 West Kirby	30	9	7	14	44	57	-13	34
12 Blacon Youth Club	30	9	6	15	42	76	-34	33
13 Christleton	30	8	8	14	39	51	-12	32
14 Southport Trinity	30	9	4	17	40	60	-20	31
15 (R) Upton A.A.	30	8	7	15	34	62	-28	31
16 (R) Heswell	30	6	4	20	37	78	-41	22

PYKE CUP

ROUND 1

Heswall	v	West Kirby	1-5
Ashville	v	Maghull	2-1
Mallaby	v	Chester Nomads	2-0
Vauxhall Motors Reserves	v	South Liverpool	4-1
Newton	v	Blacon Youth Club	10-7
Cammell Laird Reserves	v	Upton A.A.	7-0
Mossley Hill Athletic	v	Southport Trinity	3-0
Christleton	v	Hale	0-2

QUARTER FINALS

West Kirby	v	Ashville	1-3
Mallaby	v	Vauxhall Motors Reserves	0-1
Newton	v	Cammell Laird Reserves	2-1
Mossley Hill Athletic	v	Hales	2-0

SEMI FINALS

Ashville	v	Vauxhall Motors Reserves	2-0
Newton	v	Mossley Hill Athletic	2-1

FINAL

Ashville	v	Newton	3-2

DIVISION ONE	1	2	3	4	5	6	7	8	9	10	11	12	13	14	15	16
1 Ashville		3-2	2-2	1-0	3-0	2-0	2-1	1-0	4-0	4-0	1-1	0-2	1-0	4-2	1-1	1-1
2 Blacon Youth Club	0-2		1-2	1-1	0-0	0-0	3-2	2-5	1-3	0-3	2-2	0-6	3-1	0-2	2-2	2-1
3 Cammell Laird Reserves	1-2	4-1		2-0	0-3	3-5	7-1	2-5	2-0	1-1	3-3	5-2	2-1	5-1	0-3	1-1
4 Chester Nomads	1-0	2-3	4-0		3-0	2-5	0-2	0-7	3-2	7-1	2-2	3-0	2-1	1-0	3-0	1-2
5 Christleton	1-0	2-2	0-2	2-1		3-4	1-0	1-0	0-1	0-0	6-0	1-2	1-2	0-0	2-3	0-2
6 Hale	1-2	6-0	7-2	3-1	1-1		7-1	2-3	4-1	2-1	1-2	0-2	6-0	1-1	4-1	5-3
7 Heswell	2-4	0-2	0-5	2-0	2-2	1-2		1-3	1-1	1-4	3-2	1-1	0-0	3-2	1-0	2-3
8 Maghull	4-1	1-3	4-3	2-0	4-1	3-2	2-1		4-2	1-1	1-0	4-0	2-1	2-0	4-0	2-1
9 Mallaby	2-1	5-1	2-1	0-1	2-0	0-1	4-1	0-1		0-1	1-2	4-3	8-0	3-0	1-2	3-0
10 Mossley Hill Athletic	0-2	1-2	1-0	2-4	3-1	2-1	6-1	1-0	1-0		5-1	2-3	3-1	2-3	0-3	1-2
11 Newton	3-1	0-2	1-3	1-1	5-0	0-2	2-5	0-3	0-1	1-0		3-0	1-2	2-0	1-0	1-1
12 South Liverpool	3-5	3-1	2-2	2-4	3-1	3-3	2-1	1-3	3-0	3-0	1-1		2-1	5-0	2-2	3-3
13 Southport Trinity	3-0	2-3	4-0	2-2	2-2	1-5	3-0	1-2	2-0	2-1	0-4	3-4		1-0	1-3	1-1
14 Upton A.A.	1-0	3-1	1-1	1-1	2-4	0-4	2-1	3-4	0-0	1-1	1-1	1-7	1-0		3-1	2-5
15 Vauxhall Motors	3-1	8-1	4-1	0-1	1-1	3-4	5-0	1-3	0-2	1-2	1-2	0-2	0-2	2-0		2-1
16 West Kirby	1-2	4-1	1-4	3-2	1-3	1-4	1-0	0-4	1-1	0-0	1-3	1-3	1-0	0-1	1-2	

WEST CHESHIRE LEAGUE DIVISION ONE CONSTITUTION 2014-15

1 ASHVILLE	Villa Park, Cross Lane, Wallasey Village, Wallasey CH45 8RH
2 BLACON YOUTH CLUB	Cairns Crescent Playing Fields, Blacon, Chester CH1 5JG
3 CAMMELL LAIRD RESERVES	MBS Stadium, St Peters Road, Rock Ferry, Wirral CH42 1PY
4 CAPENHURST VILLA	Capenhurst Sports Ground, Capenhurst, South Wirral
5 CHESTER NOMADS	Boughton Hall Cricket Club, Boughton, Chester, CH3 5EL
6 CHRISTLETON	Little Heath Road, Christleton, Chester CH3 7AH
7 HALE	Hale Park, The High Street, Hale Village, Liverpool L24 4AX
8 HELSBY	Helsby Sports & Social club, Helsby, Cheshire
9 MAGHULL	Old Hall Field, Hall Lane, Maghull L31 7DY
10 MALLABY	Groves Sports Ground, Chester Road, Whitby, Ellesmere Port CH66 2NX
11 MOSSLEY HILL ATHLETIC	Mossley Hill Athletic Club, Mossley Hill Road, Liverpool L18 8BX
12 NEWTON	Millcroft, Frankby Road, Greasby CH49 3PE
13 SOUTH LIVERPOOL	North Field, Jericho Lane, Aigburth, Liverpool L17 5AR
14 SOUTHPORT TRINITY	JMO Sports Park, Blaguegate Playing Fields, Liverpool Road, Skelmersdale WN8 8BX
15 VAUXHALL MOTORS	Vauxhall Sports Ground, Rivacre Road, Hooton, Ellesmere Port CH66 1NJ 0151 328 1114 Clubhouse: 0151 327 2294
16 WEST KIRBY	Marine Park, Greenbank Road, West Kirby CH48 5HL

In: Capenhurst Villa (P). Helsby (P). Vauxhall Motors take the place of Vauxhall Motors Reserves.
Out: Heswell (R). Upton Athletic Association (R). Vauxhall Motors Reserves drop to Division 2 to make way for Vauxhall Motors.

DIVISION TWO	P	W	D	L	F	A	GD	Pts
1 (P) Capenhurst Villa	30	24	5	1	96	25	71	77
2 (P) Helsby	30	20	5	5	77	41	36	65
3 Richmond Mags	30	19	2	9	106	45	61	59
4 Gateacre Village	30	17	4	9	79	50	29	55
5 Manor Athletic	30	16	4	10	59	37	22	52
6 Maghull Reserves	30	15	4	11	73	52	21	49
7 Prescot Cables Reserves	30	13	4	13	73	70	3	43
8 Afc Bebington Athletic	30	14	1	15	49	60	-11	43
9 Marshalls	30	12	6	12	57	56	1	42
10 Heswall Reserves	30	13	2	15	57	65	-8	41
11 Redgate Rovers	30	10	8	12	69	69	0	38
12 Ashville Reserves (-3)	30	12	5	13	51	55	-4	38
13 Mossley Hill Athletic Reserves	30	9	9	12	54	77	-23	36
14 Willaston	30	6	3	21	58	81	-23	21
15 West Kirby Reserves (-3)	30	5	6	19	42	93	-51	18
16 (R) Mersey Royal	30	0	2	28	23	147	-124	2

DIVISION THREE	P	W	D	L	F	A	GD	Pts
1 (P) Rainhill Town	28	22	5	1	121	19	102	71
2 (P) Hales Reserves	28	20	4	4	74	40	34	64
3 South Liverpool Reserves	28	19	1	8	90	45	45	58
4 St Helens Town Reserves	28	17	5	6	64	35	29	56
5 Ford Motors	28	15	5	8	60	37	23	50
6 Capenhurst Villa Reserves	28	15	3	10	66	52	14	48
7 Bootle Reserves	28	13	5	10	56	53	3	44
8 Kirby Town Railway	28	11	10	7	83	54	29	43
9 Widnes Vikings Reserves	28	11	7	10	51	66	-15	40
10 Chester Nomads Reserves	28	10	4	14	50	63	-13	34
11 Belfry	28	7	6	15	50	89	-39	27
12 Neston Nomads	28	6	4	18	39	77	-38	22
13 Marshalls Reserves (-3)	28	5	3	20	55	97	-42	15
14 Christleton Reserves (-3)	28	4	4	20	29	78	-49	13
15 Upton A.A. Reserves (-6)	28	1	2	25	26	109	-83	-1

Mersey Police withdrew - record expumged.

WEST LANCASHIRE LEAGUE

Sponsored by: Bay Radio
Founded: 1904
Recent Champions:
2009: Charnock Richard. 2010: Blackpool Wren Rovers.
2011: Blackpool Wren Rovers. 2012: Charnock Richard.
2013: Charnock Richard.

PREMIER DIVISION	P	W	D	L	F	A	GD	Pts
1 Charnock Richard	30	23	3	4	82	32	50	72
2 Blackpool Wren Rovers	30	15	9	6	79	41	38	54
3 Fleetwood Hesketh	30	16	4	10	60	49	11	52
4 Eagley (-3)	30	16	2	12	61	53	8	47
5 Crookland Casuals	30	13	5	12	53	49	4	44
6 Thornton Cleveleys	30	13	5	12	53	55	-2	44
7 Burnley United	30	13	5	12	56	63	-7	44
8 Coppull United	30	12	7	11	43	42	1	43
9 Euxton Villa	30	11	8	11	51	42	9	41
10 Garstang (-3)	30	12	6	12	60	57	3	39
11 Norcross & Warbreck	30	10	4	16	67	85	-18	34
12 Longridge Town	30	10	3	17	40	60	-20	33
13 Slyne-with-Hest	30	9	6	15	43	65	-22	33
14 Vickerstown	30	8	8	14	53	66	-13	32
15 (R) Fulwood Amateurs	30	8	6	16	49	61	-12	30
16 (R) Tempest United	30	9	3	18	45	75	-30	30

PREMIER DIVISION	1	2	3	4	5	6	7	8	9	10	11	12	13	14	15	16
1 Blackpool Wren Rovers		3-3	1-1	2-2	2-2	0-2	2-1	4-0	3-0	3-3	1-1	8-1	2-1	5-0	4-2	3-3
2 Burnley United	1-1		0-1	0-1	1-2	2-2	4-3	4-4	0-4	3-6	2-0	1-6	3-2	1-2	3-0	5-3
3 Charnock Richard	3-0	3-0		3-0	4-1	3-0	4-1	4-1	1-0	3-1	2-0	7-1	1-1	4-0	2-1	4-2
4 Coppull United	1-1	1-2	0-3		1-0	0-1	2-0	1-1	3-0	4-1	2-1	0-4	0-1	2-0	0-0	2-3
5 Crooklands Casuals	1-2	2-0	4-1	2-0		1-4	3-1	0-0	3-2	1-4	2-1	3-0	2-0	7-0	2-2	2-0
6 Eagley	0-4	3-0	1-2	1-3	3-2		1-3	0-1	1-2	0-2	7-2	3-1	2-0	1-2	1-0	3-1
7 Euxton Villa	3-0	2-1	4-1	2-0	2-0	1-3		1-2	0-0	2-3	1-2	5-1	1-2	2-1	0-2	1-1
8 Fleetwood Hesketh	0-4	0-1	2-1	2-2	1-0	4-0	0-2		3-2	3-0	0-2	5-4	5-1	4-1	2-5	3-1
9 Fulwood Amateurs	0-4	0-2	0-3	1-0	1-4	1-2	3-3	2-4		2-0	2-0	1-0	0-0	2-2	7-1	1-1
10 Garstang	2-0	3-4	2-4	2-3	6-1	1-3	0-0	0-2	2-2		0-0	3-2	0-1	4-1	3-2	1-4
11 Longridge Town	1-4	0-3	0-3	3-1	2-0	0-1	0-0	3-1	3-2	0-1		3-1	3-2	4-2	0-2	1-3
12 Norcross & Warbreck	3-2	3-3	3-2	2-2	5-1	5-3	1-5	0-5	5-3	3-2	2-4		5-1	1-0	0-2	0-0
13 Slyne with Hest	2-5	1-3	3-3	1-3	0-2	2-4	1-1	2-1	4-1	2-2	2-0	3-2		1-7	1-2	2-0
14 Tempest United	1-0	1-3	3-5	0-0	1-1	2-1	1-3	0-2	3-2	0-3	4-3	3-2	0-2		1-3	5-3
15 Thornton Cleveleys	0-2	0-1	0-3	1-2	2-1	4-4	1-1	2-1	4-1	2-3	4-1	2-1	2-2	1-0		3-2
16 Vickerstown	1-7	4-0	0-1	2-5	1-1	2-4	0-0	0-1	0-5	0-0	3-0	3-3	3-0	3-2	4-1	

DIVISION ONE	P	W	D	L	F	A	GD	Pts
1 (P) Hesketh Bank	30	22	5	3	83	28	55	71
2 (P) Lostock St Gerards	30	22	4	4	89	36	53	70
3 Hurst Green	30	20	4	6	74	32	42	64
4 Burscough Richmond	30	15	8	7	72	45	27	53
5 BAC/EE Preston	30	14	5	11	76	58	18	47
6 Turton	30	14	5	11	75	58	17	47
7 Hawcoat Park	30	13	5	12	64	48	16	44
8 Lytham Town (-3)	30	14	5	11	69	75	-6	44
9 Bolton County	30	13	4	13	67	59	8	43
10 Poulton Town	30	13	2	15	54	59	-5	41
11 Dalton United	30	11	4	15	64	72	-8	37
12 Wyre Villa	30	10	5	15	68	74	-6	35
13 Mill Hill St Peters	30	8	2	20	40	80	-40	26
14 Ambleside United	30	8	2	20	43	108	-65	26
15 (R) Furness Rovers	30	6	6	18	32	58	-26	24
16 (R) Millom	30	3	2	25	25	105	-80	11

DIVISION TWO	P	W	D	L	F	A	GD	Pts
1 (P) Askam United	26	20	3	3	93	27	66	63
2 (P) GSK Ulverston Rangers	26	17	4	5	63	32	31	55
3 Milnthorpe Corinthians	26	16	3	7	65	42	23	51
4 Furness Cavaliers	26	16	2	8	51	37	14	50
5 Kendal County	26	15	3	8	58	38	20	48
6 Leyland United	26	14	5	7	62	36	26	47
7 CMB (-6)	26	12	6	8	55	44	11	36
8 Haslingden St. Marys	26	9	6	11	51	42	9	33
9 Croston Sports	26	9	3	14	39	54	-15	30
10 Todmorden Borough	26	8	3	15	40	55	-15	27
11 Ladybridge	26	6	6	14	39	61	-22	24
12 Stoneclough	26	7	2	17	38	71	-33	23
13 Walney Island	26	5	6	15	39	48	-9	21
14 Barrow Wanderers	26	2	0	24	16	122	-106	6

WEST LANCASHIRE LEAGUE PREMIER DIVISION CONSTITUTION 2014-15

	Club	Ground	Telephone
1	BLACKPOOL WREN ROVERS	Bruce Park, School Road, Marton, Blackpool FY4 5DX	07876 013 181
2	BURNLEY UNITED	Barden Sports Ground, Barden Lane, Burnley BB10 1JQ	01282 437 943 / 07961 604 412
3	CHARNOCK RICHARD	Mossie Park, Charter Lane, Charnock Richard, Chorley PR7 5LZ	07507 608 887
4	COPPULL UNITED	Springfield Road, Coppull PR7 5EJ	07747 606 358
5	CROOKLANDS CASUALS	Longlands Park, Greystone Lane, Dalton-in-Furness LA15 8JF	01229 465 010
6	EAGLEY	Eagley Sports Complex, Dunscar Bridge, Bolton BL7 9PQ	01204 306 178 / 07706 192 923
7	EUXTON VILLA	Jim Fowler Memorial Ground, Runshaw Hall Lane, Euxton, Chorley PR7 6HH	07778 678 221
8	FLEETWOOD HESKETH	Fylde Road, Southport PR9 9XH	07927 325 585
9	GARSTANG	The Riverside, High Street, Garstang PR3 1EB	07870 325 388
10	HESKETH BANK	Centenary Sports Ground, Station Road, Hesketh Bank, Preston PR4 6SR	01772 814 009 / 07713 158 393
11	LONGRIDGE TOWN	Inglewhite Road, Longridge, Preston PR3 2NA	07530 819 305
12	LOSTOCK ST. GERARD'S	Wateringpool Lane, Lostock Hall, Preston Lancs PR5 5UA	01772 610 636
13	NORCROSS & WARBRECK	Anchorsholme Lane, Thornton Cleveleys, Blackpool FY5 3DA	01253 859 836
14	SLYNE-WITH-HEST	Bottomdale Road, Slyne, Lancaster LA2 6BG	01524 417 193 / 07770 851 787
15	THORNTON CLEVELEYS	Bourne Road, Cleveleys, Thornton Cleveleys FY5 4QA	01253 859 907 / 07940 179 502
16	VICKERSTOWN CC	Park Vale, Mill Lane, Walney, Barrow-in-Furness LA14 3NB	07446 112 716

In: Hesketh Bank (P). Lostock St. Gerard's (P).

Out: Fulwood Amateurs (R). Tempest United (R).

RESERVE DIVISION ONE	P	W	D	L	F	A	GD	Pts
1 Charnock Richard Reserves	24	19	4	1	68	23	45	61
2 Blackpool Wren Rovers Reserves	24	18	4	2	75	24	51	58
3 Haslingden St Marys Reserves	24	13	4	7	61	35	26	43
4 Tempest United Reserves	24	13	3	8	52	44	8	42
5 Lostock St Gerards Reserves	24	13	2	9	52	37	15	41
6 Euxton Villa Reserves	24	11	6	7	67	52	15	39
7 Garstang Reserves	24	11	5	8	44	36	8	38
8 Thornton Cleveleys Reserves	24	9	3	12	57	56	1	30
9 Coppull United Reserves	24	7	9	8	39	42	-3	30
10 Wyre Villa Reserves	24	8	3	13	46	63	-17	27
11 Eagley Reserves	24	4	2	18	39	80	-41	14
12 Fulwood Amateurs Reserves	24	3	4	17	28	81	-53	13
13 Burnley United Reserves	24	1	3	20	38	93	-55	6

RESERVE DIVISION TWO	P	W	D	L	F	A	GD	Pts
1 (P) Leyland United Reserves	24	17	4	3	82	43	39	55
2 (P) Hurst Green Reserves	24	17	3	4	93	43	50	54
3 Mill Hill St Peters Reserves	24	16	3	5	68	42	26	51
4 Hesketh Bank Reserves	24	12	5	7	60	38	22	41
5 Poulton Reserves	24	11	4	9	74	70	4	37
6 Lytham Town Reserves	24	12	1	11	64	68	-4	37
7 Burscough Richmond Reserves	24	10	4	10	64	50	14	34
8 Bolton County Reserves	24	9	3	12	49	55	-6	30
9 Slyne with Hest Reserves (-3)	24	9	5	10	54	67	-13	29
10 Turton Reserves	24	8	4	12	42	58	-16	28
11 Milnthorpe Corinthians Reserves	24	6	2	16	43	71	-28	20
12 Croston Sports Reserves (-3)	24	5	1	18	51	84	-33	13
13 Longridge Town Reserves	24	4	1	19	30	85	-55	13

WEST YORKSHIRE LEAGUE

Sponsored by: Active 8
Founded: 1928
Recent Champions:
2009: Knaresborough Town
2010: Bardsey 2011: Bardsey
2012: Beeston St Anthony's 2013: Bardsey

PREMIER DIVISION	P	W	D	L	F	A	GD	Pts
1 Bardsey	30	23	5	2	84	20	64	74
2 Beeston St Anthony's	30	19	6	5	96	40	56	63
3 Leeds City	30	19	4	7	80	41	39	61
4 Field	30	19	4	7	94	58	36	61
5 East End Park	30	14	6	10	81	62	19	48
6 Oxenhope Recreation	30	13	6	11	78	63	15	45
7 Ripon City	30	13	5	12	62	68	-6	44
8 Boroughbridge	30	10	13	7	61	54	7	43
9 Horbury Town	30	11	8	11	64	63	1	41
10 Brighouse Old Boys	30	11	2	17	47	65	-18	35
11 Hunslet Club	30	9	5	16	56	71	-15	32
12 Shelley	30	9	4	17	52	72	-20	31
13 Otley Town	30	7	8	15	45	71	-26	29
14 Wetherby Athletic	30	6	6	18	50	73	-23	24
15 (R) Kippax	30	5	6	19	51	98	-47	21
16 (R) Whitkirk Wanderers (-3)	30	5	6	19	33	115	-82	18

DIVISION ONE	P	W	D	L	F	A	GD	Pts
1 (P) Robin Hood Athletic	30	24	4	2	98	35	63	76
2 (P) Knaresborough Town	30	20	3	7	74	36	38	63
3 Ilkley Town	30	19	4	7	87	46	41	61
4 Old Modernians	30	19	3	8	100	40	60	60
5 Wyke Wanderers	30	16	3	11	67	46	21	51
6 Stanley United (-3)	30	17	3	10	77	60	17	51
7 Headingley AFC	30	13	4	13	74	64	10	43
8 Aberford Albion (-3)	30	14	3	13	71	63	8	42
9 Carlton Athletic	30	12	5	13	66	67	-1	41
10 Altofts	30	12	4	14	60	63	-3	40
11 Pool	30	12	4	14	50	71	-21	40
12 Featherstone Colliery	30	10	4	16	83	94	-11	34
13 Old Centralians	30	8	7	15	60	75	-15	31
14 Sherburn White Rose	30	8	4	18	44	83	-39	28
15 (R) Baildon Trinity Athletic	30	5	2	23	35	100	-65	17
16 (R) Kellingley Welfare	30	1	3	26	49	152	-103	6

DIVISION TWO	P	W	D	L	F	A	GD	Pts
1 (P) Thornhill	24	19	1	4	98	46	52	58
2 (P) Swillington Saints	24	16	4	4	71	44	27	52
3 Howden Clough	24	16	2	6	88	45	43	50
4 Rothwell Town	23	12	2	9	55	48	7	38
5 Mount St. Mary's	23	12	0	11	50	64	-14	36
6 Hartshead	23	11	2	10	42	54	-12	35
7 Woodhouse Hill (Normanton) (-3)	24	10	5	9	52	43	9	32
8 Glasshoughton Welfare (-3)	24	11	2	11	60	58	2	32
9 Ossett Common Rovers	24	9	4	11	48	53	-5	31
10 Garforth Rangers	24	8	3	13	55	60	-5	27
11 Yorkshire Amateur	24	6	2	16	33	57	-24	20
12 Barwick (-3)	23	6	2	15	43	75	-32	17
13 Great Preston	24	2	3	19	32	80	-48	9

LEAGUE CUP

ROUND 1

Knaresborough Town	v	Ilkley Town	1-0
Great Preston	v	Featherstone Colliery	1-5
Robin Hood Athletic	v	Ossett Common Rovers	4-0
Pool	v	Mount St. Mary's	3-2
Old Centralians	v	Sherburn White Rose	0-1
Carlton Athletic	v	Howden Clough	3-2
Swillington Saints	v	Heckmondwike Town	10-5
Aberford Albion	v	Thornhill	5-7
Nostell Miners Welfare	v	Glasshoughton Welfare	AW
Garforth Rangers	v	Woodhouse Hill (Normanton)	1-2
Old Headingley	v	Wyke Wanderers	4-1
Old Modernians	v	Rothwell Town	3-4
Barwick	v	Baildon Trinity Athletic	3-0
Kellingley Welfare	v	Stanley United	1-5
Yorkshire Amateur	v	Altofts	3-6

ROUND 2

Knaresborough Town	v	Featherstone Colliery	5-3
Whitkirk Wanderers	v	Shelley	1-4
Ripon City	v	Robin Hood Athletic	1-2
Hartshead	v	Pool	0-7
Leeds City	v	Hunslet Club	2-0
Kippax	v	Bardsey	0-5
Sherburn White Rose	v	Carlton Athletic	1-2
Oxenhope Recreation	v	Beeston St Anthony's	0-1
Swillington Saints	v	Horbury Town	1-3
Wetherby Athletic	v	Thornhill	2-8
Glasshoughton Welfare	v	Woodhouse Hill (Normanton)	2-3
East End Park	v	Old Headingley	2-4
Otley Town	v	Rothwell Town	4-2
Barwick	v	Boroughbridge	0-2
Stanley United	v	Altofts	7-1
Field	v	Brighouse Old Boys	4-1

ROUND 3

Knaresborough Town	v	Shelley	4-1
Robin Hood Athletic	v	Pool	2-0
Leeds City	v	Bardsey	4-0
Carlton Athletic	v	Beeston St Anthony's	1-5
Horbury Town	v	Thornhill	5-2
Woodhouse Hill (Normanton)	v	Old Headingley	0-4
Otley Town	v	Boroughbridge	4-3
Stanley United	v	Field	1-4

QUARTER FINALS

Knaresborough Town	v	Robin Hood Athletic	1-2
Leeds City	v	Beeston St Anthony's	0-1
Horbury Town	v	Old Headingley	1-2
Otley Town	v	Field	1-6

SEMI FINALS

Robin Hood Athletic	v	Beeston St Anthony's	0-2
Old Headingley	v	Field	0-2

FINAL

Beeston St Anthony's	v	Field	0-4

PREMIER DIVISION	1	2	3	4	5	6	7	8	9	10	11	12	13	14	15	16
1 Bardsey		0-0	1-1	3-0	3-0	1-0	3-1	1-0	7-0	2-0	1-1	2-3	2-1	6-4	1-0	9-0
2 Beeston St Anthony's	1-0		5-2	6-0	2-2	6-2	1-2	3-2	4-1	2-3	4-1	0-1	4-1	1-0	5-0	8-1
3 Boroughbridge	1-4	3-0		1-3	3-3	2-2	3-3	1-3	3-1	1-0	1-1	1-4	3-1	1-1	4-0	4-0
4 Brighouse Old Boys	2-7	1-1	2-2		2-4	4-0	3-1	0-3	3-1	0-4	1-2	1-2	1-0	0-1	1-0	3-0
5 East End Park	0-4	0-6	2-2	1-0		2-3	2-0	3-6	6-1	3-1	4-3	4-1	1-4	5-1	2-3	2-3
6 Field	0-2	4-3	2-2	3-1	0-1		2-0	3-2	6-2	2-1	4-0	2-8	6-2	3-1	4-1	5-1
7 Horbury Town	1-3	1-6	3-4	2-1	2-1	2-4		2-0	1-1	2-3	1-1	5-2	3-3	2-2	3-1	7-0
8 Hunslet Club	1-3	2-8	1-1	2-4	1-1	0-6	0-4		4-1	3-5	2-0	3-0	6-1	2-3	1-4	3-0
9 Kippax	1-2	1-2	0-4	4-2	1-11	3-4	1-3	1-1		2-2	2-4	4-4	4-0	4-0	3-2	3-4
10 Leeds City	0-0	1-2	3-0	6-1	2-1	1-4	4-1	3-0	6-1		1-1	3-2	2-3	2-2	1-0	2-1
11 Otley Town	0-3	2-2	1-3	2-4	2-2	1-1	0-1	3-0	3-0	0-2		0-8	0-2	2-1	2-4	8-2
12 Oxenhope Recreation	0-0	1-3	2-3	2-1	1-4	3-2	3-1	2-2	2-5	0-3	1-1		6-0	2-4	2-2	8-0
13 Ripon City	1-3	1-1	3-3	1-0	2-3	2-2	3-3	2-1	5-1	0-6	5-1	5-1		2-1	2-1	0-1
14 Shelley	0-3	1-4	1-0	1-4	1-3	1-6	2-3	2-0	1-1	4-5	4-0	1-3	1-2		2-3	4-2
15 Wetherby Athletic	1-4	2-4	1-1	1-2	2-2	1-6	2-2	1-2	0-0	1-4	4-1	0-3	1-3	1-4		9-0
16 Whitkirk Wanderers	0-4	2-2	1-1	2-0	0-6	2-6	2-2	3-3	2-1	0-4	1-2	1-1	0-5	0-1	2-2	

WEST YORKSHIRE LEAGUE PREMIER DIVISION CONSTITUTION 2014-15

	Club	Ground	Phone
1	BARDSEY	The Sportsfield, Keswick Lane, Bardsey LS17 9AQ	01937 574 286
2	BEESTON ST ANTHONY'S	St Antony's Road, Beeston, Leeds LS11 8DP	0113 270 9141
3	BOROUGHBRIDGE	Aldborough Road, Boroughbridge YO51 9EB	01423 324 206
4	BRIGHOUSE OLD BOYS	Hipperholme & Lightcliffe School, Stoney Lane, Lightcliffe, Halifax HX3 8TL	07768 147 262
5	EAST END PARK	East End Park, Skelton Road, Leeds LS9 9EP	0113 2939 040
6	FIELD	Field Sports & Social Club, Hollingwood Lane, Bradford BD7 2RE	01274 571 750
7	HORBURY TOWN	Slazengers Sports Complex, Southfields, Horbury WF4 5BH	01924 274 228
8	HUNSLET CLUB	The Hunslet Club, Hillidge Road LS10 1BP	0113 271 6489
9	KNARESBOROUGH TOWN	Knaresborough Town A.F.C., Manse Lane, Knaresborough HG5 8LF	0777 3679 971
10	LEEDS CITY	Adel War Memorial Association, Church Lane, Adel, Leeds LS16 8DE	0113 2930 525
11	OTLEY TOWN	Old Showground, Pool Road, Otley LS21 1DY	01943 461 025
12	OXENHOPE RECREATION	The Recreation ground, Hebden Bridge Road, Oxenhope BD22 9LY	01535 642 209
13	RIPON CITY	Mallorie Park, Mallorie Park Drive, Ripon HG4 2QD	07811 788 537
14	ROBIN HOOD ATHLETIC	Behind Coach & Horses Hotel, Rothwell Haigh LS26 0SF	0113 2821 021
15	SHELLEY	Storthes Hall, Huddersfield HD8 0WA	07517 362 449
16	WETHERBY ATHLETIC	The Ings, Wetherby LS22 5HA	01937 585 699

In: Knaresborough Town (P). Robin Hood Athletic (P).

Out: Kippax (R). Whitkirk Wanderers (R).

	ALLIANCE DIVISION ONE	P	W	D	L	F	A	GD	Pts
1	Beeston St. Anthony's Reserves	24	20	1	3	98	29	69	61
2	Hunslet Club Reserves	24	18	2	4	72	28	44	56
3	Oxenhope Recreation Reserves	24	16	3	5	72	37	35	51
4	Wetherby Athletic Reserves	24	14	5	5	59	40	19	47
5	Leeds City Reserves	24	13	3	8	56	34	22	42
6	Field Reserves	24	9	3	12	60	73	-13	30
7	Brighouse Old Boys Reserves	24	8	5	11	55	59	-4	29
8	Headingley AFC Reserves	24	8	1	15	48	72	-24	25
9	Robin Hood Athletic Reserves	24	6	5	13	45	61	-16	23
10	East End Park Reserves	24	6	5	13	43	66	-23	23
11	(R) Bardsey Reserves	24	6	4	14	50	71	-21	22
12	(R) Kippax Reserves	24	5	2	17	32	76	-44	17
13	(R) Ripon City Reserves (-9)	24	6	3	15	36	80	-44	12

	ALLIANCE DIVISION TWO	P	W	D	L	F	A	GD	Pts
1	(P) Whitkirk Wanderers Reserves	22	14	6	2	67	28	39	48
2	(P) Ilkley Town Reserves	22	14	4	4	71	37	34	46
3	(P) Boroughbridge Reserves	22	13	3	6	72	36	36	42
4	(P) Aberford Albion Reserves	22	11	6	5	59	45	14	39
5	Howden Clough Reserves	22	8	8	6	52	49	3	32
6	Garforth Rangers Reserves	22	8	4	10	44	44	0	28
7	Otley Town Reserves	22	8	4	10	42	50	-8	28
8	Baildon Trinity Athletic Reserves	22	8	2	12	51	65	-14	26
9	Rothwell Town Reserves	22	8	1	13	35	56	-21	25
10	Sherburn White Rose Reserves	22	6	3	13	41	67	-26	21
11	Pool Reserves (-3)	22	6	3	13	39	66	-27	18
12	Barwick Reserves (-6)	22	5	2	15	33	63	-30	11

WILTSHIRE LEAGUE

Sponsored by: No sponsor
Founded: 1928
Recent Champions:
2010: New College - Swindon
2011: Corsham Town Reserves
2012: FC Sanford 2013: Wilts Calne Town

PREMIER DIVISION	P	W	D	L	F	A	GD	Pts
1 Southbrook	22	18	3	1	79	18	61	57
2 Supermarine Sports	22	16	3	3	66	31	35	51
3 Shrewton Utd	22	16	2	4	86	41	45	50
4 Trowbridge Town	22	13	3	6	52	34	18	42
5 Ludgershall Sports	22	12	2	8	55	42	13	38
6 FC Chippenham Youth	22	7	2	13	29	45	-16	23
7 Corsham Town Reserves (-1)	22	6	4	12	36	49	-13	21
8 Marlborough Town	22	5	6	11	34	55	-21	21
9 Wroughton	22	6	0	16	31	71	-40	18
10 Wilts Calne Town	22	3	8	11	30	50	-20	17
11 Vale of Pewsey (-3)	22	6	2	14	21	61	-40	17
12 Devizes Town Reserves	22	3	7	12	34	56	-22	16

Purton Reserves withdrew - record expunged.
SKS Blyskawica withdrew - record expunged.

SENIOR CUP

ROUND 1

Trowbridge Town	v	FC Chippenham Youth	3-2
SKS Blyskawica	-		Bye
Vale of Pewsey	v	Devizes Town Reserves	3-1
Corsham Town Reserves	v	Wroughton	2-1
Southbrook	v	Shrewton United	2-1
Purton Reserves	v	Wilts Calne Town	4-2
Ludgershall Sports	-		Bye
Marlborough Town	v	Supermarine Sports	1-2

QUARTER FINALS

Trowbridge Town	v	SKS Blyskawica	HW
Vale of Pewsey	v	Corsham Town Reserves	3-4
Southbrook	v	Purton Reserves	HW
Ludgershall Sports	v	Supermarine Sports	2-1

SEMI FINALS

Trowbridge Town	v	Corsham Town Reserves	1-2 aet
Southbrook	v	Ludgershall Sports	2-1

FINAL

Corsham Town Reserves	v	Southbrook	0-3

DIVISION ONE	P	W	D	L	F	A	GD	Pts
1 Melksham Town Reserves	24	20	2	2	101	27	74	62
2 Intel	24	15	2	7	82	45	37	47
3 Wootton Bassett Town Dev	24	15	1	8	78	53	25	46
4 Malmesbury Victoria Reserves (-3)	24	12	1	11	82	50	32	34
5 Sarum Youth Seniors	24	8	5	11	51	65	-14	29
6 Wroughton Reserves	24	6	2	16	55	92	-37	20
7 Blunsdon	24	1	1	22	24	141	-117	4

Marlborough Town Reserves withdrew - record expunged.

PREMIER DIVISION	1	2	3	4	5	6	7	8	9	10	11	12
1 Corsham Town Reserves		4-1	1-0	2-4	3-0	2-2	0-2	3-4	1-1	5-0	2-2	1-6
2 Devizes Town Reserves	3-2		0-2	1-4	1-1	1-3	0-3	1-1	1-1	5-0	2-2	4-5
3 FC Chippenham Youth	1-2	5-3		0-1	2-1	6-1	0-4	0-2	3-1	1-2	0-0	0-2
4 Ludgershall Sports	5-1	4-0	3-2		5-1	0-5	2-3	0-6	0-4	5-1	4-3	2-0
5 Marlborough Town	2-0	2-2	1-1	2-1		3-1	1-3	1-2	0-2	3-0	3-3	3-0
6 Shrewton United	3-2	5-2	8-2	3-1	8-0		2-3	2-1	3-3	5-0	1-0	7-2
7 Southbrook	4-0	1-1	5-0	1-1	4-1	5-2		6-1	7-3	5-0	3-0	6-0
8 Supermarine Sports	3-0	7-1	3-0	2-1	2-2	3-6	1-1		3-1	5-3	5-0	5-0
9 Trowbridge Town	3-2	2-1	2-1	2-0	5-2	0-1	0-2	1-2		3-1	3-1	4-1
10 Vale of Pewsey	1-0	1-0	0-1	1-1	3-2	1-5	2-1	0-4	0-4		2-3	0-1
11 Wilts Calne Town	1-1	1-1	3-0	1-4	3-3	3-5	1-5	0-1	0-2	1-1		1-0
12 Wroughton	1-2	0-3	0-2	1-7	4-0	1-8	0-5	2-3	2-5	1-2	2-1	

WILTSHIRE LEAGUE PREMIER DIVISION CONSTITUTION 2014-15

1	CORSHAM TOWN RESERVES	Southbank Ground, Lacock Road, Corsham	
2	DEVIZES TOWN RESERVES	Nursteed Road, Devizes SN10 3DX	
3	FC CHIPPENHAM YOUTH	Stanley Park, Chippenham	
4	LUDGERSHALL SPORTS	Astor Crescent, Ludgershall SP11 9QE	
5	MALMESBURY VICTORIA	Flying Monk, Gloucester Road	
6	MARLBOROUGH TOWN	Elcot Lane, Marlborough, SN8 2BG	
7	MELKSHAM TOWN RESERVES	The Conigre, Melksham	
8	SARUM YOUTH	Castle Meadows, North Street, Wilton	
9	SHREWTON UNITED	Shrewton Recreation Ground, Mill Lane, Shrewton SP3 4JY	
10	SOUTHBROOK	Southbrook Recreation Ground, Pinehurst Road, Swindon	
11	SUPERMARINE SPORTS CLUB	Hunts Copse, South Marston, Swindon	
12	TROWBRIDGE TOWN	Woodmarsh, Bradley Road, Trowbridge BA14 0SB	
13	TROWBRIDGE WANDERERS	Lambrok Playing Fields, Trowbridge	
14	VALE OF PEWSEY	Recreation Ground, Ball Road, Pewsey SN9 5BS	01672 562990
15	WESTBURY UNITED RESERVES	Meadow Lane, Westbury	
16	WILTS CALNE TOWN	Bremhill View, Calne SN11 9EE	
17	WOOTTON BASSETT TOWN DEV.	Gerrard Buxton Sports Ground, Rylands Way, Royal Wootton Bassett SN4 8AW	01793 853 880
18	WROUGHTON	The Weir Field Ground, Devizes Road, Wroughton, Wiltshire	

In: Malmesbury Victoria (R - Hellenic). Melksham Town Reserves (P). Sarum Youth (P). Trowbridge Wanderers (P - Trowbridge & District). Westbury United Reserves (P - Trowbridge & District). Wootton Bassett Town Dev. (P).
Out: Blunsdon, Intel, Malmesbury Victoria Reserves and Wroughton Town Reserves (Cirencester & District).

LEAGUE TABLES 2013-14

ALDERSHOT & DISTRICT LEAGUE

Senior Division	P	W	D	L	F	A	GD	Pts
1 Bagshot	18	16	0	2	58	20	38	48
2 West Meon & Warnford	18	11	2	5	41	33	8	35
3 West End Village	18	9	5	4	37	22	15	32
4 Hale Rovers	18	9	4	5	40	26	14	31
5 Frimley Select	18	9	3	6	40	33	7	30
6 Yateley United Res.	18	8	4	6	33	27	6	28
7 Spartans	18	6	2	10	30	37	-7	20
8 Old Farnboronians Res.	18	5	2	11	31	50	-19	17
9 Sandhurst Sports	18	4	4	10	30	43	-13	16
10 Fleet Spurs Res.	18	0	0	18	22	71	-49	0

Division One	P	W	D	L	F	A	GD	Pts
1 Wey Valley	18	15	1	2	75	33	42	46
2 Yateley United A	18	12	2	4	45	30	15	38
3 Headley Utd Res.	18	10	4	4	40	30	10	34
4 Fleet Spurs A	18	8	6	4	33	32	1	30
5 Lindford	18	8	3	7	32	24	8	27
6 Hindhead Athletic	18	5	5	8	26	35	-9	20
7 Mytchett Athletic	18	5	2	11	38	48	-10	17
8 Courtmoor	18	3	6	9	33	42	-9	15
9 Letef Select (-4)	18	4	4	10	26	42	-16	12
10 South Farnborough	18	2	3	13	28	60	-32	9

Division Two	P	W	D	L	F	A	GD	Pts
1 Alton United	18	13	3	2	51	23	28	42
2 Rushmoor Community	18	12	2	4	58	24	34	38
3 Ropley	18	11	3	4	57	36	21	36
4 AFC Petersfield	18	10	3	5	46	35	11	33
5 Headley United A	18	8	6	4	39	29	10	30
6 Hartley Wintney A	18	6	1	11	37	60	-23	19
7 Shalford Social	18	5	2	11	27	46	-19	17
8 Four Marks Res.	18	4	4	10	34	44	-10	16
9 Normandy	18	4	3	11	41	47	-6	15
10 Farnham United	18	3	1	14	29	75	-46	10

Division Three	P	W	D	L	F	A	GD	Pts
1 Bagshot Res.	18	14	3	1	75	20	55	45
2 Frogmore	18	11	5	2	60	33	27	38
3 Blackwater Town	18	9	4	5	40	25	15	31
4 South Farnborough Res.	18	9	3	6	38	44	-6	30
5 Yateley United B	18	8	2	8	32	31	1	26
6 Fleet Spurs Vet	18	7	5	6	32	40	-8	26
7 West End Village Res.	18	5	6	7	33	41	-8	21
8 Hindhead Athletic Res.	18	3	5	10	27	32	-5	14
9 Shalford Social Res.	18	4	1	13	27	54	-27	13
10 Normandy Res.	18	2	2	14	17	61	-44	8

ALTRINCHAM & DISTRICT AMATEUR LEAGUE

Division One	P	W	D	L	F	A	GD	Pts
1 AFC Quarry	22	18	3	1	102	17	85	57
2 Broadheath Central FC	22	18	2	2	71	19	52	56
3 Deans Youth	22	13	4	5	62	44	18	43
4 Sale Amateurs	22	12	2	8	62	53	9	38
5 Old Altrinchamians	22	11	4	7	46	34	12	37
6 Flixton Juniors	22	10	4	8	54	41	13	34
7 Knutsford FC	22	11	1	10	61	55	6	34
8 Swinton FC	22	8	0	14	31	55	-24	24
9 Atlantic FC	22	8	0	14	31	57	-26	24
10 Kartel Sports	22	5	2	15	14	61	-47	17
11 Cheadle Hulme	22	3	4	15	31	52	-21	13
12 Northenden Victoria	22	1	2	19	15	92	-77	5

Division Two	P	W	D	L	F	A	GD	Pts
1 FC Woodford	22	20	2	0	100	30	70	62
2 Moorlands	22	17	0	5	78	33	45	51
3 Wendover AFC	22	15	2	5	77	32	45	47
4 Broadheath JFC	22	12	3	7	56	40	16	39
5 Unicorn Athletic	22	12	2	8	76	62	14	38
6 West Didsbury & Chorlton	22	12	1	9	74	46	28	37
7 Wythenshaw Amateur	22	10	3	9	54	57	-3	33
8 APFC	22	8	2	12	48	45	3	26
9 Styal	22	6	3	13	54	70	-16	21
10 Juno United	22	4	2	16	36	75	-39	14
11 George FC	22	3	2	17	34	79	-45	11
12 Winton JFC	22	2	0	20	26	144	-118	6

AMATEUR COMBINATION

Premier Division	P	W	D	L	F	A	GD	Pts
1 Old Hamptonians	18	13	3	2	58	18	40	42
2 Old Minchendenians	18	13	1	4	45	24	21	40
3 Old Meadonians	18	8	7	3	40	20	20	31
4 Honorable Artillery Company	18	8	5	5	44	32	12	29
5 Old Suttonians	18	9	2	7	36	31	5	29
6 Old Parmiterians	18	7	1	10	35	39	-4	22
7 Old Salvatorians	18	6	3	9	31	40	-9	21
8 Enfield Old Grammarians	18	5	4	9	34	44	-10	19
9 Bealonians	18	4	0	14	22	64	-42	12
10 Parkfield	18	3	2	13	26	59	-33	11

Senior One	P	W	D	L	F	A	GD	Pts
1 Old Ignatians	20	10	4	6	58	44	14	34
2 Kings Old Boys	20	10	4	6	49	38	11	34
3 Old Aloysians	20	10	4	6	44	43	1	34
4 Dorkinians	20	10	3	7	44	43	1	33
5 UCL Academicals	20	9	4	7	45	38	7	31
6 Old Thorntonians	20	10	1	9	47	44	3	31
7 Albanian	20	9	2	9	38	34	4	29
8 London Lawyers	20	9	0	11	46	44	2	27
9 Shene Old Grammarians	20	8	3	9	25	31	-6	27
10 Honorable Artillery Company II	20	6	5	9	40	47	-7	23
11 Hale End Athletic	20	3	2	15	19	49	-30	11

Senior Two	P	W	D	L	F	A	GD	PTS
1 Old Pauline	20	15	2	3	71	15	56	47
2 Old Wokingians	20	14	4	2	59	19	40	46
3 Latymer Old Boys	20	10	5	5	52	29	23	35
4 Mayfield Athletic	20	10	3	7	57	28	29	33
5 Old Tenisonians	20	10	3	7	54	25	29	33
6 Clapham Old Xaverians	20	9	2	9	50	73	-23	29
7 Old Danes	20	8	2	10	46	47	-1	26
8 Old Suttonians II	20	6	1	13	34	69	-35	19
9 Economicals	20	4	5	11	39	57	-18	17
10 Old Parmiterians II	20	4	5	11	19	65	-46	17
11 Albanian II	20	3	2	15	32	86	-54	11

Senior Three South	P	W	D	L	F	A	GD	Pts
1 Reigatians	18	13	2	3	66	25	41	41
2 Economicals II	18	12	5	1	60	19	41	41
3 Old Vaughanians	18	12	3	3	51	22	29	39
4 Fulham Compton Old Boys	18	10	3	5	32	25	7	33
5 Wandsworth Borough	18	7	5	6	33	34	-1	26
6 Old Meadonians II	18	7	3	8	44	29	15	24
7 Sinjuns Grammarians	18	5	3	10	27	44	-17	18
8 Old Isleworthians	18	5	3	10	36	67	-31	18
9 Royal Bank of Scotland (-3)	18	3	2	13	35	76	-41	8
10 Old Hamptonians II	18	1	1	16	21	64	-43	4

Senior Three North	P	W	D	L	F	A	GD	Pts
1 Old Minchendenians II	18	14	2	2	89	29	60	44
2 Globe Rangers	18	12	1	5	60	44	16	37
3 Old Manorians	18	9	5	4	54	35	19	32
4 Old Woodhouseians	18	8	4	6	42	34	8	28
5 Old Parmiterians III	18	7	7	4	41	44	-3	28
6 Lea Valley	18	7	3	8	71	51	20	24
7 UCL Academicals II	18	7	2	9	49	48	1	23
8 Birkbeck College (-3)	18	6	6	6	37	42	-5	21
9 Bealonians II	18	2	4	12	33	67	-34	10
10 Old Uffingtonians	18	0	2	16	21	103	-82	2

Intermediate South	P	W	D	L	F	A	GD	Pts
1 Glyn Old Boys	16	10	3	3	51	25	26	33
2 National Westminster Bank	16	9	4	3	37	25	12	31
3 Old Meadonians III	16	9	3	4	33	30	3	30
4 Old St Marys	16	7	3	6	35	26	9	24
5 Citigroup	16	7	3	6	39	38	1	24
6 Fitzwilliam Old Boys	16	6	5	5	24	29	-5	23
7 Economicals III	16	5	4	7	29	34	-5	19
8 Hampstead Heathens	16	3	3	10	23	33	-10	12
9 Old Tiffinians	16	2	0	14	19	50	-31	6

Intermediate North	P	W	D	L	F	A	GD	Pts
1 Queen Mary College Old Boys	20	16	2	2	59	13	46	50
2 Old Tollingtonians	20	12	3	5	54	35	19	39
3 Oakhill Tigers	20	12	1	7	65	42	23	37
4 Old Aloysians II	20	12	1	7	42	38	4	37
5 Old Magdalenians	20	11	2	7	52	39	13	35
6 Old Salvatorians II	20	10	1	9	38	41	-3	31
7 UCL Academicals III	20	10	1	9	41	49	-8	31
8 Hale End Athletic II	20	8	3	9	41	52	-11	27
9 Old Ignatians II	20	4	3	13	31	43	-12	15
10 Leyton County Old Boys	20	2	4	14	36	57	-21	10
11 Old Buckwellians (-3)	20	1	3	16	21	71	-50	3

One North	P	W	D	L	F	A	GD	Pts
1 Old Edmontonians	18	14	2	2	59	29	30	44
2 Southgate County	18	12	1	5	63	25	38	37
3 Wood Green Old Boys	18	11	1	6	61	42	19	34
4 Enfield Old Grammarians II	18	10	3	5	63	38	25	33
5 University of Hertfordshire	18	8	3	7	48	41	7	27
6 Old Salvatorians III	18	8	1	9	41	33	8	25
7 Egbertian	18	7	4	7	34	37	-3	25
8 Albanian III	18	6	1	11	37	63	-26	19
9 Parkfield II	18	2	2	14	30	77	-47	8
10 Hale End Athletic III	18	2	2	14	29	80	-51	8

One West	P	W	D	L	F	A	GD	Pts
1 Hampstead Heathens II	14	10	1	3	47	26	21	31
2 Old Isleworthians II	14	10	1	3	46	25	21	31
3 Birkbeck College II (-3)	14	7	4	3	37	25	12	22
4 Old Challoners	14	4	5	5	28	23	5	17
5 Old Vaughanians III	14	5	2	7	32	51	-19	17
6 Old Pegasonians (-1)	14	5	2	7	36	33	3	16
7 London Welsh	14	3	4	7	20	25	-5	13
8 Brent II	14	2	1	11	20	58	-38	7

One South	P	W	D	L	F	A	GD	Pts
1 Economicals IV	20	12	3	5	47	29	18	39
2 Old Sedcopians	20	12	2	6	62	39	23	38
3 Mickleham Old Boxhillians	20	12	2	6	41	31	10	38
4 Witan	20	9	5	6	48	24	24	32
5 Old Suttonians III	20	9	5	6	40	27	13	32
6 Old Thorntonians II	20	9	4	7	40	44	-4	31
7 Royal Bank of Scotland II (-3)	20	9	3	8	38	35	3	27
8 Old Meadonians IV	20	6	4	10	30	30	0	22
9 Brent	20	6	4	10	24	50	-26	22
10 Old Pauline II	20	4	3	13	27	62	-35	15
11 Dorkinians II	20	4	1	15	29	55	-26	13

LEAGUE TABLES

Two North	P	W	D	L	F	A	GD	Pts
1 Old Manorians II	18	15	2	1	62	23	39	47
2 Old Minchendenians III	18	11	3	4	53	25	28	36
3 Old Woodhouseians II	18	10	4	4	38	23	15	34
4 Old Parmiterians IV	18	9	3	6	53	30	23	30
5 Egbertian II	18	9	3	6	29	24	5	30
6 Latymer Old Boys II	18	7	2	9	38	37	1	23
7 Old Ignatians III	18	6	3	9	29	50	-21	21
8 Enfield Old Grammarians III	18	3	4	11	24	41	-17	13
9 Old Salvatorians IV (-3)	18	3	3	12	23	50	-27	9
10 Old Aloysians III (-4)	18	2	3	13	16	62	-46	5

Two South	P	W	D	L	F	A	GD	Pts
1 Glyn Old Boys II	18	15	2	1	66	28	38	47
2 Old Suttonians IV	18	15	0	3	69	27	42	45
3 Old Strand Academicals	18	12	2	4	46	28	18	38
4 Tilburg Regents	18	10	1	7	48	36	12	31
5 Old Sedcopians II	18	7	2	9	37	40	-3	23
6 City of London (-3)	18	7	3	8	33	30	3	21
7 Clapham Old Xaverians II	18	6	0	12	35	59	-24	18
8 Sinjuns Grammarians II	18	4	4	10	19	52	-33	16
9 Old Hamptonians III	18	3	3	12	25	45	-20	12
10 Shene Old Grammarians II	18	1	3	14	18	51	-33	6

Three North	P	W	D	L	F	A	GD	Pts
1 Oakhill Tigers II	18	17	0	1	83	20	63	51
2 Old Manorians III	18	15	1	2	75	24	51	46
3 Queen Mary College Old Boys II	18	11	2	5	44	25	19	35
4 Old Aloysians IV	18	10	3	5	51	39	12	33
5 Old Minchendenians IV	18	10	0	8	51	41	10	30
6 Bealonians III	18	6	2	10	30	48	-18	20
7 Latymer Old Boys III	18	6	0	12	34	55	-21	18
8 UCL Academicals IV	18	5	1	12	40	63	-23	16
9 Old Magdalenians II	18	3	1	14	35	71	-36	10
10 Parkfield III (-3)	18	2	0	16	25	82	-57	3

Three South	P	W	D	L	F	A	GD	Pts
1 Glyn Old Boys III	18	15	1	2	55	20	35	46
2 Old Wokingians II	18	12	1	5	50	23	27	37
3 National Westminster Bank II	18	9	1	8	45	30	15	28
4 Economicals V	18	9	0	9	36	40	-4	27
5 Old Crosbeians	18	8	1	9	40	45	-5	25
6 Wandsworth Borough II	18	7	3	8	33	38	-5	24
7 Kings Old Boys II	18	7	2	9	30	33	-3	23
8 Old Meadonians V	18	7	2	9	26	33	-7	23
9 Old Guildfordians	18	4	3	11	24	47	-23	15
10 Old St Marys II	18	3	4	11	17	47	-30	13

Four North	P	W	D	L	F	A	GD	Pts
1 Old Edmontonians II	16	15	1	0	85	12	73	46
2 Comets MPSSA	16	8	3	5	46	27	19	27
3 Old Manorians IV	16	8	1	7	61	35	26	25
4 Southgate County II	16	8	1	7	35	49	-14	25
5 Albanian IV	16	6	4	6	43	49	-6	22
6 Old Buckwellians II (-3)	16	6	3	7	33	33	0	18
7 Ravenscroft Old Boys	16	4	2	10	25	66	-41	14
8 Old Salvatorians V (-6)	16	4	4	8	22	35	-13	10
9 Egbertian III	16	3	1	12	22	66	-44	10

Four South	P	W	D	L	F	A	GD	Pts
1 Old Pauline III	16	11	2	3	47	19	28	35
2 Old Meadonians VI	16	11	2	3	50	40	10	35
3 Old Whitgiftian	16	9	3	4	61	38	23	30
4 Old Wokingians III	16	9	0	7	46	31	15	27
5 Witan II	16	6	4	6	37	39	-2	22
6 Reigatians II	16	6	3	7	36	33	3	21
7 Fulham Compton Old Boys II	16	6	2	8	37	47	-10	20
8 Clapham Old Xaverians III	16	2	4	10	29	62	-33	10
9 Old Grantonians	16	1	2	13	25	59	-34	5

Five North	P	W	D	L	F	A	GD	Pts
1 Old Woodhouseians III	20	15	1	4	59	27	32	46
2 Somerville Old Boys	20	14	3	3	79	20	59	45
3 Old Kingsburians	20	12	3	5	52	35	17	39
4 Enfield Old Grammarians IV	20	11	5	4	48	28	20	38
5 Mayfield Athletic II	20	10	3	7	46	37	9	33
6 Old Tollingtonians II	20	9	2	9	51	45	6	29
7 Egbertian IV	20	5	4	11	30	48	-18	19
8 Old Edmontonians III (-3)	20	5	4	11	34	62	-28	16
9 Wood Green Old Boys II	20	4	3	13	27	58	-31	15
10 Old Parmiterians V	20	4	3	13	27	73	-46	15
11 London Hospital Old Boys	20	3	5	12	33	53	-20	14

Five South	P	W	D	L	F	A	GD	Pts
1 Old Suttonians V	16	10	4	2	58	34	24	34
2 Fulham Compton Old Boys III	16	8	5	3	45	27	18	29
3 Old Thorntonians III	16	8	3	5	40	30	10	27
4 Old Tenisonians II	16	6	6	4	46	31	15	24
5 City of London II	16	7	1	8	39	42	-3	22
6 Old Meadonians VII	16	7	1	8	38	44	-6	22
7 Dorkinians III	16	4	5	7	35	49	-14	17
8 Glyn Old Boys IV	16	4	3	9	32	58	-26	15
9 Old Sedcopians III	16	3	2	11	29	47	-18	11

Six South	P	W	D	L	F	A	GD	Pts
1 Heathrow Seniors	18	12	3	3	54	20	34	39
2 Royal Sun Alliance	18	13	0	5	69	51	18	39
3 Old Wokingians IV	18	11	2	5	45	33	12	35
4 Shene Old Grammarians III	18	10	1	7	57	32	25	31
5 Wandsworth Borough III	18	10	1	7	45	50	-5	31
6 John Fisher Old Boys II	18	6	5	7	38	38	0	23
7 Old Tiffinians II	18	7	0	11	39	57	-18	21
8 Old Tenisonians III (-3)	18	5	2	11	26	50	-24	14
9 Glyn Old Boys V	18	4	2	12	22	47	-25	14
10 Fulham Compton Old Boys IV	18	3	2	13	32	49	-17	11

Six North	P	W	D	L	F	A	GD	Pts
1 UCL Academicals V	20	17	2	1	96	23	73	53
2 Old Parmiterians VI	20	15	1	4	77	36	41	46
3 Mill Hill Village	20	14	4	2	73	35	38	46
4 Oakhill Tigers III	20	10	6	4	74	49	25	36
5 Old Salvatorians VI (-3)	20	9	2	9	51	50	1	26
6 Queen Mary College Old Boys III	20	6	5	9	39	57	-18	23
7 Old Aloysians V (-4)	20	5	6	9	47	54	-7	17
8 Lea Valley II (-3)	20	6	1	13	47	62	-15	16
9 Wood Green Old Boys III (-3)	20	5	4	11	46	86	-40	16
10 Ravenscroft Old Boys II	20	3	2	15	36	101	-65	11
11 Old Minchendenians V	20	3	1	16	54	87	-33	10

Seven North	P	W	D	L	F	A	GD	Pts
1 Old Woodhouseians IV	16	13	1	2	57	23	34	40
2 Latymer Old Boys IV	16	10	4	2	45	29	16	34
3 Mayfield Athletic III	16	9	0	7	40	41	-1	27
4 Old Manorians V	16	6	3	7	50	45	5	21
5 Bealonians IV	16	6	2	8	43	39	4	20
6 Old Ignatians IV	16	6	2	8	45	50	-5	20
7 Mill Hill Village II	16	5	4	7	35	40	-5	19
8 Old Edmontonians IV (-3)	16	5	2	9	43	56	-13	14
9 Old Parmiterians VII	16	3	0	13	22	57	-35	9

Seven South	P	W	D	L	F	A	GD	Pts
1 Reigatians III	18	15	0	3	55	21	34	45
2 Mickleham Old Boxhillians II	18	14	1	3	72	27	45	43
3 Old Wokingians V	18	12	1	5	53	38	15	37
4 Shene Old Grammarians IV	18	9	2	7	50	35	15	29
5 Old Guildfordians II	18	7	5	6	48	38	10	26
6 Old Thorntonians IV	18	8	2	8	55	46	9	26
7 Old Suttonians VI	18	7	4	7	41	33	8	25
8 Dorkinians IV	18	4	3	11	37	72	-35	15
9 Old Tiffinians III	18	2	3	13	25	60	-35	9
10 John Fisher Old Boys III	18	1	1	16	22	88	-66	4

Eight North	P	W	D	L	F	A	GD	Pts
1 Old Parmiterians VIII	16	14	1	1	68	15	53	43
2 Leyton County Old Boys II	16	12	0	4	62	28	34	36
3 Old Kingsburians II	16	10	1	5	39	31	8	31
4 Old Woodhouseians V	16	9	0	7	54	49	5	27
5 Latymer Old Boys V	16	7	2	7	40	40	0	23
6 Albanian V	16	6	0	10	49	49	0	18
7 Southgate County III	16	4	3	9	37	56	-19	15
8 Enfield Old Grammarians V	16	3	3	10	28	44	-16	12
9 Davenant Wanderers Old Boys	16	1	2	13	19	84	-65	5

Eight South	P	W	D	L	F	A	GD	Pts
1 Old Meadonians VIII	18	11	4	3	46	24	22	37
2 Clapham Old Xaverians IV	18	11	1	6	50	39	11	34
3 London Welsh II	18	10	3	5	45	24	21	33
4 Wandgas	18	9	3	6	65	39	26	30
5 Reigatians IV	18	8	5	5	47	47	0	29
6 Old Suttonians VII	18	7	5	6	52	33	19	26
7 Old Wokingians VI	18	6	4	8	42	52	-10	22
8 Sinjuns Grammarians III	18	5	2	11	31	47	-16	17
9 Wandsworth Borough IV	18	3	4	11	39	59	-20	13
10 Old Whitgiftian II	18	3	3	12	26	79	-53	12

Nine North	P	W	D	L	F	A	GD	Pts
1 Old Manorians VI	20	15	3	2	89	43	46	48
2 Old Vaughanians IV	20	14	0	6	96	50	46	42
3 Old Minchendenians VI	20	13	3	4	72	52	20	42
4 Oakhill Tigers IV	20	12	1	7	62	40	22	37
5 Old Tollingtonians III	20	11	2	7	60	50	10	35
6 Bealonians V	20	9	0	11	54	53	1	27
7 Old Edmontonians V (-3)	20	8	1	11	42	68	-26	22
8 Old Ignatians V	20	6	0	14	45	75	-30	18
9 Old Parmiterians IX	20	6	0	14	37	73	-36	18
10 Old Kingsburians III	20	4	3	13	52	77	-25	15
11 Old Challoners II (-1)	20	5	1	14	49	77	-28	15

Nine South	P	W	D	L	F	A	GD	Pts
1 Witan III	20	17	2	1	97	26	71	53
2 Old Sedcopians IV	20	15	1	4	61	29	32	46
3 Old Grantonians II	20	13	2	5	61	40	21	41
4 Old Suttonians VIII	20	12	4	4	56	36	20	40
5 Old St Columbas	20	9	2	9	40	43	-3	29
6 Old Pauline IV (-3)	20	9	2	9	59	61	-2	26
7 Old St Marys III	20	7	3	10	48	61	-13	24
8 City of London III	20	6	4	10	37	54	-17	22
9 Reigatians V	20	5	0	15	42	56	-14	15
10 Wandsworth Borough V	20	5	0	15	30	60	-30	15
11 Old Wokingians VII	20	2	0	18	28	93	-65	6

Ten South	P	W	D	L	F	A	GD	Pts
1 Old Thorntonians V	20	14	2	4	60	27	33	44
2 Old Guildfordians III	20	12	3	5	64	38	26	39
3 Old Meadonians IX	20	11	4	5	72	45	27	37
4 Old Suttonians IX	20	11	3	6	49	30	19	36
5 City of London IV	20	11	1	8	54	38	16	34
6 Tilburg Regents II	20	9	2	9	61	57	4	29
7 Old Sedcopians V	20	7	3	10	50	48	2	24
8 Reigatians VI	20	6	3	11	46	55	-9	21
9 Brent III (-1)	20	5	4	11	31	48	-17	18
10 Dorkinians V	20	4	4	12	43	73	-30	16
11 Old Wokingians VIII	20	5	1	14	33	104	-71	16

ANDOVER & DISTRICT LEAGUE

Division One	P	W	D	L	F	A	GD	Pts
1 Kingsclere	14	13	1	0	65	19	46	40
2 Andover New Street Swifts	14	9	3	2	30	18	12	30
3 Sutton Scotney	14	8	1	5	29	18	11	25
4 Kings Somborne	14	8	1	5	27	16	11	25
5 Crusaders FC	14	4	3	7	29	40	-11	15
6 South Wonston Swifts	14	3	2	9	28	43	-15	11
7 Broughton Res	14	2	2	10	21	52	-31	8
8 Sparten	14	2	1	11	19	42	-23	7

Division Two	P	W	D	L	F	A	GD	Pts
1 Kingsclere Res.	16	13	1	2	49	22	27	40
2 Swallow FC	16	9	4	3	49	22	27	31
3 AFC White Hart	16	9	2	5	44	21	23	29
4 ABC United	16	4	1	11	25	55	-30	13
5 Andover Dynamoes	16	1	0	15	14	61	-47	3

ARMY ASSOCIATION

Division One Massey Trophy	P	W	D	L	F	A	GD	Pts
1 Royal Artillery	12	9	2	1	43	18	25	29
2 Royal Engineers	12	9	1	2	28	12	16	28
3 Royal Electrical & Mechanical Engineers	12	5	2	5	26	23	3	17
4 Royal Signals	12	5	1	6	25	27	-2	16
5 Royal Logistic Corps	12	3	4	5	24	29	-5	13
6 Infantry	12	4	1	7	24	34	-10	13
7 Army Air Corps (-2)	12	1	1	10	16	43	-27	2

Division Two Massey Trophy	P	W	D	L	F	A	GD	Pts
1 Adjutants General's Corps	8	6	1	1	23	6	17	19
2 Royal Army Physical Training Corps	8	4	3	1	21	11	10	15
3 Army Medical Services	8	3	0	5	9	14	-5	9
4 Intelligence Corps	8	2	1	5	8	23	-15	7
5 Royal Armoured Corps (-2)	8	2	1	5	5	12	-7	5

ARTHURIAN LEAGUE

Premier Division	P	W	D	L	F	A	GD	Pts
1 Old Carthusians I	17	14	3	0	51	17	34	45
2 Lancing Old Boys I	18	10	1	7	39	28	11	31
3 Old Foresters I	18	8	5	5	45	25	20	29
4 Old Etonians I	18	8	4	6	38	31	7	28
5 Old Cholmeleians I	18	9	1	8	42	36	6	28
6 Old Salopians I	18	6	6	6	32	31	1	24
7 Old Brentwoods I	18	7	2	9	33	45	-12	23
8 Old Harrovians I	18	6	4	8	34	36	-2	22
9 Old Chigwellians I (-3)	17	3	6	8	23	35	-12	12
10 Old Malvernians I	18	1	2	15	21	74	-53	5

Division One	P	W	D	L	F	A	GD	Pts
1 Kings College Wimbledon I	18	16	2	0	78	20	58	50
2 Old Tonbridgians	18	10	3	5	49	30	19	33
3 Old Aldenhamians I	18	8	2	8	39	35	4	26
4 Old Reptonians	17	7	4	6	40	38	2	25
5 Old Westminsters I	18	6	6	6	42	40	2	24
6 Old Wykehamists I	18	7	3	8	47	46	1	24
7 Old Haileyburians	18	6	3	9	42	54	-12	21
8 Old Radleians	18	5	5	8	38	45	-7	20
9 Old Bradfieldians I (-6)	17	7	2	8	40	45	-5	17
10 Old King's Scholars	18	2	0	16	21	83	-62	6

Division Two	P	W	D	L	F	A	GD	Pts
1 Old Carthusians III	18	14	1	3	46	22	24	43
2 Old Marlburians	18	11	4	3	69	27	42	37
3 Old Carthusians II	16	10	4	2	47	19	28	34
4 Old Cholmeleians II	18	9	6	3	47	34	13	33
5 Old Wellingtonians	18	8	3	7	32	38	-6	27
6 Old Chigwellians II (-3)	18	6	1	11	33	37	-4	16
7 Lancing Old Boys II (-3)	17	6	1	10	26	36	-10	16
8 Old Haberdashers (-3)	17	5	2	10	33	54	-21	14
9 Old Aldenhamians II	18	4	2	12	31	66	-35	14
10 Old Salopians II	18	2	2	14	19	50	-31	8

Division Three	P	W	D	L	F	A	GD	Pts
1 Old Foresters II	16	9	4	3	32	19	13	31
2 Old Etonians II	16	9	3	4	32	25	7	30
3 Old Berkhamstedians	16	8	3	5	39	36	3	27
4 Old Epsomians	15	8	2	5	41	29	12	26
5 Kings College Wimbledon II	16	7	0	9	46	48	-2	21
6 Old Harrovians II (-3)	15	6	3	6	33	37	-4	18
7 Old Brentwoods II (-3)	16	5	2	9	32	37	-5	14
8 Old Wykehamists II	16	3	5	8	27	41	-14	14
9 Old Cholmeleians III	16	3	4	9	24	34	-10	13

Division Four	P	W	D	L	F	A	GD	Pts
1 Old Citizens	14	12	1	1	66	16	50	37
2 Old Malvernians II	14	8	2	4	31	25	6	26
3 Old Stoics I	14	6	2	6	33	35	-2	20
4 Old Brentwoods III	14	5	3	6	32	44	-12	18
5 Old Chigwellians III	14	4	3	7	27	31	-4	15
6 Old Eastbournians	14	3	4	7	28	36	-8	13
7 Old Bancroftians	14	2	7	5	17	30	-13	13
8 Old Westminsters II	14	3	4	7	19	36	-17	13

Division Five	P	W	D	L	F	A	GD	Pts
1 Old Amplefordians	12	9	0	3	43	28	15	27
2 Old Sennockians	12	8	0	4	42	31	11	24
3 Old Brentwoods IV	12	7	1	4	35	25	10	22
4 Old Millhillians	12	5	2	5	43	34	9	17
5 Old Harrovians III	12	4	1	7	29	42	-13	13
6 Old Cholmeleians IV	12	3	1	8	26	33	-7	10
7 Old Foresters III	12	3	1	8	25	50	-25	10

AYLESBURY & DISTRICT LEAGUE

Premier Division	P	W	D	L	F	A	GD	Pts
1 Walton Court Wanderers	19	16	2	1	67	19	48	50
2 Bucks CC	19	15	1	3	80	21	59	46
3 AFC Victoria	20	11	3	6	71	41	30	36
4 Aylesbury Dynamos	20	10	5	5	53	47	6	35
5 New Zealand	20	10	1	9	57	56	1	31
6 Bierton FC Wanderers	20	9	2	9	48	44	4	29
7 Downley Albion	20	8	2	10	38	52	-14	26
8 Haddenham United	20	6	3	11	35	47	-12	21
9 Berkhamsted Sports	20	6	3	11	49	63	-14	21
10 FC Spandits	20	5	2	13	42	75	-33	17
11 Bedgrove Dynamos	20	1	0	19	24	99	-75	3

Division One	P	W	D	L	F	A	GD	Pts
1 Long Marston	20	14	4	2	62	27	35	46
2 Great Milton	20	14	1	5	68	30	38	43
3 Elmhurst	20	13	3	4	56	33	23	42
4 Pond Park Rangers	20	9	2	9	60	68	-8	29
5 Wendover	20	8	2	10	45	42	3	26
6 Bedgrove United	20	8	2	10	35	51	-16	26
7 FC Mandeville	20	8	1	11	36	52	-16	25
8 Oving	20	6	4	10	53	52	1	22
9 Wingrave	20	7	0	13	46	54	-8	21
10 Ludgershall	20	5	5	10	28	42	-14	20
11 Rivets Sports	20	5	2	13	34	72	-38	17

Division Two	P	W	D	L	F	A	GD	Pts
1 Northchurch	20	16	1	3	72	25	47	49
2 Aylesbury Sports	20	15	2	3	79	38	41	47
3 Aylesbury Park Rangers	20	15	1	4	78	37	41	46
4 Tring Titans	20	14	1	5	66	44	22	43
5 Haddenham United Res.	20	7	4	9	54	62	-8	25
6 Quainton	20	7	2	11	46	58	-12	23
7 Downley Albion Res.	19	6	4	9	49	57	-8	22
8 Stone Magnets / St Johns	20	5	2	13	22	60	-38	17
9 Long Crendon	20	4	4	12	42	58	-16	16
10 Bierton FC Wanderers Res.	20	4	2	14	42	67	-25	14
11 MDM United	19	4	1	14	35	79	-44	13

Division Three	P	W	D	L	F	A	GD	Pts
1 Bucks CC Res.	20	17	1	2	72	24	48	52
2 Tetsworth	20	14	1	5	84	36	48	43
3 Brill United	19	12	4	3	51	28	23	40
4 FC Spandits Res.	20	11	1	8	49	51	-2	34
5 Rivets Sports Res.	20	10	2	8	56	49	7	32
6 Waddesdon	20	10	1	9	48	41	7	31
7 Wingrave Res.	20	8	5	7	27	32	-5	29
8 Long Marston Res.	19	6	3	10	31	35	-4	21
9 Wendover Res.	20	4	2	14	45	60	-15	14
10 Ludgershall Res.	20	3	4	13	32	58	-26	13
11 Aylesbury Wanderers	20	1	2	17	20	101	-81	5

Division Four	P	W	D	L	F	A	GD	Pts
1 Quainton Res.	24	20	2	2	121	37	84	62
2 Oving Res.	24	17	1	6	107	46	61	52
3 PIC United	24	16	2	6	90	47	43	50
4 Waddesdon Res.	24	11	7	6	54	48	6	40
5 Aylesbury ex Servicemens	24	12	2	10	65	69	-4	38
6 Bedgrove United Res.	24	11	4	9	58	54	4	37
7 Tetsworth Res.	24	9	6	9	67	58	9	33
8 Bedgrove Dynamos Res.	24	9	5	10	65	71	-6	32
9 Brill United Res.	24	9	3	12	61	66	-5	30
10 Churchill Arms	24	7	1	16	52	77	-25	22
11 Tring Titans Res.	24	6	4	14	50	101	-51	22
12 AC Meadowcroft	24	5	1	18	37	94	-57	16
13 Great Milton Res.	24	3	4	17	37	96	-59	13

BANBURY DISTRICT & LORD JERSEY

Premier Division	P	W	D	L	F	A	GD	Pts
1 Heyford Athletic	20	15	5	0	55	19	36	50
2 Bishops Itchington	20	13	5	2	73	29	44	44
3 Heyford United	20	13	2	5	50	33	17	41
4 Woodford United	20	11	3	6	41	28	13	36
5 ABBA Athletic	20	8	5	7	54	37	17	29
6 SInclair United	20	9	2	9	37	47	-10	29
7 Cropredy	20	7	4	9	32	35	-3	25
8 Deddington Town	20	6	0	14	41	50	-9	18
9 Steeple Aston	20	5	3	12	24	35	-11	18
10 KEA	20	3	3	14	17	53	-36	12
11 Highfield Old Boys	20	3	2	15	20	78	-58	11

Division One	P	W	D	L	F	A	GD	Pts
1 Banbury Rangers	20	14	2	4	84	39	45	44
2 Deddington Town Res.	20	14	2	4	45	29	16	44
3 Hornton	20	11	4	5	50	34	16	37
4 Middleton Cheney	20	11	4	5	60	46	14	37
5 Bodicote Sports	20	10	4	6	65	49	16	34
6 Bloxham	20	7	4	9	50	43	7	25
7 Kings Sutton	20	6	4	10	36	45	-9	22
8 Chesterton	20	7	1	12	41	52	-11	22
9 FC Langford	20	6	1	13	35	58	-23	19
10 Sinclair United Res.	20	5	2	13	27	53	-26	17
11 Highfield Old Boys Res.	20	3	4	13	31	76	-45	13

Division Two	P	W	D	L	F	A	GD	Pts
1 Ashton Villa	22	21	0	1	140	28	112	63
2 Diverse	22	16	3	3	91	28	63	51
3 Finmere	22	15	1	6	66	40	26	46
4 Woodford United Res.	22	12	3	7	63	37	26	39
5 Souldern	22	11	4	7	58	60	-2	37
6 Chasewell Park	22	11	2	9	61	57	4	35
7 Banbury United Youth	22	7	6	9	56	56	0	27
8 Swis FC	22	7	2	13	38	68	-30	23
9 Wroxton Sports	22	6	4	12	36	64	-28	22
10 Heyford Athletic Res.	22	6	4	12	33	61	-28	22
11 Bloxham Res.	22	3	2	17	40	117	-77	11
12 Banbury Galaxy	22	1	1	20	33	99	-66	4

Division Three	P	W	D	L	F	A	GD	Pts
1 Chacombe	20	15	2	3	65	26	39	47
2 Steeple Aston Res.	20	13	2	5	75	29	46	41
3 Bishops Itchington Res.	20	11	6	3	60	28	32	39
4 Cropredy Res.	20	11	2	7	58	48	10	35
5 Wroxton Sports Res.	20	10	3	7	47	44	3	33
6 Chasewell Park Res.	20	8	6	6	59	38	21	30
7 Kings Sutton Res.	20	9	2	9	43	54	-11	29
8 Bodicote Sports Res.	20	7	4	9	67	62	5	25
9 Finmere Res.	20	4	5	11	37	60	-23	17
10 Swis FC Res.	20	5	1	14	37	70	-33	16
11 Woodford United A	20	0	1	19	15	104	-89	1

BASINGSTOKE & DISTRICT LEAGUE

Premier Division	P	W	D	L	F	A	GD	Pts
1 Welly Old Boys	12	10	2	0	30	12	18	32
2 New Inn	12	9	0	3	33	13	20	27
3 Hook FC	12	6	2	4	27	10	17	20
4 Basingstoke Royals	12	5	4	3	17	13	4	19
5 Sherborne St John	12	4	2	6	26	36	-10	14
6 Popley FC	12	1	2	9	12	31	-19	5
7 Old Basing Rangers	12	0	2	10	13	43	-30	2

Division One	P	W	D	L	F	A	GD	Pts
1 Skewers FC	16	11	3	2	47	35	12	36
2 Tadley Calleva (A)	16	9	4	3	68	26	42	31
3 Bramley United	16	10	0	6	42	30	12	30
4 Overton Utd (A)	16	8	4	4	35	33	2	28
5 Pure Spartan	16	7	3	6	37	48	-11	24
6 Welly Old Boys (Res.)	16	7	2	7	29	28	1	23
7 Hook (Res.)	16	6	1	9	32	28	4	19
8 Chineham Albion	16	4	0	12	17	42	-25	12
9 Herriard Sports	16	1	1	14	22	59	-37	4

Division Two	P	W	D	L	F	A	GD	Pts
1 DJS Telecoms	20	16	1	3	82	38	44	49
2 Hampshire Irons	20	15	2	3	80	30	50	47
3 Basingstoke Twenty-Ten	20	11	6	3	68	42	26	39
4 Bengal Brasserie	20	11	0	9	49	48	1	33
5 Bounty Utd	20	9	5	6	56	41	15	32
6 Basingstoke Athletic	20	8	3	9	33	36	-3	27
7 Overton United 'B'	20	8	2	10	44	41	3	26
8 AFC Aldermaston (A)	20	6	2	12	48	59	-11	20
9 AFC Berg	20	5	4	11	47	68	-21	19
10 Basingstoke Labour Club	20	4	2	14	35	75	-40	14
11 Sherborne St John Res.	20	2	3	15	23	87	-64	9

BATH & DISTRICT LEAGUE

Division One	P	W	D	L	F	A	GD	Pts
1 Newbridge FC	9	9	0	0	42	7	35	27
2 Trowbridge House	9	8	0	1	42	11	31	24
3 Stockwood Wanderers	9	6	1	2	48	10	38	19
4 AFC Durbin United	9	6	0	3	55	14	41	18
5 Stothert & Pitt	9	4	2	3	39	24	15	14
6 Aces	9	4	1	4	42	32	10	13
7 Old Crown Weston	9	3	0	6	24	39	-15	9
8 Stockwood Wanderers Res.	9	2	0	7	16	46	-30	6
9 Aces Res.	9	1	0	8	11	44	-33	3
10 Westfield FC	9	0	0	9	6	98	-92	0

BIRMINGHAM AFA

Premier Division	P	W	D	L	F	A	GD	Pts
1 OLd Wulfrunians A	24	19	3	2	58	17	41	60
2 Boldmere Sports & Social A	24	15	1	8	52	33	19	46
3 AFC Somers	24	11	7	6	38	29	9	40
4 Village A	24	11	6	7	43	34	9	39
5 Smithswood Colts (-3)	24	11	5	8	59	53	6	35
6 CPA A	24	9	5	10	41	37	4	32
7 St Georges Warriors A	24	10	2	12	46	57	-11	32
8 Athletic Sparkhill	24	9	4	11	55	61	-6	31
9 Silhill A	24	7	7	10	60	62	-2	28
10 Handsworth GSOB's A	24	8	2	14	49	73	-24	26
11 Walsall Phoenix A	24	7	3	14	48	55	-7	24
12 Crusaders	24	6	6	12	37	48	-11	24
13 Wake Green AMS A	24	5	5	14	37	64	-27	20

Division One	P	W	D	L	F	A	GD	Pts
1 Kings Heath OB's	18	12	3	3	58	22	36	39
2 F.C Premier A	18	12	3	3	45	21	24	39
3 Sutton United A	18	11	2	5	51	30	21	35
4 Parkfield Amateurs A	18	11	1	6	48	37	11	34
5 Flamengo	18	10	1	7	40	37	3	31
6 Old Hill	18	9	2	7	49	32	17	29
7 Bentley Heath United (-3)	18	5	3	10	33	43	-10	15
8 Village B	18	4	2	12	27	51	-24	14
9 Shere Punjan	18	3	3	12	22	54	-32	12
10 Blackheath Town	18	3	0	15	19	65	-46	9

Division Two	P	W	D	L	F	A	GD	Pts
1 Triumph Meriden	26	20	4	2	71	17	54	64
2 OLd Wulfrunians B	26	20	3	3	69	26	43	63
3 B T FC	26	19	2	5	80	45	35	59
4 Silhill B (-2)	26	15	3	8	79	57	22	46
5 BNJS FC (-6)	26	16	1	9	70	61	9	43
6 Malremo Rangers	26	8	8	10	55	50	5	32
7 Bournville Colts (-3)	26	10	5	11	53	54	-1	32
8 Rossi & Rossi A	26	8	6	12	42	43	-1	30
9 Coldlands	26	6	10	10	42	49	-7	28
10 Wake Green Amateurs B	26	7	6	13	41	58	-17	27
11 St. Pauls	26	8	3	15	33	50	-17	27
12 Bearwood Athletic	26	6	5	15	46	85	-39	23
13 Village C	26	4	5	17	27	58	-31	17
14 Desi FC	26	3	3	20	31	86	-55	12

Division Three	P	W	D	L	F	A	GD	Pts
1 Birmingham Irish	20	16	3	1	51	17	34	51
2 Olympia 808 A	20	13	2	5	62	36	26	41
3 Pathfinder	20	11	3	6	51	34	17	36
4 Walsall Phoenix B	20	10	1	9	46	46	0	31
5 St Georges Warriors B	20	9	3	8	48	32	16	30
6 Cresconians	20	10	0	10	50	47	3	30
7 Amanah A	20	9	2	9	44	34	10	29
8 Aston FC	20	8	5	7	51	45	6	29
9 Real Riverside A	20	5	1	14	39	74	-35	16
10 Urban Athletic	20	3	5	12	36	69	-33	14
11 Wake Green Amateurs C	20	3	1	16	40	84	-44	10

Division Four	P	W	D	L	F	A	GD	Pts
1 Castle Bromwich United	24	18	3	3	106	51	55	54
2 Birmingham Medics	24	16	3	5	68	30	38	51
3 Sportsco	24	15	1	8	77	55	22	46
4 Castlecroft Rangers	24	14	2	8	55	40	15	44
5 Boldmere Sports & Social B	24	11	6	7	42	42	0	39
6 Rossi & Rossi B	24	8	7	9	48	44	4	31
7 F.C Premier B	24	8	4	12	46	42	4	28
8 Village D	24	8	4	12	46	65	-19	28
9 Parkfield Amateurs B	24	7	5	12	46	64	-18	26
10 Birmingham Citadel	24	8	2	14	37	66	-29	26
11 CPA 2nds	24	6	5	13	41	74	-33	23
12 OLd Wulfrunians C	24	6	4	14	33	61	-28	22
13 Meriden Athletic	24	3	10	11	53	64	-11	19

Division Five	P	W	D	L	F	A	GD	Pts
1 Walsall Allstars (-3)	26	20	3	3	123	33	90	60
2 Sutton United B	26	17	4	5	99	54	45	55
3 Rubery	26	16	4	6	94	39	55	52
4 Wood Wanderers	26	15	5	6	73	39	34	50
5 Roaring Lions	26	14	4	8	79	47	32	46
6 Round Oak Rangers	26	13	5	8	67	51	16	44
7 Wake Green Amateurs D	26	13	4	9	75	57	18	43
8 Hall Green United	26	12	4	10	68	64	4	40
9 Red Star Galaxy	26	11	1	14	64	93	-29	34
10 Boldmere Sports & Social C	26	10	1	15	49	78	-29	31
11 Silhill C (-2)	26	7	5	14	71	84	-13	24
12 Village E	26	7	1	18	43	82	-39	22
13 Garden House Rangers	26	4	3	19	33	80	-47	15
14 Birmingham Deaf (-9)	26	1	0	25	27	164	-137	-6

Division Six	P	W	D	L	F	A	GD	Pts
1 Silhill D	20	14	5	1	74	32	42	47
2 Walsall Phoenix C	20	14	2	4	59	29	30	44
3 Coleshill North Warwick	20	13	2	5	55	35	20	41
4 AFC Vesey	20	10	6	4	42	34	8	36
5 Amanah B	19	11	1	7	49	44	5	34
6 Coton Green	19	7	2	10	29	39	-10	23
7 Olympia 808 B	20	7	2	11	32	47	-15	23
8 Handsworth GSOB's B	20	6	3	11	42	41	1	21
9 Dudley Athletic	20	5	4	11	39	53	-14	19
10 Manchester Wanderers	20	5	3	12	39	55	-16	18
11 Real Riverside B	20	1	2	17	22	73	-51	5

Division Seven	P	W	D	L	F	A	GD	Pts
1 Spartak Monkers	20	17	3	0	99	17	82	54
2 Selly Oak Legend	20	13	2	5	76	36	40	41
3 Walsall Phoenix D	20	12	3	5	71	43	28	39
4 Coldfield Rangers	20	10	4	6	55	50	5	34
5 Saltley Stallions (-7)	20	11	5	4	88	52	36	31
6 Smethwick Raiders	20	7	2	11	54	60	-6	23
7 Sutton United C	20	7	2	11	55	68	-13	23
8 Steelhouse Lane	20	7	1	12	52	77	-25	22
9 Handsworth GSOB's C	20	6	1	13	55	80	-25	19
10 Wake Green Amateurs E (-3)	20	4	2	14	37	65	-28	11
11 Sporting FC (-3)	20	3	1	16	29	123	-94	7

BISHOP'S STORTFORD, STANSTED & DISTRICT LEAGUE

Premier Division	P	W	D	L	F	A	GD	Pts
1 Sheering	14	12	1	1	32	13	19	37
2 Northolt	14	7	4	3	45	30	15	25
3 Heath Rovers	14	6	5	3	34	24	10	23
4 Parsloe Athletic	14	7	2	5	26	27	-1	23
5 Hertfordshire Rangers	14	4	5	5	26	31	-5	17
6 Avondale Rangers	14	4	2	8	28	33	-5	14
7 Frontiers	14	2	4	8	17	37	-20	10
8 Harbridge Athletic	14	2	1	11	15	28	-13	7

Division One	P	W	D	L	F	A	GD	Pts
1 Hatfield Heath	18	16	1	1	84	22	62	49
2 North Weald	18	12	2	4	44	27	17	38
3 Lower Street	18	11	2	5	66	30	36	35
4 Fairways Corinthians	18	9	2	7	51	39	12	29
5 Avondale Rangers Res.	18	8	4	6	54	37	17	28
6 Birchanger	18	7	2	9	53	44	9	23
7 E F Lakers	18	5	4	9	32	62	-30	19
8 Albury	18	5	3	10	27	54	-27	18
9 Potter Street	18	4	0	14	23	54	-31	12
10 Sheering Res.	18	2	2	14	23	88	-65	8

BLACKBURN & DISTRICT FOOTBALL COMBINATION

Premier Division	P	W	D	L	F	A	GD	Pts
1 Rishton United	20	18	0	2	100	30	70	54
2 Blackburn United	20	14	1	5	47	26	21	43
3 Vauxhall Inn	20	11	2	7	53	45	8	35
4 Anchor	20	9	3	8	67	53	14	30
5 Hole I'th Wall	20	10	0	10	47	49	-2	30
6 Wellington Inn	20	9	2	9	59	54	5	29
7 Clifton	20	9	1	10	51	63	-12	28
8 Feildens Arms	20	7	2	11	47	54	-7	23
9 Blackburn Olympic	20	6	0	14	43	67	-24	18
10 Islington	20	5	3	12	41	75	-34	18
11 Greenfield	20	4	2	14	36	75	-39	14

Second Division	P	W	D	L	F	A	GD	Pts
1 The Ivy Veterans	18	14	2	1	77	33	44	44
2 Clayton Park (-6)	18	15	1	1	76	29	47	40
3 IMO (+3)	18	12	1	5	52	26	26	40
4 Whalley Range	18	9	2	7	39	43	-4	29
5 Blackburn United Res. (+3)	18	6	2	9	48	49	-1	23
6 The Lion	18	7	2	9	65	68	-3	23
7 Alexandra Hotel	18	6	3	9	57	48	9	21
8 Rishton United Res.	18	6	0	11	47	46	1	18
9 Worth Avenue	18	5	1	12	41	73	-32	16
10 Blackburn Eagles	18	0	2	16	20	107	-87	2

BOURNEMOUTH HAYWARD SATURDAY LEAGUE

Premier Division	P	W	D	L	F	A	GD	Pts
1 Richmond Park Con Club	22	20	0	2	92	17	75	60
2 Bournemouth Manor	22	16	3	3	63	23	40	51
3 Bournemouth Electric	22	15	1	6	67	33	34	46
4 Hamworthy Recreation	22	12	3	7	55	41	14	39
5 Mudeford Mens Club	22	9	4	9	50	49	1	31
6 Portcastrian	22	8	2	12	45	57	-12	26
7 Sway	22	7	4	11	39	50	-11	25
8 Parley Sports	22	7	4	11	34	50	-16	25
9 Westover Bournemouth	22	7	1	14	31	60	-29	22
10 Old Oakmeadians	22	5	6	11	26	47	-21	21
11 Ferndown Sports	22	5	3	14	42	64	-22	18
12 Bournemouth Poppies Res. (-1)	22	5	1	16	30	83	-53	15

Division One	P	W	D	L	F	A	GD	Pts
1 Bournemouth Electric Res.	18	12	3	3	71	34	37	39
2 BU Staff	18	12	2	4	45	26	19	38
3 Bisterne United	18	10	3	5	39	32	7	33
4 Allendale	18	9	3	6	60	38	22	30
5 Alderholt	18	8	5	5	36	38	-2	29
6 Barton Linnets	18	8	3	7	43	44	-1	27
7 Sway Res.	18	6	2	10	36	41	-5	20
8 Mploy	18	4	4	10	39	47	-8	16
9 Holt Res.	18	4	3	11	27	50	-23	15
10 Walkford	18	3	0	15	28	74	-46	9

Division Two	P	W	D	L	F	A	GD	Pts
1 Westover Bournemouth Res.	18	13	4	1	50	18	32	43
2 AFC Pennington	18	13	1	4	61	22	39	40
3 AFC Burton	18	12	4	2	57	33	24	40
4 Bournemouth Electric A	18	9	4	5	43	32	11	31
5 Boscombe Polonia	18	7	4	7	38	39	-1	25
6 Mudeford Mens Club Res.	18	7	3	8	30	40	-10	24
7 Ferndown Sports Res.	18	7	1	10	39	49	-10	22
8 Redlynch and Woodfalls	18	4	3	11	33	60	-27	15
9 St Marys	18	4	1	13	27	45	-18	13
10 Old Oakmeadians Res.	18	1	1	16	15	55	-40	4

Division Three	P	W	D	L	F	A	GD	Pts
1 Tavern Celtic	20	14	4	2	82	31	51	46
2 Fifa Standards	20	14	2	4	63	27	36	44
3 Bournemouth Manor Res.	20	11	3	6	63	41	22	36
4 Richmond Park Con Club Res.	20	10	5	5	58	36	22	35
5 West Howe (-3)	20	11	2	7	60	53	7	32
6 Bisterne United Res.	20	9	5	6	51	48	3	32
7 AFC Springbourne	20	6	4	10	49	63	-14	22
8 New Milton Eagles	20	6	4	10	45	63	-18	22
9 AFC Bransgore	20	6	1	13	36	54	-18	19
10 Redhill Rangers	20	3	3	14	38	68	-30	12
11 Fordingbridge Turks	20	3	1	16	11	72	-61	10

Division Four	P	W	D	L	F	A	GD	Pts
1 Lower Parkstone CFC	18	13	0	5	54	23	31	39
2 Allendale Res.	18	12	1	5	69	29	40	37
3 Milford	18	12	1	5	53	40	13	37
4 Alderholt Res.	18	11	3	4	47	25	22	36
5 Portcastrian Res.	18	9	2	7	46	37	9	29
6 Magpies	18	6	3	9	34	43	-9	21
7 Ringwood Athletic	18	6	2	10	38	51	-13	20
8 Witchampton Res.	18	5	4	9	22	46	-24	19
9 Burley	18	4	1	13	27	66	-39	13
10 AFC Burton Res.	18	3	1	14	27	57	-30	10

Division Five	P	W	D	L	F	A	GD	Pts
1 Gotham	20	19	1	0	139	29	110	58
2 Richmond Park Con Club A	20	14	4	2	99	28	71	46
3 Bournemouth Poppies A (-3)	20	13	2	5	78	32	46	38
4 Boldre Royals	20	12	0	8	73	44	29	36
5 Pennington St Marks	20	10	1	9	51	64	-13	31
6 Bransgore Utd	20	8	2	10	44	52	-8	26
7 Ferndown Sports A	20	7	3	10	46	59	-13	24
8 Parkstone Athletic	20	7	1	12	52	90	-38	22
9 New Milton Rovers	20	6	1	13	54	86	-32	19
10 Redhill Rangers Res.	20	4	1	15	27	83	-56	13
11 Milford Res.	20	1	2	17	22	118	-96	5

BRIGHTON & HOVE DISTRICT LEAGUE

Premier Division	P	W	D	L	F	A	GD	Pts
1 Hair Razors	18	15	2	1	44	12	32	47
2 C.C.K	18	9	5	4	39	31	8	32
3 Ovingdean	18	9	2	7	32	34	-2	29
4 Hurren & Glynn	18	8	4	6	47	43	4	28
5 Brighton Electricity	18	6	4	8	33	42	-9	22
6 Romans United	18	3	2	13	24	34	-10	11
7 Montpelier Villa	18	3	1	14	32	55	-23	10

Division One	P	W	D	L	F	A	GD	Pts
1 South Coast City	21	19	1	1	100	25	75	58
2 Bishop & Light	21	13	4	4	62	39	23	43
3 Boys Brigade Old Boys	21	10	4	7	49	42	7	34
4 The View	21	10	4	7	43	38	5	34
5 Racing Palmeira	21	10	4	7	35	37	-2	34
6 Midway	21	7	1	13	26	53	-27	22
7 Rottingdean Village Res.	21	2	2	17	19	47	-28	8
8 Southwick Rangers	21	2	2	17	19	72	-53	8

Division Two	P	W	D	L	F	A	GD	PTS
1 Boys Brigade Old Boys II	14	10	2	2	67	14	53	32
2 Southwick Rangers II	14	10	1	3	50	21	29	31
3 Portslade Athletic Res.	14	8	3	3	34	22	12	27
4 Montpelier Villa II	14	7	1	6	48	30	18	22
5 Unity	14	7	1	6	28	25	3	22
6 The Lectern	14	3	3	8	30	47	-17	12
7 C.C.K II	14	2	4	8	26	58	-32	10
8 Lansdowne United	14	1	1	12	21	87	-66	4

BRISTOL & AVON LEAGUE

Premier Division	P	W	D	L	F	A	GD	Pts
1 Bristol Sports	26	19	3	4	96	39	57	60
2 Broad Plain 'A'	26	19	3	4	100	57	43	60
3 L S United (-3)	26	18	2	6	81	49	32	53
4 Iron Acton 'B'	26	14	3	9	81	80	1	45
5 Whitchurch Phoenix	26	14	2	10	86	72	14	44
6 AFC Hartcliffe Res.	26	14	1	11	63	60	3	43
7 De-Veys Res.	26	13	2	11	83	64	19	41
8 Bristol Revolution	26	11	4	11	82	59	23	37
9 Broad Walk Community Res.	26	10	5	11	68	62	6	35
10 Westerleigh Sports Res.	26	9	4	13	65	90	-25	31
11 Dodington	26	8	2	16	73	75	-2	26
12 Wessex Wanderers 'A'	26	7	0	19	37	116	-79	21
13 Sea Mills Park 'A'	26	5	2	19	47	93	-46	17
14 Bradley Stoke Town 'B'	26	3	3	20	37	83	-46	12

BRISTOL & DISTRICT LEAGUE

Senior Division	P	W	D	L	F	A	GD	Pts
1 AEK Boco Res.	26	20	3	3	62	28	34	63
2 Crosscourt United	26	18	1	7	68	38	30	55
3 Portville Warriors (-3)	26	17	4	5	85	45	40	52
4 Bristol Barcelona	26	15	5	6	64	34	30	50
5 Pucklechurch Sports	26	13	7	6	65	45	20	46
6 De Veys	26	9	6	11	41	51	-10	33
7 Longwell Green Sports 'A'	26	11	0	15	52	63	-11	33
8 Iron Acton	26	8	6	12	49	51	-2	30
9 Shirehampton Res. (-3)	26	10	3	13	59	71	-12	30
10 Henbury Res.	26	8	5	13	54	55	-1	29
11 Hallen 'A'	26	8	4	14	63	76	-13	28
12 Wick Res. (-1)	26	7	5	14	43	87	-44	25
13 Warmley Saints	26	6	4	16	42	76	-34	22
14 Nicholas Wanderers Res.	26	4	3	19	38	65	-27	15

Division One	P	W	D	L	F	A	GD	Pts
1 Hambrook	24	20	3	1	91	24	67	63
2 Talbot Knowle United	24	16	4	4	68	30	38	52
3 Bradley Stoke Town	24	14	7	3	55	35	20	49
4 Mendip United Res.	24	15	3	6	51	34	17	48
5 Totterdown United Res.	24	11	2	11	50	50	0	35
6 St Pancras (-3)	24	10	4	10	53	56	-3	33
7 Soundwell Victoria	24	9	3	12	37	56	-19	30
8 Lebeq (Saturday) FC.Res.	24	8	5	11	50	49	1	29
9 Wnterbourne United 'A'	24	8	3	13	51	56	-5	27
10 Chipping Sodbury Town Res.	24	7	5	12	45	59	-14	26
11 Rangeworthy	24	5	5	14	41	68	-27	20
12 Seymour United Res.	24	5	5	14	34	66	-32	20
13 Stanton Drew	24	2	3	19	26	69	-43	9

Division Two	P	W	D	L	F	A	GD	Pts
1 Real Thornbury	26	26	0	0	157	14	143	78
2 Cribbs 'A'	26	19	2	5	94	44	50	59
3 Bendix	26	16	7	3	77	48	29	55
4 Frampton Athletic Res.	26	13	7	6	67	39	28	46
5 AEK Boco 'A'	26	13	5	8	64	52	12	44
6 Iron Acton Res	26	11	6	9	60	70	-10	39
7 Frys Club 'A'	26	11	3	12	68	67	1	36
8 Hanham Athletic Res.	26	10	6	10	52	65	-13	36
9 Greyfriars Athletic Res.	26	9	6	11	49	54	-5	33
10 Chipping Sodbury Town 'A'	26	7	2	17	37	68	-31	23
11 DRG Frenchay Res.	26	6	3	17	41	69	-28	21
12 Nicholas Wanderers 'A'	26	5	6	15	29	65	-36	21
13 Hartcliffe	26	5	0	21	35	119	-84	15
14 Coalpit Heath	26	4	1	21	26	82	-56	13

Division Three	P	W	D	L	F	A	GD	Pts
1 Stapleton	26	23	3	0	102	13	89	72
2 Patchway North End	26	22	3	1	73	24	49	69
3 Yate Athletic	26	13	4	9	56	44	12	43
4 Bristol Barcelona Res.	26	13	3	10	46	44	2	42
5 Pucklechurch Sports Res.	26	11	4	11	47	60	-13	37
6 South Bristol Central	26	10	6	10	51	66	-15	36
7 Olveston United Res.	26	11	1	14	63	58	5	34
8 Horfield United	26	10	3	13	55	47	8	33
9 Henbury F C 'A'	26	10	2	14	44	28	16	32
10 Hillfields Old Boys (-3)	26	9	6	11	76	77	-1	30
11 Hallen 'B'	26	9	3	14	50	67	-17	30
12 Made For Ever Res	26	8	4	14	50	57	-7	28
13 Hambrook Res.	26	7	1	18	48	94	-46	22
14 Roman Glass St George 'A'	26	3	3	20	38	120	-82	12

Division Four	P	W	D	L	F	A	GD	Pts
1 Highridge United Res.	26	21	2	3	70	21	49	65
2 Shaftesbury Crusade Res.	26	18	4	4	92	41	51	58
3 Westerleigh Sports	26	17	4	5	97	44	53	55
4 Old Sodbury Res	26	18	1	7	94	54	40	55
5 Fishponds Athletic	26	17	2	7	106	57	49	53
6 Sea Mills Park Res	26	13	3	10	58	51	7	42
7 Frys Club 'B'	26	13	2	11	76	55	21	41
8 Bradley Stoke Town Res.	26	12	4	10	66	46	20	40
9 Greyfriars Athletic 'A'	26	9	1	16	50	98	-48	28
10 Wick 'A'	26	7	5	14	39	72	-33	26
11 Talbot Knowle United (-3)	26	7	2	17	49	93	-44	20
12 Soundwell Victoria Res	26	5	4	17	28	59	-31	19
13 Bendix Res.	26	3	2	21	26	107	-81	11
14 Lawrence Rovers Res (-3)	26	3	2	21	40	93	-53	8

Division Five	P	W	D	L	F	A	GD	Pts
1 Staple Hill Orient	22	19	3	0	81	21	60	60
2 Oldland Abbotonians 'A'	22	15	2	5	74	40	34	47
3 Tormarton	22	14	3	5	51	21	30	45
4 Shireway Sports	22	13	3	6	71	47	24	42
5 Crosscourt United Res.	22	10	3	9	58	51	7	33
6 Iron Acton 'A'	22	9	2	11	59	67	-8	29
7 Mendip United 'A'	22	7	6	9	60	57	3	27
8 Patchway North End Res.	22	7	4	11	44	65	-21	25
9 Stanton Drew Res	22	7	4	11	43	68	-25	25
10 Rangeworthy Res.	22	5	2	15	47	79	-32	17
11 Highridge United 'A'	22	5	2	15	45	87	-42	17
12 Brislington Cricketers Res.	22	3	2	17	25	55	-30	11

Dlvision Six	P	W	D	L	F	A	GD	Pts
1 Stapleton Res.	22	19	1	2	90	21	69	58
2 Stoke Lane	22	18	0	4	120	30	90	54
3 Hanham Athletic Colts	22	15	3	4	71	24	47	48
4 Bradley Stoke Town 'A'	22	14	3	5	71	54	17	45
5 Saltford Res.	22	13	1	8	58	40	18	40
6 Cutters Friday	22	11	2	9	57	51	6	35
7 Yate Athletic Res.	22	9	2	11	44	59	-15	29
8 Greyfriars Athletic 'B'	22	5	3	14	35	65	-30	18
9 Bristol City Deaf	22	5	1	16	29	91	-62	16
10 Brimsham Green Res.	22	4	2	16	33	71	-38	14
11 Seymour United 'A' (-3)	22	4	4	14	34	77	-43	13
12 Cribbs 'B'	22	2	4	16	33	92	-59	10

BRISTOL DOWNS LEAGUE

Division One	P	W	D	L	F	A	GD	Pts
1 Clifton St Vincents	26	21	3	2	88	32	56	66
2 Sneyd Park	26	19	3	4	79	28	51	60
3 Torpedo	26	15	6	5	70	33	37	51
4 Ashley	26	16	1	9	60	34	26	49
5 AFC Bohemia	26	12	5	9	52	40	12	41
6 Lawes Juniors	26	12	4	10	44	45	-1	40
7 Portland Old Boys	26	11	5	10	47	40	7	38
8 Sporting Greyhound	26	10	5	11	38	50	-12	35
9 Saints Old Boys	26	10	4	12	65	56	9	34
10 Jamaica Bell	26	9	3	14	46	61	-15	30
11 DAC Beachcroft	26	9	1	16	46	63	-17	28
12 Cotswool	26	6	2	18	43	89	-46	20
13 Retainers	26	4	3	19	29	86	-57	15
14 Jersey Rangers	26	3	5	18	33	83	-50	14

Division Two	P	W	D	L	F	A	GD	Pts
1 Sneyd Park Res.	26	19	4	3	69	26	43	61
2 Torpedo Res.	26	18	3	5	71	22	49	57
3 Old Cliftonians	26	16	2	8	73	42	31	50
4 Easton Cowboys	26	14	3	9	64	43	21	45
5 Tebby AFC	26	11	5	10	47	39	8	38
6 Clifton Rockets	26	12	2	12	53	58	-5	38
7 Clifton St Vincents Res.	26	11	3	12	45	48	-3	36
8 Hare on the Hill	26	11	2	13	47	59	-12	35
9 Lion FC	26	9	4	13	52	68	-16	31
10 St Andrews	26	9	3	14	53	67	-14	30
11 Saints Old Boys Res.	26	9	2	15	39	64	-25	29
12 Ashley Res.	26	7	3	16	31	55	-24	24
13 Sporting Greyhound Res.	26	6	5	15	31	61	-30	23
14 Corinthians (-10)	26	7	5	14	37	60	-23	16

Division Three	P	W	D	L	F	A	GD	Pts
1 Easton Cowboys Res.	26	19	3	4	93	49	44	60
2 Wellington Wanderers	26	18	3	5	74	32	42	57
3 Greens Park Rangers	26	17	5	4	81	31	50	56
4 Evergreen	26	17	4	5	80	35	45	55
5 Old Elizabethans AFC	26	16	4	6	96	34	62	52
6 Helios FC	26	11	3	12	58	63	-5	36
7 Torpedo A	26	9	8	9	38	48	-10	35
8 Bengal Tigers	26	10	2	14	46	64	-18	32
9 Clifton St Vincents A	26	9	5	12	41	70	-29	32
10 Cotham Old Boys	26	8	2	16	53	76	-23	26
11 Luccombe Garage	26	7	4	15	47	90	-43	25
12 Sneyd Park A	26	6	4	16	41	69	-28	22
13 Retainers Res	26	4	5	17	47	82	-35	17
14 Portland Old Boys Res.	26	2	6	18	29	81	-52	12

Division Four	P	W	D	L	F	A	GD	Pts
1 Durdham Down Adult School	26	17	2	7	75	45	30	53
2 Clifton St Vincents B	26	16	3	7	73	52	21	51
3 West Town United	26	15	4	7	63	48	15	49
4 Tebby AFC Res.	26	15	3	8	67	44	23	48
5 Conham Rangers	26	15	2	9	65	44	21	47
6 Warmley United	26	12	4	10	64	49	15	40
7 NCSF United	26	10	8	8	61	50	11	38
8 Jersey Rangers Res.	26	10	4	12	42	60	-18	34
9 Torpedo B	26	10	3	13	54	51	3	33
10 Cosmos UK FC	26	8	7	11	44	57	-13	31
11 Sneyd Park B	26	7	6	13	45	56	-11	27
12 Clifton Rockets Res.	26	8	3	15	52	71	-19	27
13 Lion FC Res.	26	5	8	13	48	64	-16	23
14 Retainers A	26	5	1	20	29	91	-62	16

BRISTOL PREMIER COMBINATION

Premier Division	P	W	D	L	F	A	GD	Pts
1 Mendip United	28	21	4	3	58	24	34	67
2 A.E.K. Boco Res.	28	21	2	5	68	33	35	65
3 Highridge United	28	19	3	6	80	36	44	60
4 Lebeq (Saturday) FC	28	19	2	7	81	39	42	59
5 Longwell Green Res.	28	17	3	8	78	37	41	54
6 Wick	28	13	4	11	71	69	2	43
7 Hallen Res.	28	13	3	12	59	49	10	42
8 Cribbs Res.	28	12	4	12	69	64	5	40
9 Totterdown United	28	11	6	11	61	45	16	39
10 Old Sodbury	28	11	2	15	48	58	-10	35
11 Nicholas Wanderers	28	10	5	13	44	59	-15	35
12 Winterbourne United Res.	28	10	1	17	59	65	-6	31
13 Shaftesbury Crusade (-9)	28	7	1	20	25	55	-30	13
14 D R G (Frenchay)	28	4	1	23	28	94	-66	13
15 Bitton Res. (-3)	28	1	1	26	21	123	-102	1

Premier One	P	W	D	L	F	A	GD	Pts
1 Eden Grove	24	19	2	3	88	32	56	59
2 Olveston United	24	18	2	4	72	22	50	56
3 Bristol Manor Farm Res.	24	16	5	3	62	23	39	53
4 Frampton Athletic	24	17	1	6	63	24	39	52
5 Seymour United	24	11	4	9	53	36	17	37
6 Roman Glass/St George Res.	24	10	6	8	44	38	6	36
7 Sea Mills Park	24	9	5	10	42	49	-7	32
8 Brislington Cricketers	24	7	8	9	43	41	2	29
9 Patchway Town Res.	24	7	3	14	39	77	-38	24
10 Lawrence Rovers	24	7	2	15	44	78	-34	23
11 Oldland Abbotonians Res.	24	4	4	16	39	82	-43	16
12 Brimsham Green	24	4	3	17	24	69	-45	15
13 Greyfriars Athletic	24	4	1	19	33	75	-42	13

BRISTOL SUBURBAN LEAGUE

Premier Division One	P	W	D	L	F	A	GD	Pts
1 Little Stoke (-1)	24	18	2	4	75	28	47	55
2 Ashton United	24	16	2	6	50	16	34	50
3 Ridings High	24	15	5	4	56	29	27	50
4 Fishponds Old Boys	24	13	3	8	60	38	22	42
5 Easton Cowboys Suburbia	24	11	6	7	48	43	5	39
6 Avonmouth	24	12	2	10	64	57	7	38
7 Tytherington Rocks Res	24	10	4	10	35	36	-1	34
8 Mangotsfield Sports	23	10	2	11	52	54	-2	32
9 Lawrence Weston	24	9	3	12	48	67	-19	30
10 Severn Beach	24	7	3	14	35	61	-26	24
11 Stoke Gifford United	24	6	3	15	34	52	-18	21
12 Old Georgians	24	5	4	15	34	58	-24	19
13 St Aldhelms	23	3	1	19	34	86	-52	10

Premier Division Two	P	W	D	L	F	A	GD	Pts
1 Downend Foresters	22	20	0	2	83	18	65	60
2 AFC Mangotsfield	22	19	0	3	86	23	63	57
3 Lebeq United (-1)	22	15	0	7	84	42	42	44
4 Brislington A (-1)	22	13	3	6	44	41	3	41
5 Rockleaze Rangers Res. (-3)	22	11	1	10	49	42	7	31
6 Bristol Athletic	22	8	3	11	34	36	-2	27
7 Almondsbury UWE Res.	22	8	2	12	50	54	-4	26
8 Southmead CS United	22	8	1	13	33	54	-21	25
9 CAB Olympic SC (-1)	22	8	1	13	53	74	-21	24
10 Glenside 5 Old Boys	22	6	4	12	33	66	-33	22
11 Cadbury Heath Res.	22	4	2	16	33	70	-37	14
12 Wessex Wanderers	22	3	1	18	28	90	-62	10

Division One	P	W	D	L	F	A	GD	Pts
1 Stoke Rangers	24	19	4	1	90	24	66	61
2 Filton Athletic	24	17	4	3	73	27	46	55
3 Broad Plain House Res.	24	13	4	7	66	46	20	43
4 AFC Hartcliffe	24	11	8	5	60	41	19	41
5 Cleeve Colts	24	13	2	9	55	52	3	41
6 Stoke Gifford United Res.	24	13	1	10	57	57	0	40
7 Kellaway Rangers	24	11	5	8	54	44	10	38
8 Oldbury FC	24	9	4	11	43	47	-4	31
9 Avonmouth Res.	24	8	5	11	53	65	-12	29
10 Ashton Backwell Colts	24	8	3	13	47	59	-12	27
11 St Aldhelms Res.	24	8	1	15	50	48	2	25
12 Tyndalls Park Rangers	24	5	0	19	34	65	-31	15
13 Parson Street Old Boys	24	0	1	23	26	133	-107	1

Division Two	P	W	D	L	F	A	GD	Pts
1 Old Cothamians	24	20	2	2	102	20	82	62
2 Lawrence Weston Res.	24	16	4	4	77	39	38	52
3 Hydez	24	15	2	7	46	25	21	47
4 Ridings High Res.	24	12	5	7	69	49	20	41
5 Bristol Telephones Res.	24	12	3	9	65	70	-5	39
6 Wanderers	24	11	2	11	52	38	14	35
7 Fry's Club OB	24	11	1	12	41	60	-19	34
8 Ashton United Res.	24	9	5	10	56	51	5	32
9 Keynsham Town A (-1)	24	10	1	13	49	50	-1	30
10 AFC Mangotsfield Res.	24	9	1	14	44	68	-24	28
11 Almondsbury UWE A	24	6	6	12	41	66	-25	24
12 Hanham Athletic Suburbia (-1)	24	4	2	18	36	84	-48	13
13 St Annes Town	24	3	2	19	38	96	-58	11

Division Three	P	W	D	L	F	A	GD	Pts
1 Bristol Bilbao	22	22	0	0	114	19	95	66
2 Sartan United	22	18	1	3	88	31	57	55
3 Rockleaze Rangers 'A' (-3)	22	14	3	5	64	33	31	42
4 AFC Whitchurch	22	13	3	6	72	61	11	42
5 Downend Foresters Res.	22	10	4	8	64	57	7	34
6 Broadwalk Community	22	10	2	10	64	49	15	32
7 AEK Boco Colts	22	9	1	12	46	69	-23	28
8 Old Cothamians Res.	22	6	5	11	36	46	-10	23
9 Fishponds Old Boys Res.	22	6	3	13	31	72	-41	21
10 Long Ashton Res.	22	5	0	17	43	75	-32	15
11 Corinthian Sports	22	2	6	14	41	96	-55	12
12 Severn Beach Res.	22	1	4	17	22	77	-55	7

Division Four	P	W	D	L	F	A	GD	Pts
1 Park Knowle	20	17	1	2	96	29	67	52
2 Winford PH	20	16	2	2	74	21	53	50
3 Rockleaze Rangers B	20	13	2	5	59	33	26	41
4 North Bristol Catalans	20	12	3	5	61	30	31	39
5 Severnside	20	10	2	8	51	35	16	32
6 Glenside 5 Old Boys Res.	20	6	5	9	41	57	-16	23
7 Old Georgians Res.	20	6	4	10	28	39	-11	22
8 Filton Athletic Res.	20	5	3	12	23	51	-28	18
9 Brandon Sports	20	4	2	14	32	76	-44	14
10 Stoke Gifford United A	20	4	1	15	28	65	-37	13
11 Oldbury FC Res.	20	4	1	15	18	75	-57	13

Division Five	P	W	D	L	F	A	GD	Pts
1 North Bristol United	20	18	0	2	114	23	91	54
2 Real St George	20	16	1	3	74	42	32	49
3 Imperial Res.	20	13	1	6	58	41	17	40
4 Whitchurch Sports	20	12	1	7	70	52	18	37
5 Lockleaze Community	20	12	0	8	52	29	23	36
6 Lawrence Weston A	20	10	2	8	69	45	24	32
7 AFC Mangotsfield 'A'	20	8	2	10	38	44	-6	26
8 Avonmouth 'A'	20	5	3	12	24	72	-48	18
9 Kellaway Rangers Res.	20	4	1	15	21	74	-53	13
10 Wessex Wanderers Res.	20	3	2	15	27	65	-38	11
11 Fishponds Old Boys A (-1)	20	1	3	16	18	78	-60	5

DIvision Six	P	W	D	L	F	A	GD	Pts
1 Sartan United Res.	16	15	1	0	76	24	52	46
2 Bristol Spartak	16	9	3	4	51	44	7	30
3 Winford PH Res.	16	9	1	6	68	44	24	28
4 Brandon Sports Res.	16	8	1	7	49	43	6	25
5 Long Ashton 'A'	16	7	1	8	50	55	-5	22
6 AFC Mangotsfield B	16	6	2	8	40	45	-5	20
7 TC Sports	16	6	0	10	54	55	-1	18
8 Fry's OB Res.	16	5	1	10	28	50	-22	16
9 Cosmos	16	2	0	14	26	82	-56	6

BURTON & DISTRICT LEAGUE

	P	W	D	L	F	A	GD	Pts
1 Stretton Spartans	22	17	2	3	103	27	76	53
2 Real Medina FC A	21	16	1	4	67	25	42	49
3 Ashbourne FC Res.	22	15	1	6	76	38	38	46
4 TL Darby	22	14	2	6	66	42	24	44
5 Barton United	22	13	4	5	48	22	26	43
6 Blacksmiths Arms	22	11	2	9	63	78	-15	35
7 The Lamb	22	10	4	8	54	38	16	34
8 Eton Athletic	21	7	6	8	54	47	7	27
9 Rec FC	22	7	2	13	44	48	-4	23
10 Overseal Saint Matthews	22	2	5	15	35	61	-26	11
11 Tamworth United	22	2	1	19	28	120	-92	7
12 Rileys FC	22	1	2	19	24	116	-92	5

CENTRAL & SOUTH NORFOLK LEAGUE

Division One	P	W	D	L	F	A	GD	Pts
1 Castle Acre Swifts	18	16	1	1	91	30	61	49
2 Shipdham	18	12	1	5	44	37	7	37
3 Swaffham Town A	18	11	1	6	74	46	28	34
4 Tacolneston	18	11	1	6	38	35	3	34
5 Scarning	18	9	1	8	68	54	14	28
6 Bridgham Utd.	18	9	1	8	57	46	11	28
7 Yaxham	18	8	4	6	59	64	-5	28
8 Gressenhall	18	5	2	11	33	55	-22	17
9 North Elmham	18	3	0	15	30	78	-48	9
10 Rockland Utd.	18	0	0	18	15	64	-49	0

Division Two	P	W	D	L	F	A	GD	Pts
1 Stoke Ferry	20	15	3	2	64	22	42	48
2 Weeting F.C.	20	12	4	4	54	39	15	40
3 Saham Toney Res.	20	12	2	6	62	45	17	38
4 Nostro	20	10	3	7	52	39	13	33
5 Sporle	20	10	3	7	63	51	12	33
6 Necton Res.	20	10	2	8	58	46	12	32
7 Hingham Athletic Res.	20	9	3	8	56	54	2	30
8 Hethersett Athletic	20	9	3	8	45	55	-10	30
9 Rampant Horse	20	4	1	15	32	62	-30	13
10 Narborough	20	2	4	14	38	63	-25	10
11 Cockers	20	1	4	15	39	87	-48	7

Division Three	P	W	D	L	F	A	GD	Pts
1 North Pickenham	26	19	1	6	98	28	70	58
2 Mulbarton Wanderers A	26	18	4	4	96	41	55	58
3 Marham Wanderers	26	17	4	5	105	59	46	55
4 Beetley Bees	26	18	1	7	80	44	36	55
5 Feltwell Utd Res.	26	17	2	7	86	47	39	53
6 Wendling	26	15	2	9	83	65	18	47
7 Watton Utd Res.	26	11	4	11	60	60	0	37
8 Yaxham Res.	26	11	3	12	67	68	-1	36
9 Walsingham	26	9	3	14	53	70	-17	30
10 Attleborough Town A	26	7	5	14	48	80	-32	26
11 Colkirk	26	6	6	14	61	73	-12	24
12 North Elmham Res.	26	7	1	18	47	81	-34	22
13 Methwold Utd	26	6	4	16	52	93	-41	22
14 Dereham Athletic	26	1	0	25	28	155	-127	3

Division Four	P	W	D	L	F	A	GD	Pts
1 Castle Acre Swifts Res.	16	14	1	1	73	15	58	43
2 Tacolneston Res.	16	12	1	3	66	19	47	37
3 Methwold Utd Res.	16	10	1	5	62	27	35	31
4 Shipdham Res.	16	10	1	5	44	27	17	31
5 Rockland Utd. Res.	16	5	2	9	45	42	3	17
6 Scarning Res.	16	4	3	9	43	72	-29	15
7 Billingford	16	4	2	10	22	81	-59	14
8 Gressenhall Res.	16	3	3	10	28	44	-16	12
9 Narborough Res.	16	2	2	12	16	72	-56	8

CHELTENHAM ASSOCIATION FOOTBALL LEAGUE

Division One	P	W	D	L	F	A	GD	Pts
1 Charlton Rovers	24	19	3	2	94	27	67	60
2 Whaddon United	24	17	3	4	80	32	48	54
3 Kings AFC	24	12	4	8	45	40	5	40
4 Gala Wilton Res.	24	10	9	5	53	41	12	39
5 R.S.G.	24	10	5	9	52	56	-4	35
6 Falcons	24	9	5	10	44	52	-8	32
7 AC Olympia	24	8	7	9	35	44	-9	31
8 Star FC Res	24	8	4	12	42	64	-22	28
9 Upton Town	24	6	8	10	48	53	-5	26
10 Bishops Cleeve III	24	6	6	12	32	55	-23	24
11 Hanley Swan	24	5	6	13	32	50	-18	21
12 Newton FC (-1)	24	6	4	14	46	65	-19	21
13 Gloucester Elmleaze	24	4	8	12	33	57	-24	20

Division Two	P	W	D	L	F	A	GD	Pts
1 Churchdown Panthers	22	17	4	1	75	33	42	55
2 FC Lakeside	22	17	3	2	92	19	73	54
3 Andoversford	22	14	1	7	65	56	9	43
4 Staunton & Corse	22	11	3	8	40	41	-1	36
5 Chelt Civil Service Res.	22	10	3	9	46	46	0	33
6 FC Barometrics Res.	22	9	4	9	60	51	9	31
7 Tewkesbury Town	22	9	2	11	45	51	-6	29
8 Whaddon United Res.	22	8	2	12	45	51	-6	26
9 Southside FC	22	6	6	10	37	50	-13	24
10 Northleach Town (-4)	22	6	3	13	44	66	-22	17
11 Prestbury Rovers	22	3	4	15	35	71	-36	13
12 Shurdington Rovers	22	4	1	17	31	80	-49	13

Division Three	P	W	D	L	F	A	GD	Pts
1 Cheltenham Patriots	22	16	3	3	86	32	54	51
2 W.M.K.	22	16	1	5	83	36	47	49
3 Welland FC	22	15	3	4	90	24	66	48
4 Gala Wilton III	22	13	2	7	54	40	14	41
5 Fintan	22	12	2	8	45	34	11	38
6 Brockworth Albion Res.	22	10	1	11	61	52	9	31
7 Leckhampton Rovers (-3)	22	10	2	10	60	42	18	29
8 Tivoli Rovers	22	9	2	11	67	74	-7	29
9 Charlton Rovers Res.	22	6	1	15	39	70	-31	19
10 Falcons Res. (-3)	22	7	0	15	40	83	-43	18
11 Hatherley Rangers	22	4	2	16	36	81	-45	14
12 Winchcombe Town Res. (-6)	22	4	1	17	24	117	-93	7

Division Four	P	W	D	L	F	A	GD	Pts
1 Shurdington Rovers Res.	22	17	3	2	95	38	57	54
2 Newlands Athletic	22	17	3	2	88	31	57	54
3 Dowty Dynamos	22	12	4	6	82	51	31	40
4 Pittville United	22	13	1	8	71	44	27	40
5 Kings AFC Res.	22	10	3	9	51	58	-7	33
6 Southside Res. FC	22	9	5	8	56	51	5	32
7 Tewkesbury Town Res.	22	10	2	10	47	55	-8	32
8 Apperley	22	8	6	8	61	56	5	30
9 Chelt Civil Service III	22	7	3	12	52	68	-16	24
10 Star FC III (-3)	22	8	2	12	61	48	13	23
11 Bredon III (-7)	22	4	0	18	35	90	-55	5
12 Sherborne Harriers (-3)	22	1	0	21	17	126	-109	0

Division Five	P	W	D	L	F	A	GD	Pts
1 Northway (-3)	20	17	1	2	85	29	56	49
2 Smiths Athletic Res.	20	13	1	6	68	44	24	40
3 Leckhampton Rovers Res.	20	11	2	7	61	45	16	35
4 Chelt Civil Service IV	20	11	2	7	54	42	12	35
5 Bourton Rovers III	20	10	1	9	72	52	20	31
6 Staunton & Corse Res. (-3)	20	8	4	8	43	52	-9	25
7 Tewkesbury Town III	20	7	2	11	40	73	-33	23
8 FC Barometrics III	20	7	1	12	42	57	-15	22
9 Hatherley FC	20	5	4	11	42	46	-4	19
10 Cheltenham United	20	4	3	13	48	88	-40	15
11 Prestbury Rovers Res. (-6)	20	4	5	11	24	51	-27	11

Division Six	P	W	D	L	F	A	GD	Pts
1 FC Lakeside Res.	18	13	2	3	64	22	42	41
2 Andoversford Res. (-3)	18	12	1	5	68	33	35	34
3 Pittville United Res.	18	10	4	4	67	44	23	34
4 Cheltenham Athletic (-9)	18	10	2	6	68	50	18	23
5 Kingshill Sports Res.	18	7	2	9	45	47	-2	23
6 Fintan Res.	18	6	2	10	34	53	-19	20
7 Charlton Rovers III (-10)	18	7	3	8	56	54	2	14
8 Regency Town (-3)	18	3	4	11	31	55	-24	10
9 Chelt Saracens III	18	3	1	14	28	104	-76	10
10 Swindon Village Bowmen (-18)	18	7	3	8	45	44	1	6

CHESTER & DISTRICT LEAGUE

Premier Division	P	W	D	L	F	A	GD	Pts
1 Lache	22	18	3	1	105	32	73	57
2 Kelsall	22	15	5	2	69	31	38	50
3 Shaftsbury Youth	22	15	3	4	80	33	47	48
4 Whitby Athletic	22	11	1	10	72	62	10	34
5 Blacon Youth Res.	22	8	6	8	48	38	10	30
6 Kelma	22	8	6	8	62	67	-5	30
7 Ellesmere Port	22	9	2	11	50	59	-9	29
8 Uberlube	22	7	5	10	52	63	-11	26
9 Woodlands Santos	22	6	5	11	51	64	-13	23
10 Hoole Rangers	22	7	2	13	49	76	-27	23
11 Lever	22	4	7	11	46	68	-22	19
12 Crossway	22	1	1	20	30	121	-91	4

Division One	P	W	D	L	F	A	GD	Pts
1 Birkenhead Town	18	17	1	0	111	22	89	52
2 Helsby Res.	18	13	1	4	79	37	42	40
3 Ellesmere Port Town	18	10	1	7	64	38	26	31
4 Pensby Athletic	18	9	0	9	36	46	-10	27
5 Chester Celtic	18	8	2	8	39	34	5	26
6 Chester Nomads III	18	6	3	9	30	45	-15	21
7 Orange Athletic Chester	18	6	0	12	27	57	-30	18
8 Cestrian Alex	18	5	2	11	34	64	-30	17
9 Halfwayhouse Celtic	18	5	2	11	37	74	-37	17
10 Ashton	18	4	2	12	36	76	-40	14

Division Two	P	W	D	L	F	A	GD	Pts
1 Porky's Pantry	20	17	1	2	80	27	53	52
2 Deva Athletic	20	17	1	2	73	29	44	52
3 Boughton Athletic	20	11	3	6	50	31	19	36
4 Hoole Rangers Res.	20	11	2	7	67	64	3	35
5 Hooton	20	9	5	6	40	27	13	32
6 Wirral Villa	20	8	5	7	54	45	9	29
7 Peacock 09	20	7	3	10	44	56	-12	24
8 Lodge Bar	20	5	4	11	31	45	-14	19
9 Blacon Youth Colts	20	5	1	14	36	56	-20	16
10 Crossway Res.	20	3	2	15	32	65	-33	11
11 Orange Athletic Chester Res.	20	3	1	16	32	94	-62	10

Division Three	P	W	D	L	F	A	GD	Pts
1 Franklyn's	18	18	0	0	71	16	55	54
2 Neston Town	18	14	2	2	81	18	63	44
3 New Ferry United	18	14	1	3	58	32	26	43
4 Newton Athletic	18	8	1	9	46	39	7	25
5 Ellesmere Port Town Res.	18	7	2	9	38	53	-15	23
6 Kelsall Res.	18	6	3	9	41	59	-18	21
7 Bronze Social	18	5	1	12	48	50	-2	16
8 Samba	18	4	4	10	36	51	-15	16
9 Clubbies AFC	18	3	1	14	33	79	-46	10
10 Belly Full	18	2	3	13	24	79	-55	9

CIRENCESTER & DISTRICT LEAGUE

Division One	P	W	D	L	F	A	GD	PTS
1 CHQ United	20	16	1	3	93	25	68	49
2 Poulton	20	13	2	5	53	33	20	41
3 South Cerney (-1)	20	13	2	5	49	30	19	40
4 Bibury Res.	20	11	6	3	55	36	19	39
5 The Beeches (-1)	20	9	6	5	76	47	29	32
6 Siddington Sports (-1)	20	7	5	8	50	51	-1	25
7 Oaksey	20	7	0	13	44	73	-29	21
8 Lechlade FC 87 (-1)	20	6	2	12	47	69	-22	19
9 Real Fairford (-6)	20	7	3	10	53	45	8	18
10 Sherston (-1)	20	5	0	15	32	79	-47	14
11 Stratton United	20	2	1	17	22	86	-64	7

Division Two	P	W	D	L	F	A	GD	PTS
1 Kingshill Sports	18	17	1	0	85	21	64	52
2 Siddington Sports Vets (-1)	18	15	1	2	68	16	52	45
3 CHQ United Res. (-1)	18	11	2	5	52	30	22	34
4 Ashton Keynes	18	9	4	5	58	52	6	31
5 Oaksey Res. (-1)	18	7	3	8	47	41	6	23
6 Lechlade FC 87 Res. (-1)	18	7	0	11	43	57	-14	20
7 South Cerney Res. (-6)	18	6	4	8	37	47	-10	16
8 Tetbury Town 3rds (-1)	18	3	1	14	19	61	-42	9
9 Down Ampney (-6)	18	3	3	12	22	54	-32	6
10 Minety (-1)	18	1	3	14	23	75	-52	5

COLCHESTER & EAST ESSEX LEAGUE

Premier Division	P	W	D	L	F	A	GD	Pts
1 University of Essex 3rd XI	20	11	5	4	47	28	19	38
2 Oyster	20	12	2	6	38	25	13	38
3 St Osyth	20	11	2	7	55	40	15	35
4 Cinque Port	20	11	2	7	43	36	7	35
5 Castle	20	9	7	4	42	29	13	34
6 Feering United	20	8	4	8	56	53	3	28
7 Brightlingsea Regent 'A'	20	6	5	9	45	50	-5	23
8 Kelvedon Social	20	5	7	8	34	46	-12	22
9 Colchester Athletic	20	6	4	10	28	43	-15	22
10 New Field	20	4	5	11	46	53	-7	17
11 Horkesley	20	3	5	12	20	51	-31	14

Division One	P	W	D	L	F	A	GD	Pts
1 Mistley	18	15	3	0	84	25	59	48
2 Belle Vue Social	18	15	1	2	79	21	58	46
3 AFC Sudbury 'A'	18	7	5	6	40	33	7	26
4 Marks Tey	18	8	2	8	57	63	-6	26
5 Belchamps	18	7	1	10	38	45	-7	22
6 Langham Lodgers	18	7	1	10	48	61	-13	22
7 Harwich Rangers	18	5	6	7	47	42	5	21
8 Sporting Rebels	18	6	2	10	33	58	-25	20
9 University of Essex 4th XI	18	4	2	12	35	75	-40	14
10 Abbey Fields	18	3	3	12	19	57	-38	12

Division Two	P	W	D	L	F	A	GD	Pts
1 Lexden Allstars	18	13	5	0	49	13	36	44
2 Tollesbury Res.	18	13	4	1	52	11	41	43
3 Bures United Res.	18	13	2	3	42	17	25	41
4 Nayland Rangers	18	8	4	6	33	36	-3	28
5 Acton Crown	18	7	2	9	31	21	10	23
6 Little Clacton	18	6	2	10	33	33	0	20
7 Stoke-by-Nayland	18	6	2	10	23	43	-20	20
8 Riverbank Athletic	18	5	3	10	24	43	-19	18
9 Kelvedon Social Res.	18	4	0	14	20	55	-35	12
10 University of Essex 5th XI	18	2	2	14	26	61	-35	8

Division Three	P	W	D	L	F	A	GD	Pts
1 Connaught Red Star	14	11	2	1	69	16	53	35
2 Tiptree Perrywood	14	10	2	2	60	23	37	32
3 Tiptree Jobserve Blues	14	9	2	3	66	17	49	29
4 Whitehall	14	8	3	3	75	32	43	27
5 Holland 'A'	14	5	1	8	54	37	17	16
6 New Field Res.	14	4	0	10	47	58	-11	12
7 Tolleshunt D'Arcy	14	2	0	12	8	148	-140	6
8 Beacon Hill Rovers 'A'	14	1	2	11	18	66	-48	5

CORNWALL COMBINATION

		P	W	D	L	F	A	GD	Pts
1	Illogan RBL	36	31	3	2	110	31	79	96
2	Wendron United	36	29	3	4	134	35	99	90
3	St Just	36	25	5	6	103	54	49	80
4	Ludgvan	36	25	3	8	130	62	68	78
5	Redruth United	36	25	3	8	105	49	56	78
6	Mullion	36	23	5	8	105	47	58	74
7	St Ives Town	36	16	10	10	63	57	6	58
8	St Agnes	36	18	4	14	71	69	2	58
9	St Day	36	15	3	18	98	66	32	48
10	Perranwell	36	12	8	16	76	78	-2	44
11	RNAS Culdrose	36	12	5	19	61	93	-32	41
12	Penryn Athletic Res.	36	11	6	19	63	86	-23	39
13	Falmouth Town Res.	36	11	6	19	59	97	-38	39
14	Hayle	36	9	9	18	41	76	-35	36
15	Newquay Res.	36	8	10	18	63	81	-18	34
16	Falmouth Athletic (+3)	35	5	8	22	36	101	-65	26
17	Goonhavern Athletic	36	6	2	28	43	126	-83	20
18	Troon	36	5	4	27	38	131	-92	19
19	Porthleven Res. (-3)	35	4	5	26	44	104	-60	14

CRAVEN & DISTRICT LEAGUE

Premier Division		P	W	D	L	F	A	GD	Pts
1	Skipton LMS F.C.	16	14	0	2	51	21	30	42
2	Trawden Celtic F.C.	16	10	4	2	49	25	24	34
3	Cononley Sports F.C.	16	9	3	4	49	28	21	30
4	Grindleton F.C.	16	9	1	6	36	27	9	28
5	Rolls F.C.	16	9	0	7	42	33	9	27
6	Cross Hills F.C.	16	4	5	7	37	48	-11	17
7	Wilsden Athletic F.C.	16	4	2	10	24	59	-35	14
8	Cowling F.C.	16	3	2	11	30	44	-14	11
9	Embsay F.C.	16	1	1	14	25	58	-33	4

Division One		P	W	D	L	F	A	GD	Pts
1	Settle Utd F.C.	16	14	1	1	70	16	54	43
2	Earby Town F.C.	16	11	2	3	62	30	32	35
3	Grassington Utd F.C.	16	9	4	3	38	24	14	31
4	Gargrave F.C.	16	7	2	7	24	41	-17	23
5	Pendle Renegades F.C.	16	7	1	8	33	46	-13	22
6	Chatburn F.C.	16	4	4	8	32	44	-12	16
7	Silsden Whitestar F.C.	16	4	2	10	27	39	-12	14
8	Hellifield Sports F.C.	16	3	2	11	39	61	-22	11
9	Pendle F.C.	16	3	2	11	20	44	-24	11

Division Two		P	W	D	L	F	A	GD	Pts
1	Skipton Town F.C.	18	15	2	1	74	25	49	47
2	AFC Colne	18	14	2	2	68	20	48	44
3	Bingley Town F.C.	18	12	2	4	54	31	23	38
4	Bradley F.C.	18	9	3	6	47	41	6	30
5	Ingrow and Worth Valley F.C.	18	9	2	7	49	54	-5	29
6	Cononley Sports F.C. Res.	18	5	4	9	48	46	2	19
7	Rolls F.C. Res.	18	6	0	12	48	59	-11	18
8	Earby Town F.C. Res.	18	5	2	11	41	55	-14	17
9	Skipton LMS F.C. Res.	18	5	1	12	25	59	-34	16
10	Cross Hills F.C. Res.	18	1	0	17	21	85	-64	3

Division Three		P	W	D	L	F	A	GD	Pts
1	Grassington Utd F.C. Res.	18	14	1	3	50	30	20	43
2	Oxenhope Recreation F.C.	18	12	2	4	52	23	29	38
3	FC Sporting Keighley	18	11	0	7	50	35	15	33
4	Broomhill F.C.	18	9	5	4	41	24	17	32
5	Grindleton F.C. Res.	18	9	3	6	41	38	3	30
6	Salts F.C.	18	7	4	7	32	25	7	25
7	Settle Utd F.C. Res.	18	7	1	10	41	50	-9	22
8	Sutton F.C.	18	5	3	10	39	44	-5	18
9	Ilkley F.C.	18	3	1	14	18	59	-41	10
10	Cowling F.C. Res.	18	3	0	15	19	55	-36	9

Division Four		P	W	D	L	F	A	GD	Pts
1	Manningham All Stars F.C.	19	16	1	2	97	20	77	49
2	F.C. Polonia	20	14	4	2	70	33	37	46
3	Pendle Renegades F.C. Res.	19	12	3	4	57	39	18	39
4	Bradley F.C. Res.	20	12	2	6	46	44	2	38
5	Skipton Town F.C. Res.	20	10	1	9	60	60	0	31
6	Ingrow and Worth Valley F.C. Res.	20	8	4	8	71	57	14	28
7	Carleton F.C.	20	8	2	10	48	58	-10	26
8	Horton F.C.	20	8	0	12	51	55	-4	24
9	Barnoldswick Barons F.C.	20	4	2	14	30	79	-49	14
10	Addingham F.C.	20	4	1	15	33	74	-41	13
11	Sutton F.C. Res.	20	3	0	17	39	83	-44	9

CREWE & DISTRICT LEAGUE

		P	W	D	L	F	A	GD	Pts
1	Cuddington	22	18	1	3	74	27	47	55
2	Crewe FC Res.	22	15	2	5	72	44	28	47
3	Sandbach Town	22	14	2	6	59	48	11	44
4	Cuddington Res.	22	13	3	6	64	56	8	42
5	Barnton Wanderers Res.	22	12	3	7	64	55	9	39
6	Sandbach Curshaws	22	10	3	9	61	33	28	33
7	Tarporley Victoria Res.	22	6	7	9	50	60	-10	25
8	Malpas Res.	22	8	1	13	46	57	-11	25
9	AFC Alsager	22	5	4	13	41	55	-14	19
10	Winnington Avenue	22	3	10	9	35	49	-14	19
11	Winnington Avenue 1994	22	5	3	14	30	62	-32	18
12	Duddon United	22	3	1	18	26	76	-50	10

CROOK & DISTRICT LEAGUE

Division One		P	W	D	L	F	A	GD	Pts
1	Witton Park	18	14	1	3	66	30	36	43
2	Bowes	18	12	2	4	63	40	23	38
3	Middlestone Moor Masons Arms	18	10	4	4	44	35	9	34
4	Coundon Foresters Blue Star	18	8	4	6	58	47	11	28
5	Bishop Auckland Green Tree	18	7	2	9	44	51	-7	23
6	Willington W.M.C.	18	6	4	8	34	37	-3	22
7	Darlington D.S.R.M. Social Club	18	4	5	9	41	40	1	17
8	Heighington	18	5	5	8	38	53	-15	17
9	West Auckland W.M.C.	18	4	4	10	27	51	-24	13
10	Evenwood Town	18	2	5	11	23	54	-31	11

Division Two	P	W	D	L	F	A	GD	Pts
1 Shildon Railway	24	22	1	1	127	17	110	67
2 Darlington R.A. Res.	24	20	1	3	106	33	73	61
3 Wear Valley	24	20	1	3	105	33	72	61
4 Bishop Auckland Hogans	24	12	5	7	76	56	20	41
5 Wolsingham	24	12	3	9	77	56	21	39
6 Wearhead United	24	12	3	9	59	48	11	39
7 Stanhope Town Sports & Social Club	24	10	4	10	39	74	-35	34
8 Crook Town Wanderers	24	10	3	11	54	64	-10	33
9 Turbinia	24	8	3	13	76	79	-3	27
10 Howden-Le-Wear Australian	24	5	3	16	47	82	-35	18
11 Darlington Hole in the Wall	24	3	2	19	40	105	-65	11
12 Crook Albion	24	3	2	19	39	130	-91	11
13 Middleton Rangers	24	3	1	20	45	113	-68	10

CUMBERLAND COUNTY LEAGUE

Premier Division	P	W	D	L	F	A	GD	Pts
1 Netherhall	18	17	0	1	62	17	45	51
2 Longtown	18	11	4	3	46	32	14	37
3 Wigton Harriers	18	10	3	5	39	18	21	33
4 Workington Red Star	18	8	3	7	51	38	13	27
5 Workington Red House	18	8	3	7	36	32	4	27
6 Aspatria	18	7	5	6	54	49	5	26
7 Windscale	18	4	6	8	33	44	-11	18
8 Carlisle City Res.	18	4	4	10	32	55	-23	16
9 Cleator Moor Celtic Res.	18	4	2	12	36	61	-25	14
10 Whitehaven Miners	18	1	2	15	29	72	-43	5

Division One	P	W	D	L	F	A	GD	Pts
1 Silloth	13	10	1	2	68	16	52	31
2 Mirehouse	14	11	0	3	56	31	25	30
3 Cockermouth	14	9	2	3	60	28	32	29
4 Whitehaven AFC Res.	14	7	2	5	41	22	19	23
5 Borough	14	6	2	6	51	33	18	20
6 Lowca Rangers	14	5	0	9	28	63	-35	15
7 Parton United	14	3	0	11	23	70	-47	9
8 St Bees	13	0	1	12	10	74	-64	-2

DEVON & EXETER LEAGUE

Premier Division	P	W	D	L	F	A	GD	Pts
1 St Martins	28	26	0	2	118	23	95	78
2 Tiverton Town 2nds	28	22	2	4	99	22	77	68
3 Newtown	28	19	5	4	99	36	63	62
4 Feniton	20	14	7	7	74	40	34	49
5 University 2nds	28	14	6	8	45	46	-1	48
6 Thorverton	28	12	5	11	51	58	-7	41
7 Hatherleigh Town (-1)	28	11	3	14	48	56	-8	35
8 Beer Albion	28	10	5	13	40	62	-22	35
9 Budleigh Salterton 2nds	28	10	5	13	43	71	-28	35
10 Chard Town 2nds	28	9	7	12	56	52	4	34
11 Seaton Town	28	7	7	14	48	66	-18	28
12 Willand Rovers 2nds	28	8	4	16	41	73	-32	28
13 Heavitree United	28	6	2	20	38	106	-68	20
14 Topsham Town	28	5	3	20	40	81	-41	18
15 Clyst Valley	28	4	5	19	35	83	-48	17

Division One	P	W	D	L	F	A	GD	Pts
1 Elmore 2nds	28	25	2	1	108	14	94	77
2 Sidbury United	28	20	3	5	75	30	45	63
3 Bow AAC	28	18	8	2	84	32	52	62
4 Wellington Town 2nds	28	18	3	7	90	43	47	57
5 Witheridge 2nds	28	16	5	7	70	42	28	53
6 University 3rds	27	12	8	7	73	57	16	44
7 Alphington 2nds	28	12	4	12	55	54	1	40
8 East Budleigh	28	11	6	11	42	48	-6	39
9 Beacon Knights	28	10	6	12	50	56	-6	36
10 Exmouth Amateurs	28	10	1	17	56	65	-9	31
11 Bickleigh	28	9	4	15	43	67	-24	31
12 Heavitree United 2nds	28	8	3	17	50	75	-25	27
13 Cullompton Rangers 2nds	28	5	4	19	41	77	-36	19
14 Tipton St John	27	5	3	19	33	85	-52	18
15 Newton Poppleford	28	0	0	28	16	141	-125	0

Division Two	P	W	D	L	F	A	GD	Pts
1 Dolphin	26	21	3	2	72	25	47	66
2 Honiton Town	26	18	5	3	91	34	57	59
3 Exwick Villa 2nds	26	18	5	3	88	33	55	59
4 Newton St Cyres	26	15	5	6	67	30	37	50
5 Westexe Rovers	26	11	6	9	67	50	17	39
6 Lympstone	26	11	4	11	58	54	4	37
7 Dawlish United	26	10	5	11	63	48	15	35
8 Culm United	26	9	5	12	55	87	-32	32
9 Halwill	26	8	7	11	51	61	-10	31
10 Colyton	26	6	9	11	54	62	-8	27
11 Topsham Town 2nds	26	6	7	13	49	83	-34	25
12 Crediton United 2nds	26	5	3	18	36	93	-57	18
13 Clyst Valley 2nds (-3)	26	6	2	18	35	84	-49	17
14 Pinhoe	26	4	2	20	35	77	-42	14

Division Three	P	W	D	L	F	A	GD	Pts
1 University 4ths	20	16	1	3	65	29	36	49
2 Upottery	20	15	2	3	85	31	54	47
3 Chulmleigh	20	12	1	7	61	31	30	37
4 Hemyock	20	10	5	5	44	25	19	35
5 Sidmouth Town 2nds	20	10	5	5	51	39	12	35
6 Newtown 2nds	20	10	3	7	45	38	7	33
7 Woodbury	20	6	5	9	41	45	-4	23
8 Chagford	20	7	2	11	27	43	-16	23
9 Tedburn St Mary	20	5	4	11	27	47	-20	19
10 Axminster Town 2nds	20	3	4	13	23	61	-38	13
11 Exmouth Amateurs 2nds (-2)	20	0	0	20	11	91	-80	-2

Division Four	P	W	D	L	F	A	GD	Pts
1 Exmouth Town 2nds	26	19	5	2	78	32	46	62
2 Cheriton Fitzpaine	26	17	2	7	80	42	38	53
3 University 5ths	26	16	4	6	78	39	39	52
4 Thorverton 2nds	26	15	2	9	78	50	28	47
5 Axmouth United	26	13	5	8	58	56	2	44
6 Okehampton Argyle 2nds	26	14	1	11	73	69	4	43
7 Awliscombe United	26	11	8	7	41	40	1	41
8 North Tawton	26	9	5	12	43	54	-11	32
9 Lord's XI (-1)	26	10	2	14	59	65	-6	31
10 Bampton	26	8	5	13	42	55	-13	29
11 Newtown 3rds	26	8	4	14	42	50	-8	28
12 Hatherleigh Town 2nds (-1)	26	7	4	15	35	49	-14	24
13 Sandford	26	6	5	15	40	89	-49	23
14 Winkleigh (-2)	26	2	2	22	36	93	-57	6

Division Five	P	W	D	L	F	A	GD	Pts
1 Lapford	26	20	5	1	83	33	50	65
2 St Martins 2nds	26	20	2	4	72	33	39	62
3 Langdon	26	19	4	3	112	40	72	61
4 Morchard Bishop	26	14	4	8	76	63	13	46
5 Bow AAC 2nds	26	13	5	8	66	46	20	44
6 Amory Park Rangers	26	12	5	9	82	51	31	41
7 Dawlish United 2nds (-3)	26	13	3	10	62	32	30	42
8 Westexe Rovers 2nds	26	11	6	9	77	51	26	39
9 Countess Wear Dynamoes	26	11	4	11	53	64	-11	37
10 Feniton 2nds	26	7	5	14	41	65	-24	26
11 Sampford Peverell	26	8	2	16	51	80	-29	26
12 Beer Albion 2nds	26	5	2	19	43	78	-35	17
13 Dunkeswell Rovers	26	2	2	22	25	102	-77	8
14 Seaton Town 2nds	26	2	1	23	23	128	-105	7

Division Six	P	W	D	L	F	A	GD	Pts
1 Otterton	28	22	3	3	93	37	56	69
2 Uplowman Athletic	28	22	2	4	109	22	87	68
3 Starcross Generals	28	14	6	8	99	69	30	48
4 Topsham Town 3rds	28	14	5	9	92	63	29	47
5 Honiton Town 2nds	28	13	7	8	85	60	25	46
6 Halwill 2nds	28	13	5	10	95	71	24	44
7 Stoke Hill	28	13	5	10	80	75	5	44
8 Fluxton	28	11	8	9	76	59	17	41
9 Priory	28	12	5	11	56	52	4	41
10 Silverton	28	12	2	14	59	68	-9	38
11 Newton St Cyres 2nds	28	8	4	16	64	74	-10	28
12 Ottery St Mary	28	7	7	14	54	71	-17	28
13 Exwick Village	28	9	0	19	43	80	-37	27
14 East Budleigh 2nds	28	7	5	16	39	66	-27	26
15 Amory Green Rovers	28	1	0	27	17	194	-177	3

Division Seven	P	W	D	L	F	A	GD	Pts
1 Henry's Cronies	26	26	0	0	152	25	127	78
2 Kentisbeare	26	16	5	5	91	45	46	53
3 Alphington 3rds	26	16	3	7	83	57	26	51
4 Railway Club	26	15	4	7	83	79	4	49
5 Bradninch	26	15	3	8	76	56	20	48
6 Newtown 4ths	26	14	3	9	84	74	10	45
7 Langdon 2nds	26	11	4	11	73	71	2	37
8 Woodbury 2nds	26	11	2	13	68	71	-3	35
9 Pinhoe 2nds (-1)	26	9	2	15	51	77	-26	28
10 Offwell Rangers	26	8	3	15	58	62	-4	27
11 Chagford 2nds	26	7	4	15	56	72	-16	25
12 Lympstone 2nds (-2)	26	8	2	16	38	72	-34	24
13 Met Office	26	5	2	19	39	97	-58	17
14 Tedburn St Mary 2nds	26	2	1	23	30	124	-94	7

Division Eight	P	W	D	L	F	A	GD	Pts
1 Alphington 4ths	22	14	2	6	73	44	29	44
2 Hemyock 2nds	22	13	4	5	70	46	24	43
3 Elmore 3rds (-1)	22	13	4	5	73	48	25	42
4 Cheriton Fitzpaine 2nds	22	13	3	6	52	33	19	42
5 Woodbury 3rds (-1)	22	12	2	8	64	48	16	38
6 Colyton 2nds	22	9	3	10	45	58	-13	30
7 Bickleigh 2nds	22	8	5	9	55	52	3	29
8 Lapford 2nds	22	9	2	11	51	52	-1	29
9 Sandford 2nds	22	9	1	12	50	66	-16	28
10 Open Space International FC	22	8	2	12	65	62	3	26
11 Bampton 2nds	22	7	3	12	44	64	-20	24
12 Bradninch 2nds	22	0	3	19	17	86	-69	3

DONCASTER & DISTRICT LEAGUE

Premier Division	P	W	D	L	F	A	GD	Pts
1 Denaby United (-1)	14	12	1	1	53	16	37	36
2 Denaby Main	14	10	2	2	36	22	14	32
3 Hemsworth MW	14	9	1	4	37	27	10	28
4 Rossington MW (-1)	14	7	1	6	33	28	5	21
5 Armthorpe Markham Main	14	4	3	7	26	37	-11	15
6 Sutton Rovers	14	4	2	8	28	29	-1	14
7 South Elmsall United Services	14	1	4	9	21	40	-19	7
8 Yorkshire Main	14	2	0	12	11	46	-35	6

Division One	P	W	D	L	F	A	GD	Pts
1 Swinton Athletic	16	11	2	3	49	25	24	35
2 Dunscroft United	16	11	1	4	62	27	35	34
3 Scawthorpe Scorpions	16	9	4	3	49	31	18	31
4 F.C. Central	16	9	2	5	42	21	21	29
5 Brodsworth Welfare	16	6	4	6	28	29	-1	22
6 Bawtry Town	16	6	2	8	29	33	-4	20
7 Ackworth United	16	5	4	7	27	52	-25	19
8 Harworth Colliery	16	3	4	9	22	51	-29	13
9 Bentley Pumas	16	0	1	15	19	58	-39	1

DORSET FOOTBALL LEAGUE

Senior Division	P	W	D	L	F	A	GD	Pts
1 Westland Sports	26	21	4	1	82	17	65	67
2 Sturminster Marshall	25	19	1	5	70	33	37	58
3 Chickerell Utd	26	16	3	7	62	40	22	51
4 Gillingham Town Res.	26	14	5	7	49	36	13	47
5 Corfe Mullen United	25	14	4	7	65	38	27	46
6 Upwey and Broadwey	26	14	3	9	69	48	21	45
7 Portland United Res.	26	11	6	9	65	47	18	39
8 Witchampton United	26	10	5	11	46	49	-3	35
9 South Cheriton	26	8	5	13	53	76	-23	29
10 Sturminster Newton United	26	7	5	14	44	48	-4	26
11 Blandford United Res.	26	6	8	12	37	55	-18	26
12 Piddletrenthide United	26	7	4	15	42	66	-24	25
13 Kingston Lacy	26	3	4	19	37	98	-61	13
14 Okeford United	26	2	1	23	19	89	-70	7

Division One	P	W	D	L	F	A	GD	Pts
1 The Balti House	24	19	1	4	70	42	28	58
2 Wincanton Town Res.	24	16	3	5	76	41	35	51
3 Dorchester Sports	24	15	3	6	57	30	27	48
4 Kangaroos	24	13	4	7	66	40	26	43
5 Milborne Sports	24	12	3	9	67	40	27	39
6 Weymouth Spartans	24	12	3	9	51	56	-5	39
7 Poundbury Rovers	24	9	9	6	49	35	14	36
8 Poole Borough Res. (-3)	24	10	5	9	57	51	6	32
9 AFC Cobham	24	7	4	13	44	70	-26	25
10 Swanage Town & Herston Res.	24	6	3	15	40	73	-33	21
11 Bridport A	24	6	2	16	36	60	-24	20
12 Bere Regis	24	5	1	18	34	76	-42	16
13 Stourpaine (-3)	24	3	5	16	30	63	-33	11

Division Two	P	W	D	L	F	A	GD	Pts
1 Lytchett Red Triangle	26	21	1	4	119	43	76	64
2 Shaftesbury Town Res.	26	18	3	5	76	48	28	57
3 Portesham United	26	16	2	8	56	46	10	50
4 Redlands FC	26	15	4	7	57	41	16	49
5 Parley Sports Res.	26	14	3	9	73	51	22	45
6 Portland Town	26	11	6	9	78	61	17	39
7 Wareham Rangers Res.	26	12	3	11	77	66	11	39
8 Chickerell United Res.	26	11	3	12	60	62	-2	36
9 Corfe Castle	26	9	8	9	63	58	5	35
10 Wyke Regis Social Club	26	10	3	13	44	42	2	33
11 Gillingham Town A (-3)	26	7	1	18	45	79	-34	19
12 Piddlehinton United	26	4	6	16	46	80	-34	18
13 Ship Inn, Wool	26	5	3	18	43	92	-49	18
14 Sturminster Newton United Res.	26	5	2	19	39	107	-68	17

Division Three	P	W	D	L	F	A	GD	Pts
1 AFC Blandford	20	16	4	0	55	25	30	52
2 Broadstone	20	13	2	5	79	27	52	41
3 Stickland United (-3)	20	12	4	4	75	35	40	37
4 Mere Town Res.	20	10	5	5	64	34	30	35
5 Henstridge United	20	10	4	6	54	47	7	34
6 Stalbridge	20	7	5	8	37	54	-17	26
7 Maiden Newton & Cattistock	20	7	4	9	60	47	13	25
8 Handley Sports	20	6	5	9	45	61	-16	23
9 Portland Town Res.	20	5	1	14	33	77	-44	16
10 Sturminster Marshall R	20	4	2	14	38	74	-36	14
11 Donhead Utd	20	2	0	18	22	81	-59	6

Division Four	P	W	D	L	F	A	GD	Pts
1 Puddletown	22	16	5	1	79	36	43	53
2 Milborne Sports Res.	22	14	6	2	61	31	30	48
3 Weymouth Spartans Res.	22	11	8	3	56	38	18	41
4 AFC Cobham Res.	22	11	4	7	58	51	7	37
5 Owermoigne	22	10	1	11	58	53	5	31
6 Portland Town A	22	9	2	11	53	71	-18	29
7 Uniited Football Club of Poundbury	22	8	3	11	53	66	-13	27
8 Pimperne Sports Society	22	7	4	11	57	56	1	25
9 Corfe Mullen Utd Res.	22	6	4	12	31	52	-21	22
10 South Cheriton Res.	22	6	2	14	48	60	-12	20
11 Kangaroos Res.	22	5	5	12	46	74	-28	20
12 Cranborne Res. (-3)	22	5	4	13	48	60	-12	16

Division Five	P	W	D	L	F	A	GD	Pts
1 Portland United Youth	18	13	3	2	59	24	35	42
2 Broadstone Res.	18	12	3	3	59	30	29	39
3 Lytchett Red Triangle Youth (-3)	17	11	2	4	77	26	51	32
4 Corfe Castle Res.	18	8	4	6	48	46	2	28
5 Handley Sports Res. (-3)	17	6	5	6	49	41	8	20
6 Marnhull (-3)	18	7	2	9	46	38	8	20
7 Portland Town B	18	6	2	10	28	64	-36	20
8 Wool & Winfrith	18	6	0	12	30	43	-13	18
9 Piddletrenthide United Res. (-3)	18	4	2	12	33	82	-49	11
10 Okeford Utd Res. (-3)	18	3	3	12	22	57	-35	9

DUCHY LEAGUE

Premier Division	P	W	D	L	F	A	GD	Pts
1 Pensilva	18	15	0	3	52	17	35	45
2 Saltash United	18	13	4	1	59	20	39	43
3 Torpoint Athletic (+3)	18	6	4	8	31	32	-1	25
4 Lamerton	18	7	4	7	23	32	-9	25
5 Pelynt	18	7	0	11	45	45	0	21
6 St Stephen	18	6	3	9	35	42	-7	21
7 St Columb Major (-3)	18	7	3	8	38	53	-15	21
8 St Newlyn East (-3)	18	5	5	8	29	32	-3	17
9 Biscovey	18	4	5	9	26	46	-20	17
10 St Cleer	18	4	4	10	25	44	-19	16

Division One	P	W	D	L	F	A	GD	Pts
1 St Dominick	24	17	3	4	83	37	46	54
2 Padstow United (+3)	24	14	5	5	60	34	26	50
3 Lostwithiel	24	15	3	6	67	44	23	48
4 North Petherwin	24	14	0	10	73	49	24	42
5 Looe Town	24	11	5	8	60	43	17	38
6 Grampound	24	12	2	10	57	44	13	38
7 Altarnun	24	11	4	9	51	38	13	37
8 Godolphin Atlantic (-3)	24	12	3	9	68	45	23	36
9 Edgcumbe FC	24	8	3	13	66	70	-4	27
10 Polperro	24	6	6	12	35	64	-29	24
11 St Mawgan (-3)	24	6	4	14	40	69	-29	19
12 St Dennis	24	4	5	15	42	84	-42	17
13 Calstock	24	3	3	18	33	114	-81	12

Division Two	P	W	D	L	F	A	GD	Pts
1 Foxhole Stars	20	15	2	3	62	23	39	47
2 St Minver	20	14	5	1	51	15	36	47
3 LC Phoenix	20	13	3	4	52	19	33	42
4 AFC Bodmin	20	11	2	7	47	31	16	35
5 Premier Sixes	20	9	3	8	55	52	3	30
6 Sticker	20	8	5	7	32	28	4	29
7 Gunnislake	20	6	3	11	27	42	-15	21
8 Holywell and Cubert	20	5	5	10	37	52	-15	20
9 Gerrans & St Mawes Utd	20	4	4	12	33	54	-21	16
10 Boscastle	20	4	4	12	30	55	-25	16
11 St Breward	20	1	4	15	12	67	-55	7

Division Three	P	W	D	L	F	A	GD	Pts
1 Callington Town	20	15	2	3	70	28	42	47
2 North Hill	20	15	1	4	57	37	20	46
3 Stoke Climsland	20	14	1	5	77	36	41	43
4 Lifton	20	11	3	6	41	33	8	36
5 Packhorse Athletic	20	10	3	7	59	49	10	33
6 St Neot	20	8	3	9	57	44	13	27
7 Queens Rangers	20	7	4	9	38	55	-17	25
8 St Stephen Res	19	5	2	12	42	63	-21	17
9 Lanivet Inn (-3)	20	5	4	11	31	44	-13	16
10 Delabole United	20	3	1	16	32	82	-50	10
11 Lanreath (-3)	19	3	2	14	25	58	-33	8

Division Four	P	W	D	L	F	A	GD	Pts
1 Veryan	20	20	0	0	105	17	88	60
2 St Cleer Res.	20	12	3	5	82	58	24	39
3 Tintagel	20	9	4	7	65	47	18	31
4 North Petherwin Res.	20	9	4	7	59	52	7	31
5 Tregony	20	9	2	9	47	68	-21	29
6 Grampound Res.	20	7	4	9	38	50	-12	25
7 Gorran (-3)	20	7	3	10	50	65	-15	21
8 Mevagissey	20	6	3	11	40	60	-20	21
9 Wadebridge Town	20	5	5	10	54	61	-7	20
10 Pensilva Res.	20	5	5	10	51	77	-26	20
11 Roche	20	2	5	13	36	72	-36	11

Division Five	P	W	D	L	F	A	GD	Pts
1 St Merryn	22	19	2	1	89	22	67	59
2 High Street	22	15	3	4	70	26	44	48
3 Tregrehan Mills (+3)	22	14	2	6	56	39	17	47
4 Southgate Seniors (-3)	22	14	1	7	90	29	61	40
5 St Minver Res. (-3)	21	11	2	8	66	51	15	32
6 Pelynt Res.	22	9	1	12	65	65	0	28
7 Godolphin Atlantic Res.	22	8	2	12	57	62	-5	26
8 Standard Inn FC	21	8	1	12	60	61	-1	25
9 St Teath	22	6	2	14	44	69	-25	20
10 Boscastle Res.	22	6	1	15	50	91	-41	19
11 St Mawgan Res.	22	5	4	13	36	87	-51	19
12 St Newlyn East Res.	22	4	3	15	37	118	-81	15

Durham Football Alliance	P	W	D	L	F	A	GD	Pts
1 Sunderland Hylton CW	18	13	3	2	58	20	38	42
2 Coundon and Leeholm Youth FC	18	10	7	1	51	19	32	37
3 Spennymoor Town Res.	18	11	4	3	57	27	30	37
4 Durham Stonebridge	18	10	3	5	40	32	8	33
5 Murton AFC	18	8	0	10	29	33	-4	24
6 Wheatley Hill WMC	18	7	2	9	50	59	-9	23
7 Sherburn Village WMC FC	18	6	3	9	34	45	-11	21
8 Coxhoe United FC	18	5	1	12	25	67	-42	16
9 Ebchester Consett Res.	18	3	3	12	30	41	-11	12
10 Brandon United Res.	18	3	2	13	17	48	-31	11

EAST BERKSHIRE LEAGUE

Premier Division	P	W	D	L	F	A	GD	Pts
1 The Lynchpin FC	20	15	2	3	66	37	29	47
2 Chalvey (WMC) Sports	20	14	2	4	61	28	33	44
3 Iver	20	10	3	7	49	38	11	33
4 Slough Heating	20	9	4	7	53	43	10	31
5 Alpha Arms Academicals	20	9	4	7	45	56	-11	31
6 Langley Wanderers	20	8	5	7	41	29	12	29
7 Stoke Green Rovers	19	8	5	6	48	42	6	29
8 Orchard Park Rangers	20	8	4	8	33	29	4	28
9 Eton Wick	20	7	3	10	30	44	-14	24
10 FC Beaconsfield	19	2	2	15	16	54	-38	8
11 Slough Laurencians	20	1	2	17	30	72	-42	5

Henley Res. withdrew.

Division One	P	W	D	L	F	A	GD	Pts
1 Langley FC	22	18	2	2	95	37	58	56
2 Huntercombe FC (-3)	22	18	3	1	89	38	51	54
3 Iver Heath Rovers	22	14	3	5	66	31	35	45
4 Old Windsor	22	11	3	8	65	38	27	36
5 KS Gryf (+3)	22	10	1	11	44	43	1	34
6 Richings Park	22	7	6	9	48	59	-11	27
7 Upton Lea (+3)	21	5	7	9	28	50	-22	25
8 Swinley Forest (-6)	21	9	2	10	45	37	8	23
9 Windsor Great Park	21	5	5	11	43	54	-11	20
10 Robertswood (+3)	21	5	2	14	37	72	-35	20
11 AFC Ascot	22	5	1	16	34	83	-49	16
12 Slough Heating Res.	22	5	1	16	42	94	-52	16

Falcons withdrew.

Division Two	P	W	D	L	F	A	GD	Pts
1 Maidenhead Magpies	18	14	4	0	56	11	45	46
2 Iver Heath Rovers Res.	18	11	2	5	47	24	23	35
3 Burnham Beeches Seniors	18	11	2	5	44	23	21	35
4 Frontline	18	10	1	7	39	40	-1	31
5 Maidenhead Town	18	8	3	7	41	35	6	27
6 Hurley	18	8	3	7	32	43	-11	27
7 Admiral Cunningham	18	5	2	11	28	35	-7	17
8 Cippenham Sports	18	4	3	11	29	54	-25	15
9 Old Windsor Res.	18	4	2	12	35	75	-40	14
10 Newell Green FC	18	4	0	14	27	38	-11	12

Stoke Green Rovers Res. withdrew.

Division Three	P	W	D	L	F	A	GD	Pts
1 Britwell	18	13	3	2	63	22	41	42
2 Langley Galaxy	18	10	3	5	51	43	8	33
3 Real Saracens	18	9	4	5	34	26	8	31
4 Fulmer	18	9	3	6	41	27	14	30
5 FC Beaconsfield Res. (-3)	18	9	3	6	34	29	5	27
6 Braybrooke	18	6	5	7	53	47	6	23
7 Chalvey (WMC) Sports Res. (+3)	17	5	5	7	33	34	-1	23
8 Willow Wanderers	18	4	7	7	35	59	-24	19
9 Upton Park Rangers	18	5	1	12	28	46	-18	16
10 Windsor Great Park Res.	17	1	2	14	21	60	-39	5

Bracknell Cavaliers withdrew.

Division Four	P	W	D	L	F	A	GD	Pts
1 Windsor Saints	16	13	2	1	80	11	69	41
2 Britwell Res	16	10	6	0	52	17	35	36
3 Maidenhead Magpies Res.	16	10	3	3	36	18	18	33
4 Richings Park Res.	16	7	2	7	29	30	-1	23
5 Upton Lea Res.	16	5	6	5	29	38	-9	21
6 St Peters Iver	16	4	5	7	31	43	-12	17
7 Real Saracens Res.	16	4	1	11	30	53	-23	13
8 Mercian United	16	3	3	10	26	53	-27	12
9 Langley Hornets	16	2	0	14	14	64	-50	6

EAST CHESHIRE LEAGUE

Division One	P	W	D	L	F	A	GD	Pts
1 Wilmslow Town	16	16	0	0	94	11	83	48
2 Club AZ	16	14	0	2	59	21	38	42
3 High Lane	16	9	0	7	49	46	3	27
4 Prestbury FC (-3)	16	9	1	6	44	42	2	25
5 Mary Dendy	16	8	0	8	30	54	-24	24
6 Bulls Head Poynton (-3)	16	7	0	9	42	34	8	18
7 Old Alts	16	3	1	12	20	77	-57	10
8 Lacey Green	16	1	2	13	21	69	-48	5
9 Healthy Ardwick (-6)	16	3	0	13	33	38	-5	3

EAST CORNWALL LEAGUE

Premier Division	P	W	D	L	F	A	GD	Pts
1 Plymouth Parkway	30	23	3	4	96	29	67	72
2 Torpoint Athletic	30	21	4	5	88	35	53	67
3 Millbrook	30	17	4	9	90	61	29	55
4 Saltash United	30	16	5	9	74	42	32	53
5 Polperro	30	16	4	10	83	72	11	52
6 Tavistock	30	13	3	14	66	67	-1	42
7 Launceston	30	11	7	12	66	61	5	40
8 Elburton Villa	30	10	8	12	61	69	-8	38
9 St Teath	30	11	5	14	60	81	-21	38
10 Bere Alston United	30	10	7	13	56	69	-13	37
11 Callington Town	30	9	8	13	56	54	2	35
12 Liskeard Athletic	30	8	11	11	59	84	-25	35
13 Kilkhampton	30	9	6	15	58	77	-19	33
14 Morwenstow	30	9	3	18	57	101	-44	30
15 St Dominick	30	8	5	17	53	88	-35	29
16 Wadebridge Town	30	7	1	22	39	72	-33	22

Division One	P	W	D	L	F	A	GD	Pts
1 Edgcumbe	28	22	2	4	113	29	84	68
2 Fowey United	28	20	2	6	115	31	84	62
3 Plymstock United	28	19	3	6	93	38	55	60
4 St Blazey FC	28	16	7	5	76	37	39	55
5 Roche	28	17	3	8	91	35	56	54
6 Mevagissey	28	16	5	7	77	41	36	53
7 St Austell	28	14	7	7	79	65	14	49
8 Lanreath	28	16	1	11	69	56	13	49
9 St Stephens Borough	28	13	3	12	69	65	4	42
10 Probus	28	11	5	12	66	72	-6	38
11 Bude Town	28	9	3	16	60	80	-20	30
12 Bodmin Town	28	4	2	22	50	125	-75	14
13 Camelford	28	3	4	21	57	132	-75	13
14 Nanpean Rovers	28	3	3	22	41	122	-81	12
15 Holsworthy	28	1	2	25	31	159	-128	5

EAST LANCASHIRE LEAGUE

Division One	P	W	D	L	F	A	GD	Pts
1 The Ivy (+2)	26	20	5	1	97	34	63	67
2 Burnley Athletic	26	19	5	2	85	31	54	62
3 Rimington (+2)	26	16	7	3	72	34	38	57
4 Read United (-4)	26	16	3	7	84	63	21	47
5 Mill Hill	26	12	5	9	77	49	28	41
6 Oswaldtwistle SM	26	13	2	11	53	49	4	41
7 Stackstead SJ	26	10	4	12	62	81	-19	34
8 Enfield	26	10	3	13	68	55	13	33
9 Feniscowles & Pleasington	26	10	1	15	53	71	-18	31
10 Rock Rovers (-1)	26	8	6	12	52	68	-16	29
11 Calder Vale FC	26	8	4	14	50	55	-5	28
12 Langho	26	7	5	14	47	68	-21	26
13 Worsthorne (+3)	26	3	1	22	35	112	-77	13
14 Colne United	26	2	5	19	34	99	-65	11

Division Two	P	W	D	L	F	A	GD	Pts
1 Burnley Belvedere (+3)	16	11	1	4	56	26	30	37
2 Barrowford Celtic	16	11	3	2	36	18	18	36
3 Prairie United	16	9	2	5	40	29	11	29
4 Whinney HIll	16	8	4	4	38	26	12	28
5 Barnoldswick Town United	16	6	5	5	34	27	7	23
6 Pendle Forest (-3)	16	6	4	6	29	41	-12	19
7 Waddington	16	4	4	8	39	35	4	16
8 Canberra FC	16	3	4	9	29	39	-10	13
9 Peel Park	16	0	1	15	12	72	-60	1

EAST RIDING AMATEUR LEAGUE

Premier Division	P	W	D	L	F	A	GD	Pts
1 Dram Shop FC	18	13	4	1	67	21	46	43
2 AFC Northfield	18	13	4	1	66	28	38	43
3 Rapid Sol'rs Res	18	9	3	6	46	44	2	30
4 Pinefleet Wolf'n Ath	18	7	4	7	32	39	-7	25
5 Quaddy Rangers	18	7	3	8	34	34	0	24
6 AFC Preston	18	6	5	7	37	40	-3	23
7 Kingburn Athletic	18	4	8	6	34	41	-7	20
8 St Andrews Res.	18	5	2	11	43	51	-8	20
9 Cross Keys Cott'm	18	6	2	10	33	44	-11	20
10 Orchard Park United	18	2	1	15	29	79	-50	7

Division One	P	W	D	L	F	A	GD	Pts
1 AFC Ramp	20	17	2	1	111	26	85	53
2 Drum Athletic	20	14	1	5	61	32	29	43
3 AFC Hawthorn	20	12	2	6	64	46	18	38
4 AFC North	20	11	4	5	53	22	31	37
5 Apollo Rangers	20	11	1	8	57	51	6	34
6 AFC Hull	20	9	1	10	54	70	-16	28
7 Fiveways Rangers	20	8	2	10	52	56	-4	26
8 Orchard Pk Utd TSC	20	6	1	13	50	71	-21	19
9 Hoggs Head OB FC	20	6	2	12	49	75	-26	19
10 Cross Keys Cott Res.	20	4	2	14	28	75	-47	14
11 C-Force United	20	3	0	17	29	84	-55	9

EAST RIDING COUNTY LEAGUE

Premier Division	P	W	D	L	F	A	GD	Pts
1 AFC Rovers	22	16	3	3	77	36	41	51
2 Beverley Town Res.	22	15	2	5	57	38	19	47
3 Park Athletic	22	13	5	4	53	33	20	44
4 Walkington	22	11	5	6	46	31	15	38
5 Holme Rovers	22	12	2	8	41	38	3	38
6 Wawne United Res.	22	11	4	7	51	36	15	37
7 St George's FC	22	11	2	9	49	45	4	35
8 Bridlington Town Res.	22	9	4	9	57	51	6	31
9 Driffield Rangers	22	8	2	12	49	51	-2	26
10 Goole United Res.	22	6	1	15	31	60	-29	19
11 Sculcoates Amateurs Res.	22	3	1	18	29	69	-40	10
12 Easington United Res.	22	0	3	19	24	76	-52	3

Division One	P	W	D	L	F	A	GD	Pts
1 Gilberdyke Phoenix	18	15	0	3	49	20	29	45
2 Eddie Beedle AFC	18	12	0	6	67	31	36	36
3 North Ferriby United Academy	18	11	3	4	71	36	35	36
4 Leven Members Club	18	8	3	7	45	54	-9	27
5 Hornsea Town Res.	18	7	3	8	30	44	-14	24
6 Hodgsons	18	6	5	7	46	47	-1	23
7 Hedon Rangers Res.	18	7	1	10	28	44	-16	22
8 Eastern Raiders	18	5	4	9	35	39	-4	19
9 Haltemprice	18	4	2	12	41	62	-21	14
10 Skirlaugh	18	3	3	12	37	72	-35	12

Division Two	P	W	D	L	F	A	GD	Pts
1 Lord Nelson	18	16	2	0	78	19	59	50
2 Beverley Town Academy	18	12	3	3	84	30	54	39
3 West Hull Amateurs	18	12	1	5	63	34	29	37
4 Molescroft Rangers	18	12	1	5	55	42	13	37
5 Priory Athletic	18	8	3	7	51	52	-1	27
6 FC Georgies Bar	18	6	4	8	44	54	-10	22
7 Middleton Rovers	18	6	1	11	42	47	-5	19
8 Driffield Evening Institute Res.	18	5	0	13	32	51	-19	15
9 Skidby Millers	18	3	0	15	23	76	-53	9
10 Malet Lambert Youth Club Res.	18	2	1	15	28	95	-67	7

Division Three	P	W	D	L	F	A	GD	Pts
1 Newland Young Boys	20	16	3	1	57	23	34	51
2 Shiptonthorpe United	20	16	2	2	71	30	41	50
3 FC Ridings	20	10	3	7	50	38	12	33
4 Langtoft	20	9	1	10	56	61	-5	28
5 Savoy	20	8	2	10	56	63	-7	26
6 Aldbrough United	20	7	4	9	29	30	-1	25
7 Howden Res.	20	8	1	11	37	53	-16	25
8 South Cave Sporting Club Res.	20	6	2	12	43	57	-14	20
9 Skirlaugh Res.	20	6	2	12	31	47	-16	20
10 Roos	20	4	7	9	46	49	-3	19
11 Hutton Cranswick SRA	20	5	3	12	30	55	-25	18

Division Four	P	W	D	L	F	A	GD	Pts
1 Gilberdyke Phoenix Res.	16	12	2	2	60	25	35	38
2 Bluebell Nafferton	16	12	1	3	71	32	39	37
3 East Riding Rangers Res.	16	10	1	5	48	33	15	31
4 Little Driffield AFC	16	7	3	6	34	49	-15	24
5 Leven Members Club Res.	16	6	4	6	39	29	10	22
6 Withernsea Res.	16	7	1	8	61	53	8	22
7 Holme Rovers Res.	16	4	4	8	36	41	-5	16
8 Easington United Casuals	16	4	0	12	16	58	-42	12
9 Brandesburton Res.	16	2	0	14	25	70	-45	6

Division Five	P	W	D	L	F	A	GD	Pts
1 Market Weighton United	16	12	1	3	55	27	28	37
2 Hornsea Town 3rd Team (+2)	16	10	2	4	53	26	27	34
3 South Park Rangers	16	10	0	6	51	29	22	30
4 Wawne United 3rd Team	16	9	1	6	58	37	21	28
5 Cottingham Forest	16	7	1	8	45	56	-11	22
6 Harchester United (-1)	16	5	4	7	43	44	-1	18
7 Haltemprice Res.	16	5	2	9	47	64	-17	17
8 Hedon Rangers Juniors	16	4	4	8	41	48	-7	16
9 Molescroft Rangers Res.	16	2	1	13	22	84	-62	7

Division Six	P	W	D	L	F	A	GD	Pts
1 Waterloo	18	15	0	3	91	35	56	45
2 South Park Rangers Juniors	18	12	0	6	67	44	23	36
3 West Hull Amateurs Res.	18	10	1	7	70	54	16	31
4 Leven Members Club 3rd Team	18	9	2	7	56	39	17	29
5 Market Weighton United Res.	18	9	2	7	48	40	8	29
6 Howden Academy	18	8	2	8	49	38	11	26
7 Eastrington Village	18	7	4	7	51	48	3	25
8 Withernsea 3rd Team	18	6	3	9	57	85	-28	21
9 Long Riston 3rd Team	18	4	1	13	47	71	-24	13
10 Bilton Athletic Res.	18	2	1	15	32	114	-82	7

ENFIELD FOOTBALL ALLIANCE

Premier Division	P	W	D	L	F	A	GD	Pts
Broadwater United	15	9	3	3	36	19	17	30
Origin	15	9	2	4	39	31	8	29
Brimsdown Rovers	15	7	4	4	38	34	4	25
Persian	15	7	3	5	47	30	17	24
Crescent Rangers	15	3	1	11	25	49	-24	10
F.F.London	15	2	3	10	24	46	-22	9

ESKVALE & CLEVELAND LEAGUE

Division One	P	W	D	L	F	A	GD	Pts
1 Staithes Athletic	20	15	4	1	77	21	56	49
2 Lingdale United	20	12	3	5	73	38	35	39
3 Loftus Athletic	20	11	5	4	70	49	21	38
4 Stokesley SC	20	11	4	5	68	43	25	37
5 Boosbeck United AFC (-3)	20	11	3	6	61	53	8	33
6 Lealholm FC	20	9	3	8	39	37	2	30
7 Hollybush United (-3)	20	9	4	7	57	31	26	28
8 Great Ayton United	20	5	3	12	38	59	-21	18
9 Brotton Railway Arms FC (-3)	20	5	2	13	34	76	-42	14
10 Hinderwell F.C.	20	3	1	16	44	94	-50	10
11 Goldsborough United	20	2	2	16	21	81	-60	8

ESSEX BUSINESS HOMES LEAGUE

Premier Division	P	W	D	L	F	A	GD	Pts
1 FC Hamlets	16	12	1	3	39	13	26	37
2 T.L.S	16	11	3	2	37	19	18	36
3 May+Baker	16	8	0	8	31	27	4	24
4 London APSA	16	7	3	6	33	37	-4	24
5 St Johns Deaf	16	6	4	6	45	40	5	22
6 Singh Sabha Barking	16	6	2	8	14	31	-17	20
7 Newtown Wesley	16	5	3	8	26	26	0	18
8 R.W.M.C.	16	5	2	9	22	33	-11	17
9 Dagenham United	16	3	0	13	14	35	-21	9

FURNESS PREMIER LEAGUE

Premier Division	P	W	D	L	F	A	GD	Pts
1 Holker Old Boys Res.	24	19	2	3	68	25	43	59
2 Barrow Celtic	24	15	7	2	87	37	50	52
3 Vickerstown Res.	24	15	4	5	66	23	43	49
4 Bootle	24	13	4	7	64	36	28	43
5 Kirkby United	24	12	4	8	60	50	10	40
6 Hawcoat Park Res.	24	12	2	10	60	55	5	38
7 Haverigg United	24	11	3	10	50	34	16	36
8 Britannia	24	8	4	12	45	53	-8	28
9 Furness Rovers Res.	24	7	6	11	52	48	4	27
10 Crooklands Casuals Res.	24	7	1	16	32	83	-51	22
11 Millom Res.	24	7	0	17	40	76	-36	21
12 Furness Cavaliers Res.	24	5	4	15	34	79	-45	19
13 Dalton United Res.	24	4	1	19	27	86	-59	13

Division One	P	W	D	L	F	A	GD	Pts
1 Askam United Res.	18	13	2	3	75	23	52	41
2 GSK Ulverston Rangers Res.	18	13	1	4	72	21	51	40
3 Swarthmoor Social Res.	18	12	4	2	53	28	25	40
4 Barrow Island	18	12	2	4	64	42	22	38
5 Haverigg United Res.	18	8	2	8	39	45	-6	26
6 Walney Island Res.	18	7	2	9	44	51	-7	23
7 Vickerstown 'A'	18	6	2	10	39	51	-12	20
8 Holker Old Boys 'A' (-3)	18	4	2	12	28	55	-27	11
9 Barrow Wanderers Res.	18	3	2	13	28	70	-42	11
10 Britannia Res. (-3)	18	2	1	15	22	78	-56	4

Division Two	P	W	D	L	F	A	GD	Pts
1 Hawcoat Park 'A'	21	18	0	3	65	33	32	54
2 Barrow Celtic Res.	21	14	0	7	77	55	22	42
3 Furness Rovers 'A'	21	10	3	8	43	35	8	33
4 Askam United 'A' (-6)	21	11	1	9	53	42	11	28
5 Dalton United 'A'	21	6	4	11	35	48	-13	22
6 Millom 'A' (-3)	21	6	6	9	48	56	-8	21
7 Bootle Res.	21	5	4	12	40	55	-15	19
8 Walney Island 'A' (-6)	21	4	2	15	39	76	-37	8

GLOUCESTERSHIRE NORTHERN LEAGUE

Division One	P	W	D	L	F	A	GD	Pts
1 Cam Bulldogs	30	24	2	4	71	32	39	74
2 Cheltenham Civil Service	30	21	3	6	95	24	71	66
3 Broadwell Amateurs	30	20	6	4	75	29	46	66
4 Taverners	30	15	7	8	46	36	10	52
5 Stonehouse Town	30	15	5	10	61	51	10	50
6 Ruardean Hill Rangers	30	15	3	12	57	44	13	48
7 Minsterworth	30	14	5	11	67	53	14	47
8 Hardwicke	30	13	6	11	70	60	10	45
9 Harrow Hill	30	12	5	13	46	49	-3	41
10 Sharpness	30	9	9	12	48	57	-9	36
11 Brockworth Albion	30	9	7	14	42	46	-4	34
12 Star FC	30	8	9	13	43	63	-20	33
13 Ramblers	30	8	6	16	55	63	-8	30
14 Lydbrook Athletic	30	7	3	20	37	85	-48	24
15 Dursley Town	30	4	10	16	35	53	-18	22
16 Bredon (-3)	30	2	2	26	22	125	-103	5

Division Two	P	W	D	L	F	A	GD	Pts
1 FC Barometrics	28	23	3	2	95	32	63	72
2 Moreton Rangers	28	21	3	4	105	37	68	66
3 Newent Town	28	17	6	5	66	38	28	57
4 Bibury	28	15	7	6	79	47	32	52
5 Quedgeley Wanderers (-1)	28	16	5	7	60	36	24	52
6 Longford	28	13	1	14	51	52	-1	40
7 Abbeymead Rovers	28	12	3	13	49	47	2	39
8 Tuffley Rovers Res	28	11	6	11	54	68	-14	39
9 Leonard Stanley	28	12	2	14	45	53	-8	38
10 Winchcombe Town	28	11	2	15	56	56	0	35
11 Smiths Athletic	28	11	1	16	45	60	-15	34
12 Viney St Swithins	28	9	2	17	39	74	-35	29
13 Wotton Rovers	28	8	4	16	63	86	-23	28
14 Soudley	28	4	1	23	32	100	-68	13
15 Chalford	28	3	2	23	38	92	-54	11

GRANTHAM & DISTRICT LEAGUE

Premier Division	P	W	D	L	F	A	GD	Pts
1 Ancaster Rams F C	24	22	1	1	107	21	86	67
2 Greyhounders	24	16	5	3	57	35	22	53
3 AFC Three Gables	24	15	2	7	80	49	31	47
4 Bottesford	24	14	5	5	69	41	28	47
5 Barrowby Res.	24	14	4	6	63	22	41	46
6 White Horse Sleaford	24	11	5	8	49	29	20	38
7 Cranmer Arms	24	11	1	12	67	50	17	34
8 Ancaster Rovers F C	24	6	8	10	56	48	8	26
9 Croxton AFC	24	7	4	13	33	60	-27	25
10 CK Dons Res.	24	5	5	14	35	72	-37	20
11 Caythorpe	24	6	1	17	38	87	-49	19
12 Bottesford Res.	24	5	0	19	30	80	-50	15
13 Newark Flowserve F C	24	3	1	20	29	119	-90	10

GREAT YARMOUTH & DISTRICT LEAGUE

Division One		P	W	D	L	F	A	GD	Pts
1	Catfield	18	18	0	0	92	18	74	54
2	Belton	18	13	1	4	62	41	21	40
3	MK Shrubs	18	11	2	5	63	39	24	35
4	Caister FC A	18	8	2	8	50	46	4	26
5	Caister Roma	18	8	1	9	34	40	-6	25
6	Bohemians	18	7	1	10	37	47	-10	22
7	South Yarmouth	18	5	1	12	33	47	-14	16
8	Mariners FC	18	4	4	10	34	56	-22	16
9	Great Yarmouth International	18	4	4	10	27	59	-32	16
10	Wanderers	18	2	4	12	26	65	-39	10

Division Two		P	W	D	L	F	A	GD	Pts
1	Prostar Windows	14	12	1	1	42	14	28	37
2	Grange FC	14	8	5	1	34	15	19	29
3	Caister Roma Res.	14	7	3	4	25	18	7	24
4	Great Yarmouth Town Hall Res.	14	7	1	6	39	31	8	22
5	Oliver Twist	14	4	2	8	30	22	8	14
6	Hemsby Res.	14	4	1	9	22	40	-18	13
7	Bohemians Res.	14	3	3	8	22	35	-13	12
8	Filby and Runham	14	2	2	10	13	52	-39	8

GUERNSEY LEAGUE

Priaulx League		P	W	D	L	F	A	GD	Pts
1	Belgrave Wanderers	24	17	6	1	88	29	59	57
2	North	24	14	4	6	68	44	24	46
3	Rangers	24	9	7	8	41	44	-3	34
4	Vale Rec	24	10	3	11	39	53	-14	33
5	Sylvans	24	8	4	12	34	50	-16	28
6	Rovers	24	7	2	15	31	61	-30	23
7	St Martins	24	4	4	16	30	50	-20	16

Jackson League		P	W	D	L	F	A	GD	Pts
1	North	16	15	1	0	77	25	52	46
2	St Martins	16	9	3	4	50	35	15	30
3	Belgrave Wanderers	16	7	4	5	44	38	6	25
4	Vale Rec	16	6	4	6	46	41	5	22
5	Rangers	16	6	2	8	40	46	-6	20
6	Bavaria Nomads	16	5	4	7	37	43	-6	19
7	Rovers FC	16	5	1	10	24	42	-18	16
8	Sylvans	16	4	2	10	17	34	-17	14
9	Centrals	16	4	1	11	33	64	-31	13

GUILDFORD & WOKING ALLIANCE

Premier Division		P	W	D	L	F	A	GD	Pts
1	Egham Athletic	22	20	2	0	88	17	71	62
2	Lyne	22	16	3	3	72	25	47	51
3	Chertsey Old Salesians	22	15	2	5	77	41	36	47
4	Keens Park Rangers	22	12	1	9	46	36	10	37
5	FC Shepperton	22	10	5	7	48	45	3	35
6	N.L.U.	22	10	2	10	34	41	-7	32
7	Guildford United	22	9	4	9	46	53	-7	31
8	Burpham	22	8	2	12	28	59	-31	26
9	Guildford Rangers	22	7	2	13	46	67	-21	23
10	Dunsfold	22	6	2	14	39	51	-12	20
11	West Byfleet Albion	22	2	3	17	25	74	-49	9
12	Puttenham United	22	2	2	18	22	62	-40	8

Division One		P	W	D	L	F	A	GD	Pts
1	Astolat Athletic	24	19	2	3	76	27	49	59
2	Guildford Park	24	16	4	4	69	35	34	52
3	Manorcroft United	24	15	3	6	50	23	27	48
4	AFC Bedfont Green	24	14	5	5	63	33	30	47
5	Holmbury St Mary	24	13	3	8	58	37	21	42
6	Weysiders	24	12	3	9	44	43	1	39
7	Abbey Rangers 'A'	24	10	5	9	38	35	3	35
8	Hersham	24	8	3	13	39	52	-13	27
9	Elstead	24	7	2	15	47	69	-22	23
10	AFC Brooklands Seniors	24	7	2	15	33	58	-25	23
11	University of Surrey 'A'	24	6	4	14	38	56	-18	22
12	Mytchett United	24	6	2	16	42	68	-26	20
13	AFC Gomshall	24	3	2	19	26	87	-61	11

Division Two		P	W	D	L	F	A	GD	Pts
1	Parkside United	20	18	1	1	92	22	70	55
2	Heathervale	20	14	3	3	67	26	41	45
3	Addlestone	20	14	3	3	44	18	26	45
4	AFC Crown & Anchor	20	12	3	5	67	44	23	39
5	Allianz	20	9	3	8	39	35	4	30
6	AFC Bedfont Green Res.	20	7	4	9	43	46	-3	25
7	Bourne Blades	20	6	2	12	45	53	-8	20
8	Staines Lammas Res.	20	5	4	11	33	58	-25	19
9	Chertsey Old Salesians Res.	20	3	6	11	31	56	-25	15
10	Burpham Res.	20	3	2	15	18	50	-32	11
11	Knaphill Athletic 'A'	20	2	3	15	25	96	-71	9

Division Three		P	W	D	L	F	A	GD	Pts
1	Lyne Res.	24	23	1	0	92	19	73	70
2	AFC Watermans	24	15	4	5	57	38	19	49
3	Woking United	24	14	5	5	74	42	32	47
4	Laleham Res.	24	13	4	7	49	38	11	43
5	Christian Club Woking	24	11	7	6	57	29	28	40
6	Ripley Village 'A'	24	10	4	10	65	63	2	34
7	Dunsfold Res.	24	9	6	9	53	44	9	33
8	Blackwater Royals	24	9	4	11	66	41	25	31
9	Worplesdon Phoenix 'B'	24	9	2	13	64	86	-22	29
10	Elstead Res.	24	8	3	13	52	72	-20	27
11	Shottermill & Haslemere 'A'	24	7	4	13	21	49	-28	25
12	Guildford Park Res.	24	6	0	18	43	83	-40	18
13	Milford & Witley 'A'	24	0	0	24	14	103	-89	0

Division Four		P	W	D	L	F	A	GD	Pts
1	Surrey Athletic	24	17	3	4	89	40	49	54
2	Lyne 'A'	24	15	4	5	60	45	15	49
3	Woking Tigers	24	15	3	6	82	42	40	48
4	Ottershaw	24	12	5	7	76	51	25	41
5	Woking & Horsell 'A'	23	11	6	6	65	42	23	39
6	Guildford United 'A'	24	11	4	9	69	68	1	37
7	Byfleet	24	11	4	9	52	52	0	37
8	University of Surrey 'B'	24	10	3	11	48	31	17	33
9	Hersham Res.	24	10	2	12	64	63	1	32
10	Guildford Rangers Res.	23	9	4	10	52	57	-5	31
11	Weysiders Res.	24	6	3	15	32	77	-45	21
12	United Football Club of Guildford	24	3	4	17	47	74	-27	13
13	Hambledon 'A'	24	2	1	21	18	112	-94	7

HALIFAX & DISTRICT LEAGUE

Premier Division	P	W	D	L	F	A	GD	Pts
1 Ryburn United	22	16	5	1	73	19	54	53
2 Stump Cross	22	17	1	4	73	34	39	52
3 Greetland AFC	22	12	5	5	51	43	8	41
4 Midgley United	22	12	4	6	69	33	36	40
5 Elland United	22	8	5	9	60	70	-10	29
6 Calder 76	22	8	4	10	59	64	-5	28
7 Copley United	22	7	4	11	52	66	-14	25
8 King Cross Warley	22	7	3	12	50	63	-13	24
9 Sowerby United	22	6	5	11	40	58	-18	23
10 Hebden Royd RS	22	6	4	12	48	63	-15	22
11 Sowerby Bridge	22	4	7	11	45	65	-20	19
12 Holmfield	22	3	5	14	37	79	-42	14

Division One	P	W	D	L	F	A	GD	Pts
1 Northowram	22	17	4	1	97	33	64	55
2 Shelf United	22	17	2	3	88	36	52	53
3 Denholme United	22	13	5	4	78	54	24	44
4 Salem	22	10	6	6	73	60	13	36
5 Elland Allstars	22	9	6	7	48	52	-4	33
6 Ryburn United Res.	22	6	9	7	42	46	-4	27
7 Volunteer Arms	22	8	2	12	56	80	-24	26
8 Sowerby Bridge Res.	22	6	4	12	46	65	-19	22
9 Stainland United	22	5	7	10	41	61	-20	22
10 Wadsworth United	22	5	2	15	29	53	-24	17
11 Greetland AFC Res.	22	5	2	15	39	69	-30	17
12 Halifax Irish Centre	22	3	7	12	37	65	-28	16

Division Two	P	W	D	L	F	A	GD	Pts
1 AFC Crossleys	18	14	3	1	81	30	51	45
2 Spring Hall Celtic	18	12	1	5	69	29	40	37
3 Mixenden United	18	11	4	3	42	30	12	37
4 King Cross Warley Res.	18	7	5	6	44	43	1	26
5 Calder 76 Res.	18	7	3	8	28	45	-17	24
6 Denholme United Res.	18	6	5	7	52	47	5	23
7 Midgley United Res.	18	7	2	9	32	38	-6	23
0 Hcbdon Royd RS Res.	18	6	1	11	34	53	-19	19
9 Shelf United Res.	18	6	1	11	29	61	-32	19
10 Sowerby United Res.	18	1	1	16	21	56	-35	4

Division Three	P	W	D	L	F	A	GD	Pts
1 Brighouse Sports AFC	20	16	2	2	75	25	50	50
2 West Central FC	20	11	6	3	49	39	10	39
3 Shelf FC	20	9	4	7	44	26	18	31
4 Savile Arms FC	20	9	2	9	49	43	6	29
5 St Columbas	20	4	1	15	27	71	-44	13
6 Salem Res.	20	2	3	15	22	62	-40	9

HARROGATE & DISTRICT LEAGUE

Premier Division	P	W	D	L	F	A	GD	Pts
1 Kirk Deighton Rangers	22	17	1	4	70	26	44	52
2 Rawdon Old Boys	22	16	4	2	63	20	43	52
3 Harlow Hill	22	14	2	6	64	34	30	44
4 Beckwithshaw Saints	22	13	4	5	68	40	28	43
5 Otley Rovers	22	12	1	9	77	62	15	37
6 Wetherby Athletic A	22	11	3	8	58	44	14	36
7 Clifford	22	10	2	10	70	52	18	32
8 Knaresborough Celtic	22	9	1	12	49	54	-5	28
9 Kirkby Malzeard	22	8	2	12	47	53	-6	26
10 Pannal Sports	22	5	2	15	46	76	-30	17
11 Pateley Bridge	22	3	0	19	36	111	-75	9
12 Thirsk Falcons Res.	22	3	0	19	29	105	-76	9

Division One	P	W	D	L	F	A	GD	Pts
1 Bedale Town	26	23	2	1	131	37	94	71
2 Leyburn United	26	16	4	6	77	60	17	52
3 Hampsthwaite HC	26	15	5	6	91	65	26	50
4 Hampsthwaite United	26	14	3	9	81	72	9	45
5 Burley Trojans	25	14	2	9	79	54	25	44
6 Kirkstall Crusaders FC	25	12	6	7	81	53	28	42
7 Kirk Deighton Rangers Res.	26	13	2	11	69	70	-1	41
8 Dalton Athletic	26	10	1	15	58	73	-15	31
9 Beckwithshaw Saints Res.	26	8	6	12	55	73	-18	30
10 AFC Hillside	24	9	2	13	66	68	-2	29
11 Harlow Hill Res.	26	7	6	13	64	86	-22	27
12 Pannal Sports Res.	26	5	4	17	48	95	-47	19
13 Westbrook YMCA Res.	26	5	3	18	39	67	-28	18
14 Albert Sport Yeadon	26	5	2	19	41	107	-66	17

Division Two	P	W	D	L	F	A	GD	Pts
1 Bramham	22	16	6	0	66	24	42	54
2 Boroughbridge A	22	17	2	3	68	18	50	53
3 Bramhope	22	11	5	6	56	34	22	38
4 FC Harrogate	22	11	4	7	51	43	8	37
5 Ripon Red Arrows	22	10	3	9	59	71	-12	33
6 Addingham	22	9	5	8	58	41	17	32
7 Wetheby Athletic `B`	22	9	2	11	49	53	-4	29
8 Hampsthwaite United Res.	22	7	3	12	44	58	-14	24
9 Helperby United	22	6	5	11	54	48	6	23
10 Kirkby Malzeard Res.	22	6	3	13	39	57	-18	21
11 Pool A	22	5	5	12	41	74	-33	20
12 Pannal Sports A	22	2	3	17	28	92	-64	9

HEREFORDSHIRE LEAGUE

Premier Division	P	W	D	L	F	A	GD	Pts
1 Ewyas Harold	24	17	5	2	59	20	39	56
2 Leominster Town (-3)	24	16	3	5	73	33	40	48
3 Wellington Res.	24	13	6	5	74	47	27	45
4 Westfields Res. (-3)	24	14	3	7	59	38	21	42
5 Hinton	24	11	6	7	60	45	15	39
6 Shobdon	24	12	3	9	57	50	7	39
7 Fownhope	24	10	5	9	47	42	5	35
8 Kington Town	24	8	5	11	38	46	-8	29
9 Lads Club Res.	24	8	2	14	42	55	-13	26
10 Ross Juniors	24	6	4	14	38	54	-16	22
11 Pegasus Res.	24	6	2	16	32	57	-25	20
12 Weobley	24	4	6	14	33	60	-27	18
13 Bartestree Res. (-6)	24	5	2	17	30	95	-65	11

Division One	P	W	D	L	F	A	GD	Pts
1 Tenbury United	18	13	2	3	73	40	33	41
2 Orleton Colts	18	10	4	4	43	17	26	34
3 Woofferton	18	9	3	6	62	39	23	30
4 Brimfield F.C (-3)	18	10	3	5	49	29	20	30
5 Ledbury Town Res. (-3)	18	9	4	5	60	36	24	28
6 Ewyas Harold Res	18	8	3	7	23	30	-7	27
7 Wellington Colts	18	7	1	10	38	57	-19	22
8 Holme Lacy	18	6	3	9	34	41	-7	21
9 Hinton Res. (-3)	18	5	2	11	31	48	-17	14
10 Kingstone Rovers (-3)	18	0	1	17	17	93	-76	-2

Division Two	P	W	D	L	F	A	GD	Pts
1 Bromyard FC	14	13	1	0	71	8	63	40
2 Fownhope Res.	14	10	1	3	39	15	24	31
3 Tenbury Town	14	10	0	4	44	28	16	30
4 Hereford City	14	5	3	6	20	27	-7	18
5 Kingstone Harriers	14	5	1	8	25	44	-19	16
6 Pencombe	14	4	1	9	26	39	-13	13
7 Civil Service (-3)	14	3	4	7	15	39	-24	10
8 Weston (-6)	14	0	1	13	1	41	-40	-5

Division Three	P	W	D	L	F	A	GD	Pts
1 Sinkum	14	10	3	1	50	20	30	33
2 Kington Town Res.	14	9	2	3	53	22	31	29
3 Orleton Colts Res.	14	9	1	4	60	25	35	28
4 Dore Valley	14	8	1	5	59	33	26	25
5 Ross Juniors Res.	14	7	2	5	38	33	5	23
6 Shobdon Res. FC	14	3	4	7	35	51	-16	13
7 Tenbury Colts (-3)	14	2	0	12	22	84	-62	3
8 Leintwardine (-6)	14	1	1	12	24	73	-49	-2

HOPE VALLEY AMATEUR LEAGUE

Premier Division	P	W	D	L	F	A	GD	Pts
1 Bradwell	20	18	1	1	78	15	63	55
2 Dove Holes	20	16	2	2	74	16	58	50
3 Tideswell United	20	11	3	6	60	36	24	36
4 Peak Dale	20	10	3	7	49	28	21	33
5 Furness Vale	20	9	2	9	52	50	2	29
6 Tintwistle Villa	20	8	4	8	53	40	13	28
7 Bakewell Town	20	9	1	10	45	41	4	28
8 AFC Dronfield Woodhouse	20	7	5	8	40	57	-17	26
9 Dronfield Woodhouse	20	6	3	11	40	69	-29	21
10 Youlgrave United	20	3	1	16	41	75	-34	10
11 Hope Sports	20	0	1	19	23	128	-105	1

A Division	P	W	D	L	F	A	GD	Pts
1 Dronfield Town A	26	21	1	4	104	29	75	64
2 Ashover FC	26	21	0	5	104	30	74	63
3 Buxton Town	26	19	3	4	75	38	37	60
4 Buxworth	26	16	4	6	85	57	28	52
5 Hathersage	26	14	3	9	69	56	13	45
6 Blazing Rag	26	12	3	11	63	62	1	39
7 FC Utd of Tideswell	26	10	4	12	71	84	-13	34
8 Dove Holes Res.	26	9	2	15	54	83	-29	29
9 Bakewell Manners	26	8	3	15	53	59	-6	27
10 Chinley (-3)	26	10	0	16	57	114	-57	27
11 Tideswell Blue Star (-3)	26	8	5	13	52	73	-21	26
12 Grindleford	26	6	2	18	49	77	-28	20
13 Cote Heath	26	5	3	18	47	83	-36	18
14 Baslow (-3)	26	5	3	18	64	102	-38	15

B Division	P	W	D	L	F	A	GD	Pts
1 Bamford	26	19	4	3	87	37	50	61
2 Chesterfield Town	26	19	4	3	87	39	48	61
3 Dronfield Town B (-3)	26	17	2	7	84	40	44	50
4 Railway FC	26	15	3	8	74	50	24	48
5 Edale	26	15	1	10	68	61	7	46
6 Eyam	26	13	5	8	75	56	19	44
7 Stoney Middleton	26	13	1	12	60	62	-2	40
8 Calver	26	10	5	11	60	64	-4	35
9 Bakewell Town Res.	26	10	4	12	57	56	1	34
10 Darley Dale Lions	26	8	3	15	69	81	-12	27
11 Bradwell Res. (-6)	26	9	3	14	68	90	-22	24
12 Buxworth Res.	26	5	2	19	54	91	-37	17
13 Furness Vale Res.	26	4	3	19	49	89	-40	15
14 Winster FC	26	4	2	20	29	105	-76	14

HUDDERSFIELD & DISTRICT LEAGUE

Division One	P	W	D	L	F	A	GD	Pts
1 Newsome	22	17	4	1	123	41	82	55
2 Berry Brow	22	15	4	3	80	30	50	49
3 Holmbridge	22	14	4	4	76	30	46	46
4 Diggle	22	13	4	5	62	37	25	43
5 Britannia Sports	22	11	4	7	64	49	15	37
6 Hepworth Utd	22	11	3	8	68	43	25	36
7 Scholes	22	8	5	9	34	54	-20	29
8 Netherton	22	8	4	10	57	65	-8	28
9 Shepley	22	5	2	15	39	70	-31	17
10 Uppermill	22	4	4	14	32	77	-45	16
11 Heywood Irish Centre FC	22	3	2	17	29	76	-47	11
12 Lepton Highlanders	22	2	2	18	34	126	-92	8

Division Two	P	W	D	L	F	A	GD	Pts
1 Holmfirth Town	22	16	2	4	60	34	26	50
2 Shelley	22	15	1	6	53	31	22	46
3 Heyside FC	22	13	4	5	59	41	18	43
4 Honley	22	11	6	5	57	31	26	39
5 Kirkheaton Rovers	22	11	4	7	44	29	15	37
6 Skelmanthorpe	22	10	6	6	44	27	17	36
7 Slaithwaite Utd	22	8	6	8	48	50	-2	30
8 Cumberworth	22	8	4	10	39	54	-15	28
9 H.V.Academicals	22	7	4	11	46	57	-11	25
10 Meltham Athletic	22	5	5	12	45	60	-15	20
11 Linthwaite Athletic	22	3	1	18	29	68	-39	10
12 DRAM Community	22	1	5	16	29	71	-42	8

Division Three	P	W	D	L	F	A	GD	Pts
1 KKS Spartans	22	16	4	2	100	21	79	52
2 Aimbry	22	15	4	3	77	27	50	49
3 Upperthong SC	22	15	1	6	81	27	54	46
4 AFC Lindley	22	15	1	6	66	35	31	46
5 Brook Motors	22	12	5	5	57	31	26	41
6 Hade Edge	22	12	5	5	56	36	20	41
7 Scissett	22	9	4	9	55	44	11	31
8 Grange Moor	22	8	2	12	42	40	2	26
9 Paddock Rangers	22	4	2	16	28	76	-48	14
10 Wooldale Wanderers	22	3	3	16	24	81	-57	12
11 Flockton FC	22	4	0	18	22	105	-83	12
12 AFC Waterloo	22	3	1	18	22	107	-85	10

Division Four	P	W	D	L	F	A	GD	Pts
1 Royal Oak (-1)	22	16	2	4	94	34	60	49
2 Colne Valley	22	15	2	5	64	28	36	47
3 3D Dynamos	22	14	1	7	78	53	25	43
4 Moorside (-1)	22	11	5	6	59	40	19	37
5 Almondbury Woolpack	22	11	2	9	67	41	26	35
6 Cartworth Moor (-1)	22	11	1	10	82	58	24	33
7 Brow United	22	9	4	9	46	48	-2	31
8 Thornhill United (-1)	22	9	3	10	67	73	-6	29
9 Fantastic	22	8	2	12	60	71	-11	26
10 Junction	22	8	1	13	45	59	-14	25
11 Brighouse Old Boys	22	7	2	13	61	87	-26	23
12 Mount	22	0	1	21	20	151	-131	1

HUDDERSFIELD & DISTRICT WORKS & COMBINATION LEAGUE

Division One	P	W	D	L	F	A	GD	Pts
1 Yeaton Cask	12	11	0	1	46	18	28	33
2 Lindley Saddle	12	9	1	2	51	16	35	28
3 Golcar United	12	8	0	4	24	34	-10	24
4 Aimbry F.C.	12	6	1	5	34	32	2	19
5 Lepton Highlanders	12	4	0	8	19	33	-14	12
6 Sovereign Sports	12	2	1	9	20	34	-14	7
7 Fartown Force United	12	0	1	11	14	41	-27	1

Division Two	P	W	D	L	F	A	GD	Pts
1 Lindley Saddle Res.	12	10	0	2	65	22	43	30
2 AFC Craven	12	8	2	2	63	32	31	26
3 Royal Dolphins	12	8	2	2	53	23	30	26
4 Fantastic FC	12	5	1	6	32	53	-21	16
5 Railway Berry Brow	12	3	1	8	18	34	-16	10
6 Grange Moor	12	2	2	8	15	36	-21	8
7 Marsden	12	1	2	9	25	71	-46	5

I ZINGARI COMBINATION

Division One	P	W	D	L	F	A	GD	Pts
1 Essemmay OB	12	9	2	1	37	12	25	29
2 The First Dock	12	8	0	4	24	18	6	24
3 Leyfield	12	6	2	4	29	23	6	20
4 Liverpool Cavaliers	12	4	3	5	20	24	-4	15
5 Liobians	12	4	0	8	24	36	-12	12
6 BRNESC	12	2	4	6	21	30	-9	10
7 Woodstreet	12	3	1	8	16	28	-12	10

Division Two	P	W	D	L	F	A	GD	Pts
1 Liver V FC	14	12	0	2	57	23	34	36
2 Mount Athletic	14	10	3	1	52	20	32	33
3 Picton FC	14	9	3	2	47	24	23	30
4 Netherley Wood Lane Legion	14	8	3	3	45	19	26	27
5 Liverpool Hibernia	14	6	0	8	31	34	-3	18
6 Mersey Harps	14	3	1	10	22	40	-18	10
7 Woodstreet	14	2	0	12	19	52	-33	6
8 Rockville (Wallasey)	14	1	0	13	13	74	-61	3

ISLE OF MAN SENIOR LEAGUE

Premier Division	P	W	D	L	F	A	GD	Pts
1 St Georges	24	23	1	0	116	16	100	70
2 St Marys	24	17	2	5	82	20	62	53
3 Peel	24	15	3	6	79	40	39	48
4 St Johns Utd	24	13	6	5	58	37	21	45
5 DHSOB	24	13	3	8	65	43	22	42
6 Rushen Utd	24	12	5	7	72	44	28	41
7 Laxey	24	12	5	7	68	46	22	41
8 Union Mills	24	9	3	12	61	78	-17	30
9 Corinthians	24	7	4	13	44	73	-29	25
10 Ramsey	24	7	2	15	43	79	-36	23
11 Michael United	24	5	0	19	26	69	-43	15
12 RYCOB	24	3	0	21	27	108	-81	9
13 Castletown	24	2	2	20	33	121	-88	8

NON
LEAGUE DAY
06.09.14
Support your
LOCAL
FOOTBALL CLUB
nonleagueday.co.uk

Division Two	P	W	D	L	F	A	GD	Pts
1 Gymnasium	24	18	4	2	99	21	78	58
2 Ayre United	24	16	4	4	73	38	35	52
3 Colby	24	15	5	4	73	32	41	50
4 Marown	24	15	3	6	78	36	42	48
5 Douglas Royal	24	15	3	6	94	53	41	48
6 Douglas Athletic	24	13	3	8	80	46	34	42
7 Onchan	24	12	1	11	62	70	-8	37
8 Malew	24	6	7	11	37	66	-29	25
9 Pulrose United (-3)	24	8	3	13	45	60	-15	24
10 Braddan	24	6	4	14	43	78	-35	22
11 Douglas & District	24	7	1	16	38	73	-35	22
12 Ronaldsway	24	1	5	18	24	91	-67	8
13 Foxdale	24	1	3	20	28	110	-82	6

ISLE OF WIGHT LEAGUE

Division One	P	W	D	L	F	A	GD	Pts
1 West Wight	22	12	7	3	44	21	23	43
2 Brading Town	22	12	6	4	60	27	33	42
3 Northwood St Johns	22	9	6	7	51	37	14	33
4 Vectis Nomads FC	22	10	3	9	42	32	10	33
5 Cowes Sports Res.	22	10	3	9	38	35	3	33
6 Shanklin	22	10	3	9	35	40	-5	33
7 E.C.S.F.C.	22	9	5	8	39	33	6	32
8 Osborne Coburg	22	8	6	8	44	41	3	30
9 Niton	22	8	5	9	36	44	-8	29
10 Oakfield	22	8	4	10	37	38	-1	28
11 Binstead & COB FC	22	7	5	10	48	54	-6	26
12 Ryde Saints	22	2	1	19	19	91	-72	7

Division Two	P	W	D	L	F	A	GD	Pts
1 Whitecroft & Barton Sports	22	21	1	0	134	8	126	64
2 Seaview	22	17	3	2	88	28	60	54
3 Rookley	22	15	2	5	84	34	50	47
4 Shanklin VYCC	22	14	3	5	53	25	28	45
5 Ventnor	22	13	3	6	43	41	2	42
6 Brighstone	22	8	3	11	41	53	-12	27
7 Newchurch	22	8	2	12	32	82	-50	26
8 Yarmouth & Calbourne	22	6	6	10	47	58	-11	24
9 St Helens Blue Star	22	6	2	14	40	62	-22	20
10 Sandown	22	5	3	14	28	44	-16	18
11 Carisbrooke United	22	2	2	18	29	115	-86	8
12 AFC Wootton	22	0	4	18	34	103	-69	4

Division Three	P	W	D	L	F	A	GD	Pts
1 Bembridge F C	18	15	2	1	92	13	79	47
2 Holmwood Athletic	18	13	3	2	84	19	65	42
3 Wroxall	18	12	4	2	73	36	37	40
4 Cowes Sports A	18	12	0	6	75	36	39	36
5 High Park	18	8	2	8	55	40	15	26
6 Brading Town A	18	8	2	8	33	44	-11	26
7 Kyngs Towne	18	4	3	11	38	73	-35	15
8 Seaclose	18	4	2	12	23	71	-48	14
9 Shanklin A	18	3	1	14	17	75	-58	10
10 Ryde Saints A	18	0	3	15	22	105	-83	3

JERSEY FOOTBALL COMBINATION

Premiership	P	W	D	L	F	A	GD	Pts
1 St Paul's	16	13	3	0	56	14	42	42
2 Jersey Scottish	16	12	3	1	63	15	48	39
3 JTC Jersey Wanderers	16	8	2	6	35	27	8	26
4 Trinity	16	8	1	7	43	35	8	25
5 St Peter	16	6	2	8	29	36	-7	20
6 St Clement	16	5	4	7	21	38	-17	19
7 St Ouen	16	3	5	8	28	39	-11	14
8 St Brelade (-3)	16	4	1	11	25	50	-25	10
9 Grouville (+3)	16	2	1	13	11	57	-46	10

Championship	P	W	D	L	F	A	GD	Pts
1 First Tower Utd	16	14	0	2	62	14	48	42
2 St Lawrence	16	12	2	2	46	11	35	38
3 Rozel Rovers	16	11	3	2	49	11	38	36
4 St John	16	10	1	5	54	27	27	31
5 Jersey Portuguese	16	8	2	6	51	28	23	26
6 Beeches OB	16	3	1	12	25	76	-51	10
7 St Martin	16	2	3	11	13	56	-43	9
8 Magpies	16	2	2	12	19	55	-36	8
9 Sporting Academics	16	2	2	12	17	58	-41	8

KIDDERMINSTER & DISTRICT LEAGUE

Premier Division	P	W	D	L	F	A	GD	Pts
1 Hanworth Sports	15	10	2	3	29	18	11	32
2 Parkside	15	8	3	4	38	20	18	27
3 M.T.Wandgas	15	7	1	7	22	20	2	22
4 AFC West End	15	6	4	5	21	20	1	22
5 Wandle A.F.C.	15	4	5	6	22	27	-5	17
6 Darkside	15	2	1	12	17	44	-27	7

Division One	P	W	D	L	F	A	GD	Pts
1 Maori Park	21	14	4	3	48	26	22	46
2 Lennox	21	12	5	3	71	39	32	41
3 Esher United	21	12	3	5	51	30	21	39
4 Kingston Albion	21	8	5	8	35	40	-5	29
5 L.M.United	21	8	3	10	33	43	-10	27
6 Oxshott Royals	21	6	5	9	27	35	-8	23
7 Richmond & Kingston O.B	21	5	2	14	24	59	-35	17
8 N.P.L.	21	3	1	16	25	42	-17	10

Division Two	P	W	D	L	F	A	GD	Pts
1 Barnslake	18	14	0	4	54	24	30	42
2 M.C United	18	12	1	5	50	26	24	37
3 Waldergrove Wanderers	18	10	3	5	43	25	18	33
4 Sutton Celtic	18	9	2	7	32	42	-10	29
5 Surrey Fire	18	8	1	9	37	33	4	25
6 Petersham Pumas	18	7	3	7	44	39	5	24
7 N.P.L. Res.	18	7	1	10	40	45	-5	22
8 Barton Green Rovers	18	6	3	8	45	39	6	21
9 Surbiton Eagles	18	6	1	11	35	49	-14	19
10 Thornton Heath	18	2	1	15	35	93	-58	7

LEAGUE TABLES

Division Three	P	W	D	L	F	A	GD	Pts
1 Merton Social	16	13	1	2	67	26	41	40
2 AFC Kingston	16	12	0	4	64	40	24	36
3 Esher	16	10	4	2	47	32	15	34
4 Kew Association	16	8	2	5	54	37	17	26
5 New Malden Town	16	6	2	8	40	43	-3	20
6 Lower Green	16	5	2	8	29	34	-5	17
7 Hook Venturers	16	3	3	10	31	56	-25	12
8 St Martins	16	3	1	12	33	65	-32	10
9 Dynamo Kingston	16	3	1	12	27	59	-32	10

Division Four	P	W	D	L	F	A	GD	Pts
1 Darkside Res.	14	11	0	3	58	18	40	33
2 L.M.United Res.	14	9	2	3	51	23	28	29
3 Chessington K.C. Res.	14	7	2	5	46	32	14	23
4 Epsom Casuals	14	7	0	7	34	33	1	21
5 Merton Social Res.	14	6	3	5	32	31	1	21
6 AFC North Leatherhead	14	6	2	6	28	31	-3	20
7 Kew Association Res.	14	4	3	7	19	51	-32	15
8 St Martins Res.	14	0	0	14	14	63	-49	0

Division Five	P	W	D	L	F	A	GD	Pts
1 Parkside Res.	16	11	4	1	56	25	31	37
2 Ewell Saxons	16	11	2	3	67	30	37	35
3 Petersham Pumas Res.	16	9	2	5	45	30	15	29
4 Chessington K.C. III	16	8	4	4	31	26	5	28
5 AFC Hampton	16	8	2	6	48	35	13	26
6 Dynamo Kingston Res.	16	4	5	7	30	42	-12	17
7 Feltham Rangers	16	2	7	7	26	38	-12	13
8 Merton Social III	16	3	3	10	23	53	-30	12
9 AFC Kingston Res.	16	1	1	14	16	63	-47	4

LANCASHIRE & CHESHIRE LEAGUE

Premier Division	P	W	D	L	F	A	GD	Pts
1 Whalley Range	26	21	3	2	110	41	69	66
2 AFC Oldham 2005	26	18	6	2	83	39	44	60
3 Rochdalians	26	15	5	6	71	41	30	50
4 Mellor	26	14	4	8	72	50	22	46
5 Moston Brook	26	13	2	11	92	79	13	41
6 Old Ashtonians	26	12	5	9	56	59	-3	41
7 Newton 1st	26	12	4	10	49	42	7	40
8 Gorse Hill	26	9	6	11	51	56	-5	33
9 South Manchester	26	8	7	11	55	49	6	31
10 Old Stretfordians	26	8	3	15	56	83	-27	27
11 Bedians	26	7	3	16	49	66	-17	24
12 Chorltonians	26	5	8	13	42	66	-24	23
13 Spurley Hey (-3)	26	6	1	19	43	106	-63	16
14 Hooley Bridge Celtic	26	4	3	19	43	95	-52	15

Division One	P	W	D	L	F	A	GD	Pts
1 Boothstown FC 1st	24	18	5	1	80	31	49	59
2 Castleton FC First	24	16	6	2	83	36	47	54
3 Parrswood Celtic	24	13	6	5	71	41	30	45
4 Eagle	24	13	2	9	72	53	19	41
5 Moorside Rangers FC	24	10	5	9	56	57	-1	35
6 Tintwistle Athletic FC	24	10	4	10	49	42	7	34
7 Newton Heath	24	11	1	12	64	70	-6	34
8 Govan Athletic	24	8	5	11	59	64	-5	29
9 Abacus Media	24	8	4	12	42	52	-10	28
10 Milton FC	24	7	5	12	52	65	-13	26
11 Burnage Metro	24	7	3	14	48	57	-9	24
12 Stoconians 1st	24	4	5	15	37	76	-39	17
13 Santos FC	24	4	3	17	45	114	-69	15

Division Two	P	W	D	L	F	A	GD	Pts
1 Old Trafford	20	14	4	2	81	31	50	46
2 Signol Athletic FC First	20	11	7	2	64	35	29	40
3 Chorltonians Res.	20	11	5	4	45	29	16	38
4 Whalley Range Res.	20	11	2	7	58	41	17	35
5 Mellor Res.	20	11	1	8	66	46	20	34
6 Bury Amateur AFC 1st	20	10	2	8	42	35	7	32
7 Spurley Hey Res. (-3)	20	10	1	9	57	51	6	28
8 Rochdalians Res.	20	7	2	11	32	37	-5	23
9 Urmston Town 1st	20	4	2	14	36	73	-37	14
10 Heaton Mersey (-3)	20	3	1	16	29	79	-50	7
11 Hazel Grove (-6)	20	3	3	14	25	78	-53	6

Division Three	P	W	D	L	F	A	GD	Pts
1 High Lane 1st	22	17	2	3	99	16	83	53
2 Salford Victoria FC 1st	22	16	2	4	81	42	39	50
3 Ardwick FC 1st (-3)	22	16	2	4	110	31	79	47
4 Castleton FC Res.	22	14	1	7	58	48	10	43
5 Old Stretfordians Res.	22	9	3	10	39	50	-11	30
6 FC Bury Town 1st	22	7	4	11	43	58	-15	25
7 Hooley Bridge Celtic Res.	22	7	3	12	37	51	-14	24
8 Gorse Hill Res. (-3)	22	7	4	11	43	52	-9	22
9 Droylsden JFC 1st	22	7	1	14	43	104	-61	22
10 Trafford United 1st	22	6	3	13	34	60	-26	21
11 Oldham Victoria (-3)	22	6	3	13	43	83	-40	18
12 Bedians Res. (-6)	22	5	2	15	42	77	-35	11

LANCASHIRE AMATEUR LEAGUE

Premier Division	P	W	D	L	F	A	GD	Pts
1 Prestwich	26	21	2	3	81	38	43	65
2 Old Boltonians	26	19	6	1	84	23	61	63
3 Castle Hill	26	15	3	8	65	53	12	48
4 Failsworth Dynamos	26	15	2	9	66	31	35	47
5 Tottington United	26	14	2	10	73	48	25	44
6 Little Lever SC	26	14	1	11	73	64	9	43
7 Old Mancunians	26	13	3	10	55	42	13	42
8 Bury GSOB	26	11	7	8	48	55	-7	40
9 Horwich Victoria	26	10	4	12	71	62	9	34
10 Rochdale St Clements	26	9	4	13	49	48	1	31
11 Howe Bridge Mills	26	7	4	15	46	78	-32	25
12 Old Blackburnians	26	4	4	18	42	77	-35	16
13 Rossendale Amateurs (-4)	26	4	3	19	41	120	-79	11
14 Hesketh Casuals	26	2	3	21	58	113	-55	9

Division One	P	W	D	L	F	A	GD	Pts
1 North Walkden	26	18	1	7	98	48	50	55
2 Mostonians	26	17	4	5	83	48	35	55
3 Tyldesley United	26	14	8	4	67	53	14	50
4 Oldham Hulmeians	26	15	4	7	61	50	11	49
5 Chaddertonians	26	14	5	7	67	47	20	47
6 Blackrod Town	26	13	7	6	75	54	21	46
7 Bolton Wyresdale	26	14	3	9	62	44	18	45
8 Old Boltonians Res.	26	9	6	11	58	60	-2	33
9 Horwich RMI	26	7	9	10	51	59	-8	30
10 Rochdale St Clements Res.	26	8	4	14	55	63	-8	28
11 Ainsworth	26	7	6	13	68	82	-14	27
12 Roach Dynamos	26	7	4	15	51	70	-19	25
13 Thornleigh	26	5	1	20	51	92	-41	16
14 Hindley Juniors (-4)	26	2	2	22	46	123	-77	4

Division Two	P	W	D	L	F	A	GD	Pts
1 Oldham Hulmeians Res.	22	20	0	2	94	30	64	60
2 Farnworth Town	22	13	3	6	46	41	5	42
3 Wardle	22	11	7	4	52	41	11	40
4 Digmoor FC	22	11	5	6	45	35	10	38
5 Accrington Amateurs	22	11	4	7	67	39	28	37
6 Radcliffe Town	22	9	2	11	43	48	-5	29
7 Failsworth Dynamos Res.	22	8	4	10	42	52	-10	28
8 Bury GSOB Res.	22	8	3	11	47	48	-1	27
9 Old Blackburnians Res.	22	4	8	10	40	53	-13	20
10 Little Lever SC Res.	22	3	6	13	27	55	-28	15
11 Ashtonians (-4)	22	4	6	12	30	49	-19	14
12 Old Mancunians Res.	22	2	8	12	31	73	-42	14

Division Three	P	W	D	L	F	A	GD	Pts
1 Old Boltonians A	20	17	1	2	114	41	73	52
2 Mostonians Res.	20	14	2	4	59	44	15	44
3 Prestwich Res.	20	9	5	6	57	41	16	32
4 Rochdale St Clements A	20	10	1	9	59	53	6	31
5 Chaddertonians Res.	20	8	5	7	34	37	-3	29
6 Bacup United	20	8	4	8	50	49	1	28
7 Bolton Lads Club	20	8	2	10	42	55	-13	26
8 Castle Hill Res.	20	7	2	11	51	63	-12	23
9 Radcliffe Town Res.	20	6	4	10	53	73	-20	22
10 Hesketh Casuals Res.	20	5	2	13	46	60	-14	17
11 Radcliffe Boys	20	3	2	15	25	74	-49	11

Division Four	P	W	D	L	F	A	GD	Pts
1 AFC Dobbies	20	15	2	3	77	41	36	47
2 Thornleigh Res.	20	14	2	4	83	41	42	44
3 Howe Bridge Mills Res.	20	11	1	8	51	46	5	34
4 Horwich Victoria Res.	20	10	3	7	62	50	12	33
5 Wardle Res.	20	10	3	7	59	54	5	33
6 Accrington Amateurs Res.	20	9	0	11	67	58	9	27
7 Roach Dynamos Res. (-4)	20	10	1	9	49	60	-11	27
8 Blackrod Town Res.	20	5	5	10	45	50	-5	20
9 Old Blackburnians A	20	6	1	13	31	71	-40	19
10 Bolton Wyresdale Res.	20	5	3	12	49	62	-13	18
11 Horwich RMI Res.	20	3	3	14	28	68	-40	12

Division Five	P	W	D	L	F	A	GD	Pts
1 Farnworth Town Res.	18	12	1	5	51	26	25	37
2 Old Mancunians A	18	11	3	4	51	39	12	36
3 Ainsworth Res.	18	11	2	5	54	33	21	35
4 Thornleigh A	18	8	3	7	58	45	13	27
5 Lymm	18	9	0	9	39	34	5	27
6 Ashtonians Res.	18	7	4	7	37	40	-3	25
7 Old Boltonians B	18	5	6	7	43	53	-10	21
8 Hesketh Casuals A	18	6	3	9	35	51	-16	21
9 Rochdale St Clements B	18	4	2	12	32	52	-20	14
10 Bury GSOB A	18	3	4	11	39	66	-27	13

Division Six	P	W	D	L	F	A	GD	Pts
1 Oldham Hulmeians A	20	13	2	5	76	34	42	41
2 Farnworth Town 'A'	20	13	0	7	73	54	19	39
3 Mostonians A	20	11	3	6	53	47	6	36
4 Tottington United Res.	20	10	3	7	62	48	14	33
5 Howe Bridge Mills A	20	10	3	7	54	56	-2	33
6 Bolton Wyresdale A	20	8	4	8	49	48	1	28
7 Little Lever SC A	20	8	4	8	49	57	-8	28
8 Radcliffe Town A	20	7	5	8	41	49	-8	26
9 Old Mancunians B	20	6	1	13	36	54	-18	19
10 Horwich Victoria A	20	6	0	14	38	53	-15	18
11 AFC Dobbies Res.	20	5	1	14	31	62	-31	16

Division Seven	P	W	D	L	F	A	GD	Pts
1 Radcliffe Boys Res.	16	13	2	1	74	34	40	41
2 Bolton Wyresdale B	16	11	0	5	53	35	18	33
3 Old Blackburnians B	16	10	1	5	47	38	9	31
4 Thornleigh B	16	7	4	5	59	43	16	25
5 Hesketh Casuals B	16	8	1	7	34	31	3	25
6 Radcliffe Town B	16	4	3	9	31	55	-24	15
7 Bury GSOB B	16	3	3	10	35	49	-14	12
8 Horwich RMI A	16	3	3	10	30	44	-14	12
9 Oldham Hulmeians B	16	3	3	10	24	58	-34	12

LANCASHIRE LEAGUE

East Division	P	W	D	L	F	A	GD	Pts
1 FC United of Manchester Res.	20	17	2	1	90	16	74	53
2 AFC Emley Res.	20	11	5	4	54	34	20	38
3 Brighouse Town Res.	20	11	5	4	48	31	17	38
4 Hyde Res.	20	10	2	8	45	34	11	32
5 Nelson Res.	20	9	2	9	37	32	5	29
6 Garforth Town Res.	20	8	5	7	48	44	4	29
7 Ossett Albion Res.	20	7	3	10	39	49	-10	24
8 Thackley Res.	20	7	1	12	27	59	-32	22
9 Ossett Town Res.	20	6	3	11	34	51	-17	21
10 Liversedge Res.	20	5	2	13	31	62	-31	17
11 Eccleshill United A	20	3	2	15	29	70	-41	11

West Division	P	W	D	L	F	A	GD	Pts
1 AFC Fylde Res.	22	17	2	3	76	28	48	53
2 Workington Res.	22	12	4	6	59	40	19	40
3 Stalybridge Celtic Res.	22	11	6	5	62	45	17	39
4 Bootle Res.	22	11	4	7	45	47	-2	37
5 Myerscough College	22	10	6	6	62	37	25	36
6 Colne Res.	22	10	5	7	51	37	14	35
7 Curzon Ashton Res.	22	8	5	9	36	37	-1	29
8 Lancaster City Res.	22	8	4	10	31	45	-14	28
9 Witton Albion Res.	22	8	1	13	39	75	-36	25
10 Ashton Athletic Res.	22	7	2	13	31	56	-25	23
11 Eccleshill United Res.	22	5	1	16	23	41	-18	16
12 Ashton Town Res.	22	4	2	16	27	54	-27	14

LEICESTER & DISTRICT LEAGUE

Premier Division	P	W	D	L	F	A	GD	Pts
1 Braders	22	16	1	5	53	29	24	49
2 Cosby United	22	15	3	4	54	26	28	48
3 Belgrave	22	15	2	5	72	37	35	47
4 County Hall	22	13	3	6	55	38	17	42
5 Birstall RBL	22	12	4	6	50	39	11	40
6 Beaumont Town	22	11	2	9	48	30	18	35
7 Magna 73	22	10	3	9	51	43	8	33
8 Huncote	22	7	2	13	26	35	-9	23
9 Glenfield Town	22	7	0	15	28	67	-39	21
10 Kibworth Town	22	4	3	15	36	85	-49	15
11 Glen Villa	22	4	2	16	40	55	-15	14
12 North Kilworth	22	3	5	14	27	56	-29	14

Division One	P	W	D	L	F	A	GD	Pts
1 NKF Burbage	20	16	2	2	56	27	29	50
2 Kingsway Celtic	20	12	2	6	65	41	24	38
3 Oadby RBL 93	20	12	2	6	37	33	4	38
4 Midland St Andrews (-3)	20	13	0	7	55	35	20	36
5 Burbage Old Boys	20	9	3	8	48	41	7	30
6 Queniborough	20	7	5	8	46	54	-8	26
7 Fleckney Athletic	20	8	2	10	36	47	-11	26
8 Ashby Road	20	6	1	13	42	48	-6	19
9 Birstall RBL Res. (-2)	20	6	1	13	37	47	-10	17
10 Leicester Three Lions	20	5	2	13	40	53	-13	17
11 Thurlaston Magpies	20	4	4	12	28	64	-36	16

Division Two	P	W	D	L	F	A	GD	Pts
1 Whetstone Athletic	22	19	1	2	108	25	83	58
2 Magna 73 Res. (-1)	22	19	1	2	79	24	55	57
3 Thurnby Valley	22	14	2	6	58	36	22	44
4 Beaumont Town Res. (-6)	22	16	0	6	89	37	52	42
5 Broughton Astley	22	11	3	8	54	39	15	36
6 Shoemakers Ath	22	9	1	12	54	73	-19	28
7 Narborough & Enderby	22	9	1	12	35	62	-27	28
8 Belgrave Res. (-1)	22	8	2	12	39	63	-24	25
9 St Patricks	22	7	3	12	44	65	-21	24
10 North Kilworth Res.	22	5	2	15	37	76	-39	17
11 Glenfield Town Res.	22	3	3	16	27	66	-39	12
12 Thurlaston Magpies Res.	22	1	3	18	27	85	-58	6

Division Three	P	W	D	L	F	A	GD	Pts
1 Cosby United Res.	20	17	3	0	90	22	68	54
2 Old Aylestone	20	13	3	4	76	33	43	42
3 NKF Burbage Res.	20	13	3	4	65	31	34	42
4 County Hall Res. (-1)	20	12	1	7	69	48	21	36
5 Huncote Res.	20	10	6	4	42	25	17	36
6 Queniborough Res.	20	9	1	10	53	44	9	28
7 Park End 74	20	7	4	9	30	55	-25	25
8 Glen Villa Res.	20	7	3	10	40	49	-9	24
9 Kibworth Town Res.	20	2	3	15	29	76	-47	9
10 Broughton Astley Res.	20	2	3	15	18	73	-55	9
11 NKF Burbage A	20	3	0	17	26	82	-56	9

Lincoln & District League	P	W	D	L	F	A	GD	Pts
1 The Blues Club	20	17	2	1	84	23	61	52
2 RM Imp	20	15	3	2	68	31	37	48
3 AFC Ruston Sports	20	12	3	5	70	44	26	39
4 Fulbeck Utd	20	11	4	5	67	34	33	37
5 Ruston Sports Res	20	7	6	7	48	50	-2	27
6 Cherry Willingham	20	8	1	11	64	88	-24	25
7 Retford Town	20	5	5	10	45	59	-14	20
8 Middle Rasen	20	4	5	11	35	60	-25	17
9 Horncastle Town Res	20	3	6	11	31	60	-29	15
10 Monos FC	20	4	3	13	38	70	-32	15
11 Saxilby Athletic	20	4	2	14	29	60	-31	14

LINCOLNSHIRE LEAGUE

Premier Division	P	W	D	L	F	A	GD	Pts
1 Skegness Town	24	17	3	4	56	20	36	54
2 Hykeham Town (+3)	24	16	2	6	54	36	18	53
3 Gainsborough Town	24	14	5	5	64	33	31	47
4 Ruston Sports	24	14	4	6	51	33	18	46
5 Boston United Res.	24	12	6	6	46	29	17	42
6 Skegness United	24	10	5	9	47	45	2	35
7 CGB Humbertherm	24	9	5	10	41	43	-2	32
8 Lincoln United Res. (-3)	24	10	2	12	34	43	-9	29
9 Cleethorpes Town Res.	24	8	5	11	36	47	-11	29
10 Horncastle Town	24	7	3	14	26	44	-18	24
11 Sleaford Town Res.	24	5	3	16	35	60	-25	18
12 Nettleham	24	4	5	15	34	58	-24	17
13 Heckington United	24	4	4	16	22	55	-33	16

LIVERPOOL CMS LEAGUE

Premier Division	P	W	D	L	F	A	GD	Pts
1 Western Speke	16	13	3	0	52	11	41	42
2 Garston Derby	16	12	3	1	54	22	32	39
3 Mosslane	16	9	2	5	52	38	14	29
4 East Liverpool	16	7	2	7	43	36	7	23
4 A.F.C. Kirkby	16	7	2	7	29	39	-10	23
6 Northpark United	16	6	1	9	35	32	3	19
7 Elmoore	16	4	1	11	24	36	-12	13
7 Speke Dunnies	16	4	1	11	23	39	-16	13
9 Victoria Memorial	16	2	1	13	24	83	-59	7

Division One	P	W	D	L	F	A	GD	Pts
1 Everton P.L.H.	22	19	2	1	119	20	99	59
2 Strand United	22	19	1	2	96	25	71	58
3 Western Speke Res.	22	17	1	4	131	43	88	52
4 The Claremont	22	13	3	6	50	39	11	42
5 Botanic FC	22	11	3	8	101	43	58	36
6 Stuart Road	22	9	4	9	78	58	20	31
7 Leighbridge FC	22	8	1	13	58	92	-34	25
8 LH F.C.	22	7	3	12	57	98	-41	24
9 Kingy's	22	7	0	15	55	55	0	21
10 Yew Tree F.C.	22	5	3	14	47	104	-57	18
11 Walton Athletic	22	3	3	16	37	79	-42	12
12 Hope Street Raiders	22	2	0	20	25	198	-173	6

LONDON COMMERCIAL LEAGUE

Division One	P	W	D	L	F	A	GD	Pts
1 New Hanford	16	13	1	2	56	17	39	40
2 New Hanford II	16	12	1	3	52	28	24	37
3 Park View	16	9	1	5	46	16	30	28
4 Manorwood	16	9	1	6	28	34	-6	28
5 Fulham Dynamo Sports	16	8	2	6	41	39	2	26
6 Abbey National Sports & Social Club	16	4	1	10	28	68	-40	13
7 Paddington Vale	16	4	0	12	27	35	-8	12
8 Ealing Old Boys	16	3	3	10	26	45	-19	12
9 Barnet Municipal Officers	16	3	2	11	27	49	-22	11

Division Two	P	W	D	L	F	A	GD	Pts
1 D M Wanderers	18	14	3	1	67	36	31	45
2 Greenford Celtic	18	14	2	2	66	23	43	44
3 Lampton Park	18	13	1	4	63	31	32	40
4 Manor Boys FC	18	11	2	5	53	36	17	35
5 Harrow Lyons	18	9	0	9	45	52	-7	27
6 Chiswick Homefields	18	6	2	10	21	36	-15	20
7 AFC Angel Hayes	18	5	3	10	38	55	-17	18
8 Hillingdon III	18	5	1	12	35	57	-22	16
9 Old Alpertonians	18	2	2	14	20	50	-30	8
10 Sudbury Court	18	1	4	13	22	54	-32	7

LOWESTOFT & DISTRICT LEAGUE

Division Ono	P	W	D	L	F	A	GD	Pts
1 DK Consultants	20	15	4	1	83	31	52	49
2 Oulton Broad	20	16	1	3	84	35	49	49
3 Norton Athletic	20	13	1	6	78	45	33	40
4 Barsham	20	10	3	7	58	56	2	33
5 Hearts of Oak Res.	20	10	1	9	58	64	-6	31
6 Waveney Res.	20	8	2	10	46	53	-7	26
7 Mutford & Wrentham	20	8	1	11	36	56	-20	25
8 "Kirkley& Pakefield ""A"""	20	7	2	11	41	55	-14	23
9 Spexhall	20	6	4	10	39	48	-9	22
10 Great Yarmouth Town Hall	20	6	2	12	57	61	-4	20
11 Waveney Gunners	20	0	1	19	20	96	-76	1

Division Two	P	W	D	L	F	A	GD	Pts
1 Kirkley & Pakefield B	24	20	3	1	88	32	56	63
2 W.E.M.P	24	19	2	3	85	29	56	59
3 Carlton Rangers	24	14	5	5	104	52	52	47
4 Payton (-6)	24	14	5	5	54	31	23	41
5 Norton Athletic Res.	24	11	5	8	55	44	11	38
6 Waveney Hearts Res.	24	10	5	9	57	61	-4	35
7 Factory Arms	24	10	3	11	50	72	-22	33
8 Crusaders	24	9	5	10	54	62	-8	32
9 Earsham Res	24	6	5	13	37	59	-22	23
10 Beccles Caxton Res. (-3)	24	6	5	13	57	79	-22	20
11 "Bungay Town ""A"" "	24	4	6	14	41	63	-22	18
12 Telecom Rovers	24	3	3	18	47	96	-49	12
13 Spexhall Res.	24	3	2	19	36	85	-49	11

Division Three	P	W	D	L	F	A	GD	Pts
1 Hearts of Oak Res.	24	19	4	1	136	34	102	61
2 Southwold Town	24	19	2	3	111	26	85	59
3 Ellingham	24	18	2	4	101	34	67	56
4 DK Consultants Res.	24	14	4	6	105	33	72	46
5 Carlton Rangers Res.	24	14	3	7	107	45	62	45
6 Carlton Colville Town	24	14	3	7	88	36	52	45
7 Notley's 2013	24	14	2	8	123	48	75	44
8 Stanford Arms	24	11	2	11	91	57	34	35
9 Corton Seltic Res.	24	6	3	15	52	86	-34	21
10 Westhall	24	5	3	16	37	86	-49	18
11 FC Drifter	24	2	4	18	39	146	-107	10
12 Electro - Tech	24	2	2	20	33	117	-84	8
13 Lowestoft Albion (-3)	24	1	0	23	16	291	-275	0

LUTON DISTRICT & SOUTH BEDS LEAGUE

Premier Division	P	W	D	L	F	A	GD	Pts
1 Farley Boys	14	11	1	2	51	16	35	34
2 Lewsey Park	14	11	1	2	43	17	26	34
3 Four Model	14	8	1	5	40	29	11	25
4 Markyate	14	6	3	5	34	31	3	21
5 Christians in Sport	14	6	3	5	37	36	1	21
6 Jedenastka	14	4	1	9	21	42	-21	13
7 St Josephs	14	2	1	11	14	40	-26	7
8 Luton Leagrave	14	2	1	11	19	48	-29	7

Division One	P	W	D	L	F	A	GD	Pts
1 F n E Rangers	14	13	0	1	101	16	85	39
2 LU Four	14	9	2	3	40	25	15	29
3 Square Rangers	14	8	3	3	31	19	12	27
4 Markyate 2nd XI	14	6	1	7	40	32	8	19
5 Luton Leagrave 'B'	14	5	2	7	32	44	-12	17
6 FC Polonia (Luton)	14	5	0	9	26	47	-21	15
7 Blue Line Aces	14	4	2	8	30	45	-15	14
8 North Sundon Wanderers	14	0	2	12	18	90	-72	2

MAIDSTONE & DISTRICT LEAGUE

Premier Division		P	W	D	L	F	A	GD	Pts
1	Leeds SV	20	19	0	1	95	20	75	57
2	Eccles	20	14	2	4	76	42	34	44
3	Lenham Wanderers	20	12	4	4	64	42	22	40
4	Wateringbury Colts	20	12	2	6	71	42	29	38
5	Three Suttons	20	9	3	8	71	46	25	30
6	Headcorn	20	9	2	9	49	44	5	29
7	West Farleigh	20	9	2	9	58	57	1	29
8	Aylesford	20	6	2	12	38	61	-23	20
9	Leybourne Athletic	20	5	1	14	47	61	-14	16
10	Sutton Saints	20	3	2	15	38	87	-49	11
11	Hunton	20	1	2	17	23	128	-105	5

Division One		P	W	D	L	F	A	GD	Pts
1	Maidstone Kestrels	16	13	0	3	73	24	49	39
2	Loose Lions	16	12	2	2	50	24	26	38
3	Marden Minors	16	12	1	3	52	20	32	37
4	Kings Hill Res.	16	10	1	5	38	24	14	31
5	Eccles Res.	16	6	1	9	33	38	-5	19
6	Lenham Wanderers Res	16	5	3	8	39	55	-16	18
7	Duke of Edinburgh	16	3	2	11	23	57	-34	11
8	West Farleigh Res	16	3	1	12	24	64	-40	10
9	Lashings FC	16	1	3	12	28	54	-26	6

Division Two		P	W	D	L	F	A	GD	Pts
1	Trisports	18	14	2	2	58	23	35	44
2	Phoenix United	18	11	1	6	50	28	22	34
3	The Early Bird	18	11	0	7	54	43	11	33
4	Town Malling Club	18	10	2	6	62	26	36	32
5	Parkwood Jupitors	18	9	3	6	47	35	12	30
6	Ditton Minors	18	8	4	6	59	30	29	28
7	Leybourne Athletic Res.	18	6	3	9	40	45	-5	21
8	Maidstone Athletic	18	6	2	10	44	58	-14	20
9	Headcorn Res	18	2	3	13	25	52	-27	9
10	Hollingbourne	18	3	0	15	27	126	-99	9

MERCIAN REGIONAL LEAGUE

Premier Division		P	W	D	L	F	A	GD	Pts
1	Oakengates Athletic	26	15	5	6	68	44	24	50
2	Church Stretton	26	14	5	7	56	38	18	47
3	Morda Utd	26	13	5	8	72	51	21	44
4	FC Hodnet	26	11	8	7	36	31	5	41
5	Whitchurch Alport	26	10	10	6	45	33	12	40
6	Ketley Bank Utd	26	11	6	9	37	47	-10	39
7	Telford Juniors	26	11	5	10	56	43	13	38
8	Shifnal United 97	26	10	7	9	45	40	5	37
9	Wellington Amateurs Res.	26	9	8	9	45	44	1	35
10	Madeley Sports	26	8	5	13	42	49	-7	29
11	Weston Rhyn	26	8	4	14	44	64	-20	28
12	Allscott	26	6	8	12	46	63	-17	26
13	AFC Bridgnorth Res.	26	6	7	13	41	53	-12	25
14	Prees	26	7	3	16	39	72	-33	24

Division One		P	W	D	L	F	A	GD	Pts
1	Childs Ercall	28	23	0	5	121	24	97	69
2	Wroxeter Rovers	28	20	6	2	119	33	86	66
3	FC Oswestry Town	28	21	3	4	89	20	69	66
4	Rock Rovers	28	17	6	5	87	44	43	57
5	Bishops Castle Town FC	28	17	2	9	85	37	48	53
6	Hanwood United Res.	28	14	4	10	74	40	34	46
7	Clee Hill United	28	12	6	10	60	74	-14	42
8	Dawley Town	28	11	6	11	63	60	3	39
9	Brown Clee	28	11	3	14	78	70	8	36
10	Oakengates Rangers	28	11	3	14	50	69	-19	36
11	Wrockwardine Wood Juniors	28	7	2	19	34	105	-71	23
12	Oswestry Villa	28	6	4	18	51	69	-18	22
13	Meole Brace	28	6	4	18	42	118	-76	22
14	Shawbury United Res.	28	6	2	20	29	96	-67	20
15	Shrewsbury United	28	2	1	25	31	154	-123	7

Division Two		P	W	D	L	F	A	GD	Pts
1	AFC Broseley (-3)	26	23	3	0	153	22	131	69
2	Wrockwardine Wood (-3)	26	21	2	3	119	37	82	62
3	AFC Wellington	26	19	1	6	138	52	86	58
4	Donnington Community Sports & Social	26	18	2	6	122	54	68	56
5	Impact United	26	16	4	6	113	49	64	52
6	Market Drayton Tigers	26	16	1	9	103	52	51	49
7	Claverley	26	14	0	12	82	49	33	42
8	Ludlow Town Colts	26	12	2	12	110	63	47	38
9	Albrighton Juniors FC	26	8	1	17	54	92	-38	25
10	Highley Miners Welfare	26	7	3	16	58	91	-33	24
11	Spalaig Britannia	26	7	2	17	38	108	-70	23
12	Oswestry Villa Res.	26	6	2	18	30	85	-55	20
13	Shrewsbury United Res.	26	2	0	24	25	133	-108	6
14	Denso	26	1	1	24	23	281	-258	4

MID ESSEX LEAGUE

Premier Division		P	W	D	L	F	A	GD	Pts
1	Great Baddow	16	12	4	0	37	13	24	40
2	Tillingham Hotspur (+2)	16	10	3	3	45	22	23	35
3	Debden Sports Club A (-1)	16	8	3	5	47	29	18	26
4	AFC Cranham (-1)	16	7	2	7	21	27	-6	22
5	St.Clere's	16	6	3	7	29	36	-7	21
6	Braintree and Bocking United (-4)	15	7	0	8	37	37	0	17
7	Writtle Manor (+1)	15	3	5	7	23	25	-2	15
8	Silver End United (-4)	16	3	4	9	20	42	-22	9
9	United Chelmsford Churches	16	2	2	12	32	60	-28	8

Division One		P	W	D	L	F	A	GD	Pts
1	Beacon Hill Rovers	22	16	3	3	68	26	42	51
2	Stifford Town (-5)	22	14	6	2	51	17	34	43
3	Laindon Orient	22	13	3	6	73	45	28	42
4	CT 66 (-3)	22	13	4	5	84	47	37	40
5	Focus Ferrers	22	9	7	6	58	38	20	34
6	Sparta Basildon	22	10	4	8	48	32	16	34
7	Hutton A (+3)	22	8	2	12	44	55	-11	29
8	Academy Soccer (-4)	22	8	2	12	41	64	-23	22
9	Harold Wood Athletic A	22	6	3	13	46	62	-16	21
10	Battlesbridge	22	6	2	14	36	66	-30	20
11	White Hart United (-1)	22	6	3	13	32	71	-39	20
12	Frenford Senior A (-3)	22	2	3	17	26	84	-58	6

Division Two	P	W	D	L	F	A	GD	Pts
1 Dunmow Rhodes	18	11	4	3	36	20	16	37
2 White Hart United Res.	18	11	3	4	59	36	23	36
3 Haver Town Res.	18	11	2	5	53	26	27	35
4 Boreham (-4)	18	10	3	5	55	41	14	29
5 Sandon Royals	18	9	2	7	29	29	0	29
6 Manford Way A (-1)	18	9	1	8	27	37	-10	27
7 Flitch United	18	8	2	8	32	37	-5	26
8 Dunton Rangers (-1)	18	7	0	11	34	49	-15	20
9 Old Chelmsfordians A (-2)	18	4	0	14	22	46	-24	10
10 Silver End United Res. (-7)	18	1	1	16	9	35	-26	-3

Division Three	P	W	D	L	F	A	GD	Pts
1 Great Baddow Res.	24	17	1	6	74	27	47	52
2 Stock United	24	16	3	5	63	33	30	51
3 Durning (+3)	24	11	6	7	52	47	5	42
4 Runwell Hospital A	24	11	6	7	55	35	20	39
5 St.Margarets	24	11	4	9	43	45	-2	37
6 Benfleet A (-2)	24	12	1	11	56	49	7	35
7 Mundon Vics	24	10	5	9	36	36	0	35
8 Swans Athletic (-2)	24	11	1	12	61	59	2	32
9 St.Clere's Res.	24	9	3	12	58	65	-7	30
10 Latchingdon (-1)	24	8	4	12	51	58	-7	27
11 Hutton B (-4)	24	9	3	12	46	67	-21	26
12 Brendans (-1)	24	6	1	17	34	82	-48	18
13 Felsted Rovers	24	5	2	17	43	69	-26	17

Division Four	P	W	D	L	F	A	GD	Pts
1 Real Maldon	24	18	2	4	78	31	47	56
2 Mayland Village	24	16	3	5	62	31	31	51
3 Extreme United	24	16	2	6	87	39	48	50
4 Writtle	24	16	2	6	49	34	15	50
5 Harold Wood Athletic B	24	14	4	6	55	39	16	46
6 Haver Town A (-1)	24	13	3	8	51	34	17	41
7 CT 66 Res. (-2)	24	9	3	12	61	57	4	28
8 Dunmow Rhodes Res. (-1)	24	8	3	13	62	68	-6	26
9 Rayleigh Town A (-3)	24	9	2	13	38	44	-6	26
10 Beacon Hill Rovers Res. (-2)	24	6	2	16	29	67	-38	18
11 Sparta Basildon Res. (-1)	24	4	5	15	33	64	-31	16
12 Little Waltham (-9)	24	7	2	15	48	56	-8	14
13 E2V Technologies (+3)	24	2	3	19	31	120	-89	12

Division Five	P	W	D	L	F	A	GD	Pts
1 Haver Town B (-1)	20	18	1	1	109	19	90	54
2 Pro Athletic	20	14	3	3	71	38	33	45
3 Kenson	20	11	3	6	42	31	11	36
4 Burnham Athletic	20	10	2	8	45	41	4	32
5 Latchingdon Res. (-1)	20	9	2	9	37	45	-8	28
6 Battlesbridge Res. (+2)	20	7	3	10	45	68	-23	26
7 Focus Ferrers Res.	20	6	5	9	39	61	-22	23
8 Maldon Saints	20	5	4	11	32	55	-23	19
9 City Colts (-1)	20	6	1	13	40	45	-5	18
10 Frenford Senior B (-2)	20	5	2	13	36	54	-18	15
11 Writtle Manor Res. (-4)	20	6	0	14	34	73	-39	14

Division Six	P	W	D	L	F	A	GD	Pts
1 Writtle Res.	24	19	2	3	93	26	67	59
2 Leigh Ramblers A	24	19	2	3	74	27	47	59
3 Rayne United	24	17	3	4	53	27	26	54
4 Exiles (-1)	24	16	1	7	76	50	26	48
5 United Chelsmford Churches Res.	24	15	3	6	58	47	11	48
6 Flitch United A	24	13	3	8	80	62	18	42
7 Baddow Blues	24	9	5	10	46	53	-7	32
8 Mundon Vics Res. (-1)	24	8	4	12	48	64	-16	27
9 Marconi Athletic Res.	24	3	8	13	34	51	-17	17
10 Felsted Rovers Res. (-2)	24	5	4	15	53	72	-19	17
11 Dengie Athletic (-3)	24	5	3	16	41	63	-22	15
12 Parkway Sports (-4)	24	5	2	17	36	67	-31	13
13 Maldon Saints Res. (-2)	24	1	2	21	22	105	-83	3

MID LANCASHIRE LEAGUE

Premier Division	P	W	D	L	F	A	GD	Pts
1 Fulwood White Hart	22	19	2	1	108	21	87	59
2 Green Town	22	14	3	5	71	32	39	42
3 Preston Wanderers	22	13	2	7	73	47	26	41
4 Southport & Ainsdale Amateurs	22	13	2	7	51	36	15	41
5 Eccleston & Heskin	22	12	2	8	62	31	31	38
6 Penwortham Town	22	11	4	7	68	49	19	34
7 Hoole United	22	8	3	11	36	56	-20	27
8 Bolton United	22	7	4	11	38	53	-15	25
9 Deepdale	22	4	6	12	31	62	-31	18
10 Appley Bridge	22	5	2	15	28	54	-26	17
11 Highcross	22	5	2	15	37	79	-42	17
12 Adelphi	22	3	4	15	30	113	-83	13

Division One	P	W	D	L	F	A	GD	Pts
1 Walmer Bridge	24	14	7	3	81	40	41	49
2 Baxters	24	15	2	7	69	40	29	47
3 Southport Trinity	24	13	6	5	71	49	22	45
4 Broughton Amateurs	24	13	5	6	59	48	11	44
5 Walton Le Dale	24	11	7	6	60	53	7	40
6 Newman College	24	11	4	9	61	46	15	37
7 Burscough Bridge	24	11	2	11	56	58	-2	35
8 Wilbraham	24	8	9	7	70	62	8	33
9 Eccleston & Heskin Res.	24	7	5	12	58	62	-4	26
10 Springfields	24	6	7	11	46	74	-28	25
11 New Longton Rovers	24	6	5	13	40	58	-18	23
12 Goosnargh	24	5	6	13	48	68	-20	21
13 Leyland Athletic	24	3	1	20	42	103	-61	10

Division Two	P	W	D	L	F	A	GD	Pts
1 Freckleton	22	19	2	1	91	29	62	59
2 Ribble Wanderers	22	14	4	4	60	39	21	46
3 Tarleton Corinthians	22	12	7	3	58	36	22	43
4 Charnock Richard Academy	22	12	3	7	72	52	20	39
5 PLCC Nomads	22	9	6	7	48	35	13	33
6 Farington Villa	22	9	4	9	49	44	5	31
7 Ribchester	22	9	2	11	52	53	-1	29
8 AFC Preston	22	5	5	12	49	65	-16	20
9 Ribbleton Rovers	22	6	2	14	40	71	-31	20
10 Chipping	22	5	3	14	40	64	-24	18
11 Broughton Amateurs Res.	22	4	6	12	45	79	-34	18
12 Broughton Amateurs A	22	4	4	14	37	74	-37	13

Division Three	P	W	D	L	F	A	GD	Pts
1 Southport Trinity Res.	20	18	0	2	95	28	67	54
2 Cottam Corinthians	20	14	3	3	59	26	33	45
3 Broughton Amateurs B	20	12	3	5	73	55	18	39
4 AFC Blessed Sacrament	20	10	5	5	55	40	15	35
5 Walmer Bridge Res.	20	10	1	9	61	45	16	31
6 Freckleton Res.	20	9	2	9	41	49	-8	29
7 Tarleton Corinthians Res.	20	8	3	9	36	50	-14	24
8 Hoole United Res.	20	4	5	11	39	68	-29	17
9 FC Ribbleton	20	5	1	14	47	64	-17	16
10 Newman College Res.	20	5	1	14	39	78	-39	16
11 New Longton Rovers Res.	20	2	2	16	30	72	-42	8

Division Four	P	W	D	L	F	A	GD	Pts
1 Eagle	12	9	0	3	56	13	43	27
2 Whittle	12	8	2	2	44	26	18	26
3 Chorley Athletic	12	7	1	4	51	37	14	22
4 International Allstars	12	6	1	5	50	28	22	19
5 FC Clayton Brook	12	6	1	5	31	41	-10	19
6 FC Eccleston	12	2	2	8	22	38	-16	8
7 Hop Pocket	12	0	1	11	18	89	-71	1

MID SOMERSET LEAGUE

Premier Division	P	W	D	L	F	A	GD	Pts
1 Frome Town Sports	18	16	1	1	76	13	63	49
2 Pensford FC	18	13	2	3	60	35	25	41
3 Welton Arsenal	18	10	2	6	67	56	11	32
4 Coleford Athletic	18	10	1	7	55	47	8	31
5 Mells & Vobster United	18	9	1	8	57	49	8	28
6 Interhound	18	8	3	7	52	40	12	27
7 Westfield Res.	18	7	3	8	41	48	-7	24
8 Meadow Rangers	18	6	2	10	44	50	-6	20
9 Wells City A (-7)	18	3	1	14	26	61	-35	3
10 Belrose (-3)	18	0	0	18	17	96	-79	-3

Division One	P	W	D	L	F	A	GD	Pts
1 Stoke Rovers	20	17	1	2	83	23	60	52
2 Clutton Res.	20	15	4	1	88	19	69	49
3 Pilton United	20	15	0	5	89	41	48	45
4 Glastonbury Res.	20	10	4	6	52	27	25	34
5 Westfield A (-4)	20	11	1	8	78	52	26	30
6 Temple Cloud	20	8	1	11	62	52	10	25
7 Frome Collegians Res.	20	7	3	10	44	45	-1	24
8 Camerton Athletic (-2)	20	8	1	11	51	60	-9	23
9 Purnells Sports Res.	20	5	4	11	31	58	-27	19
10 Evercreech Rovers (-2)	20	3	3	14	32	81	-49	10
11 Coleford Athletic Res.	20	0	0	20	15	167	-152	0

Division Two	P	W	D	L	F	A	GD	Pts
1 Peasedown Athletic Res.	20	16	1	3	73	28	45	49
2 High Littleton FC	20	11	4	5	48	33	15	37
3 Radstock Town A (-3)	20	13	1	6	60	50	10	37
4 Frome Town Sports Res.	20	9	4	7	48	49	-1	31
5 Tunley Athletic Reserve (-3)	20	10	3	7	65	58	7	30
6 Westhill Sports FC	20	9	2	9	60	51	9	29
7 Chilcompton Sports Res. (-4)	20	8	5	7	64	55	9	25
8 Mells & Vobster United Res. (-5)	20	9	1	10	77	59	18	23
9 Farrington Gurney Res. (-1)	20	5	3	12	55	89	-34	17
10 Meadow Rangers Reserve	20	4	2	14	33	80	-47	14
11 Timsbury Athletic Res. (-1)	20	2	2	16	28	59	-31	7

Division Three	P	W	D	L	F	A	GD	Pts
1 Baltonsborough	20	16	1	3	105	29	76	49
2 Pensford Res. (-1)	20	16	2	2	63	25	38	49
3 Tor Leisure	20	15	2	3	85	33	52	47
4 Chew Magna Res.	20	12	4	4	63	46	17	40
5 Wells City B	20	7	4	9	60	60	0	25
6 Westhill Sports Res.	20	6	2	12	32	52	-20	20
7 Somer Valley FC	20	5	2	13	34	58	-24	17
8 Chilcompton Sports A	20	5	2	13	37	75	-38	17
9 Purnells Sports A (-2)	20	6	1	13	34	72	-38	17
10 Chilcompton United	20	4	3	13	33	59	-26	15
11 Temple Cloud Res. (-5)	20	6	1	13	46	83	-37	14

MID SUSSEX LEAGUE

Premier Division	P	W	D	L	F	A	GD	Pts
1 East Grinstead United	22	15	4	3	44	26	18	49
2 Willingdon Athletic	22	12	6	4	39	28	11	42
3 Peacehaven United	22	11	6	5	35	23	12	39
4 Burgess Hill Albion	22	10	6	6	36	30	6	36
5 Cuckfield Rangers (-3)	22	10	6	6	41	25	16	33
6 Rotherfield	22	9	4	9	39	39	0	31
7 Balcombe	22	8	4	10	38	40	-2	28
8 Lindfield (+3)	22	7	3	12	35	41	-6	27
9 Old Varndeanians	22	7	3	12	28	44	-16	24
10 Montpelier Villa	22	6	5	11	26	42	-16	23
11 Cuckfield Town	22	6	2	14	26	43	-17	20
12 Jarvis Brook	22	4	5	13	35	41	-6	17

Championship	P	W	D	L	F	A	GD	Pts
1 Smallfield	16	14	1	1	50	16	34	43
2 Hassocks Development (-1)	16	12	1	3	50	19	31	36
3 Buxted	16	7	4	5	43	32	11	25
4 AFC Ringmer	16	7	3	6	32	37	-5	24
5 Ditchling	16	5	4	7	24	37	-13	19
6 Copthorne	16	5	3	8	34	34	0	18
7 Portslade Athletic (+2)	16	4	3	9	36	36	0	17
8 Polegate Town	16	3	4	9	23	38	-15	13
9 Felbridge	16	2	3	11	20	63	-43	9

Division One	P	W	D	L	F	A	GD	Pts
1 Furnace Green Rovers	20	14	4	2	56	23	33	46
2 Forest Row (-3)	20	15	2	3	53	17	36	44
3 Phoenix United	20	10	5	5	56	35	21	35
4 Keymer & Hassocks	20	10	3	7	33	36	-3	33
5 Framfield & Blackboys United	20	9	4	7	36	26	10	31
6 East Court	20	8	6	6	39	43	-4	30
7 Lindfield II	20	7	3	10	42	53	-11	24
8 Old Varndeanians II	20	7	2	11	36	49	-13	23
9 Uckfield Town II (+3)	20	5	2	13	30	57	-27	20
10 Crawley Portuguese SC	20	3	4	13	24	40	-16	13
11 Furnace Green Galaxy	20	3	3	14	35	61	-26	12

Division Two	P	W	D	L	F	A	GD	Pts
1 Ashurst Wood	18	13	1	4	61	31	30	40
2 East Grinstead Town III	18	13	1	4	50	21	29	40
3 Hydraquip	18	11	1	6	51	26	25	34
4 Barcombe	18	11	1	6	39	26	13	34
5 Ardingly (+3)	18	10	1	7	47	47	0	34
6 Sporting Elite	18	8	4	6	49	44	5	28
7 Willingdon Athletic II	18	7	3	8	33	42	-9	24
8 Newick	18	3	4	11	31	48	-17	13
9 Wivelsfield Green (-3)	18	3	3	12	20	50	-30	9
10 Hartfield	18	1	1	16	16	62	-46	4

Division Three	P	W	D	L	F	A	GD	Pts
1 Copthorne II	18	10	7	1	54	24	30	37
2 North Chailey Lions	18	10	2	6	59	49	10	32
3 Burgess Hill Albion II	18	9	4	5	45	28	17	31
4 Sporting Lindfield	18	9	2	7	35	34	1	29
5 Ansty Sports & Social	18	8	3	7	54	43	11	27
6 Plumpton Athletic	18	7	2	9	38	49	-11	23
7 Balcombe II	18	6	3	9	31	34	-3	21
8 West Hoathly	18	5	5	8	24	36	-12	20
9 Cuckfield Town II	18	6	1	11	27	46	-19	19
10 Jubilee	18	3	5	10	31	55	-24	14

Division Four	P	W	D	L	F	A	GD	Pts
1 DCK Copthorne	18	14	2	2	78	18	60	44
2 Buxted II	18	13	3	2	42	23	19	42
3 Horsted Keynes	18	10	3	5	47	27	20	33
4 United Services	18	10	1	7	56	38	18	31
5 Maresfield Village II	18	8	7	3	40	38	2	31
6 Crawley Devils	18	6	3	9	30	30	0	21
7 Dormansland Rockets II	18	5	2	11	34	44	-10	17
8 Fletching	18	5	2	11	29	41	-12	17
9 Old Varndeanians III	18	5	1	12	23	63	-40	16
10 Wisdom Sports	18	1	2	15	23	80	-57	5

Division Five	P	W	D	L	F	A	GD	Pts
1 Nutley	20	17	1	2	60	19	41	52
2 Saint Hill	20	16	0	4	62	44	18	48
3 Handcross Village (+2)	20	11	2	7	48	31	17	37
4 Felbridge II	20	11	2	7	46	36	10	35
5 Ifield III	20	10	1	9	46	49	-3	31
6 Cuckfield Rangers II (-1)	20	9	3	8	34	33	1	29
7 Lindfield III	20	9	2	9	29	32	-3	29
8 Polegate Town II	20	7	1	12	42	55	-13	22
9 East Grinstead United II	20	4	3	13	35	50	-15	15
10 Ardingly II	20	4	3	13	35	61	-26	15
11 Turners Hill	20	2	2	16	24	51	-27	8

Division Six	P	W	D	L	F	A	GD	Pts
1 Hydraquip II (-1)	16	12	4	0	53	24	29	39
2 Copthorne III	16	13	0	3	40	19	21	39
3 Peacehaven United II (+2)	16	11	2	3	42	17	25	37
4 Jarvis Brook II	16	8	3	5	39	27	12	27
5 Cherry Lane	16	8	2	6	35	30	5	26
6 Rotherfield II	16	5	0	11	24	48	-24	15
7 Danehill	16	4	1	11	25	45	-20	13
8 Sporting Elite II	16	4	1	11	16	43	-27	13
9 Rottingdean Village Veterans	16	0	1	15	13	34	-21	1

Division Seven	P	W	D	L	F	A	GD	Pts
1 Framfield & Blackboys United II	16	12	3	1	53	9	44	39
2 Copthorne IV	16	10	2	4	40	13	27	32
3 Ansty Sports & Social II	16	5	6	5	28	29	-1	21
4 Ashurst Wood II	16	6	3	7	28	39	-11	21
5 Forest Row II	16	5	5	6	16	21	-5	20
6 Newick II	16	5	4	7	21	33	-12	19
7 Fairwarp II	16	5	2	9	29	34	-5	17
8 Bolney Rovers	16	5	1	10	23	37	-14	16
9 Ditchling II	16	4	4	8	23	46	-23	16

Division Eight	P	W	D	L	F	A	GD	Pts
1 AFC Haywards	20	17	3	0	66	13	53	54
2 Stones	20	15	1	4	70	29	41	46
3 Willingdon Athletic III	20	13	2	5	57	39	18	41
4 Fletching II	20	11	1	8	48	35	13	34
5 Keymer & Hassocks II	20	10	2	8	39	41	-2	32
6 Plumpton Athletic II	20	9	1	10	34	43	-9	28
7 Cuckfield Town III	20	9	0	11	46	50	-4	27
8 Pilgrims	20	7	0	13	38	52	-14	21
9 East Grinstead Town IV	20	5	0	15	37	55	-18	15
10 Maresfield Village III	20	4	3	13	27	61	-34	15
11 Hartfield II	20	2	3	15	24	68	-44	9

Division Nine	P	W	D	L	F	A	GD	Pts
1 Ridgewood	16	11	4	1	58	21	37	37
2 Handcross Village II	16	9	3	4	39	22	17	30
3 AFC Ringmer II	16	8	5	3	35	18	17	29
4 Cuckfield Rangers III	16	8	4	4	44	27	17	28
5 Burgess Hill Albion III	16	8	3	5	24	15	9	27
6 Fairfield	16	6	2	8	32	33	-1	20
7 Lindfield IV	16	5	1	10	40	51	-11	16
8 West Hoathly II	16	5	1	10	22	38	-16	16
9 Heath Rangers	16	0	1	15	9	78	-69	1

Division Ten	P	W	D	L	F	A	GD	Pts
1 Roffey III	16	13	0	3	55	19	36	39
2 Scaynes Hill II	16	12	2	2	45	21	24	38
3 Barcombe II	16	10	3	3	33	25	8	33
4 Burgess Hill Wanderers	16	7	2	7	42	33	9	23
5 Uckfield Town III	16	5	4	7	31	34	-3	19
6 Hydraquip III	16	4	3	9	33	60	-27	15
7 Cherry Lane II	16	4	2	10	21	40	-19	14
8 Buxted III	16	3	3	10	20	33	-13	12
9 Burgess Hill Athletic	16	2	5	9	27	42	-15	11

Division Eleven A	P	W	D	L	F	A	GD	Pts
1 Handcross Village III	14	10	1	3	53	25	28	31
2 East Grinstead Meads	14	9	2	3	49	28	21	29
3 Hassocks Hornets	14	8	2	4	43	29	14	26
4 Wivelsfield Wanderers	14	7	2	5	48	30	18	23
5 Nutley II	14	5	3	6	25	27	-2	18
6 Crawley United	14	4	4	6	29	46	-17	16
7 Danehill II	14	3	2	9	28	35	-7	11
8 Scaynes Hill III	14	1	2	11	13	68	-55	5

Division Eleven B	P	W	D	L	F	A	GD	Pts
1 AFC Haywards II	14	10	1	3	50	27	23	31
2 Furngate	14	8	3	3	45	34	11	27
3 Peacehaven United III	14	8	1	5	47	27	20	25
4 Rotherfield III	14	8	1	5	57	44	13	25
5 Jarvis Brook III	14	8	1	5	42	33	9	25
6 Stones II	14	7	2	5	39	34	5	23
7 Ashurst Wood III	14	2	0	12	18	57	-39	6
8 Hartfield III	14	0	1	13	11	53	-42	1

MIDLAND REGIONAL ALLIANCE

Premier Division	P	W	D	L	F	A	GD	Pts
1 Derby Rolls Royce Leisure	22	18	1	3	88	23	65	55
2 Melbourne Dynamo	22	16	4	2	101	24	77	52
3 Rowsley 86	22	15	3	4	80	29	51	48
4 Willington	22	14	3	5	58	27	31	45
5 Newhall United	22	12	4	6	45	32	13	40
6 Allestree	22	11	1	10	54	46	8	34
7 Cromford	22	10	1	11	39	48	-9	31
8 Woolley Moor United	22	8	2	12	42	56	-14	26
9 Wirksworth Town	22	6	5	11	32	54	-22	23
10 Little Eaton	22	5	2	15	28	67	-39	17
11 Sandiacre Town	22	3	0	19	23	96	-73	9
12 Chellaston	22	1	0	21	15	103	-88	3

Division One	P	W	D	L	F	A	GD	Pts
1 Rowsley 86 Res.	20	14	1	5	74	31	43	43
2 Pastures	20	12	2	6	86	48	38	38
3 Wirksworth Ivanhoe	20	11	3	6	39	27	12	36
4 Tibshelf	20	11	3	6	45	40	5	36
5 Shardlow St. James (-3)	20	10	4	6	76	36	40	31
6 Ripley Town	20	10	1	9	48	46	2	31
7 Derby Singh Brothers	20	9	3	8	47	39	8	30
8 Derby Rolls Royce Leisure Res.	20	9	3	8	46	51	-5	30
9 Ambergate	20	7	1	12	43	66	-23	22
10 Punjab United	20	4	2	14	28	74	-46	14
11 Bargate Rovers	20	1	1	18	14	88	-74	4

Division Two	P	W	D	L	F	A	GD	Pts
1 Newhall United Res.	22	17	3	2	102	37	65	54
2 Stapleford Town	22	16	3	3	114	32	82	51
3 Melbourne Dynamo Res.	22	15	2	5	98	34	64	47
4 Ambergate Res.	22	10	5	7	54	56	-2	35
5 Wirksworth Town Res.	22	11	1	10	48	50	-2	34
6 Woolley Moor United Res.	22	9	6	7	73	51	22	33
7 Little Eaton Res.	22	8	8	6	51	45	6	32
8 Sandiacre Town Res.	22	7	5	10	39	82	-43	26
9 Matlock Town (C.F.A)	22	6	6	10	36	44	-8	24
10 Roe Farm	22	4	3	15	33	102	-69	15
11 Bargate Rovers Res.	22	4	0	18	28	76	-48	12
12 Willington Sports	22	1	6	15	23	90	-67	9

NORTH DEVON LEAGUE

Premier Division	P	W	D	L	F	A	GD	Pts
1 Boca Seniors	30	28	2	0	132	33	99	86
2 Braunton	30	26	2	2	121	22	99	80
3 Torrington	30	18	3	9	89	48	41	57
4 Barnstaple AAC	30	16	6	8	93	58	35	54
5 Bideford Res.	30	17	3	10	86	63	23	54
6 Appledore Res.	30	12	10	8	48	41	7	46
7 Fremington	30	13	6	11	65	60	5	45
8 Torridgeside (-3)	30	15	2	13	90	68	22	44
9 Bradworthy	30	11	7	12	71	66	5	40
10 North Molton Sports Club	30	10	9	11	68	68	0	39
11 Ilfracombe Town Res.	30	10	4	16	71	78	-7	34
12 Shamwickshire Rovers	30	8	9	13	68	83	-15	33
13 Shebbear United	30	8	4	18	47	82	-35	28
14 Dolton	30	6	5	19	33	117	-84	23
15 Georgeham & Croyde (-3)	30	1	5	24	30	122	-92	5
16 Chittlehampton	30	0	5	25	33	136	-103	5

Senior Division	P	W	D	L	F	A	GD	Pts
1 Park United	30	27	0	3	189	41	148	81
2 Braunton Res.	30	26	2	2	133	28	105	80
3 Barnstaple FC	30	22	2	6	139	54	85	68
4 Landkey Town	30	21	2	7	140	65	75	65
5 Woolsery	30	18	5	7	125	63	62	59
6 North Molton Sports Club Res.	30	17	2	11	104	79	25	53
7 Merton	30	14	3	13	93	80	13	45
8 Putford	30	12	5	13	72	71	1	41
9 Lynton & Lynmouth	30	10	3	17	58	108	-50	33
10 Ashwater (-9)	30	12	4	14	70	74	-4	31
11 Northam Lions (-3)	30	10	2	18	55	103	-48	29
12 Torridgeside Res.	30	8	1	21	64	85	-21	25
13 Shamwickshire Rovers Res. (-3)	30	9	0	21	65	103	-38	24
14 South Molton (-3)	30	8	3	19	48	107	-59	24
15 Combe Martin (-3)	30	8	2	20	55	130	-75	23
16 Morwenstow Res.	30	0	0	30	24	243	-219	0

Intermediate One		P	W	D	L	F	A	GD	Pts
1	Woolacombe & Mortehoe	26	16	7	3	79	39	40	55
2	Hartland	26	17	3	6	97	37	60	54
3	Anchor Chiefs	26	16	5	5	77	36	41	53
4	Braunton Thirds	26	14	3	9	77	53	24	45
5	Equalizers	26	13	3	10	62	81	-19	42
6	Ilfracombe Town Thirds	26	11	5	10	56	50	6	38
7	High Bickington	26	11	5	10	44	62	-18	38
8	Pilton Academicals	26	10	4	12	63	54	9	34
9	Barnstaple FC Res.	26	10	4	12	65	71	-6	34
10	Clovelly	26	9	3	14	74	84	-10	30
11	Northam Lions Res.	26	8	5	13	64	79	-15	29
12	Barnstaple AAC Res. (-3)	26	7	6	13	47	57	-10	24
13	Torrington Res. (-3)	26	8	3	15	45	70	-25	24
14	Sporting Barum (-6)	26	3	2	21	40	117	-77	5

Intermediate Two		P	W	D	L	F	A	GD	Pts
1	Chivenor	30	23	4	3	130	42	88	73
2	North Molton Sports Club Thirds	30	23	3	4	118	37	81	72
3	Haxton Rangers	30	21	3	6	106	53	53	66
4	Appledore Academy	30	19	6	5	100	41	59	63
5	Fremington Res.	30	20	1	9	104	54	50	61
6	Braunton Fourths	30	15	5	10	78	35	43	50
7	Putford Res.	30	15	3	12	78	65	13	48
8	Woolacombe & Mortehoe Res.	30	12	4	14	66	89	-23	40
9	Woolsery Res.	30	12	3	15	47	74	-27	39
10	Anchor Chiefs Res.	30	12	2	16	78	90	-12	38
11	Georgeham & Croyde Res. (-3)	30	10	6	14	61	86	-25	33
12	South Molton Res. (-3)	30	8	3	19	47	101	-54	24
13	Hartland Res.	30	7	2	21	73	111	-38	23
14	Lynton & Lynmouth Res.	30	5	4	21	58	137	-79	19
15	Merton Res.	30	5	3	22	38	127	-89	18
16	Chittlehampton Res. (-9)	30	5	4	21	46	86	-40	10

NORTH EAST NORFOLK LEAGUE

Division One		P	W	D	L	F	A	GD	Pts
1	Runton	18	17	0	1	90	19	71	51
2	Gimingham	18	16	0	2	78	30	48	48
3	Haisboro Atheltic (-6)	18	12	2	4	72	40	32	32
4	Cromer Y O B (-3)	18	10	2	6	36	30	6	29
5	North Walsham A	18	7	0	11	36	51	-15	21
6	Mundesley	18	6	2	10	44	43	1	20
7	East Ruston (-1)	18	6	2	10	37	50	-13	19
8	Horning (-2)	18	4	2	12	31	61	-30	12
9	Corpusty (-2)	18	2	4	12	25	65	-40	8
10	Worstead	18	2	2	14	17	77	-60	8

Division Two		P	W	D	L	F	A	GD	Pts
1	Plumstead Rangers	18	17	1	0	91	15	76	52
2	Erpingham	18	11	4	3	75	29	46	37
3	Hickling (-1)	18	11	4	3	64	29	35	36
4	Holt 'A'	18	7	2	9	44	55	-11	23
5	Felmingham	18	6	4	8	46	54	-8	22
6	Trunch	18	7	1	10	39	53	-14	22
7	Southrepps	18	6	2	10	31	56	-25	20
8	Mundesley Res. (-1)	18	5	4	9	44	52	-8	18
9	Cawston (-1)	18	4	4	10	33	42	-9	15
10	Corpusty Res. (-3)	18	3	0	15	17	99	-82	6

Division Three		P	W	D	L	F	A	GD	Pts
1	Sheringham 'A'	12	9	1	2	52	25	27	28
2	AFC Coltishall	12	8	1	3	47	22	25	25
3	Plumstead Rangers Res.	12	7	1	4	36	23	13	22
4	Bacton	12	6	3	3	49	26	23	21
5	Gimingham Res.	12	3	2	7	33	54	-21	11
6	Erpingham Res.	12	1	0	11	16	75	-59	3
7	Aldborough Lions (-15)	12	3	2	7	33	41	-8	-4

NORTH GLOUCESTERSHIRE LEAGUE

Premier Division		P	W	D	L	F	A	GD	Pts
1	Woolaston	24	19	4	1	66	27	39	61
2	Milkwall	24	17	2	5	71	41	30	53
3	Lydney Town Res.	24	13	5	6	40	23	17	44
4	Whitecroft	24	14	1	9	49	34	15	43
5	English Bicknor	24	11	4	9	55	30	25	37
6	Huntley	24	9	7	8	44	45	-1	34
7	Coleford Utd	24	8	6	10	38	38	0	30
8	Westbury Utd	24	8	4	12	45	50	-5	28
9	Lydbrook Athletic Res.	24	7	4	13	27	49	-22	25
10	Broadwell Res.	24	7	3	14	32	57	-25	24
11	St Briavels	24	7	3	14	45	77	-32	24
12	Mitcheldean	24	7	2	15	32	47	-15	23
13	Bream Amts	24	4	5	15	36	62	-26	17

Division One		P	W	D	L	F	A	GD	Pts
1	Redbrook Rovers	22	17	2	3	71	28	43	53
2	Blakeney	22	14	6	2	69	29	40	48
3	Whitecroft Res.	22	13	5	4	54	28	26	44
4	Ruardean Hill Rangers Res.	22	13	4	5	55	31	24	43
5	Newent Town Res.	22	11	3	8	37	37	0	36
6	Yorkley	22	8	6	8	43	36	7	30
7	Newnham Utd	22	9	1	12	45	44	1	28
8	Ellwood Res.	22	8	3	11	30	43	-13	27
9	Puma FC	22	8	0	14	43	63	-20	24
10	Lydney Town A	22	5	2	15	32	62	-30	17
11	Mushet & Coalway Utd	22	5	2	15	24	56	-32	17
12	English Bicknor Res.	22	4	0	18	17	63	-46	12

Division Two		P	W	D	L	F	A	GD	Pts
1	Tidenham	24	20	2	2	105	27	78	62
2	Redmarley	24	20	2	2	76	25	51	62
3	Utd Longhope	24	17	2	5	101	50	51	53
4	Soudley Res.	24	15	1	8	89	51	38	46
5	Lydbrook Athletic A	24	13	2	9	45	50	-5	41
6	Howle Hill	24	12	3	9	82	55	27	39
7	Westbury Utd Res.	24	11	5	8	68	60	8	38
8	Viney St Swithins Res.	24	7	3	14	36	66	-30	24
9	Bream Amts Res.	24	7	3	14	45	76	-31	24
10	Milkwall Res.	24	6	4	14	51	98	-47	22
11	Woolaston Res.	24	6	2	16	59	90	-31	20
12	Puma FC Res.	24	3	2	19	34	108	-74	11
13	Mitcheldean Res.	24	3	1	20	36	71	-35	10

Division Three	P	W	D	L	F	A	GD	Pts
1 Aylburton Rovers	22	15	4	3	93	38	55	49
2 Newent Town A	22	15	2	5	88	26	62	47
3 Whitecroft A	22	13	3	6	63	45	18	42
4 Ruardean Utd	22	12	5	5	67	30	37	41
5 Harrow Hill Res.	22	11	5	6	46	38	8	38
6 Rank Outsiders	22	11	4	7	48	27	21	37
7 Redside	22	11	4	7	49	59	-10	37
8 Ruardean Hill Rangers A	22	7	3	12	31	40	-9	24
9 Mushet & Coalway Utd Res.	22	6	2	14	34	64	-30	20
10 Ruspidge Utd	22	6	0	16	42	90	-48	18
11 Minsterworth Res.	22	4	2	16	30	87	-57	14
12 Blakeney Res.	22	4	0	18	33	80	-47	12

Division Four	P	W	D	L	F	A	GD	Pts
1 Hilldene Athletic	22	17	3	2	81	28	53	54
2 Tidenham Res.	22	15	4	3	85	39	46	49
3 Coleford Utd Res.	22	14	3	5	96	41	55	45
4 Harrow Hill A	22	14	3	5	69	25	44	45
5 Broadwell A	22	12	2	8	52	39	13	38
6 Yorkley Res.	22	12	0	10	74	48	26	36
7 Littledean	22	11	1	10	52	57	-5	34
8 Redbrook Rovers Res.	22	10	3	9	66	60	6	33
9 Rank Outsiders Res.	22	4	3	15	33	89	-56	15
10 Puma FC A	22	4	1	17	23	103	-80	13
11 St Briavels Res.	22	3	2	17	36	73	-37	11
12 Lydney Town B	22	3	1	18	26	91	-65	10

NORTH LANCS & DISTRICT LEAGUE

Premier Division	P	W	D	L	F	A	GD	Pts
1 Carnforth Rangers	26	20	6	0	61	12	49	66
2 Caton United	26	16	6	4	68	37	31	54
3 Morecambe Royals	26	14	6	6	57	33	24	48
4 Ingleton	26	13	7	6	63	39	24	46
5 Cartmel & District	26	13	4	9	54	38	16	43
6 Trimpell & Bare Rangers	26	12	5	9	51	51	0	41
7 Galgate	26	11	8	7	36	40	-4	41
8 College AFC	26	9	3	14	33	49	-16	30
9 Bowerham	26	8	3	15	33	59	-26	27
10 Marsh United	26	7	5	14	32	58	-26	26
11 Highgrove	26	6	6	14	47	59	-12	24
12 Bentham	26	5	8	13	36	47	-11	23
13 Swarthmoor Social Club	26	6	3	17	29	52	-23	21
14 TIC Dynamos of Overton and Middleton	26	5	4	17	32	58	-26	19

Division One	P	W	D	L	F	A	GD	Pts
1 Storeys	24	18	0	6	70	53	17	54
2 Moor Lane FC	24	16	4	4	69	23	46	52
3 Heysham	24	15	3	6	76	50	26	48
4 Cartmel & District Res.	24	11	9	4	50	28	22	42
5 Carnforth Rangers Res.	24	10	6	8	50	42	8	36
6 Arnside (-3)	24	12	2	10	69	54	15	35
7 Bolton Le Sands	24	9	3	12	41	49	-8	30
8 Millhead	24	9	2	13	58	67	-9	29
9 Grange	24	7	5	12	50	55	-5	26
10 Westgate Wanderers	24	7	4	13	45	76	-31	25
11 Kirkby Lonsdale	24	6	6	12	39	61	-22	24
12 Freehold	24	5	6	13	48	67	-19	21
13 TIC Dynamos of Overton and Middleton Res	24	4	4	16	32	72	-40	16

Division Two	P	W	D	L	F	A	GD	Pts
1 Mayfield United	22	21	0	1	79	14	65	63
2 Lancaster Rovers	22	17	2	3	76	29	47	53
3 AFC Moorlands	22	12	2	8	77	51	26	38
4 Boys Club	22	11	3	8	47	43	4	36
5 Burton Thistle	22	10	4	8	54	46	8	34
6 Ingleton Res.	22	8	7	7	48	48	0	31
7 Galgate Res.	22	9	3	10	55	49	6	30
8 Morecambe Royals Res. (-4)	22	7	6	9	42	43	-1	23
9 Morecambe Gold	22	4	6	12	25	54	-29	18
10 Marsh United Res. (+2)	22	4	3	15	28	78	-50	17
11 Trimpell & Bare Rangers Res.	22	4	1	17	35	84	-49	13
12 Highgrove Res. (-10)	22	4	5	13	35	62	-27	7

Division Three	P	W	D	L	F	A	GD	Pts
1 Caton United Res.	16	14	0	2	72	29	43	42
2 CC Wanderers	16	10	3	3	42	34	8	33
3 Boys Club Res.	16	9	4	3	40	32	8	31
4 College AFC Res.	16	6	1	9	37	45	-8	19
5 Storeys Res.	16	5	2	9	31	41	-10	17
6 Torrisholme	16	4	4	8	33	41	-8	16
7 Moghuls (-3)	16	6	1	9	31	40	-9	16
8 Preesall & Pilling	16	4	3	9	42	51	-9	15
9 Lancaster Rovers Res. (-3)	16	4	2	10	37	52	-15	11

Division Four	P	W	D	L	F	A	GD	Pts
1 Mayfield United Res.	18	16	1	1	62	20	42	49
2 Carnforth Rangers A	18	13	3	2	64	22	42	42
3 FC Britannia	18	10	4	4	60	29	31	34
4 Heysham Res.	18	8	5	5	61	42	19	29
5 Cartmel & District A	18	8	5	5	34	36	-2	29
6 CC Wanderers Res.	18	3	5	10	24	52	-28	14
7 TIC Dynamos of Overton and Middleton A	18	3	3	12	27	54	-27	12
8 Morecambe Gold Res.	18	3	3	12	22	66	-44	12
9 Westgate Wanderers Res. (-6)	18	5	2	11	32	51	-19	11
10 Arnside Res. (-6)	18	3	5	10	22	36	-14	8

NORTH LEICESTERSHIRE LEAGUE

Premier Division	P	W	D	L	F	A	GD	Pts
1 Ingles FC	22	17	4	1	81	20	61	55
2 Greenhill YC	22	14	3	5	61	35	26	45
3 Loughborough FC	22	13	5	4	61	27	34	44
4 Mountsorrel Amateurs	22	12	3	7	70	39	31	39
5 Falcons FC	22	10	8	4	57	38	19	38
6 Sileby Victoria	22	11	4	7	53	30	23	37
7 Whitwick FC (-1)	22	10	2	10	42	44	-2	31
8 East Leake Athletic	22	8	3	11	42	45	-3	27
9 Kegworth Imperial	22	6	4	12	45	69	-24	22
10 Genesis FC	22	5	2	15	25	80	-55	17
11 Whitwick United	22	3	3	16	40	87	-47	12
12 Anstey Crown	22	1	3	18	24	87	-63	6

Division One	P	W	D	L	F	A	GD	Pts
1 Shelthorpe FC	20	20	0	0	114	16	98	60
2 Thringstone MW	20	13	4	3	65	27	38	43
3 Sutton Bonington Academicals	20	11	0	9	55	52	3	33
4 Ferrari FC	20	10	2	8	47	51	-4	32
5 Thurmaston Rangers	20	9	2	9	44	48	-4	29
6 Birstall Old Boys (-6)	20	11	0	9	58	60	-2	27
7 Loughborough United	20	8	2	10	62	56	6	26
8 Castle Donington Res.	20	8	2	10	56	55	1	26
9 Ingles Res. FC	20	7	2	11	40	52	-12	23
10 Loughborough Athletic	20	3	0	17	25	86	-61	9
11 Woodhouse Imperial	20	3	0	17	35	98	-63	9

Division Two	P	W	D	L	F	A	GD	Pts
1 Ravenstone United	22	18	3	1	75	29	46	57
2 Forest Road Rangers	22	16	1	5	88	30	58	49
3 Greenhill YC Res.	22	16	0	6	60	38	22	48
4 Sileby Saints	22	14	3	5	58	28	30	45
5 Belton Villa (-1)	22	11	0	11	53	49	4	32
6 Garryson FC	22	9	2	11	66	61	5	29
7 Loughborough Galaxy	22	9	2	11	54	57	-3	29
8 East Leake Athletic Res.	22	9	1	12	40	53	-13	28
9 Sutton Bonington	22	6	2	14	46	66	-20	20
10 Measham Imperial	22	6	1	15	43	85	-42	19
11 Sileby Victoria Res.	22	5	2	15	44	78	-34	17
12 Shepshed Amateurs	22	4	1	17	32	85	-53	13

Division Three	P	W	D	L	F	A	GD	Pts
1 Mountsorrel Amateurs Res.	24	20	3	1	104	26	78	63
2 Sileby WMC	24	18	5	1	111	31	80	59
3 Loughborough Emmanuel	24	16	1	7	76	46	30	49
4 Loughborough FC Res.	24	12	3	9	65	47	18	39
5 Birstall Old Boys Res.	24	11	3	10	53	70	-17	36
6 Mountsorrel FC	24	9	3	12	73	74	-1	30
7 FC Coalville	24	9	3	12	65	70	-5	30
8 Loughborough United Res.	24	8	4	12	58	77	-19	28
9 Castle Donington	24	8	2	14	60	70	-10	26
10 Nags Head Harby FC	24	7	5	12	63	81	-18	26
11 Woodhouse Imperial Res.	24	7	4	13	53	86	-33	25
12 Kegworth Imperial Res.	24	6	6	12	41	76	-35	24
13 Genesis FC Res.	24	4	0	20	36	104	-68	12

NORTH NORTHUMBERLAND LEAGUE

Division One	P	W	D	L	F	A	GD	Pts
1 Shilbottle C.W.	16	14	1	1	90	29	61	43
2 Bamburgh Castle	16	10	2	4	55	40	15	32
3 Tweedmouth Rangers (+3)	16	8	3	5	57	35	22	30
4 Red Row Welfare (-6)	16	9	3	4	54	35	19	24
5 North Sunderland	16	7	3	6	38	48	-10	24
6 Rothbury (-3)	16	5	2	9	38	55	-17	14
7 Highfields United	16	4	0	12	31	70	-39	12
8 Tweedmouth Harrow	16	3	2	11	30	63	-33	11
9 Springhill (-3)	16	3	2	11	21	39	-18	8

Division Two	P	W	D	L	F	A	GD	Pts
1 Wansbeck AFC	18	15	2	1	102	24	78	47
2 Lowick United	18	13	2	3	87	30	57	41
3 Duns	18	11	1	6	77	28	49	34
4 Craster Rovers	18	8	7	3	48	28	20	31
5 Amble St Cuthbert	18	9	2	7	49	51	-2	29
6 Alnmouth United	18	9	1	8	38	61	-23	28
7 Embleton W.R.	18	7	1	10	52	56	-4	22
8 Wooler Res. (-3)	18	5	2	11	32	78	-46	14
9 Lynemouth Anglers (-3)	18	3	1	14	32	67	-35	7
10 Hedgeley Rovers (-3)	18	0	1	17	13	107	-94	-2

NORWICH & DISTRICT LEAGUE

Division One	P	W	D	L	F	A	GD	Pts
1 Marlborough OB	18	15	0	3	72	10	62	45
2 UEA Res.	18	14	1	3	75	22	53	43
3 Jarrolds	18	10	2	6	67	61	6	32
4 Homecare United	18	10	1	7	58	48	10	31
5 Jubilee Rangers	18	8	2	8	47	39	8	26
6 Norwich Medics	18	6	4	8	41	42	-1	22
7 Eaton Beehive (-2)	18	6	5	7	72	48	24	21
8 Drayton (-2)	18	5	3	10	38	67	-29	16
9 Old Catton Rovers (-2)	18	3	2	13	20	112	-92	9
10 Wensum Albion	18	1	4	13	33	74	-41	7

Division Two	P	W	D	L	F	A	GD	Pts
1 One Love United	14	12	2	0	60	15	45	38
2 UEA A	14	11	1	2	56	22	34	34
3 Frettenham United	14	7	3	4	30	25	5	24
4 Yelverton Res.	14	5	0	9	20	39	-19	15
5 Tiger FC (-2)	14	4	4	6	25	30	-5	14
6 Hockering FC (-2)	14	4	3	7	36	44	-8	13
7 Newton Flotman Res. (-2)	14	4	2	8	26	48	-22	12
8 Taverham	14	1	1	12	22	52	-30	4

Division Three	P	W	D	L	F	A	GD	Pts
1 Dyers Arms	14	9	2	3	30	14	16	29
2 Earlham Colney	14	7	5	2	34	17	17	26
3 Norman Wanderers (-2)	14	7	5	2	45	29	16	24
4 Heartsease Athletic	14	7	2	5	35	32	3	23
5 South Walsham Res.	14	5	3	6	25	29	-4	18
6 Costessey Sports Res. (-5)	14	4	3	7	29	35	-6	10
7 Nostro Bulls Res. (-2)	14	3	3	8	31	44	-13	10
8 Anglian Knights	14	2	1	11	17	46	-29	7

NOTTS AMATEUR ALLIANCE

Premier Division	P	W	D	L	F	A	GD	Pts
1 Nottingham Sikh Lions	20	16	2	2	78	33	45	50
2 Bilborough United	20	15	3	2	75	29	46	48
3 AFC Bridgford	20	12	4	4	53	27	26	40
4 Boots Athletic Res.	20	9	1	10	56	58	-2	28
5 Nottingham All Stars	20	8	2	10	53	55	-2	26
6 Kimberley MW 'A'	20	7	3	10	51	55	-4	24
7 Netherfield Albion Res.	20	8	0	12	49	57	-8	24
8 Aspley	20	6	3	11	48	68	-20	21
9 Gedling Southbank 'A'	20	5	5	10	44	61	-17	20
10 Crusader	20	5	3	12	42	75	-33	18
11 Coopers Arms	20	5	2	13	43	74	-31	17

Division One	P	W	D	L	F	A	GD	Pts
1 Aspley Park	12	10	1	1	55	16	39	31
2 Kimberley MW 'B'	12	8	0	4	31	16	15	24
3 Ina City	12	7	2	3	43	34	9	23
4 Vernon Villa	12	7	2	3	27	23	4	23
5 Trent Bridge	12	4	1	7	30	53	-23	13
6 FC Geordie	12	2	2	8	22	30	-8	8
7 Rushcliffe Dynamo	12	0	0	12	14	50	-36	0

Division Two	P	W	D	L	F	A	GD	Pts
1 West 8	22	17	1	4	78	42	36	52
2 AFC Top Valley	22	16	3	3	82	35	47	51
3 Bingham Town Res.	22	14	5	3	69	33	36	47
4 Skegby United	22	13	2	7	73	43	30	41
5 Beeston Rylands	22	9	5	8	77	66	11	32
6 Arnold Celtic	22	9	5	8	52	44	8	32
7 Netherfield Seniors	22	9	3	10	59	63	-4	30
8 Bilborough United Res.	22	8	2	12	51	82	-31	26
9 FC Cavaliers Res.	22	7	1	14	43	76	-33	22
10 Boots Athletic 'A'	22	4	4	14	49	77	-28	16
11 Netherfield Albion 'A'	22	3	4	15	46	98	-52	13
12 Premium (-3)	22	4	3	15	42	62	-20	12

Division Three	P	W	D	L	F	A	GD	Pts
1 Ashfield Athletic	20	15	3	2	72	26	46	48
2 Gedling Southbank Colts	20	13	3	4	58	32	26	42
3 Robin Hood Colts	20	12	4	4	62	28	34	40
4 Sycamore St Anns	20	12	2	6	58	29	29	38
5 Aspley Park Res.	20	11	4	5	67	36	31	37
6 FC Samba Res.	20	9	2	9	41	41	0	29
7 Nottingham Community	20	8	4	8	52	42	10	28
8 AFC Villa	20	6	4	10	51	54	-3	22
9 Mapperley	20	6	1	13	38	73	-35	19
10 AFC Bridgford Res.	20	3	2	15	25	73	-48	11
11 Stone City	20	0	1	19	22	112	-90	1

NOTTINGHAM SENIOR LEAGUE

Senior Division	P	W	D	L	F	A	GD	Pts
1 Selston	32	24	4	4	101	42	59	76
2 Kimberley Miners Welfare	32	23	3	6	90	47	43	72
3 Hucknall Rolls Leisure	32	21	6	5	94	41	53	69
4 Beeston	32	18	5	9	91	60	31	59
5 Wollaton	32	18	4	10	81	55	26	58
6 Cotgrave	32	18	3	11	74	67	7	57
7 Awsworth Villa	32	15	5	12	69	60	9	50
8 Magdala Amateurs	32	14	4	14	81	71	10	46
9 FC Cavaliers	32	13	6	13	66	74	-8	45
10 Attenborough	32	12	6	14	59	58	1	42
11 Boots Athletic	32	10	10	12	60	65	-5	40
12 Ruddington Village	32	11	7	14	64	75	-11	40
13 Keyworth United	32	10	2	20	57	83	-26	32
14 Burton Joyce	32	8	6	18	69	93	-24	30
15 Bilborough Town	32	6	5	21	40	85	-45	23
16 Sandhurst (-6)	32	6	4	22	40	101	-61	16
17 Nottingham United	32	3	4	25	45	104	-59	13

Division One	P	W	D	L	F	A	GD	Pts
1 Kirton Brickworks	28	19	5	4	84	43	41	62
2 West Bridgford	28	20	2	6	84	44	40	62
3 Bingham Town	28	17	7	4	63	32	31	58
4 Southwell City Res.	28	14	8	6	71	50	21	50
5 Netherfield Albion	28	15	4	9	72	56	16	49
6 Underwood Villa	28	13	6	9	70	48	22	45
7 Radcliffe Olympic Res.	28	13	3	12	58	55	3	42
8 Hucknall Rolls Leisure Res.	28	12	6	10	55	60	-5	42
9 Ruddington Village Res.	28	11	2	15	73	73	0	35
10 Linby Colliery Welfare Res.	28	9	6	13	59	58	1	33
11 Wollaton Res.	28	9	4	15	36	58	-22	31
12 Awsworth Villa Res.	28	8	4	16	54	77	-23	28
13 Gedling Southbank	28	6	8	14	33	53	-20	26
14 Magdala Amateurs	28	5	4	19	36	86	-50	19
15 Nottinghamshire	28	3	3	22	32	87	-55	12

Division Two	P	W	D	L	F	A	GD	Pts
1 Moorgreen	18	14	2	2	65	21	44	44
2 Ashland Rovers	18	14	1	3	69	26	43	43
3 Newark Flowserve	18	12	0	6	63	32	31	36
4 Kimberley Miners Welfare Res.	18	11	3	4	40	31	9	36
5 FC Samba	18	8	1	9	45	39	6	25
6 Greyfriars	18	7	3	8	41	39	2	24
7 Underwood Villa Res.	18	7	0	11	41	51	-10	21
8 Nottinghamshire Res.	18	6	1	11	35	55	-20	19
9 Bilborough Town Res.	18	4	2	12	44	70	-26	14
10 Sandhurst Res.	18	0	1	17	10	89	-79	1

PERRY STREET & DISTRICT LEAGUE

Premier Division	P	W	D	L	F	A	GD	Pts
1 Crewkerne Town	20	16	2	2	74	21	53	50
2 Lyme Regis (-8)	20	14	4	2	66	21	45	38
3 Beaminster	20	12	1	7	47	24	23	37
4 Shepton Beauchamp	20	11	3	6	60	26	34	36
5 Misterton	20	9	3	8	42	48	-6	30
6 West & Middle Chinnock	20	8	2	10	39	49	-10	26
7 Perry Street	20	7	3	10	50	47	3	24
8 Combe Res. (-2)	20	8	2	10	33	54	-21	24
9 Ilminster Res.	20	7	0	13	38	58	-20	21
10 Millwey Rise	20	5	5	10	33	43	-10	20
11 Winsham	20	0	1	19	14	105	-91	1

Division One	P	W	D	L	F	A	GD	Pts
1 Perry Street Res.	18	14	2	2	78	24	54	44
2 Lyme Regis Res.	18	13	3	2	56	23	33	42
3 South Petherton	18	11	6	1	51	17	34	39
4 Barrington	18	5	7	6	50	43	7	22
5 Pymore	18	6	4	8	40	51	-11	22
6 Forton Rangers	18	7	1	10	42	54	-12	22
7 Farway United	18	6	2	10	35	52	-17	20
8 Netherbury	18	5	4	9	38	47	-9	19
9 Uplyme	18	2	7	9	36	57	-21	13
10 Beaminster Res. (-3)	18	2	2	14	20	78	-58	5

Division Two	P	W	D	L	F	A	GD	Pts
1 Chard United	20	15	1	4	60	23	37	46
2 Luso-Chard (-3)	20	15	2	3	73	19	54	44
3 Thorncombe	20	12	3	5	56	34	22	39
4 Waytown Hounds	20	10	4	6	47	28	19	34
5 Charmouth	20	10	2	8	50	38	12	32
6 Combe A	20	9	1	10	39	35	4	28
7 Crewkerne Rangers	20	8	3	9	42	46	-4	27
8 Crewkerne Res.	20	7	0	13	33	63	-30	21
9 Ilminster Colts	20	5	4	11	24	58	-34	19
10 Dowlish & Donyatt	20	3	4	13	31	64	-33	13
11 South Petherton Res. (-4)	20	2	4	14	32	79	-47	6

Division Three	P	W	D	L	F	A	GD	Pts
1 Lyme Bantams	18	11	4	3	44	24	20	37
2 Drimpton	18	11	4	3	51	32	19	37
3 Barrington Res.	18	11	2	5	58	31	27	35
4 Chard Utd. Res.	18	11	2	5	47	36	11	35
5 Hawkchurch	18	9	3	6	44	24	20	30
6 Shepton Res.	18	8	2	8	41	39	2	26
7 Millwey Rise Res.	18	7	4	7	34	34	0	25
8 Ilminster Town A	18	5	1	12	29	57	-28	16
9 Winsham Res.	18	3	2	13	24	65	-41	11
10 Chard Rangers	18	2	0	16	27	57	-30	6

Division Four	P	W	D	L	F	A	GD	Pts
1 Kingsbury	20	17	1	2	65	15	50	52
2 Merriott Dynamos	20	15	2	3	88	24	64	47
3 Thorncombe Res.	20	14	3	3	66	30	36	45
4 Forton Rangers Res. (-1)	20	13	2	5	64	29	35	40
5 Combe B (-1)	20	11	2	7	62	39	23	34
6 Misterton Res. (-1)	20	8	2	10	47	60	-13	25
7 Crewkerne Rangers Res.	20	7	3	10	46	65	-19	24
8 Uplyme Res. (-4)	20	6	1	13	54	88	-34	15
9 Chard Rangers Res.	20	4	0	16	30	76	-46	12
10 Farway Res.	20	3	1	16	35	97	-62	10
11 Hinton St George (-1)	20	3	1	16	35	69	-34	9

PLYMOUTH & WEST DISTRICT LEAGUE

Division One	P	W	D	L	F	A	GD	Pts
1 Mount Gould	20	15	0	5	56	28	28	45
2 Millbridge	20	14	2	4	58	29	29	44
3 Roborough	20	13	2	5	60	38	22	41
4 Chaddlewood Miners OB	20	11	2	7	50	37	13	35
5 University of Plymouth 'A' (-3)	20	11	1	7	45	29	16	31
6 The Windmill (Sat)	20	10	1	9	49	34	15	31
7 Hideaway Cafe (+3)	20	7	4	8	36	46	-10	28
8 Plymouth Marjon	20	5	3	12	40	46	-6	18
9 Steam Packet	20	6	0	14	37	69	-32	18
10 Tavistock Community 'A'	20	4	2	14	27	69	-42	14
11 Efford United	20	4	1	15	35	68	-33	13

Division Two	P	W	D	L	F	A	GD	Pts
1 Morley Rangers 'A'	18	14	1	3	51	21	30	43
2 Chaddlewood OB 'A'	18	12	1	5	46	29	17	37
3 Devonport Services	18	12	1	5	47	42	5	37
4 Millbrook AFC Res.	18	11	2	5	48	23	25	35
5 Plympton Athletic	18	9	2	7	36	29	7	29
6 Plymouth Hope	18	5	2	11	30	37	-7	17
7 Roborough Res.	18	5	2	11	29	43	-14	17
8 Horrabridge Rangers SA	18	4	4	10	35	46	-11	16
9 Novahomes 'A'	18	4	3	11	24	50	-26	15
10 Edgecumbe FC	18	3	4	11	26	52	-26	13

Division Three	P	W	D	L	F	A	GD	Pts
1 Sporting Plymouth	20	18	1	1	92	38	54	55
2 Horrabridge Rangers SA Res.	20	11	3	6	58	45	13	36
3 Star Garage (+3)	20	10	2	7	48	40	8	35
4 Plymouth Spurs	20	11	1	8	84	59	25	34
5 Bar Sol Ona	20	11	0	9	46	45	1	33
6 Morley Rangers 'B'	20	10	2	8	72	59	13	32
7 Plymouth Falcons	20	9	4	7	59	47	12	31
8 Millbridge Res.	20	6	3	11	44	59	-15	21
9 Chaddlewood Miners OB 'B' (-3)	20	7	1	11	53	55	-2	19
10 Staddiscombe Colts	20	4	2	14	47	67	-20	14
11 Plymouth Rangers (-6)	20	1	1	16	17	106	-89	-2

Division Four	P	W	D	L	F	A	GD	Pts
1 Ernesettle DRDE Trust	20	17	2	1	114	25	89	53
2 Belgrave FC	20	15	2	3	67	32	35	47
3 Barne Barton Rangers	20	12	2	6	69	58	11	38
4 Tavistock Community 'B'	20	10	2	8	72	57	15	32
5 Princetown	20	10	1	9	58	54	4	31
6 Hooe Rovers (+2)	20	8	4	8	64	54	10	30
7 Stoke Harriers	20	8	2	10	45	58	-13	26
8 Novahomes 'B'	20	7	2	11	48	62	-14	23
9 Woodford (-4)	20	6	4	10	66	68	-2	18
10 Kitto FC	20	4	2	14	52	93	-41	14
11 Yelverton Villa	20	0	3	17	23	117	-94	3

PORTSMOUTH LEAGUE

Premier Division	P	W	D	L	F	A	GD	Pts
1 Waterlooville Social Club	15	11	2	2	49	14	35	35
2 Meon United (-3)	15	8	3	4	44	26	18	24
3 Horndean Hawks (-3)	15	7	4	4	30	27	3	22
4 Wymering	15	6	2	7	43	43	0	20
5 AFC Hereford	15	6	1	8	21	38	-17	19
6 St Helena Bobs	15	0	2	13	19	58	-39	2

Division One	P	W	D	L	F	A	GD	Pts
1 Cosham Park Rangers	14	11	1	2	40	16	24	34
2 FC Voyers	14	8	4	2	67	21	46	28
3 Southsea Utd	14	6	4	4	40	35	5	22
4 Burrfields FC (-1)	14	6	4	4	34	41	-7	21
5 Segensworth FC	14	6	1	7	29	38	-9	19
6 Carberry	14	3	5	6	23	27	-4	14
7 Portchester Rovers	14	2	4	8	22	42	-20	10
8 Horndean Utd	14	2	1	11	12	47	-35	7

Division Two	P	W	D	L	F	A	GD	Pts
1 Budd AFC	14	13	1	0	54	18	36	40
2 Tempest Crusaders	14	10	0	4	62	29	33	30
3 Fareport Town	14	8	4	2	53	30	23	28
4 AFC Ventora	14	6	3	5	36	37	-1	21
5 Drayton Town	14	6	0	8	32	36	-4	18
6 Horndean Hawks Res. (+3)	14	3	2	9	23	39	-16	14
7 Cosham Dynamos (-3)	14	3	1	10	23	47	-24	7
8 Lee Rangers	14	1	1	12	21	68	-47	4

REDHILL & DISTRICT LEAGUE

Premier Division	P	W	D	L	F	A	GD	Pts
1 Godstone	14	10	3	1	39	15	24	33
2 RH Athletic	14	9	2	3	30	19	11	29
3 Warlingham Res.	14	9	1	4	31	29	2	28
4 Woodmansterne Hyde	14	7	3	4	30	23	7	24
5 South Park 'A'	14	4	4	6	18	26	-8	16
6 Racing Epsom	14	3	2	9	30	37	-7	11
7 Nomads	14	2	2	10	14	23	-9	8
8 Frenches Athletic	14	1	5	8	17	37	-20	8

Division One	P	W	D	L	F	A	GD	Pts
1 Dormansland Rockets	18	14	2	2	63	24	39	44
2 Bletchingley	18	12	3	3	75	30	45	39
3 Woodmansterne Hyde Res.	18	12	1	5	70	34	36	37
4 Real Holmesdale	18	9	1	8	54	60	-6	28
5 Warlingham 'A'	18	8	1	9	47	51	-4	25
6 New Nork Dynamos	18	7	2	9	34	44	-10	23
7 Edenbridge United	18	7	1	10	51	52	-1	22
8 Nutfield	18	5	2	11	31	51	-20	17
9 Farleigh Rovers 'A'	18	5	1	12	30	54	-24	16
10 South Godstone	18	3	2	13	22	77	-55	11

Division Two	P	W	D	L	F	A	GD	Pts
1 Horley AFC	20	15	4	1	55	18	37	49
2 Charlwood	20	12	4	4	62	34	28	40
3 Overton Athletic	20	12	2	6	46	21	25	38
4 Merstham Newton	20	10	6	4	41	27	14	36
5 Walton Heath	20	10	4	6	32	35	-3	34
6 Holland Sports Res.	20	9	4	7	48	28	20	31
7 RH Athletic Res.	20	8	1	11	34	38	-4	25
8 Smallfield Res.	20	6	2	12	35	32	3	20
9 Warlingham 'B'	20	5	2	13	37	50	-13	17
10 Real Holmesdale Res.	20	4	2	14	29	79	-50	14
11 Reigate Priory 'A'	20	2	3	15	16	73	-57	9

Division Three	P	W	D	L	F	A	GD	Pts
1 AFC Reigate	20	18	2	0	72	15	57	56
2 Westcott 35	20	14	2	4	79	33	46	44
3 Nomads Res.	20	12	5	3	46	25	21	41
4 Tatsfield Rovers 1st Team	20	12	3	5	34	38	-4	39
5 South Park 'B'	20	10	3	7	45	39	6	33
6 RH Athletic 'A'	20	7	5	8	33	41	-8	26
7 Sporting 50	20	7	4	9	24	25	-1	25
8 Brockham Res.	20	5	2	13	38	56	-18	17
9 AFC Sporting Horley	20	4	2	14	23	27	-4	14
10 AFC Redhill	20	3	4	13	34	54	-20	13
11 Reigate Priory 'B'	20	1	2	17	16	91	-75	5

Division Four	P	W	D	L	F	A	GD	Pts
1 Godstone Res.	20	15	2	3	70	27	43	47
2 Reigate OB	20	14	1	5	71	24	47	43
3 Westcott 35 Res.	20	12	6	2	54	34	20	42
4 Woodmansterne Hyde 'A'	20	11	4	5	44	29	15	37
5 Oxted & District 'A'	20	10	2	8	45	45	0	32
6 Walton Heath Res.	20	8	5	7	42	31	11	29
7 Frenches Athletic Res.	20	6	4	10	43	71	-28	22
8 South Godstone Res.	20	6	0	14	37	45	-8	18
9 RH Athletic 'B'	20	4	4	12	42	77	-35	16
10 Nutfield Res.	20	4	3	13	35	63	-28	15
11 Horley AFC Res.	20	3	3	14	36	73	-37	12

ROCHDALE ALLIANCE

Premier Division	P	W	D	L	F	A	GD	Pts
1 Balderstone 1st	20	16	2	2	64	32	32	50
2 FC Bury Town	20	16	0	4	56	31	25	48
3 Whitworth Valley 1st	20	15	0	5	54	25	29	45
4 Oldham Boro	20	9	4	7	58	40	18	31
5 Woodbank	20	9	1	10	30	37	-7	28
6 Fothergill & Whittles 1st	20	8	2	10	49	57	-8	26
7 King William IV	20	8	2	10	59	71	-12	26
8 Walsden C&FC	20	7	3	10	49	50	-1	24
9 White Lion	20	6	3	11	38	54	-16	21
10 Rochdale Sacred Heart	20	4	3	13	51	64	-13	15
11 Star Athletic	20	1	2	17	25	72	-47	5

Division One	P	W	D	L	F	A	GD	Pts
1 Fothergill & Whittles 2nd	22	21	0	1	144	24	120	63
2 Sudden	22	17	1	4	124	49	75	52
3 Rochdale Asia	22	16	2	4	78	45	33	50
4 Hargreaves	22	12	4	6	67	46	21	40
5 F&W Rovers	22	12	1	9	49	59	-10	37
6 Whitworth Valley 2nd	22	10	2	10	66	43	23	32
7 Mighty Dragons (-1)	22	9	1	12	44	53	-9	27
8 Wardle Old Boys	22	8	0	14	44	75	-31	24
9 Balderstone 2nd (-3)	22	7	2	13	60	62	-2	20
10 Chadderton Park	22	5	5	12	43	62	-19	20
11 Rochdale Galaxy	22	5	1	16	47	81	-34	16
12 Horse & Farrier	22	0	1	21	20	187	-167	1

SALISBURY & DISTRICT LEAGUE

Premier Division	P	W	D	L	F	A	GD	Pts
1 The Wanderers	16	12	2	2	70	21	49	38
2 Stockton & Codford	16	11	3	2	42	21	21	36
3 Porton Sports	16	8	4	4	32	28	4	28
4 Durrington Dynamoes	16	8	2	6	37	34	3	26
5 South Newton & Wishford	16	5	2	9	40	38	2	17
6 Devizes Inn	16	5	2	9	22	41	-19	17
7 Alderbury	16	5	1	10	30	48	-18	16
8 Tisbury United	16	3	4	9	21	38	-17	13
9 Nomansland & Landford	16	3	4	9	19	44	-25	13

Division One	P	W	D	L	F	A	GD	Pts
1 Chalke Valley	18	12	3	3	71	40	31	39
2 Stockton & Codford Res	18	12	1	5	60	36	24	37
3 Amesbury Kings Arms FC	18	11	3	4	33	23	10	36
4 Durrington FC	18	10	2	6	41	30	11	32
5 Whiteparish	18	10	0	8	40	46	-6	30
6 West Harnham	18	8	1	9	37	31	6	25
7 Deacon Alms FC	18	5	4	9	31	36	-5	19
8 Enford (-2)	18	6	1	11	43	58	-15	17
9 Value Cars	18	4	2	12	37	59	-22	14
10 South Newton & Wishford Res	18	3	1	14	20	54	-34	10

SCUNTHORPE & DISTRICT LEAGUE

Division One	P	W	D	L	F	A	GD	Pts
1 College Wanderers	15	15	0	0	55	13	42	45
2 Epworth Town	15	11	0	4	44	14	30	33
3 Limestone Rangers	16	10	1	5	40	21	19	31
4 Swinefleet Juniors	16	9	1	6	47	22	25	28
5 New Holland Villa	16	8	2	6	30	20	10	26
6 Messingham Juniors	16	4	3	9	24	41	-17	15
7 Scotter United	16	3	3	10	22	59	-37	12
8 Crosby Colts	16	3	1	12	22	57	-35	10
9 Barnetby United	16	2	1	13	19	56	-37	7

Division Two	P	W	D	L	F	A	GD	Pts
1 Brumby	18	16	2	0	81	16	65	50
2 Chaplins (-3)	18	13	1	4	54	30	24	37
3 Bottesford Town Res.	18	10	2	6	59	39	20	32
4 Scunthonians Res.	18	9	4	5	54	38	16	31
5 Crowle Town Colts	18	7	4	7	35	38	-3	25
6 Ashby RAOB	18	7	3	8	46	56	-10	24
7 College Wanderers Res. (+3)	18	6	0	12	40	58	-18	21
8 Crosby Colts Res.	18	6	2	10	40	58	-18	20
9 Limestone Rangers Res.	18	3	1	14	29	72	-43	10
10 Scotter United Res.	18	2	3	13	26	59	-33	9

Division Three	P	W	D	L	F	A	GD	Pts
1 Broughton Colts	18	15	2	1	76	23	53	47
2 Bruces Beacon	18	14	1	3	80	28	52	43
3 East Drayton	18	13	3	2	65	22	43	42
4 Six Bells	18	8	3	7	35	33	2	27
5 Epworth Town Res.	18	8	3	7	35	38	-3	27
6 Crosby Colts Juniors	18	8	1	9	67	43	24	25
7 Briggensians	18	5	2	11	49	49	0	17
8 Santon	18	4	1	13	42	107	-65	13
9 Luddington	18	2	3	13	29	78	-49	9
10 Barnetby United Res.	18	1	5	12	19	76	-57	8

SOUTH DEVON LEAGUE

Premier Division	P	W	D	L	F	A	GD	Pts
1 Watcombe Wanderers	24	24	0	0	89	15	74	72
2 Brixham AFC	24	18	2	4	62	25	37	56
3 Upton Athletic	24	16	2	6	94	28	66	50
4 Buckland Athletic 2nd	24	14	4	6	61	30	31	46
5 Ivybridge Town 2nd (-3)	24	12	4	8	59	48	11	37
6 Newton Abbot Spurs 2nd	24	10	4	10	52	44	8	34
7 Stoke Gabriel 2nd	24	8	6	10	42	56	-14	30
8 Waldon Athletic	24	8	4	12	53	60	-7	28
9 Loddiswell Athletic	24	8	4	12	40	54	-14	28
10 Kingskerswell & Chelston (-3)	24	8	3	13	40	55	-15	24
11 Watts Blake & Bearne (-3)	24	8	0	16	35	66	-31	21
12 Kingsteignton Athletic	24	3	3	18	33	77	-44	12
13 Ipplepen Athletic (-3)	24	1	0	23	14	116	-102	0

Division One	P	W	D	L	F	A	GD	Pts
1 Dartmouth AFC	24	20	2	2	118	34	84	62
2 Buckland Athletic 3rd	24	17	3	4	94	29	65	54
3 Bovey Tracey 2nds	24	17	2	5	85	40	45	53
4 East Allington United	24	13	2	9	62	39	23	41
5 Newton Abbot 66	24	13	1	10	55	41	14	40
6 Broadhempston United	24	13	1	10	52	46	6	40
7 Kingskerswell & Chelston 2nd	24	12	3	9	68	54	14	39
8 Buckfastleigh Rangers	24	10	2	12	51	83	-32	32
9 Brixham AFC 2nds	24	8	1	15	37	61	-24	25
10 Totnes & Dartington 2nds	24	8	0	16	38	82	-44	24
11 Teignmouth 2nd (-3)	24	7	4	13	59	69	-10	22
12 Chudleigh Athletic (-3)	24	6	0	18	44	92	-48	15
13 Abbotskerswell (-6)	24	1	1	22	22	115	-93	-2

Division Two	P	W	D	L	F	A	GD	PTS
1 Babbacombe Corinthians	26	20	1	5	100	38	62	61
2 Paignton Villa	26	18	4	4	89	31	58	58
3 Beesands Rovers	26	17	2	7	82	30	52	53
4 Stoke Gabriel 3rds	26	14	6	6	79	31	48	48
5 Newton United (-3)	26	15	1	10	68	57	11	43
6 Harbertonford	26	11	6	9	64	48	16	39
7 Kingsteignton Athletic 2nds (-3)	26	10	5	11	46	58	-12	32
8 Brixham Town	26	9	5	12	53	80	-27	32
9 Foxhole United (-3)	26	10	3	13	82	87	-5	30
10 Paignton Saints	26	7	4	15	50	78	-28	25
11 Hookhills United (-6)	26	9	3	14	60	67	-7	24
12 Brixham AFC 3rds (-3)	26	7	4	15	33	85	-52	22
13 Upton Athletic 2nds (-3)	26	7	3	16	53	90	-37	21
14 Ipplepen Athletic 2nds (-6)	26	4	1	21	27	106	-79	7

Division Three	P	W	D	L	F	A	GD	PTS
1 Buckland & Milber	24	18	0	6	110	40	70	54
2 Watts Blake & Bearne 2nd	24	17	2	5	102	42	60	53
3 South Brent	24	15	4	5	63	40	23	49
4 Ashburton	24	15	3	6	76	33	43	48
5 Waldon Athletic 2nd	24	15	2	7	74	47	27	47
6 Newton Abbot Spurs 3rd	24	15	0	9	61	46	15	45
7 Totnes & Dartington 3rd	24	9	4	11	42	42	0	31
8 Loddiswell Athletic 2nd	24	8	3	13	50	79	-29	27
9 Bishopsteignton United (-3)	24	8	3	13	47	66	-19	24
10 Teign Village	24	7	3	14	34	80	-46	24
11 Chudleigh Athletic 2nds (-3)	24	6	3	15	50	93	-43	18
12 East Allington United 2nd	24	5	1	18	36	86	-50	16
13 Liverton United 2nd (-6)	24	3	2	19	35	86	-51	5

Division Four	P	W	D	L	F	A	GD	PTS
1 Watcombe Wanderers 2nds	24	21	1	2	120	13	107	64
2 Roselands	24	20	1	3	123	25	98	61
3 Dartmouth AFC 2nd	24	12	6	6	80	50	30	42
4 South Brent 2nd	24	13	2	9	73	57	16	41
5 Salcombe Town	24	12	4	8	72	47	25	40
6 Waldon Athletic 3rds (-3)	24	12	5	7	59	45	14	38
7 Harbertonford 2nd (-3)	24	12	3	9	72	61	11	36
8 Dittisham United	24	9	4	11	64	58	6	31
9 Ilsington Villa	24	7	3	14	31	63	-32	24
10 Bovey Tracey 3rds	24	6	3	15	41	112	-71	21
11 Paignton Villa 2nds	24	6	2	16	35	121	-86	20
12 Meadowbrook Athletic	24	4	4	16	28	74	-46	16
13 Paignton Saints 2nds (-3)	24	2	2	20	22	94	-72	5

Division Five	P	W	D	L	F	A	GD	PTS
1 Buckfastleigh Rangers 2nds	26	19	5	2	106	37	69	62
2 Preston South End	26	17	6	3	91	25	66	57
3 AFC Staverton	26	17	6	3	81	39	42	57
4 Newton Rovers	26	16	3	7	64	61	3	51
5 Roselands 2nds	26	11	4	11	76	73	3	37
6 Newton Abbot 66 2nd	26	11	2	13	71	66	5	35
7 Torbay Police	26	9	7	10	59	53	6	34
8 Babbacombe Corinthians 2nd	26	10	4	12	67	62	5	34
9 Polonia Torbay (-3)	26	11	4	11	60	57	3	34
10 Riviera United	26	7	4	15	49	85	-36	25
11 Broadhempston United 2nd	26	7	4	15	45	81	-36	25
12 Newton United 2nd	26	7	1	18	33	67	-34	22
13 Moretonhampstead	26	6	4	16	45	83	-38	22
14 Buckland & Milber 2nds	26	5	4	17	48	106	-58	19

Division Six	P	W	D	L	F	A	GD	PTS
1 Watcombe Wanderers 3rds	24	15	5	4	82	39	43	50
2 Kingsbridge & Kellaton United	24	14	3	7	68	54	14	45
3 Barton Athletic	24	11	2	11	66	65	1	35
4 Malborough United	24	9	3	12	50	43	7	30
5 Ashburton 2nd (-6)	24	9	6	9	62	55	7	27
6 Stoke Fleming & Strete	24	6	7	11	36	66	-30	25
7 Teign Village 2nd	24	5	4	15	36	78	-42	19

SOUTH LONDON ALLIANCE

Premier Division	P	W	D	L	F	A	GD	Pts
1 Lewisham Athletic	24	21	0	3	83	35	48	63
2 House of Praise	24	18	4	2	82	41	41	58
3 Beehive	24	17	3	4	72	37	35	54
4 Johnson & Phillips	24	14	3	7	59	40	19	45
5 Wickham Park	24	13	3	8	76	44	32	42
6 Long Lane 'A'	24	8	6	10	41	55	-14	30
7 Southmere	24	9	2	13	65	59	6	29
8 Southwark Borough	24	7	4	13	41	59	-18	25
9 AFC Parkhurst	24	8	1	15	54	89	-35	25
10 Old Roan Res.	24	7	2	15	49	87	-38	23
11 Chislehurst Dynamoes	24	6	3	15	49	73	-24	21
12 Drummond Athletic	24	5	2	17	39	64	-25	17
13 West Bromley Albion	24	4	5	15	40	67	-27	17

Division One	P	W	D	L	F	A	GD	Pts
1 Red Velvet	20	15	4	1	54	22	32	49
2 Kingfisher Glory	20	11	7	2	50	23	27	40
3 Fleetdown United 'A'	20	11	4	5	46	27	19	37
4 Crayford Arrows	20	9	6	5	44	33	11	33
5 Blackheath Wanderers	20	8	6	6	46	40	6	30
6 Beaverwood	20	7	8	5	39	37	2	29
7 Old Roan Blue	20	5	8	7	33	47	-14	23
8 Long Lane Blue	20	4	6	10	31	42	-11	18
9 Oldsmiths	20	3	5	12	24	44	-20	14
10 Old Bromleians Res.	20	4	2	14	26	57	-31	14
11 Heathfield	20	3	4	13	31	52	-21	13

Division Two	P	W	D	L	F	A	GD	Pts
1 Seven Acre Sports	16	11	2	3	52	24	28	35
2 Lewisham Athletic Res.	16	10	4	2	61	24	37	34
3 Our Lady Seniors	16	9	3	4	59	30	29	30
4 Forest Hill Park Res.	16	6	7	3	33	25	8	25
5 Iron Tugboat City	16	6	4	6	21	40	-19	22
6 Old Colfeians	16	6	3	7	38	38	0	21
7 Meridian Sports and Social	16	4	3	9	28	56	-28	15
8 Parkwood Rangers	16	3	3	10	23	58	-35	12
9 Avery Hill College OB	16	1	3	12	19	39	-20	6

Division Three	P	W	D	L	F	A	GD	Pts
1 Bexley Sports	16	13	1	2	58	22	36	40
2 Farnborough Old Boys Guild 'A'	16	12	3	1	44	18	26	39
3 Johnson & Phillips Res.	16	10	2	4	44	32	12	32
4 Red Velvet Res.	16	10	1	5	54	41	13	31
5 Old Colfeians Res.	16	8	4	4	41	39	2	28
6 New Saints	16	4	3	9	36	53	-17	15
7 Chatterton Town	16	2	2	12	23	37	-14	8
8 Old Bromleians 3	16	2	1	13	28	61	-33	7
9 Crayford Athletic	16	1	3	12	24	49	-25	6

SOUTH YORKSHIRE AMATEUR LEAGUE

Premier Division	P	W	D	L	F	A	GD	Pts
1 Byron House	16	11	4	1	50	21	29	37
2 Millmoor Juniors	16	9	4	3	61	35	26	31
3 Brinsworth Whitehill	16	10	1	5	54	41	13	31
4 Sheffield West End	16	7	3	6	53	47	6	24
5 Sheffield Medics	16	5	6	5	44	30	14	21
6 Sheffield Bankers	16	6	3	7	46	48	-2	21
7 Ardsley Albion	16	6	2	8	39	35	4	20
8 Horse & Groom	16	3	1	12	20	62	-42	10
9 New Bohemians	16	2	2	12	15	63	-48	8

SOUTHAMPTON FOOTBALL LEAGUE

Premier Division	P	W	D	L	F	A	GD	Pts
1 Cadnam United	16	12	2	2	54	18	36	38
2 Comrades	16	12	1	3	56	12	44	37
3 BTC Southampton	16	8	4	4	31	31	0	28
4 Netley Central Sports	16	8	3	5	32	24	8	27
5 Nursling	16	8	1	7	47	42	5	25
6 Bishopstoke WMC	16	6	1	9	36	55	-19	19
7 Southampton University	16	3	5	8	27	35	-8	14
8 AFC Hiltingbury	16	3	1	12	13	55	-42	10
9 Hedge End Town	16	3	0	13	34	58	-24	9

Senior One	P	W	D	L	F	A	GD	Pts
1 AFC Grains	16	14	2	0	59	11	48	44
2 Solent Saints	16	14	1	1	42	13	29	43
3 Burridge AFC	16	7	2	7	31	29	2	23
4 Riverside	16	7	1	8	40	31	9	22
5 QK Soton Res.	16	5	4	7	31	39	-8	19
6 Harefield	16	5	2	9	28	10	18	17
7 Comrades Res.	16	5	2	9	22	36	-14	17
8 BTC Southampton Res.	16	4	2	10	22	46	-24	14
9 Durley Res.	16	2	2	12	11	71	-60	8

Junior One	P	W	D	L	F	A	GD	Pts
1 AFC Gulf Western	16	14	1	1	64	17	47	43
2 Chamberlayne Athletic	16	12	2	2	47	24	23	38
3 Langley Manor	16	8	1	7	31	29	2	25
4 Lowford FC	16	7	2	7	44	41	3	23
5 Compton	16	5	3	8	30	50	-20	18
6 West Totton	16	5	1	10	18	21	-3	16
7 Chandlers Ford	16	4	3	9	29	33	-4	15
8 FC Wellington	16	4	3	9	19	29	-10	15
9 Osborne FC	16	4	2	10	26	64	-38	14

Junior Two	P	W	D	L	F	A	GD	Pts
1 Braishfield	16	11	2	3	43	26	17	35
2 Montefiore Halls	16	9	2	5	39	30	9	29
3 Bishops Waltham Dynamo's	16	7	4	5	36	31	5	25
4 Compton Res	16	6	6	4	34	33	1	24
5 Applewood Joinery	16	7	2	7	47	38	9	23
6 Warsash Wasps	16	5	5	6	26	28	-2	20
7 Botley Village	16	6	2	8	36	43	-7	20
8 Hamble Utd	16	5	0	11	29	42	-13	15
9 London Airways	16	4	1	11	19	38	-19	13

Junior Three	P	W	D	L	F	A	GD	Pts
1 AFC Botley	14	14	0	0	50	4	46	42
2 Capital	14	8	3	3	31	24	7	27
3 Priory Rovers	14	8	2	4	40	35	5	26
4 Wellow	14	4	3	7	29	33	-4	15
5 Inmar	14	4	3	7	31	41	-10	15
6 AFC Phoenix XI	14	3	5	6	28	36	-8	14
7 Otterbourne A	14	3	3	8	27	44	-17	12
8 AFC Testwood	14	2	1	11	23	42	-19	7

Click Back in Time!

Over 37 years of publishing the Non-League Club Directory has filled a room full of information and photographs covering the game we know and love.

What we intend, over time, is to create a website that shares with you everything we have accumulated, which we hope will bring back some fond memories of season's gone by.

A unique look back at how the game has evolved since the 1940s will also make for interesting reading, including league tables from season's gone by.

Log on to **www.non-leagueclubdirectory.co.uk** today and see how many faces from teams gone by you recognise

Junior Four	P	W	D	L	F	A	GD	Pts
1 New Forest FC	16	12	3	1	69	15	54	39
2 Sporting Wessex	16	12	3	1	57	20	37	39
3 Shamblehurst	16	9	4	3	37	28	9	31
4 Athletico Romsey	16	9	3	4	43	15	28	30
5 AFC Station	16	4	4	8	29	44	-15	16
6 Mitre	16	4	1	11	33	70	-37	13
7 Weston City	16	3	4	9	29	67	-38	13
8 AFC Nemesis	16	3	3	10	38	58	-20	12
9 AFC Hiltingbury Res	16	1	5	10	23	41	-18	8

Junior Five	P	W	D	L	F	A	GD	Pts
1 New Forest FC Res.	18	15	0	3	66	26	40	45
2 BTC A	18	13	0	5	74	45	29	39
3 FC White Horse	18	12	1	5	56	35	21	37
4 Thompson FC	18	11	3	4	74	33	41	36
5 Upham Res	18	11	1	6	54	60	-6	34
6 Waltham Wolves	18	7	2	9	27	48	-21	23
7 Shield FC	18	6	0	12	35	68	-33	18
8 Braishfield Res.	18	5	1	12	33	60	-27	16
9 Hamble Utd Res.	18	4	1	13	31	49	-18	13
10 Michelmersh & Timsbury A	18	1	1	16	23	49	-26	4

SOUTHEND BOROUGH COMBINATION

Premier Division	P	W	D	L	F	A	GD	Pts
1 Railway Academicals 1st	16	12	2	2	57	25	32	38
2 Thorpe Athletic	16	11	3	2	60	28	32	36
3 Corinthians 1st	16	8	4	4	44	34	10	28
4 Leigh Town 1st	16	7	5	4	56	30	26	26
5 Shoebury Town 1st	16	7	2	7	47	41	6	23
6 Wakering Wanderers	16	5	2	9	34	42	-8	17
7 Cupids Country Club 1st	16	4	1	11	22	74	-52	13
8 White Ensign A	16	3	3	10	33	58	-25	12
9 Thundersley United 1st	16	1	6	9	26	47	-21	9

Division One	P	W	D	L	F	A	GD	Pts
1 Ashingdon 1st	18	16	1	1	55	17	38	49
2 Christchurch	18	14	3	1	81	23	58	45
3 Corinthians 2nd	18	13	1	4	56	30	26	40
4 Leigh Town 2nd	18	8	2	8	51	39	12	26
5 Rayleigh & Rawreth Sports	17	8	0	9	37	41	-4	24
6 Elmwood	17	7	0	10	39	57	-18	21
7 Earls Hall United 1st	18	6	1	11	46	58	-12	19
8 Barnsford Hurricanes	18	4	3	11	40	57	-17	15
9 Railway Academicals 2nd	18	4	2	12	28	58	-30	14
10 Old Southendian 3rd	18	2	1	15	25	78	-53	7

Division Two	P	W	D	L	F	A	GD	Pts
1 Rochford Town 2nd	14	13	0	1	55	18	37	39
2 Sceptre Elite	14	11	1	2	85	29	56	34
3 Sporting Hadleigh	14	9	1	4	33	20	13	28
4 Weir Sports 1st	14	7	0	7	49	36	13	21
5 Thundersley Rovers	14	5	1	8	29	31	-2	16
6 Shoebury Town 2nd	14	4	1	9	29	45	-16	13
7 Ashingdon 2nd	14	3	1	10	28	51	-23	10
8 Southend Collegians 1st	14	1	1	12	9	87	-78	4

Division Three	P	W	D	L	F	A	GD	Pts
1 Rayford Athletic 1st	16	12	1	3	59	22	37	37
2 B.K.S. Sports 1st	16	11	2	3	40	16	24	35
3 Bridgemarsh	16	11	1	4	48	27	21	34
4 Corinthians 3rd	16	11	0	5	35	32	3	33
5 Earls Hall United 2nd	16	6	1	9	39	42	-3	19
6 Landwick	15	6	1	8	38	53	-15	19
7 Dunton United	16	6	0	10	39	33	6	18
8 Southend Collegians 2nd	15	3	2	10	25	45	-20	11
9 Little Theatre Club	16	1	0	15	26	79	-53	3

Division Four	P	W	D	L	F	A	GD	Pts
1 Thundersley United 2nd	18	15	2	1	65	16	49	47
2 Playfootball Elite	18	15	0	3	85	23	62	45
3 Southend Rangers 1st	18	12	3	3	50	21	29	39
4 Southend Collegians 3rd	18	7	3	8	47	52	-5	24
5 Ashingdon 3rd	18	6	3	9	41	67	-26	21
6 Hullbridge Sports 3rd	18	6	2	10	45	53	-8	20
7 Old Southendian 4th	18	5	3	10	47	48	-1	18
8 Catholic United 3rd	18	6	0	12	47	62	-15	18
9 Cupids Country Club 2nd	18	4	2	12	34	77	-43	14
10 Leigh Town 3rd	18	3	4	11	25	67	-42	13

Division Five	P	W	D	L	F	A	GD	Pts
1 Rochford Town 3rd	20	19	0	1	79	24	55	57
2 Shoebury Town 3rd	20	18	0	2	129	27	102	54
3 Old Southendian 5th	20	12	2	6	63	44	19	38
4 Rayford Athletic 2nd	20	10	2	8	53	61	-8	32
5 Old Leigh Warriors	20	10	1	9	47	57	-10	31
6 Leigh Town 4th	20	9	1	10	43	61	-18	28
7 B.K.S. Sports 2nd	20	9	0	11	38	49	-11	27
8 Westcliff United 1st	20	8	1	11	52	75	-23	25
9 Southend Rangers 2nd	20	3	4	13	48	71	-23	13
10 Southend Collegians 4th	20	4	0	16	40	87	-47	12
11 Blue Boar Sports	20	1	3	16	16	52	-36	6

SOUTHERN AMATEUR LEAGUE

Senior Division One	P	W	D	L	F	A	GD	Pts
1 Old Owens	20	12	4	4	40	22	18	40
2 Winchmore Hill	20	12	2	6	41	20	21	38
3 Old Wilsonians	20	12	2	6	30	24	6	38
4 Alleyn Old Boys	20	11	3	6	44	22	22	36
5 Polytechnic	20	11	2	7	37	29	8	35
6 Nottsborough	20	8	4	8	30	28	2	28
7 Old Salesians	20	7	3	10	25	39	-14	24
8 Civil Service	20	7	2	11	27	33	-6	23
9 West Wickham	20	7	2	11	28	37	-9	23
10 Old Parkonians	20	5	2	13	27	50	-23	17
11 Alexandra Park	20	3	4	13	24	49	-25	13

LEAGUE TABLES

Senior Division Two	P	W	D	L	F	A	GD	Pts
1 Old Garchonians	22	18	4	0	63	12	51	58
2 Merton	22	15	1	6	53	32	21	46
3 Bank of England	22	11	2	9	48	39	9	35
4 BB Eagles	22	10	5	7	51	43	8	35
5 Old Finchleians	22	10	4	8	45	32	13	34
6 Weirside Rangers	22	9	5	8	51	44	7	32
7 Actonians Association	22	8	4	10	43	49	-6	28
8 Crouch End Vampires	22	8	4	10	45	55	-10	28
9 Carshalton	22	8	3	11	35	39	-4	27
10 East Barnet Old Grammarians	22	8	2	12	34	52	-18	26
11 Norsemen	22	5	6	11	38	58	-20	21
12 Broomfield (-3)	22	2	0	20	20	71	-51	3

Senior Division Three	P	W	D	L	F	A	GD	Pts
1 NUFC Oilers	20	16	3	1	76	21	55	51
2 Old Lyonians	20	12	3	5	60	33	27	39
3 HSBC	20	10	5	5	48	31	17	35
4 Southgate Olympic	20	10	2	8	51	51	0	32
5 Old Esthameians	20	9	2	9	46	49	-3	29
6 Lloyds AFC	20	8	3	9	31	37	-6	27
7 Old Westminster Citizens	20	8	3	9	47	58	-11	27
8 Kew Association	20	6	7	7	40	44	-4	25
9 Ibis	20	5	6	9	40	51	-11	21
10 Old Stationers	20	5	3	12	42	61	-19	18
11 South Bank Cuaco	20	1	3	16	24	69	-45	6

SOUTHPORT & DISTRICT LEAGUE

Premier Division	P	W	D	L	F	A	GD	Pts
1 The Herald	16	13	2	1	66	23	43	41
2 Crossens	16	10	3	3	50	29	21	33
3 Southport & Ainsdale Amateurs	16	10	1	5	48	25	23	31
4 Ship	16	9	3	4	42	29	13	30
5 FC Chivas	16	6	3	7	47	50	-3	21
6 Woodale	16	6	1	9	39	46	-7	19
7 Dales	16	5	0	11	29	47	-18	15
8 Ravenwood	16	3	1	12	18	45	-27	10
9 Altcar	16	3	0	13	37	82	-45	9

SPEN VALLEY & DISTRICT LEAGUE

Premier Division	P	W	D	L	F	A	GD	Pts
1 Route 1 Rovers	16	14	0	2	69	24	45	42
2 T.V.R United	16	12	0	4	65	36	29	36
3 Ravensthorpe Bulls	16	9	0	7	64	54	10	27
4 Vision	16	8	2	6	54	63	-9	26
5 BD3 United	16	7	0	9	43	45	-2	21
6 Girlington	16	6	1	9	39	55	-16	19
7 Savile Youth (-1)	16	5	2	9	40	55	-15	16
8 Fairbank United	16	5	0	11	32	52	-20	15
9 Abundant Life Church	16	3	1	12	38	60	-22	10

Division One	P	W	D	L	F	A	GD	Pts
1 Marsh	16	15	1	0	72	20	52	46
2 Savile United	16	11	1	4	48	28	20	34
3 Smokin Aces (-1)	16	10	2	4	45	25	20	31
4 Norfolk	16	6	4	6	45	38	7	22
5 Inter Batley	16	7	1	8	30	46	-16	22
6 Howden Clough	16	6	1	9	41	49	-8	19
7 Savile Town	16	6	1	9	28	46	-18	19
8 George Healey	16	2	2	12	36	37	-1	8
9 Cleckheaton Sporting	16	2	1	13	23	79	-56	7

STRATFORD-UPON-AVON ALLIANCE

Division One	P	W	D	L	F	A	GD	Pts
1 Badsey United	18	16	1	1	74	20	54	49
2 Southam United	18	14	1	3	63	36	27	43
3 Shipston Excelsior	18	11	2	5	49	24	25	35
4 South Redditch Athletic	18	10	2	6	61	33	28	32
5 Broadway United	18	10	1	7	58	37	21	31
6 Alveston	18	9	0	9	58	58	0	27
7 FISSC	18	7	0	11	36	49	-13	21
8 Moreton Rangers	18	4	2	12	27	52	-25	14
9 Coventry Amateurs	18	2	1	15	33	109	-76	7
10 Quinton	18	2	0	16	31	72	-41	6

Division Two	P	W	D	L	F	A	GD	Pts
1 Bidford Boys Club	16	12	0	4	54	26	28	36
2 Henley Forest	16	11	1	4	40	26	14	34
3 AFC Solihull	16	10	2	4	33	25	8	32
4 Inkberrow (-3)	16	9	0	7	38	32	6	24
5 Studley Swan	16	8	0	8	46	47	-1	24
6 Welford on Avon	16	7	1	8	39	41	-2	22
7 Tysoe United	16	5	1	10	48	55	-7	16
8 Astwood Bank	16	4	3	9	40	53	-13	15
9 Kenilworth Town (-6)	16	0	4	12	35	68	-33	-2

Division Three	P	W	D	L	F	A	GD	Pts
1 Badsey Rangers Res.	16	12	2	2	54	21	33	38
2 Wellesbourne	16	11	4	1	61	21	40	37
3 Shipston Excelsior Res.	16	8	3	5	39	32	7	27
4 Red Alert	16	8	1	7	59	42	17	25
5 Mount Pleasant F.C. (-3)	16	8	4	4	40	27	13	25
6 Claverdon AFC	16	7	2	7	53	45	8	23
7 Blockley Sports	16	3	1	12	34	64	-30	10
8 International	16	2	3	11	41	84	-43	9
9 Alcester Town Res. (-3)	16	3	0	13	30	75	-45	6

Division Four	P	W	D	L	F	A	GD	Pts
1 Bromsgove Blades	20	17	1	2	96	31	65	52
2 AFC Solihull Res.	20	13	5	2	76	40	36	44
3 PNT Royal Oak	20	12	5	3	67	47	20	41
4 Inkberrow Colts	20	12	2	6	72	44	28	38
5 Henley Forest Res.	20	9	3	8	40	58	-18	30
6 Harvington C.C. F.C. (-3)	20	7	3	10	61	52	9	21
7 Shipston Excelsior Colts (-3)	20	7	2	11	45	53	-8	20
8 FISSC Res.	20	5	2	13	40	53	-13	17
9 Astwood Bank Res.	20	5	0	15	44	90	-46	15
10 Welford Colts (-6)	20	5	4	11	43	65	-22	13
11 Tysoe United Colts	20	4	1	15	31	82	-51	13

STROUD & DISTRICT LEAGUE

Division One		P	W	D	L	F	A	GD	Pts
1	Avonvale United	22	18	1	3	70	21	49	55
2	Cashes Green	22	13	3	6	55	35	20	42
3	Didmarton	22	11	3	8	42	44	-2	36
4	Old Richians	22	10	5	7	55	41	14	35
5	Randwick	22	10	4	8	43	40	3	34
6	Upton St Leonards	22	9	5	8	40	36	4	32
7	Barnwood United	22	8	4	10	49	47	2	28
8	Kings Stanley Res.	22	8	1	13	38	43	-5	25
9	Whitminster	22	6	4	12	27	44	-17	22
10	Matson	22	5	6	11	42	64	-22	21
11	Tetbury Town	22	5	6	11	25	47	-22	21
12	Slimbridge Res.	22	5	6	11	40	64	-24	21

Division Two		P	W	D	L	F	A	GD	Pts
1	Frampton United Res.	24	22	1	1	100	12	88	67
2	Longlevens Res.	24	17	2	5	69	29	40	53
3	Quedgeley Wanderers Res.	24	17	2	5	52	30	22	53
4	Stonehouse Town Res.	24	14	1	9	57	43	14	43
5	AC Royals	24	10	8	6	48	42	6	38
6	Horsley United	24	12	1	11	47	62	-15	37
7	Kingswood Res.	24	9	4	11	55	57	-2	31
8	Tibberton United	24	6	8	10	46	52	-6	26
9	Taverners Res. (-3)	24	8	4	12	51	55	-4	25
10	AFC Phoenix (-3)	24	8	3	13	44	45	-1	24
11	Dursley Town Res.	24	5	6	13	30	53	-23	21
12	Uley	24	2	2	20	23	100	-77	8
13	Minchinhampton Town (-9)	24	3	4	17	39	81	-42	4

Division Three		P	W	D	L	F	A	GD	Pts
1	Sharpness Res	22	17	2	3	77	34	43	53
2	Tredworth Tigers	22	14	5	3	78	33	45	47
3	Charfield	22	15	2	5	73	38	35	47
4	Stroud Harriers (-3)	22	13	4	5	66	42	24	40
5	Stroud United	22	12	2	8	66	38	28	38
6	Abbeymead Rovers Res. (-6)	22	11	2	9	49	57	-8	29
7	Thornbury Town Res. (-3)	22	9	2	11	37	49	-12	26
8	Cam Bulldogs Res.	22	5	7	10	36	62	-26	22
9	Ramblers Res.	22	6	2	14	47	54	-7	20
10	Tetbury Town Res.	22	4	5	13	31	53	-22	17
11	Eastcombe	22	5	2	15	31	54	-23	17
12	Wotton Rovers Res. (-6)	22	2	3	17	21	100	-79	3

Division Four		P	W	D	L	F	A	GD	Pts
1	Longlevens 3rds	22	19	1	2	90	21	69	58
2	Hardwicke Res.	22	15	4	3	93	32	61	49
3	Bush FC	22	15	3	4	77	28	49	48
4	Arlingham	22	13	1	8	75	60	15	40
5	Nympsfield (-3)	22	10	3	9	58	45	13	30
6	Coaley Rovers	22	9	2	11	64	56	8	29
7	Whitminster Res. (-3)	22	10	2	10	48	62	-14	29
8	Leonard Stanley Res.	22	9	1	12	47	71	-24	28
9	Avonvale United Res.	22	7	1	14	53	69	-16	22
10	Berkeley Town Res. (-3)	22	8	0	14	31	85	-54	21
11	Chalford Res.	22	4	1	17	26	71	-45	13
12	Randwick Res.	22	3	1	18	26	88	-62	10

Division Five		P	W	D	L	F	A	GD	Pts
1	St Nicholas Old Boys (-3)	20	18	2	0	85	7	78	53
2	Minchinhampton	20	13	3	4	51	24	27	42
3	McCadam	20	13	1	6	65	31	34	40
4	Upton St Leonards Res.	20	12	1	7	54	50	4	37
5	Tuffley Rovers 3rds	20	11	1	8	58	47	11	34
6	Old Richians Res.	20	8	4	8	32	35	-3	28
7	Longford Res.	20	8	3	9	38	37	1	27
8	Cotswold Rangers (-3)	20	8	0	12	49	56	-7	21
9	Stonehouse Town 3rds	20	5	2	13	34	63	-29	17
10	Dursley Town 3rds (-3)	20	3	1	16	32	90	-58	7
11	Barnwood United Res.	20	2	0	18	25	83	-58	6

Divison Six		P	W	D	L	F	A	GD	Pts
1	Alkerton Rangers	22	20	0	2	116	28	88	60
2	Frocester	22	17	3	2	100	17	83	54
3	Hardwicke 3rds	22	15	2	5	92	47	45	47
4	Trident	22	14	3	5	81	31	50	45
5	Quedgeley Wanderers 3rds	22	12	3	7	53	40	13	39
6	Cashes Green Res.	22	12	2	8	59	41	18	38
7	Brockworth Albion 3rds	22	10	1	11	53	49	4	31
8	Coaley Rovers Res.	22	6	1	15	34	85	-51	19
9	Horsley United Res. (-9)	22	8	2	12	52	63	-11	17
10	Uley Res.	22	4	1	17	41	116	-75	13
11	Slimbridge 3rds	22	3	3	16	39	99	-60	12
12	Eastcombe Res. (-6)	22	0	1	21	24	128	-104	-5

Division Seven		P	W	D	L	F	A	GD	Pts
1	Hawkesbury Stallions	22	18	3	1	97	25	72	57
2	Rodborough Old Boys	22	15	3	4	98	28	70	48
3	Frampton United 3rds	22	14	5	3	76	22	54	47
4	The Village FC	22	13	4	5	90	43	47	43
5	Wickwar Wanderers Res.	22	12	2	8	62	33	29	38
6	Tuffley Rovers 4ths	22	9	2	11	47	65	-18	29
7	Charfield Res. (-3)	22	9	3	10	56	50	6	27
8	Sharpness 3rds	22	7	5	10	59	53	6	26
9	Avonvale United 3rds (-3)	22	8	4	10	60	62	-2	25
10	Cam Bulldogs 3rds (-3)	22	6	1	15	42	90	-48	16
11	Randwick 3rds (-3)	22	1	3	18	25	171	-146	3
12	Woodchester (-18)	22	2	1	19	31	101	-70	-11

Division Eight	P	W	D	L	F	A	GD	Pts
1 Alkerton Rangers Res.	20	13	3	4	70	34	36	42
2 Tredworth Tigers Res.	20	13	1	6	78	40	38	40
3 Stroud United Res.	20	12	3	5	69	46	23	39
4 Longlevens 4ths	20	11	4	5	55	35	20	37
5 Saintbridge (-3)	20	12	0	8	56	48	8	33
6 Cotswold Rangers Res.	20	9	3	8	67	48	19	30
7 Abbeymead Rovers 3rds	20	9	2	9	42	49	-7	29
8 Chalford 3rds	20	8	2	10	44	58	-14	26
9 Rodborough Old Boys Res.	20	7	4	9	46	50	-4	25
10 Uley 3rds	20	1	3	16	22	105	-83	6
11 Stonehouse Town 4ths (-3)	20	0	5	15	40	76	-36	2

SUBURBAN LEAGUE

Premier Division	P	W	D	L	F	A	GD	Pts
1 Sutton United Res.	18	14	2	2	42	15	27	44
2 Welling United Res.	18	12	0	6	42	37	5	36
3 Woking Res.	18	11	1	6	63	33	30	34
4 Boreham Wood Res.	18	9	2	7	42	31	11	29
5 Metropolitan Police Res.	18	8	4	6	46	34	12	28
6 Tonbridge Angels Res.	18	7	3	8	29	34	-5	24
7 Corinthian-Casuals Res.	18	5	4	9	28	39	-11	19
8 Carshalton Athletic Res.	18	4	3	11	23	37	-14	15
9 Bromley Res.	18	4	3	11	18	50	-32	15
10 Hampton & Richmond Borough Res.	18	4	2	12	18	41	-23	14

North Division	P	W	D	L	F	A	GD	Pts
1 Royston Town Res.	18	11	3	4	52	27	25	36
2 Tring Athletic Res.	18	11	3	4	44	22	22	36
3 Barton Rovers Res.	18	10	3	5	43	25	18	33
4 Dunstable Town Res.	18	10	3	5	41	25	16	33
5 Leighton Town Res.	18	8	2	8	27	38	-11	26
6 Northwood Res.	18	6	5	7	26	36	-10	23
7 Newport Pagnell Town Res.	18	6	4	8	27	44	-17	22
8 Berkhamsted Res.	18	4	3	11	29	36	-7	15
9 Harefield United Res.	18	3	6	9	29	48	-19	15
10 Southall Res.	18	2	6	10	28	45	-17	12

Central Division	P	W	D	L	F	A	GD	Pts
1 Uxbridge Res.	26	21	2	3	93	28	65	65
2 Tooting & Mitcham United Res.	26	18	5	3	92	26	66	59
3 North Greenford United Res.	26	16	3	7	81	37	44	51
4 Hartley Wintney Res.	26	15	4	7	73	51	22	49
5 Walton & Hersham Res.	26	14	6	6	47	33	14	48
6 Westfield Res.	26	13	2	11	74	58	16	41
7 Camberley Town Res.	26	11	4	11	46	60	-14	37
8 Hanworth Villa Res.	26	10	4	12	56	65	-9	34
9 Farnham Town Res.	26	8	6	12	50	58	-8	30
10 Chessington & Hook United Res.	26	9	3	14	54	81	-27	30
11 Ashford Town (Middlesex) Res.	26	8	4	14	38	60	-22	28
12 Molesey Res.	26	6	4	16	46	68	-22	22
13 Knaphill Res.	26	4	4	18	35	86	-51	16
14 Frimley Green Res.	26	3	1	22	29	103	-74	10

South Division	P	W	D	L	F	A	GD	Pts
1 Corinthian	20	14	2	4	82	30	52	44
2 Phoenix Sports	20	13	4	3	54	24	30	43
3 Erith Town	20	11	4	5	41	22	19	37
4 Raynes Park Vale	20	10	7	3	48	32	16	37
5 Lordswood	20	7	7	6	36	26	10	28
6 Horsham YMCA	20	8	4	8	44	51	-7	28
7 South Park	20	6	8	6	38	43	-5	26
8 East Grinstead Town	20	8	1	11	41	40	1	25
9 Chichester City	20	4	5	11	30	49	-19	17
10 Dorking Wanderers	20	4	2	14	34	69	-35	14
11 Lingfield	20	2	2	16	18	80	-62	8

SURREY INTERMEDIATE LEAGUE (WESTERN)

Premier Division	P	W	D	L	F	A	GD	Pts
1 AFC Spelthorne Sports	26	22	3	1	89	23	66	69
2 Godalming & Farncombe Athletic (-1)	26	18	5	3	87	27	60	58
3 Chobham Burymead (-4)	26	17	5	4	89	41	48	52
4 University of Surrey	26	14	3	9	90	56	34	45
5 Milford & Witley	26	10	9	7	48	43	5	39
6 Cranleigh	26	10	6	10	45	60	-15	36
7 Weston Green Sports	26	10	5	11	50	48	2	35
8 Shottermill & Haslemere	26	9	7	10	46	51	-5	34
9 Royal Holloway Old Boys	26	9	4	13	57	84	-27	31
10 Lightwater United	26	8	4	14	56	76	-20	28
11 Tongham	26	7	3	16	47	65	-18	24
12 Chiddingfold	26	6	5	15	47	73	-26	23
13 Bedfont Town	26	5	3	18	41	101	-60	18
14 Worplesdon Phoenix	26	4	4	18	32	76	-44	16

Division One	P	W	D	L	F	A	GD	Pts
1 Laleham	22	19	2	1	102	24	78	59
2 AFC Molesey	22	17	5	0	66	16	50	56
3 Elm Grove Seniors (-3)	22	16	2	4	83	35	48	47
4 Ockham	22	11	3	8	42	37	5	36
5 Farnborough North End	22	9	3	10	41	58	-17	30
6 Woking & Horsell	22	7	5	10	51	48	3	26
7 Knaphill Athletic	22	7	4	11	39	40	-1	25
8 Old Salesians	22	7	4	11	40	55	-15	25
9 Hambledon	22	7	3	12	32	51	-19	24
10 Millmead	22	6	3	13	36	45	-9	21
11 Windlesham United	22	6	1	15	35	80	-45	19
12 Shalford	22	1	3	18	21	99	-78	6

SURREY SOUTH EASTERN COMBINATION

Intermediate Division One	P	W	D	L	F	A	GD	Pts
1 Balham	22	16	4	2	79	37	42	52
2 Project Clapham (+2)	22	15	3	4	66	34	32	50
3 Cheam Village Warriors (-3)	22	14	4	4	51	27	24	43
4 Old Boys Clapham	22	12	4	6	49	31	18	40
5 Trinity	22	9	5	8	44	37	7	32
6 Old Plymouthians	22	7	7	8	40	44	-4	28
7 Old Rutlishians (-3)	22	8	6	8	44	44	0	27
8 Westminster Casuals	22	7	5	10	43	43	0	26
9 South East London	22	8	1	13	36	54	-18	25
10 Crescent Rovers (+3)	22	5	3	14	43	67	-24	21
11 Battersea (+2)	22	3	7	12	44	61	-17	18
12 Oxted & District	22	3	1	18	16	76	-60	10

Intermediate Division Two	P	W	D	L	F	A	GD	Pts
1 St Andrews	20	18	0	2	84	26	58	54
2 Chessington K C	20	17	0	3	88	27	61	51
3 Westside	20	13	1	6	52	28	24	40
4 Tooting & Mitcham Wanderers	20	10	2	8	54	42	12	32
5 Brockham	20	10	0	10	35	50	-15	30
6 AC Malden	20	8	1	11	53	57	-4	25
7 Fulham Deaf	20	7	3	10	36	54	-18	24
8 Sutton High	20	6	2	12	29	54	-25	20
9 Ashtead (+2)	20	4	5	11	21	51	-30	19
10 AFC Walcountians Kinetic (-1)	20	6	1	13	27	72	-45	17
11 UK F F	20	2	3	15	30	48	-18	9

SWINDON & DISTRICT LEAGUE

Premier Division	P	W	D	L	F	A	GD	Pts
1 Fratellos	18	18	0	0	84	23	61	54
2 Queensfield	18	13	0	5	68	32	36	39
3 Village Inn	18	11	2	5	69	45	24	35
4 Old Town United	17	10	1	6	48	33	15	31
5 Spectrum	18	9	2	7	47	53	-6	29
6 Swiss Chalet Rangers	18	7	4	7	43	42	1	25
7 Fox & Hounds	18	5	1	12	34	74	-40	16
8 DJC Marlborough	18	4	1	13	36	55	-19	13
9 Sportz Central	17	4	0	13	41	70	-29	12
10 Kingsdown	18	2	1	15	26	69	-43	7

Division One	P	W	D	L	F	A	GD	Pts
1 Lower Stratton	18	15	1	2	68	22	46	46
2 Swindon Spitfires	18	13	0	5	67	27	40	39
3 Ramsbury	18	10	3	5	50	21	29	33
4 Old Town United Res.	18	9	3	6	58	41	17	30
5 Chiseldon	18	8	4	6	53	39	14	28
6 Motaquip	18	8	3	7	40	18	22	27
7 Redhouse	18	8	2	8	32	63	-31	26
8 Bassett Bulldogs	18	6	0	12	32	49	-17	18
9 Larry's Plaice	18	2	1	15	34	66	-32	7
10 Core Construction	18	2	1	15	21	109	-88	7

TAUNTON & DISTRICT LEAGUE

Division One	P	W	D	L	F	A	GD	Pts
1 Highbridge Town	18	13	1	4	49	16	33	40
2 Locomotives	18	12	1	5	58	29	29	37
3 Bridgwater Sports	18	10	4	4	50	32	18	34
4 Middlezoy Rovers Res.	18	9	0	9	30	30	0	27
5 Sampford Blues	18	8	3	7	37	42	-5	27
6 Porlock (-3)	18	8	2	8	35	37	-2	23
7 Bishops Lydeard Res.	18	5	3	10	21	40	-19	18
8 Staplegrove Res.	18	3	8	7	29	45	-16	17
9 North Petherton	18	4	3	11	28	45	-17	15
10 Alcombe Rovers	18	4	3	11	28	49	-21	15

Division Two	P	W	D	L	F	A	GD	Pts
1 Blagdon Hill	20	16	3	1	70	21	49	51
2 Tone Youth	20	12	3	5	60	35	25	39
3 Wyvern Rangers	20	12	3	5	50	36	14	39
4 Wembdon	20	12	2	6	43	34	9	38
5 Stogursey	20	9	2	9	50	38	12	29
6 Westonzoyland	20	8	4	8	43	40	3	28
7 Minehead Res.	20	8	2	10	39	43	-4	26
8 Nether Stowey	20	5	4	11	20	48	-28	19
9 Dulverton Town	20	5	3	12	31	49	-18	18
10 Watchet Town Res.	20	4	5	11	27	55	-28	17
11 Hamilton Athletic	20	3	1	16	36	70	-34	10

Division Three	P	W	D	L	F	A	GD	Pts
1 The Gallery	18	15	2	1	76	25	51	47
2 Morganians	18	14	3	1	52	27	25	45
3 Milverton Rangers	18	10	3	5	53	34	19	33
4 Galmington Dragons	18	7	4	7	45	46	-1	25
5 Bridgwater Sports Res.	18	6	4	8	30	41	-11	22
6 Alcombe Rovers Res. (-3)	18	8	0	10	42	47	-5	21
7 Wyvern Rangers Guns (-3)	18	7	2	9	39	37	2	20
8 Sydenham Rangers	18	5	4	9	49	42	7	19
9 Redgate	18	4	2	12	30	63	-33	14
10 Highbridge Town Res.	18	2	0	16	22	76	-54	6

Division Four	P	W	D	L	F	A	GD	Pts
1 Sampford Blues Res.	18	12	2	4	48	34	14	38
2 Woolavington	18	11	3	4	60	30	30	36
3 TYFC	18	10	4	4	57	23	34	34
4 Exmoor Rangers	18	9	2	7	43	29	14	29
5 Norton Fitzwarren	18	9	1	8	53	36	17	28
6 Dulverton Town Res.	18	7	5	6	43	43	0	26
7 Porlock Res.	18	8	1	9	48	59	-11	25
8 Williton (-3)	18	5	3	10	29	56	-27	15
9 North Petherton Res.	18	3	5	10	26	46	-20	14
10 Nether Stowey Res.	18	2	2	14	21	72	-51	8

Division Five	P	W	D	L	F	A	GD	Pts
1 Ash Rangers	22	19	3	0	113	21	92	60
2 Wiveliscombe	22	17	1	4	114	53	61	52
3 Staplegrove Colts (-3)	22	15	1	6	83	56	27	43
4 Creech Cougars	22	10	5	7	63	34	29	35
5 Bridgwater Grasshoppers	22	11	2	9	61	66	-5	35
6 Galmington Dragons Res.	22	10	2	10	65	55	10	32
7 Middlezoy Athletic	22	9	5	8	67	60	7	32
8 Morganians Res.	22	8	3	11	47	47	0	27
9 East Bower (-3)	22	9	2	11	60	57	3	26
10 Hamilton Athletic Foxes	22	6	0	16	56	89	-33	18
11 Bridgwater Wolves (-3)	22	5	2	15	57	79	-22	14
12 Norton Fitzwarren Res.	22	0	0	22	15	184	-169	0

THANET & DISTRICT LEAGUE

Division One	P	W	D	L	F	A	GD	Pts
1 AFC Margate	12	8	3	1	41	23	18	27
2 Social Team United	12	7	4	1	44	24	20	25
3 EKC St Lukes	12	7	0	5	59	27	32	21
4 SI United	12	5	4	3	27	22	5	19
5 Trinity	12	5	2	5	31	35	-4	17
6 Westcliff United	12	1	2	9	15	51	-36	5
7 Minster	12	1	1	10	24	59	-35	4

TONBRIDGE & DISTRICT LEAGUE

Premier Division	P	W	D	L	F	A	GD	Pts
1 Pembury	14	11	2	1	42	18	24	35
2 Southborough	13	10	1	2	46	15	31	31
3 Tonbridge Invicta (+2)	14	7	4	3	31	28	3	27
4 Rusthall Res.	14	5	2	7	28	30	-2	17
5 Dowgate (-1)	13	4	2	7	18	28	-10	13
6 Paddock Wood	14	3	4	7	18	37	-19	13
7 Blackham & Ashurst	14	2	5	7	20	33	-13	11
8 Woodlands	14	1	4	9	18	32	-14	7

Division One	P	W	D	L	F	A	GD	Pts
1 Penshurst Park	16	11	3	2	62	28	34	36
2 Southborough Res.	16	10	1	5	49	29	20	31
3 Pembury Res.	16	10	1	5	43	32	11	31
4 Roselands	16	9	3	4	46	30	16	30
5 Yalding & Laddingford	16	8	5	3	61	31	30	29
6 AFC Valour Horsmonden	16	7	2	7	35	35	0	23
7 Capel Sports and Social	16	5	1	10	37	52	-15	16
8 Hawkenbury Res.	16	3	0	13	16	59	-43	9
9 Frant	16	1	0	15	16	69	-53	3

Division Three	P	W	D	L	F	A	GD	Pts
1 Leigh	16	14	0	2	65	17	48	42
2 Tonbridge Athletic	16	12	1	3	74	23	51	37
3 Ashton Prime	16	12	1	3	41	23	18	37
4 FC Revolution	16	11	1	4	67	32	35	34
5 Woodlands Res.	16	7	1	8	55	50	5	22
6 Rusthall 3rd	16	6	1	9	56	45	11	19
7 Paddock Wood Res.	16	5	0	11	31	50	-19	15
8 Hawkenbury 3rd	16	2	1	13	21	75	-54	7
9 Roselands Res.	16	0	0	16	11	106	-95	0

TYNESIDE AMATEUR LEAGUE

Division One	P	W	D	L	F	A	GD	Pts
1 Lindisfarne Custom Planet FC	14	9	1	4	39	23	16	28
2 Newcastle Chemfica Independent Res.	14	8	4	2	31	19	12	28
3 Walker Central Res.	14	8	1	5	34	26	8	25
4 West Jesmond	14	6	3	5	28	22	6	21
5 Wardley	14	5	3	6	29	26	3	18
6 North Shields Athletic Res.	14	5	3	6	25	28	-3	18
7 Gosforth Bohemians Res.	14	3	3	8	29	47	-18	12
8 Heaton Rifles (-3)	14	1	4	9	19	43	-24	4

Division Two	P	W	D	L	F	A	GD	Pts
1 Hazlerigg Victory	18	16	0	2	66	29	37	48
2 Newcastle East End	18	10	3	5	55	33	22	33
3 Ryton & Crawcrook Albion Res.	18	10	3	5	69	49	20	33
4 Stobswood Welfare	18	10	2	6	45	42	3	32
5 New York	18	8	4	6	52	42	10	28
6 Gosforth Bohemians 'A'	18	9	1	8	36	45	-9	28
7 Ponteland United Res.	18	8	3	7	46	51	-5	27
8 Newcastle Medicals (-3)	18	4	2	12	35	53	-18	11
9 North Shields Town	18	2	2	14	19	61	-42	8
10 Tynemouth FC	18	1	4	13	26	44	-18	7

WAKEFIELD & DISTRICT LEAGUE

Premier Division	P	W	D	L	F	A	GD	Pts
1 Rothwell FC	22	20	0	2	113	28	85	60
2 Beechwood Gate (Sat) FC	22	16	2	4	92	34	58	50
3 FC Gawthorpe	22	14	1	7	61	48	13	43
4 Prince of Wales FC (OCR)	22	12	5	5	64	42	22	41
5 Wortley FC	22	10	3	9	61	61	0	33
6 Crofton Sports FC	22	9	4	9	50	54	-4	31
7 Walton FC (-3)	22	7	4	11	55	62	-7	22
8 Fieldhead Hospital (-3)	22	7	4	11	40	55	-15	22
9 Bramley Athletic (-6)	22	8	1	13	46	79	-33	19
10 Garforth WMC AFC (-6)	22	5	5	12	38	67	-29	14
11 Dewsbury Rangers OB	22	2	5	15	39	84	-45	11
12 Eastmoor FC (-6)	22	4	2	16	36	81	-45	8

Division One	P	W	D	L	F	A	GD	Pts
1 Snydale Athletic	16	14	0	2	80	21	59	42
2 Old Bank WMC	16	11	1	4	79	43	36	34
3 Horbury Town (-3)	16	10	1	5	52	31	21	28
4 AFC Ossett	16	9	1	6	56	40	16	28
5 Altofts AFC	16	7	2	7	44	37	7	23
6 Ossett Dynamos	16	4	2	10	34	57	-23	14
7 Featherstone Colliery FC (-3)	16	4	2	10	25	52	-27	11
8 Ossett Two Brewers FC (-6)	16	5	1	10	26	62	-36	10
9 Wakefield City (-6)	16	2	2	12	36	89	-53	2

Division Two	P	W	D	L	F	A	GD	Pts
1 Crackenedge FC	22	16	5	1	96	29	67	53
2 AFC Kettlethorpe	22	17	1	4	85	39	46	52
3 FC Purston Athletic	22	14	5	3	76	39	37	47
4 Stanley United	22	14	3	5	71	45	26	45
5 New Wheel FC	22	14	1	7	72	38	34	43
6 Nostell Miners Welfare	22	7	1	14	39	61	-22	22
7 Durkar FC	22	5	5	12	51	53	-2	20
8 Adwalton AFC (-6)	22	7	2	13	46	70	-24	17
9 Red Lion Alverthorpe FC	22	5	2	15	35	87	-52	17
10 Normanton Woodhouse Hill (-9)	22	7	4	11	60	73	-13	16
11 Overthorpe SC (Wfd)	22	4	3	15	35	83	-48	15
12 Wagon FC (-3)	22	5	2	15	36	85	-49	14

Division Three	P	W	D	L	F	A	GD	Pts
1 Altofts AFC Res.	22	17	3	2	88	42	46	54
2 New Pot Oil	22	16	3	3	110	29	81	51
3 Horbury Athletic	22	16	1	5	68	42	26	49
4 White Rose FC	22	13	5	4	79	40	39	44
5 Waterloo FC	22	9	5	8	62	68	-6	32
6 Swillington Welfare	22	6	9	7	50	59	-9	27
7 Methley United	22	6	5	11	50	60	-10	23
8 Crofton Sports FC Res.	22	5	6	11	36	62	-26	21
9 Henry Boons FC	22	4	7	11	47	61	-14	19
10 Snydale Athletic Res.	22	4	5	13	33	69	-36	17
11 Dewsbury Rangers OB Res.	22	3	6	13	39	82	-43	15
12 Wrenthorpe FC (-3)	22	4	3	15	54	102	-48	12

WENSLEYDALE LEAGUE

Division One	P	W	D	L	F	A	GD	Pts
1 Hawes United	22	18	2	2	90	34	56	56
2 Unicorn FC	22	17	2	3	80	23	57	53
3 Colburn Town	22	16	3	3	112	38	74	51
4 Richmond Mavericks	22	13	3	6	84	42	42	42
5 Richmond Buck Inn	22	12	4	6	80	44	36	40
6 Catterick Garrison Football Centre	22	13	1	8	56	36	20	40
7 Spennithorne & Harmby	22	11	4	7	52	42	10	37
8 Carperby Rovers	22	5	1	16	34	76	-42	16
9 Richmond Town	22	5	0	17	29	69	-40	15
10 Reeth & District Athletic Club	22	3	3	16	27	91	-64	12
11 Askrigg United	22	3	2	17	32	112	-80	11
12 Catterick Rovers	22	3	1	18	36	105	-69	10

WEST END (LONDON) AFA LEAGUE

Premier Division	P	W	D	L	F	A	GD	Pts
1 Earlsberg Eagles	16	12	1	3	38	21	17	37
2 IB Albion	16	9	5	2	53	31	22	32
3 BUOB	16	8	4	4	37	29	8	28
4 North Acton 'A'	16	8	3	5	34	30	4	27
5 Cambridge Heath	16	8	1	7	36	26	10	25
6 Mavericks	16	6	0	10	24	38	-14	18
7 Primrose Hill	16	4	3	9	27	31	-4	15
8 Bishops Park	16	3	4	9	17	31	-14	13
9 Clissold Park Rangers	16	3	1	12	15	44	-29	10

Division One	P	W	D	L	F	A	GD	Pts
1 West London	15	11	4	0	52	19	33	37
2 Spaniards	15	11	2	2	43	26	17	35
3 Viva Capri	15	6	4	5	36	26	10	22
4 London Town	15	5	3	7	27	49	-22	18
5 Atholl 1965	14	3	2	9	26	32	-6	11
6 Primrose Hill 'A'	14	0	1	13	23	55	-32	1

Division Two	P	W	D	L	F	A	GD	Pts
1 Cambridge Heath 'A'	16	12	4	0	38	17	21	40
2 Olympic Waterloo	15	9	1	5	37	28	9	28
3 St Marks	16	8	1	7	41	39	2	25
4 Hub Athletic	16	6	4	6	29	27	2	22
5 Milton Rovers	15	6	3	6	24	25	-1	21
6 Spiders from Mars	15	5	3	7	29	32	-3	18
7 Park Stars	16	5	2	9	16	26	-10	17
8 Clissold Park Rangers 'A'	15	4	4	7	26	39	-13	16
9 Iranian Association Football Club	14	2	2	10	29	36	-7	8

WEST RIDING COUNTY AMATEUR LEAGUE

Premier Division	P	W	D	L	F	A	GD	Pts
1 Ovenden W.R	26	23	1	2	85	26	59	70
2 Bay Athletic	26	21	1	4	76	35	41	64
3 Campion	26	15	3	8	61	46	15	48
4 Storthes Hall	26	14	5	7	74	41	33	47
5 Steeton	26	12	5	9	57	46	11	41
6 Golcar Utd	26	12	5	9	55	49	6	41
7 Kirkburton AFC	26	12	4	10	60	62	-2	40
8 Littletown	26	10	4	12	43	59	-16	34
9 Salts	26	8	6	12	43	58	-15	30
10 Tyersal	26	8	4	14	59	69	-10	28
11 Huddersfield YMCA	26	6	7	13	39	46	-7	25
12 Hall Green United	26	5	3	18	38	80	-42	18
13 Halifax Irish	26	4	4	18	47	83	-36	16
14 Lepton Highlanders	26	4	4	18	45	82	-37	16

Division One	P	W	D	L	F	A	GD	Pts
1 Hunsworth	26	20	1	5	107	46	61	61
2 Lower Hopton	26	18	2	6	98	45	53	56
3 Wakefield City	26	18	2	6	49	23	26	56
4 Ventus/Yeadon Celtic	26	15	4	7	67	46	21	49
5 Wibsey	26	12	3	11	78	66	12	39
6 West Horton	26	11	4	11	60	68	-8	37
7 Westbrook YMCA	26	11	4	11	38	51	-13	37
8 Storthes Hall Res.	26	10	3	13	59	63	-4	33
9 Tingley Athletic	26	10	2	14	57	79	-22	32
10 Overthorpe Sports	26	7	4	15	63	84	-21	30
11 Campion Res.	26	8	6	12	39	49	-10	27
12 Steeton Res.	26	8	3	15	42	71	-29	27
13 Salts AFC Res.	26	6	5	15	45	67	-22	23
14 Bay Athletic Res.	26	5	2	18	44	88	-44	17

Division Two	P	W	D	L	F	A	GD	Pts
1 Dudley Hill Rangers	20	15	3	2	73	27	46	48
2 Dalton Crusaders (Dram)	20	13	4	3	84	35	49	43
3 Thorne FC	20	13	0	8	52	32	20	42
4 Lower Hopton Res.	20	12	0	8	65	45	20	36
5 Kirkburton Res.	20	9	4	7	38	42	-4	31
6 Ovenden Res.	20	9	1	10	51	58	-7	28
7 Tyersal Res.	20	7	2	10	38	46	-8	23
8 Golcar Res.	20	5	7	8	41	54	-13	21
9 Littletown Res.	20	6	3	10	33	50	-17	21
10 Hall Green United Res.	20	4	2	14	25	58	-33	16
11 Bradford FC	20	1	2	17	27	80	-53	5

WEST SUSSEX LEAGUE

Premier Division	P	W	D	L	F	A	GD	Pts
1 BOSHAM	22	15	4	3	68	32	36	49
2 NEWTOWN VILLA	22	14	4	4	76	45	31	46
3 HENFIELD	22	11	2	9	45	44	1	35
4 WEST CHILTINGTON	22	10	4	8	46	33	13	34
5 HOLBROOK	22	9	6	7	53	47	6	33
6 WITTERING UTD	22	8	3	11	34	55	-21	27
7 FAYGATE UTD	22	7	5	10	36	44	-8	26
8 LAVANT	22	7	5	10	40	51	-11	26
9 UPPER BEEDING	22	7	4	11	42	52	-10	25
10 COWFOLD	22	7	4	11	38	49	-11	25
11 HUNSTON COMMUNITY CLUB	22	6	5	11	41	60	-19	23
12 LANCING UTD	22	6	4	12	47	54	-7	22

Division One	P	W	D	L	F	A	GD	Pts
1 PREDATORS	20	17	1	2	63	21	42	52
2 OCKLEY	20	14	2	4	65	22	43	44
3 COWFOLD Res.	20	11	3	6	41	40	1	36
4 PETWORTH	20	9	5	6	53	34	19	32
5 EAST DEAN	20	10	1	9	50	47	3	31
6 SOUTHWATER	20	8	4	8	39	47	-8	28
7 RUDGWICK	20	6	4	10	34	50	-16	22
8 PULBOROUGH	20	6	3	11	25	45	-20	21
9 ALFOLD	20	5	5	10	21	39	-18	20
10 BARNS GREEN	20	4	5	11	16	30	-14	17
11 NEWTOWN VILLA Res.	20	2	3	15	34	66	-32	9

Division Two North	P	W	D	L	F	A	GD	Pts
1 AFC ROFFEY CLUB	20	14	0	6	51	37	14	42
2 PARTRIDGE GREEN	20	13	2	5	68	39	29	41
3 BILLINGSHURST Res.	20	11	2	7	41	39	2	35
4 CAPEL	20	10	4	6	69	38	31	34
5 ASHINGTON ROVERS	20	10	4	6	59	39	20	34
6 WISBOROUGH GREEN	20	10	3	7	57	32	25	33
7 FAYGATE UTD Res.	20	9	2	9	49	52	-3	29
8 NEWDIGATE	20	8	2	10	38	49	-11	26
9 SLINFOLD	20	8	1	11	44	49	-5	25
10 HOLBROOK Res.	20	5	2	13	36	79	-43	17
11 HENFIELD Res.	20	0	2	18	18	77	-59	2

Division Two South	P	W	D	L	F	A	GD	Pts
1 STEDHAM UTD	14	12	1	1	41	17	24	37
2 NYETIMBER PIRATES	14	12	0	2	62	12	50	36
3 ROGATE 08 FC	14	10	1	3	35	23	12	31
4 LODSWORTH	14	4	3	7	30	49	-19	15
5 FITTLEWORTH	14	4	2	8	34	50	-16	14
6 FERNHURST SPORTS	14	4	0	10	28	45	-17	12
7 BOXGROVE	14	3	1	10	22	40	-18	10
8 THE VARDAR VIP FC	14	1	4	9	17	33	-16	7

Division Three North	P	W	D	L	F	A	GD	Pts
1 HORSHAM TRINITY	20	14	4	2	87	30	57	46
2 T D SHIPLEY	20	13	3	4	58	24	34	42
3 UPPER BEEDING Res.	20	13	3	4	59	29	30	42
4 BORDER WANDERERS	20	12	2	6	65	27	38	38
5 BILLINGSHURST THIRDS	20	12	1	7	35	36	-1	37
6 EWHURST	20	10	3	7	38	28	10	33
7 HORSHAM OLYMPIC	20	7	5	8	28	39	-11	26
8 HENFIELD THIRDS	20	6	0	14	36	87	-51	18
9 COWFOLD THIRDS	20	5	1	14	26	49	-23	16
10 ALFOLD Res.	20	3	1	16	31	75	-44	10
11 PULBOROUGH Res.	20	2	3	15	22	61	-39	9

Division Three South	P	W	D	L	F	A	GD	Pts
1 RUSTINGTON PARK SENIORS	18	18	0	0	101	18	83	54
2 FELPHAM COLTS	18	14	0	4	81	40	41	42
3 HARTING	18	11	2	5	53	27	26	35
4 ATHLETICO ARUNDEL	18	9	2	7	40	39	1	29
5 HAMMER UTD	18	7	2	9	40	44	-4	23
6 LANCING UTD Res.	18	7	1	10	49	63	-14	22
7 AMBASSADORS	18	5	5	8	42	52	-10	20
8 HUNSTON COMMUNITY CLUB Res.	18	3	4	11	22	64	-42	13
9 BEAUMONT PARK RANGERS	18	3	3	12	25	49	-24	12
10 YAPTON Res.	18	2	3	13	32	89	-57	9

Division Four North	P	W	D	L	F	A	GD	Pts
1 FC AMBERLEY	18	12	4	2	59	19	40	40
2 SOUTHWATER Res.	18	13	1	4	57	24	33	40
3 HORSHAM BAP & AM	18	11	3	4	46	26	20	36
4 ROWFANT VILLAGE	18	10	3	5	45	46	-1	33
5 HORSHAM SPARROWS MENS FC	18	7	5	6	35	39	-4	26
6 HORSHAM CRUSADERS	18	5	5	8	52	44	8	20
7 HOLBROOK THIRDS	18	5	2	11	47	62	-15	17
8 PLAISTOW	18	4	3	11	31	49	-18	15
9 HORSHAM TRINITY Res.	18	3	5	10	32	66	-34	14
10 NEWDIGATE Res.	18	3	3	12	38	67	-29	12

Division Four South	P	W	D	L	F	A	GD	Pts
1 COAL EXCHANGE	16	14	2	0	69	21	48	44
2 THE CROWN FC	16	12	1	3	79	22	57	37
3 BOSHAM Res.	16	11	2	3	44	32	12	35
4 REAL MILLAND	16	8	2	6	50	37	13	26
5 WHYKE UTD Res.	16	6	2	8	37	42	-5	20
6 BRACKLESHAM	16	5	2	9	38	52	-14	17
7 LAVANT Res.	16	5	1	10	32	52	-20	16
8 TANGMERE	16	3	0	13	19	59	-40	9
9 HARTING Res.	16	1	2	13	16	67	-51	5

Division Five North	P	W	D	L	F	A	GD	Pts
1 CAPEL Res.	20	16	2	2	62	21	41	50
2 RUDGWICK Res.	20	14	2	4	64	28	36	44
3 BILLINGSHURST ATHLETIC	20	10	2	8	46	33	13	32
4 EWHURST Res.	20	9	5	6	32	28	4	32
5 HORSHAM BAP & AM Res.	20	7	8	5	53	40	13	29
6 HOLBROOK FOURTHS	20	8	1	11	38	65	-27	25
7 HORSHAM OLYMPIC Res.	20	6	6	8	42	44	-2	24
8 HORSHAM TRINITY THIRDS	20	6	2	12	42	35	7	20
9 BORDER WANDERERS Res.	20	5	5	10	28	57	-29	20
10 HORSHAM CRUSADERS Res.	20	5	4	11	25	64	-39	19
11 BARNS GREEN Res.	20	4	3	13	43	60	-17	15

Division Five Central	P	W	D	L	F	A	GD	Pts
1 WEST CHILTINGTON Res.	18	12	4	2	68	24	44	40
2 CHAPEL	18	12	2	4	87	40	47	38
3 WISBOROUGH GREEN Res.	18	9	3	6	36	35	1	30
4 WATERSFIELD (-6)	18	10	3	5	69	35	34	27
5 PETWORTH Res.	18	8	2	8	52	50	2	26
6 PARTRIDGE GREEN Res.	18	7	4	7	42	50	-8	25
7 FERNHURST SPORTS Res.	18	8	1	9	42	59	-17	25
8 FITTLEWORTH Res.	18	5	5	8	39	38	1	20
9 THAKEHAM VILLAGE FC	18	3	2	13	20	70	-50	11
10 SLINFOLD Res. (-1)	18	2	2	14	19	73	-54	7

Division Five South	P	W	D	l	F	A	GD	Pts
1 THE UNICORN	18	16	1	1	78	30	48	49
2 PREDATORS Res.	18	14	2	2	64	27	37	44
3 THE NELSON	18	12	3	3	56	30	26	39
4 AJAX TREES FC	18	12	1	5	64	24	40	37
5 FELPHAM COLTS Res.	18	7	2	9	38	67	-29	23
6 ELMER FC	18	6	3	9	36	43	-7	21
7 STEDHAM UTD Res.	18	6	2	10	32	47	-15	20
8 HAMMER UTD Res.	18	4	1	13	35	64	-29	13
9 ROGATE 08 FC Res.	18	3	1	14	19	48	-29	10
10 LODSWORTH Res.	18	0	4	14	15	57	-42	4

WESTMORLAND ASSOCIATION FOOTBALL LEAGUE

Division One	P	W	D	L	F	A	GD	Pts
1 Penrith Res.	22	17	1	4	85	33	52	52
2 Wetheriggs Utd	22	16	2	4	63	21	42	50
3 Kirkoswald	22	14	3	5	75	33	42	45
4 Lunesdale Utd	22	14	1	7	62	43	19	43
5 Kendal Utd	22	12	4	6	63	44	19	40
6 Keswick	22	11	4	7	78	40	38	37
7 Appleby	22	11	4	7	60	44	16	37
8 Carvetii Utd	22	9	1	12	55	66	-11	28
9 Ambleside Utd Res.	22	3	5	14	32	83	-51	14
10 Sedbergh Wanderers (-3)	22	4	4	14	37	76	-39	13
11 Burneside	22	2	3	17	30	104	-74	9
12 Staveley Utd	22	1	4	17	22	75	-53	7

Division Two	P	W	D	L	F	A	GD	Pts
1 Windermere SC	22	14	5	3	62	30	32	47
2 Kendal County Res.	22	12	6	4	53	24	29	42
3 Unisun Athletic	22	12	2	8	51	32	19	38
4 Ibis	22	11	3	8	46	35	11	36
5 Endmoor KGR	22	8	10	4	40	34	6	34
6 Kendal Celtic	22	8	6	8	37	40	-3	30
7 Wetheriggs Utd Res.	22	6	8	8	31	33	-2	26
8 Kirkby Thore Rangers	22	6	5	11	34	42	-8	23
9 Langwathby Utd	22	6	5	11	46	63	-17	23
10 Keswick Res.	22	6	5	11	39	57	-18	23
11 Shap	22	5	6	11	48	65	-17	21
12 Eden Thistle	22	5	5	12	33	65	-32	20

Division Three	P	W	D	L	F	A	GD	Pts
1 Braithwaite	16	15	1	0	65	15	50	46
2 Coniston	16	11	2	3	53	34	19	35
3 Kendal Utd Res.	16	9	1	6	58	34	24	28
4 Windermere SC Res.	16	8	2	6	28	31	-3	26
5 Greystoke	16	6	2	8	47	38	9	20
6 Dent	16	4	3	9	43	44	-1	15
7 Esthwaite Vale	16	4	3	9	25	53	-28	15
8 Kendal Celtic Res.	16	2	4	10	18	52	-34	10
9 Burneside Res.	16	2	4	10	21	57	-36	10

Division Four	P	W	D	l	F	A	GD	Pts
1 Appleby Res.	18	13	3	2	54	26	28	42
2 Lunesdale Utd Res.	18	12	4	2	58	17	41	40
3 Ibis Res.	18	10	3	5	57	37	20	33
4 Carleton Banks	18	9	3	6	48	29	19	30
5 Carvetii Utd Res.	18	9	3	6	62	45	17	30
6 Penrith Academy	18	8	4	6	51	43	8	28
7 Greystoke Res.	18	5	6	7	44	53	-9	21
8 Dent Res.	18	4	5	9	31	64	-33	17
9 Ullswater Utd	18	3	2	13	25	50	-25	11
10 Penrith Saints	18	0	1	17	20	86	-66	1

WIGAN & DISTRICT AMATEUR LEAGUE

Premier Division	P	W	D	L	F	A	GD	Pts
1 Standish St.Wilfrid's	26	18	4	4	81	30	51	58
2 Bel Air	26	17	5	4	68	36	32	56
3 Newburgh Harrock United	26	16	3	7	47	36	11	51
4 Hindley Town	26	14	8	4	61	36	25	50
5 Pemberton	26	14	4	8	65	41	24	46
6 Leigh Phoenix	26	13	3	10	84	66	18	42
7 Leigh Rangers	26	12	2	12	59	61	-2	38
8 Bickerstaffe	26	10	1	15	53	62	-9	31
9 Shevington	26	9	4	13	39	56	-17	31
10 Winstanley St.Aidans	26	9	3	14	47	53	-6	30
11 Ince Central	26	9	2	15	58	87	-29	29
12 Gidlow Athletic	26	8	4	14	47	55	-8	28
13 Atherton Royal	26	6	4	16	47	74	-27	22
14 AFC Scholes	26	2	3	21	35	98	-63	9

Division One	P	W	D	L	F	A	GD	Pts
1 St.Judes	22	16	3	3	56	29	27	51
2 Wigan Rovers	22	13	4	5	59	27	32	43
3 Rainford North End	22	12	7	3	50	30	20	43
4 AFC Tyldesley	22	9	5	8	53	39	14	32
5 Leigh Foundry	22	10	2	10	47	40	7	32
6 Bickerstaffe Res.	22	7	10	5	36	21	15	31
7 Wigan Robin Park Res.	22	8	4	10	46	52	-6	28
8 Boars Head	22	7	6	9	42	55	-13	27
9 Winstanley St.Aidans Res.	22	6	8	8	40	46	-6	26
10 Goose Green United	22	6	5	11	36	49	-13	23
11 Standish St.Wilfrid's Res.	22	5	6	11	32	54	-22	21
12 Leigh Legion	22	2	2	18	23	78	-55	8

Division Two	P	W	D	L	F	A	GD	Pts
1 Digmoor Res	26	21	4	1	103	44	59	67
2 Ormskirk West End	26	18	6	2	105	38	67	60
3 Leigh Foundry Res.	26	18	1	7	87	73	14	55
4 Ormskirk	26	17	3	6	94	70	24	54
5 Hindley Town Res.	26	13	4	9	79	70	9	43
6 Ashton Villa	26	13	3	10	85	74	11	42
7 Pemberton Res.	26	13	2	11	63	57	6	41
8 Punchbowl	26	12	4	10	71	59	12	40
9 Winstanley Warriors	26	10	0	16	59	66	-7	30
10 Springfield	26	9	2	15	72	101	-29	29
11 UpHolland	26	7	1	18	45	73	-28	22
12 Leigh Rangers Res.	26	5	3	18	55	106	-51	18
13 Black Bull (-3)	26	5	1	20	47	92	-45	13
14 A H Leisure	26	2	4	20	56	98	-42	10

Division Three	P	W	D	L	F	A	GD	Pts
1 Hurlston Hall	26	24	2	0	126	19	107	74
2 Atherton George	26	17	5	4	76	39	37	56
3 Astley and Tyldesey	26	16	3	7	75	53	22	51
4 Mitch FC	26	14	5	7	84	63	21	47
5 Atherleigh Athletic	26	11	9	6	78	66	12	42
6 Billinge Community	26	11	6	9	80	65	15	39
7 Old Hawardonians	26	10	7	9	63	69	-6	37
8 Ince Central Res.	26	10	6	10	60	60	0	36
9 Wigan Rovers Res.	26	7	7	12	56	69	-13	28
10 Abram	26	7	5	14	63	81	-18	26
11 Ormskirk Res.	26	7	4	15	47	76	-29	25
12 Gidlow Athletic Res.	26	5	4	17	47	88	-41	19
13 Winstanley Warriors Res.	26	5	3	18	44	93	-49	18
14 Ormskirk Plough	26	3	4	19	52	110	-58	13

WIMBLEDON & DISTRICT LEAGUE

Premier Division	P	W	D	L	F	A	GD	Pts
1 PWCA Wimbledon	22	18	2	2	61	20	41	56
2 Peckham United	22	17	3	2	59	18	41	54
3 Brentnal	22	14	4	4	50	26	24	46
4 Union	22	14	0	8	58	26	32	42
5 UCC Diaspora 1st XI	22	12	5	5	47	37	10	41
6 AFC Battersea	22	10	2	10	42	51	-9	32
7 Barn Elms United	22	9	4	9	47	35	12	31
8 Brentside	22	7	3	12	37	42	-5	24
9 Partizan Wandsworth	22	6	1	15	31	57	-26	19
10 Sporting Duet 1st XI	22	5	2	15	22	60	-38	17
11 AFC Cubo 2nd XI	22	5	1	16	30	56	-26	16
12 Durban United	22	1	1	20	15	71	-56	4

Division One	P	W	D	L	F	A	GD	Pts
1 Goldfingers	21	16	3	2	43	21	22	51
2 Kiwi	22	16	2	4	49	32	17	50
3 Imperial College Old Boys Res.	22	11	5	6	54	35	19	38
4 Putney Saint-Germain FC	20	10	4	6	49	34	15	34
5 South Wimbledon Dazzlers	22	10	3	9	44	30	14	33
6 Claremont	21	8	4	9	42	40	2	28
7 Merchant	22	6	6	10	29	47	-18	24
8 Wadham College Old Boys	22	5	8	9	33	50	-17	23
9 Mint Green Army Veterans	22	6	4	12	37	49	-12	22
10 Croydon Red Star	22	6	3	13	26	40	-14	21
11 Northern Town	22	4	5	13	38	59	-21	17
12 London XI (-6)	22	5	7	10	44	51	-7	16

Division Two	P	W	D	L	F	A	GD	Pts
1 FC Porto of London	16	12	2	2	57	20	37	38
2 UCC Diaspora 2nd XI	16	11	3	2	40	32	8	36
3 Boca Seniors	16	10	2	4	49	30	19	32
4 Balham Rangers	16	7	1	8	33	33	0	22
5 Inter Old Boys	16	7	1	8	42	45	-3	22
6 Rivelino Orient	16	6	2	8	34	24	10	20
7 South London Football Network 1st XI	16	5	3	8	47	39	8	18
8 South East London 2nd XI	16	3	1	12	21	50	-29	10
9 Sporting Duet 2nd XI	16	3	1	12	24	74	-50	10

Division Three		P	W	D	L	F	A	GD	Pts
1	London Box Sash FC	16	11	3	2	60	20	40	36
2	Ocean	16	11	2	3	59	33	26	35
3	FC Lokomotiv Lavender	16	10	3	3	42	26	16	33
4	Putney Ferrets	16	8	3	5	34	22	12	27
5	Clapham Cosmos	16	7	4	5	41	26	15	25
6	Battersea Lions	16	5	2	9	24	33	-9	17
7	UCC Diaspora 3rd XI	16	3	6	7	28	38	-10	15
8	Wimbledon Saints FC	16	2	3	11	15	37	-22	9
9	South London Football Network 2nd XI	16	1	2	13	8	76	-68	5

WORTHING & DISTRICT LEAGUE

Premier Division		P	W	D	L	F	A	GD	Pts
1	Worthing Leisure	14	10	2	2	44	23	21	32
2	Sompting (-1)	14	9	1	4	46	23	23	27
3	Worthing BCOB	14	6	5	3	40	28	12	23
4	KSG Chaplain Athletic (+2)	14	5	5	4	36	33	3	22
5	Goring Cricket Club	14	6	2	6	44	33	11	20
6	L&S Athletic	14	6	2	6	36	29	7	20
7	Broadwater Athletic	14	3	1	10	26	57	-31	10
8	Worthing Town	14	2	0	12	22	68	-46	6

Division One		P	W	D	L	F	A	GD	Pts
1	George & Dragon	22	18	1	3	77	27	50	55
2	Worthing Leisure Res	22	14	3	5	76	34	42	45
3	KSG Chaplain Ahtletic Res. (+3)	22	13	3	6	66	38	28	45
4	Del United	22	10	4	8	56	59	-3	34
5	Real Rustington (+3)	22	8	5	9	41	51	-10	32
6	Sompting Res.	22	9	4	9	45	52	-7	31
7	Maybridge	22	8	3	11	32	44	-12	27
8	Worthing Albion	22	8	2	12	42	50	-8	26
9	AFC Boundstone	22	7	2	13	36	68	-32	23
10	St Marys	22	6	3	13	29	53	-24	21
11	AFC Broadwater	22	6	3	13	39	66	-27	21
12	Angmering (-6)	22	8	1	13	37	34	3	19

Division Two		P	W	D	L	F	A	GD	Pts
1	Broadwater Cricket Club	20	14	2	4	61	30	31	44
2	AFC Romans	20	14	1	5	62	25	37	43
3	Worthing BCOB Res.	20	13	3	4	69	37	32	42
4	Goring Cricket Club Res.	20	12	2	6	70	50	20	38
5	Northbrook	20	11	0	9	54	48	6	33
6	Adur Athletic	20	9	3	8	40	43	-3	30
7	Goring St Theresa's	19	8	2	9	35	45	-10	26
8	Worthing Town Res.	20	7	3	10	52	50	2	24
9	West Tarring	19	7	0	12	33	62	-29	21
10	Worthing Rebels	20	3	0	17	39	75	-36	9
11	MBS United	20	3	0	17	20	70	-50	9

WYCOMBE & DISTRICT LEAGUE

Senior Division		P	W	D	L	F	A	GD	Pts
1	Stokenchurch	16	11	3	2	51	23	28	36
2	Great Missenden	16	11	1	4	66	33	33	34
3	AFC Spartans	16	10	2	4	52	39	13	32
4	Hambleden	16	10	1	5	51	33	18	31
5	Prestwood	16	6	3	7	41	45	-4	21
6	Penn & Tylers Green 'A'	16	5	5	6	46	52	-6	20
7	FC Titans	16	4	3	9	31	40	-9	15
8	Lane End	16	2	3	11	27	55	-28	9
9	Hazlemere Sports	16	1	3	12	23	68	-45	6

Premier Division		P	W	D	L	F	A	GD	Pts
1	Wycombe Athletic	21	16	4	1	72	26	46	52
2	Lane End Res.	21	10	7	4	57	45	12	37
3	AFC Amersham	21	10	3	8	42	41	1	33
4	Wizards	21	8	6	7	51	45	6	30
5	Hazlemere Sports Res.	21	7	8	6	42	37	5	29
6	FC Oakridge	21	5	4	12	32	46	-14	19
7	Chinnor 'A'	21	5	4	12	37	68	-31	19
8	Prestwood Res.	21	4	2	15	35	60	-25	14

Division One	P	W	D	L	F	A	GD	Pts
Hambleden Res.	21	16	2	3	62	25	37	50
Wycombe Athletic Res.	21	11	6	4	74	54	20	39
Walters Leisure	21	11	2	8	52	41	11	35
Hazlemere Sports 'A'	21	10	5	6	49	42	7	35
Stokenchurch Res.	21	8	3	10	43	41	2	27
Chinnor 'B'	21	7	4	10	36	47	-11	25
Flackwell Heath Dragons	21	4	2	15	30	71	-41	14
FC Leisure	21	3	4	14	41	66	-25	13

NORTHERN IRELAND TABLES 2013-14

IRELAND FOOTBALL ASSOCIATION

Premiership	P	W	D	L	F	A	GD	PTS
1 Cliftonville	38	26	7	5	88	39	49	85
2 Linfield	38	24	7	7	81	46	35	79
3 Crusaders	38	18	12	8	67	42	25	66
4 Portadown	38	18	8	12	77	53	24	62
5 Glentoran	38	16	11	11	54	42	12	59
6 Glenavon	38	15	6	17	75	79	-4	51
7 Ballymena United	38	13	8	17	48	59	-11	47
8 Dungannon Swifts	38	12	8	18	49	66	-17	44
9 Coleraine	38	10	12	16	51	61	-10	42
10 Ballinamallard United	38	10	9	19	35	70	-35	39
11 Warrenpoint Town	38	10	6	22	43	72	-29	36
12 Ards	38	6	6	26	44	83	-39	24

Championship One	P	W	D	L	F	A	GD	PTS
1 Institute	26	15	9	2	72	35	37	54
2 Bangor	26	16	5	5	65	39	26	53
3 Knockbreda	26	14	4	8	57	36	21	46
4 Dundela	26	14	4	8	65	47	18	46
5 Carrick Rangers	26	14	4	8	52	34	18	46
6 HW Welders	26	11	8	7	46	34	12	41
7 Ballyclare Comrades	26	10	4	12	53	50	3	34
8 Loughgall	26	9	6	11	48	56	-8	33
9 Larne	26	9	5	12	32	47	-15	32
10 Lisburn Distillery	26	8	7	11	43	49	-6	31
11 Donegal Celtic	26	8	5	13	41	55	-14	29
12 Dergview	26	6	8	12	30	46	-16	26
13 Coagh United	26	5	6	15	38	74	-36	21
14 Limavady United	26	4	3	19	19	59	-40	15

Championship Two	P	W	D	L	F	A	GD	PTS
1 Armagh City	30	25	2	3	90	26	64	77
2 PSNI	30	20	6	4	84	28	56	66
3 Queens University	30	19	6	5	47	32	15	63
4 Newington YC	30	15	9	6	56	32	24	54
5 Annagh United	30	15	7	8	75	53	22	52
6 Banbridge Town	30	16	2	12	60	44	16	50
7 Moyola Park	30	14	4	12	61	53	8	46
8 Portstewart	30	12	7	11	52	46	6	43
9 Ballymoney United	30	11	6	13	61	59	2	39
10 Tobermore United	30	10	4	16	47	63	-16	34
11 Glebe Rangers	30	10	3	17	48	64	-16	33
12 Lurgan Celtic	30	9	6	15	41	67	-26	33
13 Wakehurst	30	7	6	17	47	75	-28	27
14 Chimney Corner	30	7	2	21	38	75	-37	23
15 Sport	30	5	7	18	37	70	-33	22
16 Killymoon Rangers	30	5	3	22	33	90	-57	18

BALLYMENA & PROVINCIAL LEAGUE

Premier Division	P	W	D	L	F	A	GD	Pts
1 Brantwood	16	12	3	1	64	23	41	39
2 Desertmartin	16	9	5	2	50	25	25	32
3 Newtowne	16	8	4	4	43	28	15	28
4 Ballynure OB	16	8	3	5	38	27	11	27
5 Dunloy	16	8	3	5	45	35	10	27
6 Rathcoole	16	6	3	7	43	37	6	21
7 Magherafelt Sky Blues	16	6	1	9	35	39	-4	19
8 FC Ballynure	16	4	0	12	17	63	-46	12
9 Carniny Amateurs	16	0	0	16	13	71	-58	0

Junior Division One	P	W	D	L	F	A	GD	Pts
1 Ballyclare Comrades Reserves	18	14	3	1	75	27	48	45
2 Castle Star	18	12	4	2	75	38	37	40
3 Desertmartin Swifts	18	10	3	5	50	41	9	33
4 Antrim Rovers	18	9	5	4	51	31	20	32
5 Woodlands	18	7	5	6	45	52	-7	26
6 Mallusk Athletic	18	7	4	7	53	41	12	25
7 Magherafelt Sky Blues Reserves	18	5	3	10	33	72	-39	18
8 Cookstown Olympic	18	2	5	11	34	54	-20	11
9 Carnmoney FC	18	3	2	13	41	65	-24	11
10 Killymoon Rangers II	18	3	2	13	30	66	-36	11

Junior Division Two	P	W	D	L	F	A	GD	Pts
1 Cookstown Royal British Legion	20	13	4	3	79	34	45	43
2 Ballysillan Swifts	20	11	7	2	59	26	33	40
3 FC Whiteabbey	20	11	5	4	68	39	29	38
4 Moyola Park Olympic	20	11	4	5	63	50	13	37
5 Ballyclare North End	20	10	2	8	52	43	9	32
6 Sport & Leisure II	20	9	4	7	48	45	3	31
7 AFC Carrickfergus	20	8	5	7	54	50	4	29
8 Remo FC	20	8	4	8	42	45	-3	28
9 Ballynure OB B	20	4	1	15	38	82	-44	13
10 FC Larne	20	4	0	16	27	69	-42	12
11 FC Ballynure Reserves	20	2	2	16	19	66	-47	8

Junior Division Three	P	W	D	L	F	A	GD	Pts
1 Rathcoole Reserves	21	15	2	4	82	30	52	47
2 Wakehurst Strollers	21	14	4	3	70	16	54	46
3 Brantwood Reserves	21	14	2	5	94	44	50	44
4 Newington YC II	21	13	2	6	73	39	34	41
5 Red Star (Carrick)	21	9	0	12	57	68	-11	27
6 Clough Rangers Athletic	21	7	1	13	51	65	-14	22
7 1st Carrickfergus Old Boys	21	4	1	16	25	129	-104	13
8 Carrick Swifts	21	1	2	18	18	80	-62	5

NORTHERN IRELAND FOOTBALL

Junior Division Four	P	W	D	L	F	A	GD	Pts
1 Krag Albion	21	18	1	2	82	22	60	55
2 Ballysillan Swifts Reserves	21	14	4	3	71	34	37	46
3 Mallusk Athletic Reserves	21	11	3	7	68	47	21	36
4 Monkstown FC	21	9	3	9	59	47	12	30
5 Mountainview FC	21	8	3	10	69	55	14	27
6 3rd Ballyclare OB	21	6	1	14	42	92	-50	19
7 Glengormley United	21	5	3	13	27	59	-32	18
8 Carnlough Swifts II	21	4	0	17	36	99	-63	12

MID ULSTER LEAGUE

Intermediate A	P	W	D	L	F	A	GD	Pts
1 Dollingstown	24	20	2	2	101	22	79	62
2 Tandragee Rovers	24	17	5	2	78	30	48	56
3 Ballymacash Rangers	24	17	3	4	55	31	24	54
4 Broomhill	24	13	3	8	68	49	19	42
5 Camlough Rovers	24	13	2	9	69	47	22	41
6 Fivemiletown United	24	12	2	10	60	57	3	38
7 Lower Maze	24	11	2	11	76	60	16	35
8 Banbridge Rangers	24	8	5	11	54	54	0	29
9 AFC Craigavon	24	9	2	13	42	62	-20	29
10 Crewe United	24	6	7	11	43	63	-20	25
11 Lisanally Rangers	24	5	3	16	45	78	-33	18
12 Seapatrick	24	3	3	18	24	75	-51	12
13 Markethill Swifts	24	1	3	20	21	108	-87	6

Intermediate B	P	W	D	L	F	A	GD	Pts
1 Newry City AFC	26	22	3	1	88	17	71	69
2 St Marys	26	17	6	3	83	26	57	57
3 Valley Rangers	26	18	2	6	96	34	62	56
4 Moneyslane	26	17	2	7	71	32	39	53
5 Hanover	26	16	4	6	64	31	33	52
6 Dungannon Tigers	26	15	5	6	60	34	26	50
7 Laurelvale	26	9	7	10	58	50	8	34
8 Bourneview Mill	26	11	1	14	60	58	2	34
9 Oxford Sunnyside	26	9	3	12	38	58	-20	30
10 Lurgan Town	26	6	8	12	36	51	-15	26
11 Richhill	26	5	6	15	32	87	-55	21
12 Broomhedge	26	5	1	19	36	86	-50	16
13 Seagoe	26	3	6	16	34	79	-45	15
14 Banbridge AFC	26	0	0	26	14	127	-113	0

Division One	P	W	D	L	F	A	GD	Pts
1 Hill Street	22	16	5	1	79	31	48	53
2 Silverwood United	22	16	3	3	94	34	60	51
3 Ambassadors	22	12	4	6	62	34	28	40
4 Armagh Rovers	22	10	6	6	54	48	6	36
5 Scarva Rangers	22	10	5	7	51	40	11	35
6 Coalisland Athletic	22	10	3	9	51	52	-1	33
7 Derryhirk United	22	9	4	9	36	51	-15	31
8 Lurgan Institute	22	7	4	11	39	54	-15	25
9 Riverdale	22	8	1	13	42	59	-17	25
10 Ballyoran	22	7	2	13	44	54	-10	23
11 Dungannon Rovers	22	4	4	14	28	50	-22	16
12 Gilford Crusaders	22	2	1	19	29	102	-73	7

Division Two	P	W	D	L	F	A	GD	Pts
1 Tullyvallen	22	14	4	4	58	41	17	46
2 Red Star	22	13	4	5	65	40	25	43
3 Armagh Celtic	22	9	6	7	51	36	15	33
4 Portadown BBOB	22	9	5	7	39	35	4	32
5 Celtic Club (Lurgan No 1)	22	11	2	4	37	22	15	31
6 Lurgan BBOB	22	8	4	9	45	56	-11	28
7 Craigavon City	22	5	7	9	36	52	-16	20
8 Donaghmore	22	13	2	6	22	29	-7	19
9 Keady Celtic	22	5	4	12	33	48	-15	19
10 Glenavy	22	5	4	12	42	59	-17	19
11 Tullygally	22	5	3	14	33	64	-31	18
12 Stranmillis	22	5	3	13	18	57	-39	14

Division Three	P	W	D	L	F	A	GD	Pts
1 Cookstown Celtic	20	15	5	0	63	11	52	50
2 Sandy Hill	20	14	3	3	61	23	38	45
3 Rectory Rangers	20	13	2	5	62	26	36	41
4 White City	20	12	3	5	58	29	29	39
5 Lurgan United	20	10	2	8	50	39	11	32
6 Mowhan United	20	9	4	7	44	45	-1	31
7 Donacloney	20	7	2	11	37	45	-8	23
8 Santos FC	20	5	2	13	22	53	-31	17
9 Moira Albion	20	4	1	15	33	78	-45	13
10 Glenanne United	20	4	3	13	19	60	-41	11
11 Armagh Blues	20	1	5	14	21	70	-49	8

Division Four	P	W	D	L	F	A	GD	Pts
1 Knockmenagh Swifts	18	12	3	3	55	31	24	39
2 Goodyear	18	10	5	3	53	40	13	35
3 Hillsborough Boys	18	9	2	7	49	39	10	29
4 Union Lusa FC	18	8	3	7	65	47	18	27
5 Castlecaulfield	18	9	2	7	51	39	12	26
6 The Dons	18	7	4	7	40	48	-8	25
7 Lurgan Thistle	18	7	2	9	48	49	-1	23
8 Damolly	18	6	4	8	44	40	4	22
9 Newmills	18	5	4	9	53	48	5	19
10 Aghalee Village	18	1	3	14	33	113	-80	6

NORTHERN AMATEUR LEAGUE

Premier Division	P	W	D	L	F	A	GD	Pts
1 Drumaness Mills	26	17	4	5	55	32	23	55
2 Crumlin Star	26	16	4	6	58	30	28	52
3 Kilmore Rec	26	15	6	5	62	34	28	51
4 Ards Rangers	26	16	1	9	68	38	30	49
5 Nortel	26	15	3	8	50	48	2	48
6 Albert Foundry F.C.	26	11	4	11	66	49	17	37
7 Shankill United	26	9	9	8	51	47	4	36
8 Islandmagee	26	10	4	12	55	53	2	34
9 Malachians	26	10	4	12	46	56	-10	34
10 Ardglass	26	9	5	12	52	56	-4	32
11 Comber Rec F.C.	26	9	5	12	40	50	-10	32
12 Killyleagh Y.C	26	9	4	13	36	47	-11	31
13 Dunmurry Rec	26	7	2	17	38	59	-21	23
14 Dromara Village	26	0	3	23	22	100	-78	3

Division One A		P	W	D	L	F	A	GD	Pts
1	Derriaghy C C	26	18	6	2	54	21	33	60
2	Immaculata F.C. (-9)	25	22	2	1	103	27	76	59
3	Downpatrick F.C.	26	15	3	8	73	57	16	48
4	Crumlin United	26	13	6	7	45	42	3	45
5	University of Ulster at Jordanstown	26	12	7	7	38	36	2	43
6	Rathfriland Rangers	26	11	6	9	56	47	9	39
7	Larne Tech O.B. (-9)	25	12	7	6	57	45	12	34
8	Dundonald	26	9	7	10	50	43	7	34
9	Orangefield Old Boys	26	10	4	12	52	47	5	34
10	Barn United	26	7	8	11	62	66	-4	29
11	Abbey Villa	26	7	6	13	27	47	-20	27
12	Rosario Y.C.	26	5	6	15	28	60	-32	21
13	Wellington Rec	26	2	3	21	19	64	-45	9
14	East Belfast	26	1	3	22	28	90	-62	6

Division One B		P	W	D	L	F	A	GD	Pts
1	St Patricks Y.M. F.C.	26	21	0	5	77	36	41	63
2	Lisburn Rangers	26	20	2	4	83	29	54	62
3	Newcastle	26	16	2	8	77	59	18	50
4	1st Bangor Old Boys	26	15	4	7	72	44	28	49
5	Dunmurry Y. M. (-3)	25	16	1	8	76	47	29	46
6	Rathfern Rangers	26	13	2	11	69	60	9	41
7	Sirocco Wks (-3)	25	12	5	8	50	43	7	38
8	Ballynahinch United	26	9	6	11	37	47	-10	33
9	Ballywalter Rec. F.C. (-3)	26	9	5	12	62	69	-7	29
10	Bloomfield F.C.	26	8	2	16	60	64	-4	26
11	Grove United	26	7	5	14	51	66	-15	26
12	Downshire YM	26	3	10	13	46	64	-18	19
13	Saintfield United	26	3	4	19	41	103	-62	13
14	Holywood F.C.	26	3	4	19	30	100	-70	13

Division One C		P	W	D	L	F	A	GD	Pts
1	Portaferry Rovers	28	19	4	5	90	34	56	61
2	Ballynahinch Olympic	28	19	4	5	78	33	45	61
3	Colin Valley F.C.	28	18	4	6	72	32	40	58
4	Bangor Amateurs F.C.	28	17	6	5	82	36	46	57
5	Donard Hospital	28	16	1	11	74	46	28	49
6	Bryansburn Rangers	28	15	3	10	65	45	20	48
7	Shorts FC	28	14	3	11	60	56	4	45
8	Bangor Swifts	28	13	3	12	62	53	9	42
9	Iveagh United	28	11	5	12	63	65	-2	38
10	Groomsport	28	9	7	12	60	67	-7	34
11	18th Newtownabbey O.B.	28	9	5	14	59	68	-9	32
12	Mossley F.C.	28	7	7	14	58	71	-13	28
13	Newington Rangers	28	8	3	17	39	73	-34	27
14	Dromore Amateurs	28	6	2	20	43	87	-44	20
15	Kilroot Recreation	28	0	1	27	18	157	-139	1

Division Two A		P	W	D	L	GF	GA	GD	Pts
1	Woodvale F.C.	20	13	5	2	64	29	35	44
2	Rosemount Rec	20	13	3	4	55	31	24	42
3	Suffolk F.C.	20	11	3	6	38	29	9	36
4	Kelvin Old Boys	20	8	8	4	53	42	11	32
5	Ford	20	9	4	7	37	37	0	31
6	St Oliver Plunkett F.C.	20	7	6	7	38	41	-3	27
7	Greencastle Rovers F.C.	20	6	5	9	35	34	1	23
8	Kircubbin F.C.	20	5	6	9	27	30	-3	21
9	Queens Grads.	20	6	1	13	35	54	-19	19
10	Bangor Rangers	20	5	4	11	30	54	-24	19
11	Queens University 11's	20	3	3	14	36	67	-31	12

Division Two B		P	W	D	L	F	A	GD	Pts
1	Tullycarnet FC	22	19	1	2	89	23	66	58
2	St Lukes F.C.	22	15	4	3	85	26	59	49
3	Bangor Y.M.	22	14	2	6	53	29	24	44
4	Portavogie Rangers F.C.	22	12	5	5	66	33	33	41
5	Newtownbreda F C	22	9	7	6	54	36	18	34
6	Ardoyne WMC	22	10	4	8	54	49	5	34
7	Grange Rangers	22	9	4	9	40	34	6	31
8	Civil Service	22	6	5	11	43	49	-6	23
9	Temple Rangers F.C.	22	6	5	11	31	54	-23	23
10	Whitehead Eagles	22	4	4	14	38	70	-32	16
11	Drumbo F.C.	22	4	4	14	35	89	-54	16
12	Rooftop	22	1	1	20	14	110	-96	4

Division Two C		P	W	D	L	F	A	GD	Pts
1	Basement FC	18	15	1	2	79	21	58	46
2	Greenisland F.C.	18	13	4	1	57	20	37	43
3	Suffolk Swifts	18	10	6	2	45	32	13	36
4	Lower Shankill FC	18	9	4	5	45	26	19	31
5	St Teresas Y.C.	18	9	2	7	49	40	9	29
6	Carryduff F.C.	18	8	2	8	51	39	12	26
7	Finaghy F.C.	18	6	3	9	36	41	-5	21
8	Donaghadee F.C.	18	4	2	12	27	63	-36	14
9	Wesley F.C.	18	2	0	16	14	65	-51	6
10	4th Newtownabbey F.C.	18	1	2	15	23	79	-56	5

Division Three A		P	W	D	L	F	A	GD	Pts
1	Albert Foundry F.C.11's	24	21	0	3	74	26	48	63
2	Immaculata F.C.11's	24	12	5	7	64	44	20	41
3	Crumlin Star 11's	24	12	4	8	75	39	36	40
4	U.U.Jordanstown 11's	24	10	6	8	46	37	9	36
5	Orangefield O.B. 11's	24	11	3	10	41	35	6	36
6	Comber Rec F.C.11's	24	10	5	9	50	44	6	35
7	Ards Rangers 11's	24	9	8	7	35	36	-1	35
8	Rathfern Rgs 11's	24	10	4	10	53	53	0	34
9	Derriaghy CC 11's	24	6	8	10	37	47	-10	26
10	Rosario Y.C. 11's	24	7	5	12	46	65	-19	26
11	Killyleagh Y.C. 11's	24	7	5	12	46	71	-25	26
12	Dunmurry Rec 11's	24	6	3	15	32	80	-48	21
13	Malachians 11's	24	5	4	15	40	62	-22	19

Division Three B	P	W	D	L	F	A	GD	Pts
1 St Patricks YM 11's	22	18	2	2	73	26	47	56
2 Nortel 11's	22	13	2	7	70	41	29	41
3 Bloomfield F.C.11's	22	12	3	7	53	45	8	39
4 Barn Utd 11's	22	10	6	6	59	38	21	36
5 Shankill Utd. 11's	22	10	6	6	57	42	15	36
6 Crumlin Utd 11's	22	11	2	9	57	51	6	35
7 Sirocco Wks 11's (-3)	22	9	5	8	53	51	2	29
8 Larne Tech O.B. 11's	22	7	6	9	41	43	-2	27
9 Islandmagee 11's	22	6	3	13	36	68	-32	21
10 Lisburn Rgs 11's	22	6	2	14	53	59	-6	20
11 Grove Utd 11's	22	5	3	14	30	64	-34	18
12 Dromara Village 11's	22	4	2	16	22	76	-54	14

Division Three C	P	W	D	L	F	A	GD	Pts
1 Woodvale F.C.11's	26	20	5	1	101	32	69	65
2 Bangor Swifts 11's	26	18	4	4	76	34	42	58
3 Dundonald 11's	26	18	3	5	110	41	69	57
4 Abbey Villa II	26	12	5	9	66	56	10	41
5 Queens Grads 11's	26	12	3	11	66	61	5	39
6 St Lukes F.C. 11's	26	11	5	10	75	66	9	38
7 Downshire YM. 11's	26	9	9	8	66	57	9	36
8 Dunmurry Y.M.11's	26	10	4	12	62	62	0	34
9 Iveagh Utd 11's	26	10	4	12	52	58	-6	34
10 Ford F.C. 11's	26	10	2	14	47	71	-24	32
11 Shorts 11's	26	9	3	14	48	71	-23	30
12 Wellington Rec 11's	26	8	1	17	51	112	-61	25
13 Bangor Rgs 11's	26	6	4	16	48	75	-27	22
14 Mossley FC 11's	26	2	2	22	30	102	-72	8

Division Three D	P	W	D	L	F	A	GD	Pts
1 Greencastle Rovers F.C.11's	24	20	1	3	103	29	74	61
2 Bangor YM 11's	24	17	4	3	79	27	52	55
3 Colin Valley F.C.11's	24	14	3	7	71	39	32	45
4 Portaferry Rovers 11's	24	14	3	7	78	49	29	45
5 1st Bangor Old Boys 11's	24	12	4	8	84	57	27	40
6 Bryansburn Rgs. 11's	24	12	4	8	74	52	22	40
7 Ballywalter Rec. F.C.11's	24	9	4	11	67	67	0	31
8 Saintfield Utd 11's	24	7	8	9	54	61	-7	29
9 Suffolk FC 11's	24	8	4	12	57	77	-20	28
10 Newington Rgs 11's	24	8	3	13	45	79	-34	27
11 St Teresas Y.C.11's	24	8	2	14	61	57	4	26
12 Groomsport 11's	24	3	3	18	45	112	-67	12
13 Kilroot Rec 11's	24	2	1	21	23	135	-112	7

Division Three E	P	W	D	L	F	A	GD	Pts
1 Donard Hospital 11's	26	19	4	3	101	27	74	61
2 St Oliver Plunkett F.C.11's	26	19	1	6	102	32	70	58
3 Tullycarnet FC 11's	26	15	5	6	88	41	47	50
4 Ardoyne WMC 11's	26	14	5	7	84	63	21	47
5 Lower Shankill 11's	26	14	4	8	71	59	12	46
6 Kelvin OB 11's	26	13	3	10	60	50	10	42
7 18th Newtownabbey O.B. 11's	26	12	5	9	69	56	13	41
8 Newtownbreda 11's	26	11	6	9	51	44	7	39
9 Dromore Amateurs 11's	26	11	2	13	61	60	1	35
10 Drumbo F.C.11's	26	9	2	15	76	68	8	29
11 Portavogie Rangers F.C.11's	26	8	4	14	62	90	-28	28
12 Civil Service 11's	26	7	2	17	41	94	-53	23
13 4th Newtownabbey O.B. 11's	26	4	2	20	45	118	-73	14
14 Rooftop 11's	26	2	3	21	31	140	-109	9

Division Three F	P	W	D	L	F	A	GD	Pts
1 Rosemount Rec 11's	20	16	3	1	90	18	72	51
2 Bangor Amateurs 11's	20	13	3	4	58	24	34	42
3 Basement 11's	20	11	4	5	89	38	51	37
4 Temple Rgs 11's	20	11	2	7	67	37	30	35
5 Greenisland F.C.11's	20	11	1	8	60	49	11	34
6 Donaghadee FC 11's	20	10	3	7	44	42	2	33
7 Whitehead Eagles 11's	20	8	2	10	58	60	-2	26
8 Carryduff 11's	20	8	0	12	48	46	2	24
9 Suffolk Swifts 11''s	20	5	4	11	54	50	4	19
10 Grange Rgs11s	20	5	2	13	39	78	-39	17
11 Wesley FC 11's	20	0	0	20	18	183	-165	0

NORTHERN IRELAND INTERMEDIATE LEAGUE

	P	W	D	L	F	A	GD	Pts
1 Oxford United Stars	14	10	3	1	41	13	28	33
2 Strabane Athletic	14	10	0	4	37	20	17	30
3 Newbuildings United	14	9	2	3	56	22	34	29
4 Ardstraw	14	4	7	3	21	21	0	19
5 Dungiven	14	5	4	5	30	31	-1	19
6 Roe Rovers (-3)	13	3	4	6	14	29	-15	13
7 Draperstown Celtic	14	2	2	10	20	39	-19	8
8 Mountjoy United (-3)	13	0	2	11	11	55	-44	2

BELFAST & DISTRICT LEAGUE

Premier Division	P	W	D	L	F	A	GD	Pts
1 Cumann Spoirt an Phobail	14	11	1	2	45	20	25	34
2 Bheann Mhadigan	14	9	1	4	50	24	26	28
3 Shamrock	14	7	2	5	36	42	-6	23
4 Aquinas	14	7	1	6	35	32	3	22
5 St Pauls	14	5	3	6	28	28	0	18
6 St Matthews	14	5	2	7	28	33	-5	17
7 Tollymore Swifts	14	3	3	8	34	46	-12	12
8 Willowbank	14	2	1	11	23	54	-31	7

Division One		P	W	D	L	F	A	GD	Pts
1	Ballysillan YM	22	17	2	3	98	37	61	50
2	New Santos	22	14	2	6	75	55	20	44
3	St James Swifts	22	12	2	8	55	47	8	38
4	Belfast City	22	11	3	8	64	64	0	36
5	Cumann Spoirt an Phobail II	22	11	2	9	70	53	17	35
6	Kashmir Bilbao	22	9	6	7	56	50	6	33
7	St Patricks YM III	22	9	2	11	70	67	3	32
8	St Pauls II	22	10	2	10	60	66	-6	32
9	Tollymore Swifts II	22	9	2	11	55	57	-2	29
10	Colin Bhoys	22	8	2	12	49	66	-17	26
11	Glanville Rec	22	6	3	13	48	72	-24	21
12	St Malachys OB	22	2	0	20	20	86	-66	3

Division Two		P	W	D	L	F	A	GD	Pts
1	Ballysillan Elim	22	18	2	2	81	20	61	56
2	Glenpark	22	14	4	4	70	42	28	46
3	Shamrock II	22	12	3	7	70	45	25	39
4	Clonard Hibs	22	12	0	10	66	64	2	36
5	Glenbryn YM A	22	10	5	7	63	52	11	35
6	Aquinas II	22	8	6	8	56	63	-7	30
7	Ligoniel WMC	22	8	5	9	60	60	0	29
8	Glenbawn Celtic	22	8	3	11	52	55	-3	27
9	St Matthews II	22	7	5	10	48	55	-7	26
10	Holylands	22	8	1	13	34	59	-25	25
11	Sparta Belfast	22	6	3	13	62	74	-12	21
12	Colin Bhoys II	22	2	1	19	32	105	-73	7

Division Three		P	W	D	L	F	A	GD	Pts
1	St Marys FC	14	14	0	0	61	9	52	42
2	Shankill Elim YM	14	10	1	3	39	12	27	31
3	Bheann Mhadigan II	14	9	1	4	46	33	13	28
4	Broadway Swifts	14	7	3	4	37	35	2	24
5	Rock Athletic	14	4	1	9	26	42	-16	13
6	Willowbank II	14	4	1	9	19	44	-25	13
7	Sportsman	14	2	1	11	27	61	-34	7
8	New Santos II	14	1	2	11	25	44	-19	5

IRISH CUP

FIRST ROUND

Bangor 2-3 Newtowne

Newtownabbey 4-2 Lurgan Town

Ardstraw 0-1 Richhill

Bangor Amateurs 2-3 Ballynahinch United

Bangor Swifts 6-1 Groomsport

Bloomfield 0-1 Shankill United

Brantwood 2-3 Ardglass

Carniny Amateurs 2-0 Wellington Rec.

Comber Rec. 1-3 Kilmore Rec.

Crewe United 2-5 Dollingstown

Crumlin United 8-1 Draperstown Celtic

Crumlin Star 3-0 Newcastle

Derriaghy CC 6-2 Lower Maze

Donard Hospital 0-5 UU Jordanstown

Downpatrick 5-2 Saintfield United

Dromara Village 2-1 FC Ballynure

Dromore Amateurs 0-7 Banbridge Rangers

Drumaness Mills 6-0 Valley Rangers

Dunmurry Rec. 0-1 Newry City AFC

Immaculata 3-1 Ballynure OB

Islandmagee 3-2 St. Mary's

Iveagh United 2-4 Mountjoy United

Killyleagh YC 1-0 Ballymacash Rangers

Lisanally Rangers 0-6 Newbuildings United

Lisburn Rangers 3-1 Dunmurry YM

Magherafelt Sky Blues 2-3 Camlough Rovers

Moneyslane 6-2 Kilroot Rec.

Mossley 1-4 Downshire YM

Nortel 5-3 Malachians

Rathfern Rangers 3-0 Broomhill

Rathfriland Rangers 2-1 Abbey Villa

Roe Rovers 1-2 Bryansburn Rangers

Seagoe 3-0 Tandragee Rovers

Sirocco Works 3-1 Larne Tech. OB

St. Patrick's YM 2-2 (3-5p) Oxford United Stars

Strabane Athletic walkover Holywood withdrawn

SECOND ROUND

Albert Foundry 1-0 Shankill United
Ardglass 4-3 Banbridge Rangers
Ballynahinch United 0-1 Sirocco Works
Ballywalter Rec. 2-3 Rathfriland Rangers
Carniny Amateurs 1-0 Oxford United Stars
Crumlin Star 2-1 Dollingstown
Crumlin United 4-4 (3-2p) Islandmagee
Derriaghy CC 7-5 Ards Rangers
Downpatrick 5-0 UU Jordanstown
Downshire YM 1-0 Mountjoy United
Dromara Village 1-4 Kilmore Rec.
Dungiven 0-1 Newbuildings United
Immaculata v. Camlough Rovers
Lisburn Rangers 2-2 (3-2p) Barn United
Nortel 2-0 Moneyslane
Richhill 1-3 Newry City
Oxford Sunnyside 1-5 Drumaness Mills
Rathfern Rangers 3-1 Killyleagh YC
Seagoe 0-2 Bryansburn Rangers
Shorts 0-3 Bangor Swifts
Strabane Athletic 6-2 Newtowne

THIRD ROUND

Carniny Amateurs 3-5 Ardglass
Derriaghy CC 3-0 18th Newtownabbey
Downshire YM 2-2 (4-2p) Shankill United
Kilmore Rec. 0-0 (4-2p) Immaculata
Lisburn Rangers 3-1 Bryansburn Rangers
Newbuildings United 1-2 Crumlin Star
Newry City AFC 0-0 (4-3p) Downpatrick
Nortel 0-2 Drumaness Mills
Rathfern Rangers 1-2 Sirocco Works
Rathfriland Rangers 4-1 Bangor Swifts
Strabane Athletic 2-0 Crumlin United

FOURTH ROUND

Armagh City 2-0 Loughgall
Ballyclare Comrades 4-1 Larne
Banbridge Town 4-2 Rathfriland Rangers
Bangor 5-2 Knockbreda
Chimney Corner 3-0 Wakehurst
Coagh United 0-2 Carrick Rangers
Crumlin Star 4-1 Newry City AFC
Dergview 2-0 Drumaness Mills
Downshire YM 1-3 Kilmore Rec.
Glebe Rangers 3-2 Ardglass
HW Welders 8-1 Killymoon Rangers
Institute 1-1 (4-5p) Lisburn Distillery
Limavady United 2-1 Derriaghy CC
Moyola Park 2-0 Annagh United
Newington YC 1-3 Ballymoney United
Portstewart 2-5 Dundela
PSNI 2-1 Tobermore United
Queen's University 5-0 Lurgan Celtic
Sport & Leisure Swifts 2-1 Sirocco Works
Strabane Athletic 2-0 Lisburn Rangers

FIFTH ROUND

Armagh City 2-2 Ards
Ballinamallard United 0-0 Strabane Athletic
Ballyclare Comrades 3-0 Kilmore Rec.
Ballymoney United 1-0 Banbridge Town
Bangor 7-1 Glebe Rangers
Carrick Rangers 3-2 Dundela
Cliftonville 2-2 Coleraine
Crusaders 2-1 Crumlin Star
Glenavon 7-0 Sport & Leisure Swifts
HW Welders 2-2 Ballymena United
Linfield 5-0 Dergview
Lisburn Distillery 0-0 PSNI
Moyola Park 1-5 Dungannon Swifts
Portadown 1-3 Glentoran
Queen's University 1-0 Limavady United
Warrenpoint Town 2-0 Chimney Corner
Firth Round Replays
Armagh City 3-1 Ards
Ballinamallard United 1-0 Strabane Athletic
Ballymena United 1-0 HW Welders
Coleraine 4-3 Cliftonville
PSNI 0-2 Lisburn Distillery

SIXTH ROUND

Armagh City 1-1 Glentoran
Ballinamallard United 0-3 Glenavon
Ballyclare Comrades 2-1 Carrick Rangers
Coleraine 2-3 Dungannon Swifts
Crusaders 4-0 Ballymoney United
Linfield 1-2 Ballymena United
Lisburn Distillery 0-2 Queen's University
Warrenpoint Town 0-0 Bangor
Sixth Round Replays
Bangor 1-0 Warrenpoint Town
Glentoran 2-1 Armagh City

QUARTER FINALS

Ballymena United 4-1 Dungannon Swifts
Crusaders 5-0 Ballyclare Comrades
Glentoran 1-2 Glenavon
Queen's University 3-2 Bangor

SEMI FINALS

Ballymena United 3-0 Queen's University
(played at The Oval)
Glenavon 3-1 Crusaders
(played at Windsor Park)

FINAL

Ballymena United 1-2 Glenavon
(played at Windsor Park, Belfast)

SCOTTISH TABLES 2013-14

EAST OF SCOTLAND LEAGUE

Premier Division		P	W	D	L	F	A	GD	Pts
1	Lothian Thistle Hutchison Vale	18	15	1	2	46	16	30	46
2	Stirling University EOS	18	10	2	6	35	34	1	32
3	Craigroyston	18	9	4	5	36	22	14	31
4	Tynecastle	18	9	1	8	45	40	5	28
5	Edinburgh University	18	5	8	5	30	25	5	23
6	Spartans EOS	18	6	5	7	30	28	2	23
7	Leith Athletic	18	6	5	7	35	36	-1	23
8	Coldstream	18	6	2	10	23	35	-12	20
9	Civil Service Strollers	18	5	1	12	25	51	-26	16
10	Heriot-Watt University	18	3	3	12	19	37	-18	12

Division One		P	W	D	L	F	A	GD	Pts
1	Hibernian EOS	18	15	1	2	72	16	56	46
2	Easthouses Lily Miners Welfare	18	13	3	2	54	19	35	42
3	Berwick Rangers EOS	18	11	0	7	42	27	15	33
4	Peebles Rovers	18	7	4	7	35	37	-2	25
5	Kelso United	18	6	4	8	28	38	-10	22
6	Burntisland Shipyard	18	6	3	9	24	43	-19	21
7	Hawick Royal Albert	18	6	1	11	29	44	-15	19
8	Duns	18	5	3	10	29	46	-17	18
9	Ormiston	18	6	0	12	27	48	-21	18
10	Eyemouth United	18	4	3	11	31	53	-22	15

HIGHLAND LEAGUE

		P	W	D	L	F	A	GD	Pts
1	Brora Rangers	34	31	2	1	123	16	107	95
2	Inverurie Loco Works	34	23	6	5	97	39	58	75
3	Nairn County	34	24	3	7	86	39	47	75
4	Formartine United	34	22	6	6	88	36	52	72
5	Fraserburgh	34	23	2	9	89	44	45	71
6	Deveronvale	34	20	5	9	64	43	21	65
7	Cove Rangers	34	16	7	11	91	62	29	55
8	Wick Academy	34	15	8	11	83	54	29	53
9	Forres Mechanics	34	15	7	12	68	50	18	52
10	Buckie Thistle	34	13	10	11	54	48	6	49
11	Clachnacuddin	34	13	7	14	67	64	3	46
12	Turriff United	34	13	5	16	60	57	3	44
13	Huntly	34	9	8	17	55	82	-27	35
14	Keith	34	9	2	23	50	98	-48	29
15	Lossiemouth	34	4	8	22	34	93	-59	20
16	Strathspey Thistle	34	3	3	28	28	116	-88	12
17	Rothes	34	3	3	28	36	136	-100	12
18	Fort William	34	1	6	27	35	131	-96	9

NORTH CALEDONIAN LEAGUE

		P	W	D	L	F	A	GD	Pts
1	Halkirk United	12	9	3	0	43	13	30	30
2	Golspie Sutherland	12	8	1	3	45	24	21	25
3	Muir of Ord Rovers	12	6	2	4	26	25	1	20
4	Clachnacuddin	12	5	2	5	29	32	-3	17
5	Thurso	12	3	4	5	13	16	-3	13
6	Alness United	12	3	1	8	18	32	-14	10
7	Sutherland United	12	1	1	10	16	48	-32	4

SJFA EAST REGION

Superleague		P	W	D	L	F	A	GD	Pts
1	Bo'ness United	30	22	3	5	79	32	47	69
2	Linlithgow Rose	30	20	6	4	70	33	37	66
3	Bonnyrigg Rose Athletic	30	17	10	3	60	28	32	61
4	Newtongrange Star	30	19	1	10	65	34	31	58
5	Camelon Juniors	30	16	6	8	51	35	16	54
6	Hill of Beath Hawthorn	30	14	7	9	61	44	17	49
7	Broxburn Athletic	30	14	6	10	53	56	-3	48
8	Musselburgh Athletic	30	12	7	11	53	51	2	43
9	Sauchie Juniors	30	12	4	14	55	53	2	40
10	Lochee United	30	12	1	17	57	72	-15	37
11	Armadale Thistle	30	8	3	19	35	64	-29	27
12	Carnoustie Panmure	30	8	3	19	43	74	-31	27
13	Ballingry Rovers	30	7	6	17	31	67	-36	27
14	Kelty Hearts	30	5	11	14	36	54	-18	26
15	Tayport	30	5	7	18	36	62	-26	22
16	St Andrews United	30	4	9	17	42	68	-26	21

Premier League		P	W	D	L	F	A	GD	Pts
1	Penicuik Athletic	30	20	4	6	68	29	39	64
2	Fauldhouse United	30	17	8	5	86	40	46	59
3	Dalkeith Thistle	30	17	5	8	74	53	21	56
4	Jeanfield Swifts	30	17	3	10	60	42	18	54
5	Glenrothes Juniors	30	15	8	7	66	44	22	53
6	Oakley United	30	16	5	9	61	59	2	53
7	Broughty Athletic	30	14	7	9	77	50	27	49
8	Bathgate Thistle	30	14	4	12	87	53	34	46
9	Arniston Rangers	30	13	4	13	59	49	10	43
10	Kinnoull Juniors	30	10	6	14	38	48	-10	36
11	Dundee Violet	30	10	6	14	41	58	-17	36
12	Montrose Roselea	30	10	5	15	53	58	-5	35
13	Kirkcaldy YM	30	10	5	15	61	76	-15	35
14	Livingston United	30	9	2	19	38	72	-34	29
15	Kirriemuir Thistle	30	8	2	20	34	70	-36	26
16	Pumpherston Juniors	30	2	2	26	27	129	-102	8

SCOTTISH FOOTBALL

North Division	P	W	D	L	F	A	GD	Pts
1 Dundee North End	30	24	4	2	113	33	80	76
2 Forfar West End	30	20	2	8	88	44	44	62
3 Downfield Juniors	30	17	6	7	62	45	17	57
4 Newburgh Juniors	30	16	8	6	89	51	38	56
5 Kennoway Star Hearts	30	18	2	10	91	54	37	56
6 Blairgowrie Juniors	30	17	2	11	77	49	28	53
7 Thornton Hibs	30	16	3	11	97	62	35	51
8 Luncarty	30	16	2	12	90	58	32	50
9 Lochore Welfare	30	14	5	11	67	59	8	47
10 Dundee East Craigie	30	14	2	14	68	50	18	44
11 Arbroath Victoria	30	12	5	13	72	77	-5	41
12 Scone Thistle	30	12	3	15	62	76	-14	39
13 Brechin Victoria	30	8	3	19	39	65	-26	27
14 Lochee Harp	30	6	5	19	63	82	-19	23
15 Forfar Albion	30	4	0	26	37	133	-96	12
16 Coupar Angus	30	0	0	30	15	192	-177	0

South Division	P	W	D	L	F	A	GD	Pts
1 Edinburgh United (-3)	26	20	4	2	72	21	51	61
2 Dundonald Bluebell	26	19	3	4	92	38	54	60
3 Blackburn United	26	17	2	7	73	37	36	53
4 Haddington Athletic	26	17	1	8	85	45	40	52
5 Whitburn Juniors	26	13	5	8	63	45	18	44
6 Dunbar United (-3)	26	12	1	13	56	48	8	40
7 Falkirk Juniors	26	11	3	12	57	52	5	36
8 Tranent Juniors	26	8	7	11	44	63	-19	31
9 Lochgelly Albert	26	9	3	14	54	68	-14	30
10 West Calder United	26	7	7	12	37	49	-12	28
11 Stoneyburn Juniors	26	8	4	14	36	77	-41	28
12 Rosyth	26	6	6	14	39	62	-23	24
13 Crossgates Primrose	26	6	5	15	43	77	-34	23
14 Harthill Royal	26	1	5	20	23	92	-69	8

SJFA NORTH REGION

Superleague	P	W	D	L	F	A	GD	Pts
1 Culter	26	22	2	2	87	28	59	68
2 Banks o' Dee	26	16	5	5	86	35	51	53
3 Dyce Juniors	26	17	1	8	65	42	23	52
4 Hermes	26	15	5	6	74	45	29	50
5 Maud Juniors	26	11	8	7	53	45	8	41
6 Deveronside	26	11	6	9	50	46	4	39
7 Stonehaven Juniors	26	11	6	9	41	47	-6	39
8 New Elgin	26	9	7	10	44	51	-7	34
9 Hall Russell United	26	10	2	14	44	55	-11	32
10 Ellon United	26	8	3	15	37	48	-11	27
11 Banchory St Ternan	26	7	4	15	45	78	-33	25
12 FC Stoneywood	26	5	8	13	48	60	-12	23
13 East End	26	5	7	14	33	64	-31	22
14 Longside	26	2	2	22	25	88	-63	8

Division One East	P	W	D	L	F	A	GD	Pts
1 Cruden Bay Juniors	27	18	5	4	65	34	31	59
2 Bridge of Don Thistle	27	16	9	2	70	31	39	57
3 Colony Park	27	15	6	6	78	43	35	51
4 Glentanar	27	13	9	5	85	54	31	48
5 Lewis United	27	8	7	12	59	65	-6	31
6 Parkvale	27	7	10	10	42	53	-11	31
7 Fraserburgh United	27	9	2	16	62	76	-14	29
8 Sunnybank	27	8	3	16	42	72	-30	27
9 Buchanhaven Hearts	27	7	6	14	59	94	-35	27
10 Newmachar United	27	3	5	19	41	81	-40	14

Division One West	P	W	D	L	F	A	GD	Pts
1 Inverness City	27	22	3	2	100	36	64	69
2 Dufftown	27	17	5	5	72	31	41	56
3 Islavale	27	17	4	6	75	45	30	55
4 Burghead Thistle	27	13	5	9	65	51	14	44
5 Portgordon Victoria	27	13	4	10	57	48	9	43
6 Forres Thistle	27	13	3	11	51	47	4	42
7 Buckie Rovers	27	10	1	16	44	55	-11	31
8 Nairn St Ninian (-3)	27	8	1	18	48	59	-11	22
9 Whitehills	27	4	1	22	38	99	-61	13
10 Fochabers Juniors	27	4	1	22	37	116	-79	13

SJFA WESTERN REGION

Superleague Premier Premier	P	W	D	L	F	A	GD	Pts
1 Auchinleck Talbot	22	16	3	3	48	20	28	51
2 Irvine Meadow XI	22	14	4	4	38	23	15	46
3 Hurlford United	22	13	6	3	50	26	24	45
4 Clydebank	22	10	3	9	34	29	5	33
5 Cumnock Juniors	22	8	6	8	32	31	1	30
6 Glenafton Athletic	22	9	2	11	27	33	-6	29
7 Kilbirnie Ladeside	22	8	4	10	40	32	8	28
8 Petershill	22	6	7	9	34	37	-3	25
9 Arthurlie	22	6	6	10	27	41	-14	24
10 Kirkintilloch Rob Roy	22	7	2	13	33	51	-18	23
11 Pollok	22	5	4	13	39	58	-19	19
12 Largs Thistle	22	6	1	15	27	48	-21	19

Superleague Division One	P	W	D	L	F	A	GD	Pts
1 Troon	26	20	3	3	70	29	41	63
2 Beith Juniors	26	19	4	3	70	31	39	61
3 Shotts Bon Accord	26	16	2	8	62	33	29	50
4 Maybole Juniors	26	12	7	7	44	37	7	43
5 Cumbernauld United	26	11	5	10	44	40	4	38
6 Thorniewood United	26	10	6	10	55	49	6	36
7 Rutherglen Glencairn	26	11	3	12	47	46	1	36
8 Yoker Athletic	26	9	8	9	51	51	0	35
9 Greenock Juniors	26	9	5	12	41	49	-8	32
10 Kilsyth Rangers	26	9	4	13	36	55	-19	31
11 Ashfield	26	9	1	16	41	62	-21	28
12 Renfrew	26	5	4	17	32	65	-33	19
13 Kilwinning Rangers (-19)	26	10	3	13	49	45	+4	14
14 Lesmahagow Juniors	26	4	1	21	36	86	-50	13

Central District Div. One	P	W	D	L	F	A	GD	Pts
1 Neilston Juniors	24	16	4	4	50	19	31	52
2 Shettleston	24	15	3	6	58	32	26	48
3 Benburb	24	13	5	6	37	28	9	44
4 Bellshill Athletic	24	12	7	5	39	25	14	43
5 Carluke Rovers	24	13	3	8	52	43	9	42
6 Dunipace Juniors	24	12	5	7	42	29	13	41
7 Larkhall Thistle	24	11	5	8	45	34	11	38
8 St Anthony's	24	9	4	11	39	40	-1	31
9 Maryhill	24	9	4	11	40	44	-4	31
10 Lanark United	24	7	6	11	41	39	2	27
11 Cambuslang Rangers	24	8	3	13	32	35	-3	27
12 Johnstone Burgh	24	2	4	18	29	68	-39	10
13 Glasgow Perthshire	24	2	1	21	23	91	-68	7

Central District Div. Two	P	W	D	L	F	A	GD	Pts
1 Blantyre Victoria	20	17	2	1	70	23	47	53
2 Vale of Clyde	20	15	1	4	68	36	32	46
3 Wishaw Juniors	20	13	1	6	51	26	25	40
4 Forth Wanderers	20	12	3	5	57	32	25	39
5 Royal Albert	20	9	1	10	32	44	-12	28
6 Vale of Leven	20	8	3	9	50	40	10	27
7 Rossvale	20	9	0	11	34	44	-10	27
8 Port Glasgow Juniors	20	7	3	10	44	46	-2	24
9 St Roch's	20	4	4	12	36	60	-24	16
10 East Kilbride Thistle	20	2	2	16	23	57	-34	8
11 Newmains United (-3)	20	3	2	15	28	85	-57	8

Ayrshire District League	P	W	D	L	F	A	GD	Pts
1 Irvine Victoria	24	18	3	3	67	21	46	57
2 Ardeer Thistle	24	16	5	3	74	33	41	53
3 Whitletts Victoria	24	14	4	6	60	39	21	46
4 Lugar Boswell Thistle	24	13	4	7	72	40	32	43
5 Ardrossan Winton Rovers	24	11	8	5	74	43	31	41
6 Darvel	24	12	5	7	65	49	16	41
7 Girvan	24	10	6	8	60	35	25	36
8 Dalry Thistle	24	9	5	10	63	63	0	32
9 Saltcoats Victoria	24	8	6	10	51	40	11	30
10 Annbank United	24	9	3	12	56	63	-7	30
11 Kello Rovers	24	5	5	14	52	81	-29	20
12 Muirkirk Juniors	24	3	1	20	22	100	-78	10
13 Craigmark Burntonians	24	0	1	23	19	128	-109	1

SOUTH OF SCOTLAND LEAGUE

	P	W	D	L	F	A	GD	Pts
1 Wigtown & Bladnoch	20	18	1	1	75	13	62	55
2 St Cuthbert Wanderers	20	15	1	4	55	23	32	46
3 Newton Stewart	20	14	2	4	73	29	44	44
4 Nithsdale Wanderers	20	11	1	8	63	41	22	34
5 Crichton	20	9	4	7	49	45	4	31
6 Heston Rovers	20	9	3	8	61	47	14	30
7 Lochar Thistle	20	9	1	10	47	51	-4	28
8 Mid-Annandale	20	6	5	9	38	48	-10	23
9 Abbey Vale	20	3	3	14	27	72	-45	12
10 Fleet Star	20	2	4	14	27	61	-34	10
11 Creetown	20	1	1	18	20	105	-85	4

SCOTTISH AMATEUR FOOTBALL LEAGUE

Premier Division	P	W	D	L	F	A	GD	Pts
1 Oban Saints AFC	18	13	5	0	53	19	34	44
2 Haldane United AFC	18	12	3	3	54	28	26	39
3 St. Josephs FP AFC	18	11	4	3	56	32	24	37
4 Finnart AFC	18	9	3	6	47	37	10	30
5 Busby AFC	18	7	3	8	37	46	-9	24
6 Thorn Athletic AFC	18	6	3	9	28	33	-5	21
7 Castlemilk AFC	18	4	7	7	40	50	-10	19
8 Alba Thistle AFC	18	6	0	12	31	51	-20	18
9 Inverclyde AFC	18	4	4	10	33	44	-11	16
10 Kilbowie Union AFC	18	1	2	15	30	69	-39	5

Premier Division One	P	W	D	L	F	A	GD	Pts
1 Campbeltown Pupils AFC	18	11	3	4	47	27	20	36
2 Kings Park Rangers AFC	18	11	0	7	41	33	8	33
3 Eaglesham AFC	18	10	2	6	41	27	14	32
4 Hillington AFC	18	9	3	6	49	40	9	30
5 Rutherglen AFC	18	8	4	6	38	35	3	28
6 Dunoon AFC	18	7	2	9	29	38	-9	23
7 East Kilbride Rolls Royce AFC	18	6	4	8	32	36	-4	22
8 Shawlands FP AFC	18	6	4	8	42	48	-6	22
9 Centre AFC	18	5	4	9	39	49	-10	19
10 Paisley AFC	18	3	2	13	23	48	-25	11

Premier Division Two	P	W	D	L	F	A	GD	Pts
1 East Kilbride FC	18	15	1	2	68	21	47	46
2 Goldenhill AFC	18	12	3	3	69	40	29	39
3 Jamestown AFC	18	11	1	6	54	41	13	34
4 Lochgilphead Red Star	18	9	4	5	48	39	9	31
5 Easthall Star AFC	18	9	2	7	47	48	-1	29
6 Port Glasgow AFC	18	6	3	9	38	39	-1	21
7 Clydebank AFC	18	6	1	11	26	37	-11	19
8 Dunoon Athletic AFC	18	5	2	11	43	60	-17	17
9 Port Glasgow United AFC	18	3	4	11	31	66	-35	13
10 Glencastle Sparta AFC	18	2	3	13	27	60	-33	9

Division One A	P	W	D	L	F	A	GD	Pts
1 Drumchapel Amateurs Colts	20	18	0	2	103	27	76	54
2 Ferguslie Star AFC	20	17	2	1	112	24	88	53
3 Eaglesham AFC (B)	20	14	1	5	85	37	48	43
4 Tarbert AFC	20	11	4	5	68	36	32	37
5 Rosehill Star	20	10	1	9	58	59	-1	31
6 Millerston Thistle AFC	20	8	2	10	55	70	-15	26
7 Millbeg Villa AFC	20	7	3	10	62	70	-8	24
8 Inverkip Thistle AFC	20	4	4	12	38	89	-51	16
9 Shawlands F.P (B)	20	3	5	12	56	97	-41	14
10 Bothwell and Uddingston Albion	20	2	7	11	44	67	-23	13
11 Rossvale AFC	20	0	3	17	21	126	-105	3

SCOTTISH FOOTBALL

Division One B		P	W	D	L	F	A	GD	Pts
1	Motherwell Thistle AFC	20	16	2	2	70	24	46	50
2	South Camlachie YP AFC	20	13	5	2	75	29	46	44
3	Neilston AFC	20	13	2	5	87	36	51	41
4	Port Glasgow Old Boys Union AF	20	10	5	5	61	50	11	35
5	Strathaven Dynamo	20	9	3	8	62	52	10	30
6	FC Clydebank	20	7	6	7	40	37	3	27
7	Centre AFC (B)	20	6	5	9	41	63	-22	23
8	Whitehill FP AFC	20	4	7	9	39	57	-18	19
9	Carlton YMCA AFC	20	5	2	13	38	60	-22	17
10	East Kilbride YMCA AFC	20	6	2	12	35	57	-22	10
11	Kings Park Rangers (B)	20	1	1	18	28	111	-83	4

ABERDEENSHIRE AMATEUR FOOTBALL ASSOCIATION

Premier Division		P	W	D	L	F	A	GD	Pts
1	Sportsmans Club	24	19	1	4	81	40	41	58
2	Woodside	24	16	3	5	82	29	53	51
3	Cove Thistle	24	15	4	5	93	43	50	49
4	Cowie Thistle	24	13	2	9	61	53	8	41
5	Hazlehead United	24	13	1	10	60	66	-6	40
6	MS United	24	11	2	11	68	59	9	35
7	Kincorth	24	10	4	10	73	76	-3	34
8	Westdyke	24	9	5	10	49	55	-6	32
9	University	24	8	5	11	58	68	-10	29
10	Luthermuir	24	8	4	12	39	58	-19	28
11	Beacon Rangers	24	7	3	14	60	65	-5	24
12	Feughside	24	5	1	18	36	102	-66	16
13	Insch	24	3	3	18	37	83	-46	12

Division One North		P	W	D	L	F	A	GD	Pts
1	Rothie Rovers	26	20	4	2	80	41	39	64
2	Great Northern Athletic	26	19	1	6	84	44	40	58
3	Johnshaven Athletic	26	15	7	4	69	35	34	52
4	Dee Amateurs	26	15	4	7	74	49	25	49
5	Tarves	26	13	2	11	73	52	21	41
6	Halliburton	26	12	2	12	53	45	8	38
7	Echt	26	11	5	10	63	44	19	38
8	Alford	26	11	5	10	58	52	6	38
9	Dyce ITC Hydraulics	26	10	5	11	58	57	1	35
10	Stoneywood Amateurs	26	10	4	12	53	53	0	34
11	Glendale	26	8	0	18	48	74	-26	24
12	Turriff Thistle (-6)	26	7	6	13	52	61	-9	21
13	Bon Accord City	26	6	3	17	52	82	-30	21
14	Glendale XI (-3)	26	1	0	25	19	147	-128	0

Division One East		P	W	D	L	F	A	GD	Pts
1	RGU	26	20	3	3	87	31	56	63
2	Ellon Amateurs	26	17	5	4	72	40	32	56
3	AC Mill Inn	26	16	5	5	75	45	30	53
4	Newtonhill	26	15	6	5	73	44	29	51
5	Blackburn	26	14	3	9	73	54	19	45
6	Rattrays XI	26	12	6	8	43	39	4	42
7	Don Athletic	26	11	2	13	52	77	-25	35
8	Kaimhill United	26	10	4	12	59	56	3	34
9	Nicolls Amateurs	26	10	3	13	52	59	-7	33
10	Great Western United	26	8	6	12	57	70	-13	30
11	Northern United	26	9	2	15	48	62	-14	29
12	Bervie Caledonian	26	7	6	13	60	74	-14	27
13	Old Aberdonians	26	3	2	21	27	58	-31	11
14	Highland Hotel (-6)	26	1	5	20	35	104	-69	2

Division Two North		P	W	D	L	F	A	GD	Pts
1	Granite City	26	20	3	3	89	36	53	63
2	Torry Select	26	19	3	4	92	35	57	60
3	Lads Club Amateurs	26	18	4	4	70	36	34	58
4	St Laurence	26	17	3	6	76	50	26	54
5	Ellon Thistle	26	14	3	9	72	53	19	45
6	Stonehaven Athletic	26	12	2	12	65	53	12	38
7	FC Polska	26	12	1	13	66	77	-11	37
8	Cammachmore	26	10	3	13	53	67	-14	33
9	Torphins	26	8	3	15	63	76	-13	27
10	Banchory Amateurs	26	7	3	16	56	88	-32	24
11	Scotstown Rovers	26	7	2	17	64	89	-25	23
12	Torry United	26	7	2	17	34	73	-39	23
13	Newburgh Thistle (-9)	26	7	4	15	69	87	-18	16
14	Continental	26	3	6	17	34	83	-49	15

Division Two East		P	W	D	L	F	A	GD	Pts
1	Grammar FPs	26	20	0	6	89	50	39	60
2	West End	26	18	2	6	92	52	40	56
3	Bankhead	26	17	2	7	116	49	67	53
4	University Strollers	26	16	3	7	80	51	29	51
5	JS XI	26	16	3	7	92	48	44	51
6	Summerhill	26	13	2	11	75	61	14	41
7	Burghmuir	26	12	4	10	73	68	5	40
8	Glentanar Reflex	26	11	3	12	61	64	-3	36
9	University Colts	26	10	2	14	58	86	-28	32
10	Kemnay Youth	26	10	1	15	60	86	-26	31
11	Ferryhill	26	8	3	15	80	98	-18	27
12	Kintore	26	8	2	16	48	72	-24	26
13	Byron	26	3	4	19	50	100	-50	13

Division Three	P	W	D	L	F	A	GD	Pts
1 BSFC	30	24	2	4	114	62	52	74
2 Glendale Youth	30	18	7	5	107	70	37	61
3 Theologians	30	19	3	8	104	57	47	60
4 Fintray Thistle	30	17	7	6	85	47	38	58
5 Westhill *	30	20	5	5	99	51	48	56
6 Bridge of Don	30	17	5	8	99	54	45	56
7 Formartine United	30	17	4	9	90	48	42	55
8 Monymusk	30	16	5	9	89	77	12	53
9 Postal ALC	30	16	3	11	83	64	19	51
10 ARI Thistle	30	10	4	16	73	72	1	34
11 McTeagle	30	8	4	18	37	76	-39	28
12 Auchnagatt Barons	30	7	4	19	51	89	-38	25
13 Huntly Amateurs (-3)	30	8	3	19	58	81	-23	24
14 AFC Murdos	30	6	3	21	35	88	-53	21
15 RAM	30	3	3	24	39	139	-100	12
16 Aboyne	30	2	2	26	44	132	-88	8

BORDER AMATEUR LEAGUE

A League	P	W	D	L	F	A	GD	Pts
1 Gala Rovers	22	15	3	4	74	40	34	48
2 Newtown	22	13	3	6	54	44	10	42
3 Leithen Rovers	22	12	2	8	62	44	18	38
4 Pencaitland (-3)	22	12	3	7	88	55	33	36
5 Chirnside Utd	22	10	4	8	64	60	4	34
6 Tweeddale Rovers	22	9	5	8	50	50	0	32
7 Hawick Waverley	22	9	4	9	59	56	3	31
8 Hearts of Liddesdale (-3)	22	10	2	10	63	68	-5	29
9 Greenlaw	22	8	2	12	41	56	-15	26
10 West Barns Star	22	6	6	10	58	70	-12	24
11 Langholm Legion (-3)	22	6	5	11	49	69	-20	20
12 Duns Ams	22	2	1	19	33	83	-50	7

B League	P	W	D	L	F	A	GD	Pts
1 Ancrum	20	15	1	4	58	32	26	46
2 Stow	20	14	1	5	72	28	44	43
3 Eyemouth Ams (-3)	20	13	2	5	61	48	13	38
4 Hawick United (-3)	20	11	5	4	63	40	23	35
5 Selkirk Victoria	20	10	3	7	45	43	2	33
6 Jed Legion (+2)	20	8	4	8	41	36	5	30
7 Linton Hotspur (-3)	20	7	3	10	36	50	-14	21
8 Gala Hotspur	20	6	2	12	36	49	-13	20
9 Coldstream Ams (-3)	20	7	1	12	46	56	-10	19
10 Hawick Legion	20	5	3	12	42	56	-14	18
11 CFC Bowholm	20	1	1	18	22	84	-62	4

C League	P	W	D	L	F	A	GD	Pts
1 Biggar (-3)	20	16	2	2	65	20	45	47
2 Gordon	20	13	4	3	59	30	29	43
3 Tweedmouth Ams Colts	20	12	3	5	62	40	22	39
4 Lauder (-3)	20	11	6	3	41	21	20	36
5 Chirnside Utd Colts	20	10	3	7	53	39	14	33
6 Kelso Thistle	20	6	7	7	49	45	4	25
7 St.Boswells	20	7	3	10	38	55	-17	24
8 Earlston Rhymers	20	6	4	10	35	43	-8	22
9 Hawick Legion Rovers	20	5	2	13	37	72	-35	17
10 Peebles Ams	20	3	3	14	32	62	-30	12
11 Abbotsford Albion (-3)	20	2	1	17	23	67	-44	4

DUMFRIES & DISTRICT AMATEUR LEAGUE

	P	W	D	L	F	A	GD	PTS
1 Lochmaben (-3)	18	16	1	1	96	26	70	46
2 Upper Annandale	18	11	2	5	49	27	22	35
3 Terregles Athletic	18	9	3	6	70	46	24	30
4 Maxwelltown Thistle	18	9	2	7	45	53	-8	29
5 Morton Thistle	18	8	1	9	61	68	-7	25
6 Dynamo Star	18	2	4	12	36	78	-42	10
7 YMCA	18	1	1	16	34	95	-61	4

SCOTTISH JUNIOR CUP

ROUND 1

Carnoustie Panmure	v	Edinburgh United	3-1
Newmains United	v	Cambuslang Rangers	0-4
Glenrothes Juniors	v	Livingston United	0-2
Lochgelly Albert	v	Kelty Hearts	3-1
Arthurlie	v	Bridge of Don	3-0
West Calder United	v	Sauchie Juniors	0-4
Dundee North End	v	Ardeer Thistle	3-0
Irvine Meadow X1	v	Scone Thistle	2-1
Royal Albert	v	Stoneyburn	4-0
Kirkcaldy Y.M.C.A. F.C	v	Falkirk Juniors	3-3
Falkirk Juniors	v	Kirkcaldy Y.M.C.A.	3-3, 6-7p
Forth Wanderers	v	Coupar Angus	6-0
Islavale	v	Tranent Juniors	1-1
Tranent Juniors	v	Islavale	4-0
Dundee Violet	v	St. Andrew's United	0-1
Maryhill	v	Dyce	2-2
Dyce	v	Maryhill	1-2
Cruden Bay	v	Glasgow Perthshire	2-2
Glasgow Perthshire	v	Cruden Bay	1-2
Dundee East Craigie	v	Wishaw Juniors	2-3
Musselburgh Athletic	v	Arniston Rangers	6-3
Blairgowrie Juniors	v	Deveronside	0-2
Crossgates Primrose	v	Vale of Clyde	1-2
Dunbar United	v	Muirkirk Juniors	5-1
Pollok	v	Luncarty	4-1
Annbank United	v	Kello Rovers	3-1
Kinnoull F.C	v	Tayport	1-3
Irvine Victoria	v	Greenock Juniors	1-2
Glenafton Athletic	v	Inverness City	9-1
Vale of Leven	v	Thornton Hibs	1-1
Thornton Hibs	v	Vale of Leven	0-2
Blackburn United	v	Largs Thistle	1-2
Jeanfield Swifts	v	Yoker Athletic	1-3
Bonnyrigg Rose Athletic	v	Bo'ness United	2-2
B'ness United	v	Bonnyrigg Rose Athletic	1-0
Fochabers	v	Kirriemuir Thistle	0-11
Neilston Juniors	v	Port Glasgow Juniors	2-0
Saltcoats Victoria	v	Blantyre Victoria	1-2

ROUND 2

Maryhill	v	Carnoustie Panmure	1-1
Carnoustie Panmure	v	Maryhill	3-2
Arbroath Victoria	v	Beith Juniors	1-2
Kilsyth Rangers	v	Shettleston	5-1
Blantyre Victoria	v	Broughty Athletic	3-2
FC Stoneywood	v	Shotts Bon Accord	1-4
Neilston Juniors	v	Maud	2-1
Glentanar	v	Fauldhouse United	2-4
Buchanhaven Hearts	v	Banks O'Dee	2-6
Kirkcaldy Y.M.C.A. F.C	v	Longside	5-1
Burghead Thistle	v	Parkvale	
Parkvale	v	Burghead Thistle	0-2
Lochore Welfare	v	Ellon United	3-1
Dundee Downfield	v	Arthurlie	0-3
Largs Thistle	v	Oakley United	2-1
Hermes	v	Newmachars	9-0
Banchory St. Ternan	v	Pumpherston	6-1
Cambuslang Rangers	v	Portgordon Victoria	7-1
Bellshill Athletic	v	Deveronside	0-3
Forfar Albion	v	Lanark United	0-6
Johnstone Burgh	v	Hill of Beath Hawthorn	0-2
Sauchie Juniors	v	Tranent Juniors	4-0
Carluke Rovers	v	Linlithgow Rose	
Linlithgow Rose	v	Carluke Rovers	5-1
Musselburgh Athletic	v	Armadale Thistle	3-0
Livingston United	v	Vale of Clyde	4-0
Dundee North End	v	Bo'ness United	1-2
Cumnock Juniors	v	Troon	1-0
Rossvale	v	Dundonald Bluebell	3-6
Rosyth Recreation	v	Lochee United	0-6
Culter	v	Ashfield	2-3
Penicuik Athletic	v	Sunnybank	9-0
Auchinleck Talbot	v	Broxburn Athletic	7-0
Fraserburgh United	v	Ballingry Rovers	3-5
Dunipace	v	Dunbar United	2-4
Kilbirnie Ladeside	v	Newburgh	3-0
Benburb	v	Lochgelly Albert	7-0
Lewis United	v	Colony Park	0-2
Haddington Athletic	v	Newtongrange Star	1-1
Newtongrange Star	v	Haddington Athletic	1-1, 4-3p
St. Roch's	v	Thorniewood United	3-5
Tayport	v	Renfrew	4-2
St. Andrew's United	v	Whitehills	17-1
Hall Russell United	v	Cruden Bay	2-5
Whitletts Victoria	v	Bathgate Thistle	3-1
Whitburn Juniors	v	Forth Wanderers	0-2
Harthill Royal	v	Craigmark Burntonians	7-0
Dufftown	v	Pollok	1-5
Lochee Harp	v	Kirkintilloch Rob Roy	1-7
Hurlford United	v	New Elgin	8-0
Kilwinning Rangers	v	Nairn St. Ninian	12-0
Irvine Meadow X1	v	Clydebank	3-2
Dalkeith Thistle	v	Vale of Leven	6-1
Yoker Athletic	v	Ardrossan Winton Rovers	4-2
Stonehaven	v	Forfar West End	3-1
Maybole Juniors	v	Cumbernauld United	0-0
Cumbernauld United	v	Maybole Juniors	2-1
Rutherglen Glencairn	v	Annbank United	7-1
Greenock Juniors	v	Royal Albert	1-2
Larkhall Thistle	v	Kirriemuir Thistle	7-3
Brechin Victoria	v	Aberdeen East End	1-2
Forres Thistle	v	Kennoway Star Hearts	2-4
Darvel Juniors	v	Wishaw Juniors	2-2
Wilshaw Juniors	v	Darvel Juniors	2-3
St. Anthony's	v	Petershill	
Petershill	v	St. Anthony's	3-0
Lugar Boswell Thistle	v	Glenafton Athletic	0-2
East Kilbride Thistle	v	Montrose Roselea	1-1, 3-1p
Dalry Thistle	v	Buckie Rovers	9-1
Lesmahagow Juniors	v	Camelon Juniors	2-4

ROUND 3

Dunbar United	v	Arthurlie	3-2
Newtongrange Star	v	Tayport	1-5
Banks O'Dee	v	Larkhall Thistle	1-2
Lochore Welfare	v	Pollok	1-5
Carnoustie Panmure	v	Colony Park	6-0
Banchory St. Ternan	v	Whitletts Victoria	1-6
Deveronside	v	Musselburgh Athletic	3-3
Musselburgh Athletic	v	Deveronside	3-1
Bo'ness United	v	Auchinleck Talbot	1-0
Largs Thistle	v	Kilbirnie Ladeside	2-1
Montrose Roselea	v	Aberdeen East End	2-2
Aberdeen East End	v	Montrose Roselea	0-2
Irvine Meadow X1	v	Fauldhouse United	3-0
Camelon Juniors	v	Lochee United	4-1
Glenafton Athletic	v	Royal Albert	2-2
Royal Albert	v	Glenafton Athletic	0-5
Petershill	v	Ballingry Rovers	1-0
St. Andrew's United	v	Thorniewood United	2-0
Dalry Thistle	v	Burghead Thistle	4-2
Neilston Juniors	v	Stonehaven	2-0
Kilwinning Rangers	v	Hermes	4-2
Cumbernauld United	v	Cruden Bay	4-0
Kirkintilloch Rob Roy	v	Cumnock Juniors	2-3
Ashfield	v	Girvan	4-4
Girvan	v	Ashfield	4-3
Kirkcaldy Y.M.C.A. F.C	v	Kilsyth Rangers	2-6
Yoker Athletic	v	Lanark United	2-0
Benburb	v	Blantyre Victoria	1-0
Forth Wanderers	v	Hurlford United	1-1
Hurlford United	v	Forth Wanderers	4-0
Darvel Juniors	v	Rutherglen Glencairn	1-2
Cambuslang Rangers	v	Kennoway Star Hearts	2-1
Beith Juniors	v	Sauchie Juniors	1-2
Linlithgow Rose	v	Shotts Bon Accord	1-2
Livingston United	v	Penicuik Athletic	1-3
Dundonald Bluebell	v	Harthill Royal	4-0
Dalkeith Thistle	v	Hill of Beath Hawthorn	1-4

ROUND 4

Shotts Bon Accord	v	Dunbar United	2-2
Dunbar United	v	Shotts Bon Accord	4-4, 3-4p
Benburb	v	Whitletts Victoria	2-3
Camelon Juniors	v	Carnoustie Panmure	5-2
Cumnock Juniors	v	Neilston Juniors	4-1
St. Andrew's United	v	Bo'ness United	1-2
Tayport	v	Hill of Beath Hawthorn	3-2
Kilsyth Rangers	v	Largs Thistle	3-3
Largs Thistle	v	Kilsyth Rangers	3-3, 3-4
Musselburgh Athletic	v	Glenafton Athletic	1-4
Irvine Meadow X1	v	Petershill	2-2
Petershill	v	Irvine Meadow XI	0-2
Larkhall Thistle	v	Hurlford United	0-3
Cambuslang Rangers	v	Dundonald Bluebell	0-3
Yoker Athletic	v	Montrose Roselea	3-2
Pollok	v	Penicuik Athletic	1-1
Penicuik Athletic	v	Pollok	2-1
Kilwinning Rangers	v	Sauchie Juniors	1-3
Dalry Thistle	v	Cumbernauld United	
Girvan	v	Rutherglen Glencairn	2-2
Rutherglen Glencairn	v	Girvan	1-1, 5-4

ROUND 5

Dundonald Bluebell	v	Dalry Thistle	5-2
Kilsyth Rangers	v	Cumnock Juniors	0-4
Penicuik Athletic	v	Irvine Meadow X1	0-0
Irvine Meadow X1	v	Penicuik Athletic	4-3
Tayport	v	Hurlford United	1-2
Whitletts Victoria	v	Yoker Athletic	4-1
Glenafton Athletic	v	Shotts Bon Accord	3-2
Camelon Juniors	v	Sauchie Juniors	3-3
Sauchie Juniors	v	Camelon Juniors	1-3
Rutherglen Glencairn	v	Bo'ness United	1-2

QUARTER FINALS

Cumnock Juniors	v	Glenafton Athletic	2-2
Glenafton Athletic	v	Cumnock Juniors	2-1
Dundonald Bluebell	v	Hurlford United	0-3
Camelon Juniors	v	Whitletts Victoria	7-0
Irvine Meadow X1	v	Bo'ness United	1-0

SEMI FINALS

Camelon Juniors	v	Glenafton Athletic	2-3
Irvine Meadow X1	v	Hurlford United	3-4

FINAL

Glenafton Athletic	v	Hurlford United	0-3

WELSH TABLES 2013-14

WELSH PREMIER

		P	W	D	L	F	A	GD	Pts
1	The New Saints	32	22	7	3	86	20	66	73
2	Airbus UK Broughton (-1)	32	17	9	6	56	34	22	59
3	Aberystwyth Town (-3)	32	15	9	8	72	48	24	51
4	Carmarthen Town	32	14	6	12	54	51	3	48
5	Bangor City	32	14	6	12	47	50	-3	48
6	Bala Town	32	13	6	13	61	45	16	45
7	Newtown AFC	32	12	6	14	46	58	-12	42
8	Rhyl	32	11	5	16	43	49	-6	38
9	Port Talbot Town	32	10	8	14	45	53	-8	38
10	Gap Connah's Quay	32	10	8	14	47	65	-18	38
11	Prestatyn Town	32	9	8	15	42	47	-5	35
12	Afan Lido	32	3	6	23	21	100	-79	15

CYMRU ALLIANCE

		P	W	D	L	F	A	GD	Pts
1	Cefn Druids	30	22	7	1	90	20	70	73
2	Conwy Borough	30	19	6	5	66	35	31	63
3	Caernarfon Town	30	18	8	4	79	33	46	62
4	Caersws	30	17	10	3	56	32	24	61
5	Llandudno	30	12	9	9	55	42	13	45
6	Guilsfield	30	10	12	8	44	41	3	42
7	Porthmadog	30	12	6	12	55	53	2	42
8	Flint Town United	30	12	5	13	46	53	-7	41
9	Holyhead Hotspur	30	9	10	11	53	57	-4	37
10	Penycae	30	10	4	16	47	64	-17	34
11	Rhayader Town	30	8	9	13	41	60	-19	33
12	Buckley Town	30	6	13	11	41	54	-13	31
13	Llanidloes Town	30	8	6	16	44	63	-19	30
14	Rhydymwyn	30	8	4	18	32	64	-32	28
15	Penrhyncoch	30	5	8	17	35	58	-23	23
16	Llanrhaeadr (-3)	30	5	1	24	32	87	-55	13

WELSH LEAGUE

Division One

		P	W	D	L	F	A	GD	Pts
1	Monmouth Town	30	21	2	7	78	33	45	65
2	Taffs Well	30	19	6	5	63	30	33	63
3	Penybont	30	17	4	9	77	44	33	55
4	Haverfordwest County	30	16	7	7	59	37	22	55
5	Goytre	30	15	9	6	49	43	6	54
6	Cambrian & Clydach	30	15	5	10	60	44	16	50
7	Caerau (Ely)	30	12	10	8	52	51	1	46
8	Aberdare Town	30	13	5	12	49	48	1	44
9	Goytre United	30	11	6	13	56	43	13	39
10	AFC Porth	30	10	9	11	48	49	-1	39
11	Ton Pentre	30	9	11	10	36	47	-11	38
12	Pontardawe Town	30	9	6	15	34	60	-26	33
13	Cwmbran Celtic	30	7	5	18	40	58	-18	26
14	Tata Steel	30	6	7	17	29	65	-36	25
15	Aberbargoed Buds	30	4	8	18	35	66	30	20
16	West End	30	5	2	23	36	84	-48	17

Division Two

		P	W	D	L	F	A	GD	Pts
1	Cardiff Met University	30	20	6	4	86	24	62	66
2	Briton Ferry Llansawel	30	21	3	6	84	42	42	66
3	Garden Village	30	20	4	6	93	34	59	64
4	Chepstow Town	30	19	7	4	84	36	48	64
5	Undy Athletic	30	19	6	5	70	32	38	63
6	Caldicot Town	30	15	8	7	78	34	44	53
7	Ely Rangers	30	12	7	11	62	56	6	43
8	Croesyceilog	30	13	4	13	72	75	-3	43
9	Penrhiwceiber Rangers	30	12	4	14	50	52	-2	40
10	Caerleon	30	11	6	13	63	63	0	39
11	AFC Llwydcoed	30	11	4	15	63	57	6	37
12	Dinas Powys	30	8	9	13	39	46	-7	33
13	Ammanford	30	7	7	16	49	55	-6	28
14	Cardiff Corinthians	30	5	6	19	42	83	-41	21
15	Newport YMCA	30	4	3	23	37	99	-62	15
16	Caerau	30	1	0	29	31	215	-184	3

Division Three

		P	W	D	L	F	A	GD	Pts
1	Barry Town United	36	29	3	4	116	29	87	90
2	Llanwern	36	27	7	2	112	41	71	88
3	Risca United	36	23	6	7	96	51	45	75
4	Cwmamman United	36	23	4	9	106	63	43	73
5	Lliswerry	36	15	11	10	76	56	20	56
6	Llanelli Town	36	16	6	14	75	59	16	54
7	Rhoose	36	14	8	14	82	66	16	50
8	Tredegar Town	36	14	8	14	66	76	-10	50
9	Cardiff Grange Harlequins	36	13	9	14	71	67	4	48
10	Newport Civil Service	36	12	5	19	65	79	-14	41
11	Treowen Stars	36	12	5	19	49	84	-35	41
12	Bridgend Street	36	11	7	18	58	73	-15	40
13	Bettws	36	11	6	19	61	85	-24	39
14	Llantwit Major (-3)	36	12	5	19	50	72	-22	38
15	Pontypridd Town	36	10	8	18	46	81	-35	38
16	Treharris Athletic Western	36	9	10	17	61	91	-30	37
17	Abertillery Bluebirds	36	9	10	17	52	88	-36	37
18	Cwmaman Institute	36	10	4	22	50	102	-62	34
19	Newcastle Emlyn	36	8	6	22	50	79	-29	30

WELSH NATIONAL LEAGUE

Premier		P	W	D	L	F	A	GD	Pts
1	Mold Alexandra	30	21	6	3	78	26	52	69
2	Hawarden Rangers	30	22	3	5	78	30	48	69
3	Ruthin Town	30	19	3	8	67	35	32	60
4	Borras Park Albion	30	17	6	7	88	71	17	57
5	Gresford Athletic	30	17	3	10	59	47	12	54
6	Chirk AAA	30	15	8	7	69	47	22	53
7	Corwen	30	12	10	8	60	37	23	46
8	Llay Welfare	30	12	7	11	53	51	2	43
9	Saltney Town	30	13	2	15	69	58	11	41
10	Rhos Aelwyd	30	10	7	13	43	58	-15	37
11	Llangollen Town	30	10	3	17	63	81	-18	33
12	Coedpoeth United	30	8	8	14	61	77	-16	32
13	Penyffordd	30	8	7	15	55	82	-27	31
14	Brickfield Rangers	30	6	6	18	55	77	-22	24
15	Overton	30	5	3	22	29	83	-54	18
16	Brymbo	30	3	2	25	16	83	-67	11

Division One		P	W	D	L	F	A	GD	Pts
1	FC Nomads of Connah's Quay	20	20	0	0	140	11	129	60
2	Point of Ayr	20	15	2	3	106	25	81	47
3	Llanuwchllyn	20	15	2	3	80	36	44	47
4	Castell AC	20	13	2	5	71	37	34	41
5	Argoed United	20	9	4	7	52	49	3	31
6	Venture Community	20	6	4	10	48	78	-30	22
7	Lex Glyndwr	20	6	3	11	40	76	-36	21
8	Garden Village	20	3	6	11	34	73	-39	15
9	Acrefair Youth (-3)	20	5	3	12	44	101	-57	15
10	New Brighton Villa	20	2	2	16	31	77	-46	8
11	Johnstown Youth	20	1	2	17	24	107	-83	5

WELSH ALLIANCE

Division One		P	W	D	L	F	A	GD	Pts
1	Denbigh Town	28	25	3	0	96	18	78	78
2	Holywell Town	28	20	5	3	103	23	80	65
3	Llanrug United	28	18	5	5	76	43	33	59
4	Barmouth & Dyffryn United	28	14	4	10	53	58	-5	46
5	Glantraeth	28	14	4	10	67	61	6	43
6	Llanberis	28	12	3	13	69	65	4	39
7	Bodedern Athletic	28	10	7	11	49	53	-4	37
8	Gwalchmai	28	10	5	13	55	74	-19	35
9	Glan Conwy	28	8	10	10	48	64	-16	34
10	Llanrwst United	28	8	5	15	52	69	-17	29
11	Nefyn United	28	9	1	18	34	73	-39	28
12	Llandudno Junction	28	6	9	13	46	66	-20	27
13	Pwllheli	28	7	4	17	37	69	-32	25
14	Llanfairpwll	28	7	3	18	51	70	-19	24
15	Llandyrnog United	28	7	2	19	37	67	-30	23

Division Two		P	W	D	L	F	A	GD	Pts
1	Penrhyndeudraeth	24	22	1	1	114	23	91	67
2	Kinmel Bay Sports	24	16	5	3	92	38	54	53
3	Trearddur Bay	24	15	4	5	79	37	42	49
4	St Asaph (-3)	24	15	4	5	77	33	44	46
5	Nantlle Vale	24	13	3	8	69	48	21	42
6	Halkyn United	24	12	2	10	67	57	10	38
7	Meliden	24	11	2	11	60	55	5	35
8	Greenfield	24	9	4	11	51	57	-6	31
9	Penmaenmawr Phoenix	24	9	2	13	53	67	-14	29
10	Blaenau Amt	24	7	1	16	61	95	-34	22
11	Amlwch Town	24	6	2	16	31	72	-41	20
12	Gaerwen	24	3	1	20	23	86	-63	10
13	Bethesda Athletic	24	1	3	20	16	125	-109	6

MID WALES LEAGUE

Division One		P	W	D	L	F	A	GD	Pts
1	Llandrindod Wells	28	22	1	5	101	27	74	67
2	Llanfair United	28	20	6	2	74	28	46	66
3	Carno	28	19	4	5	70	33	37	61
4	Aberaeron	28	16	6	6	67	40	27	54
5	Berriew	28	16	4	8	79	39	40	52
6	Waterloo	28	15	4	9	73	50	23	49
7	Llansantffraid Village	28	12	3	13	66	69	-3	39
8	Aberystwyth University	28	9	4	15	56	66	-10	31
9	Bow Street	28	9	4	15	49	77	-28	31
10	Tywyn Bryncrug	28	9	3	16	57	86	-29	30
11	Four Crosses	28	9	3	16	49	83	-34	30
12	Montgomery	28	8	5	15	47	75	-28	29
13	Welshpool (-3)	28	8	3	17	36	66	-30	24
14	Dyffryn Banw	28	6	4	18	42	85	-43	22
15	Buith Wells	28	3	4	21	43	85	-42	13

Division Two		P	W	D	L	F	A	GD	Pts
1	Rhosgoch	18	16	0	2	72	17	55	48
2	Machynlleth	18	13	2	3	57	33	24	41
3	Knighton	18	11	5	2	49	18	31	38
4	Hay St Mary's	18	9	3	6	57	36	21	30
5	Abermule	18	9	1	8	32	27	5	28
6	Presteigne	18	7	4	7	42	51	-9	25
7	Kerry	18	3	5	10	27	49	-22	14
8	Talgarth	18	3	3	12	26	42	-16	12
9	Bont	18	1	5	12	19	58	-39	8
10	Newbridge (-3)	18	2	4	12	23	73	-50	7

CLYWD LEAGUE

Premier Division	P	W	D	L	F	A	GD	Pts
1 Llannefydd	20	17	1	2	63	32	31	52
2 Llansannan	20	13	2	5	45	35	10	41
3 Machno United	20	11	3	6	62	32	30	36
4 BRO Cernyw	20	12	0	8	40	40	0	36
5 Mochdre Sports	20	11	2	7	53	36	17	35
6 Prestatyn Rovers	20	10	2	8	47	46	1	32
7 Betws-Yn-Rhos	20	7	4	9	37	41	-4	25
8 Rhyl Athletic	20	4	5	11	43	62	-19	17
9 Rhos United	20	4	4	12	40	49	-9	16
10 Cerrigydrudion	20	3	5	12	42	62	-20	14
11 Old Colwyn	20	3	2	15	46	83	-37	11

Division One	P	W	D	L	F	A	GD	Pts
1 Conwy Legion United	18	15	1	2	99	21	78	46
2 Prestatyn Sports	18	14	1	3	81	21	60	43
3 Rhyl Town AFC	18	13	0	5	55	27	28	39
4 F.C. Tudno	18	11	1	6	58	48	10	34
5 Trefnant (-3)	18	11	1	6	76	60	16	31
6 Y Glannau	18	9	1	8	48	57	-9	28
7 Llandudno United	18	8	0	10	72	50	22	24
8 Betws-Yn-Rhos	18	3	1	14	23	77	-54	10
9 Prestatyn Albion	18	2	0	16	26	90	-64	6
10 Llysfaen	18	1	0	17	19	106	-87	3

NEATH & DISTRICT LEAGUE

Premier Division	P	W	D	L	F	A	GD	Pts
1 Ystradgynlais AFC(A)	22	18	2	2	60	17	43	56
2 Giants Grave (A)	22	16	1	5	77	33	44	49
3 Ynysygerwn (A)	22	14	4	4	65	32	33	46
4 Briton Ferry FC(A)	22	13	4	5	60	25	35	43
5 Bryn Rovers (A)	22	8	5	9	56	60	-4	29
6 Seven Sisters FC (A)	22	9	1	12	45	46	-1	28
7 Ynysymeudwy Ath (A)	22	8	4	10	43	51	-8	28
8 FC Clydach (A)	22	8	3	11	47	58	-11	27
9 Glynneath Town (A)	22	7	4	11	44	67	-23	25
10 Sunnybank WMC (A)	22	6	3	13	38	66	-28	19
11 Park Travellers (A)	22	3	5	14	31	63	-32	14
12 Resolven (A)	22	2	4	16	28	76	-48	10

Division One	P	W	D	L	F	A	GD	Pts
1 Onllwyn FC (A)	18	15	1	2	82	22	60	46
2 Cwm Wanderers (A)	18	14	1	3	66	22	44	43
3 Cambrian FC(A)	18	11	2	5	53	36	17	35
4 Harp Rovers (A)	18	8	3	7	38	52	-14	27
5 Cilfrew Rovers (A)	18	7	2	9	35	34	1	23
6 Bryncoch FC (A)	18	7	2	9	33	67	-34	23
7 FC Cimla	18	7	1	10	39	46	-7	22
8 Coelbren Ath	18	6	2	10	37	42	-5	20
9 FC Nedd	18	6	2	10	45	55	-10	20
10 Clydach Sports (A)	18	0	2	16	21	73	-52	2

Division Two	P	W	D	L	F	A	GD	Pts
1 Cwmamman Utd(A)	18	14	0	4	44	20	24	42
2 Mond FC(A)	18	12	0	6	65	45	20	36
3 Longford FC(A)	18	11	1	6	88	44	44	34
4 Tonna FC(A)	18	9	4	5	56	27	29	31
5 AFC Pontardawe (A)	18	9	3	6	67	24	43	30
6 Cimla Youth FC	18	8	4	6	49	35	14	28
7 Rhos FC (A)	18	7	4	7	55	47	8	25
8 Godregraig Ath (A)	18	6	0	12	68	72	-4	18
9 Greyhound FC	18	5	2	11	38	65	-27	17
10 Borough (A)	18	0	0	18	15	166	-151	0

NEWPORT & DISTRICT FOOTBALL LEAGUE

Premier X	P	W	D	L	F	A	GD	Pts
1 West of St Julians	18	16	0	2	72	22	+50	48
2 Villa Dino C/Ch	18	14	4	0	102	20	+82	46
3 Machen FC	18	9	4	5	66	38	+28	31
4 Cwmcarn Athletic	18	9	4	5	49	35	+14	31
5 Graig-Y-Rhacca	18	8	2	8	47	37	+10	26
6 River Usk	18	6	3	9	43	53	-10	21
7 Docks Cons	18	7	0	11	58	74	-16	21
8 The George	18	4	7	7	43	46	-3	19
9 Shaftesbury Youth	18	4	2	12	36	72	-36	14
10 Caerleon Town	18	0	0	18	23	142	-119	0
11 Pioneer FC - Withdrawn								

Premier Y	P	W	D	L	F	A	GD	Pts
1 Pill AFC	24	21	1	2	129	37	+92	64
2 AC Pontymister	24	17	4	3	95	32	+63	55
3 Trethomas Bluebirds	24	15	2	7	86	43	+43	47
4 Albion Rovers	24	15	1	8	106	57	+49	46
5 Malpas United	24	14	2	8	78	56	+22	44
6 Npt Corinthians	24	12	3	9	89	76	+13	39
7 Lliswerry	24	12	2	10	69	79	-10	38
8 Cwmbran Town	24	10	1	13	74	89	-15	31
9 Coed Eva Ath	24	8	5	11	87	80	+7	29
10 Cromwell Youth	24	8	3	13	63	96	-33	27
11 Cwmbran Celtic	24	5	3	16	54	99	-45	18
12 Lucas Cwmbran	24	2	3	19	51	114	-63	9
13 Pontnewydd United	24	1	2	21	37	160	-123	5
14 Marshfield - Withdrawn								
15 Spencer Boys Club -Withdrawn								

Division One		P	W	D	L	F	A	GD	Pts
1	Pill AFC	28	27	1	0	128	34	+94	82
2	Gaer Park AFC	28	18	0	10	91	85	+8	54
3	West of Julians	28	16	4	8	84	52	+32	52
4	Rogerstone	28	14	6	8	101	75	+26	48
5	Dock Cons	28	14	6	8	84	61	+23	48
6	Villa Dino C/Ch	28	12	9	7	87	62	+25	45
7	Croesyceiliog Athletic	28	13	5	10	88	64	+24	44
8	Spencer Boys Club	28	12	6	10	103	89	+14	42
9	K-2 AFC	28	12	4	12	76	59	+19	40
10	Albion Rovers	28	12	4	12	82	76	+6	40
11	AC Pontymister	28	10	3	15	50	73	-23	33
12	Ponthir	28	6	4	18	52	94	-42	22
13	Lliswerry	28	6	3	19	47	102	-55	21
14	Graig-Y-Rhacca	28	4	6	18	46	111	-65	18
15	Coed Eva Athletic	28	2	3	23	30	114	-84	9
16	River Usk - Withdrawn								

Division Two		P	W	D	L	F	A	GD	Pts
1	Maesglas United	28	22	2	4	138	40	+98	68
2	Pill AFC	28	21	1	6	111	36	+75	64
3	Cwmcarn Athletic	28	21	1	6	102	52	+50	64
4	Riverside Rovers	28	18	4	6	145	57	+88	58
6	CCYP AFC	28	17	1	10	118	88	+30	52
5	Lliswerry AFC	28	17	3	8	120	64	+56	54
7	Lucas Cwmbran	28	15	4	9	110	77	+33	49
8	FC Rileys	28	13	3	12	101	70	+31	42
9	Albion Rovers	28	13	2	12	90	83	+7	41
10	Risca Athletic	28	11	3	14	87	96	-9	36
11	Racing Club Npt	28	9	1	18	66	115	-49	28
12	Caerleon Town	28	6	1	21	46	155	-109	19
13	Cromwell Youth	28	4	4	20	50	121	-71	16
14	Newport Eagles	28	4	3	21	41	167	-126	15
15	Rogerstone	28	2	1	25	44	148	-104	7
16	AC Pontymister -Withdrawn								

PEMBROKESHIRE LEAGUE

Division One		P	W	D	L	F	A	GD	Pts
1	Hakin United	26	21	5	0	102	30	72	67
2	Goodwick United	26	17	6	3	77	37	40	57
3	Tenby	26	17	5	4	85	28	57	56
4	Narberth	26	15	4	7	82	47	35	49
5	Johnston	26	12	8	6	75	39	36	44
6	Merlins Bridge	26	12	5	9	73	63	10	41
7	Monkton Swifts	26	12	4	10	66	62	4	40
8	West Dragons	26	9	8	9	56	45	11	35
9	St Clears	26	9	5	12	52	68	-16	32
10	Neyland	26	7	8	11	49	56	-7	29
11	Pennar Robins	26	6	6	14	31	65	-34	24
12	Saundersfoot Sports	26	3	7	16	33	85	-52	16
13	Hundleton	26	3	2	21	32	113	-81	11
14	St Ishmaels	26	1	3	22	25	100	-75	6

Division Two		P	W	D	L	F	A	GD	Pts
1	Herbrandston	26	20	4	2	100	32	68	64
2	Angle	26	19	3	4	102	28	74	60
3	Clarbeston Road	26	19	2	5	114	30	84	59
4	Prendergast Villa	26	19	2	5	75	25	50	59
5	Solva	26	14	7	5	68	44	24	49
6	Milford United	26	10	5	11	51	52	-1	35
7	Milford Athletic	26	10	4	12	51	49	2	34
8	Carew	26	8	7	11	63	66	-3	31
9	Letterston	26	8	7	11	35	51	-16	31
10	Fishguard Sports	26	9	3	14	55	74	-19	30
11	Johnston II	26	7	1	18	45	98	-53	22
12	Goodwick United II	26	5	4	17	39	94	-55	19
13	Pennar Robins II	26	4	6	16	35	99	-64	18
14	Kilgetty	26	2	1	23	23	114	-91	7

Division Three		P	W	D	L	F	A	GD	Pts
1	Haverfordwest Cricket Club	26	21	0	5	101	43	58	63
2	Tenby II	26	18	3	5	104	38	66	56
3	Lamphey	26	16	1	9	83	58	25	49
4	Hakin United II	26	14	5	7	69	51	18	47
5	Camrose	26	13	4	9	69	58	11	43
6	Narberth II	26	12	3	11	67	78	-11	39
7	Hubberston	26	11	2	13	71	98	-27	35
8	Broad Haven	26	10	4	12	73	75	-2	34
9	Cosheston Cougars	26	11	1	14	62	72	-10	34
10	Lawrenny	26	8	6	12	61	63	-2	30
11	Clarbeston Road II	26	7	6	13	60	68	-8	27
12	Merlins Bridge II	26	9	5	12	47	49	-2	26
13	Manorbier United	26	3	6	17	53	106	-53	15
14	Pennar Robins III	26	4	4	18	52	115	-63	9

Division Four		P	W	D	L	F	A	GD	Pts
1	Milford United II	26	21	4	1	115	22	93	67
2	Carew II	26	17	4	5	84	35	49	55
3	Monkton Swifts II	26	18	3	5	109	39	70	52
4	Pendine	26	15	3	8	87	77	10	48
5	Milford Athletic II	26	12	5	9	71	60	11	41
6	West Dragons II	26	11	5	10	69	57	12	38
7	St Clears II	26	10	5	11	64	60	4	35
8	Saundersfoot Sports II	26	10	4	12	58	91	-33	34
9	St Ishmaels II	26	8	2	16	48	67	-19	26
10	Pembroke Boro	26	8	2	16	56	82	-26	26
11	Neyland II	26	8	1	17	46	87	-41	25
12	Prendergast Villa II	26	6	5	15	46	82	-36	23
13	Hundleton II	26	6	5	15	44	98	-54	23
14	St Florence	26	5	6	15	50	90	-40	21

WELSH FOOTBALL

Division Five	P	W	D	L	F	A	GD	Pts
1 Llangwm AFC	30	23	3	4	126	43	83	72
2 Herbrandston II	30	23	2	5	132	47	85	71
3 Letterston II	30	19	3	8	85	41	44	60
4 Angle II	30	17	4	9	108	60	48	55
5 Lawrenny II	30	17	4	9	84	55	29	55
6 Fishguard Sports II	30	16	3	11	110	66	44	51
7 Solva II	30	16	3	11	105	61	44	51
8 Broad Haven II	30	12	7	11	94	86	8	43
9 Cosheston Cougars II	30	15	3	12	91	60	31	42
10 Haverfordwest Cricket Club II	30	11	4	15	63	92	-29	37
11 Narberth III	30	11	2	17	73	106	-33	35
12 Carew III	30	9	3	18	65	100	-35	30
13 Camrose II	30	8	4	18	52	68	-16	28
14 Monkton Swifts III	30	9	3	18	68	128	-60	27
15 Kilgetty II	30	9	1	20	50	116	-66	25
16 Pembroke Boro II	30	0	1	29	25	202	-177	-2

WELSH CUP

FIRST QUALIFYING ROUND

Llandrindod Wells	v	Newbridge on Wye	5-0
Llanfair United	v	Kerry	9-1
Machynlleth	v	Hay St Mary	6-3
Presteigne St. Andrews	v	Llanfyllin Town	7-0
Brickfield Rangers FC	v	New Brighton Villa	H Wo
FC Nomads of Connah's Quay	v	Halkyn United	3-2
Greenfield	v	Connahs Quay Town	H Wo
Kinmel Bay Sports	v	St Asaph City FC	3-4
Lex XI	v	Castell Alun Colts	2-2, 4-2p
Llandudno Junction	v	Gaerwen	7-2
Llandyrnog United	v	Llanuwchllyn	1-3
Llangefni Town	v	Blaenau Amateur	1-2
Llannerch ym Medd	v	Amlwch Town	4-1
Llanystumdwy	v	Penmaenmawr Phoenix	3-4
Meliden	v	Dyffryn Nantlle Vale	0-2
Nefyn United	v	Trearddur Bay United	4-3
Penrhyndeudraeth FC	v	Llanfairpwll	3-1
Rhos Aelwyd	v	Llay Miners Welfare	A-A

Match Abandoned after 49 minutes, with score 9-1

Venture Community	v	Caerwys	2-5
Aber Valley YMCA	v	Cardiff Grange Harlequins	0-5
AFC Llwydcoed	v	Carnetown	10-0
AFC Rumney Juniors	v	Tonyrefail Welfare	3-2
Barry Town Utd	v	Treforest	8-0
Bettws	v	Rhoose FC	0-4
Blaenrhondda	v	Treharris Athletic Western	0-5
Butetown FC	v	Aberfan	3-1
Cardiff Corinthians	v	Brecon Corinthians FC	1-3
Chepstow Town FC	v	Clwb Cymric	3-0
Cwmbran Town	v	Cardiff Metropolitan	2-3
Dafen Welfare	v	Sully Sports	1-8
Garw	v	Kenfig Hill	7-1
Llanharry	v	Canton Rangers	2-2, 2-4p
Llantwit Fardre	v	Bridgend Street	0-1
Llantwit Major FC	v	Penrhiwfer FC	3-1
Lliswerry FC	v	Fairfield United FC	2-3
Merthyr Saints	v	Cwmaman Institute	8-1
Nelson Cavaliers	v	Cardiff Hibernian	1-2
Newcastle Emlyn	v	Llanelli Town AFC	4-1
Penygraig	v	Pontyclun	2-1
Pontllotyn FC	v	Newport Civil Service	1-5
Risca United	v	Llanwern	1-4
Splott Albion	v	RTB Ebbw Vale Ladies	3-0
Tredegar Athletic	v	Cefn Fforest	1-3
Tredegar Town	v	Trelewis Welfare	0-1
Trefelin	v	Porthcawl Town Athletic	3-1
Trethomas Bluebirds	v	Graig y Rhacca	6-0
Ynysddu Welfare	v	Abertillery Bluebirds	3-2
Ely Rangers	v	Sporting Marvels FC	8-0
Ely Valley FC	v	Pontypridd Town	0-6

SECOND QUALIFYING ROUND

Aberaeron	v	Bow Street FC	3-0
Builth Wells	v	Llanfair United	3-7
Carno	v	Barmouth & Dyffryn United	1-2
Llandrindod Wells	v	Waterloo Rovers	5-3
Llansantffraid Village	v	Berriew	1-5
Machynlleth	v	Montgomery Town	3-0
Presteigne St. Andrews	v	Four Crosses	3-2
Welshpool Town	v	Tywyn Bryncrug	A Wo
Brickfield Rangers FC	v	Llandudno Junction	3-1
Brymbo	v	Chirk AAA	0-4
Corwen	v	Caerwys	0-1
FC Nomads of Connah's Quay	v	Penmaenmawr Phoenix	3-0
Greenfield	v	Mold Alexandra	1-3
Gresford Athletic	v	Coedpoeth United	2-2, 2-4p
Holywell Town	v	Llannerch ym Medd	8-1
Lex XI	v	Denbigh Town	0-1
Llanberis	v	Hawarden Rangers	3-2
Llanllyfni	v	Llangollen Town	0-6
Llanrug United	v	St Asaph City FC	5-0
Llanrwst United	v	Llanuwchllyn	4-2
Nefyn United	v	Blaenau Amateur	7-3
Overton Recreational	v	Gwalchmai	1-3
Penyffordd	v	Glan Conwy	3-4
Pwllheli	v	Dyffryn Nantlle Vale	3-1
Ruthin Town	v	Glantraeth	1-3
Saltney Town	v	Penrhyndeudraeth FC	1-3
AFC Llwydcoed	v	Penrhiwceiber Rangers	2-1
AFC Rumney Juniors	v	Barry Town Utd	0-3
Brecon Corinthians FC	v	Cardiff Metropolitan	1-4
Butetown FC	v	Cardiff Grange Harlequins	2-1
Caerau	v	Trefelin	0-11
Caerleon	v	Briton Ferry Llansawel	1-5
Caldicot Town	v	Newport YMCA	5-0
Canton Rangers	v	Cardiff Hibernian	0-6
Croesyceiliog	v	Splott Albion	0-1
Fairfield United FC	v	Cefn Fforest	8-4
Garden Village	v	Ammanford	4-3 aet
Llantwit Major FC	v	Trelewis Welfare	6-2
Llanwern	v	Treowen Stars	2-3
Newcastle Emlyn	v	Ely Rangers	1-0
Newport Civil Service	v	Garw	3-2
Penygraig	v	Sully Sports	2-4
Pontypridd Town	v	Bridgend Street	1-1, 1-4p
Rhoose FC	v	Merthyr Saints	5-1
Treharris Athletic Western	v	Dinas Powys	2-1
Undy Athletic	v	Trethomas Bluebirds	2-1
Ynysddu Welfare	v	Chepstow Town FC	0-3

ROUND 1

Bodedern Athletic	v	Glantraeth	3-2 aet
Caernarfon Town	v	Llanrug United	4-1
Caersws	v	Denbigh Town	2-0
Coedpoeth United	v	Barmouth & Dyffryn United	2-6
FC Nomads of Connah's Quay	v	Pwllheli	3-0
Flint Town United	v	Llanberis	3-1
Glan Conwy	v	Llanidloes Town	1-3
Guilsfield Athletic	v	Machynlleth	6-1 aet
Holyhead Hotspur	v	Cefn Druids	0-3
Holywell Town	v	Penrhyncoch	3-0
Llandudno	v	Llanrhaeadr Ym Mochant	5-1
Llanfair United	v	Gwalchmai	3-2
Llangollen Town	v	Buckley Town	0-2
Llanrwst United	v	Conwy Borough FC	3-4
Nefyn United	v	Penrhyndeudraeth FC	2-1
Penycae	v	Brickfield Rangers FC	7-4 aet
Porthmadog	v	Mold Alexandra	1-0
Rhayader Town	v	Chirk AAA	1-0
Rhydymwyn	v	Caerwys	2-1
Tywyn Bryncrug	v	Berriew	2-2, 5-4p
AFC Porth	v	Monmouth Town	1-2
Barry Town Utd	v	Taffs Well	1-0
Bridgend Street	v	Tata Steel	1-3
Briton Ferry Llansawel	v	Aberbargoed Buds	3-1 aet
Caerau Ely	v	Cardiff Hibernian	4-0
Caldicot Town	v	Splott Albion	2-1
Cambrian & Clydach Vale	v	Butetown FC	4-0
Cardiff Metropolitan	v	Aberaeron	4-1
Cwmbran Celtic	v	Penybont FC	0-1
Garden Village	v	Rhoose FC	1-2
Goytre (Gwent)	v	Pontardawe Town	1-2
Goytre United	v	Trefelin	3-1
Llandrindod Wells	v	Newport Civil Service	3-0
Llantwit Major FC	v	Treharris Athletic Western	2-3
Newcastle Emlyn	v	Chepstow Town FC	1-2 aet
Sully Sports	v	AFC Llwydcoed	3-1
Ton Pentre	v	Fairfield United FC	3-0
Treowen Stars	v	Aberdare Town	2-4
Undy Athletic	v	Presteigne St. Andrews	5-2
West End	v	Haverfordwest County	2-3

ROUND 2

Barmouth & Dyffryn United	v	Cefn Druids	1-3
Bodedern Athletic	v	Tywyn Bryncrug	5-1
Buckley Town	v	Rhayader Town	1-0
Conwy Borough FC	v	Flint Town United	3-2
Holywell Town	v	Penycae	3-0
Llanfair United	v	Guilsfield Athletic	2-1
Llanidloes Town	v	Llandudno	2-0
Nefyn United	v	Caersws	1-3 aet
Rhydymwyn	v	FC Nomads of Connah's Quay	4 1
Caernarfon Town	v	Porthmadog	1-2
Barry Town Utd	v	Undy Athletic	4-3 aet
Caldicot Town	v	Penybont FC	3-0

"Caldicot disqualified for fielding an ineligible player. Penybont through to Round 3 "

Cardiff Metropolitan	v	Haverfordwest County	6-1
Llandrindod Wells	v	Caerau Ely	3-3 4-3p
Briton Ferry Llansawel	v	Aberdare Town	2-3
Cambrian & Clydach Vale	v	Pontardawe Town	2-0
Goytre United	v	Chepstow Town FC	0-1
Ton Pentre	v	Sully Sports	0-1
Treharris Athletic Western	v	Monmouth Town	1-7
Rhoose FC	v	Tata Steel	1-0

ROUND 3

Aberdare Town	v	Prestatyn Town	4-2
Afan Lido	v	Rhydymwyn	2-0
Bodedern Athletic	v	Buckley Town	2-0 aet
Caersws	v	Gap Connahs Quay	2-1 aet
Cambrian & Clydach Vale	v	Chepstow Town FC	3-1
Carmarthen Town	v	Port Talbot Town	2-1
Cefn Druids	v	Barry Town Utd	5-2
Llandrindod Wells	v	Holywell Town	1-3
Llanfair United	v	Aberystwyth Town	2-4
Monmouth Town	v	Llanidloes Town	2-1
Newtown	v	Cardiff Metropolitan	2-1
Penybont FC	v	Airbus UK Broughton	0-2
Porthmadog	v	Sully Sports	2-1
Rhoose FC	v	Bala Town	1-6
Rhyl	v	Bangor City	1-2
Conwy Borough FC	v	The New Saints	1-2 aet

ROUND 4

Newtown	v	Holywell Town	2-3
Carmarthen Town	v	The New Saints	0-2
Monmouth Town	v	Porthmadog	2-3 aet
Bala Town	v	Cefn Druids	5-0
Airbus UK Broughton	v	Bangor City	2-0
Aberdare Town	v	Bodedern Athletic	4-1
Aberystwyth Town	v	Afan Lido	5-1
Caersws	v	Cambrian & Clydach Vale	4-3 aet

QUARTER FINALS

Aberdare Town	v	Bala Town	1-2
Aberystwyth Town	v	Caersws	2-1
Holywell Town	v	Porthmadog	2-1
The New Saints	v	Airbus UK Broughton	2-0

SEMI FINALS

Aberystwyth Town	v	Holywell Town	3-1
The New Saints	v	Bala Town	2-1

FINAL

Aberystwyth Town	v	The New Saints	2-3

WELSH TROPHY

ROUND 1

AFC Rumney Juniors	v	Marshfield	0-4
Cowbridge Town FC	v	Graig y Rhacca	4-3
Creigiau	v	L&G Cosmos	2-1
Race	v	Canton Rangers	3-1
Rockspur FC	v	Ely Valley FC	4-0

ROUND 2

Barmouth & Dyffryn United	v	Montgomery Town	H Wo
Dyffryn Banw	v	Llanfyllin Town	4-2
Four Crosses	v	Bow Street FC	3-1
Kerry	v	Machynlleth	0-3
Newcastle Emlyn	v	Corwen	0-2
Presteigne St. Andrews	v	Berriew	1-3
Tywyn Bryncrug	v	Llandrindod Wells	2-1
Welshpool Town	v	Talgarth Town	H Wo
Beaumaris Town FC	v	Bodedern Athletic	2-3
Caerwys	v	Chirk AAA	1-5
Castell Alun Colts	v	New Brighton Villa	7-0
Coedpoeth United	v	Saltney Town	2-3
Connahs Quay Town	v	Brickfield Rangers FC	A Wo

Dyffryn Nantlle Vale	v	Denbigh Town	2-4
Gaerwen	v	Llanystumdwy	1-4
Glan Conwy	v	Kinmel Bay Sports	0-1
Glantraeth	v	Penmaenmawr Phoenix	8-1
Greenfield	v	Ruthin Town	0-3
Gresford Athletic	v	Mold Alexandra	2-4
Halkyn United	v	Llangollen Town	2-5
Lex XI	v	Rhos Aelwyd	0-4
Llanberis	v	Llandudno Junction	2-3
Llanllyfni	v	Blaenau Amateur	0-3
Llanrug United	v	Amlwch Town	5-1
Llanuwchllyn	v	Llanrwst United	0-3
Llay Miners Welfare	v	FC Nomads of Connah's Quay	3-3, 6-7p
Nefyn United	v	Talysarn Celts FC	3-0
Overton Recreational	v	Argoed United	2-1
Penrhyndeudraeth FC	v	Meliden	4-2
Penyffordd	v	Llandyrnog United	3-4
Pwllheli	v	Gwalchmai	1-0
St Asaph City FC	v	Llangefni Town	7-1
Trearddur Bay United	v	Llanfairpwll	1-1, 8-7p
Venture Community	v	Brymbo	3-2
Marshfield	v	Fairfield United FC	0-3
Blaenrhondda	v	Abercarn United	1-2
Bonymaen Colts	v	Tongwynlais	1-0
Bridgend Street	v	Ragged School	2-0
Cardiff Corinthians	v	Blaenavon Blues	0-1
Carnetown	v	Cardiff Metropolitan	0-9
Clydach Wasps	v	Cardiff Hibernian	5-1
Creigiau	v	Cogan Coronation	6-1
Cwm Welfare FC	v	Cowbridge Town FC	7-1
Cwmamman United	v	Canton Liberal FC	4-2
Cwmfelin Press	v	Cefn Fforest	10-3
Dafen Welfare	v	Llanharry	7-0
Garden Village	v	Swansea Dockers	1-0
Kenfig Hill	v	Penlan FC	2-6
Llanelli Town AFC	v	Bryn Rovers	9-1
Maltsters Sports	v	RTB Ebbw Vale Ladies	5-3
Nelson Cavaliers	v	Baglan Dragons	0-2
Pencoed Athletic Amateur FC	v	Tredegar Athletic	2-3
Penrhiwceiber Constitutional Athletic	v	Garw	1-1, 3-2p
Race	v	Sporting Marvels FC	5-3 aet
Rhoose FC	v	Cornelly United	5-4 aet
Rockspur FC	v	Cwmbach Royal Stars	2-3
Sully Sports	v	Abertillery Excelsiors	4-1
Ton & Gelli	v	AFC Whitchurch	4-1
Trefelin	v	STM Sports	2-1
Ynystawe Athletic	v	Lliswerry FC	1-2
Ystradgynlais	v	Stanley Town FC	5-0

ROUND 3

FC Nomads of Connah's Quay	v	Dyffryn Banw	5-0
Barmouth & Dyffryn United	v	Glantraeth	2-1
Blaenau Amateur	v	St Asaph City FC	0-2
Brickfield Rangers FC	v	Overton Recreational	3-0
Castell Alun Colts	v	Llandudno Junction	1-3
Chirk AAA	v	Four Crosses	4-1
Kinmel Bay Sports	v	Denbigh Town	3-1
Llanrug United	v	Bodedern Athletic	4-1
Llanystumdwy	v	Holywell Town	0-6
Mold Alexandra	v	Llandyrnog United	2-1
Nefyn United	v	Penrhyndeudraeth FC	1-3
Pwllheli	v	Saltney Town	3-3, 3-5p
Ruthin Town	v	Llanrwst United	1-1, 3-2p
Trearddur Bay United	v	Corwen	2-3
Tywyn Bryncrug	v	Rhos Aelwyd	3-2
Venture Community	v	Berriew	0-9
Welshpool Town	v	Llangollen Town	1-2
Treowen Stars	v	Cwm Welfare FC	3-2
Fairfield United FC	v	Ton & Gelli	1-2
Baglan Dragons	v	Race	4-0
Blaenavon Blues	v	Cwmbach Royal Stars	1-1, 3-2p
Cwmamman United	v	Clydach Wasps	5-2
Cwmfelin Press	v	Bridgend Street	1-0
Dafen Welfare	v	Penlan FC	2-2, 6-7p
Kilvey Fords FC	v	Trefelin	1-8
Llanelli Town AFC	v	Bonymaen Colts	6-1
Machynlleth	v	Creigiau	3-0
Maltsters Sports	v	Cardiff Metropolitan	0-4
Penrhiwceiber Constitutional Athletic	v	Abercarn United	2-3
Rhoose FC	v	Tredegar Athletic	0-1
Sully Sports	v	Lliswerry FC	2-1
Garden Village	v	Ystradgynlais	4-1

ROUND 4

Berriew	v	Ruthin Town	1-3
Tywyn Bryncrug	v	St Asaph City FC	1-2
Brickfield Rangers FC	v	Chirk AAA	0-4
FC Nomads of Connah's Quay	v	Barmouth & Dyffryn United	4-3
Llangollen Town	v	Corwen	1-0
Llanrug United	v	Kinmel Bay Sports	2-1
Machynlleth	v	Llandudno Junction	3-2
Penrhyndeudraeth FC	v	Holywell Town	2-0
Saltney Town	v	Mold Alexandra	1-5
Cardiff Metropolitan	v	Llanelli Town AFC	4-2
Cwmamman United	v	Garden Village	1-7
Penlan FC	v	Abercarn United	2-0
Ton & Gelli	v	Baglan Dragons	4-1
Tredegar Athletic	v	Blaenavon Blues	0-2
Trefelin	v	Cwmfelin Press	5-2
Treowen Stars	v	Sully Sports	5-4 aet

ROUND 5

Llanrug United	v	Ruthin Town	3-1
Ton & Gelli	v	Machynlleth	2-1
Penlan FC	v	Garden Village	2-1
FC Nomads of Connah's Quay	v	Llangollen Town	3-0
Penrhyndeudraeth FC	v	Mold Alexandra	3-3 aet
St Asaph City FC	v	Chirk AAA	0-1
Trefelin	v	Blaenavon Blues	2-0
Treowen Stars	v	Cardiff Metropolitan	0-8

QUARTER FINALS

Llanrug United	v	FC Nomads of Connah's Quay	3-2
Trefelin	v	Penrhyndeudraeth FC	1-2
Chirk AAA	v	Penlan FC	9-0
Ton & Gelli	v	Cardiff Metropolitan	3-2

SEMI FINALS

Chirk AAA	v	Ton & Gelli	6-1
Llanrug United	v	Penrhyndeudraeth FC	2-0

FINAL

Chirk AAA	v	Llanrug United	2-3

the
FOOTBALL ASSOCIATION COMPETITIONS

ENGLAND C

RESULTS 2013-14

No.	Date	Comp	H/A	Opponents	Att:	Result	Goalscorers
1	Sept 10	F	H	Latvia U23		L 0-1	
2	Nov 19	F	H	Czech Republic U21		D 2-2	Franks, Norwood (pen)
3	Mar 04	F	A	Jordan U23		**W** 1-0	Berry
4	May 21	F	A	Sparta Prague B		D 2-2	Taylor (2)
5	May 24	ICT	A	Slovakia U23		L 0-1	
6	May 28	F	A	Hungary U21		L 2-4	Pearson, Taylor

ICT - International Challenge Trophy (Group A). F - Friendly

ENGLAND'S RESULTS 1979 - 2014

BARBADOS
02.06.08 Bridgetown 2 - 0

BELGIUM
11.02.03 KV Ostend 1 - 3
04.11.03 Darlington 2 - 2
15.11.05 FC Racing Jets 2 - 0
19.05.09 Oxford United 0 - 1
09.02.11 Luton Town 1 - 0
12.09.12 Gemeentalijk Sportstadion 2 - 1

BERMUDA
04.06.13 Hamilton 6 - 1

BOSNIA & HERZEGOVINA
16.09.08 Grbavia Stadium 2 - 6

CZECH REPUBLIC UNDER-21
19.11.13 Home 2 - 2

ESTONIA
12.10.10 1 - 0

FINLAND UNDER-21
14.04.93 Woking 1 - 3
30.05.94 Aanekoski 0 - 2
01.06.07 FC Hakka 1 - 0
15.11.07 Helsinki 2 - 0

GIBRALTAR
27.04.82 Gibraltar 3 - 2
31.05.95 Gibraltar 3 - 2
21.05.08 Colwyn Bay 1 - 0
15.11.11 Gibraltar 1 - 3

GRENADA
31.05.08 St. George's 1 - 1

HOLLAND
03.06.79 Stafford 1 - 0
07.06.80 Zeist 2 - 1
09.06.81 Lucca 2 - 0
03.06.82 Aberdeen 1 - 0
02.06.83 Scarborough 6 - 0
05.06.84 Palma 3 - 3
13.06.85 Vleuten 3 - 0
20.05.87 Kirkaldy 4 - 0
11.04.95 Aalsmeer 0 - 0
02.04.96 Irthlingborough 3 - 1
18.04.97 Appingedam 0 - 0
03.03.98 Crawley 2 - 1
30.03.99 Genemuiden 1 - 1
21.03.00 Northwich 1 - 0
22.03.01 Wihemina FC 3 - 0
24.04.02 Yeovil Town 1 - 0
25.03.03 BV Sparta 25 0 - 0
16.02.05 Woking 3 - 0
29.11.06 Burton Albion 4 - 1

HUNGARY
15.09.09 Szekesfehervar 1 - 1
28.05.14 Budapest 2 - 4

IRAQ
27.05.04 Macclesfield 1 - 5

IRISH PREMIER LEAGUE XI
13.02.07 Glenavon FC 1 - 3

ITALY
03.06.80 Zeist 2 - 0
13.06.81 Montecatini 1 - 1
01.06.82 Aberdeen 0 - 0
31.05.83 Scarborough 2 - 0
09.06.84 Reggio Emilia 0 - 1
11.06.85 Houten 2 - 2
18.05.87 Dunfermline 1 - 2
29.01.89 La Spezia 1 - 1
25.02.90 Solerno 0 - 2
05.03.91 Kettering 0 - 0
01.03.99 Hayes 4 - 1
01.03.00 Padova 1 - 1
20.11.02 AC Cremonese 3 - 2
11.02.04 Shrewsbury 1 - 4
10.11.04 US Ivrea FC 1 - 0
15.02.06 Cambridge United 3 - 1
12.11.08 Benevento 2 - 2
28.02.12 Fleetwood Town 1 - 1

JORDAN UNDER-23
04.03.14 Jordan 1 - 0

LATVIA UNDER-23
10.09.13 Latvia 0 - 1

MALTA UNDER-21
17.02.09 Malta 4 - 0

NORWAY UNDER-21
01.06.94 Slemmestad 1 - 2

POLAND
17.11.09 Gradiszk Wielpolski 2 - 1

PORTUGAL
19.05.11 Sixfields Stadium 0 - 1

REPUBLIC OF IRELAND
24.05.86 Kidderminster 2 - 1
26.05.86 Nuneaton 2 - 1
25.05.90 Dublin 2 - 1
27.05.90 Cork 3 - 0
27.02.96 Kidderminster 4 - 0
25.02.97 Dublin 0 - 2
16.05.02 Boston 1 - 2
20.05.03 Merthyr Tydfil 4 - 0
18.05.04 Deverondale 2 - 3
24.05.05 Cork 1 - 0
23.05.06 Eastbourne Boro' 2 - 0
22.05.07 Clachnacuddin 5 - 0
26.05.10 Waterford United 2 - 1

RUSSIA
05.06.12 Russia 0 - 4

SCOTLAND
31.05.79 Stafford 5 - 1
05.06.80 Zeist 2 - 4
11.06.81 Empoli 0 - 0
05.06.82 Aberdeen 1 - 1
04.06.83 Scarborough 2 - 1
07.06.84 Modena 2 - 0
15.06.85 Harderwijk 1 - 3
23.05.87 Dunfermline 2 - 1
18.05.02 Kettering 2 - 0
24.05.03 Carmarthen Town 0 - 0
23.05.04 Deverondale 3 - 1
28.05.05 Cork 3 - 2
27.05.06 Eastbourne Boro' 2 - 0
25.05.07 Ross County 3 - 0
22.05.08 Colwyn Bay 1 - 0

SLOVAKIA UNDER-23
24.05.14 Slovakia 0 - 1

SPARTA PRAGUE B
21.05.14 Prague 2 - 2

TURKEY
05.02.13 Dartford FC 0 - 1

USA
20.03.02 Stevenage Boro. 2 - 1
09.06.04 Charleston USA 0 - 0

WALES
27.03.84 Newtown 1 - 2
26.03.85 Telford 1 - 0
18.03.86 Merthyr Tydfil 1 - 3
17.03.87 Gloucester 2 - 2
15.03.88 Rhyl 2 - 0
21.03.89 Kidderminster 2 - 0
06.03.90 Merthyr Tydfil 0 - 0
17.05.91 Stafford 1 - 2
03.03.92 Aberystwyth 1 - 0
02.03.93 Cheltenham 2 - 1
22.02.94 Bangor 2 - 1
28.02.95 Yeovil Town 1 - 0
23.05.99 St Albans 2 - 1
16.05.00 Llanelli 1 - 1
13.02.01 Rushden & Dia. 0 - 0
14.05.02 Boston 1 - 1
22.05.03 Merthyr Tydfil 2 - 0
20.05.04 Keith FC 0 - 2
26.05.05 Cork 1 - 0
25.05.06 Eastbourne Boro' 1 - 1
27.05.07 Clachnacuddin 3 - 0
21.02.08 Exeter City 2 - 1
24.05.08 Rhyl 3 - 0
15.09.10 Newtown FC 2 - 2

RESULTS SUMMARY 1979 - 2014	P	W	D	L	F	A
Barbados	1	1	0	0	2	0
Belgium	6	3	1	2	8	7
Bermuda	1	1	0	0	6	1
Bosnia & Herzegovina	1	0	0	1	2	6
Czech Republic U21	1	0	2	0	2	2
Finland Under-21	4	2	0	2	4	5
Estonia	1	1	0	0	1	0
Grenada	1	0	1	0	1	1
Gibraltar	4	3	0	1	8	7
Holland	19	14	5	0	40	8
Hungary	2	0	1	1	3	5
Iraq	1	0	0	1	1	5
Irish Premier League XI	1	0	0	1	1	3
Italy	18	5	8	4	24	22
Jordan U23	1	1	0	0	1	0
Latvia U23	1	0	0	1	0	1
Malta	1	1	0	0	4	0
Norway Under-21	1	0	0	1	1	2
Poland	1	1	0	0	2	1
Portugal	1	0	0	1	0	1
Republic of Ireland	13	10	0	3	30	11
Russia	1	0	0	1	0	4
Scotland	15	10	3	2	30	15
Slovakia U23	1	0	0	1	0	1
Sparta Prague B	1	0	2	0	2	2
Turkey	1	0	0	1	0	1
USA	2	1	1	0	2	1
Wales	24	13	7	4	34	20
TOTALS	**125**	**67**	**29**	**28**	**209**	**132**

MANAGERS 1979 - 2014

		P	W	D	L	F	A	*Win%
1979	Howard Wilkinson	2	2	0	0	6	1	-
1980 - 1984	Keith Wright	17	9	5	3	30	16	53
1985 - 1988	Kevin Verity	12	7	2	3	23	15	58
1989 - 1996	Tony Jennings	19	10	4	5	27	18	53
1997	Ron Reid	2	0	1	1	0	2	-
1998 - 2002	John Owens	14	8	5	1	22	10	57
2002 -	Paul Fairclough	59	31	12	16	101	68	53

*Calculated for those who managed for 10 games or more.

GOALSCORERS 1979 - 2014

13 GOALS...
Carter, Mark

7 GOALS...
Cole, Mitchell

6 GOALS...
Ashford, Noel

5 GOALS...
Davison, Jon
Williams, Colin

4 GOALS...
Culpin, Paul
D'Sane, Roscoe
Johnson, Jeff
Mackhail-Smith, Craig
Norwood, James

3 GOALS...
Adamson, David
Guinan, Steve
Grayson,Neil
Hatch, Liam
Kirk, Jackson
Morison, Steve
Morrison, Michael
Opponents
Taylor, Matt
Watkins, Dale

2 GOALS...
Alford, Carl
Barnes-Homer, Matthew
Barrett, Keith
Bishop, Andrew
Burgess, Andrew
Casey, Kim
Cordice, Neil
Elding, Anthony
Gray, Andre
Hayles, Barry
Hill, Kenny
Howell, David
Mutrie, Les
Patmore, Warren
Richards, Justin
Seddon, Gareth
Southam, Glen
Watson, John
Weatherstone, Simon
Whitbread, Barry

1 GOAL...
Agana, Tony
Anderson, Dale
Ashton, John
Benson, Paul
Berry
Blackburn, Chris
Boardman, Jon
Bolton, Jimmy
Boyd, George
Bradshaw, Mark
Briscoe, Louis
Brown, Paul
Browne, Corey
Carey-Bertram, Daniel
Carr, Michael
Cavell, Paul
Charles, Lee
Charley, Ken
Charnock, Kieran
Constable, James
Crittenden, Nick
Davies, Paul
Day, Matt
Densmore, Shaun
Drummond, Stewart
Fleming, Andrew
Franks, Franks
Furlong, Paul
Grant, John
Harrad, Shaun
Hine, Mark
Holroyd, Chris
Humphreys, Delwyn
Howells, Jake
Jackson, Marlon
Jennings, Connor
Kennedy, John
Kerr, Scott
Kimmins,Ged
King, Simon
Leworthy, David
McDougald, Junior
McFadzean, Kyle
Mayes, Bobby
Moore, Neil
Moore, Luke
Newton, Sean
O'Keefe, Eamon
Oli, Dennis
Pearson, Matt
Penn, Russell
Pitcher, Geoff
Porter, Max
Ricketts, Sam
Robbins, Terry
Robinson, Mark
Roddis,Nick
Rodgers, Luke
Rodman, Alex
Rogers, Paul
Ryan, Tim
Sarcevic, Antoni
Sellars, Neil
Shaw, John
Sheldon, Gareth
Simpson, Josh
Sinclair, Dean
Smith, Ian
Smith, Ossie
Spencer, Scott
Stansfield, Adam
Stephens, Mickey
Stott, Steve
Taylor, Steve
Thurgood, Stuart
Tubbs, Matthew
Venables, David
Watkins, Adam
Way, Darren
Webb, Paul
Wilcox, Russ

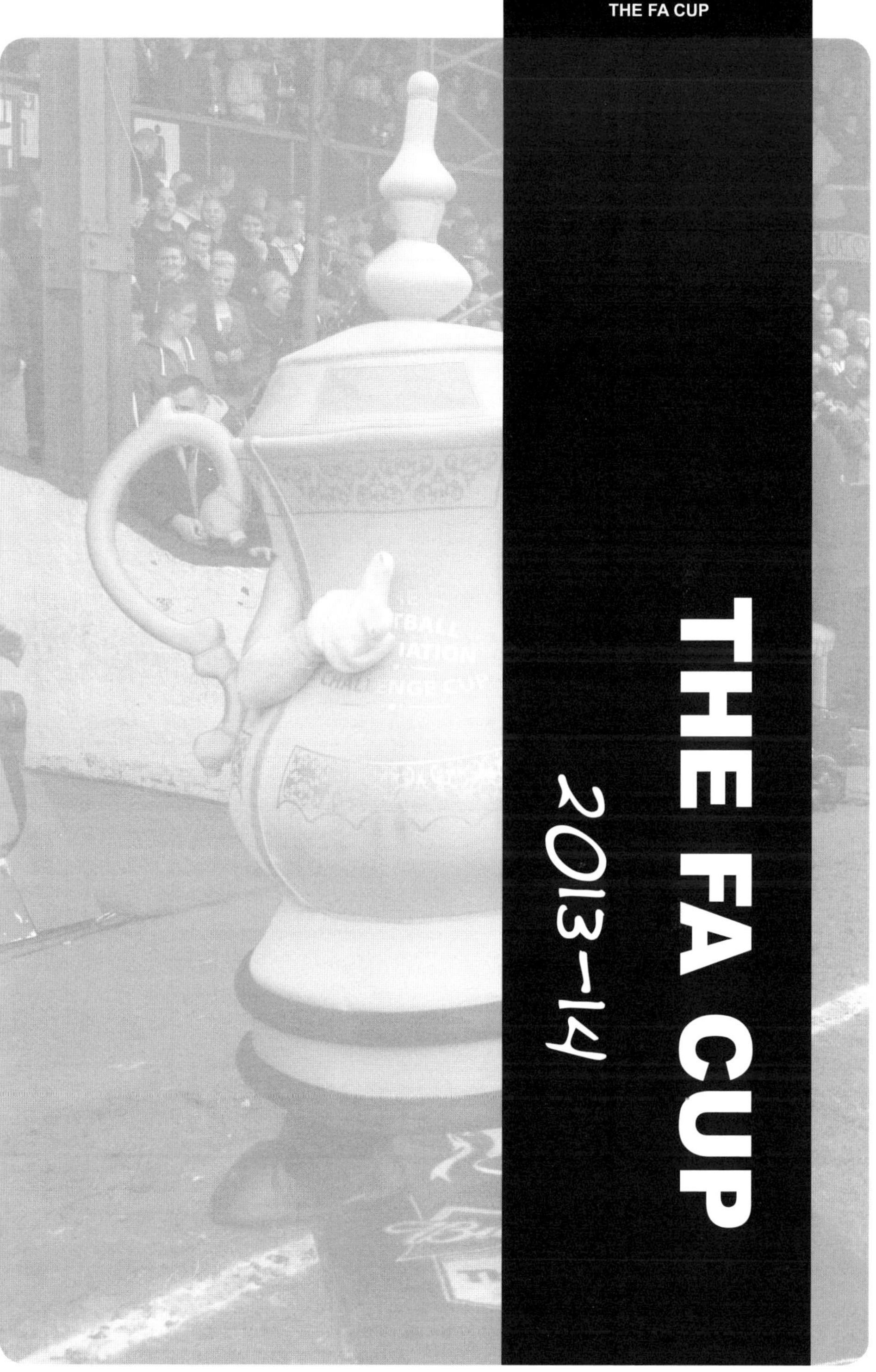

THE FA CUP 2013-14

EXTRA PRELIMINARY ROUND

Association Football's oldest and most famous knockout competition kicked off over the third week-end of August. Some of the smaller clubs probably had players still on holiday and early season league fixtures had just been played.

An FA Cup run is so important to little clubs who can receive a terrific boost from prize money earned from three or four cup victories. Little clubs can also have the fun and excitement from taking on new opponents and visiting new grounds, but of course there is always the chance of finding they are out of their depth against senior clubs.

FAC EP: Cray Valley's 'keeper, Bobby Sturgeon and defender, Joe Matthews, can only watch as Conor Sidwell, of Lancing, scores. Photo: Alan Coomes.

What a start to the season for The Combined Counties League that operates around the southerm home counties - three of their clubs produced a total of 25 FA Cup goals with 16 scored away from home!

Ashington (Northern League) and Bristol Manor Farm (Western league) both scored nine goals at home but Chessington & Hook United (Combined Counties) actually scored nine playing away.

Molesey (Combined Counties) thrilled their fans with an 8-0 victory and seven goals were scored at home by Runcorn Town and Norton United (North West Counties), Wolverhampton Casuals (West Midlands) and Horndean (Wessex League), while Hanworth Villa (Combined Counties) also managed seven goals away from home.

The first cup ties were played on the Friday evening and featured Bishop Auckland, once one of the most famous non-league clubs in the country and Winchester City, who won a Wembley Vase Final in 2002.

FAC EP: Irchester United's Judge tries to get the final touch before Biggleswade 'keeper, Harpur, can punch clear. Photo: Keith Clayton.

Each region of the country had their own special local cup ties with Spennymoor Town beating Sunderland RCA 2 -1in the North East but St Helens Town and Ashton Athletic will have to meet again after a 2-2 draw in the North West.

Two Midland clubs who have enjoyed cup headlines in the past met at Tividale, who beat Alvechurch 3-0 and from The United Counties League, Spalding United underlined their seniority with a 4-2 victory over Eynesbury Rovers.

Wantage Town, one of the favourites in the Hellenic League won convincingly at Reading Town by 4-0 and in Sussex, Horsham YMCA lost a thriller 2-3 at home to Hassocks. Two old rivals in Surrey produced an exciting tie as Epsom & Ewell earned a replay with a 3-3 draw at Whyteleafe.

While in The South West, two convincing away victories, which may not have been expected were provided by Wells City who beat Buckland Athletic 3-0 and Larkhall Athletic who stormed to a 4-0 triumph against Willand Rovers.

Whether its a match played in August or in the flrst Round Proper, FA Cup victories for non-league clubs will always be exciting and the draw for the next round will also bring more exciting expectations and of course a chance for more prize money!.

EXTRA PRELIMINARY ROUND

SATURDAY 17 AUGUST 2013 - WINNING CLUBS TO RECEIVE £1,500

1	Darlington RA	v	Newton Aycliffe	1-5	82
2	Thackley	v	Guisborough Town	1-3	78
3	Glasshoughton Welfare	v	Jarrow Roofing Boldon CA	2-3	75
4	Colne	v	South Shields	1-1	62
	South Sheilds	v	Colne	2-1	72
5	Brighouse Town	v	Seaham Red Star	3-1	75
6	Ashington	v	Pontefract Collieries	9-0	186
7	Dunston UTS	v	Pickering Town	4-1	213
8	Garforth Town	v	Shildon	1-4	166
9	Silsden	v	Bridlington Town	1-2	101
10	Crook Town	v	Billingham Town	4-2	108
11	Northallerton Town	v	Whitehaven	2-4	75
12	Morpeth Town	v	Liversedge	6-0	48
13	Billingham Synthonia	v	West Allotment Celtic	4-0	70
14	Spennymoor Town	v	Sunderland RCA	2-1	209
15	Team Northumbria	v	Whitley Bay	2-1	195
16	Bishop Auckland	v	Tadcaster Albion (16/8)	0-0	359
	Tadcaster Albion	v	Bishop Auckland	0-3	214
17	Albion Sports	v	North Shields	2-0	67
18	Hebburn Town	v	Barnoldswick Town	2-2	132
	Barnoldswick Town	v	Hebburn Town	0-2	111
19	Penrith	v	Newcastle Benfield	3-1	75
20	Marske United	v	Consett	3-1	121
21	Tow Law Town	v	West Auckland Town	0-5	100
22	Durham City	v	Hall Road Rangers	6-1	98
23	Runcorn Town	v	Winterton Rangers	7-2	83
24	Stockport Sports	v	Winsford United	1-2	74
25	Worksop Parramore	v	AFC Blackpool (16/8)	2-0	143
26	Maltby Main	v	Congleton Town	1-4	82
27	Bacup & Rossendale Borough	v	Formby	1-4	45
28	Bootle	v	Squires Gate	2-1	123
29	Barton Town OB's	v	Nostell MW	2-1	60
30	Maine Road	v	Runcorn Linnets	0-3	176
31	Parkgate	v	Shirebrook Town	0-3	96
32	AFC Emley	v	Wigan Robin Park (18/8)	3-2	
33	AFC Liverpool	v	Cheadle Town (18/8)	1-0	179
34	Armthorpe Welfare	v	Glossop North End	1-4	138
35	Alsager Town	v	Atherton Collieries	1-3	75
36	Staveley MW	v	Ashton Town	2-1	122
37	West Didsbury & Chorlton	v	Abbey Hey	2-0	122
38	St Helens Town	v	Ashton Athletic	2-2	71
	Ashton Athletic	v	St Helens Town	1-0	58
39	Boldmere St Michaels	v	Tipton Town	0-2	139
40	Bolehall Swifts	v	Causeway United	2-2	53
	Causeway United	v	Bolehall Swifts	0-4	71
41	Bewdley Town	v	Coventry Sphinx	0-3	44
42	Rocester	v	Atherstone Town	3-3	98
	Atherstone Town	v	Rocester	1-0	183
43	Gornal Athletic	v	Ellesmere Rangers	1-2	60
44	Westfields	v	Lye Town	2-3	82
45	Studley	v	Stafford Town	5-0	30
46	Heath Hayes	v	Black Country Rangers	1-3	53
47	Walsall Wood	v	Continental Star	4-1	43
48	Norton United	v	Southam United	7-1	46
49	Tividale	v	Alvechurch	3-0	88
50	Stourport Swifts	v	Coleshill Town	3-1	88
51	AFC Wulfrunians	v	Earlswood Town	4-1	85
52	Wolverhampton Casuals	v	Pegasus Juniors	7-1	53
53	Nuneaton Griff	v	Brocton	2-3	56
54	Shawbury United	v	Dudley Town	0-0	53
	Dudley Town	v	Shawbury United	1-2	83
55	Thurnby Nirvana	v	Kirby Muxloe	0-0	43
	Kirby Muxloe	v	Thurnby Nirvana	2-2	82
	(Kirby Muxloe won 4-3 on kicks from the penalty mark)				
56	Quorn	v	Holbrook Sports	5-1	109
57	Retford United	v	Heanor Town	3-1	141
58	Graham St Prims	v	Shepshed Dynamo	1-3	97
59	Harborough Town	v	Teversal	2-1	141
60	Dunkirk	v	Barrow Town	4-0	41
61	Stewarts & Lloyds Corby	v	Arnold Town	1-1	24
	Arnold Town	v	Stewarts & Lloyds Corby	2-1	74
62	Lincoln Moorlands Railway	v	Long Eaton United	2-4	19
63	Basford United	v	Holwell Sports	1-0	58
64	Borrowash Victoria	v	Louth Town	2-1	68
65	Desborough Town	v	Oadby Town	3-1	96
66	Blaby & Whetstone Athletic	v	Heather St Johns	2-0	75
67	Hucknall Town	v	Loughborough University		
	(walkover for Loughborough University – Hucknall Town removed)				
68	Gorleston	v	Deeping Rangers	2-1	102
69	Boston Town	v	Great Yarmouth Town	3-2	69
70	Godmanchester Rovers	v	Blackstones	6-3	83
71	Holbeach United	v	Norwich United	2-1	117
72	Thetford Town	v	Diss Town (16/8)	1-0	168
73	Ely City	v	Sleaford Town	0-3	97
74	Yaxley	v	Peterborough NS (16/8)	03	292
75	Huntingdon Town	v	Fakenham Town	4-1	54
76	Spalding United	v	Eynesbury Rovers	4-2	76
77	Swaffham Town	v	Wisbech Town	2-1	215
78	FC Clacton	v	Sporting Bengal United	3-1	160
79	Great Wakering Rovers	v	Halstead Town	5-0	92
80	Whitton United	v	London APSA	4-1	64
81	Kirkley & Pakefield	v	Brightlingsea Regent	2-2	86
	Brightlingsea Regent	v	Kirkley & Pakefield	1-2	95
82	Stansted	v	Brantham Athletic (18/8)	0-0	114
	Brantham Athletic	v	Stansted	6-1	
83	Clapton	v	Stanway Rovers	0-0	127
	Stanway Rovers	v	Clapton	0-1	85
84	Sawbridgeworth Town	v	Mildenhall Town	1-6	87
85	Haverhill Rovers	v	Eton Manor	3-1	86
86	Newmarket Town	v	Ilford	3-1	70
87	Ipswich Wanderers	v	Wivenhoe Town	0-0	72
	Wivenhoe Town	v	Ipswich Wanderers	0-1	
88	Barking	v	Bowers & Pitsea	3-1	71
89	Woodbridge Town	v	Hullbridge Sports	0-2	83
90	Basildon United	v	Southend Manor	2-2	53
	Southend Manor	v	Basildon United	1-2	65
91	Walsham Le Willows	v	Tower Hamlets	0-1	63
92	Takeley	v	Hadleigh United	0-2	130
93	Felixstowe & Walton United	v	Saffron Walden Town	3-0	104
94	Berkhamstead	v	AFC Dunstable	2-1	96
95	Hadley	v	Oxhey Jets (16/8)	1-1	87
	Oxhey Jets	v	Hadley	0-1	85
96	AFC Kempston Rovers	v	Wembley	0-1	100
97	Wellingborough Town	v	Greenhouse London	3-3	88
	Greenhouse London	v	Wellingborough Town	5-3aet	22
98	Hoddesdon Town	v	St Margaretsbury (16/8)	1-1	283
	St Margaretsbury	v	Hoddesdon Town	4-1	106
99	Kings Langley	v	Long Buckby	3-1	43

FAC EP: Irchester's Judge slips the ball past Harpur and the upright during the home side's 0-2 defeat against Biggleswade United. Photo: Keith Clayton.

FAC P: Russell Bedford (stripes) of Erith Town shields the ball from Corinthian Casuals' Danny Green. Photo: Alan Coomes.

FAC P: Ryan McBride, Eastbourne United, looks on as his header beats the 'keeper but finds the Herne Bay crossbar. Photo: Roger Turner.

EXTRA PRELIMINARY ROUND

SATURDAY 17 AUGUST 2013 - WINNING CLUBS TO RECEIVE £1,500

No	Home		Away	Score	Att
100	Newport Pagnell Town	v	Hatfield Town	2-0	117
101	Hillingdon Borough	v	Leverstock Green	4-2	41
102	Cogenhoe United	v	Tring Athletic	0-0	65
	Tring Athletic	v	Cogenhoe United	3-0	98
103	London Lions	v	Stotfold	1-1	30
	Stotfold	v	London Lions	1-0	65
104	Irchester United	v	Biggleswade United (18/8)	0-2	110
105	Harefield United	v	Woodford United	3-0	150
106	Codicote	v	Crawley Green	1-1	22
	Crawley Green	v	Codicote	3-1	32
107	Holmer Green	v	Ampthill Town	2-3	53
108	Hertford Town	v	Colney Heath	2-1	184
109	Northampton Spencer	v	Bugbrooke St Michaels	2-0	69
110	Haringey Borough	v	Rushden & Higham United	6-0	55
111	Enfield 1893	v	London Tigers (16/8)	0-0	90
	London Tigers	v	Enfield 1893	2-1	45
112	Cockfosters	v	Hanwell Town	1-1	94
	Hanwell Town	v	Cockforsters	0-1	110
113	London Colney	v	AFC Rushden & Diamonds	1-1	400
	AFC Rushden & Diamonds	v	London Colney	6-1	546
114	Sandhurst Town	v	Farnham Town	2-2	26
	Farnham Town	v	Sandhurst Town	4-1	60
115	Tadley Calleva	v	Ascot United	2-4	110
	(tie awarded to Tadley Calleva – Ascot United removed)				
116	Bracknell Town	v	Fairford Town	2-1	96
117	Holyport	v	Hanworth Villa	2-7	33
118	Staines Lammas	v	Badshot Lea	0-2	45
119	Ardley United	v	Thame United	4-1	51
120	Camberley Town	v	Chinnor	2-0	
121	Reading Town	v	Wantage Town	0-5	69
122	Frimley Green	v	Ash United	3-2	61
123	Flackwell Heath	v	Binfield (16/8)	0-0	207
	Binfield	v	Flackwell Heath (19/8)	3-2	210
124	Bedfont Sports	v	Abingdon United	2-2	50
	Abingdon United	v	Bedfont Sports	0-1	49
125	Westfield	v	Shrivenham	2-1	70
126	Cheltenham Saracens	v	Slimbridge	0-0	50
	Slimbridge	v	Cheltenham Saracens	1-1aet	70
	(Cheltenham Saracens won 4-1 on kicks from the penalty mark)				
127	Cove	v	Carterton	5-0	32
128	Newbury	v	Windsor	1-4	80
129	Kidlington	v	Hartley Wintney	1-1	67
	Hartley Wintney	v	Kidlington	5-2	120
130	Abingdon Town	v	Highmoor Ibis	1-5	15
131	Dorking	v	Shoreham	1-4	58
132	Alton Town	v	Selsey	3-1	74
133	Dorking Wanderers	v	Canterbury City (18/8)	5-0	
134	East Preston	v	Crowborough Athletic	0-0	99
	Crowborough Athletic	v	East Preston	2-3	75
135	Ashford United	v	Worthing United	0-0	186
	Worthing United	v	Ashford United	0-1	122
136	Sevenoaks Town	v	Horley Town	1-4	52
137	Sidley United	v	Erith Town		
	(walkover for Erith Town – Sidley United removed)				
138	Whyteleafe	v	Epsom & Ewell	3-3	118
	Epsom & Ewell	v	Whyteleafe	1-6	93
139	Holmesdale	v	East Grinstead Town	1-0	49
140	Horsham YMCA	v	Hassocks	2-3	81
141	Molesey	v	Hailsham Town	8-1	104
142	Littlehampton Town	v	St Francis Rangers (18/8)	3-1	
143	Chichester City	v	Chessington & Hook United	1-8	90
144	Pagham	v	Tunbridge Wells	2-4	148
145	Mole Valley SCR	v	South Park	0-1	26
146	Cray Valley (PM)	v	Lancing	1-1	101
	Lancing	v	Cray Valley	0-4	108
147	Arundel	v	Rye United	0-0	57
	Rye United	v	Arundel	2-1	90
	(at Arundel FC)				
148	Beckenham Town	v	Corinthian	1-2	60
149	Epsom Athletic	v	Croydon	1-3	101
150	Lordswood	v	Eastbourne United	1-4	93
151	Raynes Park Vale	v	Lingfield	2-1	40
152	Greenwich Borough	v	Ringmer	2-2	35
	Ringmer	v	Greenwich Borough	1-3	64
153	Fisher	v	Deal Town	1-2	80
154	Colliers Wood United	v	AFC Croydon Athletic	6-2	59
155	Newport (IW)	v	Verwood Town	4-1	102
156	Bournemouth	v	Highworth Town	3-1	64
157	Team Solent	v	AFC Portchester	1-3	99
158	Bradford Town	v	Longwell Green Sports	1-2	74
159	Horndean	v	Calne Town	7-2	30
160	Cowes Sports	v	Fawley	4-1	69
161	Wootton Bassett Town	v	Totton & Eling	0-2	49
162	Alresford Town	v	Winchester City (16/8)	0-3	197
163	Downton	v	Sholing	1-3	80
164	Melksham Town	v	Hamworthy United	3-3	65
	Hamworthy United	v	Melksham Town	3-1aet	108
165	Christchurch	v	Sherborne Town (16/8)	1-2	117
166	Bitton	v	Pewsey Vale	4-1	52
167	Winterbourne United	v	Folland Sports	1-4	28
	(at Folland Sports FC)				
168	Moneyfields	v	Cadbury Heath	2-1	70
169	Hallen	v	Whitchurch United	1-1	56
	Whitchurch United	v	Hallen	0-2	67
170	Corsham Town	v	Gillingham Town	3-1	70
171	Petersfield Town	v	Blackfield & Langley	4-3	64
172	Bemerton Heath Harlequins	v	Fareham Town	1-4	72
173	Romsey Town	v	Brockenhurst	1-4	38
174	Bristol Manor Farm	v	Oldland Abbotonians	9-3	78
175	East Cowes Victoria Athletic	v	Lymington Town	0-3	31
176	Hengrove Athletic	v	Bridport	0-2	50
177	Willand Rovers	v	Larkhall Athletic	0-4	81
178	St Blazey	v	Tavistock	1-0	61
179	Bishop Sutton	v	Odd Down	1-1	32
	Odd Down	v	Bishop Sutton	1-2	45
180	Shepton Mallet	v	Street	0-0	123
	Street	v	Shepton Mallet	2-0	136
181	AFC St Austell	v	Ilfracombe Town	1-4	142
182	Buckland Athletic	v	Wells City	0-3	79
183	Barnstable Town	v	Brislington	0-2	239
184	Plymouth Parkway	v	Saltash United	2-1	170
185	Radstock Town	v	Bodmin Town	1-4	57

PRELIMINARY ROUND

FAC P: Evesham striker, Marcus Palmer slips while trying to cross the ball despite the attentions of his marker, Bolehall Swifts defender, Adam Goodby. Photo: Jonathan Holloway.

The Extra Preliminary Round of the FA Cup had already produced 185 winners who had earned a win bonus of £1.500 each. Perhaps some of the clubs exempt until the Preliminary Round may have wished they too could have had the chance of an early season windfall, but their turn came on 31st August when the 160 winners would receive £1.925.

Ties at this stage of the competition are drawn on a regional basis and some local derbies are all the more exciting if the clubs come from different leagues. North Eastern teams get to know each other's strengths and weaknesses very well and half of the dozen ties in the area needed replays. FA Vase holders Spennymoor Town eventually won 3-0 but the initial 3-3 draw at Newton Aycliffe was one of the most thrilling games.

Crook Town and Scarborough Athletic proving the most successful at the first attempt with 4-2 victories over Kendal Town (away) and Ashington respectively, but Brighouse also lifted their game to achieve a 4-0 replay victory over Billingham Synthonia and a comparatively new name to the FA Cup, Worksop Parramore, earned an impressive 3-2 victory over Mossley at the second attempt.

The new Northwich Victoria revived memories of past cup excitement in the North West with a 3-0 victory at Formby. An impressive 5-0 win was achieved by Warrington Town at home to Winsford United and Ramsbottom United who beat visitors AFC Liverpool by the same score.

The Midland fixtures brought two clubs together whose structure had changed in recent years and Gresley came away from a visit to KetteringTown with a 2-0 victory in front of the best cup attendance of the day

However, it was a not so well known name, Brocton, from the Midland Combination, who recorded an emphatic 6-0 victory over Ellesmere Rangers (Midland Alliance) and Belper Town made seniority count with a 5-0 victory at home to Retford. Town. While one of the Sunday fixtures produced an 8-0 victory for Mickleover Sports against Harborough Town.

High scoring victories can occur in the early rounds of the competition with some clubs caught before they have settled into the season or perhaps just being members of very different leagues. Seven goals were scored at home by Coalville Town against Lincoln United in a tie contested by two clubs from The Northern Premier League Division One South, and Aveley also scored seven against fellow Isthmian League Division One North club Waltham Forest. One more club to score seven was Bristol Manor Farm of The Western League who beat Lymington Town (Wessex League) 7-1.

But surely one of the most puzzling results was produced by the Chiltern Saracens cup tie with Binfield, which finished in a goalless draw initially, but provided a 7-0 victory for Saracens in the replay !

PRELIMINARY ROUND

SATURDAY 31 AUGUST 2013 - WINNERS RECEIVE £1,925

No	Home		Away	Score	Att
1	Harrogate Railway Athletic	v	South Shields	1-1	72
1	Kendal Town	v	Crook Town	2-4	187
2	Billingham Synthonia	v	Brighouse Town	1-1	110
	Brighouse Town	v	Billingham Synthonia (3/9)	4-0	220
3	Jarrow Roofing Boldon CA	v	Dunston UTS	2-1	134
4	Whitehaven	v	Team Northumbria	0-2	
5	Hebburn Town	v	Marske United	1-2	101
6	Padiham	v	Clitheroe	3-1	327
7	Scarborough Athletic	v	Ashington	4-1	
8	Newton Aycliffe	v	Spennymoor Town	3-3	303
	Spennymoor Town	v	Newton Aycliffe (3/9)	3-0	510
9	Farsley	v	Lancaster City	1-3	136
10	Albion Sports	v	South Shields (1/9)	3-3	86
	South Shields	v	Albion Sports (3/9)	1-2	67
11	Shildon	v	Penrith	0-2	144
12	Goole	v	Bishop Auckland	0-2	180
13	Guisborough Town	v	Bridlington Town	1-1	153
	Bridlington Town	v	Guisborough Town (4/9)	2-4	150
14	Durham City	v	Morpeth Town	1-1	121
	Morpeth Town	v	Durham City (4/9)	3-2	77
15	Harrogate RA	v	West Auckland Town	2-2	157
	West Auckland Town	v	Harrogate Town (3/9)	4-2	241
16	Formby	v	Northwich Victoria	0-3	81
17	Bootle	v	Barton Town OB's	4-1	109
18	Ossett Town	v	AFC Emley	3-0	178
19	Mossley	v	Worksop Parramore	1-1	139
	Worksop Parramore	v	Mossley (3/9)	3-2	123
20	Atherton Collieries	v	Radcliffe Borough	1-1	108
	Radcliffe Borough	v	Atherton Collieries (3/9)	2-1	135
21	Bamber Bridge	v	Staveley MW	1-0	139
22	Cammell Laird	v	Salford City	2-0	76
23	Prescot Cables	v	Congleton Town	0-0	190
	Congleton Town	v	Prescot Cables (3/9)	0-1	173
24	Sheffield	v	Shirebrook Town	1-1	286
	Shirebrook Town	v	Sheffield (3/9)	0-4	332
25	Curzon Ashton	v	Ashton Athletic	4-0	101
26	Warrington Town	v	Winsford United	5-1	151
27	Ossett Albion	v	Runcorn Linnets	1-3	164
28	Runcorn Town	v	Glossop North End	0-1	133
29	Wakefield	v	New Mills	0-2	74
30	West Didsbury & Chorlton	v	Burscough	0-3	136
31	Ramsbottom United	v	AFC Liverpool	5-0	237
32	Newcastle Town	v	Shawbury United	2-1	60
33	Rugby Town	v	Norton United	1-1	203
	Norton United	v	Rugby Town (3/9)	1-1aet	123
	(Rugby won 3-4 on kicks from the penalty mark)				
34	Tividale	v	Wolverhampton Casuals	3-0	
35	Stourport Swifts	v	AFC Wulfrunians	1-1	113
	AFC Wulfrunians	v	Stourport Swifts (3/9)	4-1aet	140
36	Black Country Rangers	v	Halesowen Town (1/9)	1-2	165
37	Chasetown	v	Romulus	3-1	223
38	Sutton Coldfield Town	v	Bedworth United	1-0	173
39	Coventry Sphinx	v	Lye Town	2-1	131
40	Leek Town	v	Walsall Wood	2-2	176
	Walsall Wood	v	Leek Town (3/9)	2-0	126
41	Atherstone Town	v	Studley	3-1	188
42	Market Drayton Town	v	Kidsgrove Athletic	1-3	103
43	Evesham United	v	Bolehall Swifts	2-1	174
44	Brocton	v	Ellesmere Rangers	6-0	83
45	Tipton Town	v	Stratford Town	1-0	93
46	Loughborough Dynamo	v	Eastwood Town	0-1	139
47	Kettering Town	v	Gresley	0-2	862
48	Basford United	v	Quorn	2-2	153
	Quorn	v	Basford United (3/9)	1-1aet	181
	(Basford United won 5-3 on kicks from the penalty mark)				
49	Dunkirk	v	Rainworth MW	1-1	68
	Rainworth MW	v	Dunkirk (3/9)	0-1aet	118
50	Coalville Town	v	Lincoln United	7-1	152
51	Desborough Town	v	Loughborough University	2-4	57
52	Blaby & Whetstone Athletic	v	Kirby Muxloe	2-0	64
	(at Kirby Muxloe FC)				
53	Carlton Town	v	Borrowash Victoria	2-0	69
54	Arnold Town	v	Brigg Town	2-2	90
	Brigg Town	v	Arnold Town (3/9)	4-2	83
55	Long Eaton United	v	Shepshed Dynamo	4-0	182
56	Mickleover Sports	v	Harborough Town (1/9)	8-0	91
57	Belper Town	v	Retford United	5-0	218
58	Sleaford Town	v	Godmanchester Rovers	2-0	
59	Swaffham Town	v	Huntington Town	0-2	202
60	Spalding United	v	Holbeach United	4-0	341
61	Gorleston	v	Thetford Town	4-1	143
62	Peterborough Northern Star	v	Wroxham	2-4	99
63	St Ives Town	v	Soham Town Rangers	3-1	265
64	Boston Town	v	Dereham Town	1-3	93
65	Brantham Athletic	v	Barkingside	1-0	71
66	Clapton	v	Mildenhall Town	0-2	107
67	AFC Sudbury	v	Ipswich Wanderers	4-1	164
68	Waltham Abbey	v	Whitton United	1-1	105
	Whitton United	v	Waltham Abbey (3/9)	0-3	102
69	Basildon United	v	Heybridge Swifts	0-3	54
70	Harlow Town	v	Tower Hamlets	4-1	161
71	Aveley	v	Waltham Forest	7-0	52
72	Tilbury	v	Kirkley & Pakefield	2-0	63
73	Witham Town	v	Newmarket Town	0-0	61
	Newmarket Town	v	Witham Town (3/9)	0-2	115
74	Thurrock	v	Felixstowe & Walton United	3-0	66
75	Brentwood Town	v	Great Wakering Rovers	3-2	92
76	Needham Market	v	Haverhill Rovers	3-2	202
77	FC Clacton	v	Hullbridge Sports	3-0	162
78	Redbridge	v	Burnham Ramblers	1-3	70
79	Hadleigh United	v	Romford	0-5	151

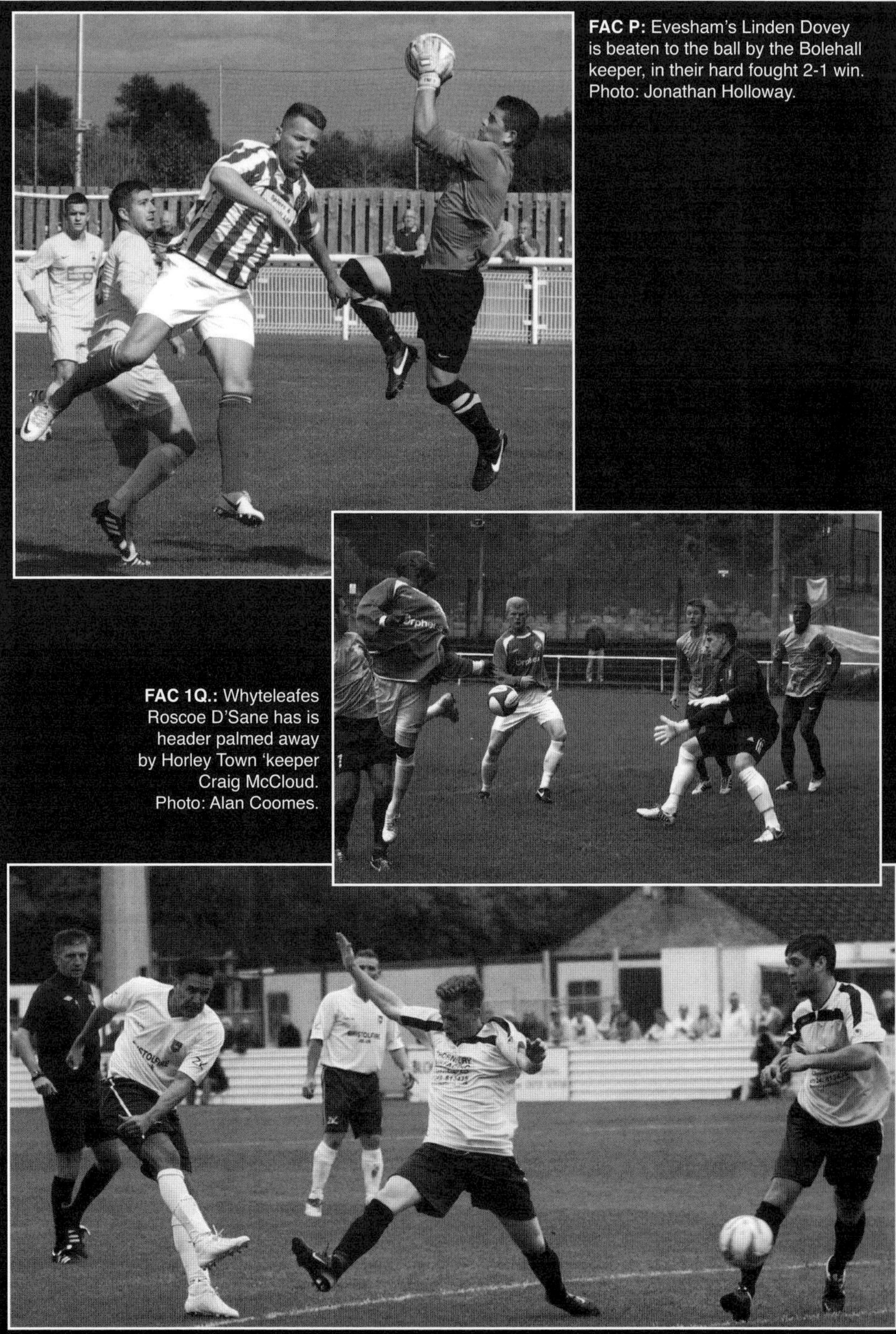

FAC P: Evesham's Linden Dovey is beaten to the ball by the Bolehall keeper, in their hard fought 2-1 win. Photo: Jonathan Holloway.

FAC 1Q.: Whyteleafes Roscoe D'Sane has is header palmed away by Horley Town 'keeper Craig McCloud. Photo: Alan Coomes.

FAC 1Q.: A Yate Town player fires in a shot against ChippenhamTown. Photo: Peter Barnes.

PRELIMINARY ROUND

SATURDAY 31 AUGUST 2013 - WINNERS RECEIVE £1,925

80	Maldon & Tiptree	v	Barking	1-1	76
	Barking	v	Malton & Tiptree (3/9)	0-1	90
81	St Margaretsbury	v	London Tigers	1-0	35
82	Kings Langley	v	Newport Pagnell Town	2-1	50
83	Uxbridge	v	Stotfold	5-1	102
84	Ware	v	Wembley	1-5	61
85	Crawley Green	v	Dunstable Town (30/8)	0-3	209
86	Barton Rovers	v	Ampthill Town	4-0	150
87	Haringey Borough	v	AFC Hayes	2-1	37
88	Potters Bar Town	v	Greenhouse London	0-3	58
89	North Greenford United	v	Tring Athletic	3-0	51
90	Royston Town	v	Northampton Spencer	3-3	165
	Northampton Spencer	v	Royston Town (3/9)	2-3	113
91	Cockfosters	v	Hadley	2-1	85
92	Daventry Town	v	Hillingdon Borough	1-0	77
93	Berkhamsted	v	Harefield United	4-1	107
94	Northwood	v	AFC Rushden & Diamonds	1-2	292
95	Hertford Town	v	Cheshunt	4-2	184
96	Leighton Town	v	Biggleswade United	1-3	140
97	Bedfont Sports	v	North Leigh	1-3	78
98	Beaconsfield SYCOB	v	Bracknell Town	5-3	75
99	Badshot Lea	v	Hartley Wintney (30/8)	2-3	116
100	Wantage Town	v	Didcot Town (30/8)	2-3	321
101	Marlow	v	Chertsey Town	1-2	102
102	Slough Town	v	Cirencester Town (1/9)	1-1	222
	Cirencester Town	v	Slough Town (3/9)	1-0	122
103	Ashford Town (Middx)	v	Bishop's Cleeve	0-0	80
	Bishop's Cleeve	v	Ashford Town (Middx) (3/9)	0-1	83
104	Binfield	v	Cheltenham Saracens	0-0	162
	Cheltenham Saracens	v	Binfield (4/9)	1-7	52
105	Shortwood United	v	Egham Town	2-1	91
106	Ardley United	v	Hanworth Villa	1-0	71
107	Chalfont St Peter	v	Tadley Calleva	5-3	91
108	Fleet Town	v	Westfield	0-1	116
109	Windsor	v	Highmoor Ibis	1-3	194
110	Aylesbury	v	Thatcham Town	2-1	118
111	Frimley Green	v	Cove	0-2	93
112	Cinderford Town	v	Aylesbury United	1-3	81
113	Farnham Town	v	Camberley Town	0-3	42
114	Erith & Belvedere	v	Chatham Town	0-5	96
115	Littlehampton Town	v	Greenwich Borough (1/9)	1-0	121
116	Raynes Park Vale	v	Alton Town	4-4	60
	Alton Town	v	Raynes Park Vale (3/9)	1-0	94
117	Eastbourne United	v	Herne Bay	2-2	142
	Herne Bay	v	Eastbourne United (3/9)	1-2	207
118	Guildford City	v	South Park	0-4	73
119	Folkestone Invicta	v	Molesey	3-3	214
	Molesey	v	Folkestone Invicta (3/9)	2-4	181
120	Colliers Wood United	v	East Preston	1-3	42
121	Merstham	v	Deal Town	4-2	75
122	Croydon	v	Whyteleafe	0-2	110
123	Hastings United	v	Ramsgate	1-0	387
124	Leatherhead	v	Tooting & Mitcham United	1-0	205
125	Shoreham	v	Walton Casuals	2-1	63
126	Crawley Down Gatwick	v	Guernsey	1-3	271
127	Horley Town	v	Holmesdale	5-3	46
128	Dorking Wanderers	v	Hassocks	0-0	42
	Hassocks	v	Dorking Wanderers (3/9)	1-0	86
129	Walton & Hersham	v	Horsham	0-2	130
130	Chipstead	v	Rye United	3-2	57
131	Eastbourne Town	v	Corinthian	1-0	109
132	Faversham Town	v	Worthing	5-1	167
133	VCD Athletic	v	Burgess Hill Town	1-3	74
134	Chessington & Hook United	v	Sittingbourne	0-1	78
135	Corinthian Casuals	v	Erith Town	3-0	60
136	Peacehaven & Telscombe	v	Ashford United	4-0	140
137	Three Bridges	v	Hythe Town	2-1	85
138	Tunbridge Wells	v	Whitstable Town	0-0	414
	Whitstable Town	v	Tunbridge Wells (3/9)	0-2	
139	Cray Valley (PM)	v	Redhill	0-2	110
140	Corsham Town	v	Sherborne Town	2-0	72
141	Moneyfields	v	Longwell Green Sports	2-2	
	Longwell Green Sports	v	Moneyfields (3/9)	1-2	72
142	Godalming Town	v	AFC Portchester	0-1	166
143	Bournemouth	v	Hallen	2-4	55
144	Winchester City	v	Swindon Supermarine	3-0	186
145	Yate Town	v	Cowes Sports	2-1	172
146	Bristol Manor Farm	v	Lymington Town	7-1	77
147	Petersfield Town	v	Horndean	1-2	121
148	Wimborne Town	v	Hamworthy United	1-3	176
149	Newport (IW)	v	Fareham Town	0-2	168
150	Brockenhurst	v	Folland Sports	2-0	59
151	Totton & Eling	v	Sholing	0-0	112
	Sholing	v	Totton & Eling (3/9)	2-1	
152	Mangotsfield United	v	Bitton	3-0	142
153	Taunton Town	v	Bridgwater Town	1-1	467
	Bridgwater Town	v	Taunton Town (3/9)	2-1	513
154	Bridport	v	Merthyr Town	2-3	146
155	Clevedon Town	v	Bishop Sutton	4-1	88
156	Plymouth Parkway	v	Ilfracombe Town	4-1	177
157	Street	v	Paulton Rovers	1-0	136
158	Wells City	v	Bodmin Town	3-2	83
159	Brislington	v	St Blazey	4-0	82
160	Larkhall Athletic	v	Tiverton Town	1-0	164

FIRST QUALIFYING ROUND

Junior non-league clubs like Runcorn Linnets in the North West, Jarrow Roofing in the North East plus Hartley Wintney and AFC Portchester in the South have earned £6,425 by mid September with their three FA Cup victories. The Wessex club even achieved a place in the Second Qualifying Round by winning all three ties away from home.

No football club official should fail to realize the importance of these early FA Cup ties and the chance of such an uplifting start to the season and a boost to their clubs' budget. What a reward for the Guernsey club's bravery and ambition! They were quite rightly allowed in the competition as they are members of the Isthmian League. Entering in The Preliminary Round they have already won at Crawley Down and Hastings United and will attract a crowd twice as large as any other club if drawn at home in the Second Qualifying Round.
Their £4,925 prize money is already a just reward for taking up the challenge.

Some famous names from the Amateur days have also reminded their older supporters of past glories. Promoted Dulwich Hamlet, who are now challenging at the top of The Isthmian Premier Division, recorded a fine 6-0 cup win over Shoreham while Skelmersdale United beat the 'new Northwich ' 3-0 away.

As expected, the FC United v Chorley tie attracted an impressive 1,318 and the visitors recorded a hard fought victory. Another well supported away victory disappointed the large Kings Lynn home crowd but saw Cambridge City storm to a 5-1 victory in front of 705.

Top scorers in the round were Burgess Hill Town (Isthmian Division One South) with an 8-1 victory over Alton Town(Combined Counties Premier). Six goals were scored at home by:-

Daventry Town (Southern Lg Div One Central) 6-1 v Berkhamstead (Spartan S. Midlands)
St Albans City (Southern League Premier Div.) 6-1 v Enfield Town (Isthmian Premier Div.)
Wealdstone (Isthmian League Premier Div.) 6-1 v Kings Langley(Spartan S. Midlands)
Dulwich Hamlet (Isthmian Lg.Premier Div.) 6-0 v Shoreham (Sussex County League)

and leading scorers away from home were:

St Margaretsbury (Spartan South Midlands) 0-7 v Hemel Hempstead T (Southern Prem)
Greenhouse London (Essex Senior League) 2-6 v Bedford Town(Southern Lg Prem Div)

High scoring draws were enjoyed at the West Country battle between Corsham Town and Bristol Manaor Farm which ended 4-4 and at Brentwood Town where an Essex' 'derby' against FC Clacton resulted in a 3-3- draw.

The 80 winners of the Second Qualifying Round will each be rewarded with £4,500, which can transform the whole season for any club playing below Step Three. But as the FA Cup ties come every fortnight early in the season, successful clubs can very quickly find themselves imagining all sorts of cup heroics with the possibility of giant killing and televised games. It's an exciting time!

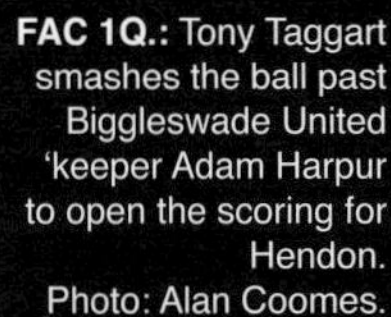
FAC 1Q.: Tony Taggart smashes the ball past Biggleswade United 'keeper Adam Harpur to open the scoring for Hendon. Photo: Alan Coomes.

FAC 1Q.: Ross Allen, Guernsey, right (partly hidden) scores from the penalty spot in the last minute against Hastings United to complete his hat-trick. Photo: Roger Turner.

FIRST QUALIFYING ROUND

SATURDAY 14 SEPTEMBER 2013 - WINNERS RECEIVE £3,000

No	Home		Away	Score	Att
1	Marske United	v	Albion Sports	3-0	222
2	Blyth Spartans	v	AFC Fylde	1-3	386
3	Whitby Town	v	West Auckland Town (17/9)	1-1	284
	West Auckland Town	v	Whitby Town	4-1	287
4	Penrith	v	Padiham	3-1	140
5	Spennymoor Town	v	Lancaster City	0-1	449
6	Team Northumbria	v	Scarborough Athletic	0-4	140
7	Brighouse Town	v	Crook Town	4-1	161
8	Guisborough Town	v	Bishop Auckland	2-2	202
	Bishop Auckland	v	Guisborough Town (17/9)	0-2	198
9	Jarrow Roofing Boldon CA	v	Morpeth Town	1-0	60
10	Stocksbridge Park Steels	v	Ramsbottom United	2-2	129
	Ramsbottom United	v	Stocksbridge Park Steels (17/9)	3-0	127
11	Marine	v	Curzon Ashton	2-4	233
12	Warrington Town	v	New Mills	0-0	130
	New Mills	v	Warrington Town (16/9)	0-1	114
13	Runcorn Linnets	v	Glossop North End	2-1	356
14	Prescot Cables	v	Buxton	0-1	220
15	FC United Of Manchester	v	Chorley	0-1	1318
16	Ashton United	v	Witton Albion	2-1	152
17	Ossett Town	v	Bamber Bridge	2-2	93
	Bamber Bridge	v	Ossett Town (17/9)	1-2	109
18	Frickley Athletic	v	Sheffield	4-1	222
19	Worksop Parramore	v	Cammell Laird (15/9)	1-3	140
20	Droylsden	v	Trafford	1-5	186
21	Worksop Town	v	Bootle	1-1	179
	Bootle	v	Worksop Town (17/9)	0-4	193
22	Burscough	v	Radcliffe Borough	2-1	144
23	Northwich Victoria	v	Skelmersdale United	0-3	187
24	Tipton Town	v	Kidsgrove Athletic	2-0	56
25	Atherstone Town	v	Redditch United	3-3	307
	Redditch United	v	Atherstone Town (16/9)	1-2	183
26	AFC Wulfrunians	v	Walsall Wood	1-1	132
	Walsall Wood	v	AFC Wulfrunians (17/9)	3-4aet	86
27	Evesham United	v	Stourbridge	0-3	265
28	Hinckley United	v	Rushall Olympic	0-3	260
29	Newcastle Town	v	Sutton Coldfield Town	2-2	81
	Sutton Coldfield Town	v	Newcastle Town (17/9)	2-0	61
30	Chasetown	v	Stafford Rangers	0-0	359
	Stafford Rangers	v	Chasetown (17/9)	2-0	311
31	Halesowen Town	v	Brocton	2-1	222
32	Coventry Sphinx	v	Tividale	2-1	180
33	Nantwich Town	v	Rugby Town	1-2	232
34	Coalville Town	v	Long Eaton United	3-2	145
35	Stamford	v	Grantham Town	0-0	318
	Grantham Town	v	Stamford (17/9)	2-3	212
36	Corby Town	v	Barwell	3-0	269
37	Mickleover Sports	v	Loughborough University	2-0	147
38	Carlton Town	v	Brigg Town	1-1	69
	Brigg Town	v	Carlton Town (17/9)	1-2	76
39	Dunkirk	v	Blaby & Whetstone Athletic	0-0	85
	Blaby & Whetstone Athletic	v	Dunkirk (17/9)	2-1	90
40	Gresley	v	Eastwood Town	3-2	300
41	Ilkeston	v	Belper Town	1-2	516
42	Basford United	v	Matlock Town	0-2	169
43	St Neots Town	v	Wroxham	3-1	232
44	Sleaford Town	v	Huntingdon Town		
	(tie abandoned after 87 minutes due to misconduct, 2-1 – both clubs removed from the competition)				
45	King's Lynn Town	v	Cambridge City	1-5	705
46	St Ives Town	v	Dereham Town	4-1	291
47	Spalding United	v	Gorleston	1-0	197
48	Billericay Town	v	Leiston	2-0	210
49	Grays Athletic	v	Romford (15/9)	2-1	217
50	Witham Town	v	Mildenhall Town	1-1	109
	Mildenhall Town	v	Witham Town (17/9)	1-3	203
51	Harlow Town	v	Lowestoft Town	2-1	236
52	AFC Hornchurch	v	East Thurrock United	1-1	273
	East Thurrock United	v	AFC Hornchurch (17/9)	1-2	156
53	Brentwood Town	v	FC Clacton	3-3	91
	FC Clacton	v	Brentwood Town (17/9)	2-1	226
54	Needham Market	v	Brantham Athletic	3-2	249
55	Bury Town	v	Thurrock	0-2	234
56	Aveley	v	Canvey Island	2-5	131
57	Tilbury	v	Waltham Abbey	2-1	77
58	Maldon & Tiptree	v	Heybridge Swifts	0-2	282
59	Burnham Ramblers	v	AFC Sudbury	1-2	119
60	Hendon	v	Biggleswade United (15/9)	7-1	138
61	Chesham United	v	Royston Town	1-2	255
62	Cockfosters	v	AFC Rushden & Diamonds	2-2	305
	AFC Rushden & Diamonds	v	Cockfosters (17/9)	8-0	421
63	Daventry Town	v	Berkhamsted	6-1	132
64	Greenhouse London	v	Bedford Town	2-6	62
65	Wingate & Finchley	v	Biggleswade Town (15/9)	0-0	108
	Biggleswade Town	v	Wingate & Finchley (17/9)	4-3	78
66	Hitchin Town	v	Arlesley Town	1-1	431
	Arlesley Town	v	Hitchin Town (17/9)	2-0	257
67	Uxbridge	v	Barton Rovers	2-3	90
68	Harrow Borough	v	North Greenford United	2-2	135
	North Greenford United	v	Harrow Borough (17/9)	2-1	135
69	Wembley	v	Haringey Borough	0-2	60
70	St Albans City	v	Enfield Town	6-1	423
71	Wealdstone	v	Kings Langley	6-1	332
72	Hertford Town	v	Dunstable Town	0-6	144
73	St Margaretsbury	v	Hemel Hempstead Town	0-7	97
74	Westfield	v	Aylesbury United	1-1	201
	Aylesbury United	v	Westfield (18/9)	2-0	149
75	Beaconsfield SYCOB	v	Burnham	2-4	133
76	Chertsey Town	v	Highmoor Ibis	4-0	121
77	Didcot Town	v	North Leigh	2-1	156
78	Hampton & Richmond Borough	v	Ashford Town (Middx)	4-2	235
79	Aylesbury	v	Shortwood United	1-5	112
80	Hungerford Town	v	Cove	4-0	100
81	Chalfont St Peter	v	Metropolitan Police	0-0	60
	Metropolitan Police	v	Chalfont St Peter (17/9)	0-1	67
82	Ardley United	v	Binfield	2-2	66
	Binfield	v	Ardley United (16/9)	4-1	189
83	Hartley Wintney	v	Camberley Town	0-0	148
	Camberley Town	v	Hartley Witney (17/9)	0-2	98
84	Banbury United	v	Cirencester Town	1-2	171
85	Leatherhead	v	Carshalton Athletic	2-1	267
86	Burgess Hill Town	v	Alton Town	8-1	203
87	South Park	v	Horsham	1-1	227
	Horsham	v	South Park (17/9)	5-2	134
88	Merstham	v	Corinthian Casuals	1-0	90
89	Peacehaven & Telscombe	v	Lewes	2-3	612
90	Three Bridges	v	Maidstone United	0-1	263
91	Thamesmead Town	v	Redhill	2-0	51
92	Hastings United	v	Guernsey	2-3	573
93	Margate	v	Kingstonian	2-1	328
94	Folkestone Invicta	v	Eastbourne United	2-0	253
95	Sittingbourne	v	Littlehampton Town	3-2	142
96	Dulwich Hamlet	v	Shoreham	6-0	341
97	Hassocks	v	Chipstead	1-2	105
98	Eastbourne Town	v	Tunbridge Wells	3-2	235
99	Whyteleafe	v	Horley Town	3-0	117
100	Cray Wanderers	v	Faversham Town (15/9)	0-3	104
101	Chatham Town	v	East Preston	2-1	147
102	Poole Town	v	Brockenhurst	2-0	278
103	Fareham Town	v	Weymouth	0-1	323
104	Hallen	v	Hamworthy United	1-2	58
105	Sholing	v	AFC Totton	4-0	312
106	Frome Town	v	Bognor Regis Town	1-1	218
	Bognor Regis Town	v	Frome Town (18/9)	4-0	310
107	Corsham Town	v	Bristol Manor Farm	4-4	70
	Bristol Manor Farm	v	Corsham Town (17/9)	1-0	104
108	Yate Town	v	Chippenham Town	3-2	248
109	Winchester City	v	Mangotsfield United	1-2	164
110	Horndean	v	AFC Portchester	0-5	195
111	Bashley	v	Moneyfields	2-0	155
112	Truro City	v	Street	1-0	365
113	Bridgwater Town	v	Merthyr Town	2-1	295
114	Bideford	v	Larkhall Athletic	3-0	221
115	Wells City	v	Brislington	1-2	109
116	Clevedon Town	v	Plymouth Parkway	1-0	107

SECOND QUALIFYING ROUND

The inclusion of clubs from the Conference North and South in The Second Qualifying Round provides the chance for some real giant killing and of the nine qualifying clubs below Step Four, the four representatives of The Northern league provided the best results.

West Auckland Town produced the result of the round with a 5-0 thrashing of Skelmersdale United, while Marske United, although playing away at Frickley Athletic, won 3-1. Both defeated clubs were in the Northern Premier League Premier Division where Skelmersdale were actually challenging at the top of the table.

With Penrith and Marske United also winning, The Northern League will have four representatives in The Third Qualifying Round. While two re-formed clubs, Runcorn Linnets and AFC Rushden & Diamonds revived memories of their predecessors with victories over Cammell Laird and Cambridge City respectively.

FAC 2Q: Merstham's Liam Harwood clears from Maidstone's Zac Attwood. Photo: Alan Coomes.

Step Five clubs in The South East will only be represented by Hartley Wintney from The United Counties League who won 5-1 at Eastbourne Town. The West also have just one representative from that level, in Western League club Brislington who beat Truro City 3-2 at home and the West Midlands provides Atherstone Town of The Midland Combination, 1-0 victors over Coalville Town.

Of the three Leagues with their three divisions, The Southern League provide 18 clubs in the Third Qualifying Round, split between Premier Division (9) Division One South West (6) and Div. One Central (3). There are 15 Isthmian clubs (Premier 8, Div One South 4 and Div One North 3) and The Northern Premier League provide 10.(Premier 4, North and South 3 each).

Conference North and South played the part of the 'Giants' in this round with little to gain other than survival. They would have to win two cup ties before they would have the chance to knock over a senior opponent, and in this round, 15 qualified from The North and 13 from The South.

Hat Tricks

The three 'Rs' provided the hat tricks on Cup Saturday with Carl Rook (AFC Hornchurch) in a 4-1 victory at Spalding, Vauxhall Motors' Jordan Rugg with three in a 4-0 win at home to Chorley and Ryan Robbins three goals in Stamford's 4-1 victory over AFC Wulfranians.

But on the Sunday, Kyle Vassell scored four, including two penalties, for Bishop's Stortford in their impressive 5-0 away victory at Hendon.

FAC 2Q: Action between Cirencester and AFC Porchester. Photo: Peter Barnes.

Attendances

Despite their fall from grace, Stockport County continued to enjoy loyal support and for the visit of Brighouse Town, who had finished as runners up in the Northern Counties East League in the previous season, a crowd of 1,704 attended.

AFC Telford United's clash with Conference North leaders Hednesford Town attracted 1,345, 'the local derby' between Trafford and Alrincham was watched by 829, the 'new Rushden & Diamonds' revived local memories for 815 as Cambridge City's challenged and Ebbsfleet United had 737 in to watch Folkestone Invicta.

Not outstanding attendances, but with the majority of ties attracting an average of about 350, this was above the normal league attendance for this level of clubs and once a team and it supporters sensed they were on a cup run, then they wouldn't want to miss it.

SECOND QUALIFYING ROUND

SATURDAY 28 SEPTEMBER 2013 - WINNERS RECEIVE £4,500

1	Runcorn Linnets	v	Cammell Laird	1-0	423
2	Guiseley	v	Bradford (Park Avenue)	1-3	595
3	Frickley Athletic	v	Marske United	1-3	302
4	Scarborough Athletic	v	Penrith	1-1	460
	Penrith	v	Scarborough Athletic (2/10)	2-2aet	230
	(Penrith won 4-3 on kicks from the penalty mark)				
5	Jarrow Roofing Boldon CA	v	Guisborough Town	3-3	87
	Guisborough Town	v	Jarrow Roofing Boldon CA (2/10)	3-1	277
6	Curzon Ashton	v	Lancaster City	0-0	302
	Lancaster City	v	Curzon Ashton (1/10)	1-2	249
7	Workington	v	Burscough	2-1	381
8	Stockport County	v	Brighouse Town	1-0	1704
9	Ossett Town	v	Warrington Town	1-1	139
	Warrington Town	v	Ossett Town (1/10)	1-3aet	133
10	AFC Fylde	v	Ashton United	0-1	302
11	Colwyn Bay	v	Harrogate Town	1-0	259
12	Vauxhall Motors	v	Chorley	4-0	366
13	Trafford	v	Altrincham	2-1	829
14	Stalybridge Celtic	v	Worksop Town	3-5	327
15	Buxton	v	North Ferriby United	1-4	284
16	West Auckland Town	v	Skelmersdale United	5-0	362
17	Barrow	v	Ramsbottom United	3-0	677
18	AFC Telford United	v	Hednesford Town	1-3	1345
19	Solihull Moors	v	Leamington	1-1	479
	Leamington	v	Solihull Moors (1/10)	1-2	368
20	Atherstone Town	v	Coalville Town	1-0	484
21	Stamford	v	AFC Wulfrunians	4-1	225
22	Stourbridge	v	Sutton Coldfield Town	3-2	373
23	Brackley Town	v	Gresley	1-1	312
	Gresley	v	Brackley Town (1/10)	0-1	302
24	Gainsborough Trinity	v	Rushall Olympic	2-0	433
	(tie awarded to Rushall Olympic – Gainsborough Trinity removed)				
25	Mickleover Sports	v	Corby Town	3-3	270
	Corby Town	v	Mickleover Sports (2/10)	5-2	228
26	Worcester City	v	Coventry Sphinx	4-0	514
27	Belper Town	v	Daventry Town	1-3	255
28	Stafford Rangers	v	Boston United	0-4	519
29	Blaby & Whetstone Athletic	v	Rugby Town	0-6	149
30	Halesowen Town	v	Tipton Town	5-0	421
31	Carlton Town	v	Matlock Town	1-0	161
32	Grays Athletic	v	Tilbury (29/9)	3-0	368
33	Spalding United	v	AFC Hornchurch	1-4	341
34	Concord Rangers	v	St Ives Town	4-3	238
35	Royston Town	v	Histon	0-4	525
36	FC Clacton	v	North Greenford United	1-1	260
	North Greenford United	v	FC Clacton (1/10)	3-1	124
37	Needham Market	v	Dunstable Town	3-1	251
38	St Albans City	v	Billericay Town	2-0	372
39	Hampton & Richmond Borough	v	Bedford Town	1-0	312
40	Arlesey Town	v	Thurrock	1-0	167
41	AFC Rushden & Diamonds	v	Cambridge City	3-2	815
42	Hemel Hempstead Town	v	Witham Town	1-1	425
	Witham Town	v	Hemel Hempstead Town (1/10)	3-4	156
43	Barton Rovers	v	Boreham Wood	0-0	172
	Boreham Wood	v	Barton Rovers (30/9)	3-0	174
44	Biggleswade Town	v	Chelmsford City	2-0	329
45	Harlow Town	v	Heybridge Swifts	2-3	263
46	Wealdstone	v	Haringey Borough	4-1	314
47	Hendon	v	Bishop's Stortford (29/9)	0-5	269
48	walkover for AFC Sudbury – Sleaford Town & Huntingdon Town removed				
49	Canvey Island	v	St Neots Town	2-2	256
	St Neots Town	v	Canvey Island (1/10)	1-2	289
50	Whitehawk	v	Sutton United	0-1	267
51	Thamesmead Town	v	Sittingbourne	1-2	123
52	Didcot Town	v	Burnham	2-1	103
53	Merstham	v	Maidstone United	1-4	306
54	Bromley	v	Burgess Hill Town	1-0	156
55	Horsham	v	Faversham Town (29/9)	2-0	361
56	Ebbsfleet United	v	Folkestone Invicta	1-0	737
57	Guernsey	v	Dover Athletic	2-3	324
	(at Sussex FA, Lancing)				
58	Oxford City	v	Maidenhead United	1-0	249
59	Eastbourne Town	v	Hartley Wintney	1-5	133
60	Whyteleafe	v	Chatham Town	1-2	166
61	Chertsey Town	v	Chipstead	1-2	143
62	Eastbourne Borough	v	Farnborough	0-0	560
	Farnborough	v	Eastbourne Borough (1/10)	0-2	332
63	Margate	v	Dulwich Hamlet	1-2	508
64	Binfield	v	Leatherhead	1-2	401
65	Aylesbury United	v	Staines Town	0-3	203
66	Hayes & Yeading United	v	Tonbridge Angels (29/9)	0-0	198
	Tonbridge Angels	v	Hayes & Yeading United (1/10)	2-1	297
67	Chalfont St Peter	v	Lewes	0-1	153
68	Dorchester Town	v	Shortwood United	0-1	279
69	Hamworthy United	v	Poole Town	2-4	350
70	Cirencester Town	v	AFC Portchester	2-0	170
71	Brislington	v	Truro City	3-2	172
72	Bristol Manor Farm	v	Bridgwater Town	4-4	182
	Bridgwater Town	v	Bristol Manor Farm (1/10)	2-1	321
73	Gloucester City	v	Havant & Waterlooville (29/9)	1-1	336
	Havant & Waterlooville	v	Gloucester City (1/10)	2-3	232
74	Eastleigh	v	Mangotsfield United	4-0	238
75	Basingstoke Town	v	Weston Super Mare	1-3	336
76	Yate Town	v	Bideford	2-1	264
77	Weymouth	v	Bognor Regis Town	2-2	598
	Bognor Regis Town	v	Weymouth (1/10)	1-4	414
78	Clevedon Town	v	Sholing	2-0	86
79	Bath City	v	Gosport Borough	2-0	411
80	Bashley	v	Hungerford Town	0-3	177

THIRD QUALIFYING ROUND

One more round to go before the Football league clubs enter the fray and there are just two Step 5 clubs definitely through. Brislington's 3-2 victory away at Weston-super-Mare of the Conference South was a sad occasion with a sending off after a brawl, and three
of the Round's 17 goals from the penalty spot, including two in the last three minutes!

Marske United beat Halesowen Town after a 3-2 thriller in front of an 807 attendance and their Northern League colleagues West Auckland Town earned an exciting replay after a 2-2 draw at high flying Hednesford Town.

Hartley Wintney from The Combined Counties held Clevedon Town to a 1-1 draw and recovered from a two goal deficit to gain a thrilling 4-3 away replay victory with a last minute winner.

The last two qualifyers stormed into the Fourth Qualifying Round, with Daventry Town winning 4-0 at Grays and Gloucester CIty, inspired by first half hour hat-trick from Joe Parker, ran out 7-0 winners against Yate Town.

Some excellent attendances were certainly encouraging for Qualifying Round ties:

Stockport County v Rushall Olympic	2135
Maidstone United v Boreham Wood	1781
Hemel Hempstead Town v Dulwich Hamlet	949
Ebbsfleet United v Eastbourne Borough	901
Atherstone Town v Barrow AFC	823
Henesford Town v West Auckland Town	820
Marske United v Halesowen Town	807

The Match watched by the biggest attendance brought an ironic 1-0 victory for Rushall Olympic. They had only been given their place back in the competition after Gainsborough Trinity had unfortunately been ejected from the competition for a registration irregularity.

Goalscoring heroes of the Round were Stefan Payne with a hat trick in AFC Hornchurch's splendid 6-1 defeat of Wealdstone, Kyle Vassell who scored three when Bishop's Stortford also produced a 6-1 scoreline at Carlton Town and Charlie Moone with a hat trick for Hampton & Richmond Borough who beat Arlesey Town 5-1.

An uplifting example of sportsmanship was shown by the compiler of the West Auckland Town website who reported on a thrilling replayed cup tie against the Conference North leaders Hednesford Town, who had two players sent off, but still managed to get through after a penalty shoot out.The writer's final line was to wish Hednesford Town good luck in the next round- how very refreshing!

The winners in The Third Qualifying Round have earned £7,500 and the excitement will be mounting in the boardrooms as they look forward to The Fourth Qualifying Round where the next bonus on offer will be £12,500!

FOURTH QUALIFYING ROUND

Its a sign of the times!

The quality of the Football Conference is developing season by season, as the majority of members are now experienced ex Football league clubs. With a little luck from the draw, which kept them away from each other in the Fourth Qualifying Round, 15/19 Premier clubs will be competing in the First Round Proper.

Also breaking records, but sadly in a disappointing fashion, are the Northern Premier League and Isthmian League who are not supplying one single member for non-league football's 32 qualifyers in the FA Cup First Round.

Sadly there will be less traditional cup romance at First Round week-end, as the standards and the reputations of the Conference clubs mean that any successes against league opposition will certainly not be surprising.

Daventry Town, of the Southern League Division One Central is the only Step Four club to qualify. Two clubs enjoying excellent league form at Step 5 level provided the match of the round at Hemel Hempstead, where the Southern League leaders drew 3-3 with Conference South challengers Sutton United in front of an excellent 1,455 attendance.

Macclesfield Town and Southport certainly made the most of home advantage with 7-0 and 6-2 scorelines against Vauxhall Motors and Marske United respectively, but it was Daventry who recorded the best away victory with a 6-1 scoreline at Hartley Wintney.

The Southern League enjoyed an impressive FA Cup afternoon with Biggleswade attracting 678 to see their victory over Canvey Island and Stourbridge, continuing their fine run of form with a 3-1 victory away to Conference North club Workington.

National Strikeforce leading scorer Elliott Durrell, scored two more from the penalty spot to win the tie for Hednesford Town at Stamford and bring his total 17 including 7 penalties.

Western League club Brislington held Conference Premier Welling United to a single goal and Shortwood United scored a last minute equaliser to force a replay at Aldershot. However, it wasn't a good day for 'the minnows' and it will be interesting to see what impact the mass Conference invasion will have on the FIrst Round proper.

THIRD QUALIFYING ROUND

SATURDAY 12 OCTOBER 2013 - WINNERS RECEIVE £7,500

1	Worcester City	v	Rugby Town	0-0	704
	Rugby Town	v	Worcester City (15/10)	0-2	327
2	Corby Town	v	Trafford	4-2	531
3	Carlton Town	v	Vauxhall Motors	1-3	153
4	Marske United	v	Halesowen Town	3-2	807
5	Stockport County	v	Rushall Olympic	0-1	2135
6	Stourbridge	v	Curzon Ashton	3-0	633
7	Stamford	v	Ashton United	4-2	301
8	Solihull Moors	v	Worksop Town	4-0	465
9	Colwyn Bay	v	Ossett Town	2-1	344
10	Hednesford Town	v	West Auckland Town	2-2	820
	West Auckland Town	v	Hednesford Town (15/10)	2-2aet	385
	(Hednesford Town won 4-2 on kicks from the penalty mark)				
11	Atherstone Town	v	Barrow	0-4	823
12	Brackley Town	v	Boston United	2-0	406
13	North Ferriby United	v	Runcorn Linnets	2-0	520
14	Bradford (Park Avenue)	v	Penrith	2-1	427
15	Guisborough Town	v	Workington	1-4	524
16	Maidstone United	v	Boreham Wood	0-2	1781
17	Biggleswade Town	v	Leatherhead	5-1	366
18	Dover Athletic	v	AFC Rushden & Diamonds	3-1	735
19	Chipstead	v	Bishop's Stortford	1-6	204
20	Horsham	v	Chatham Town	0-1	466
21	Concord Rangers	v	Histon	2-1	307
22	Hampton & Richmond Borough	v	Arlesey Town	5-1	406
23	Needham Market	v	AFC Sudbury	2-1	634
24	Staines Town	v	Sittingbourne	4-1	357
25	Lewes	v	Sutton United	0-1	1173
26	St Albans City	v	Tonbridge Angels	2-1	605
27	Hemel Hempstead Town	v	Dulwich Hamlet	3-1	949
28	AFC Hornchurch	v	Wealdstone	6-1	506
29	Canvey Island	v	North Greenford United	2-1	332
30	Ebbsfleet United	v	Eastbourne Borough	2-0	901
31	Bromley	v	Heybridge Swifts	1-2	797
32	Grays Athletic	v	Daventry Town (16/10)	0-4	196
33	Cirencester Town	v	Weymouth	1-2	366
34	Weston Super Mare	v	Brislington	2-3	315
35	Eastleigh	v	Oxford City	2-3	434
36	Hartley Wintney	v	Clevedon Town	1-1	410
	Clevedon Town	v	Hartley Wintney (14/10)	3-4	165
37	Bridgwater Town	v	Bath City	0-3	722
38	Poole Town	v	Hungerford Town	2-0	551
39	Didcot Town	v	Shortwood United	0-1	153
40	Yate Town	v	Gloucester City	2-2	609
	Gloucester City	v	Yate Town (16/10)	7-0	344

FOURTH QUALIFYING ROUND

SATURDAY 26 OCTOBER 2013 - WINNERS RECEIVE £12,500

1	Macclesfield Town	v	Vauxhall Motors	7-0	956
2	Stamford	v	Hednesford Town	0-2	668
3	Grimsby Town	v	Rushall Olympic	3-0	1456
4	Worcester City	v	Lincoln City	1-1	1019
	Lincoln City	v	Worcester City (29/10)	3-0	1344
5	Bradford (Park Avenue)	v	Kidderminster Harriers (27/10)	1-1	464
	Kidderminster Harriers	v	Bradford (Park Avenue) (29/10)	2-1	1212
6	Wrexham	v	Hyde	2-0	1848
7	Workington	v	Stourbridge	1-3	519
8	Southport	v	Marske United	6-2	943
9	Colwyn Bay	v	Corby Town	1-3	552
10	Tamworth	v	Solihull Moors	4-1	1036
11	Nuneaton Town	v	FC Halifax Town	0-2	1043
12	North Ferriby United	v	Alfreton Town	1-3	735
13	Brackley Town	v	Barrow	0-0	409
	Barrow	v	Brackley Town (29/10)	0-1aet	830
14	Chester	v	Gateshead	0-1	1659
15	Hemel Hempstead Town	v	Sutton United	3-3	1455
	Sutton United	v	Hemel Hempstead Town (29/10)	2-0	662
16	AFC Hornchurch	v	Hereford United	0-1	739
17	Ebbsfleet United	v	Dartford	1-1	2895
	Dartford	v	Ebbsfleet United (29/10)	1-0	1901
18	Barnet	v	Concord Rangers	3-0	1373
19	Chatham Town	v	St Albans City	0-2	849
20	Dover Athletic	v	Oxford City	3-0	869
21	Boreham Wood	v	Heybridge Swifts	1-0	237
22	Bath City	v	Salisbury City	0-1	1068
23	Gloucester City	v	Hampton & Richmond Borough	3-1	683
24	Weymouth	v	Braintree Town	1-2	775
25	Forest Green Rovers	v	Bishop's Stortford	0-1	789
26	Needham Market	v	Cambridge United	0-1	1784
27	Biggeswade Town	v	Canvey Island	1-0	678
28	Shortwood United	v	Aldershot Town	1-1	631
	Aldershot Town	v	Shortwood United (29/10)	1-2	1240
29	Woking	v	Luton Town	0-1	1452
30	Brislington	v	Welling United	0-1	600
31	Hartley Wintney	v	Daventry Town	1-6	1040
32	Staines Town	v	Poole Town	0-0	376
	Poole Town	v	Staines Town (29/10)	0-1	935

FAC 2Q: Goal mouth action between Gloucester City and Havant & Waterlooville. Photo: Peter Barnes.

FAC 3Q: Sutton United's Mitchell Nelson (left) puts Damian Scannel of Lewes under pressure. Photo: Roger Turner.

FAC 3Q: Gloucester City's Lewis Hogg fires a shot at goal as Yate Town's Jake Cox makes a challenge. Photo: Peter Barnes.

FAC 4Q: Shortwood United striker, Adam Mann, takes a shot at the Aldershot Town goal. Photo: Peter Barnes.

FAC 2Qr: Daryl Brown (North Greenford) gets his shot in under pressure from Steve Downres (FC Clacton). Photo: Keith Clayton.

FAC 1P: Confue (Daventry) shoots under pressure from Talbot (Chesterfield). Photo: Keith Clayton.

FAC 4Q: Brett Donnelly heads home the goal that put the Biggleswade Town into the First Round Proper for the first time, at the expence of Canvey Island. Photo: Gordon Whittington.

FAC 2Q: Eastbourne Borough's No.5, Ian Simpemba, attempts to head towards the Farnborough goal. Photo: Roger Turner.

FAC 1P: Shortwood United captain, Jake Parrott, atteempts to the clear the Port Vale wall. Photo: Peter Barnes.

FAC 1P: Gloucester City's Mike green makes a safe catch under pressure from Fleetwood Town's Mark Roberts. Photo: Peter Barnes.

FAC 1P: Burton Albion's Diamond, makes a last ditch tackle to denie Hereford United's Brown. Photo: Keith Clayton.

FIRST ROUND PROPER

SATURDAY 9 NOVEMBER 2013 - WINNERS RECEIVE £18,000

1	Morecambe	v	Southend United	0-3	1475
2	Walsall	v	Shrewsbury Town	3-0	3338
3	Boreham Wood	v	Carlisle United	0-0	901
	Carlisle United	v	Boreham Wood (19/11)	2-1	1484
4	St Albans City	v	Mansfield Town	1-8	3251
5	Milton Keynes Dons	v	FC Halifax Town	4-1	4049
6	Bristol Rovers	v	York City (8/11)	3-3	4654
	York City	v	Bristol Rovers (19/11)	2-3	2051
7	Tamworth	v	Cheltenham Town	1-0	1566
8	Grimsby Town	v	Scunthorpe United	0-0	8306
	Scunthorpe United	v	Grimsby Town (19/11)	1-2	5699
9	Bury	v	Cambridge United (19/11)	0-0	1712
	Cambridge United	v	Bury (3/12)	2-1	3342
10	Corby Town	v	Dover Athletic	1-2	1387
11	Colchester United	v	Sheffield United	2-3	2509
12	Oxford United	v	Gateshead	2-2	3114
	Gateshead	v	Oxford United (5/12)	0-1aet	2632
13	Hartlepool United	v	Notts County	3-2	3313
14	Wrexham	v	Alfreton Town	3-1	2415
15	Chesterfield	v	Daventry Town	2-0	5269
16	Bristol City	v	Dagenham & Redbridge	3-0	3763
17	AFC Wimbledon	v	Coventry City (8/11)	1-3	3379
18	Preston North End	v	Barnet	6-0	5217
19	Bishop's Stortford	v	Northampton Town (10/11)	1-2	2548
20	Burton Albion	v	Hereford United (10/11)	2-0	2069
21	Rotherham United	v	Bradford City	3-0	7667
22	Gillingham	v	Brackley Town	1-1	3004
	Brackley Town	v	Gillingham (18/11)	1-0	1772
23	Salisbury City	v	Dartford	4-2	1279
24	Accrington Stanley	v	Tranmere Rovers	0-1	1711
25	Brentford	v	Staines Town	5-0	5263
26	Stevenage	v	Portsmouth	2-1	2829
27	Shortwood United	v	Port Vale (11/11)	0-4	1247
28	Leyton Orient	v	Southport	5-2	3014
29	Peterborough United	v	Exeter City	2-0	3379
30	Torquay United	v	Rochdale	0-2	1976
31	Braintree Town	v	Newport County	1-1	1004
	Newport County	v	Braintree Town (19/11)	1-0	1406
32	Oldham Athletic	v	Wolverhampton Wanderers	1-1	3916
	Wolverhampton Wanderers	v	Oldham Athletic (19/11)	1-2	4226
33	Lincoln City	v	Plymouth Argyle	0-0	2924
	Plymouth Argyle	v	Lincoln City (20/11)	5-0	3324
34	Kidderminster Harriers	v	Sutton United	4-1	2045
35	Hednesford Town	v	Crawley Town	1-2	2321
36	Stourbridge	v	Biggleswade Town	4-1	1605
37	Welling United	v	Luton Town	2-1	1555
38	Macclesfield Town	v	Swindon Town	4-0	1835
39	Wycombe Wanderers	v	Crewe Alexandra	1-1	1929
	Crewe Alexandra	v	Wycombe Wanderers (19/11)	0-2	1605
40	Gloucester City	v	Fleetwood Town	0-2	1183

SECOND ROUND PROPER

SATURDAY 7 DECEMBER 2013 - WINNERS RECEIVE £27,000

1	Cambridge United	v	Sheffield United (8/12)	0-2	4593
2	Wycombe Wanderers	v	Preston North End	0-1	2349
3	Port Vale	v	Salisbury City (6/12)	4-1	4658
4	Bristol Rovers	v	Crawley Town	0-0	4623
	Crawley Town	v	Bristol Rovers (8/1)	1-2	2435
	(18/12 – tie abandoned after 75 mins due to waterlogged pitch, 0-0)				
5	Milton Keynes Dons	v	Dover Athletic	1-0	4060
6	Carlisle United	v	Brentford	3-2	2581
7	Macclesfield Town	v	Brackley Town	3-2	2438
8	Chesterfield	v	Southend United	1-3	4067
9	Oldham Athletic	v	Mansfield Town	1-1	3429
	Mansfield Town	v	Oldham Athletic (17/12)	1-4	2836
10	Rotherham United	v	Rochdale	1-2	4957
11	Peterborough United	v	Tranmere Rovers	5-0	3269
12	Hartlepool United	v	Coventry City	1-1	2898
	Coventry City	v	Hartlepool United (17/12)	2-1	1214
13	Kidderminster Harriers	v	Newport County	4-2	2636
14	Plymouth Argyle	v	Welling United	3-1	4706
15	Wrexham	v	Oxford United (9/12)	1-2	2906
16	Fleetwood Town	v	Burton Albion	1-1	2119
	Burton Albion	v	Fleetwood Town (17/12)	1-0	1777
17	Grimsby Town	v	Northampton Town	2-0	3828
18	Leyton Orient	v	Walsall	1-0	2604
19	Tamworth	v	Bristol City (8/12)	1-2	2860
20	Stevenage	v	Stourbridge	4-0	2160

THIRD ROUND PROPER

SATURDAY 4 JANUARY 2014 - WINNERS RECEIVE £67,500

1	Barnsley	v	Coventry City	1-2	7439
2	Yeovil Town	v	Leyton Orient	4-0	3667
3	Liverpool	v	Oldham Athletic (5/1)	2-0	44102
4	Nottingham Forest	v	West Ham United (5/1)	5-0	14397
5	Bristol City	v	Watford	1-1	10165
	Watford	v	Bristol City (14/1)	2-0	7302
6	Southend United	v	Millwall	4-1	7698
7	Middlesbrough	v	Hull City	0-2	15571
8	West Bromwich Albion	v	Crystal Palace	0-2	12700
9	Kidderminster Harriers	v	Peterborough United	0-0	3858
	Peterborough United	v	Kidderminster Harriers (14/1)	2-3	3483
10	Doncaster Rovers	v	Stevenage	2-3	3899
11	Stoke City	v	Leicester City	2-1	16844
12	Southampton	v	Burnley	4-3	15177
13	Newcastle United	v	Cardiff City	1-2	31166
14	Rochdale	v	Leeds United	2-0	8255
15	Wigan Athletic	v	Milton Keynes Dons	3-3	6960
	Milton Keynes Dons	v	Wigan Athletic (14/1)	1-3aet	8316
16	Charlton Athletic	v	Oxford United (14/1)	2-2	5566
	Oxford United	v	Charlton Athletic (21/1)	0-3	3225
17	Manchester United	v	Swansea City (5/1)	1-2	73190
18	Port Vale	v	Plymouth Argyle (3/1)	2-2	5511
	Plymouth Argyle	v	Port Vale (14/1)	2-3	6474
19	Norwich City	v	Fulham	1-1	21703
	Fulham	v	Norwich City (14/1)	3-0	11172
20	Aston Villa	v	Sheffield United	1-2	24038
21	Macclesfield Town	v	Sheffield Wednesday	1-1	5873
	Sheffield Wednesday	v	Macclesfield Town (14/1)	4-1	12302
22	Sunderland	v	Carlisle United (5/1)	3-1	21973
23	Bolton Wanderers	v	Blackpool	2-1	11180
24	Blackburn Rovers	v	Manchester City	1-1	18813
	Manchester City	v	Blackburn Rovers (15/1)	5-0	33102
25	Everton	v	Queens Park Rangers	4-0	32283
26	Brighton & Hove Albion	v	Reading	1-0	20696
27	Arsenal	v	Tottenham Hotspur	2-0	59476
28	Birmingham City	v	Bristol Rovers (14/1)	3-0	10064
29	Grimsby Town	v	Huddersfield Town	2-3	6544
30	Ipswich Town	v	Preston North End	1-1	13534
	Preston North End	v	Ipswich Town (14/1)	3-2	6088
31	Derby County	v	Chelsea (5/1)	0-2	32110
32	AFC Bournemouth	v	Burton Albion (14/1)	4-1	10343

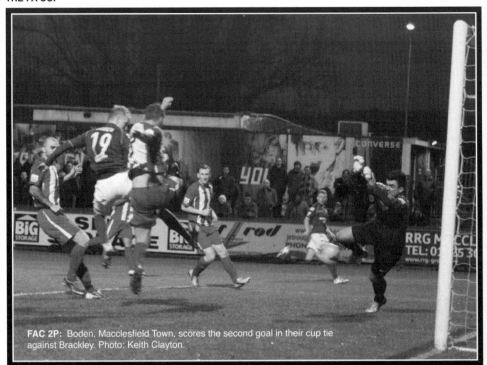

FAC 2P: Boden, Macclesfield Town, scores the second goal in their cup tie against Brackley. Photo: Keith Clayton.

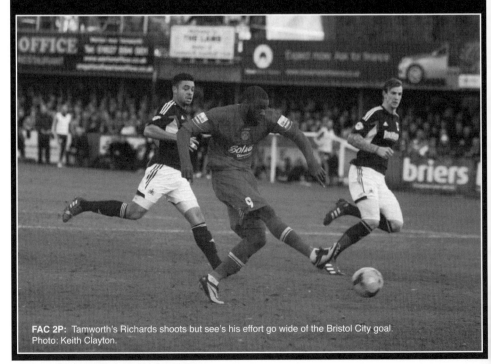

FAC 2P: Tamworth's Richards shoots but see's his effort go wide of the Bristol City goal. Photo: Keith Clayton.

FOURTH ROUND PROPER

SATURDAY 25 JANUARY 2014 - WINNERS RECEIVE £90,000

1	Sunderland	v	Kidderminster Harriers	1-0	25081
2	Bolton Wanderers	v	Cardiff City	0-1	12750
3	Southampton	v	Yeovil Town	2-0	24070
4	Huddersfield Town	v	Charlton Athletic	0-1	10120
5	Port Vale	v	Brighton & Hove Albion	1-3	7293
6	Nottingham Forest	v	Preston North End (24/1)	0-0	26465
	Preston North End	v	Nottingham Forest (5/2)	0-2	9744
7	Southend United	v	Hull City	0-2	10250
8	Rochdale	v	Sheffield Wednesday	1-2	8240
9	Arsenal	v	Coventry City (24/1)	4-0	59451
10	Stevenage	v	Everton	0-4	6913
11	Wigan Athletic	v	Crystal Palace	2-1	9542
12	Chelsea	v	Stoke City (26/1)	1-0	40845
13	Manchester City	v	Watford	4-2	46514
14	AFC Bournemouth	v	Liverpool	0-2	11475
15	Birmingham City	v	Swansea City	1-2	11490
16	Sheffield United	v	Fulham (26/1)	1-1	16324
	Fulham	v	Sheffield United (4/2)	0-1aet	10139

FIFTH ROUND PROPER

SATURDAY 15 FEBRUARY 2014 - WINNERS RECEIVE £180,000

1	Manchester City	v	Chelsea	2-0	47013
2	Sheffield United	v	Nottingham Forest (16/2)	3-1	25118
3	Arsenal	v	Liverpool (16/2)	2-1	59801
4	Brighton & Hove Albion	v	Hull City (17/2)	1-1	21352
	Hull City	v	Brighton & Hove Albion (24/2)	2-1	10795
5	Cardiff City	v	Wigan Athletic	1-2	17123
6	Sheffield Wednesday	v	Charlton Athletic (24/2)	1-2	24607
7	Sunderland	v	Southampton	1-0	16777
8	Everton	v	Swansea City (16/2)	3-1	31498

SIXTH ROUND PROPER

SATURDAY 8 MARCH 2014 - WINNERS RECEIVE £360,000

1	Arsenal	v	Everton	4-1	59719
2	Hull City	v	Sunderland (9/3)	3-0	20047
3	Sheffield United	v	Charlton Athletic (9/3)	2-0	30040
4	Manchester City	v	Wigan Athletic (9/3)	1-2	46824

SEMI FINALS

WINNERS RECEIVE £900,000 RUNNERS-UP £450,000

SATURDAY 12 APRIL 2014 - at Wembley Stadium

2	Wigan Athletic	v	Arsenal	1-1 aet	82185

(Arsenal won 3-1 on kicks from the penalty mark)

SUNDAY 13 APRIL 2014 - at Wembley Stadium

1	Hull City	v	Sheffield United	5-3	71820

THE FINAL

SATURDAY 17 MAY 2014 - at Wembley Stadium WINNERS RECEIVE £1.8m RUNNERS-UP £900,000

ARSENAL	3	2 aet	HULL CITY	89345

FAC 2P: Dan Fitchett, Salisbury City, sees his shot cross the line to equalise against Port Vale. Photo: Keith Clayton.

FAC 3P: Action from the Macclesfield Town v Sheffield Wednesday tie. Photo: Peter Barnes.

FAC 2P: Cambridge United's Liam Hughes puts pressure on Sheffield United's Jose Baxter. Photo: Peter Barnes.

FAC 3P - Joe Lolley, Kidderminster, hits the Peterborough crossbar in the first minute.
Photo: Keith Clayton.

Cambridge United lift the 2013-14 FA Trophy. Photo: Peter Barnes.

THE FA TROPHY 2013-14

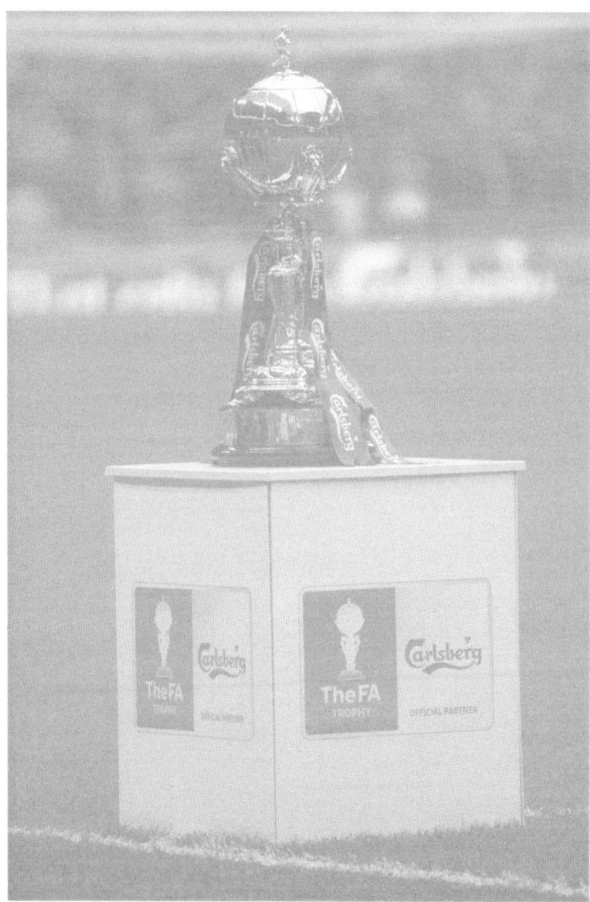

FAT P: Guernsey's Marc McGrath gets in a shot, watched closely by Barkingside's Aaron Scott.
Photo: Alan Coomes.

FAT P: Shortwood United's Mark Pritchett and Beaconsfield's Brad Hewitt challenges for the ball.
Photo: Peter Barnes.

PRELIMINARY ROUND

SATURDAY 5 OCTOBER 2013 - WINNERS RECEIVE £2,500

No	Home		Away	Score	Att
1	Brigg Town	v	Bamber Bridge	2-1	71
2	Northwich Victoria	v	Salford City	3-1	135
3	Prescot Cables	v	Scarborough Athletic	0-1	192
4	Warrington Town	v	Ramsbottom United	1-2	103
5	Goole	v	Burscough	1-5	95
6	Kendal Town	v	Farsley	3-2	153
7	Wakefield	v	Harrogate RA	2-1	51
8	Clitheroe	v	Radcliffe Borough	3-3	174
	Radcliffe Borough	v	Clitheroe (8/10)	3-0	107
9	Ossett Town	v	Darlington 1883	1-6	408
10	Padiham	v	Sheffield	1-2	202
11	Ossett Albion	v	Curzon Ashton	1-3	94
12	Lancaster City	v	New Mills	6-0	163
13	Lincoln United	v	Cammell Laird	1-2	72
14	Soham Town Rangers	v	Newcastle Town	1-0	112
15	Kettering Town	v	Romulus	1-1	561
	Romulus	v	Kettering Town (8/10)	1-2	98
16	Carlton Town	v	Gresley	2-2	114
	Gresley	v	Carlton Town (8/10)	2-0	211
17	Stratford Town	v	Coalville Town	2-2	223
	Coalville Town	v	Stratford Town (8/10)	3-1	144
18	Eastwood Town	v	Halesowen Town	0-3	145
19	Chasetown	v	Rugby Town	2-1	254
20	Evesham United	v	Market Drayton Town	3-1	152
21	Daventry Town	v	Sutton Coldfield Town	1-0	99
22	Belper Town	v	Loughborough Dynamo	2-0	152
23	Kidsgrove Athletic	v	Bedworth United	3-1	82
24	Rainworth MW	v	St Ives Town	0-1	132
25	VCD Athletic	v	Aylesbury	2-2	74
	Aylesbury	v	VCD Athletic (8/10)	2-1	63
26	Redbridge	v	Chatham Town	2-3	93
27	Ware	v	Witham Town	1-1	66
	Witham Town	v	Ware (8/10)	4-2	77
28	Sittingbourne	v	Whitstable Town	1-5	212
29	Leighton Town	v	North Greenford United	0-3	92
30	Redhill	v	Burnham Ramblers	1-3	66
31	Royston Town	v	Three Bridges	1-3	160
32	Aylesbury United	v	Faversham Town (6/10)	4-2	134
33	Dunstable Town	v	Erith & Belvedere	4-1	56
34	Tooting & Mitcham United	v	Eastbourne Town	1-2	126
35	Barton Rovers	v	Peacehaven & Telscombe	0-3	90
36	Herne Bay	v	Merstham	0-0	208
	Merstham	v	Herne Bay (8/10)	0-2	101
37	Thurrock	v	Corinthian Casuals	2-0	80
38	Waltham Abbey	v	Walton & Hersham	2-1	97
39	Uxbridge	v	Heybridge Swifts	1-2	87
40	Potters Bar Town	v	Romford	2-0	89
41	Burgess Hill Town	v	Wroxham	1-1	160
	Wroxham	v	Burgess Hill Town (8/10)	3-2	105
42	Tilbury	v	Needham Market	3-0	89
43	AFC Sudbury	v	Worthing	2-0	241
44	Folkestone Invicta	v	Waltham Forest	6-0	186
45	Walton Casuals	v	Crawley Down Gatwick	1-1	104
	Crawley Down Gatwick	v	Walton Casuals (8/10)	1-0	59
46	Horsham	v	Chipstead (4/10)	4-1	215
47	Hythe Town	v	Aveley	2-1	162
48	Barkingside	v	Guernsey (6/10)	0-6	205
49	Hastings United	v	Brentwood Town	3-2	344
50	Northwood	v	AFC Hayes	2-3	59
51	Leatherhead	v	Harlow Town	4-0	196
52	Mangotsfield United	v	Thatcham Town	2-1	109
53	Chalfont St Peter	v	Bridgwater Town	1-1	53
	Bridgwater Town	v	Chalfont St Peter (8/10)	3-3aet	156
	(Bridgewater won 5-3 on kicks from the penalty mark)				
54	Fleet Town	v	Clevedon Town	0-3	67
55	Didcot Town	v	Cirencester Town	1-1	108
	Cirencester Town	v	Didcot Town (8/10)	7-1	75
56	Merthyr Town	v	Yate Town	0-0	105
	Yate Town	v	Merthyr Town (8/10)	1-2	175
57	Swindon Supermarine	v	Taunton Town	3-0	105
58	Guildford City	v	Chertsey Town	3-4	96
59	Tiverton Town	v	Cinderford Town	1-0	147
60	Godalming Town	v	Slough Town	1-2	300
61	Bishop's Cleeve	v	Paulton Rovers	1-4	93
62	Egham Town	v	Ashford Town (Middx)	3-2	83
63	Wimborne Town	v	Marlow	3-5	151
64	Shortwood United	v	Beaconsfield SYCOB	3-1	87

FAT 1Q: Mangotsfield United players get up highest to head the ball towards the Shortwood United goal. Photo: Peter Barnes.

FAT 2Q: Jonny McNamara fires the hosts, Arlesey Town, in front during their exciting victory over Poole Town. Photo: Gordon Whittington.

FIRST QUALIFYING ROUND

SATURDAY 19 OCTOBER 2013 - WINNERS RECEIVE £2,700

1	Trafford	v	Wakefield	6-1	159
2	Whitby Town	v	Chorley	0-1	219
3	Frickley Athletic	v	Brigg Town	1-2	136
4	Cammell Laird	v	Curzon Ashton	0-1	48
5	AFC Fylde	v	Kendal Town	1-1	254
	Kendal Town	v	AFC Fylde (22/10)	1-2	170
6	Ramsbottom United	v	Worksop Town	7-2	355
7	Witton Albion	v	FC United of Manchester	2-2	693
	FC United of Manchester	v	Witton Albion (5/11)	1-2	369
	(at Witton Albion FC) (2/11 - abandoned due to waterlogged pitch after 75 mins, 2-2)				
8	Ashton United	v	Sheffield	0-3	104
9	Mossley	v	Lancaster City	3-2	186
10	Northwich Victoria	v	Radcliffe Borough	2-0	123
11	Blyth Spartans	v	Skelmersdale United	6-0	340
12	Droylsden	v	Nantwich Town	0-3	114
13	Stocksbridge Park Steels	v	Scarborough Athletic	3-4	239
14	Marine	v	Burscough	1-1	238
	Burscough	v	Marine (22/10)	0-1	205
15	Buxton	v	Darlington 1883	1-1	443
	Darlington 1883	v	Buxton (23/10)	3-3aet	766
	(Buxton won 4-3 on kicks from the penalty mark)				
16	Kettering Town	v	St Ives Town	0-1	609
17	Evesham United	v	Leek Town	0-2	167
18	Coalville Town	v	Stafford Rangers	3-2	182
19	Halesowen Town	v	St Neots Town	1-3	273
20	Redditch United	v	Chasetown (23/10)	2-0	172
	(19/10 - tie abandoned after 82 mins due to waterlogged pitch, 2-1)				
21	Gresley	v	Ilkeston	2-1	372
22	King's Lynn Town	v	Cambridge City	1-2	605
23	Belper Town	v	Mickleover Sports	2-3	225
24	Barwell	v	Rushall Olympic	0-4	153
25	Matlock Town	v	Hinckley United		
	(walkover for Matlock Town – Hinckley United removed)				
26	Stourbridge	v	Banbury United	3-2	321
27	Grantham Town	v	Soham Town Rangers	2-2	217
	Soham Town Rangers	v	Grantham Town (22/10)	4-1aet	125
28	Daventry Town	v	Corby Town	2-1	150
29	Stamford	v	Kidsgrove Athletic	1-2	151
30	Eastbourne Town	v	East Thurrock United	0-0	110
	East Thurrock United	v	Eastbourne Town (29/10)	6-2	130
31	Witham Town	v	St Albans City	0-3	85
32	Whitstable Town	v	Potters Bar Town	2-2	172
	Potters Bar Town	v	Whitstable Town (21/10)	1-2	94
33	Lewes	v	Leatherhead	1-2	417
34	Arlesey Town	v	Waltham Abbey	3-0	94
35	Cheshunt	v	Three Bridges	3-4	101
36	Thamesmead Town	v	Metropolitan Police	1-2	
37	AFC Sudbury	v	Crawley Down Gatwick	5-0	181
38	Wingate & Finchley	v	Hitchin Town	2-2	81
	Hitchin Town	v	Wingate & Finchley (21/10)	0-1	114
39	Hastings United	v	Horsham	4-2	310
40	Hampton & Richmond Borough	v	Bedford Town	1-1	209
	Brdford Town	v	Hampton&Richmond B. (22/10)	0-2	162
41	Folkestone Invicta	v	Kingstonian	2-0	230
42	Leiston	v	Wealdstone	0-3	184
43	North Greenford United	v	Aylesbury	2-1	57
44	Dunstable Town	v	Peacehaven & Telscombe	3-2	56
45	Cray Wanderers	v	Hendon	1-4	81
46	Chatham Town	v	AFC Hayes	2-0	109
47	Wroxham	v	Margate	4-9	124
48	Biggleswade Town	v	Chesham United	0-1	168
49	Grays Athletic	v	Herne Bay	1-1	154
	Herne Bay	v	Grays Athletic (22/10)	1-2aet	170
50	Guernsey	v	Billericay Town	1-2	1090
51	Bury Town	v	Dereham Town	2-0	217
52	Heybridge Swifts	v	Canvey Island	1-2	174
53	Burnham Ramblers	v	Carshalton Athletic	0-1	92
54	Hythe Town	v	Tilbury	3-1	187
55	Hemel Hempstead Town	v	AFC Hornchurch	3-2	511
56	Maldon & Tiptree	v	Maidstone United	1-3	212
57	Dulwich Hamlet	v	Harrow Borough	2-1	404
58	Bognor Regis Town	v	Thurrock	2-1	341
59	Enfield Town	v	Lowestoft Town	2-1	240
60	Aylesbury United	v	Ramsgate	0-1	210
61	Slough Town	v	Merthyr Town	1-2	216
62	Weymouth	v	Bridgewater Town	1-0	428
63	AFC Totton	v	Clevedon Town	1-2	186
64	Tiverton Town	v	Truro City	3-2	312
65	Chippenham Town	v	Chertsey Town	3-0	224
66	Egham Town	v	Cirencester Town	3-2	48
67	Shortwood United	v	Mangotsfield United	0-2	145
68	Hungerford Town	v	Bashley	4-2	1127
69	Swindon Supermarine	v	Bideford	2-3	143
70	Frome Town	v	Poole Town	1-1	224
	Poole Town	v	Frome Town (2/11)	3-1aet	245
71	Marlow	v	North Leigh	4-1	109
72	Burnham	v	Paulton Rovers	2-1	92

FIRST QUALIFYING ROUND

This year, the inter league rivalry in the First Qualifying Round was highlighted by Southern League Cambridge City's victory at Kings Lynn of The NPL in front of 605. Hemel Hempstead (Southern League) beat AFC Hornchurch (Isthmian) in a thrilling 3-2 cup tie between two clubs at the top of their respective leagues and Folkestone Invicta (Southern) will have been pleased with their 2-0 victory over a top Isthmian club Kingstonian.

The top scoring clubs included nine goals, shared between seven scorers for Margate at Wroxham, plus an incredible seven goals by Ramsbottom United (NPL Div One South) who won 7-2 against The NPL Premier Division's top scoring club Worksop Town, who had three goalscorers in 'The National Striketorce' and a goal tally in the league of 33-29.

Goals were certainly plentiful and hat tricks were recorded by Leon Spink of Rushall Olympic in their 4-0 away victory over Barwell, Michael Oates whose hat trick inspired Trafford 's 6-1 defeat of Wakefield and Craig Hubbard's three for Blyth Spartans, which were all scored in a nine minute second half spell in a 6-0 home victory over Skelmersdale United.

With fortunes changing for many senior clubs, it was perhaps not surprising to see a good attendance of 609 at Kettering, but visitors St Neots Town won 1-0. The all NPL Premier clash at Witton Albion attracted 693 for the 2-2 draw with FC United of Manchester and it was good to see a famous name from the old amateur days, Dulwich Hamlet, attracting 404 for the visit of Isthmian rivals Harrow Borough.

The biggest attendance however, was at Guernsey's first FA Trophy tie to be played on the Island. An excellent 1,090 watched Billericay Town win 2-1 but another piece of Island sporting history had been written.

The 44th FA Challenge Trophy is up and running. The last three winners have come from The North but all were from The Conference and were all ex-Football League clubs. Will the trend by changed this year?

SECOND QUALIFYING ROUND

The last round before the Conference North and South clubs enter the fray, brought some encouraging results for clubs from Step 4.

Ramsbottom United won with a Danny Warrender goal at Blyth Spartans, despite playing most of the second half with ten men. Coalville Town smashed five goals past Marine, all from different scorers. Gresley beat Trafford with two Kieran O'Connell goals scored within a minute, just before half time and Scarborough Athletic achieved an impressive away replay victory at a confident Cambridge City club.

Southern League Division One Central club Daventry Town, already looking forward toThe First Round Proper of the FA Cup, continued their excellent knock out cup form with a replay victory over Wingate & Finchley from the Isthmian Premier Division.

Two clubs who originally enjoyed FA Trophy traditions met in front of an attendance of just 138 where Northwich Victoria beat Mossley 2-1 with goals from Alex Taylor. A high powered pairing in the South took Maidstone United to Wealdstone, where 524 enjoyed an exciting 2-2 draw and 824 fans saw the Kent club go through with a last minute replay winner.

No surprise that the St Albans CIty and BIllericay Town clash produced six goals, as it featured three consistent scorers, John Frendo(16) and Mark Nwokeji (9) of Saints and Glen Poole of Billericay Town whose two goals included his fourth penalty in five games.

One of the clubs of the season so far must be Hemel Hempstead Town, who are challenging at the top of the Southern Premier Division with 49 league goals in the first thirteen games and another 30 in their FA Cup and FA Trophy matches. After losing their first game of the season, 'The Tudors' are unbeaten and have recorded a 7- 0 FA Cup victory over St Margaretsbury and their most recent 9-1 trouncing of North Greenford United in the Trophy was followed by a 10-0 victory over Bashley!

Another of the more powerful clubs at this level, who could well claim more scalps in the knock out competitions, is Stourbridge. Their away win at Mickleover Sports was their eighth consecutive victory and followed a 9-0 victory at Chippenham and an FA Cup triumph at Conference North Workington.

FAT 2Q: James Baker, AFC Sudbury, keeps the ball from Hasting United's defenders. Photo: Roger Turner.

THIRD QUALIFYING ROUND

Maidstone United attracted 1,397 for the visit of Eastleigh and the biggest FATrophy crowd of the round saw the Conference South's leaders win a closely fought cup tie with a second half penalty.

Staines Town who had met Brentford, senior local rivals in the FA Cup , this time clashed with Farnborough, another neighbour, in the Trophy and will have to meet again after a 2-2 draw.

AFC Telford United and Boston United showed their pedigree with convincing victories over Scarborough Athletic and Redditch United, but a strange change of fortunes seems to have hit Hemel Hempstead United, one of the Southern League leaders.Their nineteen goals in two games have been followed by conceding nine goals in two defeats - very confusing!

Uplifting FA Trophy victories for clubs experiencing a tough time in their respective leagues were enjoyed by Leamington, who beat Gainsborough Trinity 2-0 and Gosport Borough, who won 3-0 at home to Dorchester Town.

One of the best results was achieved by Tiverton Town from Southern League Division One South West, who conceded a late equalizer to Conference South club Weston-super-Mare.

A disappointing week for Bishops's Stortford, although they are still one of the two clubs to have scored in every game this season, they were knocked out of the FA Cup by Northampton Town and then lost by the only goal of the game at Whitehawk in the FA Trophy.

The top scorers of the round were Bury Town who won 5-1 at home to Grays Athletic and Hungerford Town who beat the mercurial Hemel Hempstead club 5-0.

The next excitement will be for some of these winners who could meet Conference Premier clubs and have the chance of giant killing which would light up their season.

SECOND QUALIFYING ROUND

SATURDAY 2 NOVEMBER 2013 - WINNERS RECEIVE £3,250

1	Witton Albion	v	Leek Town (12/11)	1-2	290
2	Mickleover Sports	v	Stourbridge	1-2	186
3	Rushall Olympic	v	AFC Fylde	0-1	121
4	Blyth Spartans	v	Ramsbottom United	0-1	298
5	Coalville Town	v	Marine	5-0	178
6	Scarborough Athletic	v	Cambridge City	0-0	442
	Cambridge City	v	Scarborough Athletic (6/11)	1-2	227
7	Redditch United	v	Brigg Town	5-0	193
8	Kidsgrove Athletic	v	Curzon Ashton	0-4	146
9	Northwich Victoria	v	Mossley	2-0	138
10	Matlock Town	v	St Neots Town	2-0	224
11	Gresley	v	Trafford	2-0	304
12	Sheffield	v	Buxton (12/11)	1-0	252
13	St Ives Town	v	Nantwich Town	1-4	282
14	Soham Town Rangers	v	Chorley	1-2	193
15	Carshalton Athletic	v	Egham Town	2-1	119
16	Chesham United	v	Weymouth	2-1	276
17	Folkestone Invicta	v	Hungerford Town	1-1	242
	Hungerford Town	v	Folkestone Invicta (5/11)	1-1aet	100
	(Hungerford won 5-4 on kicks from the penalty mark)				
18	St Albans City	v	Billericay Town	3-3	313
	Billericay Town	v	St Albans City (5/11)	2-2aet	201
	(St Albans City won 4-2 on kicks from the penalty mark)				
19	Arlesey Town	v	Poole Town (5/11)	3-2	114
20	Ramsgate	v	Three Bridges	4-1	144
21	Enfield Town	v	Grays Athletic	0-1	260
22	Hastings United	v	AFC Sudbury	0-1	375
23	Wingate & Finchley	v	Daventry Town	1-1	91
	Daventry Town	v	Wingate & Finchley (5/11)	3-1	124
24	Wealdstone	v	Maidstone United	2-2	524
	Maidstone United	v	Wealdstone (5/11)	1-0	944
25	Merthyr Town	v	Dunstable Town	3-2	236
26	Hampton & Richmond Borough	v	Metropolitan Police	2-1	227
27	Marlow	v	Burnham	2-0	201
28	Dulwich Hamlet	v	Leatherhead	3-0	296
29	Margate	v	Clevedon Town	4-1	227
30	Bury Town	v	Chatham Town	2-1	238
31	Hemel Hempstead Town	v	North Greenford United	9-1	350
32	Bognor Regis Town	v	Chippenham Town	4-1	367
33	Hendon	v	Bideford (3/11)	1-0	154
34	Canvey Island	v	East Thurrock United	0-2	266
35	Tiverton Town	v	Mangotsfield United	3-1	237
36	Hythe Town	v	Whitstable Town	2-2	303
	Whitstable Town	v	Hythe Town (6/11)	2-1	171

THIRD QUALIFYING ROUND

SATURDAY 16 NOVEMBER 2013 - WINNERS RECEIVE £4,000

1	Barrow	v	Stockport County	2-2	727
	Stockport County	v	Barrow (19/11)	2-3	812
2	Harrogate Town	v	Bradford (Park Avenue)	1-1	572
	Bradford (Park Avenue)	v	Harrogate Town (18/11)	4-0	189
3	Chorley	v	Matlock Town	2-0	772
4	Leamington	v	Gainsborough Trinity	2-0	373
5	Sheffield	v	Gresley	2-4	284
6	Stalybridge Celtic	v	Vauxhall Motors	3-0	315
7	Solihull Moors	v	Coalville Town	1-2	388
8	Stourbridge	v	North Ferriby United	2-2	437
	North Ferriby United	v	Stourbridge (19/11)	4-0	134
9	Worcester City	v	Ramsbottom United (17/11)	3-0	341
10	AFC Telford United	v	Scarborough Athletic	6-0	869
11	Brackley Town	v	Leek Town	0-0	187
	Leek Town	v	Brackley Town (27/11)	2-1aet	236
12	Hednesford Town	v	Workington	3-0	551
13	Curzon Ashton	v	AFC Fylde	2-1	217
14	Northwich Victoria	v	Nantwich Town	2-0	146
15	Guiseley	v	Histon	3-0	404
16	Boston United	v	Redditch United	4-1	784
17	Colwyn Bay	v	Altrincham (19/11)	0-2	280
	(16/11 - tie abandoned after 81 minutes due to injury to Referee, 0-2)				
18	Basingstoke Town	v	Hampton & Richmond Borough	3-1	403
19	Chelmsford City	v	St Albans City	1-2	429
20	Daventry Town	v	Ramsgate	3-2	250
21	Sutton United	v	Havant & Waterlooville	1-2	374
22	Carshalton Athletic	v	Whitstable Town	1-2	228
23	Hayes & Yeading United	v	Bognor Regis Town (17/11)	2-1	250
24	Tonbridge Angels	v	AFC Sudbury	1-1	408
	AFC Sudbury	v	Tonbridge Angels (19/11)	0-1	191
25	East Thurrock United	v	Merthyr Town	4-2	163
26	Boreham Wood	v	Gloucester City	0-1	133
27	Dover Athletic	v	Bath City	1-0	483
28	Hungerford Town	v	Hemel Hempstead Town	5-0	137
29	Ebbsfleet United	v	Bromley	4-1	956
30	Hendon	v	Oxford City (17/11)	2-1	197
31	Staines Town	v	Farnborough	2-2	299
	Farnborough	v	Staines Town (19/11)	0-2	230
32	Arlesey Town	v	Marlow	2-0	149
33	Bury Town	v	Grays Athletic	5-1	305
34	Weston Super Mare	v	Tiverton Town	1-1	385
	Tiverton Town	v	Weston Super Mare (19/11)	1-2	245
35	Whitehawk	v	Bishop's Stortford	2-1	107
36	Dulwich Hamlet	v	Concord Rangers	1-1	462
	Concord Rangers	v	Dulwich Hamlet (19/11)	4-3	156
37	Maidstone United	v	Eastleigh	1-2	1397
38	Eastbourne Borough	v	Maidenhead United	0-1	384
39	Margate	v	Chesham United	0-3	317
40	Gosport Borough	v	Dorchester Town	3-0	206

FIRST ROUND PROPER

With the 24 Conference Premier clubs entering the competition and 15 of them drawn at home. it was no surprise to see 9 through to the Second Round at the first attempt with 4 more qualifying after replays replays.

Cambridge United's disciplined defence kept a clean sheet for the sixteenth time this season when achieving a victory at Salisbury but Alfreton Town, Dartford, Hereford Town, Macclesfield and Welling United all lost to fellow Conference Premier clubs.

There were a few surprise Saturday Trophy results which reflected well on The Conference North, with Bradford PA enjoying a 2-1 home win against Kidderminster Harriers, Guiseley winning 1-0 at FC Halifax Town and Boston United winning 2-1 at Southport. Weston-super-Mare from Conference South also forced a replay with 1-1 draw away at Aldershot but lost heavily at home.

The long standing rivalry between the Southern, Northern Premier and Isthmian clubs is revived in the FA Cup and FA Trophy every year, but very few qualified for the Second Round of the Trophy this season. Chorley (NPL Premier) and Leek Town (NPL Div 1 South) formed a strong representation, with Hungerford Town and St Albans City representing The Southern Premier plus Whitstable Town from The Isthmian Div 1 South.

THIRD ROUND PROPER

The outstanding result of the round was achieved by North Ferriby United, a little club enjoying a great season at the top of the Conference North. They beat Lincoln City away 4-0 with two goals in each half, after previously eliminating Conference South club Sutton United by the same score in the Second Round.

Conference Premier clubs Aldershot Town and Grimsby Town won as expected, but the other ties were very even as the four Conference South clubs were drawn against each other and provided single goal home wins for Eastleigh over Dover Athletic and Havant & Waterlooville over Ebbsfleet United.

The two clubs from outside the Conference 'family' battled through close games with Chorley, second in the Northern Premier League, achieving a fine 1-1 draw a Tamworth but Hungerford Town, from mid table in the Southern Premier, missing a penalty when given a chance for a late equalizer against Gosport Borough.

The two senior clubs, Cambridge United and Luton Town didn't consider their first selections could cope with an extra cup tie, but the selected players produced an outstanding performance and finished with a thrilling 2-2 draw in front of 3,194. There's no doubt the supporters of both these leading Conference club would be thrilled with a Wembley appearance.

But perhaps the club officials would consider it more important to be competing against such attractions as Accrington Stanley, Bury and Hartlepool United next season - or could it just be the money?

QUARTER FINALS AND SEMI-FINALS

With waterlogged pitches ruining fixtures throughout the country, a disjointed FA Trophy competition gradually sorted itself out and the quarter finals appeared to be dominated by Hampshire clubs.

High flying Eastleigh from the Conference South played host to equally high flying Cambridge United from the Conference Premier, with the senior club just edging it by a single goal.

Grimsby Town, another club enjoying a good season in the Premier Division were red hot favourites to beat Tamworth, a struggling club in the same division, and they did just that with a 4-1 scoreline.

The Hampshire connection supplied three clubs in the other two quarter finals. Conference South strugglers Gosport Borough won 2-1 at the very confident North Ferriby United,who were enjoying a great season in the Conference North and the Havant & Waterlooville v Aldershot Town battle was hit by the weather.

A conclusive 4-1 victory for The Conference South club over Aldershot, their Premier Division Seniors, makes one wonder whether the manager's of some senior clubs really imagine two or three extra cup ties would ruin their league form. An exciting cup run lifts morale on and off the field and fully fit athletes playing, at the worst two games a week, enjoy that feeling of being in a successful team. A Wembley appearance would lift the morale of supporters, club officials and of course the players, who would all remember the occasion for the rest of their lives.

Two legged cup ties are completely different from any other games during the season. If you lose the first one by a large margin, its probably all over, but at least if you have a poor game and the deficit isn't too great, there is always a second chance.

With Luton Town streaking away with the Conference Championship and certain promotion, Cambridge United, being virtually certain of a play-off place, could concentrate on qualifying for Wembley. Grimsby Town of course were losing finalists last season, but a 2-1 lead from the home tie was enough for Cambridge to defend against The Mariners and perhaps United will also be playing at the Stadium in the play off final.

Having enjoyed my old club Hungerford Town's F A Trophy run this season and seen them rather unlucky lose 0-1 to Gosport Borough and also missing a penalty kick, I was particularly pleased to see Alex Pike's lads working their way past North Ferriby United away and then Havant & Waterloovile in the Semi-Final.

The fact that the Final is played in March, means there may not be enough time for a suitable build up for the Final, but hopefully both clubs will be well supported, although the rest of the country will still be involved in their own end of season battles.

Cambridge United v Gosport Borough is a fascinating fixture and the special occasion will bring memories that will last a lifetime for everyone involved on and off the field.

FIRST ROUND PROPER

SATURDAY 30 NOVEMBER 2013 - WINNERS RECEIVE £5,000

1	Leamington	v	Northwich Victoria	0-0	357
	Northwich Victoria	v	Leamington (3/12)	0-1	131
2	Tamworth	v	Macclesfield Town	2-0	667
3	FC Halifax Town	v	Guiseley	0-1	935
4	Southport	v	Boston United	1-2	496
5	Coalville Town	v	Grimsby Town	1-1	844
	Grimsby Town	v	Coalville Town (3/12)	3-0	1102
6	Hyde	v	North Ferriby United	1-2	256
7	Alfreton Town	v	Nuneaton Town	0-1	343
8	Chorley	v	Curzon Ashton	2-1	595
9	Bradford (Park Avenue)	v	Kidderminster Harriers	2-1	355
10	Worcester City	v	AFC Telford United	0-0	764
	AFC Telford United	v	Worcester City (3/12)	0-3	603
11	Altrincham	v	Leek Town	1-2	636
12	Wrexham	v	Gresley	2-1	1257
13	Chester	v	Barrow	1-2	1409
14	Gateshead	v	Hednesford Town	4-1	418
15	Lincoln City	v	Stalybridge Celtic	5-1	1023
16	Hereford United	v	Woking	0-3	1041
17	Bury Town	v	Eastleigh	0-3	321
18	Dartford	v	Forest Green Rovers	1-1	511
	Forest Green Rovers	v	Dartford (3/12)	1-0	459
19	Salisbury City	v	Cambridge United	0-1	721
20	Hendon	v	Whitstable Town (1/12)	1-2	211
21	Arlesey Town	v	Whitehawk	1-5	181
22	Tonbridge Angels	v	St Albans City	0-0	484
	St Albans City	v	Tonbridge Angels (2/12)	4-0	303
23	Gosport Borough	v	Concord Rangers	1-0	196
24	Aldershot Town	v	Weston Super Mare	1-1	1084
	Weston Super Mare	v	Aldershot Town (3/12)	2-5	283
25	Hungerford Town	v	Chesham United	2-0	211
26	Hayes & Yeading United	v	Barnet	0-1	302
27	Daventry Town	v	Maidenhead United	0-1	203
28	Staines Town	v	Luton Town	0-0	621
	Luton Town	v	Staines Town (3/12)	2-0	911
29	Ebbsfleet United	v	Gloucester City	3-0	740
30	Braintree Town	v	Welling United	3-0	365
31	East Thurrock United	v	Dover Athletic	1-1	273
	Dover Athletic	v	East Thurrock United (3/12)	3-1	295
32	Basingstoke Town	v	Havant & Waterlooville	0-0	354
	Havant & Waterlooville	v	Basingstoke Town (2/12)	1-0	201

SECOND ROUND PROPER

SATURDAY 14 DECEMBER 2013 - WINNERS RECEIVE £6,000

1	Luton Town	v	Wrexham	2-0	1617
2	Whitehawk	v	Havant & Waterlooville	1-1	150
	Havant & Waterlooville	v	Whitehawk (16/12)	3-1	158
3	Eastleigh	v	Gateshead	2-0	330
4	Barnet	v	Grimsby Town	1-2	972
5	Barrow	v	Maidenhead United	0-2	560
6	Gosport Borough	v	Nuneaton Town	0-0	284
	Nuneaton Town	v	Gosport Borough (17/12)	0-0aet	426
	(Gosport Borough won 4-2 on kicks from the penalty mark)				
7	St Albans City	v	Cambridge United	1-2	887
8	Guiseley	v	Bradford (Park Avenue)	3-0	476
9	Aldershot Town	v	Worcester City	4-1	1158
10	Tamworth	v	Boston United	2-0	688
11	North Ferriby United	v	Woking	4-0	201
12	Whitstable Town	v	Ebbsfleet United	1-2	742
13	Leek Town	v	Hungerford Town	0-1	426
14	Dover Athletic	v	Leamington	2-0	435
15	Braintree Town	v	Lincoln City	1-3	410
16	Chorley	v	Forest Green Rovers	0-0	790
	Forest Green Rovers	v	Chorley (17/12)	0-0aet	508
	(Chorley won 3-1 on kicks from the penalty mark)				

THIRD ROUND PROPER

SATURDAY 11 JANUARY 2014 - WINNERS RECEIVE £7,000

1	Cambridge United	v	Luton Town	2-2	3194
	Luton Town	v	Cambridge United (14/1)	0-1	2312
2	Aldershot Town	v	Guiseley	3-0	1632
3	Hungerford Town	v	Gosport Borough	0-1	384
4	Eastleigh	v	Dover Athletic	3-2	368
5	Tamworth	v	Chorley	1-1	1209
	Chorley	v	Tamworth (14/1)	2-2aet	1393
	(Tamworth won 6-5 on kicks from the penalty mark)				
6	Lincoln City	v	North Ferriby United	0-4	2037
7	Grimsby Town	v	Maidenhead United	2-1	1623
8	Havant & Waterlooville	v	Ebbsfleet United	1-0	709

FOURTH ROUND PROPER

SATURDAY 1 FEBRUARY 2014 - WINNERS RECEIVE £8,000

1	Havant & Waterlooville	v	Aldershot Town (4/2)	4-1	1125
2	Eastleigh	v	Cambridge United	0-1	957
3	North Ferriby United	v	Gosport Borough	1-2	398
4	Grimsby Town	v	Tamworth	4-1	2795

SEMI FINALS

WINNERS RECEIVE £16,000

1ST LEG – SATURDAY 15 FEBRUARY 2014					
1	Havant & Waterlooville	v	Gosport Borough (17/2)	1-1	1314
2ND LEG – SATURDAY 22 FEBRUARY 2014					
1	Gosport Borough	v	Havant & Waterlooville	2-0	2901
1ST LEG – SATURDAY 15 FEBRUARY 2014					
2	Cambridge United	v	Grismby Town	2-1	3264
2ND LEG – SATURDAY 22 FEBRUARY 2014					
2	Grimsby Town	v	Cambridge United	1-1	3931

FAT 2Q: James Baker, AFC Sudbury, scores the only goal of the game against Hastings United.
Phot: Roger Turner.

FAT 1P: Maidenhead United's Richard Paquette under pressure from Daventry Town's Ashley Deaney and Guy San
Photo: Peter Barnes.

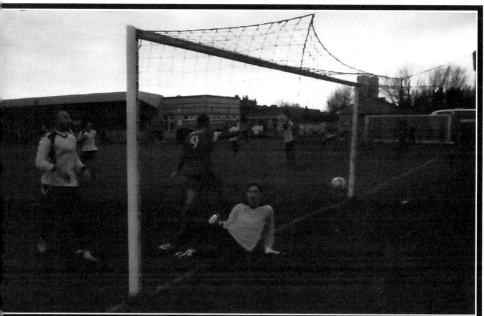

P: Alex Parsons hits home the first of the visitors goals against Arlesey Town.
: Gordon Whittington.

P: Luton Town take the lead against Wrexham from a Mark Cullen header.
: Peter Barnes.

The Final...

CAMBRIDGE UNITED 4

Bird 38, Donaldson 50, 59, Berry 78 (pen)

GOSPORT BOROUGH 0

Wembley Stadium **Att: 18,120**

CAMBRIDGE UNITED	GOSPORT BOROUGH
Will Norris	Nathan Ashmore
Greg Taylor	Lee Molyneaux
Jock Coulson	Andy Forbes
(Tom Bonner 87 min)	Jamie Brown
Ian Miller	(Rory Williams 57 min)
Ryan Donaldson	Brett Poate
Tom Champion	Sam Pearce
Richard Tait	Josh Carmichael
Liam Hughes	Danny Smith
(Nathan Arnold 73 min)	Tim Sills
Luke Berry	(Dan Woodward 57 min)
Ryan Bird	Justin Bennett
Josh Gillies	Michael Gosney
(Andy Pugh 61 min)	(Dan Wooden 72 min)
Subs not used	**Subs not used**
Kevin Roberts	Ryan Scott
Mitch Austin	Adam Wilde

Referee Craig Pawson
Assisted by Lee Betts and John Brooks.
Fourth official – Tony Harrington.

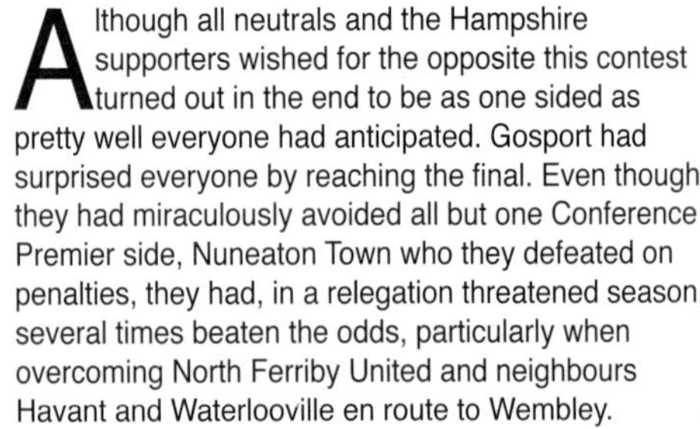

Although all neutrals and the Hampshire supporters wished for the opposite this contest turned out in the end to be as one sided as pretty well everyone had anticipated. Gosport had surprised everyone by reaching the final. Even though they had miraculously avoided all but one Conference Premier side, Nuneaton Town who they defeated on penalties, they had, in a relegation threatened season, several times beaten the odds, particularly when overcoming North Ferriby United and neighbours Havant and Waterlooville en route to Wembley.

Could there be another surprise for Borough, described by manager, Alex Pike as an "under budget side"? After all they had won the toss to wear their own colours and occupy the home dressing room so maybe luck was with them. Despite their usual gate being below 500 it was said they had brought twenty times that many supporters. A local group, 'Night of Treason', had even recorded a special song, 'Gosport Town', in their honour.

Here they were up against former Football League members Cambridge United who had been occupying second place to Luton Town in the Conference Premier for much of the season. United had been to Wembley twice before in Conference play offs so were hot favourites for a 2014 repeat. In skipper Ian Miller they had someone who had, three years previously, accepted the Trophy in his then role as captain of Darlington. For the 2013 Trophy final Miller had also been at Wembley, in the colours of Grimsby Town beaten on penalties by Wrexham.

Gosport, a side in the lower reaches of Conference South versus one, Cambridge United, extremely likely to be Conference Premier runners up; no contest thought most. Sadly that turned out to be the case although it took until seven minutes before the interval for United to show their superiority in goal terms. For half an hour Gosport more or less held their own in an opening that was noticeably less cagey than is the norm for these finals. After Gosport keeper Nathan Ashmore had made a good block following an error by his defence, his forward, Michael Gosney, failed to get any power in his shot having broken through from midfield. Tim Sills then forced Will Norris to dive to his left to save before Ashmore tore a long way out of goal to thwart Josh Gillies. Minutes later Justin Bennett, at the other end, saw Norris save his shot at the second attempt.

Luke Berry scores Cambridge United's fourth. Photo: Gordon Whittington.

Photo: Alan Coomes.

Neither side was managing to create a clear chance despite goal attempts. A free kick, given for the dangerously high foot of Gosport's Sam Pearce right on the edge of the 'D', was blocked by defenders who then stood transfixed as the rebound was lobbed over their line for Ryan Bird to touch past Ashmore for United's 38th minute opener. Too late, skipper Jamie Brown berated his defence for their inertia in not moving up and leaving Bird onside. Gosport's responses, consisting of long range efforts, were token attempts which failed to trouble Norris.

Within five minutes of the restart Cambridge's lead was doubled. Marking in their opponents' defence disintegrated as Ryan Donaldson was left to run through unchallenged, draw Ashmore and then slot the ball past him. Ten minutes later United were three up. After Luke Berry's shot rebounded off the post and Liam Hughes' two strikes had failed amidst the consequent scramble, Donaldson hit home his second.

Josh Gillies, Cambridge United, with Brett Poate of Gosport Borough in pursuit. Photo: Graham Brown.

Regular gaps were now appearing in the Gosport defence and their attacking infrequent as the Hampshire side tired. A well timed tackle by ex striker turned defender, Andy Forbes, denied United another goal but that proved to be only temporary as the fourth came from the penalty spot in the 78th minute. Pearce brought down sub Andy Pugh and Berry successfully converted.

In a game played in very good spirit Gosport's Pearce became the game's only booking before, hoping for some recompense, he saw his side's sub Dan Woodward hit the woodwork with a scorcher and Bennett, in the last minute, just unable to get his shot away before any further chance of a consolation score was taken from him.

United Manager Richard Money had previously been critical of the Trophy ties declaring they were harming his side's chances of promotion but acknowledged after the match that the win ranked with his previous successes as a Liverpool player. There he gained a European Cup winner's medal and featured in a League Cup final, and was later Walsall manager when they took the League Two title. For his part Borough's Alex Pike, who had previously managed Wimborne Town to a Vase final success, hoped that his team's fantastic team spirit and belief in their capabilities, would enable them to beat the drop from Conference South. He was also pleased to have set the whole town, his home town, buzzing as well as giving the club a sound financial basis for some time to come as a result of their Trophy exploits.

Match report by Arthur Evans.

Ryan Donaldson fires home a rebound for his second and United's third. Photo: Gordon Whittington.

Cambridge's Liam Hughes heads clear from a Gosport Borough's Michael Gosney. Photo: Alan Coomes.

Cambridge's Ryan Donaldson scores the second past Ashmore in the Gosport goal. Photo: Keith Clayton.

(Left) Richard Tait, Cambridge United, takes on Gosport Borough's Josh Carmichael. Photo: Roger Turner.

PAST FINALS

1970 MACCLESFIELD TOWN 2 (Lyons, B Fidler) — **TELFORD UNITED 0** — **Att: 28,000**
Northern Premier League — *Southern League*
Macclesfield: Cooke, Sievwright, Bennett, Beaumont, Collins, Roberts, Lyons, B Fidler,Young, Corfield, D Fidler.
Telford: Irvine, Harris, Croft, Flowers, Coton, Ray,Fudge, Hart, Bentley, Murray, Jagger. Ref: K Walker

1971 TELFORD UTD 3 (Owen, Bentley, Fudge) — **HILLINGDON BORO. 2 (Reeve, Bishop)** — **Att: 29,500**
Southern League — *Southern League*
Telford: Irvine, Harris, Croft, Ray, Coton, Carr, Fudge, Owen, Bentley, Jagger ,Murray.
Hillingdon B.: Lowe, Batt, Langley, Higginson, Newcombe, Moore, Fairchild,Bishop, Reeve, Carter, Knox. Ref: D Smith

1972 STAFFORD RANGERS 3 (Williams 2, Cullerton) — **BARNET 0** — **Att: 24,000**
Northern Premier League — *Southern League*
Stafford R.: Aleksic, Chadwick, Clayton, Sargeant, Aston, Machin, Cullerton, Chapman,Williams, Bayley, Jones.
Barnet: McClelland, Lye, Jenkins, Ward, Embrey, King, Powell, Ferry, Flatt, Easton, Plume . Ref: P Partridge

1973 SCARBOROUGH 2 (Leask, Thompson) — **WIGAN ATHLETIC 1 (Rogers) aet** — **Att:23,000**
Northern Premier League — *Northern Premier League*
Scarborough: Garrow, Appleton, Shoulder, Dunn, Siddle, Fagan, Donoghue, Franks,Leask (Barmby), Thompson, Hewitt.
Wigan: Reeves, Morris, Sutherland, Taylor,Jackson, Gillibrand, Clements, Oats (McCunnell), Rogers, King, Worswick. Ref: H Hackney

1974 MORECAMBE 2 (Richmond, Sutton) — **DARTFORD 1 (Cunningham)** — **Att: 19,000**
Northern Premier League — *Southern League*
Morecambe: Coates, Pearson, Bennett, Sutton, Street, Baldwin, Done, Webber,Roberts (Galley), Kershaw, Richmond.
Dartford: Morton, Read, Payne, Carr, Burns,Binks, Light, Glozier, Robinson (Hearne), Cunningham, Halleday. Ref: B Homewood

1975(1) MATLOCK TOWN 4 (Oxley, Dawson, T Fenoughty, N Fenoughy) — **SCARBOROUGH 0** — **Att: 21,000**
Northern Premier League — *Northern Premier League*
Matlock: Fell, McKay, Smith, Stuart, Dawson, Swan, Oxley, N Fenoughy, Scott, T Fenoughty, M Fenoughty.
Scarborough: Williams, Hewitt, Rettitt, Dunn, Marshall, Todd, Houghton, Woodall, Davidson, Barnby, Aveyard. Ref: K Styles

1976 SCARBOROUGH 3 (Woodall, Abbey, Marshall(p)) — **STAFFORD R. 2 (Jones 2) aet** — **Att: 21,000**
Northern Premier League — *Northern Premier League*
Scarborough: Barnard, Jackson, Marshall, H Dunn, Ayre (Donoghue), HA Dunn, Dale,Barmby, Woodall, Abbey, Hilley.
Stafford: Arnold, Ritchie, Richards, Sargeant,Seddon, Morris, Chapman, Lowe, Jones, Hutchinson, Chadwick. Ref: R Challis

1977 SCARBOROUGH 2 (Dunn(p), Abbey) — **DAGENHAM 1 (Harris)** — **Att: 21,500**
Northern Premier League — *Isthmian League*
Scarborough: Chapman, Smith, Marshall (Barmby), Dunn, Ayre, Deere, Aveyard,Donoghue, Woodall, Abbey, Dunn.
Dagenham: Hutley, Wellman, P Currie, Dunwell,Moore, W Currie, Harkins, Saul, Fox, Harris, Holder. Ref: G Courtney

1978 ALTRINCHAM 3 (King, Johnson, Rogers) — **LEATHERHEAD 1 (Cook)** — **Att: 20,000**
Northern Premier League — *Isthmian League*
Altrincham: Eales, Allan, Crossley, Bailey, Owens, King, Morris, Heathcote,Johnson, Rogers, Davidson (Flaherty).
Leatherhead: Swannell, Cooper, Eaton, Davies,Reid, Malley, Cook, Salkeld, Baker, Boyle (Bailey). Ref: A Grey

1979 STAFFORD RANGERS 2 (A Wood 2) — **KETTERING TOWN 0** — **Att: 32,000**
Northern Premier League — *Southern League*
Stafford: Arnold, F Wood, Willis, Sargeant, Seddon, Ritchie, Secker, Chapman, A Wood, Cullerton, Chadwick (Jones).
Kettering: Lane, Ashby, Lee, Eastell, Dixey,Suddards, Flannagan, Kellock, Phipps, Clayton, Evans (Hughes). Ref: D Richardson

1980(2) DAGENHAM 2 (Duck, Maycock) — **MOSSLEY 1 (Smith)** — **Att: 26,000**
Isthmian League — *Northern Premier League*
Dagenham: Huttley, Wellman, Scales, Dunwell, Moore, Durrell, Maycock, Horan,Duck, Kidd, Jones (Holder).
Mossley: Fitton, Brown, Vaughan, Gorman, Salter, Polliot, Smith, Moore, Skeete, O'Connor, Keelan (Wilson). Ref: K Baker

1981(3) BISHOP'S STORTFORD 1 (Sullivan) — **SUTTON UNITED 0** — **Att: 22,578**
Isthmian League — *Isthmian League*
Bishop's Stortford: Moore, Blackman, Brame, Smith (Worrell), Bradford, Abery, Sullivan,Knapman, Radford, Simmonds, Mitchell.
Sutton Utd.: Collyer, Rogers, Green, J Rains,T Rains, Stephens (Sunnucks), Waldon, Pritchard, Cornwell, Parsons, Dennis. Ref: J Worrall

1982 ENFIELD 1 (Taylor) — **ALTRINCHAM 0** — **Att: 18,678**
Alliance Premier League — *Alliance Premier League*
Enfield: Jacobs, Barrett, Tone, Jennings, Waite, Ironton, Ashford, Taylor,Holmes, Oliver (Flint), King. Ref: B Stevens
Altrincham: Connaughton, Crossley, Davison, Bailey, Cuddy, King (Whitbread), Allan, Heathcote, Johnson, Rogers, Howard.

Notes:

1 The only occasion three members of the same family played in the same FA Trophy Final team.
2 The first of the Amateurs from the Isthmian League to win the FA Trophy.
3 Goalkeeper Terry Moore had also won an Amateur Cup Winners Medal with Bishop's Stortford in 1974.

All games played at Wembley (old & new) unless stated.

1983 **TELFORD UTD** 2 (Mather 2) — NORTHWICH VICTORIA 1 (Bennett) — Att: 22,071
Alliance Premier League — *Alliance Premier League*
Telford: Charlton, Lewis, Turner, Mayman (Joseph), Walker, Easton, Barnett,Williams, Mather, Hogan, Alcock.
Northwich: Ryan, Fretwell, Murphy, Jones, Forshaw, Ward, Anderson, Abel (Bennett), Reid, Chesters, Wilson. Ref: B Hill

1984 NORTHWICH VICTORIA 1 (Chester) — BANGOR CITY 1 (Whelan) — Att: 14,200
Replay **NORTHWICH VICTORIA** 2 (Chesters(p), Anderson) — BANGOR CITY 1 (Lunn) — Att: 5,805 (at Stoke)
Alliance Premier League — *Alliance Premier League*
Northwich: Ryan, Fretwell, Dean, Jones, Forshaw (Power 65), Bennett, Anderson,Abel, Reid, Chesters, Wilson. Ref: J Martin
Bangor: Letheren, Cavanagh, Gray, Whelan, Banks,Lunn, Urqhart, Morris, Carter, Howat, Sutcliffe (Westwood 105) . Same in replay.

1985 **WEALDSTONE** 2 (Graham, Holmes) — BOSTON UNITED 1 (Cook) — Att: 20,775
Alliance Premier League — *Alliance Premier League*
Wealdstone: Iles, Perkins, Bowgett, Byatt, Davies, Greenaway, Holmes, Wainwright,Donnellan, Graham (N Cordice 89), A Cordice.
Boston: Blackwell, Casey, Ladd,Creane, O'Brien, Thommson, Laverick (Mallender 78), Simpsom, Gilbert, Lee, Cook. Ref: J Bray

1986 **ALTRINCHAM** 1 (Farrelly) — RUNCORN 0 — Att: 15,700
Gola League — *Gola League*
Altrincham: Wealands, Gardner, Densmore, Johnson, Farrelly, Conning, Cuddy,Davison, Reid, Ellis, Anderson. Sub: Newton.
Runcorn: McBride, Lee, Roberts,Jones, Fraser, Smith, S Crompton (A Crompton), Imrie, Carter, Mather, Carrodus. Ref: A Ward

1987 KIDDERMINSTER HARRIERS 0 — BURTON ALBION 0 — Att: 23,617
Replay **KIDDERMINSTER HARRIERS** 2 (Davies 2) — BURTON ALBION 1 (Groves) — Att: 15,685 (at West Brom)
Conference — *Southern League*
Kidderminster: Arnold, Barton, Boxall, Brazier (sub Hazlewood in rep), Collins (sub Pearson 90 at Wembley), Woodall, McKenzie, O'Dowd, Tuohy, Casey, Davies. sub:Jones.
Burton: New, Essex, Kamara, Vaughan, Simms, Groves, Bancroft, Land, Dorsett, Redfern, (sub Wood in replay), Gauden.
Sub: Patterson. Ref: D Shaw

1988 ENFIELD 0 — TELFORD UNITED 0 — Att: 20,161
Replay **ENFIELD** 3 (Furlong 2, Howell) — TELFORD UNITED 2 (Biggins, Norris(p)) — Att: 6,912 (at W Brom)
Conference — *Conference*
Enfield: Pape, Cottington, Howell, Keen (sub Edmonds in rep), Sparrow (sub Hayzleden at Wembley), Lewis (sub Edmonds at Wembley), Harding, Cooper, King,Furlong, Francis.
Telford: Charlton, McGinty, Storton, Nelson, Wiggins, Mayman (sub Cunningham in rep (sub Hancock)), Sankey, Joseph, Stringer (sub Griffiths at Wembley, Griffiths in replay), Biggins, Norris. Ref: L Dilkes

1989 **TELFORD UNITED** 1 (Crawley) — MACCLESFIELD TOWN 0 — Att: 18,102
Conference — *Conference*
Telford: Charlton, Lee, Brindley, Hancock, Wiggins, Mayman, Grainger, Joseph, Nelson, Lloyd, Stringer. Subs: Crawley, Griffiths.
Macclesfield: Zelem, Roberts, Tobin, Edwards, Hardman, Askey, Lake, Hanton, Imrie, Burr, Timmons. Subs: Devonshire, Kendall.

1990 **BARROW** 3 (Gordon 2, Cowperthwaite) — LEEK TOWN 0 — Att: 19,011
Conference — *Northern Premier League*
Barrow: McDonnell, Higgins, Chilton, Skivington, Gordon, Proctor, Doherty (Burgess), Farrell (Gilmore), Cowperthwaite, Lowe, Ferris.
Leek: Simpson, Elsby (Smith), Pearce, McMullen, Clowes, Coleman (Russell),Mellor, Somerville, Sutton, Millington, Norris Ref: T Simpson

1991 **WYCOMBE W.** 2 (Scott, West) — KIDDERMINSTER HARRIERS 1 (Hadley) — Att: 34,842
Conference — *Conference*
Wycombe: Granville, Crossley, Cash, Kerr, Creaser, Carroll, Ryan, Stapleton,West, Scott, Guppy (Hutchinson). Ref: J Watson
Kidderminster: Jones, Kurila, McGrath, Weir, Barnett, Forsyth, Joseph (Wilcox), Howell (Whitehouse), Hadley, Lilwall, Humphries

1992 **COLCHESTER UTD*** 3 (Masters, Smith, McGavin) — WITTON ALBION 1 (Lutkevitch) — Att: 27,806
Conference — *Conference*
Colchester: Barrett, Donald, Roberts, Knsella, English, Martin, Cook, Masters,McDonough (Bennett 65), McGavin, Smith. Ref: K P Barratt
Witton: Mason, Halliday, Coathup, McNeilis, Jim Connor, Anderson, Thomas, Rose, Alford, Grimshaw (Joe Connor), Lutkevitch (McCluskie)

1993 **WYCOMBE W*.** 4 (Cousins, Kerr, Thompson, Carroll) — RUNCORN 1 (Shaughnessy) — Att: 32,968
Conference — *Conference*
Wycombe: Hyde, Cousins, Cooper, Kerr, Crossley, Thompson (Hayrettin 65),Carroll, Ryan, Hutchinson, Scott, Guppy. Sub: Casey.
Runcorn: Williams, Bates, Robertson, Hill, Harold (Connor 62), Anderson, Brady (Parker 72), Brown, Shaughnessy, McKenna, Brabin

1994 **WOKING** 2 (D Brown, Hay) — RUNCORN 1 (Shaw (pen)) — Att: 15,818
Conference — *Conference*
Woking: Batty, Tucker, L Wye, Berry, Brown, Clement, Brown (Rattray 32), Fielder, Steele, Hay (Puckett 46), Walker. Ref: Paul Durkin
Runcorn: Williams, Bates, Robertson, Shaw, Lee, Anderson, Thomas, Connor, McInerney (Hill 71), McKenna, Brabin. Sub: Parker

1995 **WOKING** 2 (Steele, Fielder) — KIDDERMINSTER HARRIERS 1 aet (Davies) — Att: 17,815
Conference — *Conference*
Woking: Batty, Tucker, L Wye, Fielder, Brown, Crumplin (Rattray 42), S Wye, Ellis, Steele, Hay (Newberry 112), Walker. (Sub: Read(gk)
Kidderminster: Rose, Hodson, Bancroft, Webb, Brindley (Cartwright 94), Forsyth, Deakin, Yates, Humphreys (Hughes 105), Davies, Purdie. Sub: Dearlove (gk) Ref: D J Gallagher

1996 MACCLESFIELD TOWN 3 (Payne, OG, Hemmings) *Conference* **NORTHWICH VICTORIA 1 (Williams)** *Conference* **Att: 8,672**

Macclesfield: Price, Edey, Gardiner, Payne, Howarth(C), Sorvel, Lyons, Wood (Hulme 83), Coates, Power, Hemmings (Cavell 88).
Northwich: Greygoose, Ward, Duffy, Burgess (Simpson 87), Abel (Steele), Walters, Williams, Butler (C), Cooke, Humphries, Vicary.
Ref: M Reed

1997 WOKING 1 (Hay 112) *Conference* **DAGENHAM & REDBRIDGE 0** *Isthmian League* **Att: 24,376**

Woking: Batty, Brown, Howard, Foster, Taylor, S Wye, Thompson (sub Jones 115), Ellis, Steele (L Wye 108), Walker, Jackson (Hay 77).
Dagenham: Gothard, Culverhouse, Connor, Creaser, Jacques (sub Double 75), Davidson, Pratt (Naylor 81), Parratt, Broom, Rogers, Stimson (John 65).
Ref: J Winter

1998 CHELTENHAM TOWN 1 (Eaton 74) *Conference* **SOUTHPORT 0** *Conference* **Att: 26,387**

Cheltenham: Book, Duff, Freeman, Banks, Victory, Knight (Smith 78), Howells, Bloomer, Walker (sub Milton 78), Eaton, Watkins. Sub: Wright.
Southport: Stewart, Horner, Futcher, Ryan, Farley, Kielty, Butler, Gamble, Formby (sub Whittaker 80), Thompson (sub Bollard 88), Ross. Sub: Mitten.
Ref: G S Willard

1999 KINGSTONIAN 1 (Mustafa 49) *Conference* **FOREST GREEN ROVERS 0** *Conference* **Att: 20,037**

Kingstonian: Farrelly, Mustafa, Luckett, Crossley, Stewart, Harris, Patterson, Pitcher, Rattray, Leworthy (Francis 87), Akuamoah. Subs (not used): John, Corbett, Brown, Tranter
Forest Green Rovers: Shuttlewood, Hedges, Forbes, Bailey (Smart 76), Kilgour, Wigg (Cook 58), Honor (Winter 58), Drysdale, McGregor, Mehew, Sykes. Subs (not used): Perrin, Coupe
Ref: A B Wilkie

2000 KINGSTONIAN 3 (Akuamoah 40, 69, Simba 75) *Conference* **KETTERING TOWN 2 (Vowden 55, Norman 64p)** *Conference* **Att: 20,034**

Kingstonian: Farelly, Mustafa, Luckett, Crossley, Stewart (Saunders 77), Harris, Kadi (Leworthy 83), Pitcher, Green (Basford 86), Smiba, Akuamoah. Subs (not used): Hurst, Allan
Kettering Town: Sollit, McNamara, Adams, Perkins, Vowden, Norman (Duik 76), Fisher, Brown, Shutt, Watkins (Hudson 46), Setchell (Hopkins 81). Subs (not used): Ridgway, Wilson
Ref: S W Dunn

2001 CANVEY ISLAND 1 (Chenery) *Isthmian League* **FOREST GREEN ROVERS 0** *Conference* **Att: 10,007 at Villa Park**

Forest Green Rovers: Perrin, Cousins, Lockwood, Foster, Clark, Burns, Daley, Drysdale (Bennett 46), Foster (Hunt 75), Meecham, Slater. Subs (not used): Hedges, Prince, Ghent
Canvey Island: Harrison, Duffy, Chenery, Bodley, Ward, Tilson, Stimson (Tanner 83), Gregory, Vaughan (Jones 76), Parmenter. Subs (not used): Bennett, Miller, Thompson.
Ref: A G Wiley

2002 YEOVIL TOWN 2 (Alford, Stansfield) *Conference* **STEVENAGE BOROUGH 0** *Conference* **Att: 18,809 at Villa Park**

Yeovil Town: Weale, Lockwood, Tonkin, Skiverton, Pluck (White 51), Way, Stansfield, Johnson, Alford (Giles 86), Crittenden (Lindegaard 83), McIndoe. Subs (not used): O'Brien, Sheffield
Stevenage Borough: Wilkerson, Hamsher, Goodliffe, Trott, Fraser, Fisher, Wormull (Stirling 71), Evers (Williams 56), Jackson, Sigere (Campbell 74), Clarke. Subs (not used): Campbell, Greygoose
Ref: N S Barry

2003 BURSCOUGH 2 (Martindale 25, 55) *Northern Premier* **TAMWORTH 1 (Cooper 78)** *Southern Premier* **Att: 14,265 at Villa Park**

Burscough: Taylor, Teale, Taylor, Macauley (White 77), Lawless, Bowen, Wright, Norman, Martindale (McHale 80), Byrne (Bluck 84), Burns. Subs (not used): McGuire (g/k) Molyneux.
Tamworth: Acton, Warner, Follett, Robinson, Walsh, Cooper, Colley, Evans (Turner 64), Rickards (Hatton 88), McGorry, Sale (Hallam 54). Subs (not used): Grocutt, Barnes (g/k).
Ref: U D Rennie

2004 HEDNESFORD TOWN 3 (Maguire 28, Hines 53, Brindley 87) *Southern Premier* **CANVEY ISLAND 2 (Boylan 46, Brindley 48 og)** *Isthmian Premier Champions* **Att: 6,635 at Villa Park**

Hednesford Town: Young, Simkin, Hines, King, Brindley, Ryder (Barrow 59), Palmer, Anthrobus, Danks (Piearce 78), Maguire, Charie (Evans 55). Subs (not used): Evans (g/k) McGhee.
Canvey Island: Potter, Kennedy, Duffy, Chenery, Cowan, Gooden (Dobinson 89), Minton, Gregory (McDougald 80), Boylan, Midgley (Berquez 73), Ward. Subs (not used): Theobald, Harrison (g/k).
Ref: M L Dean

2005 GRAYS ATHLETIC 1 (Martin 65) Pens: 6 *Conference South* **HUCKNALL TOWN 1 (Ricketts 75) Pens: 5** *Conference North* **Att: 8,116 at Villa Park**

Grays Athletic: Bayes, Brennan, Nutter, Stuart, Matthews, Thurgood, Oli (Powell 80), Hopper (Carthy 120), Battersby (sub West 61), Martin, Cole. Subs (not used): Emberson, Bruce..
Hucknall Town: Smith, Asher, Barrick (Plummer 30), Hunter, Timons, Cooke, Smith (Ward 120), Palmer (Heathcote 94), Ricketts, Bacon, Todd. Subs (not used): Winder, Lindley.
Ref: P Dowd

2006 GRAYS ATHLETIC 2 (Oli, Poole) *Conference* **WOKING 0** *Conference* **Att: 13,997 at Upton Park**

Grays Athletic: Bayes, Sambrook, Nutter, Stuart, Hanson, Kightly (Williamson 90), Thurgood, Martin, Poole, Oli, McLean. Subs (not used): Eyre (g/k), Hooper, Olayinka, Mawer.
Woking: Jalal, Jackson, MacDonald, Nethercott (Watson 60), Hutchinson, Murray, Smith (Cockerill 60), Evans (Blackman 85), Ferguson, McAllister, Justin Richards. Subs (not used): Davis (g/k), El-Salahi.
Ref: Howard Webb (Sheffield)

THE FA TROPHY

2007 STEVENAGE BOROUGH 3 (Cole, Dobson, Morrison) **KIDDERMINSTER HARRIERS 2 (Constable 2)** **Att: 53,262**
Conference *Conference* **(New Trophy record)**
Stevenage Borough: Julian, Fuller, Nutter, Oliver, Gaia, Miller, Cole, Morrison, Guppy (Dobson 63), Henry, Beard.
Subs not used: Potter, Slabber, Nurse, McMahon.
Kidderminster Harriers: Bevan, Kenna, Hurren, Creighton, Whitehead, Blackwood, Russell, Penn, Smikle (Reynolds 90), Christie (White 75) , Constable.
Subs not used: Taylor, Sedgemore, McGrath. Ref: Chris Foy (Merseyside)

2008 EBBSFLEET UNITED 1 (McPhee) **TORQUAY UNITED 0** **Att: 40,186**
Blue Square Premier *Blue Square Premier*
Ebbsfleet United: Cronin, Hawkins, McCarthy, Smith, Opinel, McPhee, Barrett, Bostwick, Long (MacDonald 84), Moore, Akinde.
Subs not used: Eribenne, Purcell, Ricketts, Mott.
Torquay United: Rice, Mansell, Todd, Woods, Nicholson, D'Sane (Benyon 66), Hargreaves, Adams, Zebroski, Sills (Hill 88), Phillips (Stevens 46). Subs not used: Hockley and Robertson. Ref: Martin Atkinson (West Riding)

2009 STEVENAGE BOROUGH 2 (Morison, Boylan) **YORK CITY 0** **Att: 27,102**
Blue Square Premier *Blue Square Premier*
Stevenage Borough: Day, Henry, Bostwick, Roberts, Wilson, Mills, Murphy, Drury, Vincenti (Anaclet 86), Boylan, Morison.
Subs not used: Bayes, Albrighton, Maamria and Willock.
York City:Ingham, Purkiss, McGurk, Parslow, Pejic, Mackin, Greaves(McWilliams 74), Rusk (Russell 80), Brodie, McBreen (Sodje 60), Boyes. Subs not used – Mimms and Robinson. Referee: Michael Jones.

2010 BARROW 2 (McEvilly 79, Walker 117) **STEVENAGE BOROUGH 1 (Drury 10)** **Att: 21,223**
Blue Square Premier *Blue Square Premier*
Barrow: Stuart Tomlinson, Simon Spender, Paul Jones, Phil Bolland, Paul Edwards, Simon Wiles (sub Carlos Logan 63rd min), Robin Hulbert, Andy Bond, Paul Rutherford (sub Mark Boyd 109th min), Jason Walker, Gregg Blundell (sub Lee McEvilly 73rd min).
Subs not used – Tim Deasy and Mike Pearson.
Stevenage Borough: Chris Day (sub Ashley Bayes 90th min), Ronnie Henry, Jon Ashton, Mark Roberts, Scott Laird, Joel Byrom (sub Lawrie Wilson 58th min), David Bridges, Michael Bostwick, Andy Drury, Chris Beardsley (sub Charlie Griffin 64th min), Yemi Odubade. Subs not used – Stacey Long and Peter Vincenti.
Man of the match - Paul Rutherford. Referee Lee Probert.

2011 DARLINGTON 1 (Senior 120) **MANSFIELD TOWN 0** **Att: 24,668**
Blue Square Premier *Blue Square Premier*
Darlington: Sam Russell, Paul Arnison, Ian Miller, Liam Hatch, Aaron Brown, Jamie Chandler, Chris Moore, Marc Bridge-Wilkinson (sub Paul Terry 100th min), Gary Smith (sub Arman Verma 38th min), John Campbell (sub Chris Senior 75th min), Tommy Wright.
Subs not used – Danzelle St Louis-Hamilton (gk) and Phil Gray.
Mansfield Town: Alan Marriott, Gary Silk, Stephen Foster, Tom Naylor, Dan Spence, Louis Briscoe, Tyrone Thompson, Kyle Nix, Adam Smith (sub Ashley Cain 95th min), Adam Murray (sub Danny Mitchley 108th min), Paul Connor
Subs not used – Paul Stonehouse and Neil Collett (gk)
Man of the match - Jamie Chandler. Referee Stuart Atwell

2012 YORK CITY 2 (Blair 61, Oyebanjo 68) **NEWPORT COUNTY 0** **Att: 19,844**
Blue Square Premier *Blue Square Premier*
York City: Michael Ingham, Jon Challinor, Chris Smith, Daniel Parslow, Ben Gibson, Matty Blair, Lanre Oyebanjo, Patrick McLaughlan (sub Jamal Fyfield 82nd min), James Meredith, Ashley Chambers (Adriano Moke (89th min), Jason Walker (Jamie Reed 90th min).
Subs not used – Paul Musselwhite (g/k), Michael Potts.
Newport County: Glyn Thompson, David Pipe, Ismail Yakubu, Gary Warren, Andrew Hughes, Sam Foley, Lee Evans, Nat Jarvis (sub Jake Harris 68th min), Max Porter (sub Darryl Knights 79th min), Romone Rose (sub Elliott Buchanan 68th min), Lee Minshull.
Subs not used – Matthew Swan (g/k), Paul Rodgers.
Man of the match - Lanre Oyebanjo. Referee Anthony Taylor

2013 WREXHAM 1 (Thornton 82 (pen)) **GRIMSBY TOWN 1 (Cook 71)** **Att: 35,226**
Wrexham won 4-1 on kicks from the penalty mark after extra time.
Blue Square Premier *Blue Square Premier*
Wrexham: Chris Maxwell, Stephen Wright, Martin Riley, Jay Harris, Danny Wright, Brett Ormerod (Robert Ogleby 77 min), Andy Morrell (Adrian Cieslewicz 61 min), Dean Keates, Johnny Hunt, Chris Westwood, Kevin Thornton (Joe Clarke 89 min).
Subs not used - Andy Coughlin (gk) Glen Little.
Grimsby Town: Sam Hatton, Aswad Thomas, Shaun Pearson, Ian Miller, Joe Colbeck, Craig Disley, Frankie Artus, Andy Cook, James McKeown, Ross Hannah (Andi Thanoj 55 min), Marcus Marshall (Richard Brodie 87 min).
Subs not used - Jamie Devitt, Bradley Wood, Lenell John-Lewis. Referee Jonathan Moss

(Left) Cambridge's Bird shapes up to shoot past Gosport's 'keeper Nathan Ashmore. Photo: Peter Barnes.

(Right) Gosney, Gosport, skips past Tait, Cambridge. Photo: Keith Clayton.

Sholing lift the FA Vase having beaten West Auckland 1-0 in the final at Wembley Stadium. Photo: Roger Turner.

THE FA VASE 2013-14

FIRST QUALIFYING ROUND

The first FA Vase ties of the season certainly provided some glamorous names and plenty of goals. Thame United were drawn at home against local rivals Carterton and won 8-0, while seven goals were scored at home by Penrith v Yorkshire Amateurs (7-1) and Dudley Town v Leek CSOB (7-3), also by Glasshoughton v Askern Villa (7-2) away from home

High scoring from both sides must have thrilled the fans at Romsey Town who beat Bournemouth 6-4 and there was wonderful entertainment as London APSA who won 5-4 at Crawley Green.

With many clubs changing their name in recent years and many new clubs emerging, non-league enthusiasts will have noted the 3-2 scoreline as London Lions beat FC Romania and Wigan Robin Park, formed in 2005, who lost 1-2 to fellow North East Counties rivals, the more experienced Winsford United.

Of course some famous names have been re-born and AFC Rushden & Diamonds beat AFC Dunstable 3-1 but 1874 Northwich lost by the old goal in three at Oldham Borough.

Some not so famous names have also changed a little, but Runcorn Linnets, Bromsgrove Sporting, AFC Mansfield, Dorking Wanderers, Jarrow Roofing, Boldon CA and Epsom Athletic all won.

Last season Tunbridge Wells created a fairy story of their own that caught the imagination of the the town, and indeed the county of Kent. Their day at Wembley will be remembered for ever by all those involved with the club on and off the field, but some clubs featuring in this first Qualifying Round of the FA Vase have their own Wembley memories to inspire them: Guisborough Town lost in 1980, Stansted won in 1984, Southall lost in 1986, St Helens Town beat Warrington Town in 1987, Hillingdon Borough lost in 2006, Deal Town won in 2000 and all these clubs safely survived the First Qualifying Round this season.

SECOND QUALIFYING ROUND

The national knock out competition for clubs in Step 5 and below introduces many football club names to the public for the first time.

Clubs such as West Didsbury & Chorlton (North West Counties Division One), Blaby & Whetstone Athletic (East Midland Counties League) and Staines Lammas (Combined Counties Division One) won't be very well known unless one lives nearby, but all three clubs will be featuring in the next FA Vase round.

It's a wonderful competition for the little clubs with ambitions to make a name for themselves, as they hope to improve and move up the 'pyramid' of leagues. The chance to compete with senior clubs and perhaps beat them can provide valuable inspiration.

The FA Vase also provides a reminder to those clubs and their supporters who had sampled the thrill of a Wembley Final in the past. Few of the North Eastern clubs playing in The Northern League have been very keen to move up the pyramid and play in leagues which would entail much more travelling.

Consequently, many quality players chose to remain in the Northern League (Modern Step 5) and their clubs became the favourites in the old FA Amateur Cup and the present FA Vase competition.

Just look at the names of clubs featuring in Second Qualifying Round with Wembley appearances in their history:- Crook Town, Guisborough Town, North Shields and Whickham all qualified for The First Preliminary Round and the most famous of them all, Bishop Auckland, lost away to Eccleshill United.

More ex-Wembley finalists from further South who also featured in the Second Qualifying Round, included Willenhall Town, Hillingdon Borough, Epsom & Ewell, Stansted and Almondsbury although sometimes their structure and their names have altered since their glory days.

Obviously some ties produced very one sided games (especially in the Midlands!)

Bromsgrove Sporting (Midland Combination) 8-0
Stafford Town (Midland Combination)
Heanor Town (Northern Counties East)
8-2 Aylestone Park (East Mid Counties)
Bilston Town (West Midlands League)
0-7 Stourport Swifts (Midland Alliance)
Willenhall Town (West Midlands League) 0-7
RC Warwick(Midland Combination)

It was good to see FA Cup heroes AFC Portchester carrying on their winning run in the knock out competitions with a 4-0 victory over Romsey Town. However, for a high scoring thriller, Greenwich Borough's 6-4 away victory in their replay at Mole Valley Sutton Common Road Football Club must have been great to watch. I wonder how the home side's supporters cheer their team on.

Another high scoring tie was enjoyed at Willand, where The Rovers, who I fancy for another good FA Vase run, beat Sherborne Town 5-3. All the winners in this Round received £800 prize money, but its a great competition which will give inspiration to many little football clubs all over the country. Just ask the Tunbridge Wells supporters.

FIRST ROUND PROPER

It seems very early in a season for a knock out cup to have completed it's qualifying ties and to see nearly another hundred clubs knocked out of the competition in the First Round Proper.

The North East usually produce at least half a dozen possible FA Vase winners each season. So the ties for the early rounds, which are drawn on a regional basis, are the least popular in that area, as their high powered matches could see half of their favourites knocked out by local rivals.

The favourites are still to enter the fray, but The First Round saw the departure of Marske United, who have enjoyed The FA Cup this season, Penrith, Sunderland Ryhope CA and Guisborough Town with Crook Town and North Shields replaying.

West Auckland look a very serious challenger and they underlined their potential with a 5-0 home victory over South Shields. Kinsley Boys will remember their trip up from the Sheffield & Hallamshire Senior League, as they lost 7-2 to Glossop North End, but this was their third game, as AFC Darwen had been beaten 4-3 away and Appleby Frodingham 1-0 at home.

Two thrilling northern cup ties produced high scoring away victories, at Bootle, who lost 5-4 to Parkgate and at Liversedge, who were beaten 4-3 by Armthorpe Welfare.

In the MIdalnds, Alvechurch, brought back special cup memories with a 6-0 victory at Bartley Green and AFC Wulfrunians beat Artherstone Town 5-0 at home.

With twelve clubs scoring at least five goals in their home ties and another seven recording similar scores, including three with six goals ,away from home. The draw obviously brings together clubs from very different levels so its difficult to spot the real prospects so early in the season.

However, the West Country usually produces a challenger and Odd Down's 6-0 victory at Bishop Sutton and Barnstaple Town's 4-2 win at ex-Wembley finalists Almonsbury are impressive, while FA Cup heroes Brislington plus local favourites Buckland Athletic and Plymouth Parkway, both achieved solid victories.

The home counties also produced some impressive victories which may inspire a solid FA Vase run, so keep an eye on Wantage Town leaders in the Hellenic League, who beat Abingdon Town 7-0 at home. Plus Sholing who beat Winchester City 1-0 away and Saltash United who defeated the powerful Willand Rovers 2-1.

One tie that brought make memories of the old amateur Isthmian days, was Barking's 1-0 victory over East End rivals Clapton, but the biggest victory of the Round was registered by another Hellenic League club Binfield, who smashed nine past Warminster Town from The Western League Division One.

The favourites will be joining the fray in the next round but those clubs already with two or thee scalps, will be wondering whether this will be their year for a Wembley appearance.

SECOND ROUND

Saturday afternoons in November begin to create a It's not surprising that The North East dominates the FA Vase competition. Just a glance at the quality clubs battling to emerge from the regional rounds underlines the fact that the Northern League power clubs backed up by The Northern Counties East League, who survive the local derbies in the earlier rounds, will hardly ever expect to face the same quality again from clubs in other regions.

Some do have to meet clubs from the North West, many of whom are also stronger than the clubs in the southern competitions that supply Vase clubs. In general the competitive Vase standard clubs of the North are certainly stronger than those in the South.

Full marks to them all, especially the North Eastern semi-professional talent who don't have the same temptations to join senior clubs in the same way as their counterparts where various levels of leagues cover the Home Counties, the Midlands and even the North West.

Just look at some of the ties played as early as the recent Second Round of the FA Vase.-

Dunston UTS 2 Crook Town 1
West Auckland 1 Shildon 0
Whitley Bay 3 Runcorn Town 0
AFC Emley 1 Jarrow Roofing 3
Winsford United 0 Spennymoor 0

What talent!

Two home counties clubs, whose predecessors were involved in the isthmian League not so long ago, are Enfield 1893 and Barking, but both lost in the Second Round. Norwich United winning 3-2 at Enfield and Barking suffering a 7-0 thrashing at Ampthill Town.

Other clubs with some exciting cup history are Alvechurch, who won 3-0 at home against Oadby Town and Wisbech Town, who recored a fine 6-3 victory at Gornal Athletic after extra time. Rushden & Diamonds also recorded a fine a 4-2 away victory over Wulfrunians after extra time.

Reading Town are top of the Hellenic League and achieved a notable victory over Brislington but although West Country clubs do not have many opportunities to judge their quality within the FA Vase 'family' some clubs expected to emerge from the regional rounds include Plymouth Parkway, Bodmin Town, Sholing, Alresford Town and Saltash United

THIRD ROUND

Having shared their cup days, firstly with the FA Trophy on 16th November and then The FA Cup on 7th December, The FA Vase which gives a Wembley opportunity to clubs in Step 5 and below, now have just 32 clubs featuring in the Third Round

So far they have been separated in regions and the senior competitions have taken priority in the media. But the clubs who have survived and feature in the draw for the Fourth Round will begin to wonder if its going to be their year.

The powerful Northern League traditionally dominate the competition but so far they have been knocking each other out. Survivors include holders Spennymoor Town, West Auckland, Morpeth Town, Newcastle Benfield, Ashington, Dunston UTS and the winners of the Brighouse Town and Whickham tie.

So the North East will supply nearly a quarter of the last 32 and as the geographical boundaries are expended in the Second Round they had a better chance of avoiding each other in the draw. In fact six of the seven were drawn at home and West Auckland Town, the only one with an away tie were paired with Brighouse or Whickham!

Clubs geographically below the magically North East, who look strong enough to reach Wembley, include Sholing and Alresford Town from The Wessex League, but Causeway and Coleshill from The Midland Alliance both travel to the North East.

Hanwell Town enjoyed an impressive 5-0 victory over Lordswood and are drawn at home to Ashford United while Hanworth Villa, who knocked out last season's finalists Tunbridge Wells, have been rewarded with a home tie against Eastbourne United from Sussex Division Two.

FOURTH ROUND

Home advantage in the FA Vase is extremely important and once again eight out of the eleven ties played on the Saturday produced home winners with Sholing adding another on the Tuesday fixture. The best attendance was recorded at AFC Rushden, where a crowd of 948 saw St Andrews win 2-0. Brightlingsea beat Bodmin Town 3-1 in front of 567 with three individual goalscorers.

However two spectacular individual goalscoring feats were produced by Nathan Chilton who scored all three goals for Morpeth Town at home to Westfields and Phil Draycott who also scored a hat trick, for Ampthill Town who beat Norwich United 3-1.

The north eastern dominance of the competition in recent years meant that the home victories of

Newcastle Benfield, Spennymoor United and Dunston UTS were not surprising. The fact that Eastern Counties League's Wisbech Town won 2-1 at Ashington was a special achievement where Tom James scored both goals and the North East local derby as won by West Auckland 3-1 away to Whickham.

The only two Saturday games played in the South saw Hallen beat Alresford United 2-0 after the visitors had hit the woodwork three times and Larkhall Athletic beat Blackfield & Langley 3-0.

Two of the postponed games were played a week later and Eastbourne United, a name that was associated with successful senior non-league in the sixties, have come through many changes of policy over the years and have now qualified brilliantly to take their place in the FA Vase Fifth Round.

After a superb 7-2 away victory over Hanworth VIlla of the Combined Counties League, which included a fine hat trick by Joe Dryer, the Sussex club take their place alongside St Andrews as the two Step Six clubs left in the competition. While East Preston made it a great day for Sussex with a solid 3-0 victory over Brantham Athletic.

FIFTH ROUND

A good geographical balance in this round eventually Hanwell Town eventually managed to play their Fourth Round tie against Ashton United after the consistent wet weather had subsided, winning 2-1 to qualify for a trip to Ampthill Town, the only other Spartan South Midlands club left in the competition who proved too strong on the day, but have to travel to Eastbourne in the next round.

An emphatic victory was achieved by Eastbourne United who scored six against Morpeth Town, perhaps not the strongest Northern League representative, but still a capable challenger with the tough North East traditions. Dunston UTS showed their quality by beating Brightlingsea Regent 5-0 at home. They have been rewarded with a local Northern League battle against the powerful West Auckland Town in the quarter finals.

FAV SF2L: Matt MacLean, Eastbourne United, beats the Sholing defence to score his team's first goal. Photo: Roger Turner.

An intriguing tie will be sorted out at Sholing who entertain Wisbech Town. Both clubs won by just a single goal in the Fifth Round and perhaps were expected to have achieved more substantial victories, with Sholing certainly one of most powerful clubs in the Wessex League.

Form suggests that the Northern League will have two Semi-Finalists, in West Auckland Town who will be favourites to beat Northern colleagues Dunston UTS and Newcastle Benfield who travel to the only Step 6 club, Ampthill Town. Joining them should be Eastbourne United and Sholing but it's cup football and there is usually at least one surprise.

SIXTH ROUND - THE QUARTER FINALS

Tunbridge Wells reached Wembley from a Step Five League last season and it appears their example inspired clubs at all levels this season as The FA Vase semi-finals include two clubs from Step Six.

St Andrews beat the experienced Dunston UTS, winners in 2012, in front of an impressive 1, 279 attendance with a headed goal from their usual centre half and skipper Declan Towers, playing up front because of injuries. The little club from The East Midlands Counties League are currently in seventh position, twelve points behind their league leaders, with four games in hand.

To be in Division Two of the Sussex League and reach the FA Vase Semi Finals is a remarkable achievement. Eastbourne United Association FC are a rebuilt club hoping to build a more successful football future for the area and are at present favourites to win promotion back to the County's senior division. Their victory over Ampthill Town was clinched with two goals from Wes Tate but the visitors did finish with nine men on the field

In a perfect football world perhaps these two little clubs would be drawn against each other so that a Step six club would play at Wembley.

SEMI-FINALS

The two senior clubs, both won by a single goal in tough cup ties against Dunston UTs and Wisbech Town respectively. West Auckland have nine game in hand over the Northern League leaders and Sholing are favourites to win their league and gain promotion to Step Four. Both these clubs are at home in their Semi-Final first legs. They will be aiming to build substantial leads, but of course they will be clear favourites and have all to lose. While the Step Six representatives presumably should be thrilled with the prospect of the two legged semi-final, knowing they are not expected to reach Wembley- so they will have everything to gain.

So far, Eastbourne United and St Andrews have won games against the odds and they must both have a chance to go the whole way. However, the semi-final is not a one off, their senior opponents should be able to defend against a shock result, even if the first meeting proves difficult.

But there again, who has the advantage of playing the second game at home?

FIRST QUALIFYING ROUND

SATURDAY 7 SEPTEMBER 2013 - WINNERS RECEIVE £600

1	Birtley Town	v	Tadcaster Albion	4-1	85
2	Penrith	v	Yorkshire Amateur	7-1	70
3	Marske United	v	Seaham Red Star	4-1	165
4	Jarrow Roofing Boldon CA	v	Thornaby (10/9)	3-1	66
5	West Allotment Celtic	v	Stokesley	4-3	60
6	Billingham Synthonia	v	Hall Road Rangers	3-1	96
7	Whitehaven	v	Thackley	1-2	41
8	Chester-Le-Street Town	v	Newcastle Benfield	1-4	
9	Willington	v	Northallerton Town	4-3aet	124
10	Tow Law Town	v	Durham City	0-3	120
11	Esh Winning	v	Liversedge	0-3	35
12	Knaresborough Town	v	Westella Hanson	4-3aet	88
13	Newton Aycliffe	v	Guisborough Town	1-3	111
14	Whickham	v	Hebburn Town (6/9)	3-0	80
15	Alnwick Town	v	Albion Sports	2-3	126
16	Glossop North End	v	Nostell MW	3-2aet	253
17	Irlam	v	Runcorn Linnets	0-3	200
18	Wigan Robin Park	v	Winsford United	1-2	81
19	Cheadle Town	v	Daisy Hill	3-1	60
20	Maltby Main	v	Squires Gate	0-3	41
21	Abbey Hey	v	Congleton Town	0-2	82
22	Kinsley Boys	v	Appleby Frodingham	1-0	72
23	Penistone Church	v	Rossington Main	2-3	210
24	Worsborough Bridge Athletic	v	Ashton Town (8/9)	2-1aet	131
25	Armthorpe Welfare	v	AFC Liverpool	3-1	128
26	Stockport Sports	v	Atherton Collieries	5-0	40
27	Pontefract Collieries	v	St Helens Town	2-0	50
28	Askern	v	Glasshoughton Welfare	2-7	42
29	Selby Town	v	Formby	0-5	75
30	Oldham Boro	v	1874 Northwich	2-1aet	169
31	Hallam	v	Shirebrook Town (8/9)	1-2	153
32	Bottesford Town	v	Ashton Athletic	0-1aet	53
33	Wolverhampton SC	v	Ellesmere Rangers (6/9)	1-2	14
34	Wednesfield	v	Pilkington XXX	1-3	41
35	Pelsall Villa	v	Barnt Green Spartak	1-0	68
36	Bromyard Town	v	Norton United	0-2	30
37	Coventry Copsewood	v	Nuneaton Griff	3-4	41
38	Heath Hayes	v	Studley	2-3	78
39	Lichfield City	v	Brocton	3-4aet	157
40	Boldmere St Michaels	v	Tipton Town	3-1	72
41	Malvern Town	v	Coleshill Town	2-5	61
42	Bewdley Town	v	Stafford Town	2-3aet	42
43	Racing Club Warwick	v	Bustleholme	1-0	
44	Dudley Town	v	Leek CSOB	7-3	48
45	Shifnal Town	v	Earlswood Town	1-4	55
46	Black Country Rangers	v	Tividale	1-5	52
47	Bromsgrove Sports	v	Lye Town	1-0	311
48	Pegasus Juniors	v	Continental Star	2-3aet	37
49	Pershore Town	v	Wellington	2-1	43
50	Ellistown	v	Basford United		
	(walkover for Basford United – Ellistown removed)				
51	Blidworth Welfare	v	Ollerton Town	1-4	38
52	Arnold Town	v	Blaby Whetstone Athletic	2-4aet	107
53	Holwell Sports	v	Quorn	2-1aet	108
54	Stewarts & Lloyds Corby	v	Bardon Hill Sports	4-3aet	46
55	Ellistown & Ibstock United	v	Rothwell Corinthians	1-0aet	52
56	Radcliffe Olympic	v	Pinxton	4-1	61
57	Harborough Town	v	Holbrook Sports	5-3aet	77
58	AFC Mansfield	v	Gedling MW	6-2	
59	Mickleover Royals	v	Stapenhill	3-2aet	58
60	Sutton Town	v	Dunkirk	1-5	62
	(at Dunkirk FC)				
61	Clipstone	v	Belper United	4-0	57
62	Anstey Nomads	v	Heanor Town	0-4	113
63	Radford	v	Desborough Town	0-1	61
64	St Andrews	v	Lutterworth Athletic	6-2	84
65	Yaxley	v	Peterborough NS (6/9)	1-2	444
66	Cambridge Regional College	v	Harrowby United	1-2	75
67	Boston Town	v	Downham Town	6-0	68
68	Brightlingsea Regent	v	Felixstowe & Walton United	1-0	65
69	Haverhill Rovers	v	Stanway Rovers	1-2aet	99
70	Basildon United	v	Stansted	1-2	40
71	Wivenhoe Town	v	Ipswich Wanderers	1-2	92
72	Debenham LC	v	Halstead Town	0-2	84
73	Bowers & Pitsea	v	FC Clacton	2-1	59
74	Haverhill Borough	v	Norwich United (8/9)	1-4	87
75	Hillingdon Borough	v	Bedford	6-0	35
76	London Colney	v	Codicote	2-3aet	53
77	Cockfosters	v	Cogenhoe United	5-3aet	101
78	London Tigers	v	Baldock Town	1-2	28
79	Winslow United	v	Leverstock Green	6-3	72
80	Hadley	v	Biggleswade United	3-1	30
81	Harefield United	v	Wellingborough Town	0-1	65
82	Berkhamsted	v	Hertford Town	3-2aet	127
83	FC Broxbourne Borough	v	Sporting Bengal United	0-3	38
84	Wembley	v	Potton United	6-0	71
85	Holmer Green	v	AFC Kempston Rovers	1-0	36
86	Greenhouse London	v	Long Buckby	4-2aet	24
87	AFC Biggleswade	v	Sileby Rangers		
	(walkover for Sileby Rangers – AFC Biggleswade removed)				
88	Crawley Green	v	London APSA	4-5	20
89	AFC Dunstable	v	AFC Rushden & Diamonds	1-1aet	303
	AFC Rushden & Diamonds	v	AFC Dunstable (10/9)	3-1	342
90	London Lions	v	FC Romania (8/9)	3-2	30
91	Southall	v	Haringey Borough	0-2	98
92	Rushden & Higham United	v	Northampton Spencer	0-4	42
93	Langford	v	Newport Pagnell Town	1-5	41
94	Kings Langley	v	Colney Heath	1-3	51
95	Tring Athletic	v	Eton Manor	1-0	98
96	Thame United	v	Carterton	8-0	63
97	Farnham Town	v	Ardley United	2-1aet	24
98	Cheltenham Saracens	v	Hook Norton	0-2	48
99	Kidlington	v	Newbury	5-2	51
100	Frimley Green	v	Windsor	1-3	82
101	Badshot Lea	v	Knaphill (6/9)	0-1	
102	Ash United	v	Holyport	0-1	51
103	Shrivenham	v	Malmesbury Victoria	4-2	56
104	Brimscombe & Thrupp	v	Sandhurst Town	3-1	107
105	Highworth Town	v	Camberley Town	1-3	89
106	Flackwell Heath	v	Hartley Wintney	1-4	43
107	Mile Oak	v	Arundel	1-1aet	48
	Arundel	v	Mile Oak (10/9)	2-0	
108	Pagham	v	Molesey	2-1	95
109	Sevenoaks Town	v	Canterbury City	5-0	106
110	Selsey	v	Littlehampton Town	0-2	87
111	Saltdean United	v	Southwick	2-4aet	49
112	Dorking Wanderers	v	St Francis Rangers	4-3aet	25
113	Kent Football United	v	Lingfield	3-3aet	42
	(Lingfield won 5-4 on kicks from the penalty mark)				
114	Shoreham	v	Horsham YMCA	2-1	93

FAV 1Q: An aerial dual that see's the Brimscombe & Thrupp attackers come out on top as they head towards the Sandhurst Town goal. Whilst below a Brimscombe & Thrupp player again has the upper hand in a less threatening area of the pitch. Photos: Peter Barnes.

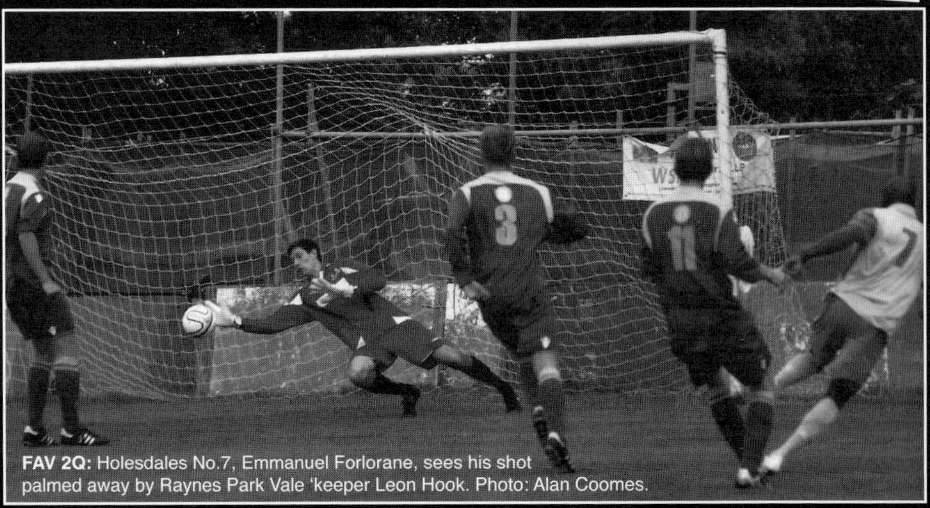

FAV 2Q: Holesdales No.7, Emmanuel Forlorane, sees his shot palmed away by Raynes Park Vale 'keeper Leon Hook. Photo: Alan Coomes.

FAV 2Q: Ryan McBride, Eastbourne United, scores against Arundel. Photo: Roger Turner.

FIRST QUALIFYING ROUND

SATURDAY 7 SEPTEMBER 2013 - WINNERS RECEIVE £600

115	Horley Town	v	Newhaven	2-6	40
116	Chichester City	v	Cray Valley (PM)	3-5aet	72
117	Raynes Park Vale	v	Holmesdale	0-2	44
118	Chessington & Hook United	v	Hailsham Town	3-1aet	48
119	Oakwood	v	Glebe	3-4	15
120	Steyning Town	v	Ashford United	0-2	150
121	Croydon	v	Seaford Town	2-0	55
122	Phoenix Sports	v	Sidley United		
	(walkover for Phoenix Sports – Sidley United removed)				
123	Colliers Wood United	v	Dorking	1-3aet	41
124	Deal Town	v	Epsom Athletic	1-3aet	84
125	East Grinstead Town	v	AFC Uckfield	2-1	60
126	Laverstock & Ford	v	Cheddar	5-2	32
127	Team Solent	v	Horndean	1-2	42
128	Chippenham Park	v	Bristol Manor Farm	2-3	81
129	United Services Portsmouth	v	Calne Town	6-1	37
130	Brockenhurst	v	Hayling United	5-0	20
131	Welton Rovers	v	Petersfield Town	0-2	69
132	Bradford Town	v	Portishead Town	5-0	74
133	Winterbourne United	v	Ringwood Town	2-1	41
	(at Ringwood Town FC)				
134	Warminster Town	v	Alton Town	4-3	114
135	Melksham Town	v	Devizes Town	4-1	85
136	Hythe & Dibden	v	Oldland Abbotonians	3-2	50
137	Fawley	v	Amesbury Town	4-2	52
138	Keynsham Town	v	Fleet Spurs	2-1	53
139	Hallen	v	Whitchurch United	2-0	46
140	Pewsey Vale	v	Folland Sports	0-5	
141	Romsey Town	v	Bournemouth	6-4	50
142	Westbury United	v	Ashton & Backwell United	1-3	31
143	Barnstaple Town	v	Witheridge	3-2	208
144	Sherborne Town	v	AFC St Austell	3-1	123
145	Bovey Tracey	v	Wells City	3-2aet	77
146	St Blazey	v	Ilfracombe Town	3-2aet	107
147	Camelford	v	Torpoint Athletic	2-1	86
148	Plymouth Parkway	v	Bridport	4-2	108
149	Elmore	v	Wadebridge Town	2-2aet	37
	Wadebridge Town	v	Elmore (10/9)	4-1	48

SECOND QUALIFYING ROUND

SATURDAY 21 SEPTEMBER 2013 - WINNERS RECEIVE £800

1	Eccleshill United	v	Bishop Auckland	3-1	135
2	Newcastle Benfield	v	Barnoldswick Town	3-1	60
3	Darlington RA	v	Thackley	1-5	32
4	Guisborough Town	v	Durham City	3-1	117
5	Penrith	v	West Allotment Celtic	4-1	80
6	Holker OB's	v	Ryton & Crawcrook Albion	5-1	56
7	Marske United	v	Knaresborough Town	2-0	202
8	Jarrow Roofing Boldon CA	v	Willington	2-1	
9	Albion Sports	v	Billingham Synthonia	2-3aet	50
10	Team Northumbria	v	Sunderland RCA	2-4	45
11	Washington	v	Morpeth Town	0-3	67
12	Pickering Town	v	Crook Town	2-6	166
13	Whickham	v	Birtley Town	5-3	
14	Consett	v	Nelson	3-4	99
15	South Shields	v	Billingham Town	4-4aet	42
	Billingham Town	v	South Shields (24/9)	1-3	97
16	Silsden	v	North Shields	2-4aet	92
17	Liversedge	v	Colne	2-1	51
18	Staveley MW	v	Ashton Athletic	3-2	116
19	Rossington Main	v	West Didsbury & Chorlton	1-2	58
20	AFC Darwen	v	Kinsley Boys	3-4aet	68
21	Glasshoughton Welfare	v	Armthorpe Welfare	1-4	66
22	Runcorn Linnets	v	Squires Gate	4-2	296
23	Winterton Rangers	v	AFC Blackpool	1-2	41
24	Winsford United	v	Pontefract Collieries	3-0	86
25	Cheadle Town	v	Worsborough Bridge Athletic	2-0	56
26	Oldham Boro	v	Congleton Town	1-5	38
27	Parkgate	v	Bacup & Rossendale Borough	4-4aet	50
	Bacup & Rossendale Borough	v	Parkgate (25/9)	0-0aet	53
	(Parkgate won 4-2 on kicks from the penalty mark)				
28	Rochdale Town	v	Dinnington Town	4-2aet	35
29	Athersley Recreation	v	Northwich Flixton Villa	5-0	128
30	Formby	v	Glossop North End	0-1	181
	(at Glossop North End FC)				
31	Alsager Town	v	Chadderton	0-1	66
32	Atherton LR	v	Shirebrook Town	1-0	91
33	Worksop Parramore	v	Hemsworth MW	4-0	59
34	Stockport Sports	v	Barton Town OB's	5-3aet	32
35	Pilkington XXX	v	AFC Wulfrunians	0-3	53
36	Brocton	v	Wolverhampton Casuals	5-3aet	51
37	Bartley Green	v	AFC Wombourne United		
	(walkover for Bartley Green – AFC Wombourne United removed)				
38	Bilston Town	v	Stourport Swifts	0-7	132
39	Tividale	v	Coventry Sphinx	1-2	88
40	Shawbury United	v	Ellesmere Rangers	3-0	59
41	Cradley Town	v	Southam United	2-1	50
42	Alvechurch	v	Eccleshall	4-1	83
43	Earlswood Town	v	Pershore Town	3-1	61
44	Norton Untied	v	Boldmere St Michaels	3-2aet	51
45	Pelsall Villa	v	Sporting Khalsa	1-0	41
46	Bromsgrove Sports	v	Stafford Town	8-0	273
47	Bolehall Swifts	v	Blackwood	2-1aet	60
48	Willenhall Town	v	Racing Club Warwick	0-7	53
49	Dudley Town	v	Studley	5-2	50
50	Causeway United	v	Continental Star (22/9)	2-1	72
51	Dudley Sports	v	Atherstone Town	1-3	42
52	Nuneaton Griff	v	Coleshill Town	2-6	68
53	Desborough Town	v	Teversal	3-0	48
54	Stewarts & Lloyds Corby	v	Thrapston Town	1-0	33
55	Holwell Sports	v	Thurnby Nirvana	3-0	60
56	Grimsby Borough	v	AFC Mansfield	1-5	51
57	Louth Town	v	Radcliffe Olympic	1-3	62
58	Mickleover Royals	v	Graham St Prims (22/9)	2-4	99
59	Lincoln Moorlands Railway	v	Heather St Johns	3-2	31
60	Basford United	v	Cleethorpes Town	0-2	74

FAV 2Q: A Brimscombe & Thrupp defender takes no chances and clears the ball before the Shrivenham striker can pounce. Photo: Peter Barnes.

Whilst (left) AFC Croydon's Joe Loyza and Fisher's Tom Carr (stripes) keep their eyes on the ball. Photo: Alan Coomes.

FAV 2Q: Glebe's Daniel Akpoveta fires in a shot watched by Dorking's Luke Milner. Photo: Alan Coomes.

FAV 2Q: An aerial battle in the middle of park between Brimscombe & Thrupp and Shrivenham. Photo: Peter Barnes.

SECOND QUALIFYING ROUND

SATURDAY 21 SEPTEMBER 2013 - WINNERS RECEIVE £800

61	Dunkirk	v	Oadby Town	0-5	63
62	Ollerton Town	v	Blaby & Whetstone Athletic	0-4	45
63	Long Eaton United	v	Ellistown & Ibstock United	0-0aet	52
	Ellistown & Ibstock United	v	Long Eaton United (24/9)	0-1	
64	Shepshed Dynamo	v	Kirby Muxloe	0-3	117
65	St Andrews	v	Clipstone	3-1	45
66	Barrow Town	v	Harborough Town	0-2	45
67	Heanor Town	v	Aylestone Park	8-2	131
68	Blackstones	v	Boston Town	0-2	44
69	Deeping Rangers	v	Swaffham Town	2-5	94
70	Peterborough Northern Star	v	Harrowby United	1-3	67
71	Eynesbury Rovers	v	Fakenham Town	3-1	73
72	Sleaford Town	v	Thetford Town	3-4	85
73	March Town United	v	Godmanchester Rovers	0-4	89
74	Saffron Walden Town	v	Norwich United	1-3	177
75	Walsham Le Willows	v	Whitton United	4-2	49
76	Mildenhall Town	v	Stowmarket Town	4-0	97
77	Brightlingsea Regent	v	Stanway Rovers	3-0	65
78	Hullbridge Sports	v	Long Melford	4-0	29
79	Southend Manor	v	Bowers & Pitsea	0-1	48
80	Diss Town	v	Stansted	3-2	108
81	Newmarket Town	v	Woodbridge Town	4-0	53
82	Cornard United	v	Great Yarmouth Town	1-2	32
83	Halstead Town	v	Team Bury	0-3	107
84	Ipswich Wanderers	v	Kirkley & Pakefield	3-1	55
85	Cockfosters	v	Buckingham Athletic	6-2	60
86	Wembley	v	Hatfield Town	2-1	56
87	AFC Rushden & Diamonds	v	Hoddesdon Town	5-1	482
88	London APSA	v	Wellingborough Whitworths	2-0	35
89	Sporting Bengal United	v	Sawbridgeworth Town	2-1	30
90	Berkhamsted	v	Buckingham Town	3-2	81
91	Welwyn Garden City	v	Irchester United	2-1	126
92	Codicote	v	Sileby Rangers	1-2	24
93	Stotfold	v	London Lions	2-0	40
94	Winslow United	v	Tower Hamlets	0-4	77
95	Hadley	v	Holmer Green (22/9)	4-3	
96	Tring Athletic	v	Greenhouse London	4-1	81
97	Hillingdon Borough	v	Newport Pagnell Town	3-2	46
98	Northampton Spencer	v	Barking	1-5	65
99	Kentish Town	v	Hanwell Town (20/9)	3-4	53
100	Wootton Blue Cross	v	Clapton	0-1aet	
101	Colney Heath	v	Broadfields United	1-0	47
102	Baldock Town	v	Bugbrooke St Michaels	4-2	42
103	Haringey Borough	v	Wellingborough Town	6-2	50
104	Lydney Town	v	Highmoor Ibis	0-1	62
105	Knaphill	v	Tadley Calleva	5-1	82
106	Windsor	v	Camberley Town	4-0	167
107	Milton United	v	Bedfont Sports	1-0	43
108	Farnham Town	v	Slimbridge	4-1	32
109	Fairford Town	v	Kidlington	0-4	45
110	New College Swindon	v	Staines Lammas	0-2	28
111	Westfield	v	Thame United	3-0	76
112	Chinnor	v	Bedfont & Feltham	2-3	75
113	Bracknell Town	v	Hartley Wintney	1-2	104
114	Brimscombe & Thrupp	v	Shrivenham	3-0	63
115	Abingdon Town	v	Hook Norton	3-1	28
116	Holyport	v	Reading Town	0-1	42
117	Pagham	v	East Grinstead Town	1-2	72
118	Lingfield	v	Worthing United	2-0	46
119	Woodstock Sports	v	Epsom Athletic (22/9)	0-2	71
120	Hassocks	v	Ringmer	3-0	49
121	Ashford United	v	Cobham	4-1	199
122	Eastbourne United	v	Arundel	3-0	79

123	Epsom & Ewell	v	Whyteleafe	2-3aet	56
124	Beckenham Town	v	Haywards Heath Town	3-0aet	55
125	Glebe	v	Dorking	2-3	65
126	Littlehampton Town	v	Shoreham	2-1	89
127	Sevenoaks Town	v	Lancing	2-1	76
128	Croydon	v	Cray Valley (PM)	1-3	40
129	Fisher	v	AFC Croydon Athletic (22/9)	0-6	88
130	Crowborough Athletic	v	Holmesdale	4-2	64
131	Chessington & Hook United	v	Dorking Wanderers	4-4aet	38
	Dorking Wanderers	v	Chessington & Hook United (24/9)	1-2	
132	Banstead Athletic	v	Phoenix Sports	0-2	42
133	Mole Valley SCR	v	Greenwich Borough (22/9)	4-6	
	(at Colliers Wood United FC)				
134	Southwick	v	Newhaven	2-4	
135	Horndean	v	Verwood Town	1-3	55
136	Bradford Town	v	Downton	4-2	62
137	Cribbs	v	Hamworthy United	0-2	50
138	Odd Down	v	Wootton Bassett Town	7-0	42
139	Hallen	v	Cowes Sports	2-0	37
140	Hengrove Athletic	v	Laverstock & Ford	0-1	30
141	East Cowes VA	v	Lymington Town	0-2	23
142	Almondsbury UWE	v	Radstock Town	1-0	32
143	Keynsham Town	v	Ashton & Backwell United	1-3	38
144	United Services Portsmouth	v	Winterbourne United	2-3	8
145	Bristol Manor Farm	v	Corsham Town	2-1aet	57
146	Folland Sports	v	Melksham Town	4-2aet	
147	Roman Glass St George	v	Longwell Green Sports	2-3	46
148	Totton & Eling	v	Hythe & Dibden	2-3aet	44
149	Fawley	v	Petersfield Town	0-1	
150	AFC Portchester	v	Romsey Town	4-0126	151
	Fareham Town	v	Bristol Academy	4-1	73
152	Brockenhurst	v	Warminster Town	0-2	55
153	Street	v	Bovey Tracey	1-2	84
154	Exmouth Town	v	Buckland Athletic	0-2	119
155	Cullompton Rangers	v	Tavistock	0-2	41
156	Plymouth Parkway	v	St Blazey	6-0	123
157	Camelford	v	Shepton Mallet	1-3	69
158	Willand Rovers	v	Sherborne Town	5-3	67
159	Saltash United	v	Wadebridge Town	5-1	86
160	Newquay	v	Barnstaple Town	2-2aet	127
	Barnstaple	v	Newquay (24/9)	5-0	134

FIRST ROUND PROPER

SATURDAY 19 OCTOBER 2013 - WINNERS RECEIVE £900

1	Newcastle Benfield	v	Marske United	3-2	85
2	Jarrow Roofing Boldon CA	v	Nelson	2-0	
3	Bridlington Town	v	Sunderland RCA	2-0	160
4	Thackley	v	Eccleshill United	1-0	147
5	North Shields	v	Crook Town	2-2aet	206
	Crook Town	v	North Shields (23/10)	4-3aet	152
6	Billingham Synthonia	v	Guisborough Town	1-0	155
7	West Auckland Town	v	South Shields	5-0	122
8	Penrith	v	Morpeth Town	1-2	85
9	Whickham	v	Holker Old Boys	1-0	103
10	Cheadle Town	v	Stockport Sports	1-0	76
11	Glossop North End	v	Kinsley Boys	7-0	230
12	Garforth Town	v	Winsford United	1-2aet	113
13	Rochdale Town	v	Congleton Town	1-3	150
14	Bootle	v	Parkgate	4-5	88
15	Worksop Parramore	v	Runcorn Linnets	3-1	114
16	AFC Blackpool	v	Norton United	1-4	57
17	Liversedge	v	Armthorpe Welfare	3-4	90
18	Chadderton	v	Athersley Recreation	2-3	70
19	Maine Road	v	Atherton LR	3-0	50
20	Staveley MW	v	West Didsbury & Chorlton	2-0	107
21	Bartley Green	v	Alvechurch	0-6	50
22	Earlswood Town	v	Causeway United	0-1	55
23	Westfields	v	Bromsgrove Sporting	3-2	204
24	Stourport Swifts	v	Brocton	0-2	83
25	Coleshill Town	v	Racing Club Warwick	4-2	49
26	Pelsall Villa	v	Coventry Sphinx	0-2	39
27	AFC Wulfrunians	v	Atherstone Town	5-0	81
28	Shawbury United	v	Bolehall Swifts	0-1	58
29	Dudley Town	v	Cradley Town	7-0	71
30	Graham St Prims	v	Harrowby United	3-1	82
31	Sileby Rangers	v	AFC Mansfield	2-5aet	67
32	Harborough Town	v	Cleethorpes Town	0-5	67
33	Heanor Town	v	Kirby Muxloe	4-2aet	148
	(both clubs removed from the competition for playing an ineligible player)				
34	Woodford United	v	AFC Rushden & Diamonds	0-6	312
35	Stewarts & Lloyds Corby	v	Loughborough University	1-2	25
36	Hucknall Town	v	Desborough Town	1-3	116
37	Radcliffe Olympic	v	Holwell Sports	2-3aet	67
38	Retford United	v	Oadby Town	0-1	178
39	St Andrews	v	Lincoln Moorlands Railway	4-0	55
40	Long Eaton United	v	Boston Town	2-0	59
41	Blaby & Whetstone Athletic	v	Holbeach United	5-1	55
42	Norwich United	v	Bowers & Pitsea	2-1aet	66
43	Diss Town	v	Eynesbury Rovers	1-3	111
44	Gorleston	v	Great Yarmouth Town	0-1	214
45	Walsham Le Willows	v	Godmanchester Rovers	5-0	52
46	Great Wakering Rovers	v	Ipswich Wanderers	5-2	92
47	Newmarket Town	v	Mildenhall Town	1-1aet	124
	Mildenhall Town	v	Newmarket Town (22/10)	0-2aet	185
48	Huntingdon Town	v	Thetford Town	3-0	67
49	Brightlingsea Regent	v	Team Bury	5-1	81
50	Swaffham Town	v	Hullbridge Sports	2-2aet	78
	Hullbridge Sports	v	Swaffham Town (29/10)	4-3aet	53
51	Tower Hamlets	v	Haringey Borough	0-3	35
52	Hanwell Town	v	London APSA	4-1	45
53	Oxhey Jets	v	Stotfold	3-2	39
54	Hillingdon Borough	v	Hadley	1-2aet	40
55	Ilford	v	Tring Athletic	2-3	57
56	Baldock Town	v	Berkhamsted	1-4	110
57	Welwyn Garden City	v	Bedfont & Feltham	1-0	105
58	Takeley	v	Sporting Bengal United	3-0	67
59	Clapton	v	Barking	0-1	
60	St Margaretsbury	v	Colney Heath	0-3	50
61	Cockfosters	v	Wembley	3-0	54
62	Dorking	v	Knaphill	2-2aet	62
	Knaphill	v	Dorking (22/10)	2-1	68
63	Farnham Town	v	East Preston	0-1	38
64	Littlehampton Town	v	Corinthian	2-1	102
65	Beckenham Town	v	Westfield	4-0	42
66	Cray Valley (PM)	v	AFC Croydon Athletic (18/10)	2-0	143
67	Ashford United	v	Greenwich Borough	4-1	201
68	Whyteleafe	v	Windsor	4-2	103
69	Crowborough Athletic	v	Epsom Athletic	1-0	84
70	Staines Lammas	v	South Park	0-5	
71	Chessington & Hook United	v	Hassocks	3-0	58
72	Newhaven	v	Cove	4-4aet	69
	Cove	v	Newhaven (5/11)	2-0	58
	(22/10 – tie abandoned after 41 mins due to waterlogged pitch, 0-1)				
73	Eastbourne United	v	Pheonix Sports	5-4aet	96
74	Erith Town	v	Lingfield	4-3	40
75	East Grinstead Town	v	Sevenoaks Town	2-0	81
76	Winchester City	v	Sholing	0-1	152
77	Hamworthy United	v	Oxford City Nomads	1-2	87
78	Kidlington	v	Lymington Town	5-1	63
79	Highmoor Ibis	v	Folland Sports	2-4	32
80	Wantage Town	v	Abingdon Town	7-0	42
81	Abingdon United	v	Fareham Town	0-3aet	110
82	Hartley Wintney	v	Petersfield Town	4-2	135
83	Moneyfields	v	Christchurch	1-1aet	
	Christchurch	v	Moneyfields (23/10)	0-1	70
84	Bradford Town	v	AFC Portchester	2-3	94
85	Verwood Town	v	Laverstock & Ford	3-1	54
86	Alresford Town	v	Hythe & Dibden	4-1	36
87	Reading Town	v	Milton United	2-0	51
88	Binfield	v	Warminster Town	9-1	130
89	Bishop Sutton	v	Odd Down	0-6	43
90	Almondsbury UWE	v	Barnstaple Town	2-4	33
91	Cadbury Heath	v	Hallen	1-3	73
92	Brimscombe & Thrupp	v	Ashton & Backwell United	3-1	97
93	Brislington	v	Longwell Green Sports	1-0	72
94	Bovey Tracey	v	Shepton Mallet	0-2	96
95	Saltash United	v	Willand Rovers	2-1	108
96	Plymouth Parkway	v	Gillingham Town	2-0	203
97	Tavistock	v	Winterbourne United	3-2	160
98	Buckland Athletic	v	Bristol Manor Farm	4-0	82

SECOND ROUND PROPER

SATURDAY 16 NOVEMBER 2013 - WINNERS RECEIVE £1,200

1	Whitley Bay	v	Runcorn Town	3-0	432
2	Cleethorpes Town	v	Morpeth Town	1-6	203
3	Maine Road	v	Billingham Synthonia	2-3	176
4	Norton United	v	Brighouse Town	0-2	71
5	AFC Emley	v	Jarrow Roofing Boldon CA	1-3	114
6	Dunston UTS	v	Crook Town	2-1	209
7	Staveley MW	v	Glossop North End	2-0	314
8	West Auckland Town	v	Shildon	1-0	534
9	Thackley	v	Armthorpe Welfare	4-0	356
10	Ashington	v	Worksop Parramore	3-1	298
11	Winsford United	v	Spennymoor Town	0-0aet	271
	Spennymoor Town	v	Winsford United (19/11)	7-0	228
12	Whickham	v	Parkgate	3-0	85
13	Newcastle Benfield	v	Cheadle Town	6-2	76
14	Athersley Recreation	v	Bridlington Town	0-1aet	249
15	Borrowash Victoria	v	Congleton Town	1-4	138
16	Causeway United	v	Dudley Town (17/11)	4-1	143
17	Walsall Wood	v	Spalding United	0-3	105
	(tie awarded to Walsall Wood – Spalding United removed)				
18	Bolehall Swifts	v	Heanor Town		
	(tie awarded to Bolehall Swifts – Heanor Town removed)				
19	Graham St Prims	v	Loughborough University	3-2aet	64
20	Alvechurch	v	Oadby Town	3-0	211
21	Westfields	v	Coventry Sphinx	6-1	59
22	Gornal Athletic	v	Wisbech Town	3-6aet	95
23	Holwell Sports	v	Rocester	2-1aet	180
24	Long Eaton United	v	Coleshill Town	0-2aet	56
25	Blaby & Whetstone Athletic	v	Desborough Town	3-0	67
26	AFC Mansfield	v	Huntingdon Town	1-1aet	102
	Huntingdon Town	v	AFC Mansfield (20/11)	1-0	72
27	AFC Wulfrunians	v	AFC Rushden & Diamonds	2-4aet	369
28	St Andrews	v	Brocton	2-1	76
29	Oxhey Jets	v	Hadleigh United	2-3	67
30	Tring Athletic	v	Eynesbury Rovers	1-0	160
31	Walsham Le Willows	v	Haringey Borough	1-4	85
32	Hullbridge Sports	v	Berkhamsted	1-0aet	75
33	Great Yarmouth Town	v	Hanwell Town	1-2	121
34	Ampthill Town	v	Barking	7-0	110
35	Great Wakering Rovers	v	Cockfosters	2-0	105
36	Hadley	v	Brantham Athletic (17/11)	1-2	82
37	Takeley	v	Brightlingsea Regent	1-2	156
38	Ely City	v	Welwyn Garden City	0-0aet	147
	Welwyn Garden City	v	Ely City (20/11)	3-0	
39	Enfield 1893	v	Norwich United	2-3	58
40	Colney Heath	v	Newmarket Town	2-1	162
41	Lordswood	v	Whyteleafe	2-1	96
42	South Park	v	Cray Valley (PM)	1-1aet	82
	Cray Valley (PM)	v	South Park (20/11)	2-3	72
43	Hanworth Villa	v	East Grinstead Town	3-1	75
44	Tunbridge Wells	v	Crowborough Athletic	1-0	1242
45	Ashford United	v	Littlehampton Town	1-0	311
46	Ascot United	v	Beckenham Town	0-1	120
47	Chessington & Hook United	v	Eastbourne United	2-3	102
48	Erith Town	v	Hartley Wintney	5-1	47
49	Knaphill	v	East Preston	0-4	141
50	Rye United	v	Cove	3-0	85
51	Buckland Athletic	v	Saltash United	0-3	78
52	Folland Sports	v	Sholing	1-2	226
53	Plymouth Parkway	v	Wantage Town	3-0	178
54	Verwood Town	v	Alresford Town	1-4	63
55	Blackfield & Langley	v	Oxford City Nomads	1-0	63
56	Bodmin Town	v	Bemerton Heath Harlequins	4-2	85
57	Barnstaple Town	v	Hallen	3-4	135
58	Reading Town	v	Brislington	1-0	84
59	Kidlington	v	Tavistock	3-0	85
60	Odd Down	v	Moneyfields	2-3	
61	Larkhall Athletic	v	Newport (IW)	2-0	150
62	Fareham Town	v	Bitton	0-3	103
63	Brimscombe & Thrupp	v	Binfield	0-3	102
64	AFC Portchester	v	Shepton Mallet	3-1	175
	(tie awarded to Shepton Mallet – AFC Portchester removed)				

FAV 2P: AFC Wulfrunians player, Craig Gregg is well marked by the Atherstone Town defence, whilst Nathan Rose-Laing rises to head in AFC Wulfrunians second goal, during his sides 5-0 win. Photo: Jonathon Holloway.

FAV 2P: Jacob Pearce, Cove, attempts to find a way past three Rye United players. Photo: Roger Turner.

FAV 2P: Erith Town's Marcus Eken tries to shield the ball from Jason Minton of Hartley Wintney. Photo: Alan Coomes.

FAV 4P: Phil Draycott's early free-kick beats the Norwich United keeper to give Ampthill the lead. Photo: Gordon Whittington.

FAV SF2L: Eastbourne United 'keeper Grant Young holds tight despite the challenge of Sholing's Lee Wort. Photo: Graham Brown.

FAV 5P: Ryan Bridge (left) beats the Morpeth Town defence to score Eastbourne United's second goal. Photo: Roger Turner.

THIRD ROUND PROPER

SATURDAY 7 DECEMBER 2013 - WINNERS RECEIVE £1,500

1	Spennymoor Town	v	Bridlington Town	2-0	440
2	West Auckland Town	v	Billingham Synthonia	2-1	177
3	Brighouse Town	v	Whickham (10/12)	3-3aet	66
	Whickham	v	Brighouse Town (17/12)	1-0	200
4	Staveley MW	v	Morpeth Town	0-2	155
5	Jarrow Roofing Boldon CA	v	Newcastle Benfield	1-2	82
6	Ashington	v	Thackley	1-0	213
7	Whitley Bay	v	Dunston UTS	0-2	542
8	Congleton Town	v	Huntingdon Town	2-1	201
9	Blaby & Whetstone Athletic	v	Causeway United	1-2	77
10	AFC Rushden & Diamonds	v	Graham St Prims	2-0	563
11	Holwell Sports	v	Coleshill Town	1-3	202
12	Walsall Wood	v	Wisbech Town	0-1	103
13	Alvechurch	v	Westfields	0-1	102
14	St Andrews	v	Bolehall Swifts	4-1	103
15	Great Wakering Rovers	v	Hullbridge Sports	0-1	147
16	East Preston	v	Rye United	2-1	107
17	Hanwell Town	v	Lordswood	5-0	150
18	Ampthill Town	v	Beckenham Town	2-1	118
19	Brightlingsea Regent	v	Colney Heath	2-2aet	120
	Colney Heath	v	Brightlingsea Regent (10/12)	0-2	224
20	Ashford United	v	Tring Athletic	1-0	335
21	South Park	v	Eastbourne United	1-2	151
22	Hadleigh United	v	Welwyn Garden City	3-2aet	186
23	Norwich United	v	Erith Town	3-0	102
24	Tunbridge Wells	v	Hanworth Villa	0-1	518
25	Haringey Borough	v	Brantham Athletic	2-3aet	69
26	Moneyfields	v	Bitton		
	(tie abandoned after 102mins due to misconduct, 1-1 – both clubs removed from the competition)				
27	Plymouth Parkway	v	Hallen	1-3	136
28	Shepton Mallet	v	Blackfield & Langley	1-2	119
29	Binfield	v	Larkhall Athletic	0-1	137
30	Reading Town	v	Sholing	1-4	80
31	Kidlington	v	Bodmin Town	2-3aet	84
32	Saltash United	v	Alresford Town	2-7	101

FOURTH ROUND PROPER

SATURDAY 18 JANUARY 2014 - WINNERS RECEIVE £2,000

1	Newcastle Benfield	v	Congleton Town	3-1	197
2	Spennymoor Town	v	Causeway United	1-0	460
3	Ashington	v	Wisbech Town	1-2	396
4	AFC Rushden & Diamonds	v	St Andrews	0-2	948
5	Morpeth Town	v	Westfields	3-0	206
6	Dunston UTS	v	Coleshill Town	2-1aet	312
7	Whickham	v	West Auckland Town	1-3aet	340
8	Larkhall Athletic	v	Blackfield & Langley	3-0	225
9	Ampthill Town	v	Norwich United	3-1	351
10	Hallen	v	Alresford Town	2-0	147
11	Sholing	v	Hullbridge Sports (21/1)	3-1	193
12	Moneyfields or Bitton	v	Hadleigh United		
	(tie awarded to Hadleigh United – Moneyfields & Bitton removed)				
13	Hanworth Villa	v	Eastbourne United (25/1)	2-7aet	210
14	Hanwell Town	v	Ashford United (13/2)	2-1	286
	(at Ashford United FC)				
15	Brightlingsea Regent	v	Bodmin Town	3-1	567
16	East Preston	v	Brantham Athletic (25/1)	3-0	214
	(at Sussex FA, Lancing)				

FIFTH ROUND PROPER

SATURDAY 15 FEBRUARY 2014 - WINNERS RECEIVE £2,500

1	Eastbourne United	v	Morpeth Town (22/2)	6-1	301
2	Ampthill Town	v	Hanwell Town	3-1aet	390
3	Dunston UTS	v	Brightlingsea Regent (22/2)	5-0	452
4	Sholing	v	Larkhall Athletic (22/2)	1-0aet	323
5	Hadleigh United	v	Wisbech Town	1-2	511
6	Spennymoor Town	v	Newcastle Benfield (22/2)	1-2	527
7	East Preston	v	St Andrews (22/2)	1-2	205
8	West Auckland Town	v	Hallen (22/2)	2-0	276

SIXTH ROUND PROPER

SATURDAY 8 MARCH - WINNERS RECEIVE £4,500

1	St Andrews	v	Newcastle Benfield	1-0	1279
2	Eastbourne United	v	Ampthill Town	2-1	456
3	Sholing	v	Wisbech Town	1-0	426
4	Dunston UTS	v	West Auckland Town	0-1	1009

SEMI FINALS

WINNERS RECEIVE £6,000

1ST LEG – SATURDAY 29 MARCH 2014

1	Sholing	v	Eastbourne United	2-0	562
1	Eastbourne United	v	Sholing	2-4	1426

(Sholing won 6-4 on aggregate)

2ND LEG – SATURDAY 05 APRIL 2014

2	West Auckland Town	v	St Andrews	0-0	1282
2	St Andrews	v	West Auckland Town	1-2	1514

(West Auckland Town won 2-1 on aggregate)

The Final...

SHOLING 1
(McLean 71)
WEST AUCKLAND TOWN 0

Wembley Stadium **Att: 5,432**

SHOLING	WEST AUCKLAND
Matt Brown	Jordan Nixon
Mike Carter	Neil Pattinson
Marc Diaper	Andrew Green
Peter Castle	(Jonathan Gibson 63 min)
(Dan Miller 53 min)	Daryll Hall
Lee Bright	Lewis Galpin
Tyronne Bowers	Brian Close
(Kevin Brewster 75 min)	Shaun Vipond
Barry Mason	(Stuart Banks 76 min)
Lewis Fennemore	Robert Briggs
(Alex Sawyer 78 min)	Mattie Moffat
Lee Wort	(Steven Richardson 74 min)
Byron Mason	John Campbell
Marvin McLean	Dennis Knight
Subs not used	**Subs not used**
Ashley Jarvis	Paul Garthwaite,
Nick Watts	Adam Wilkinson

Referee David Coote (West Riding). Assisted by Constantine Hatzidakis, and Paul Tierney. Four official - Adam Nunn.

Sholings Lee Wort (stripes) tries to go past West Auckland's Lewis Galpin. Photo: Alan Coomes.

At the conclusion of last year's final I wrote, "There still remains a major question – when will this northern domination end?" after Spennymoor had just made it five seasons in succession that a Northern League team had won the Vase. Here was the answer, provided by Sholing after what proved to be a one year voluntary drop to the Wessex League on financial grounds. Winning the title in their twelve month sojourn in Step Five they have opted to move back to the Southern League and thus will be in next year's Trophy competition rather than defending their Vase title. On the back of this success chairman/manager Dave Diaper, for whom several of the team work as electricians, decided to finish as manager. He will, however, be taking on other roles within the club as Director of Football as well as seeking to improve the Club's financial standing. Having occupied those top positions for 25 years, starting with the team playing on unenclosed grounds, he had every right to enjoy this triumphant pinnacle of his sporting career. Joining him in retirement was his 35 year old defender son, Marc, a Sholing player for the previous 14 years.

Whereas this was the Hampshire side's first Wembley visit the Northern Leaguers had, two seasons previously, lost to their neighbours, Dunston, in the 2012 final at Wembley and been knocked out of the Vase by the same club in 2013. 2014 saw the same two drawn together in the quarter final, with Auckland at last turning the tables and able to vie for a sixth consecutive Northern League Vase triumph. Six of the team had figured in the 2012 squad.

Vase finals are largely adventurous events with plenty of goalmouth action and possession being won and lost frequently. While this final could not be classed as mundane it was, for the uncommitted, only occasionally stirring. The sombre, almost funereal, music which welcomed the two sides to the arena did nothing to lift the pre- kick off spirits although, to old timers, what a great pleasure it was to see players numbered 1 to 11, even if the positions taken by some of the players did not occupy their number's appropriate berth. The crowd recompensed for its very limited numbers by the enthusiasm of its members urging on their respective heroes. They were watching people they knew well enough to be able to shout out their names and receive, in return, a waving acknowledgement during the preliminary warming up. Not even a period of piercing rain, which meant the Wembley sprinklers could stay below ground, lessened their enjoyment.

Immediately the game started we saw a Sholing winger, Marvin McLean, wearing number 11, tearing

Gibson, West Auckland, hits the Sholing crossbar in the dying minutes. Photo: Keith Clayton.

down the left wing and beating his opponent for speed. West Auckland retaliated with John Campbell the first to bring a keeper's save. His effort was safely held by Matt Brown before, seconds later, he burst through, Brown saving with his feet, a feat performed earlier by Jordan Nixon to deny Lee Wort. Auckland 's Andrew Green found himself in the book for a wild challenge on his counterpart skipper Byron Mason, the ball having departed some seconds previously. McLean again showed great pace but wasted his chance by shooting wildly over the far post. Brown had to rely on a fellow defender to clear Brian Close's shot but just before half time he made a splendid save from a fierce free kick by Robert Briggs.

The second half opened with Barry Mason spurning a chance to open Sholing's account. Two of their players, Lewis Fennemore and Lee Bright, were booked for lunging fouls as manager Peter Dixon urged his Auckland players forward. In response they earned a free kick which, only partially cleared,

Campbell (West Auckland) shoots over the Sholing crossbar. Photo: Keith Clayton.

rebounded to Campbell who shot narrowly over. Then came the break through. McLean once again tore through on the left. His attempt to score hit a defender. The deflection bounced up and over the stranded Nixon, ending fortuitously in the net. 1-0 to the Hampshire boys with twenty minutes of play remaining.

Campbell strove to pull his team level, bringing a splendid diving save from Brown who next had to push aside an effort from Briggs. Four substitutions, two for each side, in a four minute period broke up play as did two more Sholing bookings for subs Dan Miller and Alex Sawyer. Man of the match Brown turned over a Dennis Knight shot and the whole West Auckland team went up for a last minute corner which all but brought extra time, Jonathan Gibson heading against the bar. The last action saw Brian Close booked for tripping Wort as time ran out and Sholing's efforts turned to their celebrations.

Match report by Arthur Evans

Lee Bright, Sholing, clears his lines with Daryll Hall, West Auckland) looking on. Photo: Keith Clayton.

FAV F: Tyronne Bowers, Sholing, with the ball and West Auckland Town's John Campbell. Photo: Roger Turner.

FAV 6P: Declan Towers' header creeps over the line to give St Andrews the win over Newcastle Benfield. Photo: Gordon Whittington.

FAV SF2L: Nick Watts scores Sholing's fourth goal at Eastbourne United to send his team to Wembley. Photo: Roger Turner.

FAV 6P: Sholing deal with a Wisbech attack during their 1-0 win. Photo: Graham Brown.

PAST FINALS

1975 **HODDESDON TOWN** 2 *(South Midlands)* EPSOM & EWELL 1 *(Surrey Senior)* Att: 9,500
Sedgwick 2 Wales Ref: Mr R Toseland
Hoddesdon: Galvin, Green, Hickey, Maybury, Stevenson, Wilson, Bishop, Picking, Sedgwick, Nathan, Schofield
Epsom & Ewell: Page, Bennett, Webb, Wales, Worby, Jones, O'Connell, Walker, Tuite, Eales, Lee

1976 **BILLERICAY TOWN** 1 *(Essex Senior)* STAMFORD 0 (aet) *(United Counties)* Att: 11,848
Aslett Ref: Mr A Robinson
Billericay: Griffiths, Payne, Foreman, Pullin, Bone, Coughlan, Geddes, Aslett, Clayden, Scott, Smith
Stamford: Johnson, Kwiatowski, Marchant, Crawford, Downs, Hird, Barnes, Walpole, Smith, Russell, Broadbent

1977 BILLERICAY TOWN 1 *(Essex Senior)* SHEFFIELD 1 (aet) *(Yorkshire)* Att: 14,000
Clayden Coughlan og Ref: Mr J Worrall
Billericay: Griffiths, Payne, Bone, Coughlan, Pullin, Scott, Wakefield, Aslett, Clayden,Woodhouse, McQueen. Sub: Whettell
Sheffield: Wing, Gilbody, Lodge, Hardisty, Watts, Skelton, Kay, Travis, Pugh, Thornhill,Haynes. Sub: Strutt
Replay **BILLERICAY TOWN** 2 SHEFFIELD 1 Att: 3,482
Aslett, Woodhouse Thornhill at Nottingham Forest
Billericay: Griffiths, Payne, Pullin, Whettell, Bone, McQueen, Woodhouse, Aslett, Clayden, Scott, Wakefield
Sheffield: Wing, Gilbody, Lodge, Strutt, Watts, Skelton, Kay, Travis, Pugh, Thornhill, Haynes

1978 **NEWCASTLE BLUE STAR** 2 *(Wearside)* BARTON ROVERS 1 *(South Midlands)* Att: 16,858
Dunn, Crumplin Smith Ref: Mr T Morris
Newcastle: Halbert, Feenan, Thompson, Davidson, S Dixon, Beynon, Storey, P Dixon, Crumplin, Callaghan, Dunn. Sub: Diamond
Barton Rovers: Blackwell, Stephens, Crossley, Evans, Harris, Dollimore, Dunn, Harnaman, Fossey, Turner, Smith. Sub: Cox

1979 **BILLERICAY TOWN** 4 *(Athenian)* ALMONDSBURY GREENWAY 1 *(Glos. Co)* Att: 17,500
Young 3, Clayden Price Ref: Mr C Steel
Billericay: Norris, Blackaller, Bingham, Whettell, Bone, Reeves, Pullin, Scott, Clayden,Young, Groom. Sub: Carrigan
Almondsbury: Hamilton, Bowers, Scarrett, Sulllivan, Tudor, Wookey, Bowers, Shehean, Kerr, Butt, Price. Sub: Kilbaine

1980 **STAMFORD** 2 *(United Counties)* GUISBOROUGH TOWN 0 *(Northern Alliance)* Att: 11,500
Alexander, McGowan Ref: Neil Midgeley
Stamford: Johnson, Kwiatkowski, Ladd, McGowan, Bliszczak I, Mackin, Broadhurst, Hall,Czarnecki, Potter, Alexander. Sub: Bliszczak S
Guisborough: Cutter, Scott, Thornton, Angus, Maltby, Percy, Skelton, Coleman, McElvaney,Sills, Dilworth. Sub: Harrison

1981 **WHICKHAM** 3 *(Wearside)* WILLENHALL 2 (aet) *(West Midlands)* Att: 12,000
Scott, Williamson, Peck og Smith, Stringer Ref: Mr R Lewis
Whickham: Thompson, Scott, Knox, Williamson, Cook, Ward, Carroll, Diamond, Cawthra,Robertson, Turnbull. Sub: Alton
Willenhall: Newton, White, Darris, Woodall, Heath, Fox, Peck, Price, Matthews, Smith,Stringer. Sub: Trevor

1982 **FOREST GREEN ROVERS** 3 *(Hellenic)* RAINWORTH M.W 0 *(Notts Alliance)* Att: 12,500
Leitch 2, Norman Ref: Mr K Walmsey
Forest Green: Moss, Norman, Day, Turner, Higgins, Jenkins, Guest, Burns, Millard, Leitch, Doughty. Sub: Dangerfield
Rainworth M.W: Watson, Hallam, Hodgson, Slater, Sterland, Oliver, Knowles, Raine, Radzi, Reah, Comerford. Sub: Robinson

1983 **V.S. RUGBY** 1 *(West Midlands)* HALESOWEN TOWN 0 *(West Midlands)* Att: 13,700
Crawley Ref: Mr B Daniels
VS Rugby: Burton, McGinty, Harrison, Preston, Knox, Evans, ingram, Setchell, Owen,Beecham, Crawley. Sub: Haskins
Halesowen Town: Coldicott, Penn, Edmonds, Lacey, Randall, Shilvock, Hazelwood, Moss, Woodhouse,P Joinson, L Joinson. Sub: Smith

1984 **STANSTED** 3 *(Essex Senior)* STAMFORD 2 *(United Counties)* Att: 8,125
Holt, Gillard, Reading Waddicore, Allen Ref: Mr T Bune
Stanstead: Coe, Williams, Hilton, Simpson, Cooper, Reading, Callanan, Holt, Reevs,Doyle, Gillard. Sub: Williams
Stamford: Parslow, Smitheringate, Blades, McIlwain, Lyon, Mackin, Genovese, Waddicore,Allen, Robson, Beech. Sub: Chapman

1985 **HALESOWEN TOWN** 3 *(West Midlands)* FLEETWOOD TOWN 1 *(N W Counties)* Att: 16,715
L Joinson 2, Moss Moran Ref: Mr C Downey
Halesowen: Coldicott, Penn, Sherwood, Warner, Randle, Heath, Hazlewood, Moss (Smith),Woodhouse, P Joinson, L Joinson
Fleetwood Town: Dobson, Moran, Hadgraft, Strachan, Robinson, Milligan, Hall, Trainor, Taylor(Whitehouse), Cain, Kennerley

1986 **HALESOWEN TOWN** 3 *(West Midlands)* SOUTHALL 0 *(Isthmian 2 South)* Att: 18,340
Moss 2, L Joinson Ref: Mr D Scott
Halesowen: Pemberton, Moore, Lacey, Randle (Rhodes), Sherwood, Heath, Penn, Woodhouse, PJoinson, L Joinson, Moss
Southall: Mackenzie, James, McGovern, Croad, Holland, Powell (Richmond), Pierre,Richardson, Sweales, Ferdinand, Rowe

1987 ST. HELENS 3 ***(N W Counties)*** — **WARRINGTON TOWN 2** ***(N W Counties)*** — **Att: 4,254**
Layhe 2, Rigby — **Reid, Cook** — **Ref: Mr T Mills**
St Helens: Johnson, Benson, Lowe, Bendon, Wilson, McComb, Collins (Gledhill), O'Neill,Cummins, Lay, Rigby. Sub: Deakin
Warrington: O'Brien. Copeland, Hunter, Gratton, Whalley, Reid, Brownville (Woodyer), Cook,Kinsey, Looker (Hill), Hughes

1988 COLNE DYNAMOES 1 ***(N W Counties)*** — **EMLEY 0** ***(Northern Counties East)*** — **Att: 15,000**
Anderson — **Ref: Mr A Seville**
Colne Dynamoes: Mason, McFafyen, Westwell, Bentley, Dunn, Roscoe, Rodaway, Whitehead (Burke),Diamond, Anderson, Wood (Coates)
Emley: Dennis, Fielding, Mellor, Codd, Hirst (Burrows), Gartland (Cook), Carmody,Green, Bramald, Devine, Francis

1989 TAMWORTH 1 ***(West Midlands)*** — **SUDBURY TOWN 1 (aet)** ***(Eastern)*** — **Att: 26,487**
Devaney — **Hubbick** — **Ref: Mr C Downey**
Tamworth: Bedford, Lockett, Atkins, Cartwright, McCormack, Myers, Finn, Devaney, Moores,Gordon, Stanton. Subs: Rathbone, Heaton
Sudbury Town: Garnham, Henry, G Barker, Boyland, Thorpe, Klug, D Barker, Barton, Oldfield,Smith, Hubbick. Subs: Money, Hunt
Replay TAMWORTH 3 — **SUDBURY TOWN 0** — **Att: 11,201**
Stanton 2, Moores — **at Peterborough**
Tamworth: Bedford, Lockett, Atkins, Cartwright, Finn, Myers, George, Devaney, Moores,Gordon, Stanton. Sub: Heaton
Sudbury Town: Garnham, Henry, G Barker, Boyland, Thorpe, Klug, D Barker, Barton, Oldfield,Smith, Hubbick. Subs: Money, Hunt

1990 YEADING 0 ***(Isthmian 2 South)*** — **BRIDLINGTON TOWN 0 (aet)** ***(N Co East)*** — **Att: 7,932**
Ref: Mr R Groves
Yeading: Mackenzie, Wickens, Turner, Whiskey (McCarthy), Croad, Denton, Matthews, James(Charles), Sweates, Impey, Cordery
Bridlington: Taylor, Pugh, Freeman, McNeill, Warburton, Brentano, Wilkes (Hall), Noteman,Gauden, Whiteman, Brattan (Brown)
Replay YEADING 1 — **BRIDLINGTON TOWN 0** — **Att: 5,000**
Sweales — **at Leeds Utd FC**
Yeading: Mackenzie, Wickens, Turner, Whiskey, Croad (McCarthy), Schwartz, Matthews,James, Sweates, Impey (Welsh), Cordery
Bridlington: Taylor, Pugh, Freeman, McNeill, Warburton, Brentano, Wilkes (Brown), Noteman,Gauden (Downing), Whiteman, Brattan

1991 GRESLEY ROVERS 4 ***(West Midlands)*** — **GUISELEY 4 (aet)** ***(Northern Co East)*** — **Att: 11,314**
Rathbone, Smith 2, Stokes — **Tennison 2, Walling, A Roberts** — **Ref: Mr C Trussell**
Gresley: Aston, Barry, Elliott (Adcock), Denby, Land, Astley, Stokes, K Smith, Acklam,Rathbone, Lovell (Weston)
Guiseley: Maxted, Bottomley, Hogarth, Tetley, Morgan, McKenzie, Atkinson (Annan),Tennison, Walling, A Roberts, B Roberts
Replay GUISELEY 3 — **GRESLEY ROVERS 1** — **Att: 7,585**
Tennison, Walling, Atkinson — **Astley** — **at Bramall Lane**
Guiseley: Maxted, Annan, Hogarth, Tetley, Morgan, McKenzie (Bottomley), Atkinson,Tennison (Noteman), Walling, A Roberts, B Roberts
Gresley: Aston, Barry, Elliott, Denby, Land, Astley, Stokes (Weston), K Smith, Acklam, Rathbone, Lovell (Adcock)

1992 WIMBORNE TOWN 5 ***(Wessex)*** — **GUISELEY 3** ***(Northern Premier Div 1)*** — **Att: 10,772**
Richardson, Sturgess 2, Killick 2 — **Noteman 2, Colville** — **Ref: Mr M J Bodenham**
Wimborne: Leonard, Langdown, Wilkins, Beacham, Allan, Taplin, Ames, Richardson, Bridle,Killick, Sturgess (Lovell), Lynn
Guiseley: Maxted, Atkinson, Hogarth, Tetley (Wilson), Morgan, Brockie, A Roberts,Tennison, Noteman (Colville), Annan, W Roberts

1993 BRIDLINGTON TOWN 1 ***(NPL Div 1)*** — **TIVERTON TOWN 0** ***(Western)*** — **Att: 9,061**
Radford — **Ref: Mr R A Hart**
Bridlington: Taylor, Brentano, McKenzie, Harvey, Bottomley, Woodcock, Grocock, A Roberts, Jones, Radford (Tyrell), Parkinson. Sub: Swailes
Tiverton Town: Nott, J Smith, N Saunders, M Saunders, Short (Scott), Steele, Annunziata, KSmith, Everett, Daly, Hynds (Rogers)

1994 DISS TOWN 2 ***(Eastern)*** — **TAUNTON TOWN 1** ***(Western)*** — **Att: 13,450**
Gibbs (p), Mendham — **Fowler** — **Ref: Mr K. Morton**
Diss Town: Woodcock, Carter, Wolsey (Musgrave), Casey (Bugg), Hartle, Smith, Barth, Mendham, Miles, Warne, Gibbs
Taunton Town: Maloy, Morris, Walsh, Ewens, Graddon, Palfrey, West (Hendry), Fowler, Durham, Perrett (Ward), Jarvis

1995 ARLESEY TOWN 2 ***(South Midlands)*** — **OXFORD CITY 1** ***(Ryman 2)*** — **Att: 13,670**
Palma, Gyalog — **S Fontaine** — **Ref: Mr G S Willard**
Arlesey: Young, Cardines, Bambrick, Palma (Ward), Hull, Gonsalves, Gyalog, Cox, Kane,O'Keefe, Marshall (Nicholls). Sub: Dodwell
Oxford: Fleet, Brown (Fisher), Hume, Shepherd, Muttock, Hamilton (Kemp), Thomas, Spittle, Sherwood, S Fontaine, C Fontaine. Sub: Torres

1996 BRIGG TOWN 3 ***(N Co East)*** — **CLITHEROE 0** ***(N W Counties)*** — **Att: 7,340**
Stead 2, Roach — **Ref: Mr S J Lodge**
Brigg: Gawthorpe, Thompson, Rogers, Greaves (Clay), Buckley (Mail), Elston, C Stead, McLean, N Stead (McNally), Flounders, Roach
Clitheroe: Nash, Lampkin, Rowbotham (Otley), Baron, Westwell, Rovine, Butcher, Taylor (Smith), Grimshaw, Darbyshire, Hill (Dunn)

1997 WHITBY TOWN 3 ***(Northern)*** — **NORTH FERRIBY UTD. 0** ***(N Co East)*** — **Att: 11,098**
Williams, Logan, Toman — **Ref: Graham Poll**
North Ferriby: Sharp, Deacey, Smith, Brentano, Walmsley, M Smith, Harrison (Horne), Phillips (Milner), France (Newman), Flounders, Tennison
Whitby Town: Campbell, Williams, Logan, Goodchild, Pearson, Cook, Goodrick (Borthwick), Hodgson, Robinson, Toman (Pyle), Pitman (Hall)

1998 TIVERTON TOWN 1 *(Western)* TOW LAW TOWN 0 *(Northern Division 1)* Att: 13,139
Varley Ref: M A Riley
Tiverton: Edwards, Felton, Saunders, Tatterton, Smith J, Conning, Nancekivell (Rogers), Smith K (Varley), Everett, Daly, Leonard (Waters)
Tow Law: Dawson, Pickering, Darwent, Bailey, Hague, Moan, Johnson, Nelson, Suddick, Laidler (Bennett), Robinson.

1999 TIVERTON TOWN 1 *(Western)* BEDLINGTON TERRIERS 0 *(Northern)* Att: 13, 878
Rogers 88 Ref: W. C. Burns
Bedlington Terriers: O'Connor, Bowes, Pike, Boon (Renforth), Melrose, Teasdale, Cross, Middleton (Ludlow), Gibb, Milner, Bond. Subs: Pearson, Cameron, Gowans
Tiverton Town: Edwards, Fallon, Saunders, Tatterton, Tallon, Conning (Rogers), Nancekivell (Pears), Varley, Everett, Daly, Leonard. Subs: Tucker, Hynds, Grimshaw

2000 DEAL TOWN 1 *(Kent)* CHIPPENHAM TOWN 0 *(Western)* Att: 20,000
Graham 87 Ref: E. K. Wolstenholme
Deal Town: Tucker, Kempster, Best, Ash, Martin, Seager, Monteith, Graham, Lovell, Marshall, Ribbens. Subs: Roberts, Warden, Turner
Chippenham Town: Jones, James, Andrews, Murphy, Burns, Woods, Brown, Charity, Tweddle, Collier, Godley. Subs: Tiley, Cutler

2001 TAUNTON TOWN 2 *(Western)* BERKHAMPSTED TOWN 1 *(Isthmian 2)* (at Villa Park) Att: 8,439
Fields 41, Laight 45 Lowe 71 Ref: E. K. Wolstenholme
Taunton Town: Draper, Down, Chapman, West, Hawkings, Kelly, Fields (Groves), Laight, Cann (Tallon), Bastow, Lynch (Hapgood). Subs: Ayres, Parker
Berkhampsted Town: O'Connor, Mullins, Lowe, Aldridge, Coleman, Brockett, Yates, Adebowale, Richardson, Smith, Nightingale. Subs: Ringsell, Hall, Knight, Franklin, Osborne

2002 WHITLEY BAY 1 *(Northern)* TIPTREE UNITED 0 *(Eastern)* (at Villa Park) Att: 4742
Chandler 97 Ref: A Kaye
Whitley Bay: Caffrey, Sunderland, Walmsley, Dixon (Neil), Anderson, Locker, Middleton, Bowes (Carr), Chandler, Walton, Fenwick (Cuggy). Subs: Cook, Livermore
Tiptree United: Haygreen, Battell, Wall, Houghton, Fish, Streetley (Gillespie), Wareham (Snow), Daly, Barefield, Aransibia (Parnell), Brady. Subs: Powell, Ford.

2003 BRIGG TOWN 2 *(Northern Co.East)* A.F.C SUDBURY 1 *(Eastern Counties)* (at Upton Park) Att: 6,634
Housham 2, Carter 68 Raynor 30 Ref: M Fletcher
Brigg Town:- Steer, Raspin, Rowland, Thompson, Blanchard, Stones, Stead (Thompson 41), Housham, Borman (Drayton 87), Roach, Carter. Subs (not used) Nevis, Gawthorpe.
AFC Sudbury:- Greygoose, Head (Norfolk 63), Spearing, Tracey, Bishop, Anderson (Owen 73), Rayner, Gardiner (Banya 79), Bennett, Claydon, Betson. Subs (not used) Taylor, Hyde.

2004 WINCHESTER CITY 2 *(Wessex)* A.F.C SUDBURY 0 *(Eastern Counties)* (at St Andrews) Att: 5,080
Forbes 19, Smith 73 (pen) Ref: P Crossley
Winchester City:- Arthur, Dyke (Tate 83), Bicknell, Redwood, Goss, Blake, Webber, Green, Mancey, Forbes (Rogers 70), Smith (Green 90). Subs (not used) - Lang and Rastall.
AFC Sudbury:- Greygoose, Head, Wardley, Girling, Tracey, Norfolk, Owen (Banya 62), Hyde (Calver 57), Bennett, Claydon, Betson (Francis 73n). Subs (not used) - Rayner, Nower.

2005 DIDCOT TOWN 3 *(Hellenic)* A.F.C SUDBURY 2 *(Eastern Counties)*(at White Hart Lane) Att: 8,662
Beavon (2), Wardley (og) Wardley, Calver (pen) Ref: R Beeeby
Didcot Town:- Webb, Goodall, Heapy, Campbell, Green, Parrott, Hannigan, Ward, Concannon (Jones 88), Beavon (Bianchini 90), Powell. Subs (not used) – Cooper, Allen, Spurrett.
AFC Sudbury:- Greygoose, Girling, Wardley, Bennett, Hyde (Hayes 78), Owen (Norfolk 65), Claydon (Banya 59), Head, Calver, Betson, Terry Rayner. Subs (not used) – Howlett, Nower.

2006 NANTWICH TOWN 3 *(NWC 1)* HILLINGDON BOROUGH 1 *(Spartan S.Mids P.)*(at St Andrews) Att: 3,286
Kinsey (2), Scheuber Nelson
Nantwich Town:- Hackney, A.Taylor, T.Taylor, Smith, Davis, Donnelly, Beasley, Scheuber (Parkinson 69), Kinsey (Marrow 69), Blake (Scarlett 86) and Griggs. Subs (not used): O'Connor and Read.
Hillingdon Borough:- Brown, Rundell (Fenton 80),Kidson, Phillips, Croft, Lawrence, Duncan (Nelson 46), Tilbury, Hibbs, Wharton (Lyons 38). Subs (not used): O'Grady, White.

2007 TRURO 3 *(Western Division 1)* AFC TOTTON 1 *(Wessex Division 1)* Att: 27,754 (New Vase record)
Wills (2), Broad Potter Ref: P Joslin
AFC Totton: Brunnschweiler, Reacord, Troon (Stevens 60), Potter (Gregory 82), Bottomley, Austen, Roden, Gosney, Hamodu (Goss 89), Osman, Byres. Subs not used: Zammit, McCormack.
Truro City: Stevenson, Ash, Power, Smith, Martin (Pope 84), Broad, Wills, Gosling, Yetton, Watkins, Walker (Ludlam 90).
Subs not used: Butcher, Routledge, Reski.

2008 KIRKHAM & WESHAM 2 *(North West Co. Div.2)* — **LOWESTOFT TOWN** 1 *(Eastern Co. Premier)* — **Att: 19,537**
Walwyn (2) — **Thompson (og)** — **Ref: A D'Urso**

Kirkham and Wesham: Summerfield, Jackson (Walwyn 79), Keefe (Allen 55), Thompson, Shaw, Eastwood, Clark, Blackwell, Wane, Paterson (Sheppard 90), Smith. Subs not used: Moffat and Abbott
Lowestoft Town: Reynolds, Poppy, Potter, Woodrow, Saunders, Plaskett (McGee 79), Godbold, Darren Cockrill (Dale Cockrill 46), Stock, Hough, King (Hunn 55). Subs not used: McKenna and Rix.

2009 WHITLEY BAY 2 *(Northern Division One)* — **GLOSSOP NORTH END 0** *(North West Co. Prem)* — **Att: 12,212**
Kerr, Chow — **Ref: K Friend**

Whitley Bay: Burke, Taylor, Picton, McFarlane (Fawcett 60), Coulson, Ryan, Moore, Robson, Kerr, Chow (Robinson 73), Johnston (Bell 60). Subs not used: McLean and Reay.
Glossop North End: Cooper, Young, Kay, Lugsden, Yates, Gorton, Bailey (Hind 57), Morris, Allen (Balfe 65), Hamilton (Bailey 72), Hodges. Subs not used: Whelan and Parker.

2010 WHITLEY BAY 6 *(Northern Division One)* — **WROXHAM 1** *(Eastern Counties Premier Division)* — **Att: 8,920**
Chow 21(sec), Easthaugh 16 (og), Kerr, Johnston, Robinson, Gillies — **Cook 12** — **Ref: A Taylor**

Whitley Bay: Terry Burke, Craig McFarlane, Callum Anderson, Richard Hodgson, (sub Lee Picton 69th min), Darren Timmons, Leon Ryan, Adam Johnston (sub Joshua Gillies 77th min), Damon Robson, Lee Kerr, Paul Chow (sub Phillip Bell 61st min), Paul Robinson.
Subs not used – Tom Kindley and Chris Reid.
Wroxham: Scott Howie, Gavin Pauling (sub Ross Durrant 57th min), Shaun Howes, Graham Challen, Martin McNeil (sub Josh Carus 46th min), Andy Easthaugh (sub Owen Paynter 69th min), Steve Spriggs, Gavin Lemmon, Paul Cook, Danny White, Gary Gilmore.
Subs not used – Danny Self and Gareth Simpson.

2011 WHITLEY BAY 3 *(Northern Division One)* — **COALVILLE TOWN 2** *(Midland Alliance)* — **Att: 8,778**
Chow 28, 90, Kerr 61 — **Moore 58, Goodby 80** — **Ref: S Mathieson**

Whitley Bay: Terry Burke, Craig McFarlane (sub Steve Gibson 90th min), Callum Anderson, Darren Timmons, Gareth Williams (sub David Coulson 68th min), Damon Robson, Lee Kerr, Paul Chow, Paul Robinson, David Pounder (sub Brian Smith 68th min), Gary Ormston.
Subs not used – Kyle Hayes (gk) and Brian Rowe. Coalville Town: Sean Bowles, Ashley Brown (sub Matthew Gardner 88th min), Cameron Stuart, Adam Goodby, Zach Costello, Lee Miveld,
Callum Woodward, Anthony Carney (sub Craig Attwood 90th min), Ryan Robbins (sub Ashley Wells 66th min), Matt Moore, Jerome Murdock.
Subs not used – Richard Williams (gk) and James Dodd.

2012 DUNSTON UTS 2 *(Northern Division One)* — **WEST AUCKLAND TOWN 0** *(Northern Division One)* — **Att: 5,126**
Bulford 32, 79 — **Ref: R East**

Dunston UTS: Liam Connell, Ben Cattenach, Terry Galbraith, Michael Robson, Chris Swailes, Kane Young, Steven Shaw, Michael Dixon, Stephen Goddard (sub Sreven Preen 84th min), Andrew Bulford (sub Danny Craggs 88th min), Lee McAndrew.
Subs not used – Andrew Clark (g/k), Ian Herron, Jack Burns.
West Auckland Town: Mark Bell, Neil Pattinson, Andrew Green, Jonny Gibson, John Parker, Mark Stephenson (sub Daniel Hindmarsh 76th min), Stuart Banks, Mark Hudson, Mattie Moffatt, Michael Rae, Adam Nicholls (sub Martin Young 60th min).
Subs not used – Daryll Hall, Ross Preston, Matthew Coad.

2013 SPENNYMOOR TOWN 2 *(Northern Division One)* — **TUNBRIDGE WELLS 1** *(Kent League)* — **Att: 16,751**
Cogdon 18, Graydon 80 — **Stanford 78** — **Ref: M Naylor**

Spennymoor Town: Robert Dean, Kallum Griffiths, Leon Ryan, Chris Mason, Stephen Capper, Keith Graydon, Lewis Dodds, Wayne Phillips (Anthony Peacock 64 min), Joe Walton (Andrew Stephenson 73 min), Mark Davison, (Michael Rae 76 min), Gavin Congdon.
Subs not used - David Knight (g/k), Steven Richardson.
Tunbridge Wells: Chris Oladogba, Jason Bourne, Scott Whibley, Perry Spackman, Lewis Mingle, Jon Pilbeam (Richard Sinden 85 min), Andy McMath, Joe Fuller (Tom Davey 58 min), Andy Irvine, Carl Connell (Jack Harris 58 min), Josh Stanford.
Subs not used - Michael Czanner (gk), Andy Boyle.

All Finals at Wembley unless otherwise stated.

FAV 5P: A goal from close range by Shane Wardley puts Hadleigh United ahead but Wisbech hit back to win 2-1.

Photo: Gordon Whittington

PRELIMINARY ROUND

1	Gateshead	v	Ryton & Crawcrook Albion (9/9)	5-0	104
2	Formby	v	Ashton Town		
	(walkover for Ashton Town – Formby withdrawn)				
3	AFC Fylde	v	Skelmersdale United (11/9)	4-1	58
4	Northwich Victoria	v	Witton Albion		
	(walkover for Witton Albion – Northwich Victoria withdrawn)				
5	Buxton	v	Abbey Hey		
	(walkover for Abbey Hey – Buxton withdrawn)				
6	New Mills	v	Stalybridge Celtic (11/9)	3-4	69
7	Hemsworth MW	v	Westella Hanson (12/9)	1-3	56
8	FC Halifax Town	v	Thackley (11/9)	5-2	130
9	Hallam	v	Harrogate Town (9/9)	2-3	47
10	Worksop Town	v	Kinsley Boys (12/9)	9-0	58
11	St Andrews	v	Matlock Town (11/9)	2-0	35
12	Ilkeston	v	Lincoln United (9/9)	8-0	93
13	Hinckley United	v	Spalding United (11/9)	8-0	35
14	Dunkirk	v	Lincoln City (11/9)	2-4	36
15	Pelsall Villa	v	Coventry Sphinx (10/9)	2-5	37
16	Ellesmere Rangers	v	Southam United (12/9)	5-0	30
17	Wednesfield	v	AFC Telford United (12/9)	0-3	35
18	Hednesford Town	v	Racing Club Warwick (11/9)	2-1	60
19	Rugby Town	v	Chasetown (11/9)	3-2aet	52
20	Stratford Town	v	Kidderminster Harriers (12/9)	1-2	46
21	Gorleston	v	Dereham Town (12/9)	2-3	60
22	Brantham Athletic	v	Cambridge United (9/9)	1-8	45
23	Cornard United	v	Walsham Le Willows (12/9)	2-1	28
24	Leiston	v	Fakenham Town		
	(walkover for Fakenham Town – Leiston withdrawn)				
25	Brackley Town	v	Barton Rovers (11/9)	1-2	37
26	AFC Kempston Rovers	v	Kettering Town		
	(walkover for AFC Kempston Rovers – Kettering Town withdrawn)				
27	Stotfold	v	Peterborough Northern Star (11/9)	4-0	42
28	Hoddesdon Town	v	Billericay Town (18/9)	2-0	51
29	Grays Athletic	v	Tilbury (11/9)	1-0	
30	Royston Town	v	Chelmsford City (11/9)	2-4	66
31	Colney Heath	v	Stanway Rovers (11/9)	1-4	20
32	Clapton	v	AFC Hornchurch (11/9)	0-2	30
33	Canvey Island	v	Witham Town (11/9)	3-2aet	91
34	Hullbridge Sports	v	Hitchin Town (12/9)	0-3	43
35	Waltham Abbey	v	Heybridge Swifts (9/9)	1-3	49
36	FC Clacton	v	Concord Rangers (12/9)	1-2	65
37	Redbridge	v	Braintree Town	0-2	21
38	Corinthian Casuals	v	Hampton & Richmond Boro'(11/9)	0-7	
39	Northwood	v	Enfield Town (12/9)	2-1aet	45
40	Faversham Town	v	Chatham Town (12/9)	3-0	53
41	Dover Athletic	v	Corinthian (10/9)	0-1	
42	Tonbridge Angels	v	Lordswood (9/9)	7-2	94
43	Whitstable Town	v	Maidstone United (12/9)	2-5	56
44	Crowborough Athletic	v	Croydon (12/9)	3-2	31
45	East Grinstead Town	v	Erith & Belvedere (11/9)	1-0	46
46	Hastings United	v	Chipstead (12/9)	6-7aet	90
47	Shoreham	v	Pagham (11/9)	7-3aet	33
48	Bognor Regis Town	v	Kingstonian (10/9)	4-2	
49	Peacehaven & Telscombe	v	Walton & Hersham (19/9)	5-0	25
50	Lancing	v	Molesey (9/9)	4-3	50
51	Newhaven	v	Dorking (12/9)	0-1	40
52	Crawley Down Gatwick	v	Woking (12/9)	2-3	84
53	Worthing	v	Littlehampton Town (9/9)	6-0	100
54	Thame United	v	Fleet Spurs (12/9)	10-0	54
55	Thatcham Town	v	Burnham (11/9)	2 0	32
56	Danbury United	v	Marlow (11/9)	2-4	42
57	Hartley Witney	v	Flackwell Heath (12/9)	3-0	51
58	Windsor	v	Ascot United (11/9)	1-9	53
59	Cove	v	Sandhurst Town (11/9)	0-2	54
60	Kidlington	v	Fleet Town (12/9)	2-1	31
61	Salisbury City	v	Moneyfields (10/9)	1-1aet	55
	(Moneyfields won 4-2 on kicks from the penalty mark)				
62	Eastleigh	v	Hamworthy United (9/9)	3-1	
63	Cirencester Town	v	Almondsbury UWE (10/9)	6-0	71
64	Weston Super Mare	v	Wells City (9/9)	6-0	39
65	Cheltenham Saracens	v	Hengrove Athletic (9/9)	4-4aet	47
	(Cheltenham won 3-1 on kicks from the penalty mark)				
66	Ashton & Backwell United	v	Forest Green Rovers (12/9)	0-5	58
	(at Portishead Town FC)				
67	Taunton Town	v	Merthyr Town (9/9)	1-3	139

FIRST ROUND QUALIFYING

1	Newton Aycliffe	v	Consett (23/9)	0-4	14
2	Scarborough Athletic	v	Gateshead (23/9)	0-8	
	(at Pickering Town FC)				
3	Newcastle Benfield	v	Chester-Le-Street Town (23/9)	4-3	103
4	Alsager Town	v	Ashton Town (25/9)	1-3	83
5	Southport	v	Stalybridge Celtic (25/9)	0-2	72
6	Nelson	v	Lancaster City (23/9)	7-2	37
7	Nantwich Town	v	Abbey Hey (25/9)	1-8	85
8	Runcorn Town	v	Altrincham (23/9)	4-5	65
9	AFC Fylde	v	Witton Albion (23/9)	3-0	122
10	AFC Blackpool	v	Chester (23/9)	1-6	102
11	Marine	v	Macclesfield Town (25/9)	1-1aet	81
	(Macclesfield Town won 4-3 on kicks from the penalty mark)				
12	Vauxhall Motors	v	Bootle (26/9)	3-2	103
13	Wrexham	v	Hyde (18/9)	3-0	67
14	Ashton Athletic	v	Prescot Cables (26/9)	0-3	82
15	Glossop North End	v	Runcorn Linnets (26/9)	0-4	75
16	Warrington Town	v	Curzon Ashton (25/9)	4-1	70
17	Ossett Town	v	Sheffield (26/9)	0-4	85
18	Silsden	v	Westella Hanson (23/9)	0-2	26
19	Grimsby Town	v	North Ferriby United (26/9)	7-0	
20	Staveley MW	v	Farsley (23/9)	4-0	102
21	Bottesford Town	v	Selby Town (26/9)	2-6	57
22	Harrogate Town	v	FC Halifax Town (25/9)	3-2	173
23	Worksop Town	v	Ossett Albion (26/9)	4-1	73
	(at Dinnington Town FC)				
24	Guiseley	v	Brighouse Town (3/10)	3-1	65
	(At Brighouse Town FC)				
	(24/9 tie abandoned after 90 mins due to serious injury to a player, 2-2)				
25	Yorkshire Amateur	v	Hall Road Rangers		
	(walkover for Hall Road Rangers – Yorkshire Amateur withdrawn)				
26	Stocksbridge Park Steels	v	Nostell MW (26/9)	2-3	41
27	Teversal	v	St Andrews (25/9)	0-5	53
28	Deeping Rangers	v	Ilkeston (25/9)	0-6	54
29	Holwell Sports	v	Boston United (25/9)	0-4	48
30	Lincoln City	v	Basford United (23/9)	7-1	119
31	Hinckley United	v	Ellistown & Ibstock United		
	(walkover for Hinckley United – Ellistown & Ibstock United withdrawn)				
32	Blaby & Whetstone Athletic	v	Mickleover Sports (25/9)	1-4	33
33	Lutterworth Athletic	v	Retford United (25/9)	2-1	54
34	Gresley	v	Oadby Town		
	(walkover for Gresley – Oadby Town withdrawn)				
35	Stapenhill	v	Stamford (25/9)	9-0	21
36	Rugby Town	v	AFC Telford United (25/9)	3-0	35
37	Ellesmere Rangers	v	Worcester City (26/9)	2-4	25
38	Tipton Town	v	Sutton Coldfield Town (23/9)	2-1	39
39	Boldmere St Michaels	v	Stourport Swifts (23/9)	2-1	47
40	Leamington	v	Eccleshall		
	(walkover for Eccleshall – Leamington withdrawn)				
41	Hereford United	v	Newcastle Town (30/9)	2-0	125
42	Solihull Moors	v	Lye Town (23/9)	5-0	60
43	Nuneaton Town	v	Dudley Sports (26/9)	4-0	85
44	Nuneaton Griff	v	Malvern Town		
	(walkover for Nuneaton Griff – Malvern Town withdrawn)				
45	Kidderminster Harriers	v	Romulus (30/9)	5-3	
46	Coventry Sphinx	v	Atherstone Town (26/9)	1-3	51
47	Halesowen Town	v	Coleshill Town (25/9)	3-0	37
48	Walsall Wood	v	Stourbridge		
	(walkover for Stourbridge – Walsall Wood withdrawn)				
49	Pegasus Juniors	v	Hednesford Town (25/9)	5-4aet	36
50	Woodbridge Town	v	Wroxham (26/9)	4-0	52
51	Stowmarket Town	v	Newmarket Town (24/9)	0-4	26
52	Haverhill Rovers	v	Cornard United (26/9)	2-6	54
53	Needham Market	v	Cambridge United (26/9)	2-5	128
54	Swaffham Town	v	Dereham Town (26/9)	2-5aet	89
55	Long Melford	v	Ipswich Wanderers (25/9)	3-2aet	52
56	Felixstowe & Walton United	v	Bury Town (24/9)	1-3	32
57	Norwich United	v	Fakenham Town (26/9)	0-2	51
58	AFC Sudbury	v	Whitton United (25/9)	3-3aet	71
	(Whitton United won 4-2 on kicks from the penalty mark)				
59	Lowestoft Town	v	Hadleigh United (25/9)	2-0	73
60	Histon	v	Soham Town Rangers (23/9)	3-1	128
61	Stewarts & Lloyds Corby	v	Barton Rovers (23/9)	0-5	33
62	Corby Town	v	AFC Kempston Rovers (23/9)	4-3aet	40
63	St Neots Town	v	Cogenhoe United (26/9)	2-4	64

No	Home		Away	Score	Att
64	AFC Dunstable	v	Rushden & Higham United		
	(walkover for Rushden & Higham United – AFC Dunstable withdrawn)				
65	Stotfold	v	Yaxley (26/9)	12-0	48
66	St Ives Town	v	Leighton Town (26/9)	1-4	91
67	AFC Rushden & Diamonds	v	Bugbrooke St Michaels (23/9)	4-0	94
68	Bedford Town	v	Wellingborough Town (25/9)	1-3	64
69	Luton Town	v	Rothwell Corinthians (25/9)	6-0	100
70	Bishop's Stortford	v	Romford (25/9)	3-0	105
71	Stanway Rovers	v	Chelmsford City (26/9)	0-1	62
72	Bowers & Pitsea	v	Halstead Town (25/9)	3-2	41
73	East Thurrock United	v	Braintree Town (26/9)	2-0	99
74	Tower Hamlets	v	Boreham Wood (23/9)	2-6	40
75	Sawbridgeworth Town	v	Cheshunt (25/9)	3-3aet	100
	(Cheshunt won 4-2 on kicks from the penalty mark)				
76	Canvey Island	v	Barking (25/9)	1-1aet	108
	(Canvey Island won 4-3 on kicks from the penalty mark)				
77	Potters Bar Town	v	Great Wakering Rovers (24/9)	5-4	33
78	Ware	v	Barnet (25/9)	0-4	87
79	Concord Rangers	v	Heybridge Swifts (26/9)	3-2	54
80	Grays Athletic	v	Hoddesdon Town (23/9)	3-2	32
81	St Albans City	v	Brentwood Town (23/9)	2-3	77
82	Thurrock	v	Burnham Ramblers		
	(walkover for Thurrock – Burnham Ramblers withdrawn)				
83	Hitchin Town	v	AFC Hornchurch (26/9)	0-1	49
84	Staines Town	v	Hampton&Richmond Boro' (23/9)	5-4	77
85	Harefield United	v	Northwood (25/9)	2-1aet	30
86	Wingate & Finchley	v	Wealdstone (26/9)	2-2aet	71
	(Wingate won 7-6 on kicks from the penalty Mark)				
87	Kings Langley	v	North Greenford United (25/9)	2-1	30
88	Berkhamsted	v	Ashford Town (Middx) (24/9)	3-1	57
89	Metropolitan Police	v	Oxhey Jets (26/9)	3-2	
90	Bedfont Sports	v	Uxbridge (26/9)	4-6	47
91	Leverstock Green	v	Enfield 1893 (26/9)	0-1	42
92	Cockfosters	v	Hayes & Yeading United (26/9)	4-3	47
93	Fisher	v	Dulwich Hamlet (26/9)	0-6	83
94	Crowborough Athletic	v	Tonbridge Angels (26/9)	2-0	65
95	Corinthian	v	Eastbourne Town (26/9)	7-0	64
96	Thamesmead Town	v	Erith Town (26/9)	5-0	63
97	Bromley	v	Eastbourne United (24/9)	2-1	95
98	Folkestone Invicta	v	Colliers Wood United (25/9)	1-4	61
99	Welling United	v	Sutton United (26/9)	3-4	81
100	Sittingbourne	v	Holmesdale (26/9)	1-0	78
101	Margate	v	Dartford (23/9)	0-7	57
102	Ramsgate	v	Eastbourne Borough (26/9)	1-1aet	65
	(Eastbourne won 5-4 on kicks from the penalty mark)				
103	East Grinstead Town	v	Sevenoaks Town (25/9)	0-1	43
104	Faversham Town	v	Chipstead (23/9)	0-4	45
105	Ebbsfleet United	v	Cray Wanderers		
	(walkover for Cray Wanderers – Ebbsfleet United withdrawn)				
106	Tooting & Mitcham United	v	VCD Athletic (23/9)	1-4	41
107	Carshalton Athletic	v	Maidstone United (23/9)	1-3	79
108	Godalming Town	v	Havant & Waterlooville (23/9)	3-3aet	62
	(Havant & Waterlooville won 5-4 on kicks from the penalty mark)				
109	Camberley Town	v	Redhill (23/9)	3-0	32
110	Westfield	v	Horsham (25/9)	0-6	39
111	Guildford City	v	Farnham Town (25/9)	3-1	40
112	Woking	v	South Park (25/9)	4-1	45
113	Arundel	v	Horley Town (26/9)	0-6	42
114	Lancing	v	Knaphill (26/9)	2-0	52
115	Peacehaven & Telscombe	v	Whyteleafe (23/9)	3-3aet	35
	(Peacehaven & Telscombe won 4-2 on kicks from the penalty mark)				
116	Three Bridges	v	Burgess Hill Town (26/9)	1-2	73
117	Leatherhead	v	Worthing (26/9)	1-3	68
118	Dorking	v	Shoreham (25/9)	1-2	
	(at Dorking Wanderers FC)				
119	Lewes	v	Bognor Regis Town (26/9)	3-2	54
120	Binfield	v	Basingstoke Town (25/9)	3-0	20
121	Abingdon United	v	Highmoor Ibis (26/9)	3-0	30
122	Newport Pagnell Town	v	Farnborough (26/9)	0-1	62
123	Bracknell Town	v	Aylesbury (26/9)	2-5	26
124	Sandhurst Town	v	Maidenhead United (23/9)	1-9	35
125	Slough Town	v	Buckingham Athletic (23/9)	2-3	69
126	Hartley Wintney	v	Chesham United (26/9)	2-1aet	30
127	Marlow	v	Reading Town		
	(walkover for Marlow – Reading Town withdrawn)				
128	Oxford City	v	Alton Town (23/9)	2-1	25
129	Didcot Town	v	Kidlington (26/9)	4-0	54
130	Ascot United	v	Thame United (26/9)	2-6	61
131	Aldershot Town	v	Thatcham Town (25/9)	8-0	139
132	Eastleigh	v	Wimborne Town (23/9)	2-3	96
133	Moneyfields	v	Westbury United (26/9)	2-0	60
134	Chippenham Town	v	Bournemouth (23/9)	0-3	66
135	AFC Totton	v	Gillingham Town (26/9)	6-0	79
136	Dorchester Town	v	AFC Portchester (24/9)	2-1	69
137	Christchurch	v	Poole Town (24/9)	2-1	78
138	Petersfield Town	v	Chichester City (25/9)	1-4	49
139	Larkhall Athletic	v	Gloucester City (23/9)	4-3	30
140	Paulton Rovers	v	Cirencester Town (26/9)	2-3	54
141	Bitton	v	Tiverton Town		
	(walkover for Tiverton Town – Bitton removed)				
142	Lydney Town	v	Bath City		
	(walkover for Bath City – Lydney Town withdrawn)				
143	Elmore	v	Odd Down (24/9)	2-3	11
144	Cheltenham Saracens	v	Weston Super Mare (23/9)	0-1	39
145	Forest Green Rovers	v	Clevedon Town (30/9)	2-1	119
146	Bridgwater Town	v	Yate Town (23/9)	0-3	97
147	Bishop Sutton	v	Merthyr Town		
	(walkover for Merthyr Town – Bishop Sutton withdrawn)				
148	Mangotsfield United	v	Bristol Academy (25/9)	1-2	50

SECOND ROUND QUALIFYING

No	Home		Away	Score	Att
1	Guiseley	v	Hall Road Rangers (8/10)	1-1aet	67
	(Guiseley won 4-3 on kicks from the penalty mark)				
2	Consett	v	Newcastle Benfield (7/10)	5-1	49
3	Nelson	v	Gateshead (7/10)	0-4	45
4	Runcorn Linnets	v	Stalybridge Celtic (10/10)	1-2	104
5	Westella Hanson	v	Ashton Town (10/10)	3-1	24
6	Wrexham	v	AFC Fylde (9/10)	6-0	117
7	Sheffield	v	Macclesfield Town (10/10)	0-1	102
8	Prescot Cables	v	Chester (10/10)	1-3	160
9	Staveley MW	v	Nostell MW (7/10)	1-2	110
10	Grimsby Town	v	Harrogate Town (10/10)	3-1	
11	Abbey Hey	v	Selby Town (8/10)	3-3aet	
	(Selby Town won 5-4 on kicks from the penalty mark)				
12	Altrincham	v	Vauxhall Motors (10/10)	4-1	142
13	Warrington Town	v	Worksop Town (7/10)	7-2	78
14	Boston United	v	Lincoln City (9/10)	1-0	363
15	Ilkeston	v	St Andrews (8/10)	3-3aet	83
	(Ilkeston won 5-4 on kicks from the penalty mark)				
16	Lutterworth Athletic	v	Hinckley United		
	(walkover for Lutterworth Athletic – Hinckley United removed)				
17	Gresley	v	Mickleover Sports (9/10)	1-4	72
18	Stapenhill	v	Histon (9/10)	0-4	44
19	Halesowen Town	v	Eccleshall (9/10)	5-0	59
20	Stourbridge	v	Hereford United (9/10)	1-3	114
21	Solihull Moors	v	Rugby Town (8/10)	3-4aet	61
22	Kidderminster Harriers	v	Atherstone Town (10/10)	2-3	
23	Nuneaton Town	v	Nuneaton Griff (8/10)	5-0	
24	Worcester City	v	Boldmere St Michaels (9/10)	2-0	43
	(at Studley FC)				
25	Tipton Town	v	Pegasus Juniors (7/10)	2-3	61
26	Cornard United	v	Cambridge United (10/1)	1-6	38
27	Lowestoft Town	v	Woodbridge Town (9/10)	0-2aet	85
28	Bury Town	v	Dereham Town (10/10)	1-0aet	42
29	Fakenham Town	v	Long Melford (7/10)	3-4	45
30	Whitton United	v	Newmarket Town (10/10)	6-1	67
31	Cogenhoe United	v	Rushden & Higham United (10/10)	5-1	33
32	Barnet	v	Barton Rovers (16/10)	0-3	344
33	AFC Rushden & Diamonds	v	Stotfold (7/10)	0-4	91
34	Wellingborough Town	v	Leighton Town (9/10)	2-3aet	53
35	Luton Town	v	Corby Town (9/10)	5-1aet	138
36	Thurrock	v	Boreham Wood (10/10)	4-2	53
37	AFC Hornchurch	v	Cheshunt (10/10)	1-0	112
38	Canvey Island	v	Bishop's Stortford (9/10)	3-2	112
39	Grays Athletic	v	Bowers & Pitsea (9/10)	6-3 aet	
40	Potters Bar Town	v	Concord Rangers (7/10)	3-1	40
41	Chelmsford City	v	East Thurrock United (9/10)	5-0	145
42	Brentwood Town	v	Enfield 1893 (7/10)	4-2aet	67
43	Wingate & Finchley	v	Kings Langley (10/10)	4-0	73
44	Thamesmead Town	v	Staines Town (10/10)	3-2	20
45	Uxbridge	v	Berkhamsted (9/10)	3-2	44
46	Cockfosters	v	Harefield United (10/10)	1-4	65

47	Dulwich Hamlet	v	Metropolitan Police (8/10)	4-2	92
48	Crowborough Athletic	v	Colliers Wood United (10/10)	3-4	78
49	Sutton United	v	Eastbourne Borough (9/10)	2-0	109
50	Maidstone United	v	Corinthian (7/10)	2-0	233
51	Chipstead	v	Sevenoaks Town (9/10)	4-1	
52	Sittingbourne	v	Dartford (10/10)	0-5	83
53	Cray Wanderers	v	Bromley (10/10)	1-0	44
	(at Corinthian FC)				
54	VCD Athletic	v	Horsham (10/10)	1-0	63
55	Woking	v	Peacehaven & Telscombe (9/10)	1-0	
56	Lewes	v	Havant & Waterlooville (10/10)	0-3	76
57	Worthing	v	Burgess Hill Town (7/10)	0-3	
58	Horley Town	v	Lancing (10/10)	1-0	
59	Shoreham	v	Camberley Town (9/10)	1-3	43
60	Didcot Town	v	Binfield (10/10)	4-3aet	49
61	Wimborne Town	v	Guildford City (9/10)	0-2	63
62	Marlow	v	Aylesbury (9/10)	0-2	62
63	Aldershot Town	v	Buckingham Athletic (9/10)	2-0	102
64	Oxford City	v	Maidenhead United (8/10)	1-3	
65	Bournemouth	v	Chichester City (10/10)	2-1	88
66	Moneyfields	v	Dorchester Town (10/10)	1-0	70
67	Abingdon United	v	AFC Totton (10/10)	1-5	45
68	Farnborough	v	Hartley Wintney (10/10)	2-1	71
69	Thame United	v	Christchurch (10/10)	0-3	42
70	Tiverton Town	v	Bath City (8/10)	3-2	87
71	Bristol Academy	v	Larkhall Athletic (7/10)	8-0	33
72	Forest Green Rovers	v	Odd Down (7/10)	5-0	112
73	Yate Town	v	Weston Super Mare (9/10)	0-1	63
74	Merthyr Town	v	Cirencester Town (10/10)	3-5	39
	(at Cirencester Town FC)				

THIRD ROUND QUALIFYING

1	Warrington Town	v	Mickleover Sports (23/10	2-1	88
2	Stalybridge Celtic	v	Chester (24/10)	0-3	
3	Altrincham	v	Nostell MW (24/10)	10-3	139
4	Consett	v	Gateshead (24/10)	2-6	83
	(at Durham City FC)				
5	Macclesfield Town	v	Westella Hanson (23/10)	2-1	126
6	Wrexham	v	Selby Town (22/10)	3-0	92
7	Grimsby Town	v	Guiseley (23/10)	0-2aet	
8	Histon	v	Cogenhoe United (21/10)	5-1	103
9	Lutterworth Athletic	v	Halesowen Town (16/10)	0-3	
10	Boston United	v	Pegasus Juniors (23/10)	3-1	176
11	Atherstone Town	v	Hereford United (23/10)	2-5	51
12	Worcester City	v	Rugby Town (23/10)	1-0	35
	(at Studley FC)				
13	Ilkeston	v	Nuneaton Town (28/10)	2-0	85
14	Luton Town	v	Leighton Town (22/10)	3-0	148
15	Stotfold	v	Cambridge United (23/10)	1-1aet	91
	(Cambridge United won 3-1 on kicks from the penalty mark)				
16	Long Melford	v	Bury Town (24/10)	2-2aet	77
	(Bury Town won 9-8 on kicks from the penalty mark)				
17	Whitton United	v	Woodbridge Town (23/10)	0-5	146
18	Canvey Island	v	Dulwich Hamlet (23/10)	0-1	86
19	AFC Hornchurch	v	Grays Athletic (31/10)	1-2	72
20	Barton Rovers	v	Harefield United (25/10)	3-1	83
21	Brentwood Town	v	Potters Bar Town (21/10)	4-2	122
22	Uxbridge	v	Chelmsford City (23/10)	2-1	63
23	Thurrock	v	Wingate & Finchley (24/10)	0-1	101
24	Woking	v	Cray Wanderers (29/10)	5-3	
25	Dartford	v	Thamesmead Town (23/10)	4-2	118
26	Maidstone United	v	Sutton United (21/10)	1-1aet	222
	(Maidstone United won 6-5 on kicks from the penalty mark)				
27	Chipstead	v	Colliers Wood United (23/10)	2-2aet	
	(Chipstead won 4-2 on kicks from the penalty mark)				
28	Farnborough	v	Christchurch (24/10)	0-2	51
29	Horley Town	v	Aylesbury (23/10)	2-1	
30	AFC Totton	v	Aldershot Town (24/10)	1-0	111
31	Havant & Waterlooville	v	Burgess Hill Town (1/11)	1-7	76
32	Guildford City	v	Camberley Town (23/10)	1-3	65
33	Didcot Town	v	Bournemouth (24/10)	2-1	112
34	Maidenhead United	v	VCD Athletic (23/10)	0-0aet	
	(VCD won 4-2 on kicks from the penalty mark)				
35	Forest Green Rovers	v	Cirencester Town (28/10)	3-1	164
36	Moneyfields	v	Weston Super Mare (24/10)	0-0aet	50
	(Moneyfields won 3-1 on kicks from the penalty mark)				
37	Bristol Academy	v	Tiverton Town (30/10)	4-1	46

FIRST ROUND PROPER

1	Altrincham	v	Wrexham (5/11)	2-1	135
2	Chester	v	Chesterfield (7/11)	1-1	399
	(Chesterfield won 5-4 on kicks from the penalty mark)				
3	Tranmere Rovers	v	Gateshead (4/11)	4-4	304
	(Gateshead won 5-4 on kicks from the penalty mark)				
4	Preston North End	v	Mansfield Town (25/10)	6-1	522
5	Bury	v	Guiseley (6/11)	6-2	164
6	Accrington Stanley	v	Carlisle United (6/11)	3-1	172
7	Macclesfield Town	v	York City (30/10)	0-3	130
8	Morecambe	v	Hartlepool United (29/10)	3-1	76
9	Scunthorpe United	v	Bradford City (21/10)	0-2	215
10	Warrington Town	v	Rochdale (6/11)	2-6	165
11	Oldham Athletic	v	Sheffield United (30/10)	2-2aet	284
	(Sheffield United won 4-3 on kicks from the penalty mark)				
12	Rotherham United	v	Fleetwood Town (4/11)	1-1	590
	(Rotherham won 7-6 on kicks from the penalty mark)				
13	Notts County	v	Peterborough United (5/11)	1-2aet	268
14	Ilkeston	v	Northampton Town (6/11)	7-4aet	110
15	Hereford United	v	Milton Keynes Dons (6/11)	3-0	182
16	Walsall	v	Port Vale (5/11)	2-0	145
17	Boston United	v	Luton Town (6/11)	0-4	212
18	Wolverhampton Wanderers	v	Burton Albion (4/11)	5-0	319
19	Worcester City	v	Halesowen Town (6/11)	1-0	90
	(at Studley FC)				
20	Crewe Alexandra	v	Coventry City (11/11)	2-0	407
21	Histon	v	Shrewsbury Town (4/11)	1-2	247
22	Barton Rovers	v	Stevenage (15/11)	1-0	215
23	Chipstead	v	Horley Town (6/11)	2-1	
24	Maidstone United	v	Southend United (5/11)	2-3	354
	(at Southend United FC)				
25	AFC Totton	v	Leyton Orient (7/11)	0-3	202
26	Dulwich Hamlet	v	Brentwood Town (11/11)	4-1	60
27	Gillingham	v	Brentford (5/11)	1-3	224
28	Dartford	v	Christchurch (8/11)	6-1	108
29	Bury Town	v	Dagenham & Redbridge (4/11)	0-3	102
	(tie awarded to Bury Town – Dagenham & Redbridge removed for playing an ineligible player)				
30	Wingate & Finchley	v	Burgess Hill Town (5/11)	3-4	54
31	Crawley Town	v	Woodbridge Town (4/11)	5-0	
32	Cambridge United	v	Woking (7/11)	2-3	84
33	AFC Wimbledon	v	Colchester United (12/11)	1-4	212
34	Grays Athletic	v	Uxbridge (20/11)	5-2	41
	(at Uxbridge FC)				
35	Cheltenham Town	v	VCD Athletic (10/11)	7-1	130
36	Forest Green Rovers	v	Torquay United (4/11)	1-2	165
37	Exeter City	v	Swindon Town (6/11)	3-4	208
38	Didcot Town	v	Oxford United (30/10)	0-3	291
39	Bristol City	v	Newport County (11/11)	3-0	270
40	Portsmouth	v	Moneyfields (5/11)	12-0	948
41	Camberley Town	v	Bristol Rovers (4/11)	1-2	70
42	Plymouth Argyle	v	Bristol Academy (5/11)	4-1	316

SECOND ROUND PROPER

1	Sheffield United	v	Worcester City (20/11)	9-0	
2	Preston North End	v	York City (13/11)	5-0	611
3	Morecambe	v	Bradford City (20/11)	1-3	146
4	Ilkeston	v	Accrington Stanley (19/11)	0-1	228
5	Rochdale	v	Crewe Alexandra (20/11)	1-2	262
6	Wolverhampton Wanderers	v	Peterborough United (3/12)	1-2	298
7	Walsall	v	Altrincham (21/11)	4-0	179
8	Chesterfield	v	Hereford United (19/11)	0-1	162
9	Gateshead	v	Luton Town (18/11)	1-2	243
10	Rotherham United	v	Bury (19/11)	3-2	290
11	Grays Athletic	v	Dartford (28/11)	2-3	104
12	Shrewsbury Town	v	Bristol Rovers (16/11)	0-1	196
13	Southend United	v	Oxford United (25/11)	1-3	296
14	Torquay United	v	Chipstead (21/11)	4-1	
15	Brentford	v	Dulwich Hamlet (20/11)	2-0	420
16	Portsmouth	v	Barton Rovers (19/11)	1-0	349
17	Colchester United	v	Plymouth Argyle (20/11)	4-4aet	251
	(Plymouth Argyle won 4-2 on kicks from the penalty mark)				
18	Cheltenham Town	v	Bury Town (20/11)	9-0	160
19	Woking	v	Crawley Town (4/12)	1-2	182
20	Swindon Town	v	Leyton Orient (19/11)	1-4	197
21	Burgess Hill Town	v	Bristol City (21/11)	0-2aet	405

THIRD ROUND PROPER

1	Southampton	v	Portsmouth (10/12)	7-0	3814
2	AFC Bournemouth	v	Hereford United (19/12)	1-1aet	304
	(Hereford United won 4-3 on kicks from the penalty mark)				
3	Preston North End	v	Norwich City (11/12)	1-6aet	712
4	Bolton Wanderers	v	Sheffield United (13/12)	1-1aet	729
	(Sheffield United won 4-3 on kicks from the penalty mark)				
5	Bristol Rovers	v	Crewe Alexandra (17/12)	1-2aet	250
6	Accrington Stanley	v	West Ham United (10/12)	2-1aet	360
7	Leeds United	v	Reading (13/12)	1-3	620
8	Blackpool	v	Liverpool (18/12)	3-3aet	1061
	(Liverpool won 4-3 on kicks from the penalty mark)				
9	Burnley	v	Manchester United (16/12)	0-2	1489
10	Hull City	v	Peterborough United (18/12)	1-2	133
11	Sheffield Wednesday	v	Crystal Palace (10/12)	4-4aet	236
	(Sheffield Wednesday won 4-2 on kicks from the penalty mark)				
12	Nottingham Forest	v	Charlton Athletic (10/1)	2-3	527
13	Queens Park Rangers	v	Fulham (11/12)	1-4	227
14	Crawley Town	v	Watford (10/1)	0-2	230
15	Derby County	v	Wigan Athletic (10/12)	4-3	495
16	Leicester City	v	Rotherham United (18/12)	3-0	226
17	Ipswich Town	v	Sunderland (11/12)	1-1aet	391
	(Sunderland won 4-2 on kicks from the penalty mark)				
18	Arsenal	v	Torquay United (6/12)	5-0	472
19	Bristol City	v	Brentford (10/1)	1-0	245
20	Chelsea	v	Dartford (12/12)	4-0	342
21	Cardiff City	v	Blackburn Rovers (10/12)	1-0	410
22	Everton	v	Brighton & Hove Albion (9/12)	2-0	478
23	Tottenham Hotspur	v	Middlesbrough (2/12)	2-1	402
24	Huddersfield Town	v	Luton Town (8/12)	3-1aet	243
25	Swansea City	v	Oxford United (17/12)	1-3	118
26	Stoke City	v	Leyton Orient (9/12)	2-2aet	292
	(Stoke City won 5-4 on kicks from the penalty mark)				
27	West Bromwich Albion	v	Walsall (10/12)	2-1	565
28	Bradford City	v	Millwall (17/12)	0-3	970
29	Cheltenham Town	v	Birmingham City (17/12)	1-2	369
30	Aston Villa	v	Plymouth Argyle (10/12)	4-3	451
31	Manchester City	v	Doncaster Rovers (19/12)	4-0	241
32	Barnsley	v	Newcastle United (17/12)	1-2	

FOURTH ROUND PROPER

1	Tottenham Hotspur	v	Fulham (31/1)	2-3	520
2	Newcastle United	v	Sunderland (20/1)	4-0	3501
3	Reading	v	Crewe Alexandra (22/1)	3-3aet	604
	(Reading won 4-2 on kicks from the penalty mark)				
4	Leicester City	v	Manchester United (16/12)	0-1aet	964
5	Oxford United	v	Cardiff City (22/1)	2-3	279
6	Millwall	v	Sheffield United (20/1)	2-2aet	695
	(Sheffield United won 8-7 on kicks from the penalty mark)				
7	Southampton	v	Charlton Athletic (29/1)	1-3	513
8	Accrington Stanley	v	Bristol City (4/2)	4-1	310
9	Everton	v	Birmingham City (14/1)	4-3	538
10	West Bromwich Albion	v	Huddersfield Town (14/1)	2-4aet	274
11	Chelsea	v	Sheffield Wednesday (15/1)	4-1	404
12	Liverpool	v	Aston Villa (15/1)	3-1	392
13	Derby County	v	Stoke City (23/1)	3-1	652
14	Manchester City	v	Hereford United (14/1)	3-1aet	323
15	Watford	v	Norwich City (25/1)	3-1	472
16	Peterborough United	v	Arsenal (6/1)	1-6	1986

FIFTH ROUND PROPER

1	Cardiff City	v	Chelsea (18/2)	0-2	1150
2	Sheffield United	v	Everton (17/2)	0-2	1488
3	Charlton Athletic	v	Arsenal (21/2)	0-2	1198
	(at Ebbsfleet United FC)				
4	Reading	v	Accrington Stanley (12/2)	3-0	495
5	Manchester City	v	Fulham (19/2)	1-3	290
	(at Oldham Athletic FC)				
6	Huddersfield Town	v	Manchester United (14/2)	2-1	1385
7	Watford	v	Liverpool (19/2)	0-2	1933
8	Derby County	v	Newcastle United (16/2)	0-1	1275

SIXTH ROUND PROPER

1	Fulham	v	Huddersfield Town (18/3)	2-1	1102
2	Arsenal	v	Everton (10/3)	3-1	2725
3	Reading	v	Liverpool (12/3)	4-4aet	1349
	(Reading won 5-4 on kicks from the penalty mark)				
4	Newcastle United	v	Chelsea (11/3)	2-3	2506

SEMI FINALS 1ST LEG

1	Chelsea	v	Arsenal (10/4)	2-1	4961
2	Reading	v	Fulham (1/4)	2-2	1762

SEMI FINALS 2ND LEG

1	Arsenal	v	Chelsea	0-1	9655
2	Fulham	v	Reading (7/4)	3-2	1768

THE FINAL 1ST LEG

Fulham	v	Chelsea	3-2	4457

THE FINAL 2ND LEG

Chelsea	v	Fulham	5-3	13125

PREVIOUS TEN FINALS

				Aggregate Score
2013	Norwich City	v	Chelsea	4-2
2012	Chelsea	v	Blackburn Rovers	4-1
2011	Manchester Utd	v	Sheffield United	4-1
2010	Chelsea	v	Aston Villa	3-2
2009	Arsenal	v	Liverpool	6-2
2008	Manchester City	v	Chelsea	4-2
2007	Liverpool	v	Manchester Utd	2-2* 4-3p
2006	Liverpool	v	Manchester City	3-2
2005	Ipswich Town	v	Southampton	3-2
2004	Middlesbrough	v	Aston Villa	4-0

FIRST ROUND

1	West Riding	v	Westmorland (28/9)	7-0
2	Leicestershire & Rutland	v	Birmingham (12/10)	0-2
3	Northumberland	v	Durham (5/10)	3-1
4	Isle of Man	v	Cumberland (12/10)	1-6
5	Lancashire	v	East Riding (5/10)	2-1
6	Derbyshire	v	Lincolnshire (12/10)	1-2
7	Northamptonshire	v	Middlesex (6/10)	1-2
8	Devon	v	Dorset (12/10)	2-1 aet
9	Amateur Football Alliance	v	Gloucestershire (5/10)	4-3 aet
10	Cornwall	v	Guernsey (12/10)	4-2 aet
11	Herefordshire	v	Jersey (5/10)	1-0 aet
12	Essex	v	Oxfordshire (6/10)	5-1
13	Hertfordshire	v	London (13/10)	2-1

SECOND ROUND

1	Birmingham	v	Cheshire (2/11)	1-3
2	Liverpool	v	Manchester (12/10)	0-2
3	Staffordshire	v	West Riding (2/11)	0-3
4	Shropshire	v	Northumberland (16/11)	1-2 aet
5	North Riding	v	Nottinghamshire(9/11)	5-2
6	Sheffield & Hallamshire	v	Cumberland (3/11)	2-1
7	Lancashire	v	Lincolnshire (2/11)	4-2 aet
8	Cambridgeshire	v	Bedfordshire (6/10)	5-3
9	Sussex	v	Essex (23/11)	0-1
10	Middlesex	v	Hertfordshire (9/11)	3-1 aet
11	Worcestershire	v	Huntingdonshire (22/9)	8-1
12	Norfolk	v	Kent (2/11)	2-3
13	Herefordshire	v	Somerset (16/11)	4-1
14	Wiltshire	v	Devon (23/11)	0-4
15	Suffolk	v	Berks & Bucks (26/10)	6-1
16	Cornwall	v	Amateur Football Alliance (9/11)	1-2

THIRD ROUND

1	Devon	v	Kent (7/12)	1-0
2	Lancashire	v	Worcestershire (1/12)	3-2
3	Essex	v	Suffolk (7/12)	0-1
4	Cambridgeshire	v	Northumberland (15/12)	1-2
5	Herefordshire	v	Amateur Football Alliance (14/12)	1-4
6	West Riding	v	North Riding (23/11)	2-1 aet
7	Sheffield & Hallamshire	v	Middlesex (23/11)	5-2
8	Manchester	v	Cheshire (14/12)	0-1

FOURTH ROUND

1	Suffolk	v	Sheffield & Hallamshire (8/2)	1-1 aet
	(Suffolk won 6-5 on kicks from the penalty mark)			
2	Amateur Football Alliance	v	West Riding (15/3)	3-3 aet
	(AFA won 4-2 on kicks from the penalty mark) (at West Riding FA) (1/3, 1-1aet - AFA won 3-0 on kicks from the penalty mark – tie ordered to be replayed)			
3	Cheshire	v	Devon (18/1)	0-1 aet
4	Lancashire	v	Northumberland (18/1)	4-3

SEMI FINALS

1	Devon	v	Lancashire (22/2)	1-2
2	Suffolk	v	Amateur Football Alliance (22/2)	2-1

THE FINAL

SATURDAY 26 APRIL 2014 @ Portman Road (Ipswich FC)

Suffolk	v	Lancashire	2-3 aet	733

PREVIOUS TEN FINALS

2013	Bedfordshire FA	v	Manchester FA	4-4 aet
	(Bedfordshire FA won 4-2 on kicks from the penalty mark)			
2012	Essex FA	v	West Riding FA	4-2 aet
2011	Norfolk FA	v	Staffordshire FA	4-2
2010	Kent FA	v	Sheffield & Hallamshire	1-0
2009	Birmingham FA	v	Kent FA	2-1
2008	Suffolk FA	v	Cambridgeshire FA	2-1
2007	West Riding FA	v	Suffolk FA	1-1 aet, 4-3p
2006	Bedfordshire FA	v	Durham FA	3-2
2005	Suffolk FA	v	Hampshire FA	2-1
2004	Durham FA	v	North Riding FA	4-0

FIRST ROUND

1	Sunderland RCA Grangetown Flsts	v	Sportsmans	4-3
2	Newton Aycliffe WMC	v	Winlaton Commercial	1-3
3	Witton Park Rose & Crown	v	Stockton Rosegale N&SA	4-2
4	Barrington Arms	v	Humbledon Plains Farm	2-5
5	Hartlepool Rovers Quoit	v	Hartlepool Athletic Rovers	1-2
6	Burradon & New Fordley	v	Kelloe WMC	4-2
7	Northallerton Police	v	Hetton Lyons Cricket Club	1-3
8	HT Sports	v	Home & Bargain (27/10)	3-1
9	Seacroft WMC Athletic	v	The Warden	1-2
10	Thornhill Lees	v	Paddock	6-2
11	JOB	v	Nicosia	2-3
12	Kirkdale	v	Netherley Woodlane Legion	1-0
13	West Bowling	v	Allerton	0-1
14	Campfield	v	The Old Bank	1-2
15	Alder	v	Hessle Rangers	2-1
16	Fantail	v	Pineapple	0-3
17	Seymour	v	Thornton United	4-1
18	Drum	v	Canada	
	(walkover for Canada – Drum withdrawn)			
19	Garston	v	Larkspur	1-0
20	BRNESC	v	Lobster	0-3
21	Sutton Fields	v	Pumptec	2-1
22	Millhouse	v	Chapletown Fforde Grene	1-3
23	AFC Blackburn Leisure	v	Queens Park	1-4
24	St John Fisher OB	v	Mariners	1-2
25	Birstall Stamford	v	Sparta Moshdock	2-4
26	Gedling Inn	v	Whitwick Compass	0-3
27	Star & Garter	v	The New Welfare	7-0
28	Wymeswold	v	T8's	2-1
29	Kirkby Town	v	Sileby Athletic	5-2
30	Jacksdale MW	v	Thurmaston PWMC	7-5 aet
31	RHP Sports & Social	v	FC Brimington	3-0
32	Bilsthorpe Celtic	v	Nuthall	3-1
33	Punchbowl	v	Church Hill	2-2 aet
	(Church Hill won 7-6 on kick s from the penalty mark)			
34	Hundred Acre	v	Ledbury Allstars	11-1
35	Halfway	v	Sporting Khalsa (Sunday)	1-6
36	Plough FC Wellington	v	The Royal Hotel Sutton	7-4
37	Burnt Oak Builders Merchants	v	Manor House (3/11)	0-2
38	Upshire	v	Falcons	3-0
39	Flamstead End	v	New Salamis	1-7
40	Attero	v	Apoel	3-2
41	AC Sportsman	v	Bedfont Sunday	4-0
42	Nirankari	v	Two Touch	5-6 aet
43	Broadfields Laurels	v	Club Lewsey	3-1
44	Gadeside Rangers	v	Rayners Lane (Sunday)	0-2
45	Belstone (Sunday)	v	NLO	3-3 aet
	(Belstone won 4-2 on kicks from the penalty mark)			
46	AYFCS	v	Dee Road Rangers	4-4 aet
	(AYFCS won 5-4 on kicks from the penalty mark)			
47	St Josephs (Luton)	v	North Wembley	2-1 aet
48	Hillbarn Athletic	v	AFC Kumazi Strikers (10/11)	1-3
	(20/10 - tie abandoned after 33 mins due to waterlogged pitch, 1-1)			
49	Lambeth All Stars	v	Putney Town (27/10)	4-1
50	Branksome Railway	v	Kings Tamerton CA	4-2
51	The Windmill	v	All Saints	3-1

11 Clubs with Byes to the Second Round

Albion - Artois United - Bar Sol Ona - Bolton Woods - Buttershaw Whitestar - Co-op Green Man - FC Houghton Centre - Hammer - Hartlepool Lion Hillcarter - Lebeqs Tavern Courage - Loughborough Saints.

2 Clubs Exempt to the Second Round

Barnes Albion - Oyster Martyrs.

SECOND ROUND

1	Lobster	v	Queens Park	1-0
2	Canada	v	Oyster Martyrs	0-5
3	Witton Park Rose & Crown	v	Sunderland RCA Grangetown Flor	0-0 aet
	(Witton Park Rose & Crown won 7-6 on kicks from the penalty mark)			
4	Chapeltown Fford Grene	v	Garston	3-1
5	Seymour	v	Humbledon Plains Farm	3-4 aet
6	Mariners	v	Kirkdale	2-1
7	Hetton Lyons CC	v	Burradon & New Fordley	5-2
8	Buttershaw Whitestar	v	Nicosia	3-1
9	The Warden	v	Thornhill Lees	2-6
10	Allerton	v	Alder	4-0
11	Hartlepool Lion Hillcarter	v	Pineapple	0-3
12	The Old Bank	v	HT Sports	2-4
13	Sutton Fields	v	Winlaton Commercial	1-2
14	Hartlepool Athletic Rovers	v	Bolton Woods	6-3 aet
15	Albion	v	RHP Sports & Social	4-1
16	Wymeswold	v	Hundred Acre	0-1
17	Plough FC Wellington	v	Kirkby Town	5-1
18	Loughborough Saints	v	Sporting Khalsa (Sunday) (24/11)	1-1 aet
	(Sporting Khalsa won 4-3 on kicks from the penalty mark)			
19	Church Hill	v	Star & Garter	0-3
20	Jacksdale MW	v	Sparta Moshdock	
	(walkover for Sparta Moshdock – Jacksdale MW withdrawn)			
21	Bilsthorpe Celtic	v	Whitwick Compass	1-2 aet
22	Lambeth All Stars	v	FC Houghton Centre	0-3
23	New Salamis	v	Broadfields Laurels	2-0 aet
24	Two Touch	v	AC Sportsman	5-1
25	Attero	v	AFC Kumazi Strikers	1-4
26	Rayners Lane (Sunday)	v	St Josephs (Luton)	1-0
27	Belstone (Sunday)	v	Manor House	7-2
28	Co-op Green Man	v	AYFCS	1-4 aet
29	Hammer	v	Upshire	0-5
30	Barnes Albion	v	Artois United	
	(walkover for Barnes Albion – Artois United withdrawn)			
31	Bar Sol Ona	v	Branksome Railway	0-4
32	Lebeqs Tavern Courage	v	The Windmill	8-0

THIRD ROUND

1	HT Sports	v	Oyster Martyrs	1-2
2	Allerton	v	Hetton Lyons CC	1-0
3	Mariners	v	Lobster	2-1
4	Thornhill Lees	v	Hartlepool Athletic Rovers	6-0
5	Chapeltown Fforde Grene	v	Buttershaw Whitestar	2-0
6	Pineapple	v	Humbledon Plains Farm	1-5
7	Winlaton Commercial	v	Witton Park Rose & Crown (5/1)	3-6 aet
8	Whitwick Compass	v	Albion	6-1
9	FC Houghton Centre	v	Sparta Moshdock	1-0
10	Star & Garter	v	Hundred Acre	1-1 aet
	(Hundred Acre won 4-2 on kicks from the penalty mark)			
11	Plough FC Wellington	v	Sporting Khalsa (Sunday)	5-3
12	Two Touch	v	Lebeqs Tavern Courage	0-3
13	Upshire	v	Barnes Albion	1-0
14	New Salamis	v	Belstone (Sunday)	1-1 aet
	(New Salamis won 7-6 on kicks from the penalty mark)			
15	Branksome Railway	v	AFC Kumazi Strikers	4-2
16	AYFCS	v	Rayners Lane (Sunday)	4-2 aet

FOURTH ROUND

1	Witton Park Rose & Crown	v	Oyster Martyrs (2/2)	0-4
2	Humbledon Plains Farm	v	Mariners	6-0
3	Allerton	v	Whitwick Compass (16/2)	5-1
4	Thornhill Lees	v	Chapel Town Fforde Greene	2-3 aet
5	AYFCS	v	Plough FC Wellington (23/2)	2-4 aet
6	Hundred Acre	v	FC Houghton Centre	2-0
7	New Salamis	v	Branksome Railway	1-2 aet
8	Lebeqs Tavern Courage	v	Upshire (2/2)	2-5

FIFTH ROUND

1	Chapel Town Fforde Grene	v	Humbledon Plains Farm	3-6 aet
2	Allerton	v	Oyster Martyrs (23/2)	1-2
3	Branksome Railway	v	Plough FC Wellington (2/3)	0-5
4	Upshire	v	Hundred Acre	3-3 aet

(Hundred Acre won 3-1 on kicks from the penalty mark

SEMI FINALS

1	Oyster Martyrs	v	Plough FC Wellington	3-2 aet	258

(@ Marine FC)

2	Humbledon Plains Farm	v	Hundred Acre	4-2 aet	268

(@ Hartlepool United FC)

THE FINAL

SUNDAY 27 APRIL 2014

Humbledon Plains Farm	v	Oyster Martyrs	5-2	433

(@ Ewood Park - Blackburn Rovers FC)

FA INTER-LEAGUE CUP

EXTRA PRELIMINARY ROUND

1	Lancashire Amateur	v	Wearside (4/5)	3-6
	(tie reversed – at Boldon CA FC)			
2	Lancashire & Cheshire Amateur	v	Teesside	2-3
	(at Maine Road FC)			
3	West Cheshire	v	Manchester (20/3)	0-1
4	Cheshire	v	Northern Football Alliance	1-0
	(at Witton Albion FC)			
5	Essex Olympian	v	Peterborough & District (30/3)	1-2
6	Suffolk & Ipswich	v	West Riding County Amateur	2-3aet
	(at Hadleigh United FC)			
7	Cambridgeshire County	v	Essex & Suffolk Border	1-2
	(at Soham Town Rangers FC)			
8	Northamptonshire Combination	v	Yorkshire Amateur (4/5)	0-1
	(at Sileby Rangers FC)			
9	Kent County	v	Sussex County (Div 3) (2/3)	3-2aet
10	Middlesex County	v	Spartan South Midlands (Div 2)	
	(tie awarded to Middlesex County – Spartan South Midlands withdrawn)			
11	Somerset County	v	Gloucestershire County	3-1
	(at Clevedon Town FC)			
12	Reading	v	Oxfordshire Senior (17/4)	1-1aet
	(Oxfordshire Senior won 6-5 on kicks from the penalty mark - at Newbury FC)			
13	Northampton Town	v	Anglian Combination	1-1aet
	(Anglian Combination won 5-4 on kicks from the penalty mark)			

Exempt to First Round
Jersey Football Combination (Holders), Isle of Man League (Runners-up)
Byes to First Round - Brighton, Hove & District - Cumberland County - Humber Premier - Liverpool County Premier - Bedfordshire County - Birmingham AFA - Lincolnshire - West Yorkshire - Amateur Football Combination - Hertfordshire Senior County - Mid Sussex - Southern Amateur - Surrey Elite Intermediate - Worthing & District - Devon & Exeter - Dorset Premier - Guernsey - Hampshire - Wiltshire.

PRELIMINARY ROUND

1	Lincolnshire League	v	West Yorkshire League (7/9)	2-1
2	Brighton, Hove & District	v	Mid Sussex League (14/9)	3-1
	(at Shoreham FC)			

FIRST ROUND

1	Cumberland County League	v	Isle of Man League (21/9)	0-5
2	Humber Premier League	v	Teesside League (19/10)	4-2
3	Cheshire League	v	Wearside League (12/10)	0-1
4	Manchester League	v	Liverpool County League (12/10)	2-1
5	Essex & Suffolk Border League	v	West Riding CA League (26/10)	1-2
6	Birmingham AFA	v	Anglian Combination (5/10)	1-4
	(tie awarded to Birmingham AFA – Anglian Combination removed)			
7	Bedfordshire County League	v	Yorkshire Amateur League (19/10)	1-7
8	Peterborough & District League	v	Lincolnshire League (28/9)	0-2
9	Amateur Football Combination	v	Surrey Elite League (19/10)	1-2
10	Southern Amateur League	v	Kent County League (12/10)	5-6 aet
11	Herts Senior County League	v	Brighton Hove & District League(19/10)	4-2
12	Worthing & District League	v	Middlesex County League	
	(walkover for Worthing & District League – Middlesex County League withdrawn)			
13	Oxfordshire Senior League	v	Hampshire Premier League (2/10)	1-1 aet
	(Hampshire Premier League won 5-4 on kicks from the penalty mark - at Kidlington FC)			
14	Jersey Football Combination	v	Guernsey Football League (12/10)	3-1
15	Devon & Exeter League	v	Somerset County League (19/10)	5-4 aet
16	Wiltshire League	v	Dorset Premier League (9/10)	0-5

SECOND ROUND

1	Yorkshire Amateur League	v	Isle of Man League (7/12)	2-3 aet
2	Humber Premier League	v	Wearside League (14/12)	2-1 aet
3	Birmingham AFA	v	Lincolnshire League (30/11)	1-2
4	Manchester League	v	West Riding County Amateur (30/11)	0-3
5	Worthing & District League	v	Hampshire Premier League (23/11)	3-2
6	Kent County League	v	Dorset Premier League (14/12)	0-1
7	Surrey Elite Intermediate Lge	v	Herts Senior County League (7/12)	2-0
	(tie awarded to Herts Senior County - Surrey Elite removed for playing ineligible players)			
8	Devon & Exeter League	v	Jersey Football Combination (16/11)	1-2

THIRD ROUND

1	Lincolnshire League	v	Humber Premier League (25/1)	0-2
2	Isle of Man League	v	West Riding County Amateur Lge (25/1)	3-1
3	Dorset Premier League	v	Jersey Football Combination (25/1)	1-0
4	Herts Senior County League	v	Worthing & District League (15/2)	3-0

SEMI FINALS

1	Herts Senior County League	v	Dorset Premier League (22/3)	4-2 aet
	(at Colney Heath FC)			
2	Humber Premier League	v	Isle of Man League (22/3)	1-2

THE FINAL

Isle of Man League	v	Herts Senior County League	3-2

PRELIMINARY ROUND

1	Folly Lane	v	Brereton Town	3-2
2	Moulton	v	Roade	4-3
3	Fleet Town	v	Christchurch	4-2
4	Wootton Bassett Town	v	Cheltenham Civil Service (15/9)	1-0
	(at Wootton Bassett Town FC)			

FIRST QUALIFYING ROUND

1	Whitley Bay	v	Middlesbrough Lionesses	2-1
2	Boldon	v	Lowick United	5-1
3	Rutherford	v	Forest Hall	5-0
4	Workington Reds	v	Tynedale	0-5
5	Kendal Town	v	Birtley St Joseph	3-5
6	Willington	v	Seaton Carew	0-5
7	Peterlee St Francis	v	York City	3-2aet
8	Prudhoe Town	v	Kader FC Ladies	0-2
9	Birtley Town	v	Abbeytown	1-2aet
10	Whickham Fellside	v	Penrith AFC Ladies	2-2aet
	(Penrith won 3-0 on kicks from the penalty mark)			
11	Sheffield Wednesday	v	Nettleham	1-6
12	Handsworth	v	Lepton Highlanders	1-0
13	Hull City	v	Brighouse Sports	4-1
14	Ossett Albion	v	Bradford Park Avenue	3-2
15	Farsley AFC Ladies	v	Steel City Wanderers	0-4
16	Hemsworth MW	v	Malet Lambert	3-5
17	Blackpool FC Ladies	v	Burnley FC Ladies	0-3
18	Brighouse Town	v	CMB Ladies	4-1
19	Morecambe	v	Padiham FC Ladies	10-1
20	Middleton Athletic	v	Blackpool Wren Rovers	2-3
21	Chester City	v	Preston North End	
	(walkover for Chester City – Preston North End unable to fulfil fixture)			
22	Birkenhead	v	Crewe Alexandra	3-4
23	Bury Girls & Ladies	v	Woolton	1-2aet
24	City Of Manchester	v	Accrington Girls & Ladies	5-5aet
	(City of Manchester won 2-1 on kicks from the penalty mark)			
25	Asfordby Amateurs	v	Arnold Town	1-5
26	Sandiacre Town	v	West Bridgford	7-1
27	Dronfield Town	v	Ruddington Village	2-4
28	Teversal	v	Oadby & Wigston Dynamo	0-4
29	Rise Park	v	Ellistown	2-3
30	St George's	v	Long Eaton United	1-3
31	Coventrians	v	Malvern Town	2-2aet
	(Malvern Town won on kicks from the penalty mark)			
32	Walsall	v	Pelsall Villa	7-6aet
33	Crusaders	v	FC Reedswood Ladies	1-2
34	Allscott	v	TNS	0-4
35	Pegasus	v	Folly Lane	4-0
36	Cottage Farm Rangers	v	Kenilworth Town KH	1-7
37	Bilbrook	v	Lye Town	4-2
38	Netherton United	v	Peterborough Northern Star	0-15
39	Rothwell Corinthians	v	Raunds Town (29/9)	1-4
	(22/9 tie abandoned after 15 mins due to serious injury to a player, 0-0)			
40	Bar Hill	v	Moulton	2-1aet
41	Peterborough Sports	v	Brackley Sports	9-0
42	Kettering Town	v	Bedford	2-6
43	Southendian	v	Brandon	5-0
44	Colchester Town	v	Haverhill Rovers	5-0
45	Assandun Vikings	v	Waveney Wanderers	0-2
46	Lowestoft Town	v	AFC Sudbury Ladies	6-1
47	Bungay Town	v	West Billericay	2-3
48	FC Clacton Ladies	v	Billericay Town	0-15
49	Sawbridgeworth Town	v	St Albans City	1-2
50	KIKK United	v	Haringey Borough	7-0
51	Barking	v	Flitwick	6-0
52	Stevenage Borough	v	Hoddesdon Owls	5-2
53	Royston Town	v	Wootton Blue Cross	2-1
54	Maidenhead United	v	Newbury	6-2
55	Tower Hill	v	Leverstock Green	0-7
56	Colne Valley	v	Old Actonians	1-4aet
57	Oxford City	v	Marlow	2-0
58	Leighton United Vixens	v	Wealdstone	5-1
59	AFC Dunstable Ladies	v	Ascot United	4-0
60	Hemel Hempstead Town	v	Banbury United	7-0
61	Headington	v	Bracknell Town	0-3
62	Herne Bay	v	Anchorians	3-1
63	Rusthall	v	Rottingdean Village	4-1
64	London Corinthians	v	Maidstone United	2-0
65	Aylesford	v	Regents Park Rangers	5-0
66	Dartford YMCA	v	Haywards Heath Town	2-6
67	Bexhill United	v	Sheppey & Sheerness United	
	(walkover for Bexhill United – Sheppey & Sheerness United unable to fulfil fixture)			
68	Eastbourne	v	Eastbourne Town	0-6
69	Prince Of Wales	v	Tunbridge Wells Ridgewaye	
	(walkover for Prince Of Wales – Tunbridge Wells Ridgewaye withdrawn)			
70	Crystal Palace	v	Parkwood Rangers	7-4
71	Fulham Compton	v	South Park	3-0
72	Battersea & Wandsworth	v	Abbey Rangers	8-1
73	AFC Wimbledon Ladies	v	Worthing Town	5-1
74	Crawley Wasps	v	Milford & Witley	9-0
75	Westfield	v	Knaphill	11-0
76	Chertsey Town	v	AFC Wimbledon Ladies Dev	0-3
77	Andover New Street	v	Basingstoke Town	0-1
78	Southampton Women	v	New Forest	2-2aet
	(Southampton Women won 5-3 on kicks from the penalty mark)			
79	Poole Town	v	Fleet Town	6-1
80	Gosport Borough	v	Weymouth	6-0
81	Aldershot Town	v	Parley Sports	0-3
82	Cirencester Town	v	Bitton	2-1
83	Quedgeley Wanderers	v	Swindon Spitfires	0-18
84	Downend Flyers	v	Forest of Dean	3-1
85	Bristol Ladies Union	v	Wootton Bassett Town	11-0
86	Cheltenham Town	v	Pen Mill	9-0
87	Brislington	v	Stoke Lane Athletic	2-1
88	Frome Town	v	Ilminster Town	5-5aet
	(Ilminster Town won 3-0 on kicks from the penalty mark)			
89	Gloucester City	v	Longlevens	10-2
90	Bridgwater Town	v	St Nicholas	1-5
91	Truro City	v	Launceston	4-0
92	Torquay United	v	Bude Town	4-0

SECOND QUALIFYING ROUND

1	Boldon	v	Rutherford	4-1
2	Tynedale	v	Seaton Carew	4-1
3	Birtley St Joseph	v	Whitley Bay	0-2
4	Penrith AFC Ladies	v	Kader FC Ladies	2-2aet
	(Kader FC Ladies won 4-3 on kicks from the penalty mark)			
5	Abbeytown	v	Peterlee St Francis	1-8
6	Brighouse Town	v	Woolton	4-1

7	Burnley FC Ladies	v	City Of Manchester	4-5aet
8	Ossett Albion	v	Malet Lambert	0-3
9	Nettleham	v	Crewe Alexandra	6-0
10	Blackpool Wren Rovers	v	Chester City	1-1aet
	(Blackpool Wren Rovers won 5-4 on kicks from the penalty mark)			
11	Morecambe	v	Steel City Wanderers	5-3aet
12	Hull City	v	Handsworth	3-0
13	Walsall	v	Bilbrook	4-2
14	Malvern Town	v	Raunds Town	0-4
15	Oadby & Wigston Dynamo	v	Long Eaton United	4-5
16	Arnold Town	v	Kenilworth Town KH	4-3aet
17	TNS	v	Pegasus	3-1
18	FC Reedswood Ladies	v	Ellistown	4-3
19	Ruddington Village	v	Sandiacre Town	1-8
20	Bar Hill	v	Billericay Town	0-4
21	Bedford	v	Stevenage Borough	5-2
22	AFC Dunstable Ladies	v	Royston	3-1
23	Southendian	v	Peterborough Northern Star	1-3
24	Lowestoft Town	v	Peterborough Sports	4-0
25	Barking	v	West Billericay	3-1
26	Colchester Town	v	Leighton United Vixens	1-3
27	Hemel Hempstead Town	v	Leverstock Green	1-8
28	KIKK United	v	Battersea & Wandsworth	9-0
29	St Albans City	v	Waveney Wanderers	5-0
30	AFC Wimbledon Ladies	v	Oxford City	1-1aet
	(Oxford City won 3-2 on kicks from the penalty mark)			
31	London Corinthians	v	Herne Bay	5-1
32	Maidenhead United	v	Eastbourne Town	5-1
33	Bracknell Town	v	Crawley Wasps	3-1
34	Prince Of Wales	v	AFC Wimbledon Ladies Dev	1-2
35	Haywards Heath Town	v	Rusthall	2-3
36	Crystal Palace	v	Old Actonians	2-1aet
37	Westfield	v	Aylesford	7-2
38	Fulham Compton	v	Bexhill United	3-1
39	Gosport Borough	v	Bristol Ladies Union	2-0
40	St Nicholas	v	Southampton Women	11-0
41	Torquay United	v	Swindon Spitfires	0-4
42	Cirencester Town	v	Parley Sports	2-4
43	Truro City	v	Poole Town	4-0
44	Cheltenham Town	v	Ilminster Town	2-1
45	Gloucester City	v	Brislington	4-1
46	Downend Flyers	v	Basingstoke Town	0-1

THIRD QUALIFYING ROUND

1	Boldon	v	Peterlee St Francis (10/11)	1-3
2	Chester Le Street Town	v	Kader FC Ladies	10-1
3	Leeds City Vixens	v	Whitley Bay (10/11)	2-2aet
	(Whitley Bay won 3-1 on kicks from the penalty mark)			
4	Tynedale	v	Middlesbrough (10/11)	2-6
5	Brighouse Town	v	City Of Manchester	8-8aet
	(Brighouse Town won 5-4 on kicks from the penalty mark)			
6	Tranmere Rovers	v	Wakefield FC Ladies	6-0
7	Chorley	v	Morecambe (17/11)	2-1
	(tie reversed)			
8	Huddersfield Town	v	Stockport County (10/11)	2-1aet
9	Liverpool Feds	v	Malet Lambert	
	(walkover for Liverpool Feds – Malet Lambert removed)			
10	Blackpool Wren Rovers	v	Mossley Hill	4-2
11	Sheffield United Community	v	Cheadle Heath Nomads	3-2
12	Hull City	v	Curzon Ashton	4-2
13	Nettleham	v	Rotherham United	3-1
14	Arnold Town	v	Loughborough Foxes	0-1
15	Raunds Town	v	TNS	3-3aet
	(TNS won 4-3 on kicks from the penalty mark)			
16	Walsall	v	Sandiacre Town	1-4
17	Loughborough Students	v	Leafield Athletic	7-2
18	Leicester City Ladies	v	Leicester City Women	2-2aet
	(Leicester City Ladies won 3-2 on kicks from the penalty mark)			
19	FC Reedswood Ladies	v	Mansfield Town	3-2
20	Copsewood Coventry	v	Long Eaton United	7-0
21	Cambridge Women's	v	Lowestoft Town	5-1
22	Barking	v	Leverstock Green	1-4
23	KIKK United	v	Luton Town	2-2aet
	(KIKK United won 3-1 on kicks from the penalty mark)			
24	Norwich City	v	Peterborough Northern Star	7-1
25	C&K Basildon	v	Brentwood Town	4-0
26	Ebbsfleet United	v	Ipswich Town	5-3
27	Leighton United Vixens	v	Milton Keynes Dons	2-2aet
	(MK Don won 4-2 on kicks from the penalty mark)			
28	Enfield Town	v	St Albans City	6-2
29	AFC Dunstable Ladies	v	Denham United	1-5
30	Billericay Town	v	Bedford	0-0aet
	(Bedford won 5-4 on kicks from the penalty mark)			
31	Rusthall	v	University Of Portsmouth	1-3
32	Bracknell Town	v	Crystal Palace	2-2aet
	(Crystal Palace won 4-2 on kicks from the penalty mark)			
33	Maidenhead United	v	Fulham Compton	2-1
34	Oxford City	v	Queens Park Rangers	0-5
35	Shanklin	v	Gosport Borough	0-1
36	Westfield	v	London Corinthians	4-1
37	Chichester City	v	AFC Wimbledon Ladies Development	8-0
38	Truro City	v	Plymouth Argyle	0-8
39	Swindon Spitfires	v	Cheltenham Town	3-2
40	St Nicholas	v	Basingstoke Town	3-2
41	Swindon Town	v	Forest Green Rovers	0-3
42	Keynsham Town Development	v	Larkhall Athletic	1-2
43	Gloucester City	v	Southampton Saints	1-0
44	Exeter City	v	Parley Sports	6-0

FIRST ROUND

1	Chester-Le-Street Town	v	Tranmere Rovers	0-1
2	Middlesbrough	v	Sheffield United Community	3-2
3	Whitley Bay	v	Brighouse Town	2-1
4	Chorley	v	Huddersfield Town	1-6
5	Blackpool Wren Rovers	v	Hull City	1-0
6	Liverpool Feds	v	Peterlee St Francis	6-0
7	TNS	v	Sandiacre Town	4-0
8	FC Reedswood	v	Leicester City Ladies	2-1aet
9	Loughborough Students	v	Cambridge Women's	5-2
10	Copsewood Coventry	v	Nettleham	1-0
11	Loughborough Foxes	v	Milton Keynes Dons	1-3aet
12	Crystal Palace	v	Maidenhead United	2-0
13	C&K Basildon	v	KIKK United	2-1
14	Bedford	v	Westfield	
	(walkover for Bedford – Westfield failed to fulfil fixture)			
15	Leverstock Green	v	Queens Park Rangers	0-5
16	Ebbsfleet United	v	Denham United	2-5aet
17	Enfield Town	v	Norwich City	3-2

18	Exeter City	v	Gosport Borough	3-1
19	Forest Green Rovers	v	St Nicholas	0-1
20	Plymouth Argyle	v	University Of Portsmouth	
	(walkover for Plymouth Argyle – University Of Portsmouth failed to fulfil fixture)			
21	Larkhall Athletic	v	Swindon Spitfires	3-0
22	Chichester City	v	Gloucester City	6-0

SECOND ROUND

1	TNS	v	Stoke City	0-7
2	FC Reedswood	v	Copsewood Coventry (26/1)	1-2
3	Loughborough Students	v	Leeds United	1-4
4	Preston North End	v	Sporting Club Albion	
	(walkover for Preston North End – Sporting Club Albion withdrawn)			
5	Huddersfield Town	v	Coventry City	1-4
6	Derby County	v	Newcastle United (19/1)	2-0
7	Middlesbrough	v	Tranmere Rovers (19/1)	4-0
8	Nottingham Forest	v	Wolverhampton Wanderers	3-0
9	Whitley Bay	v	Blackburn Rovers	0-1
10	Sheffield FC Ladies	v	Liverpool Feds (2/2)	10-0
11	Bradford City	v	Blackpool Wren Rovers (16/2)	7-0
12	Chichester City	v	Enfield Town (2/2)	6-0
13	Lewes	v	Denham United	1-0
14	Portsmouth FC Ladies	v	Keynsham Town (26/1)	4-0
15	Charlton Athletic	v	Milton Keynes Dons (19/1)	3-0
16	Queens Park Rangers	v	Gillingham	1-2aet
17	Chesham United	v	Larkhall Athletic	1-2
18	Exeter City	v	Plymouth Argyle (2/2)	1-6
19	C&K Basildon	v	West Ham United (9/2)	3-3aet
	(West Ham United won 4-2 on kicks from the penalty mark)			
20	Brighton & Hove Albion	v	Tottenham Hotspur	3-2
21	Cardiff City	v	St Nicholas	3-0
22	Bedford	v	Crystal Palace	2-3

THIRD ROUND

1	Plymouth Argyle	v	Brighton & Hove Albion (16/2)	0-4
2	Charlton Athletic	v	Sheffield FC Ladies (16/2)	0-6
3	Nottingham Forest	v	Gillingham (16/2)	0-1
4	Preston North End	v	Yeovil Town (23/2)	3-0
5	Bradford City	v	Cardiff City (2/3)	0-1
6	Portsmouth FC Ladies	v	Lewes	3-0
7	West Ham United	v	Watford (23/2)	1-5
8	Durham Women's	v	Chichester City	4-0
9	Crystal Palace	v	Derby County (16/2)	2-0
10	Coventry City	v	Stoke City	3-1
11	Leeds United	v	London Bees (23/2)	1-3
12	Blackburn Rovers	v	Middlesbrough (16/2)	3-0
13	Copsewood Coventry	v	Larkhall Athletic	3-2aet
14	Aston Villa	v	Doncaster Rovers Belles	0-2
15	Millwall Lionesses	v	Reading Women (16/2)	1-2
16	Sunderland	v	Oxford United	5-1

FOURTH ROUND

1	Cardiff City	v	London Bees	1-0
2	Coventry City	v	Brighton & Hove Albion	2-0
3	Sunderland	v	Watford	4-1
4	Gillingham	v	Preston North End	1-0
5	Reading Women	v	Blackburn Rovers	2-0 aet
6	Crystal Palace	v	Portsmouth FC Ladies	2-3
7	Durham Women's	v	Sheffield FC Ladies	3-1
8	Doncaster Rovers Belles	v	Copsewood Coventry	4-1

FIFTH ROUND

1	Manchester City	v	Reading Women	2-1
2	Notts County	v	Coventry City	2-1
3	Arsenal	v	Gillingham	2-0
4	Birmingham City	v	Doncaster Rovers Belles	3-1
5	Portsmouth FC Ladies	v	Durham Women's	2-1
6	Chelsea	v	Bristol Academy	2-1 aet
7	Cardiff City	v	Everton	1-3
8	Sunderland	v	Liverpool	0-2

SIXTH ROUND

1	Portsmouth FC Ladies	v	Notts County	0-2
2	Liverpool	v	Everton (26/4)	0-2
3	Manchester City	v	Chelsea	1-3
4	Birmingham City	v	Arsenal (4/5)	1-2

SEMI FINALS

1	Chelsea	v	Arsenal	3-5 aet	877
(@ Woking FC)					
2	Notts County	v	Everton	1-2	638
(@ Alfreton Town FC)					

THE FINAL

Sunday 01 June 2014 - @ Milton Keynes Dons FC

Arsenal	v	Everton	2-0	15098

NATIONAL LEAGUES

NORTH	P	W	D	L	F	A	GD	Pts
1 Manchester Futsal Club	10	8	2	0	68	18	50	26
2 Sheffield Futsal Club	10	7	1	2	76	42	34	22
3 Middlesbrough Futsal Club	10	6	0	4	91	65	26	18
4 Liverpool Futsal Club	10	5	1	4	44	41	3	16
5 Leeds & Wakefield Futsal Club	10	2	0	8	26	80	-54	6
6 F.S Derby Willows	10	0	0	10	37	96	-59	0

MIDLANDS	P	W	D	L	F	A	GD	Pts
1 Oxford City Lions Futsal Team	12	10	1	1	94	29	65	31
2 Birmingham Futsal Club	12	8	2	2	98	70	28	26
3 Loughborough Student Futsal Club	12	8	1	3	80	55	25	25
4 University of Bath Futsal Club	12	8	0	4	91	62	29	24
5 Birmingham Tigers Futsal Club	12	3	0	9	53	79	-26	9
6 Gloucester Futsal Revolution	12	3	0	9	36	86	-50	9
7 University of Plymouth Futsal Club	12	0	0	12	46	117	-71	0

SOUTH	P	W	D	L	F	A	GD	Pts
1 Baku United FC	14	13	1	0	130	15	115	40
2 FC Baltic United	14	11	1	2	87	40	47	34
3 Helvecia Futsal Club	14	11	0	3	89	43	46	33
4 West London Futsal	14	7	0	7	75	96	-21	21
5 City of London Futsal Club	14	5	0	9	52	88	-36	15
6 Genesis Futsal Club	14	3	1	10	50	93	-43	10
7 FC Siauliai	14	2	2	10	45	100	-55	8
8 Kaunas FC	14	1	1	12	51	104	-53	4

SUPER LEAGUE

GROUP A	P	W	D	L	F	A	GD	Pts
1 Manchester Futsal Club	4	4	0	0	28	9	19	12
2 West London Futsal	4	1	1	2	19	19	0	4
3 Birmingham Futsal Club	4	0	1	3	10	29	-19	1

GROUP B	P	W	D	L	F	A	GD	Pts
1 Baku United FC	4	4	0	0	37	7	30	12
2 Sheffield Futsal Club	4	1	1	2	19	38	-19	4
3 University of Bath Futsal Club	4	0	1	3	14	25	-11	1

GROUP C	P	W	D	L	F	A	GD	Pts
1 Helvecia Futsal Club	4	4	0	0	25	10	15	12
2 Oxford City Lions Futsal Team	4	2	0	2	31	13	18	6
3 Middlesbrough Futsal Club	4	0	0	4	13	46	-33	0

GROUP D	P	W	D	L	F	A	GD	Pts
1 Loughborough Student Futsal Club	4	3	1	0	27	10	17	10
2 FC Baltic United	4	2	1	1	19	14	5	7
3 Liverpool Futsal Club	4	0	0	4	13	35	-22	0

GRAND FINAL

Semi Finals

Manchester Futsal Club	v	Loughborough Student Futsal Club	5-4
Baku United FC	v	Helvecia Futsal Club	3-1

Third Place Play-off

Helvecia Futsal Club	v	Loughborough Student Futsal Club	2-1

The Final

Baku United FC	v	Manchester Futsal Club	5-1

ENGLAND FUTSAL RESULTS 2013-14

Date	Opponent	H/A	Competition	Result
October 2013				
25	Qatar	A	Friendly	**W** 1-3
26	Qatar	A	Friendly	D 6-6
November 2013				
28	Lithuania	H	Friendly	**W** 2-1
29	Lithuania	H	Friendly	L 0-2
February 2014				
23	Sweden	A	Friendly	D 3-3
24	Sweden	A	Friendly	L 2-3
March 2014				
24	Wales	A	Friendly	**W** 7-4
June 2014				
5	Cyprus	H	Four Nations International	**W** 5-0
6	Qatar	H	Four Nations International	**W** 3-0
8	USA	H	Four Nations International	D 1-1

Click Back in Time!

Over 37 years of publishing the Non-League Club Directory has filled a room full of information and photographs covering the game we know and love.

What we intend, over time, is to create a website that shares with you everything we have accumulated, which we hope will bring back some fond memories of season's gone by.

A unique look back at how the game has evolved since the 1940s will also make for interesting reading, including league tables from season's gone by.

Log on to **www.non-leagueclubdirectory.co.uk** today and see how many faces from teams gone by you recognise

COUNTY FOOTBALL ASSOCIATION CONTACTS

AMATEUR FOOTBALL ALLIANCE
CEO: Mike Brown
Address: Unit 3, 7 Wenlock Road, London, N1 7SL
Tel: 020 8733 2613
Fax: 020 7250 1338
Website: www.amateur-fa.com
Email: info@amateur-fa.com
Chairman: John Maskell

ARMY FA
Secretary: Major Billy Thomson
Address: Ministry of Defence (ASCB), Clayton Barracks, Thornhill Road, Aldershot, Hampshire, GU11 2BG
Tel: 01252 348 571/4
Fax: 01252 348 630/b
Website: www.armyfa.com
Email: info@armyfa.com
Chairman: Brigadier G I Mitchell

BEDFORDSHIRE FA
CEO: Dan Robathan
Address: Century House, Skimpot Road, Dunstable, Bedfordshire, LU5 4JU
Tel: 01582 565 111
Fax: 01582 565 222/b
Website: www.bedfordshirefa.com
Email: daniel.robathan@bedfordshirefa.com
Chairman: Richard Robinson

BERKS & BUCKS FA
CEO: Liz Verrall
Address: 15a London Street, Faringdon, Oxon, SN7 7HD
Tel: 01367 242 099
Fax: 01367 242 158
Website: www.berks-bucksfa.com
Email: liz.verrall@berks-bucksfa.com
Chairman: David Grainge

BIRMINGHAM FA
CEO: Mike Pennick
Address: Ray Hall Lane, Great Barr, Birmingham, B43 6JF
Tel: 0121 357 4278
Fax: 0121 358 1661
Website: www.birminghamfa.com
Email: info@birminghamfa.com
Chairman: Mike Penn

CAMBRIDGESHIRE FA
Chief Executive: Chris Pringle
Address: Bridge Road, Impington, Cambridgeshire, CB24 9PH
Tel: 01223 209 025
Fax: 01223 209 030
Website: www.cambridgeshirefa.com
Email: info@cambridgeshirefa.com
Chairman: Bill Coad

CHESHIRE FA
CEO: Simon Gerrard
Address: Hartford House, Hartford Moss Recreation Centre, Northwich, Cheshire, CW8 4BG
Tel: 01606 871 166
Fax: 01606 871 292
Website: www.cheshirefa.com
Email: info@cheshirefa.com
Chairman: David Edmunds

CORNWALL FA
CEO: Dawn Aberdeen
Address: Kernow House, 15 Callywith Gate, Launceston Road, Bodmin, Cornwall, PL31 2RQ
Tel: 01208 269010
Fax: 01208 892665
Website: www.cornwallfa.com
Email: secretary@cornwallfa.com
Chairman: Geoff Lee

CUMBERLAND FA
CEO: Ben Snowdon
Address: 17 Oxford Street, Workington, Cumbria, CA14 2AL
Tel: 01900 872 310
Fax: 01900 616 470
Website: www.cumberlandfa.com
Email: ben.snowdon@cumberlandfa.com
Chairman: Fred Conway

DERBYSHIRE FA
CEO: Dawn Heron
Address: Units 8-9 Stadium Business Ct, Millenium Way, Pride Park, Derby, DE24 8HZ
Tel: 01332 361 422
Fax: 01332 360 130
Website: www.derbyshirefa.com
Email: info@derbyshirefa.com
Chairman: Dave Heron

DEVON FA
CEO: Paul Morrison
Address: Coach Road, Newton Abbot, Devon, TQ12 1EJ
Tel: 01626 332 077
Fax: 01626 336 814/b
Website: www.devonfa.com
Email: info@devonfa.com
Chairman: Bernard Leach

DORSET FA
CEO: Sue Hough
Address: County Ground, Blanford Close, Hamworthy, Poole, BH15 4BF
Tel: 01202 682 375
Fax: 01202 666 577
Website: www.dorsetfa.com
Email: footballoperations@dorsetfa.com
Chairman: Geoff Pike

DURHAM FA
CEO: John Topping
Address: Chester le Street Riverside South, Chester le Street, Co. Durham, DH3 3SJ
Tel: 01913 872 929
Website: www.durhamfa.com
Email: info@durhamfa.com
Chairman: Frank Pattison

EAST RIDING FA
CEO: Adam Lowthorpe
Address: Roy West Centre, 220 Inglemire Lane, Hull, HU6 7TS
Tel: 01482 221 158
Fax: 01482 221 169
Website: www.eastridingfa.com
Email: info@eastridingfa.com
Chairman: John Suddards

ENGLISH SCHOOLS FA
Secretary: John Read
Address: 4 Parker Court, Staffordshire Technology Park, Stafford, ST18 0WP
Tel: 01785 785 970
Fax: 01785 785 971
Website: www.esfa.co.uk
Email: info@schoolsfa.com
Chairman: Phil Harding

ESSEX FA
CEO: Phil Sammons
Address: The County Office, Springfield Lyons Approach, Springfield, Chelmsford, Essex, CM2 5EY
Tel: 01245 465 271
Fax: 01245 393 089
Website: www.essexfa.com
Email: info@essexfa.com
Chairman: Eddie Rhymes

GLOUCESTERSHIRE FA
CEO: David Neale
Address: Oaklands Park, Almondsbury, Bristol, BS32 4AG
Tel: 01454 615 888
Fax: 01454 618 088
Website: www.gloucestershirefa.com
Email: info@gloucestershirefa.com
Chairman: Roger Burden

GUERNSEY FA
County Secretary: Gary Roberts
Address: GFA Headquarters, Corbet Field, Grand Fort Road, St Sampsons, Guernsey, GY2 4FG
Tel: 01481 200 443
Fax: 01481 200 451
Website: www.guernseyfa.com
Email: info@guernseyfa.com
Chairman: Chris Schofield

HAMPSHIRE FA
CEO: Neil Cassar
Address: Winklebury Football Complex, Winklebury Way, Basingstoke, RG23 8BF
Tel: 01256 853 000
Fax: 01256 357 973
Website: www.hampshirefa.com
Email: info@hampshirefa.com
Chairman: John Ward

HEREFORDSHIRE FA
CEO: Jim Lambert
Address: County Ground Offices, Widemarsh Common, Hereford, HR4 9NA
Tel: 01432 342 179
Fax: 01432 279 265
Website: www.herefordshirefa.com
Email: val.lambert@herefordshirefa.com
Chairman: Bill Shorten

HERTFORDSHIRE FA
CEO: Nick Perchard
Address: County Ground, Baldock road, Letchworth, Hertfordshire, SG6 2EN
Tel: 01462 677 622
Fax: 01462 677 624
Website: www.hertfordshirefa.com
Email: secretary@hertfordshirefa.com

HUNTINGDONSHIRE FA
Secretary: Mark Frost
Address: Cromwell Chambers, 8 St Johns Street, Huntingdon, Cambridgshire, PE29 3DD
Tel: 01480 414 422
Fax: 01480 447489
Website: www.huntsfa.com
Email: info@huntsfa.com
Chairman: Maurice Armstrong

ISLE OF MAN FA
CEO: Frank Stennett
Address: The Bowl, Douglas, Isle of Man, IM2 1AD
Tel: 01624 615 576
Fax: 01624 615 578
Website: www.isleofmanfa.com
Email: ann.garrett@isleofmanfa.com
Chairman: Tony Jones

JERSEY FA
CEO: Neville Davidson
Address: Springfield Stadium, St Helier, Jersey, JE2 4LF
Tel: 01534 730 433
Fax: 01534 500 029
Website: www.jerseyfa.com
Email: neville.davidson@jerseyfa.com
President: Phil Austin

KENT FA
CEO: Paul Dolan
Address: Invicta House, Cobdown Park, London Road, Ditton, Nr Aylesford, Kent, ME20 6DQ.
Tel: Governance 01622 791850, Development 01622 792140
Fax: 01622 790658
Website: www.kentfa.com
Email: info@kentfa.com
Chairman: Barry Bright

LANCASHIRE FA
CEO: David Burgess
Address: The County Ground, Thurston Road, Leyland, Preston, PR25 2LF
Tel: 01772 624 000
Fax: 01772 624 700
Website: www.lancashirefa.com
Email: secretary@lancashirefa.com
Chairman: Brett Warburton

LEICESTERSHIRE & RUTLAND FA
CEO: Keith Murdoch
Address: Holmes Park, Dog & Gun Lane, Whetstone, Leicestershire, LE8 6FA
Tel: 01162 867 828
Fax: 01162 864 858
Website: www.leicestershirefa.com
Email: keith.murdoch@leicestershirefa.com
Chairman: David Jamieson

LINCOLNSHIRE FA
Secretary: John Griffin
Address: Deepdale Enterprise Park, Deepdale Lane, Nettleham, Lincoln, LN2 2LL
Tel: 01522 524 917
Fax: 01522 528 859
Website: www.lincolnshirefa.com
Email: secretary@lincolnshirefa.com
Chairman: Grahame Lyner

LIVERPOOL FA
CEO: David Pugh
Address: Liverpool Soccer Centre, Walton Hall Park, Walton Hall Avenue, Liverpool, L4 9XP
Tel: 01515 234 488
Fax: 01515 234 477
Website: www.liverpoolfa.com
Email: info@liverpoolfa.com
Chairman: Tommy Lloyd

LONDON FA
CEO: David Fowkes
Address: 11 Hurlington Business Park, Sulivan Road, Fulham, London, SW6 3DU
Tel: 020 7610 8360
Fax: 020 7610 8370
Website: www.londonfa.com
Email: info@londonfa.com
Chairman: Tony Sharples

MANCHESTER FA
CEO: Colin Bridgford
Address: Manchester BT Academy, Silchester Drive, Manchester, M40 8NT
Tel: 01616 047 620
Fax: 01616 047 622
Website: www.manchesterfa.com
Email: info@manchesterfa.com
Chairman: Jack Green

MIDDLESEX FA
CEO: Peter Clayton
Address: 39 Roxborough Road, Harrow, Middlesex, HA1 1NS
Tel: 020 8515 1919
Fax: 020 8515 1910
Website: www.middlesexfa.com
Email: info@middlesexfa.com
Chairman: John Taylor

NORFOLK FA
CEO: Shaun Turner
Address: 11 Meridian Way, Thorpe St Andrew, Norwich, NR7 0TA
Tel: 01603 704 050
Fax: 01603 704 059
Website: www.norfolkfa.com
Email: info@norfolkfa.com
Chairman: Richard King

NORTHAMPTONSHIRE FA
CEO: Kevin Shoemake
Address: 9 Duncan Close, Red House Square, Moulton Park, Northampton, NN3 6WL
Tel: 01604 670 741
Fax: 01604 670 742
Website: www.northamptonshirefa.com
Email: N/A
Chairman: Bob Cotter

NORTH RIDING FA
CEO: Tom Radigan
Address: Broughton Road, Stokesley, Middlesborough, TS9 5NY
Tel: 01642 717 770
Fax: 01642 717 776
Website: www.northridingfa.com
Email: info@northridingfa.com
Chairman: Len Scott

NORTHUMBERLAND FA
CEO: Clive Oliver
Address: Whitley Park, Whitley Road, Newcastle upon Tyne, NE12 9FA
Tel: 01912 700 700
Fax: 01912 700 700
Website: www.northumberlandfa.com
Email: clive.oliver@northumbderlandfa.com
Chairman: Alan Wright

NOTTINGHAMSHIRE FA
CEO: Elaine Oram
Address: Unit 6b, Chetwynd Business Park, Chilwell, Nottinghamshire, NG9 6RZ
Tel: 0115 983 7400
Fax: 0115 946 1977
Website: www.nottinghamshirefa.com
Email: info@nottinghamshirefa.com
Chairman: Malcolm Fox

OXFORDSHIRE FA
CEO: Ian Mason
Address: Unit 3, Witan Park, Avenue 2, Station Lane, Witney, Oxfordshire, OX28 4FH
Tel: 01993 894400
Fax: 01993 772 191
Website: www.oxfordshirefa.com
Email: Ian.Mason@oxfordshirefa.com
Chairman: Terry Williams

RAF FA
Secretary: Vince Williams
Address: RAF FA, RAF Brize Norton, Carterton, Oxfordshire, OX18 3LX
Tel: 01993 895 559
Fax: 01993 897 752
Website: www.raffootball.co.uk
Email: info@royalairforcefa.com
Chairman: Wg Cdr Keith Watts

ROYAL NAVY FA
CEO: Lt Cdr Steve Johnson
Address: HMS Temeraire, Burnaby Road, Portsmouth, Hampshire, PO1 2HB
Tel: 02392 722 671
Fax: 02932 724 923
Website: www.royalnavyfa.com
Email: Steve.Johnson@NavyFA.com
Chairman: Steve Dainton

SHEFFIELD & HALLAMSHIRE FA
CEO: Roger Reade
Address: Clegg House, 69 Cornish Place, Cornish Street, Shalesmoor, Sheffield, S6 3AF
Tel: 01142 414 999
Fax: 01142 414 990
Website: www.sheffieldfa.com
Email: roger.reade@sheffieldfa.com
Chairman: Brian Jones

SHROPSHIRE FA
CEO: Roy Waterfield
Address: The New Stadium, Oteley Road, Shrewsbury, Shropshire, SY2 6ST
Tel: 01743 362 769
Fax: 01743 270 494
Website: www.shropshirefa.com
Email: roy.waterfield@shropshirefa.com
Chairman: David Ralphs

SOMERSET FA
CEO: Jon Pike
Address: Charles Lewin House, Unit 10 Landmark House, Wirral Business Park, Glastonbury, BA6 9FR
Tel: 01458 832359
Fax: 01458 835588
Website: www.somersetfa.com
Email: info@somersetfa.com
Chairman: Peter Hockley

STAFFORDSHIRE FA
CEO: Brian Adshead
Address: Dyson Court, Staffordshire Technology Park, Beaconside, Stafford, ST18 0LQ
Tel: 01785 256 994
Fax: 01785 279 837
Website: www.staffordshirefa.com
Email: secretary@staffordshirefa.com

SUFFOLK FA
CEO: Laura Smith
Address: The Buntings, Cedars Park, Stowmarket, Suffolk, IP14 5GZ
Tel: 01449 616 606
Fax: 01449 616 607
Website: www.suffolkfa.com
Email: laura.smith@suffolkfa.com
Chairman: David Porter

SURREY FA
CEO: Caroline McRoyall
Address: Connaught House, 36 Bridge Street, Leatherhead, Surrey, KT22 8BZ
Tel: 01372 373 543
Fax: 01372 361 310
Website: www.surreyfa.com
Email: caroline.mcroyall@surreyfa.com
Chairman: Les Pharo

SUSSEX FA
CEO: Ken Benham
Address: SCFA Headquarters, Culver Road, Lancing, West Sussex, BN15 9AX
Tel: 01903 753 547
Fax: 01903 761 608
Website: www.sussexfa.com
Email: info@sussexfa.com

WESTMORLAND FA
CEO: Peter Ducksbury
Address: 35/37 Appleby Road, Kendal, LA9 6ET
Tel: 01539 730 946
Fax: 01539 740 567
Website: www.westmorlandfa.com
Email: info@westmorlandfa.com
Chairman: Gary Aplin

WEST RIDING FA
CEO: Hannah Simpson
Address: Fleet Lane, Woodlesford, Leeds, LS26 8NX
Tel: 01132 821 222
Fax: 01132 821 525
Website: www.wrcfa.com
Email: hannah.simpson@wrcfa.com
Chairman: Barry Chaplin

WILTSHIRE FA
Secretary: Kirsty Frior
Address: Units 2/3 Dorcan Business Village, Murdock Road, Dorcan, Swindon, SN3 5HY
Tel: 01793 486 047
Fax: 01793 692 600
Website: www.wiltshirefa.com
Email: kirsty.frior@wiltshirefa.com
Chairman: Richard Gardiner

WORCESTERSHIRE FA
CEO: Nichola Trigg
Address: Craftsman House, De Salis Drive, Hampton Lovett Industrial Estate, Droitwich, Worcestershire, WR9 0QE
Tel: 01905 827 137
Fax: 01905 798 963
Website: www.worcestershirefa.com
Email: nichola.trigg@worcestershirefa.com
Chairman: Roy Northall

COUNTY & MISCELLANEOUS CUPS

A.F.A. Senior Cup

Quarter finals

Alleyn Old Boys	v	Old Suttonians	1-1, 3-4p
BB Eagles	v	Old Wilsonians	1-2
West Wickham	v	Winchmore Hill	0-1
Kings Old Boys	v	Albanian	2-5

Semi-finals

Winchmore Hill	v	Old Suttonians	2-0
Albanian	v	Old Wilsonians	0-4

Final

Old Wilsonians	v	Winchmore Hill	3-1

A.F.A. Middlesex/Essex Senior Cup

Quarter finals

Winchmore Hill	v	Actonians Association	1-0
Old Hamptonians	v	Polytechnic	0-3
Old Salvatorians	v	Albanian	0-1
Enfield Old Grammarians	v	Civil Service	1-0 aet

Semi-finals

Polytechnic	v	Winchmore Hill	2-3
Enfield Old Grammarians	v	Albanian	0-2

Final

Albanian	v	Winchmore Hill	0-1

A.F.A. Surrey/Kent Senior Cup

Quarter finals

Weirside Rangers	v	Old Wokingians	3-1
Nottsborough	v	Carshalton	6-1
Old Tenisonians	v	Lloyds AFC	2-2, 5-4p
Honourable Artillery Company	v	Bank of England	4-0

Semi-finals

Nottsborough	v	Weirside Rangers	3-1
Honourable Artillery Company	v	Old Tenisonians	3-2

Final

Honourable Artillery Company	v	Nottsborough	2-2, 2-4p

Aldershot FA & Invitational Senior Cup

Quarter Finals

Ash United	v	Eversley & California	HW
Badshot Lea	v	Camberley Town	0-3
Reading Town	v	Hartley Wintney	3-2
Alresford Town	v	Sandhurst Town	5-1

Semi-Finals

Reading Town	v	Alresford Town	0-3
Camberley Town	v	Ash United	3-2

Final

Camberley Town	v	Alresford Town	3-4

Arthur Dunn Cup

Quarter Finals

Old Tonbridgians	v	Old Salopians	3-0
Old Westminsters	v	Old Carthusians	0-5
Lancing Old Boys	v	Old Reptonians	4-2
Old Brentwoods	v	Old Foresters	4-4 aet
Old Foresters	v	Old Brentwoods	1-0

Arthur Dunn Cup continued...

Semi-Finals

Old Tonbridgians	v	Old Carthusians	1-2
Lancing Old Boys	v	Old Foresters	0-2

Final

Old Carthusians	v	Old Foresters	3-0

Baisingstoke Senior Cup

Quarter Finals

Andover New Street	v	Alton Town	1-4
AFC Aldermaston	v	Hungerford Town	HW
Tadley Calleva	v	Overton United	1-0
Fleet Town	v	Welly Old Boys	5-0

Semi Finals

Fleet Town	v	AFC Aldermaston	1-2
Tadley Calleva	v	Alton Town	2-1

Final

Tadley Calleva	v	AFC Aldermaston	3-2

Bedfordshire Senior Challenge Cup

Quarter Finals

Leighton Town	v	Luton Town	0-2
Biggleswade United	v	Biggleswade Town	0-4
Arlesey Town	v	Barton Rovers	1-2
AFC Kempston Rovers	v	Amphill Town	0-1

Semi Finals

Ampthill Town	v	Biggleswade Town	1-2
Barton Rovers	v	Luton Town	0-0, 4-5p

Final

Luton Town	v	Biggleswade Town	1-2

Bedfordshire Senior Trophy

Quarter Finals

The 61 FC (Luton)	v	Sharnbrook	5-1
Shillington	v	Bedford	0-4
Lidlington United Sports Club	v	Wootton Blue Cross	0-5
Crawley Green	v	Potton United	2-1

Semi Finals

The 61 FC (Luton)	v	Bedford	2-3
Wootton Blue Cross	v	Crawley Green	0-3

Final

Crawley Green	v	Bedford	2-3

Bedfordshire Premier Cup

Final

Biggleswade Town	v	Luton Town	1-1, 2-3p

Bedfordshire Intermediate Cup

Final

Crawley Green Reserves	v	Elstow Abbey	2-0

Bedfordshire Junior Cup

Final

Southcott Village R.A.	v	Caddington Rangers	1-2

Bedford FC - Bedfordshire Senior Trophy winners. Photo: Gordon Whttington.

Crawley Green Reserves - Bedforshire Intermediate Cup winners. Photo: Gordon Whittington.

Caddington Rangers - Bedfordshire Junior Cup winners. Photo: Gordon Whttington.

Berks & Bucks Senior Cup

Quarter Finals

Slough Town	v	Wycombe Wanderers	0-3
Chesham United	v	Milton Keynes Dons	3-1 aet
Beaconsfield SYCOB	v	Marlow	3-1
Aylesbury United	v	Burnham	1-0

Semi Finals

Aylesbury United	v	Chesham United	1-3
Wycombe Wanderers	v	Beaconsfield SYCOB	3-3, 2-3p

Final

Beaconsfield SYCOB	v	Chesham United	0-1

Berks & Bucks Senior Trophy

Quarter Finals

Abingdon United	v	Sandhurst Town	2-1
Windsor	v	Shrivenham	7-1
Reading Town	v	Holmer Green	5-1
Binfield	v	Flackwell Heath	1-0

Semi Finals

Binfield	v	Windsor	1-2
Abingdon United	v	Reading Town	0-1

Final

Reading Town	v	Windsor	0-3

Berks & Bucks Intermediate Cup

Final

AFC Aldermaston	v	Hale Leys United	1-2 aet

Birmingham Senior Cup

Quarter Finals

Banbury United	v	Tamworth	0-1
Stourbridge	v	West Bromwich Albion	1-2
Hednesford Town	v	Birmingham City	4-3 aet
Bedworth United	v	Burton Albion	0-1

Semi Finals

Tamworth	v	Hednesford Town	5-2
Burton Albion	v	West Bromwich Albion	0-2

Final

West Bromwich Albion	v	Tamworth	2-1

Cambridgeshire Professional Cup

Final

Histon	v	Cambridge City	1-0

Cambridgeshire Invitation Cup

Quarter Finals

Histon	v	Over Sports	2-1 aet
Wisbech Town	v	CRC	1-2
Cambridge City	v	Linton Granta	3-2 aet
Soham Town Rangers	v	Foxton	9-3

Semi-Finals

Histon	v	CRC	2-4
Cambridge City	v	Soham Town Rangers	2-4

Final

CRC	v	Soham Town Rangers	1-6

Channel Islands - Muratti Vase

Final

Jersey	v	Guernsey	1-4

Cheshire Senior Cup

Quarter Finals

Tranmere Rovers	v	1874 Northwich	1-0
Hyde FC	v	Northwich Victoria	0-2
Altrincham	v	Stalybridge Celtic	2-1
Chester	v	Macclesfield Town	0-2

Semi Finals

Northwich Victoria	v	Macclesfield Town	1-0
Tranmere Rovers	v	Altrincham	2-0

Final

Northwich Victoria	v	Tranmere Rovers	2-1

Cornwall Senior Cup

Quarter Finals

Launceston	v	Saltash United	1-2 aet
AFC St Austell	v	St Day	6-3
Wendron United	v	Bodmin Town	0-3
St Blazey	v	Godolphin Atlantic	1-0

Semi Finals

Bodmin Town	v	Saltash United	2-1
AFC St Austell	v	St Blazey	3-1

Final

AFC St Austell	v	Bodmin Town	1-1, 5-3p

Cumberland Senior Cup

Quarter Finals

Silloth	v	Aspatria	1-3
Keswick	v	Cleator Moor Celtic	4-2
Workington Red Star	v	Penrith AFC	1-4
Netherhall	v	Celtic Nation	0-1

Semi-Finals

Celtic Nation	v	Penrith AFC	2-1
Keswick	v	Aspatria	0-1

Final

Aspatria	v	Celtic Nation	0-3

Derbyshire Senior Challenge Cup

Quarter Finals

Borrowash Victoria	v	Chesterfield	3-0
Buxton	v	Ilkeston	0-1 aet
Shirebrook Town	v	Glossop North End	1-3
Heanor Town	v	Graham Street Prims	3-2

Semi-Finals

Ilkeston	v	Heanor Town	2-0
Borrowash Victoria	v	Glossop North End	0-6

Final

Glossop North End	v	Ilkeston	0-2

The victorious Hale Leys United after their win over AFC Aldermaston in the final of the Berks & Bucks Intermediate Cup played at Newport Pagnell Town.
Photo: Arthur Evans.

A near miss as Hale Leys hit the post during the Berks & Bucks Intermediate Final.
Photo: Arthur Evans.

Devon St Lukes Cup

Quarter Finals

Plymouth Argyle	v	Exeter City	1-1, 0-3p
Witheridge	v	Torquay United	2-0
Barnstaple Town	v	Tiverton Town	0-2
Plymouth Parkway	v	Cullompton Rangers	11-1

Semi Finals

Plymouth Parkway	v	Exeter City	3-3, 5-3p
Tiverton Town	v	Witheridge	4-3

Final

Plymouth Parkway	v	Tiverton Town	2-0

Devon Premier Cup

Quarter Finals

Appledore	v	Willand Rovers	5-0
Tiverton Town Reserves	v	Newtown	1-2
Upton Athletic	v	Watcombe Wanderers	1-3
Brixham AFC	v	Teignmouth	4-2

Semi Finals

Watcombe Wanderers	v	Newtown	3-0
Brixham AFC	v	Appledore	3-0

Final

Watcombe Wanderers	v	Brixham AFC	3-0

Devon Senior Cup

Quarter Finals

Dartmouth	v	Honiton Town	7-1
Bow Amateur AFC	v	Park United	2-6 aet
East Allington United	v	Morley Rangers	3-1
Ashwater	v	Exwick Villa	1-3

Semi Finals

Park United	v	Exwick Villa	2-6
Dartmouth	v	East Allington United	4-1

Final

Dartmouth	v	Exwick Villa	4-2

Dorset Senior Cup

Quarter Finals

Poole Town	v	Wimborne Town	3-0
Hamworthy United	v	Dorchester Town	4-1
Weymouth	v	Bridport	4-0
Verwood Town	v	Gillingham Town	0-2

Semi Finals

Weymouth	v	Hamworthy United	2-4
Poole Town	v	Gillingham Town	2-0

Final

Poole Town	v	Hamworthy United	2-0

Dorset Senior Trophy

Quarter Finals

Blanford United Reserves	v	Kangaroos	2-1
Poole Borough Reserves	v	Sturminster Newton United	1-2
Sturminster Marshall	v	Hamworthy United Reserves	4-3
Upwey and Broadwey	v	Witchampton United	1-5

Dorset Senior Trophy continued...

Semi Finals

Witchampton United	v	Sturminster Marshall	1-2
Blanford United Reserves	v	Sturminster Newton United	2-1

Final

Blanford United Reserves	v	Sturminster Marshall	0-2

Durham Senior Challenge Cup

Quarter Finals

Spennymoor Town	v	Gateshead	2-1
West Auckland Town	v	Billingham Synthonia	6-2
Shildon AFC	v	Dunston UTS	2-1 aet
Consett AFC	v		4-2

Semi-Finals

Shildon	v	Consett AFC	3-1
West Auckland Town	v	Spennymoor Town	0-1

Final

Shildon	v	Spennymoor Town	2-1

East Riding Senior Cup

Semi Finals

North Ferriby United	v	Hull City	3-0
Beverley Town	v	Bridlington Town	0-1

Final

North Ferriby United	v	Bridlington Town	5-2

Essex Senior Cup

Quarter Finals

Braintree Town	v	Harlow Town	3-1
Colchester United	v	Thurrock	3-2
Concord Rangers	v	Canvey Island	4-0
AFC Hornchurch	v	Dagenham & Redbridge	1-0

Semi Finals

Colchester United	v	Concord Rangers	0-1
AFC Hornchurch	v	Braintree Town	1-1, 4-5p

Final

Braintree Town	v	Concord Rangers	1-2

Essex Premier Cup

Quarter Finals

Kelvedon Hatch	v	Gas Recreation	7-3
May & Baker Eastbrook Co.	v	Rayleigh Town	3-2
Frenford Senior	v	Harold Wood Athletic	1-2 aet
Manford Way	v	Newbury Forest	0-3

Semi Finals

Newbury Forest	v	Harold Wood Athletic	3-1
Kelvedon Hatch	v	May & Baker Eastbrook Community	2-1

Final

Kelvedon Hatch	v	Newbury Forest	1-3

Northwich Victoria. Photo: Keith Clayton.

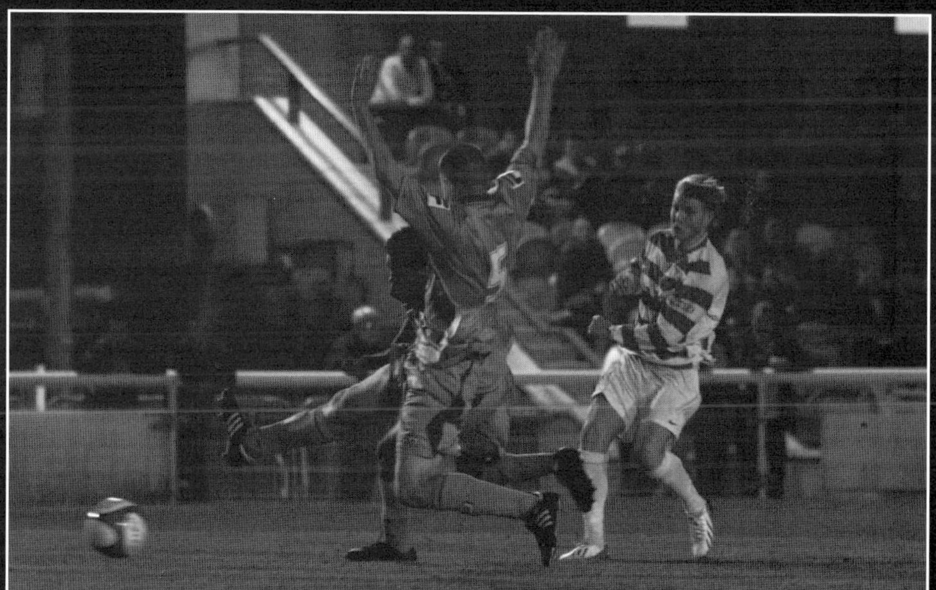

Cheshire Senior Cup Final - Summerskill (Northwich) shoots home the second goal against Tranmere Rovers. Photo: Keith Clayton.

Gloucestershire Senior Challenge Cup

Quarter Finals

Yate Town	v	Bristol Rovers Reserves	3-0
Forest Green Rovers	v	Cheltenham Town Reserves	1-2
Cinderford Town	v	Bristol City Reserves	0-2
Bishops Cleeve	v	Mangotsfield United	0-2

Semi Finals

Bristol City Reserves	v	Cheltenham Town Reserves	4-0
Mangostsfield United	v	Yate Town	2-2, 4-1p

Final

Mangotsfield United	v	Bristol City Reserves	3-0

Gloucestershire Challenge Trophy

Quarter Finals

Winterbourne United	v	Tuffley Rovers	4-1
Cadbury Heath	v	Slimbridge AFC	5-0
Bristol Manor Farm	v	Lydney Town	2-3
Hallen	v	Southmead Athletic	5-5, 3-1p

Semi Finals

Hallen	v	Lydney Town	6-0
Cadbury Heath	v	Winterbourne United	3-0

Final

Cadbury Heath	v	Hallen	1-1, 4-5p

Hampshire Senior Cup

Quarter Finals

AFC Portchester	v	Petersfield Town	3-1
Gosport Borough	v	AFC Bournemouth	2-0
Havant & Waterlooville	v	Farnborough	3-0
Whitchurch United	v	Basingstoke Town	1-2

Semi Finals

Gosport Borough	v	Basingstoke Town	2-3
Havant & Waterlooville	v	AFC Portchester	4-0

Final

Havant & Waterlooville	v	Basingstoke Town	2-3 aet

Herefordshire Challenge Cup

Quarter Finals

Hinton	v	Fownhope	4-0
Lads Club	v	Pegasus Juniors	1-3
Ledbury Town	v	Bromyard Town	3-0
Ewyas Harold	v	Westfields	0-6

Semi Finals

Hinton	v	Pegasus Juniors	0-4
Ledbury Town	v	Westfields	1-2

Final

Pegasus Juniors	v	Westfields	1-3

Herts Senior Challenge Cup

Quarter Finals

Bishop's Stortford	v	Barnet	3-0
Hitchin Town	v	Stevenage	1-0
Boreham Wood	v	Watford	2-0
Hemel Hempstead Town	v	St Albans City	4-3

Semi Finals

Bishop's Stortford	v	Hemel Hempstead Town	3-0
Hitchin Town	v	Boreham Wood	0-1

Final

Bishop's Stortford	v	Boreham Wood	1-1, 1-3p

Hertfordshire Senior Centenary Trophy

Quarter Finals

Bedmond Sports & Social	v	Wodson Park	3-2
Baldock Town	v	FC Broxbourne Borough	0-3
Codicote	v	Belstone	1-2
Sun Sports	v	Whitwell AFC	3-1

Semi Finals

FC Broxbourne Borough	v	Belstone	2-3 aet
Bedmond Sports & Social	v	Sun Sports	2-4

Final

Sun Sports	v	Belstone	0-1

Huntingdonshire Senior Cup

Round One

Eynesbury Rovers	v	Yaxley	4-2
St Neots Town Youth & Saints (U21)	v	St Ives Town	0-6
Huntingdon Town	v	Godmanchester Rovers	1-1, 8-7p

Semi Finals

St Ives Town	v	Eynesbury Rovers	4-1
St Neots Town	v	Huntingdon Town	4-1

Final

St Neots Town	v	St Ives Town	2-0

Isle of Man FA Cup

Quarter Finals

Marown	v	Ramsey	1-8
Peel	v	Pulrose United	7-0
St Marys	v	Corinthians	8-0
DHSOB	v	St Georges	1-4

SEMI-FINALS

Ramsey	v	Peel	2-0
St Marys	v	St Georges	1-5

FINAL

Ramsey	v	St Georges	2-10

Kent Senior Cup

Quarter Finals

Dartford	v	Dover Athletic	0-3
Tunbridge Wells	v	Ebbsfleet United	1-3
Whitstable Town	v	Maidstone United	1-0
Bromley	v	Hythe Town	HW

Semi Finals

Dover Athletic	v	Bromley	3-2
Whitstable Town	v	Ebbsfleet United	0-2

Final

Ebbsfleet United	v	Dover Athletic	4-0

Kent Senior Trophy

Quarter Finals

Bridon Ropes	v	Beckenham Town	0-1
Corinthian	v	Hollands & Blair	0-1
Fleet Leisure	v	West Wickham	3-0
Phoenix Sports	v	Ashford United	1-1, 2-3p

Semi Finals

Fleet Leisure	v	Beckenham Town	2-3 aet
Hollands & Blair	v	Ashofrd United	0-1

Final

Ashford United	v	Beckenham Town	0-4

Lancashire Challenge Cup

Quarter Finals

Bamber Bridge	v	Bacup & Rossendale Borough	4-0
Chorley	v	Ramsbottom United	2-0
Kendal Town	v	AFC Darwen	2-3
AFC Fylde	v	Nelson	3-2

Semi Finals

AFC Fylde	v	Bamber Bridge	2-0
AFC Darwen	v	Chorley	0-2

Final

Chorley	v	AFC Fylde	1-4

Leicestershire Challenge Cup

Quarter Finals

Oadby Town	v	Loughborough University (w/o)	
Quorn	v	Harborough Town	2-1 aet
Colaville Town	v	Barwell	2-1
Thurnby Nirvana	v	Blaby & Whetstone Athletic	1-2

Semi Finals

Quorn	v	Loughborough University	3-0
Blaby & Whetstone Athletic	v	Coalville Town	2-1

Final

Quorn	v	Blaby & Whetstone Athletic	0-2

Leicestershire Senior Cup

Quarter Finals

Coalville Town Reserves	v	Lutterworth Athletic	2-3
St Andrews	v	Bardon Hill Sports	4-2
Quorn Reserves	v	Ashby Ivanhoe	3-1
Desford	v	Barwell Reserves	2-1

Semi Finals

Quorn Reserves	v	Desford	5-0
St Andrews (w/o)	v	Lutterworth Athletic	

Final

Quorn Reserves	v	St Andrews	0-2

Lincolnshire Senior Trophy

Quarter Finals

Deeping Rangers	v	Grantham Town	0-1
Stamford AFC	v	Spalding United	1-1, 5-4p
Lincoln United	v	Bottesford Town	1-1, 4-5p
Cleethorpes Town	v	Brigg Town	0-1

Lincolnshire Senior Trophy continued...

Semi Finals

Grantham Town	v	Stamford AFC	0-1
Brigg Town	v	Bottesford Town	2-0

Final

Brigg Town	v	Stamford AFC	3-3, 5-4p

Liverpool Senior Cup

Quarter Finals

Bootle	v	Cammell Laird	1-0
Skelmersdale United	v	Southport	3-3, 4-5p
Marine	v	Everton	1-2
Burscough	v	Tranmere Rovers	1-2

Semi Finals

Bootle	v	Everton	0-0, 7-6p
Tranmere Rovers	v	Southport	5-3 aet

Final

Tranmere Rovers	v	Bootle	2-0

Liverpool Challenge Cup

Quarter Finals

South Liverpool	v	West Everton Xaviers	3-2
Garswood United	v	Waterloo Dock	2-0
Eagle Sports	v	Old Xaverians	1-2
Page Celtic	v	Aigburth Peoples Hall	4-2

Semi Finals

Old Xaverians	v	South Liverpool	3-4 aet
Garswood United	v	Page Celtic	1-1, 3-0p

Final

Garswood United	v	South Liverpool	2-1

London Senior Cup

Quarter Finals

Dulwich Hamlet	v	Metropolitan Police	3-4
Wingate & Finchley	v	Redbridge	5-1
Tooting & Mitcham United	v	Cray Valley	1-1, 7-8p
AFC Wimbledon	v	Bromley	HW

Semi Finals

Cray Valley	v	AFC Wimbledon	1-2
Metropolitan Police	v	Wingate & Finchley	3-0

Final

AFC Wimbledon	v	Metrolpolitan Police	2-1

London Senior Trophy

Quarter Finals

Bridon Ropes	v	Kent Football United	2-1
Peckham Town	v	Corinthian Casuals Reserves	2-3 aet
Metrogas	v	Enfield Town (U21)	2-4
Cockfosters Reserves	v	Erith Town Reserves	2-0

Semi Finals

Bridon Ropes	v	Enfield Town (U21)	2-1
Corinthian Casuals Reserves	v	Cockfosters Reserves	2-0

Final

Corinthian Casuals Reserves	v	Bridon Ropes	1-2 aet

Manchester Premier Cup

Final

Hyde FC	v	Trafford	2-2, 2-4p

Middlesex Senior Challenge Cup

Quarter Finals

Hampton & Richmond B.	v	Northwood	6-1
Staines Town	v	Hendon	2-3
Ashford Town (Middx)	v	Harefield United	1-2
AFC Hayes	v	Wealdstone	1-2

Semi Finals

Hendon	v	Hampton & Richmond B.	3-4
Wealdstone	v	Harefield United	4-0

Final

Hampton & Richmond B.	v	Wealdstone	3-2

Middlesex Premier Cup

Quarter Finals

Staines Lammas	v	AFC Hayes	5-3
Hampton & Richmond B. Res.	v	Bedfont & Feltham	1-2
Rayners Lane	v	Hanworth Villa Reserves	2-2, 4-2p
Northwood Reserves	v	Hanwell Town Reserves	0-6

Semi Finals

Bedfont & Feltham	v	Hanwell Town Reserves	3-1
Rayners Lane	v	Staines Lammas	1-3

Final

Bedfont & Feltham	v	Staines Lammas	1-0

Norfolk Senior Cup

Quarter Finals

Wroxham	v	Diss Town	3-0
King's Lynn Town	v	Acle United	4-0
Gorleston	v	Great Yarmouth Town	4-1
Cromer Town	v	Norwich City (U21)	0-2

Semi Finals

Gorleston	v	Norwich City	2-0
Wroxham	v	King's Lynn Town	3-2

Final

Gorleston	v	Wroxham	1-0

North Riding Senior Cup

Quarter Finals

Scarborough Athletic	v	Guisborough Town	1-2
Redcar Athletic	v	Middlesbrough Reserves	3-3, 1-3p
Redcar Newmarket	v	Grangetown Boys Club	4-2
Richmond Town	v	York City	3-0

Semi-Finals

Middlesbrough Reserves	v	Richmond Town	3-1
Guisborough Town	v	Redcar Newmarket	5-1

Final

Middlesbrough Reserves	v	Guisborough Town	0-1

Northants Hillier Senior Cup

Quarter Finals

Peterborough Northern Star	v	Corby Stewart & Lloyds	3-1
Long Buckby AFC	v	Desborough Town	2-1
Cogenhoe United	v	Corby Town	4-0
Daventry Town	v	Wellingborough Town	3-1

Semi-Finals

Peterborough Northern Star	v	Daventry Town	0-4
Cogenhoe United	v	Long Buckby AFC	3-0

Final

Cogenhoe United	v	Daventry Town	0-3

Northumberland Senior Cup

Quarter Finals

Alnwick Town	v	Whitley Bay	3-7
North Shields	v	Newcastle United Reserves (U21)	1-3
Ashington	v	Newcastle Benfield	3-1
Bedlington Terriers	v	Blyth Spartans	0-1

Semi Finals

Ashington	v	Blyth Spartans	2-2 aet
(R) Blyth Spartans	v	Ashington	3-2
Whitley Bay	v	Newcastle United Reserves (U21)	0-1

Final

Blyth Spartans	v	Newcastle United Reserves (U21)	0-4

Nottinghamshire Senior Cup

Quarter Finals

Southwell City	v	Retford United	0-1
Dunkirk	v	Rainworth MW	1-5
FC Cavaliers	v	Carlton Town	0-5
Clipstone	v	Basford United	2-3

Semi Finals

Retford United	v	Rainworth MW	0-4
Carlton Town	v	Basford United	5-3 aet

Final

Carlton Town	v	Rainworth MW	6-2

Oxfordshire Senior Cup

Quarter Finals

Kidlington	v	Oxford University Press	5-1
North Leigh	v	Ardley United	2-3
Thame United	v	Oxford United	0-2
Oxford City	v	Banbury United	6-2 aet

Semi Finals

Oxford City	v	Ardley United	0-2
Oxford United	v	Kidlington	0-0, 3-4p

Final

Kidlington	v	Ardley United	0-4

RAF Cup

Quarter Finals

RAF Northolt	v	RAF Leuchars	1-4
RAF Benson	v	RAF Marham	3-1
RAF Brize Norton	v	RAF Linton on Ouse	4-1
RAF Coningsby	v	RAF Waddington	2-1

Semi Finals

RAF Brize Norton	v	RAF Benson	4-5 aet
RAF Coningsby	v	RAF Leuchars	0-1

Final

RAF Benson	v	RAF Leuchars	2-0

RAF PLATE

Quarter Finals

RAF Digby	v	RAF High Wycombe	6-4
RAF Odiham	v	JAF Northwood	2-0
RAF Leeming	v	RAF Wittering	3-4
RAF Cosford	v	RAF Lossiemouth	5-0

Semi-Finals

RAF Cosford	v	RAF Wittering	0-1
RAF Odiham	v	RAF Digby	2-0

Final

RAF Wittering	v	RAF Odiham	1-3

Royal Navy Cup

Quarter Finals

40 Cdo Rm	v	CTCRM	7-7, 4-2p
HMS Seahawk	v	Cdo Log Regt Rm	11-3
HM Naval Base Portsmouth	v	45 Cdo Rm	2-4
HMS Sultan	v	HMS Heron	6-3

Semi Finals

HMS Seahawk	v	40 Cdo Rm	3-1
HMS Sultan	v	45 Cdo Rm	0-2

Final

45 Cdo Rm	v	HMS Seahawk	2-5

Sheffield & Hallamshire Senior Challenge Cup

Quarter Finals

Handsworth Parramore Res.	v	Frickley Athletic	0-2
Parkgate	v	Oughtibridge WMSC	1-2
Athersley Recreation	v	Houghton Main	2-2, 6-5p
Handsworth Parramore	v	Staveley Miners Welfare	2-1

Semi Finals

Frickley Athletic	v	Handsworth Parramore	3-1
Athersley Recreation	v	Oughtibridge WMSC	4-0

Final

Athersley Recreation	v	Frickley Athletic	1-0

Shropshire Challenge Cup

Semi-finals

Market Drayton Town	v	The New Saints	5-2
AFC Telford United	v	Shawbury United	3-0

Final

AFC Telford United	v	Market Drayton Town	3-1

Somerset Premier Cup

Quarter Finals

Odd Down (Bath)	v	Paulton Rovers	3-2
Frome Town (w/o)	v	Yeovil Town	
Wells City	v	Taunton Town	0-2
Cheddar	v	Bath City	1-3

Somerset Premier Cup continued...

Semi Finals

Bath City	v	Taunton Town	0-1
Frome Town	v	Odd Down (Bath)	3-2 aet

Final

Frome Town	v	Taunton Town	0-1

Somerset Senior Cup

Quarter Finals

Middlezoy Rovers	v	Portishead Town Reserves	2-3
Clutton	v	Wells City	1-3
Berrow	v	Burnham United	2-4
Minehead	v	Weston St Johns	2-1

Semi Finals

Wells City	v	Burnham United	2-0
Portishead Town Reserves	v	Minehead	1-2

Final

Minehead	v	Wells City	2-1

Staffordshire Senior Cup

Quarter Finals

Newcastle Town	v	Hednesford Town	2-0
Norton United	v	Rocester	1-0
Rushall Olympic	v	Chasetown	2-1
Stafford Rangers	v	Port Vale	1-1, 2-3p

Semi Finals

Port Vale	v	Newcastle Town	3-2
Rushall Olympic	v	Norton United	1-0

Final

Port Vale	v	Rushall Olympic	1-2

(Staffordshire) Walsall Senior Cup

Quarter Finals

Sutton Coldfield Town	v	Brocton	1-1, 4-3p
Chasetown	v	Walsall	2-0
Boldmere St Michaels	v	Rushall Olympic	2-4
Walsall Wood	v	Tividale	2-3

Semi Finals

Walsall Wood	v	Rushall Olympic	0-1
Sutton Coldfield Town	v	Chasetown	0-2

Final

Rushall Olympic	v	Chasetown	1-4

Suffolk Premier Cup

Quarter Finals

Woodbridge Town	v	Bury Town	1-5
Needham Market	v	Hadleigh United	3-0
Felixstowe & Walton United	v	Kirkley & Pakefield	3-0
Brantham Athletic	v	Leiston	1-2

Semi-Finals

Needham Market	v	Felixstowe & Walton United	0-1
Bury Town	v	Leiston	2-1

Final

Bury Town	v	Felixstowe & Walton United	4-1

Suffolk Senior Cup

Quarter Finals

Whitton United	v	Haverhill Borough	1-0 aet
Lakenheath	v	Grundisburgh	1-5
Ipswich Wanderers	v	Capel Plough	4-0
Achilles	v	Dedenham	3-0

Semi Finals

Grundisburgh	v	Whitton United	0-3 aet
Achilles	v	Ipswich Wanderers	2-3

Final

Whitton United	v	Ipswich Wanderers	1-0

Surrey Premier Cup

Quarter Finals

Frimley Green Reserves	v	Corinthian Casuals Reserves	1-4
Camberley Town Reserves	v	Worcester Park	1-2 aet
Farnham Town Reserves	v	Knaphill	1-5
Metropolitan Police Reserves	v	Raynes Park Vale Reserves	5-0

Semi-Finals

Worcester Park	v	Corinthian Casuals Reserves	2-1
Metropolitan Police Reserves	v	Knaphill	4-2

Final

Metropolitan Police Reserves	v	Worcester Park	2-0

Surrey Saturday Senior Cup

Quarter Finals

Frimley Green	v	Merstham	2-3
Metropolitan Police	v	Ash United	3-0
Walton & Hersham	v	Egham Town	0-2
Woking	v	Leatherhead	3-1

Semi-Finals

Metropolitan Police	v	Merstham	2-0
Woking	v	Egham Town	7-1

Final

Woking	v	Metropolitan Police	6-0

Sussex Senior Challenge Cup

Quarter Finals

Eastbourne Town	v	Peacehaven & Telscombe	0-4
Bognor Regis Town	v	Brighton & Hove Albion	4-2
Burgess Hill Town	v	Worthing	0-1
Horsham YMCA	v	Whitehawk	1-0

Semi Finals

Horsham YMCA	v	Bognor Regis Town	0-3
Worthing	v	Peacehaven & Telscombe	1-6

Final

Bognor Regis Town	v	Peacehaven & Telscombe	0-3

West Riding County Cup

Quarter Finals

Guiseley AFC	v	Selby Town	2-1
Harrogate Town	v	FC Halifax Town	2-1
Eccleshill United SC	v	Brighouse Town	3-1
Ossett Albion	v	Albion Sports	3-1 aet

Semi-Finals

Eccleshill United SC	v	Guiseley AFC	2-1
Harrogate Town	v	Ossett Albion	4-1

Final

Harrogate Town	v	Eccleshill United Sports Club	0-1

Westmorland Senior Cup

Quarter Finals

Appleby	v	Lunesdale United	3-1
Sedbergh Wanderers	v	Kendal County	0-7
Ambleside United	v	Corinthians	4-0
Kendal United	v	Keswick	4-2 aet

Semi-Finals

Appleby	v	Ambleside United	1-3
Kendal County	v	Kendal United	2-1

Final

Ambleside United	v	Kendal County	0-3

Wiltshire Senior Cup

Quarter Finals

Corsham Town	v	Purton	1-2
Downton	v	Bemerton Heath Harlequins	1-3
Melksham Town	v	Highworth Town	3-2
Bradford Town	v	Pewsey Vale	1-0

Semi Finals

Bemerton Heath Harlequins	v	Bradford Town	0-3
Purton	v	Melksham Town	0-4

Final

Bradford Town	v	Melksham Town	3-3, 2-3p

Worcestershire Senior Invitation Cup

Quarter Final

Redditch United	v	Kidderminster Harriers	3-2

Semi Finals

Redditch United	v	Worcester City	2-0
Stourbridge	v	Evesham United	2-3 aet

Final

Evesham United	v	Redditch United	0-2

Worcestershire Senior Invitation Urn

Quarter Finals

Alvechurch	v	Studley	1-0
Littleton	v	Stourport Swifts	3-2 aet
Malvern Town	v	Bromsgrove Sporting	0-4
Lye Town	v	Dudley Sports	5-0

Semi Finals

Bromsgrove Sporting	v	Ley Town	0-3
Alvechurch	v	Littleton	0-1

Final

Littleton	v	Ley Town	2-3

ENGLISH SCHOOLS' FOOTBALL ASSOCIATION

4, Parker Court, Staffordshire Technology Park, Beaconside, Stafford ST 18 0WP
Tel: 01785 785970; website: www.esfa.co.uk
Chief Executive: John Read (john.read@schoolsfa.com)
Competitions Manager: Darren Alcock (Darren.alcock@schoolsfa.com)
Non-League Directory Contributor: Mike Simmonds (m.simmonds31@btinternet.com)
(0115 9313299)
Photos: RWT Photogrpahy
Website: www.rwt.photography.co.uk

THE INTERNATIONAL SEASON

The English Schools' F.A. international sides both had successful seasons with the Under 18 boys' side winning the Centenary Shield and the Under 15 girls squad marking their third season by winning the Bob Docherty Cup which this season was a six nation affair staged over four days at Repton School,and also defeating the Republic of Ireland 8-0 and forcing a 1-1 draw in Glasgow with Scotland. They were thus undefeated throughout the season. The Under 18 boys' side were also undefeated, scoring 16 goals in their five full internationals of which three were victories and two were drawn.

UNDER 18 INTERNATIONAL SHIELD 2014

	P	W	D	L	F	A	Pts
England	4	2	2	0	11	8	8
Northern Ireland	4	2	1	1	11	8	7
Republic of Ireland	4	2	1	1	10	6	7
Scotland	4	1	2	1	8	6	5
Wales	4	0	0	4	3	15	0

RESULTS IN CENTENARY SHIELD

				ENGLAND GOALSCORERS
Scotland	1	Northern Ireland	1	
Republic of Ireland	3	Wales	0	
Wales	1	England	2	Haile, Hampson
Republic of Ireland	1	Northern Ireland	2	
Scotland	5	Wales	0	
England	3	Republic of Ireland	3	Hampson, Onyemah, White
Northern Ireland	3	England	5	Onyemah (2), White (2), Hickey
England	1	Scotland	1	White
Northern Ireland	5	Wales	1	
Republic of Ireland	3	Scotland	1	

OTHER ENGLAND GAMES

England A	1	RAF Under 23	1	
England B	4	Keele University	0	
England	5	Australia	0	Briggs (2), Charnley (2), Lyttle

Squad : Paul Braithwaite (Cleveland), Dean Briggs (Durham), Oliver Brown-Hill (Leicestershire and Rutland), Daniel Bruce (Cheshire), Ryan Charnley (Lancashire), Adam Curry (Durham), Tom Devitt (Northumberland), Tom Hadler (Kent), Danny Haile (Herefordshire), Michael Hampson (Lancashire), Brady Hickey (Leicestershire and Rutland), Tyler Little (Shropshire), Dominic McGiveron (Merseyside), Kieran O'Hara (Greater Manchester), Mark Onyemah (Essex), Charlie Russell (Lancashire), Andrew White (Durham), Joshua Woolley (Kent)

Back Row (L to R) : Sarah Stoneman (Team Manager), Brittany Sanderson(South Yorkshire) Jasmine Hughes (Dorset), Charlotte Newsham(Greater Manchester), Charlotte Johnson(Dorset), Olivia Dean (Greater Manchseter), Brittany Egden(Oxfordshire), Alessia Russo(Kent), Miranda Hall (Assistant Team Manager).
Middle Row: Jessica Jones(Devon), Georgia Stanway(Cumbria), Kelly Snook Dorset), Erin Hannah (Merseyside), Brenna McPartlan (Lancashire), Niamh Cashin (Nottinghamshire).
Front Row: Karolayne Byrom (Wiltshire), Ellie Brazil (Nottinghamshire), Laura Dexter (Derbyshire), Anna King (Staffordshire), Bethany Lumsden (Hertfordshire) Not in photo : Katy Gigg (Derbyshire (late call up for Alessia Russo).

E.S.F.A. GIRLS' UNDER 15 INTERNATIONAL SQUAD

Results

England	8	Republic of Ireland	0	Brazil (2), Russo, Stanway, Hughes, George, Newsham (2)
Scotland	1	England `	1	Jones (*T.S.B. Challenge Shield Trophy shared)*

Bob Docherty Under 15 Cup
Final Postions

1. England
2. Republic of Ireland
3. Scotland/Slovakia
5 Northern Ireland
6. Wales

Six nations took part in the biggest Docherty Cup competition to date with all the Home countries being joined by the Republic of Ireland and Slovakia.

The teams were divided into two groups with England drawn against Scotland and Wales.
England opened the tournament with a game against Wales and goals from Ellie Brazil and Georgia Stanway brought them a 2-0 win against a determined Welsh side. On the following day, England took on Scotland and drew 2-2 thanks to goals from Stanway and Jess Jones but the rules of the competition gave an extra point to the team winning the penalty shoot-out used to decide the winners which England won 4-3 to put them into top place in the group with 5 points against Scotland's 4. Wales lost 6-0 to Scotland so the lattercould count themselves unfortunate not to have won the group on goal difference.

In the other group, the results were : Republic of Ireland 2 Northern Ireland 0; Slovakia 0 Northern Ireland 2 and Republic of Ireland 2 Slovakia 1 which put the Republic in top place with Slovakia second and Northern Ireland third.

Wednesday brought the play-off matches, the results of which were :
1st and 2nd place : England 3 (Stanway, Brazil, Katy Gigg) Republic of Ireland 0
3rd and 4th Place : Scotland 0 Slovakia 0
5th and 6th Place : Northern Ireland 2 Wales 0

ENGLISH SCHOOLS' F.A COMPETITIONS 2013-14

Probably the biggest change in English Schools' F.A. activities since coverage of schools' first started at the end of the 1980s and again in the 21st century is the great increase in individual schools' and other competitions organised from the E.S.F.A. headquarters at Stafford. The extent of these is illustrated by the appended results during the 2013-14 season which greatly benefitted from the sponsorship of Play Station, Danone and the F>A. Premier League as well as funding from the Football Associatio to help the E.S.F.A establish a Competitions Department at Stafford.

U11 Inter Association Trophy - Sponsored By Danone Nations UK

Saturday 24 May 2014 at Bodymoor Heath, Aston Villa FC Training Ground

Dacorum SFA	1	Lewisham PSFA	2

Match postponed due to lightning storm

U11 Small Schools Soccer Sevens - Sponsored By Danone Nations UK

Saturday 24 May 2014 at Bodymoor Heath, Aston Villa FC Training Ground

Newcastle School for Boys	1	Baschurch Primary School	0
(Northumberland CSFA)		(Shropshire CSFA)	

U11 Schools Cup for School Teams - Sponsored By Danone Nations UK

Saturday 24 May 2014 at Bodymoor Heath, Aston Villa FC Training Ground

Valley Gardens Middle School	3	Lyndhurst Junior School	0
(Northumberland CSFA)		(Hampshire CSFA)	

U11 Girls Cup - Sponsored By Danone Nations UK

Saturday 24 May 2014 at Bodymoor Heath, Aston Villa FC Training Ground

St Joseph's RC Primary School	1	Orchard Junior School	2
(Greater Manchester CSFA)		(Hampshire CSFA)	

U12 Boys Indoor 5-A-Side Cup Final - Sponsored By Munich Trophies

Monday 3 March 2014 at Powerleague, Derby

Bruntcliffe High School	2	St Aloysius College	1
(Leeds SFA)		(Islington & Camden SFA)	

U12 Girls Indoor 5-A-Side Cup Final - Sponsored By Munich Trophies

Monday 3 March 2014 at Powerleague, Derby

South Hunsley School	2	St Ivo School	0
(East Riding SFA)		(Huntingdon SFA)	

U12 Boys Schools Cup Final - Sponsored By PlayStation

Monday 19 May 2014 at The Madejski Stadium, Reading FC

Thomas Telford School	8	St John The Baptist School	0
(Telford & Wrekin SFA)		(Woking SFA)	

U12 Boys Schools Cup for B Teams Final - Sponsored By PlayStation

Wednesday 21 May 2014 at The Madejski Stadium, Reading FC

Hampton School	1	St Francis Xavier's College	2
(Richmond SFA)		(Liverpool SFA)	

U13 Boys Schools Cup Final - Sponsored By PlayStation

Monday 19 May 2014 at The Madejski Stadium, Reading FC

Cardinal Heenan Sports College	3	Ravens Wood School	3
(Liverpool SFA)	6 (P)	(Bromley SFA)	7 (P)

U13 Boys Schools Cup for B Teams Final - Sponsored By PlayStation
Tuesday 20 May 2014 atThe Madejski Stadium, Reading FC
Wright Robinson College 3 Glyn School 0
(Manchester SFA) (Central Surrey SFA)

U13 Girls Schools Cup Final - Sponsored By PlayStation
Tuesday 20 May 2014 at The Madejski Stadium, Reading FC
Thomas Telford School 1 Thomas Estley Community College 4
(Telford & Wrekin SFA) (South Leicestershire SFA)

U13 Boys Small Schools Cup Final - Sponsored By PlayStation
Monday 19 May 2014 at The Madejski Stadium, Reading FC
Caistor Grammar School 0 Downend Technology College 2
(Coastal & Wolds SFA) (Bristol & South Gloucestershire SFA)

U13 Inter Association Trophy Final - Sponsored By PlayStation
Wednesday 21 May 2014 at The Madejski Stadium, Reading FC
Sunderland SFA 3 Bedford & District SFA 2

U14 Boys Inter County Trophy Final – - Sponsored By PlayStation
Wednesday 21 May 2014 at The Madejski Stadium, Reading FC
Sussex CSFA 1 Essex CSFA 3

U14 Girls Inter County Trophy Final - Sponsored By PlayStation
Monday 19 May 2014 at The Madejski Stadium, Reading FC
Kent CSFA 2 Lancashire CSFA 4

U14 Boys Schools Cup Final - Sponsored By PlayStation
Tuesday 20 May 2014 at The Madejski Stadium, Reading FC
Honley High School 2 Northampton School for Boys 2
Huddersfield SFA) 3 (P) (Northampton SFA) 2 (P)

U14 Boys Small Schools Cup Final - Sponsored By PlayStation
Wednesday 21 May 2014 at The Madejski Stadium, Reading FC
Ibstock Place School 3 Blacon High School 2
(Richmond SFA) (Chester SFA)

U14 Boys Open Schools Cup Final - Sponsored By PlayStation
Tuesday 20 May 2014 at The Madejski Stadium, Reading FC
Coombe Boys' School 4 Christleton High School 1
(Kingston SFA) (Chester SFA)

U14 Girls Schools Cup Final - Sponsored By PlayStation
Tuesday 20 May 2014 at The Madejski Stadium, Reading FC
Kibworth High School 2 Didcot Girls' School 5
(South Leicestershire SFA) (Vale of White Horse SFA)

U15 Inter Association Trophy Final First Leg - Sponsored By PlayStation
Thursday 24 April 2014 at The R Costings Abbey Stadium, Cambridge United FC
Cambridge & District SFA 2 Liverpool SFA 2

U15 Inter Association Trophy Final Second Leg - Sponsored By PlayStation
Friday 16 May 2014 at Goodison Park, Everton FC
Liverpool SFA 2 Cambridge & District SFA 1

U15 Boys Schools Cup Final - Sponsored By PlayStation
Wednesday 30 April 2014 at Hillsborough Stadium, Sheffield Wednesday FC

St Columba's Boys' School	2	Cardinal Heenan Sports College	4
(North Kent SFA)		(Liverpool SFA)	

U15 Boys Small Schools Cup Final - Sponsored By PlayStation
Monday 19 May 2014 at The Madejski Stadium, Reading FC

Ibstock Place School	0	Stanley High School	3
(Richmond SFA)		(Sefton SFA)	

U15 Girls Schools Cup Final - Sponsored By PlayStation
Wednesday 21 May 2014 at The Madejski Stadium, Reading FC

Fullbrook School	3	St Bede's RC High School	7
(Woking SFA)		(Blackburn & Darwen SFA)	

U16 Boys Inter County Trophy Final
Saturday 15 March 2014 at The Ricoh Arena, Coventry City FC

Lancashire CSFA	1 (AET)	Greater Manchester CSFA	2 (AET)

U16 Inter County Girls Trophy Final
Saturday 15 March 2014 at The Ricoh Arena, Coventry City FC

Nottinghamshire CSFA	1	Essex CSFA	0

U16 Boys Schools Cup Final - Sponsored By The Premier League
Wednesday 7 May 2014 at The Britannia Stadium, Stoke City FC

Whitgift School	4 (AET)	St Francis Xavier's College	4 (AET)
(Croydon SFA)	2 (P)	(Liverpool) SFA	4 (P)
(Croydon SFA)		(Liverpool SFA)	

U16 Girls Schools Cup Final
Thursday 13 March 2014 at The Ricoh Arena, Coventry City FC

Heckmondwike Grammar School	2	Queens' School	4
(Spen Valley SFA)		(Watford & District SFA)	

U18 Boys Inter County Trophy Final
Saturday 15 March 2014 atThe Ricoh Arena, Coventry City FC

Kent CSFA	1 (AET)	Essex CSFA	0 (AET)

U18 Girls Schools Trophy Final
Thursday 13 March 2014 at The Ricoh Arena, Coventry City FC

Balby Carr Community Sports Coll	4	John Madejski Academy	2
(Doncaster SFA)		(Reading SFA)	

U18 Boys Schools Trophy Final
Thursday 13 March 2014 at The Ricoh Arena, Coventry City FC

Thomas Telford	1 (AET)	Barking Abbey School	1 (AET)
(Telford & Wrekin SFA)	4 (P)	(Barking & Dagenham SFA)	2 (P)
(Telford & Wrekin SFA)		(Barking & Dagenham SFA)	

U18 Boys Colleges Trophy Final
Friday 14 March 2014 at The Ricoh Arena, Coventry City FC

St John Rigby College	2	Sparsholt College	3
(Wigan SFA)		(Eastleigh & Winchester SFA)	

U18 Girls Colleges Trophy Final

Friday 14 March 2014 at The Ricoh Arena, Coventry City FC

Accrington & Rossendale College	0	Solihull College	2
(Hyndburn & Ribble Valley SFA)		(Solihull SFA)	

ESFA / NDCSA Senior Boys 5-a-side Cup

Tuesday 4 February 2014 at Powerleague, Derby

Braidwood A	0	Hamilton Lodge A	1

Liverpool Schools' F.A. pictured with the Play station Trophy for the English Schools' F.A. Under 15 Inter-Association Trophy following their 2-1 win at Goodison Park (Everton) in the second leg against Cambridge which brought them a 4-3 aggregate victory.

The Nottinghamshire Schools' Under 16 Girls' squad pictured with the Cup following their 1-0 win over Essex in the Under 16 Girls Inter-County Final at the Ricoh Arena.

CLUB INDEX

CLUB INDEX

Click Back in Time!

Over 37 years of publishing the Non-League Club Directory has filled a room full of information and photographs covering the game we know and love.

What we intend, over time, is to create a website that shares with you everything we have accumulated, which we hope will bring back some fond memories of season's gone by.

A unique look back at how the game has evolved since the 1940s will also make for interesting reading, including league tables from season's gone by.

Log on to **www.non-leagueclubdirectory.co.uk** today and see how many faces from teams gone by you recognise

Hale Leys United - Spartan South Midlands Legaue Division Two champions - after a 5-1 win over Wolverton Town. Photo: Gordon Whttington.

CLUB INDEX

CLUB INDEX

CLUB INDEX

CLUB INDEX

CLUB INDEX

NON
LEAGUE DAY
06.09.14
Support your
LOCAL
FOOTBALL CLUB
nonleagueday.co.uk

CLUB INDEX

CLUB INDEX

CLUB INDEX

CLUB INDEX

For iPhone
Download on the
App Store
For iPad
Download on the
App Store
ANDROID APP ON
Google play